EIGHTH EDITION

THE KOVELS' COMPLETE ANTIQUES PRICE LIST

A guide to the 1975–1976 market
for professionals, dealers, and collectors

by **Ralph and Terry Kovel**

ILLUSTRATED

Crown Publishers, Inc., New York

BOOKS BY RALPH AND TERRY KOVEL

Dictionary of Marks—Pottery and Porcelain

Directory of American Silver, Pewter and
  Silver Plate

American Country Furniture, 1780-1875

Know Your Antiques,® Revised

The Kovels' Complete Antiques Price List

The Kovels' Official Bottle Price List

The Kovels' Collector's Guide to Limited Editions

The Kovels' Collector's Guide to American Art
  Pottery

Inquiries should be addressed to Crown Publishers, Inc.,
419 Park Avenue South, New York, N.Y. 10016
Printed in the United States of America
Published simultaneously in Canada by General Publishing Company
Limited
Library of Congress Catalog Card Number: 72-84290

ISBN: 0-517-524023

INTRODUCTION

The antiques market has remained strong through the year. Dealers report the unemployment rate and recession seem to have had little effect on antique sales. Furniture has shown a rise in prices, especially fine American pieces and golden oak furniture of the early 1900s. Rolltop desks have gained in popularity and prices are rising.

Oriental rug prices have risen in the past two years, and the trend seems to continue. New records in prices for important pieces of Tiffany glass, especially Tiffany leaded glass lamps, were set during the year. Vintage photographs and old phonograph records also showed impressive gains, up to 200% in auction prices.

Other antiques to show price rises were Indian jewelry, art nouveau items, vintage radios, prints, toys, tin containers, automatic musical instruments, art pottery, cut glass, pressed glass rarities, and Centennial materials.

The entire antiques market was strong and no single category showed a large drop in prices. In general, the sales indicate that choice items in any field are commanding the greatest price gains.

Many collectors have found back issues of this price book a useful reference source. Price trends can be seen by comparing past years' prices. We suggest you save a copy of each year's price guide and study your special antique interests. The new "collectibles," recently discovered interests, regional glass and pottery factories, and other information can be found from intelligent comparison of yearly editions of this book.

The prices included each year are reports, not estimates. This means that in some sale in the United States, the antique described was offered at the price listed. It is as accurate a method of reporting the antiques market as is possible.

Ralph M. Kovel, American Society of Appraisers, Senior Member
Terry H. Kovel, American Society of Appraisers, Senior Member

GUIDE TO USE

There are just a few simple rules to follow in using this book. Each listing is arranged in the following manner: CATEGORY (such as pressed glass, silver, or furniture); OBJECT (such as vase, spoon, table); DESCRIPTION (which includes as much information as possible about size, age, color, and pattern). All items are presumed perfect unless otherwise noted. Leaf through the book and examine the various category headings. Most of them are exactly as one would expect.

Several special categories were formed to make a more sensible listing of items possible. "Fire" includes andirons, firefighting equipment, fireplace equipment, and related pieces. "Kitchen," and "tool" include the various special equipments. It seems impossible to expect the casual collector to know the proper name for each variety of tool, such as an "adze" or a "trephine," so we have lumped them in the special categories.

This book has several idiosyncrasies of style that must be noted before it can be used properly. The prices are compiled by computer, and the machine has dictated several strange rules. Everything in the book is listed alphabetically according to the IBM alphabetic system. This means that words such as "mt." are alphabetized as "M-T," not as "M-O-U-N-T." Another peculiarity of the machine alphabetizing is that all numerals come after all letters, thus 2 comes after z. A quick glance at a listing will make this clear, as the alphabetizing is consistent throughout the book.

We have made several editorial decisions that affect the use of the book. A bowl is a bowl and not a dish unless it is a special type of dish such as a saucedish. A butter dish is a "butter" and a celery dish is a "celery." A salt dish is called a "salt" to differentiate it from a salt-shaker. A toothpick holder is called a "toothpick." It is always a "sugar and creamer," never a "creamer and sugar." Where one dimension is given, it is the height of the antique, or, if the object is round, the dimension is the diameter.

There are many new categories again this year. Personality listings, such as Amos and Andy, Charlie Chaplin, etc., have been expanded. Listings for Arita, Aventurine, Banko ware, Boy Scout memorabilia, Camark, Centennial memorabilia, Ceramic Art Co., Coors pottery, Gonder, Honesdale, Kemple, Locke Art, M Z Austria, Marblehead, Massier, Matt Morgan, Pantin, and Royal Haeger have been added. Sections for Judaica and for Negro items have been returned. The Tiffany section has been completely reorganized to include bronzes, silver, pottery, lamps, glass, and other wares.

The most important change in the book is the totally revised pressed glass section. Over 1,200 glass patterns are listed by pattern. Pictures of over 100 more popular patterns have also been included. This pressed glass listing is the most complete priced list available today and the new organization will make it easier to compare prices in coming years. The indexing of pattern names is arranged so that some of the errors of earlier researchers are now corrected and a pattern with more than one name can be easily found.

Several categories such as "milk glass" and "bottles" include special reference numbers. These numbers refer the reader to the most widely known books about the category. When these numbers appear, the name of the special book is given in the paragraph heading. All of these numbers take the form "B-22, C-103," and so forth. The letter is the author's initial; the number refers to a picture in the author's book.

All black and white pictures in KOVELS' COMPLETE ANTIQUES PRICE LIST are of antiques sold during the past year. The prices are as reported by the seller. Each piece pictured is listed with the word *illus* as part of the description. Pictures are placed as close to the price listing as is possible. Color pictures are all from the Western Reserve Historical Society collection, and no prices are given for these antiques.

All prices listed in this book were recorded from antique shows, sales, flea markets, and auctions between June 1974 and June 1975. The prices have been taken from sales in all parts of the country, and variations are sometimes due to the geographic differences in pricing. Antiques of top quality tend to be most expensive near the town where they originated because the local collectors are informed about them. We have tried to be accurate in all of the prices reported, but we cannot be responsible for any errors that may have occurred. We welcome any suggestions for future editions of this book, but cannot answer letters asking for advice or appraisals.

PICTURE ACKNOWLEDGMENTS

Antiques America (Lawrence King, Rayburn Stanley); Anton Gallery; Alice Baker; Barlow Antiques; Beechwood House Antiques; Mac Berns Antiques; Billy's & Hattie's Antiques; Sally Ann Decker; Henry DeMuth; Garth's Auction Barn; Rebecca Hahn; Frank Harding; Allan Hodges; Hugh Jordan; Knapp & Farley; Dorothy Lerner; Morton's Auction Exchange, Inc.; Northern Westchester Auction Galleries; Otto Schreiber; H. Jane Scott; Shaker Historical Society; Sotheby Parke Bernet—New York; Sotheby Parke Bernet—Los Angeles; June Stout; Bernice Sylak; Ethel Vallos; Willis House Antiques; The Wooden Bridge; Woody Auction Company.

A special thanks to Bill Brick and The William Brick Hudson Antique Show.

COLOR PICTURES

The color pictures in this book depict items from the collections of the 108-year-old Western Reserve Historical Society of Cleveland, Ohio. There are four parts to the organization. The Farm and Western Reserve Village, Peninsula, Ohio, is a group of restored nineteenth-century buildings. Original buildings were moved to the site from different villages of the Western Reserve. A Saltbox House (1825), Greek Revival House (1845), Stow House (1850), Log School House (1816), Benjamin Wade Law Office (1825), Grist Mill (1851), and Mary Ann Sears Swetland Memorial Meeting House (1851) are included. The Hale House (1826) is in its original setting surrounded by a working farm museum. Maple sugaring, weaving, dying, spinning, pottery making, candlemaking, and blacksmithing are demonstrated. All of the buildings are furnished with appropriate period antiques. The remains of the Franklin Glass Works of Kent, Ohio, have been moved to the grounds and are displayed along with pieces of Ohio glassware. The museum is continuing to acquire endangered early nineteenth-century buildings to add to the Village.

The Western Reserve Historical Museum, Cleveland, Ohio, houses a varied collection of antiques, historical memorabilia, and folk art. The costume collection is especially noteworthy. Changing exhibits in the museum feature collections of interest to the midwestern area. Tools, lighting devices, toys, period rooms, Chinese export porcelains, Shaker items, coverlets and textiles, paperweights, art glass, art pottery, and many other antiques are shown.

In the same building is The Frederick C. Crawford Auto and Aviation Museum which contains one of the finest collections of antique and classic automobiles in the country. Over two hundred vehicles are on display. The "street of shops" is a featured exhibit showing stores of the turn of the century.

The fourth part of the museum is the library, a fine research facility of over 200,000 volumes. Exceptional material concerned with genealogy, Shakers, and Napoleon are included. Ethnic and black archives for the Cleveland area have been established.

A visit to the Western Reserve Historical Society will give you and your family a glimpse of life in the old Western Reserve of more than a hundred years ago. Plan a day for the Hale Farm and a day for the Auto Museum and Historical Museum.

The cover picture is a view of the American Federal Drawing Room at the Western Reserve Historical Museum, Cleveland, Ohio. The woodwork was designed about 1820 by Jonathan Goldsmith, the famous

Painesville, Ohio, architect. The tambour writing desk of mahogany and birch was made in Massachusetts about 1795. The cherry table set with the Chinese export teaset (about 1800) is from Connecticut. The other furniture dates from 1780 to 1829. The draperies were based on an 1820 English engraving.

Our special thanks to the Western Reserve Historical Society, Mr. Jarius Barnes and his staff.

AN IMPORTANT ANNOUNCEMENT TO COLLECTORS AND DEALERS

Each year, THE KOVELS' COMPLETE ANTIQUES PRICE LIST is completely rewritten. Every entry and every picture is new because of the rapidly changing antiques market. The only way so complete a revision can be accomplished is by using a computer, making it possible to publish the bound book two months after the last price is received.

Yet many price changes occur between editions of THE KOVELS' COMPLETE ANTIQUES PRICE LIST. Important sales produce new record prices each day. Inflation, the changing price of silver and gold, and the international demand for some types of antiques influence sales in the United States.

The serious collector will want to keep up with developments from month to month rather than from year to year. Therefore, we call your attention to a new service to provide price information almost instantaneously: "Ralph and Terry Kovel on Antiques" a nationally distributed illustrated newsletter, published monthly.

This new monthly newsletter covers prices, special interest antiques, what to buy now, how to save and make money on antiques, forums and classes to attend, refinishing and first aid for your possessions, marks, decorating and displaying antiques, book reviews and other pertinent antique news.

Additional information about the newsletter and a complimentary copy are available from the authors at P.O. Box 957, Des Moines, Iowa 50304.

ABC plates, or children's alphabet plates, were popular from 1780 to 1860. The letters on the plate were meant as teaching aids for the children who were learning to read. The plates were made of pottery, porcelain, metal, or glass.

ABC, Bowl, Boys Playing Leapfrog In Center, China, 8 1/4 In.	14.00
ABC, Bowl, Campbell's Soup, 6 In.	6.50
ABC, Cup, Children & Farm Pets, Forbes Silver Co., 2 5/8 In.	29.00
ABC, Dish, Child's Feeding, Little Bopeep, 7 In.	10.00
ABC, Dish, Child's Feeding, The House That Jack Built, 7 1/2 In.	25.00
ABC, Dish, Feeding, Little Boy Blue, Deep, 7 3/4 In.	20.00
ABC, Mug, Soft Paste, Franklin Maxim, Industry Is Fortune's Handmaid	65.00
ABC, Plate, Bear Playing Xylophone, Gold Alphabet, 6 In.	8.00
ABC, Plate, Boy At Easel, Hand-Painted, 8 In.	33.00
ABC, Plate, Boys & Girls, Verse, Polychrome, Soft Paste, 6 In.	55.00
ABC, Plate, Campbell Kids, Buffalo Pottery, Non-Spill, 7 1/2 In.	35.00
ABC, Plate, Child On Tiptoe To Reach Piano, Staffordshire, 7 1/4 In.	35.00
ABC, Plate, Children, Basket Of Eggs, McNicol, East Liverpool, 8 1/2 In.	20.00
ABC, Plate, Clock Center, Pressed Glass, 7 In.	32.50
ABC, Plate, Clock Face, Alphabet & Notched Border, Clear Glass, 7 In.	28.50
ABC, Plate, Crusoe & His Pets, Brown Hills Pottery, 1872-96, 8 In.	45.00
ABC, Plate, Crusoe Finding Footprints, Brown Printed, 7 1/4 In.	35.00
ABC, Plate, Crusoe Viewing Island, Brown Printed, 7 1/4 In.	35.00
ABC, Plate, Evening Bathing Scene At Manhattan Beach, Brown, 7 In.	32.00
ABC, Plate, Falling Horseman Center, 8 3/8 In.	45.00
ABC, Plate, Fox Hunt Scene, Staffordshire, 7 1/2 In.	34.00
ABC, Plate, Franklin Maxim, Industry & No Gains, 7 1/2 In.	45.00
ABC, Plate, Franklin Maxim, Not To Oversee Workmen, Black & White, 7 1/2 In.	48.00
ABC, Plate, Franklin Maxim, Poor Richard, 5 In.	55.00
ABC, Plate, Leopard, Alphabet Around Picture, 7 1/4 In.	35.00
ABC, Plate, Lion, BP Co., 7 1/4 In.	28.00
ABC, Plate, Pony, W.A.Adams, 7 In.	32.00
ABC, Plate, Red Riding Hood Meets The Wolf, Porcelain, 7 1/4 In.	35.00
ABC, Plate, Rhino, Tiger, & Rabbit, Gold Letters, 8 In.Diameter	25.00
ABC, Plate, Sancho Panza & Dapple, Frosted Center, 6 In. 34.00 To	38.00
ABC, Plate, Stag & Hounds, Polychrome, Soft Paste, Meakin, 6 In.	55.00
ABC, Plate, The Guardian, Girl & Dog Asleep, Elsmore & Sons, 8 In.	45.00
ABC, Plate, Washington Bust Center, Tin, 5 5/8 In.	45.00
ABC, Plate, Who Killed Cock Robin, Tin, 7 1/2 In.	32.00
Abingdon, Vase, Cornucopia, Pink, Marked Abingdon USA, 5 X 9 In.	3.00

Adams china was made by William Adams and Sons of Staffordshire, England. The firm was founded in 1769 and is still working.

Adams, see also Flow Blue

Adams, Bowl, Cries Of London, A New Love Song, 6 7/8 In.	8.50
Adams, Bowl, Cries Of London, Fresh Gathered Peas, 6 7/8 In.	8.50
Adams, Bowl, Vegetable, Lake George, Pink, 12 1/2 In.	110.00
Adams, Bowl, Vegetable, Palestine, Pink, 8 3/4 In.	55.00
Adams, Bowl, Vegetable, Red Floral	20.00
Adams, Cup & Saucer, Farmer's, Landscape, Red On Cream	25.00
Adams, Cup & Saucer, Handleless, Winter	37.50
Adams, Cup & Saucer, Miniature, Boy & Girl In Garden, Blue, Wishbone Handle	19.00
Adams, Cup & Saucer, Palestine, Pink	30.00
Adams, Cup Plate, White, Blue Edge, C.1860	22.50
Adams, Jar, Powder, Covered, Cries Of London	42.50
Adams, Pitcher, Cattle Scenery, Blue & White, Bulbous, 5 1/4 In.	23.00
Adams, Pitcher, Mrs.Gummidge Casts A Damp On Our Departure, 7 1/2 In.	50.00
Adams, Plate, Arabian Sketches, Pink, 10 1/2 In.	35.00
Adams, Plate, At Mother's Grave, Black & White Transfer, 7 1/2 In.	22.00
Adams, Plate, Audubon, American Flamingo, Hand-Painted, 10 1/2 In.	40.00
Adams, Plate, Audubon, Eagle, 10 1/2 In.	13.00
Adams, Plate, Audubon, Snowy Egret, 10 1/2 In.	12.00
Adams, Plate, Caledonia, Purple, 11 In.	20.00
Adams, Plate, Castle Scene, C.1840, 9 In.	18.50
Adams, Plate, Catskill Mountain House, Pink, 10 1/4 In.	65.00
Adams, Plate, Columbus, Black & White, 10 1/2 In.	35.00
Adams, Plate, Columbus, Brown, 10 1/2 In.	35.00

Adams, Plate, Currier & Ives Scene, 10 3/4 In.	20.00
Adams, Plate, Genoa, Blue, Ironstone, C.1830, 7 1/2 In.	9.00
Adams, Plate, Montevideo, Connecticut, U.S.A., Deep Pink, 7 In.	38.00
Adams, Plate, Near Conway, N.H., Pink, 9 In.	58.00
Adams, Plate, Palestine, Pink, 10 1/2 In.	38.00
Adams, Plate, Palestine, Purple, 10 1/2 In.	38.00
Adams, Plate, Palestine, Violet, 9 In.	20.00
Adams, Plate, Scene From MacBeth, 10 In.	35.00
Adams, Plate, Soup, Caledonia, Red, 11 In.	35.00
Adams, Plate, Soup, Pearlware, American Eagle, Crimson Transfer, C.1800, Pair	650.00
Adams, Plate, Soup, Rural Village Scene, Blue, 8 7/8 In.	45.00
Adams, Plate, Soup, Yale, Light Blue, 9 In.	30.00
Adams, Plate, The Sea, Pink, 9 1/2 In.	25.00
Adams, Plate, View Near Conway, N.H., Pink, 9 In.	50.00
Adams, Plate, White, 4 Applied Blue Grape Sprigs, 7 1/2 In.	12.50
Adams, Platter, Caledonia, Brown & White, 1787-1805 Mark, 12 X 15 In.	41.00
Adams, Platter, Caledonia, Pink, 15 1/2 In.	65.00
Adams, Platter, View Of The Regent's Quadrant, Dark Blue, C.1827, 17 1/2 In.	325.00
Adams, Teapot, Italian City, Pink & Green, C.1835	75.00
Adams, Teapot, Oriental Scene, Pink, C.1835, Galley Shape	63.00
Adams, Teapot, The Huntsman, Purple	38.00

Agata glass was made by Joseph Locke of the New England Glass Company of Cambridge, Massachusetts, after 1885. A metallic stain was applied to New England Peachblow and the mottled design characteristic of agata appeared.

Agata, Pitcher, Square Mouth, 6 3/4 In.	3500.00
Agata, Toothpick, Pinched-In Square Top, 2 3/8 In.	550.00
Agata, Tumbler, Blue Black Oil Spots, Gold Tracery	695.00
Agata, Tumbler, Gloss, Gold Spiderweb Mottling, Raspberry Coloring	695.00
Agata, Tumbler, 4 In.	360.00 To 650.00
Agate, Bottle, Snuff, Chinese, Animals & Foliage, Black & White, 2 1/2 In.	900.00
Agate, Buttonhook, Carnelian Color, 5 In.	15.00
Agate, Buttonhook, Glove, Banded	8.00
Agate, Creamer, Japanese, Glazed Inside Only, Signed, 3 In.	18.00

Akro agate glass was made in Clarksburg, West Virginia, from 1932 to 1951. Before that time the firm made children's glass marbles. Most of the glass is marked with a crow flying through the letter A.

Akro Agate, Ashtray, Cobalt With White, Marbleized, Square	3.00
Akro Agate, Basket, Green Slag, 2 Handled, 3 3/4 In.	12.00
Akro Agate, Bowl, Child's, Green, 8 Sided	5.00
Akro Agate, Chocolate Set, Cobalt, Chiquita, 12 Piece	60.00
Akro Agate, Creamer, Child's, Blue, 8 Sided	5.00
Akro Agate, Cup, Child's, Blue	2.00
Akro Agate, Cup, Child's, Green, 8 Sided	3.00
Akro Agate, Cup, Child's, Opaque Green, Concentric Rings	6.00
Akro Agate, Dish, Shell, Green & White, 3 In.	3.00
Akro Agate, Jar, Mexicali, Orange & White	15.00
Akro Agate, Jar, Mortar & Pestle, Opaque Pink	25.00
Akro Agate, Jar, Powder, Covered, White, Colonial Lady	25.00
Akro Agate, Jar, Powder, Milk Glass	30.00
Akro Agate, Planter, Green, Oval, White Wire Basket, 6 X 3 In.	6.50
Akro Agate, Plate, Child's, Blue, 8 Sided	4.00
Akro Agate, Plate, Child's, Green	2.00
Akro Agate, Plate, Child's, Green, 8 Sided	4.00
Akro Agate, Pot, Green, 4 1/2 In. Opening, 4 In.	4.00
Akro Agate, Saucer, Child's, Pink, 8 Sided	5.00
Akro Agate, Set Of Dishes, Child's, Green, Signed, 14 Piece	35.00
Akro Agate, Sugar & Creamer, Child's, Orange	6.50
Akro Agate, Tea Set, Child's, Green & White, 15 Piece	45.00
Akro Agate, Tea Set, Green & White, 8 Piece	26.00
Akro Agate, Teapot, Child's, Pink	6.00
Akro Agate, Toothpick, Custard, Orange Slag, Darts, 2 In.	12.00
Akro Agate, Urn Vase, Green & White, 3 1/2 In.	5.00
Akro Agate, Vase, Custard, Darts, Signed, 9 1/2 In.	15.00

Akro Agate, Vase, Hand Holding Trumpet, Orange With White, 3 In. 5.00

Albums were popular in Victorian times to hold the myriad pictures and cutouts favored by the collectors. All sorts of scrapbooks and albums can still be found.

Album, Autograph, Leather, Ornate, C.1870 .... 6.00
Album, Card, Christmas & Greeting, 1883, 250 Cards 42.50
Album, Celluloid, Green & Rose, Poppies & Moths, Red Plush, 8 X 11 In. 25.00
   Album, Photograph, see Photography, Album
Album, Postcard, 137 Scenic Cards, C.1900 .... 24.75
Album, Trade Card, Embossed Birds & Flowers 60.00

Alexandrite glass was first made by Thomas Webb & Sons at the beginning of the 20th century. It is a transparent glass shading from pale yellow to rose to blue. Stevens & Williams later produced Alexandrite glassware by plating a transparent yellow body with rose and blue glass.

Alexandrite, Toothpick, Deep Purple To Amber, Scalloped Top, 2 1/4 In. 850.00
Alexandrite, Vase, Bud, Five-Petaled Top, Blue To Fuchsia To Citron, 3 In. 700.00
Alexandrite, Wine, Quilted, 4 1/2 In.High 1200.00
   Almanac, see Paper, Almanac
Aluminum, Cup, Child's, Nursery Rhyme Characters 3.00

Amber glass is the name of any glassware with the proper yellow-brown shade. It was a popular color after the Civil War.

Amber Glass, Bobeche, Flashed, Blown, Pair, 3 1/2 In. 12.00
Amber Glass, Bowl, Deer Head Center, B.P.O.E., 8 In. 14.00
Amber Glass, Bowl, Finger, Printed Hob, 4 1/2 In.Diameter 22.50
Amber Glass, Candlestick, Round Base, Turned, 8 1/2 In.High, Pair 20.00
Amber Glass, Candlestick, 6 1/2 In., Pair 25.00
Amber Glass, Compote, Open, Ruffled Rim, 7 1/2 In.High 40.00
Amber Glass, Condiment Set, Spoon, Clear Holder, 4 Piece 100.00
Amber Glass, Decanter, Enameled Floral, 12 X 5 1/2 In. 125.00
Amber Glass, Dish, Bird With Berry Cover 125.00
Amber Glass, Dish, Rabbit Cover 110.00
Amber Glass, Inkwell, School Desk 1.25
Amber Glass, Lemonade Set, Footed Handled Mugs, Blue Handles, 5 Piece 147.00
Amber Glass, Match Holder, Scuttle Mug 28.00
Amber Glass, Mug, Applied Blue Handle 12.50
Amber Glass, Pitcher, Crackle, Applied Handle, 7 1/4 In.High 37.50
Amber Glass, Pitcher, Water, Daisy Footed, Flattened Body, Plain 40.00
Amber Glass, Pitcher, Water, Paneled Stippled Pattern, Florals 18.00
Amber Glass, Salt, Christmas, Agitator 68.00
Amber Glass, Saltshaker, Embossed Rounded Panels 12.50
Amber Glass, Tankard, Water, Enamel Floral & Birds, Blue Handle, 9 In. 85.00
Amber Glass, Tea Set, Silver Resist, Miniature, 15 Piece 52.50
Amber Glass, Toothpick, Boiling Pot 32.00
Amber Glass, Toothpick, Boot, Round Base 30.00
Amber Glass, Toothpick, Bunch Of Cigars Tied With Ribbon, Wheeling, W.Va. ... 25.00
Amber Glass, Toothpick, Dog With Hat, Victorian 33.50
Amber Glass, Toothpick, Dollar 130.00
Amber Glass, Toothpick, Fan Top 38.00
Amber Glass, Toothpick, Little Boy About To Shoot Marble, Victorian 28.00
Amber Glass, Tray, Oblong, 8 X 11 In. 35.00
Amber Glass, Tray, Water, Round, Hobnail, Gallery Rim, 11 1/2 In.Diameter 36.00
Amber Glass, Vase, Crackle, Rounded Square, Enameled Seaweed & Fish, 5 In. ... 30.00
Amber Glass, Water Set, Melon Ribbed, 7 1/2 In.High Pitcher, 7 Piece 95.00
Amber, Bottle, Chinese, Reddish, Carved Oriental Man, Head Stopper, 3 7/8 In. 85.00

Amberina is a two-toned glassware made from 1883 to about 1900. It was patented by Joseph Locke of the New England Glass Company. The glass shades from red to amber.

   Amberina, see also Baccarat, Bluerina, Plated Amberina
Amberina, Bowl, Berry, Deep Colors, Diamond Optic, 4 1/2 In. 100.00
Amberina, Bowl, Finger, Inverted Thumbprint 90.00
Amberina, Bowl, Inverted Thumbprint, 4 In. 100.00
Amberina, Bowl, Inverted Thumbprint, 14 1/2 X 4 In. 100.00

Amberina, Bowl, Punch, Covered, Inverted Thumbprint, Reeded Finial, 13 In.	500.00
Amberina, Bowl, Ribbed, Libbey, 2 1/2 In.High, 5 In.Wide	195.00
Amberina, Canoe, Daisy & Button, 9 X 3 In.	165.00
Amberina, Castor, Pickle, Inverted Thumbprint, Enameled Flowers	245.00
Amberina, Celery, Diamond-Quilted, Square Mouth, Fuchsia _Color_	225.00
Amberina, Celery, New England, Corset Shape, Fluted Square Top, 4 3/4 In.	175.00
Amberina, Celery, New England, Fuchsia	150.00
Amberina, Celery, New England, Inverted Thumbprint, Corset Shape, 6 In.	275.00
Amberina, Compote, Libbey, Scalloped Rim, Dark Fuchsia To Golden Amber, 4 In.	325.00
Amberina, Creamer, Inverted Thumbprint, Crimped Top, Amber Handle, 3 3/4 In.	500.00
Amberina, Creamer, New England, Inverted Thumbprint, Reeded Handle	185.00
Amberina, Creamer, New England, Inverted Thumbprint, Square Top	185.00
Amberina, Cruet, Amber Handle, Ground Stopper, 7 In.High	295.00
Amberina, Cruet, Mt.Washington, Diamond-Quilted, Shell Handle, 6 In.	650.00
Amberina, Cup, Punch, Diamond-Quilted Paneled Body, Fuchsia, Reeded Handle	115.00
Amberina, Cup, Punch, New England, Fuchsia	110.00
Amberina, Decanter, Juice, Diamond-Quilted, Cut Stopper, 12 In.	250.00
Amberina, Dish, Candy, Cambridge, Honeycomb, 9 X 4 In.	115.00
Amberina, Dish, Candy, Optic Quilted Thumbprint, 4 Ball Feet	165.00
Amberina, Dish, Pressed Daisy & Button, 5 3/4 In.	68.00
Amberina, Lampshade, Daisy & Button, Ruffled, 9 In. Across, 3 3/4 In. High	90.00
Amberina, Muffineer, Pewter Top	150.00
Amberina, Mug, Child's, Applied Handle	80.00
Amberina, Pitcher, Fuchsia, Inverted Thumbprint, Ruffled Rim, 8 1/2 In.	245.00
Amberina, Pitcher, New England, Tricorner, Miniature	300.00
Amberina, Plate, Higbee, Floral Oval & Cane, Embossed Bee, Square, 7 1/4 In.	75.00
Amberina, Plate, IG Mark, Fluted, 7 1/2 In.	55.00
Amberina, Pot, Mustard, Baby Thumbprint, Pewter Top	150.00
Amberina, Pot, Mustard, Pewter Lid, Inverted Baby Thumbprint, Enamel Floral	135.00
Amberina, Rose Bowl, Fuchsia, Diamond-Quilted, Dimpled, 4 3/4 In.High	395.00
Amberina, Salt & Pepper, Baby Thumbprint, Blue Enamel Floral	150.00
Amberina, Saltshaker, New England, 3 7/8 In.	85.00
Amberina, Sauce, Flint, Daisy & Button, Boat Shape, 6 In.	110.00
Amberina, Spooner, New England, Inverted Thumbprint, Corset Shape, Crimped	215.00
Amberina, Sweetmeat, Inverted Thumbprint, Covered, 6 3/4 In.Diameter	365.00
Amberina, Tankard, Water, Applied Amber Spun-Rope Handle, 9 3/8 In.	165.00
Amberina, Tieback, Petal Loop, Metal Shank, 3 In., Pair	45.00
Amberina, Toothpick, Mt.Washington, Diamond-Quilted	115.00
Amberina, Toothpick, Tricorner	185.00
Amberina, Toothpick, Venetian Diamond, Square Top, Polished Pontil	105.00
Amberina, Toothpick, Wheeling, Daisy & Button, Footed, 3 In. 130.00 To	135.00
Amberina, Tumbler, Diamond-Quilted	95.00
Amberina, Tumbler, Diamond-Quilted, Deep Cranberry Halfway Down	75.00
Amberina, Tumbler, Diamond-Quilted, Fuchsia Coloring Halfway Down	95.00
Amberina, Tumbler, Diamond-Quilted, Fuchsia To Amber, Ground Pontil	55.00
Amberina, Tumbler, Diamond-Quilted, Polished Pontil	85.00
Amberina, Tumbler, English, Diamond-Quilted	125.00
Amberina, Tumbler, Engraved Swan & Palms	950.00
Amberina, Tumbler, Inverted Baby Thumbprint	60.00
Amberina, Tumbler, Juice, Applied Handle	195.00
Amberina, Tumbler, Juice, Diamond-Quilted	100.00
Amberina, Tumbler, Juice, Diamond-Quilted, Decorated, 3 In.	71.50
Amberina, Tumbler, Lemonade, Applied Amber Handle, 5 1/4 In.High	87.00
Amberina, Tumbler, New England Glass Co., Swirled, Polished Pontil	90.00
Amberina, Tumbler, New England, Diamond-Quilted, Deep Fuchsia, 3 3/4 In.	110.00
Amberina, Tumbler, New England, Polished Pontil	100.00
Amberina, Tumbler, Swirl	97.50
Amberina, Tumbler, Vertical Shadow Paneling, Medium Color	40.00
Amberina, Tumbler, Whiskey, New England	100.00
Amberina, Tumbler, 10 Rows Of Hobnail, Heat Check In Base	95.00
Amberina, Vase, Amber, Ruffled Cranberry Top, Lion's-Head Feet, 10 1/2 In.	525.00
Amberina, Vase, Libbey, Vertical Ridges, Signed, 7 In.	385.00
Amberina, Vase, Lily, Mt.Washington, Silver Plate Holder, 7 3/4 In.	145.00
Amberina, Vase, Reverse Trumpet Shape, Swirled, Enamel Floral, Gold, 11 In.	110.00
Amberina, Vase, Swirl, Blown, Piecrust Rim, 10 1/2 In.High, Pair	375.00
Amberina, Water Set, Inverted Thumbprint, Clear Ribbed Handle, 7 Piece	290.00

Amberina, Water Set, Swirled, Ground Pontils, 9 In. Pitcher, 7 Piece 550.00

*American Encaustic Tiling Co. of Zanesville, Ohio, worked from 1879
to 1935. Decorative glazed, embossed, and faience tiles were made.*
American Encaustic Tiling Co., Inkwell, Double, Penholder, Pink Gloss Glaze 25.00
American Encaustic Tiling Co., Plaque, Girl's Profile, L'automne, 8 1/2 In. 125.00
American Encaustic Tiling Co., Tile, Baby's Bust, Brown, Square, 6 In. 35.00
American Encaustic Tiling Co., Tile, Forest Scene, Brown, Square, 6 In. 20.00
American Encaustic Tiling Co., Tile, Scene, Blue, Renzel, Square, 6 In. 55.00
American Encaustic Tiling Co., Tile, Trees, Road, & House, Square, 6 In. 20.00
American Encaustic Tiling Co., Tile, William J.Bryan, Square, 3 In. 55.00

*Amethyst glass is any of the many glasswares made in the proper dark purple
shade. It was a color popular after the Civil War.*
Amethyst Glass, Bottle, Cologne, Cylindrical, Tapering Neck, 9 3/8 In. 65.00
Amethyst Glass, Bottle, Cologne, 12 Sided, Cork Stopper, 7 1/4 In. 75.00
Amethyst Glass, Bottle, Perfume, Art Deco, Ground Stopper, 5 In. 6.25
Amethyst Glass, Bowl, Center, Scrolls & Jewels Around Rim, 8 In. 18.00
Amethyst Glass, Bowl, Diamond-Quilted, 7 In. 35.00
Amethyst Glass, Bowl, Polished Pontil, Hand-Painted Floral, Gilded, 5 In. 12.50
Amethyst Glass, Celery, Twist Panels, Amethyst & Clear, 6 1/2 In. 14.00
Amethyst Glass, Cruet, Painted Flowers, Amethyst Handle & Stopper 40.00
Amethyst Glass, Cup, Punch, Child's 22.50
Amethyst Glass, Decanter, Faceted Crystal Stopper, 10 In. 15.00
Amethyst Glass, Pitcher, Crossbars, Applied Handle, Bulbous Base, 9 In. 95.00
Amethyst Glass, Pitcher, Water, Applied Handle, Fenton 40.00
Amethyst Glass, Planter, Dancing Nudes & Lute Players, Hess, 8 X 3 1/2 In. 20.00
Amethyst Glass, Rose Bowl, Violet, Scalloped Top, 4 1/2 X 5 7/8 In. 48.00
Amethyst Glass, Salt, Christmas, Agitator 90.00
Amethyst Glass, Salt, Floriform, Applied Vaseline Shell Trim 30.00
Amethyst Glass, Salt, Swan 11.00
Amethyst Glass, Shoe, Corn Bulges, 3 X 2 In. 18.50
Amethyst Glass, Toothpick, X-Ray Pattern, Gold Trim 38.00
Amethyst Glass, Tumbler, Leaf Medallion 45.00
Amethyst Glass, Tumbler, Straight Sided, C.1930 .... 3.25
Amethyst Glass, Tumbler, Whiskey, Set Of 6 In Metal Holder 12.00
Amethyst Glass, Vase, Fan, Sculptured, Bird, Berries, & Vine, 7 In. 20.00
Amethyst Glass, Vase, Tricorner, Grecian Dancers, Musicians, Scalloped, 7 In. 19.00
Amethyst Glass, Whiskey Taster, Enameled Grapes, Gold Bands 22.00
Amethyst, Bottle, Snuff, Chinese, Carved, Deep Purple, 2 In. 200.00
Amos & Andy, Music Sheet, Three Little Words, 1930 .... 10.00
Amos & Andy, Radio Script, Dec.25th, 1935 .... 5.00
   Amphora, see Teplitz
   Andiron, many related fireplace items, see, Fire
   Apothecary jar, see Bottle, Apothecary
   Apple Peeler, see Kitchen, Peeler, Apple
Arc-En-Ceil, Ewer, Cream To Green, Twisted, Old Man Winter On Handle, 9 In. 150.00
Arc-En-Ceil, Vase, Gold Luster, Marked, 7 3/4 In. 90.00
Arc-En-Ceil, Vase, Gold Luster, Purple, Marked, 8 1/2 In. 100.00
   Argy-Rousseau, see G. Argy-Rousseau
Arita, Bottle, Blue & White, Floral Cluster & Grasses, C.1750, 8 1/4 In. 90.00
Arita, Bottle, Blue & White, Floral Cluster, Rolled Mouth, C.1750, 10 In. 90.00
Arita, Bottle, Blue & White, Spreading Pine Tree, C.1790, 9 1/4 In. 100.00
Arita, Bottle, Blue & White, Wisteria, C.1850, 8 3/4 In. 30.00
Arita, Bowl, Blue & White, Chinese Landscape, Birds, & Floral, C.1750, 8 In. 35.00
Arita, Bowl, Blue & White, Pheasants, Rockwork, Mums, C.1750, 7 5/8 In., Pair 60.00
Artia, Charger, Tea Garden, Blue, White, & Red, C.1860, 14 In. 100.00
Arita, Kendi, Blue & White, Bulbous Spout, Landscape, Floral, C.1690, 7 In. 325.00
Arita, Vase, Birds, Fish, & Geometrics, Bamboo Effect Corners, 7 1/2 In. 140.00

*Art Deco, or Art Moderne, is a style started at the Paris Exposition
of 1925. All types of furniture and decorative arts, jewelry, bookbindings, and
even games, were designed in this style.*
Art Deco, Ashtray, Cigars, Orange Porcelain, Pewter Rim & Rests 25.00
Art Deco, Atomizer, Perfume, Sterling Silver, C.1930, 3 3/4 In., Pair 42.50
Art Deco, Bag, Enameled Gold Mesh, Whiting & Davis, Gold Chain Handle 60.00

Art Deco, Bowl, Dancing Nude, Frosted, Consolidated Glass Co., 4 3/4 In.	32.50
Art Deco, Buckle, Shoe, France, Black Satin, Steel Cut Beads, 3 In., Pair	2.75
Art Deco, Candlestick, Wood With Chrome Nudes, 8 In., Pair	18.00
Art Deco, Compact, Nailhead Decoration, Marked Mary, Volupte, Sterling	35.00
Art Deco, Figurine, Black Cat, Metal, 7 3/4 In.	24.00
Art Deco, Figurine, Dancing Man & Woman, Red, Gold, European, Plaster, 14 In.	45.00
Art Deco, Figurine, Female, Nude, Metal, 21 In.	27.50
Art Deco, Figurine, Nude Seated On Edge Of Tub, Frosted, 6 In.	16.00
Art Deco, Holder, Cigarette, Telescopic	15.00
Art Deco, Jar, Powder, Frosted Green, Clown On Lid, Angular Style	18.50
Art Deco, Plate, Cocktail, Woman At Bar With Cocktail, 8 In., Set Of 4	58.00
Art Deco, Plate, Dancing Nude, Frosted, Consolidated Glass Co., 8 1/4 In.	40.00
Art Deco, Pocket, Wall, Syroco, Cornucopia, 10 In., Pair	15.00
Art Deco, Sugar & Creamer, Red On White, C.1950	10.00
Art Deco, Tray, Card, Cast Metal, Dark Green Satin Finish	22.00
Art Deco, Vase, Parrot, Keramis, Belgium, Geometrics, Floral, 12 In., Pair	190.00
Art Deco, Vase, Pink Glass, 8 1/2 In., Pair	35.00
Art Deco, Vase, Yellow Glass, Footed, Bulbous, 5 1/2 In.	35.00

Art glass means any of the many forms of glassware made during the late nineteenth century or early twentieth century. These wares were expensive and made in limited production. Art glass is not the typical commercial glassware that was made in large quantities, and most of the art glass was produced by hand methods.

Art Glass, see also separate headings such as Burmese, Nash, Schneider, etc.

Art Glass, Ashtray, White Casing On Back, Yellow Interior, Gold Deposits	67.50
Art Glass, Basket, Cased, Blown, Milk White, Butterscotch Interior, 6 In.	65.00
Art Glass, Basket, Pink, Ruffled, Victorian, 14 X 15 In.	175.00
Art Glass, Bottle, Perfume, Purse, Green, Gold, Florals, Chain, 2 In.	40.00
Art Glass, Bowl, Bride's, Ivory To Yellow, Flame Shape, Daisies, 10 1/2 In.	75.00
Art Glass, Bowl, Bride's, White To Pink To White, Piecrust Rim, 9 7/8 In.	50.00
Art Glass, Bowl, Canary, Applied Cranberry Threading, 3 Crystal Legs, 4 In.	25.00
Art Glass, Bowl, Hobbs, Brockunier, Citron, Rose Edge, Heart Shape, 10 In.	235.00
Art Glass, Bowl, J.Beal, Etling, France, Blue, 3 Floriform Feet, 6 1/2 In.	45.00
Art Glass, Bowl, Overlay, White, Clear Edge, Roses, Ruffled, 8 1/2 In.	42.50
Art Glass, Bowl, Pink, Fluted, Irregular Shape, 9 1/2 In.	27.50
Art Glass, Chalice, Porcelain Medallion Of Young Woman, Green, Gold, 4 In.	88.00
Art Glass, Champagne, Pink & Clear, Stag, Doe, & Fawn In Forest, Rabbit, Quail	12.50
Art Glass, Cruet, Deep Blue, Amber Handle & Stopper, Pinched Sides, 9 In.	70.00
Art Glass, Cruet, Vinegar, Sapphire Blue, Amber Handle & Stopper, Enameled	68.00
Art Glass, Epergne, Opalescent To Lime, Three 8 In. Lilies, 10 In. Bowl	110.00
Art Glass, Epergne, Ruby, Vaseline, & Opalescent, 6-Way Brass Fitting	850.00
Art Glass, Epergne, Tall Trumpet & 3 Short Trumpets, Canary Threaded, 14 In	150.00
Art Glass, Epergne, 4 Lily, Cranberry Rim, Opalescent, Clear Rigaree, 14 In.	155.00
Art Glass, Jar, Powder, Pink Enamel Flower On Hinged Lid, Green, Brass, 4 In.	40.00
Art Glass, Jar, Powder, Ruby Stained, Frosted Stag's Head, Gold Trim, 6 In.	22.00
Art Glass, Jar, Sweetmeat, Opalescent, Green Threading, Pinched, 4 1/2 In.	79.00
Art Glass, Lamp Base, Mottled Purple, Blue, & Red, 29 In.	50.00
Art Glass, Lampshade, Yellow, Trees & River Scene, 4 3/4 In., Set Of 5	60.00
Art Glass, Pitcher, Orange Flecks On Frosted, Applied Reeded Handle, 4 In.	85.00
Art Glass, Pitcher, Water, Peach, Opalescent To Clear, Diamond-Quilted	95.00
Art Glass, Shade, G.V.Croismaire, Mottled Blue With White, 5 1/2 In., Pair	54.00
Art Glass, Spill, Purple Iridescent, Silver Collar, 5 1/2 In.	65.00
Art Glass, Syrup, Emerald Green, Embossed Birds On Nest Of Eggs	95.00
Art Glass, Toothpick, Gold Iridescent, Square Top, Ground Pontil	65.00
Art Glass, Toothpick, Yellow, Cranberry & Green Splashes, Leaf Spears	65.00
Art Glass, Vase, Blue, Swirled, Ruffled, 8 In.	22.50
Art Glass, Vase, Bud, Crystal, Paperweight, Cobalt Panels, Gold, 5 1/2 In.	48.00
Art Glass, Vase, Green, Poppylike Sprays, Footed, Honesdale, 9 1/2 In.	200.00
Art Glass, Vase, Hanging, Cased, Blown, Pink, White Lining, Loop Handle, 3 In.	45.00
Art Glass, Vase, Leerdam Unica, A.D.Copier, Mottled Jade, Corset, 11 In.	350.00
Art Glass, Vase, Red, Imperial Jewels, Amber At Base, 8 1/2 In.	75.00
Art Glass, Vase, Robin's-Egg Blue Opaque, Enamel Bouquet, 12 1/2 In.	89.00
Art Glass, Vase, Ruffled Edge, Luster, 5 1/2 In.	24.00
Art Glass, Vase, Triple Overlay, Custard, Clear, & Pink, Netting, 8 In.	35.00

Art Nouveau, a style characterized by free-flowing organic design, reached its zenith between 1895 and 1905. The style encompassed all decorative and functional arts from architecture to furniture and posters.

Art Nouveau, see also Furniture, Glass, etc.

Art Nouveau, **Ashtray**, Embossed Insects, Vines, Leaves, White Metal, 6 X 8 In.	24.00
Art Nouveau, **Box**, Round, Tomato Red, Acid Finish, Hess, 3 X 5 In.	85.00
Art Nouveau, **Brush**, Clothes, Sterling Silver, Full Figure Of Woman	12.00
Art Nouveau, **Buckle**, Sterling Silver, Nude Lady, Flowing Hair, 3 X 1 1/2 In.	95.00
Art Nouveau, **Buffer**, Nail, Stylized Floral	5.00
Art Nouveau, **Buttonhook**, Children & Women On Handle, 9 In.	16.00
Art Nouveau, **Buttonhook**, Sterling Silver, Embossed Cupid On Handle	15.00
Art Nouveau, **Buttonhook**, Sterling Silver, 6 1/2 In.	16.50
Art Nouveau, **Buttonhook**, Woman In Hammock, Sterling Silver	15.00
Art Nouveau, **Cigar Cutter**, Unger Brothers	22.00
Art Nouveau, **Cutter**, Cuticle, Woman In Hammock, Sterling Silver	8.00
Art Nouveau, **Dresser Set**, Lady's Head With Flowing Hair, 11 Piece	575.00
Art Nouveau, **Epergne**, Simpson Hall & Miller, Bristol Insert, 14 In.	125.00
Art Nouveau, **Figurine**, Standing Nude, Head Leaning Back, Pot Metal, 6 In.	35.00
Art Nouveau, **Iron**, Mustache Curling, Sterling Silver	8.50
Art Nouveau, **Letter Opener**, Sterling Silver, Lady's Head & Flowers	20.00
Art Nouveau, **Match Safe**, Silver, Cherubs Building Fire, Unger Bros., 3 In.	65.00
Art Nouveau, **Nail File**, Woman In Hammock, Sterling Silver	10.00
Art Nouveau, **Ornament**, Wall, Metal Vine, Silver Deposit Covalt Vase, 9 In.	27.00
Art Nouveau, **Plate**, Leaded Glass, Tulip & Leaves, Hanging Type, 12 In.	120.00
Art Nouveau, **Rose Bowl**, Green Iridescent, Brass Grill Top, 3 X 4 In.	35.00
Art Nouveau, **Spoon**, Sterling Silver, Lady's Head	8.50
Art Nouveau, **Spoon**, Sterling Silver, 5 1/2 In.	6.00
Art Nouveau, **Vase**, Women's Figures Handles, Silver Plate Rim & Frame, 8 In.	125.00
Aurene Type, **Bowl**, Blue, Ribbon Swirled, Folded Opening, 7 1/2 In.	195.00
Aurene Type, **Shade**, Gas, Gold Iridescent, Paneled, 5 1/2 In.	37.00

AURENE

Aurene glass was made by Frederick Carder of New York about 1904. It is an iridescent gold glass, usually marked Aurene or Steuben.

Aurene, see also Tiffany Glass

Aurene, **Atomizer**, Steuben, Gold, Signed F.Carder	175.00
Aurene, **Bonbon**, Gold, Blue Highlighted, Handled, Triangular, 3 1/2 In.	350.00
Aurene, **Bottle**, Cologne, Steuben, Peacock Blue, Amphora Shape, 6 1/2 In.	450.00
Aurene, **Bottle**, Perfume, Blue, Melon Ribbed	275.00
Aurene, **Bottle**, Perfume, Blue, Short Inside Stopper	225.00
Aurene, **Bottle**, Perfume, Blue, Signed, No.1414, 7 3/4 In.	325.00
Aurene, **Bottle**, Perfume, Signed & Numbered, 4 1/2 In.	375.00
Aurene, **Bottle**, Perfume, Steuben, Blue, Intaglio Cut, 10 In.	225.00
Aurene, **Bottle**, Perfume, Steuben, Blue, Melon Ribbed	375.00
Aurene, **Bottle**, Perfume, Steuben, Blue, Pinched Sided, 3 1/2 In.	575.00
Aurene, **Bottle**, Perfume, Steuben, Footed, 7 1/2 In., Pair	260.00
Aurene, **Bottle**, Perfume, Steuben, Gold, Melon Ribbed	275.00
Aurene, **Bottle**, Steuben, Blue, 3 1/2 In.	575.00
Aurene, **Bowl & Underplate**, Finger, Steuben, Gold, Signed & Numbered	195.00
Aurene, **Bowl**, Deep Iridescent Blue, Grotesque, Signed & Numbered, 5 In.	375.00
Aurene, **Bowl**, Gold To Blue, Pedestaled, 8 In.	150.00
Aurene, **Bowl**, Steuben, Amber, Flaring Rim, Sloping Cavetto, C.1905, 12 In.	250.00
Aurene, **Bowl**, Steuben, Blue & Gold, Pedestal, 8 In., Pair	550.00
Aurene, **Bowl**, Steuben, Blue, Curved-In Top Rim, 5 1/2 In.	425.00
Aurene, **Bowl**, Steuben, Blue, 10 In.	425.00
Aurene, **Bowl**, Steuben, Gold, Calcite Lining, Small Foot, Flaring, 8 In.	148.00
Aurene, **Bowl**, Steuben, Silver Blue Iridescent, 3 Handles, C.1905, 4 1/4 In.	425.00
Aurene, **Candlestick**, Steuben, Amber, Spiral Standard, C.1905, 8 In., Pair	300.00
Aurene, **Celery Dip**, Gold, Ruffled Top	135.00
Aurene, **Champagne**, Steuben, Gold, Swirl Pattern	110.00
Aurene, **Cologne**, Peacock Blue, Amphora Shape, Pedestal Base, 6 1/2 In.	425.00
Aurene, **Compote**, Steuben, Blue, Signed, No.367, 7 1/2 In.	400.00
Aurene, **Compote**, Steuben, Gold, Calcite, 8 X 3 1/4 In.	90.00
Aurene, **Compote**, Steuben, Gold, Twisted Stem, Signed Aurene 2604, 6 In.	330.00
Aurene, **Cordial**, Gold, 3 In.	150.00
Aurene, **Cup & Saucer**, Steuben, Gold	250.00
Aurene, **Dish**, Master Nut, 4 3/4 X 1 1/2 In.	150.00

Aurene, Goblet, Haviland, Gold, Twisted Stem, Signed	110.00
Aurene, Goblet, Steuben, Gold, Pink Highlights, 3 1/2 In.	140.00
Aurene, Goblet, Steuben, Gold, Twisted Stem	165.00
Aurene, Goblet, Steuben, Twisted Stem, Signed	125.00 To 150.00
Aurene, Jar, Jam, Steuben, Silver Lid & Bail, Signed 5402, 4 X 2 1/2 In.	225.00
Aurene, Lampshade, Gas, Steuben, Decorated, 5 3/4 X 5 In.	72.00
Aurene, Salt, Signed & Numbered	138.00
Aurene, Shade, Gold, 5 X 4 3/4 In.	20.00
Aurene, Shade, Steuben, Gold, Green Highlights, 3 In.	55.00
Aurene, Shade, Steuben, Gold, Squatty, 3 In.	50.00
Aurene, Sherbet & Underplate, Steuben, Gold, Pedestal Stem	175.00
Aurene, Sherbet & Underplate, Steuben, Gold & Blue, 24 Piece Set	2400.00
Aurene, Sugar & Creamer, Steuben, Gold	495.00
Aurene, Sherbet & Underplate, Steuben, Gold, Signed	150.00
Aurene, Tumbler, Liquor, Haviland, Silver, Bull's-Eye, 2 1/4 In.	135.00
Aurene, Urn, Gold, Vase Shape, 5 X 4 1/2 In.	235.00
Aurene, Vase, Bud, Carder, Tree Trunk, Gold Iridescent, Flow Blue Vase, 9 In.	350.00
Aurene, Vase, Bud, Steuben, Amber, 4 Sections, Pinched Waist, C.1905, 5 1/4 In.	125.00
Aurene, Vase, Bulbous, Signed, 4 In.	125.00
Aurene, Vase, Durand, Gold, Signed, No.20172, 5 1/2 X 3 3/4 In.	375.00
Aurene, Vase, Gold Iridescent, Ruffled Rim, Purple Lights, No.1724, 6 3/4 In.	350.00
Aurene, Vase, Gold With Pink Iridescent Highlights, 7 In.	270.00
Aurene, Vase, Gold, Applied Prunts, Raised Banding, 6 In.	475.00
Aurene, Vase, Gold, Green Spirals, Scalloped Top, 6 1/2 In.	700.00
Aurene, Vase, Gold, Signed Aurene 2776, 6 1/4 In.	150.00
Aurene, Vase, Lily, Signed & Numbered, 5 In.	285.00
Aurene, Vase, Steuben, Amber Iridescent, Bullet Shape, C.1904, 9 In.	225.00
Aurene, Vase, Steuben, Blue, Flaring Top, 5 In.	295.00
Aurene, Vase, Steuben, Blue, 5 X 5 In.	295.00
Aurene, Vase, Steuben, Deep Blue, Rolled Rim, C.1905, 12 In.	400.00
Aurene, Vase, Steuben, Gold Iridescent, Signed, 6 In.	170.00
Aurene, Vase, Steuben, Gold, Blue Highlights, Ruffled, Doughnut Base, 5 In.	195.00
Aurene, Vase, Steuben, Gold, Bulbous, 8 In.	450.00
Aurene, Vase, Steuben, Gold, Jack-In-The-Pulpit, 6 1/4 In.	395.00
Aurene, Vase, Steuben, Gold, Pink Iridescent, Classical Shape, 7 In.	270.00
Aurene, Vase, Steuben, Gold, Shape No.6213, Signed, 10 In.	235.00
Aurene, Vase, Steuben, Gold, Tree Trunk, Blue Highlights, 10 1/4 In.	235.00
Aurene, Vase, Steuben, Gold, Tree Trunk, Purple & Pink Iridescent, 6 1/2 In.	295.00
Aurene, Vase, Steuben, Gold, 6 1/4 In.	150.00
Aurene, Vase, Steuben, Gold, 10 In.	235.00
Aurene, Vase, Steuben, Pink & Purple, Tree Trunk, Mirror Finish, 6 1/4 In.	295.00
Aurene, Vase, Steuben, Turquoise Blue, Optic Rib, Footed, 5 3/4 In.	475.00
Aurene, Vase, Stick, Amber Blue, Signed, 6 In.	110.00
Aurene, Vase, Stick, Signed, 6 In.	110.00
Aurene, Wine, Steuben, Gold, Pedestal Base, 4 3/4 In.	110.00
Aurene, Wine, Steuben, Gold, Twisted Stem	95.00
Aurene, Wine, Twisted Stem, Signed	135.00

Austria, see Royal Dux, Kauffmann, Porcelain

Auto parts and accessories are collectors' items today.

Auto, Booklet, Chevrolet, 1931, Instruction	6.00
Auto, Bumper Ornament, God Bless America, White Enameled Metal, C.1935	3.00
Auto, Chair, Buffington, 1912, Folding, For Packard	24.50

Auto, Clock, see Clock, Auto

Auto, Coil Box, Ford	5.00
Auto, Eagle, Brass, Screw Threads For Radiator Cap, 10 In.	40.00
Auto, Gauge, Tire Pressure, Schrader, Firestone	6.50
Auto, Grill, 1947 Ford	4.00
Auto, Headlamp, Guido Ray, Type A	10.00
Auto, Hood Ornament, Eagle On World Globe, Bronze, C.Brau, C.1925, 9 1/2 In.	95.00
Auto, Hood Ornament, Flying Person, 14 X 4 In.	45.00
Auto, Hood Ornament, Swan With Upraised Wings, Chrome	12.00
Auto, Jar, Battery, Glass, Porcelain Cover, 10 In.	11.00
Auto, Kit, 1919	3.00
Auto, Knob, Gearshift, End-Of-Day, Monogrammed, Dated 1929	38.00
Auto, Knob, Gearshift, Model A, Black	3.00

Auto, Knob, Gearshift, Red & White	15.00
Auto, Lamp, Tung-Sol, 1940s	3.00
Auto, Lantern, Supreme, Dash Clamp, Red Reflector, Bull's-Eye Inside	24.50
Auto, License Plate, California, 1914	17.50
Auto, License Plate, Connecticut, 1923	3.50
Auto, License Plate, Connecticut, 1933	3.50
Auto, License Plate, Connecticut, 1934	3.50
Auto, License Plate, Maine, 1948, Brass	8.00
Auto, License Plate, New York, 1918-1957, Each	3.50
Auto, License Plate, New York, 1923-1948, Each	4.00
Auto, License Plate, New York, 1926, Pair	25.00
Auto, License Plate, New York, 1928, Pair	6.00
Auto, License Plate, New York, 1934, Pair	6.00
Auto, License Plate, North Dakota, 1915, Pair	6.00
Auto, License Plate, North Dakota, 1916, Pair	6.00
Auto, License Plate, North Dakota, 1917, Pair	6.00
Auto, License Plate, Pennsylvania, 1920	8.00
Auto, Light, Maxwell, Chicago, Ill. Brass Works, Red & Green, Pair	70.00
Auto, Oilcan, Ford, Metal	5.00
Auto, Ornament, Hood, Peacock, Tail Spread, Metal, 3 1/2 In.	20.00
Auto, Pencil Clip, Ford Motor Co., Metal, C.1950	3.00
Auto, Pliers, Ford	4.00
Auto, Pump, Tire, Brass	5.00
Auto, Radiator Cap Ornament, Whippet, Hand-Painted	10.00
Auto, Radiator Cap, Boyce Moto Meter, Midget Model	10.00
Auto, Stickpin, Black Crow Motor Car, 1906, Black Celluloid Crow	3.00
Auto, Token, Ford V8, 1933, Brass	8.00
Auto, Trailer, Ford 1937	24.00
Auto, Vase, see also Cloisonne, Vase, Auto	
Auto, Vase, Carnival Glass, Marigold, Holder, 7 1/2 In.	25.00
Aventurine, Rose Bowl, Purple, Pinched Top, 4 In.	90.00
Aventurine, Vase, Goldstone In Blood Red, Clear Overlay, Pontil, 9 3/4 In.	110.00
Aventurine, Vase, Goldstone, Blue Beads, Opalescent Heads, 7 In.	33.00
Aventurine, Vase, Green & White Stripes, Pot Shape, Cased, 6 1/2 X 7 In.	69.50
Aventurine, Vase, Pot Shape, Green & White Stripes, 6 1/2 In.	65.00
Avon, see Bottle, Avon	

Baccarat glass was made in France by La Compagnie des Cristalleries de Baccarat, located about 150 miles from Paris. The factory was started in 1765. The firm went bankrupt and began operating again about 1822. Famous cane and millefiori paperweights were made there during the 1860-1880 period. The firm is still working near Paris making paperweights and glasswares.

Baccarat, Bobeche, Crystal, Plain, Pair	20.00
Baccarat, Bottle, Cologne, Amberina Swirl, Stopper, 6 1/4 In.High	42.00
Baccarat, Bottle, Cologne, Cobalt Blue, Bowtie Shape, 4 In.	25.00
Baccarat, Bottle, Cologne, Gold Leaf, Pinecones, Gold Star On Top, 7 1/2 In.	49.50
Baccarat, Bottle, Perfume, Amberina Swirl, 6 1/4 In.	38.00
Baccarat, Bottle, Perfume, Amberina Swirl, 7 In.	65.00
Baccarat, Bottle, Perfume, Cobalt Blue, Bowtie Shape, 6 X 4 X 1 5/8 In.	33.00
Baccarat, Bottle, Perfume, Crystal, Gold Lion's Head On Each Side	37.50
Baccarat, Bottle, Perfume, Crystal, Guerlain, Paris, France	10.00
Baccarat, Bottle, Perfume, Green Faceted Stopper, 8 Sided Lip, 6 1/4 In.	35.00
Baccarat, Bottle, Perfume, Rubena Swirl, 5 1/2 In.	30.00
Baccarat, Bottle, Swirled, 5 3/4 In.	32.50
Baccarat, Bottle, Swirled, 6 1/4 In.	37.50
Baccarat, Candlestick, Swirl Pattern Pressed Glass, 9 In.High, Pair	45.00
Baccarat, Candlestick, Swirl, 8 In., Pair	20.00
Baccarat, Decanter, Crystal, Bulbous Stopper, 13 1/4 In.	20.00
Baccarat, Knife Rest, Crystal, Teardrop Ends, Signed	11.00
Baccarat, Knife Rest, Vaseline	33.00
Baccarat, Lamp, Amberina Swirl, Miniature	55.00
Baccarat, Paperweight, Gridel, Horse	150.00
Baccarat, Paperweight, Sulfide, Kennedy, John F., Blue Over White, Clear Case	600.00
Baccarat, Paperweight, Sulfide, Lafayette, Marquis De	225.00
Baccarat, Paperweight, Sulfide, Lee, Clear, White Cased	1000.00

Bank, Book, Lithographed,
Tin, 4 In.

Bank, Bottle, Figural,
Lincoln, 9 In.

Baccarat, Paperweight, Sulfide, Rogers, Will, Amber 200.00
Baccarat, Paperweight, Sulfide, Roosevelt, Eleanor .... 47.50 To 75.00
Baccarat, Paperweight, Sulfide, Roosevelt, Theodore, Amethyst 110.00
Baccarat, Paperweight, Sulfide, Roosevelt, Theodore, Green, Gray Cased 550.00
Baccarat, Paperweight, Sulfide, Stevenson, Adlai, Ruby 65.00
Baccarat, Paperweight, Sulfide, Truman, Harry S. 55.00
Baccarat, Paperweight, Sulfide, Wilson, Woodrow, Turquoise .... 50.00 To 100.00
Baccarat, Paperweight, Zodiac, Millefiori, 1967 .... 120.00
Baccarat, Pitcher, Wine, 7 Cut Panels, Applied Square Top Handle 40.00
Baccarat, Rose Bowl, Tiente Swirl, Scalloped Top, 9 1/2 X 3 1/2 X 1 1/2 In. 37.50
Baccarat, Tumbler, Lacy, Deep Blue Flint, C.1845, 4 1/4 In.High 70.00
Baccarat, Vase, Bud, Tulip Shape, 2 Pierced Covered Brass Cups, 7 X 6 In. 125.00
    Bag, Beaded, see Beaded Bag

*Metal banks have been made since 1868. There are still banks, mechanical
banks, and registering banks (those that total money deposited on the face of the
bank). Many old banks have been reproduced since the 1950s in iron or plastic.
The Whiting numbers refer to the book "Old Iron Still Banks" by Hubert B.
Whiting.*

    Bank, see also Bennington, Bank, Hopalong Cassidy, Bank, Kewpie,
    Bank
Bank, A & P Red Circle Coffee, Lithographed, Tin, 4 In. 4.50
Bank, Atlas Battery, 3 In. 5.00
Bank, Atlas Mason Jar, Zinc Lid, 3 1/2 In. 3.00
Bank, Aunt Jemima, Glazed 8.50
Bank, B & M Brick Oven Baked Beans, Copyright 1932, Tin, 3 1/4 X 2 5/8 In. 3.95
Bank, Barrel, Happy Days, Tin, J.Chein & Co., 4 In. .... 3.95 To 15.00
Bank, Barrel, Wooden, 6 1/4 X 4 1/2 In. 30.00
Bank, Baseball Shape, Yank, McElreath Beverage Co. 10.00
Bank, Baseball, Lithographed, Tin 2.00
Bank, Bear, Aqua 1.00
Bank, Bear, Glass, Tin Closure, 8 In. 6.50
Bank, Bear, Snow Crest Bottle 6.00
Bank, Begging Rabbit, Cast Brass 20.00
Bank, Benjamin Franklin, Metal, Wh-313 .... 4.95 To 6.95
Bank, Billiken, Painted, Cast Iron, Wh-50 .... 35.00 To 42.00
Bank, Book, Life Insurance Savings Bank, Blue Leather Over Metal, 5 1/4 In. 6.75
Bank, Book, Lithographed, Tin, 4 In. .... *Illus* 28.00
Bank, Book, Shelva-Bank, Crosley, Green Cloth Bound, 25 Cents A Day 15.00
Bank, Book, Three Pigs, Walt Disney, Green 28.00
Bank, Bottle, Figural, Lincoln, Lincoln Foods, Mass., C.1930, 8 1/2 In. 25.00
Bank, Bottle, Figural, Lincoln, Lincoln Foods, Mass., C.1930, 8 3/4 In. 20.00
Bank, Bottle, Figural, Lincoln, 9 In. .... *Illus* 18.00

Bank, Bottle, Log Cabin	2.00
Bank, British Sentry, Tin, 2 1/2 X 3 X 4 1/2 In.	37.50
Bank, Brockton Savings Bank, Ma., Patent 1913, Oval, Nickel On Brass, 4 In.	6.75
Bank, Bucket, Handle, "A Penny Saved Is A Penny Earned, " Tin, 3 In.	20.00
Bank, Budget, Washington White House Picture, Metal, Marx	15.00
Bank, Building, Black, 3 In., Wh-353	30.00
Bank, Building, Cast Iron, 6 In.	22.50
Bank, Building, Cupola, Cast Iron, 5 In.	30.00
Bank, Building, Fall River Trust Co., Metal, Bronze Finish, 4 X 3 In.	9.95
Bank, Building, Iron, Wh-422	19.75 To 20.00
Bank, Building, Miami Beach Federal Savings, Metal, 5 1/2 In.	17.00
Bank, Building, Towers At Ends, Iron, 4 X 4 In.	38.00
Bank, Building, Williamsburg Bank, Dome & Clock, Porcelain, C.1930, 8 In.	8.00
Bank, Building, Woolworth, 5 3/4 In., Wh-387	19.75 To 30.00
Bank, Building, 4 Towers, Gold Gilt, Cast Iron, 6 In.	40.00
Bank, Building, 4 Towers, Silver Gilt, Cast Iron, 6 In.	40.00
Bank, Bulldog, Seated, Cast Metal, 6 In., Wh-105	20.00
Bank, Bulldog, Sitting, Painted, Cast Iron, 4 1/2 In.	19.75
Bank, Bunnykins, Royal Doulton	47.50
Bank, Burns Co., N.Y., C.1900, Oval, Handle, Iron	9.00
Bank, Buster Brown & Tige, Cast Iron	25.00 To 55.00
Bank, Camel, Painted, Iron, 4 3/4 X 4 In., Wh-202	35.00 To 80.00
Bank, Campbell Kids	75.00
Bank, Capitalist, Gold Leaf, Cast Iron, Wh-21	60.00
Bank, Captain Kidd	130.00
Bank, Casey Jones Train, Metal, Engine 572, C.1920, 5 In.Long	22.50
Bank, Cash Register, Chas.W.Shank & Co., Patent 1905	65.00
Bank, Cash Register, Commonwealth, Shonk Works, American Can Co., 1905, 6 In.	20.00
Bank, Cash Register, Franklin, Dollar, Tin, Ornate, Miniature	12.00
Bank, Cash Register, Happy Days In Shield, 5, 10, & 25 Cents, Tin, Chein	15.00
Bank, Cash Register, Uncle Sam, 3 Coin, Red Metal	12.50
Bank, Castle, King & Puss 'n Boots, Wooden, German	4.50
Bank, Cat With Ball, Plastic	3.00
Bank, Cat, Sitting, Bowtie, Painted, Cast Iron	22.50
Bank, Chair, Coronation, 1953, Cast Iron, 8 In.	110.00
Bank, Change, Tin, Oval, Dated March 5, 1878	12.00
Bank, Chest Of Drawers, Redware, C.1850, Yellow Glaze Knobs, 7 1/2 In.	90.00
Bank, Clock, Flashlight, Alarm, Darche Mfg.Co., Patent 1910, Electric	100.00
Bank, Clock, "Time Is Money, " 1910	95.00
Bank, Clown, Grapette, Glass, Tin Closure, 7 1/2 In.	4.00
Bank, Clown, Rolypoly, Metal, Chrome Finish	7.00
Bank, Coin Deposit, Combination, Scrollwork, Nickel Finish, 5 In.	27.50
Bank, Coronation, George V & Mary, 1911, Wh-361	85.00
Bank, Court Jester, Porcelain, Blue Hat Balls	20.00
Bank, Cow, Brass	10.00
Bank, Crown, Coronation, Elizabeth, June 2, 1953, Red, Gold, Wh-321	30.00
Bank, Crying Negro Baby, Cast Iron, 7 In.	15.00 To 25.00
Bank, Deer With Antlers, Standing, Iron, Wh-196	30.00 To 39.75
Bank, Dime Register, Cash Register Shape, Lithographed, Tin, Chein	4.50
Bank, Dime Register, Jackie Robinson, Lithographed, Tin	11.00
Bank, Dime Register, Gem, 2 Coins, Lithographed, Tin	12.00
Bank, Dime Register, Little Piggy, Lithographed, Tin	4.00
Bank, Dime Register, Picture Of First Astronaut, Lithographed, Tin	4.50
Bank, Dime Register, Popeye, Lithographed, Tin, 1956	6.00
Bank, Dime Register, Popeye, Olive Oyle, & Wimpy, 1929, 2 1/2 In.	12.50
Bank, Dime Register, Statue Of Liberty	4.00
Bank, Dime, Union Savings, Building	12.00
Bank, Dog With Pack, Cast Iron, Wh-113	40.00 To 65.00
Bank, Dog, Sitting, Cast Iron, Wh-105	32.00
Bank, Dog's Head, Brown Glazed Pottery, Austria	15.00
Bank, Dog's Head, Porcelain, 1880, 2 In.	25.00
Bank, Donald Duck, Cereal Container, Hard Plastic, Metal Lid, 10 In.	9.50
Bank, Donald Duck, 11 In.	10.00
Bank, Donkey With Saddle, Iron	40.00
Bank, Donkey, Standing, Brass, 4 1/2 In.	30.00
Bank, Duck In Circus Tub, "Save For A Rainy Day, " Cast Iron, Wh-323	50.00

Bank, Dutch Banker, Transvaal Money Box, Brass, 5 1/2 In. 125.00
Bank, Dutch Boy 35.00
Bank, Dutch Girl 55.00
Bank, Eagle, Cast Iron 15.00
Bank, Eagle, Papier-Mache, 4 1/2 In. 5.00
Bank, Eight O'Clock Coffee Tin, 4 In. 2.00
Bank, Electrolux Refrigerator, Metal 25.00
Bank, Elephant On Tub, Wh-60 .... 26.50
Bank, Elephant With Howdah, Iron, Wh-68 .... 24.75
Bank, Elephant, Bisque 22.00
Bank, Elephant, Sitting, Worcester Salt, Metal, Gold Color 16.00
Bank, English Roadster, Nickel, Brass Key Lock, 5 X 2 In. 200.00
Bank, Esso, Glass Block 6.00
Bank, Excelsior, Iron 45.00
Bank, Flatiron Building, 5 1/2 In., Wh-409 .... 35.00
Bank, Foxey Grandpa 65.00
Bank, G.E.Refrigerator, Cast Iron, Green With Gold, Wh-237 .... 45.00
Bank, Gas Stove, "Save Your Money & Buy A Gas Stove, " Cast Iron, 5 In. 100.00
Bank, General Butler 450.00
Bank, Glass Block, Pittsburgh Corning, 3 1/4 In. 5.00
Bank, Globe, Chein 3.50
Bank, Globe, Medium Blue 140.00
Bank, Globe, Outline Continents & Oceans, Red 140.00
Bank, Globe, Red 140.00
Bank, Globe, World, Lithographed, Tin, Ohio Art .... 2.50 To 6.50
Bank, Globe, World's Fair, 1939, Glass, Raised Design, 4 In. 20.00
Bank, Gollywog 100.00
Bank, Gollywog, Brass, 5 5/8 In., Wh-3 .... 85.00
Bank, Graf Zeppelin, Cast Iron, Wh-171 .... 45.00
Bank, Hall's Excelsior, Cast Iron, Painted 95.00
Bank, Havoline Motor Oil 3.50
Bank, High Hat, Wh-259 .... 75.00
Bank, Hippo, Windup, Tin Lithograph, 5 In.High 5.00
Bank, Horse On Oval Base, Iron, 5 X 4 3/4 In., Wh-76 .... 19.75 To 20.00
Bank, Horse, Cast Brass 20.00
Bank, Horse, Standing, Brass, 5 In. 30.00
Bank, House, Cast Iron, Green, Orange Stripe, Wh-357 .... 30.00
Bank, Humpty Dumpty, Sitting On A Wall, Brass, 5 3/4 In. 125.00
Bank, Indian .... 30.00 To 75.00
Bank, Indian Chief's Head, Metal, Bronze Color, Key, 4 X 4 In. 6.00
Bank, Indian Warrior, Milk Glass, Coloring On Face & Headdress 17.75
Bank, Indian, Wh-39 .... 26.50
Bank, Indian's Head In Full Headdress, Cast Iron, 5 In. 40.00
Bank, Iron, Security Safe Deposit, Dated March 1, 1887, 5 In.High 30.00
Bank, Jiminy Cricket, Composition, Marked W.Disney, 6 1/2 In., Pair 25.00
Bank, Kelvinator Refrigerator, Arcade 45.00
Bank, Liberty Bell, Cast Iron 10.00
Bank, Liberty Bell, Cast Iron, Brass Finish, Embossed, Wh-229 .... 25.00
Bank, Liberty Bell, Glass 10.00
Bank, Liberty Bell, Marigold Iridescent 15.00
Bank, Lincoln's Bust, Coin Slot In Top Of Stovepipe Hat, 8 In. 4.75
Bank, Lincoln's Bust, Union Bank & Trust Of Lima, O., 1925, Bronze, 4 In. 20.00
Bank, Lion, Cast Brass .... 10.00 To 20.00
Bank, Lion, Painted, Cast Iron, Wh-89 .... 58.00
Bank, Lion, Standing, Brass, 5 In. 30.00
Bank, Log Cabin, Milk Glass, Painted 34.00
Bank, Lucky Dime 5.00
Bank, Lucky Joe, Glass, Tin Closure 4.00
Bank, Lucky Joe, Metal, Nash's Mustard Lid 4.00
Bank, Mailbox, Letters Slot Top, Hinged, Cast Iron, 4 In. 30.00
Bank, Mailbox, Patent April 8, 1902, Brass, 4 Slots, 5 1/4 X 4 1/2 In. 40.00
Bank, Mailbox, Ohio Art, Tin, 6 In. 6.00
Bank, Mailbox, U.S.A., Tin, Green, 9 In. 12.00
Bank, Mailbox, U.S.A., Wh-127 .... 19.50
Bank, Mammy, Ocean City, New Jersey 40.00
Bank, Mary & Her Lamb 50.00

Mechanical banks were first made about 1870. Any bank with moving parts is considered mechanical, although those most collected are the metal banks made before World War I. Reproductions are being made.

Bank, Mechanical, Alarm Clock	20.00
Bank, Mechanical, Always Did 'Spise A Mule .... *Illus*	225.00
Bank, Mechanical, Artillery, 4 Sided	185.00
Bank, Mechanical, Automatic Meter Register, Elves, Mother, Tin, 4 X 5 In.	35.00
Bank, Mechanical, Base With Teller, Cast Iron, 6 1/2 X 4 X 4 In.	100.00
Bank, Mechanical, Boy Scout .... *Illus*	800.00
Bank, Mechanical, Bulldog	115.00
Bank, Mechanical, Circus Elephant, Jumbo Savings, 5 In.	40.00
Bank, Mechanical, Circus Ticket Taker	55.00
Bank, Mechanical, Clock, Herkimer National Bank, Domed, Metal, Key	25.00
Bank, Mechanical, Clown On Globe, 1873	300.00
Bank, Mechanical, Clown, Chein	22.00
Bank, Mechanical, Columbus 3 Indian, World's Fair	375.00
Bank, Mechanical, Creedmore	195.00 To 250.00
Bank, Mechanical, Dentist, The	1400.00
Bank, Mechanical, Dinah, Yellow Blouse, 5 1/2 X 6 1/2 In.	135.00
Bank, Mechanical, Donald Duck, 2nd National, Tin	35.00
Bank, Mechanical, Dracula, Battery Operated	8.25
Bank, Mechanical, Eagle & Eaglettes .... *Illus*	275.00
Bank, Mechanical, Flashlight, Clock, Alarm, Electric, Darche Co., Chicago, 1906	100.00
Bank, Mechanical, Frog On Round Lattice Base	130.00
Bank, Mechanical, Girl Does Partial Striptease, Battery Operated	18.00
Bank, Mechanical, Globe On Arc	110.00
Bank, Mechanical, Gulliver, "Grow Tall, " English, 8 X 5 In.	45.00
Bank, Mechanical, Hickory Dickory Dock, Tin, C.1915, 4 X 2 In.	50.00
Bank, Mechanical, Hometown Battery	75.00
Bank, Mechanical, Hoopla	675.00
Bank, Mechanical, Joe Socko	300.00
Bank, Mechanical, Jolly Nigger, Blue Coat	135.00
Bank, Mechanical, Jolly Nigger, Bowtie, Aluminum, 6 In.	85.00
Bank, Mechanical, Jolly Nigger, Butterfly Tie	125.00
Bank, Mechanical, Jolly Nigger, Cast Iron, Painted, 6 X 5 In.	88.00
Bank, Mechanical, Jolly Nigger, Low Hat, Aluminum, 6 In.	115.00
Bank, Mechanical, Jolly Nigger, Red Coat	125.00
Bank, Mechanical, Jolly Nigger, Starlie's Patent, Straw Hat, Ears Move	85.00
Bank, Mechanical, Jolly Nigger, String Tie, Aluminum, 6 In.	100.00 To 110.00
Bank, Mechanical, Leapfrog .... *Illus*	650.00
Bank, Mechanical, Little Joe, Bowtie, Cast Iron, 5 1/4 In.	100.00 To 150.00
Bank, Mechanical, Magic Mouse, Windup, Lithographed, Tin	5.25
Bank, Mechanical, Man, "Watch Me Grow, " Lithographed, Tin, Apex Novelty	75.00
Bank, Mechanical, Money-Eating Hippopotamus, Tin, 5 X 3 In.	75.00
Bank, Mechanical, Monkey & Lion, 1783	70.00
Bank, Mechanical, Monkey, Tips Hat, Tin	12.00

Bank, Mechanical, Always Did 'Spise A Mule

Bank, Mechanical, Boy Scout

Bank, Mechanical, Leapfrog
(See Page 13)

Bank, Mechanical, Eagle & Eaglettes
(See Page 13)

Bank, Mechanical,
Speaking Dog

Bank, Mechanical,
Tammany Hall

Bank, **Mechanical,** Organ Monkey And Boy & Girl	225.00
Bank, **Mechanical,** Play-N-Save, Pinball Type, D.C.M.T.Ltd., Iron, 6 In.	75.00
Bank, **Mechanical,** Punch & Judy, Cast Iron, 1884	360.00
Bank, **Mechanical,** Punch & Judy, Tin, English, 3 X 5 In.	75.00
Bank, **Mechanical,** Rocket, Astro	12.00
Bank, **Mechanical,** Rocket, Mercury, Duro	24.00
Bank, **Mechanical,** Rooster, Cast Iron, 6 In.	95.00 To 150.00
Bank, **Mechanical,** Sambo, Aluminum	100.00
Bank, **Mechanical,** Sitting Circus Elephant, Tin, Chein	25.00
Bank, **Mechanical,** Slot Machine, Hotel Thunderbird	25.00
Bank, **Mechanical,** Slot Machine, Las Vegas, Nevada, Jackpot, Silver Plate	20.00
Bank, **Mechanical,** Southern Comfort, Soldier Shoots Coin Into Bottle	78.00
Bank, **Mechanical,** Speaking Dog *Illus*	225.00
Bank, **Mechanical,** Strato, Duro	24.00
Bank, **Mechanical,** Tammany Hall *Illus*	150.00
Bank, **Mechanical,** Uncle Sam, Cast Iron, Reproduction	22.50
Bank, **Mechanical,** William Tell *Illus*	350.00
Bank, **Mechanical,** Windmill, Lithographed, Tin, 6 In.	6.50
Bank, **Mechanical,** Wireless	375.00
Bank, **Merry-Go-Round,** Cast Iron	60.00
Bank, **Mickey Mouse,** Band Uniform, Walt Disney, C.1955, 9 1/2 In.	8.50
Bank, **Mickey Mouse,** Cereal Container, Hard Plastic, Metal Lid, 10 In.	9.50
Bank, **Mickey Mouse,** Glazed, 7 In.	9.00
Bank, **Mickey Mouse,** Walt Disney Productions, Cast Iron, 5 In.	50.00
Bank, **Middy,** Cast Iron	60.00 To 65.00
Bank, **Moon & Rocket Ship,** Strato, Metal	3.50
Bank, **Mr.Peanut,** Plastic, Beige, 8 1/2 In.	5.25
Bank, **Mr.Peanut,** Plastic, 8 In.	8.00
Bank, **Mutt & Jeff,** Cast Iron	65.00 To 110.00
Bank, **Napoleon,** Porcelain, 9 1/2 In.High	37.00
Bank, **Negro Mammy,** Glazed, 6 1/2 In.	8.50

Bank, New Deal, Red, White, & Blue Stripes, Tin, Chein, 3 1/4 In.	25.00
Bank, Oilcan, Tin	2.50
Bank, Old Fashioned Alarm Clock, Tin	19.00
Bank, Peach, Redware, 3 In.	95.00
Bank, Penny Pail, "A Penny Saved, " Tin	5.00
Bank, Phono Money Box, Tin & Plastic, Lock & Key, 5 X 7 In.	85.00
Bank, Pig & Drum, Majolica, German, 3 1/4 In.	36.00
Bank, Pig With 3 Little Pigs At Table On Side, Porcelain, 4 1/4 In.	17.00
Bank, Pig, Bennington Type, 5 1/2 In.	*Illus* 39.00
Bank, Pig, "Brother Can You Spare A Dime, " Glass, Tin Closure, 5 1/4 In.	10.00
Bank, Pig, Carnival Glass, Marigold, 4 In.	3.00 To 3.50
Bank, Pig, Cast Iron, Gold Paint	35.00
Bank, Pig, Cobalt Blue Glass, 4 In.	10.00
Bank, Pig, Heavy Metal	7.00
Bank, Pig, Pink, Form Of Purse, Green, Porcelain	19.50
Bank, Pig, Sitting, Cast Iron, 3 In.	24.00
Bank, Pig, Standing, Pink, Open Mouth, Cast Iron, 5 In.	75.00
Bank, Piggie, Bronze, Embossed Marion	40.00
Bank, Pinball, Tin & Plastic	12.00
Bank, Porcelain Boot, Russet, Cat Chasing Mouse, Japan	15.00
Bank, Pottery, Penny, American, C.1850, Jug Shape, 6 In.	30.00
Bank, Prancing Horse, Iron, 4 1/2 In.	38.00
Bank, Presto, Black, 3 1/2 In., Wh-426	35.00
Bank, Professer Pug Frog, Cast Iron, Wh-230	85.00
Bank, Radio, Iron	14.00
Bank, Refrigerator, Servel Electrolux, Metal	8.95
Bank, Register, Treasury, Tin	4.00
Bank, Rival Dog Food, Tin	3.00
Bank, Rocking Baseball, Glass, Tin Closure, 3 In.	7.50
Bank, Rolls Royce Radiator, Eagle Cap, Black Leather, Silver Finish	8.00
Bank, Rooster	20.00
Bank, Roy Rogers' Boot	12.00
Bank, Running Horse, Cast Iron, Painted, 4 1/2 In.	27.75
Bank, Safe, Coin Deposit Bank, Combination Lock, Iron, 4 X 3 In.	18.75
Bank, Safe, Combination, Black, Gold Trim, Cast Iron, 1887, 6 X 8 X 5 In.	75.00
Bank, Safe, Green Door, Gold Trim, Cast Iron, 3 X 2 1/4 In.	25.00
Bank, Safe, J.E.Steven Co., Patent 1897, Iron, Key, Wh-287	25.00
Bank, Safe, Kenton Hdwe.Co., Kenton, Ohio, Combination, Industrial Type, Iron	50.00
Bank, Safe, Picture Of 1898 Battleship, Red & Green, Tin, 5 1/2 In.	40.00
Bank, Safe, Royal Safe Deposit, Paint, Decals, Iron, 6 X 5 1/4 In.	38.75
Bank, Safe, Security Safe Deposit, March 1, 1887, Footed, Cast Iron, 5 In.	30.00
Bank, Sailor With Duffel Bag, Seamen's Savings Bank, Porcelain, C.1930	8.00
Bank, Santa & Tree	200.00
Bank, Satellite, Metal, C.1960, 10 1/2 In.	8.00
Bank, Save & Smile	100.00
Bank, Savings, Roy Rogers & Trigger, Lithographed, Tin, Metal Padlock & Key	12.50
Bank, Scottie Dog, Pewter, 6 In.	12.50
Bank, Security Safe, Cast Iron, 3 X 3 X 4 1/4 In.	32.00

Bank, Mechanical, William Tell
(See Page 14)

Bank, Pig, Bennington Type, 5 1/2 In.

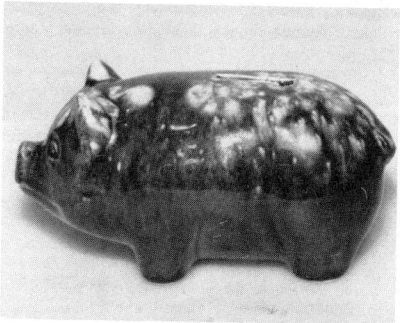

Bank, Servel Electrolux Refrigerator, Metal, 4 In. .... 8.95 To 25.00
Bank, Shaggy Dog With Pack On Back, 3 3/4 In., Wh-106 .... 30.00
Bank, Sharecropper, Ocean City, New Jersey 40.00
Bank, Sharecropper, Painted, Cast Iron, Wh-18 .... 45.00 To 65.00
Bank, Sheep, Brass 10.00
Bank, Sheep, Iron, 1880s, 3 X 4 1/2 In. 19.00
Bank, Shoe, Wooden 12.00
Bank, Simple Simon, Simon Fishing In Bucket Picture, Tin 8.50
Bank, Skookums, Glass, Painted 51.00
Bank, Skyscraper, Tin 20.00
Bank, Slot Machine, Las Vegas, Nevada, Jackpot, Silver Plate, 5 In. 20.00
Bank, Smiling Pig, Shawnee Pottery 3.00
Bank, Speedboat, Brass, C.1930 .... 8.00
Bank, Squirrel Holding Nut, Tin 9.00
Bank, Standing Lion, Bronze Paint, Cast Iron, C.1850, 5 1/2 X 3 1/4 In. 28.00
Bank, State Bank Building, Cast Iron, 4 In. 17.50
Bank, State Bank, Cast Iron, 4 1/2 In. 30.00
Bank, State Bank, Gold Gilt, 5 1/2 In., Wh-444 .... 45.00
Bank, State Bank, Penny, Cast Iron, 3 X 4 In. 12.75
Bank, Statue Of Liberty, "Save For Liberty Bank, " Cast Iron, Bronze Finish 19.00
Bank, Street Car, "Main Street, " Cast Iron, Wh-166 .... 185.00
Bank, Suitcase, Steel, James Edgar Co., Brockton, Ma., 4 1/8 In. 6.95
Bank, Tank, U.S.A., Iron 22.00
Bank, Tank, U.S.A., World War I, Black, Wh-163 .... 45.00
Bank, Telephone, Wall, Gong Bell, Metal, 5, 10, & 25 Cent Slots 6.75
Bank, Tole, Tin 10.00
Bank, Turkey, Iron 20.00
Bank, Two-Faced Devil 150.00
Bank, Two-Faced Woman, Cast Iron, Wh-44 .... 58.00 To 65.00
Bank, Uncle Sam's Register, Metal, 3 Coins, 6 In. 10.00
Bank, Uncle Scrooge & Nephews Sitting On Vault, Rubber, Disney, 7 In. 5.75
Bank, Underwood Portable Typewriter, New York World's Fair, 1939 .... 36.00
Bank, Watermelon Slice, Chalkware, 9 1/2 X 4 In. 45.00
Bank, Woodchopper, Lithographed, Tin, German 15.00
Bank, World Champions, Baseball, Tin, Ohio Art 3.50
Bank, World War I Shell, Slot At Base, Brass, Nickel Head, 8 In. 50.00
Bank, World War I Shell, 40 Mm., Engraved, Brass, 12 In. 50.00
Bank, Young Negro 50.00
Banko, Vase, Monkey In Kimono Serving Tea To 2 Monkeys, 8 1/4 In. 92.00
Banko, Vase, 3 Monkeys Playing On Red, Mottled Green & Black Top, 8 In. 75.00
Barometer, Bianchi & Compi, Amsterdam, Marquetry, 4 Ft. .... Illus 2700.00
Barometer, J.Brunner, Birmingham, Wheel, Convex Mirror, C.1790 .... 200.00
　　　Barr, see Worcester
Barum Ware, Vase, Carved Floral, Slip, Charles Brannan & J.D., 1883, 13 In. 85.00

Basalt is a black stoneware made by mixing iron and oxides into a basic clay.
It is very hard and can be finished on a lathe. Wedgwood developed his
famous black basalt in 1769, which was an improvement on a similar ware made in
Staffordshire, England, as early as 1740. Basalt is still being made in
England and on the Continent.

Basalt, Creamer, Black 125.00
Basalt, Figurine, Foo Dog, Carved, 3 In. 40.00
Basalt, Teapot, English, Black, Neoclassical Motifs, Rectangular, C.1825 .... 40.00

Battersea enamels are enamels painted on copper and made in the Battersea
District of London from about 1750 to 1756. Many similar enamels are
mistakenly called Battersea.

Battersea, Box, Verse On Top, Red Design On Blue, Mirror Inside, Oval, 2 In. 225.00
Battersea, Tieback, Curtain, Brass Fittings, Lady's Painted Portrait, 2 In. 35.00
Battersea, Tieback, Curtain, Medieval Scene, Pair 125.00
Bauer, Server, Coffee, Yellow, Wooden Handle 15.00
Bauer, Teapot, Green, Ringed, 7 In. 4.00

Bavaria was a district where many types of pottery and porcelain were made
for centuries. The words Bavaria, Germany, appeared after 1871.
Bavarian, see also Rosenthal

Bavarian, Bowl, Open Handled, Gold Border, Yellow Roses On White, 12 X 8 In. 30.00
Bavarian, Bowl, Pink Carnations, Heavy Gold Decoration, 9 1/2 In. 22.00
Bavarian, Bowl, Yellow Roses, Louise, 10 In. 15.00
Bavarian, Butter Pat, White, Embossed Edge Design, Round, 3 In. 2.35
Bavarian, Butter Pat, Young Woman In Village Scene, Crown Mark 12.00
Bavarian, Cake Set, Green & Purple Grapes, Autumn Leaves, Handled, 7 Piece 55.00
Bavarian, Cake Set, Various Fruits, Gold Edge, 7 Piece 45.00
Bavarian, Celery, Open End Handles, Sweetpeas On Blue, Gold Tracery Band 26.50
Bavarian, Chocolate Pot, White To Burnt Orange, Blue Roses, Gold 28.50
Bavarian, Chocolate Set, Prince Regent, Roses On Green & Rust, 7 Piece 165.00
Bavarian, Coffeepot, Pink Roses, Gold, 8 In. 28.00
Bavarian, Cup & Saucer, Bouillon, Gold Handle & Band Of Fleur-De-Lis 9.50
Bavarian, Cup & Saucer, Demitasse, Blue Garlands, Floral, Gold, McKnight 6.50
Bavarian, Cup & Saucer, Demitasse, Pink Roses 18.50
Bavarian, Cup & Saucer, Sterling Overlay, Marked .999, Miniature 12.00
Bavarian, Cup & Underplate, Bouillon, Gold Clover Leaf, Pink Flowers 18.50
Bavarian, Dessert Set, Hand-Painted Multicolored Flowers, Gilded, 24 Piece 50.00
Bavarian, Dessert Set, Turquoise, Flowerbasket Reserve Panel, 16 Piece 75.00
Bavarian, Dish, Egg, Floral On Green, 6 Indentations, Gold Edged, 8 In. 35.00
Bavarian, Eggcup, Double, White, Gold Trim 16.00
Bavarian, Fish Set, 7 Piece 150.00
Bavarian, Hatpin Holder, Blue At Top, Band Of Pink Roses 18.00
Bavarian, Hatpin Holder, White, Band Of Mauve Roses, Green Flowers, 7 In. 32.50
Bavarian, Pitcher, Hand-Painted Cherries, 5 1/4 In. 20.00
Bavarian, Plate, Cake, Fruit Center, Gold Design Edge, 11 In. 20.00
Bavarian, Plate, Cake, White & Pink Roses, 10 1/2 In. 14.00
Bavarian, Plate, Dinner, Floral Border, Paul Mueller, 10 In. 7.00
Bavarian, Plate, Dutch Scenes On Green, Scalloped, Gold, 10 In., Pair 35.00
Bavarian, Plate, Floral, Gold Scalloped, Schumann, 10 In. 29.50
Bavarian, Plate, Forget-Me-Nots, Raised Lacquer, Blue Border, 9 1/2 In. 30.00
Bavarian, Plate, Fuchsias, Gold Outlined, Signed Luce, 8 1/2 In. 28.00
Bavarian, Plate, Hand-Painted Floral, Stauffer, 6 In. 3.35
Bavarian, Plate, Hand-Painted Forget-Me-Nots, 6 In. 3.00
Bavarian, Plate, Ivory & 2 Shades Of Pink Roses, Gold Rim, 12 1/2 In. 27.50
Bavarian, Plate, Martha & George Washington, 8 In., Pair 20.00
Bavarian, Plate, Monbijou, Pink Wild Roses, Scalloped Gold Rim, 8 3/4 In. 8.00
Bavarian, Plate, Multicolor Floral On Cream, Z.S.& Co., 11 In. 7.50
Bavarian, Plate, Plums, Gold Line Rim, Pierced, 12 In. 20.00
Bavarian, Plate, Post Office, Albany, N.Y., Color Transfer, J & C, 6 In. 8.00
Bavarian, Plate, Raised Gold Ribbed Floral On Gold Rim, 8 1/4 In. 14.00
Bavarian, Plate, Raspberry, Cherry, & Blue Plums, Scalloped, R.K., 9 1/2 In. 18.00
Bavarian, Plate, Roman Garden, N.R.Gifford, Stauffer Studio, 11 In. 87.00
Bavarian, Plate, Service, Gold Decoration, Selb, H.& Co., 10 In. 15.00
Bavarian, Plate, Violets, Ida Sommer, 6 3/4 In. 6.50
Bavarian, Plate, White House, Color Transfer, J.C.& CHB Co., 8 1/2 In. 10.00
Bavarian, Plate, White, Roses, Gold Outlined Green Border, 7 In. 7.25
Bavarian, Plate, 2 Deer & Scenery, Hole For Hanging, 8 1/2 In. 12.00
Bavarian, Pot, Mustard, Covered, Mignon, Z.S.& Co., No.57 .... 7.50
Bavarian, Ramekin & Underplate, Green, Gold, Art Nouveau 8.00
Bavarian, Salt & Pepper, Gold Etched 9.00
Bavarian, Salt, Pepper, & Toothpick, Pink & Blue Floral On Blue, Gold Tops 30.00
Bavarian, Server, Lemon, Handled, Violets, Signed 16.50
Bavarian, Sugar & Creamer, Cover, Blue, White, Gold Trim, ZS & Co. 12.00
Bavarian, Sugar & Creamer, Moliere, Silver Luster, Gold Trim, Scrolls 20.00
Bavarian, Sugar & Creamer, Poppy 17.50
Bavarian, Tea Set, Pink Roses In Panels, Black Outline, 3 Piece 55.00
Bavarian, Teapot, Baskets Of Fruit On Sides & Lid, 6 X 11 In. 35.00
Bavarian, Tray, Dresser, Three Large Pink Peonies, 12 X 8 In. 22.00
Bavarian, Tray, Pin, Blue Forget-Me-Nots, Gold Trim, Pierced Border, Schumann 10.00
Bavarian, Tray, Pin, Cotton In Bloom, H & Co., Artist Croni, 5 1/2 In.Long 3.50
Bavarian, Vase, Colonial Ladies & Man, Handled, Sterling Rims, 3 In., Pair 35.00
Bavarian, Vase, Pink Roses, Gold Bands, Signed Schumann, 3 1/2 In. 2.50
    Bayonet, see Weapon, Bayonet
Beaded Bag, Art Deco, Blue, Gold Colored Openwork Frame 42.00
Beaded Bag, Art Nouveau Type Chain, Silver Plate Frame, Steel Beads 25.00
Beaded Bag, Pouch Shape, Purple Floral, Drawstring 12.00

Barometer, Bianchi & Compi,
Amsterdam, Marquetry, 4 Ft.
(See Page 16)

Bell, Meissen,
C.1740, 4 1/2 In.
(See Page 20)

Beaded Bag, Silver Marcasites, Ornate Metal Frame, Fringed	10.00
Beam, see Bottle, Beam	
Beatles, Decal, 5 On Card, 12 1/2 X 8 1/2 In.	125.00
Beatles, Scrapbook, Photograph Cards, 285 Scenes	35.00
Beatles, Submarine, Yellow, Corgi	12.00
Beaver Falls, Tile, Victorian Man, Brown & Beige	45.00
Beck, see also Buffalo Pottery	
Beck, Fish Set, Goodwin Pottery, Hand-Painted, 13 Piece	144.00
Beck, Plate, Fish, Striped Bass, Signed, 9 In.	12.00
Beck, Plate, Fish, Walleye Pike, Signed, 9 In.	12.00
Beck, Plate, Fowl Scene, Brown Scalloped Rim, Gold Trim, 9 1/4 In.	16.00
Beck, Plate, Game, Spaniel With Snipe In Mouth, Gold Border, 9 1/4 In.	49.00
Beck, Plate, Pheasants, Flow Blue Edge, 8 In.	17.00
Beck, Sauceboat & Underplate, Fish, Striped Bass, Signed	12.00
Beck, Sauceboat & Underplate, Fish, Walleye Pike, Signed	12.00

Beehive, Austria, or Beehive, Vienna, china includes all the many types of decorated porcelain marked with the famous beehive mark. The mark has been used since the eighteenth century.

Beehive, see also Royal Vienna	
Beehive, Bowl, Handled, Applied Flowers, Reticulated, 5 In.	95.00
Beehive, Bowl, Signed Juno Beehive, Austria On Back, 9 In.	47.50
Beehive, Bowl, Slate Color, 10 X 4 In.	15.00
Beehive, Container, Cigarette, Floral, Pink & Red Roses, Green Leaves, 3 In.	18.00
Beehive, Cup & Saucer, Empire Style, Fox Hunting Scene	105.00
Beehive, Dish, Bone, Gold Stripes & Edge, Blue Mark, No.1696, 9 X 4 In.	22.50
Beehive, Dish, Pin, Cherubs On Lid, Round, Royal Vienna	25.00
Beehive, Plate, Cherubs, 7 In.	16.50
Beehive, Plate, Floral Center & Rim, Yellow, Blue, & Pink, 9 1/2 In.	19.50
Beehive, Plate, Game, Partridge, Rococo Gold Scalloped Border, 11 In.	75.00
Beehive, Plate, People & Cherubs Center, Gold & Cobalt Border, 9 1/2 In.	85.00
Beehive, Plate, Portrait, Gypsy Lady, 9 In.	375.00
Beehive, Plate, Portrait, Turquoise & Gold Border, 9 In.	350.00
Beehive, Plate, Portrait, Young Lovers, Gold Trim, 10 1/2 In.	32.50
Beehive, Plate, Scenic, Maroon & Gold Border, 9 1/2 In., Pair	150.00
Beehive, Vase, Venus & Cherub, Double Handled, Maroon, Green, Gold, 8 1/2 In.	95.00

Bells have been made of china, glass, or metal. All types are collected.

Bell, see also Custard Glass, Bell	
Bell, Acanthus Decoration, Tepee Finial, Side Strike, C.1870	32.00
Bell, Bisque, Cupids	5.00
Bell, Bisque, Figural, Bird	4.50
Bell, Bisque, Figural, Flower	3.50
Bell, Blown Glass, Dark Amber, Folded Rim, 9 In.	75.00
Bell, Bohemian Glass, Ruby, Cut Flowers In Medallion & Scroll, 6 In.	37.00
Bell, Brass & Bronze, Ship's, 10 X 10 In.	150.00
Bell, Brass & Iron, Tap, For Desk, Patent 1856 & 1863	11.95
Bell, Brass, A.R.P. G & J 1909, English Air Raid, 9 In.	33.00
Bell, Brass, Call, 4 X 4 In.	18.00

Bell, Brass, China, Bird Handle, 4 In. 9.00
Bell, Brass, China, Brass Mallet, 7 1/2 In. 14.00
Bell, Brass, China, Monster Handle, 4 1/2 In. 8.00
Bell, Brass, Chinese, Figural 5.00
Bell, Brass, Chinese, Table, Lady In Hoop Skirt 22.00
Bell, Brass, Church, Buckeye Bell Foundry, 1855, Cincinnati, 18 In. ...-........... 435.00
Bell, Brass, Dutch Girl 10.00
Bell, Brass, Enamel, 1 1/2 In., String Of 3 .... 9.00
Bell, Brass, Engraved, 4 In. 14.00
Bell, Brass, Figural, Angel 3.50
Bell, Brass, Figural, Dutch Girl, Peaked Hat, Knitting Sock, 3 1/2 In. 27.50
Bell, Brass, Figural, French Girl, Leg Clapper, 3 In.High 24.00
Bell, Brass, Figural, Lady In Hoop Skirt, 4 1/4 In. 15.00
Bell, Brass, Figural, Napoleon 18.50
Bell, Brass, Figural, Victorian Lady, Clapper Feet, 5 In. 48.00
Bell, Brass, Hames, Double Clappers, 3 On Strap 20.00
Bell, Brass, Horse Harness, 4 On 17 In. Double Leather Strap 25.00
Bell, Brass, India, Dinner, Wooden Handle, 8 1/2 In. 7.00
Bell, Brass, Marked China, Figural, Little Red Ridinghood, Miniature 12.50
Bell, Brass, Marked China, Rearing Horse 8.00
Bell, Brass, Marked China, 2 3/4 In. 12.00
Bell, Brass, Mule-Drawn Streetcar Type, Dated 1892, Foot Powered 200.00
Bell, Brass, Nickel Plated, Cutter, 3 On 1 1/2 In. Metal Strap 15.00
Bell, Brass, Nickel Plated, Cutter, 4 On 14 In. Metal Strap 15.00
Bell, Brass, School Type, On Iron Strap, 3 In. Diameter Bells 28.00
Bell, Brass, School, Hand, Wooden, 5 In. 25.00
Bell, Brass, School, Hand, 7 1/2 In. 30.00
Bell, Brass, School, Hand, 9 In. 35.00
Bell, Brass, School, Nickel Plated, Wooden Handle, 4 1/2 In. 12.00
Bell, Brass, School, Wooden Handle, C.1850, 11 In. 45.00
Bell, Brass, School, 10 X 6 In. .... 22.00 To 34.00
Bell, Brass, School, 11 X 6 1/2 In. 36.00
Bell, Brass, Ship's, Iron Bracket, Providence, R.I., 8 In. 85.00
Bell, Brass, Ship's, On 4-Legged Stand, 28 In. 175.00
Bell, Brass, Sleigh, Buckeye, 36 On 89 In. Strap, Riveted 85.00
Bell, Brass, Sleigh, 23 Graduated On Leather Strap 95.00
Bell, Brass, Sleigh, 3 On Metal 10 3/4 In. Strap 9.95
Bell, Brass, Sleigh, 30 On String, Slotted 1 Way, Some Cotter Keys 75.00
Bell, Brass, Sleigh, 31 On String, Slotted 1 Way, 1 Bell Cotter Keyed 75.00
Bell, Brass, Streetcar Type, Pull Bell, Round, 5 In. 30.00
Bell, Brass, Tap, Iron Base, 3 3/4 In. 8.95
Bell, Brass, Tap, Ornate Iron Base, Patent 1870-74, 4 3/4 In. 11.95
Bell, Brass, Town Crier, Wooden Handle, 11 X 6 In. 52.50
Bell, Brass, Wagon, Conical, Loop For 1 1/2 In. Strap, 5 X 3 3/4 In. 10.00
Bell, Brass, Wooden Handle, 14 In. 15.00
Bell, Brass, 10 Graduated On 31 In. Rudisill, Rivets Between Each 40.00
Bell, Brass, 23 Graduated On 92 In. Strap, Rivet Between Each 250.00
Bell, Brass, 3 Embossed Eagles, Harness Type Handle, 3 3/4 X 3 1/2 In. 25.00
Bell, Bronze, C.1893, 3 1/2 In. Diameter At Mouth 12.50
Bell, Bronze, Carved Men & Mythological Figures, 4 1/4 X 3 In. 42.50
Bell, Bronze, Church, Van Duzen Co., Cincinnati, Ohio, 36 In. 890.00
Bell, Bronze, Figural, Elizabethan Lady, 4 In. 19.00
Bell, Bronze, School, Turned Maple Handle, 9 In. 25.00
Bell, Bronze, School, Turned Wooden Handle, C.1850, 11 In. 48.00
Bell, Capo-Di-Monte, Blue Crown & Shield Mark, 4 1/2 In. 27.50
Bell, Capo-Di-Monte, Table, Blue Crown Mark 20.00
Bell, Capo-Di-Monte, Table, Figural Handle 20.00
Bell, Carnival Glass, Southern Belle 8.50
Bell, Cast Iron, Minute Man 18.50
Bell, Church, Wheel & Stand, 24 In. 300.00
Bell, Cow, New England, 6 In. 8.95
Bell, Cut Glass, Dinner, Hobstar & Fan, Cut Handle, 7 1/2 In. 245.00
Bell, Cut Glass, Hobstar & Cane, American 115.00
Bell, Cut Glass, Stars, Pointed Handle, 4 In.High 16.00
Bell, Delft, Germany 23.00
Bell, Eiffel Tower, Steel Trimmed With Brass, C.1880, 6 1/4 In.High 85.00

Bell, Enamel, Chinese, Blue, Ivory Man Figural Handle, 4 1/2 In.	65.00
Bell, English Silver, Patin, London, 1724, Engraved Crest, 4 1/4 In.	2500.00
Bell, Glass, Bristol White, Red Glass Threading, 11 1/2 In.High	185.00
Bell, Glass, Souvenir, Cosmopolitan Hotel, Ruby Base & Clapper, 6 1/2 In.	20.00
Bell, Glass, Souvenir, World's Fair, 1893, Swirled Handle	38.00
Bell, Horse Shaft, 4 Graduated Half Bells, Brass & Nickel Plated, 13 In.	15.00
Bell, Hotel Front Desk	14.50
Bell, Hummel, Figural	15.00
Bell, Iron, Cow, Ball Clapper, 7 In.	15.00
Bell, Iron, Sleigh, 30 On 76 In. Strap, Slotted Both Ways, Painted Red	40.00
Bell, Luster, China, Figural, Dutch Girl	5.00
Bell, Lutz Type, Ribbon Glass	35.00
Bell, Majolica, Figural, Cat	20.00
Bell, Martingale, 36 On Strap	125.00
Bell, Meissen, C.1740, 4 1/2 In. Illus	1900.00
Bell, Metal, Griffin Openwork Handle, 4 1/2 In.	12.00
Bell, Milk Glass, Painted Lilacs, Chain Links Forming Handle	38.00
Bell, Mine, Alarm, 8 1/4 In.	25.00
Bell, Nailsea, Light Green, Clear Handle, 10 X 5 In.	52.00
Bell, Porcelain, Figural, Old-Fashioned Girl, 3 In.	6.50
Bell, Porcelain, Green Luster, Pink Roses, Wooden, Clapper	11.00
Bell, Porcelain, Smoke, Child With Umbrella, 3 In.	40.00
Bell, Pressed Glass, Dinner, Ashburton, From Cordial Mold	72.00
Bell, Royal Doulton, Red-Coated Santa Claus, Verse, 2 3/4 In.	30.50
Bell, Satin Glass, Ribbon	18.50
Bell, Silver Plate, Dinner, Figural, Lady In Old-Fashioned Gown, 1969	15.00
Bell, Silver Plate, Pairpoint, Brown Marble Base, Patent 1874	25.00
Bell, Silver Plate, Tap Type, On Standard, Patent 1863, 4 1/2 In.	25.00
Bell, Silver, Dinner Gong, Oriental, Shape Of Sea Monster, 9 1/2 In.	35.00
Bell, Sleigh, 42 On 94 1/2 In. Strap	85.00
Bell, Steel, Cow, 8 In.	14.00
Bell, Store, Over-The-Door Type	25.00
Bell, Streetcar, Conductor Rings With Foot	35.00
Bell, Tin, Cow, Handmade	9.50
Bell, Tin, Tap	5.00
Bell, Wicker, Wicker Clapper, Cow Bell Mounted Inside For Noise, 12 In.	95.00
Bell, Wood & Metal, Aunt Jemima Type Black Woman	10.00
Bell, see also Bohemian Glass, Bell	
Belle Ware, Salt & Pepper, Floral, Tapered, Signed	75.00

Belleek china was made in Ireland, other European countries, and the United States. The glaze is creamy yellow and appears wet. The first Belleek was made in 1857.

Belleek, see also Ceramic Art Co., Haviland, Lenox, Ott & Brewer	
Belleek, Ashtray, Thorn, Early Green Mark	15.00
Belleek, Basket, Basket Weave, 10 1/2 In.	52.00
Belleek, Basket, Pink & Yellow Floral, Ribbon Mark, 6 X 6 1/2 In.	325.00
Belleek, Basket, Shamrock, 3 Strand, 5 In.	150.00
Belleek, Bowl, Cabbage Leaf, 9 1/2 X 9 1/2 In.	69.00
Belleek, Bowl, Covered, Shamrock, Basket Weave, 3rd Black Mark, 4 In.	40.00
Belleek, Bowl, White & Pink, Scalloped & Pointed Edge, 2nd Black Mark, 5 In.	25.00
Belleek, Bowl, Willet, Fluted, Roses, 7 X 5 In.	80.00
Belleek, Bowl, 3 Legged, 2nd Black Mark, Miniature	28.00
Belleek, Cake Set, Handled, Black Mark, 7 Piece	250.00
Belleek, Coffee Pot, Limpet, Green Mark	33.00
Belleek, Condiment Set, Shamrock, 2nd Black Mark, 3 Piece	70.00
Belleek, Creamer, Figural, Girl Kneeling, Ivory, Rope Handle, Green Mark	67.00
Belleek, Creamer, Neptune, Green Mark	16.00
Belleek, Creamer, Pink Handle & Trim, 2nd Black Mark	76.00
Belleek, Creamer, Pink Trim, Pink Coral Handle, 2nd Black Mark	45.00
Belleek, Creamer, Shamrock, Basket Weave, 3rd Black Mark, 3 In.	40.00
Belleek, Creamer, Shell, Green Hound, Harp, & Castle Mark	16.50 To 26.00
Belleek, Creamer, Shell, Yellow Luster, 2nd Green Mark	20.00
Belleek, Creamer, Swan, 3rd Black Mark	58.50
Belleek, Creamer, Toy Shell, Pink Trim, 2nd Black Mark	58.00
Belleek, Cup & Saucer, Demitasse, Celtic, 2nd Black Mark	45.00

Belleek, Cup & Saucer, Demitasse, Hand-Painted Roses, Gold Handle 37.50
Belleek, Cup & Saucer, Echinus, 1st Black Mark 32.00
Belleek, Cup & Saucer, Erne, Yellow Luster Trim, 2nd Black Mark 27.50
Belleek, Cup & Saucer, Green Edge 40.00
Belleek, Cup & Saucer, Green Trim, Hexagonal, 2nd Black Mark 38.00
Belleek, Cup & Saucer, Harp, Shamrock, 3rd Black Mark 35.00
Belleek, Cup & Saucer, Hawthorn, 2 Shades Of Blue, Gold Rims, 1st Black Mark 125.00
Belleek, Cup & Saucer, Hexagon, 2nd Black Mark 30.00
Belleek, Cup & Saucer, Limpet, Green Mark 19.00
Belleek, Cup & Saucer, Mask, 3rd Black Mark 35.00
Belleek, Cup & Saucer, Neptune, Green Trim, 2nd Black Mark .... 40.00 To 50.00
Belleek, Cup & Saucer, Neptune, White & Green, 2nd Black Mark .... 38.00 To 45.00
Belleek, Cup & Saucer, Neptune, White With Pink, 2nd Black Mark 45.00
Belleek, Cup & Saucer, Queensware, 1st Black Mark 35.00
Belleek, Cup & Saucer, Shamrock, 2nd Black Mark 50.00
Belleek, Cup & Saucer, Tridacna, Pink Trim, 2nd Black Mark .... 36.00 To 45.00
Belleek, Cup & Saucer, Tridacna, 2nd Black Mark 30.00
Belleek, Cup, Chocolate, Willet, White Scrolled Handle 35.00
Belleek, Cup, Hexagon, Green Trim, Black Mark 27.50
Belleek, Dish, Candy, Shell Shape, Footed 30.00
Belleek, Dish, Cardium, Triple, Coral Handle, 1st Black Mark, 11 In. 115.00
Belleek, Dish, Heart Shape, Pink Trim, Fluted Sides, Green Mark, 6 1/2 In. 15.00
Belleek, Dish, Leaf Shape, Sycamore, 4 1/2 In. 15.00
Belleek, Figurine, Scottie Dog, Green Mark, 3 1/2 In. 16.00
Belleek, Figurine, Swan, 3rd Black Mark 59.00
Belleek, Flower Holder, Seahorse, 1st Black Mark 125.00
Belleek, Font, Cherub, 11 In. Wingspread, Green Mark 75.00
Belleek, Font, Sacred Heart, Red & Gold Trim, Green Mark, 6 1/2 In. 65.00
Belleek, Hatpin Holder, Willet, Blue Forget-Me-Nots, Gold Top 35.00
Belleek, Jar, Marmalade, Green Shamrocks, 1st Green Mark 40.00
Belleek, Mug, Rope Handle, Net Pattern, Yellow Luster, 2nd Black Mark 90.00
Belleek, Mug, Shamrock, Basket Weave, Belfast On Front, 2nd Black Mark 48.00
Belleek, Mug, Tankard Type, Pine Boughs & Cones In Green & Brown, 5 1/2 In. 65.00
Belleek, Mug, Willet, Brown, Monk Holding Stein, 5 1/2 In. 25.00
Belleek, Mug, Willet, "Christmas, 1914, I Am A Pirate, Tra La, " 4 3/4 In. 45.00
Belleek, Mug, Willet, Gold Swirls, 6 In. 50.00
Belleek, Mug, Willet, Miniature, 2 In. 35.00
Belleek, Mug, Willet, Tans & Yellows, Colonial Lady, 5 1/2 In. 85.00
Belleek, Mug, Wine Taster, Portrait Of Gentleman, Dated 1909, 3 In. 110.00
Belleek, Pitcher, Cauldron, 3 Legs, Black Hound, Harp, & Castle Mark, 3 In. 30.00
Belleek, Pitcher, Celtic, Harp Handled, 7 1/2 In. 65.00
Belleek, Pitcher, Ivy, Cream, 1st Black Mark, 5 In. 55.00
Belleek, Pitcher, Milk, Green Paisley Type Decoration, C.1891 .... 50.00
Belleek, Pitcher, Pear Shape, Twig Handle, Hound, Tower, & Harp Mark, 4 In. 27.50
Belleek, Pitcher, White, Pink Lining, Miniature, 2 In. 12.00
Belleek, Pitcher, Willet, White, Tricorner Top, Designs On Handle, 7 1/2 In. 60.00
Belleek, Plate, Bread, Neptune, 2nd Black Mark, 10 In. 50.00
Belleek, Plate, Brown Floral & Bird, 1st Mark In Brown, 9 3/4 In. 35.00
Belleek, Plate, Cake, Basket Weave, Irish 230.00
Belleek, Plate, Cake, Twig, Open Weave, Ribbon Mark, 10 1/2 In. 85.00
Belleek, Plate, Dessert, Mask, 3rd Black Mark 20.00
Belleek, Plate, Dessert, Willet, Raised Green, Pink, Blue, & Gold Enameling 25.00
Belleek, Plate, Hexagon, 2nd Black Mark, 7 1/2 In. 18.00
Belleek, Plate, Shamrock, 2nd Black Mark, 7 In. 30.00
Belleek, Plate, White, Pink Trim, Scalloped Rim, 2nd Black Mark, 5 In. 25.00
Belleek, Plate, 12 Shell Design, Yellow Trim, Handled, Green Mark, 9 1/2 In. 15.00
Belleek, Platter, Bacchus, Yellow Trim, Handled, 3rd Black Mark, 10 1/4 In. 69.00
Belleek, Platter, Thorn, Blue & White, Oval, 1st Black Mark, C.1877, 16 In. 75.00
Belleek, Pot, Irish, 2nd Black Mark, 7 In. 75.00
Belleek, Salt, Boat, Rowboat On Ocean, Luster In & Out, 4 1/4 X 3 In. 10.50
Belleek, Salt, Diamond Shape, Fluted Sides, Luster Inside, 3 1/2 In. 8.00
Belleek, Salt, Diamond Shape, Fluted Sides, 3 1/2 X 1 1/4 X 1 In. 7.50
Belleek, Salt, Diamond Shape, Fluted, Pink Blush To Ivory, Black Mark 18.00
Belleek, Salt, Master, Coral Trim, 2nd Black Mark 55.00
Belleek, Salt, Neptune, Sits On Shell Shaped Legs, Luster Inside 13.00
Belleek, Salt, Shamrock, Shell Shaped Sides, Green Shamrocks, 3rd Black Mark 32.00

Belleek, Salt, Shell Shaped Sides	8.50
Belleek, Salt, Teardrop Shape, Fluted Sides, 3 1/2 X 2 In.	7.50
Belleek, Salt, Tub, Pierced Handles, Luster In & Out, Green Mark	12.50
Belleek, Salt, Willet, Cream, Silver Trim, 1 1/2 In.	6.50
Belleek, Salt, Willet, Gold Rim, Luster Inside	7.00
Belleek, Salt, Willet, Gold, Pearlized Inside	8.00
Belleek, Salt, Willet, Gold, Pedestal, 1 3/4 X 1 1/4 In.	12.50
Belleek, Salt, Willet, Light Green, Gold Rim	9.00
Belleek, Salt, Willet, Light Pink, Gold Rim	9.00
Belleek, Salt, Willet, White, Gold Rim, Luster Inside, 1 3/4 X 3/4 In.	7.00
Belleek, Salt, Willet, White, Ruffled Gold Edge, 2 X 1 In.	15.00
Belleek, Shell, Irish, 1st Mark	40.00
Belleek, Spill, Basket, 2nd Black Mark	75.00
Belleek, Spill, Flowered, 2nd Black Mark	65.00
Belleek, Spill, Lily, 2nd Black Mark, 6 3/4 In.	75.00
Belleek, Spill, Owl, Green Mark, 8 In.	22.50
Belleek, Spill, Rock, 2nd Black Mark, 3 1/2 In.	27.00
Belleek, Spoon Rest, Cresting Wave Design, 1st Black Mark, 4 In.	68.00
Belleek, Stand, Teapot, Spread-Wing Dragon Lying On Back, Black Mark, 1872	575.00
Belleek, Sugar & Creamer, Bacchus & Grapes, Cream, Yellow Lining, Black Mark	85.00
Belleek, Sugar & Creamer, Cover, Celtic, 3rd Black Mark	85.00
Belleek, Sugar & Creamer, Cover, Willet, Art Nouveau Type Enamel	85.00
Belleek, Sugar & Creamer, Green Shamrocks, Harp Handles, 3rd Black Mark	47.50
Belleek, Sugar & Creamer, Hexagonal, Yellow Interiors, 2nd Black Mark	70.00
Belleek, Sugar & Creamer, Irish Pot	60.00
Belleek, Sugar & Creamer, Lines & X Band, Green Mark	30.00
Belleek, Sugar & Creamer, Mask, Yellow Luster	40.00
Belleek, Sugar & Creamer, Raised Ivy Leaves, 3rd Black Mark	45.00
Belleek, Sugar & Creamer, Shamrock, Black Mark	85.00
Belleek, Sugar & Creamer, Shamrock, Thong Handle, Green Mark	60.00
Belleek, Sugar & Creamer, Shell, Cream, Canary Inside, 2nd Black Mark	75.00
Belleek, Sugar & Creamer, Shell, Green Hound, Castle, & Harp Mark	55.00
Belleek, Sugar & Creamer, Tridacna, Green Trim, 2nd Black Mark	58.00 To 70.00
Belleek, Sugar, Hawthorn, 1st Black Mark, Toy	35.00
Belleek, Sugar, Ivy, 1st Green Mark, C.1946	8.00
Belleek, Sugar, Shamrock, Toy	35.00
Belleek, Swan, High Luster, 6 In. Long	95.00
Belleek, Tankard, Pink Dogwood, Gold Trim, Bamboo Handle, Brown Mark, 6 In.	75.00
Belleek, Tankard, Willet, Artist Signed, 5 3/4 In.	65.00
Belleek, Tankard, Willet, Gold Dragon Handle, Mask Spout, 11 In.	125.00
Belleek, Tea Set, Coral Pattern, 15 Piece	285.00
Belleek, Tea Set, Gold Lines, Green Trim, Hexagonal, 2nd Black Mark, 7 Piece	285.00
Belleek, Tea Set, Neptune, Green Mark, 17 Piece	165.00
Belleek, Tea Set, Tridacna, 2nd Black Mark, 3 Piece	150.00
Belleek, Teakettle, Echinus, 1st Black Mark	250.00
Belleek, Teakettle, Harp, Shamrock, Overhead Handle, 3rd Black Mark	85.00
Belleek, Teakettle, Tridacna, Gold Trim, 1st Black Mark	235.00 To 245.00
Belleek, Teapot, Hexagon, 2nd Black Mark	80.00
Belleek, Teapot, Neptune, Pink Trim, 2nd Black Mark, Large Size	175.00
Belleek, Teapot, Shamrock, Basket Weave, 3rd Black Mark, 10 1/2 In.	95.00
Belleek, Teapot, Tridacna, Pink Trim, 2nd Black Mark	150.00
Belleek, Teapot, Tridacna, 1st Black Mark, 8 Cup Size	165.00
Belleek, Tray, Grass, 1st Black Mark, 12 X 15 In.	150.00
Belleek, Tray, Pin, Shamrock, 2nd Green Mark	16.50
Belleek, Tray, Pink, Turned-Up Scalloped Edge, 2nd Mark, 17 X 14 In.	195.00
Belleek, Tumbler, Grass, 1st Black Mark	35.00
Belleek, Urn, Tripod Cloven Hoof Base, 1st Black Mark, 13 X 9 1/2 In.	475.00
Belleek, Urn, Yellow Enamel Trim, Tripod Cloven Hoof Base, 7 1/4 In.	135.00
Belleek, Vase, Art Nouveau Gold Peacock Feathers, Purple Hue, 12 In. High	99.00
Belleek, Vase, Bittersweet Berries & Leaves On Green Ground, 6 In. High	96.00
Belleek, Vase, Corn, White, 1st Black Mark, 6 1/4 In.	100.00
Belleek, Vase, Lily Shape, Reeded Knop, Yellow Luster Interior, 6 1/2 In.	145.00
Belleek, Vase, Nile, 2nd Black Mark, 13 In.	195.00
Belleek, Vase, Prince Arthur, Leaves & Flowers, 10 1/4 In. High	85.00
Belleek, Vase, Purse, 2nd Black Mark, 6 1/2 X 4 In.	105.00
Belleek, Vase, Shell, Green Trim, 2nd Black Mark, 9 In.	150.00

Belleek, Vase, Sunflower, Yellow Luster Trim, 2nd Black Mark, 7 1/2 In. 80.00
Belleek, Vase, Sunflower, 2nd Black Mark, 7 In. 85.00
Belleek, Vase, Tree Stump, No Limbs, 1st Black Mark, 5 In., Pair 145.00
Belleek, Vase, Tree Stump, Shamrock, Green, 3rd Black Mark, 6 1/4 In.High 60.00
Belleek, Vase, Willet, Grapes & Vines On Cream, Green, & Gray, 12 1/2 In. 165.00
Belleek, Vase, Willet, Lavender Flowers Trailing On Body, 12 In. 55.00
Belleek, Vase, Willet, Mermaid & Baby Mermaid On Blue Green, 16 1/2 In. 350.00
Belleek, Vase, Willet, Purple Flowers On Yellow & Orange, 12 In. 95.00
Bennington Type, Creamer, Brown Cow, Covered 12.50
Bennington Type, Cup, Custard 35.00
Bennington Type, Pen Holder, Dog, 5 In. .... *Illus* 85.00
Bennington Type, Pitcher, Brown, Hunter, Dog, & Gun, 5 1/4 In.High 50.00
Bennington Type, Pitcher, Tankard Style, Mottled, Glazed, 1/2 Gallon 38.00
Bennington Type, Teapot, Rebecca At The Well, Dark Brown, 6 Cup .... 28.00 To 55.00

Bennington ware was the product of two factories working in Bennington, Vermont. Both firms were out of business by 1896. The wares include brown and yellow mottled pottery, Parian, scroddled ware, stoneware, graniteware, yellowware, and Staffordshire-like vases.

Bennington, see also Rockingham

Bennington, Bank, 6 1/2 X 5 1/4 In. 375.00
Bennington, Bedpan, Man's, Malted Yellow 39.75
Bennington, Bottle, Coachman, Signed Norton, 7 1/2 In. .... 200.00 To 300.00
Bennington, Bowl, Brown & Yellow Mottled, 11 In. 30.00
Bennington, Box, Trinket, Parian, Dead Game On Lid, Blue & White .... 38.50 To 40.00
Bennington, Bust, Young Girl, Parian, Low-Cut Dress, 4 1/2 In. 65.00
Bennington, Compote, White Unglazed Shell, 3 Dolphins Support, 4 1/2 In. 39.50
Bennington, Creamer, Cow, Rockingham Glazed, Covered, Brown, C.1849, 6 In. 200.00
Bennington, Dish, Pudding, Brown Glaze, Yellow Mottling, 9 1/2 In. 55.00
Bennington, Figurine, Lion, Flint Enamel .... *Illus* 1300.00
Bennington, Flask, Flint Enamel, Book Shape, Battle, Brown, C.1849, 7 3/4 In. 350.00
Bennington, Inkwell, 3 1/4 In.High 200.00
Bennington, Jar, Cream, Norton, Cobalt Floral, Eared, 2 Gallon 65.00
Bennington, Jar, Tobacco, Alternating Ribs, Marked 129B, 10 In. 450.00
Bennington, Jug, Blue Slip, 3 Gallon 52.00
Bennington, Mug, Rockingham Type, Leaf Decoration 28.00
Bennington, Pan, Milk, Rockingham Type, Mottled, 10 1/2 X 2 1/2 In. 55.00
Bennington, Pitcher, American Eagle Under Spout, Birds, Animals On Side 325.00
Bennington, Pitcher, Flint Enamel, Ribbed, Brown Glaze, C.1849, 9 In. 140.00
Bennington, Pitcher, Gray Green, Geometric Arabesque, C.1850, 7 In. 125.00
Bennington, Pitcher, Hound Handle, 6 Quart, 11 1/2 In. 600.00
Bennington, Pitcher, Peacock, 8 X 5 In. 75.00
Bennington, Plate, Parian, Strawberries, Grapes, & Vines, Scalloped, 8 1/2 In. 48.50
Bennington, Plate, Pie, 10 In. 35.00
Bennington, Plate, Pie, 10 1/2 In. 40.00
Bennington, Spittoon, Brown Glaze, Shell Pattern 27.00
Bennington, Spittoon, Brown, Flint Enamel, Lyman Fenton & Co., 9 1/2 In. 175.00
Bennington, Spittoon, Flint Enamel, Fenton's Enamel, Patent 1849, 9 In. 175.00
Bennington, Spittoon, Gray & Beige Scroddle On White, Diamond, 10 1/2 In. 250.00
Bennington, Spittoon, Norton & Fenton, 8 In. .... *Illus* 225.00
Bennington, Spittoon, Shell Pattern, 4 X 8 In. 50.00
Bennington, Syrup, Graniteware, Gray, Fern, C.1853, 8 1/2 In. 55.00
Bennington, Toby Mug, 6 In. 65.00
Bennington, Vase, Parian, Blue, Applied White Grapes, Twig Handles, 11 In. 195.00
Bicycle, Child's, Velocipede 225.00

Bing and Grondahl is a famous Danish factory making fine porcelains from 1853 to the present. Their Christmas plates are especially well known.

Bing & Grondahl, see also Collector, Plate

Bing & Grondahl, Figurine, Cat, Gray & White, 4 In.High 45.00
Bing & Grondahl, Figurine, Collie Dog, 10 1/2 In.Long 68.00
Bing & Grondahl, Figurine, Duck, Tan, 3 1/2 In. 28.00
Bing & Grondahl, Figurine, Duckling, 3 X 2 1/2 In.High 25.00
Bing & Grondahl, Figurine, The Cobbler, Signed Alex Locher, 8 1/4 In. 185.00
Bing & Grondahl, Figurine, Water Baby, No.2209, 4 1/2 In. 19.00
Bing & Grondahl, Vase, Landscape, Snow Hills, Signed L.N., C.1915, 4 1/2 In. 35.00

Bennington Type, Penholder, Dog, 5 In.
(See Page 23)

Bennington, Spittoon, Norton & Fenton, 8 In.
(See Page 23)

Bennington, Figurine, Lion, Flint Enamel
(See Page 23)

Bing & Grondahl, Vase, Sea Gulls, Soft Blue, White, & Gold, 5 1/2 In.	20.00
Binoculars, Swift, Leather Case, 7 X 35 In.	38.00

Bisque is an unglazed baked porcelain. Finished bisque has a slightly sandy texture with a dull finish. Some of it may be decorated with various colors. Bisque gained favor during the late Victorian era when thousands of bisque figurines were made.

Bisque, see also Disneyana

Bisque, Barrel, Boston Baked Beans, Pig, 2 In.	12.00
Bisque, Box, Ring, Hand-Painted Woman & Man On Cover, Round	20.00
Bisque, Bust, Shakespeare, German, White, 5 In.	5.00
Bisque, Dish, Soap, 2 Cupids In Bottom, 1812	22.50
Bisque, Figurine, Black Boy On Potty, Head In Hands, 4 In.	20.00
Bisque, Figurine, Boy Holding Bird, Pink & White, 12 In.	37.50
Bisque, Figurine, Boy, Bow, Fruit, W.K.C. Germany No.3098, 7 In.	20.00
Bisque, Figurine, Cupid, Reclining, White, Marked Japan, 1 1/2 X 3 In.	4.00
Bisque, Figurine, Dancing Coachman, Russian, Popov, C.1850, 8 In.	400.00
Bisque, Figurine, Doe & Fawn, White, Germany, 1 7/8 & 1 1/16 In., Pair	35.00
Bisque, Figurine, Doe, W.D.Dwarf, 3 In.	8.00
Bisque, Figurine, Girl Holding Dove & Boy Holding Fish, 10 In., Pair	52.00
Bisque, Figurine, Girl Wearing Hat, Pastel Colors, French, 9 In.	45.00
Bisque, Figurine, Girl With Tambourine & Boy With Castanet, 8 In., Pair	65.00
Bisque, Figurine, Girl, Milk Pitcher, No.4241, Weiss Kuhnert Co., 7 In.	20.00
Bisque, Figurine, Kwan Yin, Holding Scroll, White, C.1850, 16 3/4 In.	200.00
Bisque, Figurine, Lady Holding Branch Of Flowers Over Head, 8 In.	25.00
Bisque, Figurine, Little Girl Dancing, Hornberg, 6 1/2 In.	28.00
Bisque, Figurine, Maggie & Jiggs, 4 In., Pair	65.00
Bisque, Figurine, Peasant Man Eating Lunch, Ikonnikov, Russian, C.1890, 5 In.	525.00
Bisque, Figurine, Rebecca At The Well, 8 1/2 In.	40.00
Bisque, Figurine, Santa Claus, Painted, 1 1/2 In.	2.75
Bisque, Figurine, Santa Claus, 4 In.	8.50
Bisque, Figurine, Standing White Bear, Germany, 4 In.	7.00

Bisque, Figurine, Woman & Man, Pastels, 16 In., Pair 127.50
Bisque, Group, Monkey In Colorful Dress Riding Dog, C.1900, 5 In. 28.00
Bisque, Group, Mother & Child With Dog, 17 1/2 X 17 1/2 In. 325.00
Bisque, Holder, Cigar, Reclining Dog, Sheaves Of Wheat, Marked R, 5 In. 38.00
Bisque, Match Holder, Boots, Pastel, Gold Decoration, Striker Base, 4 In. 20.00
Bisque, Match Holder, Boy In Elegant Dress With Basket, C.1900, 7 In. 30.00
Bisque, Match Holder, Bulldog 25.00
Bisque, Match Holder, Collie Dog's Face, Pewter Rim, Striker On Back, 3 In. 34.00
Bisque, Match Holder, Dog Seated By Champagne Cork 28.50
Bisque, Match Holder, German, Little Girl With Basket On Back, 4 In. 45.00
Bisque, Salt Dip, Floral, Gold, Oval 4.00
Bisque, Spice Set, Glazed, Labeled, 5 Piece 20.00
Bisque, Teapot, White, Blue Enamel, Left Wicker Handle 6.50
Bisque, Toothpick, Boy Leaning On Tree Trunk Playing Mandolin 28.00
Bisque, Toothpick, Boy Taking Shirt Off 35.00
Bisque, Toothpick, Brown Tree Stump, White Owl, Blown-Out Face 16.00
Bisque, Toothpick, Dog & Puppy In Doghouse, Glazed, Germany 17.50
Bisque, Toothpick, German Clown Holding Ice Cream Cone, Drum Holder, 4 In. 40.00
Bisque, Toothpick, German, Baby Kneeling On Green Base, Pumpkin Holder 40.00
Bisque, Toothpick, Germany, Cat On Bottle, Yellow Holder 7.50
Bisque, Toothpick, Peacock At Well, Numbered 4485 .... 9.00
Bisque, Toothpick, Pigs, Pink 25.00
Bisque, Toothpick, Rabbit Leaning On Cabbage 32.00
Bisque, Toothpick, Rooster Chasing Chick Up Ladder To Coop, German 25.00
Bisque, Toothpick, Tricornered, Bulldog, Pig, & Owl On Corners 22.00
Bisque, Vase, English, Triangular Shape, Boy Picking Grapes, 5 In. 25.00
Bisque, Vase, German, Figural, Maiden On Horn Of Plenty Base, 9 1/2 In. 100.00
Bisque, Vase, German, Figural, Man In Victorian Dress, Gold Trim, 11 In. 100.00

Black amethyst glass appears black until it is held to the light, then a dark
purple can be seen. It was made in many factories from 1860 to the present
time.

Black Amethyst, Bottle, Cologne, Gold On Stopper, 9 In. 36.00
Black Amethyst, Bottle, Cologne, Raised Gold Design, 9 In. 35.00
Black Amethyst, Bottle, Figural, Bear, Seated, 11 1/2 In., Pair 50.00
Black Amethyst, Butter, Covered, McKee 10.00
Black Amethyst, Candlestick, Square Base, 7 In., Pair 18.00
Black Amethyst, Carafe, Coffee, McKee 8.50
Black Amethyst, Dish, Candy 10.00
Black Amethyst, Dish, Candy, Swan, L.E.Smith, 9 1/2 In. 25.00
Black Amethyst, Dish, Elephant Cover, 8 In. 28.50
Black Amethyst, Figurine, Bulldog, Glass Eyes, 2 1/2 In. 8.00
Black Amethyst, Jar, Cracker, Silver Decoration 30.00
Black Amethyst, Plate, Scalloped Edge, 8 In. 2.50
Black Amethyst, Plate, Shells, 8 1/2 In. 3.00
Black Amethyst, Plate, Sterling Overlay, 8 In. 2.50
Black Amethyst, Salt & Pepper, McKee 10.00
Black Amethyst, Saucer, Square 2.00
Black Amethyst, Saucer, Sterling Overlay 2.00
Black Amethyst, Tray, Serving, Gold Encrusted Border, Handled, 15 X 10 In. 14.00
Black Amethyst, Vase, Greek Key At Top, Bulbous Base, 6 In. .... 10.00 To 15.00
Bloor Derby, Pitcher, Applied Floral & Leaves, Gold Handle, 5 1/2 In. 145.00
Bloor Derby, Plate, Oriental, Blue, Gold, & Orange, 7 1/4 In. 50.00

Blown glass was formed by forcing air through a rod into molten glass.
Early glass and some forms of art glass were hand blown. Other types of
glass were molded or pressed. The McKearin numbers refer to the book
"American Glass" by George and Helen McKearin.

Blown Glass, Ashtray, Amethyst & White, Stretch, Art Deco, 4 3/4 In. 15.00
Blown Glass, Beaker, Cobalt, Round, Lip, Ground Pontil, 3 1/2 X 2 3/4 In. 4.50
Blown Glass, Bowl, Amethyst Leaf Glass, Footed, Ribbed, C.1815, 10 In. 550.00
Blown Glass, Bowl, Aqua, Thin Metal, Conical Base, 6 X 6 In. 100.00
Blown Glass, Bowl, Cleveland, N.Y., Aqua, Flaring Sides, Footed, 7 1/2 In. 95.00
Blown Glass, Bowl, Cobalt, 2 Lip, Ground Pontil, 5 3/4 X 3 1/2 In. 12.50
Blown Glass, Bowl, Cobalt, 2 Lip, Straight Sided, Pontil, 5 1/4 X 3 3/4 In. 10.00
Blown Glass, Bowl, Finger, Amethyst, Pontil, Pair 28.00

Blown Glass, Bowl, Finger, Blue Color Spiraling On Top, Clear, 4 7/8 In.	55.00
Blown Glass, Bowl, Finger, Cobalt, Free-Blown, Straight Sides	15.00
Blown Glass, Bowl, Flint, Blue Opalescent, Pontil, 4 1/2 X 2 3/4 In.	20.00
Blown Glass, Bowl, Flint, Engraved Leaf, Notch Cutting, Footed, C.1800, 4 In.	15.00
Blown Glass, Bowl, Flint, McK G I-6, 6 In.	65.00
Blown Glass, Bowl, Flower, Flint, Crown Shape, Applied Loops At Top, 6 In.	30.00
Blown Glass, Bowl, Light Green, Broken Swirl, C.1950, 5 1/2 In. Diameter	30.00
Blown Glass, Bowl, Light Green, Swirled, Footed, C.1950, 6 In. Diameter	15.00
Blown Glass, Bowl, Lutz Type Gold Threading, Scalloped, Flared, 4 1/2 In.	40.00
Blown Glass, Bowl, Medium Green, Hat Shape, 5 1/4 In.	35.00
Blown Glass, Bowl, Midwestern, Light Green Thin Metal, Folded Rim, 9 1/2 In.	105.00
Blown Glass, Bowl, Molded, McK G III-24, 6 1/2 In.	80.00
Blown Glass, Bowl, New England Glass Co., Amethyst, 11 3/4 X 3 1/2 In.	55.00
Blown Glass, Bowl, New York State, Amber, Wide Folded Rim, 5 1/2 X 2 1/2 In.	75.00
Blown Glass, Bowl, New York State, Aqua, Folded-Under Rim, Footed, 6 3/4 In.	155.00
Blown Glass, Bowl, New York State, Aqua, Folded-Under Rim, 7 In.	100.00
Blown Glass, Bowl, New York State, Aqua, Folded-Under Rim, 8 In.	90.00
Blown Glass, Bowl, New York State, Aqua, Hollow Folded-Under Rim, 8 1/4 In.	100.00
Blown Glass, Bowl, New York State, Medium Green, Folded-In Rim, 3 1/2 In.	55.00
Blown Glass, Bowl, Redwood, N.Y., Aqua, Hat Shape, Folded-Under Rim, 12 In.	85.00
Blown Glass, Bowl, Redwood, N.Y., Golden Amber, Tall, 4 3/4 X 4 1/4 In.	55.00
Blown Glass, Bowl, Serving, Clear Lutz Type Stripes, Latticinio, 10 In.	145.00
Blown Glass, Bowl, South Jersey, Yellow Green, 2 Handled, Footed, 2 1/2 In.	55.00
Blown Glass, Bowl, Three Mold, McK G II-21, 5 In.	95.00
Blown Glass, Bowl, White Opalescent, Three Mold, Hobnail, Ruffled, 6 In.	5.00
Blown Glass, Breast Pump, Flint, 3 In.	12.00
Blown Glass, Candlestick, Flint, Pressed Bottom, McK 199-27, C.1830	95.00
Blown Glass, Celery, Copper Wheel Scrolls, Applied Stem & Foot, Flint	35.00
Blown Glass, Celery, Pittsburgh, Pillar Mold, Swirled To Right, Stem, 8 In.	125.00
Blown Glass, Claret, Flint, Engraved Tassels & Swags, C.1800, 6 3/4 In.	30.00
Blown Glass, Compote, Flint, Cut Diamond & Horizontal Steps, C.1800, 7 In.	55.00
Blown Glass, Compote, Flint, Folded Rim, 7 X 7 In.	100.00
Blown Glass, Compote, Flint, Free-Blown, Folded Rim, Rough Pontil, 7 X 7 In.	100.00
Blown Glass, Compote, Lockport, N.Y., Light Blue, Footed, 6 3/4 X 6 1/2 In.	200.00
Blown Glass, Cordial, Ruby Stained, Free-Blown, Knop Stem, Open Pontil	9.50
Blown Glass, Cruet, Amethyst, Applied Handle, Painted Flowers, Gold, 8 In.	45.00
Blown Glass, Cruet, Bitters, Three Mold, McK G II-29, 6 In.	20.00
Blown Glass, Cruet, Blue, Clear Handle & Ball Stopper, Enamel, 6 In.	46.50
Blown Glass, Cruet, Castor, Flint, McK G II-11	24.00
Blown Glass, Cruet, Castor, Flint, McK G III-31	28.00
Blown Glass, Cruet, Castor, McK G I-7	20.00
Blown Glass, Cruet, Flint, Stiegel Type, 16 Molded Ribs, 5 3/4 In.	30.00
Blown Glass, Cruet, Green, Clear Handle & Faceted Stopper, Enamel, 9 1/2 In.	51.00
Blown Glass, Cruet, Sapphire Blue, Paneled, Crystal Stopper & Handle, 7 In.	55.00
Blown Glass, Decanter, Amber, Sterling Overlay & Stopper, 12 In.	75.00
Blown Glass, Decanter, Amber, Thumbprint, 7 In.	35.00
Blown Glass, Decanter, Bar, Flint, C.1800	28.00
Blown Glass, Decanter, Flint, Amelung Type, Tapered, Quart	40.00
Blown Glass, Decanter, Flint, Barrel Shape, McK G II-27, Pint	120.00
Blown Glass, Decanter, Flint, C.1800, Quart	30.00
Blown Glass, Decanter, Flint, Folded Lip, C.1790, 1/2 Pint	35.00
Blown Glass, Decanter, Flint, McK G III-14, 1/2 Pint	120.00
Blown Glass, Decanter, Flint, McK G III-24, Quart	90.00
Blown Glass, Decanter, Flint, McK G IV-7, Quart	145.00
Blown Glass, Decanter, Flint, Pattern Molded Panels, C.1790, 1/2 Pint	40.00
Blown Glass, Decanter, Flint, Pressed Mushroom Stopper, C.1850, Quart	38.00
Blown Glass, Decanter, Gold Threading, Applied Amber Rigaree, 10 1/2 In.	140.00
Blown Glass, Decanter, Hollow Stopper, Wheel Cut Grapes, Long Neck, Pint	18.00
Blown Glass, Decanter, Keene, Dark Green, Geometric, Pint, McK G III-16	300.00
Blown Glass, Decanter, Keene, Light Green, Geometric, McK G III-16	275.00
Blown Glass, Decanter, Keene, Olive Green, Geometric, McK G III-16	300.00
Blown Glass, Decanter, Pittsburgh, Flint, Blue, 8 Panel Flute, C.1824, Quart	275.00
Blown Glass, Decanter, Ring Type Stopper, 3 Applied Neck Rings, 9 1/2 In.	35.00
Blown Glass, Decanter, Sunburst, 3 Rigaree Rings, McK G III-5, Quart	100.00
Blown Glass, Decanter, Three Mold, McK G I-29, Quart	90.00
Blown Glass, Decanter, Three Mold, McK G III-14, 1/2 Pint	120.00

Blown Glass, Decanter, Victorian, Enameled, 13 1/2 In.	35.00
Blown Glass, Egg, Easter, Applied Decoration	29.50
Blown Glass, Egg, Easter, End-Of-Day, Hen Size	20.00
Blown Glass, Egg, Easter, Painted, 3 In.	10.00
Blown Glass, Flip, Flint, Stiegel Type, Paneled, Engraving, C.1750, 6 In.	135.00
Blown Glass, Flip, Flint, Stiegel Type, 26 Panels, 5 In.	62.00
Blown Glass, Flip, Three Mold, McK G I-6, 6 In.	85.00
Blown Glass, Flip, Three Mold, McK G II-22, 6 1/4 In.	175.00
Blown Glass, Flytrap, Free-Blown, Bottle Shape, 3 Footed, C.1825, 7 In.	65.00
Blown Glass, Fruit Stand, Irish, Columnar Stem, C.1820, 8 3/4 In.	70.00
Blown Glass, Goblet, Flint, Blue Opalescent, Pontil, 7 In.	35.00
Blown Glass, Goblet, Flint, Soda Lime, Cone Bowl, C.1800, 5 In.	20.00
Blown Glass, Hat, Amethyst, Turned-Up Brim, 7 X 5 1/2 X 4 1/2 In.	18.00
Blown Glass, Hat, Quaker, Free-Blown, Turned-Down Brim, 1 In.	10.00
Blown Glass, Hat, Sunburst, Folded-In Edge, 2 In.	135.00
Blown Glass, Hat, Three Mold, McK Giii-5	100.00
Blown Glass, Inkwell, Amber, School Desk Size	1.25
Blown Glass, Jug, Flint, Handled, Pontil Mark, Quart	22.00
Blown Glass, Mug, South Jersey, Blue	94.00
Blown Glass, Pan, Mantua, Amber, 16 Broken Swirled Ribs, Folded Rim, 5 In.	800.00
Blown Glass, Pan, Mantua, Yellow, Folded-Under Rim, 5 3/4 In.	175.00
Blown Glass, Pen, Green & Amethyst, Umbrella Shape	15.00
Blown Glass, Pipe, Yellow, Opalescent, Ribbing, 14 In.	85.00
Blown Glass, Pitcher, Amethyst, Opalescent Coin Spot, Crimped, 9 1/2 In.	48.00
Blown Glass, Pitcher, Apple Green, Opalescent Coin Spot, Crimped, 9 1/2 In.	48.00
Blown Glass, Pitcher, Blue, Thumbprint, Applied Handle, 4 Lip, 8 In.	45.00
Blown Glass, Pitcher, Clevenger, N.J., Pale Sea Green, 5 1/2 In.	45.00
Blown Glass, Pitcher, Emil Larson, Amber, Lily Pad, Crimped Foot, 1950s, 6 In.	115.00
Blown Glass, Pitcher, New York, Green, Threaded Neck, Crooked, 5 In.	70.00
Blown Glass, Pitcher, South Jersey, Aqua, Threaded Neck, Footed, 5 1/2 In.	300.00
Blown Glass, Pitcher, Water, Blue, Applied Clear Reeded Handle, 9 In.	98.00
Blown Glass, Pitcher, Water, Blue, Inverted Thumbprint, Amber Handle, 7 In.	60.00
Blown Glass, Pitcher, Water, European, C.1840, Polished Pontil, 12 In.	62.00
Blown Glass, Pitcher, Water, Ruffled Edge, Enamel Daisies, Gold, 10 3/4 In.	32.50
Blown Glass, Pitcher, Water, Ruffled Top, Pink To Clear, Enameled, 10 In.	70.00
Blown Glass, Pot, Preserve, Lemon, White Cased, Silver Holder & Lid, C.1870	65.00
Blown Glass, Rake, Victorian, 14 1/2 In.	16.50
Blown Glass, Rinser, Wine, Swirl Marks, 14 X 4 In.	25.00
Blown Glass, Rose Bowl, Green, Paneled Inside, Crimped Rim, Gold Trim, 4 In.	20.00
Blown Glass, Salt & Pepper, Hat With Cane	3.00
Blown Glass, Salt, Lutz Type, White Latticinio, Pink Ribbons, Pedestal	25.00
Blown Glass, Saltshaker, Flint, 22 Ribs, Coin Silver Tip	28.00
Blown Glass, Shaker, Castor, Flint, McK G I-12	20.00
Blown Glass, Shaker, Castor, Flint, McK G I-15	22.00
Blown Glass, Shaker, Castor, Three Mold, McK G I-12	20.00
Blown Glass, Shaker, Castor, Three Mold, McK G I-13	20.00
Blown Glass, Shaker, Castor, Three Mold, McK G I-14	20.00
Blown Glass, Spittoon, Lady's, Blue, Tooled Rim, Applied Handle	60.00
Blown Glass, Spittoon, Sapphire Blue, Rough Pontil, C.1860, 7 1/2 In.	95.00
Blown Glass, Sugar & Creamer, White Opaque, Applied Handles, Swirled	22.00
Blown Glass, Sugar, Zanesville, Blue Aqua, Covered, Tapered Sides, 5 3/4 In.	1100.00
Blown Glass, Syllabub Set, Blown, Enamel Floral, Gilt, Silver Ladle, 8 Piece	450.00
Blown Glass, Tankard, Applied Handle, 3 Amber Rings At Base, Enamel, 13 In.	49.50
Blown Glass, Tankard, Cobalt, Swirled, 10 X 6 In.	50.00
Blown Glass, Tazza, Pittsburgh Type, Sea Green, Lid, 11 In.	105.00
Blown Glass, Teapot, Painted Decoration, Gold Trim, 5 In.	45.00
Blown Glass, Tumbler, Ale, Clambroth Base & Stem, 9 In.	45.00
Blown Glass, Tumbler, Black Decals, Cocktail Recipes, C.1930	1.00
Blown Glass, Tumbler, Cobalt To Lavender, Vertical Ribs	35.00
Blown Glass, Tumbler, Cobalt, Hand-Blown, 2 Ozs.	5.85
Blown Glass, Tumbler, Cranberry To Pale Apricot, Ribbed	28.00
Blown Glass, Tumbler, Etched Castle, Birds, & Floral, 8 1/2 In.	55.00
Blown Glass, Tumbler, Flint, Stiegel Type, 31 Ribs, 3 3/4 In.	45.00
Blown Glass, Tumbler, Kent, Citron, 20 Broken Swirled Ribs, 4 1/2 In.	500.00
Blown Glass, Tumbler, Sapphire Blue, Diamond-Quilted	27.50
Blown Glass, Tumbler, Threaded, Etched Top Rim, World's Fair, 1933	25.00

Blown Glass, Vase, Amber, Hobnail, Hand-Blown, 6 In., Pair 15.00
Blown Glass, Vase, Amethyst, Gold Enamel Floral, 11 In. 85.00
Blown Glass, Vase, Aqua To Clear, Swirl, Ruffled Aqua Edge, 6 In. 14.00
Blown Glass, Vase, Bischoff, Green, Flared Ruffled Top, 8 In. 19.00
Blown Glass, Vase, Black Amethyst, Enamel Water Lilies, Ruffled, 12 In. 35.00
Blown Glass, Vase, Blue Green, Inverted Bowl, 8 1/2 In. 140.00
Blown Glass, Vase, Cobalt, Corset Shape, Scalloped, Daisies, 13 In., Pair 85.00
Blown Glass, Vase, Cobalt, White Hand-Painted Lilies-Of-The-Valley, 10 In. .. 47.50
Blown Glass, Vase, Coventry, Conn., Olive Amber Hat Form, 4 In. 50.00
Blown Glass, Vase, English, Cobalt Blue, White Looping, 13 1/2 In. 65.00
Blown Glass, Vase, Engraved Cockfight, Applied Foot, 6 3/4 In. 75.00
Blown Glass, Vase, Expanded Diamond, Ruffled Top, Flared Base, 12 1/2 In. .. 60.00
Blown Glass, Vase, Free-Blown, Trumpet Bowl, Applied Foot, Engraved, 10 In. .. 50.00
Blown Glass, Vase, Green, Folded Foot, Flared Top, Lily Pad, 11 In. 85.00
Blown Glass, Vase, Hyacinth, Deep Amethyst, Rough Pontil, 8 3/4 In., Pair ... 45.00
Blown Glass, Vase, Light Aqua To Clear Base, Pointed Ruffle, 6 In. 12.00
Blown Glass, Vase, New York State, Aqua, Footed, 5 1/2 In. 40.00
Blown Glass, Vase, Opalescent, Flared Scalloped Top, Painted Floral, 5 In. ... 19.50
Blown Glass, Vase, Pittsburgh, Milk White, Trumpet, Folded-Over Rim, 14 In. .. 180.00
Blown Glass, Vase, Ruby, Free-Blown, Flaring, Open Pontil, 3 3/4 In. 18.00
Blown Glass, Vase, Silver Overlay, Floral & Concentrics, Pedestal, 10 In. 10.00
Blown Glass, Vase, Yellow To Clear, Zipper Cut Edge, 6 Panels Base, 9 In. ... 175.00
Blown Glass, Vigil Light, Amber, Flint, Stiegel Type, 16 Diamond 52.00
Blown Glass, Vigil Light, Green, Flint, Stiegel Type, 16 Diamond 52.00
Blown Glass, Water Set, Applied Handle, Ruffled Rim, Enameled, 5 Piece 85.00
Blown Glass, Wine Set, Threaded, Rough Pontil, 3 Piece 55.00
Blown Glass, Wine, Amelung Type, Engraved, Flint 35.00
Blown Glass, Wine, Flint, Bucket Bowl 15.00
Blown Glass, Wine, Flint, Cone & Bucket Bowl 15.00
Blown Glass, Wine, Flint, Cone Bowl 15.00
Blown Glass, Wine, Flint, Cone Bowl, Cut Stem 15.00
Blown Glass, Wine, Flint, Engraved, Flute Cutting, Cut Stem & Foot, C.1800 .. 15.00
Blown Glass, Wine, Flint, Engraved, Folded Foot, C.1800, 4 1/4 In. 20.00
Blown Glass, Wine, Flint, Folded-Under Base Rim 15.00
Blown Glass, Wine, Flint, Goblet Bowl 15.00
Blown Glass, Wine, Flint, Gold Spray Decoration 15.00
Blown Glass, Wine, Flint, Stiegel Type, Engraved 18.00
Blown Glass, Wine, Flint, Stiegel Type, Ribbed, Applied Foot, C.1750 .... 38.00
Blown Glass, Wine, Hand Blown, Etched 8.00
Blown Glass, Wine, Ribbed Bowl, Heavy Bottom 14.00
Blown Glass, Witch's Ball On Vase, Green, White Opaque Looping, 7 1/2 In. .. 95.00
Blown Glass, Witch's Ball, Amethyst, Clear Standard, 6 In. Diameter 35.00
Blown Glass, Witch's Ball, Aqua, 2 1/2 In. 15.00
Blown Glass, Witch's Ball, Opalescent Swirl, 15 In. 38.00
Blown Glass, Witch's Ball, Pink, Blue & White Loopings, Clear Stem, 5 In. ... 140.00
Blown Glass, Witch's Ball, Sapphire Blue, Swirled, Vase Stem, 5 In. 65.00
Blue Amberina, see Bluerina
Blue Glass, see Cobalt Blue
Blue Onion, see Onion

*Blue Willow pattern has been made in England since 1780. The pattern
has been copied by factories in many countries, including Germany, Japan, and
the United States. It is still being made. Willow was named for a
pattern that pictures a bridge, birds, willow trees, and a Chinese landscape.*

Blue Willow, Bowl, Vegetable, Buffalo Pottery, Deep 15.00
Blue Willow, Butter Pat, Buffalo China 10.00
Blue Willow, Butter Pat, Wedgwood, England 8.00
Blue Willow, Cake Set, Gilded Borders, Royal Worcester, 1904, 13 Piece 250.00
Blue Willow, Creamer, Allerton 10.00
Blue Willow, Creamer, Buffalo Pottery, Dated 1911, 4 In. 12.00
Blue Willow, Creamer, Buffalo Pottery, Dated 1918, 4 In. 17.00
Blue Willow, Cup & Saucer, Allerton 18.00
Blue Willow, Cup & Saucer, Maruta China, Occupied Japan 4.00
Blue Willow, Cup & Saucer, Miles Mason, Staffordshire, C.1800 .... 22.00
Blue Willow, Dishes, Child's, Japan, 26 Pieces 45.00
Blue Willow, Drain, Fish, C.1850, 10 1/2 X 14 In. 55.00

Blue Willow, Gravy Boat, Buffalo Pottery .... 12.00 To 28.50
Blue Willow, Gravy Boat, 5 1/4 X 4 In. 18.00
Blue Willow, Jug, Octagonal, Serpent Handle, Mason's Ironstone, 7 In.High 95.00
Blue Willow, Muffineer, Hexagonal 68.00
Blue Willow, Plate, Amber Glaze, Crown Doulton, Burslem, England, 10 In. 39.00
Blue Willow, Plate, Breakfast, Gold Trim, English 2.00
Blue Willow, Plate, Buffalo Pottery, Dated 1905, 8 In. 30.00
Blue Willow, Plate, Cake, Buffalo Pottery, Reticulated, 1915 .... 15.00
Blue Willow, Plate, Doves, Wm.Adams, 8 In. 30.00
Blue Willow, Plate, Gilt Trim, Davenport, C.1810, Anchor Mark, 7 In. 25.00
Blue Willow, Plate, Grill, English, 10 In. 7.50
Blue Willow, Plate, Ironstone, 10 In. 28.50
Blue Willow, Plate, Soup, Allerton, 7 3/4 In. 4.00
Blue Willow, Plate, Soup, 8 In. 8.00
Blue Willow, Plate, Swinnerton, 8 In. 5.00
Blue Willow, Plate, 10 In. 10.00
Blue Willow, Platter, Marked Stone China & Impressed Star, 11 3/4 In. 22.00
Blue Willow, Platter, Mayer, 14 In. 30.00
Blue Willow, Platter, Oval, Ridgway, 12 1/8 X 15 5/8 In. 30.00
Blue Willow, Platter, Staffordshire, 15 1/2 In. 35.00
Blue Willow, Platter, Tree & Well, Dark Blue, Minton, 17 X 14 In. 55.00
Blue Willow, Saucer, Japanese 2.50
Blue Willow, Sugar & Creamer, Allerton 27.50
Blue Willow, Sugar, Ridgway 32.00
Blue Willow, Tea Set, Made In Japan, Miniature, 11 Piece .... 33.00 To 40.00
Blue Willow, Tureen, Buffalo Pottery, 8 In. 35.00

*Bluerina is a type of art glass which shades from light blue to ruby. It is
often called blue amberina.*
Bluerina, Pitcher, Water, New England 200.00

*Bohemian glass is an ornate, overlay, or flashed glass made during the
Victorian era. It has been reproduced in Bohemia, which is now a part of
Czechoslovakia. Glass made from 1875 to 1900 is preferred by collectors.*
Bohemian Glass, Bell, Bird In Flight, Castle, & Trees, Ruby, 5 1/2 In.High 75.00
Bohemian Glass, Bottle, Ruby & Clear Panels, Steeple Stopper, 5 In., Pair 85.00
Bohemian Glass, Bowl, Dark Blue, Etched White Grape & Vine, 9 In. 35.00
Bohemian Glass, Castor Set, 5 Bottle, Deer & Pine Tree, Amber 175.00
Bohemian Glass, Cordial Set, Ruby, Birds, Gold Decoration, 7 Piece 125.00
Bohemian Glass, Creamer, Dark Red, Bird & Castle 25.00
Bohemian Glass, Cruet, Red, Deer 33.00
Bohemian Glass, Cruet, Red, Deer & Castle 35.00
Bohemian Glass, Cruet, Ruby, Vintage 47.50
Bohemian Glass, Decanter, Blown, Vintage, Blown Stopper, 12 In. 75.00
Bohemian Glass, Decanter, Captain's, Deer & Pine, Quart 90.00
Bohemian Glass, Decanter, Ruby To Clear, House & Animal Design, 12 1/2 In. 85.00
Bohemian Glass, Decanter, Wine, Ruby, Vintage, 15 1/2 In. 47.50
Bohemian Glass, Goblet, Red, Deer & Castle 6.75
Bohemian Glass, Mug, Amber, Intaglio Cut City Scenes, 1840, Footed 75.00
Bohemian Glass, Mug, Engraved Floral & With Friendship In German, C.1850 .... 32.00
Bohemian Glass, Pitcher, Dark Red, Bird & Castle, 7 3/4 In. 65.00
Bohemian Glass, Pokal, Domed Lid, Deer, Trees, & Vines, C.1850, 23 1/2 In. 65.00
Bohemian Glass, Pokal, Ruby To Clear, Deer & Castle, Faceted Finial, 15 In. 145.00
Bohemian Glass, Punch Set, Ruby To Clear, Flower & Fan, C.1910, 14 Piece 525.00
Bohemian Glass, Sugar & Creamer, Ruby, Cut & Frosted, Birds, Trees 65.00
Bohemian Glass, Sugar, Dark Red, Bird & Castle 25.00
Bohemian Glass, Tumble-Up, Cut To Clear, Daisy, Thumbprint 75.00
Bohemian Glass, Tumbler, Portrait Insert Of Woman On Porcelain, C.1820 .... 100.00
Bohemian Glass, Vase, Ale Glass Shape, Amber Overlay, Deer, 9 1/2 In.High 135.00
Bohemian Glass, Vase, Cobalt, Matte Gold Decoration, Tube Shape, 11 1/2 In. 35.00
Bohemian Glass, Vase, Etched Elephant & Jungle Scene, 14 In. 80.00
Bohemian Glass, Vase, Red To Clear, Deer & Foliage, 5 In., Pair 75.00
Bohemian Glass, Vase, Red, Vintage, 6 1/2 In., Pair 50.00
Bohemian Glass, Vase, Ruby To Clear, Castle & Flying Birds, 12 1/2 In., Pair 275.00
Bohemian Glass, Vase, Ruby, Castle, Birds, Trees, & Scrolls, 12 1/2 In., Pair 275.00
Bohemian Glass, Vase, White Cut To Dark Blue, Enamels, C.1835, 6 3/4 In. 245.00

Bohemian Glass, Wine Set, Deer & Castle, 4 Piece	165.00
Bohemian Glass, Wine Set, Enameled White Cut To Clear, Gold, 5 Piece	48.50
Bohemian Glass, Wine, Amethyst, Grapes & Leaves	15.00
Bohemian Glass, Wine, Red, Deer & Castle	12.00
Bohemian Glass, Wine, Rhine, Red, Deer & Castle	20.50
Bohemian Glass, Wine, Ruby, Deer & Pine Tree, 3 3/4 In.	12.50
Bohemian Glass, Wine, Ruby, Grapes & Leaves, Knob Stem, 3 1/2 In.High	15.00

Book, see Charlie Chaplin, Book, Coronation, Book, Hopalong
Cassidy, Book, Paper, Book, Shirley Temple, Book
Boston & Sandwich Co., see Sandwich, Fireglow, Lutz

Bottle collecting has become a major American hobby. There are several general categories of bottles such as historic flasks, bitters, household, figural, and others.

Bottle, see also Hopalong Cassidy, Bottle, Shaker, Bottle

Bottle, Allover Vertical Ribs, Oval, Light Aqua, Quart, 9 1/4 In.	22.50
Bottle, Apothecary, Ball Stopper, C.1850, Amethyst, 16 1/2 In.	70.00
Bottle, Apothecary, Black Amethyst, Gallon	115.00
Bottle, Apothecary, Chenopod On Front, Ground Stopper, 10 In.	20.00
Bottle, Apothecary, Deep Amber, 8 1/4 In.	12.00
Bottle, Apothecary, Parcel Gilt Label, Tole Lid, C.1850, 19 1/4 In., Pair	100.00
Bottle, Apothecary, Round, Label Under Glass, 7 In.	3.50
Bottle, Apothecary, Round, Label Under Glass, 10 In.	3.50
Bottle, Apothecary, Square, Label Under Glass, 7 In.	3.50
Bottle, Apothecary, Square, Label Under Glass, 10 In.	3.50
Bottle, Apothecary, Theodore Campbell, Overbrook, Cobalt, 5 In.	10.00

Avon started in 1886 as the California Perfume Company. It was not until 1929 that the name Avon was used. In 1939 it became the Avon Products, Inc. Each year Avon sells many figural bottles filled with cosmetic products. Ceramic, plastic, and glass bottles are made in limited editions.

Bottle, Avon, Air Lady Set, 1945	100.00
Bottle, Avon, Alpine Flask, 1966	55.00
Bottle, Avon, Angler, 1970	5.00
Bottle, Avon, Apothecary Jar Soap, 1965	13.00
Bottle, Avon, Apple Blossom Cologne, 1936, 6 Ozs.	75.00
Bottle, Avon, Attention Cologne, 1947, 6 Ozs.	75.00
Bottle, Avon, Baa Baa Black Sheep, 1954	55.00
Bottle, Avon, Barber Bottle, 1963	25.00
Bottle, Avon, Bath Urn, 1963	3.00
Bottle, Avon, Bay Rum Gift Set, 1964	25.00
Bottle, Avon, Bay Rum, 1969	7.00
Bottle, Avon, Beehive, 1951	100.00
Bottle, Avon, Blue Blazer Soap Set, 1964	13.00
Bottle, Avon, Book, 1967, 1st Edition	5.00
Bottle, Avon, Bugle, 1965	7.00
Bottle, Avon, Caddy, 1968, Set Of 6	12.00
Bottle, Avon, Candlestick, 1966, Pair	19.00
Bottle, Avon, Captain's Choice, 1964	8.00
Bottle, Avon, Casey's Lantern, 1966, Green	25.00
Bottle, Avon, Casey's Lantern, 1966, Red	25.00
Bottle, Avon, Charlie Brown Mug, 1969, Charlie Brown	4.00
Bottle, Avon, Charlie Brown Mug, 1969, Snoopy	4.00
Bottle, Avon, Christmas Fragrance, 1965, Set Of 3	50.00
Bottle, Avon, Christmas Ornament, 1967, Round	5.00
Bottle, Avon, Christmas Ornament, 1968, Indented	4.00
Bottle, Avon, Christmas Ornament, 1970, Pointed Tip	3.00
Bottle, Avon, Classics, Books, 1969, Set Of 4	16.00
Bottle, Avon, Clock, 1968	3.00
Bottle, Avon, Copper Penny, 1970	3.00
Bottle, Avon, Courting Lamp, 1970	7.00
Bottle, Avon, Cream Shampoo, 1938, California Perfume Company	100.00
Bottle, Avon, Crystal Glory Spray Essence, 1962	8.00
Bottle, Avon, Cuckoo Clock Bubble Bath, 1965, 10 Ozs.	6.00
Bottle, Avon, Decisions, 1965	20.00

Bottle, Avon, Defender Cannon, 1966	15.00
Bottle, Avon, Dollars & Scents, 1966	20.00
Bottle, Avon, Duck Organizer, 1971	22.00
Bottle, Avon, Duck, 1960, Frilly	7.00
Bottle, Avon, Eagle Organizer, 1972	25.00
Bottle, Avon, Elephant Soap, 1962	8.00
Bottle, Avon, Fife, 1965	7.00
Bottle, Avon, Football Helmet, 1968, Gold Top	20.00
Bottle, Avon, Football Helmet, 1968, White Stripe	9.00
Bottle, Avon, Football, 1961	10.00
Bottle, Avon, Fragrance Belle Cologne, 1965, Full	10.00
Bottle, Avon, French Telephone, 1971	20.00
Bottle, Avon, Futura, 1969	15.00
Bottle, Avon, Gavel, 1967	10.00
Bottle, Avon, Gentlemen's Caddy, 1968	15.00
Bottle, Avon, Golden Vanity & Mirror, 1967	25.00
Bottle, Avon, Gun, 1964	10.00
Bottle, Avon, Hickory Dickory Clock Shampoo, 1971	2.69
Bottle, Avon, Inkwell, 1969	5.00
Bottle, Avon, Island Lime, 1966, Canary Yellow, Basket Weave	7.00
Bottle, Avon, Jewel Collection, 1964	50.00
Bottle, Avon, Just Two, 1965, Boxed	75.00
Bottle, Avon, Kingpin, 1969	4.00
Bottle, Avon, Koffee Klatch, 1971	13.00
Bottle, Avon, L'il Captain, 1963	9.00
Bottle, Avon, L'il Folks Time Bubble Bath, 1961, 8 Ozs.	7.00
Bottle, Avon, L'il Helper Iron, 1964	10.00
Bottle, Avon, L'il Mate, 1963	9.00
Bottle, Avon, Leather Boot, Amber Glass, 6 1/2 In.	4.75
Bottle, Avon, Leisure Hours Clock, 1970	5.00
Bottle, Avon, Mad Hatter Decanter Bubble Bath, 1970, 6 Ozs.	1.99
Bottle, Avon, Man's World, 1969	5.00
Bottle, Avon, Perfumed Candle, 1967, Frosted	2.00
Bottle, Avon, Petite Mouse Perfume, 1970	10.00
Bottle, Avon, Pig, 1964	10.00
Bottle, Avon, Pipe Dream, 1966	15.00
Bottle, Avon, Pony Decanter, 1968, Short	3.00
Bottle, Avon, Pony Post, 1966, Tall	8.00
Bottle, Avon, Pump, 1968	6.00
Bottle, Avon, Pyramid, 1969, Boxed	13.00
Bottle, Avon, Rose Fragrancy, 1956, Frosted Stopper	10.00
Bottle, Avon, Royal Orb, 1965, White Letters	20.00 To 75.00
Bottle, Avon, Royal Vase, 1970, Blue	7.00
Bottle, Avon, School Belle, 1965	13.00
Bottle, Avon, Scimitar, 1968	15.00
Bottle, Avon, Skin-So-Soft Urn, 1960, Milk Glass	13.00
Bottle, Avon, Slugger, 1961	10.00
Bottle, Avon, Snail Perfume, 1968	6.00
Bottle, Avon, Snoopy Ace, 1969	3.00
Bottle, Avon, Splash & Spray Set, 1968	19.00
Bottle, Avon, Stein, 1965, 8 Ozs.	8.00
Bottle, Avon, Stein, 1968, 6 Ozs.	6.00
Bottle, Avon, Swinger Golfbag, 1969	5.00
Bottle, Avon, Telephone, 1969	8.00
Bottle, Avon, Tic Toc Tiger Bubble Bath, 1967, 8 Ozs.	4.00
Bottle, Avon, Tic Toc Turtle Bubble Bath, 1968, 8 Ozs.	2.29
Bottle, Avon, Turtle Soap, 1962	8.00
Bottle, Avon, Twenty Paces, 1968, Blue	95.00
Bottle, Avon, Twenty Paces, 1968, Red	35.00
Bottle, Avon, Viking Horn, 1966	13.00
Bottle, Avon, Warrior, 1967, Cobalt	15.00
Bottle, Avon, Watering Can, 1962	8.00
Bottle, Avon, Western Choice Steer Horns, 1967	15.00
Bottle, Avon, White Moire Cologne, 1947, 6 Ozs.	75.00
Bottle, Avon, Wild Rose Cologne, 1955	9.00
Bottle, Avon, Wise Choice Owl, 1969	5.00

Bottle, Avon, Wishing Coin Trio Set, 1963 .... 30.00
Bottle, Barber, Bristol Type, Enameled Floral Sprays, Original Stopper 39.00
Bottle, Barber, Cobalt Blue Satin Glass, 4 Sided, Two Ovals, C.1880 .... 75.00
Bottle, Barber, Cobalt Blue, Blown, Enameled Flowers, Porcelain Stopper 75.00
Bottle, Barber, Enamel Decoration, Amethyst, 6 3/4 In. 45.00
Bottle, Barber, Enamel Decoration, Sapphire Blue, 6 3/4 In. 45.00
Bottle, Barber, Green, Blown, Enameled Flowers, Metal Stopper 65.00
Bottle, Barber, Opaque Blue, Bubbles, White Porcelain Top, Noonan & Co. 40.00

Beam bottles are made to hold Kentucky Straight Bourbon made by the
James B.Beam Distilling Company. The Beam series of ceramic
bottles began in 1953.
Bottle, Beam, Alaska Purchase .... 10.00 To 10.95
Bottle, Beam, Bluejay 7.95
Bottle, Beam, Cat, Burmese 10.00
Bottle, Beam, Civil War, North 34.00
Bottle, Beam, Civil War, Pair 74.95
Bottle, Beam, Club, Dutch 19.95
Bottle, Beam, Colorado 37.00
Bottle, Beam, English Setter, 1959 .... 38.00
Bottle, Beam, Executive, 1955 .... 225.00 To 295.00
Bottle, Beam, Executive, 1956 .... 115.00 To 119.00
Bottle, Beam, Executive, 1957 .... 68.95
Bottle, Beam, Executive, 1958 .... 259.00 To 265.00
Bottle, Beam, Executive, 1959 .... 64.00 To 72.50
Bottle, Beam, Executive, 1960 .... 139.00 To 160.00
Bottle, Beam, Executive, 1961 .... 69.00
Bottle, Beam, Executive, 1962 .... 48.00
Bottle, Beam, Executive, 1963 .... 47.00
Bottle, Beam, Executive, 1964 .... 45.00
Bottle, Beam, Executive, 1965 .... 70.00
Bottle, Beam, Executive, 1965, Case 69.95
Bottle, Beam, Executive, 1966 .... 36.00
Bottle, Beam, Executive, 1967, Case 15.00
Bottle, Beam, Executive, 1968, Case 8.00
Bottle, Beam, Executive, 1969, Case 10.95
Bottle, Beam, Executive, 1972, Case 12.00
Bottle, Beam, Harold's Pinwheel 65.00
Bottle, Beam, Genie, Smoked 7.00
Bottle, Beam, Idaho 67.00
Bottle, Beam, Illinois 6.95
Bottle, Beam, Kansas 59.00
Bottle, Beam, Montana 86.00
Bottle, Beam, Musicians On Wine Cask 7.00
Bottle, Beam, New Hampshire 7.95
Bottle, Beam, New Jersey, Gray 67.50
Bottle, Beam, North Dakota 89.00
Bottle, Beam, Oregon 32.50
Bottle, Beam, Pennsylvania 4.95
Bottle, Beam, Pheasant 14.00
Bottle, Beam, Political, Elephant, 1956 .... 12.50
Bottle, Beam, Robin 7.95
Bottle, Beam, Santa Fe .... 199.00 To 200.00
Bottle, Beam, Speckled Beauty, Pink 650.00
Bottle, Beam, St.Louis Arch 16.00
Bottle, Beam, State, Alaska Star 68.00
Bottle, Beam, State, Idaho 67.00
Bottle, Beam, State, Kansas 59.00
Bottle, Beam, State, Kentucky, Black 9.95
Bottle, Beam, State, Maine 4.00
Bottle, Beam, State, Montana 86.00
Bottle, Beam, State, Nevada 56.00
Bottle, Beam, State, New Jersey, Gray 67.50
Bottle, Beam, State, New Jersey, Yellow 55.00
Bottle, Beam, State, North Dakota 89.00
Bottle, Beam, State, Ohio 10.00

Bottle, Beam, State, South Carolina 4.00
Bottle, Beam, State, West Virginia 159.00
Bottle, Beam, State, Wyoming 67.00
Bottle, Beam, Stein, Milwaukee 37.50
Bottle, Beam, Twin Bridges 55.00
Bottle, Beam, World's Fair, New York 14.00
Bottle, Beam, Wyoming 67.00
Bottle, Beam, Zimmerman, 2 Handled Jug 90.00
Bottle, Beer, A.Palmthe & Co., Eureka, Cal., Blob Top, Amber, Quart 12.00
Bottle, Beer, Acme, Miniature 2.50
Bottle, Beer, Blatz, Miniature 2.50
Bottle, Beer, Budweiser, Miniature 2.50
Bottle, Beer, Buffalo Brewing Co., Cal., Porcelain Stopper, Amber, Quart 12.00
Bottle, Beer, Burger, Cincinnati, O., Display, Labels, 30 In. 62.00
Bottle, Beer, Carling's Black Label, Miniature 6.00
Bottle, Beer, Eastside, Miniature 5.00
Bottle, Beer, Embossed, Blob, Amber, 9 In. 4.00
Bottle, Beer, Enterprise Brewing Co., Cal., Blob Top, Amber, Quart 8.95
Bottle, Beer, Falstaff, Embossed, Green, 11 1/2 In. 10.00
Bottle, Beer, Fort Pitt, Miniature 3.00
Bottle, Beer, Fredericksburg Bottling Co., San Francisco, Blob, Amber, Quart ... 8.00
Bottle, Beer, George Bechtel Brewing Co., Crown Lip, Seeds, Amber, 9 1/4 In. .. 12.00
Bottle, Beer, Hamm's, Miniature 5.00
Bottle, Beer, J.A.Blaffer, New Orleans, Squat, Amber, 9 1/2 In. 25.00
Bottle, Beer, John Rapp & Son, San Francisco, Cal., Blob Top, Amber, Quart 12.00
Bottle, Beer, L.Speidel & Co., Boston, Embossed Hop Leaf, Blob Top, 8 1/2 In. . 8.00
Bottle, Beer, Lemon, Stoneware, Cobalt Glaze, 10 In. 18.00
Bottle, Beer, Miller High Life, Miniature 6.00
Bottle, Beer, National Lager, H.Roltrabacher, Cal., Blob Top, Amber, Pint 6.95
Bottle, Beer, Pabst, Arched, BIMAL, Amethyst, 9 1/2 In. 7.00
Bottle, Beer, Park Brewing Co., Winona, Minn., Picnic, Gold Amber, 1/2 Gallon . 25.00
Bottle, Beer, Royal Ruby, Anchor Glass, ABM, Red, Quart 5.90
Bottle, Beer, Schlitz, Label, Ruby Red, 7 Ozs. 10.00
Bottle, Beer, Stars & Stripes, Omaha, Quart 12.00
Bottle, Bellows, New England, Applied Decoration, 6 1/4 In. 40.00
Bottle, Bellows, New York State, Applied Decoration, Pale Green, 6 3/4 In. 35.00
Bottle, Bellows, New York State, Applied Rigaree, Aqua, 9 1/2 In. 45.00
Bottle, Bitters, American Deobstruent, Oval, Applied Lip, Label, 6 1/2 In. 75.00
Bottle, Bitters, American Stomach, Meyer's Remedy Co., C.1905, Label, 9 In. 27.50
Bottle, Bitters, Boerhave's Holland, Aqua, 8 In. 56.00
Bottle, Bitters, C.K.Wilson's Wa-Hoo, Ohio, Label, 8 1/2 In. 20.00
Bottle, Bitters, Carter's Aromatic Scotch, 4 Panels, Label, Aqua, 8 In. 30.00
Bottle, Bitters, Clark's Vegetable Sherry Wine, 75 Cents, Aqua, 11 1/4 In. 55.00
Bottle, Bitters, Delhi Kidney & Liver, Square, Label, Amber, 8 1/2 In. 50.00
Bottle, Bitters, Dr.Buzzell's Vegetable Bilious, Label, Aqua, 7 1/2 In. 35.00
Bottle, Bitters, Dr.Gerrish Standard, Salt Glaze Jug, 2 Quart, 9 In. 500.00
Bottle, Bitters, Dr.Harter's Wild Cherry, 4 1/2 In. 25.00
Bottle, Bitters, Dr.Harter's, 3 3/4 In. 25.00
Bottle, Bitters, Dr.Hicks' Stomach & Liver, Ga., Oval, Label, 5 In. 35.00
Bottle, Bitters, Dr.Hoofland's German, 9 In. 32.00
Bottle, Bitters, Dr.J.C.Chesley's Golden, 9 In. 95.00
Bottle, Bitters, Dr.Kaufmann's, Oval, Label, Light Aqua, 8 In. 20.00
Bottle, Bitters, Dr.Langley's 99 Union St., Amber, 7 In. 45.00
Bottle, Bitters, Dr.Langley's 99 Union St., Amber, 8 1/2 In. 60.00
Bottle, Bitters, Dr.Sawens' Life Invigorating, Amber, 9 3/4 In. 35.00
Bottle, Bitters, Dr.Van Dyke's Holland, 1896, 4 Panels, 9 3/4 In .... 10.00 To 29.50
Bottle, Bitters, Dr.Warren's Bilious, Boston, Flask, Aqua, 6 1/2 In. 50.00
Bottle, Bitters, Dr.Williams, Doolittle & Smith, Mass., Oval, Label, 8 3/4 In. 30.00
Bottle, Bitters, Drake's Plantation X, 6 Log, Amber 65.00
Bottle, Bitters, Drake's Plantation X, 6 Log, Puce 125.00
Bottle, Bitters, Drake's Plantation, 4 Log 50.00
Bottle, Bitters, Drake's Plantation, 4 Log, Light Amber 75.00
Bottle, Bitters, Drake's Plantation, 4 Log, Medium Amber 55.00
Bottle, Bitters, Drake's Plantation, 5 Log, Burst Bubble 140.00
Bottle, Bitters, Drake's Plantation, 5 Log, Golden Citron 250.00
Bottle, Bitters, Drake's Plantation, 6 Log 60.00

Bottle, Bitters, Drake's Plantation, 6 Log, Amber .... 60.00 To 65.00
Bottle, Bitters, Drake's Plantation, 6 Log, Dark Cherry Red 140.00
Bottle, Bitters, Drake's Plantation, 6 Log, Light Orange Amber 75.00
Bottle, Bitters, Drake's Plantation, 6 Log, Puce 125.00
Bottle, Bitters, Durand's Stomach, Ohio, 4 Indented Panels, C.1900, 7 1/2 In. 30.00
Bottle, Bitters, E.A.Smith, M.D., Oval, Embossed, Label, Aqua, 9 1/2 In. 35.00
Bottle, Bitters, Erso Anti-Bilious, Pa., C.1906, Label, 8 1/4 In. 30.00
Bottle, Bitters, Gold Lion Celery, Label, Whiskey Shape, 6 In. 15.00
Bottle, Bitters, Golden, Cabin Shape, Aqua, W-L190 .... 50.00
Bottle, Bitters, H.P.Herb Wild Cherry, 9 In. 250.00
Bottle, Bitters, H.P.Herb Wild Cherry, 10 1/4 In. 250.00
Bottle, Bitters, Hansard's Genuine Hop, Swansea & Llanelly, Pottery, 8 In. 60.00
Bottle, Bitters, Hartwig Kantorwicz, Embossed Trees & Sun, 13 1/2 In. 65.00
Bottle, Bitters, Hentz Curative, Free Sample, Square, BIMAL, Dug, 3 In. 25.00
Bottle, Bitters, Hoofland's German, 9 In. 35.00
Bottle, Bitters, HUA, Lady's Leg, Crooked Neck, Red Amber, 12 1/4 In. 30.00
Bottle, Bitters, HUA, Lady's Leg, 12 1/4 In. 12.50
Bottle, Bitters, Hufeland Original Swiss Stomach Tonic, Label, 9 1/2 In. 30.00
Bottle, Bitters, Inspector Braesig Stomach, Adolf Prince, Label, 9 3/4 In. 50.00
Bottle, Bitters, King Solomon's, 7 1/4 In. .... 55.00 To 60.00
Bottle, Bitters, Lady's Leg, Inside Stain, Amber, 12 1/2 In. 25.00
Bottle, Bitters, Lash's Natural Tonic Laxative, Label, Amber, 9 1/2 In. 8.65
Bottle, Bitters, Liver, C M Co., N.Y., In Slug Plate, Oval, Amber, 8 1/2 In. 34.95
Bottle, Bitters, N.K.Brown's Iron & Quinine, 4 Panels, Label, 8 1/2 In. 25.00
Bottle, Bitters, S.O.L.Darling's Indian Herb Tonic, C.1903, Label, 8 1/4 In. 35.00
Bottle, Bitters, Oscoda Herbal, Continental Products, Label, Amber, Quart 20.00
Bottle, Bitters, Panwee Too-Re, Embossed, Label, Amber, 8 1/4 In. 60.00
Bottle, Bitters, Peychaud's Aromatic Cocktail, Applied Top, Amber, 11 In. 35.00
Bottle, Bitters, Peychaud's Aromatic Cocktail, Label, Amber, 9 3/4 In. 12.00
Bottle, Bitters, Saxlehner's Bitterquelle, Blob, Emerald Green, 9 1/4 In. 2.45
Bottle, Bitters, Shamrock, Round, Label, 16 Ozs., 9 1/2 In. 30.00
Bottle, Bitters, Sonny Stomach, Whiskey Shape, Label, Amber, Quart 45.00
Bottle, Bitters, Sonoma Wine, 1867, Applied Lip, Label, Amber, 9 1/2 In. 37.50
Bottle, Bitters, Tonic With Bitters On 3 Panels, 12 Panels, Green, 7 1/2 In. 39.95
Bottle, Bitters, Tuft's Tonic, 3 Indented Panels, Label, Aqua, 9 In. 35.00
Bottle, Bitters, Turner's Modoc Indian, Label, Amber, 8 1/2 In. 42.50
Bottle, Bitters, Udolpho Wolfe's Aromatic Schnapps, Stain, Green, 8 In. 15.00
Bottle, Bitters, Udolpho Wolfe's Schiedam Aromatic Schnapps, Green, 8 In. 35.00
Bottle, Bitters, Warner's Safe, 7 1/2 In. 500.00
The McK numbers refer to the book American Glass by George and
Helen McKearin
Bottle, Blown, Applied Top, Whittled, Deep Olive, Quart 15.00
Bottle, Blown, Barrel, Threaded Top & Bottom, Blue On White, 6 In. 60.00
Bottle, Blown, Wafer With R.Lenox, Round, Deep Olive Amber, 10 3/4 In. 30.00
Bottle, Carboy, Free-Blown, Aqua, 24 X 17 In. 150.00
Bottle, Case, Amelung Type, Flint, Gilt Decoration, 7 In. 35.00
Bottle, Case, Amelung Type, Flint, Soda Lime, 5 1/4 In. 35.00
Bottle, Case, Gin, Blown In Mold, Olive Green, 11 In. 22.00
Bottle, Case, Gin, Quart 8.00
Bottle, Case, Gin, 7 1/2 In. 6.00
Bottle, Case, Gin, 10 1/2 In. 12.00
Bottle, Case, Stiegel Type, Blob Type Stopper, C.1750, Pint 25.00
Bottle, Castor, Blown, Three Mold, McK G I-12 .... 20.00
Bottle, Castor, Blown, Three Mold, McK G I-13 .... 20.00
Bottle, Castor, Blown, Three Mold, McK G I-14 .... 20.00
Bottle, Castor, Mold Blown, Applied Rim, 6 1/2 In. 10.00
Bottle, Castor, Mustard, Blown, McK G II-31 .... 26.00
Bottle, Chemical, C.W.Merchant, Chemist, Lockport, N.Y., Green, 7 In. 60.00
Bottle, Chemical, H.E.Geman Co., Chemists, Aqua, 10 1/2 In. 10.00
Bottle, Chemical, Rumford Chemical Works, 8 Sided, Teal Green, 5 1/2 In. 5.00
Bottle, Chemical, Winchester Hpyophosphite Of Manganese, Aqua, 6 3/4 In. 5.00
Bottle, Coca-Cola, see Coca-Cola, Bottle
Bottle, Cologne, Aqua, 5 1/4 In. 60.00
Bottle, Cologne, Aqua, 5 3/4 In. 35.00
Bottle, Cologne, Blown In Mold, Paneled, Floral, McK 243-14 .... 30.00

Bottle, Cologne, Blown, Gilt Decoration, Turquoise	75.00
Bottle, Cologne, Blown, Pear Shape, Hollow Stopper, Ruby Stain, 10 In.	32.00
Bottle, Cologne, Embossed Man In Doorway, Aqua, 3 In.	35.00
Bottle, Cologne, Figural, Woman's Shoe, C.1880, 4 1/2 In.	38.00
Bottle, Cologne, Flint, Lions On 4 Corners, Seeing Eyes, 7 1/2 In.	100.00
Bottle, Cologne, Floral Tree, 4 In.	40.00
Bottle, Cologne, French, Faceted Stopper, Ormolu Collar & Holder	45.00
Bottle, Cologne, J.M.Farina, 6 Sided, Pontil, 4 3/8 In.	25.00
Bottle, Cologne, Melon Ribbed, Pink Satin, Enamel Decoration, 2 1/2 In.High	28.00
Bottle, Cologne, Pot Of Flowers, Pale Green, 4 1/4 In.	35.00
Bottle, Cosmetic, Barbasol, 8 Panels, Screw-On Tin Cap, C.1915, 3 1/4 In.	8.50
Bottle, Cosmetic, Noxzema, Embossed Across Base, Cobalt, 1/2 Gallon	100.00
Bottle, Cosmetic, Paragon Hair Coloring, Amber, 3 1/2 In.	6.00
Bottle, Decanter, Crystal, Inverted Thumbprint, Facet Cut Stopper, 10 In.	12.50
Bottle, Decanter, Russia, Czarina Alexandra Feodorovna, C.1894, 9 5/8 In.	800.00
Bottle, Decanter, Russia, Narishkin Coat Of Arms, C.1890, 9 1/4 In.	900.00
Bottle, Demijohn, Blob Top, Brown, 18 In.	65.00
Bottle, Demijohn, Hand-Blown, Impressed Seal, Pontil, C.1700, Green, 36 In.	50.00
Bottle, Demijohn, Olive Green, 1/2 Gallon	10.00
Bottle, Demijohn, Open Pontil, Green, 13 In.	35.00
Bottle, Demijohn, Open Pontil, 3 Gallon	55.00
Bottle, Demijohn, "Our Little Pet Jug, " Crimped, Applied Handle, 2 3/4 In.	12.00
Bottle, Drug, American Drug & Press Assn., Decorah, I., Amber, 5 In.	10.00
Bottle, Drug, Cobalt Blue, White Glass Label, 9 1/2 In.High	42.50
Bottle, Drug, Glyco-Heroin, Smith, Dug, Amber, 8 3/4 In.	4.00
Bottle, Drug, New York Pharmaceutical Association, Cobalt, 12 In.	25.00
Bottle, Dyottville Glass Works, Phila. On Bottom, Round, Citron, 12 In.	15.00
Bottle, Embossed Key On One Side, Aqua, Pint	12.50
Bottle, Error, A.Nicholson, Backward S, Blue, 8 3/4 In. *Illus*	400.00
Bottle, Error, K.Konishi & Co., Apohercary, Embossed, Green Blue, 8 In.	8.00
Bottle, Error, Swayzee's Imppover, Fruit Jar, Quart	6.00
Bottle, Figural, Austrian Woman, Robj, Paris, 11 1/4 In.	60.00
Bottle, Figural, Barrel, Embossed LAM & A & F ON BASE, GREEN, 10 IN.	24.50
Bottle, Figural, Barrel, Hoops, Mold Blown, 5 In.	12.00
Bottle, Figural, Barrel, Pub, Porcelain, Castle Scenes, White, 3 1/4 In.	3.50
Bottle, Figural, Barrel, Pub, Porcelain, Cottage Scenes, White, 3 1/4 In.	3.50
Bottle, Figural, Barrel, Pub, Porcelain, English Maps, White, 3 1/4 In.	3.50
Bottle, Figural, Barrel, Pub, Porcelain, Water Scenes, White, 3 1/4 In.	3.50
Bottle, Figural, Big Ben Tower, Black Base, 6 1/2 In.	5.00
Bottle, Figural, Blackpool Tower, Porcelain, Tan, 3 1/2 In.	4.00
Bottle, Figural, Book, 4 1/2 In.	65.00
Bottle, Figural, Bull-Nosed Morris, Porcelain, Gold, Platinum, 1965, 3 1/2 In.	6.00
Bottle, Figural, Bullfighter, 12 In.	4.00
Bottle, Figural, Bunny Rabbit, Germany, C.1920, 2 1/2 In.	5.50
Bottle, Figural, Christmas Tree, 14 1/2 In. *Illus*	275.00
Bottle, Figural, Dickens' Olde Curiosity Shop, Porcelain, Tan, 2 1/4 In.	5.50
Bottle, Figural, Doe's Head, Porcelain, Tan, 3 3/4 In.	4.50
Bottle, Figural, Dog, Miniature	20.00

Bottle, Error,
A.Nicholson, Backward S,
Blue, 8 3/4 In.

Bottle, Figural, Pretzel, 5 1/2 In.
(See Page 36)

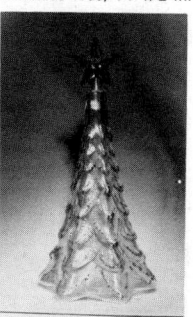

Bottle, Figural,
Christmas Tree, 14 1/2 In.

Bottle, Figural, George Washington, 9 1/2 In. 6.95
Bottle, Figural, Koala Bear Climbing Tree, Molded, Black Base, 3 1/2 In. 5.00
Bottle, Figural, Lighthouse, Red Trim, Brown Base, Porcelain, White, 4 1/4 In. 3.50
Bottle, Figural, Madonna, Mexican, Cobalt, 12 In. 15.00
Bottle, Figural, Madonna, 14 In. 9.00
Bottle, Figural, Mermaid On Rock, Molded Glass, Black Base, 3 1/2 In. 5.00
Bottle, Figural, Mr.Pickwick, 9 In. 6.95
Bottle, Figural, Nude Dancing Girls, Chas. Stenet Freres, 5 1/4 In. 20.00
Bottle, Figural, Pig Smoking Pipe, Stocking Cap, Porcelain, 6 1/4 In. 50.00
Bottle, Figural, Pretzel, 5 1/2 In. .... *Illus* 35.00
Bottle, Figural, Robert Burns' Bust, Ceramic, Matte Finish, White, 4 In. 4.95
Bottle, Figural, Scottish Warrior, Tam & Tartan Kilt, Porcelain, 4 In. 4.50
Bottle, Figural, Shakespeare's Birthplace House, Tan & Brown, 2 In. 5.95
Bottle, Figural, Shoe, 3 3/4 In. 15.00
Bottle, Figural, Soldier With Pig's Head, German Lettering, China, 7 1/2 In. 69.50
Bottle, Figural, Tam-O'-Shanter, Blue, Red Pompon, Porcelain, 1 1/2 In. 4.00
Bottle, Figural, Toilet, Toilet Water, 2 1/2 In. 3.00
Bottle, Figural, Violin, Musical Scale, Hanger, 10 In. 10.00
Bottle, Figural, Woman & Man, Volendam, Blue, 3 1/2 X 3 3/4 In., Pair 10.00
Bottle, Figural, Ye Olde Beer Handle, Hunting Scenes, Gold, Porcelain, 6 In. 4.00

*The McK numbers refer to the book American Glass by George and
Helen McKearin.*

Bottle, Flask, Anchor & Baltimore Glass & Sheaf Of Rye, Aqua, 1/2 Pint 40.00
Bottle, Flask, Anchor & Baltimore Glass Works & Resurgam, Amber, Pint 105.00
Bottle, Flask, Anchor & Baltimore Glass Works & Resurgam, Aqua, Pint 68.00
Bottle, Flask, Anchor & New London Glassworks & Flying Eagle, Amber, Pint 225.00
Bottle, Flask, Anchor & Ravenna Glass Co. & Eagle & 13 Stars, Amber, Pint 95.00
Bottle, Flask, Anchor, Amber, Pint 20.00
Bottle, Flask, Applied Metal Vines & Floral, Silver Cap, Green, 9 In. 75.00
Bottle, Flask, Baltimore Glass Works & Resurgam, Aqua, Pint 80.00
Bottle, Flask, Calabash, Jenny Lind & Glass House, McK G I-103, Aqua 30.00
Bottle, Flask, Calabash, Union & Masonic, Aqua, McK G IV-42 .... 65.00
Bottle, Flask, Charlie Ross, 5 In. 22.00
Bottle, Flask, Chestnut, New England, 6 1/4 In. 55.00
Bottle, Flask, Chestnut, Red Amber, 8 1/4 In. 25.00
Bottle, Flask, Chestnut, Zanesville, 24 Ribs Swirled To Left, Amber, 1/2 Pint 250.00
Bottle, Flask, Chestnut, Zanesville, 24 Vertical Ribs, Amber, Pint, 7 In. 375.00
Bottle, Flask, Clasped Hands & Eagle & Shield, Aqua, Quart 30.00
Bottle, Flask, Coffin, Embossed Key On Front, Aqua, Pint 30.00
Bottle, Flask, Corn Whiskey, Ear Of Corn Shape, Pewter Screw Cap, 6 1/2 In. 85.00
Bottle, Flask, Cornucopia & Urn, Dark Amber, Pint 65.00
Bottle, Flask, Cornucopia & Urn, Olive Green, 1/2 Pint 40.00
Bottle, Flask, Crossed Keys, McK G IV-30 .... 2000.00
Bottle, Flask, Double Eagle & Granite Glass Co. & Stoddard, Amber, Pint 85.00
Bottle, Flask, Double Eagle & Granite Glass Co. & Stoddard, Green, Pint 160.00
Bottle, Flask, Double Eagle & Pittsburgh, Pa. In Oval, Amber, Pint 60.00
Bottle, Flask, Double Eagle & Stoddard, Glass In Bottom, Amber, 1/2 Pint 85.00
Bottle, Flask, Double Eagle & Stoddard, N.H. In Oval, Olive Amber, Pint 150.00
Bottle, Flask, Double Eagle & Stoddard, Open Pontil, Smoky Amber, 1/2 Pint 85.00
Bottle, Flask, Double Eagle Over Oval, Aqua, Pint 40.00
Bottle, Flask, Double Eagle Over Oval, Iron Pontil, Deep Aqua, Pint 47.50
Bottle, Flask, Double Eagle, Amber, Pint 90.00
Bottle, Flask, Double Eagle, Cunningham, Aqua, 1/2 Pint 75.00
Bottle, Flask, Double Eagle, Haze, Aqua, Pint 34.50
Bottle, Flask, Double Eagle, Olive Green, Pint 85.00
Bottle, Flask, Eagle & A & DH, C In Oval & Girl On Bicycle, Blue, Pint 80.00
Bottle, Flask, Eagle & Cornucopia & Zanesville, Dark Amber, 1/2 Pint 250.00
Bottle, Flask, Eagle & Cornucopia, Open Pontil, Olive Green, Pin .... 80.00 To 90.00
Bottle, Flask, Eagle & Flag, McK G II-54, Aqua, Pint 195.00
Bottle, Flask, Eagle & Kensington Glassworks, C.1850, Aqua, 1/2 Pint 275.00
Bottle, Flask, Eagle & Liberty, McK G II-65, Olive Green, 1/2 Pint 85.00
Bottle, Flask, Eagle & Shield & Flag & For Our Country, Pale Aqua, Pint 85.00
Bottle, Flask, Eagle & Westford, McK G II-65, Amber, 1/2 Pint 135.00
Bottle, Flask, Eagle & Willington, Amber, Quart 130.00
Bottle, Flask, Eagle In Oval & Louisville, Ky., Ribbed, Amber, 1/2 Pint 160.00

Bottle, Flask, Eagle Lengthwise, McK G II-71, Amber, 1/2 Pint	170.00
Bottle, Flask, Eagle, Aqua, Quart	40.00
Bottle, Flask, Eagle, McK G II-20, Deep Aqua, Pint	1275.00
Bottle, Flask, Embossed Columbus, Medallion Shape, Screw Cap, 6 1/4 In.	17.50
Bottle, Flask, Embossed Small Eagle, Short Neck, Clear Amber, 5 3/4 In.	30.00
Bottle, Flask, Etched Pennsylvania Tulip, C.1790, 1/2 Pint	135.00
Bottle, Flask, Flat Chestnut, Ohio, 25 Swirled Ribs, Dark Amber, Pint	200.00
Bottle, Flask, For Pike's Peak & Eagle & Shield & Streamer, Aqua, Pint	40.00
Bottle, Flask, For Pike's Peak & Eagle Over Oval, Haze, Aqua, Quart	38.50
Bottle, Flask, For Pike's Peak & Old Rye, Aqua, Pint	75.00
Bottle, Flask, For Pike's Peak, Aqua, 1/2 Pint	38.00
Bottle, Flask, For Pike's Peak, Green, Pint	90.00
Bottle, Flask, Franklin & Dr.Dyott, Pint	50.00
Bottle, Flask, Girl On Bicycle & Not For Joe On Streamer, Aqua, Pint	100.00
Bottle, Flask, Glass, Metal Lid, 8 In.	12.50
Bottle, Flask, Granite Glass Co. & Stoddard, N.H., Amber, Pint	60.00
Bottle, Flask, Granite Glass Co. & Stoddard, N.H., Pontil, Olive Green, Pint	200.00
Bottle, Flask, Grant, McK G I-79, Aqua	210.00
Bottle, Flask, Grapevine, McK G X-5	295.00
Bottle, Flask, Green Aqua, 6 1/4 In.	15.00
Bottle, Flask, Honest Measure In Banner, Strap Sided, Lip Ring, 4 1/2 In.	5.50
Bottle, Flask, Justus Perry, McK G IV-1, Deep Aqua, Pint	300.00
Bottle, Flask, Lafayette, S & C & DeWitt Clinton & C & T, Olive, 1/2 Pint	350.00
Bottle, Flask, Liberty & Willington Glass Co., Dark Olive Green, 1/2 Pint	75.00
Bottle, Flask, Light Yellow Amber, 6 3/4 In.	7.50
Bottle, Flask, Louisville, Ribbed, McK G II-33, Amber, 1/2 Pint	500.00
Bottle, Flask, Lowell Railroad, McK G V-10, Amber, 1/2 Pint	210.00
Bottle, Flask, Masonic & Eagle & Keene In Oval, Yellow Amber, Pint	175.00
Bottle, Flask, Masonic & Eagle & Oval, McK G IV-24, Olive, 1/2 Pint	250.00
Bottle, Flask, Masonic & Eagle & Zanesville, O., McK G IV-32, Blue	275.00
Bottle, Flask, Masonic & Keene, McK G IV-17, Amber, Pint	170.00
Bottle, Flask, Masonic & Keene, McK G IV-21, Olive Green	245.00
Bottle, Flask, Masonic & Keene, McK G IV-24, AMBER, 1/2 PINT	185.00
Bottle, Flask, Masonic & Steubenville, O., Ceramic, 3 In.	29.00
Bottle, Flask, Masonic, McK G IV-11, , Pint	320.00
Bottle, Flask, Picnic, Spiderweb, Blown In Mold, Pint	6.00
Bottle, Flask, Picnic, 5 Pointed Star, Blob Lip With Ring, 3 1/2 In.	5.50
Bottle, Flask, Pitkin, Green, Pint	185.00
Bottle, Flask, Pumpkinseed, A.F.Benard, Larkin & Fulton St., 5 1/2 In.	22.00
Bottle, Flask, Pumpkinseed, Blob Lip With Skirt, Blue Aqua, 4 1/2 In.	6.00
Bottle, Flask, Pumpkinseed, Blob Lip With Skirt, Yellow Green, 4 3/4 In.	7.00
Bottle, Flask, Pumpkinseed, Cobweb, Bent Neck, Dug, Aqua, Pint	10.00
Bottle, Flask, Ravenna Glass Works & 5 Pointed Star, Aqua, Pint	75.00
Bottle, Flask, Saddle, Blob Top, Amber, 10 In.	65.00
Bottle, Flask, Saddle, London, 1892, Silver Collar & Hinged Lid, 9 3/4 In.	28.00
Bottle, Flask, Scroll, Marked S.McKee, McK G IX-26, Aqua, Pint	400.00
Bottle, Flask, Scroll, McK G IX-34, Aqua	80.00
Bottle, Flask, Scroll, Open Pontil, Medium Aqua, Quart	75.00
Bottle, Flask, Scroll, Uneven Lip, McK G IX-36, Aqua, 1/2 Pint	49.50
Bottle, Flask, Seated Monkey & Banjo & Dancing Monkey, Amber, 1/2 Pint	130.00
Bottle, Flask, Seeing Eye & G.R.J.A., Sheared Lip, Amber, Pint	195.00
Bottle, Flask, Sheaf Of Rye & Tools & 5 Pointed Star, Dark Amber, 1/2 Pint	165.00
Bottle, Flask, Sheaf Of Wheat & Tools & Westford Glass Co., Amber, Pint	50.00
Bottle, Flask, Sheaf Of Wheat & Westford, Conn., Olive Amber, Pint	80.00
Bottle, Flask, Shield & Rampant Lion & Grapes, Europe, Cobalt, 6 1/2 In.	32.50
Bottle, Flask, Shield & Rampant Lion & Grapes, Europe, Green, 6 1/2 In.	10.00
Bottle, Flask, Shield & Rampant Lion, Swirled, Europe, Cobalt, 6 1/2 In.	35.00
Bottle, Flask, Soldier On Horse & Dog, Cloudy, Aqua, Quart	25.00
Bottle, Flask, Stoddard Type, Double Ring Top, Whittled, Amber, Pint	12.00
Bottle, Flask, Stoddard, Double Rolled Collar, Pint	20.00
Bottle, Flask, Strap Sided, Amber, 1/2 Pint	5.00
Bottle, Flask, Strap Sided, Amber, Pint	6.00
Bottle, Flask, Success To The Railroad, McK G V-4, Aquamarine, Pint	125.00
Bottle, Flask, Success To The Railroad, McK G V-5, Olive Green, Pint	180.00
Bottle, Flask, Sunburst, McK G VIII-16, Yellow Olive	350.00
Bottle, Flask, Traveler's Companion, Dark Olive Green, Quart	120.00

Bottle, Flask, Union & A.& D.H.Chambers, Aqua, Quart	52.00
Bottle, Flask, Union & Eagle & Shield, Amber, 1/2 Pint	60.00
Bottle, Flask, Union & Wm.Frank & Sons, Pitt. & Cannon & Flag, Blue, Pint	65.00
Bottle, Flask, Violin, Aqua, Pint	45.00
Bottle, Flask, Washington & Eagle & T.W.D., McK G I-16, Green, Pint	75.00
Bottle, Flask, Washington & Taylor, Blob Top, McK G I-41, Aqua, Pint	115.00
Bottle, Flask, Washington & Taylor, Light Amber, 1/2 Pint	195.00
Bottle, Flask, Washington & Taylor, Reproduction, C.1950, Cobalt, Pint	15.00
Bottle, Flask, Washington, McK G I-2	500.00
Bottle, Flask, Washington, McK G I-10	300.00 To 500.00
Bottle, Flask, Whiskey, New Hampshire Officer's, 1862, Pewter Cap, 6 In.	50.00
Bottle, Flask, Whiskey, 1886, Pewter Lip, Cap, & Bottom Half, 6 In.	20.00
Bottle, Flask, Will You Take A Drink-Will A Duck Swim, Aqua, Pint	75.00
Bottle, Food, E.R.Durkee & Co., N.Y., Belt & Gloved Hand, 1877, 8 1/2 In.	5.95
Bottle, Food, Heinz Apple Butter, 36 Ozs. *Illus*	25.00
Bottle, Food, Jamaican Ginger, Decanter, White Enamel Letters, Pint	10.00
Bottle, Food, Jumbo Peanut Butter, Embossed Elephant, ABM, Pint	2.25
Bottle, Food, McMacher's, Always The Best, 7 1/4 In. *Illus*	45.00
Bottle, Food, Olive Oil, Open Pontil, Stain, 10 1/2 In.	2.95
Bottle, Food, Planter's Peanut, Square Peanut On Top, 7 1/2 In.	65.00
Bottle, Food, Rose's Lime Juice, 11 In.	8.00
Bottle, Food, Sara-A-Lee Salad Dressing, 1920, 8 1/2 In.	5.95
Bottle, Food, Sauce, Honeywell Type, Concave Panels, Aqua, 6 In.	5.95
Bottle, Food, Sunshine Coffee, Embossed, Pound	2.50
Bottle, Fruit Jar, A.G.Smalley, Large Mouth, Embossed, Milk Glass, Quart	30.00
Bottle, Fruit Jar, A.P.Donagho, W.Va., Wax Sealer, Pottery, 9 In.	15.00
Bottle, Fruit Jar, A.Stone & Co., Chipped, Aqua, 8 1/2 In *Illus*	250.00
Bottle, Fruit Jar, Air Tight, Iron Pontil, Quart	500.00
Bottle, Fruit Jar, Atlas E-Z Seal, Wire Bail, Orange Amber, Quart	35.00
Bottle, Fruit Jar, Atlas E-Z Seal, 48 Ozs.	7.00
Bottle, Fruit Jar, Atlas E-Z Seal, 58 Ozs.	7.00
Bottle, Fruit Jar, Atlas Strong Shoulder, Pint	1.00
Bottle, Fruit Jar, Atlas Strong Shoulder, Quart	1.00
Bottle, Fruit Jar, Atlas Strong Shoulder, Salesman's Sample, 3 In.	10.00
Bottle, Fruit Jar, Atlas, Amber, 1/2 Gallon	25.00
Bottle, Fruit Jar, Atlas, Cornflower Blue, Pint	12.75
Bottle, Fruit Jar, Atlas, Cornflower Blue, Quart	12.75
Bottle, Fruit Jar, Atlas, Olive Green, Pint	4.50
Bottle, Fruit Jar, Atlas, 1/2 Pint	1.25
Bottle, Fruit Jar, Ball Ideal, Patent July 1908, Glass Lid, Aqua, Pint	2.00
Bottle, Fruit Jar, Ball Improved, Quart	4.00
Bottle, Fruit Jar, Ball Mason, Deep Olive Green, Pint	30.00
Bottle, Fruit Jar, Ball Perfect Mason, Deep Olive Green, Pint	30.00
Bottle, Fruit Jar, Ball Perfect Mason, Deep Olive Green, Quart	30.00
Bottle, Fruit Jar, Ball Perfect Mason, 1/2 Gallon	20.00
Bottle, Fruit Jar, Ball Special, Aqua, Pint	4.00
Bottle, Fruit Jar, Ball Special, Aqua, 1/2 Gallon	5.00
Bottle, Fruit Jar, Ball, Olive Amber, 1/2 Gallon	28.00
Bottle, Fruit Jar, Beaver, Amber, Quart	300.00
Bottle, Fruit Jar, Best Fruit Keeper, Aqua, Quart	32.00
Bottle, Fruit Jar, Best, Quart	21.50
Bottle, Fruit Jar, Best, 1/2 Gallon	21.50
Bottle, Fruit Jar, Boldt Mason, Zinc Lid, Aqua, Quart	10.00
Bottle, Fruit Jar, Boyd, Pint	5.00
Bottle, Fruit Jar, Canton Domestic, Quart	40.00
Bottle, Fruit Jar, Chef, Embossed Face, Quart	2.75
Bottle, Fruit Jar, Clarke Co., Cleveland, O., Aqua, Quart	35.00
Bottle, Fruit Jar, Cohansey On Base, Haze, Amber, Quart	15.00
Bottle, Fruit Jar, Cohansey, Aqua, Quart	15.00
Bottle, Fruit Jar, Cohansey, Pint	50.00
Bottle, Fruit Jar, Cohansey, Quart	14.00
Bottle, Fruit Jar, Cunningham & Co., Pittsburgh, Iron Pontil, Quart	142.00
Bottle, Fruit Jar, Curtis & Moore, 1/2 Gallon	20.00
Bottle, Fruit Jar, Dandy, The, Trademark, Aqua, Pint	26.00
Bottle, Fruit Jar, Diamond, Quart	5.00
Bottle, Fruit Jar, Dictator, D.I.Holcomb, Wax Sealer, Tin Lid, Aqua, Quart	60.00

Bottle, Food,
Heinz Apple Butter,
36 Ozs.
(See Page 38)

Bottle, Food,
McMacher's,
Always The Best,
7 1/4 In.
(See Page 38)

Bottle, Fruit Jar, A.Stone & Co.,
Chipped, Aqua, 8 1/2 In
(See Page 38)

Bottle, Fruit Jar, Doolittle, Quart	20.00
Bottle, Fruit Jar, Double Safety, S.K.O., Pint	7.00
Bottle, Fruit Jar, E.Hazard, Quart	9.50
Bottle, Fruit Jar, E-Z Seal, 1/2 Pint	2.00
Bottle, Fruit Jar, Eclipse, The, Embossed Side, Wax Sealer, Amber, Quart	600.00
Bottle, Fruit Jar, FA & Co., Embossed Base, Iron Pontil, Aqua, 1/2 Gallon	124.00
Bottle, Fruit Jar, Folded-In Lip, Iron Pontil, Aqua, 8 In.	85.00
Bottle, Fruit Jar, Foster Seal Fast, Pint	5.00
Bottle, Fruit Jar, Franklin Dexter, Haze, Aqua, Quart	20.00
Bottle, Fruit Jar, GJCo Monogram, Domed Zinc Insert Lid, Aqua, Quart	12.00
Bottle, Fruit Jar, Gem, Aqua, Quart	8.00
Bottle, Fruit Jar, Gem, Maltese Cross, Aqua, Midget	5.00
Bottle, Fruit Jar, Gem, The, Quart	12.50
Bottle, Fruit Jar, Genuine Mason, Pint	2.00
Bottle, Fruit Jar, Gilberd's Improved, Quart	95.00
Bottle, Fruit Jar, Glassboro Trade Mark Improved, Aqua, Pint	12.50
Bottle, Fruit Jar, Globe, Amber, Quart	35.00
Bottle, Fruit Jar, Globe, Aqua, Pint	12.00
Bottle, Fruit Jar, Globe, Aqua, Quart	10.00
Bottle, Fruit Jar, Globe, Quart	11.00
Bottle, Fruit Jar, Golden State, Pint	12.00
Bottle, Fruit Jar, Golden State, Quart	12.00
Bottle, Fruit Jar, Golden State, 1/2 Gallon	12.00
Bottle, Fruit Jar, Great Western Wier, Stoneware, Gallon	18.00
Bottle, Fruit Jar, Hazel Atlas E-Z Seal, Pint	8.00
Bottle, Fruit Jar, Helme's Railroad Mills, Amber, Quart	8.00
Bottle, Fruit Jar, Hero, Gallon	285.00
Bottle, Fruit Jar, Heroine, The, Glass Lid, Bubbles, Aqua, Quart	25.00
Bottle, Fruit Jar, Howe, The, 2 Quart	45.00
Bottle, Fruit Jar, Johnson & Johnson, Amber, 1/2 Pint	7.00
Bottle, Fruit Jar, Kivlan & Onthank, Pat'd June 28, '21, Boston, Quart	4.00
Bottle, Fruit Jar, Knowlton Vacuum, 1/2 Gallon	19.00
Bottle, Fruit Jar, Knowlton, Pint	20.00
Bottle, Fruit Jar, Lafayette, Amber, Pint	165.00
Bottle, Fruit Jar, Lafayette, Amber, Quart	85.00
Bottle, Fruit Jar, Lafayette, Script, Quart	65.00
Bottle, Fruit Jar, Lamb Mason, Quart	2.00
Bottle, Fruit Jar, Leader, Amber, Quart	80.00
Bottle, Fruit Jar, Lightning Trademark Registered, Putnam On Base, Pint	2.50
Bottle, Fruit Jar, Lightning, Amber, Pint	18.00
Bottle, Fruit Jar, Lightning, Amber, Quart	29.00
Bottle, Fruit Jar, Lightning, Amber, 1/2 Gallon	30.00
Bottle, Fruit Jar, Lightning, Aqua, Pint	1.00
Bottle, Fruit Jar, Lightning, Aqua, Quart	1.00
Bottle, Fruit Jar, Lightning, Pint	8.00
Bottle, Fruit Jar, Lorillard, Amber, Quart	7.00
Bottle, Fruit Jar, Ludlow's Patent, Quart	95.00
Bottle, Fruit Jar, Lyman, Circled 2 Dates, Pint	48.00
Bottle, Fruit Jar, Macomb, 1899, Pottery, 1/2 Gallon	15.00

Bottle, Fruit Jar, Marion, The, Aqua, 1/2 Gallon 6.50
Bottle, Fruit Jar, Marion, The, Mason's Patent Nov.30th, 1858, Aqua, Quart 8.00
Bottle, Fruit Jar, Mason, Liberty Bell, 1776-1876, Pint 3.00
Bottle, Fruit Jar, Mason, Liberty Bell, 1776-1876, Quart 3.00
Bottle, Fruit Jar, Mason, The, Bubbles, 1/2 Gallon 6.00
Bottle, Fruit Jar, Mason's CFJ Co., Improved, Midget .... 6.00 To 10.00
Bottle, Fruit Jar, Mason's CFJ Co., Patent Nov.30th, 1858, Midget 7.00
Bottle, Fruit Jar, Mason's CFJ, Patent Nov.30th, 1858, Apple Green, Quart 25.00
Bottle, Fruit Jar, Mason's CFJ, Patent Nov.30th, 1858, Lime Green, Pint 25.00
Bottle, Fruit Jar, Mason's Improved CFJ, Aqua, Midget 6.00
Bottle, Fruit Jar, Mason's Improved, May 1870 On Base, Midget 6.00
Bottle, Fruit Jar, Mason's Improved, Midget 7.25
Bottle, Fruit Jar, Mason's Patent Nov.30th, 1858, Amber, 1/2 Gallon 60.00
Bottle, Fruit Jar, Mason's Patent Nov.30th, 1858, Maltese Cross, Midget 10.00
Bottle, Fruit Jar, Mason's Patent Nov.30th, 1858, 1/2 Gallon 4.50
Bottle, Fruit Jar, Mason's Patent, 1830, Midget 17.00
Bottle, Fruit Jar, Mason's, Amber, Pint 35.00
Bottle, Fruit Jar, McDonald Perfect Seal, Quart 2.50
Bottle, Fruit Jar, McDonald, Pint 6.00
Bottle, Fruit Jar, McDonald, Quart 5.00
Bottle, Fruit Jar, Middleby, 1/2 Gallon 5.50
Bottle, Fruit Jar, Millville, Amber, 1/2 Pint 50.00
Bottle, Fruit Jar, Millville, Quart 20.00
Bottle, Fruit Jar, Millville, 1/2 Pint .... 41.00 To 45.00
Bottle, Fruit Jar, Model Mason, Quart 11.00
Bottle, Fruit Jar, Moore's, Aqua, 1 1/2 Quart 65.00
Bottle, Fruit Jar, Moore's, Whittled, Aqua, 1 1/2 Quart 80.00
Bottle, Fruit Jar, Moore's, 1861, Aqua, Quart 55.00
Bottle, Fruit Jar, Myer's Test, Whittled, Aqua, 2 Quart 200.00
Bottle, Fruit Jar, N.W.Electroglas, Quart 5.00
Bottle, Fruit Jar, Pansy, Aqua Insert, Amber, Quart 310.00
Bottle, Fruit Jar, Perfection, Pint 27.50
Bottle, Fruit Jar, Petal, 10 Petals, Iron Pontil, Emerald Green, Quart 1200.00
Bottle, Fruit Jar, Pettit, Pint 14.00
Bottle, Fruit Jar, Porcelain Lined, Aqua, Quart 15.00
Bottle, Fruit Jar, Potter & Bodine, Straight Sides, Quart 215.00
Bottle, Fruit Jar, Protector, Quart 15.00
Bottle, Fruit Jar, Quick Seal, Quart 3.00
Bottle, Fruit Jar, Ravenna Glass Works Air Tight, Iron Pontil, Pint 1200.00
Bottle, Fruit Jar, Red Key Mason, Aqua, Quart 7.50
Bottle, Fruit Jar, Red Key Mason, Aqua, 1/2 Gallon 8.50
Bottle, Fruit Jar, Root Mason, Aqua, Pint 3.00
Bottle, Fruit Jar, Root Mason, Aqua, Quart 2.50
Bottle, Fruit Jar, Root Mason, Aqua, 1/2 Gallon 4.00
Bottle, Fruit Jar, Root Mason, Pint 2.00
Bottle, Fruit Jar, S.G.Co., 1858, Pint 5.00
Bottle, Fruit Jar, S.McKee, Wax Seal, Quart 10.00
Bottle, Fruit Jar, Safety Valve, No Embossing, Sun Colored, 1/2 Pint 6.00
Bottle, Fruit Jar, Sanford's, Quart 12.50
Bottle, Fruit Jar, Schram, Pint .... 2.00 To 6.00
Bottle, Fruit Jar, Schram, Quart 5.00
Bottle, Fruit Jar, Selco, Pint 5.00
Bottle, Fruit Jar, Selco, 1/2 Gallon 7.00
Bottle, Fruit Jar, Simplex, Pint 8.00
Bottle, Fruit Jar, Smalley's Nu Seal, Royal Trade Mark In Crown, Quart 4.00
Bottle, Fruit Jar, Snowflake Mason, Quart 12.00
Bottle, Fruit Jar, Standard Mason, Quart 6.00
Bottle, Fruit Jar, Standard Mason, 1/2 Gallon 7.00
Bottle, Fruit Jar, Stoddard, Preserve, Open Pontil, C.1800, Light Green, 6 In. 50.00
Bottle, Fruit Jar, Sun, Amber, Quart 45.00
Bottle, Fruit Jar, Sun, Haze, Quart 44.00
Bottle, Fruit Jar, Tight Seal, Pint 4.00
Bottle, Fruit Jar, Trademark Lightning, Cornflower Blue, Quart 25.00
Bottle, Fruit Jar, Tudor Rose, Mason's Patent 1858, Stain, Aqua, Quart 25.00
Bottle, Fruit Jar, Valve, Aqua, Quart 130.00
Bottle, Fruit Jar, Van Vliet, 1/2 Gallon 260.00

Bottle, Fruit Jar, Wan-Eta Cocoa, Boston, Amber, Quart	5.50
Bottle, Fruit Jar, Wan-Eta Cocoa, Boston, Embossed, Aqua, Quart	5.00
Bottle, Fruit Jar, Western Stoneware, White, 2 Quart	16.00
Bottle, Fruit Jar, Woodbury, Aqua, Quart	15.00
Bottle, Gin, Bininger, 19 Broad St., Amber, Pint	48.00
Bottle, Gin, Embossed, Olive Green, 4 In.	40.00
Bottle, Gin, Free-Blown, Squashed Lip, Pontil, 10 In.	35.00
Bottle, Glenn & Co., Phila., Ointment, Jar, Three Mold, Brass Lid, 4 In.	20.00
Bottle, Globular, 12 Ribs, Long Neck, Yellow Green, 8 In.	300.00
Bottle, Glue, Bell Mucilage, Sheared Lip, Bimal, 3 In.	3.00
Bottle, Glue, Bell Mucilage, Sheared Lip, Neck Ring, Blue Aqua, 3 1/4 In.	5.00
Bottle, Glue, Egyptian Tenexine, Pyramid Shape, Sheared Lip, Blue, 2 3/4 In.	7.00
Bottle, Glue, Spalding's, Cylindrical, Pontil, Stain, Dug, Aqua, 3 1/4 In.	7.50
Bottle, Hand-Blown, Fancy Design, Ground Top, Amber, 7 Gallon	50.00
Bottle, Household, Soap Co., Tippecanoe City, O., Rectangular, 6 In.	2.45
Bottle, Household, Use Whitine For Kid, Albion Mfg.Co., N.Y., Aqua, 5 1/4 In.	2.00
Bottle, I.W.Harper, Figural, Porcelain, White, 16 1/2 In.	18.00
Bottle, I.W.Harper, Nelson Co., Ky., Incised, Jug, 1/4 Pint	17.50
Bottle, Ink, Angus & Co., Schoolhouse Type, Pen Rest, Blue Aqua, 2 In.	10.95
Bottle, Ink, Barrel, Part Label, 2 X 2 In.	15.00
Bottle, Ink, Billing's Mauve, Beehive Shape, Rolled Lip, Aqua, 1 1/2 In.	15.00
Bottle, Ink, Blown, Three Mold, McK G III-18, Olive Amber	135.00
Bottle, Ink, Bristol Recorder, Waterbury, Conn., Square, 2 1/2 In.	20.00
Bottle, Ink, Carter's Indelible, 8 Sided, 1 3/4 In.	6.00
Bottle, Ink, Carter's Red Fountain Pen, Cube Shape, Wood Cork, 2 1/2 In.	8.50
Bottle, Ink, Carter's, Cathedral, Blue, Pint	55.00
Bottle, Ink, Carter's, Cathedral, Cobalt, 1/2 Pint	85.00
Bottle, Ink, Carter's, Cathedral, Cobalt, Amber	35.00 To 50.00
Bottle, Ink, Carter's, Cobalt, Quart, 9 3/4 In.	30.00 To 45.00
Bottle, Ink, Carter's, Conical, Double Ring Lip, Bubbles, M On Base, 2 1/2 In.	7.00
Bottle, Ink, Carter's, Cylindrical, V Band, Aqua, 8 1/4 In.	6.95
Bottle, Ink, Carter's, Master, Patent Feb.14, '99, Neck Ring, Aqua, 1/2 Pint	10.00
Bottle, Ink, Carter's, No.63, Cone, Blue Aqua, 2 1/2 In.	5.00
Bottle, Ink, Carter's, Stoneware, Embossed, C-996	20.00
Bottle, Ink, Carter's, 1897, Made In U.S.A., Cone, Seeds, Emerald, 2 1/2 In.	12.00
Bottle, Ink, Carter's, 1897, U.S.A., Cone, Burst Bubble, Aqua, 2 1/2 In.	5.00
Bottle, Ink, Caw's, Master, Sheared Lip, Neck Ring, Teal Blue Green, 7 7/8 In.	45.00
Bottle, Ink, Cone, Aqua, 2 1/2 In.	1.00
Bottle, Ink, Denby Pottery, England, Brown, 3 Sun Streaks, 9 1/2 In.	16.00
Bottle, Ink, Derby All British, Embossed, Pyramid Shape, Sealed, C-709	15.00
Bottle, Ink, Diamond Co., Patent 12-1-03, 2 Lip Rings, Sun Color, 2 3/8 In.	6.00
Bottle, Ink, E.S.Curtis, Pottery, Eagle, Red, White, & Blue, C-934	30.00 To 45.00
Bottle, Ink, Flint, Three Mold, Olive Amber, McK G II-18	135.00
Bottle, Ink, Harrison's Columbian, 8 Sided, 3 3/4 In.	65.00
Bottle, Ink, Hollidge, Pen Ledge, Olive Green, C-506	30.00
Bottle, Ink, J.& I.E.M. Turtle, 6 Panels, Sheared Lip, Blue Aqua, 1 1/4 In.	17.00
Bottle, Ink, J.R.Nichols & Co., Master, Lip Ring, Whittled, Green, 7 In.	13.00
Bottle, Ink, Ma & Pa Carter, Pair	75.00
Bottle, Ink, Master, Pottery, Pour Spout, White Glaze, Pint	6.00
Bottle, Ink, Master, Three Mold, Pinch Pour Spout, Emerald Green, Pint	15.00
Bottle, Ink, P.& J. Arnold, London, Pottery, 7 In.	10.00
Bottle, Ink, Pottery, Spout, 5 1/2 In.	4.50
Bottle, Ink, S.S.Stafford's, Master, Pour Spout, Double Rings, Cobalt, 6 In.	18.00
Bottle, Ink, Sanford's, Labels, Amber, 5 Gallon	17.00
Bottle, Ink, Sanford's, Metal Pour Spout, Ground Lip, Amber, 7 In.	8.50
Bottle, Ink, Sanford's, Pouring Spout, Labels, Amber, Pint, 8 1/2 In.	24.00
Bottle, Ink, Schoolhouse Type, Tin On Shoulder, Aqua, 2 X 2 X 1 1/2 In.	8.95
Bottle, Ink, Signet, Cobalt, Pint	6.00
Bottle, Ink, Signet, Cobalt, Quart	12.00
Bottle, Ink, Stafford's, Master, Pour Spout, Cobalt, Pint	10.00
Bottle, Ink, Stafford's, Pouring Lip, Cobalt, Quart	30.00
Bottle, Ink, T On Bottom, Cone, Aqua, 2 1/2 In.	3.50
Bottle, Ink, Three Mold, Master, Pour Spout, Teal Green Blue, 3/4 Quart	15.00
Bottle, Ink, Traveling, Figural, Man's Brown Leather Shoe, 3 3/4 In.	60.00
Bottle, Ink, Turtle, Embossed Bird In Tree On Dome, Whittled, Aqua, 1 3/8 In.	35.00
Bottle, Ink, Umbrella, Green Iridescent, 2 1/2 In.	35.00

Bottle, Ink, Underwood's, Cobalt, 32 Ozs. 28.00
Bottle, Ink, Underwood's, Pouring Spout, Cobalt, 5 In. 25.00
Bottle, Jar, South Jersey, Blown, Covered, Applied Glass Bands, 10 In. 95.00
Bottle, Jug, Applied Handle, Amber, 8 1/2 In. 10.00
Bottle, Jug, Flat Globular, Deep Amber, 8 In. 30.00
Bottle, Lady's Leg, Dug, Amber, 12 In. 15.00
Bottle, Liqueur, Dom Benedictine, Sheared Lip, Part Ring, Green, 3 1/4 In. 5.50
Bottle, Medicine, Atwood's, L.F.Monogram, H.H.Hayes Co., 6 5/8 In. 99.00
Bottle, Medicine, Ayer's Cherry Pectoral, Light Green, 7 1/2 In. 8.00
Bottle, Medicine, Ayer's Cherry Pectoral, Lowell, Mass., Aqua, 7 1/2 In. 10.75
Bottle, Medicine, Ayer's Cherry Pectoral, Rectangular, Haze, Aqua, 7 In. 16.00
Bottle, Medicine, Ayer's Hair Vigor, Flask, Blob Lip, 7 1/2 In. 30.00
Bottle, Medicine, Baker's Specific, Embossed Uncle Sam, 6 In. 7.00
Bottle, Medicine, Barry's Tricopherous For The Skin & Hair, Aqua, 6 1/4 In. 6.00
Bottle, Medicine, Barry's Tricopherous For The Skin & Hair, 6 In. 16.00
Bottle, Medicine, Calder's Dentine, 4 In. 1.00
Bottle, Medicine, Castor Oil, Dull, Cobalt, 8 In. 5.00
Bottle, Medicine, Cod Liver Oil, Fish Shape, Amber, 6 1/4 In. 8.50
Bottle, Medicine, Cod Liver Oil, Fish Shape, Light Amber, 10 In. 12.50
Bottle, Medicine, Cough & Cold Cure, Barby, Rectangular, Aqua, 5 5/8 In. 5.95
Bottle, Medicine, Cough Cure In Sunken Panel, Square Collar, Aqua, 6 1/4 In. 9.95
Bottle, Medicine, Cure For The Throat & Lungs, B.H.Bacon, Aqua, 6 In. 6.95
Bottle, Medicine, D.Jayne's Tonic Vermifuge, Aqua, 5 5/8 In. 1.65
Bottle, Medicine, Doctor C.McLane's Worm Specific, Blue Aqua, 3 1/2 In. 5.50
Bottle, Medicine, Dr.Coles' Catarrh Cure, Ring Collar, Aqua, 2 3/8 In. 7.95
Bottle, Medicine, Dr.Goerss Chaulmoogra, The East India Cure, Amber, 6 In. 8.00
Bottle, Medicine, Dr.H.Kelsey, Lowell, Mass., Oval, Aqua, 6 In. 22.00
Bottle, Medicine, Dr.Hay's Hair Health, Sunken Panels, Amber, 6 3/4 In. 2.45
Bottle, Medicine, Dr.Haynes' Arabian Balsam, R.I., 12 Sided, Aqua, 4 1/4 In. 2.95
Bottle, Medicine, Dr.Kilmer's Swamp Root Kidney Cure, Blue Aqua, 3 In. 4.00
Bottle, Medicine, Dr.Kilmer's, Label, 7 In. 5.00
Bottle, Medicine, Dr.M.M.Fenner's Peoples' Remedies, N.Y., Amber, 10 In. 20.00
Bottle, Medicine, Dr.Pinkham's Emmenagogue, Square, Deep Aqua, 6 In. 35.00
Bottle, Medicine, Dr.S.Pitcher's Castoria, Bubbles, C.1880, Aqua, 5 1/4 In. 5.75
Bottle, Medicine, Dr.Simmons' Liver, Man's Picture, Square, 2 In. 1.00
Bottle, Medicine, Dr.Swayne's Panacea, Round, 8 In. 15.00
Bottle, Medicine, Fahrney's Panacea, Aqua, 9 1/2 In. 12.00
Bottle, Medicine, Fenner's Cure, Amber, 11 In. 22.00
Bottle, Medicine, Florida Water, Murry S.Lannon, Druggist, N.Y., Aqua, 9 In. 2.00
Bottle, Medicine, Foley's Cream, Chicago, Square, Amethyst, 4 In. .... .75
Bottle, Medicine, Four Fold Liver Tonic, Simmons Co., Rectangular, 8 In. 3.50
Bottle, Medicine, Fruitcura Woman's Tonic, Blob Lip, Ring, 8 1/2 In. 8.00
Bottle, Medicine, Gargling Oil, Lockport, N.Y., Emerald Green, 7 1/2 In. 20.00
Bottle, Medicine, Gargling Oil, Lockport, N.Y., Haze, 2 1/4 X 1 1/2 In. 16.00
Bottle, Medicine, Glover's Imperial Mange, Amber, 6 1/2 Ozs. 5.00
Bottle, Medicine, Granitonic, Hair & Scalp Food, Rectangular, Stain, 5 In. 8.00
Bottle, Medicine, Granitonic, Hair Food, 12 Sided, Cylindrical, Stain, 3 In. 8.00
Bottle, Medicine, Hagan's Magnolia Balm, Rectangular, Milk Glass, 5 1/8 In. 7.95
Bottle, Medicine, Hagan's Magnolia Balm, Rectangular, Milk Glass, 5 1/4 In. 8.95
Bottle, Medicine, Hagan's Magnolia Balm, Rectangular, Milk Glass, 5 1/2 In. 8.95
Bottle, Medicine, Harper's Brain Food, Rectangular, Aqua, 5 In. 3.90
Bottle, Medicine, Harper's Cephalcine For Headache, Aqua, 5 In. 1.90
Bottle, Medicine, Haywood's Balm Of Savannah, Dandruff, Oval, Aqua, 6 In. 40.00
Bottle, Medicine, Haywood's Balm Of Savannah, Dandruff, Oval, Aqua, 8 In. 40.00
Bottle, Medicine, Haywood's Balm Of Savannah, Rectangular, Aqua, 8 In. 35.00
Bottle, Medicine, Healey & Bigelow Kickapoo Indian Oil, Aqua, 3 In. 11.00
Bottle, Medicine, Henery, Johnson & Hord, Burlington, Vt., Aqua, 7 1/4 In. 4.95
Bottle, Medicine, Hollis' Balm Of America, Lip Ring, Ice Blue, 5 In. 6.50
Bottle, Medicine, Hood's Pills Cure Liver Ills, Aqua, 2 In. 10.00
Bottle, Medicine, Household Panacea & Family Liniment, Aqua, 5 1/8 In. 2.25
Bottle, Medicine, Hyposulph, Whittled, Part Label, Pontil, Aqua, Pound 10.00
Bottle, Medicine, Indian Sagwa, Embossed Indian's Head, Aqua, 8 1/2 In. 15.00
Bottle, Medicine, Instant Cough Cure, Mt.Morris, N.Y., Green Aqua, 7 In. 6.95
Bottle, Medicine, J.B.Wilder & Co., Louisville, Rectangular, Aqua, 6 1/2 In. 35.00
Bottle, Medicine, Kickapoo Oil, Aqua, 5 1/2 In. 3.00
Bottle, Medicine, L.C.Hood's Blood & Nerve Tonic, 9 In. 12.00

Bottle, Medicine, Maxi Nerve Food, Cylindrical, Stain, Aqua, Quart 7.50
Bottle, Medicine, Medical Smith's Wonder Worker, Tiffin, O., Amber, Pint 10.00
Bottle, Medicine, National Remedy Company, N.Y., Aqua, 5 1/2 In. 2.00
Bottle, Medicine, Old Indian Liver & Kidney Tonic, Label, Blue Aqua, 8 In. 15.00
Bottle, Medicine, Phillip's Emulsion Cod Liver Oil, Amber, 9 In. 7.50
Bottle, Medicine, Pills Cure Liver Ills, Oval, 1 3/4 In. 5.95
Bottle, Medicine, Pine Tree Tar Cordial, 1859, Emerald Green, 7 3/4 In. 45.00
Bottle, Medicine, Piso's Cure For Consumption, Yellow Olive Green, 5 In. 6.00
Bottle, Medicine, Reed & Carnrick Peptenzyme, Cobalt, 2 1/4 In. 6.00
Bottle, Medicine, Rosewood Dandruff Cure, Stain, Amethyst, 6 1/2 In. 8.95
Bottle, Medicine, Sanitol For The Teeth, 8 Sided, Milk Glass, 5 In. 10.00
Bottle, Medicine, Scott's Emulsion, Aqua, 9 In. 1.00
Bottle, Medicine, Scott's Emulsion, Fisherman, Light Aqua, 9 1/4 In. 3.50
Bottle, Medicine, Shiloh's Consumption Cure .... *Illus* 6.00
Bottle, Medicine, Sim's Tonic Elixir Of Pyrophosphate Of Iron, Amber, 7 In. 5.75
Bottle, Medicine, Sloan's Liniment For Man Or Beast, Stain, Aqua, 9 1/2 In. 15.00
Bottle, Medicine, Sloan's Ointment, Square, Aqua, 2 1/2 In. 13.50
Bottle, Medicine, St.Jakob's Oel, Vogeler Co., Blob Lip, Aqua, 6 1/2 In. 5.00
Bottle, Medicine, Stella Vitae, Thatcher Co., Rectangular, Aqua, 8 1/2 In. 4.00
Bottle, Medicine, Stoddard Type, Pontil, Olive Green, 7 In. 18.00
Bottle, Medicine, Thatcher's Liver Pills, Square, Amber, 2 1/2 In. 3.75
Bottle, Medicine, Thatcher's Liver Pills, Square, Aqua, 2 1/2 In. 3.75
Bottle, Medicine, Thysolol Antiseptic For The Mouth & Teeth, 3 1/2 In. 1.00
Bottle, Medicine, Vegetable Tonic Syrup, Blown In Mold, Aqua, 5 1/2 In. 2.65
Bottle, Medicine, Warner's Kidney & Liver Cure, 16 Ozs. 21.00
Bottle, Medicine, Warner's Nervine, 1/2 Pint 25.00
Bottle, Medicine, Warner's Safe Cure, London, Red Amber, 9 1/2 In. 125.00
Bottle, Medicine, Warner's Safe Cure, 7 1/2 In. 20.00
Bottle, Medicine, Warner's Safe Kidney & Liver Cure, Dark Amber, 9 1/2 In. 15.00
Bottle, Medicine, Westerman's Opodel Liniment, Ky., C.1880, 6 1/2 In. 6.00
Bottle, Medicine, Westlake's Vegetable Ointment, Square, Aqua, 3 In. 30.00
Bottle, Medicine, Wm.Radam's Microbe Killer No.1, Porcelain, White, Gallon 20.00
Bottle, Medicine, Wyeth, Dose Bottle, 5 1/2 In. 6.00
Bottle, Milk, Aiyukpa, Golden Guernsey Products, N.Y., 1/3 Quart 3.00
Bottle, Milk, Baby Face, Quart 5.00
Bottle, Milk, Bartlett Farms, Wichita, Embossed, Quart 2.50
Bottle, Milk, Bill's, Pawhuska, Okla., Painted, Quart 2.00
Bottle, Milk, Borden's, Eagle Emblem, Tin Top, Quart 15.00
Bottle, Milk, Brookfield, Double Baby Face, Quart .... *Illus* 12.00
Bottle, Milk, Carlton Hall Dairy, Coffeyville, Kans., Painted, Quart 2.00
Bottle, Milk, Castles, Lockport, N.Y., Embossed, 1/2 Pint 2.50
Bottle, Milk, Chestnut Farms, Washington, D.C., Embossed, 1/2 Pint 1.75
Bottle, Milk, Cream Top, Quart 3.00
Bottle, Milk, Deerfoot Farm Heavy Cream, Plum Shape, Screw Cap, 1/2 Pint 1.50
Bottle, Milk, Figural, Double Headed Lady, Cream Top, Quart 20.00
Bottle, Milk, Horn & Farris, Muskogee, Okla., Painted, Quart 2.00
Bottle, Milk, Mellow Gold, Grade A, Square, 1/2 Pint 4.00
Bottle, Milk, Mellow Gold, Taste Tells, Square, 1/2 Pint 4.00
Bottle, Milk, Missouri Pacific, Embossed, 1/2 Pint 2.00
Bottle, Milk, Missouri Pacific, Embossed, Quart 3.00
Bottle, Milk, Parker's, Erie, Pa., Embossed, 1/2 Pint 2.50
Bottle, Milk, Pennsylvania Dairy, Cream Top, Quart 6.00
Bottle, Milk, Pyroglazed Rojeck's Sour Cream, Tonawanda, N.Y., Pint 2.00
Bottle, Milk, Quality Dairy, Hannibal, Mo., War Slogan, Cream Top, Quart 3.50
Bottle, Milk, Round, Embossed, 1/2 Pint 2.50
Bottle, Milk, Sheffield Embossed On Side, Quart 1.50
Bottle, Milk, Somerset Dairy, Somerset, Ky., Painted, Quart 2.00
Bottle, Mineral Water, Buffalo Spring, Label, Aqua, 1/2 Gallon 10.00
Bottle, Mineral Water, Byron Acid Spring, Iron Pontil, Emerald, 7 3/4 In. 85.00
Bottle, Mineral Water, Champion Spouting Spring, Aqua, Pint 30.00
Bottle, Mineral Water, Clarke & White, Olive Green, Quart 40.00
Bottle, Mineral Water, Congress & Empire, Whittled, Quart 30.00
Bottle, Mineral Water, Empire, Quart 25.00
Bottle, Mineral Water, Excelsior, Saratoga, N.Y., Green, 10 In. 30.00
Bottle, Mineral Water, Florida Water, Solon Palmers, N.Y., Stain, Aqua, 9 In. 2.95
Bottle, Mineral Water, Geyser Spring, Aqua, Pint 26.00

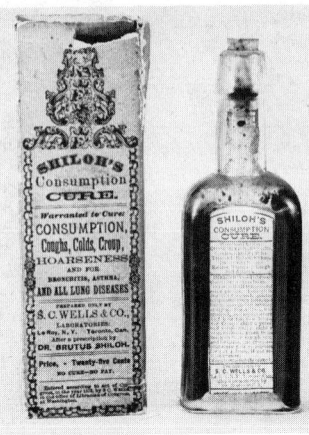

Bottle, Milk, Brookfield,
Double Baby Face, qt.
(See Page 43)

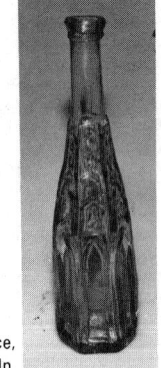

Bottle, Medicine, Shiloh's Consumption Cure
(See Page 43)

Bottle, Pepper Sauce,
Cathedral, Blue, 9 In.

Bottle, Mineral Water, Guilford Mineral & Spring, Green, Quart	31.00
Bottle, Mineral Water, Hathorn Springs, Saratoga, Bubbly, Green, Quart	25.00
Bottle, Mineral Water, Oak Orchard Acid Springs, N.Y., Emerald, 9 In.	25.00
Bottle, Mineral Water, Old Gum Spring, Long Bros., Stoneware, Jug, 1/4 Pint	11.75
Bottle, Mineral Water, W.H.Bostwick, Agnt., N.Y., Amber, 9 In.	22.50
Bottle, Nailsea Type, Rose Looping On Milk White Glass, 7 3/4 In.	250.00
Bottle, Nursing, Cleaneasy Sanitary Sterilizer, Whitall Tatum, 12 Ozs.	9.00
Bottle, Pepper Sauce, Cathedral, Blue, 9 In. ....*Illus*	55.00
Bottle, Pepper Sauce, Gothic Arches, Square, Aqua, 8 1/4 In.	27.50
Bottle, Pepper Sauce, Gothic Arches, 6 Sided, Aqua, 8 1/2 In.	20.00
Bottle, Pepper Sauce, H.E.Swan, Flint, Horn Of Plenty, 8 1/2 In.	68.00
Bottle, Perfume, Art Deco, Ground Stopper, Amethyst, 5 In.	6.25
Bottle, Perfume, Art Deco, Ground Stopper, Golden Amber, 5 In.	6.25
Bottle, Perfume, Aventurine, Red, Silver Opening, Lay-Down Type	29.50
Bottle, Perfume, E.W.Hoyt & Co., Lowell, Mass., Labeled, 3 1/2 In.	2.00
Bottle, Perfume, Figural, Barrel, Blown, Three Mold, Brass Lid, McK I-19	20.00
Bottle, Perfume, Lay Down, Engraved Silver Neck & Cap, Opalescent, 5 In.	45.00
Bottle, Perfume, Lead Crystal, West Germany, Gold Sticker, 5 In.	2.50
Bottle, Perfume, Mouson & Co., Parfumeur, Jar, Flared Lip, Amber, 2 1/2 In.	75.00
Bottle, Perfume, Opalescent Coin Spot, Bulb, 5 In.	22.00
Bottle, Perfume, Overlay, White To Clear, Steeple Stopper, Floral, 9 In., Pair	125.00
Bottle, Perfume, Paperweight, Frosted Stopper, 3 1/2 In.	5.00
Bottle, Perfume, Porcelain Egg, Tan & Brown, Sterling Cap, 1885, 1 3/4 In.	45.00
Bottle, Perfume, Porcelain, Mauve, White, Gold Circles, 7 1/2 In., Pair	35.00
Bottle, Perfume, Purse, Gold Collar, Goldstone, Orange, 1 1/2 In.	50.00
Bottle, Perfume, Purse, Marked Coralene, Dome Twist Top, Emerald, 4 In.	15.00
Bottle, Perfume, Pyramid Shape, Red Glass, Silver Top & Bottom, 3 1/2 In.	45.00
Bottle, Perfume, Shoe Shape, Raised Design On Toe, 3 3/4 In.	38.00
Bottle, Perfume, Shoe Shape, 3 3/4 In.	15.00
Bottle, Perfume, Silver Deposit, 3 7/8 In.	7.00
Bottle, Perfume, Silver Overlay, 3 3/4 In.	25.00
Bottle, Perfume, Train Engine, 3 3/4 In.	8.50
Bottle, Pickle, Bunker Hill, Round, Honey Amber, 7 1/2 In.	25.00
Bottle, Pickle, Bunker Hill, Stain, Aqua, 1/2 Pint	2.75
Bottle, Pickle, Cathedral, Applied Rolled Lip, Square, Aqua, 11 In.	65.00
Bottle, Pickle, Cathedral, Square, Applied Rolled Lip, Aqua, 11 1/2 In.	107.50
Bottle, Pickle, Cathedral, Square, Applied Rolled Lip, Emerald, 11 In.	165.00
Bottle, Pickle, Cathedral, 4 Flat Sides, Embossed Flowers, Aqua, 13 1/2 In.	45.00
Bottle, Pickle, Cathedral, 4 Sided, Aqua, 7 In.	40.00
Bottle, Pickle, Cathedral, 4 Sided, Aqua, 11 In.	45.00
Bottle, Pickle, Cathedral, 4 Sided, Aqua, 11 1/2 In.	38.00
Bottle, Pickle, Cathedral, 4 Sided, Embossed Lattice On 3 Panels, Aqua, 7 In.	55.00
Bottle, Pickle, Gothic Arches, Square, Wide Mouth, Aqua, 7 1/4 In.	25.00

Bottle, Pickle, Henry C.Kellogg, Philada., Embossed, Dug, Aqua, Pint	8.00
Bottle, Pickle, Paneled, Square, Embossed Leaves, Whittled, Aqua, 11 In.	65.00
Bottle, Pickle, Paneled, Square, Iron Pontil, Light Aqua, 11 1/2 In.	100.00
Bottle, Pickle, 4 Sided, Amber, 7 In.	30.00
Bottle, Pickle, 4 Sided, Yellow, 8 1/2 In.	30.00
Bottle, Poison, Big Letters, Triangles, Ribbed Edges, BIMAL, Amber, 8 In.	42.00
Bottle, Poison, Lewis & Whitly, Poisonous, Rectangular, Amber, 8 In.	22.00
Bottle, Poison, Not To Be Taken, Fluted Panels, Hexagonal, Amber, 2 1/4 In.	10.00
Bottle, Poison, Not To Be Taken, Fluted Panels, Hexagonal, Amber, 2 3/4 In.	10.00
Bottle, Poison, Not To Be Taken, Fluted Panels, Hexagonal, Amber, 3 In.	10.00
Bottle, Poison, Not To Be Taken, Fluted Panels, Hexagonal, Amber, 4 In.	10.00
Bottle, Poison, Not To Be Taken, Fluted Panels, Hexagonal, Amber, 6 1/2 In.	10.00
Bottle, Poison, Not To Be Taken, Fluted Panels, Hexagonal, Cobalt, 2 1/4 In.	10.00
Bottle, Poison, Not To Be Taken, Fluted Panels, Hexagonal, Cobalt, 2 3/4 In.	10.00
Bottle, Poison, Not To Be Taken, Fluted Panels, Hexagonal, Cobalt, 3 In.	10.00
Bottle, Poison, Not To Be Taken, Fluted Panels, Hexagonal, Cobalt, 4 In.	10.00
Bottle, Poison, Not To Be Taken, Fluted Panels, Hexagonal, Cobalt, 6 1/2 In.	10.00
Bottle, Poison, Wyeth, Quilted, Square Oval, Ring Lip, Cobalt, 2 1/2 In.	5.50
Bottle, Round, Emerald Green, 7 1/2 In.	7.50
Bottle, Rum, Three Mold, Blob Lip With Skirt, Bubbles, Black Amethyst, 10 In.	12.00
Bottle, Sarsaparilla, Bristol's Genuine, Aqua, Quart	18.00
Bottle, Sarsaparilla, Dr.Green's, Sunken Panels, Rectangular, Aqua, 9 1/4 In.	12.95
Bottle, Sarsaparilla, Hobson's, Paper Label, Contents, Box, 8 In.	5.00
Bottle, Scent, Figural, Shoe, Blown In Mold, Flint, 3 1/2 In.	18.00
Bottle, Scent, Paperweight, Yellow Lilies, Green, 4 3/4 In.	25.00
Bottle, Snuff, Amber *Illus*	250.00
Bottle, Snuff, Amber, Bird Crested *Illus*	250.00
Bottle, Snuff, Amber, Ring Handles *Illus*	250.00
Bottle, Snuff, Aquamarine, Chinese, Carved, 2 1/2 In.	1000.00
Bottle, Snuff, Blue Cameo Floral & Insects On Opaque White, 2 3/4 In.	95.00
Bottle, Snuff, Blue Floral Decorated Porcelain, Jade Stopper, Chinese	30.00
Bottle, Snuff, Carnelian Agate, Chinese, Eagle, Moth, & Floral, 2 1/2 In.	650.00
Bottle, Snuff, Carved Ivory, Oriental Figures, 2 1/2 In.	55.00
Bottle, Snuff, Chinese, Lapis Lazuli, Carved Lizard	125.00
Bottle, Snuff, Cobalt Blue, 4 X 2 1/4 In.	15.00
Bottle, Snuff, Coral, Chinese, Twin, Carved, Deep Red, 2 In.	525.00
Bottle, Snuff, Crystal, Chinese, Carved Fine Hairs, 2 1/2 In.	225.00
Bottle, Snuff, Hornbill, Chinese, Carved Dragons, 3 1/2 In.	200.00
Bottle, Snuff, Hornbill, Chinese, Carved, Red Casque On Sides, 2 1/2 In.	600.00
Bottle, Snuff, Ivory, Carved Dragon & Birds	85.00
Bottle, Snuff, Jade, Chinese, Monkeys & Dogs, White, 2 5/8 In.	400.00
Bottle, Snuff, Jade, Chinese, Silver Trim, Opens From Side, White, 3 In.	250.00
Bottle, Snuff, Jadeite, Pendant, Gold Dragon & Phoenix, Green, 2 1/2 In.	475.00
Bottle, Snuff, Lion Handles, Gold Hair Crystal, 2 1/2 In.	225.00
Bottle, Snuff, Malachite, Chinese, Carved, 2 3/4 In.	200.00
Bottle, Snuff, Midwestern, 24 Ribs, Cut Corners, Aqua, 5 1/2 In.	250.00
Bottle, Snuff, Mother-Of-Pearl, Carp *Illus*	70.00
Bottle, Snuff, Mother-Of-Pearl, Double Gourd *Illus*	90.00
Bottle, Snuff, Mother-Of-Pearl, Woman *Illus*	160.00
Bottle, Snuff, Opal Matrix, Chinese, Carved, Black, 2 1/2 In.	700.00
Bottle, Snuff, Opal, Chinese, Carved, Fire, 2 1/2 In.	350.00
Bottle, Snuff, Opal, Chinese, Dragons & Phoenix, Red & Green Fire, 2 3/8 In.	500.00
Bottle, Snuff, Opal, Chinese, Pendant, Carved Dragons, Red & Green, 2 1/2 In.	750.00
Bottle, Snuff, Tigereye, Chinese, Carved Fish In Skin, Blue, 2 1/2 In.	150.00
Bottle, Snuff, Tourmaline, Chinese, Carved Dragons, Watermelon, 2 In.	250.00
Bottle, Snuff, Turquoise, Chinese, Carved, 2 3/8 In.	475.00
Bottle, Soda, B.F.Tatman, Owensboro, Ky., Blob, Paneled, Dug, Aqua, 9 In.	4.50
Bottle, Soda, C.Cleminshaw, Troy, N.Y., Blob Lip, Whittled, Aqua, 7 In.	12.00
Bottle, Soda, Drewry's, Embossed R.C.M.P. Effigy, C.1920, Green, 6 Ozs.	4.00
Bottle, Soda, Embossed, Blob, 9 In.	1.50
Bottle, Soda, Gilbert, Minn., Hutchinson, Quart	15.00
Bottle, Soda, J.C.Parker, Blob Top, Cloudy, Blue, 7 1/2 In.	14.00
Bottle, Soda, Jackson Napa, Aqua, 7 1/4 In.	8.00
Bottle, Soda, Lime, Blown, Flint, Amelung Type, Case, 5 1/4 In.	35.00
Bottle, Soda, O-T Cordial New Drinks Ltd., San Francisco, Square, Quart	15.00
Bottle, Soda, Schmuck's Ginger Ale, Hutchinson Type, Stain, Aqua, 8 In.	20.00

Bottle, Snuff, Mother-Of-Pearl, Carp
(See Page 45)

Bottle, Snuff, Amber
(See Page 45)

Bottle, Snuff, Mother-Of-Pearl,
Double Gourd
(See Page 45)

Bottle, Snuff, Amber, Bird Crested
(See Page 45)

Bottle, Snuff, Mother-Of-Pearl, Woman
(See Page 45)

Bottle, Snuff, Amber, Ring Handles
(See Page 45)

Bottle, Soda, W.L.Rose & Co., Wheeling, W.Va., Hutchinson, Aqua, 7 In.	8.75
Bottle, Stiegel Type, Pewter Neck, Enamel Decoration, 5 1/2 In.	150.00
Bottle, Stiegel, Half Post Method, Pewter Cap, Painted, 10 In.	145.00
Bottle, Stoneware, F.Rober, Savannah, Ga., 7 In.	15.00
Bottle, Stoneware, J.Kornahrens, Charleston, S.C., 8 In.	15.00
Bottle, Stoneware, Thomas Meager, 7 In.	10.00
Bottle, Talcum, Cut Glass, Sterling Top, Unger Brothers, 3 1/8 In.	40.00
Bottle, Toilet, Blown, Peacock Blue, Inverted Thumbprint, 8 3/4 In.High	50.00
Bottle, Toilet, Flint, Deep Blue, 1/2 Pint, McK G I-7	170.00
Bottle, Toilet, Flint, Three Mold, Blue, 1/2 Pint	175.00
Bottle, Toilet, Sandwich, Three Mold, Fine Swirl, Sapphire Blue, McK G I-3	85.00
Bottle, Toilet, Three Mold, Blue, McK G I-7	200.00
Bottle, Toilet, Three Mold, McK G I-7	45.00
Bottle, Toilet, Three Mold, McK G I-11	45.00
Bottle, Toilet, Three Mold, Tam-O'-Shanter Top, Blue, 1/2 Pint	170.00
Bottle, Vinegar, White House, Picture Of White House, Aqua, Pint	5.00
Bottle, Warner's Safe Remedies, Stain, Light Amber, 6 Ozs.	15.00
Bottle, Whiskey, Banded Flask, Embossed Eagle, Sun Colored Amethyst, Quart	4.00
Bottle, Whiskey, Bininger, Barrel, Quart	250.00
Bottle, Whiskey, Brook Hill, Railway Exchange Buffet, Jug, 1/4 Pint	16.00
Bottle, Whiskey, C.Berry & Co., Boston, Flask, Strap Side, Sun Color, 1/2 Pint	12.00
Bottle, Whiskey, C.Koepper, Indianapolis, Drum Shape, Porcelain, Quart	35.00
Bottle, Whiskey, Carnival Glass, 1/2 Pint	15.00
Bottle, Whiskey, Carstair's White Seal, Embossed, 1788, Amber, 1/2 Pint	12.00
Bottle, Whiskey, Cascade, Label, Quart	10.00
Bottle, Whiskey, Cedar Brook, Label, Quart	10.00
Bottle, Whiskey, Compliments Of Hirsch Bros. & Co., Ky., Jug, 1/4 Pint	13.50
Bottle, Whiskey, Compliments Of J.& O., Jug, 1/4 Pint	15.00
Bottle, Whiskey, Compliments Of John Schmitt, Jug, 1/4 Pint	15.98
Bottle, Whiskey, Compliments Of Pomona Co-Op Union, Cal., Jug, 1/4 Pint	15.00
Bottle, Whiskey, Compliments Of T.W.Chafee, Mich., Jug, 1/4 Pint	16.99
Bottle, Whiskey, Compliments Of Wm.Ellebrecht, St.Louis, Mo., Jug, 1/4 Pint	17.50
Bottle, Whiskey, Coon Hollow, Label, Quart	10.00
Bottle, Whiskey, Cutter Old Bourbon, A.P.Hotaling & Co., Amber, Quart	17.95
Bottle, Whiskey, Cylinder, Collared Lip With Ring, Olive Green, 4 1/4 In.	5.50
Bottle, Whiskey, Dallemand, Basket Weave, Blown In Mold, 1/2 Pint	6.00

Bottle, Whiskey, Detrick Distilling Co., Dayton, O., Motto Jug, 1/2 Pint 17.75
Bottle, Whiskey, East Liverpool, O., Medicinal, Green Letters, China, Quart 55.00
Bottle, Whiskey, Elk's, Ear Of Corn, 5 In. 75.00
Bottle, Whiskey, F.Chevalier Old Castle, San Francisco, Screw Cap, Fifth 20.00
Bottle, Whiskey, Flask, Strap Sided, Amethyst, Registered Full Pint 15.00
Bottle, Whiskey, Fluted Neck & Shoulders, Quart 2.00
Bottle, Whiskey, Golden Wedding, Screw Top, Carnival, Pint 15.00
Bottle, Whiskey, Golden Wedding, Screw Top, Carnival, Quart 15.00
Bottle, Whiskey, Green River, Paper Label, 6 In. 12.00
Bottle, Whiskey, Green River, 2 Labels On Negro & Horse, Quart 9.00
Bottle, Whiskey, Grommes & Ullrich National Club Bourbon, Jug, Quart 28.50
Bottle, Whiskey, H.B.Mitchell, Bull & Best St., Jug, 1/4 Pint 15.94
Bottle, Whiskey, Handled Jug, Red Amber, Pint 14.50
Bottle, Whiskey, Hayner Distilling Co., Quart 30.00
Bottle, Whiskey, Hayner's, Fancy Design, Oval, Mazy, Amber, Pint .... 45.00 To 50.00
Bottle, Whiskey, Hayner's, Quart 1.00
Bottle, Whiskey, Hayner's, Quilted, Blown In Mold, 1/2 Pint 6.00
Bottle, Whiskey, Hayner's, Stain, Amber, Quart 13.75
Bottle, Whiskey, Henry Schroder, 401 Broughton St., Jug, 1/4 Pint 15.95
Bottle, Whiskey, I.W.Harper, Nelson Co., Ky., Compliments, Jug, 1/4 Pint 17.50
Bottle, Whiskey, J.H.Cutter Old Bourbon, A.P.Hotaling & Co., Amber, Quart 17.95
Bottle, Whiskey, J.Rieger & Co., Kansas City, Embossed, Purple, Quart 16.00
Bottle, Whiskey, Jesse Moore & Co., Louisville, Ky., Amber, Quart 23.95
Bottle, Whiskey, Julius Kessler Bourbon Co., Quart 8.00
Bottle, Whiskey, Klein Bros. & Hyman Keystone Rye, Gold Script, Quart 11.00
Bottle, Whiskey, Lotus Club Hand Made Sour Mash, Gold Script, Quart 24.50
Bottle, Whiskey, Meredith's Diamond Club Pure Rye, Medicinal, China, Pint 65.00
Bottle, Whiskey, Meredith's Diamond Club Pure Rye, Medicinal, China, Quart 50.00
Bottle, Whiskey, Meredith's, Jug, Gold, Porcelain, 1/2 Pint, 4 In. 64.00
Bottle, Whiskey, Miller's Game Cock, Boston, Oval Flask, Seeds, Aqua, Pint 7.00
Bottle, Whiskey, Mt.Vernon Pure Rye, Amber, Pint 16.00
Bottle, Whiskey, Mt.Vernon, Square, Amber, Quart 10.00
Bottle, Whiskey, Myers & Co. Pure Fulton, Covington, Ky., Jug, Aqua, 9 In. 12.50
Bottle, Whiskey, Old Blue House, Sample, Brown & White Glaze, 4 In. 18.00
Bottle, Whiskey, Old Hermitage, Quart 10.00
Bottle, Whiskey, Old Maryland, Jug, Gold, Porcelain, Quart 48.00
Bottle, Whiskey, Old Plantation Distilling Co., Los Angeles, Amber, Gallon 50.00
Bottle, Whiskey, Paul Jones, Blob Seal, Quart 9.00
Bottle, Whiskey, Paul Jones, Miniature 5.00
Bottle, Whiskey, Salzman & Siegelman Pure Old Rye, Crockery, 7 In. 25.00
Bottle, Whiskey, Samuel Westheimer, Pint 1.00
Bottle, Whiskey, Scotch, Monarch, Stoneware, Handle, Brown & Tan, 3 3/4 In. 6.00
Bottle, Whiskey, South Carolina Dispensary, Union Flask, Amber, Quart 325.00
Bottle, Whiskey, Straight Sided, Collared Lip With Ring, Amber, 3 3/4 In. 4.50
Bottle, Whiskey, Strauss Bros., Chicago, Kenwood Sour Mash, Script, Quart 25.00
Bottle, Whiskey, Strauss Bros., Chicago, Old Crow, Gold Script, Quart 55.00
Bottle, Whiskey, Strauss Bros., Chicago, Pint 1.00
Bottle, Whiskey, Taylor & Williams, 1/2 Pint 1.00
Bottle, Whiskey, Taylor & Williams, Pint 1.00
Bottle, Whiskey, Taylor & Williams, Quart 1.00
Bottle, Whiskey, Telusky Bros.Fine, N.Y., Strap-Sided Flask, 1/2 Pint 5.00
Bottle, Whiskey, Three Mold, Cylindrical, Pontil, Aqua, 10 In. 4.00
Bottle, Whiskey, Three Mold, Green, 12 In. 15.00
Bottle, Whiskey, Uri & Co., Louisville, Ky., Stain, Amber, 4 3/4 In. 6.00
Bottle, Whiskey, Walker's Kilmarnock, Bubbles, Dug, Corker, Aqua, 10 In. 20.00
Bottle, Whiskey, Weston's Special Reserve, Oval, Amber, Quart 10.00
Bottle, Whiskey, Wharton's, 1850, Chestnut Grove, Flat Flask, Amber, 5 In. 95.00
Bottle, Whiskey, Wharton's, 1850, Chestnut Grove, Flat Flask, Sapphire, 5 In. 115.00
Bottle, Whiskey, Wharton's, 1850, Whitney Glass Works, Jug, Amber, 10 In. 155.00
Bottle, Whiskey, Wheat, Seal, Mineral Water Shape, Amber, Quart 80.00
Bottle, Whiskey, Wright & Taylor, Amber, Quart 2.75
Bottle, Whiskey, 1879 Old Jug, Freiberg Bros., O., Crockery, 10 1/2 In. 60.00
Bottle, Wine, Garrett Co., Embossed, Blown In Mold, Quart 15.00
Bottle, Wine, George Drewry, Crockery Jug, Gray & Blue, Gallon 25.00
Bottle, Wine, Hock, Applied Collar, Red Amber, 15 In. 3.85
Bottle, Wine, L.Jacobs, San Francisco, Hock Type, Amber, 13 In. 95.00

Bottle, Wine, Meder & Zoom, Holland, Clay, 12 In. 6.50
Bottle, Wine, Pinch, Pewter Stopper & Grapes, Olive Green, 9 1/2 In., Pair 100.00
Bottle, Wine, Sol Rath, 1014 Mt.Vernon Ave., Columbus, Ohio, Pint 12.00
Bottle, Wine, Viarengo, Clown, Hand-Painted, 10 In. 14.00
Bow, Inkwell, Girl With Basket, Quill Holder, Gold, White Base, C.1786 .... 130.00

*Boxes of all kinds are collected. They were made of thin strips of inlaid
wood, metal, tortoiseshell, embroidery, or other material.*
Box, see also Charlie Chaplin, Box, Ivory, Box, Porcelain, Box,
Shaker, Box, Store, Box, Tin, Box, and various porcelain
categories.
Box, Battersea, see Battersea, Box
Box, Bible, Wooden, Carved, Slant Lid, Carved, 1718, 27 1/2 X 17 In. 350.00
Box, Bridal, Wood, Handmade Nails, Painted, C.1790, 10 X 19 In. 184.00
Box, Bride's, Covered, Wood Latches, Floral, Oval, 6 X 3 In. 38.00
Box, Candle, Pine, Dovetailed, Sliding Cover, 12 X 5 X 5 In. .... 50.00 To 55.00
Box, Candle, Pine, Hewn, Sliding Top 55.00
Box, Candle, Pine, Made From 1 Piece, Green Sliding Cover, 8 1/4 In. 25.00
Box, Candle, Pine, Sliding Lid, 15 X 6 X 7 1/2 In. 40.00
Box, Candle, Walnut, Dovetailed, Sliding Lid, 10 X 2 1/4 X 6 1/2 In. 50.00
Box, Candle, Walnut, Sliding Cover, Dovetailed, 10 X 6 1/2 X 2 1/4 In. 50.00
Box, Cigar, Leather, Mosaic Plaque On Top, 2 Cottages On Road, 4 X 6 In. 115.00
Box, Cigarette, Brass Lid, Red To Almost Black Frosted 15.00
Box, Cigarette, Hand-Carved Onyx, Mexico 7.50
Box, Collar Button, Aluminum, Footed, Embossed Where's My Collar Button 3.50
Box, Collar Button, Silver Plate, Embossed Friend In Need 9.50
Box, Deed, Black Leather, Brass Escutcheon & Ring Handle, 14 X 8 1/2 In. 150.00
Box, Desk, Walnut, Copper Dragon On Lid, Inkwell & Compartments, 10 In. 30.00
Box, Dough, Pine, Covered, 2 Handles, 28 In.Long 35.00
Box, Egg Shape, Leather Covered, Landscape Under Glass On Ivory, 2 1/2 In. 40.00
Box, Glass, Sapphire Blue, Hinged, Decorated, Brass Fittings, Round, 6 In. 135.00
Box, Inlaid, 3 Milking Maids, Velvet Lined, Key, 10 1/4 X 4 3/4 X 3 1/8 In. 35.00
Box, Jewel Casket, Lime Green Glass, Brass Mounts, Enamel Cupid On Lid 285.00
Box, Jewel Casket, Victorian, Rosewood, Mother-Of-Pearl, C.1890, 12 In. 100.00
Box, Jewel, Cast Iron Safe, Lock & Key, Union Clothing Co., 7 1/2 In. 65.00
Box, Jewel, Crossed Arrows & S8847 Mark, Portrait, Hinged, Ormolu, 3 1/4 In. 68.00
Box, Jewel, Heart Shape, Hinged, Gold Colored Metal, 3 1/4 X 4 In. 8.50
Box, Jewel, Marked China, Frosted Glass, Enamel, Brass Frame, 5 X 3 In. 50.00
Box, Jewel, Porcelain, Hinged, Green & Gold, Brass Fittings, Round, 3 3/4 In. 14.00
Box, Knife, Walnut, Dovetailed, Chip Carved, Heart Cutout, High Arch 30.00
Box, Lacquer, Japanese, Covered, Gold Bird & Cherry Tree On Green, 9 3/4 In. 110.00
Box, Lacquer, Russian, Troika Scene, Painted Lid, 6 X 4 X 2 In. 100.00
Box, M.Hess On Pewter Design On Top, Red, Acid Finish, Round, 5 In. 85.00
Box, Pill, Brass, Mosaic Star Design On Cover, Scrolled Sides & Bottom 35.00
Box, Pine, Dome Top, Snipe Hinges, Red & Black Paint, Dovetailed, 30 In. 95.00
Box, Pine, Dovetailed, Hex Signs On Lid, 19 X 49 X 18 In. 200.00
Box, Pine, Lift Cover, 38 X 24 In. 39.00
Box, Pine, Red & Black Maine Paint Decorated, Dovetailed, 15 X 10 In. 68.00
Box, Pipe, New England, C.1750, Maple, Painted, Drawer, 17 1/4 In. 1000.00
Box, Pipe, Pine, Drawer, Serpentine Base, C.1800, 22 1/2 X 6 3/4 In. 650.00
Box, Porcelain, Colonial Figures On Hinged Lid, Cobalt, Round, 3 1/2 In. 27.50
Box, Powder, Hinged, Green, Gold Trim, Floral, White & Blue Beading, 4 In. 60.00
Box, Powder, Porcelain, Hinged, Ormolu, Green, Enameled, Rectangular, 4 In. 29.00
Box, Russian, Troika Scene On Lid, Brass Hinge, 5 In. Square 150.00
Box, Silver, Persian Style Pattern, Wood Lines, 3 1/4 X 4 1/4 In. 22.50
Box, Stamp, Banded Agate Top & Bottom, Carnelian Color, Chrome Fittings 45.00
Box, Stamp, Hinged, Silver, Victorian, Footed, Floral & Scrolls, 2 1/4 In. 15.00
Box, Stamp, Sterling Silver, Embossed Stamps 22.00
Box, Stamp, Sterling Silver, Hinged 17.00
Box, Stamp, Wooden, Black Transfer Print, German 12.00
Box, Stamp, Wooden, Black Transfer, Summit House, Mass. 12.00
Box, Stamp, Wooden, Hand-Carved Flowers & Leaves 12.00
Box, Stamp, Wooden, Hand-Carved Oak Leaves 14.00
Box, Sugar, Covered, Wooden Handle, Wire Bail, Green Paint, 12 X 8 In. 25.00

Box, Tea Caddy, see also Brass, Tea Caddy, Furniture, Tea
Caddy, Silver, Sterling, Tea Caddy, Tin, Tea Caddy, and various
porcelain categories.

Box, Tobacco, Lead, Negro's Head Finial, Octagonal, C.1750, 5 X 5 1/4 In.	135.00
Box, Tool, Mahogany, Dovetailed, Brass Hardware, 18 X 8 1/2 X 11 In.	70.00
Box, Traveling, Leather, Hinged, Brass Tacks, American, C.1850, 6 X 11 In.	100.00
Box, Trinket, Fireplace, Baby In Basin With Oars On Lid, 3 X 2 In.	40.00
Box, Trinket, Leather, Brass Nailheads & Ring Handle, American, C.1835, 9 In.	80.00
Box, Trinket, Silver, Hinged, Oval, Open Filigree, 2 1/2 X 1 1/2 In.	65.00
Box, Walnut, Brass Sunken Handle On Top, C.1840, 6 X 9 X 4 1/2 In.	40.00
Box, Weights, Wooden, 13 Holes, 2 Solid Hinged Blocks, 9 1/4 X 4 In.	6.00
Box, Wooden, Acorn Shape, Covered, 4 1/2 X 5 In.	7.00
Box, Wooden, Oval, 6 1/2 X 4 1/2 In. .... *Illus*	65.00

Box, Wooden, Oval, 6 1/2 X 4 1/2 In.

Box, Writing, Mahogany, Book Shape, Inlaid Lid, 4 Sections, C.1850, 10 In.	50.00
Boy Scout, Diary, 1926	5.00
Boy Scout, Match Safe, Metal	8.95
Boy Scout, Sheet Music, 1907, March Of The Boy Scouts	3.00
Boy Scout, Yearbook, 1928	6.50
Bradley & Hubbard, Candleholder, Brass, 12 In., Pair	85.00
Bradley & Hubbard, Candlestick, Brass, 13 In., Pair	45.00
Bradley & Hubbard, Desk Set, Brass, Art Deco Design, 4 Piece	125.00
Bradley & Hubbard, Desk Set, Brass, Ornate Design, 3 Piece	45.00
Bradley & Hubbard, Holder, Stationery & Pen, Brass, Signed, 2 Piece	65.00
Bradley & Hubbard, Inkwell, Brass, Relief Floral, 3 X 5 In.	26.00
Bradley & Hubbard, Lamp, Banquet, Kerosene, Brass, 8 In. Floral Ball Shade	150.00
Bradley & Hubbard, Lamp, Brass Base & Frame, 8 Tan Slag Panels, 21 In.	250.00
Bradley & Hubbard, Lamp, Nickel Over Brass, Embossed, White Shade, 21 In.	52.50
Bradley & Hubbard, Lamp, Table, Bronze, 14 In. Shade	375.00
Bradley & Hubbard, Lamp, 1904, Oil, Rayo Type, Brass, Milk Glass, 17 In.	50.00
Bradley & Hubbard, Letter Rack, Brass, Double, No.1913, 7 1/2 X 10 1/2 In.	85.00
Bradley & Hubbard, Stand, Match, Brass, Ornate	14.00
Brass & Copper, Teakettle, Top Half Copper, Tin Lining, 7 In.	12.00

*Brass has been used for decorative pieces and useful tablewares since ancient
times. It is an alloy of copper, zinc, and other metals.*

Brass, see also Bell, Miniature, Tool, Trivet, etc.

Brass, Ashtray, Art Nouveau Full Figure, 7 In.	15.00
Brass, Ashtray, China, Enameled, 2 Attached Slippers, 4 In.	12.00
Brass, Ashtray, Made In China, Full Figure Of Pug Attached	15.00
Brass, Ashtray, Marked China, Round, 5 5/8 In.	3.95
Brass, Ashtray, World's Fair, 1939	4.00
Brass, Bar, Towel, Bathroom Fixture, Victorian	24.00
Brass, Basin, Openwork, Engraved, Flared, Rolled Rim, 9 1/4 In.	12.00
Brass, Basket, Russian, Czarist Seal, Flared Top, Rolled Edge, 3 3/4 In.	12.00
Brass, Bookrack, Art Nouveau Ladies' Faces, Expandable	32.50
Brass, Bootjack, Beetle, 10 In.	60.00
Brass, Bootjack, The Moland, Oak Base, 15 1/2 In.	25.00
Brass, Bottle Opener, Jolly Nigger	12.00
Brass, Bowl, Art Nouveau, Footed, 14 X 9 In.	45.00
Brass, Bowl, Chinese, Gong Metal, Decorated, 4 3/4 In.	12.50

Brass, Bowl, Flowers & Leaves Design, 7 1/2 X 3 In. 9.75
Brass, Bowl, Hand Hammered, C.1750, 14 In. 90.00
Brass, Bowl, Made In China, Pedestal Base, 5 1/2 X 3 1/2 In. 12.00
Brass, Bowl, Marked China, Dragon Design, 10 In. 11.75
Brass, Bowl, Marked China, Dragon Design, 4 1/4 In. 4.95
Brass, Bowl, Marked China, Lady In Garden Scene, Wooden Base, 10 In. 14.75
Brass, Box, Cigarette, Cylindrical, Dragon, Jade On Top, 3 X 2 1/4 In. 35.00
Brass, Box, Cigarette, Hinged, Footed, Relief Figures, Signed J.B., 7 1/2 In. 35.00
Brass, Box, Cigarette, Marked China, Embossed Buddha, 4 Faces In Corners 8.50
Brass, Box, Cigarette, Marked China, Flower & Leaves On Hinged Lid 9.95
Brass, Box, Jewelry, Painting On Ivory Under Glass On Hinged Lid, 5 1/4 In. 75.00
Brass, Box, Stamp, Applied Oriental Lady & Child On Hinged Lid, 1 1/2 In. 12.00
Brass, Box, Stamp, Bronze Finish, 3 1/4 X 1 3/4 X 1 1/2 In. 5.95
Brass, Box, Stamp, Chatham Electric Switching Device Co., Ky., 1919 .... 14.00
Brass, Box, Stamp, Hinged, 3 Compartments, Extended Base, 3 3/4 X 1 7/8 In. 15.00
Brass, Box, Stamp, Shakespeare's House, 4 Claw Feet 12.00
Brass, Box, Stamp, Vienna, Hinged, 3 Compartments, Footed, 5 X 3 In. 25.00
Brass, Box, Tobacco, English, C.1800, Boat Shape, Dome Lid, Paw Feet, 6 In. 180.00
Brass, Brazier, Copper Bottom, 2 Handles, 1860, 15 X 5 In. 65.00
Brass, Bucket, American Brass Kettle Co., Bail Handle, 9 X 13 1/2 In. 42.00
Brass, Bucket, Connecticut, 1851, Handwrought Iron Bail Handle, 13 3/4 In. 65.00
Brass, Bucket, Hammered Surface, Wrought Iron Bail Handle, C.1850 .... 70.00
Brass, Buckle, Belt, K.K.K., Dated 1926 .... 18.50
Brass, Buckle, Blue Lapis Nugget Insets, 2 Parts, Filigree, 1 1/2 In. 5.00
Brass, Bust, Shakespeare, 3 In. 7.00
Brass, Canary Songbird, Victory, C.1920, Tin Bulb For Water, 5 In. 13.00
Brass, Candelabra, Louis XVI Style, Gilt, Cut Glass Pendants, 22 In., Pair 250.00
Brass, Candelabrum, Marked China, 3 Arm, 7 1/2 In. 20.00
Brass, Candelabrum, Marked China, 5 Arm, 9 1/2 In. 14.00
Brass, Candelabrum, Marked China, 5 Arm, 10 1/2 In. 14.00
Brass, Candelabrum, Serpents, 3 Arm, 17 In. 25.00
Brass, Candleholder, Capstan, 5 In. 260.00
Brass, Candleholder, China, 2 Arm, Engraved, 4 1/2 In. 4.00
Brass, Candleholder, Cobra, 9 In. 15.00
Brass, Candleholder, Figural, Man Holding Candles, 14 In. 50.00
Brass, Candleholder, Made In China, Handled, 4 1/2 In., Pair 20.00
Brass, Candleholder, Marked China, Decorated Octagonal Base, 4 In., Pair 40.00
Brass, Candleholder, 3 Crisscrossed Rifles, 3 In. 18.00
Brass, Candlesnuffer, Chinese, Twisted Handle 12.50
Brass, Candlesnuffer, Marked China, 8 1/2 In. 4.95
Brass, Candlestick, Art Nouveau Design, 5 Arm, 25 1/2 X 20 In., Pair 395.00
Brass, Candlestick, Art Nouveau, Cobra, 4 Parts Screw Together, 8 1/2 In. 26.00
Brass, Candlestick, Baluster Stem, Bracket Feet, C.1820, 9 In., Pair 110.00
Brass, Candlestick, Bell-Shaped Base, Footed, C.1820, 9 In., Pair 150.00
Brass, Candlestick, Chinese, 3 Arm, 11 3/4 In., Pair 45.00
Brass, Candlestick, Chinese, 9 3/4 In., Pair 38.00
Brass, Candlestick, Court Jester Support, Pierced Diamond Shaped Stem, 9 In 20.00
Brass, Candlestick, Dollhouse Size, Pair 7.50
Brass, Candlestick, Dutch, Bell Form Base, Bun Feet, C.1850, 9 In., Pair 125.00
Brass, Candlestick, Dutch, Lobed Dish, 7 Footed, C.1850, 10 3/4 In., Pair 80.00
Brass, Candlestick, Electrified, Cranberry Shade, 10 Prisms, Pair 75.00
Brass, Candlestick, Embossed Faces On Triangular Base, 18 In., Pair 35.00
Brass, Candlestick, England, Beehive, Push-Up, 10 In., Pair 75.00
Brass, Candlestick, Hand-Turned, Polished, 9 In., Pair 16.00
Brass, Candlestick, Hand-Turned, Polished, 11 In., Pair 24.00
Brass, Candlestick, Hand-Turned, Polished, 16 In., Pair 28.00
Brass, Candlestick, Jade Insert, 1 X 1 1/2 In., Pair 75.00
Brass, Candlestick, Lions, 3 Arm, 12 In., Pair 40.00
Brass, Candlestick, Louis XVI, 10 1/2 In., Pair 238.00
Brass, Candlestick, Marked China, Round Base, 5 1/4 In., Pair 9.95
Brass, Candlestick, Metal Plated, Engraved, Art Nouveau, 1909, 7 3/4 In., Pair 39.00
Brass, Candlestick, Push-Up, C.1810, 11 In., Pair 88.00
Brass, Candlestick, Push-Up, C.1850, 15 1/2 In., Pair 175.00
Brass, Candlestick, Push-Up, C.1880, 8 3/4 In., Pair 88.00
Brass, Candlestick, Push-Up, Octagonal Base, 7 In. 22.50
Brass, Candlestick, Push-Up, 5 In. 12.75

Brass, Candlestick, Push-Up, 6 In.	12.75
Brass, Candlestick, Push-Up, 12 In., Pair	75.00
Brass, Candlestick, Queen Anne, Bell Form Base, Canted Foot, 9 In., Pair	100.00
Brass, Candlestick, Russian, Turned Design, Cyrillic Mark, 8 In.	30.00
Brass, Candlestick, Russian, 6 1/2 In. *Illus*	55.00
Brass, Candlestick, Saucer Base, Push-Up, Finger Ring, 5 X 4 In.	15.00
Brass, Candlestick, Scalloped Domed Base, Baluster, C.1750, 8 In., Pair	550.00
Brass, Candlestick, Shell On Base, Baluster Turned, C.1750, 8 In., Pair	425.00
Brass, Candlestick, Signed Warsaw, Embossed Roses, 12 In., Pair	125.00
Brass, Candlestick, Square Base, Push-Up, Straight Shank, C.1790, 6 In., Pair	45.00
Brass, Candlestick, Square Footed Base, C.1850, 4 In., Pair	25.00
Brass, Candlestick, Unscrew At Base, 4 In., Pair	35.00
Brass, Candlestick, 1 1/2 In., Pair	4.00
Brass, Candlestick, 19 In., Pair	45.00
Brass, Candlestick, 6 Sided Base, 2 1/2 In., Pair	30.00
Brass, Censer, Openwork Case, Multicolored Jewels, Chain, 4 1/2 X 8 In.	85.00
Brass, Cigar Cutter, Ship's Wheel Shape, 6 In.	26.00
Brass, Cigar Cutter, Watch Charm, Bottle Shape, 2 In.	9.00
Brass, Cigar Holder, 3 Section, Design	12.00
Brass, Cigar Snuffer, Marked China, Cat, 2 1/2 In.	17.50
Brass, Clip, Bill, Hanging, Fleur-De-Lis, 2 3/4 In.	7.50
Brass, Clip, Bill, Hanging, Hand, Patented, Dark Finish, 5 1/2 In.	12.50
Brass, Compass, German, Closed Face, 1 3/4 In.	12.00
Brass, Compote, Marked China, 9 1/2 In.	10.00
Brass, Container, Ink Drying Sand, C.1850, 2 In.	35.00
Brass, Cruet, 6 Bottles, Brass Caps	58.00
Brass, Cup & Saucer, Chinese, Etched	3.00
Brass, Cup, Collapsible, Nickel Plated, Niles Patent, June 5, 1860	4.95
Brass, Cup, Cyclist's, Folding	3.50
Brass, Cup, Cyclist's, Nickel Plated, Collapsible, 1897, Couple On Bicycle	16.00
Brass, Cup, Nut, Chinese, Etched	2.00
Brass, Dish, Soap, Bathroom Fixture, Victorian	30.00
Brass, Dish, Soap, Hammered, Covered, Traveling, Tin Lined, Oval, 3 1/2 In.	5.00
Brass, Door Knocker, see also Coronation	
Brass, Door Knocker, Figure Of Aladdin, Aladdin Homes, 6 In.	25.00
Brass, Door Knocker, Grinning Satin With Horns, Sits Cross-Legged, 3 In.	20.00
Brass, Door Knocker, Woodpecker, 4 In.Long	35.00
Brass, Doorknob, Public School, City Of New York, Oval, 3 In., Pair	5.75
Brass, Doorknob, Statue Of Liberty Medallion, 2 1/2 In., Pair	10.00
Brass, Doorstop, Folding	2.50
Brass, Eagle, American, C.1850, Iron Mounting Piece, 39 In. Wingspread	695.00
Brass, Easel, Patent 1908, 7 1/8 X 5 1/8 In.	4.95
Brass, Fernery, Claw Feet, Russian, Signed, 6 In.Diameter	45.00
Brass, Figurine, Old Man, Chinese, Bearded, Head Ornament, 7 1/4 In.	78.00
Brass, Fork, Toasting, Shakespeare, English, C.1865, 16 In.	30.00
Brass, Frame, American & Italian Flag On Top, C.1917, 9 1/2 X 6 1/4 In.	15.00
Brass, Frame, Easel, Leaf Corners, Ball Feet, Curved Glass, 6 1/4 X 4 1/8 In.	6.95
Brass, Frame, Footed, 1 1/4 X 1 In.	18.00
Brass, Frame, Mosaic Inserts, Easel Back, 2 In. Diameter	12.50
Brass, Frame, Picture, Easel, Patent 1894, 6 3/4 X 12 In.	18.00
Brass, Frame, Picture, Ornate, Oval, 10 X 8 In.	12.50
Brass, Grinder, Pepper, Cylindrical, 4 Engraved Bands, 1860, 6 1/4 In.	37.00
Brass, Holder, Banner, American Eagle, Spread Winged, N.Y., C.1881, 29 In.	150.00
Brass, Holder, Cup, Bathroom Fixture, Victorian	20.00
Brass, Holder, Pocket Watch, Sandwich Glass Center, 3 1/2 In. Diameter	35.00
Brass, Holder, Watch, Figure Of Cobbler Pointing, Iron Plinth, 9 In.	35.00
Brass, Horn, Bicycle, Rubber Bulb, Mounting Bracket, 12 In.	18.00
Brass, Incense Burner, Chinese Character Writing, Footed, 6 3/4 In.High	65.00
Brass, Inkwell, Austria, Hinged, Reticulated Leaves, 1 1/4 In.	13.00
Brass, Inkwell, B&H, Covered, Oval, 4 Ball Feet & Handle, 2 X 3 1/2 In.	15.00
Brass, Inkwell, Chinese, Brush Holder, C.1850, 13 1/4 In.	95.00
Brass, Inkwell, Crab, Glass Insert	35.00
Brass, Inkwell, Dog's Bust, Hinged Jaw, 2 Attached Puppies, 4 X 6 In.	52.00
Brass, Inkwell, Dome Shaped Well, Hinged, Scrolls, Ceramic Insert, 3 3/4 In.	45.00
Brass, Inkwell, Hinged Domed Cover, Glass Insert, 5 In. Diameter At Base	9.95
Brass, Inkwell, Hinged Lid, Clear Glass Insert, Pen Rack, 5 3/4 In.	12.75

Brass, Inkwell, Hinged, Repousse Floral & Cherubs, Attached Tray, 4 Legs	35.00
Brass, Inkwell, K & Co., Square, Hinged, Glass Insert, Embossed, 3 X 2 1/2 In.	18.00
Brass, Inkwell, Lift-Up Cover, Clear Glass Insert, 4 1/2 X 3 1/2 X 2 In.	6.95
Brass, Inkwell, Shell Shaped, Hinged Lid, Pen Tube With Hinged Lid, 9 In.	50.00
Brass, Inkwell, Top Opens, White Glass Insert	70.00
Brass, Jar, Openwork, Copper & Silver Trim, 3 1/4 In.	35.00
Brass, Key, Screws Into Itself To Become Compact, Patent 1885	4.75
Brass, Key, 4 3/4 In.	2.95
Brass, Knife, Paper, Oriental, Peacock Feather Shape, Village Scene, 12 In.	22.50
Brass, Letter Holder, Art Nouveau, 4 Ladies, Floral, 5 1/2 In.	45.00
Brass, Letter Holder, Rex Carnival, New Orleans, 1908, Art Nouveau	20.00
Brass, Letter Opener, Bird On Flowering Branch, Dragonfly, 10 1/2 In.	14.00
Brass, Letter Opener, Cutout Design, 9 In.	4.75
Brass, Letter Opener, Dagger, Knight In Armor Handle, 9 1/2 In.	9.00
Brass, Letter Opener, Elephant On Handle, 8 In.	5.95
Brass, Letter Opener, Full Figure Of Venus Handle	9.00
Brass, Letter Opener, Marked China, Shape Of Crocodile, 8 1/4 In.	5.95
Brass, Letter Opener, St.Louis, Louisiana Purchase Centennial, 1904	20.00
Brass, Letter Opener, Standing Indian Handle, 7 In.Long	20.00
Brass, Letter, A, 4 In.	4.00
Brass, Letter, D, 4 In.	4.00
Brass, Letter, O, 4 In.	4.00
Brass, Lighter, Cigar, Bowers, Kalamazoo, Mich.	20.00
Brass, Lighter, R.K.Premier, Acorn On Pedestal Shape, 4 1/2 In.	6.95
Brass, Lighter, Tinder, English, C.1800, 5 In.Long	395.00
Brass, Lock & Key, Belt Buckle Shape, L.H.& Co., Patent 1902, 1 3/4 In.	10.00
Brass, Lock, Imperial 6 Lever, Chain	5.00
Brass, Mailbox, Raised Star In Center, 12 X 5 1/2 In.	28.00
Brass, Match Holder, Beetle, Hinged Lid, 3 3/4 X 2 1/4 X 1 1/2 In.	15.00
Brass, Match Holder, Pocket, Man On Horseback	17.50
Brass, Match Safe, Pig, English, Garnet Over Nose	45.00
Brass, Match Safe, Pocket, Mid-Winter Fair, San Francisco, C.1894, Nickel	9.95
Brass, Match Safe, Pocket, Milwaukee Beer Is Famous, Pabst Has Made It	9.95
Brass, Match Safe, Wall, Dog's Head Center Top, 2 Compartments, 6 1/2 In.	30.00
Brass, Matchbox Holder, Marked China, Hand-Tooled Dog On Top, Etched	7.50
Brass, Matchbox Holder, Mutton Fat Jade Insert On Top, Etched, 1 In.	13.00
Brass, Measure, To Determine Grade Of Wheat At Mill, Howe	85.00
Brass, Mirror, Hand, Art Nouveau, Blown-Out Decoration	12.00
Brass, Mortar & Pestle, Plain Sides, 4 X 3 In.	25.00
Brass, Mortar & Pestle, Round Ball Handle, 4 X 3 1/2 In.	25.00
Brass, Nutcracker, Figural, Bill Sikes & Fagin Handle	35.00
Brass, Nutcracker, Parrot	16.00
Brass, Pail, Copper-Riveted Brass Loops, Iron Handle, C.1850, 8 In.	30.00
Brass, Pail, Spun, Bail, 6 In.	35.00

Brass, Candlestick, Russian, 6 1/2 In.
(See Page 51)

Brass, Paper Clip, Graceful Hand, 4 In.	18.00
Brass, Paper Clip, Spencerian	10.00
Brass, Pencil Holder, Marked China, Turtle, Paperweight	25.00
Brass, Pillbox, Fired Enamel Lid, Pink & Cobalt On White	10.00
Brass, Pipe Tamper, Nude Bust Of George Washington, C.1790	110.00
Brass, Pitcher, Curved Spout, Thumb Lift Cover, 10 1/2 In.	35.00
Brass, Planter, Russian, 6 In. Diameter	39.00
Brass, Plaque, Beethoven, Left Profile, Wooden Frame, 7 X 11 In.	125.00
Brass, Plaque, Bust Of Lincoln, Facing Left, Powell, 1865, Silvered, 7 X 5 In.	125.00
Brass, Plaque, Shakespeare, Left Profile Head, Bronze Frame, Round, 4 1/2 In.	65.00
Brass, Plate, White House Of 1800s, Relief Floral Rim, 4 1/4 In.	18.00
Brass, Pot, Spun, Copper Rivets & Bail Handle, 15 In. X 11 In.	85.00
Brass, Ruler, 12 In.	7.50
Brass, Salt Dip, Signed China, Pair	15.00
Brass, Samovar, Russian, Pierced Cover To Heating Column, C.1890, 33 1/2 In.	200.00
Brass, Sander, Engraved Cable Rim, Button Finial, 2 In. Diameter	18.00
Brass, Scoop, 6 X 4 In.	15.00
Brass, Server, Coffee, Turkish, Engraved	14.00
Brass, Skimmer, Iron Handle	40.00
Brass, Spittoon, Old West Style, 6 X 8 In.	11.50
Brass, Spittoon, 9 X 7 In.	22.50
Brass, Spoon, Tea Caddy, Admiral Dewey Handle, Ship In Bowl	7.50
Brass, Spoon, Yogurt, 2 In. Across Bowl	10.00
Brass, Spurs, U.S.Cavalry, Pair	10.00
Brass, Stencil Set, 26 Letters, 7 Numbers, Brush, Paste	25.00
Brass, Strainer, Tea, Embossed Cupids & Floral, Footed Stand	18.00
Brass, Sundial, Octagonal, C.1905, My Face Marks Sunny Hours, 11 In.	65.00
Brass, Tag, Dog, Wichita, 1929	5.00
Brass, Tea Caddy, Cobalt Glass Knob, Enamel Scenic Panels, 4 In.	32.50
Brass, Tea Caddy, Hand Hammered, Square, Indented Corners, 4 3/4 In.	14.75
Brass, Tea Caddy, Octagonal, 7 In.	22.50
Brass, Tea Caddy, 8 Sided, Lift-Off Cap, 5 1/4 X 2 3/4 In.	22.50
Brass, Teakettle On Stand, Creamer, N.Y., Burner, Paw Feet, C.1850, 9 1/4 In.	85.00
Brass, Teakettle On Stand, New York, Paw Feet, 9 1/4 X 5 3/4 In.	68.00
Brass, Teakettle, Amber Handle, Button Feet	55.00 To 68.00
Brass, Teakettle, Scottish, Victorian, Blue Wooden Handle, Footed, 1/2 Gallon	75.00
Brass, Teakettle, Stand & Burner, Manning Bowman, 1907	40.00
Brass, Teakettle, 4 Button Feet, Amber Handle, Signed	78.00
Brass, Teapot, Chinese, Wooden Handle, 3 1/2 X 5 In.	25.00
Brass, Teapot, English, Whistle Top, C.1890, Signed, 13 1/2 In.High	195.00
Brass, Teapot, Footed, Milk Glass Handle	75.00
Brass, Teapot, Snake Mouth, Quart	29.00
Brass, Tieback, Curtain, Relief Rosette Center, C.1850, 2 1/2 In., Pair	14.00
Brass, Tieback, Petaled Flower Center, 3 1/4 In., Pair	20.00
Brass, Tray, American, Hand Hammered, Spun, 12 1/2 In.	35.00
Brass, Tray, China, Flowers & Leaves Design, 2 Handled, 8 1/4 In.	9.75
Brass, Tray, China, Rounded, 12 In.	28.00
Brass, Tray, Round, Benares India, Stylized Peacock In Center, 15 In.	25.00
Brass, Tray, Round, Man & Woman Figures, China, 11 1/2 In.	25.00
Brass, Tray, Russian, 8 3/8 In.	10.75
Brass, Tray, Samovar, Russian, Nickel Plated, Double Eagle Mark, 1889, 18 In.	17.75
Brass, Tray, Souvenir, Lincoln Exhibit, Chicago Exposition, 1933, 5 X 3 In.	4.75
Brass, Tray, St.Louis Exposition, 1904, 6 X 5 In.	15.00
Brass, Tumbler Holder, Wall, Nickel Plated, Pair	12.00
Brass, Urn, Coffee, Spigot On Turnkey, 3 Footed, 9 X 7 In.	75.00
Brass, Urn, Coffee, 3 Feet, 9 X 7 In.	70.00
Brass, Urn, Griffins' Heads Handles, Leaves & Palmettes, C.1890, 17 In., Pair	80.00
Brass, Vase, Bud, Hand Hammered, 6 X 1 1/4 In.	4.75
Brass, Vase, Chinese, Mother & 2 Children In Relief, 6 In.	38.00
Brass, Vase, Priest Of Palace, 1905, Kansas City, Square Base, 9 In.	45.00
Brass, Vase, Spiral Threading, Bulbous Base, Flanging Out, 9 In., Pair	12.50
Brass, Warmer, Bed, Rooster & Floral On Lid, C.1800, 47 1/2 In.	160.00
Brass, Warmer, Bed, Stanley Cup Air Races, 1929, Oak Handle, 9 In.	25.00
Brass, Warmer, Bed, Susan Grafton, C.1800, Ring Handle, Engraved, 41 1/4 In.	475.00
Brass, Whistle, Arm For Cord, 12 In.	45.00
Brass, Whistle, Police Special	4.00

Brass, Whistle, Regulation, U.S.Army 5.00
Brass, Whistle, Steam, 12 In. 50.00
Brass, Whistle, Steam, 15 In. 44.00
Brayton Laguna, Figurine, Swan, Hand-Painted, Copyrighted 1941, 3 1/2 In. 25.00
Bread Plate, see also Silver Plate, Plate, Bread
Bread Plate, Glass, Blaine, Frosted Portrait, 1884, 11 1/2 In. 120.00
Bread Plate, Glass, Deer & Doe Border, Frosted Center, Iowa City 65.00
Bread Plate, Glass, Double Horseshoe With Prayer Rug .... 42.00 To 55.00
Bread Plate, Glass, G.A.R. Commemorative, 11 1/8 X 7 5/8 In. 90.00
Bread Plate, Glass, Garfield Memorial .... 20.00 To 35.00
Bread Plate, Glass, Garfield, Frosted Bust, 101 Border, 9 In. .... 42.50 To 45.00
Bread Plate, Glass, Grant's Memorial, Square 30.00
Bread Plate, Glass, Grant's Peace .... 22.00 To 25.00
Bread Plate, Glass, Grant's Peace, Amber .... 25.00 To 36.00
Bread Plate, Glass, Grant's Peace, Apple Green 38.00
Bread Plate, Glass, Grant's Peace, Blue .... 25.00 To 30.00
Bread Plate, Glass, Grapes .... 20.00 To 22.50
Bread Plate, Glass, Heroes Of Bunker Hill, 13 1/2 X 9 In. 37.50
Bread Plate, Glass, Knights Of Labor, Amber 200.00
Bread Plate, Glass, Knights Of Labor, Blue 200.00
Bread Plate, Glass, In Remembrance, Washington, Lincoln, McKinley 45.00
Bread Plate, Glass, Independence Hall, Bear Paw Handles .... 75.00 To 95.00
Bread Plate, Glass, "It Is Pleasant To Labor, " Grape Handles .... 24.00 To 35.00
Bread Plate, Glass, John Logan, Portrait, 1884, 11 1/2 In. 120.00
Bread Plate, Glass, John Mitchell, Gilded Portrait Center 125.00
Bread Plate, Glass, Lady & The Lions 35.00
Bread Plate, Glass, Liberty Bell, Shell Handles, Oval, 11 X 7 In. ....Illus 110.00
Bread Plate, Glass, Liberty Bell, Shell Handles, Oval, 11 1/4 X 7 In. 95.00
Bread Plate, Glass, Lion & His Mate, Frosted Center 65.00
Bread Plate, Glass, Louisiana Purchase Centennial, 7 1/4 In. .... 14.00 To 18.00
Bread Plate, Glass, Maltese Cross In Circles 18.00
Bread Plate, Glass, McKinley Memorial, Stippled Leaf Border, 10 1/2 In. 35.00
Bread Plate, Glass, Old Statehouse, Philadelphia, Sapphire Blue 85.00
Bread Plate, Glass, Old Statehouse, Philadelphia, 12 1/4 In. 75.00
Bread Plate, Glass, Pope Leo XIII .... 20.00 To 27.00
Bread Plate, Glass, Puck, Dog Cart & Rabbit, Frosted, 10 In. 90.00
Bread Plate, Glass, Railroad Train .... 55.00 To 75.00
Bread Plate, Glass, Reaper 68.00
Bread Plate, Glass, Rock Of Ages, Milk Glass Insert 125.00
Bread Plate, Glass, Royal Crying Baby .... 30.00 To 55.00
Bread Plate, Glass, Saint Bernard Dog In Mountain, Frosted, 10 In. 90.00
Bread Plate, Glass, Sheaf Of Wheat, Give Us This Day, 10 In. 22.50
Bread Plate, Glass, Sheaf Of Wheat, Turned Down Edge 16.00
Bread Plate, Glass, Sheaf Of Wheat, 12 X 10 In. 25.00
Bread Plate, Glass, Sheridan Memorial 48.00
Bread Plate, Glass, Theodore Roosevelt, Frosted, 10 1/4 X 7 3/4 In. 77.50
Bread Plate, Glass, Three Graces, Frosted & Clear 35.00
Bread Plate, Glass, Three Presidents, 12 1/2 In. 45.00
Bread Plate, Glass, Train, 12 In. 30.00
Bread Plate, Glass, Virginia Dare 42.50
Bread Plate, Glass, Waste Not, Want Not 35.00
Bread Plate, Glass, Warrior, Frosted, Classic Border, Jacobus 95.00
Bread Plate, Glass, Warrior, 11 1/4 In. 100.00
Bread Plate, Glass, Washington, Frosted Bust Center 110.00

*Brides' baskets of glass were usually one-of-a-kind novelties made in
American and European glass factories. They were especially popular about
1880 when the decorated basket was often given as a wedding gift. Cut-glass
baskets were popular after 1890. All brides' baskets lost favor about 1905.*
Bride's Basket, Cased Apricot Fluted Bowl, Silver Plate Frame, 10 In. 150.00
Bride's Basket, Chartreuse, 8 In. 84.75
Bride's Basket, Clear Glass, Multicolor Enameled Flowers, Holder 80.00
Bride's Basket, Deep Pink, Scalloped, Ornate Silver Plate Holder, 9 In. 125.00
Bride's Basket, White Satin Glass, Red Petaled Edge, 6 1/2 In. 105.00
Bride's Bowl, Amethyst, Ruffled, Enamel Florettes, 11 In. 65.00
Bride's Bowl, Blue & Opalescent, 10 3/4 In. 53.00

Bride's Bowl, Heart Shape, Fuchsia To White, Bellflowers, Gold, 8 In. 60.00
Bride's Bowl, Shaded Pink, Ruffled, Crimped Edge, 11 1/2 In. 75.00
Bride's Bowl, White, Ruffled Clear Edge, Pink Interior 40.00
Bridle Rosette, Brass & Gilt, Hand-Engraved, Initial D, C.1905, Pair 12.50
Bridle Rosette, Brass & Glass, Initial O On Black, Patent 1882, Pair 7.75

Bristol glass was made in Bristol, England, after the 1700s. The
Bristol glass most often seen today is a Victorian, lightweight opaque glass
that is often blue. Some of the glass was decorated with enamels.

Bristol, Bell, Smoke, Opaque White, Crimped, Applied Blue Rim, 8 1/2 In. 18.00
Bristol, Bottle, Cologne, Pink, Blue, & White Floral Medallion, Gold Trim 12.00
Bristol, Bowl, Finger, Emerald Green, Pair 95.00
Bristol, Box, Brown To Tan, Hinged, Orchids, Brass Fittings, Round, 4 3/4 In. 110.00
Bristol, Box, Jewel, Hinged, Rose Decoration, Round, 5 1/2 In. 165.00
Bristol, Box, Jewel, Violets, 3 Footed, 5 X 6 In. 135.00
Bristol, Cologne, Bulbous Base, Slim Neck, Light Green, Gold Line Trim 20.00
Bristol, Cracker Jar, White To Pink, Blue & Rose Morning Glory 75.00
Bristol, Dish, Sweetmeat, Blue, Enamel Floral, Silver Lid, Handle, & Rim, 3 In. 67.00
Bristol, Dresser Set, Blue, Decorated, 3 Piece 45.50
Bristol, Inkwell, Paperweight, Clear Over Yellow, C.1850, 4 1/4 In. 75.00
Bristol, Jar, Cookie, Green To Cream Top, Floral Bouquet & Deer, 7 In. 60.00
Bristol, Jar, Cracker, Aqua, Floral, Brass Fittings, 1879, 7 In. 88.00
Bristol, Jar, Cracker, Coffee Color, Pink & Brown Floral, Silver Fittings 65.00
Bristol, Jar, Cracker, Green, Pansies, Silver Lid & Bail 78.00
Bristol, Lamp, Miniature, Hand-Painted Florals, Marked Sterling, 9 1/2 In. 60.00
Bristol, Lamp, Oil, Hand-Painted Cupid On Bottom, Miniature 45.00
Bristol, Lamp, Oil, Hand-Painted Top & Bottom, Miniature 50.00
Bristol, Mug, White, Red Roses, Inscribed Remember Me, Pair 75.00
Bristol, Plate, Concave, Pansies, 11 In. 12.00
Bristol, Plate, Delft, Blue & White, Floral Sprigs, C.1730, 9 In., Pair 125.00
Bristol, Ring Tree, Blue, Enameled Flowers 35.00
Bristol, Rose Bowl, Crimped Top, Yellow To White 25.00
Bristol, Rose Bowl, Robin's Egg Blue, Cased, Scalloped Top, 3 1/2 In. 45.00
Bristol, Salt, White, Christmas, 1877, Tan Winter Scene 45.00
Bristol, Teapot, Floral Finial, C.1780, 6 3/4 In.High 500.00
Bristol, Vase, Beige, Enameled Ducks, 8.In., Pair 55.00
Bristol, Vase, Beige, Red & Gold Geometrics, Urn Shape, Footed, 10 In., Pair 45.00
Bristol, Vase, Blue Flowers, Green, Yellow, 10 In. 35.00
Bristol, Vase, Blue Glass, Enameled Flowers & Bird, 10 In.High 30.00
Bristol, Vase, Blue, Enameled Floral, Ruffled Crimped Top, 6 1/2 In. 16.00
Bristol, Vase, Blue, White Cased, 2 1/2 In., Pair 35.00
Bristol, Vase, Cream, Brown On Base, Enameled Floral, 8 In., Pair 32.00
Bristol, Vase, Custard Satin, Floral On White Band, 8 3/4 In., Pair 47.50
Bristol, Vase, Enamel Portrait Of Little Blonde Girl, 10 In. 20.00
Bristol, Vase, Enameled Floral On Caramel Ground, 12 In.High 25.00
Bristol, Vase, Frosted White, Gold Band At Top, Footed, 4 1/2 In., Pair 32.00
Bristol, Vase, Gray, Fluted Top, Enamel Bird & Flower Basket, 7 1/2 In. 30.00
Bristol, Vase, Gray, Orange, Gold, Pink, & Blue Enameling, 8 1/2 In., Pair 38.50
Bristol, Vase, Green, Gleaners, The, 12 1/2 In. 75.00
Bristol, Vase, Light Blue, Cobalt Layer, Bird, Bee, & Flower Enamel, 5 In. 18.50
Bristol, Vase, Milk White, Green Leaves, Red Cranberries, 9 1/2 In., Pair 25.00
Bristol, Vase, Opaque Blue Green, Enameled Floral, Fan Top, 7 In. 25.00
Bristol, Vase, Opaque Blue Green, Enameled Flowers, 7 In.High 25.00
Bristol, Vase, Pink & White Panels, Courting Scenes, Flowers, 5 3/4 In. 27.50
Bristol, Vase, Pink Cased, Hand-Painted Birds On Branch, 12 In., Pair 115.00
Bristol, Vase, Pink, Enameled Strawberries & Flowers, 13 In., Pair 65.00
Bristol, Vase, Pink, Enameled, 12 In., Pair 95.00
Bristol, Vase, Pink, Jeweled, Hand-Painted Scrolls & Floral, 7 1/4 In. 110.00
Bristol, Vase, Portrait Of Lady, Bulbous Body & Narrow Neck, 7 In.High 40.00
Bristol, Vase, Robin's Egg Blue, Blown, Fluted Top, 9 In. 30.00
Bristol, Vase, Violets & Horseshoe, 9 In., Pair 48.00
Bristol, Vase, White, Floral Decoration, Opalescent, 9 In. 22.50
Bristol, Vase, White, Floral, Tan Trim, Scalloped Rim, 11 1/2 In. 35.00
Bristol, Vase, White, Jack-In-The-Pulpit, Hand-Painted, Fluted, 8 In., Pair 25.00
Bristol, Vase, White, Ruffled Top, Hand-Painted Floral, Rough Pontil, 7 In. 15.00

Bristol, Vase, White, Ruffled Top, Hand-Painted Flowers, 18 In.	18.00
Bronze, Ashtray, Armor Bronze Corp., 1927, Art Deco Nude Woman, 8 In.	65.00
Bronze, Ashtray, Art Deco, Kneeling Egyptian Woman, Footed Vase, 5 X 5 In.	65.00
Bronze, Ashtray, General Motors, 1930s	6.50
Bronze, Ashtray, Hitler's Hearth	30.00
Bronze, Ashtray, N.Y.State Bankers Assoc., 9/22/28, 8 1/2 In.	5.00
Bronze, Ashtray, Susse, C.1900, Figural, Moroccan Woman, Silvered, 6 In.	150.00
Bronze, Bookend, Barefoot Girl & Boy, 1927, 6 3/8 In., Pair	10.00
Bronze, Bookend, Herzel, Tiger, 6 X 6 In., Pair	200.00
Bronze, Bookend, Trail's End, 1920 On Bottom, 5 X 12 1/2 In., Pair	20.00
Bronze, Box, Jewelry, French, Painting On Ivory On Lid, Dore, Oval, 8 In.	275.00
Bronze, Box, Silver Crest, Dore, Art Nouveau, 2 1/2 X 4 1/2 X 1 In.	20.00
Bronze, Box, 2 Dogs On Marble Top, Carved Dogs, 6 1/2 X 3 1/2 In.	190.00
Bronze, Burner, Incense, Foo Dog Finial, Mongoose Handles, 3 X 3 In.	45.00
Bronze, Burner, Incense, Foo Dog Lid	16.00
Bronze, Burner, Incense, Houseboat Shape, 7 X 5 In.	75.00
Bronze, Burner, Incense, Nippon, Turtles On Sides, Footed, 3 1/4 In.	19.75
Bronze, Burner, Incense, Tao T'ieh Masks, Foo Dog Finial, C.1850, 19 1/4 In.	375.00
Bronze, Bust, Canova, 1808, Napoleon I, Gray Marble Socle, 17 3/8 In.	375.00
Bronze, Bust, Carpeaux, C.1890, Le Genie De La Danse, 14 1/2 In.	450.00
Bronze, Bust, Carrier, C.1890, Napoleon III, P.G.Pottier, 16 1/2 In.	600.00
Bronze, Bust, Dante, Marble Base, C.1900, 5 1/2 In.High	75.00
Bronze, Bust, Emerson, Copyright 1897, 4 In.	65.00
Bronze, Bust, Faralla, C.1890, Young Maiden, 7 3/4 In.	200.00
Bronze, Bust, Geflowski, 1901, Queen Victoria, Mappin Brothers, 7 In.	195.00
Bronze, Bust, Goethe, 2 In.	62.50
Bronze, Bust, Houdon, C.1890, Lady, Hair Pulled Back, Marble Socle, 18 In.	300.00
Bronze, Bust, Houdon, C.1890, Lady, 18th Century Style, 18 5/8 In.	275.00
Bronze, Bust, King Oscar Of Norway, 5 1/2 In.	55.00
Bronze, Bust, Marchand, 1908, Charles M.Russell, 8 1/2 In.	1100.00
Bronze, Bust, Mypatia, Fancy Headdress, 3 X 3 In.	148.00
Bronze, Bust, Renevez, Indian Head, Full Headdress, Giving War Call, 4 X 4 In	375.00
Bronze, Bust, Rude, C.1850, Gaul Man, 12 In.	800.00
Bronze, Bust, Svatopolk, Silvered, 1867, 12 In.	300.00
Bronze, Bust, Tereszezuk, C.1890, Young Lady, Hair Pulled Back, 10 In.	275.00
Bronze, Bust, Van Der Straaten, Art Nouveau Woman, Plumed Hat, 26 In.High	850.00
Bronze, Candelabra, Pradier, C.1890, Female Figure, 7 Arm, Marble, 23 In., Pair	150.00
Bronze, Candleholder, Marble Plinth, 24 Cut Glass Prisms, 15 In., Pair	195.00
Bronze, Candleholder, Oriental, Figural, Cranes On Turtle Backs, 13 In., Pair	150.00
Bronze, Candlesnuffer, Figural, Monk, Teacup Handle, 2 1/4 X 1 3/4 In.	40.00
Bronze, Candlestick, Japanese, C.1850, 9 1/2 In., Pair	100.00
Bronze, Censer, Foo Dog Finial, Birds, Flowers, Phoenix Bird Handles, 15 In.	145.00
Bronze, Compote, Mythological Gods, Dolphins, & Seahorses, Cutout, 6 In.	85.00
Bronze, Container, 2 Enclosed Dish Type Weights, Geometrics, C.1790, 2 In.	35.00
Bronze, Crucifix, Gorham, Wall, C.1895, 9 In.	60.00
Bronze, Ewer, Art Nouveau, Lady Forms Handle, 6 In.	16.50
Bronze, Figurine, A.Bros., C.1890, Magellan, 14 In.	80.00
Bronze, Figurine, Anfrie, C.1890, Maiden, Standing, 16 In.	225.00
Bronze, Figurine, Arhat, Holding Ghanta In Right Hand, C.1850, 16 1/4 In.	200.00
Bronze, Figurine, Arson, Rooster, 3 3/4 In.	215.00
Bronze, Figurine, Art Union, 1854, Queen Victoria On Horseback, 26 In.	2000.00
Bronze, Figurine, Austrian, Irish Setter, 4 X 2 1/2 In.	60.00
Bronze, Figurine, Barbedienne, C.1850, Dying Slave, 18 In.	150.00
Bronze, Figurine, Barbedienne, C.1890, Ariadne, 13 In.	100.00
Bronze, Figurine, Barbedienne, Nude Woman & Shell, 6 X 5 1/2 In.	295.00
Bronze, Figurine, Barrias, 1926, Nature Unveiling Before Science, 23 In.	2000.00
Bronze, Figurine, Barye, C.1890, African Elephant, Charging, 8 In.	650.00
Bronze, Figurine, Barye, C.1890, Indian Elephant, 7 1/2 In.	450.00
Bronze, Figurine, Barye, C.1890, Indian Elephant, 10 1/2 In.	450.00
Bronze, Figurine, Barye, C.1890, Jaguar, Walking, 8 3/4 In.	650.00
Bronze, Figurine, Barye, Elephant, Walking, 10 1/2 X 6 In.	650.00
Bronze, Figurine, Barye, Jaguar, Standing, 8 X 6 1/2 In.	750.00
Bronze, Figurine, Barye, Jaguar, 9 1/2 X 7 1/2 In.	650.00
Bronze, Figurine, Barye, Lion, Standing, 6 X 4 1/2 In.	275.00
Bronze, Figurine, Barye, Lion, 12 1/2 X 6 In.High	425.00
Bronze, Figurine, Barye, Lion, 14 X 9 In.	850.00

Bronze, Figurine, Bissell, 1898, Abraham Lincoln, Gorham Co., 8 1/4 In. 550.00
Bronze, Figurine, Bissell, 1898, Abraham Lincoln, Gorham Co., 9 In. 550.00
Bronze, Figurine, Boar, Seated, C.1850, 4 1/4 In. 50.00
Bronze, Figurine, Boar, Striding, C.1850, 11 In. 175.00
Bronze, Figurine, Bonheur, Cow, 5 1/2 In.Long, 3 1/2 In.High 325.00
Bronze, Figurine, Bonheur, Ram, Reclining, 9 X 4 In. 850.00
Bronze, Figurine, Borghese Gladiator, C.1850, 13 1/2 In. 100.00
Bronze, Figurine, Boulton, Gnawing Rodent, American Art Foundry, N.Y., 3 In. 150.00
Bronze, Figurine, Boulton, The Great Longhorn Owl, 7 1/2 X 7 In. 750.00
Bronze, Figurine, Boy Sitting On Potty, 2 1/4 In. 35.00
Bronze, Figurine, Carles, C.1890, La Jeunesse, Gilt, 10 3/4 In. 275.00
Bronze, Figurine, Carrier-Belleuse, Melodie, 31 In. 1200.00
Bronze, Figurine, Causse, Woman, Brown Patina, 31 In. 1200.00
Bronze, Figurine, Cecioni, Enfant En Coq, 21 1/2 X 12 In. 750.00
Bronze, Figurine, Cesari, Chestnut Vendor, Ivory Face, 11 1/2 In. 475.00
Bronze, Figurine, Cheret, C.1890, Seminude Child With Baskets, 6 3/8 In. 150.00
Bronze, Figurine, Chiparus, Boy With Toy Elephant, Ivory Face, 7 1/4 In. 395.00
Bronze, Figurine, Ciampi, 1918, Nude Young Woman, 19 3/8 In. 275.00
Bronze, Figurine, Clesinger, Roman Bull, 11 X 6 In.High 950.00
Bronze, Figurine, Collas, C.1890, Diane De Gabies, 16 1/4 In. 100.00
Bronze, Figurine, D'Astanieres, C.1890, Young Boy, Gilt, 24 In. 650.00
Bronze, Figurine, D'Orsay, 1848, Louis Napoleon, 22 1/2 In. 750.00
Bronze, Figurine, Dachshund Holding Tail In Mouth, 2 In. .... 55.00 To 58.00
Bronze, Figurine, Dalou, C.1890, Nude, Seated, 8 5/8 In. 425.00
Bronze, Figurine, Danzmann, Nude Female Dancer, Art Deco, 17 In. 30.00
Bronze, Figurine, Deer, Standing, French Style, 12 1/2 In. 225.00
Bronze, Figurine, Deer, 9 In. 295.00
Bronze, Figurine, Dog & Ball, 4 In. 65.00
Bronze, Figurine, Dog Looking At Ball, 3 In. 175.00
Bronze, Figurine, Dragon, Coiled, 13 1/4 In. 150.00
Bronze, Figurine, Drouot & Etling, C.1890, American Indian On Horse, 22 In. 700.00
Bronze, Figurine, Drouot, C.1890, Seminude Maiden, 21 3/4 In. 125.00
Bronze, Figurine, Dubucand, Greyhound, 9 1/2 X 7 1/2 In. 450.00
Bronze, Figurine, Dumaige, C.1890, Seminude Athlete, Standing, 22 3/4 In. 250.00
Bronze, Figurine, Dumaige, Joan Of Arc, Gilt Bronze, 20 In. 795.00
Bronze, Figurine, Dying Gladiator, C.1850, 15 In. 70.00
Bronze, Figurine, Elephant, Raised Trunk, 6 1/4 In. 75.00
Bronze, Figurine, Elephant, Raised Trunk, Ivory Tusks, 9 X 6 In. 85.00
Bronze, Figurine, Elephant, Raised Trunk, 13 X 11 In. 75.00
Bronze, Figurine, Fame, Allegorical, Seminude Female, C.1850, 23 1/2 In. 200.00
Bronze, Figurine, Fratin, Elephant, Walking, 7 X 5 In. 350.00
Bronze, Figurine, Fremiet, Horse, 12 X 12 In. 1100.00
Bronze, Figurine, French, C.1890, Noble On Horse, 25 In. 350.00
Bronze, Figurine, French, Greyhound, Sitting On Hind Legs, 8 X 7 1/2 In. 165.00
Bronze, Figurine, French, Jester, Ivory Face & Hands, Dore, 5 1/2 In. 185.00
Bronze, Figurine, Gamboge, C.1890, Miner Holding Pick, 14 1/2 In. 300.00
Bronze, Figurine, Gautheri, C.1890, Sower, 14 In. 175.00
Bronze, Figurine, Geschutzt, Dancing Arab, Polychrome, 7 In. 225.00
Bronze, Figurine, Geschutzt, Doe, 3 X 3 In. 95.00
Bronze, Figurine, Geschutzt, Horse, Marble Plinth, 10 1/2 X 10 In. 450.00
Bronze, Figurine, Geschutzt, Rhinoceros, 5 X 2 1/4 In. 125.00
Bronze, Figurine, Geschutzt, Saddled Horse, Marble Plinth, 10 1/4 In. 450.00
Bronze, Figurine, Girl Child On Tummy Reading, Marble Base, 6 In. 125.00
Bronze, Figurine, Gnome, Sitting Hunched Up, Pedestal Base, 4 In. 45.00
Bronze, Figurine, Goddess Giva, 4 In. 35.00
Bronze, Figurine, Gorham Co., Scottie Dog, Sitting, 3 In. 125.00
Bronze, Figurine, Gorham Co., Wolfhound, Dark Patina, 6 In. 165.00
Bronze, Figurine, Gregoire, C.1890, Bacchus, 15 1/2 In. 150.00
Bronze, Figurine, Hasse, Female Nude On Horseback, 23 In. 900.00
Bronze, Figurine, Herzel, 1922, Leopard, Pompeiian Bronze Co., 6 1/2 In., Pair 90.00
Bronze, Figurine, Herzel, 1922, Leopard, 5 In. Base, 6 1/2 In. 125.00
Bronze, Figurine, Hooded Skeleton & Dagger, Silver Plate, C.1835, 3 3/4 In. 175.00
Bronze, Figurine, Huger, Girl, Long Hair, Art Deco, Signed, 15 1/2 In. 390.00
Bronze, Figurine, K.B.W., Sitting Monk Reading Book, 7 1/4 In. 40.00
Bronze, Figurine, Knig Tengu, Holding Cauldron, C.1850, 24 In. 400.00
Bronze, Figurine, Knight Standing With His Visor, 14 In. 60.00

Bronze, Figurine, Lady, Art Deco, Saddle At Feet, Colored, Silver Shoes, 7 In. 225.00
Bronze, Figurine, Lanceray, Cossack Chasing Ram, 10 X 8 In. 1300.00
Bronze, Figurine, LeBlanc, Dog With Snail, 7 X 4 In. 450.00
Bronze, Figurine, LeVasseur, C.1850, Vainqueur, Seminude, 14 3/8 In. 175.00
Bronze, Figurine, LeVasseur, Nude Youth With Loincloth, Sword, 14 3/8 In. 325.00
Bronze, Figurine, Lion Roaring, Holding Eagle On Ground, 6 1/2 X 5 In. 325.00
Bronze, Figurine, Lion, Stalking, Marble Base, C.1850, 4 3/8 In. 110.00
Bronze, Figurine, Lion, Stalking, Paws On Orb, C.1850, 13 3/4 In., Pair 550.00
Bronze, Figurine, Llama, Standing, 1 1/4 In. 25.00
Bronze, Figurine, MacMonnies, 1894, Youth & Heron, 27 1/4 In. 1000.00
Bronze, Figurine, Mene, C.1890, Pointer, Gilt, 11 In. 325.00
Bronze, Figurine, Mene, Dog, Pointer, 11 1/2 X 8 In. 500.00
Bronze, Figurine, Mene, Goat, 10 X 6 In. 425.00
Bronze, Figurine, Mene, Mountain Goat, 10 X 6 In. 550.00
Bronze, Figurine, Mene, Pheasant, 7 In. 295.00
Bronze, Figurine, Mene, Pointer, 11 1/2 In.Long, 8 In.High 550.00
Bronze, Figurine, Mene, Whippet With Ball, 10 X 7 In. 350.00
Bronze, Figurine, Mercury, On Left Leg, C.1850, 26 1/4 In. 200.00
Bronze, Figurine, Meunier & Atelier, C.1890, Dock Worker, 19 In. 375.00
Bronze, Figurine, Moigniez, Reeve With Fish In Beak, Dore, 11 1/2 X 9 In. 695.00
Bronze, Figurine, Moreau, Classical Female, Seated, 12 X 11 X 6 In. 475.00
Bronze, Figurine, Moreau, Lady With Ewer, Dark Patina, 12 X 11 In. 425.00
Bronze, Figurine, Moreau, Le Toile Du Matin, Lady With Star On Head, 22 In. 75.00
Bronze, Figurine, Nepalese, C.1850, Cunda, Seated, 6 3/4 In. 90.00
Bronze, Figurine, Nepalese, C.1850, Tara, On Lotus Throne, 6 1/4 In. 100.00
Bronze, Figurine, Nepalese, Tara, Seated On Brocaded Cushion, 7 3/8 In. 175.00
Bronze, Figurine, Nude Lady, Art Nouveau, Frog On Base, 1922, 12 In. 135.00
Bronze, Figurine, Oni, Standing, Holding Cup, C.1850, 22 3/4 In. 350.00
Bronze, Figurine, Owl, On Left Foot, Marble Base, C.1850, 6 1/2 In. 525.00
Bronze, Figurine, Paeef, Doberman Pinscher, 12 X 7 1/2 In. 750.00
Bronze, Figurine, Pandora & Her Box, 7 1/2 X 6 1/2 In. 75.00
Bronze, Figurine, Pautrot, Bird, 7 X 6 In. 325.00
Bronze, Figurine, Perdua & La Stele, C.1890, Lady & Her Cat, 7 In. 90.00
Bronze, Figurine, Perrin, Bull, 5 1/4 X 3 1/2 In. 225.00
Bronze, Figurine, Picault, C.1890, Le Penseur, Eagle On Throne, 18 In. 175.00
Bronze, Figurine, Piniole, Fisherman Casting Life Preserver, 10 In. 165.00
Bronze, Figurine, Pompeiian, Scottie Dog, 5 1/2 X 5 In. .... 25.00 To 35.00
Bronze, Figurine, Proctor, Princeton Tiger, 22 X 10 In. 2500.00
Bronze, Figurine, Puyl, Panther Crouching On Boulder, 10 X 8 In. 195.00
Bronze, Figurine, Ragnault & Jones, C.1890, Executioner, 24 1/2 In. 275.00
Bronze, Figurine, Samurai On Black Stallion, Gilt Lacquer, C.1850, 21 In. 425.00
Bronze, Figurine, Schmidikler, Prussian Soldier, Marble Base, 5 3/4 In. 195.00
Bronze, Figurine, Schwallenbach, Barefoot Peasant Girl, 7 1/2 In. 225.00
Bronze, Figurine, Seifert, C.1890, Nude Woman Kneeling, 17 3/4 In. 325.00
Bronze, Figurine, Shonard, Frog, 5 X 4 In. 550.00
Bronze, Figurine, Silvestre, C.1920, Leda & The Swan, Reclining Nude, 32 In. 375.00
Bronze, Figurine, Solkowski, Goat, Dark Patina, 6 X 5 In. 125.00
Bronze, Figurine, Somme, Lady Holding Jewel Chest, Ivory Head & Hands, 9 In. 425.00
Bronze, Figurine, Spinario, C.1850, 7 In. 90.00
Bronze, Figurine, Stouffer, C.1890, Satyr Astride Goat, 5 In. 180.00
Bronze, Figurine, Susse, C.1890, Nude Girl Dancer, Parcel Gilt, 11 1/2 In. 375.00
Bronze, Figurine, Tengu, Holding Ghanta In Left Hand, C.1850, 16 In. 225.00
Bronze, Figurine, Thai, Hand Of The Buddha, 9 1/2 In. 75.00
Bronze, Figurine, Tibetan, Abbot, Gilt, 3 3/4 In. 70.00
Bronze, Figurine, Tibetan, Buddha, Gilt, 3 5/8 In. 200.00
Bronze, Figurine, Tibetan, C.1750, Abbot, 6 1/8 In. 120.00
Bronze, Figurine, Tibetan, C.1750, Dhyanibuddha Amitayus, Gilt, 8 1/8 In. 325.00
Bronze, Figurine, Tibetan, C.1790, Maitreya As Bodhisattva, Gilt, 5 3/4 In. 425.00
Bronze, Figurine, Tibetan, C.1790, Tara Khadiravani, 6 In. 120.00
Bronze, Figurine, Tibetan, C.1850, Abbot, Seated, 3 3/4 In. 60.00
Bronze, Figurine, Tibetan, Tsong-Kha-Pa, Gilt, 6 1/8 In. 325.00
Bronze, Figurine, Vienna, Bear, Polychrome, 3 In. 75.00
Bronze, Figurine, Vienna, Bear, Polychrome, 5 1/2 X 3 1/2 In. 110.00
Bronze, Figurine, Vienna, Bear, Sitting, Drinking Milk From Bottle, 1 1/8 In. 55.00
Bronze, Figurine, Vienna, Cat Orchestra, Gray Cats, 5 In., 6 Piece 275.00
Bronze, Figurine, Vienna, Cockatoo, Pink, Gray, & White, 10 In. 185.00

Bronze, Figurine, Vienna, Crane, Enameled, 2 1/2 X 2 In. 45.00
Bronze, Figurine, Vienna, Dog In Woman's Glove, 3 X 1 1/2 In. 75.00
Bronze, Figurine, Vienna, Donkey, Enameled, 2 3/4 X 2 In. 45.00
Bronze, Figurine, Vienna, Dutch Boy, Sitting, Crystal Base, 2 X 1 1/4 In. 75.00
Bronze, Figurine, Vienna, Elephant, Pen & Penholder, Marble Base, Miniature 35.00
Bronze, Figurine, Vienna, English Sheepdog, 3 1/2 In. 125.00
Bronze, Figurine, Vienna, Greyhound, 4 In. 95.00
Bronze, Figurine, Vienna, Jockey On Horse, Wooden Plinth, 7 1/2 X 5 3/4 In. 225.00
Bronze, Figurine, Vienna, Magpie, 1 1/2 In. 26.00
Bronze, Figurine, Vienna, Mallard Duck, Sitting Up, 3 X 2 In. 50.00
Bronze, Figurine, Vienna, Negro Boy With Old-Fashioned Telephone, 1 1/8 In. 50.00
Bronze, Figurine, Vienna, Parrot, Green, Red-Topped Head, 5 X 4 In. 135.00
Bronze, Figurine, Vienna, Parrot, Red Head, 5 1/2 X 4 1/2 In. 125.00
Bronze, Figurine, Vienna, Pheasant, Red, Gold, & Brown, 5 1/2 X 2 3/4 In. 95.00
Bronze, Figurine, Vienna, Shetland Sheepdog, 3 1/2 X 3 In. 105.00
Bronze, Figurine, Vienna, Wild Boar, 6 1/2 X 3 In. 150.00
Bronze, Figurine, Vrai, Paris, C.1890, L'Hirondelle De Mere, 36 In. 375.00
Bronze, Figurine, Winged Woman On Marble Ball & Base, 17 In. 395.00
Bronze, Fork, Toasting, Figural, Standing Bear Finial, Victorian, 20 In. 18.00
Bronze, Frame, Picture, French, Vellum, 10 In. Diameter 175.00
Bronze, Group, Barbedienne, C.1890, La Sirene, Gazing At Nude Male, 22 In. 3100.00
Bronze, Group, Barbedienne, C.1890, Satyr & 2 Bear Cubs, 13 In. 300.00
Bronze, Group, Barbedienne, C.1890, 3 Male Runners, 19 1/2 In. 800.00
Bronze, Group, Barge With 5 Passengers & Monkey, C.1850, 3 Ft.3 In. 900.00
Bronze, Group, Benin, Mother With Child, 5 5/8 In. 400.00
Bronze, Group, Bitter, C.1920, Infant Satyr & 2 Fawns, 26 1/4 In .... 400.00 To 450.00
Bronze, Group, Boreas, C.1850, Rape Of Orithyia, 23 In. 300.00
Bronze, Group, Campiaiola, 1913, Biga & A Charioteer, 30 1/2 In. 650.00
Bronze, Group, Chateignon, Lady Knitting & 5 Sheep, C.1850, 13 X 12 In. 750.00
Bronze, Group, Chinese, Tigers Attacking Elephant, Ivory Tusks, 12 X 9 In. 485.00
Bronze, Group, Colin & Cie., C.1890, Electricity, Allegorical, 37 1/2 In. 850.00
Bronze, Group, David, Foot On Goliath's Head, C.1850, 27 1/2 In. 750.00
Bronze, Group, Debucand, 2 Hunting Hounds, 11 1/2 X 6 In. 875.00
Bronze, Group, DeLabriere, Bull Fighting A Dog, 7 1/2 X 4 1/2 In. 325.00
Bronze, Group, Dog Chasing Cat, 7 1/2 X 6 In. 450.00
Bronze, Group, Fratin, C.1890, Hounds Attacking A Boar, 18 In. 600.00
Bronze, Group, Fremiet, C.1890, Cupid Attacking Peacock, 17 In. 875.00
Bronze, Group, Guillemin, 2 Men Fighting Over Card Game, Silver Plate, 8 In. 550.00
Bronze, Group, Herbert, C.1890, Shepherdess & Shepherd, 17 In. 225.00
Bronze, Group, Hercules & Lichas, Gilt, C.1850, 17 In. 500.00
Bronze, Group, Jaquemin, Skaters, Art Deco, Ivory Faces, 14 X 13 In. 700.00
Bronze, Group, Lane, Deer & Stag, Gorham Co., 15 In. 1000.00
Bronze, Group, Mene, 3 Burrowing Dogs, 15 X 8 1/2 In. 750.00
Bronze, Group, Moigniez, Birds In Marshes, Dore, 10 X 8 In. 650.00
Bronze, Group, Naps, C.1890, Barefoot Boy On Horse, Dog, 8 1/8 In. 1200.00
Bronze, Group, Romulus & Remus Being Suckled By She Wolf, 6 In. 125.00
Bronze, Group, Russian, C.1850, Horse Pulling Man In Cart, 10 In. 700.00
Bronze, Group, Saku, C.1850, Manchurian Cranes & Turtles, 24 In. 275.00
Bronze, Group, Susse, C.1920, Infant Satyr & 2 Panthers, 31 1/4 In. 700.00
Bronze, Group, Vienna, Bulldogs, Tan & Brown, 2 X 1 In. 45.00
Bronze, Group, Vienna, Elephant In Washtub, Negro Boy Washing Him, 7/8 In. 55.00
Bronze, Group, Vienna, Lovebirds Facing Each Other, Colored, 2 3/4 In. 75.00
Bronze, Group, Vienna, Negro Girl & Boy Sitting On Bench, 2 1/2 X 1 3/4 In. 95.00
Bronze, Group, Vienna, 2 Dancing Mice, Enameled, 3 X 2 In. 65.00
Bronze, Group, Vienna, 2 Negro Children On Movable Seesaw, 1 3/4 In. 50.00
Bronze, Group, Vienna, 3 Negro Acrobats On Seated Elephant, 1 1/2 In. 60.00
Bronze, Group, Wolff, C.1890, Horse Pulling Woman & Man On Wagon, 15 In. 2100.00
Bronze, Helmet, Russian, C.1890, Order Of St.Andrew, Gilt, 4 1/2 In. 1100.00
Bronze, Humidor, Sterling Trim, Signed, No.2609, 6 1/4 X 5 3/4 In. 110.00
Bronze, Inkwell, Basket Weave Design, Sea Life In Relief, 2 1/2 X 1 1/2 In. 35.00
Bronze, Inkwell, Indian's Head Cover, Feathers In Hair, 4 In. 70.00
Bronze, Inkwell, Jester's Head Lid, 6 X 4 In. 75.00
Bronze, Jar, Incense, Foo Dog Finial, Champleve Cloisonne Band, Footed 67.50
Bronze, Knife, Letter, Austrian, Owl With Amethyst Eyes On Handle, 10 In. 18.00
Bronze, Letter Opener, Al Smith's Garage, Hudson-Essex Service, Ma., 8 In. 3.95

Bronze, Letter Opener, Centenary Pawtucket Royal Arch Chapter, 1820-1920	4.95
Bronze, Letter Opener, Combination Ruler, Blue Porcelain Medallion, 9 In.	4.00
Bronze, Letter Opener, Garland Mfg.Co., Loom Harnesses, Me., 9 1/4 In,	3.95
Bronze, Letter Opener, Knox & Morse Co., Waxes & Gums, Ma., 8 In.	3.95
Bronze, Letter Opener, Metropolitan Life Insurance Co., 8 3/4 In.	2.95
Bronze, Letter Opener, Quaker State Motor Oils, 7 3/4 In.	3.75
Bronze, Match Container, Rosettes & Scrolls, Striker On Base, 2 1/4 In.	12.75
Bronze, Mirror, Japanese, Birds & Trees, Calligraphy On Back, 7 In.	55.00
Bronze, Mirror, Japanese, Storklike Birds, 8 In. Diameter	85.00
Bronze, Nutcracker, Rooster	15.00
Bronze, Palette, Painter's, 12 In. Tubular Handle, Hinged Covered Pot	150.00
Bronze, Plaque, Calverly, Lincoln, 10 1/2 In.	60.00
Bronze, Plaque, Commemorative, Nurse Edith Cavell, 5 1/2 X 7 1/2 In.	25.00
Bronze, Plaque, French, C.1850, Religious Procession, 5 3/4 In.	10.00
Bronze, Plaque, Germany, 1918, Deer In Woodland Scene, 10 1/2 X 7 3/8 In.	110.00
Bronze, Plaque, Gorham, 1931, Washington Bicentennial, 8 In.	24.00
Bronze, Plaque, Left Profile Of Abraham Lincoln, 6 3/4 X 4 1/2 In.	65.00
Bronze, Plaque, Lindbergh, 7 X 5 In.	35.00
Bronze, Plaque, Paul Manship, 1927, 5 1/2 In.	185.00
Bronze, Plaque, Paul Manship, 5 1/2 In.	150.00
Bronze, Plaque, Profile James A.Garfield, 5 X 7 1/2 In.	85.00
Bronze, Plaque, Reliance Lock, Dec.1851, Shield Shape, Red Paint, 9 1/2 In.	25.00
Bronze, Plaque, Scharda, Cesso Obec Sokolska, Czechoslovakia, 13 In.	150.00
Bronze, Seal, Art Nouveau Lady, 5 In.	55.00
Bronze, Seal, Devil With Large Wings, Holds Long Horn, 9 1/2 In.High	190.00
Bronze, Spoon, Figural, Miner, Bowl Is Spade, 6 1/2 In.	42.00
Bronze, Tazza, AC, Insects, Floral, & 2 Cranes Catching Fish, 7 In.	295.00
Bronze, Tray, Art Nouveau Flowers, Leaves, & Stems, Stem Handles, 11 X 8 In.	90.00
Bronze, Tray, Art Nouveau, Relief Flowers, 11 X 8 In.	90.00
Bronze, Tray, Pin, Gorham, Applied Silver Bird & Flower, 5 1/2 X 4 In.	15.00
Bronze, Tray, Teresezezuk, C.1895, 2 Females, Dog, Moose, & Swan, 17 1/2 In.	225.00
Bronze, Urn, Dragon Holding Tama In Claw At Neck, C.1850, 10 In.	60.00
Bronze, Urn, 4 Bacchanalian Heads In Relief, Footed, 17 In.	145.00
Bronze, Vase, Applied Dragon At Neck, Trumpet Shape, C.1850, 22 1/8 In.	300.00
Bronze, Vase, Bulbous, Chased, Fish In Water, Birds In Bamboo, 9 In., Pair	125.00
Bronze, Vase, Carl Sorenson, 8 1/2 In., Pair	75.00
Bronze, Vase, Chinese, Champleve Enamel, C.1750, 8 5/8 In.	85.00
Bronze, Vase, J.Marionnet, C.1900, Parcel Gilt, Grapes & Vines, 15 In., Pair	275.00
Bronze, Vase, Korean, Koryo Dynasty, Ring Foot, Tear Shape, 12 In.	250.00
Bronze, Vase, Seifusai Buntei, C.1850, Plum Trunks, Eagle With Snake, 28 In.	300.00
Bronze, Vase, Stick, Japanese, Elephants' Heads Handles, C.1850, 11 In.	55.00
Bronze, Vase, Trumpet, Gouli Meddor, Art Nouveau Lady's Bust, 8 In.	175.00
Bronze, Vase, Turtles, Wood Stand, C.1850, 9 1/2 In.	650.00
Bronze, Vase, Wani Supporting Lantern Base, C.1850, 25 In., Pair	675.00
Bronze, Wax Seal, Mummy Case, Opens, Nude Girl Inside	225.00
Brownie, Book, Another Brownie Book, Palmer Cox, 1890, 8 1/2 X 10 In.	17.00
Brownie, Book, Around The World, Palmer Cox, 1894, 10 X 8 1/2 In.	17.00
Brownie, Book, Many More Nights, Cox, 1913	45.00
Brownie, Book, The Brownies Abroad, Hard Cover, 1899	20.00
Brownie, Book, Their Book, Palmer Cox, 1887, 8 1/2 X 10 In.	17.00
Brownie, Book, Through The Union, Palmer Cox, 1895, 8 1/2 X 10 In.	17.00
Brownie, Box, Embossed Metal, 3 1/2 In.	20.00
Brownie, Butterpat, Palmer Cox, Chinaman Brownie, TST Mark, 3 1/4 In.	8.00
Brownie, Cup & Saucer, Cox, Brownies Playing Tug Of War	44.00
Brownie, Fork, Palmer Cox	6.00
Brownie, Knife, Palmer Cox	6.00
Brownie, Mug, Brown Matte Glaze, 7 Brownies, 6 In.	75.00
Brownie, Music Sheet, Dance Of The Brownies, Palmer Cox, 1895	15.00
Brownie, Pin, Little Pinkies, The Sailor, Dated 1890, Pepsin Gum Co.	8.00
Brownie, Plate, Crimped, Goat In Center, Gold Rim, 7 In.	30.00
Brownie, Plate, Palmer Cox, 7 In.	9.50
Brownie, Ring Toss, Palmer Cox, Tin	12.00
Brownie, Saltshaker, Palmer Cox Brownies, Satin Finish	30.00
Brownie, Sauce, Palmer Cox, 3 Brownies, TST Mark, 4 1/2 In.	10.00
Brownie, Stamp, Rubber	3.00

Brownie, Tea Set, Doll's, Dancing Brownies, Service For 4 .... 85.00
Brownie, Vase, Pixie Leaning On Tree Trunk, Palmer Cox, Japan, C.1920, 5 In. 22.00
Buck Rogers, Gun, Sonic Ray, Flashlight 16.00
Buck Rogers, Gun, Sonic Ray, Official .... 25.00 To 32.50
Buck Rogers, Gun, Sonic Ray, 1950s 18.50
Buck Rogers, Gun, U235 Atomic, Daisy Mfg.Co., Boxed 55.00
Buck Rogers, Pistol, Water, Metal, Paint 55.00

Buffalo pottery was made in Buffalo, New York, after 1902. The company was established by the Larkin Company, famous manufacturers of soap. The wares are marked with a picture of a buffalo and the date of manufacture. Deldare ware is the most famous pottery made at the factory. It is a khaki-colored transfer-decorated ware.

Buffalo Pottery, see also Blue Willow
Buffalo Pottery, Bedpan, White High Glaze, Standing Buffalo 22.00
Buffalo Pottery, Deldare, Bowl, Cereal, Fallowfield Hunt, The Start, 6 In. 75.00
Buffalo Pottery, Deldare, Bowl, Cereal, Ye Olden Days, 6 In. 75.00
Buffalo Pottery, Deldare, Bowl, Dated 1908, 9 In. 210.00
Buffalo Pottery, Deldare, Bowl, Fallowfield Hunt, Breaking Cover, 9 In. 275.00
Buffalo Pottery, Deldare, Candleholder, Shieldback, Village Life 475.00
Buffalo Pottery, Deldare, Charger, Fallowfield Hunt, The Start, 1908, 14 In. 650.00
Buffalo Pottery, Deldare, Creamer, Village Life, 1909, 2 1/2 In. .... 65.00 To 175.00
Buffalo Pottery, Deldare, Cup & Saucer, Ye Olden Days, 1909 .... 115.00 To 125.00
Buffalo Pottery, Deldare, Cup & Saucer, Ye Village Street, A.Hall 125.00
Buffalo Pottery, Deldare, Humidor 450.00
Buffalo Pottery, Deldare, Jar, Tobacco 275.00
Buffalo Pottery, Deldare, Mug, Ye Lion Inn 135.00
Buffalo Pottery, Deldare, Pitcher, Manner Of Telling Stories, 6 1/2 In. 175.00
Buffalo Pottery, Deldare, Pitcher, To Spare A Soldier, 7 1/4 In. 210.00
Buffalo Pottery, Deldare, Plaque, Breakfast At Three Pigeons, 11 1/2 In. 215.00
Buffalo Pottery, Deldare, Plaque, Ye Lion Inn, 12 In. 350.00
Buffalo Pottery, Deldare, Plate, Art Nouveau, 8 1/4 In. 235.00
Buffalo Pottery, Deldare, Plate, At Ye Lion Inn, 6 1/4 In. .... 75.00 To 115.00
Buffalo Pottery, Deldare, Plate, Bread & Butter, No.172, 6 1/4 In. 72.50
Buffalo Pottery, Deldare, Plate, Chop, Fallowfield & 3 Pigeons, Laney, 13 In. 265.00
Buffalo Pottery, Deldare, Plate, Chop, Fallowfield Hunt, 14 In. 375.00
Buffalo Pottery, Deldare, Plate, Dr.Syntax Soliloquising, Emerald, 7 1/4 In. 245.00
Buffalo Pottery, Deldare, Plate, Dr.Syntax, Courtship, Emerald, 10 In. 320.00
Buffalo Pottery, Deldare, Plate, Dr.Syntax, Floral Offering, Emerald, 6 In. 180.00
Buffalo Pottery, Deldare, Plate, Emerald, 1911, 8 In. .... *Illus* 325.00
Buffalo Pottery, Deldare, Plate, Fallowfield Hunt, Breaking Cover, 10 In. 125.00
Buffalo Pottery, Deldare, Plate, Fallowfield Hunt, Death, Sheehan, 1909, 9 In. 125.00
Buffalo Pottery, Deldare, Plate, Fallowfield Hunt, The Start, 1908, 9 1/4 In. 150.00
Buffalo Pottery, Deldare, Plate, Fallowfield Hunt, The Start, 9 1/4 In. 165.00
Buffalo Pottery, Deldare, Plate, Fallowfield Hunt, 6 1/4 In. 70.00

Buffalo Pottery, Deldare, Plate,
Emerald, 1911, 8 In.

Buffalo Pottery, Deldare, Plate, Fallowfield Hunt, 9 In.	95.00
Buffalo Pottery, Deldare, Plate, Fallowfield Hunt, 9 1/2 In.	150.00
Buffalo Pottery, Deldare, Plate, Fallowfield Hunt, 10 1/2 In.	145.00
Buffalo Pottery, Deldare, Plate, J.Gerhardt, 1908, 7 1/2 In.	59.50
Buffalo Pottery, Deldare, Plate, Ye Olden Times, P.Hall, 1909, 9 1/4 In.	95.00
Buffalo Pottery, Deldare, Plate, Ye Olden Times, 1909, 9 3/4 In.	97.50
Buffalo Pottery, Deldare, Plate, Ye Town Crier, L.Newman, 8 1/4 In.	100.00
Buffalo Pottery, Deldare, Plate, Ye Town Crier, 1908, 8 3/8 In.	85.00
Buffalo Pottery, Deldare, Plate, Ye Town Crier, 8 1/2 In.	110.00 To 120.00
Buffalo Pottery, Deldare, Plate, Ye Village Gossips, Fazter, 1908, 10 1/4 In.	170.00
Buffalo Pottery, Deldare, Plate, Ye Village Gossips, L.Streissel, 10 In.	115.00
Buffalo Pottery, Deldare, Plate, Ye Village Gossips, M.Laird, 10 In.	125.00
Buffalo Pottery, Deldare, Plate, Ye Village Gossips, 1908, 10 In.	115.00 To 250.00
Buffalo Pottery, Deldare, Plate, Ye Village Street, E.Hacker, 1908, 7 1/4 In.	100.00
Buffalo Pottery, Deldare, Plate, Ye Village Street, H.Ford, 7 1/2 In.	95.00
Buffalo Pottery, Deldare, Sugar, Covered, Village Life, G.H.S., 1925	125.00
Buffalo Pottery, Deldare, Tankard, Ye Village Street, 1909, 9 In.	225.00
Buffalo Pottery, Deldare, Teapot, Village Life, 6 Sided	225.00
Buffalo Pottery, Deldare, Tile, Tea, Fallowfield Hunt, Breaking Cover	110.00
Buffalo Pottery, Deldare, Tray, Calling Card, Dr.Syntax	250.00
Buffalo Pottery, Deldare, Tray, Dancing Ye Minuet, L.Anna, 12 X 9 1/4 In.	300.00
Buffalo Pottery, Deldare, Tray, Dresser, Dancing Ye Minuet, 9 X 12 In.	265.00
Buffalo Pottery, Deldare, Vase, Village Scenes, 7 In.	135.00 To 235.00
Buffalo Pottery, Dish, Feeding, Campbell Kids, Signed Drayton	35.00
Buffalo Pottery, Feeder, Child's, Little Bopeep, No.611	11.00
Buffalo Pottery, Fish Set, Signed R.K.Beck, 7 Piece	115.00
Buffalo Pottery, Jar, Mustard, Hotel, Maroon On White, C.1910	4.25
Buffalo Pottery, Jug, Dutch, Dated 1907	130.00
Buffalo Pottery, Luncheon Set, Bluebird, 1919, Service For 6	140.00
Buffalo Pottery, Mug, Calumet Club, Buffalo, N.Y., Jan.26, 1915, Green, 5 In.	55.00
Buffalo Pottery, Mug, Calumet Club, 1913	55.00
Buffalo Pottery, Mug, Saturn Club, 1914	55.00
Buffalo Pottery, Pitcher, George Washington, 1907, 7 1/2 In.	135.00 To 180.00
Buffalo Pottery, Pitcher, Milk, Cinderella, Signed, Dated 1907	265.00
Buffalo Pottery, Plate, Bluebird China, 7 1/2 In.	3.00
Buffalo Pottery, Plate, Christmas, 1957	25.00
Buffalo Pottery, Plate, Christmas, 1958	25.00
Buffalo Pottery, Plate, Faneuil Hall, Blue, 10 1/4 In.	32.00
Buffalo Pottery, Plate, General Wolfe, Portraits & Monument, 1908, 7 1/2 In.	65.00
Buffalo Pottery, Plate, Niagara Falls, Blue & White, 10 In.	23.00
Buffalo Pottery, Plate, Niagara Falls, Green, 7 1/2 In.	18.00
Buffalo Pottery, Plate, Niagara Falls, 7 3/4 In.	20.00
Buffalo Pottery, Plate, The Gunner, Dated 1907, 9 1/4 In.	52.00
Buffalo Pottery, Plate, Vienna, 9 In.	5.00
Buffalo Pottery, Plate, White House, Dark Blue Green, 7 1/2 In.	42.00
Buffalo Pottery, Platter, Buffalo Hunt, 11 1/4 X 14 In.	55.00
Buffalo Pottery, Pot, Cream, Hotel, Brown On Buff, C.1910	3.25
Buffalo Pottery, Sugar & Creamer, Forget-Me-Not	30.00
Buffalo Pottery, Sugar, Hotel, Green On White, C.1910	4.00
Buffalo Pottery, Sugar, Hotel, Maroon On White, C.1910	4.00
Buffalo Pottery, Teapot, Argyle, Blue & White, 1914	25.00 To 32.50
Buffalo Pottery, Teapot, Blue On White Argyle, Gold Trim, 1911	20.00

*Burmese glass was developed by Frederick Shirley at the Mt.Washington
Glass Works in New Bedford, Massachusetts, in 1885. It is a two-toned
glass, shading from peach to yellow. Some have a pattern mold design. A few
Burmese pieces were decorated with pictures or applied glass flowers of
colored Burmese glass.*

Burmese, see also Gunderson

Burmese, Condiment Set, Mt.Washington, Pairpoint Silver Holder, 3 Piece	350.00
Burmese, Creamer, Mt.Washington, Fluted Top, Applied Handle, 2 1/2 In.	395.00
Burmese, Cruet, 6 In.	250.00
Burmese, Lamp, Fairy, Signed Clarke Base, 5 In.	225.00
Burmese, Nappy, Mt.Washington, Handled, 5 In.	350.00
Burmese, Pear, Mt.Washington, Shiny	175.00
Burmese, Pitcher, Pairpoint Bryden, 3 In.	45.00 To 55.00

Burmese, Pitcher, Scalloped Top, Applied Reeded Handle, 7 In. 75.00
Burmese, Pitcher, Water, Mt.Washington, Applied Yellow Handle, 1/2 Gallon 795.00
Burmese, Rose Bowl, Mt.Washington, Hobnail, Applied Yellow Rigaree, 3 In. 450.00
Burmese, Rose Bowl, Yellow & Salmon Turned-In Scalloped Rim, 2 1/2 In. 265.00
Burmese, Rose Bowl, 6 Sided, 2 1/2 In. 265.00
Burmese, Salt & Pepper, Mt.Washington, Pewter Tops 295.00
Burmese, Sugar, Mt.Washington 375.00
Burmese, Sugar, Mt.Washington, 3 Footed 310.00
Burmese, Toothpick, Mt.Washington, Glossy, Tricorn, Venetian Diamond, 2 In. 335.00
Burmese, Toothpick, Mt.Washington, Tricorner, Venetian Diamond, 3 In. 335.00
Burmese, Toothpick, Mt.Washington, Venetian Diamond, Square Top 350.00
Burmese, Toothpick, Mt.Washington, 2 1/2 In.High 225.00
Burmese, Toothpick, Satin, Melon Sections, Blue Forget-Me-Nots 275.00
Burmese, Toothpick, Tricornered, Applied Pastel Beads, Floral, Satin Finish 350.00
Burmese, Toothpick, Tricornered, Hand-Painted Florals, 2 In. 300.00
Burmese, Tumbler, Diamond-Quilted 295.00
Burmese, Tumbler, Lemonade, Ring Handle Near Base, Lemon To Pink 325.00
Burmese, Tumbler, Mt.Washington, Acid, Salmon Pink To Base 185.00
Burmese, Tumbler, Three-Fired 250.00
Burmese, Tumbler, Whiskey, Mt.Washington, Diamond-Quilted, 2 7/8 In. 195.00
Burmese, Vase, Ball Shape, Flared Ruffled Rim, 3 In. 300.00
Burmese, Vase, Five Petals Turned In At Top, 4 In. 265.00
Burmese, Vase, Mt.Washington, Lilac Enameled Flowers & Leaves, Ovoid, 10 In. 475.00
Burmese, Vase, Mt.Washington, 2 Monkeys, Encrusted Gold Leaf, 14 In. 2350.00
Burmese, Vase, Pink To Yellow, Hexagonal Top, Acid Finish, 2 1/2 In. 180.00
Burmese, Vase, Ruffled Rim, Bulbous, Satin Finish, 3 1/4 In. 300.00
Burmese, Vase, Stick, Enameled Flowers & Leaves, Mt.Washington, 5 In. 1150.00
Burmese, Vase, Stick, Mt.Washington, Variation Queen's Design, Acid, 10 In. 1200.00
Burmese, Vase, Urn Shape, Pink To Lemon, 2 Handles, 8 In. 450.00
    Burmese, Webb, see Webb Burmese
Buster Brown, Camera, Box, Album & Instructions 16.00
Buster Brown, Clicker, Advertising 5.00
Buster Brown, Creamer, Buster & Tige, Porcelain 37.00
Buster Brown, Cup & Saucer, Buster & Tige, Porcelain 35.00
Buster Brown, Neckerchief, Buster & Tige, Slide Clip, Pictures 22.00
Buster Brown, Noisemaker, Tige, Cricket, Advertising Shoes 18.00
Buster Brown, Periscope 3.00
Buster Brown, Spoon 15.00
Buster Brown, Teapot, Buster & Tige, Ornate Shape, Porcelain 65.00
    Buttermilk Glass, see Custard Glass

    Buttons have been known throughout the centuries, and there are millions of
    styles. Only a few of the most common types are listed for comparison.
    Button, see also Carnival Glass, Button, Centennial, Button,
    Coronation, Button, Store, Button, Wedgwood, Button
Button, Santa Claus, Pinback, Merry Christmas & Happy New Year, 1 1/2 In. 1.25
    Buttonhook, see Art Nouveau, Buttonhook, Brass, Buttonhook, Silver,
    Sterling, Buttonhook, Store, Buttonhook
    Calcite, see also Steuben
Calcite, Vase, Pedestal Base, 4 1/2 In. 65.00

    Calendar plates were very popular in the United States from 1906 to 1929.
    Since then plates have been made every year. A calendar, the name of a
    store, a picture of flowers, a girl, or a scene was featured on the plate.
Calendar Plate, 1909, Cherries, Wreaths Around Months, 7 1/2 In. 15.00
Calendar Plate, 1909, Coalinga, California, Holly & Berries, Rose, 9 In. 18.00
Calendar Plate, 1909, Green Bird In Center, 8 1/2 In. 17.00
Calendar Plate, 1909, Horse's Head Center, 9 In. 14.00
Calendar Plate, 1909, Lancaster, Pa., Holly, Gold & Green Border, 8 In. 16.00
Calendar Plate, 1909, Pink Roses & Buds Center, Scenes, 9 In. 16.00
Calendar Plate, 1909, Roses & Buds Center, Scenes Around Border, 9 In. 18.00
Calendar Plate, 1909, Roses In Center, Spring & Winter Scene, Green, 8 In. 16.50
Calendar Plate, 1910, Breslin, New York, Holly, 7 1/2 In. 10.00
Calendar Plate, 1910, Indian's Portrait, 7 3/4 In. 29.00
Calendar Plate, 1910, Old Swimming Hole, Verse, 7 1/4 In. 25.75
Calendar Plate, 1911, Betsy Ross, 8 1/2 In. 18.00

Calendar Plate, 1911, Clock Vases, Violets In Center, 8 3/8 In.	17.00
Calendar Plate, 1911, Flower Pods & Foliage In Center, 8 1/4 In.	16.00
Calendar Plate, 1911, Portrait Of Young Girl With Green Hat, 9 In.	15.00
Calendar Plate, 1912, Lady, Sporting Items By Month, 9 In.	24.00
Calendar Plate, 1912, Natural Bridge, Va., 8 5/8 In.	18.00
Calendar Plate, 1912, Owl On Open Book, 8 1/2 In.	22.00
Calendar Plate, 1913, Aircraft Over Coastal Town, 9 1/4 In.	20.00
Calendar Plate, 1913, Horseshoe, Two Horses' Heads, 7 In.	14.00
Calendar Plate, 1913, Robin On Heart-Shaped Florals, 8 In.	24.00
Calendar Plate, 1920, Victory, 9 In.	22.50
Calendar Plate, 1954, Blue On White, 10 In.	12.00
Calendar Plate, 1961, English Country Scene, 9 In.	14.00
Calendar Plate, 1967, House Scene, Sepia & White, Meakin, 9 In.	4.00
California Faience, Tile, Flower Basket On Blue, Round, 5 1/4 In.	5.00
California Faience, Tile, Spanish Mission Church, Round, 5 In.	35.00
Camark, Bowl, Turquoise, Double Shell, Impressed Mark, 12 X 5 1/2 In.	10.00
Camark, Bowl, Turquoise, 9 1/2 X 3 1/2 In.	5.00
Camark, Jardiniere, Fall Leaves On High Gloss Brown Ground, Fluted Rim	85.00
Camark, Vase, Classic Shape, Blue & Green Mottled Matte Glaze, Figure, 20 In	100.00

CAMBRIDGE

Cambridge art pottery was made in Cambridge, Ohio, from about 1895 until World War I. The factory made brown glazed decorated wares marked with a variety of marks including an acorn, the name Cambridge, the name Oakwood, or the name Terrhea.

Cambridge Pottery, Creamer, Browns, Silver Deposit, Art Deco Design, 3 In.	88.00
Cambridge Pottery, Creamer, Guernsey Cooking Ware, Brown, Silver Overlay	125.00
Cambridge Pottery, Ewer, Oakwood, Marked, 7 1/2 In.	150.00
Cambridge Pottery, Jug, Waldorf, Ear Of Corn, 2 Tone Brown Metallic, 6 In.	100.00
Cambridge Pottery, Vase, Oakwood, Green, Brown, & Blue, Marked, 5 1/2 In.	85.00
Cambridge Pottery, Vase, Oakwood, Whites, Greens, & Yellows On Brown, 4 In.	100.00
Cambridge Pottery, Vase, Standard Glaze, Floral, Marked CAP, 5 In.	150.00
Cambridge Pottery, Vase, Terrhea, Marked Terrhea CAP, 10 In.	210.00

C

The Cambridge Glass Company made pressed glass in Cambridge, Ohio. It was marked with a C in a triangle about 1902. The words "near-cut" were used after 1906.

Cambridge, Ashtray Set, Blue, Crystal, & Yellow, Caprice, Nest Of 3	15.00
Cambridge, Ashtray, Amethyst, Gadroon, Square, 3 In.	2.00
Cambridge, Ashtray, Blue, Seashell, 3 Footed	4.00
Cambridge, Ashtray, Crown Tuscan, Nude, Black Base	85.00
Cambridge, Ashtray, Crown Tuscan, 5 In.	11.00
Cambridge, Ashtray, Topaz, Seashell, 3 Footed	4.00
Cambridge, Basket, Thistle, Applied Reeded Handle, 7 1/4 In.	45.00
Cambridge, Bonbon, Wildflower, Handled, Gold Encrusted, 7 In.	10.00
Cambridge, Bottle, Cordial, Royal Blue, 120 Ozs.	22.00
Cambridge, Bowl & Base, Tomato Glass, 10 In.	80.00
Cambridge, Bowl & Underplate, Mayonnaise, Wildflower, Footed Bowl	15.00
Cambridge, Bowl, Amber Insert, Handled Farber Tray With Spoon, Oval, 7 In.	14.00
Cambridge, Bowl, Amethyst, Farber Bros. Metal Holder, 7 1/2 In.	20.00
Cambridge, Bowl, Amethyst, Gold Thistles & Leaves, 4 Toed, 12 In.	90.00
Cambridge, Bowl, Amethyst, Square, 6 In.	7.00
Cambridge, Bowl, Berry, Green, Marked, 5 1/2 In.	1.65
Cambridge, Bowl, Blue, Parrot, 8 1/2 In.	35.00
Cambridge, Bowl, Candy, Crown Tuscan, Oval Shell, Shell Feet	48.00
Cambridge, Bowl, Caprice, Silver Deposit Leaves, Handled, Oval, 12 X 4 In.	22.00
Cambridge, Bowl, Caprice, Sterling Silver Overlay, 4 Footed, 13 X 4 In.	28.00
Cambridge, Bowl, Center, Octagon Thumbprint, 9 In.	150.00
Cambridge, Bowl, Centerpiece, Experimental Tomato Glass	125.00
Cambridge, Bowl, Console, Green, Heavy Gold Border	35.00
Cambridge, Bowl, Console, Heliotrope, 11 1/2 In.	65.00
Cambridge, Bowl, Console, Tomato Glass, 10 1/2 In.	90.00
Cambridge, Bowl, Crown Tuscan, Globe, 5 1/2 In.	20.00
Cambridge, Bowl, Emerald Green, Mt.Vernon, Oval, 13 In.	18.00
Cambridge, Bowl, Etched Lorna, 13 In.	22.00
Cambridge, Bowl, Fruit, Jade, 12 In.Diameter	80.00
Cambridge, Bowl, Green, Crimped, 4 Footed, 13 In.	19.00

Cambridge, Bowl, Green, Inverted Thistle, Gold In Design, Near Cut, 9 In. 58.00
Cambridge, Bowl, Green, 3 Sections, Farber Bottom, 6 1/2 X 3 In. 14.00
Cambridge, Bowl, Helio, Gold Band, 10 X 3 In. 47.50
Cambridge, Bowl, Inverted Strawberry, 6 1/2 In. 35.00
Cambridge, Bowl, Inverted Thistle, Scalloped, Gold Trim, Near-Cut, 9 In. 55.00
Cambridge, Bowl, Jade, 10 In. 30.00
Cambridge, Bowl, La Rosa Alpine, Footed, 10 1/2 X 4 1/2 In. 23.00
Cambridge, Bowl, Milk Glass, Seashell, Footed, 4 1/2 In. 18.00
Cambridge, Bowl, Moonlight, Caprice, Scalloped Edge, 4 Footed, 13 In. 15.00
Cambridge, Bowl, Roselyn, Etched, 2 Handles, 7 X 2 In. 12.00
Cambridge, Bowl, Rosepoint, Fluted, 12 In. 28.00
Cambridge, Bowl, Serving, Blue, Caprice 22.50
Cambridge, Bowl, Trinket, Crown Tuscan, Elephant, Patina Frame, 3 In. 25.00
Cambridge, Box, Candy, Covered, Crown Tuscan, 3 Compartments 38.00
Cambridge, Box, Cigarette, Covered, Caprice 15.00
Cambridge, Box, Cigarette, Covered, Crown Tuscan, Dolphin Footed .... 15.00 To 32.00
Cambridge, Box, Cigarette, Covered, Crystal, Nude Figure, 7 1/2 In. 55.00
Cambridge, Box, Cigarette, Crystal, Nude Figure, Carmen 45.00
Cambridge, Box, Covered, Crown Tuscan, Shell, Dolphin Feet, 4 X 3 In. 47.50
Cambridge, Box, Covered, Crown Tuscan, Shell, 5 X 4 In. 38.00
Cambridge, Box, Covered, Etched, Round, Farber Reticulated Tray, 4 1/2 In. 12.00
Cambridge, Box, Covered, Shell, Dolphin Feet, 4 X 4 In. 50.00
Cambridge, Box, Covered, Tricornered, Set In Metal Art Deco Nudes, 8 X 5 In. 29.00
Cambridge, Box, Crown Tuscan, Seashell, Dolphin Feet, Gold Trim, 5 X 4 In. 40.00
Cambridge, Box, Flowered Farber Cover, Handled, 7 In. Long 11.00
Cambridge, Bridge Set, Pink, Etched No.704, 5 Piece 17.50
Cambridge, Bucket, Ice, Black Glass, Tongs, Signed 12.00
Cambridge, Bucket, Ice, Frosted & Crystal, Caprice 3.50
Cambridge, Bucket, Ice, Pink, Signed 42.50
Cambridge, Butter, Pink, Chrome Top, Signed 10.00
Cambridge, Butter, Rosepoint, Covered 18.00
Cambridge, Cake Stand, Squared Daisy & Diamond 12.00
Cambridge, Candelabra, Three Light, Clear, 11 X 13 1/2 In. 75.00
Cambridge, Candleholder, Caprice, Prism, 7 In., Pair 17.00
Cambridge, Candlestick, Amberina, Red To Amber To Red, 8 1/2 In.High, Pair 65.00
Cambridge, Candlestick, Black Amethyst, Twisted Stems, 10 1/4 In, Pair 34.00
Cambridge, Candlestick, Blue, Caprice, Single Prism, 7 1/2 In., Pair 24.00
Cambridge, Candlestick, Crystal, Everglades, Footed, Flared, 2 1/2 In., Pair 18.00
Cambridge, Candlestick, Experimental Tomato Glass, 9 In., Pair 125.00
Cambridge, Candlestick, Jade, Twisted Stem, 10 1/2 In., Pair 45.00
Cambridge, Candlestick, Jade, 8 1/2 In.High, Pair 47.50
Cambridge, Candlestick, Red Slag, 8 1/2 In. 150.00
Cambridge, Candlestick, Red, Carmen, 2 1/2 In., Pair 25.00
Cambridge, Candlestick, Ring Stem, 5 In., Pair 17.50
Cambridge, Candlestick, Tomato Glass, 9 In., Pair 95.00
Cambridge, Celery, Apple Green, 10 1/4 In. 20.00
Cambridge, Celery, Blockade 20.00
Cambridge, Celery, Rosepoint 14.00
Cambridge, Centerpiece, Primrose, Swan, 13 X 7 In. 145.00
Cambridge, Champagne, Rosepoint .... 12.00 To 15.00
Cambridge, Champagne, Topaz, Versailles 6.00
Cambridge, Cigarette Set, Crown Tuscan, Box & 2 Ashtrays 45.00
Cambridge, Compote, Crown Tuscan, Nude Supporting Shell, 5 1/2 In. 85.00
Cambridge, Compote, Crown Tuscan, Seashell, Nude Standard, 8 In. 75.00
Cambridge, Compote, Crown Tuscan, Seashell, 7 In. 45.00
Cambridge, Compote, Crystal, Nude Figure, Carmen Top, 8 1/2 In. 85.00
Cambridge, Compote, Helio, Sweet Pea, Footed, 6 1/4 In. 28.00
Cambridge, Compote, Ivory, 9 1/2 In. 38.00
Cambridge, Compote, Royal Blue, Ring Stem, 5 1/2 In. 40.00
Cambridge, Compote, Tomato Glass, Black Base, 5 X 7 In. 80.00
Cambridge, Compote, Tomato Glass, 7 X 5 In. 95.00
Cambridge, Compote, Tomato Glass, 7 X 7 In. 135.00
Cambridge, Console Set, Amber, 3 Piece 65.00
Cambridge, Console Set, Amethyst, Gadroon, Marked C In Circle, 3 Piece 35.00
Cambridge, Console Set, Azurite, 3 Piece 50.00
Cambridge, Console Set, Crown Tuscan, Flying Lady, 3 Piece 300.00

Cambridge, Console Set, Ivory, 3 Piece 125.00
Cambridge, Console Set, Jade, 3 Piece 90.00
Cambridge, Console Set, Primrose, Black & Gold Greek Key Band, 3 Piece 125.00
Cambridge, Cordial Set, Amethyst, Farber Holders, 6 Piece 55.00
Cambridge, Cornucopia, Milk Glass, 3 1/4 In. 15.00
Cambridge, Creamer, Colonial, Miniature .... 9.75 To 16.00
Cambridge, Cruet Set, Blue, Caprice, 3 Piece 40.00
Cambridge, Cruet Set, Etched Floral, Tray, Signed, 3 Piece 35.00
Cambridge, Cup & Saucer, Amber 5.00
Cambridge, Cup & Saucer, Bouillon, Amber, Marked 32.00
Cambridge, Cup & Saucer, Clear Cup, Black Saucer, Signed 7.00
Cambridge, Cup & Saucer, Rosepoint 18.00
Cambridge, Cup & Saucer, Topaz, Versailles, Footed 6.00
Cambridge, Cup, Caprice 6.00
Cambridge, Cup, Nut, Diane, Marked C, Set Of 6 .... 50.00
Cambridge, Cup, Punch, Crystal, Swan, 5 Ozs. 2.00
Cambridge, Decanter, Wine, Amethyst, Crystal Stopper 15.00
Cambridge, Dish, Blue, Shell, 3 In. 4.00
Cambridge, Dish, Candy, Covered, Crown Tuscan, Gadroon, 8 In. 42.50
Cambridge, Dish, Candy, Covered, Moonlight Blue, 3 Compartments 22.00
Cambridge, Dish, Candy, Covered, Wheel Etching, 3 Sections, Gold Trim 35.00
Cambridge, Dish, Candy, Swan, 6 1/2 In. 15.00
Cambridge, Dish, Coral & Opal, Shell, 13 X 10 1/2 In. 125.00
Cambridge, Dish, Crown Tuscan, Shell, Footed, Floral, Gold Trim, 3 In. 17.50
Cambridge, Dish, Crown Tuscan, Shell, Hand-Painted Flower, Gold Rim, 4 In. 30.00
Cambridge, Dish, Crown Tuscan, Shell, 3 Footed, 8 1/4 In. 15.00
Cambridge, Dish, Deviled Egg, Opaque 6.00
Cambridge, Dish, Honey, Farber Cover, Gadroon, 2 Handles 18.50
Cambridge, Dish, Honey, Farber Cover, Gadroon .... 9.50 To 10.00
Cambridge, Dish, Mint, Amethyst Insert, Farber Tray With Finger Lifts, 6 In. 12.00
Cambridge, Dish, Mint, Cobalt Insert, Farber Tray With Finger Lifts, Oval 12.00
Cambridge, Dish, Nut, Crown Tuscan, Seashell 9.00
Cambridge, Dish, Pale Green, 3 Sections, Handled Farber Holder, 9 In. 11.00
Cambridge, Dish, Pink, Divided, Handled, Farber Holder, 9 In. 12.00
Cambridge, Dish, Yellow, Shell, 3 In. 4.00
Cambridge, Figurine, Horse, 2 1/4 In., Pair 5.00
Cambridge, Flower Frog, Blue Jay 25.00
Cambridge, Flower Frog, Draped Nude 25.00
Cambridge, Flower Frog, Flying Sea Gull, 9 3/4 In. 32.50
Cambridge, Flower Holder, Camphor Glass, Girl, 12 In. 65.00
Cambridge, Flower Holder, Crown Tuscan, Nautilus, Seashell, 7 1/2 In. 40.00
Cambridge, Flower Holder, Light Green, Nude Lady, Numbers On Inside, 9 In. 38.00
Cambridge, Flower Holder, Primrose Color, Nude Lady, Numbered, 13 In. 55.00
Cambridge, Goblet, Caprice 7.00
Cambridge, Goblet, Cocktail, Amethyst Bowl, Nude Stem, Satin Finish 35.00
Cambridge, Goblet, Cocktail, Mandarin Gold Bowl, Nude Stem 35.00
Cambridge, Goblet, Cocktail, Rosepoint, 3 Ozs. 9.00
Cambridge, Goblet, Colonial 8.00
Cambridge, Goblet, Crystal, Etched Poppies 10.00
Cambridge, Goblet, Queen 12.50
Cambridge, Goblet, Rosepoint .... 2.10 To 12.00
Cambridge, Goblet, Topaz, Versailles, Footed 8.00
Cambridge, Goblet, Wildflower .... 10.00 To 11.00
Cambridge, Ice Bucket, Caprice, Tongs 6.50
Cambridge, Ice Bucket, Yellow, Etched Flowers, Handled 25.00
Cambridge, Ivy Ball, Amethyst, Melon Ribbed, Ring Stem, 8 1/2 In. 21.00
Cambridge, Ivy Ball, Crown Tuscan, Open Stem, 9 In. 30.00
Cambridge, Ivy Ball, Red Crystal, Ribbed Optic, Footed, 8 1/2 In. 38.00
Cambridge, Jar, Candy, Mt.Vernon, Silver Overlay, Covered, Pedestal 35.00
Cambridge, Jar, Powder, Frosted, Elephant Finial, Round, 5 In. 30.00
Cambridge, Jar, Tobacco, Crown Tuscan, Figural, Man With Green Alpine Hat 25.00
Cambridge, Jug, Amber, Ball, 7 In. 18.00
Cambridge, Jug, Amber, Corinth, Ball, 80 Ozs. 16.40
Cambridge, Jug, Peachglo, Corinth, Ball, 80 Ozs. 16.40
Cambridge, Lamp, see Lamp, Cambridge
Cambridge, Luncheon Set, Apple Green, Marked, C.1901, 19 Piece 70.00

Cambridge, Mayonnaise Set, Azurite, 3 Piece 35.00
Cambridge, Mug, Carmen Red, Thumbprint 8.00
Cambridge, Parfait, Pink 4.00
Cambridge, Pitcher, Water, Emerald Green, Martha Washington 28.00
Cambridge, Plate, Amber, Caprice, 8 In. 2.75
Cambridge, Plate, Bread & Butter, No.3400/62 .... 7.00
Cambridge, Plate, Cake, Alpine, Caprice, 4 Footed, 14 1/2 In. 18.00
Cambridge, Plate, Carmen, Mt.Vernon, 6 In. 6.00
Cambridge, Plate, Crown Tuscan, Scalloped 2 Scrolled Edge, 9 In. 26.00
Cambridge, Plate, Crystal, Cape Cod, 6 In. 1.50
Cambridge, Plate, Dinner, No.3400/62, 10 In. 8.00
Cambridge, Plate, Helio, 7 3/4 In. 9.00
Cambridge, Plate, Honey Color, Etched Grapes & Leaves, 8 Sided, 8 1/2 In. 5.00
Cambridge, Plate, Honey Color, Etched Grapes & Leaves, 10 Sided, 8 1/2 In. 5.00
Cambridge, Plate, Luncheon, Opaque Black, Square, 7 1/2 In. 3.50
Cambridge, Plate, Luncheon, Rosepoint 9.00
Cambridge, Plate, Square, Labels, 7 In. 1.00
Cambridge, Plate, Topaz, Versailles, 7 1/4 In. 3.00
Cambridge, Platter, Moonlight Blue, Everglades, Tulips, 16 In. 45.00
Cambridge, Relish, Crown Tuscan, 3 Compartments, Handled, 8 In. 35.00
Cambridge, Relish, Crystal, Etched, 3 Sections, 3 Handles, Signed 8.00
Cambridge, Relish, Etched Elaine, 3 Part 15.00
Cambridge, Relish, Green, Etched, 3 Sections, 3 Handles, Signed 8.00
Cambridge, Relish, Heatherbloom, 3 Part, Marked C In Circle 45.00
Cambridge, Relish, Rosepoint, Divided 15.00
Cambridge, Rose Bowl, Moonlight, Caprice, 4 In. 18.50
Cambridge, Salt & Pepper, Amber, Farber Holder, 3 In. 10.00
Cambridge, Salt & Pepper, Near-Cut, No.2631 .... 14.50
Cambridge, Salt, Apple Green, Swan, Marked, 3 1/2 In. 21.00
Cambridge, Salt, Blue, Caprice, Footed 4.50
Cambridge, Salt, Crown Tuscan, Swan, Turned Head, Gold Trim, 3 1/2 In. 25.00
Cambridge, Salt, Crown Tuscan, Swan, Twisted Neck, 3 In. 20.00
Cambridge, Salt, Individual, Crown Tuscan, Shell On Shell Feet 9.50
Cambridge, Salt, Swan 10.00
Cambridge, Salt, Yellow, Footed 4.50
Cambridge, Saltshaker, Amberina, 4 1/2 In. 15.00
Cambridge, Saucer, Etched Elaine 4.00
Cambridge, Sherbet, Adonis, Liner 185.00
Cambridge, Sherbet, Rosepoint, Stemmed .... 1.25 To 10.00
Cambridge, Sherbet, Topaz, Versailles, Stemmed 6.00
Cambridge, Sherbet, Wildflower 9.00
Cambridge, Sherry Set, Amber, Stemmed Glasses, Chrome Holder, 7 Piece 70.00
Cambridge, Smoking Set, Crystal, Caprice, Triangular Shape, 4 Piece 10.00
Cambridge, Spooner, Child's, Cobalt, Colonial 24.00
Cambridge, Spooner, Child's, Colonial .... 9.75 To 16.00
Cambridge, Sugar & Creamer On Stand, Pink, Marked 15.00
Cambridge, Sugar & Creamer On Tray, Crystal, Caprice 17.00
Cambridge, Sugar & Creamer, Blue, Caprice 12.50
Cambridge, Sugar & Creamer, Caprice 10.00
Cambridge, Sugar & Creamer, Crystal, Caprice 10.00
Cambridge, Sugar & Creamer, Etched 12-Point Star & Leaves, Footed 25.00
Cambridge, Sugar & Creamer, Heirloom, Miniature 15.00
Cambridge, Sugar & Creamer, Light Amber, Floral 14.00
Cambridge, Sugar & Creamer, Rosepoint 20.00
Cambridge, Sugar, Blockade 15.00
Cambridge, Sugar, Caprice, Footed 6.00
Cambridge, Sugar, Colonial, Miniature 18.00
Cambridge, Sugar, Creamer, & Tray, Mandarin Gold, Cascade, Paper Label 25.00
Cambridge, Sugar, Daisies & Hobstars, Handled, Footed, Near-Cut 18.50
Cambridge, Sugar, Square 5.00
Cambridge, Swan, Black Amethyst, 8 In. 60.00
Cambridge, Swan, Camphor Glass, Signed, 4 1/2 In. 35.00
Cambridge, Swan, Crown Tuscan, 3 In. 28.00
Cambridge, Swan, Crystal, Signed, 3 In. .... 15.00 To 18.50
Cambridge, Swan, Ebony, 3 1/2 In. 24.50
Cambridge, Swan, Green, Signed, 5 1/4 In. 35.00

Cambridge, Swan, Pink, Signed, 4 1/2 In.	24.00
Cambridge, Swan, Yellow, 3 1/2 In.	17.00
Cambridge, Table Set, Child's, Colonial, 3 Piece	35.00 To 45.00
Cambridge, Table Set, Cobalt, Colonial, Miniature, 3 Piece	85.00
Cambridge, Table Set, Colonial, Miniature, 4 Piece	55.00
Cambridge, Table Set, Green, Colonial, Miniature, 3 Piece	85.00
Cambridge, Tea Set, Child's, Colonial, 3 Piece	35.00
Cambridge, Toothpick, Inverted Strawberry, Scalloped Rim, 3 Footed, Near-Cut	30.00
Cambridge, Tray, Card, Marjorie, Spade, Marked Near-Cut	12.50
Cambridge, Tray, Nut, Azurite, Wreath Edge, Handled, 9 In.	22.00
Cambridge, Tray, Sandwich, Pink, Etched Magnolia, 10 1/2 In.	23.00
Cambridge, Tumbler, Georgian, 9 Ozs.	9.00
Cambridge, Tumbler, Heatherbloom, Georgian	7.00
Cambridge, Tumbler, Iced Tea, Rosepoint, 10 Ozs.	2.00
Cambridge, Tumbler, Juice, Amethyst, 4 In.	7.00
Cambridge, Tumbler, Juice, Blue, Caprice, Stemmed	3.10
Cambridge, Tumbler, Juice, Rosepoint	8.00
Cambridge, Tumbler, Milk Glass, Mt.Vernon, 5 Ozs.	2.50
Cambridge, Tumbler, Moonlight Blue, Gyro Optic, 13 Ozs.	3.00
Cambridge, Tumbler, Red	12.50
Cambridge, Tumbler, Royal Blue, 3 1/2 In.	8.00
Cambridge, Tumbler, Topaz, Versailles, Footed, 4 1/4 In.	5.00
Cambridge, Tumbler, Topaz, Versailles, Footed, 6 In.	6.00
Cambridge, Vase, Amethyst, Crystal Foot, 10 In.	25.00
Cambridge, Vase, Black Amethyst, Crisscross Lines, Tricorner, 6 1/2 In.	20.00
Cambridge, Vase, Crown Tuscan, Cornucopia, Shell Base, 10 In.	36.50
Cambridge, Vase, Crown Tuscan, Cornucopia, 4 Shell & Pebble Base, 9 1/2 In.	45.00
Cambridge, Vase, Crown Tuscan, Everglades, 10 1/2 In.	165.00
Cambridge, Vase, Crown Tuscan, Gold, Roses, Pedestal, Gold Trim, 5 1/2 In.	22.00
Cambridge, Vase, Crown Tuscan, Shell, 7 1/2 In.	80.00
Cambridge, Vase, Crystal, Corn, 9 1/2 In.	9.00
Cambridge, Vase, Crystal, Rosepoint, 10 3/4 In.	45.00
Cambridge, Vase, Emerald Green, Clear Base, Paneled, 13 In.	38.00
Cambridge, Vase, Frosted Gold Tone, Tulip, Farber Holder, 6 1/2 In.	16.00
Cambridge, Vase, Gold Flowers, Pedestal, 11 In.	40.00
Cambridge, Vase, Gold, Portia, Paper Label, 10 In.	25.00
Cambridge, Vase, Helio, Sweet Pea, 7 X 8 1/4 In.	35.00
Cambridge, Vase, Jade, Black Dragon Etching, 4 1/2 In.High	65.00
Cambridge, Vase, Pearl Green, 7 1/2 In.	25.00
Cambridge, Vase, Rosepoint, Footed, 11 In.	10.00
Cambridge, Vase, Rosepoint, Gold Band, 10 In.	27.60
Cambridge, Vase, Royal Blue, 10 3/4 In.	45.00
Cambridge, Vase, Tomato Glass, 10 In.	75.00
Cambridge, Wine, Black Nude Lady Stem, Clear Bowl & Foot, 6 1/2 In.	25.00
Cambridge, Wine, Caprice	2.25
Cambridge, Wine, Pink	4.00
Cambridge, Wine, Portia	8.50
Cambridge, Wine, Rosepoint, 5 Ozs.	9.00 To 12.00

*Cameo glass was made in layers in much the same manner as a cameo in jewelry.
Part of the top layer of glass was cut away to reveal a different colored
glass beneath. The most famous cameo glass was made during the nineteenth
century.*

Cameo, see also De Vez, Daum Nancy, Galle, Le Verre Francais, Richard, Webb

Cameo, Bottle, Perfume, English, Citron, Cut Flowers	225.00
Cameo, Bottle, Perfume, English, Lay Down, Sterling Cap, Lily, Blue, 8 1/2 In.	625.00
Cameo, Bottle, Perfume, Lay Down, White Floral On Yellow, 10 In.	750.00
Cameo, Bottle, Shot Stopper, Cranberry Floral, 9 1/2 In.	265.00
Cameo, Bowl, Finger, New England, Raspberry, Acid, Ruffled, 5 1/4 In.	450.00
Cameo, Box, G.Raspiller, Egg Shape, Brown Floral On Yellow, Footed, 5 In.	410.00
Cameo, Compote, English, White To Cranberry To Pink, Geometrics, 5 7/8 In.	65.00
Cameo, Cordial, C.Nessiere, Nancy, Frosted Thistles On Pink, 5 In.	175.00
Cameo, Flask, Perfume, English, Silver Cap, Butterfly On Red, C.1880, 7 In.	300.00
Cameo, Jar, Cracker, English, Bright Yellow, Cut, Metal Lid	795.00
Cameo, Pitcher, Water, French, Burnt Orange, Green Base, Acid Finish, 7 In.	295.00
Cameo, Spittoon, Lady's, English, White, Pink Floral Band, Ruffled Top	550.00

Cameo, Vase, Acid Stripe & Enamel Swirled Thistle, Pedestal, 12 In. 50.00
Cameo, Vase, English, Deep Red, Carved Flower & Leaves, 4 1/2 In .... 750.00 To 850.00
Cameo, Vase, English, Fox Hunt Scene, Cobalt & Frosted, 10 1/4 In. 400.00
Cameo, Vase, English, White On Clear, Cranberry Interior, Floral, 6 In. 1150.00
Cameo, Vase, English, Yellow, Red Orange Overlay, Florets, C.1890, 4 1/4 In. 1700.00
Cameo, Vase, French, Brown & White Spatters, Leaves, Gold Leaf, 6 In. 85.00
Cameo, Vase, French, Lilies & Cattails On Frosted & Etched, 11 In. 195.00
Cameo, Vase, French, Signed Bry, Orange On White, Brass Base, 14 In. 425.00
Cameo, Vase, Heckert, Brown Floral On Green Gray Satin, 5 3/4 In. 140.00
Cameo, Vase, Lamiral, Scenic, Apple Green, 3 3/4 In. 165.00
Cameo, Vase, Lecert, Buff, Red & Green Berries & Leaves, C.1910, 3 1/2 In. 150.00
Cameo, Vase, Leves, Deep Pink, Maroon Daisies & Leaves, 11 1/2 In. 200.00
Cameo, Vase, Nancy, France, Gray, Etched Trees & Berries, C.1930, 16 1/4 In. 175.00
Cameo, Vase, P.Nicholas, Nancy, Fruit On Frosted Gold, 7 7/8 In. 295.00
    Campaign, see Political Campaign
    Campbell Kid, see also Buffalo Pottery
Campbell Kid, Cup, Rogers Silver Plate 12.00
Campbell Kid, Doll, Ideal, Vinyl, Dressed, 8 In. 8.00
Campbell Kid, Spoon, Boy 4.00
Campbell Kid, Spoon, Girl 4.00
Campbell Kid, Spoon, M-M-M Good 8.00

    Camphor glass is a cloudy white glass that has been blown or pressed. It
    was made by many factories in the Midwest during the mid-nineteenth century.
Camphor Glass, Basket, Rectangular, Scalloped, Stem & Berries, 7 X 5 In. 125.00
Camphor Glass, Decanter, Pewter Handle, Hinged Lid, & Beak Spout, 10 In. 35.00
Camphor Glass, Figurine, Donkey & Cart, 8 In. 35.00
Camphor Glass, Jar, Powder, Covered, 4 In. 25.00
Camphor Glass, Mug, Beer 6.00
Camphor Glass, Pipe, Liberal, Kansas, Painted Flower, 12 In. 12.00
Camphor Glass, Salt & Pepper, Blue, Pedestal 12.50
Camphor Glass, Toothpick, Green, Baby's Shoe 32.50
Camphor Glass, Vase, Hand, Centennial, 1876, 8 In. 45.00
Camphor Glass, Vase, Quilted Base, Bulbous, Hand-Painted Roses, 9 In. 20.00
    Canary Glass, see Vaseline Glass
    Candleholder, see Brass, Candleholder, Pewter, Candleholder,
    Pressed Glass, Sandwich Glass, Candleholder, Silver Plate,
    Candleholder, Silver Sterling, Candleholder, Vaseline Glass,
    Candleholder, Wooden, Candleholder, and various porcelain categories.
    Candlestick, see Brass, Candlestick, Pewter, Candlestick,
    Pressed Glass, Sandwich Glass, Candlestick, Silver, Sterling,
    Candlestick, Vaseline Glass, Candlestick, and various porcelain
    categories.

    Candy containers, especially those made of glass, were popular during the late
    Victorian era.
    Candy Container, see also Kewpie, Candy Container
Candy Container, Army Bomber, Embossed, Paper Closure, Candy .... 15.00 To 17.50
Candy Container, Army Jeep, Embossed, Paper Closure, Candy 17.50
Candy Container, Army Tank 10.00
Candy Container, Auto 12.00
Candy Container, Auto, Station Wagon, 1939 Style, Paneled Body, 5 In. 24.00
Candy Container, Auto, 1935 Style, Screw Opening In Rear, 4 In. 20.00
Candy Container, Auto, 1938 Style, Sloped Back, 4 5/8 In. 18.00
Candy Container, Battleship, 5 1/2 In. 21.00
Candy Container, Boat, Cabin Cruiser, 5 In. 14.00
Candy Container, Bomber, J.H.Millstein Co., 4 In. 18.00
Candy Container, Boot 4.50
Candy Container, Buster Brown, Hat Shaker 12.00
Candy Container, Car, Blue, 5 In. .... *Illus* 28.00
Candy Container, Charlie Chaplin, Borgfeldt, Original Paint 60.00
Candy Container, Charlie Chaplin, Tin Closure Slotted For Bank 55.00
Candy Container, Chicken, Papier-Mache, 6 1/2 In. .... *Illus* 30.00
Candy Container, Coupe With Long Hood, U.S.A. 28.00
Candy Container, Cruiser 3.00
Candy Container, Dog, Sitting 10.00

Candy Container, Lantern, 4 1/2 In.

Candy Container, Chicken,
Papier-Mache, 6 1/2 In.
(See Page 69)

Candy Container, Car, Blue, 5 In.
(See Page 69)

Candy Container, Duck	20.00
Candy Container, Fire Engine, Closure	11.00 To 21.00
Candy Container, Fire Pumper, Tin Wheels, 5 In.	40.00
Candy Container, Fire Truck With Driver, Bell On Hood, 5 In.	24.00
Candy Container, Fire Truck With Driver, Steam Boiler On Back, 4 3/4 In.	25.00
Candy Container, Fire Truck With Driver, 5 In.	20.00
Candy Container, Fire Truck, Victory Glass Co., 5 In.	18.00
Candy Container, Flatiron, 4 1/2 In.	15.00
Candy Container, French Telephone, Candy	6.50
Candy Container, Hen On Nest, 4 1/2 In.	10.00 To 13.00
Candy Container, Hen On Nest, 4 3/4 In.	8.00 To 12.50
Candy Container, Hen, Cardboard Closure	8.00
Candy Container, Horse & Cart	10.00
Candy Container, Horse & Wagon	12.00
Candy Container, Hot Doggie	100.00
Candy Container, Hound Dog	5.00 To 9.50
Candy Container, House, Painted, Tin Slip Bottom, 3 In.	20.00
Candy Container, Lantern, Red Metal Top & Bail, Victory Glass Co.	10.00
Candy Container, Lantern, Ribbed Globe, Marked	14.00
Candy Container, Lantern, Tin Cover, 2 1/2 In.	8.00
Candy Container, Lantern, Tin Cover, 2 3/4 In.	8.00
Candy Container, Lantern, Tin Cover, 3 In.	8.00
Candy Container, Lantern, Tin Cover, 3 5/8 In.	4.50
Candy Container, Lantern, 4 1/2 In. *Illus*	4.00
Candy Container, Liberty Bell, Gold Paint, 4 In.	15.00
Candy Container, Liberty Bell, Wire Bail	22.00
Candy Container, Locomotive	8.95
Candy Container, Locomotive, Switch Type, Lamp On Front Top, 4 1/4 In.	25.00
Candy Container, Military Hat	7.50
Candy Container, Piano, Glass Cover	20.00
Candy Container, Pistol, 7 1/2 In.	6.50 To 15.00
Candy Container, Rabbit	10.00 To 12.00

Candy Container, Rabbit Eating Carrot, 4 1/2 In. .... 7.50 To 12.00
Candy Container, Rabbit, J.H.Millstein Co., 6 1/2 In. 18.00
Candy Container, Radio, Tune In, Horn, J'ne't, Pa., Paint 30.00
Candy Container, Railroad Engine, Covered, 6 In. 92.50
Candy Container, Railroad Lantern 10.00
Candy Container, Revolver, Amethyst Glass, Screw Cap, 6 In. 20.00
Candy Container, Revolver, Cap, 7 1/2 In. 12.00
Candy Container, Rolling Pin, Glass Center, Wooden Handles, Tin Closure 25.00
Candy Container, Sad Dog, Geneva, O. 5.00
Candy Container, Santa Claus, 5 In. .... 25.00 To 27.00
Candy Container, Santa Claus, Boot Section Holds Candy, Cardboard, Germany 8.00
Candy Container, Santa Claus, West Germany, Cardboard, Boots Container 8.00
Candy Container, Satchel, Handle, Tin Slide 22.00
Candy Container, Scottie Dog, 4 In. .... 9.00 To 15.00
Candy Container, Scottie Dog, Back Opening, 5 1/2 In. 6.00
Candy Container, Sitting Puppy 3.95
Candy Container, Spirit Of Goodwill 20.00
Candy Container, Steamer Trunk, Closure, Milk Glass, Souvenir N.Y. 35.00
Candy Container, Suitcase, Milk Glass, Decal Of Victorian Ladies 30.00
Candy Container, Suitcase, Tin Closure, Metal Handle .... 12.50 To 17.50
Candy Container, Suitcase, Victorian Decal Scene, Tin Closure 28.00
Candy Container, Tank, Victory Glass Co., 4 In. 18.00
Candy Container, Tank, 2 Cannons, U.S.A. & Star, 4 1/4 In. 25.00
Candy Container, Telephone .... 12.50 To 25.00
Candy Container, Telephone, Desk, Contents 12.50
Candy Container, Three Naked Children, Germany 75.00
Candy Container, Touring Car, Opaline 19.50
Candy Container, Uncle Sam Hat, White Opaque Glass 28.00
Candy Container, Willys Jeep With Driver 18.00
Candy Container, Windmill 35.00
Cane, Horse's Head With Hidden Blade, 11 1/2 In. 20.00
Cane, Ice Blue Glass, Tapered, 48 In. 32.75
Cane, Ivory Top 35.00
Cane, Silver Plate Top 35.00
Cane, Walking Stick, Bands Of Gold & Mother-Of-Pearl Handle 15.00
Cane, Walking Stick, Gold Fancy Top, 1888 .... 90.00
Cane, Walking Stick, Horn & Hoof Handle, Applied Sterling Death's Head 15.00
Cane, Wooden, Raised Carving, N.G.Berkley, Sept.30, 1874, Bent Roots End 29.75

Canton china is a blue-and-white ware made near Canton, China, from about
1785 to 1895. It has hand-decorated Chinese scenes.

Canton, Basket & Stand, Blue & White, Willow, Reticulated, C.1820, 9 1/4 In. 300.00
Canton, Basket & Stand, Fruit, Blue & White, Reticulated, 8 In. 345.00
Canton, Basket & Stand, Fruit, Blue & White, Reticulated, 9 In. 375.00
Canton, Basket & Stand, Fruit, Blue & White, Reticulated, 10 In. 410.00
Canton, Basket & Stand, Fruit, Blue & White, Reticulated, 10 1/2 In. 495.00
Canton, Basket & Stand, Willow, Blue & White, Oval, C.1850, 10 3/4 In. 325.00
Canton, Bottle, Water, Blue & White, 8 1/2 In. 295.00
Canton, Bottle, Water, Blue & White, 10 In. 360.00
Canton, Bowl, Blue & White, Cut Corners, 8 1/2 In. 425.00
Canton, Bowl, Blue & White, Cut Corners, 11 In. 425.00
Canton, Bowl, Blue & White, Scalloped, 8 1/2 In. .... 265.00 To 275.00
Canton, Bowl, Blue & White, Scalloped, 8 1/2 X 3 In. 315.00
Canton, Bowl, Blue & White, Scalloped, 8 1/2 X 3 1/2 In. 315.00
Canton, Bowl, Blue & White, Scalloped, 10 X 2 In. 310.00
Canton, Bowl, Curry, Blue & White, Footed, 15 X 11 X 3 1/2 In. 385.00
Canton, Bowl, Rice, Blue & White, 4 In. 35.00
Canton, Bowl, Rice, Blue & White, 4 1/2 In. 35.00
Canton, Bowl, Serving, Blue & White, Deep, 10 1/2 In. 180.00
Canton, Bowl, Serving, Blue & White, Diamond Shape, 9 X 6 In. 75.00
Canton, Bowl, Serving, Blue & White, Diamond Shape, 9 1/2 X 6 In. 125.00
Canton, Bowl, Serving, Blue & White, Oval, 9 1/2 X 7 1/2 In. 115.00
Canton, Bowl, Serving, Blue & White, Oval, 10 X 8 In. 120.00
Canton, Bowl, Serving, Blue & White, Oval, 10 1/2 X 8 1/2 In. 150.00
Canton, Bowl, Serving, Blue & White, Oval, 11 X 8 1/2 In. 145.00
Canton, Bowl, Serving, Blue & White, Oval, 11 X 9 X 2 In. 240.00

Canton, Bowl, Serving, Blue & White, Rectangular, 10 X 6 1/2 In.	140.00
Canton, Bowl, Serving, Blue & White, Square, 9 In.	155.00
Canton, Bowl, Serving, Blue & White, Square, 9 X 2 In.	155.00
Canton, Bowl, Serving, Blue & White, 8 1/2 X 6 1/2 In.	120.00
Canton, Bowl, Serving, Blue & White, 10 X 8 In.	135.00
Canton, Bowl, Serving, Blue & White, 10 X 8 1/2 In.	135.00
Canton, Bowl, Serving, Blue & White, 12 1/2 X 10 X 2 In.	175.00
Canton, Bowl, Vegetable, Blue & White, Octagonal, 11 In.	185.00
Canton, Bowl, Vegetable, Blue & White, 9 X 7 In.	135.00
Canton, Bowl, Vegetable, Blue & White, 11 In.	125.00
Canton, Bowl, Vegetable, Covered, Blue & White, Lozenge Shape, C.1840, 11 In.	90.00
Canton, Bowl, Vegetable, Covered, Blue & White, Oval, 7 1/2 In.	155.00
Canton, Bowl, Vegetable, Covered, Blue & White, Oval, 8 In.	170.00
Canton, Bowl, Vegetable, Covered, Blue & White, Oval, 8 X 6 In.	170.00
Canton, Bowl, Vegetable, Covered, Blue & White, Oval, 8 1/2 In.	175.00
Canton, Bowl, Vegetable, Covered, Blue & White, Oval, 9 In.	185.00
Canton, Bowl, Vegetable, Covered, Blue & White, Oval, 9 1/2 In.	195.00
Canton, Bowl, Vegetable, Covered, Blue & White, Oval, 10 In.	185.00
Canton, Bowl, Vegetable, Covered, Blue & White, Oval, 10 1/2 In.	220.00
Canton, Bowl, Vegetable, Covered, Blue & White, Oval, 11 In.	225.00
Canton, Bowl, Vegetable, Covered, Blue & White, Oval, 11 1/2 In.	225.00
Canton, Bowl, Vegetable, Covered, Blue & White, 6 1/2 X 5 1/2 In.	155.00
Canton, Bowl, Vegetable, Covered, Blue & White, 8 X 7 In.	85.00 To 175.00
Canton, Bowl, Vegetable, Covered, Blue & White, 9 1/2 X 8 In.	185.00 To 195.00
Canton, Bowl, Vegetable, Covered, Blue & White, 9 1/2 X 8 1/2 In.	195.00
Canton, Bowl, Vegetable, Covered, Willow, Blue & White, C.1820, 11 In., Pair	150.00
Canton, Bowl, Vegetable, Pinecone Knop, Blue & White, Willow, C.1820, 9 In.	212.50
Canton, Bowl, Vegetable, Pinecone Knop, Willow, Blue & White, C.1850, 11 In.	175.00
Canton, Bowl, White, Blue Scenic Bottom, Melon Ribbed, Oblong, 5 X 3 In.	36.50
Canton, Bowl, White, Polychrome Figures In Landscape, 4 3/4 In., Pair	50.00
Canton, Creamer, Blue & White, 3 In.	90.00
Canton, Creamer, Blue & White, 3 1/2 In.	85.00 To 95.00
Canton, Creamer, Blue & White, 4 In.	110.00
Canton, Cup & Saucer, Demitasse, Blue & White	15.00
Canton, Cup, Blue & White, Handleless, 3 1/2 In.	35.00
Canton, Cup, Bouillon, Covered, Blue & White, 2 Handles	29.00
Canton, Cup, Covered, 3 1/2 In.	*Illus* 135.00
Canton, Dish, Hot Water, Blue & White, 9 1/4 In.	115.00
Canton, Dish, Leaf Shape, Willow, Blue & White, C.1850, 8 1/8 In., Pair	325.00
Canton, Dish, Leaf, Blue & White, 8 X 6 1/4 In.	100.00
Canton, Dish, Shrimp, Blue & White	220.00
Canton, Ewer, Blue & White, Mallet Form, Pinched Spout, 1820, 11 3/8 In.	200.00
Canton, Ewer, Wine, Blue & White, Narrow Neck, Small Spout, 10 In.	495.00

Canton, Jar, Ginger,

Blue & White, C.1820, 10 1/4 In.

(See Page 73)

Canton, Cup, Covered, 3 1/2 In.

Canton, Gravy Boat, Blue & White, 5 1/2 X 3 In. 90.00
Canton, Jar, Ginger, Blue & White, C.1820, 10 1/4 In. .... *Illus* 285.00
Canton, Jar, Ginger, Blue & White, Wrought Steel Double-Hinged Lid, Lock 355.00
Canton, Jar, Ginger, Blue & White, 6 In. 85.00
Canton, Jar, Ginger, Blue & White, 7 In. 125.00
Canton, Mug, Blue & White, Twist Handle, 3 1/2 In. .... 170.00 To 200.00
Canton, Mug, Blue & White, Twist Handle, 4 In. 230.00
Canton, Mug, Blue & White, Twist Handle, 5 In. 265.00
Canton, Pitcher, Cider, Foo Dog Cover, Blue & White, 6 1/2 X 6 In. 560.00
Canton, Pitcher, Cider, Foo Dog Cover, Blue & White, 7 1/2 X 7 In. 690.00
Canton, Pitcher, Cider, Foo Dog Cover, Blue & White, 8 1/2 X 7 1/2 In. 695.00
Canton, Pitcher, Cider, Foo Dog Cover, Blue & White, 9 X 8 In. 710.00
Canton, Pitcher, Milk, Blue & White, Fishtail Handle, 6 1/2 In. 375.00
Canton, Pitcher, Milk, Blue & White, Scalloped Top Edge, 10 1/2 In. 575.00
Canton, Pitcher, Milk, Blue & White, 3 1/2 In. 65.00
Canton, Pitcher, Milk, Blue & White, 5 In. 310.00
Canton, Pitcher, Milk, Blue & White, 5 1/2 In. 345.00
Canton, Pitcher, Milk, Blue & White, 7 In. 465.00
Canton, Pitcher, Milk, Blue & White, 7 1/2 In. 465.00
Canton, Pitcher, Milk, Blue & White, 8 1/2 In. 595.00
Canton, Pitcher, Washstand, Blue & White, 14 In. 695.00
Canton, Plate, Blue & White, Willow, Bamboo Sprays, C.1820, 13 1/2 In. 250.00
Canton, Plate, C.1820, 6 In. 14.00
Canton, Plate, Hot Water, Blue & White, 9 In. .... 175.00 To 185.00
Canton, Plate, Hot Water, Blue & White, 9 1/2 In. 185.00
Canton, Plate, Hot Water, Covered, Blue & White, 8 1/2 In. 350.00
Canton, Plate, Rice Border, Blue & White, Marked China, 6 In. 4.50
Canton, Plate, Rice Border, Blue & White, Marked China, 9 In. 12.50
Canton, Platter, Blue & White, Nanking Scene, Octagonal, 13 X 16 In. 112.00
Canton, Platter, Blue & White, Octagonal, Scalloped Corners, 15 X 12 In. 150.00
Canton, Platter, Blue & White, Scenic, 16 X 12 1/2 In. 29.00
Canton, Platter, Deep Blue, 12 1/4 X 9 1/2 In. 125.00
Canton, Platter, Hot Water, Beefsteak, Blue & White, 13 X 10 In. 475.00
Canton, Platter, Shrimp, Blue & White, 10 X 9 1/2 In. .... 265.00 To 295.00
Canton, Platter, Shrimp, Blue & White, 10 1/2 X 9 In. 290.00
Canton, Sauceboat & Underplate, Willow, Blue & White, Strap Handle, C.1850 .... 175.00
Canton, Sauceboat, Blue & White, 6 1/2 X 1 1/2 In. 120.00
Canton, Sauceboat, Blue & White, 7 1/2 X 2 In. 120.00
Canton, Sauceboat, Handle, 17 1/2 In. 85.00
Canton, Server, Vegetable, Blue & White, Vented, Oval, 10 1/2 In. .... 195.00 To 295.00
Canton, Sugar, Crab On Cover 145.00
Canton, Tazza, Blue & White, 3 X 8 In. 350.00
Canton, Tea Caddy, Blue & White, Square, 4 X 3 1/2 In. 410.00
Canton, Tea Set, Willow, Blue & White, C.1850, 3 Piece 250.00
Canton, Teacup & Saucer, Blue & White 28.00
Canton, Teacup, Blue & White, Gold Trim .... 20.00 To 22.00
Canton, Tureen & Stand, Horn-Shaped Knop, Willow, Blue & White, C.1850, 12 In 450.00
Canton, Tureen & Stand, Stalk Knop, Blue & White, Willow, C.1820, 14 In. 550.00
Canton, Tureen & Underplate, Vegetable, Covered, Blue & White, 7 X 3 1/2 In. 225.00
Canton, Tureen, Covered, Blue & White, 5 3/4 X 13 In. 525.00
Canton, Tureen, Vegetable, Cone Knop, Willow, Blue & White, C.1820, 11 1/4 In. 200.00
Canton, Washstand Set, Blue & White, Brown Edge, 11 In. Bowl, 2 Piece 850.00
Capo-Di-Monte Type, Vase, 14 1/2 In., Pair 700.00

*Capo-Di-Monte porcelain was first made in Naples, Italy, from 1743 to
1759. The factory moved near Madrid, Spain, and reopened in 1771 and worked
to 1834. Since that time the Doccia factory of Italy acquired the molds
and style, even using the N and crown mark, which was made famous by the
factory.*

Capo-Di-Monte, Box, Hinged, Floral, Blue N Mark, 3 3/4 X 2 1/2 In. 80.00
Capo-Di-Monte, Box, Round, King Neptune With Horses, 3 1/2 In.Diameter 105.00
Capo-Di-Monte, Charger, Achilles & Muses, Putto, Medici Arms, C.1890, 23 In. 800.00
Capo-Di-Monte, Cup & Saucer, Demitasse, Ducks & Swans, Footed, N Mark 75.00
Capo-Di-Monte, Cup, Demitasse, Covered, People In Landscape 115.00
Capo-Di-Monte, Cup, 3 1/2 In. Diameter .... *Illus* 15.00
Capo-Di-Monte, Ewer, Putti & Dolphins Banding, Satyr Handle, 14 3/8 In. 125.00

Capo-Di-Monte, Cup, 3 1/2 In. Diameter
(See Page 73)

Capo-Di-Monte, Figurine, Man With Hat, Woman With Mandolin, 6 1/2 In., Pair	95.00
Capo-Di-Monte, Figurine, Tumbler, 4 1/2 In., Pair	125.00
Capo-Di-Monte, Urn, Rococo, Turned Up Handles, 11 1/2 In.	150.00
Capo-Di-Monte, Wall Pocket, Cherub In Center, Birds On Sides, C.1700s	295.00
Captain Midnight, Pin, Coding & Decoding, Official Squadron, Secret	42.00
Caramel Slag, see Chocolate Glass	
Card, see also Postcard	
Card, Advertising, Currier & Ives, Caught Napping, 1879	15.00
Card, Advertising, Currier & Ives, Longfellow, 1881	15.00
Card, Advertising, Gargling Oil Liniment, Baseball Comics Of Fat Man	2.00
Card, Advertising, Hassan Cigarettes, Lighthouse Series, 37	9.75
Card, Advertising, Hires, 1892	3.00
Card, Advertising, Larkin Soap Co., Folding, People Holding Babies	10.00
Card, Advertising, Milson Fertilizer Co., Baseball Comics Of Pixies	2.00
Card, Advertising, Soapine, Prang, 8 1/2 X 4 In.	10.00
Card, Advertising, Sulphur Bitters, Mrs.Grover Cleveland, 6 1/2 X 4 In.	8.00
Card, Advertising, Thomson's Rein Holder, Horse & Buggy	1.75
Card, Advertising, Yosemite Beer, 1906, Celluloid	8.00
Card, Fortune Telling, Astrologer, Prof.A.F.Seward's, Box	5.00
Card, Greeting, Christmas, Clapsaddle	2.50
Card, Greeting, Christmas, Birds On Snow-Laden Boughs, Louis Prang, 1884	5.00
Card, Greeting, Valentine, see also Kewpie, Card, Valentine	
Card, Greeting, C.1840, Envelope	20.00
Card, Greeting, Valentine, Die Cut, Girl, Cupid Strumming Mandolin, 8 In.	9.50
Card, Greeting, Valentine, Pop-Out, 1900, Angel & Horn Of Plenty, 10 In.	8.50
Card, Greeting, Valentine, Punch-Out, Similar To Grace Drayton, 4 In.	4.00
Card, Greeting, Valentine, Stand-Up, 5 Dimensional, Angels, Roses, 9 X 6 In.	10.00
Card, Greeting, Valentine, 1900, 3 Little Girls In Auto, 5 X 7 In.	9.00
Card, Playing, see also Railroad, Cards, Playing	
Card, Playing, Automatic, Magician's, 1913, Deck, Instruction Sheet	7.00
Card, Playing, Green Hornet, 1966, 52	1.50
Card, Playing, Little Duke, 1 1/4 X 1 3/4 In., Pack	2.95
Card, Playing, N.F.L.	2.00
Card, Playing, Old Maid, Comic Sheet Characters, C.1905, Deck Of 39	15.00
Card, Playing, Old Style Lager Beer, Deck, Boxed	8.00
Card, Playing, Panama, Souvenir, Inaugural Edition, Sepia Photographs	15.00
Card, Playing, Railroad, C.1915, Southern Pacific, Sunset Scenes	15.00
Card, Playing, Sutherland's Circular Coon Cards, Round, Tin Box	30.00
Card, Playing, Texas Scenes, C.1910, Deck	20.00
Card, Playing, Winchester Centennial, Deck	5.00
Card, Playing, World's Fair, 1933, Skyride Scene, Deck	6.00
Card, Playing, 10th Olympics & Movie Stars, 1932, Deck	20.00
Card, Tarot, Switzerland, 78	3.00
Carder, see Steuben, Aurene	

Carlsbad, Germany, is a mark found on china made by several factories in Germany. Most of the pieces available today were made after 1891.

Carlsbad, Butter Pat, Hand-Painted	6.00
Carlsbad, Can, Sprinkling, Victorian, 4 1/4 In.	30.00
Carlsbad, Cup & Saucer, Demitasse, Floral Spray, Red Brown Border	15.00
Carlsbad, Jar, Sweetmeat, Gold Decoration, Silver Fittings	38.50
Carlsbad, Plate, Portrait, Lady Pompadour, 9 In.	24.00
Carlsbad, Plate, Scenic Center, Green Border, Gold Trim, 8 In.	18.00
Carlsbad, Plate, State Capitol, Nashville, Sepia Transfer, 8 1/4 In.	10.00
Carlsbad, Vase, Portrait Babies, Light Blue, Gold, Handled, 10 In.	26.00

Carnival, or taffeta, glass was an inexpensive, pressed, iridescent glass made
from about 1900 to 1920. Carnival glass is currently being reproduced. Over
200 different patterns are known.

Carnival Glass, see also Northwood

Carnival Glass, Banana Boat, Cherry Wreath, Amethyst	95.00 To 132.00
Carnival Glass, Banana Boat, Grape & Cable, Dark Purple	175.00
Carnival Glass, Banana Boat, Grape & Cable, Marigold	85.00 To 90.00
Carnival Glass, Banana Boat, Grape & Cable, White, Frosty	250.00
Carnival Glass, Banana Boat, Kitten, Marigold	60.00
Carnival Glass, Banana Boat, Wreathed Cherry, White	195.00
Carnival Glass, Basket Weave, Green, Grape & Cable Inside, N, 9 3/4 In.	55.00
Carnival Glass, Berry Set, Butterfly & Berry, Marigold, Balled Feet, 5 Piece	75.00
Carnival Glass, Berry Set, Butterfly & Berry, Marigold, 7 Piece	175.00
Carnival Glass, Berry Set, Feathered Serpent, Purple, 7 Piece	80.00
Carnival Glass, Berry Set, Grape & Cable With Thumbprint, Purple, 7 Piece	275.00
Carnival Glass, Berry Set, Little Flowers, Purple, Blue Base, 7 Piece	215.00
Carnival Glass, Berry Set, Open Rose, Marigold, 5 Piece	55.00
Carnival Glass, Bonbon, Basket Weave, Amethyst, Roses On Handle, N, 6 In.	25.00
Carnival Glass, Bonbon, Birds & Boughs, Green, Two Handles	75.00
Carnival Glass, Bonbon, Butterfly, Amethyst	27.50
Carnival Glass, Bonbon, Butterfly, Marigold, 2 Handles	28.00
Carnival Glass, Bonbon, Daisy & Plume, Marigold, Tulip Shape, N, 5 In.	27.50
Carnival Glass, Bonbon, Drapery, Amethyst, 2 Handled	23.00
Carnival Glass, Bonbon, Grape & Cable, Green, N	25.00
Carnival Glass, Bonbon, Persian Medallion, Blue, 2 Handles	27.50
Carnival Glass, Bonbon, Persian Medallion, Marigold, Ruffled Edge	14.75
Carnival Glass, Bonbon, Pinecone, Blue	25.00
Carnival Glass, Bonbon, Pond Lily, White	35.00
Carnival Glass, Bonbon, Stippled Rays, Green, 2 Handles	30.00
Carnival Glass, Bottle, Cologne, Grape & Cable, Amethyst, Northwood	450.00
Carnival Glass, Bottle, Cologne, Grape & Cable, Marigold	45.00
Carnival Glass, Bottle, Cologne, Grape & Cable, Purple	140.00
Carnival Glass, Bottle, Horn Of Plenty, Marigold	12.00
Carnival Glass, Bowl & Base, Punch, Heavy Grape, Marigold, Fenton	275.00
Carnival Glass, Bowl & Base, Punch, Multifruits, Purple, Millersburg	550.00
Carnival Glass, Bowl & Base, Punch, Orange Tree, Marigold	75.00
Carnival Glass, Bowl & Base, Punch, Peacock At Fountain, Marigold, Northwood	215.00
Carnival Glass, Bowl, Acorn & Autumn Leaves, Green, Rust Tones, 8 1/2 In.	45.00
Carnival Glass, Bowl, Acorn Burr, Purple, Marked N, 9 1/2 In.	90.00
Carnival Glass, Bowl, Acorn, Amethyst, Scallops Turn Out, Signed N, 6 In.	30.00
Carnival Glass, Bowl, Acorn, Green, 7 In.	20.00
Carnival Glass, Bowl, Basket Weave & Grape, Purple, 3 Fruits Inside, 8 In.	40.00
Carnival Glass, Bowl, Basket Weave, Green, Grape & Cable Inside, N, 8 1/2 In.	45.00
Carnival Glass, Bowl, Basket Weave, Red, 2 Rows Open Lace Edge, 5 1/2 In.	80.00
Carnival Glass, Bowl, Berry, Banded Daisy, Deep Marigold	16.00
Carnival Glass, Bowl, Berry, Dahlia, Purple	24.00
Carnival Glass, Bowl, Berry, Field Thistle, Marigold	12.00
Carnival Glass, Bowl, Berry, Geometric, Marigold	10.00
Carnival Glass, Bowl, Berry, Master, Acorn Burr, Green, N	150.00
Carnival Glass, Bowl, Berry, Peach, White, 9 In.	100.00
Carnival Glass, Bowl, Berry, Singing Bird, Green, Northwood	20.00
Carnival Glass, Bowl, Berry, Split Diamond, Marigold	14.00
Carnival Glass, Bowl, Berry, Sunflower, Marigold, 8 1/2 In.	65.00
Carnival Glass, Bowl, Berry, Three In One, Marigold	10.00
Carnival Glass, Bowl, Berry, Water Lilies, Marigold	9.00
Carnival Glass, Bowl, Berry, Zipper & Diamond Band, Marigold, Scroll Inside	15.00
Carnival Glass, Bowl, Butterfly & Berry, Cobalt, Ball & Claw Feet, 9 In.	138.00

Carnival Glass, Bowl, Butterfly & Berry, Green, Footed, 9 In. 195.00
Carnival Glass, Bowl, Butterfly & Berry, Marigold, Panther Interior, 5 In. 30.00
Carnival Glass, Bowl, Captive Rose, Blue, Fluted, 7 In. 42.50
Carnival Glass, Bowl, Centerpiece, Double Scroll, Red, 10 5/8 In. 125.00
Carnival Glass, Bowl, Centerpiece, Grape & Cable, Marigold, N 225.00
Carnival Glass, Bowl, Cherries, Peach, 3 Footed, Crimped & Scalloped, 9 In. 41.00
Carnival Glass, Bowl, Cherry Delight, Cobalt, 9 In. 58.00
Carnival Glass, Bowl, Child's, Kittens, Marigold, Ruffled 95.00
Carnival Glass, Bowl, Chrysanthemum & Roman Key, Purple, 9 In. 70.00
Carnival Glass, Bowl, Chrysanthemum, Marigold, Footed, 11 In. 65.00
Carnival Glass, Bowl, Chrysanthemums & Windmills, Marigold, Fluted, 9 In. 30.00
Carnival Glass, Bowl, Coin Dot, Purple, Ruffled, 8 1/2 In. 28.00
Carnival Glass, Bowl, Coin Dot, Purple, Ruffled, 8 1/4 In. 28.00
Carnival Glass, Bowl, Coin Dot, Purple, Shallow, 8 3/4 In.Diameter 21.00
Carnival Glass, Bowl, Daisy & Leaves, Amethyst, 8 In. 45.00
Carnival Glass, Bowl, Dessert, Butterfly & Berry, Marigold 15.00
Carnival Glass, Bowl, Diamond Ring, Marigold, 9 In. 25.00
Carnival Glass, Bowl, Dogwood Sprays, Purple, Dome Footed, 9 In. 45.00
Carnival Glass, Bowl, Dragon & Lotus, Blue, Ruffled, 9 In. 42.50
Carnival Glass, Bowl, Dragon & Lotus, Cobalt, Collared Base, 8 1/2 In. 48.00
Carnival Glass, Bowl, Dragon & Lotus, Cobalt, 8 In. 47.50
Carnival Glass, Bowl, Dragon & Lotus, Marigold, Collared Bottom, 9 1/4 In. 27.50
Carnival Glass, Bowl, Dragon & Lotus, Marigold, Fluted, 8 3/4 In. 18.00
Carnival Glass, Bowl, Dragon & Lotus, Marigold, 8 1/2 In.Diameter 37.50
Carnival Glass, Bowl, Embossed Scroll, Amethyst, 7 In. 30.00
Carnival Glass, Bowl, Fishscale & Beads, Peach Opalescent, 7 In. 27.50
Carnival Glass, Bowl, Flowering Dill, Marigold, Hat Shape, 6 In. 18.75
Carnival Glass, Bowl, Good Luck, Blue, 9 In.Diameter 99.00
Carnival Glass, Bowl, Good Luck, Cobalt, Fluted, 8 1/2 In. 110.00
Carnival Glass, Bowl, Grape & Cable, Lavender, Shallow, 8 1/2 In. 45.00
Carnival Glass, Bowl, Grape & Cable, Marigold, 8 In. 18.00
Carnival Glass, Bowl, Grape & Cable, Pastel Blue, Northwood, 9 In. 60.00
Carnival Glass, Bowl, Grape & Cable, Purple, Fluted, 8 In. 55.00
Carnival Glass, Bowl, Grape & Cable, Purple, Persian Medallion Inside, 10 In 125.00
Carnival Glass, Bowl, Grape With Thumbprint, Purple, Marked N, 4 1/2 In. 22.50
Carnival Glass, Bowl, Heart & Vine, Blue, Piecrust Edge, 8 1/2 In. 33.00
Carnival Glass, Bowl, Heavy Grape, Amethyst, Star-Shaped Border, 7 In. 33.00
Carnival Glass, Bowl, Holly Sprig, Amber, Millersburg, 6 1/2 In. 35.00
Carnival Glass, Bowl, Holly, Marigold, 8 1/2 In. 20.00
Carnival Glass, Bowl, Holly, Purple, Hat Shape, Ruffled Top, 6 In. 22.75
Carnival Glass, Bowl, Horses' Heads, Marigold, Fluted, 8 1/2 In. 40.00
Carnival Glass, Bowl, Horses' Heads, Marigold, Fluted, 8 5/8 In. 45.00
Carnival Glass, Bowl, Horses' Heads, Marigold, Greek Key Inside, 8 1/2 In. 70.00
Carnival Glass, Bowl, Ice Cream, Grape & Cable, Marigold 135.00
Carnival Glass, Bowl, Ice Cream, Persian Garden, White, 5 3/4 In. 27.00
Carnival Glass, Bowl, Ice Cream, Persian Garden, White, 11 In. .... 95.00 To 150.00
Carnival Glass, Bowl, Ice Cream, Persian Garden, White, 11 1/2 In. 155.00
Carnival Glass, Bowl, Ice Cream, Stretch, White, Stemmed 18.00
Carnival Glass, Bowl, Imperial Grape, Marigold, 7 In. 20.00
Carnival Glass, Bowl, Imperial Jewels, Sapphire Blue, 9 3/4 X 2 1/2 In. 22.00
Carnival Glass, Bowl, Iris Herringbone, Marigold, 8 In. 14.00
Carnival Glass, Bowl, Jeweled Heart, Purple, Stippled Feather Inside, 10 In. 70.00
Carnival Glass, Bowl, Little Fishes, Amethyst, Footed, 6 In. 95.00
Carnival Glass, Bowl, Little Fishes, Marigold, Footed, 10 In. 85.00
Carnival Glass, Bowl, Mayan, Green, 8 In. 42.00
Carnival Glass, Bowl, Nesting Swan, Amethyst, 9 1/2 In. 135.00
Carnival Glass, Bowl, Nesting Swan, Purple, Ruffled, Millersburg, 10 In. 180.00
Carnival Glass, Bowl, Nut, Grape, Purple, 6 Footed 65.00
Carnival Glass, Bowl, Open Rose, Marigold, 3 Footed, 10 In. 45.00
Carnival Glass, Bowl, Orange Tree, Amethyst, Berries Inside, 9 In. 33.00
Carnival Glass, Bowl, Orange, Grape & Cable, Amethyst, Footed 150.00
Carnival Glass, Bowl, Orange, Grape & Cable, Frosty White, N, 9 3/4 In. 265.00
Carnival Glass, Bowl, Orange, Grape & Cable, Marigold, Footed, 10 In. 45.00
Carnival Glass, Bowl, Orange, Grape & Cable, Marigold, Persian Medallion In 75.00
Carnival Glass, Bowl, Orange, Grape & Cable, Purple 125.00
Carnival Glass, Bowl, Pansy, Purple, 9 In. 45.00

Carnival Glass, Bowl, Panther, Marigold, 5 1/2 In. 29.00
Carnival Glass, Bowl, Peacock & Grape, Blue, 8 In. 45.00
Carnival Glass, Bowl, Peacock & Grape, Marigold, Fluted, 8 3/4 In. 18.00
Carnival Glass, Bowl, Peacock & Grape, Marigold, 9 In. 47.50
Carnival Glass, Bowl, Peacock At Urn, Marigold, Scalloped Edge, 10 In. 70.00
Carnival Glass, Bowl, Peacock On Fence, Marigold, Fluted, 9 In. 48.00
Carnival Glass, Bowl, Peacock With Grape, Cobalt, Ruffled, 8 1/2 In. 40.00
Carnival Glass, Bowl, Peacock's Tail, Amethyst, 7 In. 35.00
Carnival Glass, Bowl, Persian Medallion, Green, 7 In. 35.00
Carnival Glass, Bowl, Pineapple, Marigold, 6 1/2 In. 32.50
Carnival Glass, Bowl, Posie & Pod, Green, Ruffled Edge, 8 1/2 X 2 1/2 In. 57.50
Carnival Glass, Bowl, Punch, Imperial Grape, Marigold 95.00
Carnival Glass, Bowl, Punch, Orange Tree, Blue 135.00
Carnival Glass, Bowl, Punch, Orange Tree, Marigold 65.00
Carnival Glass, Bowl, Ribbon & Rays, Amethyst, 9 In. 68.00
Carnival Glass, Bowl, Rose Show, Amber, 8 3/4 In. 150.00
Carnival Glass, Bowl, Rose Show, Purple, 9 In. 135.00
Carnival Glass, Bowl, Roses, Orange, 3 Footed, 10 In. 45.00
Carnival Glass, Bowl, Sailboat, Cobalt, Ruffled, 6 In. 50.00
Carnival Glass, Bowl, Show, Green, 9 In. 175.00
Carnival Glass, Bowl, Single Flower Framed, Peach, 7 In. 25.00
Carnival Glass, Bowl, Single Flower, Peach, Opalescent, Scalloped, 8 1/4 In. 28.00
Carnival Glass, Bowl, Stag & Holly, Amethyst, Spatula Footed, Fluted, 8 In. 65.00
Carnival Glass, Bowl, Stag & Holly, Blue, Footed 135.00
Carnival Glass, Bowl, Stag & Holly, Blue, Footed, 7 In. 65.00
Carnival Glass, Bowl, Stag & Holly, Green, 3 Footed, 7 1/2 In. 65.00
Carnival Glass, Bowl, Stag & Holly, Marigold, Footed, 11 In. 75.00
Carnival Glass, Bowl, Stag & Holly, Marigold, 3 Footed, 9 1/2 In. 65.00
Carnival Glass, Bowl, Star & File, Marigold, 7 In. 20.00
Carnival Glass, Bowl, Star Of David, Amethyst, Fluted, Imperial, 9 3/8 In. 55.00
Carnival Glass, Bowl, Stork In Rushes, Amethyst, 4 1/2 In. 10.00
Carnival Glass, Bowl, Strawberry, Ice Green, 10 In. 85.00
Carnival Glass, Bowl, Strawberry, Pastel Green, Scalloped, Northwood, 9 In. 65.00
Carnival Glass, Bowl, Sunflower, Green, Footed, Fluted, 8 3/8 In. 40.00
Carnival Glass, Bowl, Thistle, Blue, 8 In. 42.50
Carnival Glass, Bowl, Thistle, Green, Frilled Edge, 8 1/2 In. 45.00
Carnival Glass, Bowl, Three Fruits, Aqua, Opalescent, Footed, 9 In. 75.00
Carnival Glass, Bowl, Three Fruits, Blue, Basket Weave Inside, 10 In. 50.00
Carnival Glass, Bowl, Triplets, Marigold, 7 In. 20.00
Carnival Glass, Bowl, Trout & Fly, Amethyst, 9 In. 275.00
Carnival Glass, Bowl, Vintage, Blue, Candy Ribbon Top, 8 X 4 In. 38.00
Carnival Glass, Bowl, Whirling Leaves, Marigold, 10 In. 85.00
Carnival Glass, Bowl, Wild Rose, Green, Scroll Footed, Northwood, 6 3/8 In. 40.00
Carnival Glass, Bowl, Windflower, Blue, 9 In. 45.00
Carnival Glass, Bowl, Windmill, Green, 6 1/2 In. 35.00
Carnival Glass, Bowl, Wishbone, Green, Piecrust Edge, Marked N, 10 In. 95.00
Carnival Glass, Bowl, Wishbone, Purple, Footed, Signed N, 9 In. 62.50
Carnival Glass, Bowl, Wishbone, Purple, Footed, 8 1/2 In. 65.00
Carnival Glass, Bowl, 24 Panels, Marigold, 10 1/2 In. 15.00
Carnival Glass, Bride's Basket, Strawberry, Purple, Plated Holder, N, 7 In. 85.00
Carnival Glass, Butter, Grape & Cable With Thumbprint, Purple, Covered, N 225.00
Carnival Glass, Butter, Grape & Cable, Marigold, Covered, Marked N 75.00
Carnival Glass, Butter, Grape & Cable, Purple .... 185.00 To 210.00
Carnival Glass, Butter, Grapes, Purple, Covered, Marked N 195.00
Carnival Glass, Butter, Luster Rose, Marigold 85.00
Carnival Glass, Butter, Peacock At Fountain, Amethyst, Covered 200.00
Carnival Glass, Button, Owl, Purple 225.00
Carnival Glass, Candleholder, Imperial Jewels, Sapphire Blue, 8 In., Pair 38.00
Carnival Glass, Candlestick, Tree Of Life, Marigold, 7 In., Pair 35.00
Carnival Glass, Compote, Double Stem Rose, Marigold, 8 1/2 In.Diameter 27.50
Carnival Glass, Compote, Holly, Marigold, Miniature 38.50
Carnival Glass, Creamer, Acorn Burr, Purple 65.00
Carnival Glass, Creamer, Beaded Shell, Marigold, Footed 30.00
Carnival Glass, Creamer, Butterfly & Berry, Marigold 25.00
Carnival Glass, Creamer, Hanging Cherry, Green, Millersburg 45.00
Carnival Glass, Creamer, Long Thumbprint, Marigold 12.00

Carnival Glass, Creamer, Luster & Clear Clambroth, Marigold	10.00
Carnival Glass, Creamer, Luster & Clear, Marigold	7.00
Carnival Glass, Creamer, Luster Flute, Marigold, Marked N	22.50
Carnival Glass, Creamer, Lustre Rose, Green	80.00
Carnival Glass, Creamer, Maple Leaf, Purple	55.00
Carnival Glass, Creamer, Octagon, Light Marigold	22.50
Carnival Glass, Creamer, Pineapple, Marigold	35.00
Carnival Glass, Creamer, Singing Bird, Purple, Marked N	60.00
Carnival Glass, Creamer, Star & File, Marigold	18.50
Carnival Glass, Cup & Saucer, Bouquet & Lattice, Marigold	3.75
Carnival Glass, Cup & Saucer, Imp, Green	69.00
Carnival Glass, Cup & Saucer, Kitten, Marigold	110.00
Carnival Glass, Cup, Loving, Orange Tree, Marigold	75.00
Carnival Glass, Cup, Memphis, White, Northwood	15.00
Carnival Glass, Cup, Punch, Acorn Burr, Ice Blue	65.00
Carnival Glass, Cup, Punch, Acorn Burr, Marigold, Marked N	16.00
Carnival Glass, Cup, Punch, Acorn Burr, Purple	25.00
Carnival Glass, Cup, Punch, Colonial, Green	15.00
Carnival Glass, Cup, Punch, Fruits, Pastel Marigold, Millersburg	22.00
Carnival Glass, Cup, Punch, Grape & Cable, Marigold, Signed N	17.00
Carnival Glass, Cup, Punch, Grape & Cable, Purple	20.00
Carnival Glass, Cup, Punch, Grape & Cable, Purple Amethyst	22.00
Carnival Glass, Cup, Punch, Grape & Cable, Purple, Marked N	25.00
Carnival Glass, Cup, Punch, Grape & Leaf, Purple	12.00
Carnival Glass, Cup, Punch, Memphis, Amethyst, Marked N	17.00
Carnival Glass, Cup, Punch, Multifruits, Marigold	12.50
Carnival Glass, Cup, Punch, Peacock At Fountain, Amethyst, Northwood	32.00
Carnival Glass, Cup, Punch, Peacock At Fountain, Ice Blue	65.00
Carnival Glass, Cup, Punch, Peacock At Fountain, Marigold, Northwood	15.00
Carnival Glass, Cup, Punch, Stork In Rushes, Amethyst	28.50
Carnival Glass, Cup, Punch, Stork In Rushes, Dark Marigold	18.00
Carnival Glass, Cup, Punch, Stork In Rushes, Light Marigold	18.00
Carnival Glass, Cup, Punch, Vintage, Deep Purple	25.00
Carnival Glass, Cup, Punch, Wreath Of Roses, Amethyst, Vintage Inside	11.25
Carnival Glass, Cup, Punch, 474, Green	22.50
Carnival Glass, Decanter, Whiskey, Grape & Cable, Marigold	625.00
Carnival Glass, Decanter, Wine, Golden Harvest, Marigold	95.00
Carnival Glass, Dish, Candy, Basket Weave, Red, Fenton	140.00
Carnival Glass, Dish, Candy, Green Band Of White Enamel, Marigold, Stemmed	10.00
Carnival Glass, Dish, Candy, Imperial Grape, Marigold, Flared Top	15.00
Carnival Glass, Dish, Candy, Shell, Amethyst	24.00
Carnival Glass, Dish, Candy, Twins, Deep Smoke	19.00
Carnival Glass, Dish, Candy, Twins, Marigold	12.00
Carnival Glass, Dish, Hen Cover, Marigold	90.00
Carnival Glass, Dish, Pickle, Pansy, Amber, Oval	35.00
Carnival Glass, Dish, Pickle, Windmill, Purple, Oval	35.00
Carnival Glass, Dish, Swan Cover, Marigold	135.00
Carnival Glass, Epergne, Vintage, Purple, 1 Lily	110.00
Carnival Glass, Fernery, Luster Rose, Green, 7 1/2 In.	150.00
Carnival Glass, Goblet, Buttermilk, Iris, Green	75.00
Carnival Glass, Goblet, Flute, Marigold	12.50
Carnival Glass, Goblet, Imperial Grape, Deep Marigold	29.00
Carnival Glass, Goblet, Imperial Grape, Pastel Marigold	22.00
Carnival Glass, Goblet, Star Medallion, Marigold	20.00
Carnival Glass, Hatpin Holder, Butterfly & Berry, Blue	625.00
Carnival Glass, Hatpin Holder, Butterfly & Berry, Cobalt, 7 1/4 In.	475.00
Carnival Glass, Hatpin Holder, Grape & Cable, Green	140.00
Carnival Glass, Hatpin Holder, Grape & Cable, Purple, Signed N	125.00 To 140.00
Carnival Glass, Hatpin Holder, Orange Tree, Blue	115.00
Carnival Glass, Hatpin Holder, Orange Tree, Marigold	95.00
Carnival Glass, Hatpin, Butterfly Form	29.00
Carnival Glass, Hatpin, Flying Bat With 3 Stars, Rainbow Iridescent	28.00
Carnival Glass, Hatpin, Flying Bat, Dark Background	28.00
Carnival Glass, Hatpin, Rooster, Sapphire Blue	10.00
Carnival Glass, Hatpin, Scarab	8.00
Carnival Glass, Hatpin, Top-O'-Walk	8.00

Carnival Glass, Humidor, Tobacco, Grape & Cable, Marigold, N 225.00
Carnival Glass, Jar, Cookie, Grape & Cable, Amethyst 425.00
Carnival Glass, Jar, Cookie, Grape & Cable, Marigold, N 175.00
Carnival Glass, Jar, Cookie, Grape & Cable, Purple, Covered, Marked N 395.00
Carnival Glass, Jar, Powder, Grape & Cable, Marigold, Signed N 35.00
Carnival Glass, Jar, Powder, Inverted Strawberry, Marigold 110.00
Carnival Glass, Jar, Powder, Orange Tree, Marigold 60.00
Carnival Glass, Jar, Powder, Zipper, Marigold 16.00
Carnival Glass, Match Holder, Autumn, Pastel Marigold 18.00
Carnival Glass, Mug, Beaded Shell, Purple, Set Of 6 .... 200.00
Carnival Glass, Mug, Dandelion, Ice Green, Alleg.Commandry, May 1912 .... 100.00
Carnival Glass, Mug, Dandelion, Marigold, Alleg.Commandry, May 1912 .... 100.00
Carnival Glass, Mug, Fisherman, Purple .... 65.00 To 70.00
Carnival Glass, Mug, Heron, Purple 145.00
Carnival Glass, Mug, Orange Tree, Aqua 43.00
Carnival Glass, Mug, Orange Tree, Marigold .... 15.00 To 28.50
Carnival Glass, Mug, Orange Tree, Red 85.00
Carnival Glass, Mug, Parfait, Marigold 40.00
Carnival Glass, Mug, Shell & Jewel, Marigold 65.00
Carnival Glass, Mug, Singing Bird, Blue, Marked N 45.00
Carnival Glass, Mug, Singing Bird, Marigold 33.00
Carnival Glass, Mug, Singing Bird, Marigold, Marked N 35.00
Carnival Glass, Mug, Singing Bird, Purple, Marked N 42.00
Carnival Glass, Mug, Stork In Rushes, Marigold 18.00
Carnival Glass, Nappy, Butterfly, Green, 2 Handles, 7 In. 38.50
Carnival Glass, Nappy, Cherry Circle, Pastel Green, 2 Handled 65.00
Carnival Glass, Nappy, Grape & Cable, Marigold, 2 Handled 20.00
Carnival Glass, Nappy, Grape & Cable, Marigold, 2 Handled, Marked N 30.00
Carnival Glass, Nappy, Leaf Rays, Purple 28.00
Carnival Glass, Nappy, Leaf Rays, White Iridescent 35.00
Carnival Glass, Nappy, Leaf, Peach Opalescent 21.00
Carnival Glass, Nappy, Stippled Leaves, Marigold 15.00
Carnival Glass, Nappy, Strawberry, Amber, 2 Handled 27.00
Carnival Glass, Pitcher, Milk, Poinsettia, Marigold 35.00
Carnival Glass, Pitcher, Milk, Raspberry, Green, Northwood 140.00
Carnival Glass, Pitcher, Milk, Star Medallion, Marigold 27.00
Carnival Glass, Pitcher, Near-Cut, Green, 1 1/2 Quart 27.50
Carnival Glass, Pitcher, Octagon, Marigold, 8 In. 52.50
Carnival Glass, Pitcher, Raspberry, Marigold, N, 7 In. 49.00
Carnival Glass, Pitcher, Water, Apple, Marigold 145.00
Carnival Glass, Pitcher, Water, Crackle, Marigold 38.00
Carnival Glass, Pitcher, Water, Fashion, Marigold 75.00
Carnival Glass, Pitcher, Water, Floral & Grape, Amethyst 185.00
Carnival Glass, Pitcher, Water, Floral & Grape, Marigold 75.00
Carnival Glass, Pitcher, Water, Grape & Cable, Marigold 125.00
Carnival Glass, Pitcher, Water, Heavy Iris, Marigold 225.00
Carnival Glass, Pitcher, Water, Imperial Grape, Green 95.00
Carnival Glass, Pitcher, Water, Marilyn, Green 700.00
Carnival Glass, Pitcher, Water, Raspberry, Marigold, Northwood 125.00
Carnival Glass, Pitcher, Water, Robin, Marigold 190.00
Carnival Glass, Pitcher, Water, Singing Bird, Dark Purple 325.00
Carnival Glass, Pitcher, Water, Singing Bird, Marigold, Marked N .... 105.00 To 150.00
Carnival Glass, Pitcher, Water, Singing Bird, Purple, Northwood 325.00
Carnival Glass, Pitcher, Water, Split Diamond, Marigold, 3 X 2 In. 75.00
Carnival Glass, Plate, Acanthus, Marigold, 10 In. 125.00
Carnival Glass, Plate, Apple Twig, Marigold, 7 In. 19.00
Carnival Glass, Plate, Chop, Four Flowers, Purple 650.00
Carnival Glass, Plate, Chop, Wishbone & Spades, Purple 475.00
Carnival Glass, Plate, Chop, Wishbone, Marigold .... 250.00 To 295.00
Carnival Glass, Plate, Floral & Optic, Frosty White, Footed, 11 In.Diameter 105.00
Carnival Glass, Plate, Grape & Cable, Purple, Basket Weave Back, 9 In. 58.00
Carnival Glass, Plate, Grape & Cable, Purple, Marked N, 6 In. 70.00
Carnival Glass, Plate, Grape & Leaf, Marigold, Basket Weave Ground, 9 In. 30.00
Carnival Glass, Plate, Heavy Grape, Amethyst, Fenton, 8 In. 67.00
Carnival Glass, Plate, Heavy Grape, Purple, 8 In. 80.00
Carnival Glass, Plate, Holly, Cobalt Blue, 9 1/2 In. 80.00

Carnival Glass, Plate, Horses' Heads, Marigold, 7 1/2 In.	75.00
Carnival Glass, Plate, Imperial Jewels, Ice Blue, 8 1/2 In., Pair	20.00
Carnival Glass, Plate, Laurel Leaves, White, 6 In.	19.00
Carnival Glass, Plate, Leaf Chain, Green, 9 In.	75.00
Carnival Glass, Plate, Lion, Marigold, 6 In.	20.00
Carnival Glass, Plate, Luncheon, Stretch, White	18.50
Carnival Glass, Plate, Lustre Rose, Marigold, 9 In.	30.00
Carnival Glass, Plate, Peacock At Urn, Marigold, 9 In.	90.00
Carnival Glass, Plate, Peacock On Fence, White, Frosty, 9 In.	160.00
Carnival Glass, Plate, Peacock On Fence, White, N, 9 In.	165.00
Carnival Glass, Plate, Persian Garden, White, Fluted, 9 1/2 In.	90.00
Carnival Glass, Plate, Persian Garden, White, 6 In.	50.00
Carnival Glass, Plate, Persian Garden, White, 6 1/2 In.	67.50
Carnival Glass, Plate, Persian Medallion, Cobalt Blue, 9 In.	95.00
Carnival Glass, Plate, Pinecone, Gold, Iridescent, 6 1/4 In.	27.00
Carnival Glass, Plate, Pinecone, Marigold, 6 In.	19.00
Carnival Glass, Plate, Rose Show, Green, 9 1/2 In.	350.00
Carnival Glass, Plate, Rose Show, Ice Green, 9 1/2 In.	300.00
Carnival Glass, Plate, Rose Show, White, 9 In.	285.00
Carnival Glass, Plate, Scales, Marigold, 6 In.	21.00
Carnival Glass, Plate, Strawberry & Leaf, White, Basket Weave Outside, 8 In.	52.00
Carnival Glass, Plate, Strawberry, Green, N, 9 In.	75.00
Carnival Glass, Plate, Three Fruits, Amethyst, 9 In.	150.00
Carnival Glass, Plate, Three Fruits, Marigold, 9 In.	50.00
Carnival Glass, Plate, Three Fruits, Purple, 9 In.	70.00
Carnival Glass, Plate, Tree Bark, Marigold, 8 In.	12.50
Carnival Glass, Punch Set, Orange Tree, Blue, 8 Piece	260.00
Carnival Glass, Punch Set, Orange Tree, Marigold, 6 Piece	195.00
Carnival Glass, Relish, Pansy, Amber	29.00
Carnival Glass, Relish, Pansy, Amber, Handled, Round	16.00
Carnival Glass, Rose Bowl, Daisy & Plume, Marigold, 3 Footed, 5 In.	38.00
Carnival Glass, Rose Bowl, Louisa, Green, 3 Reeded Scroll Feet, 4 In.	45.00
Carnival Glass, Sauce, Acorn Burr, Marigold, Northwood	12.00
Carnival Glass, Sauce, Beaded Shell, Marigold	15.00
Carnival Glass, Sauce, Butterfly & Berry, Marigold, Claw Feet	22.00
Carnival Glass, Sauce, Grape & Gothic Arches, Dark Marigold	12.00
Carnival Glass, Sauce, Heavy Grape, Purple, Fenton	25.00
Carnival Glass, Sauce, Imperial Grape, Marigold	10.00
Carnival Glass, Sauce, Orange Tree, Marigold, Footed	18.00
Carnival Glass, Sauce, Peacock At Fountain, Amethyst	29.00
Carnival Glass, Sauce, Peacock At Fountain, Purple, Marked N	30.00
Carnival Glass, Sauce, Peacock's Tail, Amethyst	9.00
Carnival Glass, Sauce, Windflower, Marigold, Handled	22.00
Carnival Glass, Sauce, Windmill, Marigold	15.00
Carnival Glass, Sauce, Zippered Heart, Purple	20.00
Carnival Glass, Saucer, Kittens, Marigold, Turned-Up Sides, 4 1/2 In.	70.00
Carnival Glass, Saucer, Luster & Clear Clambroth, Marigold	10.00
Carnival Glass, Saucer, Soda Gold, Marigold	10.00
Carnival Glass, Sconce, Wall, Hammered Bell, White, Pair	350.00
Carnival Glass, Shade, Daisy, Marigold, 7 In.	35.00
Carnival Glass, Sherbet, Button & Cane, Deep Marigold	6.65
Carnival Glass, Spooner, Acorn Burr, Marigold, Marked N	37.00
Carnival Glass, Spooner, Grape & Gothic Arch, Dark Marigold	30.00 To 35.00
Carnival Glass, Spooner, Grape & Gothic Arch, Marigold	20.00
Carnival Glass, Spooner, Luster Rose, Marigold	22.00
Carnival Glass, Spooner, Maple Leaf, Blue	65.00
Carnival Glass, Spooner, Wreathed Cherry, Purple	65.00
Carnival Glass, Sugar & Creamer, Fire King, White	5.00
Carnival Glass, Sugar & Creamer, Grape & Cable, Purple, N	225.00
Carnival Glass, Sugar & Creamer, Pansy Spray, Marigold	38.00
Carnival Glass, Sugar & Creamer, Pansy, Marigold	31.00
Carnival Glass, Sugar & Creamer, Shell & Jewel, Green, Covered	25.00
Carnival Glass, Sugar, Colonial, Purple	30.00
Carnival Glass, Sugar, Grape & Gothic Arch, Marigold	35.00 To 38.00
Carnival Glass, Sugar, Grape & Gothic Arch, Pearl	95.00
Carnival Glass, Sugar, Strutting Peacock, Purple, Covered	47.00 To 48.00

Carnival Glass, Table Set, Butterfly & Berries, Marigold, Fenton, 5 Piece	175.00
Carnival Glass, Table Set, Grape & Cable, Purple, St.Joseph, Mich., 4 Piece	425.00
Carnival Glass, Table Set, Grape, Marigold, Northwood, 4 Piece	145.00
Carnival Glass, Table Set, Lustre Rose, Marigold, 4 Piece	125.00
Carnival Glass, Table Set, Maple Leaf, Purple, 3 Piece	235.00
Carnival Glass, Tankard, Rose Marie, Cobalt, 8 3/4 X 4 In.	200.00
Carnival Glass, Tankard, Water, Tree Bark, Marigold, 8 3/4 In.	24.75
Carnival Glass, Toothpick, Bicentennial, Red	6.00
Carnival Glass, Toothpick, Flute, Green	55.00
Carnival Glass, Toothpick, Flute, Purple	60.00
Carnival Glass, Toothpick, Kitten, Marigold	70.00
Carnival Glass, Toothpick, S Repeat, Amethyst	50.00
Carnival Glass, Town Pump, Purple	475.00
Carnival Glass, Tray, Dresser, Grape & Cable, Ice Blue, 11 In.	265.00
Carnival Glass, Tray, Dresser, Grape & Cable, Marigold	125.00
Carnival Glass, Tray, Dresser, Grape & Cable, Purple	150.00
Carnival Glass, Tray, Pin, Butterfly, Pink	45.00
Carnival Glass, Tumbler, Acorn Burr, Green, N	50.00
Carnival Glass, Tumbler, Acorn Burr, Purple, Marked N	42.00 To 50.00
Carnival Glass, Tumbler, Apple Tree, Blue	30.00
Carnival Glass, Tumbler, Blackberry & Butterfly, Marigold	17.00
Carnival Glass, Tumbler, Blackberry Block, Blue	45.00
Carnival Glass, Tumbler, Blackberry, Blue	39.50
Carnival Glass, Tumbler, Blueberry, Blue	50.00
Carnival Glass, Tumbler, Bouquet, Marigold	22.00
Carnival Glass, Tumbler, Butterfly & Berry, Blue	33.00
Carnival Glass, Tumbler, Butterfly & Berry, Cobalt	30.00
Carnival Glass, Tumbler, Butterfly & Berry, Marigold	15.00 To 17.50
Carnival Glass, Tumbler, Butterfly & Berry, Purple	15.00 To 20.00
Carnival Glass, Tumbler, Butterfly & Fern, Marigold	32.00
Carnival Glass, Tumbler, Butterfly, Cobalt Blue	35.00
Carnival Glass, Tumbler, Crocus, Ice Green, Enameled	35.00
Carnival Glass, Tumbler, Daisy & Lattice, Light Marigold	12.50
Carnival Glass, Tumbler, Dandelion, Purple, Northwood	45.00
Carnival Glass, Tumbler, Diamond & Daisy, Marigold	35.00
Carnival Glass, Tumbler, Diamond, Amethyst, Millersburg	40.00
Carnival Glass, Tumbler, Diamond, Green, Millersburg	35.00
Carnival Glass, Tumbler, Double Star, Green	55.00
Carnival Glass, Tumbler, Fashion, Marigold	18.00 To 40.00
Carnival Glass, Tumbler, Fentonia, Blue	47.00
Carnival Glass, Tumbler, Floral & Grape, Amethyst	25.00 To 30.00
Carnival Glass, Tumbler, Floral & Grape, Marigold	15.00
Carnival Glass, Tumbler, Fluffy Peacock, Amethyst	65.00
Carnival Glass, Tumbler, Flute, Marigold, 7 Panels	30.00
Carnival Glass, Tumbler, God & Home, Amethyst	175.00
Carnival Glass, Tumbler, Grape & Cable, Marigold	18.00
Carnival Glass, Tumbler, Grape & Cable, Marigold, Signed N	26.00
Carnival Glass, Tumbler, Grape & Cable, Purple	25.00
Carnival Glass, Tumbler, Grape & Cable, Purple, Signed N	28.00 To 31.00
Carnival Glass, Tumbler, Grape & Gothic Arch, Blue	40.00
Carnival Glass, Tumbler, Grape & Gothic Arch, Cobalt	25.00
Carnival Glass, Tumbler, Grape & Gothic Arch, Green	49.00
Carnival Glass, Tumbler, Grape & Gothic Arch, Marigold	12.00 To 18.00
Carnival Glass, Tumbler, Grape Arbor, Marigold	25.00
Carnival Glass, Tumbler, Grape, Brown Iridescent, Signed N	25.00
Carnival Glass, Tumbler, Grapevine & Lattice, Amethyst	37.00
Carnival Glass, Tumbler, Harvest Flower, Marigold	95.00
Carnival Glass, Tumbler, Heavy Iris, Marigold	40.00
Carnival Glass, Tumbler, Hobstar Band, Marigold	35.00
Carnival Glass, Tumbler, Imperial Grape, Marigold	8.00 To 15.00
Carnival Glass, Tumbler, Inverted Coin Dot, Marigold	30.00
Carnival Glass, Tumbler, Jeweled Heart, Marigold	66.65
Carnival Glass, Tumbler, Lattice & Daisy, Marigold	15.00
Carnival Glass, Tumbler, Lattice & Grape, Blue	40.00
Carnival Glass, Tumbler, Lattice & Grape, Cobalt Blue	35.00
Carnival Glass, Tumbler, Lattice & Grape, Marigold	10.00

Carnival Glass, Tumbler, Louisa, Light Marigold 15.00
Carnival Glass, Tumbler, Lustre Rose, Marigold 15.00
Carnival Glass, Tumbler, Lustre Rose, Marigold, Imperial 15.00
Carnival Glass, Tumbler, Lustre Rose, Purple 39.00
Carnival Glass, Tumbler, Orange Tree, Marigold, Footed 30.00
Carnival Glass, Tumbler, Oriental Poppy, Green 45.00
Carnival Glass, Tumbler, Oriental Poppy, Green, N 45.00
Carnival Glass, Tumbler, Oriental Poppy, Marigold 30.00
Carnival Glass, Tumbler, Oriental Poppy, Purple, N 45.00
Carnival Glass, Tumbler, Paneled Dandelion, Blue 38.00
Carnival Glass, Tumbler, Peach, Blue 55.00
Carnival Glass, Tumbler, Peacock At Fountain, Blue 25.00
Carnival Glass, Tumbler, Peacock At Fountain, Purple, N 35.00
Carnival Glass, Tumbler, Peacock At Fountain, White 55.00
Carnival Glass, Tumbler, Rambler Rose, Amethyst 32.00
Carnival Glass, Tumbler, Rambler Rose, Blue 32.00
Carnival Glass, Tumbler, Rambler Rose, Marigold .... 12.50 To 18.00
Carnival Glass, Tumbler, Raspberry, Amethyst 30.00
Carnival Glass, Tumbler, Raspberry, Purple, Northwood 45.00
Carnival Glass, Tumbler, Scale Band, Marigold 20.00
Carnival Glass, Tumbler, Shasta Daisy, Marigold, Enameled 15.00
Carnival Glass, Tumbler, Singing Bird, Deep Purple 40.00
Carnival Glass, Tumbler, Singing Bird, Green 25.00
Carnival Glass, Tumbler, Singing Bird, Green, Signed N 24.00
Carnival Glass, Tumbler, Singing Bird, Purple, Northwood 50.00
Carnival Glass, Tumbler, Soda Gold, Marigold 27.00
Carnival Glass, Tumbler, Soda Gold, Marigold, Cone Shape 10.00
Carnival Glass, Tumbler, Star Medallion, Marigold .... 29.00 To 32.00
Carnival Glass, Tumbler, Stork In Rushes, Blue 28.00
Carnival Glass, Tumbler, Stork In Rushes, Marigold 15.00
Carnival Glass, Tumbler, Strawberry Scroll, Blue 185.00
Carnival Glass, Tumbler, Ten Mums, Blue 45.00
Carnival Glass, Tumbler, Ten Mums, Marigold .... 29.00 To 45.00
Carnival Glass, Tumbler, Thumbprint, Marigold, Signed N 26.00
Carnival Glass, Tumbler, Thumbprint, Purple, Signed N 30.00
Carnival Glass, Tumbler, Tree Bark, Marigold 4.95
Carnival Glass, Tumbler, Vineyard, Green 25.00
Carnival Glass, Tumbler, Vineyard, Marigold .... 17.50 To 19.00
Carnival Glass, Tumbler, Vintage, Marigold, Fenton 17.00
Carnival Glass, Tumbler, Vintage, Purple 35.00
Carnival Glass, Tumbler, Water Lily & Cattail, Marigold 11.00
Carnival Glass, Tumbler, Water Lily & Cattail, Marigold, Marked N 15.00
Carnival Glass, Tumbler, 474, Marigold 15.00
Carnival Glass, Vase, Beaded Bull's-Eye, Marigold, 11 In. 25.00
Carnival Glass, Vase, Beaded Bull's-Eye, Marigold, 12 In. 25.00
Carnival Glass, Vase, Diamond & Rib, Green, 10 In. 8.00
Carnival Glass, Vase, Diamond & Rib, Green, 16 In.High 24.00
Carnival Glass, Vase, Drapery, Ice Blue, Tricornered, Signed N 80.00
Carnival Glass, Vase, Fine Rib, Purple, Crimped & Ruffled Top, 15 3/4 In. 39.50
Carnival Glass, Vase, Fine Rib, Purple, Crimped & Ruffled Top, 16 1/2 In. 39.50
Carnival Glass, Vase, Knotted Beads, Blue, 9 1/2 In.High 17.50
Carnival Glass, Vase, Lined Lattice, Pastel Marigold, 8 In. 25.00
Carnival Glass, Vase, Mary Ann, Deep Marigold, Handled, 6 3/8 In. 35.00
Carnival Glass, Vase, Mary Ann, Marigold, Amethyst Base, 2 Handled, 6 1/2 In. 35.00
Carnival Glass, Vase, Mary Ann, Purple, Amethyst Base, 2 Handled, 6 1/2 In. 60.00
Carnival Glass, Vase, Pinecone, Dark Blue, 7 1/2 In. 45.00
Carnival Glass, Vase, Pulled Loop, Purple, 10 1/2 In. 15.00
Carnival Glass, Vase, Ribbed, Purple, Signed N, 9 1/4 In. 28.00
Carnival Glass, Vase, Ripple, Green, 11 In.High 17.50
Carnival Glass, Vase, Ripple, Marigold, Scalloped Top, 8 3/4 In. 10.00
Carnival Glass, Vase, Ripple, Marigold, 11 In.High 12.50
Carnival Glass, Vase, Ripple, Purple, 8 In. 8.50
Carnival Glass, Vase, Ripple, Purple, 11 In. 21.00
Carnival Glass, Vase, Rustic, White, 10 In. 25.00
Carnival Glass, Vase, Ten Fluted, Marigold To Clear, Northwood, 14 In. 40.00
Carnival Glass, Vase, Tree Bark, Amethyst, Northwood, 10 In. 30.00

Carnival Glass, Vase, Tree Bark, Marigold, 7 1/2 In., Pair	23.00
Carnival Glass, Vase, Tree Bark, Purple, Marked N, 10 1/2 In.	20.00
Carnival Glass, Vase, Tree Trunk, Green, 10 In.High	21.00
Carnival Glass, Vase, Twig, Purple, 4 1/2 In.	295.00
Carnival Glass, Water Set, Acorn Burr, Marigold, N, 7 Piece	350.00 To 495.00
Carnival Glass, Water Set, Grape & Cable, Marigold, 7 Piece	265.00 To 275.00
Carnival Glass, Water Set, Grape & Cable, Purple, N, 7 Piece	375.00 To 450.00
Carnival Glass, Water Set, Grape & Cable, Purple, 7 Piece	300.00
Carnival Glass, Water Set, Imperial Grape, Marigold, 7 Piece	175.00
Carnival Glass, Water Set, Lattice & Grape, Marigold, 7 Piece	175.00
Carnival Glass, Water Set, Louisa, Marigold, 9 Piece	135.00
Carnival Glass, Water Set, Peacock At Fountain, Blue, 7 Piece	365.00
Carnival Glass, Water Set, Robin, Cobalt Blue, Imperial, 7 Piece	135.00
Carnival Glass, Water Set, Singing Bird, Green, 7 Piece	325.00
Carnival Glass, Water Set, Tiger Lily, Marigold, Iridescent, 5 Piece	175.00
Carnival Glass, Water Set, Tiger Lily, Marigold, 7 Piece	200.00
Carnival Glass, Water Set, Tree Bark, Marigold, 3 Piece	29.75
Carnival Glass, Water Set, Tree Bark, Marigold, 6 Piece	55.00
Carnival Glass, Water Set, Tree Bark, Marigold, 9 Piece	45.00 To 49.75
Carnival Glass, Wine Set, Golden Harvest, Marigold, 9 Piece	175.00
Carnival Glass, Wine, Orange Tree, Marigold	12.00
Carousel, Horse, Carved & Painted Wood, Iron Stand, 48 X 43 In.	425.00
Carousel, Horse, Painted, 38 1/2 In. *Illus*	550.00
Carousel, Horse, Spillman, C.1910, Roman Type, Wooden, Saddle, 63 In.	525.00
Carousel, Horse, Wooden, C.1890	250.00
Carousel, Polar Bear, Painted Wood, Iron Wheels, C.1850, 39 In.	650.00

Carousel, Horse, Painted, 38 1/2 In.

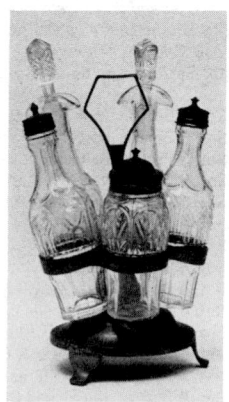

Castor Set, 5 Bottles, Pewter,
American, C.1840
(See Page 84)

Cased glass is made with one thin layer of glass over another layer or layers
of colored glass. Many types of art glass were cased. Cased glass is
usually a well-made piece by a reputable factory.

Cased Glass, Basket, White Outside, Cranberry Inside, Amber Handle, 6 1/2 In	75.00
Cased Glass, Bowl, Amethyst To Clear, Grapes & Willow Leaves, 12 In.	57.50
Cased Glass, Celery, Cranberry Overlay, Decorated	110.00
Cased Glass, Condiment Set, Three Petal, Pink, Metal Loop Center Handle	122.00
Cased Glass, Decanter, Green & Pink, White Gold Swirls, 16 In., Pair	45.00
Cased Glass, Goblet, Ale, Cranberry, Engraved Barley & Hops, C.1820	43.50
Cased Glass, Muffineer, Blue To White, Tin Star Top, 6 3/8 In.	57.00
Cased Glass, Muffineer, Pale Green, Pinecone	58.00
Cased Glass, Muffineer, Pink, Cone	68.00
Cased Glass, Pitcher, Water, Pink, Cone	175.00
Cased Glass, Pitcher, Water, White Overlay, Honeycomb, Cranberry Lined	175.00
Cased Glass, Rose Bowl, White Casing, Blue To Pale Blue, Crimped, 5 1/2 In.	75.00

Cased Glass, Rose Bowl, White Casing, Rose To Pink, Crimped Edge, 4 In.	68.00
Cased Glass, Salt & Pepper, Pink & Blue, Pinecone	45.00
Cased Glass, Salt, Overshot, Gilt Edge, Square, 2 In.	7.00
Cased Glass, Saltshaker, Blue, Leaf Umbrella	22.00
Cased Glass, Saltshaker, Blue, Shell	22.00
Cased Glass, Saltshaker, Green, Shell	22.00
Cased Glass, Saltshaker, Pink, Shell	22.00
Cased Glass, Saltshaker, Yellow, Ribbed	22.50
Cased Glass, Shade, Dome Shape, Dark Green, 10 In.	85.00
Cased Glass, Shade, Dome Shape, Light Green, 10 In.	75.00
Cased Glass, Toothpick, Blue, Florette	42.00
Cased Glass, Toothpick, Yellow, Florette Pattern	55.00
Cased Glass, Tumbler, Pink, Cone	24.00
Cased Glass, Tumbler, White, Cranberry Interior, Eye Dots	30.00
Cased Glass, Vase, Apple Green, Opalescent Hobnail Casing, Ruffled, 6 In.	32.00
Cased Glass, Vase, Bud, French, Applied Clear Handles, 4 3/4 In.	22.00
Cased Glass, Vase, Clear Over White, Ruffled Crimped Top, 8 1/2 In., Pair	18.00
Cased Glass, Vase, Pink, Enamel Decoration, 8 1/2 In.	75.00
Cased Glass, Vase, Pink, Hand-Painted Mountain Scenes, 3 3/4 In., Pair	95.00
Cased Glass, Vase, Ruby, Cut To Clear, Engraved Floral, Miter & Oval, 10 In.	90.00
Cased Glass, Vase, White & Yellow, 9 1/4 In.	12.50
Cased Glass, Witch's Ball, Bright Colors On White, 4 1/2 In. Diameter	49.75

Castor sets have been known as early as 1705. Most of those that have been found today date from Victorian times. A castor set usually consists of a silver-plated frame that holds three to seven condiment bottles. The pickle castor was a single glass jar about six inches high and held in a silver frame. A cover and tongs were kept with the jar. They were popular from 1890 to 1900. The McK numbers refer to the book American Glass by George and Helen McKearin.

Castor Set, see also Bohemian Glass, Castor Set, Rubena, Castor Set

Castor Set, 3 Bottles, Leaf & Lattice, Silver Holder, Miniature	30.00
Castor Set, 3 Bottles, Porcelain, Hand-Painted	27.50
Castor Set, 3 Bottles, Rubena Cut Panels, English Silver Plate Holder	110.00
Castor Set, 3 Bottles, Waffle, Glass Triangular Base, Pewter Tops	90.00
Castor Set, 4 Bottles, American Pattern, Miniature	50.00
Castor Set, 4 Bottles, Blown, Three Mold, Eben Smith Pewter Frame	160.00
Castor Set, 4 Bottles, Cut Glass	65.00
Castor Set, 4 Bottles, Etched & Cut Glass, 2 Pewter Tops, Silver Holder	95.00
Castor Set, 4 Bottles, Flint, McK G I-14, Pewter Frame, Eben Smith Mark	160.00
Castor Set, 4 Bottles, Four Panel, Blue, Blue Glass Frame	125.00
Castor Set, 4 Bottles, Rubena Glass, Silver Plate Frame	165.00
Castor Set, 5 Bottles, Bellflower & Fine Rib, Single Vine, Pewter Holder	275.00
Castor Set, 5 Bottles, Blown, Three Mold, McK G I-14, Pewter Frame	95.00
Castor Set, 5 Bottles, Cut Etched Grape, Revolving Silver Plate Frame	62.50
Castor Set, 5 Bottles, Etched, Revolving Silver Frame With Bell, 1870	175.00
Castor Set, 5 Bottles, Flint, Blown, Pewter Frame, McK G I-14	95.00
Castor Set, 5 Bottles, Gothic, Pewter Frame	40.00
Castor Set, 5 Bottles, Honeycomb & Fern, Silver Plate Frame, 14 1/2 In.	77.50
Castor Set, 5 Bottles, Paneled Wheat, Round	75.00
Castor Set, 5 Bottles, Pewter, American, C.1840 .... *Illus*	100.00
Castor Set, 5 Bottles, Silver Stand, Bone Spoon	225.00
Castor Set, 5 Bottles, Vaseline Glass, Revolving Gallery Type Frame	100.00
Castor Set, 6 Bottles, Blown, Three Mold, R.Gleason Frame, McK G I-14	180.00

Castor, Pickle, see also Amberina, Castor, Pickle, Mt. Washington, Castor, Pickle

Castor, Pickle, Almond Thumbprint, Etched Floral, Silver Plate Frame, Hinged	110.00
Castor, Pickle, Amber Button Insert, Footed Silver Frame & Tongs	95.00
Castor, Pickle, Beaded Band, Footed Frame	55.00
Castor, Pickle, Bulbous Insert, Cover, Frame, & Tongs	55.00
Castor, Pickle, Buttons & Bows, Ornate Frame, Tongs	95.00
Castor, Pickle, Clear & Stippled Glass Insert, Boston Silver Co.	145.00
Castor, Pickle, Clear Glass Insert, Openwork Flower Holder, Barbour	85.00
Castor, Pickle, Clear Patterned Insert, Fancy Footed Frame & Tongs	63.00
Castor, Pickle, Clear Swirl Line	85.00

Castor, Pickle, Cranberry Glass, Enamel Flowers, Tongs & Fancy Frame	225.00
Castor, Pickle, Cranberry Glass, Silver Frame, 10 In.	165.00
Castor, Pickle, Cranberry Thumbprint, Tongs	150.00
Castor, Pickle, Cranberry, Enamel & Gold, Poole Silver Frame & Tongs	178.00
Castor, Pickle, Cranberry, Floral Overlay	175.00
Castor, Pickle, Cut Diamond, Fan, & Nailhead Vesica, Silver Plate Tongs	60.00
Castor, Pickle, Daisy & Button, Amber, Silver Collar, Lid, Handle, & Tongs	89.50
Castor, Pickle, Daisy Insert, Silver Plate Frame & Tongs, Victorian	57.50
Castor, Pickle, Diamond Block, Rogers-Smith Co. Silver Frame & Tongs	62.00
Castor, Pickle, Double Swirled Insert, Middletown Center Handle Frame	30.00
Castor, Pickle, Double, Cucumber & Vine Glass Inserts, 12 1/2 In.High	85.00
Castor, Pickle, Embossed Birds & Floral, Clear & Frosted, Reed & Barton	135.00
Castor, Pickle, Enameled Daisies, Sapphire Blue, Maple Leaves Silver Frame	150.00
Castor, Pickle, Etched, Double, Footed Silver Frame	98.00
Castor, Pickle, Fancy Clear Insert, Ornate Silver Plate Frame & Tongs	55.00
Castor, Pickle, Frosted & Clear Cherubs & Birds, Reed & Barton Frame	125.00
Castor, Pickle, Frosted, Reed & Barton Handled Silver Holder	95.00
Castor, Pickle, Inverted Thumbprint, Amber, Swirled Top, Silver Holder	75.00
Castor, Pickle, Inverted Thumbprint, Clear, Enamel Decoration, Fork	65.00
Castor, Pickle, Pairpoint, Scenic Jar, Silver Plate Frame	70.00
Castor, Pickle, Paneled Insert, Engraved Floral, Tongs, Union Silver Co.	32.00
Castor, Pickle, Pressed Glass, Brooklyn Silver Co. Frame & Domed Lid	42.00
Castor, Pickle, Red Block Insert, Silver Plate Frame	45.00
Castor, Pickle, Reed & Barton Frame, Prismatic Jar	31.00
Castor, Pickle, Russian Cut Crystal, Embossed Meriden Frame & Lid	63.00
Castor, Pickle, Sapphire Blue Insert, Floral & Gold, Silver Plate Frame	225.00
Castor, Pickle, Sawtooth & Fan Insert, Silver Frame & Ornate Fork	55.00
Castor, Pickle, Silver Plate, Victorian, Glass Liner, H.Schade Co., N.Y.	65.00
Castor, Pickle, Sunk Daisy, Silver Plate Frame & Tongs, 11 1/2 In.	63.00
Castor, Pickle, Tree Of Life, Silver Frame, Cover, & Tongs, 14 In.	87.50
Castor, Pickle, Vaseline Insert, Fancy Top, Bird Cutout Tongs	150.00
Castor, Pickle, Zipper & Panel, Repousse Silver Plate Frame & Tongs	65.00
Castor, Sugar, Blue Inverted Thumbprint, Rogers Footed Frame & 12 Spoons	125.00

Catalogue, see Paper, Catalogue

Cauldon is an English pottery factory working after 1905.

Cauldon, see also Indian Tree

Cauldon, Bowl, Vegetable, Covered, Chariot	45.00
Cauldon, Cup & Saucer, Roses & Coin Gold On Mint Green	16.50
Cauldon, Plate, Greek Key Bands, Burley & Co., 5 7/8 In.	4.50
Cauldon, Plate, Roses & Pansies, Cobalt & Gold Trim, 9 5/8 In.	18.50
Cauldon, Pot, Chocolate, Tankard Type, Ivory Ground, Gold Scrolls, 9 In.High	45.00

Celadon is a Chinese porcelain having a velvet-textured green-gray glaze.
Japanese and Korean factories also made a celadon-colored glaze.

Celadon, Bottle, Korean, Tear Shape, Mums & Lotus Petal, C.1250, 12 7/8 In.	200.00
Celadon, Bowl, Birds & Flowers, Scalloped Edge, 5 1/2 In.	8.00
Celadon, Bowl, Medium Green, Fern Leaf Decoration, 5 In.	30.00
Celadon, Bowl, Molded Fish, Sung, 8 In.	375.00
Celadon, Charger, Peony, Shasta Daisies, & Butterflies, Chien Lung, 10 In.	70.00
Celadon, Figurine, Kirin, Uplifted Head, C.1850, 10 1/2 In.	110.00
Celadon, Incense Burner, Foo Dog, Dark Green, C.1900, 7 In.	40.00
Celadon, Jar, Korean, Black & White Mums & Cranes, C.1190, 11 5/8 In.	175.00
Celadon, Koro, Silvered Lid, Decorated Burner, Footed, C.1850, 4 1/2 In.	75.00
Celadon, Maebyong, Korean, Black & White Cranes, C.1250, 11 3/8 In.	1750.00
Celadon, Plate, Cabbage & Butterfly, 6 In.	28.00
Celadon, Platter, Birds, Butterflies, & Flowering Branches, C.1750, 14 In.	225.00
Celadon, Teapot, Bulbous, Raised Pastel Floral Design, C.1800s, 5 X 7 1/2 In	45.00
Celadon, Teapot, Green, Decorated	35.00
Celadon, Teapot, Raised Pastel Floral, Bulbous, C.1850, 5 X 7 1/2 In.	45.00
Celadon, Vase, Buddhistic Symbols, Flared Mouth, Baluster, 13 In.	50.00
Celadon, Vase, Enamel Trees, White Flowers, & Bluebird On Branch, 14 In.	240.00
Celluloid, Box, Collar, Hinged, Ivory, Holly & Berries, 7 X 6 In.	18.00
Celluloid, Dresser Set, Brown, Tray & 6 Pieces	10.00
Celluloid, Dresser Set, Child's, Bluebird In Pink Ribbon, 3 Piece	15.00
Celluloid, Dresser Set, Ivory Color, 7 Piece	20.00
Celluloid, Dresser Set, 8 Piece	29.00

Centennial, Ale Glass, Paneled, Star, 1776 & 1876	58.00
Centennial, Ale Glass, Star & 1776, Star & 1876 On Reverse	25.00
Centennial, Bandana, Philadelphia, 1876, Buildings, 27 X 23 In.	75.00
Centennial, Button, Philadelphia Sesquicentennial, 1776-1926	3.50
Centennial, Mirror, Hand, Philadelphia Sesquicentennial, 1776-1926	10.00
Centennial, Ribbon, Philadelphia, 1876, Silk, Brass Eagle Pin	25.00
Centennial, Tumbler, 1964, Hoover Dam	5.00
Ceramic Art Co., Barrel, Ivory, Indented Staves, Raised Hoops, 3 1/2 In.	35.00
Ceramic Art Co., Bowl, Green, Floral Festoons Inside, 4 X 1 3/4 In.	22.50
Ceramic Art Co., Box, Domed Lid, Pink Roses, Gold Rococo, 4 X 1 3/4 In.	68.00
Ceramic Art Co., Cup & Saucer, Belleek, Ribbed, Gold Leaves, Ornate Handle	85.00
Ceramic Art Co., Cup & Saucer, Child's, Belleek, Cox Type Brownies, Gold	45.00
Ceramic Art Co., Cup & Saucer, Chocolate, Gold Paste Floral On Pale Blue	85.00
Ceramic Art Co., Mug, Belleek, Gentlemen Carousing On Gold, Gold Handle	65.00
Ceramic Art Co., Mug, Gray, White Band With Vines & Grapes	35.00
Ceramic Art Co., Perfume Burner, Belleek, Floral, 24K Gold Trim, 2 1/2 In.	75.00
Ceramic Art Co., Pitcher, Cider, Belleek, Vintage Decoration	75.00
Ceramic Art Co., Pitcher, Cider, Cherries & Green Leaves On Mocha, 6 In.	69.95
Ceramic Art Co., Salt, Belleek, Gold Design Edge, Palette Mark	8.00
Ceramic Art Co., Salt, Belleek, Pink & Gold Coral, 6 Shells Form Sides	38.00
Ceramic Art Co., Salt, Belleek, Swan, Gold Trim, Pink Palette Mark	12.00
Ceramic Art Co., Sherbet, Belleek, Matte, Gold Floral, 2 Handles, Ruffled	85.00
Ceramic Art Co., Tankard, Belleek, Green, Berries, German Verse, 1898, 15 In.	110.00
Ceramic Art Co., Tankard, Portrait Of Monk, Signed, 5 1/2 In.	95.00
Ceramic Art Co., Vase, Belleek, Oriental Maiden, Water Scene, Howe, 11 In.	100.00
Ceramic Art Co., Vase, Belleek, Yellow Daffodils, Green, Brown, 1906, 11 In.	95.00
Ceramic Art Co., Vase, Belleek, Yellow Roses, Gold, Palette Mark, 11 1/2 In.	65.00

Chalkware is really plaster of Paris decorated with watercolors. The pieces were molded from known Staffordshire and other porcelain models and painted and sold as inexpensive decorations. Most of this type of chalkware was made from about 1820 to 1870.

Chalkware, Box, Pennsylvania Dutch, Hand-Painted Designs, C.1820, 5 X 4 In.	65.00
Chalkware, Bust, Negro Man, 15 In.	72.00
Chalkware, Figurine, see also Kewpie	
Chalkware, Figurine, Circus Elephant, Sequins, 9 1/2 In.	15.00
Chalkware, Figurine, Dog Leaning Against A Tub, Frock Coat, 4 1/2 In.	15.00
Chalkware, Figurine, Dutch Milkmaid, Fisherman, 20 In.High, Pair	67.50
Chalkware, Figurine, Eagle, Marked God Bless America, 11 In.	6.00
Chalkware, Figurine, Lion Holding Green Serpent In Paw, 7 X 7 In., Pair	65.00
Chalkware, Figurine, Santa Claus, Japan, 3 In.	.85
Chalkware, Figurine, Scottie, 6 In.	8.50
Chalkware, Figurine, Stag, Reclining, Pennsylvania, C.1850, Painted, 9 In.	250.00
Chalkware, Figurine, Stork With Baby On Back, Metal Legs, Paper Box, 5 In.	6.50
Chalkware, Figurine, Victorian Child Dancing, Oil Colors, 17 In.High	85.00
Chalkware, Holder, Watch, American, C.1850, Bird, Painted, 12 In.	375.00
Chalkware, Plaque, The Storm, Gold Border, Oval, 16 1/2 X 13 1/2 In.	30.00
Charlie Chaplin, see also Candy Container, Charlie Chaplin	
Charlie Chaplin, Book, Comic, Funny Stunts, 1917, 12 X 15 In.	26.00
Charlie Chaplin, Box, Pencil, Tin	12.00
Charlie Chaplin, Doll, Straw Body, 8 In.	60.00
Charlie Chaplin, Film, The Stolen Umbrella, Keystone, C.1930, 16mm.	16.00
Charlie Chaplin, Music Sheet, Funniest Man Of Them All, 1915, 11 X 14 In.	20.00
Charlie Chaplin, Photograph, Autographed, C.1915, 5 X 7 In.	7.00
Charlie Chaplin, Puppet, Dancing, Jointed, C.1930, 16 In.	9.50
Charlie Chaplin, Puppet, Magic Illusion, Cardboard, C.1930, 10 In.	30.00
Charlie McCarthy, Book, A Day With Charlie McCarthy, 1938, Picture	6.00
Charlie McCarthy, Doll, Paper, Cut	10.00
Charlie McCarthy, Dummy, 20 In.	45.00
Charlie McCarthy, Radio, Metal, Charlie On Front	175.00
Charlie McCarthy, Spoon, Detective	5.00
Charlie McCarthy, Spoon, Duchess, 5 In.	3.00

Chelsea grape pattern was made before 1840. A small bunch of grapes in a raised design, colored with purple or blue luster, is on the border of the white plate. Most of the pieces are unmarked. The pattern is sometimes called Aynsley or Grandmother.

Chelsea Grape, Cup Plate, Luster, 4 In.	15.00
Chelsea Grape, Plate, 7 In.	20.00
Chelsea Grape, Saucer	5.00
Chelsea Grape, Sugar, Covered	30.00

Chelsea porcelain was made in the Chelsea area of London from about 1745 to 1784. Recent copies of this work have been made from the original molds.

Chelsea, Cup & Saucer, Sprig	25.00
Chelsea, Pitcher, Milk, Blue & White Birds	55.00
Chelsea, Plate, Blue Flower, 8 In.	6.00
Chelsea, Plate, Kakiemon, Red Anchor Period, 9 In. *Illus*	320.00
Chelsea, Plate, Sprig, 7 In.	7.00
Chesapeake, Pitcher, Egyptian Desert Scene, Browns, Footed, C.1900, 7 In.	75.00

Chinese export porcelain is all the many kinds of porcelain made in China for export to America and Europe in the 18th and 19th centuries. Included in the category are Nanking, Canton, Chinese Lowestoft, Armorial, Jesuit, and other types of the ware.

Chinese Export, see also Canton, Celadon, Nanking

Chinese Export, Basin, Blue & White, Bird & Peony Tree, C.1750, 15 1/8 In.	300.00
Chinese Export, Basin, Famille Rose, Lotus, Insects, C.1820, 14 1/8 In.	450.00
Chinese Export, Basin, Ladies & Child At Table, C.1850, 13 1/2 In.	80.00
Chinese Export, Beaker & Saucer, Famille Rose, Armorial, Rigby, C.1750	400.00
Chinese Export, Beaker, Blue & White, Shou & Peonies, C.1850, 15 1/2 In.	150.00
Chinese Export, Beaker, Famille Verte, Court Figures, C.1850, 9 1/4 In.	125.00
Chinese Export, Beaker, Mandarin Palette, C.1780, 10 3/8 In.	150.00
Chinese Export, Bottle, White, Floral & Leaf Neck, 12 1/2 In., Pair	225.00
Chinese Export, Bowl & Saucer, Bouillon, Famille Rose, Armorial, C.1790, Pair	500.00
Chinese Export, Bowl, American Eagle, Gilt, Square, 9 1/2 In., Pair	700.00
Chinese Export, Bowl, Batavian Ware, Famille Rose, Landscapes, C.1750, 10 In.	450.00
Chinese Export, Bowl, Berry, Famille Rose, Floral Bouquets, C.1760, 6 1/2 In.	54.50
Chinese Export, Bowl, Blue & White, Figure Crossing Bridge, C.1800, 11 In.	225.00
Chinese Export, Bowl, Court Figures, Floral Branch, C.1780, 7 7/8 In.	125.00
Chinese Export, Bowl, Crimson Floral Center, C.1790, 8 3/4 In.	125.00
Chinese Export, Bowl, Deep Blue Border, Gold Stars, Gold Sprigs, 4 1/2 In.	45.00
Chinese Export, Bowl, Dignitary On Donkey, Floral, C.1820, 5 7/8 In.	70.00
Chinese Export, Bowl, En Grisaille, Famille Rose, Armorial, C.1760, 5 In.	70.00
Chinese Export, Bowl, En Grisaille, Seamstress, C.1750, 5 1/2 In.	250.00
Chinese Export, Bowl, Famille Rose, Armorial, Gordon, C.1780, 9 1/4 In.	375.00
Chinese Export, Bowl, Famille Rose, Cockerel, Rockwork, Floral, C.1750, 15 In.	600.00
Chinese Export, Bowl, Famille Rose, Crested, Birds, Floral, C.1755, 8 In.	175.00
Chinese Export, Bowl, Famille Rose, Figures In Garden, C.1770, 15 1/4 In.	400.00
Chinese Export, Bowl, Famille Rose, Figures, Peonies, C.1790, 15 1/8 In.	600.00
Chinese Export, Bowl, Famille Rose, Floral & Diaper Bands, C.1790, 12 In.	300.00
Chinese Export, Bowl, Famille Rose, Floral & Masks, C.1780, 10 1/4 In.	400.00
Chinese Export, Bowl, Famille Rose, Floral Bouquet Center, C.1790, 8 5/8 In.	50.00
Chinese Export, Bowl, Famille Rose, Floral Bouquets, C.1790, 8 In.	130.00
Chinese Export, Bowl, Famille Rose, Floral Medallion, C.1780, 7 3/4 In.	150.00
Chinese Export, Bowl, Famille Rose, Flower-Filled Vases, C.1780, 9 1/4 In.	275.00
Chinese Export, Bowl, Famille Rose, Gold & Red Pheasants, C.1755, 10 5/8 In.	200.00
Chinese Export, Bowl, Famille Rose, La Pompadour, C.1740, 10 In.	400.00
Chinese Export, Bowl, Famille Rose, Oriental Figures, C.1750, 11 1/8 In.	700.00
Chinese Export, Bowl, Famille Rose, Oriental Figures, C.1780, 11 1/4 In.	400.00
Chinese Export, Bowl, Famille Rose, Peafowl, Octagonal, C.1765, 9 7/8 In.	275.00
Chinese Export, Bowl, Famille Rose, Peonies, Octagonal, C.1760, 12 3/8 In.	250.00
Chinese Export, Bowl, Famille Rose, Pheasants, Squirrels, C.1770, 10 1/2 In.	500.00
Chinese Export, Bowl, Famille Rose, Puce Camaieu Landscape, 1775, 9 1/8 In.	275.00
Chinese Export, Bowl, Famille Verte, Floral & Fence, Fluted, C.1720, 9 In.	175.00
Chinese Export, Bowl, Famille Verte, Phoenix, Butterflies, C.1850, 13 In.	125.00
Chinese Export, Bowl, Famille Verte, The Cherry Pickers, C.1750, 8 1/8 In.	700.00
Chinese Export, Bowl, Fish, Dragon & Phoenix On Cream, C.1850, 21 In.	900.00
Chinese Export, Bowl, Fish, Famille Verte, Warriors, C.1850, 12 In.	550.00
Chinese Export, Bowl, Fish, Yellow, Pink & Blue Dragon, C.1820, 13 1/2 In.	1400.00
Chinese Export, Bowl, Fisherman & House Medallion, C.1790, 6 7/8 In.	250.00

Chelsea, Plate, Kakiemon,
Red Anchor Period, 9 In.
(See Page 87)

Chinese Export, Charger, Armorial, C.1720, 15 In., Pair

Chinese Export, Bowl, Fisherman & House Medallion, C.1790, 9 In.	450.00
Chinese Export, Bowl, Fitzhugh, Blue, Handled, Rectangular, C.1820, 14 In.	525.00
Chinese Export, Bowl, Fitzhugh, Orange, Deep, 9 3/4 X 1 3/4 In.	275.00
Chinese Export, Bowl, Floral Bouquet Center, Blue Scrolls, C.1750, 11 In.	87.50
Chinese Export, Bowl, Floral Bouquet, Blue Scrolls, C.1790, 10 3/4 In., Pair	200.00
Chinese Export, Bowl, Floral Clusters & Sprigs, Dogtooth Band, C.1780, 7 In.	100.00
Chinese Export, Bowl, Gold Bands On Rim, 4 Gilt Flower Sprigs, C.1790, 9 In.	50.00
Chinese Export, Bowl, Iron Red Floral & Insects, Gilding, C.1820, 9 3/8 In.	450.00
Chinese Export, Bowl, Lotus, Pink & Yellow Petals, C.1850, 9 1/8 In., Pair	675.00
Chinese Export, Bowl, Lotus, Pink Petals, Gilding, Floral, C.1760, 7 1/8 In.	500.00
Chinese Export, Bowl, Lotus, Pink To Pale Green, Gilt, C.1760, 11 1/8 In.	600.00
Chinese Export, Bowl, Marco Polo, White Ware, Leaf Design, Sung, 3 1/2 In.	75.00
Chinese Export, Bowl, Polychrome Figures Outside, Floral Inside, 9 In.	425.00
Chinese Export, Bowl, Punch, Blue & White, Oriental Hunters, C.1790, 16 In.	350.00
Chinese Export, Bowl, Punch, Famille Rose, Figures, Animals, C.1765, 14 In.	550.00
Chinese Export, Bowl, Punch, Famille Rose, Figures, Birds, C.1850, 14 1/2 In.	450.00
Chinese Export, Bowl, Punch, Famille Rose, Figures, Birds, Gilt, C.1850, 13 In.	450.00
Chinese Export, Bowl, Punch, Famille Rose, Floral Bouquet, Gilt, C.1755	1800.00
Chinese Export, Bowl, Punch, Famille Rose, Oriental Figures, C.1775, 16 In.	1300.00
Chinese Export, Bowl, Punch, Famille Rose, Oriental Woman Medallion, C.1780	500.00
Chinese Export, Bowl, Punch, Mandarin Palette, Hunt Scenes, C.1780, 16 In.	5200.00
Chinese Export, Bowl, Serving, Fitzhugh, Orange, Beasts, C.1820, 11 1/4 In.	400.00
Chinese Export, Bowl, Serving, Oval Monogram, Star & Florette, C.1795, 13 In.	100.00
Chinese Export, Bowl, Vegetable, Cone Knop, Armorial, Silveira, C.1795, 11 In.	1400.00
Chinese Export, Bowl, Vegetable, Covered, Armorial, East India Co., 9 7/8 In.	450.00
Chinese Export, Bowl, Vegetable, Fitzhugh, Green, Scalloped, 10 1/4 X 8 In.	600.00
Chinese Export, Bowl, Vegetable, Fitzhugh, Green, Scalloped, 10 1/2 X 8 In.	600.00
Chinese Export, Bowl, Vegetable, Gilt Cone Knop, Fitzhugh, Blue, C.1815, Pair	1000.00
Chinese Export, Bowl, Vegetable, Pinecone Knop, Fitzhugh, Blue, C.1820	725.00
Chinese Export, Box, Covered, Famille Rose, Court Figures, C.1820, 7 3/4 In.	400.00
Chinese Export, Box, Covered, Fitzhugh, Blue, 7 1/2 X 4 X 2 1/2 In.	500.00
Chinese Export, Box, Cricket, White, Lobed Oval Shape, Floral, 5 X 6 In.	65.00
Chinese Export, Box, Duck Cover, Color On Black, C.1850, 9 1/2 In., Pair	550.00
Chinese Export, Box, Gilt Ball Knop, Lotus Blossom, Pink, C.1800, 5 3/4 In.	1800.00
Chinese Export, Box, Glove, Covered, Fitzhugh, Blue, 7 1/2 X 4 X 2 1/2 In.	500.00
Chinese Export, Cachepot, Famille Rose, Armorial, Mask Handles, C.1735, 5 In.	1850.00
Chinese Export, Candlestick, Famille Rose, Floral, C.1730, 8 1/8 In., Pair	2600.00
Chinese Export, Candlestick, Famille Rose, Floral, C.1820, 7 3/8 In., Pair	950.00
Chinese Export, Charger, Armorial, C.1720, 15 In., Pair *Illus*	3600.00
Chinese Export, Charger, Armorial, Gough Of Oddfallings, C.1720, 15 In.	1800.00
Chinese Export, Charger, Blue & White, Jardiniere & Floral, C.1750, 14 In.	225.00
Chinese Export, Charger, Blue & White, Meandering Floral, C.1750, 15 1/2 In.	225.00
Chinese Export, Charger, En Grisaille, Armorial, Patten, C.1755, 15 In., Pair	650.00
Chinese Export, Charger, En Grisaille, Oriental Figures, C.1740, 14 In., Pair	1400.00
Chinese Export, Charger, Famille Rose, Floral & Insects, C.1820, 24 In.	1700.00
Chinese Export, Charger, Famille Rose, Floral Bouquet, Gilt, C.1760, 16 In.	250.00
Chinese Export, Charger, Famille Verte, Aubergine Foo Dog, C.1850, 16 In.	175.00

Chinese Export, **Charger,** Flower Filled Vase, Gilding, C.1725, 15 3/8 In.	350.00
Chinese Export, **Coffeepot,** Mandarin Palette, Pear Shape, C.1780, 9 1/8 In.	425.00
Chinese Export, **Coffeepot,** Sepia Camaieu, Figures, Floral Vases, C.1800	200.00
Chinese Export, **Compote,** En Grisaille, Armorial, Nelson, C.1815, 13 In.	475.00
Chinese Export, **Cooler,** Wine, Famille Rose, Van Goudriaen, C.1770, 6 3/4 In.	3700.00
Chinese Export, **Creamer,** Covered, Famille Rose	125.00
Chinese Export, **Cup & Saucer,** Bouillon, Famille Rose, Meissen Style, C.1780	64.50
Chinese Export, **Cup & Saucer,** Coffee, Empress Elizabeth Portrait, C.1750	575.00
Chinese Export, **Cup & Saucer,** Coffee, En Grisaille, Gilding, C.1780	30.00
Chinese Export, **Cup & Saucer,** Coffee, En Grisaille, Juno, C.1745	150.00
Chinese Export, **Cup & Saucer,** Coffee, En Grisaille, Seamstress, C.1750	175.00
Chinese Export, **Cup & Saucer,** Coffee, Famille Rose, Armorial, Griffiths, 1785	450.00
Chinese Export, **Cup & Saucer,** Coffee, Famille Rose, Armorial, Rigby, C.1750	250.00
Chinese Export, **Cup & Saucer,** Coffee, Figures In Scene, C.1760	800.00
Chinese Export, **Cup & Saucer,** Famille Rose, Meissen Style, C.1780	65.00
Chinese Export, **Cup & Saucer,** Fitzhugh, Blue	175.00
Chinese Export, **Cup,** Double Handled, American Eagle & Great Seal, C.1795	2500.00
Chinese Export, **Dish & Stand,** Potted Meat, Pod Knop, Floral, C.1780, 7 In.	175.00
Chinese Export, **Dish & Underplate,** Meat, Covered, Eagle Crest, C.1790, 7 In.	300.00
Chinese Export, **Dish,** Bat Shape, Apple Green, Peonies, C.1820, 7 1/2 In.	125.00

Chinese Export, Dish, Hot Water,
Blue & White, C.1750
(See Page 90)

Chinese Export, Plate, Eagle,
Red, White, Blue, 1800, 8 In.
(See Page 91)

Chinese Export, Jug, Milk,   Chinese Export, Teapot,   Chinese Export, Dish, Leaf Shape,
Famille Rose, C.1820, 4 In.   1820, 5 7/8 In.   Famille Rose, C.1820
(See Page 90)   *(See Page 94)*   *(See Page 90)*

Chinese Export, Dish, Bat Shape, Famille Rose, Floral, C.1820, 8 3/8 In., Pair	150.00
Chinese Export, Dish, Hot Water, Blue & White, C.1750 .... *Illus*	175.00
Chinese Export, Dish, Hot Water, Blue Enamel, M In Medallion, C.1790, 8 In.	200.00
Chinese Export, Dish, Hot Water, Fitzhugh, Blue, C.1820, 11 1/4 In.	200.00
Chinese Export, Dish, Hot Water, Fitzhugh, Blue, Floral Rim, C.1820, 11 In.	175.00
Chinese Export, Dish, Kidney Shape, Armorial, Hamilton, C.1795, 10 1/4 In.	500.00
Chinese Export, Dish, Kidney Shape, Famille Rose, Celadon, C.1820, 11 In.	125.00
Chinese Export, Dish, Leaf Shape, Famille Rose, C.1820 .... *Illus*	100.00
Chinese Export, Dish, Leaf Shape, Willow, Blue & White, C.1800, 7 In., Pair	250.00
Chinese Export, Dish, Lotus Leaf, Green, Fruits & Flowers, C.1775, 10 3/4 In.	275.00
Chinese Export, Dish, Lotus, Flowering Tree & Mum, C.1760, 10 7/8 In.	800.00
Chinese Export, Dish, Lotus, Oriental Floral, Gilt, C.1760, 11 7/8 In.	450.00
Chinese Export, Dish, Meat, Gilt Knop, Mandarin Palette, C.1780, 11 3/4 In.	350.00
Chinese Export, Dish, Pseudo Tobacco Leaf, Oriental Floral, C.1790, 14 In.	1000.00
Chinese Export, Dish, Shell Shape, Blue Enamel, Gilt Star Bands, C.1850, 7 In	150.00
Chinese Export, Dish, Shell Shape, Fitzhugh, Green, C.1820, 10 1/4 In.	400.00
Chinese Export, Dish, Shell Shape, Tobacco Leaf, Famille Rose, C.1800, 10 In.	800.00
Chinese Export, Figurine, Cockerel, Blue & White, C.1750, 4 1/2 In.	100.00
Chinese Export, Figurine, Foo Dog, 2 Pups, Earthenware, 16 X 16 In.	175.00
Chinese Export, Figurine, Horse, White, 9 1/2 In.	1500.00
Chinese Export, Figurine, Kneeling Boy, Famille Rose, Ormolu, C.1850, 7 In.	1050.00
Chinese Export, Figurine, Parrot, Glazed Bisque, C.1850, 7 1/2 In., Pair	225.00
Chinese Export, Figurine, Parrot, Pierced Rockwork, C.1850, 13 3/4 In.	550.00
Chinese Export, Figurine, Parrot, Yellow, Green, Gilt, C.1850, 8 1/2 In., Pair	500.00
Chinese Export, Figurine, Pigeon, Grays & Green, C.1790, 6 1/2 In.	350.00
Chinese Export, Figurine, Pigeon, White, Ocher Beak, C.1750, 6 3/4 In., Pair	1300.00
Chinese Export, Figurine, Pillow, Enameled Figurines & Bats, 5 1/2 In.	60.00
Chinese Export, Figurine, Pu Tai, Seated, Wooden Base, C.1850, 10 1/8 In.	250.00
Chinese Export, Figurine, Rooster, Famille Rose, C.1900, 10 In.	50.00
Chinese Export, Fruit, Altar, Peach, Applied Stalks & Buds, C.1850, 12 In.	325.00
Chinese Export, Fruit, Altar, Peach, Pink & Green, 5 1/2 In.	70.00
Chinese Export, Fruit, Altar, Peach, Pink & Green, 6 1/2 In., Pair	125.00
Chinese Export, Jar, Conical Lid, Peonies On Peach, C.1850, 12 3/8 In., Pair	200.00
Chinese Export, Jar, Cosmetic, Covered, Polychrome, Shou, Bats, C.1850, 5 In.	40.00
Chinese Export, Jar, Covered, Famille Rose, Buddhistic, C.1850, 17 In.	225.00
Chinese Export, Jar, Domed Lid, Blue & White, Phoenix, Dragon, C.1850, 10 In.	70.00
Chinese Export, Jar, Domed Lid, Famille Rose, Boys, Buddhistic, C.1850, 17 In.	175.00
Chinese Export, Jar, Ginger, Blue & White, Floral, Calligraphic, C.1790, 8 In.	350.00
Chinese Export, Jar, Ginger, Blue & White, Ming Style Floral, C.1790, 9 In.	250.00
Chinese Export, Jar, Ginger, Famille Rose, Phoenix, Rockwork, C.1850, 9 In.	200.00
Chinese Export, Jar, Ginger, Famille Rose, Shrubbery, Rockwork, C.1765, 9 In.	375.00
Chinese Export, Jar, Ginger, Famille Verte, Pheasant & Floral, C.1850, 10 In.	150.00
Chinese Export, Jar, Ginger, Figures, Puce & Green, Teak Stand	45.00
Chinese Export, Jar, Ginger, Powder Blue, Red Carp On Dark Blue, 1850, 7 In.	75.00
Chinese Export, Jar, Storage, Foo Dog Finial, River Scenes, C.1850, 30 In.	275.00
Chinese Export, Jar, Tear Finial, Famille Rose, Court Ladies, C.1850, 13 In.	80.00
Chinese Export, Jar, Tear Finial, Polychrome, Immortal, Woman, C.1850, 11 In.	80.00
Chinese Export, Jardiniere, Famille Rose, Birds, Branches, C.1850, 13 In.	450.00
Chinese Export, Jardiniere, Famille Rose, C.1820, 13 X 7 In.	500.00
Chinese Export, Jug, Covered, Famille Rose, Figures At Tea, C.1770, 15 In.	750.00
Chinese Export, Jug, En Grisaille, Ship Flying American Flag, C.1800, 10 In.	1800.00
Chinese Export, Jug, Famille Rose, Floral, Helmet Shape, C.1790, 8 1/8 In.	100.00
Chinese Export, Jug, Hot Water, Famille Rose, Floral Bouquet, C.1770, 6 In.	100.00
Chinese Export, Jug, Milk, Armorial, State Of New York, Helmet Shape, 5 In.	950.00
Chinese Export, Jug, Milk, En Grisaille, Seamstress, C.1750, 4 1/8 In.	275.00
Chinese Export, Jug, Milk, European Harbor & 2 Men-O'-War, 1760, 5 In.	750.00
Chinese Export, Jug, Milk, Famille Rose, C.1820, 4 In. .... *Illus*	90.00
Chinese Export, Jug, Milk, Fitzhugh, Green, Scroll Handle, C.1820, 4 1/4 In.	325.00
Chinese Export, Liner, Vegetable Bowl, Roses & Iris Bouquet, C.1790, 11 In.	175.00
Chinese Export, Pillow, Reclining Cat, Ivorine, Dark Spots, 14 In.	185.00
Chinese Export, Pillow, Reclining Cat, Ivorine, Luster Spots, 14 X 8 In.	145.00
Chinese Export, Pitcher, Blue & White, Kakiemon Floral, Chien Lung, 5 In.	75.00
Chinese Export, Pitcher, Iris On Cobalt, White Inside, 8 1/4 In.	65.00
Chinese Export, Plaque, Dowager & Attendants, 21 1/2 X 13 1/2 In.	600.00
Chinese Export, Plate, American Eagle, Gilding, C.1800, 7 5/8 In.	750.00
Chinese Export, Plate, Armorial, English, Octagonal, C.1780, 9 1/8 In.	75.00

Chinese Export, Plate, Armorial, Newton, Negro Crest, C.1745, 9 In., Pair 375.00
Chinese Export, Plate, Armorial, Silveira, C.1795, 7 3/4 In. 325.00
Chinese Export, Plate, Birds In Flowering Tree, C.1750, 9 1/8 In. 150.00
Chinese Export, Plate, Birds, Insects, Fruits, & Flowers, C.1820, 10 In. 118.50
Chinese Export, Plate, Blue & White, Birds, Floral, C.1750, 14 1/4 In. 200.00
Chinese Export, Plate, Blue On White, Band Of 11 Bats, 12 In. 100.00
Chinese Export, Plate, Butter, Fitzhugh, Brown, 6 1/8 In., Pair 350.00
Chinese Export, Plate, Cherry Pickers, Pink Scalework, C.1780, 9 1/8 In. 175.00
Chinese Export, Plate, Court Figures, Ornithological, C.1780, 7 7/8 In., Pair 325.00
Chinese Export, Plate, Dessert, Fisherman & House Medallion, C.1790 .... 50.00
Chinese Export, Plate, Dinner, Fisherman & House Medallion, C.1790 .... 100.00
Chinese Export, Plate, Eagle, Red, White, Blue, 1800, 8 In. ....*Illus* 9000.00
Chinese Export, Plate, En Grisaille, Amorous Lady & Gentleman, C.1745, 9 In. 700.00
Chinese Export, Plate, En Grisaille, Armorial, Bucknall, C.1735, 9 In., Pair 425.00
Chinese Export, Plate, En Grisaille, Armorial, Continental, C.1775, 6 In. 200.00
Chinese Export, Plate, En Grisaille, Armorial, Continental, C.1775, 9 1/4 In. 175.00
Chinese Export, Plate, En Grisaille, Armorial, Gilt Shield, C.1745, 9 In. 225.00
Chinese Export, Plate, En Grisaille, Armorial, Reticulated, C.1790, 7 1/2 In. 175.00
Chinese Export, Plate, En Grisaille, Armorial, Van Herzeele, C.1750, 9 In. 525.00
Chinese Export, Plate, En Grisaille, Armorial, Vautenay, C.1740, 9 1/4 In. 500.00
Chinese Export, Plate, En Grisaille, Seamstress, C.1750, 9 In. 275.00
Chinese Export, Plate, Famille Rose, Armorial, Ducal Coronet, C.1770, 9 In. 100.00
Chinese Export, Plate, Famille Rose, Armorial, Gamon, C.1780, 9 1/2 In., Pair 450.00
Chinese Export, Plate, Famille Rose, Armorial, Gordon, C.1780, 9 3/4 In. 325.00
Chinese Export, Plate, Famille Rose, Armorial, Llandaff, C.1755, 9 In. 100.00
Chinese Export, Plate, Famille Rose, Armorial, Octagonal, C.1750, 8 3/8 In. 185.00
Chinese Export, Plate, Famille Rose, Armorial, Reticulated, C.1780, 9 1/2 In. 400.00
Chinese Export, Plate, Famille Rose, Armorial, Swedish, C.1750, 10 In., Pair 375.00
Chinese Export, Plate, Famille Rose, Birds In Trees, C.1760, 9 In. 120.00
Chinese Export, Plate, Famille Rose, Brown Ducks & Peonies, C.1735, 9 In. 200.00
Chinese Export, Plate, Famille Rose, Central Floral Bouquet, C.1760, 9 In. 100.00
Chinese Export, Plate, Famille Rose, Chrysanthemum Center, C.1745, 9 In. 165.00
Chinese Export, Plate, Famille Rose, Cockerel, Blue Rockwork, C.1735, 10 In. 525.00
Chinese Export, Plate, Famille Rose, Floral & Fruit, C.1760, 9 1/4 In. 150.00
Chinese Export, Plate, Famille Rose, Floral & Ribbon Bouquet, C.1760, 10 In. 55.00
Chinese Export, Plate, Famille Rose, Floral Bouquet, C.1760, 12 1/2 In. 200.00
Chinese Export, Plate, Famille Rose, Floral Bouquet, C.1770, 9 3/8 In. 105.00
Chinese Export, Plate, Famille Rose, Floral Bouquet, Gilt, C.1760, 8 7/8 In. 66.50
Chinese Export, Plate, Famille Rose, Floral Bouquets, C.1750, 9 1/8 In., Pair 325.00
Chinese Export, Plate, Famille Rose, Floral, Gilt Ribbons, C.1760, 9 In. 58.50
Chinese Export, Plate, Famille Rose, Floral, Octagonal, C.1770, 8 7/8 In. 25.00
Chinese Export, Plate, Famille Rose, Neptune & Amphitrite, C.1760, 8 7/8 In. 300.00
Chinese Export, Plate, Famille Rose, Neptune & Amphitrite, C.1760, 9 In. 375.00
Chinese Export, Plate, Famille Rose, Palette & Pomegranate, C.1765, 9 In. 50.00
Chinese Export, Plate, Famille Rose, Peonies In Vase, C.1750, 11 1/4 In. 375.00
Chinese Export, Plate, Famille Verte, Armorial, De Vassey, 1702, 7 7/8 In. 3500.00
Chinese Export, Plate, Fisherman & House Medallion, C.1790, 6 1/4 In. 11.75
Chinese Export, Plate, Fitzhugh, Blue, C.1820, 7 7/8 In. .... 25.00 To 37.50
Chinese Export, Plate, Fitzhugh, Blue, C.1820, 9 7/8 In. 62.50
Chinese Export, Plate, Fitzhugh, Blue, Gilt Border, C.1815, 9 3/4 In. 29.50
Chinese Export, Plate, Fitzhugh, Green, C.1820, 8 In., Pair 300.00
Chinese Export, Plate, Fitzhugh, Green, 9 1/2 In. 185.00
Chinese Export, Plate, Floral Bouquet Center, C.1790, 8 3/4 In. 16.65
Chinese Export, Plate, Floral Bouquet, Greek Key Band, C.1800, 9 7/8 In. 75.00
Chinese Export, Plate, Floral Bouquets, Gilt, C.1780, 8 7/8 In. 25.00
Chinese Export, Plate, Floral Sprigs Center Panel, C.1760, 8 7/8 In., Pair 50.00
Chinese Export, Plate, Island Pavillion, Floral Vignettes, C.1720, 8 7/8 In. 90.00
Chinese Export, Plate, Islands & Bridge, Octagonal, C.1700, 8 5/8 In. 200.00
Chinese Export, Plate, Lotus Blossom & Shrubbery, Octagonal, C.1720, 9 In. 300.00
Chinese Export, Plate, Mandarin Palette, Acrobats, C.1775, 6 1/4 In., Pair 275.00
Chinese Export, Plate, Mandarin Palette, Oriental Figures, C.1780, 9 3/4 In. 83.50
Chinese Export, Plate, Octagonal, Floral Clusters, C.1760, 8 7/8 In., Pair 200.00
Chinese Export, Plate, Pink Rose Sprig, Gros Blue Band Border, C.1790, 9 In. 80.00
Chinese Export, Plate, Pomegranate Branch, Gilt Scrolls, C.1750, 8 3/4 In. 45.50
Chinese Export, Plate, Sepia Crickets In Roses, C.1760, 9 In., Set Of 4 .... 250.00
Chinese Export, Plate, Soup, Blue & White Floral, 1 In. Rim, 9 In. 35.00

Chinese Export, Plate, Soup, En Grisaille, Carp, Famille Rose, C.1750, Pair 100.00
Chinese Export, Plate, Soup, Famille Rose, Armorial, Dalyell, C.1773, 8 In. 312.50
Chinese Export, Plate, Soup, Famille Rose, Armorial, Gordon, C.1780, 9 In. 360.00
Chinese Export, Plate, Soup, Famille Rose, Armorial, MacGregor, 1760, 9 In. 137.50
Chinese Export, Plate, Soup, Famille Rose, Floral & Roses, C.1760, 9 1/4 In. 75.00
Chinese Export, Plate, Soup, Famille Rose, Floral Bouquets, C.1760, 8 7/8 In. 75.00
Chinese Export, Plate, Soup, Figures In Scene, C.1760, 9 In. 700.00
Chinese Export, Plate, Soup, Fitzhugh, Orange, Shield & Initials, 9 1/2 In. 200.00
Chinese Export, Plate, Vase Of Flowers, Clobbered, C.1750, 9 1/8 In. 150.00
Chinese Export, Platter, Armorial, Duke Of Norfolk, C.1740, 11 In., Pair 325.00
Chinese Export, Platter, Armorial, Silveira, C.1795, 14 3/4 In. 1250.00
Chinese Export, Platter, Blue & White, Lake Scene, C.1750, 13 3/4 In. 150.00
Chinese Export, Platter, Blue & White, Peonies, Octagonal, C.1790, 12 In. 125.00
Chinese Export, Platter, Blue & White, 1790, 12 5/8 In. .... *Illus* 200.00
Chinese Export, Platter, Clipped Corners, C.1750, 15 X 11 1/2 In. 188.00
Chinese Export, Platter, Eagle Crest, Gilt & Iron Red Rim, C.1790, 13 In. 275.00
Chinese Export, Platter, En Grisaille, Armorial, German, C.1750, 14 3/4 In. 1350.00
Chinese Export, Platter, Famille Rose, Armorial, Barnes, C.1790, 15 7/8 In. 250.00
Chinese Export, Platter, Famille Rose, Bouquets, Gilding, C.1755, 17 In. 400.00
Chinese Export, Platter, Famille Rose, Court Figures, C.1765, 15 1/2 In. 400.00
Chinese Export, Platter, Famille Rose, Crested, C.1810, 14 5/8 In., Pair 600.00
Chinese Export, Platter, Famille Rose, Floral & Fruit, C.1780, 14 5/8 In. 175.00
Chinese Export, Platter, Famille Rose, Floral, Gilding, C.1790, 10 7/8 In. 187.50
Chinese Export, Platter, Famille Rose, Floral, Octagonal, C.1770, 16 1/8 In. 375.00
Chinese Export, Platter, Famille Rose, Flowering Plants, C.1750, 11 1/2 In. 200.00
Chinese Export, Platter, Famille Rose, Peacock & Hen, Floral, C.1765, 14 In. 450.00
Chinese Export, Platter, Fitzhugh, Blue, Center Medallion, C.1800, 18 1/2 In. 300.00
Chinese Export, Platter, Fitzhugh, Blue, Well & Tree, Oval, C.1800, 21 In. 350.00
Chinese Export, Platter, Fitzhugh, Blue, 14 In. 195.00
Chinese Export, Platter, Fitzhugh, Blue, 14 1/2 X 12 In. 195.00
Chinese Export, Platter, Fitzhugh, Green, C.1790, 21 In. 1750.00
Chinese Export, Platter, Floral Bouquet Center, C.1790, 16 3/8 In. 200.00
Chinese Export, Platter, Floral Clusters, Gilt, C.1765, 10 1/4 In., Pair 550.00
Chinese Export, Platter, Mandarin Palette, Figures, Terrace, C.1780, 16 In. 350.00
Chinese Export, Platter, Purple Butterfly On Pink Rose, C.1775, 16 1/2 In. 325.00
Chinese Export, Pot, Bough, Pierced Lid, Squirrels & Vines, C.1820, 9 In. 300.00
Chinese Export, Pot, Punch, Fruit Knop, Armorial, Van Goudriaen, C.1770, 7 In. 3500.00
Chinese Export, Sauceboat & Underplate, Famille Rose, Peacocks, C.1765, Pair 425.00
Chinese Export, Sauceboat, Famille Rose, Cranes, Peonies, C.1750, 9 1/4 In. 175.00
Chinese Export, Saucer, Armorial, Famille Rose, Dogs, Horse, Dove, C.1760 .... 175.00
Chinese Export, Saucer, Armorial, Hamilton Of Dalzell, C.1778, 5 1/2 In. 125.00
Chinese Export, Saucer, Batavian Ware, Vase Of Flowers, C.1750, 5 1/4 In. 50.00
Chinese Export, Saucer, En Grisaille, Armorial, Shipwrights' Company, 1795 .... 900.00
Chinese Export, Saucer, Famille Rose Birds & Flowering Tree, C.1755, Pair 110.00
Chinese Export, Saucer, Fitzhugh, Brown, C.1800, 5 1/2 In., Pair 300.00
Chinese Export, Saucer, Gilt Floral Sprigs, Sepia Leaf Border, C.1780, Pair 60.00
Chinese Export, Seat, Garden, Famille Rose, Floral, Pierced, C.1850, 10 In. 125.00
Chinese Export, Seat, Garden, Famille Rose, Scenic, C.1820, 18 In., Pair 3000.00
Chinese Export, Snuffbox, Famille Rose Floral Bouquet, Bombe, C.1760, 3 In. 1600.00
Chinese Export, Snuffbox, Scallop Shell, Silver Mounts, C.1750, 3 1/8 In. 1200.00
Chinese Export, Stand, Fruit, Fitzhugh, Blue, Diamond Shape, C.1820, 14 In. 425.00
Chinese Export, Stand, Teapot, Famille Rose Floral Bouquet, C.1775, 5 In. 70.00
Chinese Export, Stand, Teapot, Famille Rose Floral Medallions, C.1770 .... 60.00
Chinese Export, Stand, Teapot, Fluted, Rose Camaieu Floral, C.1780, 4 7/8 In. 30.00
Chinese Export, Stand, Teapot, Hexagonal, Center Bouquet, Scrolls, C.1765 .... 80.00
Chinese Export, Stand, Teapot, Pink Monochrome, Pink & Iron Floral, C.1775 .... 60.00
Chinese Export, Stand, Teapot, Willow, Blue & White, C.1790, 5 1/4 In. 40.00
Chinese Export, Sugar, Covered, Strap Handles, Gold Finial, 5 3/4 In. 188.00
Chinese Export, Sugar, Gold Finial & Rim, Blue Fitzhugh, 2 Handled 250.00
Chinese Export, Tankard, Bell Shape, 6 Oriental Figures, C.1780, 4 5/8 In. 150.00
Chinese Export, Tankard, Blue & White, Island Pavillions, C.1800, 4 7/8 In. 110.00
Chinese Export, Tankard, Famille Rose, Armorial, English, C.1775, 5 3/8 In. 350.00
Chinese Export, Tankard, Famille Rose, Figural Medallion, C.1780, 4 5/8 In. 325.00
Chinese Export, Tankard, Floral Rice, Strap Handle, C.1850, 4 3/4 In. 60.00
Chinese Export, Tankard, Oriental Riverscape, C.1750, 6 1/8 In. 250.00
Chinese Export, Tankard, Sepia English Manor House Medallion, C.1790, 5 In. 400.00

Chinese Export, Platter, Blue & White, 1790, 12 5/8 In.
(See Page 92)

Chinese Export, Tea Caddy, C.1795

Chinese Export, Teapot,
Fitzhugh, C.1790
(See Page 94)

Chinese Export, **Tankard,** Serpent Handle, Floral, Scalework, C.1790, 4 3/4 In.	125.00
Chinese Export, **Tea Caddy,** American Eagle, Gilding, C.1790, 4 7/8 In.	225.00
Chinese Export, **Tea Caddy,** Blue & White, Willow, C.1750, 4 7/8 In.	200.00
Chinese Export, **Tea Caddy,** C.1795 .... *Illus*	300.00
Chinese Export, **Tea Caddy,** Famille Rose Floral Medallion, C.1780, 5 In.	200.00
Chinese Export, **Tea Caddy,** Floral Bouquets In Brown Urn, C.1780, 5 1/4 In.	175.00
Chinese Export, **Tea Caddy,** Floral On Pale Yellow, Gilt Trim, 6 1/2 In.	75.00
Chinese Export, **Tea Set,** Grasshoppers & Leaves, Rope Handles, 3 Piece	220.00
Chinese Export, **Teabowl & Saucer,** Allegorical, Hope, C.1790	500.00
Chinese Export, **Teabowl & Saucer,** American Eagle, Sepia, Gilt, C.1790	450.00
Chinese Export, **Teabowl & Saucer,** Batavian Ware, Peonies, C.1750, Pair	110.00
Chinese Export, **Teabowl & Saucer,** En Grisaille, Famille Rose, Armorial, 1770	225.00
Chinese Export, **Teabowl & Saucer,** En Grisaille, Seamstress, C.1750	275.00
Chinese Export, **Teabowl & Saucer,** Famille Rose, Armorial, Burgoyne, C.1750	110.00
Chinese Export, **Teabowl & Saucer,** Famille Rose, Armorial, Rigby, C.1750	275.00
Chinese Export, **Teabowl & Saucer,** Famille Rose, Floral Bouquets, C.1780	37.50
Chinese Export, **Teabowl & Saucer,** Sepia Camaieu Fishermen, C.1790, Pair	275.00
Chinese Export, **Teacup & Saucer,** Bouquets, Ogee Form, C.1770, Pair	120.00
Chinese Export, **Teacup & Saucer,** Fitzhugh, Green, C.1820, Pair	225.00
Chinese Export, **Teapot,** American Eagle, Gilding, C.1790, 5 7/8 In.	1800.00
Chinese Export, **Teapot,** Armorial, State Of New York, C.1790, 5 1/4 In.	1600.00
Chinese Export, **Teapot,** Blue Enamel & Gilding, M In Shield, C.1790	150.00
Chinese Export, **Teapot,** En Grisaille, Lady & Suitor, Cupid, C.1745	335.00
Chinese Export, **Teapot,** En Grisaille, Pink Rosebush, Blue, C.1750	225.00
Chinese Export, **Teapot,** European Figures Loading Bales At Harbor, C.1760	300.00
Chinese Export, **Teapot,** Famille Jaune, C.1662, 1/4 Cup Size	45.00

Chinese Export, Teapot, Famille Rose, Black Urns With Flowers, Bird, C.1795 .... 350.00
Chinese Export, Teapot, Famille Rose, European Floral, Gold, C.1750 .... 300.00
Chinese Export, Teapot, Famille Rose, Floral & Insects, Octagonal, C.1764 .... 200.00
Chinese Export, Teapot, Famille Rose, Floral Bouquet, Gilt Bows, C.1760 .... 125.00
Chinese Export, Teapot, Famille Rose, Floral Panels, Pink Scalework, C.1760 .... 250.00
Chinese Export, Teapot, Famille Rose, Floral Spray, Fruit Knop, C.1790 .... 150.00
Chinese Export, Teapot, Famille Rose, Floral Sprigs & Vines, C.1790 .... 200.00
Chinese Export, Teapot, Fitzhugh, C.1790 .... *Illus* 425.00
Chinese Export, Teapot, Fitzhugh, Green, Shield Shape, C.1820, 8 1/2 In. 850.00
Chinese Export, Teapot, In Padded Basket, 8 In. 95.00
Chinese Export, Teapot, Lotus, Pink, Turquoise Spout & Handle, C.1765 .... 850.00
Chinese Export, Teapot, Man-O'-War Crest, Fitzhugh Border, C.1790 .... 425.00
Chinese Export, Teapot, Mandarin Palette, Figures On Terraces, C.1780 .... 250.00
Chinese Export, Teapot, Oriental Figures Continuous Scene, C.1820 .... 200.00
Chinese Export, Teapot, 1820, 5 7/8 In. .... *Illus* 200.00
Chinese Export, Tray, Famille Rose, Peonies, Octagonal, C.1760, 12 3/4 In. 200.00
Chinese Export, Tray, Spoon, Famille Rose Floral Bouquet, C.1770, 4 3/4 In. 100.00
Chinese Export, Tray, Spoon, Famille Rose Floral, Hexagonal, C.1765, 5 In. 130.00
Chinese Export, Tray, Spoon, Famille Rose Vase Of Flowers, C.1765, 5 1/8 In. 150.00
Chinese Export, Trencher, Salt, En Grisaille, Armorial, Continental, C.1775 .... 225.00
Chinese Export, Tureen & Stand, Covered, Famille Rose, C.1775, 15 1/2 In. 2200.00
Chinese Export, Tureen & Stand, Kylin Knop, Blue & White, C.1750, 14 1/8 In. 800.00
Chinese Export, Tureen & Stand, Sauce, Pinecone Knop, C.1790, 7 7/8 In., Pair 2400.00
Chinese Export, Tureen & Stand, Soup, Flower Knop, Famille Rose Floral, 1790 .... 2100.00
Chinese Export, Tureen, Covered, Peach Form, Pink & Green, 11 In. 350.00
Chinese Export, Tureen, Crown Knop, Famille Rose, Floral, C.1765, 11 In. 700.00
Chinese Export, Tureen, Crown Knop, Rabbit Handles, Floral, C.1780, 12 In. 650.00
Chinese Export, Tureen, Sauce, Flower Knop, Famille Rose Floral, C.1790, Pair 1400.00
Chinese Export, Tureen, Sauce, Flower Knop, Fitzhugh, Green, C.1820, Pair 1600.00
Chinese Export, Tureen, Sauce, Pod Knop, Crested, Gilt Handles, C.1795, 8 In. 700.00
Chinese Export, Tureen, Scroll Knop, Armorial, Famille Rose, C.1785, 13 In. 2500.00
Chinese Export, Tureen, Soup, Flower Knop, Fitzhugh, Blue, C.1815, Pair 3200.00
Chinese Export, Tureen, Tortoise, Aubergine Glaze, C.1790, 8 1/4 In. 700.00
Chinese Export, Tureen, Vegetable, Cone Knop, Willow, Blue & White, C.1800 .... 350.00
Chinese Export, Urn, Cobalt, Silver Inlay, Covered, 13 In., Pair 325.00
Chinese Export, Vase, Blue & White, Scenic, Pierced Handles, C.1850, 24 In. 100.00
Chinese Export, Vase, Blue & White, 12 X 6 In., Pair 195.00
Chinese Export, Vase, Famille Noire, Birds & Branches, 35 In., Pair 350.00
Chinese Export, Vase, Famille Rose, Figures In Landscape, C.1850, 11 1/4 In. 125.00
Chinese Export, Vase, Famille Rose, Figures, Foo Dogs, Dragons, C.1850, 25 In. 450.00
Chinese Export, Vase, Famille Verte, 9 3/4 In. 95.00
Chinese Export, Vase, Figures In Landscape On White, C.1850, 25 1/2 In. 200.00
Chinese Export, Vase, Foo Dog Handles, Famille Rose, Taoist, C.1800, 14 In. 150.00
Chinese Export, Vase, Hawthorn, Green, Trumpet Neck, Birds, C.1850, 33 In. 1500.00
Chinese Export, Vase, Kylin Knop, Mandarin Palette, C.1780, 14 3/4 In., Pair 900.00
Chinese Export, Vase, Kylin Knop, Mandarin Palette, Handled, C.1780, 11 In. 325.00
Chinese Export, Vase, Mandarin Palette, Beaker Shape, C.1780, 13 In., Pair 650.00
Chinese Export, Vase, Ormolu Mounted, Floral, 23 1/4 In., Pair 400.00
Chinese Export, Vase, Polychrome, Peacock & Hen On Black, C.1850, 10 In. 160.00
Chinese Export, Vase, Polychrome, 17 In., Pair 698.00
Chinese Export, Vase, Potpourri, Covered, Famille Rose, C.1740, 8 In. 1100.00
Chinese Export, Vase, Turquoise, Dragon Handles, C.1890, 27 In., Pair 300.00
Chinese Export, Vase, Wall, Carp Form, Mauve, Black Eyes, C.1850, 9 3/4 In. 200.00
Chinese Export, Vase, 8 Immortals, Shanghai, C.1850, 5 1/2 In. 125.00
Chinese Export, Water Dropper, Lotus Flower, Pink, Green Stalk, 8 In. 350.00

*Chocolate glass, sometimes mistakenly called caramel slag, was made by the
Indiana Tumbler and Goblet Company of Greentown, Indiana, from 1900
to 1903.*

Chocolate Glass, Bowl, Berry, Cactus, Greentown, 7 1/4 In. 59.00
Chocolate Glass, Bowl, Fruit, Cactus, Deep 75.00
Chocolate Glass, Bowl, Fruit, Leaf Bracket, Deep 57.50
Chocolate Glass, Bowl, Fruit, Shell, Deep 57.50
Chocolate Glass, Butter, Covered, Cactus, Greentown .... 120.00 To 135.00
Chocolate Glass, Butter, Dewey, Dome Top 75.00
Chocolate Glass, Butter, Swan Cover, Finial & 3 Handles 195.00

Chocolate Glass, Celery, Leaf & Bracket, Greentown	45.00
Chocolate Glass, Compote, Melrose, Greentown, 5 In.	135.00
Chocolate Glass, Creamer, Dewey	75.00
Chocolate Glass, Cruet, Cactus, Darker Shade Than Usual	85.00
Chocolate Glass, Cruet, Leaf Bracket	120.00
Chocolate Glass, Dish, Chicken Cover, Basket Weave Base, White Lid, 4 In.	45.00
Chocolate Glass, Dish, Cow Cover	555.00
Chocolate Glass, Dish, Fish Cover, Dolphin, Greentown *Illus*	150.00
Chocolate Glass, Dish, Rabbit Cover, Greentown	250.00 To 350.00
Chocolate Glass, Dish, Robin With Berry Cover, Greentown, Indiana	400.00
Chocolate Glass, Mug, Cactus	52.00
Chocolate Glass, Mug, Outdoor Drinking Scene, Greentown	65.00
Chocolate Glass, Mug, Serenade, Greentown	85.00
Chocolate Glass, Nappy, Leaf Bracket, Tricornered, Handled	39.50
Chocolate Glass, Nappy, Shell, Tricornered, Handled	39.50 To 75.00
Chocolate Glass, Pitcher, Cactus, Greentown, 6 In.	62.00 To 72.00
Chocolate Glass, Pitcher, Water, Heron, Greentown	295.00 To 325.00
Chocolate Glass, Plate, Cactus, 7 1/2 In.	45.00
Chocolate Glass, Sauce, Cactus	35.00
Chocolate Glass, Sauce, Leaf Bracket, Round	35.00
Chocolate Glass, Sauce, Shell, Round	35.00
Chocolate Glass, Shade, Dome, 12 In.	28.00
Chocolate Glass, Spooner, Cactus	60.00
Chocolate Glass, Syrup, Cord Drapery, Metal Top	125.00
Chocolate Glass, Syrup, Shuttle, Greentown	95.00
Chocolate Glass, Syrup, Strigil, Greentown	110.00
Chocolate Glass, Toothpick, Cactus	40.00
Chocolate Glass, Toothpick, Witch's Head, Greentown	86.00
Chocolate Glass, Tumbler, Cactus, 4 In.	50.00
Chocolate Glass, Tumbler, Cactus, 5 In.	40.00
Chocolate Glass, Tumbler, Geneva	65.00
Chocolate Glass, Tumbler, Iced Tea, Uneeda Milk Biscuit	38.00
Chocolate Glass, Tumbler, Leaf Bracket, Greentown	42.00 To 60.00
Chocolate Glass, Tumbler, Rose In Bowknot	95.00
Chocolate Glass, Tumbler, Shuttle, Greentown	55.00
Chocolate Glass, Vase, Knobbed, Fluted & Narrow Bottom, Flared Top, 6 In.	59.00
Christmas Plate, see Collector, Plate	
Christmas Tree Ornament, see also Disneyana, Light	
Christmas Tree Ornament, Blown, Flint, Stiegel Type, Amber	55.00
Christmas Tree Ornament, Candleholder, Frosted Blue, Smoke Bell, 8 In.	25.00
Christmas Tree Ornament, House, Snow On Roof, Bisque Santa, 6 X 4 In.	10.00
Christmas Tree Ornament, Light Bulb, Church, Milk Glass, Electric	5.00
Christmas Tree Ornament, Light Bulb, Pinecone, Red, Electric, 2 1/4 In.	4.00
Christmas Tree Ornament, Light Bulb, Santa's Head, Milk Glass, Electric	5.00
Christmas Tree Ornament, Light Bulb, Snowflake, Electric, 2 1/2 In.	4.00
Christmas Tree Ornament, Light Bulb, Snowman, Milk Glass, Electric	5.00
Christmas Tree Ornament, Light Set, Noma, 1930s	10.00
Christmas Tree Ornament, Light, Apple	5.00
Christmas Tree Ornament, Light, Candle, Amber	6.00
Christmas Tree Ornament, Light, Candle, Green	6.00
Christmas Tree Ornament, Light, Candle, Quilted, Blue	6.00
Christmas Tree Ornament, Light, Cobalt Blue, Diamond Point	12.50
Christmas Tree Ornament, Light, Christ, Electric Connection	4.00
Christmas Tree Ornament, Light, Diamond Pattern, Dark Amber	14.00
Christmas Tree Ornament, Light, Diamond Sawtooth, Deep Blue	5.00
Christmas Tree Ornament, Light, Opalescent, 1, 000-Eye	27.00
Christmas Tree Ornament, Light, Pressed Glass, Diamond Point, Amber	22.00
Christmas Tree Ornament, Light, Santa	5.00
Christmas Tree Ornament, Light, 1, 000-Eye, Jade Green	32.50
Cigar Cutter, see Brass, Cigar Cutter, Gold, Cigar Cutter	
Cigar Store Indian, see Wooden, Cigar Store Indian	

Cinnabar is a vermilion or red lacquer. Some pieces are made with hundreds of thicknesses of the lacquer that is later carved.

Cinnabar, Box, Cigarette, Chinese, White, Blue Interior, 3 1/2 In.	40.00
Cinnabar, Box, Covered, Lacquer, Figures In Landscape, C.1850, 10 3/4 In.	130.00

Cinnabar, Box, Domed Lid, Carved, Maiden In Landscape, C.1850, 4 In., Pair 70.00
Cinnabar, Box, Lacquer, Covered, Bats & Floral, C.1850, 8 In. 80.00
Cinnabar, Box, Trees, Man, Birdcage, Brass Bound, 5 3/4 X 4 X 2 In. 48.00
Cinnabar, Platter, Geometrics & Floral, C.1900, Round, 11 In. 160.00
Cinnabar, Vase, People & Trees, 7 X 4 1/2 In. 72.00

Civil War mementos are important collectors' items. Most of the pieces
are military items used from 1861 to 1865.

Civil War, Artificial Leg, Iron Frame, Leather Shoe, Jewett, Mass., 1865 .... 195.00
Civil War, Banner, Victory Parade, 32 Stars Form 27 In. Heart, 26 X 34 In. 100.00
Civil War, Bible, Brass Edged Cover, Massachusetts Volunteers, 1863 .... 22.00
Civil War, Broadside, Honorable Discharge, Fort Brooke, Fla., 1858 .... 60.00
Civil War, Buckle, Belt, Union Officer's 35.00
Civil War, Canteen, Confederate, Wooden, Leather Shoulder Strap 65.00
Civil War, Canteen, Oak, Drum Type Center, Outer Hoops, 8 1/2 In. 115.00
Civil War, Canteen, Tin, Hagerstown, 1867, Braided Handle, 2 1/4 In. 15.00
Civil War, Canteen, Wooden, Drum Type, Blue Paint, Nails, Single Rim, 7 In. 94.50
Civil War, Canteen, Wooden, Drum Type, Convex Sides, Nails, Red Paint, 8 In. 145.00
Civil War, Canteen, Wooden, Drum Type, Single Rim, Nails, 7 In. 94.50
Civil War, Canteen, Wooden, Nails, Drum Type, Gray Paint, 6 1/2 In. 84.50
Civil War, Canteen, Wooden, Red Paint, Eyelet & Buttonhole Hoops, 10 In. 115.00
Civil War, Coat, Officer's 35.00
Civil War, Cup, Collapsible, Silver On Pewter, New Bedford, Mass. 59.50
Civil War, Epaulette, Union Colonel, Brass Nameplate, Pair 145.00
Civil War, Knapsack, U.S.Army, Canvas, Loops For Blanket Roll 49.50
Civil War, Knapsack, Union Army 35.00
Civil War, Knife, Homemade, Confederate, Iron, Folding, "Hail To Lee" 145.00
Civil War, Poster, Steuben Rangers, N.Y., "Preserve The Union, " 16 X 14 In. 20.00
Civil War, Pouch, Cap, Infantryman's, Black Leather, Belt Loops 22.50
Civil War, Saddlebag, Surgeon's, Russet Leather, Dr.J.R.Heald, Pair 185.00
Civil War, Shoulder Scale, Noncommissioned Officer's, Brass, Gettysburg 22.50
Civil War, Shoulder Straps, U.S.Infantry Officer's, Gilt Brass, Velvet 24.50

Clambroth glass, popular in the Victorian era, is a grayish color and is
semiopaque like the soup.

Clambroth, Candlestick, Crucifix, 11 In.High, Pair 75.00
Clambroth, Hat, Fedora, Painted Violet Spray 31.00
Clambroth, Mug, Birds & Wheat, Raised, Fence Post Handle 18.00
Clambroth, Tumbler, Button Arches, Souvenir, Watertown, S.D. 8.00

Clews pottery was made by George Clews & Co.of Brownhill Pottery,
Tunstall, England, from 1806 to 1861.
Clews, see also Flow Blue

Clews, Bowl, Water Girl Series, Deep Blue, 5 3/4 In. 110.00

Clews, Platter,
Winter View Of Pittsfield, Mass.
(See Page 97)

Chocolate Glass, Dish,
Fish Cover, Dolphin, Greentown
(See Page 95)

Clews, **Compote,** Playing At Draughts, Wilkie, Blue, C.1830, 11 In. 275.00
Clews, **Cup & Saucer,** English River & Tower Scene, Deep Blue .... 88.00 To 95.00
Clews, **Cup Plate,** Hudson River Series, Pink, 3 3/4 In. 48.00
Clews, **Plate,** Christmas Eve, Dark Blue, Wilkie, 6 3/4 In. 175.00
Clews, **Plate,** Christmas Eve, Dark Blue, Wilkie, 9 In. 125.00
Clews, **Plate,** Dr.Syntax Returned From His Tour, Light Blue, 8 1/2 In. 110.00
Clews, **Plate,** Dr.Syntax Star Gazing, Blue & White, 7 In. 85.00
Clews, **Plate,** Near Fishkill, Hudson River, Brown, 10 In. 70.00
Clews, **Plate,** Near Fishkill, Hudson River, Brown, 11 In. 75.00
Clews, **Plate,** Near Fishkill, Hudson River, Sepia, 10 1/2 In. 75.00
Clews, **Plate,** Near Hudson River, Black & White, 9 In. 55.00
Clews, **Plate,** Near Sandy Hill, Hudson River, Black, 7 In. 45.00
Clews, **Plate,** Near Sandy Hill, Hudson River, Sepia, 7 3/4 In. 35.00
Clews, **Plate,** Near Sandy Hill, Hudson River, Sepia, 8 In. 55.00
Clews, **Plate,** Peace & Plenty, Dark Blue, 10 In. 110.00
Clews, **Plate,** States, Dark Blue, 8 3/4 In. 195.00
Clews, **Plate,** States, Deep Blue, 10 1/2 In. 240.00
Clews, **Plate,** The Valentine, Dark Blue, Wilkie, 10 In. 125.00
Clews, **Platter,** Knight Of The Wood Conquered, Quixote, Blue, C.1825, 17 In. 150.00
Clews, **Platter,** Newburg, Pittsfield Elm, Black & White, 8 In. 125.00
Clews, **Platter,** Teresa Panza & The Messenger, Quixote, Blue, C.1825, 15 In. 200.00
Clews, **Platter,** Winter View Of Pittsfield, Mass. .... *Illus* 150.00
Clifton, **Vase,** Robin's Egg Blue, Signed, Dated 1905, 9 In. 75.00
    Clock, see also Brass, Sundial, Coca-Cola, Clock, Disneyana,
    Clock, Kewpie, Clock, Store, Clock
Clock, **A.Munger,** Empire Case, Flat Top, Spiraled Side Column 750.00
Clock, **A.Willard,** Jr., Banjo, Wooden Bezel, Weight Driven, 8 Day 1300.00
Clock, **Aaron Willard,** Mass., C.1820, Banjo, Mahogany, Parcel Gilt, 33 In. 2300.00
Clock, **Aaron Willard,** Tall, C.1800 .... 4900.00
Clock, **Advertising,** Calumet Baking Powder 275.00
Clock, **Advertising,** Carling's Black Label Beer, Plastic, Oblong, Oval Face 39.95
Clock, **Advertising,** Empire Shirt Co., Man's Shirt Shape, Germany, Pearl 35.00
Clock, **Advertising,** Griesedieck Bros. Beer, Illuminated 30.00
Clock, **Advertising,** Iroquois Beer & Ale, Indian's Head, Metal, Glass, 7 In. 89.95
Clock, **Advertising,** Jewel Tea, Hall's 45.00
Clock, **Advertising,** Old Mr.Boston, Bottle Shape, Key Wind 275.00
Clock, **Alden Atkins,** 30 Hour, Strikes 85.00
Clock, **Animated,** Blacksmith Shop .... *Illus* 425.00
Clock, **Animated,** Blinking Eye Organ Grinder .... *Illus* 500.00
Clock, **Ansonia Copper & Brass Co.,** Steeple, 30 Hour, Alarm, Miniature 150.00
Clock, **Ansonia Copper & Brass Co.,** Terry's Patent, Rosewood Case, Calendar 605.00
Clock, **Ansonia,** Calendar, Strikes, 19 In. 187.50
Clock, **Ansonia,** Carriage, Brass Case 160.00
Clock, **Ansonia,** Carriage, Embossed Metal Case, 30 Hour, 6 X 4 3/4 In. 100.00
Clock, **Ansonia,** Carriage, Nickel Case, Alarm 110.00
Clock, **Ansonia,** Cigar Box, Strikes 100.00
Clock, **Ansonia,** Combination Safe, Alarm 75.00
Clock, **Ansonia,** Crystal, Regulator, Brass Case, Open Escapement On Face 185.00
Clock, **Ansonia,** Cut Glass, Similar To Tuthill's Primrose, 8 Day 375.00
Clock, **Ansonia,** Jenny Lind, Mirror Side 275.00
Clock, **Ansonia,** Mantel, Iron, Black Enamel, 4 Brass Columns, Porcelain Dial 110.00
Clock, **Ansonia,** Mantel, Porcelain Dial, Brass Columns, Black Enamel 110.00
Clock, **Ansonia,** Marble Case, Pillars, Filigree Brass Dome, 15 X 16 In. 120.00
Clock, **Ansonia,** Marble, Ship Gallery, 3 Steeples 70.00
Clock, **Ansonia,** Ornate Iron Case, Strikes, 8 Day 50.00
Clock, **Ansonia,** Peep-O-Day, Alarm 50.00
Clock, **Ansonia,** Plush Covered, Humpback, 8 Day, 1/2 Hour Cathedral Gong 100.00
Clock, **Ansonia,** Regulator, Crystal 400.00
Clock, **Ansonia,** Rhinestone Bezel, Porcelain Plaque 125.00
Clock, **Ansonia,** Royal Bonn Case, Red & Yellow Roses On Green, Gold 165.00
Clock, **Ansonia,** Royal Bonn, Cream, Green Case, Flowers, 11 1/2 In. 165.00
Clock, **Ansonia,** Swing, Huntress, 25 In. 625.00
Clock, **Ansonia,** Swinging Arm .... 375.00 To 475.00
Clock, **Ansonia,** Walnut Case, Glass, Strikes, 19 In. 155.00
Clock, **Atkins & Whiting & Co.,** Wall, Octagonal, 30 Day .... *Illus* 675.00
Clock, **Atkins,** Cottage 75.00

Clock, Atkins, Drop Octagon, Piecrust Trim, Spring Wind, 8 Day 295.00
Clock, Atkins, Fife Type Case, Gold Column, Brass Works, 8 Day 135.00
Clock, Atkins, Venetian, Round Top 100.00
Clock, Austin Chittenden, Lexington, Mass., Hollow Column, Wooden Works 400.00
Clock, Austin Chittenden, Shelf, Hollow Column, 30 Hour 395.00
Clock, Auto, Brevet, Swiss Movement, Brass, Porcelain, Stem Wind, 8 Day 20.00
Clock, Auto, Waltham, 8 Day, Black Enamel, 3 1/4 In. 25.00
Clock, Automaton, French Clock In Tower, Musicians, C.1880, 24 X 18 In. 3650.00
Clock, Banjo, C.1820 .... 900.00
Clock, Banjo, Mahogany, Brass Eagle & Trim 125.00
Clock, Beehive, Wooden, Brass Works 90.00
Clock, Big Ben, Alarm 10.00
Clock, Birge & Fuller, C.1835, Shelf, Double Steeple, Mahogany, 8 Day 700.00
Clock, Birge & Fuller, Steeple On Steeple, Wagon Spring Movement 2000.00
Clock, Birge & Fuller, 4 Candle Wagon Spring, 8 Day 2350.00
Clock, Birge & Peck Co., C.1850, Shelf, Weights, Strikes, 8 Day 400.00
Clock, Birge & Peck Co., Empire Case, Strap Movement, 8 Day 375.00
Clock, Bishop & Bradley, Pillar & Scroll 1000.00
Clock, Black Forest, Carved Dog, Eyes Tell Time 130.00
Clock, Black Forest, Wag-On-Wall, Dial Dated 1836 .... 225.00

Clock, Animated,
Blacksmith Shop
(See Page 97)

Clock, Brewster & Ingraham,
Sharp Twin Gothic Steeple
(See Page 99)

Clock, Atkins & Whiting & Co., Wall,
Octagonal, 30 Day
(See Page 97)

Clock, Animated,
Blinking Eye Organ Grinder
(See Page 97)

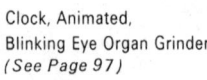

Clock, Chinese,
Bracket, Carved, C.1730
(See Page 99)

Clock, Blin, French, Wag-On-Wall, Porcelain Dial, Brass Pendulum	195.00
Clock, Brass, 17 Jewel	20.00
Clock, Brewster & Ingraham, Bristol, Conn.	175.00
Clock, Brewster & Ingraham, Gothic Twin Steeple, Fusee Movement	500.00
Clock, Brewster & Ingraham, Kirk's Patent, Steeple, Brass Spring, 8 Day	320.00
Clock, Brewster & Ingraham, Sharp Twin Gothic Steeple Illus	500.00
Clock, Brewster & Ingraham, Steeple, 30 Hour	120.00
Clock, Brewster & Ingraham, Twin Gothic Steeple, Brass Works, 8 Day	450.00
Clock, Brille Master, Regulator, Short Pendulum	500.00
Clock, Bronze, Napoleon, Porcelain & Bronze Face, Bronze Pendulum, 16 In.	325.00
Clock, C.& L.C. Ives, Shelf, Half Column, Carved Eagle Crest, 3 Tiered Case	275.00
Clock, C.& N. Jerome, Bristol, Conn., Empire Case, Repeating Brass Movement	375.00
Clock, C.& N. Jerome, Bristol, Conn., Shelf, Round End, Zinc Dial, Weight	130.00
Clock, Carriage, Brass, Beveled Glass, Porcelain Face, 4 1/2 X 3 In.	225.00
Clock, Carriage, Enamel & Bronze, 2 1/4 In.High	125.00
Clock, Charles Stratton, Shelf, Scroll Top, Wooden Works, 30 Hour	300.00
Clock, Chauncey Jerome, Bristol, Ogee	130.00
Clock, Chauncey Jerome, Drop Octagonal Case, Piecrust Trim, Double Fusee	425.00
Clock, Chauncey Jerome, Fusee Movement, 8 Day	150.00
Clock, Chauncey Jerome, Shelf, Half Column	160.00
Clock, Chauncey Jerome, Silver Plate	75.00
Clock, Chauncey Jerome, Steeple	145.00
Clock, Chelsea Claremont, Ship, Barometer	300.00
Clock, Chelsea Clock Co., Boston	475.00
Clock, Chelsea, Ship's, Bronze Case, Wooden Stand 195.00 To	225.00
Clock, Cherub, Patent 1890-1894, Paste Brilliance Bezel, 7 1/2 In.	55.00
Clock, China, Blue, Floral, Open Escapement, Strikes, 11 In.	167.50
Clock, Chinese, Bracket, Carved, C.1730 Illus	1000.00
Clock, Columbia Time Products, Woody Woodpecker, Woody's Cafe, Animated	80.00
Clock, Cornelius Miller, N.Y., C.1750, Tall Case, Queen Anne, Maple, 7 1/2 Ft.	4750.00
Clock, Cut Glass, Boudoir, Harvard, 5 1/2 X 4 In.	185.00
Clock, Daniel Pratt, Jr., Papier-Mache Case, Mother-Of-Pearl Inlaid	200.00
Clock, Daniel Pratt, Shelf, Empire Case, 30 Hour	160.00
Clock, David Wood, Grandfather	950.00
Clock, Dey, Oak Case, Dated 1894	375.00
Clock, Diptych, Stockert, Bavaria, Wooden Dial, Compass, C.1790	80.00
Clock, E.& G.W. Bartholomew, Stenciled Splat, Wooden Works	115.00
Clock, E.C.Brewster & Son, Bristol, Conn., Shelf, Ripple Door	220.00
Clock, E.Henry Dumaige, Bronze, 3 Piece Set	425.00
Clock, E.Manross, Steeple	115.00
Clock, E.N.Welch, Forestville, Conn., Steeple, Reverse Painting On Glass	145.00
Clock, E.N.Welch, Miniature	80.00
Clock, E.N.Welch, Ship Bell, Octagonal Oak Case, Round Face, 30 Hour	475.00
Clock, E.N.Welch, Steeple, 30 Hour	85.00
Clock, E.W.Adams, Seneca Falls, N.Y., Empire Case, Wooden Works	300.00
Clock, Edward Meeks, Jr., N.Y., C.1795, Tall Case, Mahogany, Inlaid, 8 Ft.	1900.00
Clock, Electric, Bronze Nude Holding Clock, 11 X 13 In.	135.00
Clock, Eli & Samuel Terry, Reverse Painting, Urn Finials	1250.00
Clock, Eli Terry, Jr., Transition	450.00
Clock, Eltime, U.S.A., Carriage, Music Box	20.00
Clock, English, Mantel, Oak, Portico Style, Marquetry, Brass, Strikes	75.00
Clock, English, Schoolhouse, Long Drop, Single Fusee Movement, C.1850	95.00
Clock, Ephraim Downs, Bristol, C.1825, Shelf, Mahogany, Pillar & Scroll	550.00
Clock, Ephraim Downs, Shelf, Stenciled Column, Wooden Works, 30 Hour	300.00
Clock, F.C.Andrews, Weight Driven, Miniature	170.00
Clock, F.Kroeber, Shelf	165.00
Clock, F.Kroeber, Wall, Strikes	275.00
Clock, F.Welch, Forestville, Conn., Mantel, Walnut, 8 Day, Alarm	99.00
Clock, Figure Eight, Brass Bezels & Buttons, Strikes, 8 Day, 18 In.	145.00
Clock, Forestville Mfg.Co., Bristol, Acorn Illus	3750.00
Clock, Forestville Mfg. Co., Bristol, Conn., Empire Case, Carved Eagle Top	325.00
Clock, Forestville, Conn., Shelf, Hollow Column, Brass Movement, 8 Day	175.00
Clock, French, Black Marble, 3 Piece, 8 Day	125.00
Clock, French, Carriage, Brass, Beveled Glass, Alarm, 3 X 4 1/4 In.	185.00
Clock, French, Carriage, Brass, Beveled Glass, Bell Alarm, 5 3/4 In.	200.00
Clock, French, Carriage, Brass, Beveled Glass, Fancy Case, 6 1/4 In.	235.00

Clock, French, Carriage, Brass, Beveled Glass, Porcelain Dial, 5 1/2 In. 175.00
Clock, French, Carriage, Brass, Beveled Glass, Porcelain Dial, 5 3/4 In. 165.00
Clock, French, Carriage, Brass, Beveled Glass, 3 X 4 1/2 In. 165.00
Clock, French, Carriage, Repeater 900.00
Clock, French, Cloisonne Case, 6 1/4 In. 365.00
Clock, French, Grandfather, Hand-Carved 6000.00
Clock, French, Mantel, Wooden, Metal Cupids & Trim, Porcelain Face, 18 In. 95.00
Clock, French, Pendulum, Gold Castings On Case, Silver Dial 1750.00
Clock, French, Polished Brass, Beveled Glass, Mercury Pendulum, 10 In. 325.00
Clock, French, Statue, Strikes 85.00
Clock, French, Wag-On-Wall, Porcelain Calendar Dial, Strikes, 30 In. 525.00
Clock, G.E.Coil-Top Refrigerator Shape, Electric 70.00
Clock, German, Cuckoo, 8 In. 14.50
Clock, German, Patent 1895, Porcelain, Blue Forget-Me-Nots, 6 1/2 In. 40.00
Clock, Germany, Table, Brass 22.50
Clock, Gilbert, Banjo Type, Back Wind 50.00
Clock, Gilbert, Banjo, Daggett, Presentation Case 1100.00
Clock, Gilbert, Banjo, 8 Day, 29 In. 115.00
Clock, Gilbert, Kitchen, Oak, Strikes 85.00
Clock, Gilbert, Mantel 47.50
Clock, Gilbert, School, Rosewood Case, Calendar 165.00
Clock, Gilbert, School, Round Top, Long Drop 155.00
Clock, Gilbert, Wall, Dark Oak, Calendar, Regulator, Rectangular, 38 X 20 In. 150.00
Clock, Gilbert, Wall, Regulator, Single Wind, 2 Weights 400.00
Clock, Goddard-Townsend, R.I., C.1760, Tall Case, Mahogany, 8 Ft.2 In. 8000.00
Clock, Grandfather, Symphonium, Walnut Case .... Illus 3450.00
Clock, H & M, Carriage, Beveled Glass, Brass Case, 3 1/4 X 4 1/4 In. 165.00
Clock, H.Welton & Co., Successor To Eli Terry & Co., Conn., Gold Front 125.00
Clock, H.Welton & Co., Successor To Eli Terry & Co., 3 Weights 110.00
Clock, Hebdomas, Nickel Case, 8 Day 75.00
Clock, Hopkins & Alfred, Harwington, Conn., Pawfoot, Stenciled, Wooden Works 205.00
Clock, Hopkins & Alfred, Harwington, Conn., Wooden Movement, Stenciled 325.00
Clock, Hotchkiss & Benedict, Auburn, N.Y., Mahogany .... Illus 650.00
Clock, Hotchkiss & Benedict, N.Y., Munger Patent, Mahogany, Eagle Pendulum 650.00
Clock, Hourglass, Tartan Ware, Wood Frame, Stuart Plaid Paper, C.1845, 7 In. 65.00
Clock, Howard, Banjo, No.5 .... 900.00
Clock, Howard, Banjo, 50 In. 40.00
Clock, Howard, Hanging, 2 Face, Weight Driven, 30 Day 175.00
Clock, Howard, Jeweler's Floor, Regulator, Mercury Pendulum 2150.00
Clock, Howard, Ship's 250.00
Clock, Howard, Weight Driven, 2 Face 250.00
Clock, Huxtable Newton-Abbot, 1887, Bracket, 44 In. 950.00
Clock, Ingraham & Co., Venetian, Round Top 70.00
Clock, Ingraham, A.A.Schadow & Sons Art Nouveau Lamp, Brass, Spelter, 19 In. 110.00
Clock, Ingraham, Admiral Dewey 200.00
Clock, Ingraham, Cottage, Round Top, 30 Hour, Strikes 50.00
Clock, Ingraham, Dewdrop, Calendar 225.00
Clock, Ingraham, Iron Front 120.00
Clock, Ingraham, Kitchen, Oak Case, 8 Day, Time & Strike .... Illus 105.00
Clock, Ingraham, Kitchen, Oak, Calendar 175.00
Clock, Ingraham, Kitchen, Walnut .... 85.00 To 100.00
Clock, Ingraham, Kitchenette, Pendulum View Window, Oak, 13 X 13 5/8 In. 45.00
Clock, Ingraham, Roy Rogers, Animated, Desert Scene, Alarm 25.00
Clock, Ingraham, School, Round Top, 11 In.Dial, 16 X 23 1/2 In. 115.00
Clock, Ingraham, Store, Regulator 35.00
Clock, Ingraham, Wall, Calendar Dial 225.00
Clock, Ingraham, Wall, Ionic Model, Gold Front, 8 Day, Strikes 225.00
Clock, Ingraham, Wall, Ionic, Strikes 175.00
Clock, International Alarm, Art Nouveau Winged Cherub, 6 1/2 In. 65.00
Clock, Isaac Grotz, Easton, Pa., C.1810, Tall Case, Chippendale, Cherry, 7 Ft. 2000.00
Clock, Ithaca, Bank Model, No.2, Walnut Case, Calendar, Double Dial 2000.00
Clock, Ithaca, Calendar, Walnut, Double Dial 1500.00
Clock, Ithaca, Cottage Model, Calendar, Double Dial 500.00
Clock, Ithaca, Farmer's Model, Calendar, Double Dial 425.00
Clock, Ithaca, Fashion Model, Walnut Case, Calendar, Double Black Dials 1800.00
Clock, Ithaca, Granger Model, Calendar, Double Dial 550.00

Clock, Japanese, Lantern, 30 In.
(See Page 102)

Clock, Grandfather, Symphonium, Walnut Case
(See Page 100)

Clock, L.Gilbert, Wall,
Walnut, Calendar
(See Page 102)

Clock, Hotchkiss & Benedict,
Auburn, N.Y., Mahogany
(See Page 100)

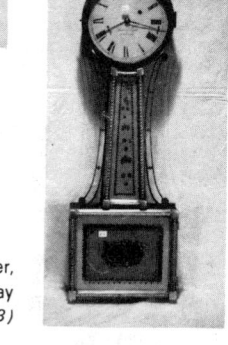

Clock, Sawin & Dyer,
Banjo, Gold Front, 8 Day
(See Page 103)

Clock, Forestville Mfg.Co.,
Bristol, Acorn
(See Page 99)

Clock, Ingraham,
Kitchen, Oak Case,
8 Day, Time & Strike
(See Page 100)

Clock, Putnam Bailey, Conn.,
Transition, Paw Feet
(See Page 103)

Clock, **Ithaca**, Library Model, Calendar, Double Dial 600.00
Clock, **Ithaca**, Parlor Model, Calendar, Double Dial 1300.00
Clock, **Ithaca**, 1866, Walnut Case, Calendar, 25 In. 550.00
Clock, **J.C.Brown**, Forestville, Conn., 8 Day 135.00
Clock, **J.C.Brown**, Ripple Beehive, Etched Glass, Painted Dial 525.00
Clock, **J.N.Dunning**, N.Y., C.1850, Wall, Mahogany, Carved, Acorn Finial, 5 Ft. 1600.00
Clock, **J.R.Mills & Co.**, N.Y., Aaron D.Crane Design, C.1845, Torsion, 8 Day 1150.00
Clock, **Jacob Gorgas**, Ephrata, Pa., Grandfather, Brass Dial, C.1780 .... 1600.00
Clock, **Japanese**, Lantern, 30 In. .... *Illus* 3500.00
Clock, **Japanese**, Stick 2000.00
Clock, **Japanese**, Temple, Stand 4800.00
Clock, **Japy Freres & Cie**, Med D'Honneur, Porcelain, Bronze, 12 In. 295.00
Clock, **Japy Freres**, Mantel, Mahogany, Blue & White Tile Front, 12 1/2 In. 275.00
Clock, **Japy Freres**, Onyx Case, Urn Top 185.00
Clock, **Jennings Brothers**, Bridgeport, Conn., Second Hand, 7 1/2 In. 50.00
Clock, **Jerome & Darrow**, Gronner Movement, Stenciled Column & Splat 160.00
Clock, **Jerome**, Cottage, Colorful Glass, 11 In. 62.50
Clock, **Jerome**, Dneister, Wall, Walnut, Calendar, Double Dial, 8 Day, Strikes 750.00
Clock, **Jerome**, Keyhole, 8 Day 375.00
Clock, **John Bailey**, Hanover, Miniature 2000.00
Clock, **John Birge**, Bristol, Conn., Sleigh Front, Weight Driven, 8 Day 250.00
Clock, **John Everitt**, Easton, Pa., Grandfather, Tambour Door 1500.00
Clock, **John J.Krause**, Northhampton, Pa., Grandfather, Maple Case, C.1800 .... 1900.00
Clock, **John Kirk**, Alarm, Stenciled Column & Splat 750.00
Clock, **John Kirk**, Bristol, Conn., Shelf, Weight Driven, Alarm, Strikes 190.00
Clock, **Jonathan Frost**, Wooden Works, 30 Hour, Alarm, Strikes 145.00
Clock, **Jos.Dudds**, London, C.1750, Long Case, Black Lacquer, 7 Ft.5 In. 1600.00
Clock, **Joseph Ives**, Hills & Goodrich, Plainville, Conn. Designed Case 375.00
Clock, **Joseph Ives**, Mirror, C.1818, Long Pendulum 1500.00
Clock, **Joseph Ives**, Regulator, 2 Weight Drop, 30 Day 1200.00
Clock, **Kitchen**, Oak, Chimes, 8 Day 75.00
Clock, **Krocher**, Calendar, Wall, Walnut Case, 14 In. 325.00
Clock, **Kuell**, Carriage, Music Box 75.00
Clock, **L.Gilbert**, Wall, Walnut, Calendar .... *Illus* 425.00
Clock, **Lalique**, C.1930, Pale Blue Opaque, Mermaids In Water, 11 In. 800.00
Clock, **LeBouthier & Co.**, N.Y.C., Swinger, Nude Lady Statue, Porcelain Dial 475.00
Clock, **Liverpool**, Mantel, Brass Face & Works, Beveled Glass Door, 8 Day 145.00
Clock, **London**, 112 Regent St., Carriage, French, Brass Case, Porcelain, 6 In. 225.00
Clock, **Lovell**, Meriden, Conn., Calendar, Figure Eight, 8 Day, Strikes 325.00
Clock, **Lux Mfg.Co.**, Alarm, Red Metal, Family Scene On Face, 4 1/2 In. 30.00
Clock, **Lux**, Clown, Pendulette, Key 25.00
Clock, **Lux**, Cottage 12.50
Clock, **Lux**, Happy Days, Animated 35.00
Clock, **Lux**, Spinning Wheel, Animated, Alarm 20.00
Clock, **Man With Hammer On Top**, Toy, Pendulum, Metal, 5 In. 60.00
Clock, **Mantel**, Pressed Glass, Daisy & Button, Amber .... 95.00 To 125.00
Clock, **Mantel**, Pressed Glass, Daisy & Button, Amber, C.1800, 14 In. 145.00
Clock, **Mantel**, Strikes, 8 Day 15.00
Clock, **Marcus & Co.**, N.Y., Mercury Pendulum, Brass & Glass 135.00
Clock, **Marcus Smith**, Empire Case, Swiss Movement, Weight Driven 325.00
Clock, **Medaille D'Argent Vincenti**, 1855, Black Stone Case, 15 X 12 In. 175.00
Clock, **Merriman & Birge**, Ives Roller Pinion Movement, Scroll Top, 30 Hour 800.00
Clock, **Molineux**, Bracket, Strikes, Miniature 325.00
Clock, **Moore Ipswich**, Bracket, Repeater 3500.00
Clock, **Morbier**, Crown Wheel, Folding Pendulum, Strikes, C.1850, 8 Day 200.00
Clock, **Mr.Zimmer**, C.1930, Pillar & Scroll, Miniature 310.00
Clock, **N.Pomeroy**, Cottage, Alarm, Strikes 75.00
Clock, **Neuchatel**, Bracket 2000.00
Clock, **New Hampshire**, Mirror, Weight Driven, Rattrap Movement, 8 Day 600.00
Clock, **New Haven**, Advertising, Clothing, Calendar 210.00
Clock, **New Haven**, Advertising, Schenley's, Season's Greetings, 1939 .... 24.50
Clock, **New Haven**, Alarm, Patent Nov.29, 1898, 4 3/8 In. 15.00
Clock, **New Haven**, Art Nouveau, Second Hand, 6 1/2 In. 45.00
Clock, **New Haven**, Banjo, Mahogany, Eagle Finial, Reverse Paintings, 18 In. 75.00
Clock, **New Haven**, Banjo, Painted Tablet, 12 Day, 18 In. 127.50
Clock, **New Haven**, Banjo, Scenic, Eagle Finial, Metal Scrolls, 29 X 9 In. 120.00

Clock, New Haven, Banjo, Strikes, 20 In. 150.00
Clock, New Haven, Double Cherub, Brass Colored Base, 10 In. 60.00
Clock, New Haven, Double Cherub, Brass, 6 In. 57.50
Clock, New Haven, Gallery, C.1875 .... 150.00
Clock, New Haven, Gallery, Mahogany Case, C.1875, 22 X 21 In. 150.00
Clock, New Haven, Mantel, Iron, 11 X 11 In. 45.00
Clock, New Haven, Mantel, Walnut Case, Key Wind, Strikes, 8 Day 60.00
Clock, New Haven, Oak Case, Regulator, 30 Day 250.00
Clock, New Haven, Painting, Alarm, Strikes 50.00
Clock, New Haven, Regulator, Single Weight 345.00
Clock, New Haven, Steeple, Mahogany, Stenciled, Alarm 135.00
Clock, New Haven, Steeple, 30 Hour 120.00
Clock, Niagara, Wall, Oak, Square 70.00
Clock, Norris North, C.1820, Torrington Wooden Works, Shelf, Pillar & Scroll 3100.00
Clock, Octava Pillow, Bronze Case, 8 Day, 15 Jewel, 3 1/2 X 2 1/2 X 1/2 In. 25.00
Clock, Phillip Barnes & Co., Empire Case, Brass Works, Weight Driven, 8 Day 285.00
Clock, Plymouth, Mantel, Camelback, Chimes Quarter Hour, Gongs Hour 85.00
Clock, Prestone, Windup 50.00
Clock, Putnam Bailey, Conn., Transition, Paw Feet ....Illus 275.00
Clock, Raingo Freres, Paris, Louis XVI Style, Marble, Ormolu, 15 In. 550.00
Clock, Regulator, Iowa Jewelry Store, Burled Cherry Case, Carved, 10 In. 3500.00
Clock, Regulator, Jeweler's, Cherry Case, Carved Deer Head, 10 In.High 3500.00
Clock, Regulator, Wall, Carved Greek Key On Door Frame, Strikes, 34 In. 125.00
Clock, Riley Whiting, Grandfather, Wooden Movement, 30 Hour 500.00
Clock, Rodney Brace, Shelf, Wooden Works, Full Column 250.00
Clock, Royal Bonn China, 12 X 11 In. 195.00
Clock, S.B.Terry, Wall, Octagonal 400.00
Clock, S.Hoadley, Alarm, Reverse Painting On Glass 450.00
Clock, Sawin & Dyer, Banjo, Gold Front, 8 Day ....Illus 1200.00
Clock, Sawin & Dyer, Banjo, Presentation Case 2000.00
Clock, Schatz, German, Anniversary, 400 Day, Dome 85.00
Clock, School, Maple, Hexagon Face, Glass Door, Pendulum, 8 Day 135.00
Clock, Seikoska, Regulator, Wall, Lyre Pendulum, 55 In. 285.00
Clock, Sessions, Banjo, 36 In. 200.00
Clock, Sessions, Forestville, Conn., Wooden, Gothic, Key Wind, 8 Day 65.00
Clock, Sessions, Kitchklok On Label, Salesman's Sample, 13 In. 147.50
Clock, Sessions, Mantel, Humpback, 8 Day, Strikes 25.00
Clock, Sessions, Mantel, Lion's Head, Key Wind 60.00
Clock, Sessions, Mantel, Oak Case, 8 Day, Strikes 65.00
Clock, Sessions, Mantel, Walnut, 8 Day 22.50
Clock, Sessions, Mission, Wall, Striking, 13 X 25 In. 50.00
Clock, Sessions, School, Drop, Salesman's Sample, 14 In. 137.50
Clock, Sessions, School, Miniature 135.00
Clock, Sessions, School, Regulator, Oak, Short Drop, 24 In. 175.00
Clock, Sessions, Wall, Oak Case, Regulator, 2 Weights 350.00
Clock, Seth Thomas & Sons, Colored Brass, Strikes, 13 In. 67.50
Clock, Seth Thomas, Advertising, John Finzer Tobacco, Gesso Type 450.00
Clock, Seth Thomas, Banjo, Flowers On Case, 18 In. 117.50
Clock, Seth Thomas, Calendar, Double Dial 550.00
Clock, Seth Thomas, Calendar, Rosewood Case, 42 1/2 In. High 800.00
Clock, Seth Thomas, Cottage, 8 Day, Strikes 90.00
Clock, Seth Thomas, Fashion, Walnut Case, Big Bell, Short Pendulum, 32 In. 875.00
Clock, Seth Thomas, Grandfather, Cherry Case 1400.00
Clock, Seth Thomas, Kitchen, Walnut 145.00
Clock, Seth Thomas, Mantel, Carved Wooden Eagle, Sonora Chime 275.00
Clock, Seth Thomas, Mantel, Empire Case 145.00
Clock, Seth Thomas, Mantel, Gold Column, Lyre Movement, 3 Day, Strikes 125.00
Clock, Seth Thomas, Mantel, Glass Sides, Front, & Back, Roses & Vines, Bronze 175.00
Clock, Seth Thomas, Mantel, Mahogany, 7 1/2 X 11 In. 40.00
Clock, Seth Thomas, Mantel, Oak Case, 8 Day, Strikes 55.00
Clock, Seth Thomas, Mantel, Rosewood Case, Strikes 130.00
Clock, Seth Thomas, Mantel, White & Gold 87.00
Clock, Seth Thomas, Miniature Ogee, 30 Hour, Time & Strike, 10 X 16 In. 60.00
Clock, Seth Thomas, No.6, Double Dial, Calendar 565.00
Clock, Seth Thomas, Office Calendar, No.3, Rosewood Case, Weight Driven 575.00
Clock, Seth Thomas, Pillar & Scroll 525.00

Clock, **Seth Thomas,** Plymouth Hollow, Burglar & Fire Detective Alarm	650.00
Clock, **Seth Thomas,** Plymouth Hollow, Cottage, Miniature	125.00
Clock, **Seth Thomas,** Plymouth Hollow, Mantel, Rosewood Case, Octagonal Top	110.00
Clock, **Seth Thomas,** Plymouth Hollow, Round Top Regulator, Single Weight	400.00
Clock, **Seth Thomas,** Polished Brass, Strikes Ship's Bell, 5 In. Dial	250.00
Clock, **Seth Thomas,** Railroad Station, Wall, Drop, Brass Works & Weights	200.00
Clock, **Seth Thomas,** Regulator, Oak	375.00 To 400.00
Clock, **Seth Thomas,** School, Miniature	105.00
Clock, **Seth Thomas,** Schoolhouse, Oak	180.00
Clock, **Seth Thomas,** Shelf, Empire Case, Gold Column	170.00
Clock, **Seth Thomas,** Ship's, Brass, Round, 5 In. Dial	145.00
Clock, **Seth Thomas,** Ship's, Outside Bell	295.00
Clock, **Seth Thomas,** Ship's, Outside Bell, Nickel Plated	270.00
Clock, **Seth Thomas,** Steeple, Walnut	85.00
Clock, **Seth Thomas,** Thomaston, Conn., Cottage, Alarm, Strikes	100.00
Clock, **Seth Thomas,** Violin	575.00
Clock, **Seth Thomas,** Weight, Mirror, Half Columns, 5 X 15 X 25 In.	135.00
Clock, **Seth Thomas,** Westminster Sonora Chime, Bell Cluster	125.00
Clock, **Seymour Williams & Porter,** Conn., C.1835, Shelf, Mahogany, 8 Day	600.00
Clock, **Ship's,** U.S.Navy, Phenolic Case, 11 Jewel	85.00
Clock, **Shreve, Crump & Low,** Boston & C.H.Hour, France, Marble, 6 1/4 In.	85.00
Clock, **Silas Hoady,** Grandfather, Wooden Works, 30 Hour	1350.00
Clock, **Simon Willard,** Banjo, Large Movement	3500.00
Clock, **Single Train Skeleton,** Dome *Illus*	575.00
Clock, **Spencer Wooster & Co.,** Salem Bridge, Rack & Snail Movement, 8 Day	375.00
Clock, **Spilhaus,** Space, Electric World Time Piece	140.00
Clock, **Standard Electric,** Springfield, Mass., Slave Movement	30.00
Clock, **Steeple,** Fusee	185.00
Clock, **Store,** Oak Case, Key Wind, Chimes, Round	70.00
Clock, **Sundial,** American, 1762, Pewter, 4 1/2 In. Diameter	350.00
Clock, **Sundial,** Bronze, Hourglass & Wings, "Count None But The Sunny Hours"	65.00
Clock, **Sundial,** German, C.1820, Brass, Wooden, Square Base, Compass	145.00
Clock, **Sundial,** N.Bion A Paris, C.1690, Butterfield Type, Brass, Compass	540.00
Clock, **Swartzwald,** Alarm, 4 Porcelain Dials	75.00
Clock, **Terhune & Edwards,** C.1840, Steeple, Mahogany, 20 In.	300.00
Clock, **Terry & Andrews,** Beehive, 8 Day	120.00
Clock, **Terry & Andrews,** Steeple, 30 Hour	85.00
Clock, **Terry Clock Co.,** Waterbury, Conn., Skeleton Under Glass, China Dial	325.00
Clock, **Terryville,** Black Iron, Round Top	30.00
Clock, **Thomas Lister,** Luddenden, C.1790, Long Case, Oak, 7 Ft.2 In.	575.00
Clock, **Thos.Lister,** Halifax, Grandfather, Carved Oak Case, Brass Dial, C.1780	1200.00
Clock, **Tiffany,** see Tiffany, Clock	
Clock, **Topsy,** Negro Girl Blinking Eye, 15 In.	525.00
Clock, **Tudric,** England, Pewter, Hammered Art Deco Design	115.00
Clock, **U.Nardin,** Chronometer, Ship's	1250.00
Clock, **United Clock Co.,** Animated, Man Beating Drum, Will Rogers, Gold Paint	47.50
Clock, **Vienna,** Regulator, 8 Day, 2 Weights	265.00 To 375.00
Clock, **Vonschierholz,** Porcelain, Cupids On Each Side, Floral, 12 1/2 In.	250.00
Clock, **Wall,** Oak, Square, Plate Rack, Brass Weight & Pendulum	50.00
Clock, **Waltham,** Gimbaled Boxed, 8 Day	200.00
Clock, **Waltham,** Traveling, Premier, Folding, 8 Day	50.00
Clock, **Waterbury,** Carriage, Porcelain Face, Beveled Glass, Brass Case, 2 In.	95.00
Clock, **Waterbury,** Carriage, Repeater, Strikes, 5 1/2 In.	185.00
Clock, **Waterbury,** Conn., Mantel, Gold Plated Bronze, Porcelain Face, C.1870	375.00
Clock, **Waterbury,** Daintie No.2, 12 1/2 In.	145.00
Clock, **Waterbury,** Kitchen, Walnut, Calendar	175.00
Clock, **Waterbury,** Mantel, Mahogany, Multicolor Inlay, 14 X 9 In.	125.00
Clock, **Waterbury,** No.44, Oak Case, Double Dial, Calendar, Alarm, Strikes	450.00
Clock, **Waterbury,** School, Calendar Dial, Long Drop	225.00
Clock, **Waterbury,** Ship's Bell, Desk Model	115.00
Clock, **Welch,** Cottage, Alarm *Illus*	55.00
Clock, **Westclock,** Big Ben, 5 In. Nickel Over Brass Face	15.00
Clock, **Westminster,** Chiming Alarm, 4 Bells On Top, Second Hand, 9 1/2 In.	275.00
Clock, **Westminster,** General Electric Refrigerator, Chrome	20.00
Clock, **Willard's Patent,** C.1815, Banjo, Mahogany, Parcel Gilt, Brass, 33 In.	3250.00
Clock, **Willard's Patent,** Mass., C.1815, Banjo, Mahogany, Parcel Gilt, 42 In.	3600.00

Clock, Single Train Skeleton,
Dome
(See Page 104)

Clock, Windmill, Novelty,
Brass Case, 20 In.

Clock, Welch, Cottage, Alarm
(See Page 104)

Clock, William Crane, Grandfather 700.00
Clock, William Gilbert, Columbia Model, Wall, Walnut, Calendar 125.00
Clock, William Gilbert, Teardrop, Calendar, 8 Day, Strikes 375.00
Clock, William Johnson, Flat, Matching Mirror, Strikes 205.00
Clock, William Johnson, Shelf, Ripple Front, Fusee Movement, 30 Hour 210.00
Clock, Windmill, Novelty, Brass Case, 20 In. .... *Illus* 600.00
Clock, Younghans, Elephant Swinger 210.00
Clock, Younghans, Flying Trapeze 275.00
Clock, Younghans, Swinging Arm .... 200.00 To 225.00

*Cloisonne Enamel was developed during the nineteenth century. A glass
enamel was applied between small ribbonlike pieces of metal on a metal base.
Most Cloisonne is Japanese.*

Cloisonne, Ashtray, Light Blue, Multicolored Floral, Spring Scrolls 10.00
Cloisonne, Ashtray, Three Leaf Clover Shape, Floral, 4 3/4 In. 80.00
Cloisonne, Bottle, Snuff, Floral On White, Blue Panels, 2 In. 100.00
Cloisonne, Bottle, Snuff, Floral, 2 1/2 In. 125.00
Cloisonne, Bottle, Snuff, Twin Gourd Shape, 2 1/2 In. 150.00
Cloisonne, Bowl, Black Mirror, Chinese Symbol In Center, 3 X 5/8 In., Pair 45.00
Cloisonne, Bowl, Brass, C.1750, 13 In. 450.00
Cloisonne, Bowl, Chinese Red, Floral, Marked China, 3 5/8 In. 12.00
Cloisonne, Bowl, Covered, Gold Flecks, Insects, 10 X 10 In. 295.00
Cloisonne, Bowl, Dragon & Goldstone, Covered, 5 1/2 X 5 In. 145.00
Cloisonne, Bowl, Dragon, Turned-In Rim, 10 In. 215.00
Cloisonne, Bowl, Fish Scale, Light Blue, Marked China, 8 In. 50.00
Cloisonne, Bowl, Flower Rim Top & Bottom, Floral On Black, 4 1/4 In. 40.00
Cloisonne, Bowl, Lotus, Scrolls On Black, Simulated Ming Marks, 12 In. 425.00
Cloisonne, Bowl, Rice, Light Blue, Marked China 22.00
Cloisonne, Bowl, Rust, Spring Scroll Pattern, Oval, 8 1/2 In. 225.00
Cloisonne, Bowl, Teal Blue, White & Lavender Flower & Bird, 19 In. 100.00
Cloisonne, Bowl, Three Dragons, Flaming Pearl, Black Ground, 8 In.Diameter 185.00
Cloisonne, Box, Cake, Japanese, Lid, Pattern On Goldstone, 10 X 4 In. 950.00
Cloisonne, Box, Covered, Black, Spring Scroll Pattern, Round, 8 In. 275.00
Cloisonne, Box, Covered, Yellow, Floral & Scrollwork, 4 1/2 X 3 In. 220.00
Cloisonne, Box, Cylindrical, Openwork, Lotus & Scrolls, 7 .... *Color* 95.00
Cloisonne, Box, Desk, Foo Dogs On Lid, Oil Burner, White, Brass, 11 X 6 In. 225.00
Cloisonne, Box, Hinged, Gold Wires & Geometrics On White, C.1880, 10 In. 59.00
Cloisonne, Box, Jewelry, Brass, Floral, Turquoise, Green, Yellow, & Pink, 5 In. 40.00
Cloisonne, Box, Open Technique, Multicolor On Gold, C.1850, 2 1/2 In. 55.00
Cloisonne, Box, Patch, Blue Floral, 1 3/4 In. 16.50
Cloisonne, Box, Powder, Floral On Rust, Spiral Cloisons, Round, 3 1/2 In. 55.00
Cloisonne, Box, Powder, Spiral Cloisons, Pastel Flower On Rust, 3 3/4 In. 55.00
Cloisonne, Box, Scrolls On Black, Wood Lined, 5 X 3 1/2 In. 150.00
Cloisonne, Box, Square, Dragons, Green, Blue, & Black, 5 1/2 X 2 1/2 In. 65.00

Cloisonne, Box, Tobacco, Over Bronze 110.00
Cloisonne, Burner, Incense, Globe, Dragons In Clouds On White, C.1850, 9 In. 600.00
Cloisonne, Burner, Incense, Iron, Hirata School, Silver Figure, C.1850, 5 In. 750.00
Cloisonne, Candleholder, White, Yellow & Red Flower, Yellow Butterfly, 3 In. 55.00
Cloisonne, Candlestick, Ormolu Mounts, F.Barbedienne, C.1890, 13 In., Pair 500.00
Cloisonne, Candlestick, Scrolls On Turquoise, 14 In., Pair 395.00
Cloisonne, Charger, Bird & Floral Center, 17 In. 675.00
Cloisonne, Charger, Brilliant Colors, Scalloped, 17 In. 675.00
Cloisonne, Charger, Floral, Green & Red Foliage & Bird, Blue Ground, 12 In. 245.00
Cloisonne, Charger, Flying Bats & Floral On Robin's-Egg Blue, 12 In. 295.00
Cloisonne, Charger, White & Gray & White Doves On Turquoise, 10 In. 235.00
Cloisonne, Charger, White & Green Blossoms On Red, 11 1/2 In. 135.00
Cloisonne, Coffee Pot, Miniature, Tankard Shape, Green, Floral, 4 In. 95.00
Cloisonne, Compact, Sterling Silver, Pink Floral, Chain, 2 In. Diameter 14.00
Cloisonne, Container, Cigarette, Covered, Cobalt Dragon, Geometrics, China 70.00
Cloisonne, Container, Cigarette, Covered, Pale Green, Colored Floral, China 42.00
Cloisonne, Container, Cigarette, Covered, Royal Blue, Prunus, China, 3 In. 40.00
Cloisonne, Cup & Saucer, Coffee, Diaper Pattern 150.00
Cloisonne, Cup & Saucer, Coffee, Floral & Diaper 145.00
Cloisonne, Cup & Saucer, Sake, Dainty Floral 250.00
Cloisonne, Cup & Saucer, Sake, Floral On Blue, U.S.& Imperial China Flags 65.00
Cloisonne, Cup, Sake, Black, Prunus, Spring Scrolls, China 10.00
Cloisonne, Cup, Sake, Light Blue, White Floral, Spring Scrolls, China 10.00
Cloisonne, Dish, Candy, Brass Foo Dog Lid, Black, White Floral, Scrolls 58.00
Cloisonne, Dish, Candy, Covered, Maroon, Prunus, China, 15 1/2 In. 42.50
Cloisonne, Ewer, Phoenix Form, Powder Blue, Chicken On Lid, C.1850, 9 In. 450.00
Cloisonne, Figurine, Crane, Standing, Blue, Yellow, & Red, Brass Wings, 15 In. 600.00
Cloisonne, Figurine, Foo Dog, Gilt Mane & Tail, Blue, C.1850, 9 In., Pair 800.00
Cloisonne, Figurine, Foo Dog, Scrolls On Blue, 5 1/2 In., Pair 800.00
Cloisonne, Flowerpot, Blue Mums On Gray, Mineral Flowers Pewter Base, 3 In. 225.00
Cloisonne, Humidor, Tobacco, Foo Dog Finial, Floral On Red, 7 In. 95.00
Cloisonne, Jar, Covered, Chrysanthemums, Blue, Red, White, Turquoise, 14 In. 125.00
Cloisonne, Jar, Covered, Red & Yellow Flowers On Blue & Green, 5 In. 50.00
Cloisonne, Jar, Ginger, White, Yellow Rose & Bird, Green Flower, 18 In. 135.00
Cloisonne, Jar, Incense, Copper, Yellow 5-Toed Dragon, Covered, Miniature 35.00
Cloisonne, Jar, Potpourri, Covered, Knob Feet, Flowers, Butterflies, 3 1/2 In. 80.00
Cloisonne, Jar, Temple, Covered, Green Cross T Pattern, Floral, 8 In. 195.00
Cloisonne, Lamp Base, Cobalt, Goldstone, Butterflies, Floral, Brass, 19 In. 95.00
Cloisonne, Lamp Base, 23 X 11 In. 145.00
Cloisonne, Match Holder, Maroon, Colored Prunus, 2 3/4 In. 13.50
Cloisonne, Match Holder, White, Fleur-De-Lis, Cloud Scrolls, 2 3/4 In. 15.00
Cloisonne, Matchbox, Blue, Marked China 10.00
Cloisonne, Matchbox, Yellow, Marked China 10.00
Cloisonne, Pipe, Opium, Multicolored Pattern 150.00
Cloisonne, Plaque, Flowers & Butterfly On Black, Beaded Frame, 7 X 7 1/2 In 105.00
Cloisonne, Plaque, Gray, Blue, & Black Geometrics, Brass Base, 12 In., Pair 495.00
Cloisonne, Plate, Flying Bird & Lily Pads On Blue, Gold Border, 6 In. 135.00
Cloisonne, Plate, Red Ground, Colorful Flowers, Brass Rim, 6 In. 75.00
Cloisonne, Pot, Covered, Butterflies, Diaper Pattern, 4 In. 58.00
Cloisonne, Rose Bowl, Covered, Florals On Dark Blue, 3 In.High 26.00
Cloisonne, Rose Bowl, Covered, Footed, Butterfly & Floral, 6 X 7 In. 185.00
Cloisonne, Salt & Pepper, Dragons, Miniature 27.00
Cloisonne, Salt & Pepper, Marked China, Open, Floral On Black 35.00
Cloisonne, Salt & Pepper, Marked China, Open, Floral On Blue 35.00
Cloisonne, Salt & Pepper, Open Salt, Dragon & Floral On Copper 15.00
Cloisonne, Salt, Individual 15.00
Cloisonne, Smoking Set, Dragonflies & Red Scrolls, 6 Piece 90.00
Cloisonne, Spoon, Nut, Dragon Handle 7.00
Cloisonne, Tea Set, Rust Ground, Green Border, Miniature, 5 Piece 375.00
Cloisonne, Teapot, Birds & Floral On Green, Miniature 98.00
Cloisonne, Teapot, Blue, Brown Floral & Butterfly Panels, Goldstone, 5 In. 175.00
Cloisonne, Teapot, Butterflies, Diaper Pattern, 2 3/4 In. 120.00
Cloisonne, Teapot, Floral & Dice Pattern On Blue Ground, 2 1/2 In.High 110.00
Cloisonne, Teapot, Floral & Geometric, Brass Feet, 3 In. 48.00
Cloisonne, Teapot, Green, Blue Floral & Butterfly Panels, 6 1/2 In. 275.00
Cloisonne, Teapot, Pear Shape, Medallion Center, Birds, Butterflies, 6 In. 185.00

Cloisonne, Tray, Brass, Blue, Mikado Rings, C.1720, 14 1/2 X 11 In.	275.00
Cloisonne, Tray, Butterflies & Flowers On Red Ground, Footed, 8 In.Long	90.00
Cloisonne, Tray, Floral & Butterflies On Goldstone, 9 1/2 X 7 1/2 In.	150.00
Cloisonne, Tray, Floral Design, 5 1/2 X 4 1/4 In.	19.00
Cloisonne, Tray, Flowering Plants & 5 Butterflies On Black, C.1850, 9 In.	290.00
Cloisonne, Tray, Flying Bird On Blue, Footed Brass Holder, 10 X 8 In.	200.00
Cloisonne, Tray, Multicolor Floral, Footed, Fretwork Brass Rim, 14 In.	225.00
Cloisonne, Tray, Pin, Bluebird Center	22.00
Cloisonne, Vase, Auto, Green & Dark Blue Panels, Flowers & Butterflies, 7 In	85.00
Cloisonne, Vase, Baluster, Pink & Yellow Blossoms, 3 In.	45.00
Cloisonne, Vase, Birds & Flowering Tree On Blue Gray, 7 In.	50.00
Cloisonne, Vase, Birds & Flowers On Blue, 16 In.	190.00
Cloisonne, Vase, Blue & White, Prunus, Brass, China, Small Neck, 4 In., Pair	95.00
Cloisonne, Vase, Blue, Dragon, 6 In. *Illus*	125.00
Cloisonne, Vase, Bud, Butterflies & Floral, Goldstone Specks, 6 In.	55.00
Cloisonne, Vase, Burgundy, 7 1/2 X 4 In., Pair	250.00
Cloisonne, Vase, Cathedral Panels, Floral & Geometrics, 5 In.	70.00
Cloisonne, Vase, Chrysanthemums On Robin's-Egg Blue Ground, 3 In., Pair	145.00
Cloisonne, Vase, Covered, Japanese, Dragons & Birds, 7 1/4 In.	225.00
Cloisonne, Vase, Cranes On Black, Silver Base, Japan, C.1880, 9 1/2 In.	160.00
Cloisonne, Vase, Fighting Cock On Yellow, 2 1/2 In.	125.00
Cloisonne, Vase, Floral & Butterflies, Goldstone, Cobalt, & Copper, 6 1/8 In.	80.00
Cloisonne, Vase, Floral, Copper Goldstone Panels, Multicolor, 6 1/8 In.	75.00
Cloisonne, Vase, Goldfish & Blue Waterlilies On Red, Silver Foil, 4 In.	135.00
Cloisonne, Vase, Gray, C.1850, 12 1/4 In. *Illus*	550.00
Cloisonne, Vase, Green Ground, Whooping Cranes, Prunus Tree, 10 In., Pair	275.00
Cloisonne, Vase, Green, Brass, Stamped China, 9 1/4 In.	80.00
Cloisonne, Vase, House Scene On Blue, Silver Base, Japan, C.1880, 7 In., Pair	180.00
Cloisonne, Vase, Iris & Butterfly, 4 In.	25.00
Cloisonne, Vase, Japanese, Blue, 8 1/2 In.	165.00
Cloisonne, Vase, Mother-Of-Pearl, Scale Ground, Cranes, 4 1/2 In.	95.00
Cloisonne, Vase, Multicolor Medallions On Black, 7 1/2 In.	75.00
Cloisonne, Vase, Ovoid, Blue Ground, Purple, White, & Orange Floral, 7 In.High	105.00
Cloisonne, Vase, Pea Green Ground, Geese In Fish Scale, C.1870, 7 1/2 In.	155.00
Cloisonne, Vase, Pigeons, Dragons, Plum Blossoms, Dark Blue, C.1850, 4 Ft.	2700.00
Cloisonne, Vase, Pink Cherry Blossom On Cerulean Blue Ground, 7 1/2 In.	72.00
Cloisonne, Vase, Polychrome, Hunt Scenes, C.1850, 31 In., Pair	175.00
Cloisonne, Vase, Prunus Blossoms, Cloud Scrolls, Teak Stands, 3 3/4 In., Pair	60.00
Cloisonne, Vase, Royal Blue, 2 Dancing Cranes, 5 In., Pair	195.00
Cloisonne, Vase, Serpentine Dragon On Chocolate, 6 Sided, 9 In.	139.00
Cloisonne, Vase, Swallows, Iris, & Cherry Blossoms, Pale Blue, C.1850, 36 In.	1250.00
Cloisonne, Vase, Tree Trunk, Bird & Floral, Orange & Red, Japan, 6 1/4 In.	125.00
Cloisonne, Vase, Trumpet, Green Ferns On Black, 11 In.	195.00
Cloisonne, Vase, Vines, Flowers, & Leaves, Royal Blue Ground, 13 In.	95.00
Cloisonne, Vase, Whooping Cranes & Prunus Tree On Mint Green Ground, 10 In	140.00
Cloisonne, Vase, Yellow Dragons On Black, Blue Top & Base, 9 In.	110.00
Cloisonne, Vase, Yellow, Scale, Leaves, & Scrolls, Gilt, 12 In.	175.00
Clothing, see Textile	

Cluthra glass is a two-layered glass with small air pockets that form white spots. The Steuben Glass Works of Corning, New York, made it after 1903. Kimball Glass Company of Vineland, New Jersey, made Cluthra from about 1925.

Cluthra, see also Steuben

Cluthra, Bowl, Apricot, White Inclusions, Spiderweb Effect, 14 1/2 In.	125.00
Cluthra, Bowl, White, Fried Egg Effect, 9 In.Diameter	56.00
Cluthra, Vase, Bubbly Ruby With Blue, C.1888, 10 1/4 In.	150.00
Cluthra, Vase, Emerald Green, Bubbles, Glass Ring Forms Bow, 7 3/4 In.	95.00
Cluthra, Vase, Gray, Yellow Streaked With Red, Signed, 8 1/2 In.	125.00
Cluthra, Vase, Kimball, Urn Shape, Blue, Lemon Patches, 8 1/4 In.	250.00

Coalbrookdale was made by the Coalport porcelain factory of England during the Victorian period. The pieces are heavily decorated with floral encrustations.

Coalbrookdale, Inkstand, Flowers, C.1830	600.00
Coalbrookdale, Mansion, White, Flower Encrusted, 2 Chimneys, C.1830, 5 In.	375.00

Coalbrookdale, Vase, Flowers, Handled, 8 In. 75.00

Coalport ware has been made by the Coalport Porcelain Works of England from 1795 to the present time.

Coalport, Bowl, Covered, Indian Tree, Ring Handle, 11 In. 75.00
Coalport, Bust, H.R.H.P. Of Wales, Parian, John Rose & Co., 1863, 12 In. 275.00
Coalport, Cup & Saucer, Demitasse, Aqua To Ivory, Fluted, Scalloped 39.00
Coalport, Cup & Saucer, Demitasse, Coin Gold Lining, Blue & Pink Trim 68.00
Coalport, Cup & Saucer, Demitasse, Ornate 35.00
Coalport, Plate, Blue Decoration, 6 5/8 In. 5.00
Coalport, Plate, Luncheon, Enameled Gold Flowers & Wreaths, 8 3/4 In. 15.75
Coalport, Plate, Ornate Gold Border, 9 1/2 In. 10.75
Coalport, Sugar & Creamer, Blue Floral On White, Gold Handles & Trim, 2 In. 55.00
Coalport, Vase, Oyster Color, Shell Shape, 8 X 4 In., Pair 75.00

Cobalt blue glass was made using oxide of cobalt. The characteristic bright dark blue identifies it for the collector. Most cobalt glass found today was made after the Civil War.

Cobalt Blue, see also Shirley Temple

Cobalt Blue, Bottle, Perfume, Gold Encrusted, Enameled Leaves, 5 1/2 In. 35.00
Cobalt Blue, Bottle, Perfume, Laydown, Brass Collar & Hinged Cap, 4 In. 30.00
Cobalt Blue, Bottle, Perfume, White, Pink, & Yellow Daisies, 3 1/2 In., Pair 100.00
Cobalt Blue, Bowl, Centerpiece, Ribbed, Footed, C.1920, 12 In. 15.00
Cobalt Blue, Butter Pat, Band 2.00
Cobalt Blue, Cake Set, C.1920, 19 Piece 45.00
Cobalt Blue, Candlestick, Gold Encrusted, Colored Leaves, 7 In. 24.00
Cobalt Blue, Chalice, Enamel Figures All Round, 12 In.High 200.00
Cobalt Blue, Compote, Cut To Clear Quatrefoils, Silver Standard, 8 In. 95.00
Cobalt Blue, Decanter, Rum In Gold, Silver Ring, 13 In. 50.00
Cobalt Blue, Eyecup, Wyeth 6.00
Cobalt Blue, Jar, Candy, Covered, New Martinsville, 8 1/2 In. 20.00
Cobalt Blue, Jar, Dresser, Ball Finial, Urn Shape, White & Gold, Flint, 7 In. 65.00
Cobalt Blue, Jar, Powder, Gold Encrusted, Colored Leaves, 2 1/2 In. 25.00
Cobalt Blue, Pitcher, Water, Gold Around Lip & Base, Enameled Ship 65.00
Cobalt Blue, Plate, Ground Bottom, 11 In. 40.00
Cobalt Blue, Ring Tree, Gold Encrusted, Colored Leaves 35.00
Cobalt Blue, Salt & Pepper, Christmas 125.00
Cobalt Blue, Salt, Master, Silver Plate Frame 16.50
Cobalt Blue, Salt, Sawtooth 95.00
Cobalt Blue, Spooner, Bird Design 8.50
Cobalt Blue, Sugar & Creamer, Square 7.50
Cobalt Blue, Toothpick, Souvenir, Courthouse, Manitowoc, Wis. 10.00

Cloisonne, Vase, Blue, Dragon, 6 In. *(See Page 107)*

Cloisonne, Vase, Gray, C.1850, 12 1/4 In. *(See Page 107)*

Coca-Cola, Bottle *(See Page 109)*

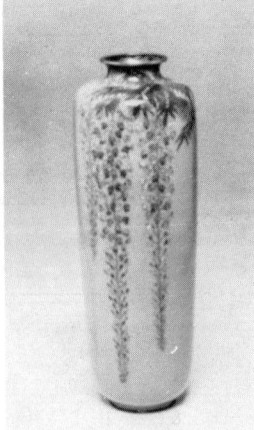

Cobalt Blue, Toothpick, Top Hat	15.00 To 17.00
Cobalt Blue, Tray, Gold Encrusted, Colored Leaves, 7 X 9 In.	28.00
Cobalt Blue, Tumbler, Leaf Medallion	30.00
Cobalt Blue, Tumbler, Painted Flowers	20.00
Cobalt Blue, Urn, Etched San Diego, 1937, Gold Letters, 9 1/2 In.	19.00
Cobalt Blue, Vase, Ball, 4 In., Pair	10.00
Cobalt Blue, Vase, Hat Shape, 3 1/2 In.High	15.00
Cobalt Blue, Vase, Overlay, Allover Cutting, 7 1/4 In.High	148.00
Cobalt Blue, Vase, Scalloped Clear Base, 8 3/4 In.	16.00
Cobalt Blue, Water Set, Royal Lace, 7 In. Pitcher, 5 Piece	110.00
Cobalt Blue, Water Set, Silver Overlay, 7 Piece	125.00

Coca-Cola advertising items have become a special field for collectors.

Coca-Cola, Ad, 1904, Opera Star, Color, 6 1/2 X 9 3/4 In.	45.00
Coca-Cola, Bill Holder, C.1950, English Morocco, Drink Coca-Cola In Gold	15.00
Coca-Cola, Billfold, 1917, "Drink Coca-Cola"	20.00
Coca-Cola, Blotter, 1951	2.00
Coca-Cola, Blotter, 1956, 7 1/2 X 3 1/2 In.	.50 To 2.00
Coca-Cola, Blotter, 1960	2.00
Coca-Cola, Booklet, 1943, Know Your War Planes	20.00
Coca-Cola, Bottle	*Illus* 3.00
Coca-Cola, Bottle Protector, C.1940 U.S.Patent 6-14-27, No Drip	1.00
Coca-Cola, Bottle, Donald Duck, Walt Disney Productions, 7 Ozs.	3.00 To 3.50
Coca-Cola, Bottle, Seltzer, Blue	47.50
Coca-Cola, Bottle, Taiwan, Embossed, 2 1/2 In.	.50
Coca-Cola, Bottle, 12 Embossed, 12 White Script, Wooden Case, 6 1/2 Ozs., 24	18.00
Coca-Cola, Buckle, Belt, Nickel Set In Blue Porcelain, 2 X 3 In.	10.00
Coca-Cola, Calendar, 1927	125.00
Coca-Cola, Calendar, 1937, Picture By N.C.Wyeth	47.50
Coca-Cola, Calendar, 1948, Coke Girls, 6 Pages, 12 X 24 In.	12.00
Coca-Cola, Calendar, 1951	12.50
Coca-Cola, Calendar, 1958	10.00
Coca-Cola, Calendar, 1973	2.00
Coca-Cola, Calendar, 1974	2.00
Coca-Cola, Cards, Playing, Tiffany, Boxed	6.00
Coca-Cola, Cards, Playing, 1943	12.50
Coca-Cola, Cards, Playing, 1944	12.50
Coca-Cola, Carton, 1912, Wooden, 6 Pack, Showing Christmas Bottle	8.00
Coca-Cola, Carton, 1923 Christmas Bottle, 6 Pack	8.00
Coca-Cola, Case, C.1910, Porcelain, 12 Bottles	78.00
Coca-Cola, Clip, Money, Copper, Drink Coca-Cola In White On Red Circle	7.50
Coca-Cola, Clock, C.1950	22.50
Coca-Cola, Cooler, 1932, Glascock Bros., Mfg.Co., 18 X 31 In.	175.00
Coca-Cola, Counter, C.1910, Perpetual, 6 Revolving Scales, 3 1/4 In.	15.00
Coca-Cola, Cuff Links, Pair	4.00
Coca-Cola, Fan, C.1930, Hand	6.00
Coca-Cola, Fan, 1942, Hand	5.00
Coca-Cola, Film, 1950, Ladies Amateur Golf Tournament, 16mm.	35.00
Coca-Cola, Key & Chain, C.1950, Gold Dipped, Miniature	2.00
Coca-Cola, Key Chain, Bottle	3.00
Coca-Cola, Kit, Sewing, U.S.Army	4.00
Coca-Cola, Knife, 1933, World's Fair, Chicago, 4 Blades, Corkscrew	22.00
Coca-Cola, Letterhead, Atlanta Factory & Offices, C.1890	40.00
Coca-Cola, Menu With Message Board, 1940, Restaurant, Tin, 20 X 30 In.	30.00
Coca-Cola, Opener, Bottle, 1925, Wall Type, Cast Iron	5.00 To 10.00
Coca-Cola, Opener, Bottle, 1940, Starr, Plastic, 6 In.	15.00
Coca-Cola, Paperweight, C.1950, Bubbles, Red Background	30.00
Coca-Cola, Paperweight, Red Coke Is Coca-Cola On Glass Ball	25.00
Coca-Cola, Paperweight, 1948, Glass, 11 In.	20.00
Coca-Cola, Pencil Sharpener, Bottle Type, 1933	12.50
Coca-Cola, Purse, Change, C.1930, Leather	50.00
Coca-Cola, Ruler, C.1920, Wooden, "Drink Coca-Cola, 5 Cents"	3.00
Coca-Cola, Ruler, 1936, Wooden	1.50
Coca-Cola, Sharpener, Pencil, 1933	10.00
Coca-Cola, Sign, Drink Coca Cola, Red, White, & Green Tin, 54 X 18 In.	20.00
Coca-Cola, Sign, 1936, Cutout Girl's Head & Coke Bottles, Cardboard, 40 In.	85.00

Coca-Cola, Sign, 1937, 1923 Bottle & Drink Coca-Cola, Tin, 27 X 19 1/2 In. 50.00
Coca-Cola, Sign, 1940s, Join The Friendly Circle, Cardboard, 36 X 23 In. 45.00
Coca-Cola, Thermometer, Dec.25, 1923, 17 In.Long 12.00
Coca-Cola, Thermometer, Red & White, Oval Ends, Convex Shape, 30 In. 48.00
Coca-Cola, Thermometer, 1923, On Metal Bottle, 16 In. 32.00
Coca-Cola, Thermometer, 1941, 2 Bottles 17.50
Coca-Cola, Tietack, 1930 .... 4.00
Coca-Cola, Tray, Change, Mexico City, 1860 Street Scene, Tin .... .65 To 1.25
Coca-Cola, Tray, Change, 1904, Hilda Clark 395.00
Coca-Cola, Tray, Change, 1904, World's Fair 79.00
Coca-Cola, Tray, Change, 1905, Gibson Girl Drinking Coke, Round 110.00
Coca-Cola, Tray, Change, 1905, Juanita 175.00
Coca-Cola, Tray, Change, 1906, Relieves Fatigue, Oval 150.00
Coca-Cola, Tray, Change, 1909, Coca-Cola Girl, Hamilton King .... 95.00 To 98.50
Coca-Cola, Tray, Change, 1912, World's Fair .... 55.00 To 75.00
Coca-Cola, Tray, Change, 1914, Betty .... 75.00 To 85.00
Coca-Cola, Tray, Change, 1917, Elaine .... 50.00 To 65.00
Coca-Cola, Tray, Coke Bottle, Tin, Round, 13 In. 2.00
Coca-Cola, Tray, Mexico, Coke Bottle & People, Tin, Round, 13 In. 2.50
Coca-Cola, Tray, 1905, Juanita 175.00
Coca-Cola, Tray, 1909, Hamilton King Girl's Picture 160.00
Coca-Cola, Tray, 1920, Garden Girl, Rectangular .... 95.00 To 120.00
Coca-Cola, Tray, 1921, Summer Girl 48.00
Coca-Cola, Tray, 1923, Brunette Flapper .... 50.00 To 75.00
Coca-Cola, Tray, 1925, Girl At Party .... 42.00 To 65.00
Coca-Cola, Tray, 1926, Golfers 45.00
Coca-Cola, Tray, 1927, Curb Service 40.00
Coca-Cola, Tray, 1929, Girl Holding Glass Of Coke 40.00
Coca-Cola, Tray, 1930, Bathing Beauty .... 29.00 To 40.00
Coca-Cola, Tray, 1930, Telephone Girl .... 39.00 To 50.00
Coca-Cola, Tray, 1932, Girl In Swimsuit Holding Bottle 95.00
Coca-Cola, Tray, 1933, Frances Dee 45.00
Coca-Cola, Tray, 1934, Johnny Weissmuller 185.00
Coca-Cola, Tray, 1935, Madge Evans .... 35.00 To 45.00
Coca-Cola, Tray, 1936, Hostess 40.00
Coca-Cola, Tray, 1937, Bathing Beauty Running On Beach .... 25.00 To 40.00
Coca-Cola, Tray, 1938, Girl In Yellow Dress .... 28.00 To 41.00
Coca-Cola, Tray, 1939, Springboard, Girl In Swimsuit .... 20.00 To 35.00
Coca-Cola, Tray, 1940, Sailor Girl .... 20.00 To 35.00
Coca-Cola, Tray, 1941, Ice Skater .... 25.00 To 40.00
Coca-Cola, Tray, 1942, Two Girls In Roadster .... 23.00 To 36.00
Coca-Cola, Tray, 1943, Redhead Girl With Wind In Her Hair .... 15.00 To 19.00
Coca-Cola, Tray, 1950, Girl With Menu .... 10.00 To 16.00
Coca-Cola, Tray, 1961, Hand Pouring Bottle Of Coke 8.00
Coca-Cola, Tray, 1961, Pansy Garden, Metal, 10 3/4 X 13 1/4 In. 6.50
Coca-Cola, Tray, 1971, Hamilton King Girl 5.00
Coca-Cola, Tray, 1972, Girl In Duster 8.00
Coca-Cola, Truck, Buddy L 20.00
Coca-Cola, Truck, Metalcraft, With Bottles, C.1930 .... 125.00
Coca-Cola, Truck, Windup, Tin, Marx, 11 In.Long, 1940s 35.00
Coca-Cola, Truck, 1945 .... 35.00 To 45.00
Coca-Cola, Truck, 1960 .... 30.00
Coca-Cola, Whistle, C.1950, Made To Look Like Bottle Cap, Spanish Ads 2.00
    Coffee grinders, home size, were first made about 1894. They lost favor by
    the 1930s.
Coffee Grinder, Arcade, Crystal, Cast Iron, Wall, Crank Type 25.00
Coffee Grinder, Coles, Phila., Crank, Drawer, Red, 12 In. 85.00
Coffee Grinder, Elgin National, 5 1/2 Ft. 475.00
Coffee Grinder, Enterprise, Electric, Cast Iron, Red 75.00
Coffee Grinder, Iron & Wood, 1 Drawer, C.1850 .... 28.00
Coffee Grinder, Iron Cup, Lid, Handle, & Crank, Dovetailed Wood, 12 In. 25.00
Coffee Grinder, Iron, Hinged Tin Lid On Top 16.00
Coffee Grinder, Kupples King, Double 35.00
Coffee Grinder, Lap Type, Tin 25.00
Coffee Grinder, Lee, Glass, Turned Purple 18.50

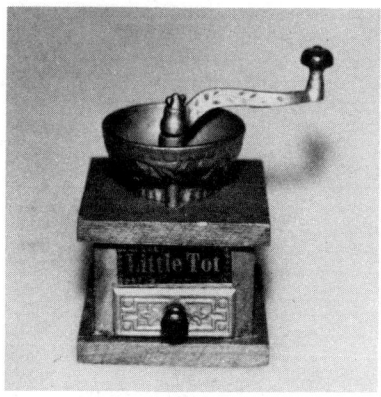

Coffee Grinder, Little Tot, Toy, 4 In.

Coffee Grinder, Little Tot, Toy, 4 In. ....*Illus*	35.00
Coffee Grinder, Regal, No.44, Screws On Wall, Sheet Metal Canister & Cup	22.50
Coffee Grinder, Swift, Stenciled, Tin Drawer, 2 12 In. Wheels	170.00
Coffee Grinder, The Cha's Parker Co., Meriden, Conn., Iron, Red Paint	295.00
Coffee Grinder, Toy, Dollhouse, Red, Wheel Turns	4.50
Coffee Grinder, Universal, No.014, Wall, Patent Aug.31, 1909, 13 In.	18.00
Coffee Grinder, Wall, Iron, White China Jar, Blue Delft Type Scene, Germany	55.00
Coffee Grinder, Wall, Tin, King, Blue & White	14.00
Coffee Grinder, Wood, Dovetailed, Pewter Top, Porcelain Pull	60.00
Coffee Grinder, 6 Ft.	300.00

Christmas plates were made by several firms. The most famous were made by
The Bing & Grondahl Factory of Denmark, after 1895, and the Royal
Copenhagen Factory, after 1908. Each of these plates has a blue-and-white
glaze with a scene in the center, the date, and the word Jule.

Collector, Bell, Bing & Grondahl, Christmas, 1973	175.00
Collector, Bell, Bing & Grondahl, Christmas, 1974	220.00
Collector, Bell, Bing & Grondahl, Christmas, 1975	60.00
Collector, Egg, Furstenberg, Easter, 1973, 1st Issue	14.00
Collector, Egg, Noritake, Easter, 1972	18.00
Collector, Plaque, Royal Doulton, Christmas, 1972	30.00

Collector, Plate, see also Buffalo Pottery, Plate, Christmas

Collector, Plate, Bareuther, Christmas, 1969	15.00
Collector, Plate, Berta Hummel, Christmas, 1971, 1st Issue	20.00
Collector, Plate, Bing & Grondahl, Christmas, 1896	795.00
Collector, Plate, Bing & Grondahl, Christmas, 1897	550.00
Collector, Plate, Bing & Grondahl, Christmas, 1901	250.00
Collector, Plate, Bing & Grondahl, Christmas, 1906	65.00
Collector, Plate, Bing & Grondahl, Christmas, 1908	55.00
Collector, Plate, Bing & Grondahl, Christmas, 1909	65.00
Collector, Plate, Bing & Grondahl, Christmas, 1910	60.00
Collector, Plate, Bing & Grondahl, Christmas, 1911	60.00
Collector, Plate, Bing & Grondahl, Christmas, 1913	60.00
Collector, Plate, Bing & Grondahl, Christmas, 1914	55.00
Collector, Plate, Bing & Grondahl, Christmas, 1915	88.00
Collector, Plate, Bing & Grondahl, Christmas, 1916	55.00
Collector, Plate, Bing & Grondahl, Christmas, 1917	50.00 To 55.00
Collector, Plate, Bing & Grondahl, Christmas, 1920	50.00
Collector, Plate, Bing & Grondahl, Christmas, 1921	50.00
Collector, Plate, Bing & Grondahl, Christmas, 1922	50.00
Collector, Plate, Bing & Grondahl, Christmas, 1923	50.00
Collector, Plate, Bing & Grondahl, Christmas, 1924	50.00
Collector, Plate, Bing & Grondahl, Christmas, 1925	50.00
Collector, Plate, Bing & Grondahl, Christmas, 1926	50.00
Collector, Plate, Bing & Grondahl, Christmas, 1928	50.00
Collector, Plate, Bing & Grondahl, Christmas, 1932	60.00
Collector, Plate, Bing & Grondahl, Christmas, 1935	50.00

Collector, **Plate,** Bing & Grondahl, Christmas, 1937 .... *Illus*   65.00
Collector, **Plate,** Bing & Grondahl, Christmas, 1938 .... 90.00
Collector, **Plate,** Bing & Grondahl, Christmas, 1940 .... 110.00
Collector, **Plate,** Bing & Grondahl, Christmas, 1944 .... 90.00
Collector, **Plate,** Bing & Grondahl, Christmas, 1945 .... 110.00
Collector, **Plate,** Bing & Grondahl, Christmas, 1946 .... 50.00
Collector, **Plate,** Bing & Grondahl, Christmas, 1948 .... 50.00 To 65.00
Collector, **Plate,** Bing & Grondahl, Christmas, 1949 .... 50.00
Collector, **Plate,** Bing & Grondahl, Christmas, 1950 .... 70.00
Collector, **Plate,** Bing & Grondahl, Christmas, 1951 .... 75.00
Collector, **Plate,** Bing & Grondahl, Christmas, 1952 .... *Illus*   50.00
Collector, **Plate,** Bing & Grondahl, Christmas, 1953 .... 55.00
Collector, **Plate,** Bing & Grondahl, Christmas, 1954 .... 75.00
Collector, **Plate,** Bing & Grondahl, Christmas, 1956 .... 100.00
Collector, **Plate,** Bing & Grondahl, Christmas, 1957 .... 100.00
Collector, **Plate,** Bing & Grondahl, Christmas, 1958 .... 75.00 To 80.00
Collector, **Plate,** Bing & Grondahl, Christmas, 1960 .... 140.00
Collector, **Plate,** Bing & Grondahl, Christmas, 1962 .... 50.00
Collector, **Plate,** Bing & Grondahl, Christmas, 1964 .... 27.00 To 30.00
Collector, **Plate,** Bing & Grondahl, Christmas, 1965 .... 27.50

Collector, Plate, Bing & Grondahl, Christmas, 1937

Collector, Plate, Bing & Grondahl, Christmas, 1952

Collector, Plate, Royal Copenhagen,
Christmas, 1927
(See Page 113)

Collector, Plate, Royal Copenhagen,
Christmas, 1964
(See Page 113)

Collector, Plate, Bing & Grondahl, Christmas, 1967 .... 16.00 To 22.50
Collector, Plate, Bing & Grondahl, Christmas, 1968 .... 18.00 To 25.00
Collector, Plate, Bing & Grondahl, Christmas, 1969 .... 12.00 To 19.00
Collector, Plate, Bing & Grondahl, Christmas, 1970 .... 12.00 To 20.00
Collector, Plate, Bing & Grondahl, Christmas, 1971 .... 18.00
Collector, Plate, Bing & Grondahl, Christmas, 1972 .... 18.00
Collector, Plate, Bing & Grondahl, Christmas, 1973 .... 16.50
Collector, Plate, Bing & Grondahl, Christmas, 1974 .... 17.00 To 22.00
Collector, Plate, Bing & Grondahl, Jubilee, 1955 .... 120.00
Collector, Plate, Bing & Grondahl, Jubilee, 1960 .... 100.00
Collector, Plate, Bing & Grondahl, Jubilee, 1965 .... 67.50
Collector, Plate, Bing & Grondahl, Jubilee, 1970 .... 15.00 To 22.00
Collector, Plate, Bing & Grondahl, Jubilee, 1975 .... 30.00
Collector, Plate, Bing & Grondahl, Mother's Day, 1969 .... 245.00
Collector, Plate, Bing & Grondahl, Mother's Day, 1970 .... 14.00 To 25.00
Collector, Plate, Bing & Grondahl, Mother's Day, 1971 .... 6.00 To 10.00
Collector, Plate, Bing & Grondahl, Mother's Day, 1972 .... 10.50
Collector, Plate, Bing & Grondahl, Mother's Day, 1973 .... 14.50 To 20.00
Collector, Plate, Bing & Grondahl, Mother's Day, 1974 .... 16.50
Collector, Plate, Bing & Grondahl, Mother's Day, 1975 .... 15.00 To 19.50
Collector, Plate, Frankoma, Christmas, 1965 .... 150.00
Collector, Plate, Haviland, Christmas, 1970 .... 100.00
Collector, Plate, Hummel, Schmid, Mother's Day, 1972 .... 20.00
Collector, Plate, Hummel, Schmid, Mother's Day, 1973 .... 40.00
Collector, Plate, Hummel, Schmid, Mother's Day, 1974 .... 18.50
Collector, Plate, Rosenthal, Christmas, 1926 .... 65.00
Collector, Plate, Rosenthal, Christmas, 1960 .... 47.50
Collector, Plate, Royal Copenhagen, Bicentennial, 1975, 1st Issue 24.00
Collector, Plate, Royal Copenhagen, Christmas, 1909 .... 100.00
Collector, Plate, Royal Copenhagen, Christmas, 1917 .... 75.00
Collector, Plate, Royal Copenhagen, Christmas, 1921 .... 50.00
Collector, Plate, Royal Copenhagen, Christmas, 1922 .... 50.00
Collector, Plate, Royal Copenhagen, Christmas, 1923 .... 55.00
Collector, Plate, Royal Copenhagen, Christmas, 1925 .... 70.00
Collector, Plate, Royal Copenhagen, Christmas, 1926 .... 55.00
Collector, Plate, Royal Copenhagen, Christmas, 1927 .... *Illus* 75.00
Collector, Plate, Royal Copenhagen, Christmas, 1930 .... 60.00
Collector, Plate, Royal Copenhagen, Christmas, 1932 .... 60.00
Collector, Plate, Royal Copenhagen, Christmas, 1938 .... 155.00
Collector, Plate, Royal Copenhagen, Christmas, 1950 .... 87.50
Collector, Plate, Royal Copenhagen, Christmas, 1952 .... 60.00 To 65.00
Collector, Plate, Royal Copenhagen, Christmas, 1953 .... 65.00
Collector, Plate, Royal Copenhagen, Christmas, 1957 .... 50.00 To 70.00
Collector, Plate, Royal Copenhagen, Christmas, 1958 .... 85.00
Collector, Plate, Royal Copenhagen, Christmas, 1959 .... 100.00
Collector, Plate, Royal Copenhagen, Christmas, 1960 .... 75.00
Collector, Plate, Royal Copenhagen, Christmas, 1962 .... 85.00
Collector, Plate, Royal Copenhagen, Christmas, 1964 .... *Illus* 45.00
Collector, Plate, Royal Copenhagen, Christmas, 1966 .... 25.00 To 40.00
Collector, Plate, Royal Copenhagen, Christmas, 1967 .... 24.00
Collector, Plate, Royal Copenhagen, Christmas, 1968 .... 15.00 To 25.00
Collector, Plate, Royal Copenhagen, Christmas, 1969 .... 20.00
Collector, Plate, Royal Copenhagen, Christmas, 1970 .... 18.00
Collector, Plate, Royal Copenhagen, Christmas, 1971 .... 18.00
Collector, Plate, Royal Copenhagen, Christmas, 1973 .... 16.50
Collector, Plate, Royal Copenhagen, Christmas, 1974 .... 17.00 To 22.00
Collector, Plate, Royal Copenhagen, Mother's Day, 1971 .... 22.00 To 27.50
Collector, Plate, Royal Copenhagen, Mother's Day, 1972 .... 13.00 To 13.50
Collector, Plate, Royal Copenhagen, Mother's Day, 1973 .... 16.00 To 16.50
Collector, Plate, Royal Copenhagen, Mother's Day, 1974 .... 16.50
Collector, Plate, Veneto Flair, Easter, 1973 .... 100.00
Collector, Plate, Wedgwood, Christmas, 1969, 1st Issue .... 165.00 To 195.00
Collector, Plate, Wedgwood, Mother's Day, 1971 .... 20.00
Collector, Plate, Wedgwood, Mother's Day, 1972 .... 20.00
Collector, Plate, Wedgwood, Mother's Day, 1973 .... 20.00
Collector, Plate, Wedgwood, Mother's Day, 1974 .... 20.00

Commemoration items have been made to honor members of royalty and those of great national fame. World's fairs and important historical events are also remembered with commemoration pieces.

Commemoration, see also Coronation

Commemoration, Beaker, George V, 1935, Silver Jubilee	15.00
Commemoration, Beaker, Princess Anne & Mark, 1973, Royal Wedding	6.00
Commemoration, Bookmark, Washington, 1893, Woven Silk	15.00
Commemoration, Bowl, Queen's Jubilee, 1887, Amber, Scalloped, 9 1/2 In.	45.00
Commemoration, Goblet, Arden House World Hunger Conference, 1966, Silver	15.00
Commemoration, Mug, George V, 1935, Silver Jubilee	15.00
Commemoration, Mug, Queen Victoria, County Borough Of Brighton, 1897	35.00
Commemoration, Plate, Victoria Jubilee, 1887, Clear Glass, Scalloped, 10 In.	29.95
Commemoration, Salt & Pepper, Columbian Exhibition, 1873, Laydown, Egg Shape	92.50
Commemoration, Spoon, King Edward & Queen Alexandra	6.50
Commemoration, Throne, Queen Victoria, Jubilee, 1887, Cast Iron, 7 3/4 In.	62.00
Commemorative, Plate, Reign Of Queen Wilhelmina, Blue, 1893, 1923, 9 In.	36.50
Coors, Vase, Blue, White Interior, Handles From Top To Bottom, 7 1/2 In.	15.00
Coors, Vase, Medium Blue, Gold Top Rim, 2 Handled, Golden ....*Color*	7.50
Coors, Vase, Tan Matte Glaze, Green Interior, Handled, 9 In.	8.00

W.T.Copeland & Sons, Ltd., ran the Spode Works in Staffordshire, England, from 1847 to the present. Copeland & Garrett was the firm name from 1833 to 1847.

Copeland Spode, Bowl, June, Medium Blue, 10 In.	15.00
Copeland Spode, Bust, Princess Alexandria, Parian, 1863, F.M.Miller, 12 In.	95.00
Copeland Spode, Cake Set, Patricia, 19 Piece	100.00
Copeland Spode, Cup & Saucer, Demitasse, Red	30.00
Copeland Spode, Cup & Saucer, Doll's, Colored Leaf Design	22.00
Copeland Spode, Figurine, Cherub Holding Bellflower, Unglazed, 13 In.	45.00
Copeland Spode, Figurine, Cupid With Bellflower, Unglazed, 13 In.High	47.50
Copeland Spode, Jug, Cerulean Blue Jasper On Buff, Drinking Scene, 7 In.	45.00
Copeland Spode, Pitcher, Jasperware, Football Scene On Blue, C.1895, 7 In.	100.00
Copeland Spode, Pitcher, Mayflower In Plymouth Harbor, Blue, C.1897, 6 In.	35.00
Copeland Spode, Pitcher, Tavern Scene & White Grapes On Blue, 6 3/4 In.	68.00
Copeland Spode, Plate, Bird, Swirl Rim, 9 In.	65.00
Copeland Spode, Plate, Blue, Green, & Red Peacocks, 10 In.	15.00
Copeland Spode, Platter, Tuscan, 15 X 11 In.	10.00
Copeland Spode, Platter, Winter, Medium Blue, 14 1/2 X 11 In.	30.00
Copeland Spode, Teapot, Tower, Cup O' Kindness, Pint	14.00
Copeland Spode, Tray, Blue Floral & Trim On White, 11 In.	12.00
Copeland Spode, Tureen, Morocco, Floral Finial & Handles, Footed, 10 In.	85.00
Copeland Spode, Vase, Double Lily, Blue & Pink, Gold Snake Around Base, 9 In	80.00
Copeland Spode, Vase, White Horn Of Plenty On Shell, C.1930, 8 In., Pair	45.00
Copeland Spode, Washstand Set, Italian Scenes, Dark & Light Blue, 2 Piece	125.00

Copeland, see also Spode

Copeland, Compote & Underplate, Gravy, Covered, Openwork Handles, Roses	150.00
Copeland, Compote, Off-White, Butterflies, Heron, & Floral, 4 1/4 X 9 In.	25.00
Copeland, Compote, Tan White, Heron, Butterflies, & Foliage, C.1850, 8 1/2 In.	22.50
Copeland, Creamer, Black Transfer Village Scene, C.1880	22.00
Copeland, Cup & Saucer, Demitasse, Allover Gold Dots, Roses, Gold Rim	22.00
Copeland, Cup & Saucer, 1851-1885 Mark	40.00
Copeland, Figurine, John Wilson Known As Christopher North, Parian, 18 In.	185.00
Copeland, Pitcher, Salt Glazed, Corset Shape, Water Lily Pads, 1874, 5 In.	45.00
Copeland, Pitcher, White Lily Pads On Blue, 1878, 5 In.High	35.00
Copeland, Plate, Cake, Apple Green, Yellow Bands, Hand-Painted Flowers	75.00
Copeland, Platter, Copper Luster Border, Pink & Yellow Floral, 11 In.	30.00
Copeland, Platter, Pink & Yellow Floral, Brown Figural Border, 11 In.	35.00
Copeland, Teapot, Cadogan, Pink, Blue Floral, Yellow Fruit, 6 1/2 In.	110.00
Copeland, Tray, Pen, Pearlware, Covered, Checkerboard, C.1850, 8 3/4 In.	30.00
Copeland, Vase, Urn Shape, Jeweled Turquoise Beading, Gold Enamel, 6 In.	115.00

Copper Luster, see Luster, Copper

Copper, Ashtray, Chicago World's Fair, 1933, Chrysler Motors	4.50
Copper, Ashtray, Handmade, Rolled Edge, C.1840, 4 1/2 In.	6.50
Copper, Ashtray, Hanging Gypsy Pot, Chicago World's Fair, 1933, Brass, Glass	12.00
Copper, Ashtray, Indian Made, Engraved Thunderbird & Arrows, C.1920	6.50
Copper, Basket, Flower, 12 1/2 In. To Top Of Handle	12.00

Copper, Boiler, Tin Lid	20.00
Copper, Box, Letter, Hanging	18.00
Copper, Bucket, Paul Revere, Heavy Chain, Gallon	30.00
Copper, Bucket, Two Handles At Base, Two Pouring Lips, 11 1/2 X 18 In.	60.00
Copper, Coffeepot, Brass Lid, 6 In.	32.00
Copper, Dipper, Signed Reed, Burnished, 7 1/4 X 4 3/4 In.	60.00
Copper, Ewer, Marked China, Engraved, 7 1/2 X 5 In.	12.00
Copper, Ewer, Riveted Brass Bands, 10 In.	12.50
Copper, Foot Warmer, Victorian, 9 1/2 In. Diameter	30.00
Copper, Funnel, Brewer's, 14 In.	50.00
Copper, Holder, Matchbox, Sterling Inlay Of Parrot	22.00
Copper, Holder, Plant, Ornate, Brass Handle & Pad Feet, 8 1/4 X 6 3/4 In.	55.00
Copper, Inkwell, Austria, Double, Hand Hammered, Insert, 12 X 8 1/2 In.	75.00
Copper, Inkwell, Hammered, Crest On Top, Square, 3 In.	24.00
Copper, Kettle, Apple Butter, Iron Handle, 35 Gallon, Brass Dovetail, 14 X 24	145.00
Copper, Kettle, Water, Aldrich, Buffalo, Gooseneck Spout, 3 Quart	21.00
Copper, Match Safe, English, Leaf & Ship Engraving, 1 1/2 X 2 1/8 In.	45.00
Copper, Measure, Dovetailed, 4 1/2 X 2 1/2 In.	20.00
Copper, Mug, Beer, N.G.Wood, Boston, Brass Handle & Hoops, 4 In.	15.00
Copper, Mug, Pub, Marked V.R., Tin Lined, C.1880, 1/2 Pint	27.50
Copper, Pitcher, Water, Handwrought, Dovetailed Seams, 16 In.	30.00
Copper, Plaque, George Washington's 200th Birthday, Mutual Co., 1931, 8 In.	8.00
Copper, Plate, Seattle, 1909, 7 In.	15.00
Copper, Plate, 9 In.	9.00
Copper, Pot, Bail Handle & 2 Applied Handles On Sides, 11 X 9 In.	59.00
Copper, Pot, Hanging, Handwrought, Dovetailed Seams, 7 X 9 In.	24.00
Copper, Pot, Pouring Lip, Chain Attached To Cover, Bail Handle, 7 X 6 In.	49.00
Copper, Saucepan, Lewis & Conger, N.Y., Covered, Iron Handle, 5 Quart	75.00
Copper, Skimmer, Handwrought, 16 In.	12.00
Copper, Sugar & Creamer, Bail, Pedestal Bases	15.00
Copper, Teakettle, D.Bentley, Phila., C.1850 *Illus*	450.00
Copper, Teakettle, Dated 1885	17.00
Copper, Teakettle, Gooseneck, Dovetailed, Blade Handle Folds Down	230.00
Copper, Teakettle, Gooseneck Spout, Wooden Handle	15.00
Copper, Teakettle, Handwrought, Dovetailed Seams, 7 X 10 In.	24.00
Copper, Teakettle, Imperial, 10 In.	45.00
Copper, Teakettle, 2 Gallon	37.50
Copper, Teapot, Black Wooden Handle & Finial, Tapering From Bottom, 9 In.	23.00
Copper, Tray, St.Louis Exposition, 1904, Louisiana Purchase, 6 X 5 In.	20.00
Copper, Trout Creel, Brass Rings & Hooks For Shoulder Strap, Tin Lined	38.00
Copper, Urn, Hot Water, Benham & Sons, England, Brass Spout, C.1750, 20 In.	125.00
Copper, Vase, Floral, Silver Inlay, 8 In.	45.00
Copper, Warmer, Brandy, French, Handled, C.1900	20.00

Copper, Teakettle, D. Bentley,
Phila., C.1850

Coralene glass was made by firing many small colored beads on the outside of glassware. It was made in many patterns in the United States and Europe in the 1880s. Reproductions are made today.

Coralene, Bottle, Perfume, Blue, Pastel Coralene Beads, 6 In.	150.00
Coralene, Bottle, Perfume, Geometrics On Transparent Blue, 6 In.	140.00
Coralene, Planter, Browns & Green, Gold Beads, Pink Floral, U.S., 1902, 5 In.	80.00
Coralene, Saltshaker, Coralene Decoration On Bristol Ground	45.00
Coralene, Tumbler, Butterscotch Satin, Diamond-Quilted, Blue Seaweed, 6 In.	175.00
Coralene, Tumbler, Diamond-Quilted, Raspberry Satin, Yellow Seaweed, Cased	225.00
Coralene, Tumbler, Orange Seaweed On Blue Diamond-Quilted Satin, 4 In.	235.00
Coralene, Urn, Aladdin's Lamp Style, Gold, Cobalt, & Pink, U.S., 1902, 7 In.	165.00
Coralene, Vase, Bleeding Hearts, Lime To Dark Green, Japanese, 13 In.High	175.00
Coralene, Vase, Coral Branch Beading, Camphor Ground, 8 In.High	135.00
Coralene, Vase, Diamond-Quilted, Satin, Yellow, Purple Flowers, Puffed, 3 In.	265.00
Coralene, Vase, Fan, Shaded Blue Satin, Yellow Seaweed, 5 3/4 In.	360.00
Coralene, Vase, Japan, Blue & Green, Pink Mum, Gold Trim, 1909, 11 In.	135.00
Coralene, Vase, Japanese, Daffodils, Gold Top, 2 Handled, 11 In.	95.00
Coralene, Vase, Peachblow, Yellow Seaweed, Double Lip, White Lined, 6 1/2 In.	235.00
Coralene, Vase, Ribbed, Diamond-Quilted, White To Yellow, Blue Seaweed, 5 In.	310.00
Coralene, Vase, Violet & Purple, Beaded Iris, Bisque Ground, Japanese, 10 In.	185.00
Coralene, Vase, 2 Animal Faces Handles, Browns, Coralene Floral, 7 3/4 In.	195.00

Coronation cups have been made since the 1800s. Pieces of pottery or glass with a picture of the monarch and the date have been made as souvenirs for many coronations.

Coronation, see also Commemoration

Coronation, Ashtray, Edward VIII, 1937, Royal Doulton, Set Of 4, Holder	62.00
Coronation, Basket, Serving, George VI, Raised Diamonds, 7 1/4 In.	35.00
Coronation, Beaker, Elizabeth II, 1953	9.50
Coronation, Beaker, George VI, 1937	12.50
Coronation, Beaker, George VI, 1939	12.50
Coronation, Book, Coloring & Paper Dolls, Elizabeth, 1953	5.00 To 11.50
Coronation, Book, Coloring, Elizabeth, 1953	4.00 To 11.00
Coronation, Box, Candy, Elizabeth II, 1953, Tin	6.00
Coronation, Button, Elizabeth II, Picture, 2 In.	1.75
Coronation, Creamer, Edward VIII	17.00
Coronation, Cup & Saucer, Edward VIII	15.00
Coronation, Cup & Saucer, Elizabeth II	16.00
Coronation, Cup & Saucer, Elizabeth II, Green	10.00
Coronation, Cup & Saucer, 1939, King, Queen, & Princess	20.00
Coronation, Cup, Edward VIII, Pottery, 3 In.	10.00
Coronation, Cup, George & Elizabeth, 1937, Signed Laura Knight	35.00
Coronation, Cup, Mustache, British Crests, Rose, Shamrock, 1902	24.50
Coronation, Door Knocker, Elizabeth II, Brass	15.00
Coronation, Medal, 1911, Box & Label	20.00
Coronation, Mug, Edward VIII, Belleek Type Glase, Salisbury China	15.00
Coronation, Mug, Edward VIII, Pottery, 4 In.	8.00
Coronation, Mug, Elizabeth II, Crystal, Etched Crown, 4 X 4 1/2 In.	25.00
Coronation, Mug, Elizabeth II, 1953	9.50
Coronation, Mug, Elizabeth II, 1953, Adams	12.50
Coronation, Mug, George V, 1911, Pottery, 3 1/2 In.	10.00
Coronation, Mug, George VI, 1937	12.50
Coronation, Plate, Butter, Edward VIII	10.00
Coronation, Plate, Elizabeth, 1952, Porcelain, English, Square, 6 1/2 In.	7.25
Coronation, Plate, George V & Mary, Semiporcelain, Roses Border, 10 In.	15.00
Coronation, Plate, Victoria, Porcelain, Picture In Color, C.1860, 8 1/2 In.	30.00
Coronation, Tray, Pin, Edward VIII, Square	12.00
Coronation, Tumbler, Czar Nicholas II, 1896, Enamel On Tin, Russian	185.00
Coronation, Tumbler, Edward VII & Alexandra, 1902, Porcelain, 4 In.	25.00
Coronation, Tumbler, Edward VIII	15.00

Cosmos pattern glass is a pattern of pressed milk glass with colored flowers.

Cosmos, Butter, Covered, Colored Flowers	160.00 To 193.00
Cosmos, Butter, Covered, Pink Band	165.00
Cosmos, Butter, Domed Lid	150.00 To 165.00
Cosmos, Dresser Set, Blue, Painted Flowers On Jar, Tray, 3 Piece	95.00
Cosmos, Lamp, Kerosene, Dore Bronze & French Enamel, Miniature	200.00

Cosmos, Lamp, Milk Glass, Miniature 150.00
Cosmos, Lamp, Miniature .... 37.00 To 100.00
Cosmos, Lamp, Painted, Miniature 60.00
Cosmos, Muffineer, Apple Blossoms On Netted Milk 78.00
Cosmos, Muffineer, Oak Leaf Pattern 65.00
Cosmos, Pitcher, Water, Apple Blossom, Blue Band 195.00
Cosmos, Salt & Pepper Inserts, Pair 55.00
Cosmos, Salt & Pepper, Apple Blossom 65.00
Cosmos, Saltshaker 35.00
Cosmos, Sugar, Covered, Pink Band 145.00
Cosmos, Syrup, Milk Glass, Lattice Back 175.00
Cosmos, Syrup, Pink Band, Spring Lid 185.00
Cosmos, Table Set, 4 Piece 475.00
Cosmos, Table Set, 5 Piece 215.00
Cosmos, Tumbler, Pink Band, Milk Glass 41.50
Cosmos, Water Set, 7 Piece 420.00
     Country Store, see Store

Cowan pottery was made in Cleveland, Ohio, from 1913 to 1920. Most pieces
of the art pottery were marked with the name of the firm in various ways.

Cowan, Bowl, Blue Iridescent, Signed, 7 1/2 In. 14.00
Cowan, Candlestick, Blue Iridescent, 7 1/2 In., Pair 22.00
Cowan, Candlestick, Green, Seahorse Base, Impressed Mark, 4 1/2 In. 7.50
Cowan, Candlestick, Ivory Seahorse, 4 1/2 In., Pair 25.00
Cowan, Candlestick, Peach Color, Semigloss, Incised Cowan, 2 1/4 In., Pair 15.00
Cowan, Console Set, 8 Sided Shape, Signed, 3 Piece 32.00
Cowan, Match Holder, Ivory Seahorses, Stem Footed, 3 1/4 In. 10.00
Cowan, Vase, Art Deco, Ovoid, Green With Gold, 8 In. 25.00
Cowan, Vase, Purple On Semigloss Teal Blue, Incised Cowan, 7 1/8 In. 18.00

Crackle glass was originally made by the Venetians, but most of the ware
found today dates from the 1800s. The glass was heated, cooled, and refired so
that many small lines appeared inside the glass. It was made in many
factories in the United States and Europe.
     Crackle Glass, see also Fry
Crackle Glass, Cruet, Amber, 7 In. 20.00
Crackle Glass, Rose Bowl, Amber, 4 In. 10.00
Crackle Glass, Sauce, Berry, Rainbow, Royal Ivy 42.00

Cranberry glass is an almost transparent yellow red glass. It resembles the
color of cranberry juice.
     Cranberry Glass, see also Rubena Verde, etc.
Cranberry Glass, Basket, Bride's, Flared, Silver Plate Holder, 9 1/2 In. 195.00
Cranberry Glass, Basket, Diamond-Quilted, Applied Clear Handle, 6 In. 125.00
Cranberry Glass, Basket, Sugar, Filigree Brass Frame 50.00
Cranberry Glass, Bottle, Perfume, Gold & Enamel Overlay, 5 In. 85.00
Cranberry Glass, Bottle, Scent, Hinged Silver Cap, 2 3/4 In. 50.00
Cranberry Glass, Bowl, Coin Spot, Ruffled, 7 In. 24.00
Cranberry Glass, Bowl, Crystal Rigaree, English Silver Holder, 4 3/4 In. 75.00
Cranberry Glass, Bowl, Finger, Blown, C.1850 .... 32.00
Cranberry Glass, Bowl, Finger, Cartouche Shape, 3 In. 38.00
Cranberry Glass, Bowl, Finger, Raised Moire, Blown, 5 In. 25.00
Cranberry Glass, Bowl, Frilled, Flared, 9 Clear Thumbprint Feet, 6 In. 70.00
Cranberry Glass, Bowl, Opalescent Thumbprint, 3 X 4 1/2 In. 45.00
Cranberry Glass, Bowl, Powder, Covered, Applied Clear Thorn Knob, 4 In. 75.00
Cranberry Glass, Bowl, Serving, Overshot, Scalloped Shell, Gold, 9 X 9 In. 165.00
Cranberry Glass, Bowl, White Stringing, 7 Thumbprint Feet, 6 In. 70.00
Cranberry Glass, Box, Covered, Gold Scrolls, Round, 2 1/2 In. 40.00
Cranberry Glass, Box, Enamel Blossoms, Trellis, & Ribbons, Round, 3 1/2 In. 165.00
Cranberry Glass, Box, Hinged, Enamel Lattice, Floral, & Bows, Gold, 3 1/4 In. 135.00
Cranberry Glass, Butter, Covered, Clear Applied Feet & Lacy Edge 70.00
Cranberry Glass, Butter, Covered, Inverted Thumbprint, Cranberry & Clear 65.00
Cranberry Glass, Butter, Covered, Royal Ivy, Cranberry To Clear 110.00
Cranberry Glass, Butter, Crystal Ball Finial, 6 1/2 In. Diameter 95.00
Cranberry Glass, Castor, Pickle, Inverted Thumbprint, Floral .... 175.00 To 250.00

Cranberry Glass, **Chimney**, Lamp, Dorflinger 38.00
Cranberry Glass, **Cologne**, Gold Leaves All Over, Ormolu Feet, 7 In.High 65.00
Cranberry Glass, **Compote**, Clear Knobbed Stem, Teardrop, 5 In.High 65.00
Cranberry Glass, **Cordial Set**, 6 Piece 150.00
Cranberry Glass, **Cruet**, Clear Reeded Handle & Faceted Stopper, 6 In. 49.25
Cranberry Glass, **Cruet**, Cloverleaf Neck, Applied Handle, 7 In. 65.00
Cranberry Glass, **Cruet**, Diamond-Quilted, Rigaree At Center, 6 1/2 In. 95.00
Cranberry Glass, **Cruet**, Wine, French, Pewter Casing, Gargoyles' Heads, 12 In. 195.00
Cranberry Glass, **Cup**, Loving, 3 Clear Handles, Gold & Enamel Decoration 67.50
Cranberry Glass, **Cup**, Punch, Clear Handle 10.00
Cranberry Glass, **Cup**, Punch, Delaware, Gold Trim 27.00
Cranberry Glass, **Decanter**, Ovoid, Long Neck, Diamond Point Band, 12 In. 160.00
Cranberry Glass, **Decanter**, Wine, Pewter Holder, 11 1/2 In.High 245.00
Cranberry Glass, **Dish**, Candy, Applied Clear Handle, Blown, 4 In. 35.00
Cranberry Glass, **Epergne**, Four Trumpet-Shaped Vases, Ruffled, 21 In. 265.00
Cranberry Glass, **Epergne**, Opalescent To Green Yellow, Single Lily, 24 In. 190.00
Cranberry Glass, **Epergne**, Ruffled Compote, Athena, Metal Stand, 20 X 11 In. 100.00
Cranberry Glass, **Epergne**, 2 Clear Canes, Clear Lacing, 19 In. 150.00
Cranberry Glass, **Epergne**, 3 Lilies Entwined With Gold Flecked Vine, 16 In. 198.00
Cranberry Glass, **Jar**, Biscuit, Silver Plate Cover & Bail Handle, 6 In. 85.00
Cranberry Glass, **Jar**, Bonbon, Crystal Ball Finial & Stem, Flower Design 75.00
Cranberry Glass, **Jug**, Claret, Thumbprint, 8 In. .... 60.00 To 85.00
Cranberry Glass, **Muffineer**, Blown, Silver Plate Dome Top & Rim, 6 In. 45.00
Cranberry Glass, **Muffineer**, Bulbous, 6 1/2 In. 50.00
Cranberry Glass, **Muffineer**, E.P.N.S. Lid 38.50
Cranberry Glass, **Muffineer**, Inside Ribs 55.00
Cranberry Glass, **Muffineer**, Inverted Thumbprint, 9 Panels 85.00
Cranberry Glass, **Muffineer**, Metal Top, 6 In. 50.00
Cranberry Glass, **Muffineer**, Nickel Top 50.00
Cranberry Glass, **Muffineer**, Opalescent & Reverse Swirl 95.00
Cranberry Glass, **Muffineer**, Opalescent Coin Spot 80.00
Cranberry Glass, **Muffineer**, Opalescent Swirl 55.00
Cranberry Glass, **Muffineer**, Opalescent Swirl, Chrysanthemum Base 88.00
Cranberry Glass, **Muffineer**, Paneled, 5 1/2 In.High 38.50
Cranberry Glass, **Muffineer**, Silver Plate Dome Top, 6 1/2 In. 65.00
Cranberry Glass, **Muffineer**, 10 Panels, Domed Top 30.00
Cranberry Glass, **Muffineer**, 12 Panels, Silver Domed Top 55.00
Cranberry Glass, **Muffineer**, 5 1/2 In.High 60.00
Cranberry Glass, **Mug**, White Enamel Floral, Applied Clear Handle, 2 In. 20.00
Cranberry Glass, **Pillbox**, Gold Mesh Overlay 65.00
Cranberry Glass, **Pitcher**, Crimped Top, Ribbed Base, Clear Handle, 7 In. 98.00
Cranberry Glass, **Pitcher**, Heart-Shaped Top, White Applied Edge, 6 In. 60.00
Cranberry Glass, **Pitcher**, Inverted Thumbprint, Clear Handle, Gold, 8 1/2 In. 165.00
Cranberry Glass, **Pitcher**, Opalescent Hobnail, 8 In.High 125.00
Cranberry Glass, **Pitcher**, Ribbed, Clear Handle, 8 In. 75.00
Cranberry Glass, **Pitcher**, Thumbprint, Applied Clear Reeded Handle, 10 In. 165.00
Cranberry Glass, **Pitcher**, Water, Clear Handle, Sloping Sides, 8 1/2 In. 120.00
Cranberry Glass, **Pitcher**, Water, Hex Block, Cranberry To Clear, 12 1/2 In. 150.00
Cranberry Glass, **Pitcher**, Water, Inverted Thumbprint, Clear Reeded Handle 175.00
Cranberry Glass, **Pitcher**, Water, Opalescent Swirls, Bulbous, 8 1/2 In. 88.00
Cranberry Glass, **Pitcher**, Water, Ruffled Top, Floral Enamel Decoration 110.00
Cranberry Glass, **Pitcher**, Water, Thumbprint, Clear Rope Collar 250.00
Cranberry Glass, **Pitcher**, 8 In. 65.00
Cranberry Glass, **Plate**, Amber Glass Edge, 8 In. 67.50
Cranberry Glass, **Plate**, Greek Key Around Edge, 8 In. 27.50
Cranberry Glass, **Rose Bowl**, Coin Spot, Crimped, Overlay, 3 1/2 X 5 In. 60.00
Cranberry Glass, **Rose Bowl**, Diamond-Quilted, Applied Clear Top, 4 1/2 In. 72.00
Cranberry Glass, **Rose Bowl**, Diamond-Quilted, Clear Rigaree, 4 In. 65.00
Cranberry Glass, **Rose Bowl**, Diamond-Quilted, Ruffled Fluted Rim, 5 In. 110.00
Cranberry Glass, **Rose Bowl**, Royal Ivy, 5 In. 95.00
Cranberry Glass, **Salt & Pepper**, Crisscross, Opalescent 75.00
Cranberry Glass, **Salt & Pepper**, Enamel Trim, Double Pewter Tops 125.00
Cranberry Glass, **Salt & Pepper**, Ribbed, Enameled Flowers 58.00
Cranberry Glass, **Salt & Pepper**, Thumbprint, Silver Tops .... 75.00 To 85.00
Cranberry Glass, **Salt**, Clear Footed Shells At Base, English 60.00
Cranberry Glass, **Saltshaker** 30.00

Cranberry Glass, Saltshaker, Fern, Opalescent 35.00
Cranberry Glass, Saltshaker, Inverted Thumbprint, Squat Type 28.00
Cranberry Glass, Shade, Hanging, Diamond-Quilted, 11 7/8 In. 275.00
Cranberry Glass, Shade, To Clear Opalescent, Hobnail Ruffled Edge, 4 In. 26.00
Cranberry Glass, Shot Glass, Swirl 12.00
Cranberry Glass, Sugar & Creamer, Hobnail, Crimped Top, Applied Handles 45.00
Cranberry Glass, Sugar & Creamer, White Threading 110.00
Cranberry Glass, Syrup, Opalescent Swirl, Reeded Handle 125.00
Cranberry Glass, Syrup, Silver Plate Top 55.00
Cranberry Glass, Syrup, Thumbprint, Silver Lid .... 95.00 To 110.00
Cranberry Glass, Tankard, Applied Crystal Handle, Polished Pontil, 8 In. 75.00
Cranberry Glass, Tankard, Blown, Ribbed, Applied Clear Reeded Handle, 10 In. 115.00
Cranberry Glass, Tankard, Enamel Decoration, Crimped Top, 11 In. 98.00
Cranberry Glass, Toothpick, Ribbed, Quilted, Opalescent 32.00
Cranberry Glass, Toothpick, Royal Ivy, Cranberry To Clear 48.00
Cranberry Glass, Toothpick, Royal Oak, Cranberry To Clear 50.00
Cranberry Glass, Toothpick, Thumbprint 60.00
Cranberry Glass, Toothpick, Thumbprint, Ground Pontil 45.00
Cranberry Glass, Tumble-Up, Thumbprint 140.00
Cranberry Glass, Tumbler, Enameled Decoration 30.00
Cranberry Glass, Tumbler, Hobnail 15.00
Cranberry Glass, Tumbler, Hobnail, Fenton, Opalescent 10.00
Cranberry Glass, Tumbler, Hobnail, Opalescent 130.00
Cranberry Glass, Tumbler, Inverted Baby Thumbprint, Set Of 6 .... 110.00
Cranberry Glass, Tumbler, Inverted Thumbprint .... 12.00 To 35.00
Cranberry Glass, Tumbler, Inverted Thumbprint, Enamel Honeysuckles 65.00
Cranberry Glass, Tumbler, Inverted Thumbprint, Etched 35.00
Cranberry Glass, Tumbler, Juice, Swirled, 4 In. .... 9.00 To 15.00
Cranberry Glass, Tumbler, Opalescent Coin Spot 27.50
Cranberry Glass, Tumbler, Royal Ivy, Cranberry To Clear 35.00
Cranberry Glass, Tumbler, Thumbprint, Hand-Blown 23.00
Cranberry Glass, Tumbler, Vertical Panels, Blue Enamel Forget-Me-Nots 22.00
Cranberry Glass, Tumbler, White Swirl Overlay 30.00
Cranberry Glass, Vanity Set, 3 Piece 40.00
Cranberry Glass, Vase, Applied Vaseline Flower, Crystal Thorn Feet, 7 In. 65.00
Cranberry Glass, Vase, Blown, Ruffled Top, Expanded Diamond, 12 1/2 In.High 60.00
Cranberry Glass, Vase, Bottle Shape, Gold Encrusted Design, 11 1/2 In. 60.00
Cranberry Glass, Vase, Bottle Shape, Gold Overlay, 11 1/2 In. 50.00
Cranberry Glass, Vase, Coin Dot, Opalescent, Ruffled Top, Fenton, 7 In. 30.00
Cranberry Glass, Vase, Crimped Top, Floral Decoration, 5 In.High 65.00
Cranberry Glass, Vase, Floriform, Squirrel Frame, Sonhall & Miller, 9 In. 75.00
Cranberry Glass, Vase, Frilled Fan Top, Slender Neck, 4 1/2 In. 45.00
Cranberry Glass, Vase, Jack-In-The-Pulpit, English, 12 In. 135.00
Cranberry Glass, Vase, Melon Shape, 4 In., Pair 85.00
Cranberry Glass, Vase, Quilted, Ruffled Top, 6 X 5 In. 47.50
Cranberry Glass, Vase, Rigaree Collar, Crimped, Rough Pontil, 6 3/4 In.High 45.00
Cranberry Glass, Vase, Vertical Ribbing, Enamel Floral, Bulbous, 4 In. 45.00
Cranberry Glass, Washstand Set, Applied Crystal Handle, 7 In., 2 Piece 95.00
Cranberry Glass, Water Set, Grapes, Gold Trim, 5 Piece 35.00
Cranberry Glass, Wine Set, Intaglio Cut, Clear Stems & Bases, 7 Piece 130.00

Creamware, or queensware, was developed by Josiah Wedgwood about 1765. It is a cream-colored earthenware that has been copied by many factories.

Creamware, Bowl, Broth, Cushion Knop, Double Shell Handles, C.1760, 4 1/4 In. 60.00
Creamware, Dish, Hot Water, I.Warburton, Oval, C.1795, 10 1/2 In. 50.00
Creamware, Mug, Boy & Dog, Red Transfer, "Reward For Industry, " C.1810 .... 50.00
Creamware, Plate, Prince & Princess William V Of Orange, C.1790, 9 7/8 In. 170.00
Creamware, Plate, Prince Of Orange, Dutch Decorated, C.1780, 11 5/8 In. 300.00
Creamware, Plate, Rebecca At The Well, En Grisaille, C.1780, 10 In. 120.00
Creamware, Plate, Virgin & Child, Dutch Decorated, C.1780, 9 3/4 In. 175.00
Creil, Plate, Canary Yellow, Black Transfer Bataille De Waterloo, 1825, 9 In9 .... 100.00

Croesus glass is a special pattern of pressed glass made about 1897. It was made in clear glass, emerald green, or amethyst. Each piece was decorated with gold.

Croesus, Amethyst, Bowl, Berry 25.00

Croesus, Amethyst, Butter, Covered, Gold Trim 165.00
Croesus, Amethyst, Sugar, Covered, Gold Trim, Breakfast Size, 5 1/2 In. 85.00
Croesus, Amethyst, Toothpick .... 35.00 To 65.00
Croesus, Clear, Pitcher, Water .... 90.00 To 95.00
Croesus, Clear, Toothpick 40.00
Croesus, Green, Berry Set, Gold, 7 Piece 285.00
Croesus, Green, Bowl, Berry 35.00
Croesus, Green, Butter, Covered, Gold Trim, Round 110.00
Croesus, Green, Butter, Gold 150.00
Croesus, Green, Creamer, Breakfast, Gold 135.00
Croesus, Green, Creamer, Gold 95.00
Croesus, Green, Creamer, Gold, 3 Legs 65.00
Croesus, Green, Pitcher, Water 125.00
Croesus, Green, Salt & Pepper, Gold Plated Tops 75.00
Croesus, Green, Sauce, Gold 35.00
Croesus, Green, Spooner, Gold Trim .... 50.00 To 73.00
Croesus, Green, Sugar 50.00
Croesus, Green, Sugar, Covered 75.00
Croesus, Green, Sugar, Covered, Gold, 3 Legs 95.00
Croesus, Green, Toothpick, Gold Trim .... 55.00 To 75.00
Croesus, Green, Tray, Condiment, Fan Shaped 27.00
Croesus, Green, Water Set, Gold Trim, 4 Piece 225.00
Croesus, Green, Water Set, Gold, 7 Piece .... 400.00 To 485.00
Croesus, Purple, Berry Set, 7 Piece 390.00
Croesus, Purple, Butter, Covered, Gold Trim .... 225.00 To 230.00
Croesus, Purple, Creamer .... 135.00 To 145.00
Croesus, Purple, Salt & Pepper, Gold Plated Tops 85.00
Croesus, Purple, Sauce, Footed, Gold Trim 45.00
Croesus, Purple, Spooner 100.00
Croesus, Purple, Sugar, Covered .... 135.00 To 200.00
Croesus, Purple, Toothpick 88.00

Crown Derby is the nickname given to the works of the Royal Crown Derby Factory which began working in England in 1859. An earlier and more famous English Derby factory existed from 1750 to 1848. The two factories were not related. Most of the porcelain found today with the Derby mark is the work of the later Derby factory.

Crown Derby, see also Royal Crown Derby
Crown Derby, Pitcher, Canary Yellow, Gold Encrusted Floral, 8 1/2 In. 225.00
Crown Derby, Teapot, Floral Finial, 6 In.High 85.00
Crown Devon, Pitcher, Floral On Light Beige, Stoke-On-Trent, 6 In. 20.00
Crown Devon, Vase, Luster, Bird Decoration, 5 1/2 In. 18.00
Crown Ducal, Plate, Sam Weller Composes His Valentine, 10 1/2 In. 18.00
Crown Ducal, Plate, Washington & His Family, Square, 8 1/4 In. 25.00
Crown Ducal, Plate, Washington & His Mother, Square, 8 1/4 In. 25.00
Crown Ducal, Plate, Washington At Trenton, Della Robbia Border, 11 In. 22.00
Crown Ducal, Plate, Washington's Birthplace, Della Robbia Border, 11 In. 22.00

Crown Milano glass was made by Frederick Shirley about 1890. It had a plain biscuit color with a satin finish. It was decorated with flowers, and often had large gold scrolls.

Crown Milano, Creamer, Floral Decoration, Applied Reed Handle, 5 In. 1050.00
Crown Milano, Jar, Cookie, Peachblow Color 475.00
Crown Milano, Jar, Cracker, Beige, Gold Leaves & Flowers, Silver Bail 450.00
Crown Milano, Jar, Cracker, Mt.Washington, Bulbous, Floral 470.00
Crown Milano, Jar, Sweetmeat, Floral & Gold On Off-White, Silver Fittings 575.00
Crown Milano, Jar, Sweetmeat, Melon Ribbed, Off-White, Silver Fittings 575.00
Crown Milano, Jar, Sweetmeat, Off-White, Ribbed, Pansies, Silver Fittings 450.00
Crown Milano, Muffineer, Melon Shape, Floral Decoration, 4 X 2 1/2 In. 175.00
Crown Milano, Toothpick, Mt.Washington, Floral & Gold, 4 Footed 150.00
Crown Milano, Vase, Acorns & Oak Leaves On Biscuit, 2 Handled, Gold, 8 In. 725.00
Crown Milano, Vase, Allover Floral Design, Biscuit Ground, 11 1/2 In.High 850.00
Crown Milano, Vase, Biscuit Body, Acorns & Oak Leaves, Handles, 8 In.High 725.00
Crown Milano, Vase, Coin Gold On White Satin, Signed, 9 3/4 In. 700.00
    Crown Tuscan, see Cambridge

Jasperware urn. Wedgwood. England. c. 1800.

Copper luster pitcher. England. c. 1825.

Faience and pewter stein. European. 1700–1750.

Staffordshire pottery pitcher. England. c. 1835.

Parian pitcher by Samuel Alcock & Co.. England. c. 1840.

Hound handled pitcher, Bennington, Vt., c. 1850.

Pottery pitcher, East Liverpool, Ohio, c. 1850.

Chinese export porcelain bowl, "Cherry Pickers," c. 1780. Chinese export plate depicting Governor Duf, c. 1750.

Spatterware sugar bowl, England, c. 1800–20.

Gaudy Welsh pitcher, England, c. 1800–1825.

Lotus ware bowl, East Liverpool, Ohio, 1895.

Wedgwood vase, England, mid-19th century.

Parian pitcher, Bennington, Vt., c. 1850.

Leeds creamware plate made for the American market, c. 1810. Staffordshire bust of George Washington, early 19th century.

Rookwood pottery bowl, M. A. Daly, Cincinnati, 1885.

Salt glazed plate, 1750–70.

Cowan pottery plate, Cleveland, c. 1930.

French porcelain punch bowl, decorated in America by Jennie Munger Cregany, c. 1900.

English vase in style of 18th-century Sevres, c. 1840.

Porcelain teapot, England, c. 1840.

Chinese export porcelain plate, "Sewing Lady," c. 1750.

Copper and pink luster pitcher, England, early 19th century.

Porcelain vases, Paris, pair, c. 1870 (front and back view).

Soft-paste-porcelain tea set, England, c. 1825.

Spode cottage, 5 inches high.

Rookwood pottery urn, Cincinnati. 1894.

Redware jug. Pennsylvania, c. 1800. Slipware plate. New England, c. 1800–1825.

Vienna porcelain tea set, 18th century.

Rookwood pottery vases, Cincinnati, 1915, 1925, 1911.

English delft pitcher, England, 17th century.

English delft punch bowl, mid-18th century.

Pressed glass sugar bowl, Westward Ho, c. 1870.

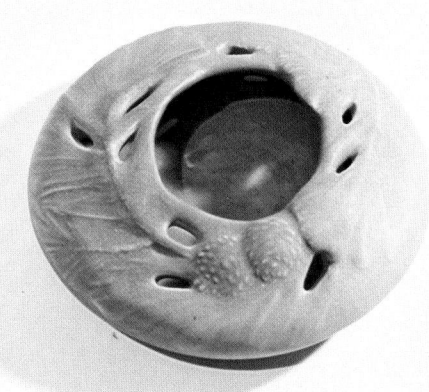

Statuettes of Benjamin Franklin and Louis XVI, Niderviller, France.

Rookwood pottery bulb bowl, Cincinnati, 1907.

Porcelain pitcher and basin, Paris, 1820.

Porcelain urn, Paris, c. 1825–30.

Porcelain pitcher, England, c. 1830.

Creamware pottery candlestick, England, c. 1775–1800. Whieldon tortoiseshell glazed plate, England, mid-18th century.

Leeds pottery plate, England, 18th century. Worcester pitcher, England, mid-18th century. Bow cup and saucer, England, mid-18th century.

Pressed glass pitcher, Moon and Star pattern, Adams & Co., Pittsburgh, c. 1888.

Reticulated Queensware basket, England.

Cut glass punch bowl, New York, c. 1905.

Lacy Sandwich glass dish, Massachusetts, c. 1835.

Cruets of glass or porcelain were made to hold vinegar or oil. They were especially popular during Victorian times.

Cruet, see also, Amber Glass, Pressed Glass, and other glass sections

Cruet, Gimmel, One Side Blue, One Side Amber, Wafer Foot	175.00
Cruet, Olive Green, Floral Decoration, Applied Handle, 7 In.High	69.00
Cruet, Vinegar, Deep Red, Acorn Shape, Cut Panels, Brass Chain & Hinged Lid	78.00

Currier & Ives made the famous American lithographs marked with their name from 1857 to 1907.

Currier & Ives, A Side Wheeler Bustin' A Trotter, 1880, 5 1/4 X 3 1/4 In.	30.00
Currier & Ives, Birth Of Our Savior, 1867, 14 X 10 In.	28.50
Currier & Ives, Card, Advertising, A Crack Trotter, Between The Heats, 1880	15.00
Currier & Ives, Clipper Ship, Three Brothers, 1875, Lithograph, Color, 27 In.	250.00
Currier & Ives, Little Charlie, Copyright, 1874, 14 X 11 In.	45.00
Currier & Ives, Little Ella, Framed, 8 X 11 In.	34.00
Currier & Ives, Mother's Pet, Lithograph, 13 X 10 In.	22.00
Currier & Ives, The Political Gymnasium, Lincoln, Aug.1860, 17 X 11 In.	100.00
Currier & Ives, The Soldier's Home, Small Folio	45.00
Currier & Ives, Washington's Birthplace, Color, 18 X 12 In.	110.00
Currier, Woodcock Shoot, 1952, 12 X 16 In.	77.50

Custard glass is an opaque glass sometimes known as buttermilk glass. It was first made after 1886 at La Belle Glass Works, Bridgeport, Ohio.

Custard Glass, see also Maize

Custard Glass, Banana Boat, Blue, Chrysanthemum Sprig, Gold, N	375.00 To 395.00
Custard Glass, Banana Boat, Chrysanthemum Sprig, Script Signed	155.00
Custard Glass, Banana Boat, Chrysanthemum Sprig, 10 In.Long	185.00
Custard Glass, Banana Boat, Louis XV	125.00 To 135.00
Custard Glass, Banana Boat, Louis XV, Gold Trim	125.00 To 150.00
Custard Glass, Bell, Souvenir	125.00
Custard Glass, Berry Set, Argonaut Shell, Gold Trim, 7 Piece	445.00
Custard Glass, Berry Set, Intaglio, Blue & Gold Decoration, 5 Piece	250.00
Custard Glass, Berry Set, Louis XV, Footed, Northwood, 7 Piece	475.00
Custard Glass, Bonbon, Prayer Rug, Handled	33.00
Custard Glass, Bowl, Banana, Louis VX, Footed, Oval	135.00
Custard Glass, Bowl, Banana, Louis XV, Gold Trim, Footed, Oval	110.00
Custard Glass, Bowl, Berry, Green, Louis XV, Gold Trim, Northwood	60.00
Custard Glass, Bowl, Berry, Master, Fluted Scrolls, 8 In.	25.00
Custard Glass, Bowl, Berry, Winged Scroll	95.00
Custard Glass, Bowl, Blackberry & Sprigs, Birds Inside, Ruffled, 9 1/2 In.	45.00
Custard Glass, Bowl, Blackberry, Flying Robins Interior, Painted, 8 In.	46.00
Custard Glass, Bowl, Centerpiece, Pearlized Grape & Cable, Fernery Shape	450.00
Custard Glass, Bowl, Fluted Scrolls With Flower Band, Footed, 8 1/2 In.	75.00
Custard Glass, Bowl, Fruit, Green, Button & Arches, 9 X 4 In.	65.00
Custard Glass, Bowl, Fruit, Ivorina, 8 1/2 X 3 1/2 In.	90.00
Custard Glass, Bowl, Fruit, Little Gem, Gold & Hand-Painted Floral	75.00
Custard Glass, Bowl, Fruit, Little Gem, 10 X 3 1/2 In.	85.00
Custard Glass, Bowl, Grape & Cable, Scalloped, 8 1/2 In.	42.00
Custard Glass, Bowl, Green, Georgia, Footed, 10 In.	62.00
Custard Glass, Bowl, Intaglio Butterflies & Dragons, Wheaton, N.J., 10 In.	75.00
Custard Glass, Bowl, Opaline, Applied Edge, 3 Blue Ball Feet, 5 1/8 In.	58.00
Custard Glass, Bowl, Pink, Grape & Cable, Pedestal, Northwood, 11 In.	1200.00
Custard Glass, Bowl, Pink, Poinsettia, Footed, 8 7/8 In.	46.75
Custard Glass, Bowl, Punch, Grape & Cable, Northwood, Mark Inside, 11 In.	600.00
Custard Glass, Bowl, Ruffled, Grape & Cable, 7 1/2 In.Diameter	37.50
Custard Glass, Box, Powder, Georgia Gem, Covered, Roses, Souvenir Wisconsin	42.50
Custard Glass, Butter, Beaded Circle	200.00
Custard Glass, Butter, Covered, Beaded Circle, Gold	235.00
Custard Glass, Butter, Covered, Green, Button & Arches	75.00
Custard Glass, Butter, Covered, Green, Georgia	87.00
Custard Glass, Butter, Covered, Green, Intaglio, Gold Trim	135.00
Custard Glass, Butter, Covered, Ivorina	100.00 To 130.00
Custard Glass, Butter, Covered, Ivorina, Gold Trim	130.00
Custard Glass, Butter, Covered, Louis XV	145.00
Custard Glass, Butter, Covered, Maple Leaf, Northwood	165.00

Custard Glass, Butter, Intaglio 145.00
Custard Glass, Butter, Louis XV 145.00
Custard Glass, Celery, Gem, Lavender Flowers 210.00
Custard Glass, Celery, Georgia Gem, Enameled Decoration 210.00
Custard Glass, Celery, Green, Button Arches, Gold Trim 60.00
Custard Glass, Celery, Scalloped Top, Gold Flowers & Leaves, Heisey, 5 In. 35.00
Custard Glass, Compote, Jelly, Argonaut Shell, Gold Trim .... 105.00 To 145.00
Custard Glass, Compote, Jelly, Argonaut Shell, 5 In. High 125.00
Custard Glass, Compote, Jelly, Chrysanthemum Sprig .... 35.00 To 50.00
Custard Glass, Compote, Jelly, Chrysanthemum Sprig, Gold Trim 45.00
Custard Glass, Creamer, Baby Thumbprint, Souvenir, St.Paul, 3 In. 25.00
Custard Glass, Creamer, Blue, Intaglio, Gold Trim 75.00
Custard Glass, Creamer, Chrysanthemum Sprig .... 90.00 To 95.00
Custard Glass, Creamer, Chrysanthemum Sprig, Gold Decoration 75.00
Custard Glass, Creamer, Decorated, "Conneaut Lake, Pa." 39.00
Custard Glass, Creamer, Diamond With Peg, Red Rose, Souvenir 55.00
Custard Glass, Creamer, Everglades 100.00
Custard Glass, Creamer, Green, Intaglio 65.00
Custard Glass, Creamer, Individual, Little Gem, McGregor, Iowa 45.00
Custard Glass, Creamer, Individual, Ring & Beads 35.00
Custard Glass, Creamer, Louis XV, Gold Trim 90.00
Custard Glass, Creamer, Ponca City, Oklahoma, 5 In. 37.00
Custard Glass, Creamer, Ribbed Thumbprint, "Menton, Minn." 22.00
Custard Glass, Creamer, Ribbed Thumbprint, Pink Decoration 25.00
Custard Glass, Creamer, Ring Band, Gold Trim, Heisey .... 85.00 To 95.00
Custard Glass, Creamer, Sunkist 22.00
Custard Glass, Creamer, Tankard Shape, Beaded, Rose, Souvenir, Salena, Kan. 35.00
Custard Glass, Creamer, Tankard Shape, Souvenir, Rulo, Neb. High School, 5 In 35.00
Custard Glass, Cruet, Blue, Chrysanthemum Sprig, Faceted Stopper 115.00
Custard Glass, Cruet, Chrysanthemum Sprig 125.00
Custard Glass, Cruet, Intaglio, Gold & Green Decoration, Crystal Stopper 125.00
Custard Glass, Cruet, Ivorina Verde, Gold Trim, Heisey 220.00

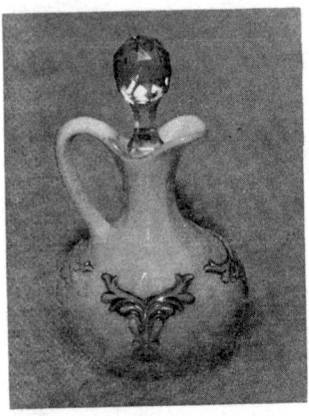

Custard Glass, Cruet, Winged Scroll, 6 1/2 In.

Custard Glass, Cruet, Winged Scroll, 6 1/2 In. .... Illus 165.00
Custard Glass, Cup, Punch, Diamond Peg, Beloit, Kansas 35.00
Custard Glass, Dish, Candy, Prayer Rug, Gold Paint Flecks, 5 In. 35.00
Custard Glass, Dish, Candy, Prayer Rug, 2 Handles 32.00
Custard Glass, Dish, Card, Green, Button & Arches, Turned-Up Edges, 6 1/2 In. 28.00
Custard Glass, Dish, Pickle, Poppy 65.00
Custard Glass, Fruit Set, Grape & Cable With Thumbprint, 5 Piece 350.00
Custard Glass, Fruit Set, Green, Button & Arches, 7 Piece 155.00
Custard Glass, Fruit Set, Louis XV, 7 Piece 365.00
Custard Glass, Goblet, Beaded Swag With Rose, Dow City, Iowa 55.00
Custard Glass, Goblet, Grape & Gothic Arches, Nutmeg Trim, N .... 45.00 To 55.00
Custard Glass, Hair Receiver, Jefferson, Red Roses, Gold 58.00
Custard Glass, Hat, Leaf & Berry Border, 3 X 5 1/2 In. 27.50
Custard Glass, Hat, Northwood Grape 40.00

Custard Glass, **Jar**, Powder, Winged Scroll, "Mankato, Kansas, " Heisey	42.00
Custard Glass, **Match Holder**, Green, Georgia	25.00
Custard Glass, **Muffineer**, Blue, Melon	78.00
Custard Glass, **Muffineer**, Ribbed	65.00
Custard Glass, **Mug**, Fish Design, Gold On Fish & Handle, Signed N, 5 In.	50.00
Custard Glass, **Mug**, Krystol, "Stratton, Maine, " 3 3/4 In.	20.00 To 22.00
Custard Glass, **Mug**, Singing Bird, Northwood	65.00
Custard Glass, **Mug**, Souvenir, Columbia, S.D., Hand-Painted Roses, Miniature	18.50
Custard Glass, **Mug**, Souvenir, Lloyd's, Beloit, Kansas	12.50
Custard Glass, **Mug**, Souvenir, School Building, Hillsboro, Kansas, 2 1/2 In.	20.00
Custard Glass, **Mug**, Souvenir, 2 In.	20.00
Custard Glass, **Mug**, Souvenir, 3 1/4 In.	16.50
Custard Glass, **Nappy**, Prayer Rug, 2 Handled	22.50
Custard Glass, **Nappy**, White, Indiana, 5 1/2 In.	2.50
Custard Glass, **Nappy**, White, Orange Blossom, 5 1/2 In.	2.50
Custard Glass, **Pitcher**, Water, Grape & Gothic Arches, Northwood	155.00
Custard Glass, **Pitcher**, Water, Green, Louis XV, Gold Trim	85.00
Custard Glass, **Pitcher**, Water, Louis XV	130.00 To 150.00
Custard Glass, **Pitcher**, Water, Louis XV, Gold	165.00
Custard Glass, **Pitcher**, Water, Ribbed Drape	145.00
Custard Glass, **Plate**, Grape, Nutmeg, Basket Weave Rim, Northwood, 7 5/8 In.	85.00
Custard Glass, **Salt & Pepper**, Argonaut Shell	375.00 To 450.00
Custard Glass, **Salt & Pepper**, Chrysanthemum Sprig	20.00
Custard Glass, **Salt & Pepper**, Green, Intaglio, Gold Trim, Pewter Tops	110.00
Custard Glass, **Salt & Pepper**, Intaglio	135.00
Custard Glass, **Salt & Pepper**, Intaglio, Green Trim	135.00
Custard Glass, **Salt & Pepper**, Ribbed	16.00
Custard Glass, **Salt & Pepper**, White, Everglades, Northwood	110.00
Custard Glass, **Saltshaker**, Chrysanthemum Sprig	45.00
Custard Glass, **Saltshaker**, Georgia Gem, No Decoration	14.00
Custard Glass, **Saltshaker**, Intaglio	35.00
Custard Glass, **Saltshaker**, Punty Band, Heisey, Souvenir, Butte, Mont.	22.50
Custard Glass, **Saltshaker**, Ring Band, Gold Trim, Heisey, H In Diamond Mark	38.00
Custard Glass, **Saltshaker**, Ring Band, Rose Decoration, Heisey	38.00
Custard Glass, **Sauce**, Argonaut Shell	60.00
Custard Glass, **Sauce**, Argonaut Shell, Gold Trim	55.00
Custard Glass, **Sauce**, Argonaut Shell, Northwood	45.00
Custard Glass, **Sauce**, Argonaut Shell, Northwood, 1890, Oval	50.00
Custard Glass, **Sauce**, Blue, Chrysanthemum Sprig, Northwood In Script	95.00
Custard Glass, **Sauce**, Blue, Skirted Base, Northwood, 4 3/4 X 3 5/8 In.	65.00
Custard Glass, **Sauce**, Fluted Scrolls With Flower Band, Footed, 5 In.	30.00
Custard Glass, **Sauce**, Fluted Scrolls, Footed, Northwood	18.00
Custard Glass, **Sauce**, Intaglio, Blue & Gold Decoration, 4 1/2 In.	40.00
Custard Glass, **Sauce**, Intaglio, Blue Trim	52.50
Custard Glass, **Sauce**, Intaglio, Green & Gold	40.00
Custard Glass, **Sauce**, Intaglio, Green Trim	45.00 To 52.50
Custard Glass, **Sauce**, Inverted Fan & Feather, Gold & Pink Trim, Footed, N	75.00
Custard Glass, **Sauce**, Inverted Fan & Feather, Gold, Footed, Northwood	75.00
Custard Glass, **Sauce**, Louis XV	45.00
Custard Glass, **Sauce**, Louis XV, Oval	45.00
Custard Glass, **Sauce**, Ring Band, Moss Rose, Heisey	32.50
Custard Glass, **Sauce**, Wild Bouquet, Iris	55.00
Custard Glass, **Sauce**, Winged Scroll, Gold Trim	20.00
Custard Glass, **Sherbet**, Grape & Cable	42.50 To 45.00
Custard Glass, **Shot Glass**, Decal Martin Luther College, Sterling, Nebr.	22.50
Custard Glass, **Spooner**, Argonaut Shell, Northwood In Script	110.00 To 125.00
Custard Glass, **Spooner**, Blue, Chrysanthemum Sprig, Gold Trim, Northwood	150.00
Custard Glass, **Spooner**, Brown Stain, Grape & Cable With Thumbprint	85.00
Custard Glass, **Spooner**, Chrysanthemum Sprig	75.00 To 95.00
Custard Glass, **Spooner**, Chrysanthemum Sprig, Footed	95.00
Custard Glass, **Spooner**, Everglades	85.00
Custard Glass, **Spooner**, Fluted Scrolls, Northwood	35.00
Custard Glass, **Spooner**, Grape & Gothic Arch	38.00
Custard Glass, **Spooner**, Green, Button & Arches	38.00
Custard Glass, **Spooner**, Green, Intaglio	65.00
Custard Glass, **Spooner**, Green, Intaglio, Gold Trim	65.00 To 70.00

Custard Glass, Spooner, Green, Maple Leaf, Gold Trim, Northwood	69.50
Custard Glass, Spooner, Honeycomb, Flower	50.00
Custard Glass, Spooner, Intaglio, Blue Trim	80.00
Custard Glass, Spooner, Intaglio, Gold & Blue Decoration	50.00
Custard Glass, Spooner, Intaglio, Northwood	65.00
Custard Glass, Spooner, Louis XVI, Gold Trim, Northwood	65.00
Custard Glass, Spooner, Louis XV	65.00 To 79.00
Custard Glass, Spooner, Louis XV, Gold Trim	90.00
Custard Glass, Spooner, Maple Leaf	55.00 To 70.00
Custard Glass, Spooner, Winged Scroll, Enamel Floral	59.00
Custard Glass, Sugar & Creamer, Breakfast, Brown Stain, Grape & Cable	85.00
Custard Glass, Sugar & Creamer, Brown Stain, Grape & Cable	90.00
Custard Glass, Sugar & Creamer, Chrysanthemum Sprig, Northwood	100.00 To 150.00
Custard Glass, Sugar & Creamer, Green, Georgia Belle, Heisey	48.00
Custard Glass, Sugar & Creamer, Grape, Northwood	90.00
Custard Glass, Sugar & Creamer, Louis XV	150.00
Custard Glass, Sugar & Creamer, Louis XV, Gold Decoration	120.00
Custard Glass, Sugar & Creamer, Narcissus, Heisey	23.00
Custard Glass, Sugar, Chrysanthemum Sprig, Script Signed	125.00
Custard Glass, Sugar, Covered, Chrysanthemum Sprig	100.00 To 145.00
Custard Glass, Sugar, Covered, Flower With Leaf Band	18.50
Custard Glass, Sugar, Covered, Louis XV	65.00
Custard Glass, Sugar, Covered, Louis XV, Gold Trim	72.00
Custard Glass, Sugar, Grape Band	9.00
Custard Glass, Sugar, Individual, Cut Block, Souvenir, Heisey	30.00
Custard Glass, Syrup, Spiderweb, C.1890	135.00
Custard Glass, Table Set, Argonaut Shell, 4 Piece	475.00 To 540.00
Custard Glass, Table Set, Chrysanthemum Sprig, Gold, Northwood, 4 Piece	375.00
Custard Glass, Table Set, Ivorina Verde, Winged Scroll, 3 Piece	300.00
Custard Glass, Table Set, Krystol, 3 Piece	350.00
Custard Glass, Table Set, Louis XV, Gold Trim, 3 Piece	250.00
Custard Glass, Table Set, Louis XV, Gold Trim, 4 Piece	350.00
Custard Glass, Table Set, Louis XV, 4 Piece	375.00
Custard Glass, Toothpick, Argonaut Shell	225.00
Custard Glass, Toothpick, Beaded Top, "Pierre, S.D. Capitol"	22.00
Custard Glass, Toothpick, Chrysanthemum Sprig	175.00
Custard Glass, Toothpick, Color Scene, Bradford, Vt.	22.00
Custard Glass, Toothpick, Harvard, Souvenir Miller's Falls	18.00
Custard Glass, Toothpick, Light Green, Bulging Loop	25.00
Custard Glass, Toothpick, Punty Band, Flowers, Heisey	75.00
Custard Glass, Toothpick, Punty Band, Heisey, Souvenir	50.00
Custard Glass, Toothpick, Punty Band, Rose Buds, Heisey, "Rosecrans, Wisc."	45.00
Custard Glass, Toothpick, Ring Band	45.00
Custard Glass, Toothpick, Ring Band Roses, Heisey	75.00
Custard Glass, Toothpick, Ring Band, Souvenir, State Fair	39.00
Custard Glass, Toothpick, Ring Band, Souvenir, Traverse City	35.00
Custard Glass, Toothpick, Souvenir, Shattuck, Okla. High School	25.00
Custard Glass, Toothpick, Souvenir, Wilber, Neb., Heisey	39.00
Custard Glass, Toothpick, Tarentum's Harvard	40.00
Custard Glass, Toothpick, Thumbprint, "Westboro, Wisconsin"	22.00
Custard Glass, Tray, Narcissus, Heisey, 14 In.	24.50
Custard Glass, Tray, Pin, Scalloped Scrolled Edges, 4 X 6 In.	22.00
Custard Glass, Tumbler, Argonaut Shell	65.00
Custard Glass, Tumbler, Blue, Chrysanthemum Sprig, Gold Trim	150.00
Custard Glass, Tumbler, Chrysanthemum Sprig	57.50 To 60.00
Custard Glass, Tumbler, Chrysanthemum Sprig, Gold	60.00
Custard Glass, Tumbler, Diamond Peg, Souvenir, Plymouth, Mass.	35.00
Custard Glass, Tumbler, Fluted Scrolls, Northwood	18.00
Custard Glass, Tumbler, Geneva	42.50 To 44.00
Custard Glass, Tumbler, Green, Button & Arches	25.00 To 35.00
Custard Glass, Tumbler, Intaglio	39.50 To 55.00
Custard Glass, Tumbler, Intaglio, Blue Trim	55.00
Custard Glass, Tumbler, Intaglio, Northwood	39.50
Custard Glass, Tumbler, Louis XV	50.00
Custard Glass, Tumbler, Louis XV, Gold Trim	30.00 To 150.00
Custard Glass, Tumbler, Louis XV, Northwood, C.1898	62.50

Custard Glass, Tumbler, Plain, Signed McKee	10.00
Custard Glass, Tumbler, Punty Band, Painted Roses, Heisey	35.00
Custard Glass, Tumbler, Punty Band, Roses, Souvenir, Heisey	48.00
Custard Glass, Tumbler, Raised Wild Roses, Marked N	32.25
Custard Glass, Tumbler, Ring Band	35.00
Custard Glass, Tumbler, Ring Band, Roses, Souvenir, Heisey	52.00
Custard Glass, Tumbler, Roses, Souvenir, Yankton, S.D.	24.00
Custard Glass, Tumbler, Souvenir, Heisey	45.00
Custard Glass, Tumbler, Wild Rose	34.00
Custard Glass, Tumbler, Winged Scroll	65.00
Custard Glass, Tumbler, Winged Scroll, Gold Trim, Heisey	52.00
Custard Glass, Vase, Beaded Rim, Pedestal, Souvenir, Ponca City, Okla., 6 In.	35.00
Custard Glass, Vase, Clear Rigaree, 5 1/2 In.	145.00
Custard Glass, Vase, Colored Bird & Decoration, 9 1/4 In.	95.00
Custard Glass, Vase, Trumpet, High Waterloo, La., 6 In.	28.00
Custard Glass, Water Set, Chrysanthemum Sprig, 7 Piece	500.00
Custard Glass, Water Set, Diamond With Peg, Souvenir, Cuba, S.D., 7 Piece	325.00
Custard Glass, Water Set, Geneva, Painted, 7 Piece	375.00
Custard Glass, Water Set, Grape & Cable, 7 Piece	600.00
Custard Glass, Water Set, Louis XV, 7 Piece	400.00
Custard Glass, Wine, Beaded Swag, Souvenir, Blue Mounds, Wis.	30.00
Custard Glass, Wine, Diamond & Peg	75.00
Custard Glass, Wine, Ribbed Thumbprint, "McVille, N.D.," Marked Krystol	32.00

*Cut glass has been made since ancient times, but the large majority of the
pieces now for sale date from the brilliant period of glass design, 1880 to
1905. These pieces had elaborate geometric designs with a deep miter cut.*

Cut Glass, Atomizer, Ruby To Clear, 5 In.	65.00
Cut Glass, Banana Boat, Cane & Hobstar Bands, 12 X 5 In.	90.00
Cut Glass, Basket, Applied Twisted Rope Handle, 6 1/4 X 6 In.	200.00
Cut Glass, Basket, Comet Pattern, Notched Handle, 6 X 4 1/2 X 5 In.High	150.00
Cut Glass, Basket, Geometrics, Twisted Handle, 7 1/2 X 4 1/2 In.	180.00
Cut Glass, Basket, Graphic Flowers, Press Cut Leaves, 16 In.	50.00
Cut Glass, Basket, Hobstar & Diamond Point Vesica, Notched Handle, 8 In.	225.00
Cut Glass, Basket, Hobstar & Pinwheel, Twisted Handle, 6 1/4 X 5 In.	95.00
Cut Glass, Basket, Hobstar, Crosshatched Vesica, & Fan, 6 1/4 In.	125.00
Cut Glass, Basket, Hobstars, Clarke, 6 X 7 In.	185.00
Cut Glass, Basket, Intaglio & Fine Crosshatching, Thumbprint Handle, 6 In.	175.00
Cut Glass, Basket, Intaglio Floral, Bull's-Eye, Floral, & Leaf, Libbey, 12 In.	525.00
Cut Glass, Bonbon, Leaf Shape, Hobstar, Prism, Crosshatching & Vesica, 7 In.	85.00
Cut Glass, Bonbon, Rolled-Up Sides, Deep Cuttings, 5 1/2 In. Long	25.00
Cut Glass, Bottle, Cologne, Flat, Silver Plate Cap	35.00
Cut Glass, Bottle, Cologne, Gravic, Carnation, Sterling Top, Hawkes, 6 1/4 In.	120.00
Cut Glass, Bottle, Cologne, Vertical Cuttings, Faceted Stopper, 5 1/2 In.	35.00
Cut Glass, Bottle, Cordial, Hobstar & Pinwheel, 9 In.	90.00
Cut Glass, Bottle, Cordial, Russian, Buttons, Shot Glass Cover, 3 Piece, 6 In.	225.00
Cut Glass, Bottle, Cordial, Trellis Variation, 8 1/2 In.High	175.00
Cut Glass, Bottle, Ink, Cube Shape, Ground Lip, Pewter Cap, 1 1/2 In.	8.00
Cut Glass, Bottle, Ketchup, Strawberry Diamond, Fan, & Hobstar, Hawkes, 8 In.	135.00
Cut Glass, Bottle, Medicine, Tumbler Insert, Stopper, 8 1/2 In.	350.00
Cut Glass, Bottle, Oil & Vinegar, Sterling Cap, Hawkes, 1916, 7 3/8 In.	59.95
Cut Glass, Bottle, Perfume, Brass Top, 6 1/2 In., Pair	63.00
Cut Glass, Bottle, Perfume, Cut Stopper, 4 1/2 In., Pair	40.00
Cut Glass, Bottle, Perfume, Enameled	100.00
Cut Glass, Bottle, Perfume, French, 18K Gold Overlay	175.00
Cut Glass, Bottle, Perfume, Hobstar, Block, Bull's-Eye, & Prism, 4 3/4 In.	50.00
Cut Glass, Bottle, Perfume, Intaglio Floral, Enamel Sterling Top, 4 1/2 In.	40.00
Cut Glass, Bottle, Perfume, Orchid To Purple Top, 16 Point Star, 6 1/4 In.	22.50
Cut Glass, Bottle, Perfume, Sterling Fittings, Notched Prism, Purse Size	30.00
Cut Glass, Bottle, Perfume, Sterling Stopper, 3 Rows Panels, 3 1/4 In.	45.00
Cut Glass, Bottle, Perfume, Sterling Top, Engraved Floral, Hawkes, 5 1/2 In.	39.00
Cut Glass, Bottle, Perfume, Thumbprint & Engraved Carnation, 6 In.	77.75
Cut Glass, Bottle, Smelling Salts, Sterling Hinged Lid, 3 In.	20.00
Cut Glass, Bottle, Smelling Salts, Sterling Rim, Lid, & Finial, 3 In.	45.00
Cut Glass, Bottle, Talcum, Star & Diamond, Sterling Top, Unger Bros., 3 In.	40.00
Cut Glass, Bowl & Base, Punch, Allover Cuttings, Hoare, 12 X 11 In.	1100.00

Cut Glass, Bowl & Base, Punch, Harvard, 9 3/4 X 13 In.	675.00
Cut Glass, Bowl & Base, Punch, Harvard, 10 X 11 In.	995.00
Cut Glass, Bowl & Base, Punch, Hobstars, 10 In.	425.00
Cut Glass, Bowl & Base, Punch, Hobstars, 16 X 17 In.	1200.00
Cut Glass, Bowl & Base, Punch, Pinwheel Variant, Fans & Hobstars	400.00
Cut Glass, Bowl & Base, Punch, Pinwheel, Hobstar Centers, Cane, 10 X 9 1/2 In	300.00
Cut Glass, Bowl & Base, Punch, Salesman's Sample, Cane, Star, 5 1/2 In.	69.00
Cut Glass, Bowl & Underplate, Finger, Canary, Flute & Miter, Pairpoint	45.00
Cut Glass, Bowl & Underplate, Finger, Kalana Lily, Dorflinger	22.50
Cut Glass, Bowl & Underplate, Finger, Vaseline, 4 1/2 In.	44.50
Cut Glass, Bowl & Underplate, Mayonnaise, Hobstar & Diamond Point, 6 In.	75.00
Cut Glass, Bowl & Underplate, Mayonnaise, Hobstar & Fan, American	90.00
Cut Glass, Bowl & Underplate, Tom & Jerry, 12 X 9 In.	425.00
Cut Glass, Bowl & Underplate, Whipped Cream, Hobstar & Crosshatching	95.00
Cut Glass, Bowl On Stand, Punch, Hobstar, Fan, Nailhead, & Diamond, 10 In.	465.00
Cut Glass, Bowl Set, Russian, American, 5 In., 4 Piece	250.00
Cut Glass, Bowl, Allover Hobstars, Harvard, Diamond, Sawtooth, 7 In.Long	65.00
Cut Glass, Bowl, Banana, Corinthian, 11 X 4 In.	140.00
Cut Glass, Bowl, Banana, Pinwheel & Hobstar, Flared Sides, Oval, 11 3/4 In.	60.00
Cut Glass, Bowl, Berry, Hobstar & Star, Sawtooth Edge, 8 X 3 1/4 In.	60.00
Cut Glass, Bowl, Blaze, Engraved Swags & Floral, Star Base, Pairpoint, 11 In.	85.00
Cut Glass, Bowl, Brilliant Cut, American, 9 X 2 In.	80.00
Cut Glass, Bowl, Brilliant Cut, Rectangular, 11 3/8 X 3 1/4 X 6 3/4 In.	55.00
Cut Glass, Bowl, Bull's-Eye & Notched Prism, Low, 7 In.	75.00
Cut Glass, Bowl, Buzz, Star, & Miter, 8 In.	70.00
Cut Glass, Bowl, Center Handle, Intaglio Floral & Butterfly, 10 In.	150.00
Cut Glass, Bowl, Centerpiece, Cuspidor Shape, Primrose, Jewel Cut Glass Co.	195.00
Cut Glass, Bowl, Centerpiece, Stars, Openwork German Silver, C.1900, 17 In.	320.00
Cut Glass, Bowl, Chain Of Hobstars On Base, Engraved Thistles, Clarke, 8 In.	65.00
Cut Glass, Bowl, Chrysanthemum, Notched Handles, Turned-In Sides, 5 1/2 In.	155.00
Cut Glass, Bowl, Claret, Chain Of Hobstars, Vesica, 2 Piece, 9 1/4 X 9 In.	280.00
Cut Glass, Bowl, Cloverleaf, Hobstars, & Crosshatch, 9 In.Diameter	125.00
Cut Glass, Bowl, Comet, Medallion, Hobstar & Horizontal Cuttings, 8 In.	68.00
Cut Glass, Bowl, Corinthian, Folded-In Sides, Libbey, Square, 8 1/4 In.	175.00
Cut Glass, Bowl, Daisy & Button, 9 In.	65.00
Cut Glass, Bowl, Expanding Star, 8 In.Diameter, 3 1/2 In.High	175.00
Cut Glass, Bowl, Fan, Floral, Prism, & Hobnail, Scalloped, 8 1/4 X 3 1/4 In.	115.00
Cut Glass, Bowl, Finger, Pluto, Hoare, Corning, 1853, 4 3/4 In.	47.50
Cut Glass, Bowl, Footed, Covered, Finial, Strawberry Diamond, Vesica, 5 In.	130.00
Cut Glass, Bowl, Fortuna, Turned-Out Edges, 9 X 4 In.	135.00
Cut Glass, Bowl, Fruit, Hobstars, American, Brilliant Period, 7 7/8 In.	57.00
Cut Glass, Bowl, Fruit, Honeycomb, Bobbin Knop, English, C.1820, 8 1/2 In.	300.00
Cut Glass, Bowl, Gravic Cosmos, Paperweight Base, Footed, Hawkes, 6 X 9 In.	595.00
Cut Glass, Bowl, Gravic Cut, Carnation, Hawkes, 8 X 2 In.	175.00
Cut Glass, Bowl, Gravic Iris, Hawkes, 9 In.	235.00
Cut Glass, Bowl, Gravic Strawberries, Hobstar & Diamond Center, 6 In.	160.00
Cut Glass, Bowl, Handled, Hobstar, Cane, Strawberry Diamond, & Fan, 11 1/2 In.	65.00
Cut Glass, Bowl, Harvard & Intaglio, Bowl, Boat Shape, 8 X 4 1/2 In.	40.00
Cut Glass, Bowl, Harvard, Scalloped Rim, Hawkes, 8 X 4 In.	125.00
Cut Glass, Bowl, Hobstar & Cane, American, 5 X 2 1/2 In.	25.00
Cut Glass, Bowl, Hobstar & Cane, Shallow, 8 In.	60.00
Cut Glass, Bowl, Hobstar & Fan, American, 8 In.	80.00
Cut Glass, Bowl, Hobstar & Panels Of Fern & Vesicas, 9 In.	50.00
Cut Glass, Bowl, Hobstar, Crosshatching, & Star, Scalloped, 8 In.	85.00
Cut Glass, Bowl, Hobstar, Fan, Split Vesica, & Bead, Paneled, Hoare, 8 In.	95.00
Cut Glass, Bowl, Hobstar, Strawberry Diamond, & Crosscut, Scalloped, 8 In.	77.50
Cut Glass, Bowl, Hobstar, Vesica, & Crosscut, 8 1/4 X 3 1/4 In.	67.50
Cut Glass, Bowl, Hobstars & Notched Prisms, Hawkes, 7 X 3 1/2 In.	85.00
Cut Glass, Bowl, Hobstars Allover, Sinclaire, 8 X 2 In.High	125.00
Cut Glass, Bowl, Hobstars, Strawberry Diamond In Corners, Hawkes, 7 1/2 In.	150.00
Cut Glass, Bowl, Intaglio Flowers & Leaves, Clarke, 9 X 3 1/2 In.	80.00
Cut Glass, Bowl, Intaglio Grape & Leaf, Hand-Blown, Libbey, 4 1/2 In.	60.00
Cut Glass, Bowl, Intaglio, Hawkes, 8 X 4 In.	75.00
Cut Glass, Bowl, Intaglio, Shallow, Low Pedestal, Libbey, 7 1/4 In.	125.00
Cut Glass, Bowl, Kimberly, Star Cut, 8 In.	70.00
Cut Glass, Bowl, Notched Prisms, Hobstars, & Fans, Libbey, 8 In.Diameter	85.00

Cut Glass, Bowl, Octagonal, Column & Sunburst, C.1750, 10 X 8 1/4 In.	150.00
Cut Glass, Bowl, Orange, Blue On Clear, 12 X 6 1/2 In.	150.00
Cut Glass, Bowl, Orange, Harvard Hobnail, Intaglio Floral, 8 X 5 X 4 In.	95.00
Cut Glass, Bowl, Orange, Harvard, 10 X 6 X 4 1/4 In.	275.00
Cut Glass, Bowl, Orange, Innovation, 12 In.	37.50
Cut Glass, Bowl, Orange, Pinwheel, Fan, & Cane Vesica, Engraved Floral, 9 In.	95.00
Cut Glass, Bowl, Pineapple Shape, Deep Cuttings, 12 In.	195.00
Cut Glass, Bowl, Pinwheel, Hobnail, & Vesica, 3 Footed, 7 3/8 In.	75.00
Cut Glass, Bowl, Plymouth, Empire C.G.Co., 7 1/2 X 5 In.	45.00
Cut Glass, Bowl, Prism Flower, 3 Footed, 8 In.	82.50
Cut Glass, Bowl, Punch, Rolled-Over Edge, American, 15 In.	300.00
Cut Glass, Bowl, Rectangular, Brilliant Hobstars, Prism, Fans, 12 X 8 In.	325.00
Cut Glass, Bowl, Royal, Hunt, 8 1/4 X 3 1/4 In.	250.00
Cut Glass, Bowl, Ruby To Clear, Hobstars, Footed, 9 1/2 In.	65.00
Cut Glass, Bowl, Salad, Arcadia, Sterling, 10 In.	200.00
Cut Glass, Bowl, Salad, Scalloped Top, Hawkes, 9 1/2 In.	100.00
Cut Glass, Bowl, Salad, Sharp Cuttings, 3 Footed, 9 X 3 1/2 In.	70.00
Cut Glass, Bowl, Salad, Signed Maple Leaf, Hobstars, 8 X 4 In.	75.00
Cut Glass, Bowl, Salad, Straus, Gorham Sterling Rim, 8 In.	175.00
Cut Glass, Bowl, Spoon, & Fork, Serving, 7 1/2 In. Diameter	67.50
Cut Glass, Bowl, Sterling Rim, Hawkes, 4 3/4 In.	32.00
Cut Glass, Bowl, Straus Davies, Pinched Sides, 9 In.	145.00
Cut Glass, Bowl, Straus, Gorham Sterling Edge, 8 In.	125.00
Cut Glass, Bowl, Strawberry Diamond & Fan, Rayed Base, 9 1/4 In.	85.00
Cut Glass, Bowl, Triangular, Scenic, Airplane & Lighthouse, 5 In.	275.00
Cut Glass, Bowl, Triple Square, Shallow, Clarke, 8 1/2 X 2 1/4 In.	220.00
Cut Glass, Bowl, Vesica, Cane, Hobstar, Crosshatching, & Star, Hoare, 9 In.	120.00
Cut Glass, Bowl, Vintage, Grape & Leaf Center, Hobstar Band, Tuthill, 6 In.	137.50
Cut Glass, Bowl, Whip Cream, Wedgemere, 20 Point Hobstar Base, 8 In.	125.00
Cut Glass, Bowl, Windmill Center, Hobstars, Straight Sided, 8 In.	74.00
Cut Glass, Bowl, 8 Petal Flower & Leaf, 8 Petal Flower Base, 9 X 4 In.	85.00
Cut Glass, Box, Butter, Hinged, Butterfly & Floral, 5 In.	145.00
Cut Glass, Box, Butter, Hinged, Butterfly & Floral, 6 In.	175.00
Cut Glass, Box, Candy, Pinwheels, 3 Feet, 6 X 6 1/2 In.	35.00
Cut Glass, Box, Dresser, Hinged, Garland Type Pattern, Silver, 6 3/4 In.	165.00
Cut Glass, Box, Dresser, Intaglio Floral, Silver Bound, Hinged, Round, 5 In.	110.00
Cut Glass, Box, Glove, Intaglio Daisies On Hinged Lid, Rayed Base, 11 In.	275.00
Cut Glass, Box, Hinged, Flashed Hobstar, 7 3/4 In.	375.00
Cut Glass, Box, Hinged, Intaglio Daisy, Thumbprint, & Crosshatching, 5 In.	65.00
Cut Glass, Box, Hinged, 8 Point Hobstar On Lid, 5 X 3 In.	145.00
Cut Glass, Box, Jewel, Hinged, Cosmos & Leaf, 24 Point Star Base, 5 X 3 In.	160.00
Cut Glass, Box, Powder, Hobstars, Fans, Star Cut Bottom, 4 1/2 X 3 In.	34.50
Cut Glass, Box, Powder, Pinwheel & Fan, Clarke, Round, 4 1/4 In.	75.00
Cut Glass, Box, Rock Crystal, Gorham Sterling Lid, Hawkes, Round, 5 In.	155.00
Cut Glass, Brandy Set, Strawberry Diamond, Dahlia Base, 6 Piece	285.00
Cut Glass, Bucket, Ice, Brilliant Period, Tab Handles	83.00
Cut Glass, Bucket, Ice, Georgian Style, Quadruple Plate Holder, C.1850	135.00
Cut Glass, Bucket, Ice, Harvard, Checkered Button Base, Tab Handles, 7 In.	265.00
Cut Glass, Bucket, Ice, St.Louis Diamond, Sterling Fittings, Hawkes, 8 In.	250.00
Cut Glass, Butter Pat, Notched Edge	18.00
Cut Glass, Butter Pat, Strawberry Diamond & Fan, 3 In.Diameter, 12	225.00
Cut Glass, Butter, Covered, Double Hobstar Chain & Crosscut, 8 X 5 1/4 In.	225.00
Cut Glass, Butter, Covered, Hobstars	250.00
Cut Glass, Butter, Covered, Pinwheels	165.00
Cut Glass, Butter, Covered, Russian	425.00
Cut Glass, Butter, Covered, Russian & Daisy	120.00
Cut Glass, Butter, Dome Lid, Brilliant Period	250.00
Cut Glass, Butter, Dome Lid, Harvard, Geometric, Hobstar, & Nailhead, 6 In.	350.00
Cut Glass, Butter, Dome Lid, Hobstar, Strawberry Diamond, & Fan, Scalloped	175.00
Cut Glass, Butter, Dome Lid, Hobstar, Sunburst, & Miter	265.00
Cut Glass, Butter, Engraved Floral, 1/4 Pound Shape, Hawkes	25.00
Cut Glass, Butter, Floral Design, Hawkes	25.00
Cut Glass, Butter, Hobstar, Fan, & Diamond	175.00
Cut Glass, Cake Stand, Intaglio, Strawberry & Leaves, Silver Border, 7 In.	90.00
Cut Glass, Candelabra, Charles X, Ormolu Mounted, 4 Arm, 13 1/4 In., Pair	300.00
Cut Glass, Candelabra, Enamel, 4 S Scroll Arms, C.1850, 34 1/4 In., Pair	700.00

Cut Glass, Candelabra, Geometrics, 3 Silver Plate Arms & Snuffer, 15 In.	275.00
Cut Glass, Candelabra, 2 Arm, 4 Section, Prisms, Czechoslovakia, 14 In., Pair	150.00
Cut Glass, Candleholder, Harvard & Intaglio, Teardrop Stem, 10 In., Pair	295.00
Cut Glass, Candlestick, Double Teardrops, Blank, 9 In., Pair	275.00
Cut Glass, Candlestick, Floral Sprays, Turned-Down Top, Hawkes, 5 In., Pair	640.00
Cut Glass, Candlestick, Hawkes, 12 In., Pair	175.00
Cut Glass, Candlestick, Hollow Stem, Hobstar, Panel, & Beading, 8 In., Pair	275.00
Cut Glass, Candlestick, Prisms, Maple Leaf, 10 In.	50.00
Cut Glass, Candlestick, Russian, Strawberry Diamond, Teardrop Center, 9 In.	150.00
Cut Glass, Candlestick, Square Column & Base, Intaglio Floral, 9 In., Pair	27.50
Cut Glass, Candlestick, Teardrop, 7 In.	50.00
Cut Glass, Candlestick, 6 Sided, Zipper Sides, Deep Teardrop Center, 8 In.	45.00
Cut Glass, Carafe, Bubbles Around Bottom, 1880, 10 In.	80.00
Cut Glass, Carafe, Intaglio Daisy, Leaf, & Fern, 24 Point Star Base, 9 In.	65.00
Cut Glass, Carafe, Oregon, Bergen, 7 X 6 1/2 In.	65.00
Cut Glass, Carafe, Star & Zipper, Stepped Neck, 8 In.	55.00
Cut Glass, Carafe, Water, Buzz Star, Diamond, & Leaf, 8 1/2 In.	37.50
Cut Glass, Carafe, Water, Florence	92.00
Cut Glass, Carafe, Water, Hand-Blown, Beaded Sides, Swirls & Stars, 7 In.	40.00
Cut Glass, Carafe, Water, Star & Fan	90.00
Cut Glass, Case, Jewel, Acid Floral & Intaglio Lid, Harvard, Pewter Trim	225.00
Cut Glass, Celery, Acid Etched Floral & Butterfly, 11 1/2 In.	29.50
Cut Glass, Celery, Brilliant Cut, G.CCo. In Clover Signed, 10 In.	35.00
Cut Glass, Celery, G.C.Co., Birks, 11 In.	40.00
Cut Glass, Celery, Cabbage Rose, 12 X 5 In.	52.50
Cut Glass, Celery, Carnations, Gravic, Turned-In Sides, Boat Shape, Hawkes	155.00
Cut Glass, Celery, Daisy & Button, 10 1/2 X 4 1/2 In., Pair	52.50
Cut Glass, Celery, Etched Flying Bird, Peony, & Butterfly, 11 1/4 X 5 In.	37.50
Cut Glass, Celery, Harvard, Heavy Blank, Serrated Rim, 6 Sided, 12 In.	89.00
Cut Glass, Celery, Hobstar & Star Center, Egginton, 11 In.	62.00
Cut Glass, Celery, Hobstar, Strawberry Diamond, & Prism, 5 1/2 In.	45.00
Cut Glass, Celery, Honeycomb, 7 1/2 In.	45.00
Cut Glass, Celery, 3 Intaglio Cut Flowers, 12 1/4 X 4 1/2 In.	60.00
Cut Glass, Champagne, Diamond Band, Star Bottom, Cut Stem, 4 1/2 In.	15.00
Cut Glass, Champagne, Diamonds, 4 1/2 In.	15.00
Cut Glass, Champagne, Emerald To Clear, Flute, Double Teardrop Stem	25.00
Cut Glass, Champagne, Engraved Grapes	8.75
Cut Glass, Champagne, Intaglio Daisy & Leaf, 9 1/4 In.	18.75
Cut Glass, Champagne, Strawberry Diamond, 3 1/2 X 4 1/2 In.	15.00
Cut Glass, Clock, see Clock	
Cut Glass, Coaster, Webster Sterling Chased Rim, Overlay, 6 In.	25.00
Cut Glass, Coffee Pot, Fine Line Cutting, 6 1/2 In.High	300.00
Cut Glass, Compote, Arcadia, Notched Teardrop Stem, Hobstar Base, 6 In.	75.00
Cut Glass, Compote, British Cane, Square Notched Standard, 8 1/4 In.	62.00
Cut Glass, Compote, Candy, Buzz Star & Fan, Tall Stemmed, 6 In.	75.00
Cut Glass, Compote, Cane Medallion & Pinwheel, Notched Stem, 6 In.	295.00
Cut Glass, Compote, Diamond & Flute, English, C.1830, 5 1/2 In., Pair	50.00
Cut Glass, Compote, Feathered Star, Star, & Crosshatching, 9 1/2 In., Pair	210.00
Cut Glass, Compote, Gravic Strawberries, Hawkes, 7 1/2 In.	375.00
Cut Glass, Compote, Hobstar & Flute, Teardrop Stem, Hobstar Base, 8 In.	130.00
Cut Glass, Compote, Hobstar, Cane, Strawberry Diamond, & Crosshatching, 7 In.	250.00
Cut Glass, Compote, Hobstar, Feathered Fan, & Nailhead, Teardrop Stem, 9 In.	225.00
Cut Glass, Compote, Hobstars, Cane Blaze, Rayed Base, 10 X 8 In.	170.00
Cut Glass, Compote, Intaglio Engraved Floral & Leaf, Tuthill, 4 1/2 In.	48.00
Cut Glass, Compote, Intaglio Sunflower, 9 1/4 X 8 1/4 In.	300.00
Cut Glass, Compote, Jelly, Hobstar, Strawberry Diamond, & Fan, 9 In., Pair	450.00
Cut Glass, Compote, Jelly, Hobstars, 6 1/2 X 4 In.	95.00
Cut Glass, Compote, Jelly, Twisted Hollow Stem	40.00
Cut Glass, Compote, Lacy & Bright Cut, Pedestal, American, 8 1/2 In.	75.00
Cut Glass, Compote, Pinwheel, Strawberry Diamond, & Fan, Star Base, 5 In.	50.00
Cut Glass, Compote, Salesman's Sample, 2 1/2 In.	60.00
Cut Glass, Compote, Sawtooth, Salesman's Sample, 2 1/2 X 1 1/2 In.	60.00
Cut Glass, Compote, Tall Stem With Teardrop, Hawkes, 7 1/4 In.High	185.00
Cut Glass, Compote, Viscaria, Teardrop Stem, Pairpoint, 8 In.	65.00
Cut Glass, Compote, Zippered Prism, Stemmed, Rayed Base, 9 In.	130.00
Cut Glass, Console Set, Dark Blue, Footed Bowl, 11 1/2 In. Candles, 3 Piece	375.00

Cut Glass, **Cordial**, Paneled Stems Become Flutes At Bowl, Teardrop Stem 7.50
Cut Glass, **Creamer**, Hobstar & Fan, American 35.00
Cut Glass, **Cruet**, Daisy & Thumbprint, 6 In. 25.00
Cut Glass, **Cruet**, Deep Claret Cut To Clear, Applied Clear Handle, 8 In. 55.00
Cut Glass, **Cruet**, Faceted Stopper, Oval Bull's-Eyes, Paneled Neck, 6 In. 25.50
Cut Glass, **Cruet**, Hobstar, Crosshatching, & Fan, Notched Handle, 6 In., Pair 145.00
Cut Glass, **Cruet**, Hobstars, 5 1/2 In. 45.00
Cut Glass, **Cruet**, Hollow Stopper, Hobstar, Fine Cut, & Miter, 11 In. 55.00
Cut Glass, **Cruet**, Oil & Vinegar, Engraved Floral, Sterling Stopper, 2 Lips 22.50
Cut Glass, **Cruet**, Oil & Vinegar, Etched Floral & Leaf, Hawkes, 1916, 8 In. 85.00
Cut Glass, **Cruet**, Pinwheel, Fan, & Prism, 3 Lip, Diamond Stopper, 7 In. 75.00
Cut Glass, **Cruet**, Teardrop Stopper, Strawberry Diamond & Fan, 8 In. 22.50
Cut Glass, **Cruet**, Vinegar, Middlesex, Sterling Stopper, Notched Neck 59.00
Cut Glass, **Cup**, Loving, Geometric Cutting, 3 Handles, Silver Rim, 5 X 4 In. 235.00
Cut Glass, **Cup**, Nut, Kalana Lily, Pedestal, Dorflinger, 2 1/2 In. 22.50
Cut Glass, **Cup**, Punch, Cane, Diamond, & Star, Hobstar Base 20.50
Cut Glass, **Cup**, Punch, Chain Hobstar, Vesica, & Fine Cut 20.00
Cut Glass, **Cup**, Punch, Notched Prism & Bull's-Eye, American 15.00
Cut Glass, **Cup**, Punch, Strawberry & Fan, Applied Curled Handle 15.00
Cut Glass, **Decanter**, Amethyst To Clear, Brilliant Period, 14 In. 135.00
Cut Glass, **Decanter**, Ball Shape, Hobstars & Fans, 11 1/2 In.High 145.00
Cut Glass, **Decanter**, Brandy, Czechoslovakia, C.1885, 8 In., Pair 88.00
Cut Glass, **Decanter**, Bulbous Base, Hobstars, Hobnail Diamonds, 12 1/2 In. 195.00
Cut Glass, **Decanter**, Captain's, Flat Bottom, American 150.00
Cut Glass, **Decanter**, Cobalt, Crosshatched Drape & Swag & Bull's-Eye, 15 In. 250.00
Cut Glass, **Decanter**, Double Lozenge, Ball Stopper, 12 In. 110.00
Cut Glass, **Decanter**, Faceted Stopper, Gadroons, English, C.1790, 11 In., Pair 110.00
Cut Glass, **Decanter**, Faceted Stopper, Notched Handle, Shamrock, 13 In. 100.00
Cut Glass, **Decanter**, Hobstar Diamond Point Cane & Blaze, Panels, 15 In. 225.00
Cut Glass, **Decanter**, Honey Amber, Ducks In Water & Cattails, 15 In. 45.00
Cut Glass, **Decanter**, Mushroom Stopper, Waterford, 13 In. 75.00
Cut Glass, **Decanter**, Nailhead, 13 1/2 In. 100.00
Cut Glass, **Decanter**, Ship's, Harvard, Floral, & Leaf, Prisms Handle, Ring Neck 145.00
Cut Glass, **Decanter**, St.Louis Pattern, Double Fans, 11 1/2 In.High 150.00
Cut Glass, **Decanter**, Sunburst, Bulbous Base, 12 In. 225.00
Cut Glass, **Decanter**, Thumbprint, Amber To Clear, 12 1/2 In. 80.00
Cut Glass, **Decanter**, Wine, Emerald Flashed, Floral Sprays, 12 1/2 In. 65.00
Cut Glass, **Decanter**, Wine, Green To Clear, Grape, Leaf, & Thumbprint, 13 In. 65.00
Cut Glass, **Decanter**, Wine, Hobstar & Jacob's Ladder, Thumbprint Stopper 75.00
Cut Glass, **Decanter**, Wine, Mushroom Stopper, Waterford 75.00
Cut Glass, **Dish**, Candy, Harvard Cuttings, Rectangular, 7 1/2 X 1 1/4 In. 65.00
Cut Glass, **Dish**, Candy, Hobstar & Cane, 2 Handled, 4 Sections, 9 In. 95.00
Cut Glass, **Dish**, Candy, Square, Clear Buttons, Russian, 5 3/4 X 1 3/4 In. 85.00
Cut Glass, **Dish**, Caviar, Gold-Washed Sterling Chatillon Lid, Hawkes 285.00
Cut Glass, **Dish**, Cheese, Covered, Hobstars 365.00
Cut Glass, **Dish**, Cheese, Dome Top, Hobstar & Oval Sunburst, 9 1/4 In. 325.00
Cut Glass, **Dish**, Cheese, Harvard & Cornflower 150.00
Cut Glass, **Dish**, Dessert, Copper Wheel Holly & Berries, Libbey, 7 In. 54.50
Cut Glass, **Dish**, Heart Shape, 7 X 6 In. 49.00
Cut Glass, **Dish**, Hobstar & Finecut, 4 Section, 2 Handles, 7 In. 75.00
Cut Glass, **Dish**, Hobstar, Cane, & Feathered Fan, Handled, 4 Sections, 11 In. 160.00
Cut Glass, **Dish**, Mint, Square, Libbey, 5 1/2 In. 95.00
Cut Glass, **Dish**, Olive, G.C.Co., 7 1/2 In. 36.00
Cut Glass, **Dish**, Olive, Hobstar, Fan, & Strawberry Diamond, 8 In. 28.75
Cut Glass, **Dish**, Olive, Thistles, Deep, 8 X 2 In. 32.50
Cut Glass, **Dish**, Pickle, Oblong, Brilliant Cut, G.C.Co., 6 1/4 In. 27.00
Cut Glass, **Dish**, Pickle, Tapered Ends, Brilliant Cut, Maple Leaf, 7 1/4 In. 35.00
Cut Glass, **Dram Glass**, Funnel Bowl, Diamond & Flute, Stem, C.1750 .... 25.00
Cut Glass, **Egg**, Easter, Russia, Faceted Diamonds, C.1890, 4 In. 150.00
Cut Glass, **Eggcup**, Stars, 2 1/2 In. 20.00
Cut Glass, **Epergne**, 3 Sections, Engraved Grape Leaves, C.1850, 18 In. 115.00
Cut Glass, **Ferner**, Oval Shape, Harvard, 4 Feet, 9 X 7 X 3 3/4 In. 75.00
Cut Glass, **Ferner**, Pinwheels, Stars, & Fans, 8 1/2 X 4 In.High 100.00
Cut Glass, **Flask**, Lady's, Stopper & Cap, 1/2 Pint 75.00
Cut Glass, **Flip**, Dutch Diamond Bottom, Engraved Floral Top, St.Louis, C.1776 .... 175.00
Cut Glass, **Flower Center**, Hobstar & Strawberry Diamond, Clarke, 23 In. 145.00

Cut Glass, Flower Center, Hobstar, Fan, Hobnail, & Strawberry Diamond, 6 In.	195.00
Cut Glass, Flower Center, Hobstars, Fluted Neck, 10 In.	165.00
Cut Glass, Flower Center, Pinwheel & Fan, Salesman's Sample, 3 1/2 In.	48.00
Cut Glass, Goblet, Cranberry To Clear, Pineapple, Clear Stem	25.00
Cut Glass, Goblet, Diamonds, 6 In.	18.00
Cut Glass, Goblet, Engraved Swirling Floral, Paper Thin, Hawkes	38.50
Cut Glass, Goblet, Floral, Fry	18.00
Cut Glass, Goblet, Footed, Trefoil, Star Cut Base, Signed Hawkes, 6 In.	23.00
Cut Glass, Goblet, Hobnail, Knobbed Teardrop Stem, American, 7 In.	75.00
Cut Glass, Goblet, Pinwheel, Diamond, & Fan, Long Stem, 7 1/4 In.	70.00
Cut Glass, Goblet, Russia, Engraved Elizabeth Petrovna Monogram, C.1741	325.00
Cut Glass, Goblet, Russian, 6 In.	125.00
Cut Glass, Goblet, Strawberry Diamond & Fan, Notched Stem, Star Base	35.00
Cut Glass, Goblet, Strawberry Diamond, Crosscut Diamond, & Fan, Notched Stem	30.00
Cut Glass, Goblet, 24 Point Star Base, Hoare	53.75
Cut Glass, Hair Receiver, Cut Cover, 3 Hobstars & 3 Pinwheels	69.00
Cut Glass, Hair Receiver, Elongated Thumbprint, Floral, Sterling Lid	35.00
Cut Glass, Hair Receiver, Harvard, Flowers & Leaves, 3 1/2 X 4 In.	30.00
Cut Glass, Heart, Hobstar Center, Strawberry Diamond & Fan, 7 In.	85.00
Cut Glass, Highball Glass, Albany, Flared Rim, Meriden	65.00
Cut Glass, Inkwell, Blue, Hinged, Brass Collar, 2 3/8 In.	42.00
Cut Glass, Inkwell, Hinged Sterling Silver Top	25.00
Cut Glass, Jar, Biscuit, Diamond-Shaped Finial, Square, 9 In.	155.00
Cut Glass, Jar, Cookie, Middlesex, Sterling Rim, Dorflinger, 6 1/2 In.	500.00
Cut Glass, Jar, Covered, Monarch, 6 In.	95.00
Cut Glass, Jar, Covered, Strawberry Diamond & Fan, Round, 6 1/2 X 3 1/4 In.	63.00
Cut Glass, Jar, Cracker, Barrel Shape, Floral, Star, & Fan, Silver Fittings	85.00
Cut Glass, Jar, Ginger, Ruby Cut To Clear	68.50
Cut Glass, Jar, Marmalade, Sterling Lid, Geometrics, Rayed Under Foot	55.00
Cut Glass, Jar, Mustard, Faceted Finial, Notched & Serrated Prisms	28.00
Cut Glass, Jar, Mustard, Silver Collar & Lid, Strawberry & Fan, American	25.00
Cut Glass, Jar, Powder, Emerald Cut To Clear, Flute & Bull's-Eye, 3 In.	75.00
Cut Glass, Jar, Powder, Hobstar On Lid, Hobstars, 5 X 3 In.	95.00
Cut Glass, Jar, Powder, Hobstars & Geometrics, 4 X 6 1/4 In.	40.00
Cut Glass, Jar, Powder, Kirk & Son Silver Top	40.00
Cut Glass, Jar, Powder, Sterling Cover, Embossed, Scrolled, 3 3/4 In.	35.00
Cut Glass, Jar, Sachet, Strawberry Diamond, Sterling Top, Unger Bros., 2 In.	25.00
Cut Glass, Jar, Silver Lid, Hobstar, Crosshatching, & Bull's-Eye	225.00
Cut Glass, Jar, Strawberry Diamond & Fan, 6 3/4 In.	75.00
Cut Glass, Jar, Sweetmeat, Allover Diamond Point, Thumbprint, Pairpoint	145.00
Cut Glass, Jar, Tobacco, Crosscut Diamond & Fan, Sterling Lid, 1896, 6 In.	250.00
Cut Glass, Jar, 12 Panels, Starred Base, Sterling Cover, 2 1/2 In.	18.50
Cut Glass, Jardiniere, Hobstars, Pinwheels, Fans, 8 X 9 In.	185.00
Cut Glass, Jug, Catsup, Beaded Vesicas, Crosshatching, Cane, Diamond	95.00
Cut Glass, Jug, Cider, Moon, Comet, & Hobstar, American	114.00
Cut Glass, Jug, Claret, German, Etched Grapevine, Silver Mount, C.1850, 13 In.	237.50
Cut Glass, Jug, Claret, Silver Plate, 10 1/2 In.	240.00
Cut Glass, Jug, Water, Tumble-Up, Ruby Overlay, Thumbprint & Floral, 8 In.	65.00
Cut Glass, Jug, Wine, Stars, Silver Mounted, E.& J.Barnard, 1860, 15 In.	450.00
Cut Glass, Knife Rest, Ball Ends With Star, Paneled Center, 4 1/2 In.	18.50
Cut Glass, Knife Rest, Checkered Diamond, 4 1/2 In.Long	25.00
Cut Glass, Knife Rest, Faceted Cutting, Ball Ends, 4 1/2 In.	17.50
Cut Glass, Knife Rest, Faceted Ends, 3 In.Long	25.00
Cut Glass, Knife Rest, Faceted, 5 1/2 In.	15.00
Cut Glass, Knife Rest, Fan, Strawberry & Diamond, 5 1/2 In.	28.00
Cut Glass, Knife Rest, Hourglass Shape, Hallmarked Silver Bands On Ends	25.00
Cut Glass, Knife Rest, Knob Ends, Hawkes, 4 In.	22.00
Cut Glass, Knife Rest, Lapidary Cut, 4 1/2 In.	24.00
Cut Glass, Knife Rest, Master, Faceted Ends, 5 1/2 In., Pair	49.00
Cut Glass, Knife Rest, Master, Hobstar & Strawberry Diamond, 5 1/2 In.	38.00
Cut Glass, Knife Rest, Master, Hobstar Ends, Strawberry Diamond, 5 1/2 In.	38.00
Cut Glass, Knife Rest, Signed Hawkes, Ball Ends	35.00
Cut Glass, Knife Rest, St.Louis Diamond Knobs, Notched Prisms Center, 5 In.	35.00
Cut Glass, Knife Rest, Starred Ends With Teardrop In Each	45.00
Cut Glass, Knife Rest, Step Cutting On Ends, 5 1/2 In.	28.00
Cut Glass, Ladle, Egginton, Silver Handle & Bowl, Pairpoint, 1899, 16 1/2 In.	225.00

Cut Glass, Lamp Base, Bedroom, Leaf & Cosmos, Prisms, Notched Stem, 12 In. 50.00
   Cut Glass, Lamp, see Lamp
Cut Glass, Liqueur Set, Silver Overlay, Brown To Green, Dorflinger, 8 Piece 450.00
Cut Glass, Liqueur, Plain Bowl, Cut Stems, Star Cut Base, Hawkes, Set Of 6 .... 65.00
Cut Glass, Muffineer, Domed Silver Top 48.00
Cut Glass, Muffineer, Engraved Floral & Leaf, Silver Plate Top, 7 In. 26.00
Cut Glass, Muffineer, Paneled, Ferns, Sterling Top, English 37.50
Cut Glass, Muffineer, Paneled, Flares Out To 8 Point Base, Silver Lid, 6 In. 27.00
Cut Glass, Muffineer, Ruby To Clear, Brass Top 75.00
Cut Glass, Muffineer, Silver Top, Waterford 65.00
Cut Glass, Muffineer, 5 3/4 In.High 85.00
   Cut Glass, Napkin Ring, see Napkin Ring
Cut Glass, Nappy, Arc Handled, 9 In. 44.00
Cut Glass, Nappy, Buzz Star, Hobstar, & Zippered Fan, Handled, 6 In. 50.00
Cut Glass, Nappy, Divided, Hobstars, Crosscut, 2 Handles, Hoare, 7 X 1 1/2 In. 95.00
Cut Glass, Nappy, Double Handled, Hobstar & Fan, Salesman's Sample, American 50.00
Cut Glass, Nappy, Floral & Button, 2 Handled, 8 In. 52.50
Cut Glass, Nappy, Floral & Leaf, Irving, 5 In. 39.50
Cut Glass, Nappy, Frosted Sides, Elongated Thumbprint & Star, Hawkes, 6 In. 55.00
Cut Glass, Nappy, Harvard & Etched Floral, Handled, 7 1/2 In. 25.00
Cut Glass, Nappy, Harvard Border, Comet Base, Handled, Round, 7 In. 39.00
Cut Glass, Nappy, Heart Shape, Loop Handle, Serrated Edges, 9 In. 43.00
Cut Glass, Nappy, Heart Shape, Strawberry, Hawkes, 7 3/4 X 6 In. 130.00
Cut Glass, Nappy, Hobstar & Fan, Hawkes, 6 In. 49.50
Cut Glass, Nappy, Hobstars, Clover Shape, Stepped Handle 35.00
Cut Glass, Nappy, Joan, Handled, Straus, 6 In.Diameter 75.00
Cut Glass, Nappy, Lacy & Hobstars, 2 Handles, 8 1/2 In. 45.00
Cut Glass, Nappy, Rose & Cane, Scalloped Edge, 6 In. 22.50
Cut Glass, Nappy, Strawberry Diamonds, Hobstars, Scalloped Edge 38.00
Cut Glass, Nappy, Triangular, Pinwheels, Hobstar, Fans 30.00
Cut Glass, Perfume, Cane, Hinged Silver Plate Cap With Leaf, 3 In. 21.00
Cut Glass, Perfume, Straight Side, Clear Button Cane, 6 In.High 75.00
Cut Glass, Pitcher, Buttermilk, Deep Cuttings, Hawkes, 8 1/2 In. 165.00
Cut Glass, Pitcher, Cider, Hobstar & Crosscut Diamond, Star Base, 7 In. 140.00
Cut Glass, Pitcher, Cider, Maple Leaf, 7 1/2 In. 75.00
Cut Glass, Pitcher, Claret, Hobstar, Diamond, & Fan, Double Notched, 12 In. 180.00
Cut Glass, Pitcher, Cornflower & Leaf, Double Cut Handle, 9 In. 49.00
Cut Glass, Pitcher, Diamond & Button, 5 In.High 38.00
Cut Glass, Pitcher, Flora, International Silver Co., 10 In. 110.00
Cut Glass, Pitcher, Floral, Leaf, Crosshatched Diamond, & Star, 8 In. 80.00
Cut Glass, Pitcher, Harvard & Stepped, Superior Blank, Hawkes, 9 In. 175.00
Cut Glass, Pitcher, Harvard, Floral, & Leaf, Prismed Handle, 7 In. 60.00
Cut Glass, Pitcher, Hobstar, Crosshatching, Star, & Fan, 8 In. 115.00
Cut Glass, Pitcher, Hobstar, Diamond, & Cane, 13 In. 95.00
Cut Glass, Pitcher, Hobstars, 36 Point Star Base, Notched Handle, 9 3/4 In. 85.00
Cut Glass, Pitcher, Intaglio Thistle Cutting, Star Base, 8 X 5 In. 225.00
Cut Glass, Pitcher, Lemonade, Zipper, Floral Sterling Top, Applied Handle 80.00
Cut Glass, Pitcher, Milk, Ruby & Clear Buttons, Notched Handle, 5 In. 175.00
Cut Glass, Pitcher, Milk, Russian, Starred Buttons, 4 3/4 In. 375.00
Cut Glass, Pitcher, Milk, Squatty, Brilliant Cut 265.00
Cut Glass, Pitcher, Monarch, Bulbous, Hoare, 9 In. 190.00
Cut Glass, Pitcher, Notched Handle, 8 In. 48.50
Cut Glass, Pitcher, Prism & Bull's-Eye, 32 Point Hobstar Base, 9 1/2 In. 150.00
Cut Glass, Pitcher, Russian, Barrel Shape, 7 In. 625.00
Cut Glass, Pitcher, Squat, Hawkes, 5 3/8 In. 150.00
Cut Glass, Pitcher, Water, Ball Shape, Hobstars, Fans, Hawkes, 8 X 6 In. 150.00
Cut Glass, Pitcher, Water, Brunswick, Hawkes, 9 In. 145.00
Cut Glass, Pitcher, Water, Festoon & Hobstar, Hawkes 125.00
Cut Glass, Pitcher, Water, Flashed Star & Fan, Thumbprint Base, 8 In. 160.00
Cut Glass, Pitcher, Water, Harvard Bottom, Floral Top 60.00
Cut Glass, Pitcher, Water, Intaglio Sunflower, 12 1/4 In. 250.00
Cut Glass, Pitcher, Water, Pinwheel, Fan, & Crosshatching, 16 Point Star Base 87.50
Cut Glass, Pitcher, Water, Primrose, Tuthill, 9 1/2 In.High 140.00
Cut Glass, Pitcher, Water, Silsbee, Pairpoint, 1910, 8 In. 89.50
Cut Glass, Pitcher, Water, Star & Diamond, Double-Notched Handle, 10 In. 95.00
Cut Glass, Pitcher, Water, Swirling Star & Fan, Notched Handle 80.00

Cut Glass, Planter, Miter & Silver Diamond, Dorflinger, 9 1/2 X 3 In.	85.00
Cut Glass, Plate, Beverly, 9 In.	95.00
Cut Glass, Plate, Bonbon, Aberdeen Type, 6 Sided, Scalloped, 6 1/2 In.	32.00
Cut Glass, Plate, Bread, Blown-In Sides, Hobstar, Cane, & Vesica, 12 X 3 In.	210.00
Cut Glass, Plate, Bread, Flora, International Silver Co., 12 3/4 X 5 1/2 In.	115.00
Cut Glass, Plate, Cake, Clarke, 9 3/4 In.	275.00
Cut Glass, Plate, Cake, Paperweight Base, Signed Bergen, 8 In.Diameter	125.00
Cut Glass, Plate, Diamonds, 8 1/2 In.	15.00
Cut Glass, Plate, Engraved Greek Key Rim, 36 Point Star, Sterling Rim, 8 In.	25.00
Cut Glass, Plate, Floral & Leaf, 6 1/2 In.	10.00
Cut Glass, Plate, Fortuna, Maple City, 9 1/2 In.	140.00
Cut Glass, Plate, Hobstar & Cane, American, 6 In.	25.00
Cut Glass, Plate, Hobstar & Intaglio Strawberry, Hawkes, 7 In.	95.00
Cut Glass, Plate, Hobstar Chain At Edge, Whirling Star Center, 7 In.	32.00
Cut Glass, Plate, Hobstar, Strawberry Diamond, & Crosscut, Scalloped, 10 In.	65.00
Cut Glass, Plate, Hobstar, Vesica Of Notched Prism & Fan, Maple Leaf, 7 In.	85.00
Cut Glass, Plate, Ice Cream, Wide Rim	8.00
Cut Glass, Plate, Intaglio, Hawkes, 7 In.	55.00
Cut Glass, Plate, Large, Medium, & Small Hobstars, 9 1/2 In.	95.00
Cut Glass, Plate, Russian Rayed Buttons, 7 1/4 In.	95.00
Cut Glass, Plate, Sandwich, Hawkes	275.00
Cut Glass, Plate, Scalloped Edge, 9 1/2 In.	55.00
Cut Glass, Plate, Sheraton 6 Diamond Shape, Hobstars, Hawkes, 9 3/4 In.	75.00
Cut Glass, Plate, Tuthill, 8 In.	75.00
Cut Glass, Plate, Wedgemere, Libbey, 7 In.	125.00
Cut Glass, Plate, Wheat Design At Edge, 8 1/2 In.	10.00
Cut Glass, Platter, Etched Flying Bird, Peony, & Butterfly, Footed, 9 3/8 In.	47.50
Cut Glass, Punch Set, Hobstar, Strawberry Diamond, & Russian, 10 Piece	2400.00
Cut Glass, Relish, Brilliant Cut, American, 7 1/2 In.	20.00
Cut Glass, Relish, Chrysanthemum, Blank, Hawkes, 12 X 6 X 2 In.	165.00
Cut Glass, Relish, Daisies & Leaves, Sawtooth Edge, 7 1/2 X 4 1/2 In.	18.00
Cut Glass, Relish, Divided, 2 Handled, 6 In.	35.00
Cut Glass, Relish, Harvard, 7 1/2 X 3 1/2 In.	85.00
Cut Glass, Relish, Hoare, Corning	55.00
Cut Glass, Relish, Iris Patterns, Handled, Hawkes, 6 In.	42.00
Cut Glass, Relish, Step Pattern, Silver Plate Cover, 3 In.	7.50
Cut Glass, Relish, Windmill Design, Leaves & Flowers, Serrated, 8 X 5 In.	35.00
Cut Glass, Relish, 2 Handled, Oval, 7 X 4 1/2 In.	40.00
Cut Glass, Rose Bowl, Chrysanthemum, Ribbed Top, 5 1/4 In.	135.00
Cut Glass, Rose Bowl, Harvard & Intaglio, 3 Legs, 8 X 6 1/4 In.	110.00
Cut Glass, Rose Bowl, Hobstar Medallions, Brilliant Period, American, 6 In.	75.00
Cut Glass, Rose Bowl, Hobstar, Crosscut Diamond, & Strawberry Diamond, 5 In.	95.00
Cut Glass, Rose Bowl, Hobstar, Vesica, & Fine Line, 19 In.	150.00 To 175.00
Cut Glass, Rose Bowl, Hobstars, 6 X 8 In.	55.00
Cut Glass, Rose Bowl, Strawberry Diamonds, 4 1/2 X 3 1/2 In.	85.00
Cut Glass, Rose Bowl, Wheeler, 6 X 4 In.	85.00
Cut Glass, Salt & Pepper, Brilliant Cut, Sterling Tops, Hawkes, 2 1/2 In.	32.00
Cut Glass, Salt & Pepper, Cut Tops	12.50
Cut Glass, Salt & Pepper, Intaglio Flowers, Sterling Tops, Libbey, 2 3/4 In.	40.00
Cut Glass, Salt & Pepper, Notched Prism, Sterling Tops, 3 1/4 In.	20.00
Cut Glass, Salt & Pepper, Sheraton Variation, Cut Tops, Hawkes, 3 1/4 In.	50.00
Cut Glass, Salt & Pepper, Sterling Silver Cap, 3 1/2 In.	12.50
Cut Glass, Salt Dip, Amber, Faceted, Round	9.50
Cut Glass, Salt Dip, Leaf & Star, Star Base, Serrated & Scalloped Edge	12.00
Cut Glass, Salt Dip, Pink, 6 Sided	9.50
Cut Glass, Salt, Boat Shape, Fine Cut Band, Pedestal, Notched Edge, Waterford	28.00
Cut Glass, Salt, Diamonds, Bucket Shape, Pair	30.00
Cut Glass, Salt, Individual, Harvard, Sterling Silver Spoon	16.00
Cut Glass, Salt, Intaglio Cutting, 1 1/2 In. Diameter At Base, Pair	10.00
Cut Glass, Salt, Master, Russian With Buttons, 3 1/4 In., Pair	200.00
Cut Glass, Salt, Master, Strawberry Diamond & Fan, 8 Point Star Base	75.00
Cut Glass, Saltshaker, Harvard, Star Bottom, Gold Washed Top	15.00
Cut Glass, Shade, Gaslight, Star, Fan, & Crosscut, 7 1/2 In. Diameter	65.00
Cut Glass, Shade, Oil Chandelier, Ribbed, Ruffled, Screw Top, 4 In.	5.00
Cut Glass, Shaker, Martini, Sterling Top, Hawkes	150.00
Cut Glass, Sherbet & Underplate, Calla Lily, Dorflinger	70.00

Cut Glass, Sign, Libbey, 2 Piece, 5 1/2 In.

Cut Glass, Sherbet, Kalana Chinese Daisies, Teardrop Stem, Dorflinger	15.00
Cut Glass, Sherbet, Kalana Poppy, Teardrop Stem, Dorflinger	15.00
Cut Glass, Sherry, Prism & Chain, Notched Stem, Rayed Base, 4 3/8 In.	25.00
Cut Glass, Sign, Libbey, 2 Piece, 5 1/2 In. .... *Illus*	425.00
Cut Glass, Spittoon, Cranberry To Clear, Bull's-Eye & Panel, 2 In.	125.00
Cut Glass, Spoon & Fork, Salad, Hobstar, Star, Fan, & Notching, Meriden Silver	275.00
Cut Glass, Spooner, Corinthian & Harvard Base, Scalloped & Serrated Rim	95.00
Cut Glass, Spooner, Harvard Cuttings, 2 Handled, American	150.00
Cut Glass, Sugar & Creamer, Allover Harvard Pattern	110.00
Cut Glass, Sugar & Creamer, Allover Hobstars, Notched Handles, Libbey	75.00
Cut Glass, Sugar & Creamer, Columbia, Harvard Border	75.00
Cut Glass, Sugar & Creamer, Daisy & Button	80.00
Cut Glass, Sugar & Creamer, Daisy & Criscross, Star Bases	30.00
Cut Glass, Sugar & Creamer, Frosted Iris, Signed Hawkes	225.00
Cut Glass, Sugar & Creamer, Harvard & Floral	70.00
Cut Glass, Sugar & Creamer, Hobstar & Zipper, 16 Point Star Bases	60.00
Cut Glass, Sugar & Creamer, Hobstar Band & Engraved Primrose	70.00
Cut Glass, Sugar & Creamer, Hobstar, 3 Vesicas, & Fine Line Cutting	145.00
Cut Glass, Sugar & Creamer, Hobstars, Double Cane Handle, American	70.00
Cut Glass, Sugar & Creamer, Hobstars, Prism Bottoms, Libbey	135.00
Cut Glass, Sugar & Creamer, Inverted Thumbprint & Hobstar	30.00
Cut Glass, Sugar & Creamer, Pedestal, Notched Handles	175.00
Cut Glass, Sugar & Creamer, Pinwheel & Harvard	67.50
Cut Glass, Sugar & Creamer, Pinwheel, Hobstar, & Intaglio Leaf, American	65.00
Cut Glass, Sugar & Creamer, Pinwheels	40.00
Cut Glass, Sugar & Creamer, Pinwheels, C.1913, 2 1/2 In.	136.50
Cut Glass, Sugar, Hobstars, Notched Prism Handles	18.00
Cut Glass, Sugar, Intaglio	15.00
Cut Glass, Sugar, Intaglio, Tuthill	55.00
Cut Glass, Sugar, Pedestal, Pinwheel & Hobstar, 2 Cut Handles, American	18.00
Cut Glass, Sugar, Pinwheel & Strawberry Diamond, 2 Handled, Squatty	38.00
Cut Glass, Sugar, Pinwheels, C.1913, 3 In.	55.00
Cut Glass, Sugar, Starred Buttons	24.00
Cut Glass, Syrup, Beaded Rim, Claw Lift	54.00
Cut Glass, Syrup, Diamond & Fan, Pewter Lid, 5 In.High	35.00
Cut Glass, Syrup, Individual, Etched & Cut, Sterling Top, Hawkes	30.00
Cut Glass, Syrup, Nine Vertical Rows Fine Line, Hawkes, 7 3/4 In.High	67.50
Cut Glass, Syrup, Silver Plate Lid	10.00
Cut Glass, Syrup, Sterling Silver Lid	75.00
Cut Glass, Syrup, Strawberry Diamond & Horizontal Step, Silver Fittings	88.00
Cut Glass, Tankard, Buzz & Chair Cane, Notched Handle, 10 In.High	85.00
Cut Glass, Tankard, Buzz, Hobnail, & Inverted Heart, Notched Handle, 9 In.	155.00
Cut Glass, Tankard, Buzz, Star, Strawberry Diamond, Prism, & Fan, 11 In.	145.00
Cut Glass, Tankard, Finecut, 11 In.	110.00
Cut Glass, Tankard, Floral & Leaf, 12 In.	70.00

Cut Glass, Tankard, Hobstar, Pinwheel, & Leaf, Fluted Spout, American, 9 In. 77.00
Cut Glass, Tankard, Hobstar, Pinwheel, & Sunburst, American, 9 1/2 In. 65.00
Cut Glass, Tankard, Intaglio Floral & Butterfly, Notched Rim, 10 In. 120.00
Cut Glass, Tankard, Pinwheel & Hobstar, American, 8 7/8 In. 70.00
Cut Glass, Tankard, Pinwheel & Hobstar, Fluted Spout, 9 In.High 75.00
Cut Glass, Tankard, Pinwheel & Hobstar, Fluted Under Spout, 9 In. 75.00
Cut Glass, Tankard, Russian, Intaglio Floral, Hobstar, & Leaf, 10 In. 125.00
Cut Glass, Tea Caddy, Hobstars, Lions On Silver Frame, Ivory Handle 550.00
Cut Glass, Teapot, Flutes, Greek Key, Floral Chain, Sinclaire, 9 In. 1250.00
Cut Glass, Tooth Powder Dispenser, 10 Panels, Sterling Cover, 3 3/4 In. 22.00
Cut Glass, Toothpick, Corset Shape, Deep Cuttings, 2 1/2 In. 24.00
Cut Glass, Toothpick, Icicle, 2 1/2 In. 25.00
Cut Glass, Toothpick, Serrated Top, Pinwheel & Hobstar, Cut Under Base 24.00
Cut Glass, Toothpick, Star, Crosshatching, & Notched Column, Handled, 2 In. 22.00
Cut Glass, Toothpick, Strawberry Diamond & Fan, Square Beveled Base 30.00
Cut Glass, Toothpick, Vertical Notch & Pinwheel 22.50
Cut Glass, Tray, Chain Of Hobstars, Engraved Floral, Hawkes, 13 X 9 In. 175.00
Cut Glass, Tray, Condiment, Hawkes 37.50
Cut Glass, Tray, Engraved, Silver Rim, Hawkes, 11 3/4 In. Diameter 135.00
Cut Glass, Tray, Harvard, Small Button, Scalloped, Oval, 8 1/4 X 5 1/2 In. 95.00
Cut Glass, Tray, Ice Cream, Chain Of Hobstars, Vesica, Strawberry, 14 X 8 In. 190.00
Cut Glass, Tray, Ice Cream, Harvard, Hobstar, Diamond, & Fan, American, 18 In. 375.00
Cut Glass, Tray, Ice Cream, Hobstar & Vesica, 14 X 8 1/4 In. 125.00
Cut Glass, Tray, Ice Cream, J.Hoare Co., Corning, 12 X 8 In. 200.00
Cut Glass, Tray, Ice Cream, Strawberry & Fan 185.00
Cut Glass, Tray, Ice Cream, Strawberry & Fan, Oblong 175.00
Cut Glass, Tray, Oval, Harvard, Scalloped Rim, 8 1/4 X 5 1/2 In. 95.00
Cut Glass, Tray, Peaches & Cherries, Oval, 10 1/2 In.Diameter 165.00
Cut Glass, Tray, Rectangular, Vesica Pattern, Hawkes, 5 X 11 X 1 3/4 In. 68.00
Cut Glass, Tray, Venetian, 9 X 5 3/4 In. 235.00
Cut Glass, Tub, Ice, Hobstar & Intaglio Floral, Star Base, Signet, 7 In. 185.00
Cut Glass, Tumble-Up, Intaglio Roses 55.00
Cut Glass, Tumbler, Brilliant Period, Libbey 22.00
Cut Glass, Tumbler, Cane, Hobstars, & Fans, 4 In.High, Set Of 6 .... 150.00
Cut Glass, Tumbler, Chain Of 8-Pointed Hobstar & Flute, Hawkes 25.00
Cut Glass, Tumbler, Crosscut Diamond & Fan 10.00
Cut Glass, Tumbler, Diamond & Fan 10.00
Cut Glass, Tumbler, Double Lozenge 22.50
Cut Glass, Tumbler, Engraved, Stag, Doe, & Lion Holding Flag, European 60.00
Cut Glass, Tumbler, Hobstar, Fan & Crosshatching, American 24.10
Cut Glass, Tumbler, Hobstar, Star, Fan, & Crosshatching, Star & Circle Signed 17.50
Cut Glass, Tumbler, Hobstars & Fan, 3 1/2 In. 15.00
Cut Glass, Tumbler, Intaglio Grape, 5 In. 45.00
Cut Glass, Tumbler, Pinwheel & Fan 5.00
Cut Glass, Tumbler, Pinwheel, Hobstar, & Geometric 12.00
Cut Glass, Tumbler, Pinwheel, Tapered 25.00
Cut Glass, Tumbler, Pinwheels, American 27.50
Cut Glass, Tumbler, Russian Buttons, Star Base, 4 In. 70.00
Cut Glass, Tumbler, Russian, 4 In. 65.00
Cut Glass, Tumbler, Strawberry Diamond 14.65
Cut Glass, Tumbler, Strawberry Diamond, Fan, & Star, American 29.50
Cut Glass, Tumbler, Sunburst 35.00
Cut Glass, Tumbler, Sunburst & Arc, American 21.00
Cut Glass, Tumbler, Three Diamonds & Feather 15.00
Cut Glass, Tumbler, Whiskey, Applied Raspberry Prunts On Sides 15.00
Cut Glass, Tumbler, Whiskey, Double, Lozenge, 2 3/4 In. 18.00
Cut Glass, Vase, Basket Weave & Floral, Hawkes, 10 In. 85.00
Cut Glass, Vase, Brilliant Cut, Hoare, 15 In. 225.00
Cut Glass, Vase, Bud, Russian, Clear Button, 6 In.High 75.00
Cut Glass, Vase, Bud, Strawberry Diamond & Notched Flute, American, 6 In. 21.00
Cut Glass, Vase, Bulbous, Intaglio Floral, Signed Libbey, 10 In.High 115.00
Cut Glass, Vase, Carnation, Gravic, Hawkes, 15 X 5 1/2 In. 225.00
Cut Glass, Vase, Chalice Shape, Hobstars, 12 In. 275.00
Cut Glass, Vase, Corset Shape, Gravic Iris, Hawkes, 8 In. 275.00
Cut Glass, Vase, Corset Shape, Scalloped Top, 12 In. 175.00
Cut Glass, Vase, Cosmos & Overall Cutting, Flared Top, 14 In.High 215.00

Cut Glass, Vase, Cranberry Cased, Diamond & Fan, 16 Point Star Vase, 10 In. 70.00
Cut Glass, Vase, Cranberry To Clear, Engraved Floral, Footed, 10 In. 18.50
Cut Glass, Vase, Daisy & Cane, Corset Shape, 11 In. 50.00
Cut Glass, Vase, Diamonds, Fan Top, 9 In. 35.00
Cut Glass, Vase, Double Harvard Borders, Daisy & Leaves, 11 3/4 In. 75.00
Cut Glass, Vase, Emerald To Clear, Nailhead & Crosscut Fan, 10 1/4 In. 95.00
Cut Glass, Vase, Engraved & Cut, Footed, Hawkes, 10 1/4 In. 125.00
Cut Glass, Vase, Engraved Floral & Leaf, Crosshatching, Libbey, 12 In. 95.00
Cut Glass, Vase, Engraved Lily Of The Valley, Footed, Sinclaire, 15 3/8 In. 135.00
Cut Glass, Vase, Etched & Cut, 10 X 6 In. 110.00
Cut Glass, Vase, Etched Design, Hawkes, 8 In. 50.00
Cut Glass, Vase, Etched, Sterling Fluted Rim, 9 In. 13.50
Cut Glass, Vase, Fan, Engraved & Etched, Green Base, Hawkes, 7 1/2 In. 40.00
Cut Glass, Vase, Finecut Floral, Tapered, 10 In. 95.00
Cut Glass, Vase, Floral, Daisy Band With Honeycomb, Flutes, Hawkes, 9 In. 95.00
Cut Glass, Vase, Floriform, American, 12 In. 125.00
Cut Glass, Vase, Footed, Almy-Thomas, 1903/17, 12 1/2 In., Pair 185.00
Cut Glass, Vase, Hobstar, Vesica, & Flute, Star Base, 8 1/2 In. 75.00
Cut Glass, Vase, Hourglass, Middlesex, Notched Prism, Dorflinger, 12 In. 285.00
Cut Glass, Vase, Intaglio, Horn Top, 26 In.High 100.00
Cut Glass, Vase, Millicent, Hawkes, 9 1/2 In. 110.00
Cut Glass, Vase, Palm Leaf Fan, Hobstars, Facet Knob, 12 In. 215.00
Cut Glass, Vase, Rose, Brilliant Period, 8 1/2 In. 29.00
Cut Glass, Vase, St.Louis Diamond, Hobstar Base, Dorflinger, 16 X 6 In. 325.00
Cut Glass, Vase, Thistle, Silver Plate Stand, 4 1/2 In. 9.00
Cut Glass, Vase, Trumpet, Pinwheel & Russian Fan, Star Base, 10 In. 55.00
Cut Glass, Vase, Trumpet, Rambler Rose, 6 Panel Stem, Notched, 10 In. 55.00
Cut Glass, Vase, Tudor, 6 1/2 In. 37.00
Cut Glass, Vase, Vesica & Star, Engraved Butterfly & Floral, 11 1/2 In. 35.00
Cut Glass, Vase, Waterford, C.1910, 10 In., Pair 40.00
Cut Glass, Water Set, Brilliant Cut, Signed Clarke, 7 Piece 275.00
Cut Glass, Water Set, Buzz Stars, Fans, 6 Piece 175.00
Cut Glass, Water Set, Flying Bird, 5 Piece 225.00
Cut Glass, Water Set, Leaf & Floral, 11 Piece 100.00
Cut Glass, Water Set, Roxana, Dorflinger, 3 Piece 150.00
Cut Glass, Whiskey Set, Bright Cut, American, Brilliant Period, 6 Piece 155.00
Cut Glass, Whiskey Set, Diamond Stopper, Handled Decanter, 9 Piece 575.00
Cut Glass, Wine Set, Intaglio Tulips & Leaf Sprays, G.C.Co., 2 Piece 140.00
Cut Glass, Wine, Blown, Pittsburgh, Panel Cut Stem, Flute Top, C.1840 .... 16.00
Cut Glass, Wine, Cranberry To Clear, Lozenge & Crosshatching, Faceted Stem 95.00
Cut Glass, Wine, Crosscut Diamond & Fan, Zipper Stem, Rayed Base, Libbey 35.00
Cut Glass, Wine, Dutch Diamond, Libbey, 5 In. 14.00
Cut Glass, Wine, Edwardian Lady Center Panel, Multicolor, Lobmeyer 135.00
Cut Glass, Wine, Hobstar & Fern, Double Teardrop Stem, American, 8 1/2 In. 210.00
Cut Glass, Wine, Hobstar, V, & Fan, Knobbed Teardrop Stem, Libbey, Star Base 40.60
Cut Glass, Wine, Knob & Teardrop Panel, Hobstars & Blaze, Beading, 5 In.High 65.00
Cut Glass, Wine, Prism & Chain Variation, Notched Stems, Rayed Base 25.00
Cut Glass, Wine, Ruby To Clear, Crystal Cut Stem, 8 In. 25.00
Cut Glass, Wine, Ruby To Clear, Floral & Butterfly, Dated 1892 .... 20.00
Cut Glass, Wine, St.Louis Diamond, Vines & Flowers, Pairpoint, 5 1/2 In. 13.50
Cut Glass, Wine, Strawberry Diamond & Fan 15.00
Cut Glass, Wine, Strawberry Diamond, Zippercut Panel, Cranberry To Clear 65.00

> *Cut velvet is a special type of art glass made with two layers of blown glass, which shows a raised pattern. It usually had an acid finish or velvetlike texture. It was made by many glass factories during the late Victorian years.*

Cut Velvet, Creamer, Butterscotch, White Lining, Amber Handle, 4 1/4 In. 135.00
Cut Velvet, Tumbler, Blue, Diamond-Quilted Overlay Satin, White Lining 100.00
Cut Velvet, Tumbler, Pink, Diamond-Quilted 75.00
Cut Velvet, Tumbler, Tan 85.00
Cut Velvet, Tumbler, Yellow, Diamond-Quilted, Square Top 110.00
Cut Velvet, Vase, Blue, 6 In. 95.00
Cut Velvet, Vase, Butterscotch, Applied Camphor Acorns & Feet, 10 In. 215.00
Cut Velvet, Vase, Orchid, Ruffled Top, Bulbous Bottom, 9 In. 325.00
Cut Velvet, Vase, Stick, Mt.Washington, Deep Blue Over White, 7 In. 85.00

Cut Velvet, Water Set, Butterscotch, Diamond-Quilted, 8 In. Pitcher, 7 Piece 695.00
     D'Albret, Paperweight, see Paperweight, D'Albret
> *D'Argental was a French cameo glassmaker of the late Victorian period.*
> *The D'Argental factory made multi-layered, acid-cut cameo glass in*
> *France in the late 19th century. The glass is decorated with floral or*
> *scenic designs.*

D'Argental, Bowl, Cameo, Olive, Orange & Yellow Flowers & Leaves, 5 1/2 In 375.00
D'Argental, Bowl, Trees & Mountains, Gold, Apricot, & Chestnut, 2 7/8 In. 175.00
D'Argental, Lamp, Cameo, Signed, 18 In. 1350.00
D'Argental, Vase, Autumn Colors, 3 Layers, Signed, 24 In. 775.00
D'Argental, Vase, Houses & Landscape Scene On Red & Yellow, C.1900, 8 In. 375.00
D'Argental, Vase, Intaglio Leaves & Fireflies On Golden, 7 1/2 In. 595.00
D'Argental, Vase, Scenic, Brown, Russet, & Gold, 18 In. 850.00
     Daguerreotype, see Photography, Daguerreotype
     Danish Christmas Plate, see Collector, Plate
     Dant, see Bottle, Dant

Daum Nancy is the mark used by Auguste and Antonin Daum on pieces of French cameo glass made after 1875.

Daum Nancy, Ashtray, Heart Shape, French Writing & White Floral, Gold, Green 95.00
Daum Nancy, Beaker, Frosted, Lavender & Green Iris, C.1900, 3 1/2 In. 175.00
Daum Nancy, Bottle, Perfume, Reddish-Orange, Fruits & Leaves, 4 1/2 In. 475.00
Daum Nancy, Bottle, Scent, Frosted Amber, Spiderwebs, Fuchsias, 1900, 6 In. 140.00
Daum Nancy, Bowl, Autumn Colors, 2 Handles, 11 In. 450.00
Daum Nancy, Bowl, Etched Stylized Floral On Gilt, C.1925, 7 5/8 In. 70.00
Daum Nancy, Bowl, Green Cut To Orange & Yellow Sunset Scene, 6 In. 275.00
Daum Nancy, Bowl, Handled, Autumn Colors, Leaf & Berries, 11 X 4 In. 375.00
Daum Nancy, Bowl, Peacock's-Eyes On Blue To Purple, C.1900, 6 1/4 In. 650.00
Daum Nancy, Bowl, Red, Brown & Green Carving, 5 3/4 In. 225.00
Daum Nancy, Bowl, Silveria, Gold Foil Spatters, Orange Glass, 4 1/2 In. 55.00
Daum Nancy, Card Holder, Sunset, Water Scene, 3 Cuttings, 3 3/4 X 5 In. 265.00
Daum Nancy, Compote, Green, Black, & Orange, Leaves, Yellow Lined, 6 1/2 In. 425.00
Daum Nancy, Dish, Mint, Red Orange, Blue Green Yellow Interior, 2 1/4 In. 110.00
Daum Nancy, Jardiniere, Yellow & Red Lilies, Green Leaves, 6 X 8 1/4 In. 375.00
Daum Nancy, Lamp Base, Cameo Poppies, 4 Colors, 10 1/2 X 7 In. 475.00
Daum Nancy, Lamp Base, Light Green, Water Lilies, Metal Mounts, C.1900, 9 In. 125.00
Daum Nancy, Lamp, Dragonfly, Signed, 20 In. 2000.00
Daum Nancy, Lamp, Forest Scene Base, Sailing Scene Dome Shade, 10 In. 1100.00
Daum Nancy, Lamp, Grapes On Orange & Yellow Helmet Shade, C.1900, 20 In. 1100.00
Daum Nancy, Lamp, Orange Cameo, Deep Cutting, Signed, 18 In. 925.00
Daum Nancy, Liqueur Set, Enamel Grapes & Vines On Clear, C.1910, 7 Piece 375.00
Daum Nancy, Napkin Holder, Mushrooms On Yellow & Green, 3 1/4 X 4 In. 450.00
Daum Nancy, Napkin Holder, Mushrooms, Orange, Yellow, Brown, 3 1/4 In. 650.00
Daum Nancy, Night-Light, Rose Trees, Blue, Yellow, White, Silver Top, 8 In. 650.00
Daum Nancy, Planter, Mottled Green & Blue, 4 1/2 X 6 1/2 In. 195.00
Daum Nancy, Tumbler, Orange Berries & Yellow & Green On Yellow Green 245.00
Daum Nancy, Tumbler, Summer Scene, Green, 5 In.High 395.00
Daum Nancy, Tumbler, Winter Scene, Barrel Shape, Frosted Gold 225.00
Daum Nancy, Tumbler, Yellow Flowers On Green Leaves, White Ground, 5 In. 310.00
Daum Nancy, Vase, Baluster, Flaring Foot, Grapes & Vines On Oranges, 12 In. 400.00
Daum Nancy, Vase, Beaker Form, Opalescent, Enamel Wildflowers, C.1910, 5 In. 225.00
Daum Nancy, Vase, Black & Gold, Cut To Clear, Floral Design, 10 In. 275.00
Daum Nancy, Vase, Blown, Oranges, Majorelle, 15 In. 465.00
Daum Nancy, Vase, Brown Floral & Leaves On Yellow & Purple, 16 In. 300.00
Daum Nancy, Vase, Crystal, Signed Daum-France, 8 In. 30.00
Daum Nancy, Vase, Dark Green Leaves On Green, 6 In. 375.00
Daum Nancy, Vase, Enameled, Trees, 9 In. .... *Illus* 525.00
Daum Nancy, Vase, Fire Scene, 19 In.High 1450.00
Daum Nancy, Vase, Green Floral & Leaves On Orange & Yellow, 12 1/2 In. 350.00
Daum Nancy, Vase, Green Leaf & Branch On Hammered Matte, 9 In. 900.00
Daum Nancy, Vase, Green, Cameo, 8 X 3 In. 95.00
Daum Nancy, Vase, Lime Green & Yellow Ground, Rust Clouds, Sailboats, 5 In. 475.00
Daum Nancy, Vase, Mottled Orange, Iron Mounted, Rope Handles, C.1920, 6 In. 250.00
Daum Nancy, Vase, Olive Green & Cameo Leaves On Orange, Enamel, 2 In. 125.00
Daum Nancy, Vase, Orange & Purple, Bubbles, Signed, 3 In.High 65.00

Daum Nancy, Vase,
Wheel Carved Tulips,
C.1915, 9 1/4 In.

Daum Nancy, Vase,
Enameled, Trees, 9 In.
(See Page 136)

Daum Nancy, Vase, Paperweight, Cameo, Intaglio, Enamel Fish, C.1890, 16 In.	2100.00
Daum Nancy, Vase, Pumpkins In Ground, Green Leaves, 5 X 6 In.	400.00
Daum Nancy, Vase, Purple & Red Gladiola On Yellow Mottled Ground, 10 In.	380.00
Daum Nancy, Vase, Purple, White & Green, Enameled Violets, 3 In.High	195.00
Daum Nancy, Vase, River Scene On Mottled Yellow, C.1900, 4 3/4 In.	350.00
Daum Nancy, Vase, Salmon & Purple, Gilt Inclusions, C.1930, 4 1/2 In.	100.00
Daum Nancy, Vase, Scenic, Pink & Yellow Shades, 3 Color, 17 In.	335.00
Daum Nancy, Vase, Signed & Cross Of Lorraine, 21 In.	400.00
Daum Nancy, Vase, Silver Mounted, Cranberry, Green Hibiscus, C.1900, 4 In.	275.00
Daum Nancy, Vase, Spring Scenic On Blue, Enameled, 7 1/2 In.	425.00
Daum Nancy, Vase, Summer Scene, Green, Blue, & Yellow, 13 In.High	295.00
Daum Nancy, Vase, Sunset Scene, Mottled Peach & Yellow Frosted, 9 3/4 In.	335.00
Daum Nancy, Vase, Trumpet, Gray, Yellow, & Orange, Enamel Fruit, C.1910, 12 In.	160.00
Daum Nancy, Vase, Tulips On Hammered Gray, C.1895, 9 1/2 In.	500.00
Daum Nancy, Vase, Violets On Frosted To Purple, Enamel, Flattened, 2 In.	150.00
Daum Nancy, Vase, Wheel Carved Tulips, C.1915, 9 1/4 In. ....Illus	450.00
Daum Nancy, Vase, White, Avocado & Yellow Snapdragons, C.1900, 4 3/4 In.	250.00
Daum Nancy, Vase, Winter Scene, Cylinder, Blue Ground, 6 3/4 X 2 In.	195.00
Daum Nancy, Vase, Wooded Lakeshore Scenes, Sunset, Square, 4 5/8 In.	180.00
Daum Nancy, Vase, Yellow & Orange, Applied Maple Leaves & Webs, 1900, 14 In.	1600.00
Daum Nancy, Vase, Yellow, Rust, & Brown Water Lilies, 10 1/2 In.	375.00

DAVENPORT
LONGPORT
STAFFORDSHIRE

Davenport pottery and porcelain were made at the Davenport Factory in Longport, Staffordshire, England, from 1793 to 1887. Earthenwares, creamwares, porcelains, ironstone wares, and other products were made. Most of the pieces are marked with a form of the word Davenport.

Davenport, Cabaret Set, White, Blue Butterflies & Ivy, Gilt, C.1805, 10 Piece	150.00
Davenport, Cup Plate, Pearlware, Sepia Eagle Center, C.1805, 3 7/8 In.	225.00
Davenport, Plate, Cyprus, 9 In.	22.50
Davenport, Plate, Dessert, Songbird & Floral, Blue, Signed	10.00
Davenport, Plate, Genoa, Mulberry, 9 1/4 In.	19.50
Davenport, Plate, Luncheon, Allover Floral, C.1792, Set Of 8	195.00
Davenport, Plate, Raised Gold Border, 1850, 9 In.	9.00
Davenport, Plate, Scenic, Dark Blue, White Feathered Border, 9 In.	38.00
Davenport, Plate, Soup, Transfer Printed Oriental Shrubbery, C.1805, 9 In.	25.00
Davenport, Platter, Friburg, Blue Transfer, Octagonal, C.1848, 16 In.	25.00
Davenport, Platter, Meat, Oval, Blue Floral Bands, Birds, 16 1/2 X 13 In.	35.00
Davenport, Platter, Medium Blue, 20 1/2 X 15 1/4 In.	125.00
Davenport, Platter, Woman, Children, & Dog, Mulberry, C.1800, 10 1/2 X 8 In.	45.00
Davy Crockett, Chalk, Graphic Box, 12 Sticks	.65
Davy Crockett, Gun, Flintlock, Hard Plastic, 7 In.	3.50
Davy Crockett, Lunch Box & Thermos, Metal, Lithographed	7.50
Davy Crockett, Thermos, Tin Cup	3.00

*De Vez is a name found on special pieces of French cameo glass made by
the Cristallerie de Pantin about 1890. Monsieur de Varreux was the art
director of the glassworks and he signed pieces "De Vez."*

De Vez, Vase, Black On Baby Blue, Birds & Leaves, Signed, 6 In.High	395.00
De Vez, Vase, Blue Waterfall Scene On Pink To Yellow, C.1900, 8 In.	325.00
De Vez, Vase, Boat Shape, River & Forest Scene, Pink & Green, 10 In.	295.00
De Vez, Vase, Cameo, Blue Grapes, Leaves & Vines On Lavender, 8 1/2 In.	290.00
De Vez, Vase, Cameo, Boy Of Naples, Pink To Blue To Brown, 8 In.High	485.00
De Vez, Vase, Car, River, Trees, & Mountains On Gold Frosted, 7 In.	365.00
De Vez, Vase, River & Mountain Scene On Pale Blue, C.1900, 15 7/8 In.	425.00
De Vez, Vase, Macaw & Jungle Scene On Blue Over Yellow, Scalloped, 8 In.	450.00
De Vez, Vase, Mountains, Foliage, & Birds, Blue & Green, 11 3/4 In.High	365.00
De Vez, Vase, Navy To Yellow Scene On Pink Frosted, 4 In.	235.00
De Vez, Vase, River & Mountains Scene On Yellow, C.1910, 3 3/4 In.	400.00
De Vez, Vase, Scenic Cameo, Ovoid, Macaw On Limb, Blue & Yellow, 8 In.High	450.00
De Vez, Vase, Shorebirds On Lavender, 5 3/4 In.	275.00
De Vez, Vase, Stick, Pink & Green Scene On Blue, Vines At Opening, 8 In.	365.00
De Vez, Vase, Venetian Scene, Dark Blue, Gray, & Pink, 3 Layers, 12 In.	595.00

*Decoys are carved or turned wooden copies of birds. The decoy was placed in
the water to lure flying birds to the pond for hunters.*

Decoy, Barrow's Goldeneye, Drake, E.Elmer Crowell, Mass., 1890	350.00
Decoy, Black Duck, Chauncey Wheeler, N.Y., Painted	200.00
Decoy, Bluebill, Wooden	6.00
Decoy, Broadbill, Ernest Fox, Brockville, Ont., 1950, Sgrafitto Feathering	20.00
Decoy, Broadbill, Hen & Drake, Dodge Factory, Sgrafitto, Pair	70.00
Decoy, Broadbill, Hen, Fort Covington, N.Y., C.1880, Pair	40.00
Decoy, Broadbill, Hen, Relief Feathers, Painted	40.00
Decoy, Broadbill, Jean Boucher, Boucherville, P.Q., 1930, Pair	30.00
Decoy, Broadbill, Lake St.Peter, P.Q., Pair	30.00
Decoy, Canada Goose, Dan Wolfe, Clayton, N.Y., C.1940	50.00
Decoy, Canada Goose, Luke Dodge, N.Y., C.1790, White Pine, Painted, Pair	525.00
Decoy, Canada Goose, Painted	50.00
Decoy, Canada Goose, Tuckerton, New Jersey, Hollow, 25 1/2 X 9 In.	100.00
Decoy, Canvasback Drake, Mason, No.2	125.00
Decoy, Canvasback Drake, New England, 5 X 3 In.	160.00
Decoy, Canvasback, Joseph Standard, St.Clair Flats, Mich., 1930, Pair	30.00
Decoy, Duck, Cloth, Painted Details, Glass Eyes	11.00
Decoy, Duck, Hand-Carved Wood, Painted	39.00
Decoy, Goose, Wooden, Painted, 17 X 12 In.	45.00
Decoy, Hooded Merganser, Drake, New England, Pair	50.00
Decoy, Mallard Duck, Mason, Mackby Collection, 18 In.	150.00
Decoy, Mallard, Female, Wooden, Glass Eyes, Painted, Rudder, Weights	18.00
Decoy, Redheaded Duck, Drake, Joseph Standard, St.Clair Flats, Mich., 1930	60.00
Decoy, Scoup Drake, Mackby Collection, 13 In.	100.00
Decoy, Snow Goose, Hand-Carved, Wooden	15.00

*The Dedham Pottery Company of Dedham, Massachusetts, started making
pottery in 1866. It was reorganized as the Chelsea Pottery Company in
1891, and became the Dedham Pottery Company in 1895. The factory was
famous for its crackleware dishes, which picture blue outlines of amimals,
flowers, and other natural motifs.*

Dedham, Bowl, Rabbit, Decorated On Inner Side, 6 In.	60.00
Dedham, Bowl, Rabbit, 5 1/4 In.Diameter	68.00
Dedham, Bowl, Snow Tree, Crackle, 5 X 2 In.	95.00
Dedham, Creamer, Rabbit, 3 1/4 X 4 1/4 In.	65.00
Dedham, Cup & Saucer, Pond Lily	85.00
Dedham, Cup & Saucer, Rabbit	65.00 To 80.00
Dedham, Cup Plate, Rabbit	25.00 To 115.00
Dedham, Mug, Rabbits At Base, Fruit At Top, 4 1/4 X 4 In.	125.00
Dedham, Plate, Bread & Butter, Bears	55.00
Dedham, Plate, Bread & Butter, Butterfly	45.00
Dedham, Plate, Bread & Butter, Duck, 6 1/2 In.	45.00
Dedham, Plate, Bread & Butter, Rabbit	65.00
Dedham, Plate, Bread & Butter, Turkey	50.00
Dedham, Plate, Bunny, 6 In.	38.00

Dedham, Plate, Butterfly, 8 In. .... 55.00 To 125.00
Dedham, Plate, Duck, 10 In. 70.00
Dedham, Plate, Horse Chestnuts, 6 In. 40.00
Dedham, Plate, Lily, 8 1/2 In. 46.00
Dedham, Plate, Lily, 10 In. 90.00
Dedham, Plate, Lobster, 8 1/2 In. 135.00
Dedham, Plate, Magnolia Pattern Over Rabbit Blank, 8 1/2 In. 125.00
Dedham, Plate, Mushroom, 10 In. 95.00
Dedham, Plate, Polar Bear, 10 In. 135.00
Dedham, Plate, Pond Lily, 8 1/2 In. 48.00
Dedham, Plate, Rabbit, Blue Green, C.1897, 8 1/2 In. 37.50
Dedham, Plate, Rabbit, Blue, 8 1/2 In. 37.50
Dedham, Plate, Rabbit, 6 In. .... 30.00 To 35.00
Dedham, Plate, Rabbit, 8 1/2 In. 43.50
Dedham, Plate, Rabbit, 10 In. .... 40.00 To 65.00
Dedham, Plate, Raised Rabbit, C.P.U.S. Mark, 8 1/2 In. 52.00
Dedham, Plate, Water Lily, Blue, 10 In. 65.00
Dedham, Salt & Pepper, Rabbits .... 125.00 To 135.00
Dedham, Sugar, Covered, Rabbit, Handled 75.00
Dedham, Tile, Leaf & Flower, Blue, C.1897, Square, 5 1/2 In. 65.00
Dedham, Tray, Swan Border, 9 1/2 X 6 In. 150.00
Dedham, Trivet, Rabbits, Round, 5 7/8 In. 65.00
DeGue, Bowl, Art Deco, Triangular, Aztec On Green, Cameo, 5 In. 132.50
DeGue, Lamp, Silvered Iron Base, Domical Frosted Shade, C.1935, 14 In. 100.00
DeGue, Vase, Burnt Orange & Green Floral On Blue Frosted, C.1930, 11 In. 250.00
DeGue, Vase, Red, Orange, & Green, 10 In. 135.00

Delatte glass is a French cameo glass made by Andre Delatte. It was
first made in Nancy, France, in 1921. Lighting fixtures and opaque
glassware in imitation of Bohemian opaline were made.

Delatte, Rose Bowl, Pink Casing, Signed, 8 X 8 In. 75.00
Delatte, Vase, Ball Shape, Mottled Oranges & Browns, Narrow Neck, 7 1/2 In. 55.00
Delatte, Vase, Cameo, Pink Satin Ground, Maroon Leaves & Vines, 7 1/2 In. 365.00
Delatte, Vase, Pear Shape, Dark Blue Mottling On Orange Red, 4 1/2 In. 75.00
   Delaware, see Pressed Glass
   Deldare, see Buffalo Pottery, Deldare

Delft is a tin-glazed pottery that has been made since the seventeenth
century. It is decorated with blue on white or with colored decorations.
Most of the pieces sold today were made after 1891, and the name Holland
appears with the Delft factory marks.

Delft, Ashtray, Hand-Painted Windmill Scene, Marked Holland 17.00
Delft, Bottle, Polychrome, Bird & Floral, Hand-Painted, 3 In. 9.00
Delft, Bowl, Bristol, Polychrome, Blue, Farm & Figures, C.1740, 12 1/8 In. 750.00
Delft, Bowl, Bristol, Polychrome, Flowering Oriental Shrub, C.1760, 9 In. 130.00
Delft, Bowl, Covered, English, Floral, C.1850, 11 1/2 X 8 1/2 In. 120.00
Delft, Bowl, English, Blue & White, Church & Buildings, C.1720, 14 1/4 In. 160.00
Delft, Bowl, Irish, Deep, Blue, 12 5/8 X 9 1/4 In. 248.00
Delft, Bowl, Lambeth, Pomegranate, Ocher & Turquoise, C.1670, 13 1/2 In. 575.00
Delft, Celery, House & Trees, Open Handles, RC Germany, 12 In. 36.00
Delft, Chamberstick, Polychrome, Flowers, Dated 1786, 8 1/2 In. 90.00
Delft, Charger, English, Blue & White, Chinoiserie Figure, C.1750, 13 5/8 In. 175.00
Delft, Creamer, Bear With Overcoat & Muff, 3 1/2 In. 30.00
Delft, Creamer, Cow 25.00
Delft, Creamer, Cow, Reclining, Dutch Windmills & Landscape, 7 1/2 In. 55.00
Delft, Creamer, Sailboat & Windmill, Germany 40.00
Delft, Dish, Pin, On Pedestal, Blue & White Windmill Scene, Germany, 3 1/2 In 24.00
Delft, Figurine, Cow, Dutch, C.1763, 5 1/2 In. .... *Illus* 675.00
Delft, Figurine, Dutch Girl & Boy On Base, Blue & White, 4 1/2 In., Pair 6.50
Delft, Mug, Windmill Design, Crossed Pipes, German 22.50
Delft, Mug, Windmill Scene, Hand-Painted, Blue, 5 1/8 In. 15.00
Delft, Pitcher, Blue & White, Windmill, 8 1/2 In. 40.00
Delft, Plaque, V & BM, 17 1/2 In. 90.00
Delft, Plaque, Waterfront Scene, Gray, Browns, & Greens, Enamel, 12 X 7 In. 150.00
Delft, Plate, Brislington, Polychrome, Floral & Fruit, C.1760, 11 7/8 In. 250.00
Delft, Plate, Bristol, Blue & White, Lady & Gallant Scene, C.1750, 8 5/8 In. 187.50

Delft, Figurine, Cow, Dutch, C.1763, 5 1/2 In.
(See Page 139)

Delft, Plate, Dutch, Blue & White, C.1750

Delft, Plate, Bristol, Rooster, Manganese Spongework, C.1720, 7 In., Pair	1200.00
Delft, Plate, Bristol, Rooster, Manganese Spongework, C.1720, 8 7/8 In.	500.00
Delft, Plate, De Paeuw, Blue & White, Floral Medallions, C.1720, 8 3/4 In.	75.00
Delft, Plate, Dutch, Blue & White, C.1750 .... *Illus*	100.00
Delft, Plate, Dutch, Blue & White, Flowering Shrubbery & Fence, C.1740, 9 In.	70.00
Delft, Plate, English, Blue & White, Vase Of Flowers, C.1740, 8 3/4 In.	50.00
Delft, Plate, English, Blue & White, William & Mary, C.1700, 11 1/2 In.	800.00
Delft, Plate, English, Chinese Fisherman In Boat, Blue & White, C.1740, 8 In.	85.00
Delft, Plate, English, Flying Insect & Island Pavillion, C.1760, 9 In.	90.00
Delft, Plate, Lambeth, Blue & White, Fenced Garden, Insect, C.1740, 14 3/8 In.	175.00
Delft, Plate, Lambeth, Blue & White, Floral Bouquet, C.1740, 8 1/2 In.	100.00
Delft, Plate, Lambeth, Blue & White, Flowering Tree Peonies, C.1750, 13 In.	150.00
Delft, Plate, Lambeth, Blue & White, Island Pavillion, C.1760, 9 In.	60.00
Delft, Plate, Lambeth, Blue & White, Willow Tree, Fence, C.1750, 13 5/8 In.	150.00
Delft, Plate, Lambeth, Polychrome, Chinoiserie Figure, C.1750, 11 5/8 In.	425.00
Delft, Plate, Lambeth, Polychrome, Oriental Shrubbery, C.1740, 8 7/8 In.	100.00
Delft, Plate, Pierced For Hanging, Signed, 8 1/2 In.	27.50
Delft, Plate, Soup, Bristol, Polychrome, Fisherman, C.1770, 8 3/4 In.	150.00
Delft, Plate, Soup, English, Blue & White, Buildings, Smoke, C.1750, 8 3/8 In.	75.00
Delft, Plate, Windmill Scene, 9 3/4 In.	38.00
Delft, Pocket, Wall, Blue, Rococo Shape, Floral, People, C.1750, MP	200.00
Delft, Shoe, Dutch, Blue & White Flowers, 4 In.	6.00
Delft, Teapot, Monkey Figural, Tasseled Cover, 9 In.High	195.00
Delft, Vase, Bud, Floral, Square, 11 In.	32.50
Delft, Vase, English, Ginger Jar Shape, Oriental Landscapes, 4 1/2 In.	175.00
Delft, Washstand Set, Maddox, Blue & White, 2 Piece	135.00

Depression glass was an inexpensive glass manufactured in large quantities during the 1920s and early 1930s. It was made in many colors and patterns by dozens of factories in the United States. The name depression glass is a modern one.

Depression Glass, Ashtray, Clover, Black	35.00
Depression Glass, Ashtray, Crystal, Clear, 3 3/4 In.	5.25
Depression Glass, Ashtray, Floragold	1.50
Depression Glass, Ashtray, Florentine, 5 1/2 In.	8.00
Depression Glass, Ashtray, Madrid, Green	49.50
Depression Glass, Berry Set, Cameo, Green, 7 Piece	25.00
Depression Glass, Bonbon, No.173, Moonstone, Heart Shape	3.75 To 5.00
Depression Glass, Bowl, Adam, Green, 8 1/2 In.	8.00
Depression Glass, Bowl, Adam, Pink, Covered, 9 In.	8.00
Depression Glass, Bowl, Adam, Pink, 8 In.	4.00
Depression Glass, Bowl, American Sweetheart, Pink, 6 In.	2.00
Depression Glass, Bowl, American Sweetheart, Pink, 9 In.	8.00
Depression Glass, Bowl, Berry, Floral, Pink, 4 In.	1.75
Depression Glass, Bowl, Berry, Moderntone, Blue, Platonite, 5 In.	1.00

Depression Glass, Bowl, Berry, Moderntone, Green, Platonite, 5 In. 1.00
Depression Glass, Bowl, Berry, Moderntone, Pink, Platonite, 5 In. 1.00
Depression Glass, Bowl, Berry, Moderntone, Pink, Platonite, 8 3/4 In. 3.50
Depression Glass, Bowl, Berry, Moderntone, Yellow, Platonite, 5 In. 1.00
Depression Glass, Bowl, Berry, No.139, Cobalt, Ruffled, 4 1/2 In. 2.00
Depression Glass, Bowl, Berry, Normandie, Iridescent 1.25
Depression Glass, Bowl, Berry, Royal Lace, Blue, 5 In. 7.00
Depression Glass, Bowl, Berry, Royal Lace, Blue, 10 In. 15.00
Depression Glass, Bowl, Berry, Sharon, Pink, 5 In. 1.75
Depression Glass, Bowl, Block, Green, 8 3/4 In. 4.00
Depression Glass, Bowl, Bubble, Light Blue, 4 In. 1.50
Depression Glass, Bowl, Bubble, Pink, 8 1/2 In. 3.50
Depression Glass, Bowl, Cameo, Green, Low, 8 1/2 In. 7.00
Depression Glass, Bowl, Cameo, Green, 8 1/4 In. 6.00
Depression Glass, Bowl, Cameo, Green, 8 1/2 In. 5.00
Depression Glass, Bowl, Center, Rock Crystal, Amber, Footed, 12 1/2 In. 37.50
Depression Glass, Bowl, Cereal, American Sweetheart, Monax, 6 In. 6.00
Depression Glass, Bowl, Cereal, American Sweetheart, Pink, 6 In. 3.00
Depression Glass, Bowl, Cereal, Bubble, Blue, 4 In. 1.75
Depression Glass, Bowl, Cereal, Dogwood, Pink, 5 1/2 In. 3.00
Depression Glass, Bowl, Cereal, Lace Edge 1.50
Depression Glass, Bowl, Cereal, Lace Edge, Pink, 6 1/2 In. 3.00
Depression Glass, Bowl, Cereal, Mayfair Open Rose, Pink, Hocking, Square 4.00
Depression Glass, Bowl, Cereal, Miss America, Pink 6.50
Depression Glass, Bowl, Cereal, Miss America, 6 1/4 In. 3.00
Depression Glass, Bowl, Cereal, Normandie, Carnival, 6 1/2 In. 1.75
Depression Glass, Bowl, Cereal, Normandie, Iridescent 2.00
Depression Glass, Bowl, Cereal, Patrician Spoke, Amber, 6 In. .... 3.00 To 5.00
Depression Glass, Bowl, Cereal, Petalware, White 1.50
Depression Glass, Bowl, Cereal, S Pattern, Topaz, 5 1/2 In. 3.00
Depression Glass, Bowl, Cereal, Windsor, Pink, Deep, 5 1/2 In. 3.00
Depression Glass, Bowl, Cherry Blossom, Green, 3 Footed, 10 1/2 In. 16.50
Depression Glass, Bowl, Cherry Blossom, Green, 4 3/4 In. 3.50
Depression Glass, Bowl, Cherry Blossom, Pink, Round, 8 1/2 In. 5.00
Depression Glass, Bowl, Cherry Blossom, Pink, 8 In. 6.25
Depression Glass, Bowl, Cherry Blossom, Pink, 9 In. 8.00
Depression Glass, Bowl, Colonial, Green, 9 In. 7.00
Depression Glass, Bowl, Console, American Sweetheart, Monax 275.00
Depression Glass, Bowl, Console, Swirl, Ultramarine, Footed, 10 1/2 In. 10.00
Depression Glass, Bowl, Coronation, Ruby, 6 1/2 In. 4.00
Depression Glass, Bowl, Cream Soup, American Sweetheart, Pink, 4 1/2 In. 10.00
Depression Glass, Bowl, Cream Soup, Cameo, Green 25.00
Depression Glass, Bowl, Cream Soup, Diana 2.50
Depression Glass, Bowl, Cream Soup, Florentine No.2, Yellow 5.00
Depression Glass, Bowl, Cream Soup, Florentine No.2, 4 3/4 In. 2.00
Depression Glass, Bowl, Cream Soup, Florentine, Green, 4 3/4 In. 3.00
Depression Glass, Bowl, Cream Soup, Madrid, Amber 3.00
Depression Glass, Bowl, Cream Soup, Mayfair Open Rose, Pink, 5 In. 9.00
Depression Glass, Bowl, Cream Soup, Moderntone, Blue 2.50
Depression Glass, Bowl, Cream Soup, Moderntone, Blue, Platonite, 2 Handled 3.50
Depression Glass, Bowl, Cream Soup, Moderntone, Blue, Round 2.50
Depression Glass, Bowl, Cream Soup, Moderntone, Green, Platonite, 2 Handled 3.50
Depression Glass, Bowl, Cream Soup, Moderntone, Pink, Platonite, 2 Handled 3.50
Depression Glass, Bowl, Cream Soup, Newport, Burgundy 2.00
Depression Glass, Bowl, Cream Soup, Old Florentine, 4 3/4 In. 3.00
Depression Glass, Bowl, Cream Soup, Patrician Spoke, Amber .... 2.50 To 3.00
Depression Glass, Bowl, Cream Soup, Patrician Spoke, Pink .... 7.00 To 12.00
Depression Glass, Bowl, Cream Soup, Petalware, Pink, 4 In. 3.50
Depression Glass, Bowl, Cream Soup, Rosemary, Amber, 5 In. 2.50
Depression Glass, Bowl, Cream Soup, Rosemary, Green 10.00
Depression Glass, Bowl, Cream Soup, Royal Lace, Cobalt 9.50
Depression Glass, Bowl, Cream Soup, Sharon, Amber 4.50
Depression Glass, Bowl, Cream Soup, Sharon, Green 10.00
Depression Glass, Bowl, Cream Soup, Sharon, Pink 8.00
Depression Glass, Bowl, Crystal, 8 In. 2.00
Depression Glass, Bowl, Cubist, Pink, Covered, 3 Legs, 3 1/2 In. 3.00

Depression Glass, Bowl, Cubist, Pink, 4 1/2 In. .... 1.50 To 2.00
Depression Glass, Bowl, Dessert, Moonstone, Crimped 2.00
Depression Glass, Bowl, Diana, Scalloped, 12 In. 6.00
Depression Glass, Bowl, Dogwood, Pink, 5 1/2 In. 3.00
Depression Glass, Bowl, Dogwood, Pink, 8 1/2 In. 8.00
Depression Glass, Bowl, Doric, Pink, Handled, 9 In. 5.50
Depression Glass, Bowl, Doric, Pink, 4 1/2 In. 1.25
Depression Glass, Bowl, Doric, Pink, 8 In. 3.75
Depression Glass, Bowl, Fiesta, Blue, 7 1/2 X 2 3/4 In. 3.00
Depression Glass, Bowl, Fiesta, Green, 4 3/4 X 1 3/4 In. 2.50
Depression Glass, Bowl, Floragold No.174, Scalloped, 5 1/2 In. 2.00
Depression Glass, Bowl, Floragold No.174, Scalloped, 9 In. 6.00
Depression Glass, Bowl, Floragold No.174, Scalloped, 12 In. 6.00
Depression Glass, Bowl, Floragold, Iridescent, Ruffled, 12 In. 5.00
Depression Glass, Bowl, Floragold, Scalloped, 11 1/2 In. 3.75
Depression Glass, Bowl, Floragold, Square, 4 1/2 In. 1.25
Depression Glass, Bowl, Floragold, Square, 8 1/2 In. 3.25
Depression Glass, Bowl, Floral, Green, 7 1/2 In. 4.75
Depression Glass, Bowl, Floral, Pink, 7 1/2 In. 8.00
Depression Glass, Bowl, Florentine No.2, Yellow, 8 In. 7.00
Depression Glass, Bowl, Florentine, Yellow, 4 1/2 In. 2.50
Depression Glass, Bowl, Fruit, Cherry Blossom, Pink, 3 Footed, 10 1/2 In. 18.00
Depression Glass, Bowl, Fruit, Floragold No.174, Square, 4 1/2 In. 1.75
Depression Glass, Bowl, Fruit, Floragold, Scalloped, 5 1/2 In. 1.50
Depression Glass, Bowl, Fruit, Floral, Green, 8 In. 1.50
Depression Glass, Bowl, Fruit, Heritage, White, 10 1/2 In. 8.00
Depression Glass, Bowl, Fruit, Mayfair, Pink, Flared, Anchor Hocking, 12 In. 9.50
Depression Glass, Bowl, Fruit, Miss America, Deep, 8 1/2 In. 15.00
Depression Glass, Bowl, Fruit, Miss America, Pink, Curved-In Sides, 8 1/2 In. 23.00
Depression Glass, Bowl, Fruit, Miss America, Pink, Curved-In Top, 8 In. 22.00
Depression Glass, Bowl, Fruit, Miss America, Pink, Straight, 8 3/4 In. 19.00
Depression Glass, Bowl, Fruit, Sharon, Pink, 10 1/2 In. 4.90
Depression Glass, Bowl, Heritage, 10 1/2 In. 4.50
Depression Glass, Bowl, Ice, Cameo, Green .... 15.00 To 69.00
Depression Glass, Bowl, Iris, Amber, Scalloped, 5 1/2 In. 2.00
Depression Glass, Bowl, Iris, Amber, Scalloped, 9 1/2 In. 6.00
Depression Glass, Bowl, Iris, Amber, Scalloped, 11 1/2 In. 6.00
Depression Glass, Bowl, Iris, Flared, 11 In. 5.00
Depression Glass, Bowl, Iris, Fluted, 5 1/2 In. 2.00
Depression Glass, Bowl, Iris, Fluted, 11 In. 5.00
Depression Glass, Bowl, Iris, Ruffled, 9 In. 3.00
Depression Glass, Bowl, Iris, Scalloped, 11 1/2 In. 5.00
Depression Glass, Bowl, Iris, 11 In. 5.00
Depression Glass, Bowl, Jam, Normandie, Sunburst Carnival, 6 1/2 In. 3.00
Depression Glass, Bowl, Lace Edge, Pink, Ribbed, 9 1/2 In. .... 4.00 To 4.50
Depression Glass, Bowl, Lace Edge, Pink, 7 3/4 In. 3.00
Depression Glass, Bowl, Lace Edge, Pink, 9 1/2 In. .... 4.50 To 5.00
Depression Glass, Bowl, Madrid, Green, 5 In. 2.00
Depression Glass, Bowl, Mayfair, Pink, Anchor Hocking, 11 3/4 In. 10.50
Depression Glass, Bowl, Mayfair, Pink, Flared, 12 In. 15.00
Depression Glass, Bowl, Mayfair, Pink, Handled, 7 In. 5.00
Depression Glass, Bowl, Mayfair, Pink, Handled, 10 In. .... 4.00 To 6.00
Depression Glass, Bowl, Mayfair, Pink, 11 3/4 In. 15.00
Depression Glass, Bowl, Mayfair, Pink, 12 In. 10.00
Depression Glass, Bowl, Miss America, 6 1/4 In. 3.00
Depression Glass, Bowl, Moonstone, Covered, 4 1/2 In. 4.00
Depression Glass, Bowl, Moonstone, Crimped, 5 1/2 In. 2.25
Depression Glass, Bowl, Moonstone, Crimped, 7 3/4 In. 2.75
Depression Glass, Bowl, Moonstone, Crimped, 9 1/2 In. 5.75
Depression Glass, Bowl, Moonstone, Handled, Crimped, 6 1/2 In. 3.50
Depression Glass, Bowl, No.173, Moonstone, Crimped, 9 1/2 In. 8.50
Depression Glass, Bowl, Normandie, Carnival, 5 In. .... .75
Depression Glass, Bowl, Normandie, Carnival, 8 1/2 In. 3.50
Depression Glass, Bowl, Oatmeal, Princess, Green 4.75
Depression Glass, Bowl, Orange, Princess, Pink, Hat Shape, 9 1/2 In. 8.00
Depression Glass, Bowl, Oyster & Pearl, Milk Glass With Rose, 10 1/2 In. 6.75

Depression Glass, Bowl, Patrician Spoke, Amber, 8 1/2 In.	6.00
Depression Glass, Bowl, Petalware, Cremax, 8 1/4 In.	4.00
Depression Glass, Bowl, Petalware, Cremax, 8 1/2 In.	6.00
Depression Glass, Bowl, Petalware, Pink, 5 3/4 In.	2.00
Depression Glass, Bowl, Petalware, Pink, 8 1/4 In.	3.50
Depression Glass, Bowl, Princess, Green, Octagonal, Handled, 8 In.	4.50
Depression Glass, Bowl, Princess, Pink, Octagonal, 9 In.	5.00
Depression Glass, Bowl, Princess, Pink, 4 1/2 In.	3.50
Depression Glass, Bowl, Quilted Diamond, Pink, 4 3/4 In.	2.50
Depression Glass, Bowl, Quilted Diamond, Pink, 7 In.	2.00
Depression Glass, Bowl, Royal Lace, Blue, 3 Legs, Straight Edge, 10 In.	18.00
Depression Glass, Bowl, Royal Lace, Cobalt, Footed, 10 X 4 1/2 In.	40.00
Depression Glass, Bowl, Royal Lace, Footed, 10 In.	10.00
Depression Glass, Bowl, Royal Lace, Green, 10 In.	6.00 To 8.50
Depression Glass, Bowl, Royal Lace, Pink, Footed, 10 In.	8.00
Depression Glass, Bowl, Royal Lace, Pink, Ruffled, 3 Footed, 10 In.	10.00
Depression Glass, Bowl, Royal Lace, Pink, 10 In.	3.00
Depression Glass, Bowl, Royal Lace, Pink, 3 Legs, 10 In.	8.50 To 10.00
Depression Glass, Bowl, Royal Ruby, 4 1/2 In.	2.00
Depression Glass, Bowl, Salad, Floragold No.174, 5 1/2 In.	2.00
Depression Glass, Bowl, Salad, Royal Ruby, 11 1/2 In.	10.00
Depression Glass, Bowl, Sandwich, Anchor Hocking, 4 1/2 In.	2.00
Depression Glass, Bowl, Sandwich, Desert Gold, Deep, 9 In.	7.00
Depression Glass, Bowl, Sandwich, Green, Anchor Hocking, 6 1/2 In.	15.00
Depression Glass, Bowl, Sandwich, Pink, 4 3/4 In.	1.50
Depression Glass, Bowl, Sandwich, Ruby, Scalloped, Anchor Hocking, 8 In.	14.00
Depression Glass, Bowl, Serving, Bubble, Blue, 8 In.	3.00
Depression Glass, Bowl, Sharon, Amber, 8 1/2 In.	2.50
Depression Glass, Bowl, Sharon, Amber, 10 1/2 In.	5.00
Depression Glass, Bowl, Sharon, Green, 8 1/2 In.	5.00
Depression Glass, Bowl, Sharon, Pink, 5 In.	2.00
Depression Glass, Bowl, Sharon, Pink, 6 In.	2.90
Depression Glass, Bowl, Sharon, Pink, 7 1/2 In.	6.50
Depression Glass, Bowl, Sharon, Pink, 10 1/2 In.	6.00
Depression Glass, Bowl, Soup, Bubble, Light Blue, 7 3/4 In.	3.00
Depression Glass, Bowl, Soup, Holiday, Pink	5.00
Depression Glass, Bowl, Soup, Iris	8.00
Depression Glass, Bowl, Soup, Madrid, Amber, 7 In.	3.25
Depression Glass, Bowl, Soup, Royal Ruby, 7 1/2 In.	3.50
Depression Glass, Bowl, Soup, Sharon, Pink, 7 1/2 In.	6.50
Depression Glass, Bowl, Swirl, Ultramarine, 9 In.	6.00 To 6.50
Depression Glass, Bowl, Three Flower, Pink, 9 1/2 In.	5.00
Depression Glass, Bowl, Vegetable, Adam, Pink, Oval, 10 In.	6.00
Depression Glass, Bowl, Vegetable, American Sweetheart, Monax, Oval	23.50
Depression Glass, Bowl, Vegetable, American Sweetheart, Pink, Oval, 11 In.	8.00
Depression Glass, Bowl, Vegetable, American Sweetheart, 9 In.	22.00
Depression Glass, Bowl, Vegetable, Cameo, Green, Oval, 9 In.	5.00
Depression Glass, Bowl, Vegetable, Cameo, Yellow, Oval, 10 In.	5.00
Depression Glass, Bowl, Vegetable, Floral, Green, Oval, 9 In.	5.00
Depression Glass, Bowl, Vegetable, Floral, Pink, Covered, 8 In.	8.00
Depression Glass, Bowl, Vegetable, Floral, Pink, Oval, 9 In.	4.00
Depression Glass, Bowl, Vegetable, Laurel	7.00
Depression Glass, Bowl, Vegetable, Madrid, Amber, Oval, 10 In.	5.00
Depression Glass, Bowl, Vegetable, Mayfair Open Rose, Ice Blue, Covered	30.00
Depression Glass, Bowl, Vegetable, Miss America, Oval	4.75
Depression Glass, Bowl, Vegetable, Miss America, Pink, Oval, 10 In.	7.50
Depression Glass, Bowl, Vegetable, Parrot, Green, Oval	12.50
Depression Glass, Bowl, Vegetable, Patrician Spoke, Amber, Oval, 10 In.	3.50
Depression Glass, Bowl, Vegetable, Patrician Spoke, Green, Oval, 10 In.	6.00
Depression Glass, Bowl, Vegetable, Poinsettia, Pink, Covered, 8 In.	10.00
Depression Glass, Bowl, Vegetable, Princess, Green, Oval, 10 In.	4.00
Depression Glass, Bowl, Vegetable, Princess, Green, 10 In.	3.50
Depression Glass, Bowl, Vegetable, Royal Lace, Blue, Oval	14.00
Depression Glass, Bowl, Vegetable, Sharon, Green, Oval	8.00
Depression Glass, Bowl, Vegetable, Sharon, Pink, Oval, 9 1/2 In.	4.50
Depression Glass, Bowl, Vegetable, Tea Room, Green, Oval	5.00

Depression Glass, Bowl, Vegetable, Tea Room, Green, Tan Handles, Oval 11.50
Depression Glass, Bowl, Windsor, Pink, Handled, 9 1/2 In. 5.00
Depression Glass, Bowl, Windsor, Pink, 5 1/4 In. 1.25
Depression Glass, Bowl, Windsor, Pink, 8 1/2 In. 5.50
Depression Glass, Bowl, Windsor, 8 1/2 In. 2.75
Depression Glass, Butter, Cherry Blossom, Pink .... 30.00 To 45.00
Depression Glass, Butter, Columbia 15.00
Depression Glass, Butter, Columbia, Covered 10.00
Depression Glass, Butter, Columbia, Covered, Round 6.75
Depression Glass, Butter, Cubist, Green 32.50
Depression Glass, Butter, Cubist, Pink 20.00
Depression Glass, Butter, Floragold, Round 17.50
Depression Glass, Butter, Floral, Pink, Covered 35.00
Depression Glass, Butter, Florentine No.1, Green 45.00
Depression Glass, Butter, Florentine No.2, Yellow 62.50
Depression Glass, Butter, Florentine, Yellow 48.00
Depression Glass, Butter, Hazel Atlas Block, Green, Covered 20.00
Depression Glass, Butter, Holiday, Pink 20.00
Depression Glass, Butter, Holiday, Pink, Covered 15.00
Depression Glass, Butter, Iris, Amber, Covered 15.00
Depression Glass, Butter, Lace Edge, Pink .... 18.00 To 22.00
Depression Glass, Butter, Lace Edge, Pink, Covered 25.00
Depression Glass, Butter, Madrid, Amber, Covered 50.00
Depression Glass, Butter, Mayfair Open Rose, Pink 22.00
Depression Glass, Butter, Mayfair Open Rose, Pink, Covered, Hocking 30.00
Depression Glass, Butter, Miss America, Pink, Covered 310.00
Depression Glass, Butter, Old Florentine, Green 55.00
Depression Glass, Butter, Parrot, Green 155.00
Depression Glass, Butter, Parrot, Green, Covered 135.00
Depression Glass, Butter, Patrician Spoke, Amber 40.00
Depression Glass, Butter, Patrician Spoke, Green 50.00
Depression Glass, Butter, Princess, Green 45.00
Depression Glass, Butter, Princess, Green, Covered 48.00
Depression Glass, Butter, Princess, Pink 40.00
Depression Glass, Butter, Princess, Pink, Covered .... 40.00 To 60.00
Depression Glass, Butter, Royal Lace, Blue 197.50
Depression Glass, Butter, Sandwich 17.50
Depression Glass, Butter, Sandwich, Anchor Hocking 16.50
Depression Glass, Butter, Sharon, Amber .... 24.00 To 30.00
Depression Glass, Butter, Sharon, Amber, Covered .... 30.00 To 35.00
Depression Glass, Butter, Sharon, Green 75.00
Depression Glass, Butter, Sharon, Pink 30.00
Depression Glass, Butter, Sharon, Pink, Covered .... 20.00 To 30.00
Depression Glass, Butter, Sierra, Pink 35.00
Depression Glass, Butter, Waterford 12.00
Depression Glass, Butter, Waterford, Crystal, Covered 10.00
Depression Glass, Butter, Windsor, Pink 22.50
Depression Glass, Candlestick, Adam, Pink, 3 7/8 In., Pair 20.00
Depression Glass, Candlestick, Dolphin, Blue, 4 1/2 In., Pair 35.00
Depression Glass, Candlestick, Sandwich, Green, Indiana, 8 1/2 In., Pair 20.00
Depression Glass, Casserole, Lydia Ray, Covered, 9 In. 20.00
Depression Glass, Celery, Miss America 4.00
Depression Glass, Celery, Miss America, Pink, Oval 6.75
Depression Glass, Celery, Miss America, Pink, 10 1/2 In. 6.00
Depression Glass, Champagne, Cameo 10.50
Depression Glass, Claret, Colonial, 5 1/4 In., 4 Ozs. 6.00
Depression Glass, Coaster, Adam, Pink, 3 7/8 In. 4.00
Depression Glass, Coaster, Cherry Blossom, Green 4.50
Depression Glass, Coaster, Cherry Blossom, Pink 3.25
Depression Glass, Coaster, Cubist, Green 2.00
Depression Glass, Coaster, Doric, Pink 4.00
Depression Glass, Coaster, Floral, Green 2.50
Depression Glass, Coaster, Florentine, Topaz, 3 1/4 In. 3.50
Depression Glass, Coaster, Hot Dish, Madrid, Amber, 5 In. 20.00
Depression Glass, Coaster, Madrid, Green, Ring 27.50
Depression Glass, Coaster, Manhattan 1.00

Depression Glass, Coaster, Miss America 8.00
Depression Glass, Coaster, Princess, Green 8.00
Depression Glass, Coaster, Waterford 1.00
Depression Glass, Coaster, Waterford, Crystal, 4 In. 1.25
Depression Glass, Cocktail Glass, Royal Ruby, Chrome Base 4.00
Depression Glass, Cocktail Shaker, Angelfish, Blue 10.00
Depression Glass, Compote, Lace Edge, Pink, 7 In. .... 1.75 To 3.00
Depression Glass, Compote, Miss America, Pink, 5 In. 5.00
Depression Glass, Compote, Miss America, 5 In. 6.00
Depression Glass, Console Set, Sierra, Pink, 3 Piece 30.00
Depression Glass, Cordial, Colonial, 3 3/4 In., 1 Oz. 6.00
Depression Glass, Creamer, Bubble, Blue 5.00
Depression Glass, Creamer, Child's, Cherry Blossom, Delfite 22.50
Depression Glass, Creamer, Child's, Cherry Blossom, Pink 22.00
Depression Glass, Creamer, Child's, Doric & Pansy, Pink 20.00
Depression Glass, Creamer, Child's, Doric, Pink 20.00
Depression Glass, Creamer, Cloverleaf, Black 5.00
Depression Glass, Creamer, Cloverleaf, Yellow 4.50
Depression Glass, Creamer, Diamond-Quilted, Blue 6.00
Depression Glass, Creamer, Dogwood, Pink 3.00
Depression Glass, Creamer, English Hobnail, Octagonal Base 3.50
Depression Glass, Creamer, Floragold 3.00
Depression Glass, Creamer, Floragold No.174 .... 3.00
Depression Glass, Creamer, Floragold, Iridescent 4.00
Depression Glass, Creamer, Floral, Pink .... 3.00 To 4.50
Depression Glass, Creamer, Florentine No.2, Yellow .... 2.50 To 5.00
Depression Glass, Creamer, Florentine, Green .... 3.00 To 3.50
Depression Glass, Creamer, Holiday, Pink 2.50
Depression Glass, Creamer, Iris .... 2.50 To 3.00
Depression Glass, Creamer, Madrid, Amber .... 2.00 To 2.50
Depression Glass, Creamer, Madrid, Green 2.00
Depression Glass, Creamer, Mayfair Open Rose, Pink .... 4.00 To 6.00
Depression Glass, Creamer, Miss America, Pink .... 5.00 To 6.00
Depression Glass, Creamer, Moderntone, Pink, Platonite 1.25
Depression Glass, Creamer, Moderntone, Ritz Blue 2.50
Depression Glass, Creamer, Moderntone, Yellow, Platonite 1.25
Depression Glass, Creamer, Normandie, Carnival 2.50
Depression Glass, Creamer, Normandie, Iridescent 2.50
Depression Glass, Creamer, Patrician Spoke, Amber .... 2.00 To 3.00
Depression Glass, Creamer, Patrician Spoke, Green 3.00
Depression Glass, Creamer, Petalware, Cremax 3.00
Depression Glass, Creamer, Petalware, Monax 2.75
Depression Glass, Creamer, Princess, Yellow 8.00
Depression Glass, Creamer, Queen Mary 2.00
Depression Glass, Creamer, Ribbon, Green 1.75
Depression Glass, Creamer, Royal Lace 5.00
Depression Glass, Creamer, Royal Lace, Blue 12.00
Depression Glass, Creamer, Royal Lace, Pink 4.00
Depression Glass, Creamer, Royal Ruby 3.00
Depression Glass, Creamer, Sharon, Pink .... 3.00 To 3.50
Depression Glass, Creamer, Strawberry, Green 5.00
Depression Glass, Creamer, Windsor, Pink, 3 In. 2.50
Depression Glass, Cup & Saucer, American Sweetheart, Monax ... 7.00 To 7.50
Depression Glass, Cup & Saucer, Aurora, Cobalt 4.50
Depression Glass, Cup & Saucer, Block, Green 2.75
Depression Glass, Cup & Saucer, Bubble, Blue 3.25
Depression Glass, Cup & Saucer, Cameo 6.25
Depression Glass, Cup & Saucer, Cameo, Green 4.50
Depression Glass, Cup & Saucer, Cameo, Topaz 3.00
Depression Glass, Cup & Saucer, Cameo, Yellow .... 3.50 To 5.00
Depression Glass, Cup & Saucer, Cherry Blossom, Blue 22.50
Depression Glass, Cup & Saucer, Cherry Blossom, Green 9.00
Depression Glass, Cup & Saucer, Cherry Blossom, Pink 6.75
Depression Glass, Cup & Saucer, Child's, Cherry Blossom, Pink, Delphite 20.00
Depression Glass, Cup & Saucer, Child's, Homespun, Pink 15.00
Depression Glass, Cup & Saucer, Child's, Moderntone 5.00

Depression Glass, Cup & Saucer, Cloverleaf, Green	3.25 To 4.00
Depression Glass, Cup & Saucer, Daisy, Amber	4.50
Depression Glass, Cup & Saucer, Diana	2.75
Depression Glass, Cup & Saucer, Diana, Pink	4.50
Depression Glass, Cup & Saucer, Dogwood, Pink, Thick	3.50
Depression Glass, Cup & Saucer, Dogwood, Pink, Thin	4.50
Depression Glass, Cup & Saucer, Doric, Pink	4.50
Depression Glass, Cup & Saucer, Floragold	3.75
Depression Glass, Cup & Saucer, Floral, Pink	3.75
Depression Glass, Cup & Saucer, Florentine No.2, Green	3.50
Depression Glass, Cup & Saucer, Florentine No.2, Yellow	4.50
Depression Glass, Cup & Saucer, Fruits, Green	2.35
Depression Glass, Cup & Saucer, Georgian, Green	3.00
Depression Glass, Cup & Saucer, Holiday, Pink	4.25 To 4.50
Depression Glass, Cup & Saucer, Holiday, Pink, Rayed	3.50
Depression Glass, Cup & Saucer, Iris	3.50
Depression Glass, Cup & Saucer, Lace Edge, Pink	7.50
Depression Glass, Cup & Saucer, Laurel	5.00
Depression Glass, Cup & Saucer, Madrid, Amber	2.90 To 4.50
Depression Glass, Cup & Saucer, Madrid, Topaz	5.00
Depression Glass, Cup & Saucer, Mayfair Open Rose, Pink	6.50 To 7.00
Depression Glass, Cup & Saucer, Moderntone, Blue	2.50 To 4.50
Depression Glass, Cup & Saucer, Moderntone, Blue With White Stripes	3.00
Depression Glass, Cup & Saucer, Moderntone, Blue, Gold Rim	3.00
Depression Glass, Cup & Saucer, Moderntone, Ritz Blue	3.75
Depression Glass, Cup & Saucer, Moonstone	4.25
Depression Glass, Cup & Saucer, Newport, Blue	3.25
Depression Glass, Cup & Saucer, Newport, Cobalt	4.50
Depression Glass, Cup & Saucer, No.612, Green	4.75
Depression Glass, Cup & Saucer, Normandie, Iridescent	3.50
Depression Glass, Cup & Saucer, Normandie, Pink	3.50 To 4.50
Depression Glass, Cup & Saucer, Old Cafe, Red, Crystal Saucer	3.00
Depression Glass, Cup & Saucer, Ovide, Black	4.50
Depression Glass, Cup & Saucer, Parrot, Green	9.00
Depression Glass, Cup & Saucer, Patrician Spoke, Pink	4.25
Depression Glass, Cup & Saucer, Petalware, Cremax	4.00
Depression Glass, Cup & Saucer, Petalware, Cremax, Pastel Bands	4.50
Depression Glass, Cup & Saucer, Petalware, Monax, Painted Flower	6.50
Depression Glass, Cup & Saucer, Petalware, Pink	3.50 To 4.50
Depression Glass, Cup & Saucer, Princess, Green	3.25 To 3.50
Depression Glass, Cup & Saucer, Princess, Pink	5.00
Depression Glass, Cup & Saucer, Princess, Yellow	3.00 To 5.00
Depression Glass, Cup & Saucer, Rosemary, Amber	4.00
Depression Glass, Cup & Saucer, Roulette, Green	3.50
Depression Glass, Cup & Saucer, Royal Lace, Blue	8.00 To 13.00
Depression Glass, Cup & Saucer, Royal Lace, Pink	6.00
Depression Glass, Cup & Saucer, Royal Ruby	2.00 To 3.00
Depression Glass, Cup & Saucer, Ruby Red, Square	3.00
Depression Glass, Cup & Saucer, Sandwich, Dark Green, Anchor Hocking	10.00
Depression Glass, Cup & Saucer, Sandwich, Green, Anchor Hocking	12.00
Depression Glass, Cup & Saucer, Sharon, Amber	5.00
Depression Glass, Cup & Saucer, Sharon, Pink	2.90 To 5.00
Depression Glass, Cup & Saucer, Swirl, Ultramarine	5.50
Depression Glass, Cup & Saucer, Tea Room, Pink	6.00
Depression Glass, Cup & Saucer, Waterford, Crystal	1.75
Depression Glass, Cup & Saucer, Waterford, Pink	3.50
Depression Glass, Cup, Adam, Pink	3.00 To 4.00
Depression Glass, Cup, American Sweetheart, Monax	5.50
Depression Glass, Cup, American Sweetheart, Pink	3.00
Depression Glass, Cup, Block, Green	1.50
Depression Glass, Cup, Block, Pink	1.00 To 2.50
Depression Glass, Cup, Bubble, Blue	2.00
Depression Glass, Cup, Bubble, Light Blue	1.50
Depression Glass, Cup, Cameo, Green	3.00
Depression Glass, Cup, Cameo, Yellow	2.00 To 2.25
Depression Glass, Cup, Child's, Diana	1.00

Depression Glass, Cup, Child's, Doric & Pansy, Pink	15.00
Depression Glass, Cup, Child's, Doric & Pansy, Ultramarine	25.00
Depression Glass, Cup, Cloverleaf, Pink	2.00
Depression Glass, Cup, Coffee, Sandwich, Anchor Hocking	2.00
Depression Glass, Cup, Crystal	1.00
Depression Glass, Cup, Custard, Sandwich, Dark Green, Anchor Hocking	1.00
Depression Glass, Cup, Diana, Amber	3.00
Depression Glass, Cup, Dogwood, Pink, Thin	3.00
Depression Glass, Cup, Doric & Pansy, Pink	20.00
Depression Glass, Cup, Floragold	2.00
Depression Glass, Cup, Floragold No.174	2.50
Depression Glass, Cup, Floral, Green	3.50
Depression Glass, Cup, Floral, Pink	2.50
Depression Glass, Cup, Florentine, Topaz	3.00
Depression Glass, Cup, Fluted, Pink	1.50
Depression Glass, Cup, Georgian, Green	3.00
Depression Glass, Cup, Hobnail, Pink	1.50
Depression Glass, Cup, Holiday, Pink	2.25
Depression Glass, Cup, Lace Edge, Pink	5.00
Depression Glass, Cup, Madrid, Amber	2.50
Depression Glass, Cup, Madrid, Blue	10.00
Depression Glass, Cup, Miss America	4.50
Depression Glass, Cup, Miss America, Pink	5.75 To 7.00
Depression Glass, Cup, Moderntone, Blue, Platonite	2.25
Depression Glass, Cup, Moderntone, Green, Platonite	2.25
Depression Glass, Cup, Moderntone, Pink, Platonite	2.25
Depression Glass, Cup, Moderntone, Yellow, Platonite	2.25
Depression Glass, Cup, Moonstone	2.00 To 3.00
Depression Glass, Cup, No.612, Green	2.25
Depression Glass, Cup, Normandie, Pink	2.00
Depression Glass, Cup, Old Cafe, Red	2.25
Depression Glass, Cup, Old Florentine	2.25 To 2.50
Depression Glass, Cup, Orange Peel	2.25
Depression Glass, Cup, Patrician Spoke	2.00
Depression Glass, Cup, Patrician Spoke, Amber	2.50 To 2.75
Depression Glass, Cup, Patrician Spoke, Green	2.00 To 3.25
Depression Glass, Cup, Petalware, Monax	3.00
Depression Glass, Cup, Princess, Blue	35.00
Depression Glass, Cup, Princess, Green	2.50
Depression Glass, Cup, Princess, Pink	2.50
Depression Glass, Cup, Princess, Topaz	2.50
Depression Glass, Cup, Princess, Yellow	2.00
Depression Glass, Cup, Punch, Royal Ruby	2.00 To 2.50
Depression Glass, Cup, Ribbon Candy	1.50
Depression Glass, Cup, Rosemary, Amber	2.00
Depression Glass, Cup, Royal Lace	2.50
Depression Glass, Cup, Royal Lace, Pink	2.00 To 2.50
Depression Glass, Cup, S Pattern, Topaz	2.00
Depression Glass, Cup, Sandwich, Indiana	1.50
Depression Glass, Cup, Sandwich, Teal	4.25
Depression Glass, Cup, Sharon, Pink	2.50
Depression Glass, Cup, Sunflower, Pink	3.50
Depression Glass, Cup, Swirl, Ultramarine	2.50 To 4.00
Depression Glass, Cup, Waterford, Crystal	1.25
Depression Glass, Cup, Windsor Diamond, Pink	3.00
Depression Glass, Dish, Candy, Adam, Green, Covered	59.50
Depression Glass, Dish, Candy, Block Optic, Pink, Covered, 2 1/4 In.	7.00
Depression Glass, Dish, Candy, Block Optic, Yellow, Covered, Low	14.75
Depression Glass, Dish, Candy, Block, Green, Covered	10.00
Depression Glass, Dish, Candy, Cameo, Covered, 4 In.	19.75
Depression Glass, Dish, Candy, Cameo, Yellow, Covered, 4 In.	35.00
Depression Glass, Dish, Candy, Cloverleaf, Moonstone	4.00
Depression Glass, Dish, Candy, Doric, Green, Covered, 8 In.	14.00
Depression Glass, Dish, Candy, Floragold No.174, Handled	3.50
Depression Glass, Dish, Candy, Floral, Green	15.00
Depression Glass, Dish, Candy, Manhattan, Pink	2.50

Depression Glass, Dish, Candy, Mayfair, Ice Blue, Covered	55.00
Depression Glass, Dish, Candy, Mayfair, Moonstone, Heart Shape, Handled, 6 In.	4.00
Depression Glass, Dish, Candy, Miss America, Metal Lid, 6 1/4 In.	12.00
Depression Glass, Dish, Candy, Miss America, Pink, Covered	45.00
Depression Glass, Dish, Candy, Old Cafe, Pink, Low	2.50
Depression Glass, Dish, Candy, Royal Ruby Top, Clear Bottom	6.00
Depression Glass, Dish, Candy, Sandwich, Footed, Westmoreland, 5 In.	4.25
Depression Glass, Dish, Candy, Sharon, Pink	12.50
Depression Glass, Dish, Candy, Sharon, Pink, Covered	15.00 To 16.50
Depression Glass, Dish, Candy, Ultramarine	3.50
Depression Glass, Dish, Cheese, Laurel, Jade	37.50
Depression Glass, Dish, Cheese, Sharon, Amber, Covered	75.00
Depression Glass, Dish, Jam, Madrid	3.00
Depression Glass, Dish, Jam, Madrid, Amber	2.50
Depression Glass, Dish, Nut, Floragold No.174, Footed, Oblong	3.50
Depression Glass, Goblet, Block, Green, 4 3/4 In.	3.50
Depression Glass, Goblet, Cameo, Green, 6 In.	12.00
Depression Glass, Goblet, Fruit Cocktail, New Century, Green, Footed	1.25
Depression Glass, Goblet, Iris, 3 Ozs.	5.00
Depression Glass, Goblet, Iris, 8 Ozs., 5 3/4 In.	4.25
Depression Glass, Goblet, Juice, Miss America	9.50
Depression Glass, Goblet, Miss America, Pink, 5 1/2 In., 10 Ozs.	17.00
Depression Glass, Goblet, Moonstone	5.00
Depression Glass, Gravy Boat & Underplate, Florentine No.2, Yellow	45.00
Depression Glass, Gravy Boat, Florentine No.2, Yellow	30.00
Depression Glass, Jar, Candy, Cubist, Green, Covered	9.50
Depression Glass, Jar, Candy, Cubist, Light Pink, Covered	6.00
Depression Glass, Jar, Candy, Floral, Pink	12.00 To 14.00
Depression Glass, Jar, Candy, Floral, Pink, Poinsettia	8.00
Depression Glass, Jar, Candy, Mayfair, Pink	12.50
Depression Glass, Jar, Candy, Mayfair, Pink, Anchor Hocking	8.00
Depression Glass, Jar, Candy, Mayfair, Pink, Footed	11.00
Depression Glass, Jar, Candy, Miss America, Covered	35.00
Depression Glass, Jar, Candy, Miss America, Pink, Covered	45.00
Depression Glass, Jar, Candy, Miss America, Pink, 11 3/4 In.	47.50
Depression Glass, Jar, Candy, Princess, Pink	20.00
Depression Glass, Jar, Cookie, Cameo, Green	10.00 To 15.00
Depression Glass, Jar, Cookie, Cameo, Green, Covered, Sticker	15.00
Depression Glass, Jar, Cookie, Lace Edge, Pink	8.00
Depression Glass, Jar, Cookie, Madrid, Amber	18.00 To 25.00
Depression Glass, Jar, Cookie, Madrid, Pink	12.75
Depression Glass, Jar, Cookie, Mayfair Open Rose, Blue	69.50
Depression Glass, Jar, Cookie, Mayfair Open Rose, Pink	8.00 To 9.00
Depression Glass, Jar, Cookie, Mayfair Open Rose, Pink, Anchor Hocking	8.00
Depression Glass, Jar, Cookie, Princess, Green	9.50 To 12.50
Depression Glass, Jar, Cookie, Princess, Pink	8.00
Depression Glass, Jar, Cookie, Royal Lace	12.00 To 15.00
Depression Glass, Jar, Cookie, Royal Lace, Blue	50.00 To 65.00
Depression Glass, Jar, Cookie, Royal Lace, Pink, Covered	15.00
Depression Glass, Jar, Cookie, Sandwich, Amber	17.50
Depression Glass, Jar, Powder, Cubist, Pink	5.00
Depression Glass, Jar, Powder, Windsor	4.50
Depression Glass, Juice Set, Royal Ruby, Ball Pitcher, 9 Piece	25.00
Depression Glass, Juicer, Sunkist, Milk Glass	3.50
Depression Glass, Juicer, Swirled, Green	2.50
Depression Glass, Lampshade, Petalware, Monax, 8 1/2 In.	7.00
Depression Glass, Lazy Susan, Waterford, Green, 5 Milk Glass Inserts, 14 In.	12.75
Depression Glass, Liner, Custard Cup, Sandwich, Dark Green, Anchor Hocking	1.00
Depression Glass, Little Hostess Party Set, Moderntone, Platonite, 14 Piece	32.50
Depression Glass, Mold, Jello, Madrid, Amber, 2 In.	4.00
Depression Glass, Mug, Cherry Blossom, Green	58.00
Depression Glass, Nappy, Adam, Pink, 7 3/4 In.	4.00
Depression Glass, Nappy, Aunt Polly, Blue	3.25
Depression Glass, Nappy, Cameo, Rose, 5 In.	1.50
Depression Glass, Nappy, Cherry Blossom, Pink, 8 1/2 In.	6.00
Depression Glass, Nappy, Crystal, Platinum Trim, 4 1/4 In.	3.00

Depression Glass, **Nappy,** Cubist, Pink, 4 1/2 In. 1.00
Depression Glass, **Nappy,** Diana, Pink, 9 In. 3.50
Depression Glass, **Nappy,** Doric, Pink, 4 1/2 In. 1.25
Depression Glass, **Nappy,** Floral & Diamond Band, Aqua, Handled 7.50
Depression Glass, **Nappy,** Floral, Pink, 4 In. 2.25
Depression Glass, **Nappy,** Floral, Pink, 7 1/2 In. 5.00
Depression Glass, **Nappy,** Fortune, Pink, Handle, 4 1/2 In. .... .40
Depression Glass, **Nappy,** Georgian, Green, Lovebirds, 5 3/4 In. 2.50
Depression Glass, **Nappy,** Georgian, Green, 4 1/2 In. 1.50
Depression Glass, **Nappy,** Heritage, 5 In. 1.00
Depression Glass, **Nappy,** Iris, Scalloped, 5 1/2 In. 2.00
Depression Glass, **Nappy,** Lace Edge, Pink, 9 1/2 In. 3.00
Depression Glass, **Nappy,** Madrid, Amber, 5 In. .... 1.50 To 2.00
Depression Glass, **Nappy,** Madrid, Blue, 8 1/2 In. 9.50
Depression Glass, **Nappy,** Madrid, 5 In. 2.00
Depression Glass, **Nappy,** Moderntone, Blue, Platonite, 4 3/4 In. 1.00
Depression Glass, **Nappy,** Moderntone, Blue, Platonite, 5 In. 1.25
Depression Glass, **Nappy,** Moderntone, Blue, 9 In. 7.00
Depression Glass, **Nappy,** Moderntone, Green, Platonite, 4 3/4 In. 1.00
Depression Glass, **Nappy,** Moderntone, Green, Platonite, 5 In. 1.25
Depression Glass, **Nappy,** Moderntone, Pink, Platonite, 4 3/4 In. 1.00
Depression Glass, **Nappy,** Moderntone, Pink, Platonite, 5 In. 1.25
Depression Glass, **Nappy,** Moderntone, Yellow, Platonite, 4 3/4 In. 1.00
Depression Glass, **Nappy,** Moderntone, Yellow, Platonite, 5 In. 1.25
Depression Glass, **Nappy,** Moonstone, Crimped, 7 3/4 In. 3.75
Depression Glass, **Nappy,** No.612, Green, Horseshoe, 7 1/2 In. 5.00
Depression Glass, **Nappy,** Normandie, Sunburst Carnival, 5 In. .... 1.50 To 3.75
Depression Glass, **Nappy,** Normandie, Sunburst Carnival, 8 1/2 In. 6.00
Depression Glass, **Nappy,** Old Florentine, 4 In. 2.00
Depression Glass, **Nappy,** Patrician Spoke, Pink, 8 1/2 In. 6.00
Depression Glass, **Nappy,** Rosemary, Amber, 5 In. 2.00
Depression Glass, **Nappy,** Royal Lace, Blue, 2 Handled 7.00
Depression Glass, **Nappy,** Royal Lace, Green, 10 In. 8.00
Depression Glass, **Nappy,** Sandwich, Dark Green, Anchor Hocking 1.00
Depression Glass, **Nappy,** Sharon, Amber, 5 In. 1.25
Depression Glass, **Nappy,** Sharon, Amber, 8 1/2 In. 3.00
Depression Glass, **Nappy,** Sharon, Pink, 5 In. 2.00
Depression Glass, **Nappy,** Windsor, Pink, 4 3/4 In. .... 1.50 To 2.00
Depression Glass, **Parfait,** Poppy, Yellow 18.00
Depression Glass, **Pitcher,** Adam, Pink, 8 In. 10.00
Depression Glass, **Pitcher,** Cameo, Green, 8 1/2 In. 15.00
Depression Glass, **Pitcher,** Floral, Pink, Cone Shape, 8 In. 12.00
Depression Glass, **Pitcher,** Florentine No.2, 7 1/2 In. 18.00
Depression Glass, **Pitcher,** Florentine, Green, Footed, 6 3/4 In. 17.50
Depression Glass, **Pitcher,** Holiday, Pink, 4 1/2 In., 16 Ozs. 12.50
Depression Glass, **Pitcher,** Holiday, Pink, 7 In. 9.00
Depression Glass, **Pitcher,** Holiday, Pink, 52 Ozs. 9.75
Depression Glass, **Pitcher,** Iris, 9 1/2 In., 60 Ozs. .... 8.00 To 9.50
Depression Glass, **Pitcher,** Juice, Madrid, Amber 11.50
Depression Glass, **Pitcher,** Juice, Mayfair, Pink, Anchor Hocking 7.50
Depression Glass, **Pitcher,** Juice, Princess, Green 12.50
Depression Glass, **Pitcher,** Juice, Sandwich, Green, Anchor Hocking 65.00
Depression Glass, **Pitcher,** Lemonade, Floral, Green 90.00
Depression Glass, **Pitcher,** Madrid, Amber, 8 In. 17.50
Depression Glass, **Pitcher,** Madrid, Blue, Square, 8 In. 115.00
Depression Glass, **Pitcher,** Mayfair Open Rose, Pink, 6 In. 7.00
Depression Glass, **Pitcher,** Mayfair Open Rose, Pink, 8 In. 11.00
Depression Glass, **Pitcher,** Mayfair Open Rose, Pink, 83 Ozs. .... 25.00 To 35.00
Depression Glass, **Pitcher,** Milk, Holiday, Pink 12.00
Depression Glass, **Pitcher,** Patrician Spoke, Green, 8 In. 75.00
Depression Glass, **Pitcher,** Patrician Spoke, Pink, 8 In. 16.00
Depression Glass, **Pitcher,** Poppy, Yellow, 7 1/2 In. 9.75
Depression Glass, **Pitcher,** Princess, Green, 37 Ozs. 8.50
Depression Glass, **Pitcher,** Princess, Pink, 8 In. 17.50
Depression Glass, **Pitcher,** Princess, Pink, 60 Ozs. 18.00
Depression Glass, **Pitcher,** Royal Lace, Blue, Straight Sided, 54 Ozs. 40.00

Depression Glass, Pitcher, Royal Lace, 96 Ozs., 8 1/2 In. 27.50
Depression Glass, Pitcher, Royal Ruby, 3 Quart 15.00
Depression Glass, Pitcher, Sandwich, Green, Anchor Hocking, 1/2 Gallon 97.50
Depression Glass, Pitcher, Sharon, Pink, 9 In. 35.00
Depression Glass, Pitcher, Water, Floragold No.174, 64 Ozs. 15.00
Depression Glass, Pitcher, Water, Iris 8.50
Depression Glass, Pitcher, Water, Miss America, Pink 35.00
Depression Glass, Pitcher, Water, Miss America, Pink, Ice Lip 40.00
Depression Glass, Pitcher, Water, Poppy No.2 .... 6.50
Depression Glass, Pitcher, Water, Princess, Green 10.00
Depression Glass, Pitcher, Water, Princess, Pink 10.00
Depression Glass, Pitcher, Water, Royal Lace, Cobalt, Ice Lip 37.50
Depression Glass, Pitcher, Water, Sharon, Amber, Ice Lip 45.00
Depression Glass, Pitcher, Water, Sharon, Pink 40.00
Depression Glass, Pitcher, Waterford, Crystal, 42 Ozs. 3.50
Depression Glass, Pitcher, Waterford, Crystal, 80 Ozs. 6.50
Depression Glass, Pitcher, Windsor, Green, 6 1/2 In. 18.00
Depression Glass, Pitcher, Windsor, Pink, 6 1/2 In. 10.00
Depression Glass, Pitcher, Windsor, 4 1/2 In. 3.50
Depression Glass, Plate, Adam, Green, 7 3/4 In. 3.00
Depression Glass, Plate, Adam, Pink, 6 In. 1.00
Depression Glass, Plate, American Sweetheart, Monax, 6 In. 2.50
Depression Glass, Plate, American Sweetheart, Monax, 8 In. 3.50
Depression Glass, Plate, American Sweetheart, Monax, 9 In. .... 4.25 To 5.00
Depression Glass, Plate, American Sweetheart, Monax, 10 In. 6.50
Depression Glass, Plate, American Sweetheart, Monax, 15 1/2 In. .... 75.00 To 129.50
Depression Glass, Plate, American Sweetheart, Pink, 10 In. 3.25
Depression Glass, Plate, American Sweetheart, Pink, 12 In. 5.00
Depression Glass, Plate, American Sweetheart, Red, 8 In. 65.00
Depression Glass, Plate, Block, Green, 6 In. .... .75
Depression Glass, Plate, Block, Green, 8 In. 1.25
Depression Glass, Plate, Block, Pink, 6 In. 1.25
Depression Glass, Plate, Block, Pink, 8 1/2 In. 1.50
Depression Glass, Plate, Bread & Butter, American Sweetheart, Monax 3.00
Depression Glass, Plate, Bread & Butter, American Sweetheart, Pink, 6 In. 1.50
Depression Glass, Plate, Bread & Butter, Bubble, Light Blue, 6 3/4 In. .... .75
Depression Glass, Plate, Bread & Butter, Dogwood, Pink, 6 In. 1.50
Depression Glass, Plate, Bread & Butter, Mayfair Open Rose, Pink, 6 In. 2.00
Depression Glass, Plate, Bread & Butter, Normandie, Sunburst Carnival, 6 In. 1.50
Depression Glass, Plate, Bread & Butter, Pineapple & Floral, Amber 1.50
Depression Glass, Plate, Bread & Butter, Royal Lace, Pink, 6 In. 1.50
Depression Glass, Plate, Bread & Butter, S Pattern, Topaz, 6 In. 1.50
Depression Glass, Plate, Bread & Butter, Sharon, Pink, 6 In. 1.50
Depression Glass, Plate, Bubble, Blue, 9 1/2 In. 2.00
Depression Glass, Plate, Cake, Adam, Green, Footed 4.50
Depression Glass, Plate, Cake, Adam, Pink .... 4.50 To 7.00
Depression Glass, Plate, Cake, Adam, Pink, Footed, 10 In. 6.00
Depression Glass, Plate, Cake, American Sweetheart, Monax, 12 In. 10.00
Depression Glass, Plate, Cake, Cameo, Green 5.50
Depression Glass, Plate, Cake, Cameo, Green, Footed, 10 In. 7.00
Depression Glass, Plate, Cake, Cherry Blossom, Pink, Footed, 10 1/4 In. 6.00
Depression Glass, Plate, Cake, Dogwood, Green, 13 In. 23.00
Depression Glass, Plate, Cake, Doric, Green, Footed 6.00
Depression Glass, Plate, Cake, Holiday, Pink 10.00
Depression Glass, Plate, Cake, Mayfair Open Rose, Pink 3.90
Depression Glass, Plate, Cake, Mayfair Open Rose, Pink, Footed 5.00
Depression Glass, Plate, Cake, Mayfair Open Rose, Pink, Footed, Hocking, 10 In 6.00
Depression Glass, Plate, Cake, Miss America, Footed, 12 In. .... 9.00 To 10.00
Depression Glass, Plate, Cake, Miss America, Pink 9.75
Depression Glass, Plate, Cake, Miss America, Pink, Footed 10.00
Depression Glass, Plate, Cake, Patrician Spoke, Pink 5.50
Depression Glass, Plate, Cake, Petalware, Monax, 11 In. 4.00
Depression Glass, Plate, Cake, Petalware, Pink, 11 In. 4.00
Depression Glass, Plate, Cake, Princess, Green, Footed 7.50
Depression Glass, Plate, Cake, Queen Mary, Pink, 12 In. 4.00
Depression Glass, Plate, Cake, Rock Crystal, Amber, Footed, 11 In. 15.00

Depression Glass, Plate, Cake, Sharon, Pink, Footed, 11 1/2 In.	8.50
Depression Glass, Plate, Cake, Sunflower, Green, 10 In.	3.00
Depression Glass, Plate, Cake, Sunflower, Pink & Green, Footed	3.00
Depression Glass, Plate, Cake, Swirl, Aqua	8.00
Depression Glass, Plate, Cake, Swirl, Ultramarine, 12 3/4 In.	8.00
Depression Glass, Plate, Cameo, Green, Closed Handles, 10 1/2 In.	3.00
Depression Glass, Plate, Cameo, Green, Handled, 10 1/2 In.	3.00 To 4.50
Depression Glass, Plate, Cameo, Green, 6 In.	1.25
Depression Glass, Plate, Cameo, Green, 9 1/4 In.	1.85
Depression Glass, Plate, Cameo, Green, 9 1/2 In.	4.50
Depression Glass, Plate, Cameo, Green, 10 In.	4.00
Depression Glass, Plate, Cameo, Topaz, 6 In.	1.25 To 1.50
Depression Glass, Plate, Cameo, Yellow, 9 1/2 In.	3.00
Depression Glass, Plate, Cherry Blossom, Pink, 7 In.	2.25
Depression Glass, Plate, Cherry Blossom, Pink, 9 In.	3.50
Depression Glass, Plate, Child's, Doric & Pansy, Ultramarine, 6 In.	5.00
Depression Glass, Plate, Child's, Homespun, Pink	4.00
Depression Glass, Plate, Chinex, Ivory, 10 In.	4.50
Depression Glass, Plate, Chop, American Sweetheart, Monax, 11 In	7.00 To 8.00
Depression Glass, Plate, Cloverleaf, Green, 8 In.	1.50 To 2.50
Depression Glass, Plate, Colonial, Pink, 8 In.	1.25
Depression Glass, Plate, Columbia, 11 3/4 In.	2.75
Depression Glass, Plate, Crystal, Platinum Trim, 6 3/4 In.	1.75
Depression Glass, Plate, Cubist, Pink, 8 In.	1.75
Depression Glass, Plate, Daisy, Amber, 8 3/8 In.	2.00
Depression Glass, Plate, Daisy, Amber, 9 3/8 In.	2.75
Depression Glass, Plate, Diamond-Quilted, Pink, 6 In.	1.00
Depression Glass, Plate, Diamond-Quilted, Pink, 8 In.	1.75
Depression Glass, Plate, Diamond-Quilted, Pink, 8 1/4 In.	1.50
Depression Glass, Plate, Diana, Amber, 11 3/4 In.	5.00
Depression Glass, Plate, Diana, Pink, 6 In.	1.50 To 1.75
Depression Glass, Plate, Dinner, American Sweetheart, Pink, 10 In.	3.25
Depression Glass, Plate, Dinner, Bubble, Blue	2.00
Depression Glass, Plate, Dinner, Bubble, Light Blue, 9 1/4 In.	1.75
Depression Glass, Plate, Dinner, Cameo	4.50
Depression Glass, Plate, Dinner, Cameo, Green, 9 1/4 In.	4.00
Depression Glass, Plate, Dinner, Cameo, Yellow, 9 1/2 In.	2.25
Depression Glass, Plate, Dinner, Cherry, Delphite	10.00
Depression Glass, Plate, Dinner, Cherry, Green	4.75
Depression Glass, Plate, Dinner, Cherry, Pink	4.25
Depression Glass, Plate, Dinner, Colonial, Green	7.00
Depression Glass, Plate, Dinner, Doric, Pink	2.50
Depression Glass, Plate, Dinner, Floragold No.174	6.00
Depression Glass, Plate, Dinner, Floral, Green, 9 In.	3.00
Depression Glass, Plate, Dinner, Floral, Pink, 9 In.	2.25 To 3.00
Depression Glass, Plate, Dinner, Florentine No.2	2.50
Depression Glass, Plate, Dinner, Florentine No.2, Green	1.75
Depression Glass, Plate, Dinner, Florentine No.2, Yellow	2.00
Depression Glass, Plate, Dinner, Florentine, Topaz, 9 1/2 In.	2.00
Depression Glass, Plate, Dinner, Homespun, Pink	1.75 To 2.75
Depression Glass, Plate, Dinner, Iris, Amber, 9 In.	5.00
Depression Glass, Plate, Dinner, Lace Edge, Pink, 10 1/2 In.	3.50
Depression Glass, Plate, Dinner, Madrid, Amber, 10 1/2 In.	7.00
Depression Glass, Plate, Dinner, Mayfair, Pink, 9 1/4 In.	8.00
Depression Glass, Plate, Dinner, Miss America	2.25
Depression Glass, Plate, Dinner, Miss America, Pink, Label, 10 1/4 In.	7.50
Depression Glass, Plate, Dinner, Miss America, Pink, 10 1/2 In.	7.50
Depression Glass, Plate, Dinner, Miss America, 10 1/4 In.	4.50
Depression Glass, Plate, Dinner, Normandie, Iridescent	3.00
Depression Glass, Plate, Dinner, Normandie, Sunburst	4.75
Depression Glass, Plate, Dinner, Old Cafe, Pink	2.25
Depression Glass, Plate, Dinner, Old Florentine, 9 3/4 In.	2.75
Depression Glass, Plate, Dinner, Patrician, Amber, 10 1/2 In.	2.50
Depression Glass, Plate, Dinner, Patrician Spoke, Green, 10 1/2 In.	2.50
Depression Glass, Plate, Dinner, Patrician Spoke, Pink	3.75
Depression Glass, Plate, Dinner, Petalware, Monax, 9 1/4 In.	3.00

Depression Glass, Plate, Dinner, Princess, Pink, 9 1/2 In. 3.00
Depression Glass, Plate, Dinner, Princess, Topaz, 9 In. 3.00
Depression Glass, Plate, Dinner, Princess, Yellow 1.90
Depression Glass, Plate, Dinner, Rosemary, Amber, 9 1/2 In. 2.00
Depression Glass, Plate, Dinner, Royal Lace, Blue 9.00
Depression Glass, Plate, Dinner, Royal Ruby 2.00
Depression Glass, Plate, Dinner, Royal Ruby, Square 2.00
Depression Glass, Plate, Dinner, S Pattern, Yellow 4.00
Depression Glass, Plate, Dinner, Sandwich, Anchor Hocking 5.00
Depression Glass, Plate, Dinner, Sandwich, Green, Anchor Hocking 12.00
Depression Glass, Plate, Dinner, Sandwich, Light Green 2.75
Depression Glass, Plate, Dinner, Sharon, Amber .... 2.00 To 5.00
Depression Glass, Plate, Dinner, Sharon, Green, 9 1/4 In. 3.50
Depression Glass, Plate, Dinner, Sharon, Pink, 9 1/2 In. 2.50
Depression Glass, Plate, Dinner, Swirl, Ultramarine 2.50
Depression Glass, Plate, Dinner, Waterford, Crystal 1.25
Depression Glass, Plate, Dinner, Windsor 1.50
Depression Glass, Plate, Dinner, Windsor, Pink .... 2.00 To 2.25
Depression Glass, Plate, Dogwood, Pink, 6 In. 1.75
Depression Glass, Plate, Dogwood, Pink, 8 In. .... 1.40 To 2.25
Depression Glass, Plate, Dogwood, Pink, 9 In. 4.00
Depression Glass, Plate, Doric, Green, 6 In. 1.25
Depression Glass, Plate, Doric, Pink, 6 In. 1.00
Depression Glass, Plate, English Hobnail, Pink, 8 In. .... 2.75 To 4.50
Depression Glass, Plate, English Hobnail, 6 In. 1.25
Depression Glass, Plate, Fiesta, Blue, 9 1/2 In. 1.00
Depression Glass, Plate, Fiesta, Green, 9 1/2 In. 1.00
Depression Glass, Plate, Floral, Green, 8 In. 1.50
Depression Glass, Plate, Floral, Pink, 6 In. 1.00
Depression Glass, Plate, Florentine No.2, Yellow, 6 In. 1.50
Depression Glass, Plate, Fruits, Green, 8 In. .... 1.25 To 2.00
Depression Glass, Plate, Grill, Adam, Pink .... 1.90 To 3.00
Depression Glass, Plate, Grill, Cameo, Green .... 1.90 To 3.00
Depression Glass, Plate, Grill, Cameo, Topaz, 10 1/2 In. 3.00
Depression Glass, Plate, Grill, Cameo, Yellow, Closed Handles, 10 1/2 In. 2.50
Depression Glass, Plate, Grill, Cameo, Yellow, 10 1/2 In. 2.50
Depression Glass, Plate, Grill, Cherry Blossom, Green .... 3.00 To 4.00
Depression Glass, Plate, Grill, Cherry Blossom, Pink, 10 In. 3.50
Depression Glass, Plate, Grill, Cloverleaf, Green 3.75
Depression Glass, Plate, Grill, Daisy, 10 1/2 In. 1.50
Depression Glass, Plate, Grill, Dogwood, Pink 2.75
Depression Glass, Plate, Grill, Florentine, Topaz, 10 1/2 In. 2.00
Depression Glass, Plate, Grill, Lace Edge, Pink, 10 1/2 In. 3.50
Depression Glass, Plate, Grill, Madrid, Amber, 10 1/2 In. 4.00
Depression Glass, Plate, Grill, Madrid, Yellow 2.00
Depression Glass, Plate, Grill, Miss America, Pink .... 5.00 To 6.50
Depression Glass, Plate, Grill, Miss America, 10 1/4 In. 4.00
Depression Glass, Plate, Grill, Normandie, Sunburst Carnival .... 2.00 To 4.25
Depression Glass, Plate, Grill, Parrot, Amber 4.50
Depression Glass, Plate, Grill, Parrot, Green, Compartments 7.00
Depression Glass, Plate, Grill, Patrician Spoke, Amber 2.00
Depression Glass, Plate, Grill, Patrician Spoke, Green 3.00
Depression Glass, Plate, Grill, Patrician Spoke, 10 1/2 In. 2.00
Depression Glass, Plate, Grill, Princess, Pink, Handled, 11 1/2 In. 2.50
Depression Glass, Plate, Grill, Princess, Topaz, 10 1/4 In. 2.00
Depression Glass, Plate, Grill, Princess, Yellow 1.50
Depression Glass, Plate, Grill, Princess, Yellow, Handled, 10 1/2 In. 2.50
Depression Glass, Plate, Grill, Royal Lace, Blue 7.00
Depression Glass, Plate, Grill, Royal Lace, 10 In. 2.50
Depression Glass, Plate, Heritage, 6 In. 1.00
Depression Glass, Plate, Hobnail, Pink, 6 In. .... 1.00 To 1.50
Depression Glass, Plate, Hobnail, Pink, 8 1/2 In. 1.25
Depression Glass, Plate, Holiday, Pink, 5 7/8 In. 1.00
Depression Glass, Plate, Holiday, Pink, 6 In. 1.15
Depression Glass, Plate, Holiday, Pink, 9 In. .... 2.50 To 2.75
Depression Glass, Plate, Iris, 5 1/2 In. 1.25

Depression Glass, Plate, Iris, 9 In.	5.00
Depression Glass, Plate, Lace Edge, Pink, 8 In.	2.00
Depression Glass, Plate, Lace Edge, Pink, 8 1/2 In.	2.75
Depression Glass, Plate, Lace Edge, Pink, 10 1/2 In.	5.00
Depression Glass, Plate, Leaf No.132, Green, 8 In.	1.50
Depression Glass, Plate, Leaf No.132, Pink, 8 In.	1.50
Depression Glass, Plate, Lorain, Green, 5 1/2 In.	1.50
Depression Glass, Plate, Luncheon, American Sweetheart, Monax, 9 In.	5.00
Depression Glass, Plate, Luncheon, American Sweetheart, Pink, 9 In.	2.00
Depression Glass, Plate, Luncheon, Cameo, Green, Square	12.50
Depression Glass, Plate, Luncheon, Cameo, Green, 8 In.	2.50
Depression Glass, Plate, Luncheon, Cloverleaf, Black	6.00
Depression Glass, Plate, Luncheon, Cloverleaf, Green	1.50
Depression Glass, Plate, Luncheon, Dogwood, Green	3.00
Depression Glass, Plate, Luncheon, Dogwood, Pink, 8 In.	1.50
Depression Glass, Plate, Luncheon, English Hobnail, Green	3.50
Depression Glass, Plate, Luncheon, Floral & Diamond Band, Aqua, 8 In.	5.50
Depression Glass, Plate, Luncheon, Floral, Green	2.00
Depression Glass, Plate, Luncheon, Florentine, Yellow	2.00
Depression Glass, Plate, Luncheon, Georgian, Green, Lovebirds, 8 In.	1.75
Depression Glass, Plate, Luncheon, Georgian, Green, 8 1/2 In.	12.00
Depression Glass, Plate, Luncheon, Madrid, Amber, 8 7/8 In.	1.50
Depression Glass, Plate, Luncheon, Madrid, Amber, 9 In.	1.50
Depression Glass, Plate, Luncheon, Mayfair, Blue, 8 1/2 In.	7.50
Depression Glass, Plate, Luncheon, Mayfair, Pink, 8 1/2 In.	3.00
Depression Glass, Plate, Luncheon, No.173, Moonstone	4.00
Depression Glass, Plate, Luncheon, Old Florentine, 8 In.	1.75
Depression Glass, Plate, Luncheon, Pineapple & Floral, Amber	2.00
Depression Glass, Plate, Luncheon, Poppy No.2, Yellow	2.50
Depression Glass, Plate, Luncheon, Princess, Green	1.50
Depression Glass, Plate, Luncheon, Princess, Pink	3.75
Depression Glass, Plate, Luncheon, Royal Lace, Blue, 8 1/2 In.	5.90
Depression Glass, Plate, Luncheon, S Pattern, Topaz, 8 In.	1.50
Depression Glass, Plate, Luncheon, Sandwich, Anchor Hocking, 9 In.	2.50
Depression Glass, Plate, Madrid, Amber, 9 In.	1.00 To 2.50
Depression Glass, Plate, Madrid, Ice Blue, 9 In.	8.00
Depression Glass, Plate, Madrid, 10 1/2 In.	5.50
Depression Glass, Plate, Manhattan, 6 In.	1.00
Depression Glass, Plate, Manhattan, 10 1/4 In.	1.75
Depression Glass, Plate, Mayfair Open Rose, Blue, 9 1/2 In.	15.00
Depression Glass, Plate, Mayfair Open Rose, Pink, Anchor Hocking, 8 1/2 In.	3.50
Depression Glass, Plate, Mayfair Open Rose, Pink, 6 1/2 In.	2.00
Depression Glass, Plate, Mayfair Open Rose, Pink, 9 1/2 In.	7.50
Depression Glass, Plate, Miss America, Pink, 10 1/2 In.	5.50
Depression Glass, Plate, Moderntone, Blue With White Stripes, 9 In.	2.50
Depression Glass, Plate, Moderntone, Blue, Platonite, 9 In.	1.50
Depression Glass, Plate, Moderntone, Blue, 6 In.	.75
Depression Glass, Plate, Moderntone, Blue, 7 In.	1.00
Depression Glass, Plate, Moderntone, Blue, 8 In.	1.50
Depression Glass, Plate, Moderntone, Blue, 9 In.	2.00
Depression Glass, Plate, Moderntone, Blue, 10 1/2 In.	3.00
Depression Glass, Plate, Moderntone, Cobalt, 6 In.	1.25
Depression Glass, Plate, Moderntone, Cobalt, 7 In.	1.75
Depression Glass, Plate, Moderntone, Cobalt, 8 In.	2.50
Depression Glass, Plate, Moderntone, Cobalt, 9 In.	3.00
Depression Glass, Plate, Moderntone, Green, Platonite, 9 In.	1.50
Depression Glass, Plate, Moderntone, Pink, Platonite, 9 In.	1.50
Depression Glass, Plate, Moderntone, Ritz Blue, 7 3/4 In.	1.75
Depression Glass, Plate, Moderntone, Ritz Blue, 10 3/4 In.	6.00
Depression Glass, Plate, Moderntone, Yellow, 9 In.	1.50
Depression Glass, Plate, Moonstone, Crimped, 10 3/4 In.	5.50
Depression Glass, Plate, Moroccan, Amethyst, 9 1/2 In.	3.00
Depression Glass, Plate, Newport, Burgundy, 6 In.	1.25
Depression Glass, Plate, No.612, Green, 6 In.	1.50 To 2.00
Depression Glass, Plate, No.612, Green, 8 1/4 In.	2.25
Depression Glass, Plate, No.612, Green, 9 1/2 In.	2.50

Depression Glass, Plate, Normandie, Pink, 6 In. 1.25
Depression Glass, Plate, Normandie, Pink, 8 In. 1.50
Depression Glass, Plate, Old Florentine, 8 In. 1.50
Depression Glass, Plate, Oyster & Pearl, Ruby, 13 1/2 In. 10.00
Depression Glass, Plate, Patrician Spoke, Amber, 9 In. 1.50
Depression Glass, Plate, Patrician Spoke, Amber, 10 1/2 In. .... 1.25 To 2.00
Depression Glass, Plate, Patrician Spoke, Pink, 6 In. 2.25
Depression Glass, Plate, Patrician Spoke, Pink, 9 In. 3.00
Depression Glass, Plate, Patrician Spoke, Pink, 10 1/2 In. 7.50
Depression Glass, Plate, Petalware, Cremax, 6 1/2 In. 1.50
Depression Glass, Plate, Petalware, Cremax, 9 In. 3.00
Depression Glass, Plate, Petalware, Cremax, 11 In. 4.00
Depression Glass, Plate, Petalware, Monax, Rings, 9 1/2 In. 3.00
Depression Glass, Plate, Petalware, Monax, 6 In. 2.00
Depression Glass, Plate, Petalware, Monax, 8 In. 1.50
Depression Glass, Plate, Petalware, Monax, 11 In. 3.00
Depression Glass, Plate, Petalware, Pink, 6 In. 1.50
Depression Glass, Plate, Petalware, Pink, 8 In. 1.50
Depression Glass, Plate, Petalware, 11 In. 3.00
Depression Glass, Plate, Princess, Green, 7 1/2 In. 1.00
Depression Glass, Plate, Princess, Green, 8 In. .... 1.75 To 2.75
Depression Glass, Plate, Princess, Green, 9 In. .... 3.25 To 4.00
Depression Glass, Plate, Princess, Green, 9 1/2 In. .... 2.00 To 4.00
Depression Glass, Plate, Princess, Pink, Handled, 11 1/2 In. 3.75
Depression Glass, Plate, Princess, Yellow, 6 In. 1.25
Depression Glass, Plate, Princess, Yellow, 8 In. 2.00
Depression Glass, Plate, Princess, Yellow, 8 1/4 In. 3.00
Depression Glass, Plate, Roses, Pink, 10 In. 5.00
Depression Glass, Plate, Roulette, Green, 8 1/2 In. 1.00
Depression Glass, Plate, Royal Lace, Blue, 6 In. 2.90
Depression Glass, Plate, Royal Lace, Cobalt, 10 In. 10.00
Depression Glass, Plate, Royal Lace, Green, 10 1/2 In. 7.00
Depression Glass, Plate, Royal Ruby, 6 1/2 In. 1.50
Depression Glass, Plate, Salad, Adam, Green 2.00
Depression Glass, Plate, Salad, Adam, Pink, 7 3/4 In. 2.00
Depression Glass, Plate, Salad, American Sweetheart, Monax, 8 In. 4.00
Depression Glass, Plate, Salad, American Sweetheart, Pink 2.50
Depression Glass, Plate, Salad, Cherry Blossom, Green 3.50
Depression Glass, Plate, Salad, English Hobnail, 8 In. 1.50
Depression Glass, Plate, Salad, Floral, Green, 8 In. 2.00
Depression Glass, Plate, Salad, Floral, Pink, 8 In. 2.50
Depression Glass, Plate, Salad, Florentine No.2, Yellow 1.50
Depression Glass, Plate, Salad, Florentine, Green, 8 1/2 In. 1.75
Depression Glass, Plate, Salad, Horseshoe, Green, 8 3/8 In. 2.25
Depression Glass, Plate, Salad, Lace Edge, Pink 3.50
Depression Glass, Plate, Salad, Madrid, Amber, 7 1/2 In. 2.25
Depression Glass, Plate, Salad, Miss America, Pink, 8 1/2 In. 4.00
Depression Glass, Plate, Salad, Miss America, 8 1/2 In. 3.00
Depression Glass, Plate, Salad, Moderntone, Blue, Platonite, 6 3/4 In. 1.00
Depression Glass, Plate, Salad, Moderntone, Cobalt 1.00
Depression Glass, Plate, Salad, Moderntone, Green, Platonite, 6 3/4 In. 1.00
Depression Glass, Plate, Salad, Moderntone, Pink, Platonite, 6 3/4 In. 1.00
Depression Glass, Plate, Salad, Moderntone, Yellow, Platonite, 6 3/4 In. 1.00
Depression Glass, Plate, Salad, Petalware, Cremax, 3 Band, 8 In. 3.00
Depression Glass, Plate, Salad, Princess, Green 1.75
Depression Glass, Plate, Salad, Princess, Pink, 8 In. 2.00
Depression Glass, Plate, Salad, Royal Ruby, 7 3/4 In. 2.50
Depression Glass, Plate, Salad, Royal Ruby, 13 3/4 In. 8.00
Depression Glass, Plate, Salad, S Pattern, Yellow 2.75
Depression Glass, Plate, Salad, Swirl, Ultramarine 2.00
Depression Glass, Plate, Sandwich, Anchor Hocking, 8 In. 2.00
Depression Glass, Plate, Sandwich, Crystal 2.00
Depression Glass, Plate, Sandwich, Desert Gold, 12 In. 6.00
Depression Glass, Plate, Sandwich, English Hobnail, Green, 11 In. 6.00
Depression Glass, Plate, Sandwich, Indiana, Oval, Indent, 8 In. 2.00
Depression Glass, Plate, Sandwich, Light Green, 13 In. 7.50

Depression Glass, Plate, Sandwich, No.612 Horseshoe, Green, 11 1/2 In. 5.00
Depression Glass, Plate, Sandwich, Rock Crystal, Clear, Pres Cut, 11 In. 8.00
Depression Glass, Plate, Sharon, Amber, 6 In. 1.25
Depression Glass, Plate, Sharon, Amber, 7 1/2 In. 1.50
Depression Glass, Plate, Sharon, Pink, 6 In. 2.00
Depression Glass, Plate, Sharon, Pink, 8 In. 1.75
Depression Glass, Plate, Sharon, Pink, 9 In. 1.90
Depression Glass, Plate, Sharon, Pink, 9 1/4 In. 2.50
Depression Glass, Plate, Sherbet, Adam, Pink, 6 In. 1.50
Depression Glass, Plate, Sherbet, Aunt Polly, Blue, 6 In. 2.50
Depression Glass, Plate, Sherbet, Cameo, Yellow, 6 In. 1.25
Depression Glass, Plate, Sherbet, Cherry Blossom, Pink, 6 In. 2.00
Depression Glass, Plate, Sherbet, Floral, Green, 6 In. 1.50
Depression Glass, Plate, Sherbet, Floral, Pink, 6 In. 1.50
Depression Glass, Plate, Sherbet, Florentine, Green, 6 In. 1.50
Depression Glass, Plate, Sherbet, Florentine, Topaz, 6 In. 1.50
Depression Glass, Plate, Sherbet, Iris, Amber, 5 3/4 In. 2.00
Depression Glass, Plate, Sherbet, Knife & Fork, Pink, 6 1/2 In. 1.50
Depression Glass, Plate, Sherbet, Mayfair Open Rose, Pink 1.50
Depression Glass, Plate, Sherbet, Miss America, 5 3/4 In. 1.50
Depression Glass, Plate, Sherbet, No.612 Horseshoe, Green, 6 In. 2.00
Depression Glass, Plate, Sherbet, Normandie, Carnival .... 1.00 To 1.25
Depression Glass, Plate, Sherbet, Old Florentine, 6 In. 1.50
Depression Glass, Plate, Sherbet, Patrician Spoke, Green 1.50
Depression Glass, Plate, Sherbet, Princess, Pink, 6 In. 1.50
Depression Glass, Plate, Sherbet, Princess, Topaz, 6 In. 1.50
Depression Glass, Plate, Sherbet, Royal Lace, Blue 2.50
Depression Glass, Plate, Sherbet, Royal Lace, 6 In. 1.50
Depression Glass, Plate, Sherbet, Swirl, Ultramarine, 6 1/2 In. 2.25
Depression Glass, Plate, Sherbet, Windsor, Pink 1.00
Depression Glass, Plate, Sierra, Green, 9 In. 4.00
Depression Glass, Plate, Snack, Sandwich, Teal, Oval 5.75
Depression Glass, Plate, Soup, Bubble, Blue 2.50
Depression Glass, Plate, Swirl, Ultramarine, 8 3/4 In. 2.75
Depression Glass, Plate, Thistle, Pink, 8 In. 3.50
Depression Glass, Plate, Three Flower, Pink, 13 In. 5.00
Depression Glass, Plate, Windsor, Pink, 7 In. 1.50
Depression Glass, Platter, Adam, Green, 11 5/8 In. 6.00
Depression Glass, Platter, Adam, Pink, 11 5/8 In. 4.00
Depression Glass, Platter, American Sweetheart, Pink, 13 In. 8.00
Depression Glass, Platter, Bubble, Light Blue, 12 In. 3.00
Depression Glass, Platter, Cameo, Green, 10 1/2 In. 5.00
Depression Glass, Platter, Cherry Blossom, Green, 11 In. 6.50
Depression Glass, Platter, Floral, Green, 10 3/4 In. 5.00
Depression Glass, Platter, Floral, Pink, 10 3/4 In. 4.00
Depression Glass, Platter, Florentine, Topaz, 11 In. 6.00
Depression Glass, Platter, Florentine, Yellow, 11 1/2 In. 7.50
Depression Glass, Platter, Gravy Boat, Florentine No.2, Yellow 20.00
Depression Glass, Platter, Gravy Boat, Poppy No.2, Yellow 7.50
Depression Glass, Platter, Horseshoe, Green, 10 1/2 In. 6.50
Depression Glass, Platter, Lace Edge, Pink, 12 3/4 In. 5.00
Depression Glass, Platter, Madrid, Blue, 11 In. 9.50
Depression Glass, Platter, Mayfair, Pink, 12 In. 5.00
Depression Glass, Platter, Meat, Floral, Pink 4.00
Depression Glass, Platter, Meat, Princess, Green 4.00
Depression Glass, Platter, Miss America, Pink, Oval, 12 In. 8.00
Depression Glass, Platter, Miss America, Pink, 12 In. .... 6.00 To 8.00
Depression Glass, Platter, Miss America, 12 In. 6.00
Depression Glass, Platter, Moderntone, Blue, 11 In. 4.00
Depression Glass, Platter, Moderntone, Platonite, 12 In. 3.00
Depression Glass, Platter, Normandie, Sunburst Carnival, 12 In. 6.00
Depression Glass, Platter, Patrician Spoke, Green, 11 1/2 In. 6.00
Depression Glass, Platter, Petalware, Pink, 13 In. 5.00
Depression Glass, Platter, Princess, Pink, 12 In. 4.00
Depression Glass, Platter, Rosemary, Amber, 12 In. 4.00
Depression Glass, Platter, Rosemary, Pink, 12 In. 5.50

Depression Glass, **Platter**, Royal Lace, Pink, 13 In. .... 5.00 To 8.00
Depression Glass, **Platter**, Sharon, Amber, 12 1/2 In. .... 4.00 To 6.00
Depression Glass, **Platter**, Sharon, Pink, 12 1/2 In. 6.00
Depression Glass, **Punch Set**, Royal Ruby, 13 Piece 32.50
Depression Glass, **Reamer**, Sunkist, Green Opaque 15.00
Depression Glass, **Relish**, Adam, Pink, Divided 3.25
Depression Glass, **Relish**, Adam, Pink, 2 Sections, 8 In. 4.00
Depression Glass, **Relish**, Doric, Green 2.50
Depression Glass, **Relish**, Doric, Pink, Square, 8 In. 3.75
Depression Glass, **Relish**, Floral, Green, 2 Sections .... 3.75 To 4.00
Depression Glass, **Relish**, Floral, Pink 5.00
Depression Glass, **Relish**, Floral, Pink, 2 Sections 4.00
Depression Glass, **Relish**, Lace Edge, Pink, Oval, 5 Part 6.50
Depression Glass, **Relish**, Lace Edge, Pink, 10 In. 4.00
Depression Glass, **Relish**, Lace Edge, Pink, 3 Sections, 10 1/2 In. 5.00
Depression Glass, **Relish**, Madrid, Amber 2.75
Depression Glass, **Relish**, Madrid, Pink, 4 Sections, 10 1/4 In. 3.50
Depression Glass, **Relish**, Mayfair, Pink, 4 Sections 5.00
Depression Glass, **Relish**, Miss America, Divided, 12 In. 6.75
Depression Glass, **Relish**, Miss America, Pink, Round 5.00
Depression Glass, **Relish**, Miss America, Pink, 4 Sections 5.00
Depression Glass, **Relish**, Miss America, Pink, 8 3/4 In. 7.00
Depression Glass, **Relish**, Moonstone, Divided 3.00
Depression Glass, **Relish**, Moonstone, 2 Sections 3.50
Depression Glass, **Relish**, No.173, Moonstone, Divided 5.00
Depression Glass, **Relish**, No.612, Green, Divided 8.00
Depression Glass, **Relish**, No.612, Green, 3 Sections 5.00
Depression Glass, **Relish**, Princess, Pink, 4 Sections, 7 1/2 In. 4.50
Depression Glass, **Relish**, Three Flower, Pink 4.00
Depression Glass, **Salt & Pepper**, Adam, Green 35.00
Depression Glass, **Salt & Pepper**, Adam, Pink .... 12.00 To 22.00
Depression Glass, **Salt & Pepper**, American Sweetheart, Pink 125.00
Depression Glass, **Salt & Pepper**, Block Optic, Green 7.50
Depression Glass, **Salt & Pepper**, Block, Green .... 8.00 To 10.00
Depression Glass, **Salt & Pepper**, Cameo, Green .... 15.00 To 22.50
Depression Glass, **Salt & Pepper**, Cherry Blossom, Green 550.00
Depression Glass, **Salt & Pepper**, Cloverleaf, Green .... 9.00 To 25.00
Depression Glass, **Salt & Pepper**, Cubist, Green 12.00
Depression Glass, **Salt & Pepper**, Cubist, Pink 16.00
Depression Glass, **Salt & Pepper**, Doric, Pink 13.00
Depression Glass, **Salt & Pepper**, Dove, Green 8.00
Depression Glass, **Salt & Pepper**, English Hobnail, Milk Glass 9.75
Depression Glass, **Salt & Pepper**, Etched Band, Cobalt, Footed 8.00
Depression Glass, **Salt & Pepper**, Etched, Green, 4 In. 8.00
Depression Glass, **Salt & Pepper**, Floral, Green, 4 In. 20.00
Depression Glass, **Salt & Pepper**, Floral, Pink, Footed, 4 In. 15.00
Depression Glass, **Salt & Pepper**, Floral, Pink, 4 In. 15.00
Depression Glass, **Salt & Pepper**, Florentine No.1 .... 14.00
Depression Glass, **Salt & Pepper**, Florentine No.1, Green 18.00
Depression Glass, **Salt & Pepper**, Florentine No.2, Green .... 15.00 To 16.50
Depression Glass, **Salt & Pepper**, Florentine No.2, Yellow 20.00
Depression Glass, **Salt & Pepper**, Florentine, Green 20.00
Depression Glass, **Salt & Pepper**, Florentine, Poppy 5.00
Depression Glass, **Salt & Pepper**, Frosted, Painted Fruit, Anchor Hocking 8.00
Depression Glass, **Salt & Pepper**, Hazel Atlas, Cobalt 7.50
Depression Glass, **Salt & Pepper**, Hazel Atlas, Green 5.00
Depression Glass, **Salt & Pepper**, Madrid, Amber .... 18.00 To 22.00
Depression Glass, **Salt & Pepper**, Madrid, Amber, Footed 22.00
Depression Glass, **Salt & Pepper**, Madrid, Green 25.00
Depression Glass, **Salt & Pepper**, Manhattan, Pink, Square 4.00
Depression Glass, **Salt & Pepper**, Mayfair Open Rose 13.00
Depression Glass, **Salt & Pepper**, Mayfair Open Rose, Pink .... 15.00 To 30.00
Depression Glass, **Salt & Pepper**, Miss America .... 14.00 To 16.00
Depression Glass, **Salt & Pepper**, Miss America, Pink .... 22.00 To 22.50
Depression Glass, **Salt & Pepper**, Moderntone 9.50
Depression Glass, **Salt & Pepper**, Moderntone, Blue .... 5.00 To 9.00

Depression Glass, Salt & Pepper, Moderntone, Cobalt .... 9.50 To 15.00
Depression Glass, Salt & Pepper, Moderntone, Monax 8.00
Depression Glass, Salt & Pepper, Moderntone, Pink 5.00
Depression Glass, Salt & Pepper, No.119, Green, Anchor Hocking 5.00
Depression Glass, Salt & Pepper, No.121, Green, Anchor Hocking 5.00
Depression Glass, Salt & Pepper, No.201, Cobalt 7.00
Depression Glass, Salt & Pepper, Paneled, Green, Anchor Hocking 6.00
Depression Glass, Salt & Pepper, Parrot, Green 135.00
Depression Glass, Salt & Pepper, Patrician Spoke, Amber 9.00
Depression Glass, Salt & Pepper, Patrician Spoke, Green 35.00
Depression Glass, Salt & Pepper, Patrician Spoke, Pink 58.00
Depression Glass, Salt & Pepper, Poinsettia, Pink 12.00
Depression Glass, Salt & Pepper, Princess, Green, 4 1/2 In. 25.00
Depression Glass, Salt & Pepper, Princess, Pink 30.00
Depression Glass, Salt & Pepper, Princess, Yellow 28.00
Depression Glass, Salt & Pepper, Ribbed, Cobalt 5.00
Depression Glass, Salt & Pepper, Ribbon, Green .... 4.75 To 8.50
Depression Glass, Salt & Pepper, Royal Lace, Cobalt 80.00
Depression Glass, Salt & Pepper, Royal Lace, Pink .... 12.00 To 18.75
Depression Glass, Salt & Pepper, Sharon, Amber .... 10.00 To 20.00
Depression Glass, Salt & Pepper, Sharon, Green 27.50
Depression Glass, Salt & Pepper, Sharon, Pink .... 18.00 To 25.00
Depression Glass, Salt & Pepper, Swirl, Ultramarine 17.00
Depression Glass, Salt & Pepper, Tea Room, Pink 19.50
Depression Glass, Salt & Pepper, Waterford 4.00
Depression Glass, Salt & Pepper, Waterford, Crystal 3.00
Depression Glass, Salt & Pepper, Windsor 7.00
Depression Glass, Salt & Pepper, Windsor, Pink 8.75
Depression Glass, Salt Dip, Crystal 2.00
Depression Glass, Salt, English Hobnail, Clear, Pedestal 2.00
Depression Glass, Salt, English Hobnail, Pink, Pedestal 2.50
Depression Glass, Salt, Madrid, Ritz Blue, Footed 25.00
Depression Glass, Saltshaker, Adam, Pink 12.00
Depression Glass, Saltshaker, Bouquet & Lattice, Pink 15.00
Depression Glass, Saltshaker, English Hobnail, Pink 10.00
Depression Glass, Saltshaker, Floral, Green, Footed, 4 In. 7.50
Depression Glass, Saltshaker, Floral, Pink 12.50
Depression Glass, Saltshaker, Florentine, Yellow 6.00
Depression Glass, Saltshaker, Madrid, Amber 7.75
Depression Glass, Saltshaker, Moderntone, Cobalt 5.00
Depression Glass, Saltshaker, Normandie, Amber 8.00
Depression Glass, Salver, American Sweetheart, Monax, 12 In. .... 7.50 To 8.00
Depression Glass, Salver, American Sweetheart, Pink, 12 In. .... 3.75 To 5.00
Depression Glass, Salver, American Sweetheart, Ruby Red, 12 In. 95.00
Depression Glass, Salver, Dogwood, Monax, 12 In. 18.50
Depression Glass, Salver, Dogwood, Pink, 12 In. 6.00
Depression Glass, Salver, Petalware, Cremax, 3 Band, 11 In. 4.00
Depression Glass, Sauce, Mayfair Open Rose, Pink 2.00
Depression Glass, Sauce, Sharon, Amber 1.25
Depression Glass, Saucer, Adam, Green .... 1.50 To 2.00
Depression Glass, Saucer, Adam, Pink 1.50
Depression Glass, Saucer, American Sweetheart, Monax 2.25
Depression Glass, Saucer, American Sweetheart, Pink 1.50
Depression Glass, Saucer, Block, Pink 1.50
Depression Glass, Saucer, Bubble, Blue 1.00
Depression Glass, Saucer, Bubble, Light Blue 1.00
Depression Glass, Saucer, Cameo, Green 1.00
Depression Glass, Saucer, Cherry Blossom, Blue 5.00
Depression Glass, Saucer, Cherry Blossom, Green 1.75
Depression Glass, Saucer, Cherry Blossom, Pink 2.00
Depression Glass, Saucer, Child's, Cherry Blossom, Delphite 4.75
Depression Glass, Saucer, Child's, Diana 1.00
Depression Glass, Saucer, Child's, Doric & Pansy, Ultramarine 6.50
Depression Glass, Saucer, Chinex, Ivory 2.50
Depression Glass, Saucer, Cloverleaf, Black 2.50
Depression Glass, Saucer, Cloverleaf, Green .... .50 To 1.25

Depression Glass, Saucer, Cloverleaf, Pink 1.25
Depression Glass, Saucer, Daisy, Amber 1.00
Depression Glass, Saucer, Diana, Pink 1.75
Depression Glass, Saucer, Dogwood, Pink 1.50
Depression Glass, Saucer, Doric & Pansy, Pink 5.00
Depression Glass, Saucer, Doric, Green 1.00
Depression Glass, Saucer, Doric, Pink .... 1.25 To 1.75
Depression Glass, Saucer, Floragold No.174 .... 1.75
Depression Glass, Saucer, Floral, Pink 1.50
Depression Glass, Saucer, Florentine No.2, Yellow 1.50
Depression Glass, Saucer, Florentine, Topaz 3.00
Depression Glass, Saucer, Horseshoe, Green 2.50
Depression Glass, Saucer, Lace Edge, Pink .... 1.00 To 3.00
Depression Glass, Saucer, Lorain, Green 1.50
Depression Glass, Saucer, Madrid, Amber 1.50
Depression Glass, Saucer, Mayfair, Moonstone 1.50
Depression Glass, Saucer, Mayfair, Pink, Cup Ring 5.00
Depression Glass, Saucer, Miss America 2.00
Depression Glass, Saucer, Miss America, Pink .... 1.50 To 2.50
Depression Glass, Saucer, Moderntone, Blue, Platonite .... .50
Depression Glass, Saucer, Moderntone, Green, Platonite .... .50
Depression Glass, Saucer, Moderntone, Pink, Platonite .... .50
Depression Glass, Saucer, Moderntone, Yellow, Platonite .... .50
Depression Glass, Saucer, No.612 Horseshoe, Green 1.75
Depression Glass, Saucer, No.612, Green .... 2.00 To 2.25
Depression Glass, Saucer, Normandie, Sunburst Carnival 1.50
Depression Glass, Saucer, Old Florentine 1.50
Depression Glass, Saucer, Patrician Spoke, Amber 1.50
Depression Glass, Saucer, Patrician Spoke, Green 1.50
Depression Glass, Saucer, Patrician Spoke, Pink 1.50
Depression Glass, Saucer, Petalware .... .80
Depression Glass, Saucer, Petalware, Cremax .... 1.00 To 1.25
Depression Glass, Saucer, Petalware, Monax 2.00
Depression Glass, Saucer, Princess, Pink 1.50
Depression Glass, Saucer, Princess, Yellow 1.50
Depression Glass, Saucer, Ribbon Candy .... .75
Depression Glass, Saucer, Rosemary, Amber 1.50
Depression Glass, Saucer, Royal Lace, Pink 1.50
Depression Glass, Saucer, S Pattern, Topaz 1.50
Depression Glass, Saucer, Sandwich, Amber, Indiana 1.00
Depression Glass, Saucer, Sandwich, Anchor Hocking .... 1.00 To 1.50
Depression Glass, Saucer, Sandwich, Green, Lacy 1.00
Depression Glass, Saucer, Sharon, Amber .... 1.25 To 1.50
Depression Glass, Saucer, Sharon, Pink .... 1.00 To 1.50
Depression Glass, Saucer, Swirl, Ultramarine .... 1.00 To 2.00
Depression Glass, Saucer, Waterford, Pink 1.00
Depression Glass, Server, Tidbit, Dogwood, Pink, 2 Tiers 39.00
Depression Glass, Sherbet, Adam, Pink 4.00
Depression Glass, Sherbet, American Sweetheart, Metal Holder 5.00
Depression Glass, Sherbet, American Sweetheart, Monax, 4 1/4 In. 6.50
Depression Glass, Sherbet, American Sweetheart, Monax, 4 1/2 In. 8.00
Depression Glass, Sherbet, American Sweetheart, Pink, Low Footed, 4 In. 3.25
Depression Glass, Sherbet, Block Optic, Green 2.50
Depression Glass, Sherbet, Block, Green, 5 In. 3.75
Depression Glass, Sherbet, Block, Pink, Round 1.50
Depression Glass, Sherbet, Cameo, Green, Stemmed, 5 In. 9.75
Depression Glass, Sherbet, Cherry Blossom, Green .... 4.00 To 4.50
Depression Glass, Sherbet, Cherry Blossom, Pink .... 3.25 To 3.50
Depression Glass, Sherbet, Cloverleaf, Black .... 6.50 To 7.50
Depression Glass, Sherbet, Cloverleaf, Green .... 1.50 To 2.00
Depression Glass, Sherbet, Colonial, Footed 2.00
Depression Glass, Sherbet, Colonial, Pink 1.75
Depression Glass, Sherbet, Crystal 1.50
Depression Glass, Sherbet, Cubist, Pink 2.00
Depression Glass, Sherbet, Dogwood, Pink, Low Footed 3.00
Depression Glass, Sherbet, Floragold No.174, Low Footed 3.00

Depression Glass, Sherbet, Floral & Diamond, Green 2.00
Depression Glass, Sherbet, Floral, Green .... 2.50 To 3.00
Depression Glass, Sherbet, Floral, Pink .... 2.25 To 2.50
Depression Glass, Sherbet, Florentine No.1, Footed 2.00
Depression Glass, Sherbet, Florentine No.1, Pink 2.00
Depression Glass, Sherbet, Florentine No.2, Yellow 2.50
Depression Glass, Sherbet, Florentine, Green 2.50
Depression Glass, Sherbet, Georgian, Green .... 2.00 To 2.50
Depression Glass, Sherbet, Georgian, Green, Lovebirds 2.00
Depression Glass, Sherbet, Holiday, Pink 1.50
Depression Glass, Sherbet, Iris, Amber, Low Footed, 2 1/2 In. 3.00
Depression Glass, Sherbet, Iris, 4 In. 3.00
Depression Glass, Sherbet, Knife & Fork, Pink 3.00
Depression Glass, Sherbet, Madrid, Amber .... .90 To 1.75
Depression Glass, Sherbet, Madrid, Topaz 10.00
Depression Glass, Sherbet, Manhattan 1.00
Depression Glass, Sherbet, Manhattan, Pink 2.00
Depression Glass, Sherbet, Mayfair, Pink, 3 1/4 In. 3.00
Depression Glass, Sherbet, Miss America 3.50
Depression Glass, Sherbet, Miss America, Pink .... 3.50 To 6.50
Depression Glass, Sherbet, Moderntone, Blue 1.50
Depression Glass, Sherbet, Moderntone, Blue, Platonite, Footed 2.00
Depression Glass, Sherbet, Moderntone, Green, Platonite, Footed 2.00
Depression Glass, Sherbet, Moderntone, Pink, Platonite, Footed 2.00
Depression Glass, Sherbet, Moderntone, Yellow, Platonite, Footed 2.00
Depression Glass, Sherbet, Moonstone .... 2.50 To 3.00
Depression Glass, Sherbet, New Century, Green 1.25
Depression Glass, Sherbet, No.612 Horseshoe, Green 3.00
Depression Glass, Sherbet, No.612, Green 4.50
Depression Glass, Sherbet, Normandie, Pink .... 1.25 To 2.00
Depression Glass, Sherbet, Normandie, Sunburst Carnival .... 2.00 To 3.50
Depression Glass, Sherbet, Old Florentine .... 2.00 To 2.50
Depression Glass, Sherbet, Optic Paneled No.187 .... 1.25
Depression Glass, Sherbet, Parrot, Green, 3 In. 3.50
Depression Glass, Sherbet, Patrician Spoke, Amber .... 1.50 To 2.50
Depression Glass, Sherbet, Patrician Spoke, Green 3.00
Depression Glass, Sherbet, Petalware, Monax 2.50
Depression Glass, Sherbet, Pineapple & Floral, Clear 5.00
Depression Glass, Sherbet, Princess, Green .... 2.50 To 3.00
Depression Glass, Sherbet, Princess, Pink .... 1.50 To 3.00
Depression Glass, Sherbet, Roulette, Green 1.00
Depression Glass, Sherbet, Royal Lace, Blue 7.00
Depression Glass, Sherbet, Royal Lace, Green, Footed 6.50
Depression Glass, Sherbet, Royal Lace, Pink 3.00
Depression Glass, Sherbet, Royal Ruby 2.00
Depression Glass, Sherbet, Sandwich, Light Pink, Footed, Westmoreland 3.75
Depression Glass, Sherbet, Sandwich, Rose Pink, Footed, Westmoreland 3.75
Depression Glass, Sherbet, Sharon, Pink .... 2.75 To 3.00
Depression Glass, Sherbet, Swirl, Ultramarine 2.50
Depression Glass, Sherbet, Tea Room, Pink, Footed 3.50
Depression Glass, Sherbet, Twisted Optic, Green 2.50
Depression Glass, Sherbet, Windsor 1.25
Depression Glass, Sherbet, Windsor, Green 4.50
Depression Glass, Spice Shaker, Princess, Green, Tall 17.50
Depression Glass, Squeezer, Orange, Fine Ribbed, Green 3.00
Depression Glass, Squeezer, Orange, Sunkist, Milk Glass 6.00
Depression Glass, Sugar & Creamer On Tray, Sandwich, Indiana ....
Depression Glass, Sugar & Creamer, American Sweetheart, Monax .... 9.00 To 15.00
Depression Glass, Sugar & Creamer, American Sweetheart, Monax, Cover 100.00
Depression Glass, Sugar & Creamer, American Sweetheart, Opalescent 15.00
Depression Glass, Sugar & Creamer, American Sweetheart, Pink 6.00
Depression Glass, Sugar & Creamer, Block Optic, Green, Low 4.00
Depression Glass, Sugar & Creamer, Block Optic, Pink 7.50
Depression Glass, Sugar & Creamer, Block, Green .... 4.00 To 5.00
Depression Glass, Sugar & Creamer, Block, Green, Cone Shape 4.00
Depression Glass, Sugar & Creamer, Bubble 5.00

Depression Glass, Sugar & Creamer, Bubble, Green 5.50
Depression Glass, Sugar & Creamer, Bubble, Light Blue 7.00
Depression Glass, Sugar & Creamer, Cameo, Green, Sunflower Shape 6.50
Depression Glass, Sugar & Creamer, Cherry Blossom, Green .... 10.50 To 13.00
Depression Glass, Sugar & Creamer, Cherry Blossom, Pink 9.00
Depression Glass, Sugar & Creamer, Cherry Blossom, Pink, Cover 10.00
Depression Glass, Sugar & Creamer, Child's, Cherry Delphite, Blue 50.00
Depression Glass, Sugar & Creamer, Child's, Moderntone, Pink 6.00
Depression Glass, Sugar & Creamer, Child's, Scottie Dog, Laurel 60.00
Depression Glass, Sugar & Creamer, Cloverleaf, Black .... 2.50 To 12.00
Depression Glass, Sugar & Creamer, Cloverleaf, Green .... 6.00 To 8.00
Depression Glass, Sugar & Creamer, Colonial Block, Green 7.00
Depression Glass, Sugar & Creamer, Colonial, Green, Cover 13.50
Depression Glass, Sugar & Creamer, Colonial, Green, Fluted 5.50
Depression Glass, Sugar & Creamer, Crystal, Anchor Hocking 4.00
Depression Glass, Sugar & Creamer, Cubist 3.50
Depression Glass, Sugar & Creamer, Cubist, Amber 5.00
Depression Glass, Sugar & Creamer, Cubist, Green 7.50
Depression Glass, Sugar & Creamer, Cubist, Green, Cover, 3 In. 12.00
Depression Glass, Sugar & Creamer, Cubist, Pink, Cover 6.00
Depression Glass, Sugar & Creamer, Cubist, Pink, Short 3.50
Depression Glass, Sugar & Creamer, Daisy, Amber 5.00
Depression Glass, Sugar & Creamer, Diamond-Quilted, Pink .... 4.50 To 5.50
Depression Glass, Sugar & Creamer, Diana, Amber 6.00
Depression Glass, Sugar & Creamer, Dogwood, Pink 10.00
Depression Glass, Sugar & Creamer, Doric, Pink, Cover 9.00
Depression Glass, Sugar & Creamer, English Hobnail 5.00
Depression Glass, Sugar & Creamer, English Hobnail, Footed 7.00
Depression Glass, Sugar & Creamer, Floragold No.174 .... 6.00
Depression Glass, Sugar & Creamer, Floragold, Cover 5.50
Depression Glass, Sugar & Creamer, Floral Sterling No.392, Black 8.00
Depression Glass, Sugar & Creamer, Floral, Pink, Cover .... 6.50 To 12.00
Depression Glass, Sugar & Creamer, Florentine No.2, Yellow, Cover 7.50
Depression Glass, Sugar & Creamer, Florentine, Topaz 7.00
Depression Glass, Sugar & Creamer, Florentine, Yellow 9.00
Depression Glass, Sugar & Creamer, Georgian, Green, Lovebirds 5.00
Depression Glass, Sugar & Creamer, Georgian, Green, 3 In. 3.00
Depression Glass, Sugar & Creamer, Holiday, Pink, Cover 7.50
Depression Glass, Sugar & Creamer, Iris 5.50
Depression Glass, Sugar & Creamer, Iris, Amber, Cover 9.00
Depression Glass, Sugar & Creamer, Iris, Cover .... 5.25 To 12.50
Depression Glass, Sugar & Creamer, Lace Edge, Pink 11.00
Depression Glass, Sugar & Creamer, Lightning, Green 7.50
Depression Glass, Sugar & Creamer, Lorain, Amber 7.00
Depression Glass, Sugar & Creamer, Lovebirds, Green, Short 7.00
Depression Glass, Sugar & Creamer, Lydia Ray, Green 9.00
Depression Glass, Sugar & Creamer, Madrid, Amber .... 2.00 To 5.50
Depression Glass, Sugar & Creamer, Madrid, Amber, Cover 7.50
Depression Glass, Sugar & Creamer, Manhattan 4.00
Depression Glass, Sugar & Creamer, Mayfair Open Rose, Amber, Federal 8.75
Depression Glass, Sugar & Creamer, Mayfair Open Rose, Moonstone 5.00
Depression Glass, Sugar & Creamer, Mayfair Open Rose, Pink .... 6.00 To 10.00
Depression Glass, Sugar & Creamer, Miss America .... 10.00 To 12.50
Depression Glass, Sugar & Creamer, Modern Art, Green 8.50
Depression Glass, Sugar & Creamer, Moderntone, Blue .... 3.50 To 9.00
Depression Glass, Sugar & Creamer, Moderntone, Cobalt 7.00
Depression Glass, Sugar & Creamer, Moonstone 6.00
Depression Glass, Sugar & Creamer, Newport, Cobalt 7.75
Depression Glass, Sugar & Creamer, Newport, Platonite 2.25
Depression Glass, Sugar & Creamer, No.173, Moonstone .... 5.00 To 7.00
Depression Glass, Sugar & Creamer, No.612, Green .... 7.50 To 9.50
Depression Glass, Sugar & Creamer, Old Florentine 6.00
Depression Glass, Sugar & Creamer, Old Florentine, Green 6.00
Depression Glass, Sugar & Creamer, Old Florentine, Topaz 6.00
Depression Glass, Sugar & Creamer, Ovide, Black .... 9.50 To 10.50
Depression Glass, Sugar & Creamer, Parrot, Green 15.00

Depression Glass, Sugar & Creamer, Patrician Spoke, Amber .... 4.00 To 6.00
Depression Glass, Sugar & Creamer, Patrician Spoke, Pink, Cover 7.50
Depression Glass, Sugar & Creamer, Petalware, Monax .... 6.00 To 7.00
Depression Glass, Sugar & Creamer, Petalware, Monax, Flowers 7.50
Depression Glass, Sugar & Creamer, Pineapple & Floral, Amber 6.50
Depression Glass, Sugar & Creamer, Poppy No.2, Amber 7.00
Depression Glass, Sugar & Creamer, Princess, Green .... 6.00 To 9.50
Depression Glass, Sugar & Creamer, Princess, Topaz 6.00
Depression Glass, Sugar & Creamer, Princess, Yellow 7.00
Depression Glass, Sugar & Creamer, Queen Mary 5.00
Depression Glass, Sugar & Creamer, Queen Mary, Pink 5.00
Depression Glass, Sugar & Creamer, Ribbon Candy 8.00
Depression Glass, Sugar & Creamer, Ripple, Green 5.50
Depression Glass, Sugar & Creamer, Rosemary, Amber 5.00
Depression Glass, Sugar & Creamer, Royal Lace 8.00
Depression Glass, Sugar & Creamer, Royal Lace, Blue 19.00
Depression Glass, Sugar & Creamer, Royal Lace, Cover 9.50
Depression Glass, Sugar & Creamer, Royal Lace, Green 10.00
Depression Glass, Sugar & Creamer, Royal Lace, Pink .... 8.00 To 10.00
Depression Glass, Sugar & Creamer, Royal Lace, Pink, Cover 11.00
Depression Glass, Sugar & Creamer, Royal Ruby .... 5.00 To 6.00
Depression Glass, Sugar & Creamer, Ruby Thumbprint, Dinner Size 12.00
Depression Glass, Sugar & Creamer, Sandwich 7.00
Depression Glass, Sugar & Creamer, Sandwich, Anchor Hocking 4.50
Depression Glass, Sugar & Creamer, Sandwich, Cover, Anchor Hocking 5.00
Depression Glass, Sugar & Creamer, Sandwich, Dark Green, Anchor Hocking 14.25
Depression Glass, Sugar & Creamer, Sandwich, Green 17.50
Depression Glass, Sugar & Creamer, Sandwich, Westmoreland 4.75
Depression Glass, Sugar & Creamer, Sharon, Amber .... 5.00 To 6.50
Depression Glass, Sugar & Creamer, Sharon, Amber, Cover .... 10.00 To 12.00
Depression Glass, Sugar & Creamer, Sharon, Green, Cover 25.00
Depression Glass, Sugar & Creamer, Sharon, Pink 4.50
Depression Glass, Sugar & Creamer, Sharon, Pink, Cover .... 9.50 To 11.00
Depression Glass, Sugar & Creamer, Starlight 4.00
Depression Glass, Sugar & Creamer, Sunflower, Pink 8.00
Depression Glass, Sugar & Creamer, Swirl, Pink 6.00
Depression Glass, Sugar & Creamer, Swirl, Ultramarine 7.00
Depression Glass, Sugar & Creamer, Tea Room, Pink .... 7.00 To 8.50
Depression Glass, Sugar & Creamer, Vitrock 6.50
Depression Glass, Sugar & Creamer, Waterford, Cover .... 4.50 To 5.00
Depression Glass, Sugar & Creamer, Waterford, Crystal, Cover .... 3.25 To 5.50
Depression Glass, Sugar & Creamer, Windsor, Pink 7.00
Depression Glass, Sugar & Creamer, Windsor, Pink, Cover .... 7.00 To 8.50
Depression Glass, Sugar, American Sweetheart, Monax 5.00
Depression Glass, Sugar, American Sweetheart, Pink 3.00
Depression Glass, Sugar, Block Optic, Green, Conical 2.50
Depression Glass, Sugar, Block, Green, Cone Shape 4.00
Depression Glass, Sugar, Block, Pink, Cone Shape 4.00
Depression Glass, Sugar, Cameo, Green, 3 1/4 In. 2.50
Depression Glass, Sugar, Cherry Blossom, Delphite .... 12.75 To 14.00
Depression Glass, Sugar, Cherry Blossom, Green, Covered 5.50
Depression Glass, Sugar, Child's, Cherry Blossom, Blue 22.50
Depression Glass, Sugar, Child's, Doric & Pansy, Pink 25.00
Depression Glass, Sugar, Child's, Doric & Pansy, Ultramarine 25.00
Depression Glass, Sugar, Cloverleaf, Black 5.00
Depression Glass, Sugar, Creamer, & Tray, Block, Green, Handled Tray 16.00
Depression Glass, Sugar, Creamer, & Tray, Candlewick, Kidney-Shaped Tray 7.50
Depression Glass, Sugar, Crystal 1.50
Depression Glass, Sugar, Cubist 1.25
Depression Glass, Sugar, Doric, Green 3.00
Depression Glass, Sugar, Floragold No.174 .... 3.00
Depression Glass, Sugar, Floragold, Iridescent, Covered 5.00
Depression Glass, Sugar, Floral, Green 2.50
Depression Glass, Sugar, Floral, Green, Covered 4.00
Depression Glass, Sugar, Floral, Pink 3.00
Depression Glass, Sugar, Floral, Pink, Covered .... 4.50 To 6.50

Depression Glass, Sugar, Florentine, Yellow 4.00
Depression Glass, Sugar, Georgian, Green, 4 In. 3.00
Depression Glass, Sugar, Iris, Covered 3.50
Depression Glass, Sugar, Lace Edge, Pink 4.00
Depression Glass, Sugar, Lovebirds, Green 3.25
Depression Glass, Sugar, Madrid, Blue 6.00
Depression Glass, Sugar, Mayfair, Pink, Anchor Hocking 4.00
Depression Glass, Sugar, Miss America .... 3.25 To 3.50
Depression Glass, Sugar, Miss America, Pink 6.00
Depression Glass, Sugar, Moderntone, Green, Platonite 1.25
Depression Glass, Sugar, Moderntone, Pink, Platonite 1.25
Depression Glass, Sugar, Moderntone, Ritz Blue 2.50
Depression Glass, Sugar, No.612 Horseshoe, Green 4.00
Depression Glass, Sugar, No.612, Green 4.00
Depression Glass, Sugar, Normandie, Amber, Covered 97.50
Depression Glass, Sugar, Normandie, Iridescent 2.50
Depression Glass, Sugar, Patrician Spoke, Amber 3.00
Depression Glass, Sugar, Patrician Spoke, Green 5.00
Depression Glass, Sugar, Patrician Spoke, Pink 3.00
Depression Glass, Sugar, Petalware, Cremax 2.00
Depression Glass, Sugar, Petalware, Monax 3.00
Depression Glass, Sugar, Poppy, Covered 7.50
Depression Glass, Sugar, Princess, Green, Covered 10.00
Depression Glass, Sugar, Princess, Yellow, Covered 10.00
Depression Glass, Sugar, Queen Mary, Pink 2.00
Depression Glass, Sugar, Royal Lace .... 3.00 To 3.75
Depression Glass, Sugar, Royal Lace, Blue 13.00
Depression Glass, Sugar, Royal Lace, Pink, Covered 15.00
Depression Glass, Sugar, Sandwich, Hocking 2.00
Depression Glass, Sugar, Sharon, Amber 2.75
Depression Glass, Sugar, Sharon, Pink 2.75
Depression Glass, Sugar, Sharon, Pink, Covered .... 5.50 To 7.50
Depression Glass, Sugar, Swirl, Ultramarine 3.50
Depression Glass, Sugar, Tea Room, Green 3.00
Depression Glass, Sugar, Waterford, Crystal 1.00
Depression Glass, Sugar, Waterford, Pink 2.25
Depression Glass, Sugar, Windsor, Covered 3.00
Depression Glass, Sugar, Windsor, Pink .... 2.00 To 7.00
Depression Glass, Tea Set, Child's, Doric & Pansy, 14 Piece 135.00
Depression Glass, Tray, Candy, Old Cafe, Pink, Flared 3.00
Depression Glass, Tray, Cherry Blossom, Green, 10 1/4 In. 6.00
Depression Glass, Tray, Domino, Cameo, Green 25.00
Depression Glass, Tray, Doric & Pansy, Ultramarine, Handled, 10 In. 10.00
Depression Glass, Tray, Doric, Green, Handled, 10 In. 4.25
Depression Glass, Tray, Floral, Pink, Handled, Square, 6 In. 7.00
Depression Glass, Tray, Mint, Old Cafe, Pink, Low, 8 In. 1.50
Depression Glass, Tray, Sandwich, Cherry Blossom, Pink 7.00
Depression Glass, Tray, Sandwich, Cherry Blossom, Pink, Handled, 10 1/2 In. 6.00
Depression Glass, Tray, Sandwich, Etched, Green, Center Handle 6.00
Depression Glass, Tray, Sandwich, Iris, Amber, 12 In. 6.00
Depression Glass, Tray, Sandwich, Mayfair, Pink, Center Handle 6.50
Depression Glass, Tray, Sandwich, Princess, Green 4.00
Depression Glass, Tray, Sandwich, Windsor, Pink 4.00
Depression Glass, Tray, Serving, Doric, Pink, 8 X 8 In. 4.00
Depression Glass, Tray, Serving, Waterford, Crystal, 13 1/2 In. 4.25
Depression Glass, Tray, Serving, Windsor, Pink, 13 1/2 In. 8.00
Depression Glass, Tray, Sierra, Green, Handled, 10 1/2 In. 4.50
Depression Glass, Tray, Swirl, Ultramarine, 12 In. 6.50
Depression Glass, Tray, Torte, Floragold 6.00
Depression Glass, Tray, Windsor, Pink, 10 1/4 In. 3.50
Depression Glass, Tub, Ice, Angelfish, Blue 5.00
Depression Glass, Tumbler, Adam, Pink, 4 1/2 In. 8.00
Depression Glass, Tumbler, American Sweetheart, Pink, 4 1/2 In. ..... 10.00 To 13.00
Depression Glass, Tumbler, Block, Topaz, Footed, 9 Ozs. 4.00
Depression Glass, Tumbler, Cameo, Green, Footed, 5 In. 7.50
Depression Glass, Tumbler, Cameo, Green, 11 Ozs. 7.50

Depression Glass, Tumbler, Cameo, Green, 4 In., 9 Ozs. 5.00
Depression Glass, Tumbler, Cameo, Rose 2.75
Depression Glass, Tumbler, Cameo, Rose, Cone, Footed, 5 In. 3.00
Depression Glass, Tumbler, Cameo, Yellow, Footed, 5 In. 6.50
Depression Glass, Tumbler, Cherry Blossom, Blue, Delphite, 8 Ozs. 13.00
Depression Glass, Tumbler, Cherry Blossom, Green, Footed 8.00
Depression Glass, Tumbler, Cherry Blossom, Pink, Footed, 4 Ozs. 7.50
Depression Glass, Tumbler, Colonial, Footed, 3 Ozs., 3 1/4 In. 2.75
Depression Glass, Tumbler, Colonial, 4 In. 3.50
Depression Glass, Tumbler, Crystal 2.00
Depression Glass, Tumbler, Crystal Ring, Footed, 5 3/4 In. 3.00
Depression Glass, Tumbler, Cubist, Pink 5.50
Depression Glass, Tumbler, Dogwood, Pink, Decorated, 4 In. 8.00
Depression Glass, Tumbler, Dogwood, Pink, Decorated, 5 In. 9.50
Depression Glass, Tumbler, English Hobnail, 4 In. 3.50
Depression Glass, Tumbler, Floragold, Footed, 10 Ozs. 4.50
Depression Glass, Tumbler, Floral & Diamond Band, Aqua, 4 In. 7.50
Depression Glass, Tumbler, Floral, Green, Footed, 4 3/4 In. 3.50
Depression Glass, Tumbler, Floral, Green, 4 3/4 In. 6.50
Depression Glass, Tumbler, Floral, Pink, Footed, 4 3/4 In., 7 Ozs .... 3.50 To 5.00
Depression Glass, Tumbler, Floral, Pink, Footed, 5 1/2 In., 9 Ozs. 7.00
Depression Glass, Tumbler, Floral, Pink, Footed, 6 In. 7.50
Depression Glass, Tumbler, Florentine No.1, Green, Footed, 5 In. 7.50
Depression Glass, Tumbler, Florentine No.2, Pink, 4 1/4 In. 4.00
Depression Glass, Tumbler, Florentine No.2, 4 1/4 In. 3.00
Depression Glass, Tumbler, Florentine No.7, Green, 4 1/4 In. 3.25
Depression Glass, Tumbler, Florentine, Topaz, Footed, 4 In., 5 Ozs. 5.00
Depression Glass, Tumbler, Florentine, Topaz, Footed, 6 In., 5 Ozs. 6.00
Depression Glass, Tumbler, Florentine, 4 1/4 In. 5.00
Depression Glass, Tumbler, Georgian, Green, 4 In., 9 Ozs. 7.00
Depression Glass, Tumbler, Holiday, Pink, 4 In. .... 5.00 To 5.25
Depression Glass, Tumbler, Homespun, Pink, Footed 6.00
Depression Glass, Tumbler, Honeycomb, Green, 5 1/2 In. 1.50
Depression Glass, Tumbler, Iced Tea, Adam, Pink, 5 1/2 In. 11.00
Depression Glass, Tumbler, Iced Tea, Crystal 10.00
Depression Glass, Tumbler, Iced Tea, Madrid, Amber, Footed, 5 1/2 In., 12 Ozs. 7.50
Depression Glass, Tumbler, Iced Tea, Parrot, Amber 45.00
Depression Glass, Tumbler, Iced Tea, Princess, Topaz, 5 In., 12 1/2 Ozs. 8.00
Depression Glass, Tumbler, Iced Tea, Princess, Yellow, 5 1/4 In. 8.50
Depression Glass, Tumbler, Iced Tea, Sharon, Green 24.50
Depression Glass, Tumbler, Iced Tea, Sharon, Pink, Thin, 5 In. 10.00
Depression Glass, Tumbler, Iris, Amber, Footed, 6 In. 5.00
Depression Glass, Tumbler, Iris, Footed, 6 In. .... 4.00 To 5.00
Depression Glass, Tumbler, Iris, Footed, 7 In. .... 5.00 To 5.25
Depression Glass, Tumbler, Iris, 6 In. 3.00
Depression Glass, Tumbler, Iris, 6 1/2 In. 6.00
Depression Glass, Tumbler, Juice, Cameo, Green 8.00
Depression Glass, Tumbler, Juice, Cherry Blossom, Pink 3.50
Depression Glass, Tumbler, Juice, Cherry Blossom, Pink, Footed, 3 1/2 In. 7.50
Depression Glass, Tumbler, Juice, Colonial, Pink 3.50
Depression Glass, Tumbler, Juice, Diamond Line, Pink 2.00
Depression Glass, Tumbler, Juice, Dogwood, Pink, 3 1/2 In. 3.00
Depression Glass, Tumbler, Juice, Madrid, Amber 6.00
Depression Glass, Tumbler, Juice, Mayfair, Pink, 3 1/2 In., 5 Ozs. 10.00
Depression Glass, Tumbler, Juice, Old Cafe, Pink 1.75
Depression Glass, Tumbler, Juice, Old Florentine, Footed, 3 1/4 In. 2.75
Depression Glass, Tumbler, Juice, Princess, Green 7.50
Depression Glass, Tumbler, Juice, Royal Lace, Blue, 5 Ozs. 10.00
Depression Glass, Tumbler, Juice, Royal Lace, Cobalt, 3 In. 9.00
Depression Glass, Tumbler, Juice, Royal Lace, Green 13.50
Depression Glass, Tumbler, Juice, Royal Lace, 3 1/2 In. 4.50
Depression Glass, Tumbler, Juice, Sandwich, Green 2.00
Depression Glass, Tumbler, Juice, Sandwich, Green, Anchor Hocking 1.00
Depression Glass, Tumbler, Lace Edge, Pink, Footed, 5 In. 8.00
Depression Glass, Tumbler, Lace Edge, Pink, 4 1/2 In. 4.00
Depression Glass, Tumbler, Lace Edge, Pink, 5 In. 9.00

Depression Glass, Tumbler, Madrid, Amber, 4 In., 5 Ozs. 5.50
Depression Glass, Tumbler, Madrid, Amber, 5 1/2 In. .... 6.00 To 7.00
Depression Glass, Tumbler, Madrid, Blue, 5 1/2 In. 10.00
Depression Glass, Tumbler, Mayfair Open Rose, Blue, 4 3/4 In. 30.00
Depression Glass, Tumbler, Mayfair Open Rose, Pink, Footed, 5 1/2 In., 10 Ozs 6.50
Depression Glass, Tumbler, Mayfair Open Rose, Pink, 4 In. 8.00
Depression Glass, Tumbler, Miss America, Pink, 4 1/2 In. 12.00
Depression Glass, Tumbler, Miss America, 4 In., 10 Ozs. 6.00
Depression Glass, Tumbler, Moderntone, Blue, Platonite, 4 1/4 In. 6.00
Depression Glass, Tumbler, Moderntone, Blue, 4 1/8 In. 3.00
Depression Glass, Tumbler, Moderntone, Green, Platonite, 4 1/4 In. 6.00
Depression Glass, Tumbler, Moderntone, Pink, Platonite, 4 1/4 In. 6.00
Depression Glass, Tumbler, No.612, Green, Footed, 4 3/4 In. 7.00
Depression Glass, Tumbler, Normandie, Amber, 5 In. 6.00
Depression Glass, Tumbler, Old Florentine, Green, Footed, 5 In. 7.75
Depression Glass, Tumbler, Patrician Spoke, Green, 4 1/4 In. 6.00
Depression Glass, Tumbler, Patrician Spoke, Pink, Footed 5.75
Depression Glass, Tumbler, Patrician Spoke, Pink, 4 1/4 In., 9 Ozs. 9.50
Depression Glass, Tumbler, Princess, Green, Footed, 5 1/2 In. 6.00
Depression Glass, Tumbler, Princess, Green, 4 In. 6.00
Depression Glass, Tumbler, Princess, Pink, Footed, 5 1/4 In., 10 Ozs. 6.00
Depression Glass, Tumbler, Princess, Pink, 9 Ozs., 4 In. 6.40
Depression Glass, Tumbler, Princess, Yellow, Footed, 11 Ozs., 5 1/2 In. 7.50
Depression Glass, Tumbler, Rose Cameo, Green, Footed, 5 In. 3.50
Depression Glass, Tumbler, Roulette, Green, 4 In. 3.75
Depression Glass, Tumbler, Roulette, Green, 5 1/8 In. 4.75
Depression Glass, Tumbler, Royal Lace, Blue, 4 1/4 In. 14.00
Depression Glass, Tumbler, Royal Lace, Blue, 9 Ozs. 11.00
Depression Glass, Tumbler, Royal Lace, Blue, 13 Ozs. 12.00
Depression Glass, Tumbler, Royal Lace, Cobalt, Footed, 5 In. 6.25
Depression Glass, Tumbler, Royal Lace, Green, 4 1/8 In. 12.50
Depression Glass, Tumbler, Royal Lace, Green, 4 1/2 In., 9 Ozs. 12.00
Depression Glass, Tumbler, Royal Lace, Green, 4 7/8 In., 12 Ozs. 13.00
Depression Glass, Tumbler, Royal Lace, Pink, 12 Ozs., 5 In. 6.00
Depression Glass, Tumbler, Royal Ruby, Footed, 5 In. 3.75
Depression Glass, Tumbler, Royal Ruby, Footed, 5 1/2 In. 3.00
Depression Glass, Tumbler, Royal Ruby, 3 In. 1.50
Depression Glass, Tumbler, Royal Ruby, 4 In. 2.00
Depression Glass, Tumbler, Royal Ruby, 10 Ozs. 4.00
Depression Glass, Tumbler, S Pattern, Silver Band, 4 1/4 In. 3.50
Depression Glass, Tumbler, S Pattern, Topaz, 5 In., 9 Ozs. 5.00
Depression Glass, Tumbler, S Pattern, Yellow, 5 Ozs. 4.50
Depression Glass, Tumbler, Sailboat, Blue, 3 1/4 In. 2.00
Depression Glass, Tumbler, Sailboat, Red 4.50
Depression Glass, Tumbler, Sandwich, Dark Green, 4 In. 2.00
Depression Glass, Tumbler, Sandwich, Green, Anchor Hocking 1.50
Depression Glass, Tumbler, Sharon, Amber, Thick, 4 In. 7.50
Depression Glass, Tumbler, Sharon, Amber, 4 In. 5.00
Depression Glass, Tumbler, Sharon, Green, Thick 22.50
Depression Glass, Tumbler, Sharon, Green, 4 In. 22.50
Depression Glass, Tumbler, Sharon, Pink, Footed, 6 1/2 In., 15 Ozs. 10.00
Depression Glass, Tumbler, Sharon, Pink, 4 In., 9 Ozs. .... 4.90 To 8.25
Depression Glass, Tumbler, Waterford, Footed, 5 In. 3.25
Depression Glass, Tumbler, Whiskey, Colonial, Pink, 1 1/2 Ozs. 4.25
Depression Glass, Tumbler, Windsor Diamond, Pink, 4 In. 4.50
Depression Glass, Tumbler, Windsor, Footed, 5 In. 3.25
Depression Glass, Tumbler, Windsor, Pink, 4 In., 9 Ozs. 5.00
Depression Glass, Tumbler, Windsor, Pink, 5 In. 5.00
Depression Glass, Tumbler, Windsor, Pink, 5 Ozs. 3.00
Depression Glass, Vase, Cameo, Green, Ground, 5 3/4 In. 30.00
Depression Glass, Vase, Cameo, Green, 8 In. .... 4.90 To 7.50
Depression Glass, Vase, Cameo, Green, 8 1/2 In. .... 7.00 To 10.50
Depression Glass, Vase, Fine Rib, Bulbous, 1 1/2 In. Opening, 3 1/2 In. 1.50
Depression Glass, Vase, Florentine No.2, Yellow, 6 In. 25.00
Depression Glass, Vase, Flower Garden With Butterflies, Pink, Footed, 10 In. 15.00
Depression Glass, Vase, Flower Garden With Butterflies, Pink, 10 In. 22.50

Depression Glass, Vase, Iris, Crimped, 9 In. 5.00
Depression Glass, Vase, Iris, Iridescent, 9 In. 7.00
Depression Glass, Vase, Moonstone, 5 In. 5.50
Depression Glass, Vase, Princess, Green, 8 In. 7.00
Depression Glass, Vase, Rock Crystal, Amber, 11 In. 35.00
Depression Glass, Vase, Swirl, Ultramarine, 8 1/2 In. 8.00
Depression Glass, Water Set, Ruby Red, Ice Lip, 64 Oz. Pitcher, 7 Piece 45.00
Depression Glass, Wine, Cameo 42.50
Depression Glass, Wine, Colonial, 2 1/2 Ozs., 4 1/2 In. 3.75
Depression Glass, Wine, English Hobnail 6.50
Depression Glass, Wine, Miss America, Pink 29.50
Depression Glass, Wine, Miss America, 4 3/4 In. 9.00

Derby porcelain was made in Derby, England, from 1756 to the present. The factory changed names and marks several times. Chelsea Derby (1770-1784), Crown Derby (1784-1811), and the modern Royal Crown Derby are some of the most famous periods of the factory.

Derby, see also Chelsea, Crown Derby, Royal Crown Derby

Derby, Cup & Saucer, Demitasse, Yellow & Gold Bands On White, C.1861 ...... 40.00
Derby, Cup, Gilt Garlands & Lavender Floral On White, C.1782, Puce Mark 60.00
Derby, Inkstand, Japan Pattern, Scroll Handle, Quill Holes, C.1800, 6 In. 100.00
Derby, Plate, Floral Center, Hand-Painted, Gilt Rim, C.1800, 8 In. 24.00
Derby, Sugar & Creamer, Sheffield Holder With Spoon, John Nodder 85.00
DeVilbiss, Atomizer, Clear & Opalescent Coin Spot, 4 In. 15.00
DeVilbiss, Atomizer, Custard Glass, Swirled Feather, Gold Top 17.50
DeVilbiss, Atomizer, Gold Satin Pedestal, Art Deco Top, Signed 22.50
DeVilbiss, Atomizer, Porcelain, Pink Roses, Green Leaves 6.50
DeVilbiss, Atomizer, Squatty, Coin Spot 15.00
DeVilbiss, Box & Tray, Powder, Covered, Frosted Blue, Black Stripe 15.00
Dick Tracy, Book, Adventures Of Dick Tracy & Jr., 1933, Big Little Books 7.50
Dick Tracy, Salt & Pepper, Figural, Dick & Junior 8.50
Dionne Quintuplet, Book, Cutout 12.00
Dionne Quintuplet, Book, Now We Are Three Years Old 4.00
Dionne Quintuplet, Book, Primer, Jean Ayer 10.00
Dionne Quintuplet, Book, The Country Doctor, Movie Edition 12.00
Dionne Quintuplet, Book, We Are Two Years Old 4.00
Dionne Quintuplet, Bowl, Feeding, Signed 6.50
Dionne Quintuplet, Calendar, 1939 .... 6.00
Dionne Quintuplet, Calendar, 1940 .... 4.00
Dionne Quintuplet, Calendar, 1941 .... 4.00
Dionne Quintuplet, Calendar, 1947 .... 3.50
Dionne Quintuplet, Calendar, 1948 .... 3.50
Dionne Quintuplet, Calendar, 1949 .... 3.50
Dionne Quintuplet, Calendar, 1952 .... 3.50
Dionne Quintuplet, Calendar, 1953 .... 3.50
Dionne Quintuplet, Cards, Playing, Dated 1936, Full Deck 45.00
Dionne Quintuplet, Doll, Madame Alexander, 7 In., Set Of 5 .... 125.00
Dionne Quintuplet, Doll, Marked, 7 1/2 In. 300.00
Dionne Quintuplet, Doll, Paper, All Aboard For Shut Eye Town, 1937, Uncut ... 25.00
Dionne Quintuplet, Fan, Milk Advertisement 7.50
Dionne Quintuplet, Fan, Pictures Of Quints, Cardboard, Wooden Handle 8.00
Dionne Quintuplet, Fan, St.Paul Milk Co. 6.00
Dionne Quintuplet, Scrapbook, 1934 .... 12.00
Dionne Quintuplet, Spoon, Annette, Silver Plate .... 10.00 To 11.50
Dionne Quintuplet, Spoon, Cecile, Silver Plate .... 10.00 To 11.50
Dionne Quintuplet, Spoon, Emile, Silver Plate .... 10.00 To 11.50
Dionne Quintuplet, Spoon, Marie .... 6.00 To 11.50
Dionne Quintuplet, Spoon, Yvonne .... 4.95 To 11.50
Dionne Quintuplet, Teaspoon, Set Of 5 .... 50.00

Disneyana, see also Coca-Cola, Bottle

Disneyana, Book, Adventures Of Mickey Mouse, McKay, 1931 .... 38.00 To 75.00
Disneyana, Book, Donald Duck & His Nephews, 1940 .... 8.50
Disneyana, Book, Donald's Lucky Day, Friday, The 13th, 1939, Whitman 25.00
Disneyana, Book, Mickey Mouse Has A Party, A School Reader, Whitman, 1938 ... 30.00
Disneyana, Book, Mickey Mouse, Phila., 1934 .... 25.00
Disneyana, Book, Paint, Pinocchio, Whitman, 1939 .... 20.00

Item	Price
Disneyana, **Book**, Pinocchio, G.& D., 1939	3.00
Disneyana, **Book**, The Seven Dwarfs, Walt Disney, 1936	10.00
Disneyana, **Bottle**, Hot Water, Donald Duck Figural, 12 In.	7.00
Disneyana, **Camera**, Donald Duck	7.00
Disneyana, **Camera**, Mickey Mouse, Dated 1957	40.00
Disneyana, **Canasta Set**, Junior, Mickey Mouse	4.00
Disneyana, **Clock**, Big Bad Wolf, Animated, Alarm	225.00
Disneyana, **Cookie Cutter**, Mickey Mouse	5.00
Disneyana, **Costume**, Mickey Mouse, 1940, Original Box	20.00
Disneyana, **Crayon Set**, Donald Duck, Lithographed Tin Box, 1946	5.50
Disneyana, **Cup Plate**, Mickey Mouse, China	7.50
Disneyana, **Cup**, Child's, Mickey Mouse	10.00
Disneyana, **Cutout**, Mickey & Minnie Mouse, Iron, Painted, C.1935, 9 In., Pair	45.00
Disneyana, **Dish Set**, Mickey Mouse, 10 Piece	35.00
Disneyana, **Doll**, Bashful, Hard Rubber, 6 In.	9.00
Disneyana, **Doll**, Doc, Hard Rubber, 6 In.	9.00 To 30.00
Disneyana, **Doll**, Donald Duck, Composition, 9 In.	30.00
Disneyana, **Doll**, Dopey, Hard Rubber, 6 In.	9.00
Disneyana, **Doll**, Grumpy, Hard Rubber, 6 In.	9.00
Disneyana, **Doll**, Happy, Hard Rubber, 6 In.	9.00
Disneyana, **Doll**, Huey, Stuffed, Matador Dress, 10 1/2 In.	35.00
Disneyana, **Doll**, Mickey Mouse, Cloth, 8 In.	50.00
Disneyana, **Doll**, Mickey Mouse, Sun Rubber, 8 In.	10.00
Disneyana, **Doll**, Mouseketeer, Rubber, Jointed, 12 In.	10.00
Disneyana, **Doll**, Paper, Mickey Mouse, Uncut, 1933	40.00
Disneyana, **Doll**, Pinocchio, Vinyl Head, Plush Body, 1950s, 9 In.	4.00
Disneyana, **Doll**, Pinocchio, Wooden, 7 In.	9.50
Disneyana, **Doll**, Sleepy, Hard Rubber, 6 In.	9.00
Disneyana, **Figurine**, Donald Duck, China, 5 In.High	6.00
Disneyana, **Figurine**, Dopey, Bisque, 2 3/4 In.High	12.50
Disneyana, **Figurine**, Dopey, Bisque, 3 In.High	5.00
Disneyana, **Figurine**, Grumpy, Bisque, 3 In.	7.00
Disneyana, **Figurine**, Mickey Mouse, Bisque, Japanese, Walt Disney, 4 In.	18.00
Disneyana, **Figurine**, Mickey Mouse, Glazed, 4 1/2 In.	7.50
Disneyana, **Figurine**, Mickey Mouse, Latex, Signed Walt Disney, 3 1/2 In.	25.00
Disneyana, **Figurine**, Mickey Mouse, Papier-Mache, Painted, 9 In.High	25.00
Disneyana, **Figurine**, Mickey Mouse, Porcelain, 5 In.	5.50
Disneyana, **Figurine**, Mickey Mouse, 1960, 5 In.	6.50
Disneyana, **Figurine**, Mickey Mouse, 5 1/2 In.	5.00
Disneyana, **Figurine**, Minnie Mouse, Porcelain, 4 In.	4.00
Disneyana, **Figurine**, Pinocchio, Bisque, 4 In.	10.00
Disneyana, **Figurine**, Snow White, Porcelain, 5 In.	4.75
Disneyana, **Guitar**, Mickey Mousegetar, Picture, 14 In.	7.50
Disneyana, **Jar Opener**, Mickey Mouse	2.50
Disneyana, **Light**, Christmas Tree, Mickey Mouse & Friends	8.00
Disneyana, **Lunch Box**, Mickey Mouse, School Bus Shape	12.50
Disneyana, **Magazine**, Donald Duck, 1935	45.00
Disneyana, **Magazine**, Mickey Mouse, November, 1937	35.00
Disneyana, **Mask**, Minnie Mouse, 1933	10.00
Disneyana, **Mold**, Mickey Mouse Mask, Metal, 13 In.	12.00
Disneyana, **Mouseketeer Ears**, Mickey Mouse	6.00
Disneyana, **Mouseketeer Outfit**, Mickey Mouse Club	7.50
Disneyana, **Movie**, Donald Duck Down Mexico Way, 1936, 16mm., 100 Ft.	35.00
Disneyana, **Movie**, Mickey Mouse, Running Wild, 1934, 16mm., 100 Ft.	35.00
Disneyana, **Movie**, Mickey Mouse, 16 Mm.	8.00
Disneyana, **Mug**, Donald Duck, Made In Japan	4.50
Disneyana, **Mug**, Mickey Mouse, Mickey With No.5 Fire Helmet & Ax, S.C.Co.	10.00
Disneyana, **Music Sheet**, Der Fuehrer's Face, Donald Duck & Hitler, 1942	11.00
Disneyana, **Music Sheet**, Snow White, 1937	3.50
Disneyana, **Pencil Set**, Mickey Mouse	15.00
Disneyana, **Phonograph**, Mickey Mouse Club, Speartone, Electric, Lionel	85.00
Disneyana, **Pillow**, Mickey & Minnie Mouse	35.00
Disneyana, **Plate**, Mickey Mouse Playing Drums, 7 1/2 In.	25.00
Disneyana, **Plate**, Mickey Mouse, 7 In.	25.00
Disneyana, **Poster**, Victory Through Air Power Film, 1943, 28 X 40 In.	20.00
Disneyana, **Program**, Theater, Fantasia, Original Showing, 1940	5.00

Disneyana, Projector, Mickey Mouse Newsreel, Plastic, C.1955, 2 Films, 10 In.	12.00
Disneyana, Projector, Mickey Mouse, C.1933, Black Enameled Metal	27.00
Disneyana, Ring, Pluto	18.00
Disneyana, Salt & Pepper, Donald Duck, Hand-Painted China, C.1940	6.00
Disneyana, Soap, Snow White & The 7 Dwarfs, 1938, Boxed	30.00
Disneyana, Soap, Soaky, Characters On Wrapper, Box Of 24	12.00
Disneyana, Spoon, Mickey Mouse, C.1930	5.00
Disneyana, T.V.Set, Plastic, Spring Wound, C.1954, 4 Films	10.00
Disneyana, Tea Set, Snow White & The Seven Dwarfs, 17 Piece	44.00
Disneyana, Telephone, Mickey Mouse	100.00
Disneyana, Toothbrush Holder, 3 Pigs With Musical Instruments, Bisque	22.00
Disneyana, Toy, Disneyland Express Train, Tin, Windup	37.50
Disneyana, Toy, Donald Duck Duet, Windup, Tin, Marx	100.00
Disneyana, Toy, Dopey, Tin, Mechanical, Marx, 8 In.High, 1938	100.00
Disneyana, Toy, Mickey Mouse Band, Mechanical, Tin, Marx, C.1930	200.00
Disneyana, Toy, Mickey Mouse, Electric, Papier-Mache, 36 In.	300.00
Disneyana, Toy, Pinocchio, Tin, Windup, 1939	32.00
Disneyana, Toy, Tractor, Mickey Mouse, Rubber	45.00
Disneyana, Tray, Donald Duck, Lithographed, Tin, Ohio Art Co., 6 X 7 1/2 In.	7.50
Disneyana, Watch, Bambi, U.S.Time	65.00
Disneyana, Watch, Cinderella	15.00
Disneyana, Watch, Wrist, Mickey Mouse, Oblong, Ingersoll	65.00
Disneyana, Watch, Wrist, Snow White, U.S.Time, 1940s	45.00
Disneyana, Zipper Bag, Snow White & The 7 Dwarfs, C.1950, 8 In.	4.50
Doccia, Cup & Saucer, Village Scenes, Crown & Star Mark	26.50
Doctor, Apparatus, Electricity At Home, 1904, Wooden Box	18.50
Doctor, Bandage, Triangular, Teaching, Illustrated, Civil War, 24 X 48 In.	50.00
Doctor, Container, Intravenous Feeding, German, World War I, Glass, Chrome	45.00
Doctor, Doll, Carved Ivory, Lying Nude On Wood Base, 6 In.	48.00
Doctor, Doll, Carved Ivory, Lying Nude On Wood Base, 7 1/4 In.	85.00
Doctor, Doll, Carved Ivory, Reclining On Side, Wooden Base, 9 In.	70.00
Doctor, Doll, Ivory, Lady, Lying On Wooden Base, 7 1/4 In.	85.00
Doctor, Fleam, Veterinarian's, 3 Blades, Folding, Horn Handles, Silver Trim	25.00
Doctor, Home Medical Apparatus, Quack, Oak Case, Electrical, C.1800	35.00
Doctor, Kit, Surgical, Wooden, 4 Scalpels	10.00
Doctor, Kit, Veterinarian's, 1900	12.00
Doctor, Machine, Geiger Electroshock	16.00
Doctor, Machine, Master Violet Ray	15.00
Doctor, Machine, Millivolter	20.00
Doctor, Machine, Renu Generator	15.00
Doctor, Machine, Sanitax Radiolux Ray	15.00
Doctor, Machine, Violet Ray, Marble Displaying Table, Case	25.00
Doctor, Pessary, 10K Gold	24.00
Doctor Syntax, see Adams, Staffordshire	
Doctor, Table, Chiropractic, Portable, Carrying Case	28.50
Doll, see also Campbell Kid, Doll, Charlie Chaplin, Doll,	
Dionne Quintuplet, Doll, Disneyana, Doll, Kewpie, Doll, Popeye,	
Doll, Shirley Temple, Doll	
Doll, A.B.G., Baby, 12 In.	95.00
Doll, A.M., see also Doll, Armand Marseille	
Doll, A.M. G 253, Girl, Bisque Head, Composition Body, Googlie Eyes, 7 In.	565.00
Doll, A.M. 323, Girl, Bisque Head, Googlie Eyes, Composition Body, 7 In.	560.00
Doll, A.M. 341, Dream Baby, Bisque Head, Celluloid Hands, 10 1/2 In.	145.00
Doll, A.M. 341-12 Germany, Dream Baby, Cloth Body, Composition Hands, 9 In.	145.00
Doll, A.M. 351, Baby, Composition Body, 14 In. Head	200.00
Doll, A.M. 370 D.E.P., Ball Jointed, Brown Eyes & Wig, 23 In.	85.00
Doll, A.M. 370, Bisque Head & Hands, Kid Body, Open Mouth, 22 In.	125.00
Doll, A.M. 370, Bisque Head, Kid & Composition Body, Blue Eyes, 15 In.	95.00
Doll, A.M. 390, Bisque, Jointed Body, Blue Eyes, Open Mouth, 29 In.	195.00
Doll, A.M. 390, Girl, Jointed Body, Sleep Eyes, Evening Gown, 18 1/2 In.	110.00
Doll, A.M. 390, Nun, Brown Sleep Eyes, Open Mouth, 20 In.	145.00
Doll, A.M. 900, Open Mouth, Blue Sleep Eyes, Human Hair Wig, 12 1/2 In.	145.00
Doll, A.M. 971, Baby, Blue Sleep Eyes, Human Hair, 10 1/2 In. Head	125.00
Doll, A.M. 971, Baby, 13 In.	75.00
Doll, A.M. 985, Baby Girl, Bisque Head, Blue Sleep Eyes, Blonde, 9 1/2 In.	175.00
Doll, A.M. 1894, Composition Body, 17 In.	75.00

Doll, A.M. 1894, Girl, Blue Eyes, 25 In.	160.00
Doll, A.M. 1894, 20 In.	155.00
Doll, A.M., Ball Jointed, Blue Eyes, 33 In.	275.00 To 340.00
Doll, A.M., Ball Jointed, Brown Eyes, Wig, 22 In.	75.00
Doll, A.M., Ball Jointed, Brown Eyes, 28 In.	145.00
Doll, A.M., Ball Jointed, Brown Eyes, 35 In.	395.00
Doll, A.M., Blue Eyes, 8 In.	95.00
Doll, A.M., Blue Eyes, 14 In.	45.00
Doll, A.M., Dream Baby, Bisque Head, Celluloid Hands, Cloth Body, 12 In.	150.00
Doll, A.M., Dream Baby, Bisque Head, Composition Body, Blue Eyes, 12 In.Tall	125.00
Doll, A.M., Dream Baby, Cloth Body, Brown Sleep Eyes, 9 In.	95.00
Doll, A.M., Dream Baby, Cloth Body, Composition Hands, Blue Eyes, 13 In.	155.00
Doll, A.M., Dream Baby, Cloth Body, 13 In. Head	150.00
Doll, A.M., Dream Baby, Composition Toddler Body, Dressed, 20 In. Head	350.00
Doll, A.M., Dream Baby, Papier-Mache Body, Blue Sleep Eyes, 8 In.	75.00
Doll, A.M., Dream Baby, Stuffed Body, Open Mouth, Dressed, 21 In.	250.00
Doll, A.M., Dream Baby, 16 1/2 In.	140.00
Doll, A.M., Floradora, Kid Body, Hair Eyebrows, 36 In.	395.00
Doll, A.M., Frowning Indian, Compostion Body, Costume & Wig, 9 In.	185.00
Doll, A.M., Germany, Boy Oriental Toddler, Bisque Head, Cloth Body, 9 In.	395.00
Doll, A.M., Girl, Bisque Head, Kid Body, Dark Eyes & Hair, 17 In.	50.00
Doll, A.M., Googlie, Bisque Head, Mohair Wig, 7 In.	325.00
Doll, A.M., Green Velvet Dress & Hat, 27 In.	195.00
Doll, A.M., Hair Eyelashes, 25 In.	125.00
Doll, A.M., Long French Wig, 16 In.	125.00
Doll, A.M., Nun, Bisque Head, 12 In.	60.00
Doll, A.M., Oriental Girl, Jointed Composition Body, Brown Eyes, 8 In.	275.00
Doll, A.Wolf & Co., Bisque Shoulder Head & Hands, Kid Body, 23 In.	111.00
Doll, ABG, Baby, Brown Sleep Eyes, 25 In.	245.00
Doll, Adalina Patti, Girl, China Head, Cloth Body, 19 1/2 In.	335.00
Doll, Alexander, see Doll, Madame Alexander	
Doll, Alice In Wonderland, Composition, Painted Face, 7 In.	65.00
Doll, Alice, Incised, Bisque Hands, Brown Eyes, 12 In.	125.00
Doll, Alma Incised On Head, Blue Eyes, Blonde Hair, 13 1/2 In.	65.00 To 95.00
Doll, Alma, Brown Eyes, 22 In.	175.00
Doll, Amberg 1928, Edwina, Composition, 13 In.	75.00
Doll, Amberg, Baby, Cloth Body, Blue Eyes, 8 In.Tall	135.00
Doll, Amberg, Baby, 6 1/2 In.	95.00
Doll, American Youth, 11 In.	275.00
Doll, American, Sweet Sue, Hard Plastic, Walker, 15 In.	17.00
Doll, Armand Marseille, see also Doll, A.M.	
Doll, Armand Marseille, 370-AM-10 DEP, Bisque Shoulder Head, 28 In.	225.00
Doll, Arrow Plastics, Lady, Vinyl & Hard Plastic, Blue Eyes, 1956, 25 In.	12.00
Doll, Artisan, Raving Beauty, Walker, Hard Plastic, Dressed, 19 In.	35.00
Doll, Astri Campbell, NIADA, Becky, 12 In.	150.00
Doll, Aunt Jemima, Oilcloth, 13 In.	26.00
Doll, A10/0 Germany, DRGM, Googlie, Boy, Intaglio Eyes, 6 1/2 In.	195.00
Doll, A14M, Baby Girl, Bisque, Ball Jointed Body, Blue Sleep Eyes, 30 In.	250.00
Doll, A14M, Girl, Jointed Body, Brown Stationary Eyes, 29 In.	235.00
Doll, B O, American Schoolboy, Bisque Shoulder Head, Dressed, 12 1/2 In.	295.00
Doll, BSW, Heart Mark, Sleep Eyes, Dressed, 19 In.	165.00
Doll, Baby Dainty, 14 In.	42.00
Doll, Baby First Step, Battery Operated, 1964, 18 In.	17.50
Doll, Baby June, Ideal, 1956, 15 In.	16.50
Doll, Baby Sandy, Composition, Jointed, Sleep Eyes, 1930s, 14 In.	75.00
Doll, Baby Sandy, Composition, Jointed, Sleep Eyes, 1930s, 17 In.	85.00
Doll, Baby, Bisque, C.1940, 4 In.	7.50
Doll, Baby, Composition Shoulder Head, Cloth Body, Dressed, 17 In.	25.00
Doll, Baby, Composition, Painted Hair & Features, 9 In.	4.00
Doll, Baby, 154/1, Blue Sleep Eyes, Painted Brown Hair, 10 In.	175.00
Doll, Baby, 5 Piece Body, Brown Eyes, 14 In.	150.00
Doll, Bahr Proschild, No.585, Baby, Blue Eyes, Blonde Hair, 16 In.	250.00
Doll, Barbara Eden As I Dream Of Jeannie, Pink Harem Outfit, 19 In.	22.50
Doll, Baseball Player, Celluloid Head, Stuffed Body, 4 In.	1.50
Doll, Beja, Holland, Dutch Girl, Vinyl, Blonde Braids, 16 In.	35.00

Doll, **Belton Type**, Lady, Bisque Shoulder Head, Cloth Body, 14 In.	365.00
Doll, **Belton**, Baby, Bisque Head, Jointed Composition Body, 16 In.	475.00
Doll, **Belton**, Girl, Blue Paperweight Eyes, Closed Mouth, Human Hair, 26 In.	675.00
Doll, **Belton**, Indian, Closed Mouth, 11 In.	350.00
Doll, **Bester**, Composition, Ball Jointed, 55 In.	55.00
Doll, **Betty Boop**, Celluloid Head Swings Side To Side, 7 1/4 In.	80.00
Doll, **Biedermeier**, China Head & Limbs, Cloth Body, Dressed, 15 1/2 In.	385.00
Doll, **Bisque Head**, Kid Body, Blonde Mohair Wig, German, 27 In.	175.00
Doll, **Bisque**, Girl & Boy, Jointed Shoulders & Hips, Painted Eyes, 4 In., Pair	35.00
Doll, **Bisque**, Housekeeper, Molded Gray Hair, 6 In.	38.00
Doll, **Bisque**, Incised Viola, Jointed Body, Brown Stationary Eyes, 22 In.	175.00
Doll, **Bisque**, Molded Indian Headdress, 5 In.	23.50
Doll, **Bisque**, 2 1/2 In.	5.00
Doll, **Bonnet Head**, Cloth Body, 10 In.	75.00
Doll, **Boy**, Bisque, Intaglio Eyes, Papier-Mache Body, Boots, Velvet Suit, 8 In.	67.50
Doll, **Boy**, Composition Head & Arms, Felt Body, 13 In.	245.00
Doll, **Bride & Groom**, Nippon, Bisque, 4 1/2 In., Pair	30.00
Doll, **Brikette**, Ballerina, Vogue, 22 In.	35.00
Doll, **Bru**, Nursing Mouth, Kid Body, Blue Paperweight Eyes, 13 In.	1750.00
Doll, **Bruno Schmidt**, B.S.In Heart, Boy Toddler, 16 In.	300.00
Doll, **Bruno Schmidt**, Tommy Tucker, Molded Hair, 24 1/2 In.Tall	800.00
Doll, **Bye-Lo**, Babe, Bisque, Blue Intaglio Eyes, Brown Hair, 6 1/2 In.	390.00
Doll, **Bye-Lo**, Bisque, Painted, 10 In.	125.00
Doll, **Bye-Lo**, Blue Sleep Eyes, 10 In. Head, 12 In. Tall	295.00
Doll, **Bye-Lo**, Blue Sleep Eyes, 12 1/4 In. Head, 13 In. Tall	325.00
Doll, **C.M.Bergmann**, see also Doll, S.&H., Doll, Simon & Halbig	
Doll, **C.M.Bergmann**, Ball Jointed, Blue Sleep Eyes, 27 In.	225.00
Doll, **C.M.Bergmann**, Simon & Halbig, Bisque Head, 25 1/2 In.	165.00
Doll, **C-K-192**, Girl, Pale Bisque Head, 28 In.	185.00
Doll, **Cameo Doll Co.**, Miss Peep, Negro, 16 In.	16.50
Doll, **Carl Bergner**, Marked CB, 3 Faced Baby, Bisque Head, 11 In.	1050.00
Doll, **Carmen Miranda**, Composition, Dressed, 11 1/4 In.	18.00
Doll, **Cast Iron**, Dollhouse, Hand-Painted Green Dress, 1 1/2 In.	12.50
Doll, **Celluloid**, Campbell Kid Type Face, Movable Arms, C.1930, 2 1/2 In.	8.50
Doll, **Celluloid**, Carnival, Feathers, Hat, & Cane, 9 In.	8.00
Doll, **Charlie McCarthy**, Plastic Head & Hands, Tuxedo & Top Hat, 30 In.	29.00
Doll, **Chase**, Baby, 25 In.	125.00
Doll, **Chase**, Marked On Thigh, 17 In.	80.00
Doll, **Chase**, Stockinette, Boy, Hand-Painted, 16 1/2 In.	110.00
Doll, **Chase**, Stockinette, Hand-Painted Face & Body, Jointed, 38 1/2 In.	519.00
Doll, **Chase**, Stockinette, Jointed, Blonde Hair, Blue Eyes, 24 In.	150.00
Doll, **Chase**, 20 In.	30.00
Doll, **Cherie**, Pierced Ears, 26 In.	225.00
Doll, **China Head**, Black Bow In Block Molded Hair, 14 In. Circumference	120.00
Doll, **China Head**, Kid Body, Black Hair, Blue Eyes, 16 In.	750.00
Doll, **China Head**, Marked With Crossed Lines, Black, Red Line On Eyes, 5 In.	55.00
Doll, **China Shoulder Head & Arms**, Cloth Body, Apple Cheeks, 15 1/2 In.	45.00
Doll, **China**, Black Hair, 16 In.	45.00
Doll, **Chinese Character**, Papier-Mache, 10 In.Tall, Pair	160.00
Doll, **Chubby Boy**, Bisque, Painted Googlie Eyes, Movable Arms, 5 1/4 In.	135.00
Doll, **Cinderella**, Hard Plaster, 18 In.Tall	40.00
Doll, **Cissette**, Hard Plastic, Dressed, 9 In.	20.00
Doll, **Cissy**, Hard Plastic, Dressed, 20 In.	35.00
Doll, **Clover/88**, Child, Dressed, 18 In.	450.00
Doll, **Composition Head & Limbs**, Cloth Body, 15 In.	35.00
Doll, **Composition**, Jointed At Shoulders & Hips, Sleep Eyes, 12 In.	15.00
Doll, **Composition**, Jointed, Painted Features, Mohair Wig, 11 1/2 In.	15.75
Doll, **Composition**, Molded Hair, Painted Features, Dressed, 4 In.	3.75
Doll, **Cowboy**, Celluloid, Lasso & Gun, 7 In.	4.75
Doll, **Cowgirl**, Celluloid, Jointed Arms, Painted Features, C.1930, 4 In.	2.50
Doll, **Cragstan**, Charlie Chaplin, Hard Plastic, Moves, Jointed, 1970, 5 In.	5.50
Doll, **Crawling Baby**, Celluloid, 4 1/2 In.	8.50
Doll, **Crown Over CW 120 4/0**, Girl, 14 In.	95.00
Doll, **Cuno O.Dressel**, Bisque, Sleep Eyes, Dressed, 21 In.	165.00
Doll, **Curly Top**, China, 11 In.	275.00
Doll, **Czechoslovakian**, Boy & Girl, Bisque Face, 4 In., Pair	20.00

Doll, D * R 117, Pouty Face, Jointed Body, Flirty Eyes, Human Hair, 23 In. 395.00
Doll, D * R 128, 30 In. 400.00
Doll, D.E.P. 960, Kid Body, Brown Eyes, Blonde Wig, 18 In. 95.00
Doll, DRGM-A.M. Germany, Bisque Swivel Head, Composition Body, 14 In. 65.00
Doll, Deluxe, Baby Magic, Battery Operated, 1966, 18 In. 5.00
Doll, Denny Dimwit, Nodder, Composition, 1948, 12 In. 38.50
Doll, Depose Tete Jumeau Bth S.G.D.G., Girl, Composition Body, 16 In. 595.00
Doll, Dick Van Dyke As Mr.Potts, Talking, Stuffed, 23 In. 16.50
Doll, Dolly Dingles, Composition Head & Arms, Stuffed Body, 12 In.Tall 75.00
Doll, Dy-Dee Baby, 15 In. 25.00
Doll, E 9 D Depose, Girl, Jointed Composition Body, Paperweight Eyes, 22 In. 350.00
Doll, E 12 D, Girl, Composition Body, Pierced Ears, Brown Eyes, 28 In. 550.00
Doll, E.D., Closed Mouth, Blue Paperweight Eyes, 17 In. 695.00
Doll, E.D., E9D Depose, Jointed Composition Body, Blue Eyes, 23 In. 475.00
Doll, E.D., French Girl, Open Mouth, Blue Paperweight Eyes, 18 In. 345.00
Doll, E.D., French, Jointed Body, Open Mouth, Blue Paperweight Eyes, 23 In. 450.00
Doll, E.U.Steiner, Composition Body, Open Mouth, Brown Eyes, 15 In. 125.00
Doll, Eden Bebe, Closed Mouth, Dressed, 15 In. 625.00
Doll, Edie, Germany, Negro, Celluloid, Walking, Dressed, 6 1/2 In. 12.00
Doll, Eegee, Baby Puppetrina, 16 In. 14.00
Doll, Eegee, Puppetrina, Teen, 1963, 22 In. 10.00
Doll, Eegee, Puttetrina, 23 In. .... 21.50 To 24.50
Doll, Eegee, Susan Stroller Bride, Vinyl Head, Hard Plastic, 13 In. 16.50
Doll, Eegee, Susan Stroller, Vinyl & Hard Plastic, 1950s, 23 In. 5.00
Doll, Effanbee, Baby Grumpy, Composition, 11 In. 67.50
Doll, Effanbee, Colonial Lady, Historical Series, 14 1/2 In. 100.00
Doll, Effanbee, Fluffy, Dressed, 10 1/2 In. 13.50
Doll, Effanbee, Honey Walker, Hard Plastic, 1951, 18 1/2 In. .... 15.00 To 25.00
Doll, Effanbee, Mickey Mouse, Dressed As Policeman, 11 In. 11.75
Doll, Effanbee, Miss Chips, Dressed, 18 In. 15.50
Doll, Effanbee, Mommy's Baby, Plastic Head, Magic Skin, Talks, 19 In. 22.50
Doll, Effanbee, Negro Girl, Green Dress, 8 1/4 In. 22.00
Doll, Effanbee, Patsy Ann, Composition, Fur Coat, 19 In.Tall 75.00
Doll, Effanbee, Patsy, 14 In. 25.00
Doll, Effanbee, Skippy, Composition, 14 In. 62.50
Doll, Effanbee, Susie Sunshine, 1961, 17 1/2 In. 3.50
Doll, Effanbee, Suzanne, Composition, 1942, Dressed, 13 1/2 In. 40.00
Doll, Elise, Hard Plastic, Dressed, 16 In. 30.00
Doll, Emmett Kelly, The Clown, Rubber, 5 In. 7.00
Doll, Empire, Boy, Bisque Head, Molded Hair, Celluloid Hands, 21 In. 155.00
Doll, Eskimo, Composition Face, Stuffed Body, 12 In.Tall 15.00
Doll, Ethel, China Head, Cloth Body, 10 In. 110.00
Doll, F.G. In Scroll, Girl, Blue Paperweight Eyes, 2 Rows Of Teeth, 26 In. 495.00
Doll, F.G., Girl, Bisque Head, Teeth, Jointed Composition Body, 15 1/2 In. 395.00
Doll, F.3 G., French Child, Cork Head, Jointed Composition Body, 12 In. 795.00
Doll, FY Nippon, Baby, 2 Teeth, Open Mouth, Brown Sleep Eyes, 16 In. 125.00
Doll, Fanny Brice, 12 1/2 In. 150.00
Doll, Fashion, French, Bisque Shoulder Head, Kid Body, 17 In. 575.00
Doll, Fashion, French, Bisque Swivel Head On Shoulder Plate, 15 In. 550.00
Doll, Flapper, Permanent Wave Dollcraft, Composition Head, 28 In. 38.50
Doll, Flower Girl, Composition, Painted Features, Molded Hair, 4 In. 5.00
Doll, Flying Nun, From TV Show, Original Box, 12 In. 18.50
Doll, Franz Schmidt, No.1271/32Z, Baby, Solid Dome, 12 In. 550.00
Doll, French Court Man, Bisque Shoulder Head, Kid Body, Dressed, 15 In. 595.00
Doll, French Fashion, Brown Eyes, Human Hair, Green Dress, 25 In. 695.00
Doll, French Fashion, Kid Body, Blue Paperweight Eyes, 16 In. 365.00
Doll, French Fashion, Wooden, Jointed, Blue Paperweight Eyes, 16 In. 950.00
Doll, French, Baby, Celluloid, Jointed At Shoulders & Hips, 13 In. 7.50
Doll, French, Bisque, Swivel Neck, 3 In. 50.00
Doll, French, D.E.P., Brown Sleep Eyes, 28 In. 250.00
Doll, French, D.E.P., Girl, Brown Eyes, Honey Hair, 22 In. 285.00
Doll, French, Girl, Celluloid, Jointed At Shoulders & Hips, 11 In. 8.00
Doll, French, 227, Baby, Molded Hair, Blue Paperweight Eyes, 17 In. 650.00
Doll, Frozen Charlotte, Luster, Molded Hair, Blue Eyes, 14 In. 495.00
Doll, Fulper, Baby, 4 Part Fat Composition Body, 2 Teeth, 15 In. Head 350.00
Doll, Fulper, Girl, Composition Body, 2 Teeth, Blue Eyes, Open Mouth, 18 In. 185.00

Doll, **Furga,** Boy, Anatomically Correct, Drinks, Wets, 16 1/2 In. 26.50
Doll, **Furga,** Elena, Blue Sleep Eyes, Blonde Curls, Blue Satin Dress, 23 In. 58.00
Doll, **Furga,** Fiorenza, Pink Velvet Outfit, 18 In. 36.00
Doll, **Furga,** Italy, Tomasino, Anatomically Correct, Wets, Drinks, 17 In. 26.50
Doll, **GS Putnam 1922,** Bye-Lo Baby, Bisque, 4 In. 275.00
Doll, **George Borgfeldt,** Ball Jointed, 24 In. 150.00
Doll, **Georgene Averill,** Baby, Cloth Body, Composition Limbs, 20 1/2 In. 695.00
Doll, **Georgene Averill,** Bonnie Babe, Blue Eyes, 16 1/2 In. 650.00
Doll, **Georgene Averill,** Bonnie Babe, 8 In. Head 500.00
Doll, **Georgene Averill,** Cloth Body, Composition Limbs, Sleep Eyes, 18 In. 565.00
Doll, **Gerber Baby,** Jointed, Painted Features, Feeding Set & Food, 14 In. 12.00
Doll, **Gerber Baby,** Molded Hair, Jointed, Foods & Feeding Dish, C.1970, 14 In. 12.00
Doll, **Gerbruder Krauss,** 4 Piece Jointed Body, 8 1/2 In. 68.50
Doll, **German,** Bisque Head & Arms, China Legs, Bonnet Head, 12 1/2 In. 150.00
Doll, **German,** Boy, Bisque, Molded Blonde Hair, 9 In. 39.00
Doll, **German,** Fashion, China Head & Limbs, Cloth Body, Red Hair, 16 In. 850.00
Doll, **German,** Flirty Eye, Jointed, Wobbly Tongue, 25 In. 350.00
Doll, **German,** Girl, Bisque Head, Kid Body, Blonde Hair, Blue Eyes, 13 In. 35.00
Doll, **German,** Girl, Brown Paperweight Eyes, Closed Mouth, 16 In. 395.00
Doll, **German,** Girl, Closed Mouth, Dressed, 12 In. 250.00
Doll, **German,** No.39-17, Child, Soldier Outfit, Closed Mouth, 8 1/2 In. 175.00
Doll, **German,** Pincushion Head, Gray Short Hair, Molded Dress, 3 3/4 In. 42.00
Doll, **German,** Pincushion Head, Holding Binoculars, Molded Hat, 2 1/2 In. 42.00
Doll, **German,** Toddler Boy, Bisque Head, Composition Body, 18 In. 60.00
Doll, **German,** 639, Baby, Bald Head, Cloth Body, Blue Eyes, 19 In. 285.00
Doll, **Germany 9,** China Shoulder Head & Limbs, Dressed, 7 In. 50.00
Doll, **Germany,** Baby, Porcelain, Hands & Legs Attached By Wire, 2 In. 25.00
Doll, **Germany,** Cupid With Sword, Bisque, Tufted Hair, 5 In. 47.50
Doll, **Germany,** Girl, China Head, Bisque Arms & Legs, 6 In. 32.00
Doll, **Germany,** Kiddiejoy, Baby, 14 1/2 In. Bisque Head, Cloth Body 300.00
Doll, **Germany,** U.S.Zone, Lady, Molded Hair, Painted Eyes, Closed Mouth, 4 In. 4.00
Doll, **Ginger,** Walker, Vinyl Head, Plastic, Mickey Mouse Costume, 8 In. 12.75
Doll, **Girl,** Bisque, Jointed Shoulders & Hips, Brown Eyes, Blonde Hair, 6 In. 90.00
Doll, **Girl,** Papier-Mache Shoulder Head, Kid Body, Dressed, 11 In. 285.00
Doll, **Girl,** Parian Bisque Head & Arms, Cloth Body, Pierced Ears, 16 In. 495.00
Doll, **Googlie,** Composition, Brown Eyes, 25 In. 18.00
Doll, **Grace S.Putnam,** Bye-Lo Baby, Bisque Head, Cloth Body, 13 1/2 In. 350.00
Doll, **Greiner,** Girl, Cloth Body, Kid Arms, 16 In. 350.00
Doll, **Greiner,** Lady, Papier-Mache, Cotton Body, Kid Arms, 20 In. 350.00
Doll, **H.C. Over 1361 62 Germany,** Baby, Curly Hair, 23 In. 240.00
Doll, **H.Steiner,** 15, Germany, Dream Baby, 8 In. 110.00
Doll, **H-K 300,** Girl Toddler, Brown Sleep Eyes, Brown Hair, 23 In. 270.00
Doll, **H-K 300,** Toddler, Blue Sleep Eyes, 16 In. 275.00
Doll, **H-K 300,** Toddler, Brown Sleep Eyes, Wig, 23 In. 290.00
Doll, **Harriet Hubbard Ayer,** Box With Cosmetics, 14 In. 35.00
Doll, **Heinrich Handwerck Simon & Halbig,** Ball Jointed, Blue Eyes, 30 In. 225.00
Doll, **Heinrich Handwerck Simon & Halbig,** Inset Eyebrows, Dressed, 32 In. 395.00
Doll, **Heinrich Handwerck Simon & Halbig,** 24 In. 135.00
Doll, **Heinrich Handwerck,** Ball Jointed, Sleep Eyes, 30 In. 225.00
Doll, **Heinrich Handwerck,** Bisque Head, Ball Jointed Body, Dressed, 26 In. 135.00
Doll, **Heinrich Handwerck,** Bisque Head, Kid Body, Blue Sleep Eyes, 19 In. 175.00
Doll, **Heinrich Handwerck,** Horseshoe Mark, Boy, Bisque Arms, Kid Body, 15 In. 85.00
Doll, **Heinrich Handwerck,** Kid Body, Brown Stationary Eyes, 14 In. 105.00
Doll, **Hendren,** Cloth & Composition, Dressed, 28 In. 50.00
Doll, **Herman Steiner 245,** Infant, Solid Dome Bisque Head, 13 1/4 In. 175.00
Doll, **Herman Steiner,** 14 In. 230.00
Doll, **Heubach Kopplesdorf 250,** Girl, Jointed Papier-Mache Body, 9 In. 95.00
Doll, **Heubach Kopplesdorf 275,** Bisque Shoulder Head, Cloth Body, 19 In. 95.00
Doll, **Heubach Kopplesdorf 300 Germany,** Baby, Composition Body, 18 In. 240.00
Doll, **Heubach Kopplesdorf 300,** Baby, Blue Eyes, 8 In. 115.00
Doll, **Heubach Kopplesdorf 349,** Infant, Cloth Body, Closed Mouth, 9 In. 235.00
Doll, **Heubach Kopplesdorf 3208 Germany,** Baby, Breather, Blue Eyes, 24 In. 285.00
Doll, **Heubach Kopplesdorf,** Boy, African, Bisque Head, Grass Skirt, 7 1/2 In. 260.00
Doll, **Heubach Kopplesdorf,** Toddler, Breather, Blue Sleep Eyes, 27 In. 350.00
Doll, **Heubach,** Baby Boy, Intaglio Eyes, 8 In. 185.00
Doll, **Heubach,** Baby, 11 In. 110.00

Doll, **Heubach**, Bisque Head, Brown Eyes, Composition Body 150.00
Doll, **Heubach**, Bisque Head, Kid Body, Brown Eyes, Blonde Hair, 13 1/2 In. 140.00
Doll, **Heubach**, Bisque Head, Pouty, Blue Sleep Eyes, Closed Mouth, 11 1/2 In. 375.00
Doll, **Heubach**, Boy, Bisque Head & Arms, Kid Body, Intaglio Eyes, 12 1/2 In. 350.00
Doll, **Heubach**, Boy, Bisque Head & Arms, Kid Body, Molded Hair, 13 In. 575.00
Doll, **Heubach**, Boy, Bisque Head & Arms, Kid Body, Pouty, 11 In. 365.00
Doll, **Heubach**, Boy, Bisque Head, Jointed Body, Applied Ears, 20 In. 400.00
Doll, **Heubach**, Boy, Bisque Shoulder Head & Limbs, Kid Body, Teeth, 14 In. 350.00
Doll, **Heubach**, Coquette, 13 In. 350.00
Doll, **Heubach**, Infant, Solid Dome, Molded Hair, Composition Body, 9 In. 185.00
Doll, **Heubach**, K444, Toddler, Indian Costume, 8 1/2 In. 170.00
Doll, **Heubach**, Negro, Bent Limb Body, 5 Teeth, 11 In.Tall 265.00
Doll, **Heubach**, Pouty Girl, Bisque Head, Glass Eyes, 13 In.Tall 395.00
Doll, **Heubach**, 2 Under Square Mark, Boy, 5 Piece Body, 8 1/2 In. 140.00
Doll, **Heubach**, 9 In. 205.00
Doll, **Hilda**, 21 In. 695.00
Doll, **Holtz Masse**, 26 In. 230.00
Doll, **Horseman**, Campbell Kid Girl, 1918, Composition, 12 In. 65.00
Doll, **Horseman**, Composition Head, Arms, & Legs, Stuffed Body, C.1911, 19 In. 65.00
Doll, **Horseman**, Just Born Tynie Baby, 15 In. 30.00
Doll, **Horseman**, Mary Poppins, 12 In. .... 12.75 To 16.50
Doll, **Hummel**, Gretel & Hansel, Bee Mark On Back, Dressed, 11 In., Pair 175.00
Doll, **Hummel**, Knitting Girl, 10 1/2 In. 29.50
Doll, **Hummel**, Merry Wanderer, Composition Head, Felt Body, Jointed, 18 In. 750.00
Doll, **Hummel**, Tinder Girl, Dressed, 10 1/2 In. 29.95
Doll, **Hummel**, Tinder Girl, 10 In. 29.95
Doll, **Hummel**, Traveling Boy, Dressed, 10 1/2 In. 29.95
Doll, **Hummel**, Traveling Boy, 10 In. 29.95
Doll, **Hummel**, Traveling Boy, 10 1/2 In. 29.50
Doll, **Ideal**, Bambam, Jointed, 1963, 16 1/2 In. 5.00
Doll, **Ideal**, Betsy Wetsy, Vinyl, Rooted Hair, 1956, 15 1/2 In. 5.00
Doll, **Ideal**, Cinnamon, Red Grow Hair, 1971, 12 In. 2.00
Doll, **Ideal**, Deputy Dawg, 1961, Vinyl Head, Rag, Metal Badge, 19 In. 5.00
Doll, **Ideal**, Dinah, Blonde Grow Hair, Adult Body, Swivel Waist, 1971, 15 In. 4.00
Doll, **Ideal**, Giggles, Flirty Eyes, 1966, 18 In. 8.00
Doll, **Ideal**, Kerry, Beige Blonde Grow Hair, Adult Body, 1969, 18 In. 4.00
Doll, **Ideal**, Kissy, 1962, 22 In. 5.00
Doll, **Ideal**, Larry, Hand Puppet, From 3 Stooges, Vinyl Head, 1959 .... 4.50
Doll, **Ideal**, Mia, Dark Brown Grow Hair, 1970, 15 1/2 In. 3.00
Doll, **Ideal**, Patti Partridge, Plays Patticake, 16 In. 19.50
Doll, **Ideal**, Pete & Repete Twin, Magic Skin, 1950, 9 In. 5.00
Doll, **Ideal**, Plassie, Hard Plastic Head, Cloth Body, Latex Limbs, 1948, 20 In. 18.00
Doll, **Ideal**, Real Live Lucy, Blonde Baby, Shakes Head, 21 In. 11.00
Doll, **Ideal**, Saucy Walker, Hard Plastic, Dressed, 22 In. 22.00
Doll, **Ideal**, Toni Walker, Hard Plastic, Blue Sleep Eyes, 1949, 14 In. 17.00
Doll, **Ideal**, Toni Walker, Hard Plastic, Blue Sleep Eyes, 1949, 20 In. 22.00
Doll, **Indian Girl**, Bisque, Movable Arms, Leather Dress, C.1950, 5 In. 4.00
Doll, **Indian, see Indian, Doll**
Doll, **Izanhah Walker**, Rag, Brown Drop Curls By Ears, Dressed, 16 In. 800.00
Doll, **J.D.K., see also Doll, Kestner**
Doll, **J.D.K. 200**, Girl, Bisquloid Head, Brown Eyes, Black Hair, 18 1/2 In. 130.00
Doll, **J.D.K. 211**, Baby, Brown Eyes, 23 In. 550.00
Doll, **J.D.K. 211**, Baby, Closed Mouth, Brown Eyes, 10 In. 295.00
Doll, **J.D.K. 211**, Baby, 16 In. 200.00
Doll, **J.D.K. 211**, 25 In. 475.00
Doll, **J.D.K. 214**, Ball Jointed, Blue Eyes, Human Hair Wig, 29 In. 275.00
Doll, **J.D.K. 226**, Baby, Brown Sleep Eyes, 12 In. Head, 18 In. Tall 245.00
Doll, **J.D.K. 257**, Baby, Blue Sleep Eyes, 15 In. Head, 23 In. Tall 275.00
Doll, **J.D.K. 260**, Baby Girl, Composition Body, Blue Sleep Eyes, 15 In. 175.00
Doll, **J.D.K.**, Baby, Solid Dome, Jointed Body, Brown Eyes, 18 In. 295.00
Doll, **J.D.K.**, Germany, Baby, Bisque Head, Jointed Composition Body, 17 In. 250.00
Doll, **J.D.K.**, Girl, Teeth, Fur Eyebrows, Open & Close Eyes, 29 In. 250.00
Doll, **J.D.K.**, Toddler, Bald Head, Brown Sleep Eyes, 14 In. 300.00
Doll, **J.F.Kennedy**, Puppet, Vinyl Head, 1962, 14 In. 11.50
Doll, **J.Fred Muggs**, Hand Puppet, 8 In. 4.75
Doll, **Jack Frost Sugar**, Lithographed, Stuffed Cloth, 18 In. 9.00

Doll, Japan, Bisque, Jointed, Molded Hair, Painted Features, 5 In.	5.00
Doll, Japan, Boy, Bisque, 2 1/2 In.	3.00
Doll, Japan, Geisha Girl, Composition, Glass Eyes, 8 In.	25.00
Doll, Japan, Girl, Bisque, 2 1/2 In.	3.00
Doll, Japan, Oriental Baby, Bisque, Dressed, 6 1/4 In.	45.00
Doll, Japan, Quintuplets, Bisque, Jointed Arms, 3 In., 5 In Original Box	125.00
Doll, Joel Ellis, Woman, Rock Maple, Pewter Limbs, C.1873, 15 In.	550.00
Doll, Joy, Baby, Molded Hair, Blue Sleep Eyes, 17 In.	165.00
Doll, Jumeau 1907 11, Girl, Bisque Head, Jointed Composition Body, 24 In.	425.00
Doll, Jumeau 1907, Girl, Blue Paperweight Eyes, Human Hair Wig, 24 In.	575.00
Doll, Jumeau 1907, Girl, Blue Paperweight Eyes, Human Hair Wig, 30 In.	775.00
Doll, Jumeau, Bebe, Cork Head, Jointed Composition Body, Voice Box, 21 In.	450.00
Doll, Jumeau, Closed Mouth, Blue Paperweight Eyes, 16 In.	680.00
Doll, Jumeau, Closed Mouth, Paperweight Blue Eyes, Voicebox Torso, 23 In.	795.00
Doll, Jumeau, French Fashion, Brown Eyes, 14 In.	475.00
Doll, Jumeau, French Fashion, Jointed Body, Blue Paperweight Eyes, 21 In.	795.00
Doll, Jumeau, Girl, Bisque Head, Jointed Composition Body, 15 In.	335.00
Doll, Jumeau, Girl, Bisque, Blue Paperweight Eyes, Open Mouth, 20 In.	550.00
Doll, Jumeau, Girl, Blue Paperweight Eyes, Closed Mouth, Auburn Hair, 18 In.	785.00
Doll, Jumeau, Girl, Blue Paperweight Eyes, Human Hair Wig, 19 1/2 In.	550.00
Doll, Jumeau, Girl, Human Hair Wig, Blue Paperweight Eyes, 14 1/2 In.	775.00
Doll, Jumeau, Girl, Jointed Body, Closed Mouth, 18 In.	800.00
Doll, Jumeau, Girl, Marked Head & Body, 25 In.	550.00
Doll, Jumeau, Girl, Walks, Talks, & Kisses, Blue Sleep Eyes, 22 In.	495.00
Doll, Jumeau, Incised Dep., French Child, Blue Eyes, 14 1/2 In.	200.00
Doll, Jumeau, Jointed Composition Body, 24 In. _Illus_	1000.00
Doll, Jumeau, Lady, Bisque, Blue Paperweight Eyes, Open Mouth, 14 1/2 In.	525.00
Doll, Jumeau, Marked Dep., Bisque Swivel Head, Jointed Body, 27 In.	350.00
Doll, Jumeau, Marked 1907, Negro, Bisque Swivel Head, Jointed Body, 11 In.	525.00
Doll, Jumeau, Medaille D'Or Body, Brown Paperweight Eyes, 26 In.	850.00
Doll, Jumeau, Open Mouth, 18 In.	315.00
Doll, Jumeau, S.F.J.B., Paris 230, Bebe, Jointed, Open Mouth, 20 In.	550.00
Doll, Jumeau, 17 In.	285.00
Doll, Jumeau, 19 1/3 In.	110.00
Doll, Jumeau, 1907, 14 In.	310.00
Doll, Jutta, Flirty Eyes, 20 In.	225.00
Doll, K & H, Boy, Bisque Head, Composition Toddler Body, 15 1/2 In.	745.00
Doll, K & H, Boy, Bisque, Molded Hair, Brown Eyes, 13 In.	375.00
Doll, K & H, Tommy Tucker, Bisque Head, Brown Glass Eyes, 14 In.	385.00
Doll, K * R Simon Halbig, Baby, Bisque Swivel Head, Composition Body, 17 In.	126.00
Doll, K * R 11, Girl, Ball Jointed, Blue Sleep Eyes, 23 In.	165.00
Doll, K * R 21 S & H, Bisque, 5 Part Composition Body, 7 1/2 In.	135.00
Doll, K * R 121 Simon & Halbig, Boy Baby, Bisque Head, 16 In.	335.00
Doll, K * R 121, Boy Toddler, Brown Eyes, 2 Teeth, Blonde Mohair Wig, 24 In.	395.00
Doll, K * R 122, Baby, 2 Top Teeth, Blue Eyes, Dressed, 17 In.	250.00
Doll, K * R 126, Baby Girl, Blue Sleep Eyes, Blonde Wig, Jointed, 14 In.	155.00
Doll, K * R 126, 25 In.	325.00
Doll, K * R, Baby Girl, Bisque, Flirty Eyes, Blonde Wig, 21 In.	385.00
Doll, K * R, Baby, Jointed Body, Brown Flirty Eyes, 21 In.	385.00
Doll, K * R, Bisque Head, Composition Body, 12 In.High	65.00
Doll, K * R, Bisque Head, Jointed Composition Body, Flirty Eyes, 15 In.	250.00
Doll, K * R, Boy Toddler, Buster Brown Outfit, Composition Body, 24 In.	325.00
Doll, K * R, Boy, Celluloid Head, Kid Body, Brown Sleep Eyes, 19 In.	125.00
Doll, K * R, Brown Sleep Eyes, 28 In.	235.00
Doll, K * R, Girl, Bisque Shoulder Plate, Kid Body, Open Mouth, 16 In.	135.00
Doll, K * R, Kaiser Baby, 11 In.	340.00
Doll, K * R, Kaiser Baby, 13 In.Tall	300.00
Doll, K * R, Lady, Jointed Body, Blue Sleep Eyes, Human Hair, 30 In.	235.00
Doll, K * R, 126, Infant, Composition Toddler Body, 15 In.	300.00
Doll, K.P.M., Boy, C.1870, Painted Blue Eyes, 4 1/2 In. Head	1400.00
Doll, Kaiser, Baby, Blue Intaglio Eyes, 9 1/2 In.	225.00
Doll, Kaiser, Baby, Blue Painted Eyes, 14 In.	295.00
Doll, Kallas, Plaything, Baby, Composition Head, Stuffed Body, 14 In.Tall	50.00
Doll, Kamkins, Girl, Dressed, 19 In.	235.00
Doll, Kerr & Hinz, Miss Peg O' My Heart, Bisque, C.1940, Jointed, 7 In.	3.25
Doll, Kestner, see also Doll, J.D.K.	

Doll, Kestner 1 1/2, Bisque, 4 Part Composition Body, Blue Eyes, 8 In.	125.00
Doll, Kestner 7 3/4 154 DEP C 3/4, Germany, Kid Body, Brown Eyes, 21 In.	150.00
Doll, Kestner 142, Baby, Solid Dome, Jointed Body, Blue Eyes, 14 1/2 In.	195.00
Doll, Kestner 142, Baby, Solid Dome, Jointed Body, Gray Intaglio Eyes, 12 In.	195.00
Doll, Kestner 142, Ball Jointed, Brown Sleep Eyes, 36 In.	425.00
Doll, Kestner 151, Baby, Solid Dome, Jointed Body, Blue Eyes, 21 In.	395.00
Doll, Kestner 151, Boy, Jointed Body, Blue Intaglio Eyes, Molded Hair, 14 In.	215.00
Doll, Kestner 152, Character Baby, Gray Eyes, 11 In.	140.00
Doll, Kestner 152-4, Baby Boy, Brown Eyes, Brown Wig, 14 In.	125.00
Doll, Kestner 154, Shoulder Head, Brown Sleep Eyes, 26 In.	175.00
Doll, Kestner 162, Bride, Jointed Body, Blue Sleep Eyes, Open Mouth, 23 In.	435.00
Doll, Kestner 166, Dark Human Hair Curls, 23 In.	130.00
Doll, Kestner 166, Shoulder Head, Blue Sleep Eyes, 14 In.	115.00
Doll, Kestner 171 Germany, Girl, Sleep Eyes, 3 Teeth, 17 1/2 In.	122.00
Doll, Kestner 171, Ball Jointed, 24 In.	150.00
Doll, Kestner 171, Daisy, Dressed, 24 In.	300.00
Doll, Kestner 174, Ball Jointed Body, Brown Sleep Eyes, Mohair Wig, 11 In.	90.00
Doll, Kestner 211, Baby, Bald Head, 11 In.	195.00
Doll, Kestner, Baby, Jointed Body, Open & Close Mouth, 10 In.	175.00
Doll, Kestner, Bisque, Kid Body, Open Mouth, Blue Eyes, C.1880, 26 In.	175.00
Doll, Kestner, Boy, Brown Eyes, 2 Teeth, 17 In.	240.00
Doll, Kestner, Darling, 5 Piece Papier-Mache Body, 8 In.	80.00
Doll, Kestner, Girl, Bisque, 4 Teeth, Blue Sleep Eyes, 7 In.	160.00
Doll, Kestner, Girl, Brown Sleep Eyes, Kid Body, Human Hair, 18 In.Tall	140.00
Doll, Kestner, Girl, 4 Teeth, Blue Sleep Eyes, 7 In.	160.00
Doll, Kestner, Hilda, Porcelain Head, Composition Body, 13 In.Circumference	125.00
Doll, Kestner, Kid Body, Bisque Hands, Blue Sleep Eyes, 23 In.	175.00
Doll, Kestner, Leather Body, Bisque Head, Brown Eyes, 20 In.Tall	150.00
Doll, Kewpie, see Kewpie, Doll	
Doll, King Features, Popeye, Stuffed Body, Plastic Face, 9 In.	10.00
Doll, Klay & Hahn, Baby, Blue Sleep Eyes, Molded Hair, 20 In.	265.00
Doll, Klay & Hahn, Walker, Bisque Head, Jointed Body, Blue Eyes, 23 In.	155.00
Doll, Knickerbocker, Bozo Clown, 1950s, Rag, Capitol Records, 22 In.	6.00
Doll, Lenci, Buccaneer Boy, 20 In.	85.00
Doll, Lenci, Girl, Green Outfit, 12 In.	70.00
Doll, Lenci, Girl, Painted Eyes, Mohair Wig, Felt, 12 1/2 In.	55.00
Doll, Leslie Uggams, Singer, Hard Plastic, 16 In.	85.00
Doll, L'il Imp, Vogue, Sister to Brikette, 11 In.	14.75
Doll, Limbach, Bisque, Molded Shoes, 5 1/2 In.	55.00
Doll, Limoges, Bisque Head, 4 In.	15.00
Doll, Limoges, Cherie No.3, Blue Sleep Eyes, Pierced Ears, Dressed, 13 In.	150.00
Doll, Limoges, Mechanical Legs & Head, Blue Paperweight Eyes, 21 In.	375.00
Doll, Lindstrom, Betty, Clockwork, Tin, 8 In.	30.00
Doll, Little Favorite, Bonnet Head, Porcelain, Pine Trunk, C.1870, 7 In.	55.00

Doll, Jumeau, Jointed
Composition Body, 24 In.
(See Page 173)

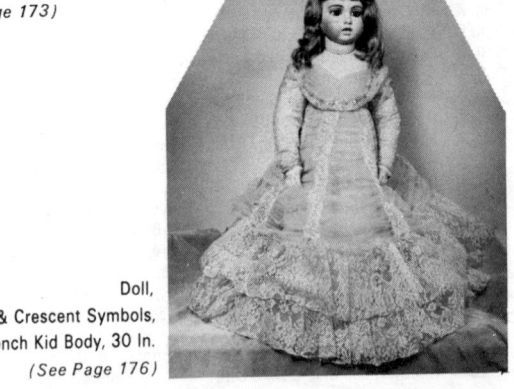

Doll,
Moon & Crescent Symbols,
French Kid Body, 30 In.
(See Page 176)

Doll, Little Lulu, Celluloid Face, Cloth Body, 14 In.	12.00
Doll, Little Lulu, Cloth, Stuffed, Yarn Hair, C.1970, 19 In.	8.50
Doll, Little Max, From Joe Palooka, 20 In.	30.00
Doll, Little Sis, Composition, Dressed, 13 In.	24.00
Doll, Lois Jane, Composition Face, 16 In.	38.00
Doll, Lori, Baby, Molded Head, Brown Sleep Eyes, 9 1/2 In.	395.00
Doll, M.B. 22, Baby, Open Mouth, Brown Sleep Eyes, 14 In.	65.00
Doll, M.B., Japan, Girl, Toddler, Cloth Body, Smiling, 13 1/2 In.	62.00
Doll, M.F., Straight Limb Body, Blue Eyes, Human Hair Wig, 12 In.	45.00
Doll, M.O.A., 27 In.	185.00
Doll, Mabel, Pink Cloth Body, Blonde Wig, Blue Eyes, 15 In.	120.00
Doll, Mabel, 15 In.	65.00
Doll, Madame Alexander, Alexanderkin Bride, Hard Plastic, 7 1/2 In.	12.50
Doll, Madame Alexander, Alexanderkins, 7 In.	35.00
Doll, Madame Alexander, Alice In Wonderland, Composition, Dressed, 14 In.	35.00
Doll, Madame Alexander, Amish Boy, 8 In.	26.50 To 33.50
Doll, Madame Alexander, Amy Of Little Women, Bent Knee, 8 In.	26.50
Doll, Madame Alexander, Argentine Boy, Hard Plastic, Jointed, 8 In.	26.50
Doll, Madame Alexander, Babs, The Ice-Skating Girl, 1948, Hard Plastic, 14 In.	26.00
Doll, Madame Alexander, Baby Genius, 1940s, Hard Plastic, Cloth Body, 18 In.	12.00
Doll, Madame Alexander, Baby Lynn, White Organdy Dress, 20 In.	24.00
Doll, Madame Alexander, Baby McGuffy, Vinyl, Dressed, 18 In.	34.50 To 38.75
Doll, Madame Alexander, Baby, Composition Head, Rubber Arms & Legs, 18 In.	35.00
Doll, Madame Alexander, Baby, 25 In.	20.00
Doll, Madame Alexander, Beth Of Little Women, Bent Knee, 8 In.	23.00 To 26.50
Doll, Madame Alexander, Boy, 23 In.	20.00
Doll, Madame Alexander, Bride, Bent Knee, 8 In.	24.00
Doll, Madame Alexander, Bride, Composition, 14 In.	55.00
Doll, Madame Alexander, Bride, Hard Plastic, Jointed, 8 In.	26.50
Doll, Madame Alexander, Canada, Bent Knee, 8 In.	23.00
Doll, Madame Alexander, China, Bent Knee, 8 In.	23.00
Doll, Madame Alexander, Cissy, Hard Plastic Face, 19 In.	30.00
Doll, Madame Alexander, Cissy, 20 In.	48.00
Doll, Madame Alexander, Elsie Bridge, 17 In.	30.00
Doll, Madame Alexander, France, Bent Knee, 8 In.	23.00
Doll, Madame Alexander, Godey Lady, 1953, Hard Plastic, Blue Eyes, 14 In.	50.00
Doll, Madame Alexander, Greek Boy, 8 In.	26.50
Doll, Madame Alexander, Gretel From The Sound Of Music, 8 In.	27.50
Doll, Madame Alexander, Hansel, Hard Plastic, Jointed, 8 In.	23.00 To 26.50
Doll, Madame Alexander, Indonesia, Bent Knee, 8 In.	23.00
Doll, Madame Alexander, Jane Withers, 15 In.	95.00
Doll, Madame Alexander, Janie Baby, 14 In.	26.50
Doll, Madame Alexander, Janie Baby, 20 In.	33.00
Doll, Madame Alexander, Japanese, Hard Plastic, Jointed, 8 In.	26.50
Doll, Madame Alexander, Kathy, Dressed, 15 In.	14.50
Doll, Madame Alexander, Leslie, Negro, Ballerina Costume, 17 In.	55.00
Doll, Madame Alexander, Leslie, Negro, Bride Dress, 17 In.	65.00
Doll, Madame Alexander, Leslie, Negro, Pink Formal Gown, 17 In.	53.00
Doll, Madame Alexander, Little Genius, Vinyl Body, Caracul Wig, 7 In.	35.00
Doll, Madame Alexander, Maggie, Plaid Skirt, Straw Hat, 17 In.	35.00
Doll, Madame Alexander, Marge, Hard Plastic Face, 10 In.	16.00
Doll, Madame Alexander, Marta From The Sound Of Music, 8 In.	27.50
Doll, Madame Alexander, Mary Martin, Sailor Outfit, 17 In.	58.00
Doll, Madame Alexander, McGuffy Anna, Composition, 12 In.	50.00
Doll, Madame Alexander, McGuffy Anna, Composition, 13 In.	40.00
Doll, Madame Alexander, Polly Ballerina, 1965, Vinyl, Blue Eyes, 17 In.	22.00
Doll, Madame Alexander, Portuguese, Hard Plastic, Jointed, 8 In.	26.50
Doll, Madame Alexander, Princess Elizabeth, Dressed, 15 In.	45.00
Doll, Madame Alexander, Queen, Plastic, 10 In.	26.00
Doll, Madame Alexander, Russia, Bent Knee, 8 In.	23.00
Doll, Madame Alexander, Scarlett O'Hara, Vinyl, Green Dress, 12 In.	28.00
Doll, Madame Alexander, Scotland, Bent Knee, 8 In.	23.00
Doll, Madame Alexander, Snow White, 8 In.	21.00
Doll, Madame Alexander, So Big, Vinyl, Rooted Wig, 22 In.	30.00
Doll, Madame Alexander, Southern Belle, Portrette, 11 In.	27.50
Doll, Madame Alexander, Victoria, Original Box, 18 In.	22.50

Doll, **Madame Alexander**, Vietnam, Bent Knee, 8 In. 27.50
Doll, **Made In Germany**, No.151, Baby, Composition Body, 22 1/2 In. 250.00
Doll, **Majestic**, Nun, Bisque Head, Jointed Body, Blue Eyes, 34 In. .... 345.00 To 350.00
Doll, **Margo**, Ballerina, Hard Plastic, 18 In. 30.00
Doll, **Matell**, Baby First Step, Battery Operated, Talks, 1964, 18 In. 6.00
Doll, **Matell**, Chatty Baby, Pull String, Talks, 1964, 16 In. 5.00
Doll, **Matell**, Twiggy, British Model, 11 In. 19.00
Doll, **Mechanical**, French, Music Hall Costume, Smokes Cigarettes, 10 In. 200.00
Doll, **Mexican Boy**, Bisque, Jointed Arms, Painted Features, 5 In. 3.50
Doll, **Mexican Girl**, Bisque, Jointed Arms, Painted Features, 5 In. 3.50
Doll, **Mike**, Monkees, Finger Puppet, Movable Head & Arms, 5 In. 2.00
Doll, **Milliner's Model**, Papier-Mache Shoulder Head, Kid Body, 10 In. 285.00
Doll, **Milton Bradley Co.**, Charlie Chaplin, 1972, 19 In. 11.00
Doll, **Minerva**, Tin Shoulder Head, 3 In. 8.50
Doll, **Minerva**, Tin Shoulder Head, 3 3/8 In. 12.50
Doll, **Miss Peep**, Negro, Cameo, 16 In. 16.50
Doll, **Mon Cheri**, Brown Paperweight Eyes, 12 In. 175.00
Doll, **Mon Tresor**, Girl, Blue Eyes, Blonde Wig, Lace Trimmed Dress, 18 In. 325.00
Doll, **Moon & Crescent Symbols**, French Kid Body, 30 In. .... *Illus* 4000.00
Doll, **Mr.Peanut**, Wooden, Jointed, 8 In. 35.00
Doll, **Nancy Lee**, Bonnet Hat, 8 1/2 In. 225.00
Doll, **Negro Mammy**, New Orleans, 1880, Sitting, Molded Bust, 25 In. 75.00
Doll, **Negro**, Bisque Head, 5 Piece Composition Body, Glass Eyes, 6 In. 66.00
Doll, **Negro**, Bisque, Jointed At Shoulders, Painted Features, 5 In. 6.50
Doll, **Negro**, Celluloid, Jointed Arms, Molded Hair, Dressed, C.1930, 2 1/2 In. 1.10
Doll, **Negro**, Composition Head, Aunt Jemima Type Face, C.1930, 4 1/2 In. 6.25
Doll, **Negro**, Rubber, Molded Hair & Clothes, 5 In. 5.00
Doll, **Nippon 18**, Marked Flower Bud, Girl, 20 In. 110.00
Doll, **Nippon**, Bisque Head, Papier-Mache Body, Brown Intaglio Eyes, 5 In. 75.00
Doll, **Nippon**, Girl, Bisque, Bathing Suit, Fat Tummy, 5 1/2 In. 65.00
Doll, **Nippon**, Girl, Jointed Kid Body, Blue Stationary Eyes, 18 In. 55.00
Doll, **Nippon**, H In Diamond, Baby, 13 1/2 In. 95.00
Doll, **Nippon**, Oriental Baby, Bisque, Brown Slanted Eyes, 12 In. 225.00
Doll, **No.125**, French Fashion, Bisque Swivel Head, Cloth Body, 13 In. 650.00
Doll, **No.187**, 122X On Solid Dome Bisque Head, Jointed, 13 In. 600.00
Doll, **No.2015 & Anchor With W**, Bisque Head, Kid Body, 19 In. 135.00
Doll, **No.263 Over 38**, Baby, Brown Eyes & Hair, 14 1/2 In. 195.00
Doll, **Nora Wellings**, 12 In. 15.00
Doll, **Nun**, Composition, Swivel Head, Blue Sleep Eyes, Dressed, 18 In. 40.00
Doll, **Occupied Japan**, Boy, Celluloid, Knickers, Holding Football, 4 In. 3.00
Doll, **Occupied Japan**, Fat Baby Boy, Celluloid, Jointed Arms, Bottle, 7 In. 6.00
Doll, **Occupied Japan**, Fat Baby Boy, Movable Arms, Holds Bottle, 7 In. 6.00
Doll, **Occupied Japan**, Flapper Type Girl, Bisque, Blonde Hair, 3 1/2 In. 9.00
Doll, **Occupied Japan**, Flapper Type Girl, Bisque, Blonde Hair, 5 In. 10.00
Doll, **Occupied Japan**, Little Boy With Football, Celluloid, 4 In. 3.00
Doll, **Open & Closed Mouth**, Kid Body, 21 In. 190.00
Doll, **Orphan Annie**, Stuffed Cloth, Molded Face, 1972, 23 In. 12.50
Doll, **P 2/1 Germany**, Baby, Bisque, Solid Dome Head, 7 In. 95.00
Doll, **Palmer Cox**, 1897, Old Woman, Rag, Papier-Mache Face, 11 In. 65.00
Doll, **Papier-Mache**, Sleep Eyes, 23 In. 55.00
Doll, **Paris**, Bebe, Closed Mouth, Blue Paperweight Eyes, 21 In. 695.00
Doll, **Patsy Baby**, 10 In. 55.00
Doll, **Patsy Jr.**, Gold Bracelet, 11 In. 12.00
Doll, **Patsy**, Sleep Eyes, 13 In. 12.00
Doll, **Patsyette**, 9 1/2 In. 35.00
Doll, **Patsykins**, 11 In. 23.00
Doll, **Peddler Woman**, C.1850 .... *Illus* 800.00
Doll, **Peddler**, Terra-Cotta, Old Lady Carrying Basket With Bread, 11 In. 52.00
Doll, **Poland**, The Whistler, Stuffed Body, Hard Mask Face, 20 In. 30.00
Doll, **Poured Wax**, Long Blonde Braids, Glass Eyes, 4 1/2 In. 75.00
Doll, **Premier Khrushchev**, Puppet, Vinyl Head, 1962, 14 In. 11.50
Doll, **Queen Louise**, Bisque Socket Head, Blue Eyes, 24 In. .... 130.00 To 150.00
Doll, **Queen Louise**, German, Bisque Head, 27 In. 135.00
Doll, **R & B**, Debuteen, Wrist Tag, 14 In. 37.50
Doll, **R.& B.**, Littlest Angel, Hard Plastic, Brown Eyes, Blonde Wig, 11 In. 10.50
Doll, **R.W.**, Baby, Boy, 5 Piece Body, Intaglio Eyes, 8 In. 200.00

Doll, Remco, Barry Goldwater, Hat & Glasses, 1964, 6 In.	8.00
Doll, Remco, Linda Lee, 1970, 12 In.	2.50
Doll, Remco, Lyndon B.Johnson, Vinyl, Jointed Arms, 1964, 6 In.	9.00
Doll, Remco, Lyndon B.Johnson, 8 In.	35.00
Doll, Remco, Orphan Annie, 1966, 16 In.	17.50
Doll, Revlon, 18 In.	23.75
Doll, Rex Harrison As Dr.Doolittle, Talking, 24 In.	23.50
Doll, Ricky Jr., From I Love Lucy Show, American, 16 In.	33.00
Doll, Rootie Kazootie, Marionette, 16 In.	12.00
Doll, Rosebud, 21 In.	125.00
Doll, S & C, Ball Jointed, Blue Sleep Eyes, 29 In.	225.00 To 265.00
Doll S & H, see also Doll, C.M.Bergmann, Doll, Simon & Halbig	
Doll, S & H 1/950, Solid Dome Bisque Shoulder Head, Kid Body, 13 In.	195.00
Doll, S & H 103, Pierced Ears, Brown Eyes, 16 In.	150.00
Doll, S & H 550, Velvet Dress, 22 In.	190.00
Doll, S & H 550, Velvet Dress, 24 In.	190.00
Doll, S & H 939, Bisque, Jointed Body, Brown Paperweight Eyes, 14 In.	180.00
Doll, S & H 939, Top & Bottom Teeth, 14 In.	275.00
Doll, S & H 1039, Lady, 24 In.	240.00
Doll, S & H 1078, Girl, Jointed Body, Blue Eyes, Human Hair, 36 In.	395.00
Doll, S & H 1160, Shoulder Head, Closed Mouth, Brown Eyes, 1 1/2 In.	65.00
Doll, S & H 1249, Girl, Jointed Composition Body, Brown Eyes & Hair, 18 In.	225.00
Doll, S & H, Bisque Head, Jointed Body, Teeth, Pierced Ears, 21 In.	155.00
Doll, S & H, CMB, Character Face, Blue Eyes, 22 In.	120.00
Doll, S & H, Girl, Blue Eyes, Honey Hair, 23 In.	160.00
Doll, S & H, Girl, Brown Eyes, 35 In.	360.00
Doll, S & H, H.H., Dressed, 21 In.	195.00
Doll, S & H, K * R 126, Baby, Jointed Body, Flirty Eyes, 18 In.	250.00
Doll, S & H, K * R 126, Little Lord Fauntleroy, Composition Body, 24 In.	290.00
Doll, S & H, Walker, Girl, Throws Kisses, 21 1/2 In.	275.00
Doll, S.F.B.J. Paris, French Child, Blue Eyes, Open Mouth, 20 In.	255.00
Doll, S.F.B.J. 25-301, Girl, Composition Body, Brown Sleep Eyes, 22 In.	325.00
Doll, S.F.B.J. 230, Brown Sleep Eyes, 23 In.	350.00
Doll, S.F.B.J. 235, Baby, Sleep Eyes, 10 In.	260.00
Doll, S.F.B.J. 236 Paris 6, Laughing Child, Composition Body, 14 In.	425.00
Doll, S.F.B.J. 236 Paris, Laughing Child, Jointed Composition Body, 24 In.	485.00
Doll, S.F.B.J. 236, Baby, Sleep Eyes, Brown Hair, 26 In.	595.00
Doll, S.F.B.J. 236, Toddler, Blue Sleep Eyes, 21 In.	625.00
Doll, S.F.B.J. 236, Toddler, 27 In.	695.00
Doll, S.F.B.J. 237, Boy, Paperweight Eyes, 16 In. .... *Illus*	1650.00
Doll, S.F.B.J. 251, Character Face, Blue Sleep Eyes, Human Hair Wig, 13 In.	450.00
Doll, S.F.B.J. 251, 17 In.	500.00
Doll, S.F.B.J. 301 Paris, Clown, Bisque Head, Composition Body, 19 In.	375.00
Doll, S.F.B.J. 301, Blue Sleep Eyes, 15 In.	295.00

Doll, S.F.B.J. 237, Boy,
Paperweight Eyes, 16 In.

Doll, Peddler Woman,
C.1850
(See Page 176)

Doll, S.F.B.J. 301, Boy, 18 In.	255.00
Doll, S.F.B.J. 301, Brown Sleep Eyes, 27 In.	295.00
Doll, S.F.B.J. 60 Paris, Girl, Bisque Head, Jointed Composition Body, 15 In.	195.00
Doll, S.F.B.J., Blue Paperweight Eyes, Open Mouth, Human Hair Wig, 29 In.	495.00
Doll, S.F.B.J., Boy, French Costume, 9 In.	135.00
Doll, S.F.B.J., French Child, 22 In.	275.00
Doll, S.F.B.J., Girl, French Costume, 9 1/2 In.	150.00
Doll, S.F.B.J., Girl, Painted Shoes, Dressed, 13 In.	125.00
Doll, S.F.B.J., Harem Girl, Painted Blue Eyes, Mohair Wig, 12 In.	135.00
Doll, S.F.B.J., Jumeau Label On Body, Open Mouth, 23 In.	295.00
Doll, S.F.B.J., Walker, Kisses, 20 In.	295.00
Doll, Sally, Marked, 11 In.	38.00
Doll, Schoenau & Hoffmeister, Bisque Head, Composition Body, 18 In.	175.00
Doll, Schoenau & Hoffmeister, Girl, Jointed Composition Body, 1909, 9 In.	135.00
Doll, Schoenhau & Hoffmeister, Hannah, Sleep Eyes, 6 1/2 In.	95.00
Doll, Schoenhut, Boy, Sleep Eyes, 17 In.	250.00
Doll, Schoenhut, Girl Toddler, Walking, Painted Eyes, Wooden, 17 In.	225.00
Doll, Schoenhut, Girl, Carved Head, Middy Dress, 15 In.	460.00
Doll, Schoenhut, Girl, Open Mouth, Teeth, Blonde Hair, 16 In.	295.00
Doll, Schoenhut, Girl, Sleep Eyes, Dressed, 18 In.	250.00
Doll, Schoenhut, Negro, Wooden, 9 In.	75.00
Doll, Schoenhut, Roly-Poly, Negro Face, 4 In.	75.00
Doll, Schoenhut, Roly-Poly, Patent Dec.15, 1905, Clown Face, 12 1/2 In.	150.00
Doll, Schoenhut, Roly-Poly, White Face, 4 In.	75.00
Doll, Schoenhut, Walker, Gray Velvet Suit, 11 In.	250.00
Doll, Shoen & Hoff, Bisque Head, Wood & Composition Body, Lies On Sled, 6 In	110.00
Doll, Shutz-Marke, Celluloid Head, Wood Body, C.1915, 8 1/2 In.Tall	125.00
Doll, Simon & Halbig, see also Doll, C.M.Bergmann, Doll, S.&H.	
Doll, Simon & Halbig 156, Baby, Flirty, Open Mouth, 26 In.	375.00
Doll, Simon & Halbig 949, Upper Teeth, Jointed Composition Body, 32 In.	385.00
Doll, Simon & Halbig 1009, Composition Body, Brown Sleep Eyes, 24 In.	125.00
Doll, Simon & Halbig 1009, Girl, Celluloid Body, Wood & Mache Limbs, 19 In.	135.00
Doll, Simon & Halbig 1010, Turned Bisque Head, Dressed, 16 In.	210.00
Doll, Simon & Halbig 1079, Ball Jointed, Blue Eyes, 22 In.	95.00
Doll, Simon & Halbig 1079, Girl, Jointed Body, Brown Eyes, 36 In.	550.00
Doll, Simon & Halbig 1079, Girl, Pierced Ears, Blue Sleep Eyes, 35 In.	355.00
Doll, Simon & Halbig 1129, Oriental, Jointed Body, Brown Eyes, 12 In.	700.00
Doll, Simon & Halbig 1249, Pull String, Cries, 16 In.	165.00
Doll, Simon & Halbig, Gibson Girl, Jointed Body, High Heel Feet, 14 In.	495.00
Doll, Simon & Halbig, Girl, Bisque Shoulder Head, Kid Body, 14 In.	295.00
Doll, Simon & Halbig, Girl, Brown Sleep Eyes, Wig, Dressed, 3 Ft.	495.00
Doll, Simon & Halbig, Girl, Jointed Composition Body, 22 In.	185.00
Doll, Simon & Halbig, Girl, Pierced Ears, Blue Stationary Eyes, 30 In.	225.00
Doll, Simon & Halbig, Lady, Bisque Turned Head, Jointed Kid Body, 26 In.	225.00
Doll, Solid Dome, F Mark On Composition Body, Pouty, Closed Mouth, 12 In.	210.00
Doll, Sonja Henie, Costume With Skates, 17 In.	125.00
Doll, Sonja Henie, U.S.A., Composition, Skating Outfit, Skates, 15 In.	50.00
Doll, Steiner, Girl, Jointed Body, Blue Paperweight Eyes, 12 In.	725.00
Doll, Steiner, 89 *, Girl, Jointed Composition Body, Paperweight Eyes, 18 In.	650.00
Doll, Tete Jumeau, Baby, Bisque Head, Jointed Composition Body, 24 In.	375.00
Doll, Tete Jumeau, Girl, Jointed Composition Body, Paperweight Eyes, 12 In.	525.00
Doll, Tete Jumeau, Girl, Jointed Composition Body, Paperweight Eyes, 26 In.	435.00
Doll, Tete Jumeau, Girl, Jointed Composition Body, Paperweight Eyes, 29 In.	485.00
Doll, Tete Jumeau, 1907, Girl, Jointed Composition Body, Brown Eyes, 25 In.	375.00
Doll, Thomasino, Anatomically Correct, Jointed, Drinks, Wets, 17 In.	26.50
Doll, Tiny Tears, American, Rooted Hair, Original Box, 13 In.	12.50
Doll, Toddler, Composition Head & Limbs, Cloth Body, Tin Eyes, C.1920, 20 In.	20.00
Doll, Tommy Tucker, Closed Mouth, Brown Sleep Eyes, 8 In. Head, 11 In. Tall	475.00
Doll, Toni, 11 In.	5.00
Doll, Topper, Smarty Pants, Talks, Blonde, 1971, 19 In.	5.00
Doll, Toys Incorporated, Baltimore, Negro, Dancing, Wooden, Jointed, 15 In.	29.00
Doll, Turtle, Boy, Celluloid, Composition Arms, Wooden Feet, Cap On, 8 In.	20.00
Doll, Turtle, Boy, Celluloid, 10 1/2 In.	25.00
Doll, Turtle, Boy, Celluloid, 14 In.	85.00
Doll, Turtle, Girl, Celluloid, Wig, Dressed, 9 In.	20.00
Doll, Twiggy, British Model, Original Box, 11 In.	21.50

Doll, U.S.A., Sailor, Roly-Poly, Wooden, 1946, 10 In.	7.00
Doll, Uneeda, Pollyanna, Walt Disney Productions, Hard Plastic, 20 In.	25.00
Doll, Unis France 60, Lady, Brown Coloring, Jointed Composition Body, 11 In.	150.00
Doll, Unis France 71-149 301, Walker, Composition Body, Sleep Eyes, 22 In.	275.00
Doll, Unis France, Bisque Head, French Costume, 6 1/2 In.	95.00
Doll, Unis France, Girl, Papier-Mache & Composition, 20 In.	50.00
Doll, Vogue, Bride Medford, 7 In.	11.00
Doll, Vogue, Dearest One, Baby, Vinyl, Black Sleep Eyes, 1967, 17 In.	10.00
Doll, Vogue, Ginny, Hard Plastic, Dressed, 8 In.	12.00
Doll, Vogue, P-90, Hard Vinyl, Blue Sleep Eyes, Closed Mouth, 13 In.	15.00
Doll, W & C Thuringia, Girl, Bisque, Ball Jointed, Open Mouth, 20 1/2 In.	135.00
Doll, Wax Over Composition, Wooden Limbs, Dressed, 12 In.	85.00
Doll, Wax Over Composition, 30 In.	120.00
Doll, Wedding Cake, Bride & Groom, Bisque, Jointed, 4 1/4 In., Pair	45.00
Doll, Wee Imp, Ballerina, Vogue, Sister To Brikette, 8 In.	12.50
Doll, Wee Patsy, Marked Torso, Painted Eyes, 6 In.	12.00
Doll, Wendy, 14 In.	22.00
Doll, Wendykins Bride, 1965, 8 In.	30.00
Doll, Whiskbroom, Hair Bristles, 1920, 3 In.	15.00
Doll, Young Adult Girl, Composition, Jointed, Painted Features, 12 In.	23.50
Doll, 100 11/0, Bisque Head, Composition Body, Black Eyes, 10 In.	50.00
Donald Duck, see Disneyana	
Doorstop, see Iron, Doorstop	
Dorchester, Sugar & Creamer, Cover, Blueberry Design	35.00
Dorchester, Sugar & Creamer, Pinecones	60.00

Doulton, Bottle, Nelson,
Stoneware, C.1820, 16 1/4 In.

*Doulton pottery and porcelain were made by Doulton and Co.of Burslem,
England, after 1882. The name Royal Doulton appeared on their wares
after 1902.*

Doulton, see also Royal Doulton

Doulton, Bottle, Nelson, Stoneware, C.1820, 16 1/4 In.	*Illus*	500.00
Doulton, Bowl, Punch, Blue, Gold, & Gilt, Burslem, Vernon, 16 X 10 In.		220.00
Doulton, Breakfast Set, Dickensware, Signed Noke, 3 Piece		120.00
Doulton, Candlestick, Silicon Ware, Blue, Gilt & Gold, C.1875, 6 3/4 In., Pair		120.00
Doulton, Chocolate Pot, Cobalt Floral, Gold Trim, Burslem, C.1885		65.00
Doulton, Cistern, Robert Burns, Spigot, Stoneware, Lambeth, C.1820, 10 1/2 In.		200.00
Doulton, Compote, Brown Floral, Burslem, 7 3/4 X 4 3/4 In.		22.00
Doulton, Creamer, Stoneware, Tan To Blue, Silver Top, 1876		94.00
Doulton, Cup & Saucer, Demitasse, Flowers, Gold Trim, Raised Scrolls		24.00
Doulton, Ewer, Red & White Floral On Beige Tapestry, Slater, Lambeth, 7 In.		72.50
Doulton, Ewer, Tans, Floral, Sterling Mount, Tinworth, Lambeth, 1872, 11 In.		265.00
Doulton, Figurine, Spaniel Curled On Round Cushion, 1 1/2 X 1 In.		65.00
Doulton, Foot Warmer, Black On Beige, Stoneware, Lambeth	25.00 To	35.00
Doulton, Jar, Biscuit, Silicone		150.00
Doulton, Jar, Mustard, Lambeth, 3 1/4 In.High		35.00
Doulton, Jar, Tobacco, Classical Medallions, Lambeth		55.00

Doulton, Jar, Tobacco, Dolphin Figural, Green, Brown, & Ivory, C.1875, 6 1/4 In.	150.00
Doulton, Jar, Tobacco, Holly Berries, Brown, Tan, & Blue, Slater, Lambeth, 5 In.	67.50
Doulton, Jug, Buff, Applied Blue Floral, Silver Rim, Barlow, Lambeth, 7 In.	350.00
Doulton, Jug, Buff, Sheep, Hannah Barlow, Lambeth, 1875, 6 1/2 In.	350.00
Doulton, Jug, Herons In Water, Blue Slip On White, Barlow, 1874, Lambeth, 7 In.	375.00
Doulton, Jug, High Glaze Pale Brown, Leaf Tips, Silver Rim, 8 In.High	92.50
Doulton, Jug, Horses Incised, Florence Barlow, 1876, Lambeth, 9 1/2 In.	395.00
Doulton, Jug, Hunt, Irish Silver Cover, 9 1/2 In.High	188.00
Doulton, Jug, Imitation Copper With Rivets & Dents, 7 In.	165.00
Doulton, Jug, Lambeth, Stoneware, Herons In Water, Bulrushes, 1874, 7 1/2 In.	350.00
Doulton, Jug, Pony & Sheep On Buff, Barlow, Lambeth, 1873, 10 1/2 In.	375.00
Doulton, Jug, Puzzle, Five Spouts, Brown Band Design, Stoneware, 8 3/4 In.	145.00
Doulton, Jug, Puzzle, 3 Shades Of Brown Stoneware, Humorous Verse, 7 3/4 In.	98.50
Doulton, Jug, Queen Victoria Commemorative, 3 Colors, 1897, 7 In.	110.00
Doulton, Jug, Stoneware, Brown & Tan, Strap Handle, Lambeth, C.1895, 8 In.	78.00
Doulton, Jug, Stoneware, White Flowering Plants, Lambeth, C.1895, 5 1/2 In.	45.00
Doulton, Jug, Three Horse Scene, Hannah Barlow, 9 1/2 In.	435.00
Doulton, Jug, White, Blue, Herons, Bulrushes, F.Barlow, 1874, Lambeth, 7 1/2 In.	350.00
Doulton, Jug, William Ewart Gladstone, 1809-1898, Browns, Lambeth, 8 In.	95.00
Doulton, Keg, Whiskey, Silver Tap, Lion & Unicorn, Watts, C.1827, 3 Gallon	175.00
Doulton, Match Holder, Man's Head Through Life Preserver, Lambeth, C.1890	90.00
Doulton, Mug, 3 Handles, Beige, Slip, Sterling Rim, McLennan, Lambeth	175.00
Doulton, Pitcher, Embossed Hunting Scene, Hand-Turned, Lambeth, 6 In.	140.00
Doulton, Pitcher, Gold & Cobalt, Tapestry, 7 In.High	60.00
Doulton, Pitcher, He Who Buys Land Buys Stones, Tans, A.P., C.1891, 6 In.	72.00
Doulton, Pitcher, Hunting Scene, Burslem, 1901, 7 In.	80.00
Doulton, Pitcher, Hunting Scene, Geo.Morland Pinxit, 1901, Burslem, 7 In.High	95.00
Doulton, Pitcher, Stoneware, Blue To Brown, Stars, 1878, 5 1/2 In.	82.00
Doulton, Pitcher, Stoneware, Floral Applied, Atkins, Lambeth, 7 1/2 In.	95.00
Doulton, Pitcher, Stoneware, Stippled, Deer, H.Barlow, Lambeth, C.1891, 11 In.	225.00
Doulton, Plate, Dog In Center, Burslem, 9 1/4 In.	37.00
Doulton, Plate, Floral, Matte Ivory Border, Gold Rim, Burslem, C.1887, 9 In.	45.00
Doulton, Plate, Madras Pattern, Green, Yellow, Gold Edge, 10 1/2 In., Set Of 6	75.00
Doulton, Shoe, Woman's, Stoneware, Lambeth, C.1825, 5 In.	85.00
Doulton, Teapot, Stoneware, White Egyptians On Tan, Lambeth	125.00
Doulton, Tray, Three Musketeers, Lion & Shield Border, Noke, 11 3/4 In.	46.00
Doulton, Vase, Blue Ground, Green, Blue, & Yellow Sgraffito Tulips, 10 In.	60.00
Doulton, Vase, Blue, Green, & Tans, RB, No.6445, Slater, 12 In.	65.00
Doulton, Vase, Bluebirds, Cream Color, Florence Barlow, Lambeth, 11 In., Pair	500.00
Doulton, Vase, Brown Design On Gray Blue, Lambeth, 11 1/2 In., Pair	75.00
Doulton, Vase, Burro & Cart, Horses, Hannah Barlow, Lambeth, 11 In.	395.00
Doulton, Vase, Dickensware, Cap'n Cuttle, 5 1/2 In.High	35.00
Doulton, Vase, Dickensware, Dick Swiveller, Handled, 6 1/2 In.High	68.00
Doulton, Vase, Dickensware, Old Peggotty, Coach Stop Scene, 11 1/2 In.	29.00
Doulton, Vase, Flambe Top, No.1603, Rouge Et Noir, 7 3/4 In.	95.00
Doulton, Vase, Frieze Of Donkeys, Brown & Blue Slip, Barlow, 18 In., Pair	650.00
Doulton, Vase, Horses Grazing, Browns, Hannah Barlow, Lambeth, 12 In.	375.00
Doulton, Vase, Incised Blue Horses On Deep Tan, Hannah Barlow, 7 In.	235.00
Doulton, Vase, Mr.Pickwick & Sam Weller At Work, Square, 5 1/2 In.	120.00
Doulton, Vase, Pate-Sur-Pate, Dog's Head, Stoneware, Dunn, 1883, Lambeth, 5 In.	175.00
Doulton, Vase, Pixies Among Cattails On Robin's-Egg Blue, 7 In.	125.00
Doulton, Vase, Sheep Grazing, Blues, Hannah Barlow, Lambeth, 10 In.	395.00
Doulton, Vase, Slender Neck, Deer, Hannah Barlow, 1877, Lambeth, 12 1/2 In.	390.00
Doulton, Vase, Steers & Calves, Greens, Hannah Barlow, Lambeth, 15 In.	375.00
Doulton, Vase, Stoneware, Dark To Pale Blue, Beading, 1877, 6 1/2 In.	64.00
Doulton, Vase, Stoneware, Plant Forms, Martha Rogers, Lambeth, 1881, 12 In.	148.00
Doulton, Vase, Stoneware, Run, Beige Tapestry, Blue, Green, Beading, 13 In.	52.00
Doulton, Vase, Tapestry, American Beauty, Lavender Flowers, Gold, 5 1/2 In.	65.00
Doulton, Vase, Tapestry, Blue Ground, Signed Slater, 5 1/2 In., Pair	125.00
Doulton, Vase, Windsor Castle, Tan & Sepia, L.Bentley, Burslem, 7 In.	55.00

*Dresden china is any china made in the town of Dresden, Germany. The
most famous factory in Dresden is the Meissen Factory.*

Dresden, see also Meissen

Dresden, Barrel, Biscuit, Floral On White, Scalloped Collar, 8 1/2 In.	120.00

Dresden, **Basket,** Latticework Border, Hand-Painted Flowers, Vine, 4 X 1 In. 38.00
Dresden, **Bonbonniere,** Boy's Head Form, Fool's Cap, C.1850, 2 3/4 In. 200.00
Dresden, **Bowl,** Serving, Floral, Ornate Handle, 3 Sections, 11 In. 65.00
Dresden, **Candelabra,** Tree Form, White, 3 Branch, C.1890, 18 3/8 In., Pair 125.00
Dresden, **Chocolate Pot,** Hand-Painted Roses On White, Rococo Handle, 8 In. 45.00
Dresden, **Clock Case,** Blue & White, Flowers, Cupid On Top, C.1850 .... 50.00
Dresden, **Compote,** Florals, Pierced Borders, 8 1/2 X 3 1/4 In., Pair 200.00
Dresden, **Compote,** Openwork Basket On Tree, Putti, Floral, C.1890, 16 In. 90.00
Dresden, **Creamer,** Yellow, Black Austrian Eagles, Blue, Green, & Red Enamel 115.00
Dresden, **Cup & Saucer,** Demitasse, Octagonal Scallop, Paneled 85.00
Dresden, **Cup & Saucer,** Farmer's, Roses & Leaves 18.00
Dresden, **Cup & Saucer,** Floral, Lamb Mark 8.50
Dresden, **Cup & Saucer,** Watteau Of Lovers, Marked Dresden, Saxony With Lamb 32.50
Dresden, **Cup,** Loving, 3 Gold Handles & Trim, Floral, 4 Women Scene, Coburg 62.00
Dresden, **Cup,** Loving, 3 Handled, 3 Lovers Medallions, Gold Scrolls, Floral 185.00
Dresden, **Dessert Set,** Bouquets In Gold Cartouches, Service For 8 .... 275.00
Dresden, **Dessert Set,** Yellow & Gold, Floral Design, 24 Piece 295.00
Dresden, **Dish,** Leaf, Ribbed, Floral Decoration, Grapes, 9 In.Diameter 65.00
Dresden, **Etui,** Babe Form, Silver Gilt Mounts, C.1850, 3 5/8 In. 160.00
Dresden, **Figurine,** Boy & Girl Bringing Fish & Game, 22 In.High, Pair 490.00
Dresden, **Figurine,** Dog, English Pug, Pink Collar, Bell, 8 1/2 In., Pair 200.00
Dresden, **Figurine,** Harlequin With Dog Under Arm, 6 1/2 In.High 115.00
Dresden, **Figurine,** Hen & Rooster Mating, 3 X 5 In. 45.00
Dresden, **Figurine,** Macaw On Tree Stump, 16 In., Pair 450.00
Dresden, **Figurine,** Macaw, Red, Green, Blue, & Yellow Feathers, 16 In., Pair 465.00
Dresden, **Figurine,** Marshall Soult On White Horse, 5 X 6 1/2 In. 40.00
Dresden, **Figurine,** Pug Dog, Sitting, Tan & White, 7 1/2 In., Pair 220.00
Dresden, **Figurine,** Pug, Sitting, Tan, Black Mask, Blue Collar, 5 In., Pair 135.00
Dresden, **Figurine,** Woman Representing American Continent, 6 1/2 In. 125.00
Dresden, **Garniture,** Mantel, Lady & Gentleman, & Cherub, C.1890, 3 Piece 575.00
Dresden, **Group,** Bacchic, Scrollwork Base, C.1890, 8 1/2 In. 325.00
Dresden, **Group,** Lady & Gentleman, C.1760, Hayfork Mark, 8 3/4 In. 175.00
Dresden, **Inkwell & Attached Tray,** Double, Scalloped Edge, 10 1/2 X 8 In. 135.00
Dresden, **Mirror,** Lady's Hand, Lavender, White Violets, C.1900, 5 1/2 In. 35.00
Dresden, **Pitcher,** Water, Florals, Squat, 6 In. 85.00
Dresden, **Plate,** Battleship Maine Destroyed, Havana, 1898, 7 In. 37.50
Dresden, **Plate,** Bouquet Center, Gold & Floral Bouquets Border, 5 3/4 In. 20.00
Dresden, **Plate,** Bread & Butter, Florals, 6 In. 15.00
Dresden, **Plate,** Cake, Hand-Painted Pink Roses, Gold Border, 8 1/2 In. 17.00
Dresden, **Plate,** Opera, Rienzi, Gold Border, 8 1/4 In. 125.00
Dresden, **Plate,** Opera, Walkure, Act I, Gold Border, 8 1/4 In. 125.00
Dresden, **Plate,** Opera, Wotans Abachilit Brunnhilde, Gold Border, 8 1/2 In. 125.00
Dresden, **Plate,** Salad, Empress 5.00
Dresden, **Plate,** Service, Bouquet Center, Gold Bordered Medallions, 10 In. 35.00
Dresden, **Plate,** Wall, Rose Floral, 9 1/2 In., Pair 7.00
Dresden, **Ramekin & Saucer,** Floral, Scalloped 38.00
Dresden, **Relish,** Top Handled, 2 Sections, Hand-Painted 32.00
Dresden, **Salt,** Basket Shape, Branch Form Handles, Floral Decoration, 4 .... 48.00
Dresden, **Spooner,** Pink Roses 7.50
Dresden, **Tea Caddy,** Floral, Gold Trim, Crown & D Mark 45.00
Dresden, **Tea Strainer,** Florals, 5 7/8 In. 35.00
Dresden, **Vase,** Blue, Shake Handles, Gilding, C.1850, 18 1/2 In., Pair 475.00
Dresden, **Vase,** 3 Scenic Medallions, 3 Handled, 6 1/2 In. 250.00
Duncan & Miller, **Ashtray,** Duck, Red Flashed, 4 In. 11.00
Duncan & Miller, **Banana Boat,** Canterbury, 13 X 3 1/4 In. 12.00
Duncan & Miller, **Bowl,** Hat Shape, Canterbury, Open Lattice Edge, 11 1/4 In. 28.00
Duncan & Miller, **Bowl,** Pink, Canterbury, Scalloped, 9 1/2 X 3 1/2 In. 45.00
Duncan & Miller, **Box,** Candy, Covered, Canterbury, Gold Floral 23.00
Duncan & Miller, **Butter Pat,** No.42, Paneled English Hobnail With Prisms 12.00
Duncan & Miller, **Candlestick,** Pink Opalescent, 3 In., Pair 26.00
Duncan & Miller, **Compote,** Jelly, No.42 .... 16.50 To 18.50
Duncan & Miller, **Creamer,** No.24 .... 6.00
Duncan & Miller, **Cruet Set,** Sandwich, Oval Tray, 3 Piece 30.00
Duncan & Miller, **Cruet,** No.48, Faceted Stopper 24.00
Duncan & Miller, **Cup & Saucer,** Demitasse, Teardrop 6.85
Duncan & Miller, **Cup,** No.40, 3 In. 6.50

Duncan & Miller, Dish, Mint, No.48, Diamond Ridge, Oval	9.50
Duncan & Miller, Goblet, No.42	17.00
Duncan & Miller, Goblet, Sandwich	4.00
Duncan & Miller, Horn Of Plenty, Crystal, 8 In.	23.00
Duncan & Miller, Jar, Cracker, No.42, Mardi Gras	35.00
Duncan & Miller, Pitcher, Water, No.42, Gold Band	32.50 To 40.00
Duncan & Miller, Plate, No.24, 7 In.	9.75
Duncan & Miller, Plate, Sandwich, Canterbury, 15 In.	15.00
Duncan & Miller, Plate, Sandwich, Green, 8 In.	9.35
Duncan & Miller, Plate, Sandwich, 7 In.	9.35
Duncan & Miller, Plate, Sherbet, Green, Sandwich	2.50
Duncan & Miller, Relish, No.30, Turned-In Sides	11.00
Duncan & Miller, Rose Bowl, Pink Opalescent, 3 1/2 In.	25.00
Duncan & Miller, Salt Dip, No.30	5.50
Duncan & Miller, Salt Dip, No.42, Oval	3.35
Duncan & Miller, Shell, Light Blue Opalescent, Sanibel, Divided, 9 In.	18.00
Duncan & Miller, Sherbet, Green, Sandwich	7.25
Duncan & Miller, Sherry, No.42	15.00
Duncan & Miller, Spooner, No.42, Miniature	25.00
Duncan & Miller, Spooner, No.42, Ring Neck	19.50
Duncan & Miller, Spooner, No.63	12.50
Duncan & Miller, Sugar & Creamer, Pink, Swirl	9.00
Duncan & Miller, Sugar, Child's, No.42	42.00
Duncan & Miller, Swan, Avocado Body, 12 In.	50.00
Duncan & Miller, Swan, Crystal, 7 In.	9.50 To 10.00
Duncan & Miller, Swan, Green & Crystal, 12 In.	37.50
Duncan & Miller, Swan, Ruby, Clear Neck, 10 X 4 In.	40.00
Duncan & Miller, Swan, 4 1/2 X 4 In.	14.90
Duncan & Miller, Swan, 7 In.	11.00
Duncan & Miller, Swan, 8 In.	9.00
Duncan & Miller, Swan, 11 1/2 In.	30.00
Duncan & Miller, Syrup, No.42	26.00
Duncan & Miller, Toothpick, No.42	12.50
Duncan & Miller, Toothpick, No.44	21.50
Duncan & Miller, Tray, Opalescent Yellow, Shell, Sanibel, Divided, 13 In.	25.00
Duncan & Miller, Tumbler, Green, Sandwich, 13 Ozs.	4.25
Duncan & Miller, Tumbler, Iced Tea, Sandwich	4.00
Duncan & Miller, Tumbler, Juice, No.42	5.00
Duncan & Miller, Tumbler, No.44, Gold Trim	7.50
Duncan & Miller, Vase, American Way, Crystal, 6 In.	20.00
Duncan & Miller, Vase, No.42, Flared, 10 1/2 In.	22.50
Duncan & Miller, Vase, No.42, 8 In., Pair	20.00
Duncan & Miller, Vase, Pink, Top Hat Fluted Shape, Hobnail, 4 1/4 In.	22.00
Duncan & Miller, Wine, No.42, Gold	10.00
Duncan & Miller, Wine, No.45, Starred Loop	12.50
Duncan & Miller, Wine, No.48, Diamond Ridge	20.00

Durand glass was made by Victor Durand from 1879 to 1935 at several factories. Most of the iridescent Durand glass was made by Victor Durand, Jr., from 1912 to 1924 at the Durand Art Glass Works in Vineland, New Jersey.

Durand, Bowl, Mottled Silver Over Gold, Wavy Stretch Border, 6 In.	175.00
Durand, Candlestick, Blue, White Hearts, Gold Base, 10 In., Pair	895.00
Durand, Candlestick, Green Bobeches & Stem On Amber Foot, 3 In.	95.00
Durand, Console Set, Feather Pattern, Cranberrry, Pink, & White, 3 Piece	795.00
Durand, Cup & Saucer, Gold Luster, Pink & Blue Highlights	210.00
Durand, Jar, Cracker, Platinum, Egyptian, Crackle, Amber Finial, 9 In.	575.00
Durand, Lamp Base, Blue Iridescent, Gold Threading, 12 In.	195.00
Durand, Lamp, Floor, Brass & Green Onyx Base, White & Green Shade, 66 In.	950.00
Durand, Lamp, MS & Co. Base, Gold Spiderweb On Amber Shade, 30 In.	550.00
Durand, Parfait, Blue, Feather Cutting	158.00
Durand, Rose Bowl, King Tut, Green Over Orange Yellow, 4 In.High	425.00
Durand, Shade, Gold Luster Ground, Pulled Feathers, 3 1/2 In., Pair	130.00
Durand, Shade, Pulled Decoration, Zipper Pattern, 3 In.	85.00
Durand, Sherbet, Blue, Feather Cutting, Yellow Stem	190.00
Durand, Sherbet, Red, Feather Cutting, Yellow Stem	175.00

Durand, Vase, Amber, Bulbous, 5 X 6 1/2 In. 85.00
Durand, Vase, Blue Iridescent, Beehive Shape, Signed, 7 In. .... 450.00 To 675.00
Durand, Vase, Blue Iridescent, Gold Pedestal, Signed, 12 In. 475.00
Durand, Vase, Blue Iridescent, Wide Mouth, Straight Sided, C.1900, 6 1/4 In. 130.00
Durand, Vase, Blue Luster, Opal Heart & Clinging Vine, 8 In. 750.00
Durand, Vase, Blue Luster, Opal Luster Coil Pattern, 4 1/2 In. 290.00
Durand, Vase, Blue, Amber, 3 X 8 3/4 In. 250.00
Durand, Vase, Bulbous, Blue, Short Neck, Flaring Mouth, 4 1/2 X 4 In. 200.00
Durand, Vase, Candlestick Type, Iridescent Blue, 9 3/4 In.High 575.00
Durand, Vase, Crackle, Silver Splatter On Red, 6 1/2 X 4 1/2 In. 190.00
Durand, Vase, Deep Blue Iridescent, White Heart & Vine, C.1900, 10 1/4 In. 400.00
Durand, Vase, Deep Blue, Signed, 7 1/2 In. 495.00
Durand, Vase, Gold Iridescent, Rose Bowl Shape, Signed, 4 In. 210.00
Durand, Vase, Golden Orange Iridescent, Yellow Interior, 8 X 4 1/2 In. 350.00
Durand, Vase, King Tut Pattern, Gold Luster With Green, 4 1/2 In. 375.00
Durand, Vase, King Tut, Gold On White, 9 In. 650.00
Durand, Vase, Opal, Moorish, Crackle, Green Luster, Lava Decoration, 8 In. 525.00
Durand, Vase, Orange Iridescent, 7 In. 225.00
Durand, Vase, Peachblow, Enameled Leaves & Flowers, Bulbous, 9 In.High 235.00
Durand, Vase, Peacock Blue, Egyptian Style, Signed, 1812-6, 6 1/2 X 4 In. 400.00
Durand, Vase, Peacock Blue, Threading, Pedestal, Signed 2028-8, 8 1/2 In. 310.00
Durand, Vase, Red, Pulled Feather Design On Bottom, 13 In.High 675.00
Durand, Vase, Silver, Etched Grape & Leaf, Pulled Decoration, 6 1/2 In. 295.00
Durand, Vase, Spiderwebbing, Pulled Feather, Gold, 9 In. 275.00
Durand, Vase, White Hearts & Vines On Blue Iridescent, 6 1/2 In. 850.00
Durand, Vase, Yellow, Gold, Green & Blue Coils, 9 1/2 In. 375.00
Durand, Vase, Yellow, Triple Cased, Orange Neck Interior, 6 1/2 In. 225.00
Elvis Presley, Button, Pinback, I Like Elvis, Wooden Guitar Attached 2.50
Elvis Presley, Music Sheet, Love Me Tender, 1956, Elvis On Cover, 14 In. 4.00
Elvis Presley, Scrapbook 15.00
· Enamelware, see Graniteware
Enamel, Austrian, Spoon, Strassburg, 800 Silver 24.00
Enamel, Bowl, East Indian, Metal, Blues, Pink, & Green, 5 In., Pair 45.00
Enamel, Box, Copper, Pastoral, Courting Couple, Brass Hinge, C.1750, 6 1/8 In. 750.00
Enamel, Chinese, Box, Brass, Foo Dogs, Peking Bead, Cloisonne, 3 1/2 In. 45.00
Enamel, Chinese, Box, Globe, Black Interior, 9 X 4 1/2 In. 16.00
Enamel, Chinese, Pillbox, Green 10.00
Enamel, Chinese, Tray, Copper, People Scene, Pink & Greens, Square, 4 1/2 In. 20.00
Enamel, Clip, Paper, Sterling Silver, Chester, 1904, Pheasant, 2 1/2 In. 68.00
Enamel, Desk Set, Champleve, 4 Piece 250.00
Enamel, English, Spoon, Demitasse, Sterling Silver, Gold Washed, 6 Colors 20.75
Enamel, French, Holder, Letter, Footed, Burgundy, Blues, Green, & Pale Yellow 90.00
Enamel, French, Pen Staff, Checkerboard Design 44.00
Enamel, French, Plaque, Fortuna, Barbedienne On Frame, 1879, Round, 10 In. 425.00
Enamel, French, Plaque, The Nativity, C.1890, 6 X 4 1/2 In. 175.00
Enamel, French, Snuffbox & Scent Bottle, Gold, Champleve, Black, C.P., C.1810 .... 1400.00
Enamel, French, Switch, Wall, On Silver, Pink, Yellow, & White, C.1900, 3 In. 60.00
Enamel, French, Vase, Limoges, On Sterling, C.Faurt, 4 In. 750.00
Enamel, French, Vase, On Metal, Art Deco, Gold Birds, Color Floral, 12 3/4 In. 85.00
Enamel, German, Box, River Scenes On White, Gilt Metal Mounts, C.1760, Double 325.00
Enamel, German, Snuffbox, Gallant & Girl, Gilt Metal Mounts, C.1760, 3 In. 500.00
Enamel, German, Snuffbox, Hunter & Stag On White, Metal Mounts, C.1790, 4 In. 80.00
Enamel, German, Snuffbox, Travelers On White, Gilt Metal Mounts, C.1760 .... 150.00
Enamel, German, Snuffbox, Upright, Landscapes On White, Metal Mounts, C.1750 .... 125.00
Enamel, Plate, On Copper, Birds & Flowers, 6 3/4 In. 17.50
Enamel, Plate, On Copper, Birds, Flowers, & Animals, 9 3/4 In. 37.50
Enamel, Portrait, Art Nouveau Woman, Shadowbox Frame, 3 In. Diameter 225.00
Enamel, Russian, see also Coronation, Faberge, Napkin Ring
Enamel, Russian, Basket, Sugar, Gilt Silver, Floral & Scroll, Klingert, 1893 .... 1200.00
Enamel, Russian, Beaker, Copper, Coronation, Nicholas II, 1896, 4 1/8 In. 150.00
Enamel, Russian, Beaker, Gilt Silver, Floral, Geometric, Sbitnev, C.1900, 3 In. 500.00
Enamel, Russian, Beaker, Gilt Silver, Floral, Ovchinnikov, C.1900, 3 In. 1600.00
Enamel, Russian, Beaker, Gilt Silver, Floral, Ovchinnikov, 1887, 2 1/2 In. 1100.00
Enamel, Russian, Belt, Gilt Silver, Cartouche Shaped Buckle, C.1900, 30 In. 475.00
Enamel, Russian, Bowl, Gilt Silver, Tulips, Ovchinnikov, C.1900, 4 1/4 In. 1800.00
Enamel, Russian, Box, Gilt Silver, Covered, Floral & Geometric, C.1900, 3 In. 300.00

Enamel, Russian, Box, Gilt Silver, Hinged, Stippled Ground, P.F., C.1900, 3 In. 800.00
Enamel, Russian, Box, Powder, Gilt Silver, Champleve, Ovchinnikov, 1884, 3 In. 1400.00
Enamel, Russian, Box, Powder, Gilt Silver, Hinged Lid, Floral, Saltykov, C.1900 .... 1600.00
Enamel, Russian, Candleholder, Gilt Silver, Ovchinnikov, 1884, 4 In., Pair 3500.00
Enamel, Russian, Cap, Hussar Officer's, Parcel Gilt Silver, C.1900, 3 3/8 In. 3500.00
Enamel, Russian, Cap, Military, Gilt Silver, Artillery, 1916, 3 1/2 In. 2250.00
Enamel, Russian, Cap, Officer's, Gilt Silver, M.P., C.1870, 2 1/8 In. 2500.00
Enamel, Russian, Cap, Officer's, Silver, Order Of St.Andrew, C.1890, 3 5/8 In. 2700.00
Enamel, Russian, Case, Cigarette, Gilt Silver, Blue Stone Cabochon, C.1900 .... 900.00
Enamel, Russian, Case, Cigarette, Gilt Silver, Butterflies, Swans, V.A., C.1900 .... 1200.00
Enamel, Russian, Case, Cigarette, Gilt Silver, Central Diamond, C.1900 .... 800.00
Enamel, Russian, Case, Cigarette, Gilt Silver, Champleve, Ovchinnikov, C.1880 .... 2000.00
Enamel, Russian, Case, Cigarette, Gilt Silver, Diamond Chips, A.A., C.1900 .... 350.00
Enamel, Russian, Case, Cigarette, Gilt Silver, Floral & Beads, C.1900 .... 1700.00
Enamel, Russian, Case, Cigarette, Gilt Silver, Floral & Geometrics, C.1900 .... 800.00
Enamel, Russian, Case, Cigarette, Gilt Silver, Floral, Klingert, 1892 .... 600.00
Enamel, Russian, Case, Cigarette, Gilt Silver, Floral, Scroll, Nikolaev, C.1900 .... 550.00
Enamel, Russian, Case, Cigarette, Gilt Silver, Floral, Scrolls, Zverev, C.1900 .... 1900.00
Enamel, Russian, Case, Cigarette, Gilt Silver, Floral, V.L., C.1900, 4 1/2 In. 2000.00
Enamel, Russian, Case, Cigarette, Gilt Silver, Floral, 1896, 4 1/2 In. 1450.00
Enamel, Russian, Case, Cigarette, Gilt Silver, Swan In Pond, C.1900, 5 1/8 In. 2100.00
Enamel, Russian, Casket, Gilt Silver, Cock Handles, Ovchinnikov, 1884, 4 In. 2400.00
Enamel, Russian, Casket, Gilt Silver, Hinged Top, Handles, P.F., C.1900, 7 In.. .... 9500.00
Enamel, Russian, Casket, Silvered Bronze, Double, Floral, Hinged, C.1790, 6 In. 425.00
Enamel, Russian, Charka, Gilt Silver, Jeweled, Ovchinnikov, 1877, 1 1/2 In. 1100.00
Enamel, Russian, Cup & Saucer, Gilt Silver, Floral, N.A., C.1900 .... 3100.00
Enamel, Russian, Cup & Saucer, Gilt Silver, Scrolling Foliage, E.C., C.1900 .... 3000.00
Enamel, Russian, Cup, Drinking, Hallmarked, 2 1/2 In. 450.00
Enamel, Russian, Cup, Gilt Silver, Champleve, Mosaic, Klingert, 1886, 3 In. 350.00
Enamel, Russian, Cup, Vodka, Gilt Silver, Floral Cartouches, 1895, 2 In. 400.00
Enamel, Russian, Dish, Nut, Silver, 5 Colors, 3 3/4 In. 135.00
Enamel, Russian, Egg, Easter, Gilt Silver, Center Opening, G.S., C.1900, 2 In. 4900.00
Enamel, Russian, Egg, Easter, Gilt Silver, Footed, Kuzmitchev, C.1890, 3 In. 2000.00
Enamel, Russian, Egg, Easter, Gilt Silver, Ovchinnikov, C.1890, 2 1/2 In. 5000.00
Enamel, Russian, Egg, Easter, Green & Pink, Silver Loop On Top, 3/4 X 1/2 In. 150.00
Enamel, Russian, Goblet, Gilt Silver, Plique A Jour, Kuzmitchev, C.1900, 7 In. 3500.00
Enamel, Russian, Handle, Cane, Gilt Silver, Crook, Yellow, Floral, N.A., C.1900 .... 1000.00
Enamel, Russian, Helmet, Gilt Silver, St.Andrew, Gratchev, C.1900, 3 3/4 In. 2500.00
Enamel, Russian, Helmet, Parcel Gilt Silver, K.P., C.1900, 3 1/4 In. 1300.00
Enamel, Russian, Holder, Tea Glass, Champleve, Man In Window, G.A., 1887 .... 2100.00
Enamel, Russian, Holder, Tea Glass, Gilt Silver, Champleve, A.Ya.S., C.1890 .... 1000.00
Enamel, Russian, Holder, Tea Glass, Gilt Silver, Champleve, Ovchinnikov, 1878 .... 1500.00
Enamel, Russian, Holder, Tea Glass, Gilt Silver, Champleve, Pan Slavic, C.1890 .... 1200.00
Enamel, Russian, Holder, Tea Glass, Gilt Silver, Foliage, Klingert, C.1900 .... 1000.00
Enamel, Russian, Holder, Tea Glass, Gilt Silver, Kiev In Cyrillic, C.1850 .... 275.00
Enamel, Russian, Jar, Covered, Filigree, 5 In. 325.00
Enamel, Russian, Kovsh, Gilt Silver, Birds, Insects, Nikolaev, C.1900, 9 In. 1400.00
Enamel, Russian, Kovsh, Gilt Silver, Floral & Scroll, Semenova, C.1900, 3 In. 1400.00
Enamel, Russian, Kovsh, Gilt Silver, Floral, Geometrics, Artel, C.1900, 6 In. 3500.00
Enamel, Russian, Kovsh, Gilt Silver, Floral, R Handle, Semenova, C.1900, 6 In. 4500.00
Enamel, Russian, Kovsh, Gilt Silver, Floral, R Handle, Semenova, C.1900, 7 In. 6250.00
Enamel, Russian, Kovsh, Gilt Silver, Floral, R Handle, Ya.B., C.1900, 5 1/4 In. 1700.00
Enamel, Russian, Kovsh, Gilt Silver, Floral, Saltykov, C.1900, 2 7/8 In. 675.00
Enamel, Russian, Kovsh, Silver, Champleve, Strapwork, Sazikov, C.1890, 11 In. 1600.00
Enamel, Russian, Pillbox, Gilt Silver, Floral, Saltykov, 1895, 1 3/4 In. 400.00
Enamel, Russian, Pillbox, Gilt Silver, Hinged, Floral, C.1900, 2 In. 400.00
Enamel, Russian, Pillbox, Gilt Silver, Wire Twist Scrolls, Saltykov, C.1890 .... 225.00
Enamel, Russian, Plate, Gilt Silver, Champleve, Ovchinnikov, C.1890, 8 3/4 In. 5250.00
Enamel, Russian, Purse, Change, Gilt Silver, Floral, Agafonov, C.1900 .... 400.00
Enamel, Russian, Salt Chair, Champleve, Pan Slavic Style, U.G., 1891, 8 In. 2800.00
Enamel, Russian, Salt Dip, On Silver, 5 Color Geometrics, 3 Footed 375.00
Enamel, Russian, Salt, Master, 3 Ball Feet, Silver, 1889, 2 3/4 In. 400.00
Enamel, Russian, Seal, Gold, Bloodstone, Military, Arnd, C.1890, 3 7/8 In. 8000.00
Enamel, Russian, Shako, Silver, Paul I Infantry Guard, M.C., C.1900, 2 3/4 In. 2750.00
Enamel, Russian, Spoon, Demitasse, Gilt Silver, Beading, Saltykov, C.1880, 6 .... 350.00
Enamel, Russian, Spoon, Gold Over Silver, Marked, 7 In. 75.00

Enamel, Russian, Spoon, Hallmarked, Set Of 6 .... 500.00
Enamel, Russian, Spoon, Serving, Gilt Silver, Floral, Geometrics, C.1900, 8 In. 350.00
Enamel, Russian, Spoon, Serving, Gilt Silver, Floral, Klingert, 1891, 7 1/4 In. 500.00
Enamel, Russian, Spoon, Serving, Gilt Silver, Floral, Lubavin, C.1900, 8 In. 525.00
Enamel, Russian, Spoon, Serving, Gilt Silver, Floral, Zverev, C.1900, 7 3/4 In. 550.00
Enamel, Russian, Tazza, Gilt Silver, Cartouches, Klingert, C.1900, 5 In. 3100.00
Enamel, Russian, Teaspoon, Gilt Silver, Twisted Handle, Floral, C.1900, 5 .... 500.00
Enamel, Russian, Tray, Gilt Silver, Floral, Kuzmitchev, C.1890, 6 5/8 In. 1400.00
Enamel, Russian, Urn On Stand, Gilt Silver, Champleve, Chlebnikov, 1833, 5 In. 1100.00
Enamel, Russian, Vase, Gilt Silver, Pierced, Geometrics, Dome Base, 1872, 5 In. 1800.00
Enamel, Russian, Vase, Gilt Silver, Plique A Jour, Cloisonne, C.1900, 5 In. 4500.00
Enamel, Salt & Spoon, On Silver, Viking Ship Design, Glass Liner 65.00
Enamel, Spoon, Demitasse, Sterling Silver, Calla Lily On Handle 35.00
Enamel, Spoon, Demitasse, Sterling Silver, Forget-Me-Nots On End, Twisted 15.00
Enamel, Spoon, Demitasse, Sterling Silver, Man In High Hat & Cane End 18.50
Enamel, Spoon, Silver, Champleve Dragonfly, Bird, & Leaf, 4 7/8 In. 30.00
Enamel, Teaspoon, On Sterling, Crown Handle, Ships Scenes, Gold Washed 23.00
Enamel, Viennese, Ewer & Stand, Silver Gilt, Watteau, C.1850, Miniature 525.00
Enamel, Viennese, Flask, Scent, Silver Gilt Mounts, Birds, C.1890, 4 1/8 In. 160.00
Enamel, Viennese, Flask, Scent, Silver Gilt Mounts, Watteau, C.1850, 3 In. 130.00

*End-of-Day glass is now an out-of-fashion name for spattered glass. The
glass was made of many bits and pieces of colored glass. Traditionally, the
glass was made by workmen from the odds and ends left from the glass used
during the day. Actually it was a deliberately manufactured product popular
about 1880 to 1900, and some of it is still being made.*

End-Of-Day, Basket, Red, Blue, & White, Blue Rim, Clear Handle, 7 In. 55.00
End-Of-Day, Bowl, Bride's, Strawberry, 12 In. 80.00
End-Of-Day, Candlestick, Pink & Green, 7 In., Pair 55.00
End-Of-Day, Ewer, Red, Yellow, & Green, Applied Crystal Handle, 7 In. 50.00
End-Of-Day, Muffineer, Pink & White Spatter 58.00
End-Of-Day, Pitcher, Water, Swirl, Royal Ivy Overlay, Clear Handle, 8 In. 175.00
End-Of-Day, Vase, Flared Top, Light Blue & Clear Base, 8 In. 45.00
End-Of-Day, Vase, Multicolor, Clear Handles, 7 1/4 In. 17.50
End-Of-Day, Vase, Red, White, Applied Cobalt Handles, 5 In. 65.00
End-Of-Day, Witch's Ball, Cased, Clear Standard, 4 1/2 In. 40.00
ES Germany, Holder, Toothbrush, Swags Of Pastel Florals, Gold Trim 25.00
Eskimo, Basket, Sea Grass & Dyed Seal Gut, Lid, Potbellied, 7 1/2 X 6 1/2 In 64.50
Eskimo, Basket, Sea Grass & Dyed Seal Gut, Lid, Potbellied, 7 1/2 X 7 In. 69.50
Eskimo, Basket, Sea Grass & Dyed Seal Gut, Lid, Potbellied, 9 X 8 In. 89.50
Eskimo, Basket, Sea Grass & Dyed Seal Gut, Lid, Potbellied, 10 1/2 In. 110.00
Eskimo, Basket, Sea Grass & Dyed Seal Gut, Oval Open Top, 5 1/2 In. 34.50
Eskimo, Basket, Sea Grass & Dyed Seal Gut, Oval Open Top, 6 1/2 X 4 1/2 In. 34.50
Eskimo, Basket, Sea Grass & Dyed Seal Gut, Round Open Star, 10 1/2 In. 34.50
Eskimo, Basket, Sea Grass & Dyed Seal Gut, Star Design, 10 1/2 X 1 1/2 In. 34.50
Eskimo, Boot, Tanned Moosehide, Beaver Trim, Beaded, Pair 79.50
Eskimo, Boot, Tanned Moosehide, Muskrat Trim, Beaded, Pair 79.50
Eskimo, Boot, Tanned Moosehide, Rabbit Trim, Beaded, Pair 79.50
Eskimo, Boots, Smoke Tanned Moosehide, Beaver Trim, Beaded, Pair 79.50
Eskimo, Boots, Smoke Tanned Moosehide, Muskrat Trim, Beaded, Pair 79.50
Eskimo, Boots, Smoke Tanned Moosehide, Rabbit Trim, Beaded, Pair 79.50
    Etruscan Majolica, see Majolica
    Ezra Brooks, see Bottle, Ezra Brooks

*Faberge, Carl Gustavovich, was a goldsmith and jeweler to the Russian
Imperial Court from about 1870 to 1914.*

Faberge, Blotter, Desk, Gilt Silver, Enamel, Guilloche Ground, Perchin, C.1900 .... 1800.00
Faberge, Bowl, Cut Glass, Silver Mounted, C.1900, 7 1/4 In. 500.00
Faberge, Brooch, Diamond, Enamel, 2 Color Gold, Pierced, C.1900, 2 3/8 In. 1600.00
Faberge, Brooch, Gold Mounted, Enamel, Jeweled, Silver, Perchin, C.1890 .... 2000.00
Faberge, Brooch, Gold, Enamel & Diamond, Diamond Shape, Thielemann, C.1900 .... 2000.00
Faberge, Buckle, Belt, Gold Mounted Gilt Silver, Enamel, Wigstrom, C.1900 .... 1400.00
Faberge, Bust, Warrior, Carved Topaz Quartz, C.1900, 6 1/2 In. 5000.00
Faberge, Cane Handle, Gold, Diamond, Amethyst, Orange Enamel, Perchin, C.1900 .... 7500.00
Faberge, Cane Handle, Jeweled, Gold Mounted, Red Enamel, C.1900, 1 3/8 In. 700.00
Faberge, Case, Card, Gold, Enamel, Jeweled, Nephrite Mounted, Wigstrom, C.1900 .... 7500.00

Faberge, Case, Cigarette, Gold, Cabochon Sapphire, Rappaport, C.1900 .... 2500.00
Faberge, Case, Cigarette, Silver, Cabochon Garnet, Tinder, Hollming, C.1900 .... 1000.00
Faberge, Case, Cigarette, Silver, Cabochon Sapphire, Lake Scene, C.1900 .... 1400.00
Faberge, Case, Cigarette, Silver, Imperial Eagle, Diamond, C.1900 .... 1000.00
Faberge, Case, Cigarette, Silver, Jeweled, Nevalainen, C.1900 .... 1150.00
Faberge, Case, Cigarette, Silver, Mauve Enamel, Hollming, C.1900 .... 1200.00
Faberge, Case, Cigarette, 2 Color Gold, Diamond Chips, Wigstrom, C.1900 .... 2200.00
Faberge, Charm, Enamel, 2 Color Gold Mounted, Nephrite Cabochon, 1900, 1 In. 1600.00
Faberge, Cup, Gold & Blue Enamel, Footed, Thielemann, C.1900, 2 1/4 In. 8500.00
Faberge, Egg, Easter, Gold & Enamel, Imperial Eagle, C.1900, 11/16 In. 3200.00
Faberge, Egg, Easter, Gold & Jadeite, Helmet On Top, C.1900, 7/8 In. 1900.00
Faberge, Egg, Easter, Gold & Purpurin, Helmet On Top, F.H., C.1900, 1 In. 2000.00
Faberge, Figurine, Hornbill, Bowenite, Seated, Ruby Eyes, C.1900, 1 3/4 In. 2000.00
Faberge, Frame, Picture, Gold, Nephrite, Jeweled, Armfelt, C.1900, 2 1/2 In. 4200.00
Faberge, Helmet, Parcel Gilt Silver, Enamel, Perchin, C.1890, 5 3/8 In. 3800.00
Faberge, Helmet, Parcel Gilt Silver, Enamel, Rappaport, C.1900, 3 1/2 In. 2500.00
Faberge, Holder, Cigar, Gold, Enamel, Tortoiseshell, C.1900, 4 In. 800.00
Faberge, Inkwell, Traveling, Silver, Hinged, Glass Well, C.1890, 1 7/8 In. 750.00
Faberge, Knife, Paper, Gold, Rhodonite, Chased, Perchin, C.1890, 9 1/4 In. 3500.00
Faberge, Kovsh, Cut Glass, Silver Mounted, Cabochon Amethyst, C.1900, 7 In. 1200.00
Faberge, Kovsh, Silver, Blue & Red Enamel, Scroll Handle, C.1900, 3 1/2 In. 1700.00
Faberge, Kovsh, Silver, Peter The Great Bust, Oval, C.1900, 4 3/4 In. 5250.00
Faberge, Pendant, Alexandra Feodorovna, Gilt Silver, Enamel, Thielemann, 1900 ...... 510.00
Faberge, Salt Cellar, Double, Jade, Silver Mounted, 1900 .... Illus 3000.00

Faberge, Salt Cellar, Double,
Jade, Silver Mounted, 1900

Faberge, Salt, Silver, Figural Owl, Moonstone Eyes, C.1900, 2 1/2 In. 1100.00
Faberge, Seal, Anastasia Nicholaevna, Jade, Gold, Enamel, Perchin, C.1900 .... 4500.00
Faberge, Seal, Bust Of Warrior, Carved Rock Crystal, C.1900, 5 In. 2400.00
Faberge, Seal, Egg Form, Gold, Enamel, Nephrite, Afanassiev, C.1900, 3 1/2 In. 9500.00
Faberge, Seal, Helmet, Parcel Gilt Silver, Enamel, C.1890, 1 1/2 In. 1500.00
Faberge, Seal, Jade & Carnelian, 2 Color Gold, Perchin, C.1900, 2 1/2 In. 3600.00
Faberge, Snuffbox, Gold, Diamonds, Imperial Eagle, C.1910, 1 1/8 In. 9000.00
Faberge, Stamp Moistener, Gold Mounted, White Enamel, Wigstrom, C.1900, 2 In. ... 4000.00
Faberge, Tray, Desk, Boxwood, Gilt Silver, Pen Rack, Nevalainen, C.1900, 11 In. 300.00
Faberge, Tray, Gold Mounted Nephrite, Imperial Eagle, Wigstrom, C.1900, 3 In. 4000.00
Faience, Dresser Set, Cobalt & White, 21 X 6 In. Tray, 7 Piece 185.00
Faience, Ewer, Ansbach, Blue & White, Pewter Mounted, C.1730, 11 In. 900.00
Faience, Plaque, Italian Pastoral Scene, Faience Frame, 19 1/2 X 18 In. 400.00
Faience, Porringer, Double Handled, 6 X 2 1/8 In. 18.00

*Fairings are, among other items, small souvenir china boxes sold at country fairs during the
nineteenth century.*
Fairing, Child Pushing Up Lid, Staffordshire, 2 3/4 In. 35.00
Fairing, Returning At 1 A.M., 4 In. 75.00
Fairing, Shall We Sleep First Or Hmm, Twiddling Thumbs, 3 In. 90.00
Fairing, Welsh Tea Party, Hollow, Oval Base, 4 7/8 In. 60.00

Fairing, You Naughty Boy, Springer & Co., 6 1/2 In.	85.00
Fairing, Young Boy In Period Costume Holding Rabbit, German, 5 In.High	38.00
Famille Rose, see Chinese Export	
Fan, Black Peacock Feathers, Tortoiseshell Frame, C.1880	35.00
Fan, Celluloid, Birds & Flowers, Folding	8.50
Fan, Child's, Hand-Painted Floral & Sticks, Applied Ring, 7 X 12 In.	4.50
Fan, Hand-Painted Satin, Mother-Of-Pearl Sticks, Marshall Field	30.00
Fan, Hand, McPeek's Mortuary	2.00
Fan, Ivory Open Fretwork Sticks, Threaded Blue Ribbon	10.00
Fan, Ivory Sticks, Purple Silk, Black Lace, Sequins	15.00
Fan, Mandarin, Ivory Faces, Silk Robes, 58 People, Lacquer	195.00
Fan, Ostrich Feather, Black, 23 X 15 In.High	22.00
Fan, Ostrich Feathers, Carved & Perforated Ivory Sticks, 12 In.	32.00
Fan, Snow White & The Seven Dwarfs, Folding	8.00
Fan, White Feathers, Wooden Sticks, Silver Inlay, 17 In.	18.00
Fan, White Ostrich Feathers, Ivory Sticks, Gold Decorated, 10 X 10 In.	22.50

*Fenton Art Glass Company, founded in Martins Ferry, Ohio, by
Frank L.Fenton, is now located in Williamstown, West Virginia. It
is noted for early carnival glass produced between 1907 and 1920. Many other
types of glass were also made.*

Fenton, Lemonade Set, Vaseline, Stretch, Cobalt Handles & Coasters, 5 Piece	350.00
Fenton, Pitcher, Water, Light Blue, Jacqueline Pattern, Cased	75.00
Fenton, Vase, Jade, Flared Top, 5 1/2 X 4 1/2 X 2 1/2 In.	16.00
Fenton, Vase, Mosaic, Urn Shape, Black, Free-Form Color Splashes, 8 In.	85.00
Ferrier, Vase, Brown River Scene On Salmon, Enameled, C.1910, 7 3/4 In.	200.00

*Fiesta dinnerware was produced by the Homer Laughlin Company at East
Liverpool, Ohio, from 1936 to 1972. It can be distinguished from its
imitations by the graduated width of its rings. Older Fiesta can be
distinguished from the very recent Fiesta Ironstone by its straight sides
on all pieces.*

Fiesta Ware, Ashtray, Chartreuse	18.50
Fiesta Ware, Ashtray, Cobalt	15.00
Fiesta Ware, Ashtray, Dark Green	15.00
Fiesta Ware, Ashtray, Green	15.00
Fiesta Ware, Ashtray, Ivory	15.00
Fiesta Ware, Ashtray, Rose	18.50
Fiesta Ware, Ashtray, Turquoise	15.00
Fiesta Ware, Ashtray, Yellow	15.00
Fiesta Ware, Bowl, Cream Soup, Ivory	3.75
Fiesta Ware, Bowl, Cream Soup, Light Green, 2 Handled	6.50
Fiesta Ware, Bowl, Dessert, Turquoise, 6 In.	6.00
Fiesta Ware, Bowl, Fruit, Chartreuse, 5 1/2 In.	4.50
Fiesta Ware, Bowl, Fruit, Dark Blue, 5 1/2 In.	4.50
Fiesta Ware, Bowl, Fruit, Gray, 5 1/2 In.	4.50
Fiesta Ware, Bowl, Fruit, Ivory, 4 3/4 In.	3.50
Fiesta Ware, Bowl, Fruit, Light Green, 5 1/2 In.	4.50
Fiesta Ware, Bowl, Fruit, Red, 5 1/2 In.	6.00
Fiesta Ware, Bowl, Fruit, Turquoise, 4 3/4 In.	3.50
Fiesta Ware, Bowl, Soup, Light Green, 8 In.	3.00
Fiesta Ware, Candlestick, Yellow, Square Base, Round, 4 In.	3.00
Fiesta Ware, Coffeepot, Yellow, Stick Handle	25.00
Fiesta Ware, Compote, Green, 12 In.	22.50
Fiesta Ware, Creamer, Ivory	3.00
Fiesta Ware, Creamer, Ivory, Ring Handle	2.50
Fiesta Ware, Creamer, Light Green	3.00
Fiesta Ware, Creamer, Turquoise	3.00
Fiesta Ware, Creamer, Yellow	3.00
Fiesta Ware, Creamer, Yellow, Round Handle	2.50
Fiesta Ware, Creamer, Yellow, Stick Handle	15.00
Fiesta Ware, Cup & Saucer, Demitasse, Cobalt	12.50
Fiesta Ware, Cup & Saucer, Red	6.50 To 9.00
Fiesta Ware, Jug, Ivory, 2 Pint	12.00
Fiesta Ware, Jug, Turquoise, Disk, 2 Quart	12.00
Fiesta Ware, Jug, Water, Dark Blue, Disk	10.00

Fiesta Ware, Jug, Water, Light Green, Disk	10.00
Fiesta Ware, Jug, Water, Rose Color, Disk	10.00
Fiesta Ware, Mug, Tom & Jerry, Green	10.00
Fiesta Ware, Nappy, Ivory, 8 1/2 In.	5.50
Fiesta Ware, Nappy, Red, 9 1/2 In.	10.00
Fiesta Ware, Nappy, Turquoise, 4 3/4 In.	1.75
Fiesta Ware, Nappy, Yellow, 8 1/2 In.	3.50 To 5.50
Fiesta Ware, Nappy, Yellow, 9 1/2 In.	7.00
Fiesta Ware, Pepper Shaker, Dark Blue	2.00
Fiesta Ware, Pepper Shaker, Light Green	2.00
Fiesta Ware, Pepper Shaker, Red	3.50
Fiesta Ware, Pitcher, Juice, Yellow	5.00
Fiesta Ware, Pitcher, Turquoise, Narrow Neck & Lip, 9 In.	9.00
Fiesta Ware, Pitcher, Yellow, Disk, 2 Quart	6.50
Fiesta Ware, Plate, Bread & Butter, Ivory, 7 In.	1.00
Fiesta Ware, Plate, Bread & Butter, Light Green, 7 3/8 In.	1.00
Fiesta Ware, Plate, Bread & Butter, Royal Blue, 7 In.	1.00
Fiesta Ware, Plate, Bread & Butter, Turquoise, 7 In.	1.00
Fiesta Ware, Plate, Bread & Butter, Turquoise, 7 3/8 In.	1.00
Fiesta Ware, Plate, Bread & Butter, Yellow, 7 In.	1.00
Fiesta Ware, Plate, Bread & Butter, Yellow, 7 3/8 In.	1.00
Fiesta Ware, Plate, Chartreuse, Deep, 8 In.	6.00
Fiesta Ware, Plate, Chartreuse, Deep, 8 1/2 In.	5.00
Fiesta Ware, Plate, Chop, Gold	8.50
Fiesta Ware, Plate, Chop, Ivory, 13 In.	2.50
Fiesta Ware, Plate, Chop, Yellow, 13 In.	2.50 To 8.00
Fiesta Ware, Plate, Cobalt, 9 In.	3.00
Fiesta Ware, Plate, Dark Blue, Deep, 8 1/2 In.	5.00
Fiesta Ware, Plate, Dessert, Chartreuse, 6 In.	1.00
Fiesta Ware, Plate, Dessert, Dark Blue, 6 3/8 In.	.75
Fiesta Ware, Plate, Dessert, Gray, 6 In.	1.00
Fiesta Ware, Plate, Dessert, Ivory, 6 In.	1.00
Fiesta Ware, Plate, Dessert, Red, 6 In.	1.50
Fiesta Ware, Plate, Dessert, Red, 6 3/8 In.	1.50
Fiesta Ware, Plate, Dessert, Royal Blue, 6 In.	1.00
Fiesta Ware, Plate, Dessert, Turquoise, 6 In.	1.00
Fiesta Ware, Plate, Dessert, Turquoise, 6 3/8 In.	.75
Fiesta Ware, Plate, Dessert, Yellow, 6 In.	1.00
Fiesta Ware, Plate, Dinner, Gray, 10 In.	2.50
Fiesta Ware, Plate, Forest Green, Deep, 8 In.	6.00
Fiesta Ware, Plate, Gray, Deep, 8 In.	6.00
Fiesta Ware, Plate, Green, 9 In.	3.00
Fiesta Ware, Plate, Grill, Chartreuse, Compartments	12.50
Fiesta Ware, Plate, Grill, Cobalt, Compartments	10.00
Fiesta Ware, Plate, Grill, Green, Compartments	10.00
Fiesta Ware, Plate, Grill, Light Green, 10 1/2 In.	2.50
Fiesta Ware, Plate, Grill, Red, Compartments	12.50
Fiesta Ware, Plate, Grill, Rose, Compartments	12.50
Fiesta Ware, Plate, Grill, Yellow, Compartments	10.00
Fiesta Ware, Plate, Luncheon, Chartreuse, 9 In.	1.50
Fiesta Ware, Plate, Luncheon, Dark Blue, 9 1/2 In.	1.00
Fiesta Ware, Plate, Luncheon, Dark Green, 9 1/2 In.	10.00
Fiesta Ware, Plate, Luncheon, Gray, 9 1/2 In.	1.00
Fiesta Ware, Plate, Luncheon, Ivory, 9 In.	1.50
Fiesta Ware, Plate, Luncheon, Ivory, 9 1/2 In.	1.00
Fiesta Ware, Plate, Luncheon, Red, 9 In.	2.25
Fiesta Ware, Plate, Luncheon, Red, 9 1/2 In.	4.00
Fiesta Ware, Plate, Luncheon, Turquoise, 9 In.	1.50
Fiesta Ware, Plate, Luncheon, Yellow, 9 In.	1.50
Fiesta Ware, Plate, Soup, Ivory, 8 In.	3.00
Fiesta Ware, Plate, Turquoise, 6 In.	2.00
Fiesta Ware, Plate, Turquoise, 9 In.	3.00
Fiesta Ware, Plate, Yellow, Deep, 8 In.	6.00
Fiesta Ware, Plate, Yellow, Deep, 8 1/2 In.	5.00
Fiesta Ware, Plate, Yellow, 9 In.	3.00
Fiesta Ware, Platter, Dark Blue, 12 1/2 In.	7.50

Fiesta Ware, Platter, Gray, 12 1/2 In.	7.50
Fiesta Ware, Platter, Light Green, 12 1/2 In.	7.50
Fiesta Ware, Platter, Turquoise, 12 In.	9.00
Fiesta Ware, Platter, Yellow, Oval, 13 In.	3.00
Fiesta Ware, Relish, Dark Blue, 6 Sections	25.00
Fiesta Ware, Salt & Pepper, Red	2.00
Fiesta Ware, Salt & Pepper, Yellow	4.00
Fiesta Ware, Saltshaker, Dark Blue	2.00
Fiesta Ware, Saltshaker, Turquoise	2.00
Fiesta Ware, Saltshaker, Yellow	2.00
Fiesta Ware, Sauceboat, Chartreuse	10.00
Fiesta Ware, Sauceboat, Dark Blue	9.50
Fiesta Ware, Sauceboat, Ivory	9.50
Fiesta Ware, Sauceboat, Yellow	9.50
Fiesta Ware, Saucer, Blue	1.50
Fiesta Ware, Saucer, Chartreuse	1.00
Fiesta Ware, Saucer, Cobalt	1.00
Fiesta Ware, Saucer, Dark Blue	.75
Fiesta Ware, Saucer, Dark Green	.75
Fiesta Ware, Saucer, Gray	1.00
Fiesta Ware, Saucer, Green	1.00
Fiesta Ware, Saucer, Ivory	.75 To 1.00
Fiesta Ware, Saucer, Light Green	.75
Fiesta Ware, Saucer, Rose Color	.75
Fiesta Ware, Saucer, Royal Blue	1.00
Fiesta Ware, Saucer, Turquoise	1.00
Fiesta Ware, Saucer, Yellow	1.00
Fiesta Ware, Server, Coffee, Ivory	18.00
Fiesta Ware, Sugar, Dark Blue, Covered	5.00
Fiesta Ware, Sugar, Green	2.00
Fiesta Ware, Sugar, Ivory, Covered	4.00
Fiesta Ware, Sugar, Light Green, Covered	5.00
Fiesta Ware, Sugar, Yellow	2.00
Fiesta Ware, Sugar, Yellow, Covered	4.00
Fiesta Ware, Syrup, Cobalt	45.00
Fiesta Ware, Syrup, Yellow	45.00
Fiesta Ware, Teacup, Dark Blue	6.00
Fiesta Ware, Teacup, Red	8.50
Fiesta Ware, Teacup, Turquoise	6.00
Fiesta Ware, Teapot, Gold	10.00
Fiesta Ware, Tray, Utility, Light Green	5.00
Fiesta Ware, Tray, Utility, Red	5.00
Fiesta Ware, Tumbler, Juice, Dark Blue	6.50
Fiesta Ware, Tumbler, Juice, Ivory, 5 Ozs.	7.50
Fiesta Ware, Tumbler, Juice, Turquoise, 6 Ozs.	7.50
Fiesta Ware, Tumbler, Rose, 5 Ozs.	3.00
Fiesta Ware, Tumbler, Turquoise, 5 Ozs.	3.00
Fiesta Ware, Tumbler, Turquoise, 10 Ozs.	12.00
Fiesta Ware, Tumbler, Yellow, 5 Ozs.	3.00
Fiesta Ware, Vase, Bud, Green, 6 1/4 In.	100.00
Fiesta Ware, Vase, Flower, Turquoise, 8 In.	25.00

Findlay, or onyx, glass was made using three layers of glass. It was manufactured by the Dalzell Gilmore Leighton Company about 1889 in Findlay, Ohio. The silver, ruby, or black pattern was molded into the glass. The glass came in several colors, but was usually white or ruby.

Findlay Onyx, Celery, Silver & Cream	225.00
Findlay Onyx, Creamer, Platinum & Stark White, Applied Opalescent Handle	400.00
Findlay Onyx, Muffineer	95.00 To 275.00
Findlay Onyx, Salt & Pepper, Pewter Tops	250.00
Findlay Onyx, Sugar, White With Platinum Decoration, 5 3/4 In.High	450.00
Findlay Onyx, Toothpick, Cinnamon	750.00
Fire, Andiron, Brass & Wrought Iron, American, C.1750, Urn Finial, Pair	40.00
Fire, Andiron, Brass, American, C.1815, Ball Top, 14 In., Pair	200.00
Fire, Andiron, Brass, American, C.1820, Ball Feet, Baluster Standard, Pair	130.00
Fire, Andiron, Brass, American, C.1820, Ball Finial, Pair	400.00

Fire, Hat, Fireman's, Leather,
American, C.1850

Fire, Andiron, Brass, American, C.1825, Ring Turned Standard, Pair	125.00
Fire, Andiron, Brass, American, C.1825, Steeple Finial, 17 1/2 In., Pair	225.00
Fire, Andiron, Brass, American, C.1830, Ring Turned Standard, Pair	180.00 To 325.00
Fire, Andiron, Brass, R.I., C.1760, Ball Top, Ball & Claw Feet, 20 In., Pair	1200.00
Fire, Andiron, R.Whittingham, N.Y., C.1780, Brass, Ball Top, Pair	600.00
Fire, Andiron, Wrought Iron, Penny Footed, Ram's Horn, Pair	165.00
Fire, Ax, Warren, Pa., Painted Red	80.00
Fire, Bellows, Fireplace, Iron Rivets	29.75
Fire, Bomb, Red Comet, Red, Liquid	6.00
Fire, Box, Fireplace, Brass, Hinged Cover, Hammered Ships, 12 X 20 In.	85.00
Fire, Box, Fireplace, Paper Picture On Top, Raised Ship Design, 14 In.	85.00
Fire, Box, Wood, Fireplace, Iron, Raised Stag, Doe, & Fawn, 26 X 20 In.	75.00
Fire, Bucket, Parmelee No.1, New England, Leather, C.1800	150.00
Fire, Bucket, S.Jones, 1824, Leather, Painted, Green, 13 In.	125.00
Fire, Coal Hod, Helmet Shape, Grecian Design, Finial, Brass, Shovel	168.00
Fire, Crane, Fireplace, 25 In. Pins	30.00
Fire, Extinguisher, Minamax, N.Y.C., Red, Brass Fittings, 2 Gallon	55.00
Fire, Extinguisher, Southwest Fire Equipment Co., Purple Flashed Glass	12.00
Fire, Fireplace Fender, Brass, C.1850, 54 X 14 In.	175.00
Fire, Fireplace Top, Hand-Forged Iron, Wishbone-Shaped Handle	21.00
Fire, Fireplace Trivet, Footman, Home Sweet Home, C.1830, 12 X 13 X 10 In.	198.00
Fire, Hat, Fireman's, Leather, American, C.1850 .... Illus	1000.00
Fire, Hat, Fireman's, Taylor Hose Co., American, C.1850, Leather, Red, 7 In.	1000.00
Fire, Hat, Fireman's, White, Aluminum, Foxboro, Mass.	45.00
Fire, Hat, Leather, Eagle Finial	32.00
Fire, Hearth Set, Brass, 14 In. Closed Stand, Tier Base, 4 Piece	72.50
Fire, Heater, Hard Coal, Ornamental, C.1913	750.00
Fire, Hod, Coal, Copper, Delft Handle, 11 X 7 1/2 In.	18.00
Fire, Hook, Fireplace Tools, Jamb, Brass	4.95
Fire, Horn, Fireman's, Silver Plate, Inscribed Champion, 19 1/2 In.	200.00
Fire, Mark, Buildings, Man With Hose, Copper, 8 X 7 In.	50.00
Fire, Mark, Fire Hydrant With Hose, Oval, Cast Iron	70.00
Fire, Mark, Hand-Forged Iron, Cut Log Center, 1873	110.00
Fire, Nozzle, Fire Hose, Brass, 30 In.	30.00
Fire, Plug, Cast Iron	35.00
Fire, Poker, Stove, Wire Handle	2.50
Fire, Pot, Fireplace, Cast Iron, Brass Lid, Footed, Bail, 9 1/2 In.	29.00
Fire, Pumper, Chemical, Wooden Wheels, Red, 1923	175.00
Fire, Reel, Hose, Hand, Fireman's, Wooden Wheels	200.00
Fire, Screen, George III Style, Mahogany, Needlepoint, Tripod, 5 Ft.2 In.	40.00
Fire, Screen, Inlaid Mahogany, Arched Crest, Bird On Branch, C.1820, 37 In.	120.00
Fire, Screen, Mahogany, Parcel Gilt, Shield Shape, C.1810, 5 Ft.3 In., Pair	600.00
Fire, Screen, Pole, Inlaid Mahogany, Urn Finial, Needlework, C.1840, 5 Ft.	100.00
Fire, Screen, Silkwork Map, Gilt Wood Frame, Tripod, C.1790, 4 1/2 Ft., Pair	275.00
Fire, Screen, Soapstone Carvings, Birds & Butterflies, 2 Panels, 34 X 15 In.	52.00
Fire, Screen, Table, Papier-Mache, Mother-Of-Pearl Inlay, C.1750, 13 In., Pair	40.00
Fire, Screen, Tiffany, Amber Tiles, Bronze Hooks, C.1890, 44 In.	2000.00

Fire, Stove, see also Shaker, Stove

Fire, Stove, Excelsior, Quincy, Ill., National Cycloidal Furnace, Sample, Case	150.00
Fire, Stove, Cook, Cast Iron, 30 In. X 2 Ft. X 3 Ft.	125.00
Fire, Stove, Farm, 60 Gallon Kettle, 6 Cows' Heads, 1902	450.00
Fire, Stove, Jiffy National, Outing, Tin & Cast Iron, 11 X 9 In.	12.00
Fire, Stove, Kitchen Range, White, Coal & Wood	55.00
Fire, Stove, Moore Bros.Co., Joliet, Illinois, Blue Enamel, Nickel, 46 In.	475.00
Fire, Stove, Parlor, Cast Iron, Foliated Smoke Chamber, Paw Feet, 50 In.	275.00
Fire, Tongs, Ember, Steel, 2 To 15 In.	135.00
Fire, Tongs, Ember, Steel, 3 To 20 1/2 In.	145.00
Fire, Trumpet, Fireman's Parade, Silver Plate, American, C.1900, 22 In.	200.00
Fire, Trumpet, Fireman's Parade, Silver Plate, N.Y., Engraved, C.1900, 20 In.	225.00

Fireglow glass resembles English Bristol glass. But a reddish-brown color can be seen when the piece is held to the light. It is a form of art glass made by the Boston and Sandwich Glass Co.of Massachusetts, and other companies.

Fireglow, Vase, Blue White, Hand-Painted Brown Floral, 9 In.	25.00
Fireglow, Vase, Enameled Blue Flower On Beige, Gold Trim, PK8c.1870, 9 In.	125.00
Fireglow, Vase, Sailboat Scene, 6 1/4 In.	20.00

Fireplace Tools, see Fire, Tongs, etc.

Fischer porcelain was made in Herend, Hungary. The factory was founded in 1839, and has continued working into the twentieth century. The wares are sometimes referred to as Herend porcelain.

Fischer, Ewer, Brown, Green, & Ivory Majolica Coloring, 15 In., Pair	80.00
Fischer, Ewer, Budapest, Pink & Green Luster, Allover Cutout, 20 In.	300.00
Fischer, Ewer, Ivorine, Pastel Floral, 9 1/2 In.	120.00
Fischer, Figurine, Chicken, Berry In Beak, 8 In.	105.00
Fischer, Figurine, Male Dancer, Signed Tertis, 12 In.High	75.00
Fischer, Figurine, Owl, White, 12 In.	50.00
Fischer, Figurine, Two Ducks, White, Black Eyes, Yellow Beaks, 1939, 2 1/2 In.	65.00
Fischer, Figurine, White Ducks Cuddling Together, Marked 1839-1939	38.00
Fischer, Inkwell, Dome Cover, Butterflies & Fruit On White, 2 1/2 In.	32.00
Fischer, Inkwell, Hand-Painted	40.00
Fischer, Pitcher, Ivorine, Pastel Floral, 9 1/2 In.	120.00
Fischer, Vase, Corset, Reticulated, Pansies & Leaves On Cream, 6 1/2 In.	55.00
Fish Set, Figural Fish, Gold With Green Trim, Shorter & Son, 10 Piece	150.00
Fish Set, Pike In Pond, Water Lilies, Sterling China, 7 Piece	150.00

Flatiron, see Kitchen, Flatiron

Florian Ware, Sugar & Creamer, Light To Cobalt Blue Design, Silver Frame	200.00
Florian Ware, Vase, Light Blue To Cobalt Design, Signed WR, 8 1/2 In.	400.00

Flow blue, or flo blue, was made in England about 1830 to 1900. The plates were printed with designs using a cobalt blue coloring. The color flowed from the design to the white plate so the finished plate had a smeared blue design. The plates were usually made of ironstone china.

Flow Blue, Bowl, Abbey, Jones & Sons, 8 In.	25.00
Flow Blue, Bowl, Albany, English, 6 In.	24.00
Flow Blue, Bowl, Babes In Woods, 3 Girls & Collie, Royal Doulton, 6 1/4 In.	60.00
Flow Blue, Bowl, Basket Of Flowers In Center, Floral Sprays, 10 1/4 In.	38.00
Flow Blue, Bowl, Berry, Floral, J.Hughes, 5 In.	7.00
Flow Blue, Bowl, Blossom, 9 1/4 In.	28.00
Flow Blue, Bowl, Cereal, Non Pareil, 6 In.	12.00
Flow Blue, Bowl, Conway, New Wharf, 9 In.	29.00
Flow Blue, Bowl, Delft, Burslem, 10 In.	22.50
Flow Blue, Bowl, Egypt, 9 3/4 In.	47.50
Flow Blue, Bowl, Fairy Villas, 10 In.	45.00 To 47.50
Flow Blue, Bowl, Grape Clusters & Leaves, 10 In.Diameter	30.00
Flow Blue, Bowl, Pevano, Rimmed, 10 1/2 In.	45.00
Flow Blue, Bowl, Soup, Conway, New Wharf Pottery, C.1891, 9 In.	18.00
Flow Blue, Bowl, Soup, Kyber, Adams, 7 1/2 In.	22.00
Flow Blue, Bowl, Soup, Kyber, W.Adams & Co., 9 In.	22.00
Flow Blue, Bowl, Soup, Linda, Maddock, 7 1/2 In.	15.00
Flow Blue, Bowl, Soup, Lorne, Grindley	14.00
Flow Blue, Bowl, Soup, Normandy, Johnson Bros., England, 9 1/2 In.	18.50

Flow Blue, Bowl, Soup, Waldorf, 9 1/4 In.	20.00
Flow Blue, Bowl, Vegetable, Baronia, Wood & Sons, 10 1/2 In.	41.00
Flow Blue, Bowl, Vegetable, Covered, Danube, Oval	20.00
Flow Blue, Bowl, Vegetable, Covered, Hizen, Pedestal Base, Ashworth, C.1870	47.50
Flow Blue, Bowl, Vegetable, Covered, Hong Kong, Octagonal	115.00
Flow Blue, Bowl, Vegetable, Covered, Scinde, 13 In.	325.00
Flow Blue, Bowl, Vegetable, Covered, Shell, Challinor, 10 In.	110.00
Flow Blue, Bowl, Vegetable, Daisies & Violets, American Saxon, 10 1/2 In.	18.00
Flow Blue, Bowl, Vegetable, Floral, Oval, J.Hughes, 10 X 6 In.	25.00
Flow Blue, Bowl, Vegetable, Hizen, Ashworth & Bros., C.1870, 10 In.	24.50
Flow Blue, Bowl, Vegetable, Non Pareil, 8 3/4 In.	42.50
Flow Blue, Bowl, Vegetable, Round, Lily, 9 3/4 In.	30.00
Flow Blue, Bowl, Vegetable, Watteau, Round, Royal Doulton, 10 In.	27.00
Flow Blue, Bowl, Waldorf, Straight Edge, 9 1/4 In.	25.00
Flow Blue, Bowl, Waldorf, 9 In.	24.00
Flow Blue, Bowl, Waste, Gironde	20.00
Flow Blue, Butter Pat, Argyle	10.00
Flow Blue, Butter Pat, Fairy Villas, Adams	6.00
Flow Blue, Butter Pat, Hamilton	10.00
Flow Blue, Butter Pat, Keele	7.00
Flow Blue, Butter Pat, La Belle	15.00
Flow Blue, Butter Pat, La Francaise	4.50
Flow Blue, Butter Pat, Marie	5.00
Flow Blue, Butter Pat, Melbourne	7.50
Flow Blue, Butter Pat, Messina, Meakin	10.00
Flow Blue, Butter Pat, Normandy, Johnson Bros.	9.00 To 12.50
Flow Blue, Butter Pat, Touraine, Stanley	12.00 To 16.50
Flow Blue, Butter Pat, Virginia	6.50
Flow Blue, Butter Pat, Windmill On White	9.00
Flow Blue, Butter, Covered, Indian Jar	125.00
Flow Blue, Butter, Covered, Waverly, Insert	35.00
Flow Blue, Butter, Normandy, Covered, Drainer Insert, Gold Trim	75.00
Flow Blue, Chocolate Pot, Gold Scrolls & Handle, Victoria, Carlsbad, Austria	62.00
Flow Blue, Clock, Figures, Pagodas, Flowers, 6 2/3 X 7 1/2 In.	150.00
Flow Blue, Compote, Fruit, Argyle, 8 Feet, Open, 11 X 8 1/2 In.	95.00
Flow Blue, Compote, Oriental Design, Handled, B & B New Stone, 11 1/2 In.	45.00
Flow Blue, Creamer, Floral, J.Hughes	30.00
Flow Blue, Creamer, Kyber, W.Adams & Son	75.00 To 80.00
Flow Blue, Creamer, Lorne, Grindley	35.00
Flow Blue, Cup & Saucer, Coffee, Normandy, Gold Trim	36.00
Flow Blue, Cup & Saucer, Demitasse, Chiswick, Ridgway	17.50
Flow Blue, Cup & Saucer, Farmer's, Birds, Flowers, Gold Trim, 8 In. Saucer	58.00
Flow Blue, Cup & Saucer, Floral, J.Hughes	22.50
Flow Blue, Cup & Saucer, Florida	35.00
Flow Blue, Cup & Saucer, Hindustan, Maddock	55.00
Flow Blue, Cup & Saucer, Nankin, Davenport	50.00
Flow Blue, Cup & Saucer, Normandy	30.00
Flow Blue, Cup & Saucer, Oriental	35.00
Flow Blue, Cup & Saucer, Portrait	17.50
Flow Blue, Cup & Saucer, Scinde, Alcock	55.00
Flow Blue, Cup & Saucer, Scinde, Handleless, Octagonal	59.00
Flow Blue, Cup & Saucer, Seville	35.00
Flow Blue, Cup & Saucer, Temple, The, Pearl Stoneware	45.00 To 55.00
Flow Blue, Cup & Saucer, Touraine, Alcock	25.00 To 30.00
Flow Blue, Cup Plate, Amoy	25.00 To 26.00
Flow Blue, Cup Plate, Floral, 14 Sided, Impressed Walley	32.50
Flow Blue, Cup Plate, Landscape, Minaret Center, Floral Medallions, C.1840	30.00
Flow Blue, Cup Plate, Shell, 4 1/8 In.	24.50 To 30.00
Flow Blue, Cup, Martha Washington & 14 States, Gold Trim	15.00
Flow Blue, Cup, Two Handled, Minton	7.00
Flow Blue, Dish, Bone, Malta	7.00
Flow Blue, Dish, Bone, Touraine, Crescent Shape	10.50 To 18.00
Flow Blue, Dish, Bun, La Belle, 2 X 13 1/2 In.	80.00
Flow Blue, Dish, Cheese, Covered, Flowers	40.00
Flow Blue, Gravy Boat & Underplate, Covered, Hizen, Ashworth, C.1870	47.50
Flow Blue, Gravy Boat, Marie	20.00

Flow Blue, **Gravy Boat,** Nelson, New Wharf Pottery	25.00
Flow Blue, **Gravy Boat,** Sobraon	50.00
Flow Blue, **Mug,** Shanghai, Furnivals	20.00
Flow Blue, **Pitcher,** Chinese Temple, Snake Handle, 6 1/2 In.	55.00
Flow Blue, **Pitcher,** Clarence, W.H.Grindley, C.1900, 6 3/4 In.	75.00
Flow Blue, **Pitcher,** Clarence, W.H.Grindley, C.1900, 7 3/4 In.	95.00
Flow Blue, **Pitcher,** Lotus, C & H Co., C.1840, 12 In.	125.00
Flow Blue, **Pitcher,** Milk, Cherub Babies, Copper Luster Trim, 6 In.	45.00
Flow Blue, **Pitcher,** Milk, Floral Decoration, Gold Band, C.1860, 5 In.High	40.00
Flow Blue, **Pitcher,** Nonpareil, Middleport Pottery, 5 In.	32.00
Flow Blue, **Pitcher,** Vinranka, Sweden, 5 X 6 1/2 In.	40.00
Flow Blue, **Pitcher,** Water, Floral, J.Hughes, 7 In.	75.00
Flow Blue, **Plate,** Alaska Yukon Pacific Exposition, R&M, 9 3/4 In.	50.00
Flow Blue, **Plate,** Alhambra, 7 In.	8.00
Flow Blue, **Plate,** Amoy, Davenport, 7 1/2 In.	38.00
Flow Blue, **Plate,** Amoy, 10 1/4 In.	45.00
Flow Blue, **Plate,** Amoy, 10 1/2 In.	45.00
Flow Blue, **Plate,** Art Nouveau, Trent, 10 In.	14.00
Flow Blue, **Plate,** Asiatic Pheasants, J.Meir & Sons, 9 In.	25.00
Flow Blue, **Plate,** Battle Creek, Michigan, R & M Co., 10 In.	35.00
Flow Blue, **Plate,** Blue Danube, 9 In.	20.00
Flow Blue, **Plate,** Blue Danube, 10 In.	25.00
Flow Blue, **Plate,** Blue Rose, Grindley, 9 In.	18.00
Flow Blue, **Plate,** Bread, Gothic, 8 X 10 In.	48.00
Flow Blue, **Plate,** Bread, Kremling, C.1843	65.00
Flow Blue, **Plate,** Cake, Handled, Oriental, Alcock, Square	58.00
Flow Blue, **Plate,** Carlton, 8 1/4 In.	18.50
Flow Blue, **Plate,** Chusan, Eagle Mark, 8 1/4 In.	59.00
Flow Blue, **Plate,** Chusan, Wedgwood, 10 1/4 In.	45.00
Flow Blue, **Plate,** Clifton, Ford & Son, 9 1/2 In.	18.50
Flow Blue, **Plate,** Coburg, J.E., 9 In.	32.00
Flow Blue, **Plate,** Coburn, 11 In.	35.00
Flow Blue, **Plate,** Constance, Adderley, 10 In.	8.00
Flow Blue, **Plate,** Country Scenes, 7 In.	17.50
Flow Blue, **Plate,** Del Monte, 7 In.	7.00
Flow Blue, **Plate,** Dinner, Decal, 9 1/2 In.	19.50
Flow Blue, **Plate,** Dinner, Hizen, Ashworth & Bros., C.1870, 10 1/2 In.	20.00
Flow Blue, **Plate,** Dinner, Marguerite, Gilt Trim, 10 In.	12.50
Flow Blue, **Plate,** Dinner, Normandy, 10 In.	18.00
Flow Blue, **Plate,** Excelsior, 9 In.	8.00
Flow Blue, **Plate,** Fairy Villas, 7 3/4 In.	9.25
Flow Blue, **Plate,** Floral Pastoral, Wm.Adams, 10 In.	30.00
Flow Blue, **Plate,** Floral, J.Hughes, 7 In.	10.00
Flow Blue, **Plate,** Floral, J.Hughes, 8 In.	12.00
Flow Blue, **Plate,** Floral, J.Hughes, 9 In.	18.00
Flow Blue, **Plate,** Formosa, 10 1/2 In.	47.50
Flow Blue, **Plate,** Game, Turkey, Rippled Rim, Cauldon, 10 In.	25.00
Flow Blue, **Plate,** Gold Tracery, Ridgeley, 6 In.	18.00
Flow Blue, **Plate,** Gorinde, 5 In.	8.00
Flow Blue, **Plate,** Grace, 9 In.	20.00
Flow Blue, **Plate,** Haddon, 8 In.	20.00
Flow Blue, **Plate,** Hindustan, Maddock, 10 1/2 In.	42.00
Flow Blue, **Plate,** Holland, Johnson Bros., 9 In.	16.00
Flow Blue, **Plate,** Kyber, Adams, 7 1/4 In.	20.00
Flow Blue, **Plate,** Kyber, Adams, 9 In.	19.00
Flow Blue, **Plate,** Kyber, Adams, 10 In.	32.00
Flow Blue, **Plate,** Kyber, 9 In.	35.00
Flow Blue, **Plate,** Kyber, 10 In.	24.00
Flow Blue, **Plate,** Kyber, 10 1/2 In.	28.00
Flow Blue, **Plate,** Ladybug & Blue Floral On White, Davenport, 9 In.	18.00
Flow Blue, **Plate,** Lahore, 10 In.	37.50
Flow Blue, **Plate,** Leaf & Floral Vine Border, Thomas Hughes Son, 9 In.	14.00
Flow Blue, **Plate,** Linda, Maddock, 8 In.	14.00
Flow Blue, **Plate,** Linda, Maddock, 9 In.	17.50
Flow Blue, **Plate,** Linda, Maddock, 10 In.	17.50
Flow Blue, **Plate,** Lonsdale, Ridgway, 9 In.	15.00

Flow Blue, Plate, Lonsdale, 10 In. 25.00
Flow Blue, Plate, Lorne, Grindley, 7 In. 10.00
Flow Blue, Plate, Lorne, Grindley, 10 In. 20.00
Flow Blue, Plate, Lorne, 6 In. 8.50
Flow Blue, Plate, Louise, New Wharf, 9 In. 7.00
Flow Blue, Plate, Lozere, Ironstone, E.Challinor, 8 1/2 In. 27.00
Flow Blue, Plate, Madras, Doulton, 8 3/4 In. 18.00
Flow Blue, Plate, Madras, 7 1/2 In. 23.50
Flow Blue, Plate, Manila, 9 1/2 In. 40.00
Flow Blue, Plate, Marechal Niel, Grindley, 9 In. 16.00
Flow Blue, Plate, Marechal, Niel, Grindley, 7 In. 9.50
Flow Blue, Plate, Marie, Grindley, 10 In. 20.00
Flow Blue, Plate, Martha Washington & 14 States, 8 3/4 In. 20.00
Flow Blue, Plate, Melbourne, 8 In. 10.00
Flow Blue, Plate, Messina, Meakin, 9 In. 12.00
Flow Blue, Plate, Messina, Meakin, 10 In. 15.00
Flow Blue, Plate, Milan, Grindley, 10 In. 18.00
Flow Blue, Plate, Mogul, 9 In. 19.75
Flow Blue, Plate, Monarch, Myott, 10 In. 24.00
Flow Blue, Plate, Mongolia, Johnson Bros., 9 In. 20.00
Flow Blue, Plate, Morea, J.Goodwin, Longton, 10 In. 20.00
Flow Blue, Plate, Normandy, Gold Trim, 10 In. 18.00
Flow Blue, Plate, Nonpareil, 6 In. 12.50
Flow Blue, Plate, Nonpareil, 6 3/4 In. 24.00
Flow Blue, Plate, Nonpareil, 10 In. 25.00
Flow Blue, Plate, Normandy, Johnson Bros., England, 9 1/4 In. 20.00
Flow Blue, Plate, Old Curiosity Shop, 10 In. 30.00
Flow Blue, Plate, Oregon, 9 1/2 In. 40.00
Flow Blue, Plate, Oregon, 9 3/4 In. 40.00
Flow Blue, Plate, Oriental, Alcock, 8 In. 48.00
Flow Blue, Plate, Oriental, New Wharf, 9 In. 22.00
Flow Blue, Plate, Oriental, 9 In. 19.00
Flow Blue, Plate, Osborne, Grindley, 9 In. .... 16.00 To 22.50
Flow Blue, Plate, Osborne, 7 3/4 In. 18.00
Flow Blue, Plate, Pekin, Gold Trim, Royal Staffordshire, 10 In. 22.00
Flow Blue, Plate, Pelesy, 8 1/2 In. 9.50
Flow Blue, Plate, Pelew, Challinor, 8 1/2 In. 50.00
Flow Blue, Plate, Persian, 9 In. 25.00
Flow Blue, Plate, Poppy, 8 In. 20.00
Flow Blue, Plate, Poppy, 9 In. 25.00
Flow Blue, Plate, Progress, Grindley, 8 In. 9.00
Flow Blue, Plate, Ramsey, C.1830, 10 1/2 In. 30.00
Flow Blue, Plate, Rhone, C.1845, 9 In. 25.00
Flow Blue, Plate, Rose, Grindley, 8 In. .... 9.00 To 14.00
Flow Blue, Plate, Sobraon, C.1850, 12 Sided, 9 1/4 In. 35.00
Flow Blue, Plate, Scinde, Alcock, 7 3/8 In. 28.75
Flow Blue, Plate, Scinde, 10 1/2 In. .... 47.50 To 49.50
Flow Blue, Plate, Shanghai, Grindley, 7 7/8 In. 28.00
Flow Blue, Plate, Soup, Floral, Ledged, J.Hughes, 9 In. 14.00
Flow Blue, Plate, Soup, Hong Kong, 10 1/2 In. 20.00
Flow Blue, Plate, Soup, Marguerite, Gilt Trim 14.00
Flow Blue, Plate, Soup, Waldorf, New Wharf Pottery, 9 In. 20.00
Flow Blue, Plate, States, 9 In. .... 14.00 To 20.00
Flow Blue, Plate, Temple, PW & Co., 7 3/4 In. 22.00
Flow Blue, Plate, Temple, The, Pearl Stoneware, C.1830, 8 3/4 In. 35.00
Flow Blue, Plate, Temple, 7 In. 30.00
Flow Blue, Plate, Temple, 8 In. 35.00
Flow Blue, Plate, Togo, 9 3/4 In. 18.00
Flow Blue, Plate, Tonquin, 8 1/2 In. 35.00
Flow Blue, Plate, Touraine, Alcock & Son, 7 1/2 In. 11.00
Flow Blue, Plate, Touraine, Stanley, 6 1/2 In. 12.50
Flow Blue, Plate, Touraine, Stanley, 9 In. 25.00
Flow Blue, Plate, Touraine, 7 1/2 In. .... 14.50 To 16.50
Flow Blue, Plate, Treat, Hand-Painted Fruit Center, Wood & Son, 8 3/4 In. 22.50
Flow Blue, Plate, Venus, T.Till & Sons, England, 7 1/2 In. 12.00
Flow Blue, Plate, Waldorf, New Wharf, 10 In. 28.00

Flow Blue, Plate, Watteau, Doulton, 6 1/2 In.	8.95
Flow Blue, Plate, Watteau, Doulton, 8 1/2 In.	14.95
Flow Blue, Plate, Watteau, Doulton, 9 In.	26.00
Flow Blue, Plate, Watteau, Doulton, 10 1/2 In.	18.00
Flow Blue, Plate, Watteau, Gold Outlines, Royal Doulton, 9 In.	25.00
Flow Blue, Plate, Watteau, Royal Doulton, 10 1/4 In.	15.00
Flow Blue, Plate, Yedo, Floral, Ashworth, 10 1/2 In.	26.00
Flow Blue, Plate, Yedo, 10 1/2 In.	25.00
Flow Blue, Platter, Belmont, 11 X 16 In.	35.00
Flow Blue, Platter, Belmont, 13 X 18 In.	45.00
Flow Blue, Platter, Birds, Elsmore, Parisian Granite, C.1887, 8 X 12 In.	22.00
Flow Blue, Platter, Chusan, 17 In.	210.00
Flow Blue, Platter, Clarissa, Johnson Bros., No.285459, 18 X 13 3/4 In.	70.00
Flow Blue, Platter, Coburg, 9 1/2 X 12 1/2 in.	75.00
Flow Blue, Platter, Colonial, Scalloped Edge, 18 X 14 In.	42.50
Flow Blue, Platter, Conway, New Wharf, 8 X 10 3/4 In.	18.00
Flow Blue, Platter, Cyprus, Oval, JRB, C.1860, 15 3/4 X 12 1/2 In.	70.00
Flow Blue, Platter, Devon, Meakin, 12 In.	42.50
Flow Blue, Platter, F.& Sons, Burslem, 15 1/2 X 11 In.	37.50
Flow Blue, Platter, Floral, J.Hughes, 9 X 6 In.	22.00
Flow Blue, Platter, Floral, J.Hughes, 13 X 8 In.	30.00
Flow Blue, Platter, Floral, J.Hughes, 15 X 9 In.	35.00
Flow Blue, Platter, Ghent, 15 1/2 X 13 3/4 In.	45.00
Flow Blue, Platter, Hizen, Ashworth & Bros., C.1870, 11 X 8 1/4 In.	35.00
Flow Blue, Platter, Hizen, Ashworth & Bros., C.1870, 14 X 11 In.	50.00
Flow Blue, Platter, Hizen, Ashworth & Bros., C.1870, 15 1/2 X 12 In.	65.00
Flow Blue, Platter, Hizen, Ashworth & Bros., C.1870, 20 X 16 In.	75.00
Flow Blue, Platter, Hizen, Well & Tree, Flanged Base, Ashworth, C.1870, 21 In.	95.00
Flow Blue, Platter, Indian, 13 1/4 X 10 1/4 In.	60.00
Flow Blue, Platter, Indian, 13 1/2 X 10 1/2 In.	65.00
Flow Blue, Platter, Knox, New Wharf, 10 1/2 In.	25.00
Flow Blue, Platter, Lorida, Johnson Bros., 12 X 8 In.	28.00
Flow Blue, Platter, Lorne, Oval, 16 X 11 1/2 In.	27.50 To 30.00
Flow Blue, Platter, Melbourne, 16 X 11 1/2 In.	28.00
Flow Blue, Platter, Mentone, English, C.1900, 13 X 17 In.	75.00
Flow Blue, Platter, Nonpareil, 13 X 11 In.	75.00
Flow Blue, Platter, Oregon, Mayer, 16 In.	125.00
Flow Blue, Platter, Oriental, Ridgway, 17 1/4 X 15 In.	140.00
Flow Blue, Platter, Scinde, Alcock, 16 In.	125.00
Flow Blue, Platter, Scinde, 18 3/4 X 15 1/4 In.	200.00
Flow Blue, Platter, Shanghai, W.& E.Corn, 10 X 8 In.	24.50
Flow Blue, Platter, Simla, Ellsmore, 16 In.	12.50
Flow Blue, Platter, Sobraon, 13 1/2 X 10 3/4 In.	67.50
Flow Blue, Platter, Togo, Oval, 11 1/2 In.	17.00
Flow Blue, Platter, Togo, Oval, 12 X 9 1/4 In.	20.00
Flow Blue, Platter, Turkey, Salem China Co., O., 18 1/2 X 22 In.	198.00
Flow Blue, Platter, Turkey, Whampoa, Mellor & Venables, C.1840, 19 1/2 In.	165.00
Flow Blue, Platter, Vermont, 12 X 16 In.	22.00
Flow Blue, Platter, Waldorf, N.Wharf, 10 1/4 X 8 In.	22.50
Flow Blue, Relish, Floral, Oval, J.Hughes, 6 X 4 1/2 In.	16.00
Flow Blue, Ring Tree, Ironstone, Staffordshire, England	20.00
Flow Blue, Sauce, Nonpareil	9.75
Flow Blue, Sauce, Togo	6.50
Flow Blue, Sauce, Touraine, Stanley, 5 In.	15.00
Flow Blue, Saucer, Ebor	3.50
Flow Blue, Saucer, Kelvin, Alfred Meakin, England	10.00
Flow Blue, Saucer, Oregon	12.00
Flow Blue, Saucer, Oriental	6.50
Flow Blue, Saucer, Poppy	4.00
Flow Blue, Saucer, Touraine, 6 In.	8.00
Flow Blue, Saucer, Waldorf	7.00
Flow Blue, Saucer, Watteau, Doulton	2.95 To 3.50
Flow Blue, Saucer, Wild Rose, Ironstone, W.Adams & Co., Tunstall, England	8.00
Flow Blue, Sugar & Creamer, Linda, Maddock	110.00
Flow Blue, Sugar, Covered, Octagonal, Morning Glory	75.00
Flow Blue, Sugar, English Scenery, Enoch Wood Woodware	12.50

Flow Blue, Sugar, Oriental 67.50
Flow Blue, Syrup, La Belle 48.00
Flow Blue, Tea Caddy, Hallmarked Cover & Base 60.00
Flow Blue, Teapot, Country Life, Arthur Wood & Son 42.00
Flow Blue, Teapot, La Belle, 10 In. 95.00
Flow Blue, Teapot, McDonnough's Victory, 3 3/4 X 6 X 4 1/2 In. 200.00
Flow Blue, Tile, Tea, Vista, Mason's Ironstone, Square, 5 In. 28.00
Flow Blue, Tile, Tea, Watteau, Doulton, Round, 6 In. 35.00
Flow Blue, Tray, Dresser, Warrick 16.50
Flow Blue, Tureen & Ladle, Gravy, Covered, Hong Kong, 8 X 5 1/2 X 4 1/2 In. 140.00
Flow Blue, Tureen, Como, Open Handled, W A A Co., 11 1/2 In. 38.00
Flow Blue, Tureen, Covered, Normandy, Footed, Oval, Johnson Bros., 10 In. ... 60.00
Flow Blue, Tureen, Covered, Scinde, 11 X 9 In. 325.00
Flow Blue, Tureen, Covered, Touraine, Oval, 11 X 7 In. 75.00
Flow Blue, Tureen, Florence, Open Handled, Pedestal, Wood & Son, 12 In. ... 45.00
Flow Blue, Tureen, Sauce, Hong Kong 48.00
Flow Blue, Vase, Floral Design, Gold Trim, Pedestal Base, 6 1/2 In., Pair ... 110.00
Flow Blue, Washstand Set, Athena, Pedestal Pitcher, Grindley, 13 In., 2 Piece ... 250.00
*Foo dogs are mythical Chinese figures, part dog and part lion. They were
made of pottery, porcelain, carved stone, and wood.*
Foo Dog, Electric Blue, 8 1/2 In., Pair 110.00
Foo Dog, Japan, Blue Green, 1920s, 7 In., Pair 50.00

FOSTORIA

*Fostoria glass was made in Fostoria, Ohio, from 1887 to 1891. The factory
was moved to Moundsville, West Virginia, and most of the glass seen in
shops today is a twentieth-century product.*

Fostoria, see also Milk Glass
Fostoria, Block, Candle, Green, Paradise, 2 In., Pair 8.50
Fostoria, Bonbon, American, 3 Toed 4.00
Fostoria, Bowl, Centerpiece, Green, Versailles, 12 In. 25.00
Fostoria, Bowl, Etched Roses, 9 In. 6.00
Fostoria, Bowl, Topaz, June, Handled, 8 1/2 In. 11.00
Fostoria, Bucket, Ice, Etched 25.00
Fostoria, Candleholder, Duncan, 3 1/2 In., Pair 12.50
Fostoria, Celery, Brazilian 17.00
Fostoria, Champagne, Blue, June 10.75
Fostoria, Champagne, Emerald Green, Versailles, Clear Footed Base 5.00
Fostoria, Console Set, Footed Bowl, Double Candlesticks, 3 Piece 25.00
Fostoria, Creamer, American 2.50
Fostoria, Creamer, Baroque 5.00
Fostoria, Creamer, Pink, Fairfax 2.00
Fostoria, Cup & Saucer, Amber, Fairfax .... 3.50 To 4.50
Fostoria, Cup & Saucer, Crystal, Colony 4.50
Fostoria, Cup & Saucer, Duncan 7.50
Fostoria, Cup & Saucer, Topaz, June 7.00
Fostoria, Cup, Bouillon, Pink, Fairfax, Wheel Cut Design 2.00
Fostoria, Dish, Candy, Amber, Versailles, Handled 9.00
Fostoria, Dish, Candy, Covered, Orchid, Grape, Brocade Etching, 3 Sections ... 20.00
Fostoria, Epergne, Single Vase, Fluted Bowl, Pink Opalescent, 16 X 6 1/2 In. ... 70.00
Fostoria, Goblet, Amber, Royal 6.35
Fostoria, Goblet, Amber, Versailles 9.00
Fostoria, Goblet, American, Hexagonal Base, 6 7/8 In. 3.00
Fostoria, Goblet, Azure, Versailles 20.00
Fostoria, Goblet, Chintz 7.50
Fostoria, Goblet, Crystal, Etched, Green Stem & Base, 1930 Wedding Gift ... 6.25
Fostoria, Goblet, Green, Etched, Milk Glass Stem & Base 6.00
Fostoria, Jar & Spoon, Mustard, Covered, Sunray, Blue Paint Decoration .. 6.50
Fostoria, Jar, Cookie, Pink Satin, Quilted, Matching Lid 200.00
Fostoria, Jar, Cookie, Silver Plate Lid & Handle 48.00
Fostoria, Nappy, Baroque, Handled, Square 3.75
Fostoria, Nappy, Victoria, Triangular, Marked Patent 17.50
Fostoria, Pitcher, Water, Florette, Pink Satin 250.00
Fostoria, Plate, Cake, Topaz, June, Handled, 11 1/2 In. 17.00
Fostoria, Plate, Etched Roses, 7 In. 3.50
Fostoria, Punch Set, American, 16 Piece 165.00

Fostoria, Relish, Amber, Versailles, Divided	9.00
Fostoria, Relish, Chintz, Blue Paint Decoration, 2 Part, Square	4.25
Fostoria, Relish, Topaz, June, 11 1/2 In.	10.00
Fostoria, Relish, Topaz, Round, 9 1/2 In.	4.25
Fostoria, Rose Bowl, Pink Frosted, Grape, 5 In.	35.00
Fostoria, Salt Dip, American	2.50
Fostoria, Sherbet, American	3.50
Fostoria, Sherbet, Emerald Green, Versailles, Clear Footed Base	5.00
Fostoria, Spooner, Green, Priscilla	24.00
Fostoria, Sugar & Creamer, Baroque	6.00
Fostoria, Sugar & Creamer, Daisy	6.00
Fostoria, Sugar, American	2.50
Fostoria, Syrup, Wedding Bells, Gold Stripe	29.50
Fostoria, Tumbler, Emerald Green, Versailles, Clear Footed Base, 4 Ozs.	5.00
Fostoria, Tumbler, Emerald Green, Versailles, Clear Footed Base, 5 Ozs.	5.00
Fostoria, Tumbler, Emerald Green, Versailles, Clear Footed Base, 8 Ozs.	7.00
Fostoria, Tumbler, Emerald Green, Versailles, Clear Footed Base, 9 Ozs.	7.00
Fostoria, Tumbler, Westar, C.1941	5.00
Fostoria, Wine, Amber, Versailles	9.00
Fostoria, Wine, American Crystal, 2 1/2 Ozs.	3.25
Fostoria, Wine, Amethyst, Clear Stem, Signed	10.00

Foval, see Fry Foval

Frame, see Furniture, Frame, Faberge, Frame

Francisware is an amber hobnail glassware made by Hobbs Brockunier and Company, Wheeling, West Virginia, in the 1880s.

Francisware, Basket, Bride's, Silver Plate Holder, 10 In.	175.00
Francisware, Berry Set, Round Bowls, 7 Piece	175.00
Francisware, Bowl, Finger, Amber & Clear Hobs, 4 In.	36.00
Francisware, Box, Round, Covered, Frosted, 5 3/8 In.	62.50
Francisware, Celery, Amber Ruffled Rim, Opalescent Ribs On Clear, 5 1/2 In.	42.00
Francisware, Creamer, Frosted Block, Amber Rim	40.00
Francisware, Pitcher, Clear Hobnails, Amber Neck, 4 Sided Rim, 8 1/2 In.High	225.00
Francisware, Relish, Frosted Swirl, Amber Rim	35.00
Francisware, Salt & Pepper, Frosted & Amber, Swirled	45.00
Francisware, Sauce	14.50
Francisware, Spooner, Frosted Block, Amber Rim	35.00
Francisware, Spooner, Frosted Hobnails, Amber Band	45.00
Francisware, Sugar & Creamer, Covered	100.00
Francisware, Sugar, Frosted, Amber, 4 In.	22.00
Francisware, Sugar	40.00
Francisware, Table Set, Frosted Hobnail With Amber Band, 4 Piece	200.00
Francisware, Table Set, 3 Piece	130.00
Francisware, Toothpick, Frosted Hobnail, Amber Top, 2 1/2 In.	45.00
Francisware, Toothpick, Hobnail, Frosted	42.00
Francisware, Tumbler, Frosted Block, Amber Rim	30.00
Francisware, Water Set, Frosted Hobnail, Yellow Rim, 7 Piece	450.00
Francisware, Water Set, Frosted Hobs & Amber Rims, 5 Piece	325.00
Franklin Tile, Viking Ship Scene, Marked, Square, 9 In.	10.00
Frankoma, Cup & Saucer, Demitasse, Impressed Mark	15.00
Frankoma, Vase Bowl, Mottled Brown With Yellow, 12 In.	10.00
Frankoma, Vase Bowl, Mottled Green With Brown, 12 In.	10.00
Frankoma, Vase, Brown, Impressed Frankoma 38, 6 In.	6.00
Frankoma, Vase, Globe Shape, Blue Metallic-Like Finish, 4 1/2 In.	8.00
Frankoma, Vase, Raised Desert Scene, Footed, 7 In.	12.50
Fraunfelter, Vase, Blue Luster On White, C.1923, 6 In.	20.00
Fraunfelter, Vase, Lessell Ware, Red Floral On Pink, 4 1/2 In.	85.00

Fry glass was made by the famous H.C.Fry Glass Company of Rochester, Pennsylvania. It includes cut glass, but the famous Fry glass today is the foval, or pearl, art glass. This is an opal ware decorated with colored trim. It was made from 1922 to 1933.

Fry, see also Cut Glass

Fry Foval, Bowl, Fruit, Jade Base, Sterling Rim & Base, 13 1/2 In.	250.00
Fry Foval, Candlestick, Opalescent Threading, 10 1/2 In., Pair	225.00
Fry Foval, Candlestick, Teal Blue At Top & Bottom, 11 In.High, Pair	175.00

Fry Foval, Champagne, Jade Stem	75.00
Fry Foval, Cup & Saucer, Blue Handle	50.00 To 65.00
Fry Foval, Cup & Saucer, Green Handle	38.00 To 50.00
Fry Foval, Cup & Saucer, Pink Handle	65.00
Fry Foval, Cup & Saucer, Plain Handle	40.00
Fry Foval, Cup & Saucer, Smoky Blue, Dark Blue Handles	85.00
Fry Foval, Lemonade Set, Jade Handles & Bases, Sterling Rims, 7 Piece	650.00
Fry Foval, Pitcher, Ruby Red Applied Handle, Ribbed, 12 In.High	225.00
Fry Foval, Plate, Delft Blue Rim, 9 1/2 In.	45.00
Fry Foval, Server, Lemon, Blue Delft Handle	75.00
Fry Foval, Sugar & Creamer, Blue Delft Handles & Bases	175.00
Fry Foval, Tea Set, Miniature, 11 Piece	350.00
Fry Foval, Vase, Striped, 12 In.High	145.00
Fry Foval, Vase, Trumpet, Cobalt Base, 10 In., Pair	225.00
Fry, Bowl, Oval, Basket Pattern, 6 1/4 X 8 1/2 In.	160.00
Fry, Candlestick, Opalescent, Blue Wafer, Green Threading, 10 1/2 In., Pair	175.00
Fry, Candlestick, Opalescent, Teardrop Stem, 7 1/4 In., Pair	75.00
Fry, Candlestick, Pearlware, Blue Knobs, Spiral Stripes, Pair	325.00
Fry, Candlestick, Pearlware, Double Knob, Blue Spiral Stripes, 11 In., Pair	295.00
Fry, Case, Clock, Cut Glass, 10 X 5 X 8 In.	250.00
Fry, Creamer, Clear To Blue, Applied Handle	15.00
Fry, Cup & Saucer, Swirled	75.00
Fry, Juicer, Deep, Open Handle, Marked	10.00
Fry, Mug, Striped, Applied Blue Handle	30.00
Fry, Pan, Marked, 11 X 8 1/2 In.	8.00
Fry, Plate, Pie, Dated 5-27-'19, 9 In.	7.00
Fry, Platter, Cut Flower & Vine, 10 3/4 In.	15.00
Fry, Reamer, Orange Juice, Embossed	35.00
Fry, Toothpick, Blue Handles, Signed, 2 In.	85.00
Fry, Trivet, Opalescent, 3 Footed	25.00
Fry, Vase, Applied Green Leaves, 7 X 5 In.	65.00
Fry, Vase, Crackle, Applied Green Leaves, 9 X 5 In.	85.00
Fry, Vase, Crackle, Applied Green Rosettes, Bulbous, 11 X 9 In.	95.00
Fry, Vase, Crackle, 3 Applied Green Leaves, 10 In.	28.00
Fry, Vase, Crackle, 3 Applied Purple Leaves On Lavender, 6 3/4 In.	25.00
Fry, Vase, Lemon Yellow, Royal Blue Rim & 3 Handles, 6 In.	42.00
Fry, Vase, Opalescent, Pink Drag Loop Pattern, 12 In.	155.00
Fry, Wine, Art Deco, Green, Black Stem	8.50
Fulham, Bottle, Peasant Woman, Salt Glaze, Stoneware, Buff, Brown, 1850, 10 In.	50.00
Fulham, Box, Money, Salt Glaze, Stoneware, Buff, Brown Decoration, 1867, 5 In.	30.00
Fulham, Box, Money, Salt Glaze, Stoneware, Cottage, Roof Cover, C.1850, 7 In.	30.00
Fulham, Inkwell, Salt Glaze, Stoneware, Buff, 3 Quill Holes, 1823, 2 3/4 In.	20.00
Fulham, Pitcher, Salt Glaze, Stoneware, Buff, Hunting Scenes, C.1850, 7 In.	70.00

FULPER

Fulper is the mark used by the American Pottery Company of Flemington, New Jersey. The art pottery was made from 1910 to 1929. The firm had been making bottles, jugs, and housewares from 1805. Doll heads were made about 1928. The firm became Stangl Pottery in 1929.

Fulper, Bowl, Centerpiece, Turquoise, Ribbed, Scalloped, Flared, Oval, 18 In.	30.00
Fulper, Bowl, Flower, Blue Streaks On Pink, Rose, Mauve, & Turquoise, 13 In.	33.00
Fulper, Bowl, Green, Candleholder Handle *Illus*	45.00
Fulper, Box, Powder, Lady	75.00
Fulper, Figurine, Duck, Signed, 3 X 3 1/2 In.	38.00
Fulper, Figurine, Nude Boy Sitting On Lily Pad, 5 1/2 In.	17.50
Fulper, Flower Frog, Pelican, Leafy Base, 16 Holes, 7 In.	42.00
Fulper, Lamp, Fairy, Art Deco Girl In Full Skirt, Orange To Natural, 6 In.	58.00
Fulper, Lamp, Green Glass Shade, 24 1/2 In. *Illus*	1350.00
Fulper, Lamp, Perfume, Ballerina, Bisque Finish, Beige & Cream, Marked, 6 In.	95.00
Fulper, Pot, Blue, 2 Handles, 10 In. At Widest Part, 7 In.	18.50
Fulper, Vase, Aqua Green, Gold Rim, Crystalline, 3 In.High	9.00
Fulper, Vase, Aqua, Flecked & Decorated With Tan, Handled, 10 1/2 In.	18.50
Fulper, Vase, Blue Crystalline Effect, Ruffled Sides, Signed, 6 1/2 X 4 In.	25.00
Fulper, Vase, Bowl Shape, Brown Metallic, Gold Speckling, 5 X 5 1/2 In.	15.00
Fulper, Vase, Bowl Type, Mauve With Purple & Cobalt Flambe, 3 1/2 X 6 In.	42.50
Fulper, Vase, Crackle, Blue & Green Top, White & Blue Bottom, 3 Handles, 7 In.	60.00

Fulper, Bowl, Green, Candleholder Handle
(See Page 198)

Fulper, Lamp, Green Glass Shade,
24 1/2 In.
(See Page 198)

Fulper, Vase, Dark Blue On Light Blue, 5 1/2 In.	35.00
Fulper, Vase, Earth Tone, Squat, Handled, 6 X 6 1/2 In.	35.00
Fulper, Vase, Flambe, Gray, Tan, & Brown, Shiny Glaze, Vertical Mark, 8 In.	30.00
Fulper, Vase, Gray & Blue Flambe On Green, Round, 2 1/2 X 5 In.	38.50
Fulper, Vase, Gray Flambe, Horizontal Ribs, Glaze Drips, 2 Handled, 9 In.	43.50
Fulper, Vase, High Glaze Brown To Tan, 2 Handles, 8 In.High	40.00
Fulper, Vase, Medium Blue High Glaze, Off-White Interior, 10 X 6 In.	39.00
Fulper, Vase, Mottled Green, Browns, Silver Flecks, 12 In.	38.00
Fulper, Vase, Mottled Green, 2 Strap Handles, Everted Neck, C.1900, 12 In.	100.00
Fulper, Vase, Pink Drip Glaze, Three Handles, 5 In.High	16.00
Fulper, Vase, Sky Flambe Blue, 9 In.High	25.00
Furniture, see also Shaker, Rocker, Store, Chair, etc.	
Furniture, Armchair, Art Nouveau, Gilt Wood, Pierced Backrest, C.1895, Pair	650.00
Furniture, Armchair, Art Nouveau, Mahogany, Cabriole Legs, C.1895, Pair	700.00
Furniture, Armchair, Child's, Ladder Back, Painted Red, Acorn Finials	120.00
Furniture, Armchair, Child's, Windsor, Maple, Turned, Comb Back, C.1775	2600.00
Furniture, Armchair, Child's, Windsor, Pennsylvania, C.1780, Bow Back	800.00
Furniture, Armchair, Chinese, C.1650	*Illus* 2400.00
Furniture, Armchair, Chinese, Huang Hua Li, Pair	*Illus* 3750.00
Furniture, Armchair, Chippendale Style, Mahogany, Wing, Carved Arms	200.00
Furniture, Armchair, Chippendale, Mahogany, Carved, Pierced Vase Splat	850.00
Furniture, Armchair, Chippendale, Mahogany, Carved, Wind, Floral Chintz	425.00
Furniture, Armchair, Federal, Mahogany, Carved, Shield Back, Spade Feet	75.00
Furniture, Armchair, French, C.1930, Burr Walnut, Upholstered, C.1930, Pair	800.00
Furniture, Armchair, George III Style, Mahogany, Serpentine Top Rail	150.00
Furniture, Armchair, George III, Mahogany, French Style, Pair	525.00
Furniture, Armchair, Hudson River Valley, C.1720, Maple & Cherry, Rush Seat	1500.00
Furniture, Armchair, Jacobean, Walnut, Turned & Carved, Ball Feet	300.00
Furniture, Armchair, Library, George II Style, Mahogany, Carved Knees	400.00
Furniture, Armchair, Library, George III Style, Mahogany, Serpentine Rail	800.00
Furniture, Armchair, Library, Mahogany, Ball & Claw Feet, C.1790	1200.00
Furniture, Armchair, Mahogany, Arched Top Rail, Carved Front Rail, C.1790	350.00
Furniture, Armchair, Mahogany, Bowfront, Cane Seat, Arched Top Rail, C.1850	50.00
Furniture, Armchair, Martha Washington, Lolling, Mahogany, Mass., C.1790	2200.00
Furniture, Armchair, Mendlesham, Elm & Yew, Pierced Splat, C.1790	250.00
Furniture, Armchair, N.Y., C.1760, Mahogany, Carved, Ogival Wings, Canted Back	4000.00
Furniture, Armchair, New York, C.1760, Mahogany, Carved, Wing, Spoon Back	4000.00
Furniture, Armchair, New York, C.1800, Mahogany, Wing, Canted Back	1500.00
Furniture, Armchair, Parcel Gilt & Paint, Black & Gold, Cane Seat, C.1820	325.00
Furniture, Armchair, Pennsylvania, C.1740, Maple, Turned, Rush Seat	850.00
Furniture, Armchair, Pennsylvania, C.1740, Maple, Turned, Slat Back	1050.00
Furniture, Armchair, Queen Anne Style, Black Japanned, Chinoiserie Scenes	225.00
Furniture, Armchair, Queen Anne Style, Turned Maple, Banister Back, Rush	100.00

Furniture, Armchair, Queen Anne Style, Walnut, Wing, Bowfront Seat	300.00
Furniture, Armchair, Queen Anne Style, Walnut, Wing, Turned, Balloon Seat	1000.00
Furniture, Armchair, Rhode Island, C.1725, Maple, Turned, Banister Back	800.00
Furniture, Armchair, Rhode Island, C.1740, Wing, Walnut, Cream Damask	3000.00
Furniture, Armchair, William & Mary Style, Maple, Turned, Rush Seat	225.00
Furniture, Armchair, Windsor, Elm, Saddle Seat, Serpentine Top Rail, C.1790	150.00
Furniture, Armchair, Windsor, Pennsylvania, C.1800, Bamboo Turned	550.00
Furniture, Armchair, Windsor, Pennsylvania, C.1800, Low Back, Saddle Seat	1700.00
Furniture, Armchair, Windsor, Pennsylvania, C.1800, Low Back, Turned Feet	600.00
Furniture, Armchair, Windsor, Rhode Island, Brace Back .... *Illus*	650.00
Furniture, Armchair, Windsor, Rhode Island, C.1800, Comb Back	700.00
Furniture, Armoire, D.G.Savard, C.1750, 8 Ft. .... *Illus*	3100.00
Furniture, Armoire, French, Hand-Carved, Clock At Top	4000.00
Furniture, Armoire, Walnut, Fruitwood Pulls, 7 Ft.	100.00
Furniture, Bed Steps, Mahogany, 18 In.Square	105.00
Furniture, Bed, Child's, Federal, Tester, Turned Maple, Vase Posts	300.00
Furniture, Bed, Day, Mahogany, Brassbound, 2 Drawer, C.1850, 6 Ft.4 In.	9500.00
Furniture, Bed, Federal Style, Maple, Ring Turned, 6 Ft.7 1/2 In., Pair	225.00
Furniture, Bed, Federal, Maple, Turned, Pencil Post, 6 Ft.2 In.	425.00
Furniture, Bed, Federal, Pine, Ring Turned Posts, 5 Ft.1 1/2 In. High	425.00
Furniture, Bed, Field, Maple, Cannonball, Double	100.00
Furniture, Bed, Italian, C.1775, Carved, Painted, Gilt .... *Illus*	800.00
Furniture, Bed, Jenny Lind, Spool, Walnut	188.00
Furniture, Bed, Journeyman's Sample, Walnut, Rococo Style, C.1875, 21 In.	35.00
Furniture, Bed, Mahogany, Carved, 4 Poster, Reeded & Turned, C.1760, 4 Ft.5 In	2800.00
Furniture, Bed, Marquetry, 4 Poster, C.1850, 6 Ft. X 4 Ft.11 In.	175.00
Furniture, Bed, New England, C.1800, Cherry, Turned, 4 Poster, 6 Ft.9 In.	400.00
Furniture, Bed, New England, C.1800, Pine & Ash, Turned Posts, 6 1/2 Ft.	80.00
Furniture, Bed, New England, C.1810, Curly Maple, 19 X 13 In.	250.00
Furniture, Bed, Pencil Post, Maple, Red Paint, 5 Ft.8 In. X 6 Ft.	375.00
Furniture, Bed, Pennsylvania, C.1815, Maple, Tester, 5 Ft.3 In. X 6 Ft.	675.00
Furniture, Bed, Philadelphia, C.1810, Mahogany, Carved, Tester, 8 Ft.High	2700.00
Furniture, Bed, Philadelphia, C.1810, Mahogany, Carved, 4 Poster, 7 1/2 Ft.	1600.00
Furniture, Bed, Rhode Island, C.1750, Maple & Curly Maple, Pencil Post, 8 Ft.	1100.00
Furniture, Bed, Tiger Maple, Double, Rope	700.00
Furniture, Bed, Walnut, Turned, Pencil Post, Tester, Arched Canopy, 7 Ft.	175.00
Furniture, Bench, Art Nouveau, Stained Oak, Carved, C.1900, 35 In.	175.00
Furniture, Bench, Bucket, Pine, Natural Finish, C.1700, 20 1/2 In. High	475.00
Furniture, Bench, Chiropractor's, Oak Legs, Folds Into Suitcase	75.00
Furniture, Bench, Cobbler's, American, C.1850, Pine, 18 In .... *Illus*	350.00
Furniture, Bench, Cobbler's, New England, C.1850, Pine, Cupboard Section	650.00
Furniture, Bench, Cobbler's, 19 X 20 X 14 In.	125.00
Furniture, Bench, Nursing, New England, C.1800, Stenciled .... *Illus*	375.00
Furniture, Bench, Shaker, Prayer	95.00
Furniture, Bench, Shaker, 6 Ft.	90.00
Furniture, Bench, Water, Pine & Poplar, Cupboards Above & Below, 68 In.High	1200.00
Furniture, Bench, Water, Shaker	85.00
Furniture, Bibliotheque, Marquetry, Glass Doors, Ormolu, C.1890, 5 Ft.7 In.	950.00
Furniture, Bonheur Du Jour, Kingwood, Ormolu, 8 Drawer, C.1890, 40 1/2 In.	2500.00
Furniture, Bonheur Du Jour, Sevres Portrait Medallions, Ormolu, C.1890	1600.00
Furniture, Bookcase Cabinet, George III Style, Mahogany, C.1850, 7 Ft.	950.00
Furniture, Bookcase Chest, George I, Walnut, 2 Drawer, Glass Doors, 79 In.	1300.00
Furniture, Bookcase, Chippendale Style, Mahogany, Carved, Bonnet Top, 9 Ft.	1300.00
Furniture, Bookcase, Empire Style, Mahogany, Ormolu Mounted, C.1890, 6 Ft.	600.00
Furniture, Bookcase, New York, C.1760, Mahogany, 2 Parts, Glass Doors, 8 Ft.	1500.00
Furniture, Bookcase, Virginia, C.1810, Walnut, Carved, Glass Doors, 7 Ft.8 In.	1600.00
Furniture, Box On Stand, James I, C.1600, Bible	785.00
Furniture, Box, Bible, Oak, Hinged, Metal Lock Flap, Bun Feet, C.1620, 30 In.	275.00
Furniture, Box, Bible, Pilgrim Century, Oak, Carved, Hinged, C.1690, 30 In.	300.00
Furniture, Box, Knife, Mahogany, Floral Marquetry On Hinged Lid, C.1790	250.00
Furniture, Box, Knife, Mahogany, Hinged Sloping Top, Copper Lined, C.1890	130.00
Furniture, Box, Knife, Mahogany, Inlaid, Hinged Slant Lid, C.1790, 15 In.	300.00
Furniture, Box, Letter, Burr Walnut, Inlaid Rosewood, Hinged, Handles, C.1820	100.00
Furniture, Box, Pipe, Wall, Pine, Drawer At Base, Mustard Colored Paint	1400.00
Furniture, Box, Writing, Burr Walnut, Hinged Fall Front, Drawers, C.1820	130.00
Furniture, Bureau Bookcase, Dutch, C.1750, Walnut, Mirror Doors, 7 1/2 Ft.	4200.00

Furniture, Armchair, Chinese,
C.1650
(See Page 199)

Furniture, Armchair, Chinese,
Huang Hua Li, Pair
(See Page 199)

Furniture, Armchair, Windsor,
Rhode Island, Brace Back
(See Page 200)

Furniture, Armoire, D.G.Savard, C.1750, 8 Ft.
(See Page 200)

Furniture, Bench, Cobbler's, American, C.1850, Pine, 18 In
(See Page 200)

Furniture, Bed, Italian, C.1775, Carved, Painted, Gilt
(See Page 200)

Furniture, Candlestand,
New England, Maple, Adjustable
(See Page 202)

Furniture, Bench, Nursing, New England, C.1800, Stenciled
(See Page 200)

Furniture, Bureau Bookcase, George I, Burr Walnut, Mirror Doors, 6 1/2 Ft.	4500.00
Furniture, Bureau Plat, Kingwood, Parquetry, Ormolu Mounted, C.1890, 30 In.	1300.00
Furniture, Bureau Plat, Louis XVI Style, Leather Top, C.1890, 28 3/4 In.	400.00
Furniture, Bureau Plat, Marquetry, Brass Mounted, C.1890, 20 1/2 In.	750.00
Furniture, Bureau, Burr Walnut, Slant Front, 4 Drawer, C.1720, 41 In.	1600.00
Furniture, Bureau, Dutch, C.1790, Marquetry, Roll Top, Bombe Front, 45 In.	3200.00
Furniture, Bureau, William & Mary Style, Walnut, Seaweed Marquetry, 38 In.	500.00
Furniture, Cabinet, China, Oak, Paw Feet	1400.00
Furniture, Cabinet, China, Walnut, Carved, 2 Glass Doors, 18 X 10 3/4 In.	85.00
Furniture, Cabinet, Chinese Export, Black Lacquer, Paintings, C.1820, 24 In.	1550.00
Furniture, Cabinet, Chinese, Brass Mounted, Landscape, 12 7/8 In.	60.00
Furniture, Cabinet, Corner, George III, Oak, Cupboard Door, 45 In.	125.00
Furniture, Cabinet, Curio, Chippendale, Mirrored Back	375.00
Furniture, Cabinet, Hanging, Pine, Bonnet Top, C.1720, 36 X 37 In.	1100.00
Furniture, Cabinet, Medicine, Pine	25.00
Furniture, Cabinet, Pipe Smoker's, Oak, Drawer, Pipe Rack, C.1850, 12 X 6 In.	55.00
Furniture, Cabinet, Rosewood & Ebonized Wood, Glass Top, C.1932, 4 Ft.7 In.	450.00
Furniture, Cabinet, Serge Chermayeff, C.1930, Silvered & Ebonized, 4 Ft.	2100.00
Furniture, Cabinet, Side, George III, Bowfront, Mythological Scene, 36 In.	3000.00
Furniture, Cabinet, Side, Mahogany, Bowfront, Brass Grillwork, C.1820, 33 In.	150.00
Furniture, Cabinet, Side, Mahogany, Bowfront, Frieze Drawer, C.1790, 37 In.	800.00
Furniture, Cabinet, Side, Marquetry, Chrome Lamp Top & Feet, C.1930, 44 In.	800.00
Furniture, Cabinet, Side, Rosewood, 3 Open Shelves, Doors, Bun Feet, 29 In.	200.00
Furniture, Cabinet, Specimen, Walnut, 2 Tiers Of 5 Drawers, C.1850, 16 In.	450.00
Furniture, Candlestand, Cherry, Octagonal Top, Tripod Base, 28 In.	150.00
Furniture, Candlestand, Cherry, Tilt Top, Vase Standard, C.1780, 28 In.	350.00
Furniture, Candlestand, Chippendale, Mahogany, Carved, Tilt Top, Birdcage	2600.00
Furniture, Candlestand, Chippendale, Walnut, Oval Top, Vase Standard, 28 In.	525.00
Furniture, Candlestand, Conn., C.1800, Inlaid Mahogany & Cherry, 29 1/2 In.	500.00
Furniture, Candlestand, Country Sheraton, Cherry & Birch, American, C.1850	80.00
Furniture, Candlestand, Federal, Cherry, Conn., C.1800, Square, Tripod, 28 In.	550.00
Furniture, Candlestand, Federal, Mahogany, Carved, Tilt Top, Oval, 28 In.	150.00
Furniture, Candlestand, Mahogany, Urn Standard, Snake Feet, C.1790, 27 In.	400.00
Furniture, Candlestand, Mass., C.1800, Inlaid Mahogany, Tilt Top, Oval, 28 In.	500.00
Furniture, Candlestand, New England, C.1700, Pilgrim, Century, Octagonal Top	200.00
Furniture, Candlestand, New England, C.1750, Pine, Ring Turned Standard	400.00
Furniture, Candlestand, New England, C.1755, Maple, Turned, 35 In.	800.00
Furniture, Candlestand, New England, Maple, Adjustable *Illus*	400.00
Furniture, Candlestand, Pennsylvania, C.1740, Mahogany, Carved, Tilt Top	375.00
Furniture, Candlestand, Pennsylvania, C.1800, Walnut, Tilt Top, Tripod	125.00
Furniture, Candlestand, Rhode Island, C.1750, Chestnut, Adjustable, 54 In.	275.00
Furniture, Candlestand, Walnut, Circular Top, Tripod Base, C.1780, 29 In.	275.00
Furniture, Candlestand, Walnut, Turned, Urn Standard, C.1800, 28 In.	300.00

Furniture, Case, Liqueur, George III, Mahogany, Medallions, Handles, 9 In.	70.00
Furniture, Case, Liqueur, Thuyawood, Hinged, Bohemian Glass Medallion, C.1875	425.00
Furniture, Cellarette On Stand, Federal Style, Inlaid Mahogany, 34 1/2 In.	500.00
Furniture, Cellarette On Stand, Mahogany, Brass Fittings & Handles, C.1790	500.00
Furniture, Cellarette On Stand, Mahogany, Brass Lions' Heads Handles, 1790	650.00
Furniture, Chair, American, C.1825, Black Paint, Decorated, Cane Seat, Pair	250.00
Furniture, Chair, American, C.1825, Black Paint, Stenciled, Set Of 6	450.00
Furniture, Chair, Barber's, Iron, Brass, & Porcelain	245.00
Furniture, Chair, Child's Lawn, Iron	8.50
Furniture, Chair, Child's, Bentwood	10.00
Furniture, Chair, Child's, Mass., C.1720, Maple, Turned, Slat Back	900.00
Furniture, Chair, Corner, New England, C.1760, Maple, Pierced Splats	175.00
Furniture, Chair, Corner, Walnut, Pillow Crest, Vase Splats, C.1760	850.00
Furniture, Chair, Country, Fiddleback, Decorated, Set Of 4	265.00
Furniture, Chair, Dining, Chippendale Style, Mahogany, Set Of 12	2800.00
Furniture, Chair, Dining, Chippendale Style, Pierced Splat, Set Of 10	1200.00
Furniture, Chair, Dining, Federal Style, Mahogany, Carved, Set Of 8	1200.00
Furniture, Chair, Dining, Federal Style, Mahogany, Carved, Shield Back	85.00
Furniture, Chair, Dining, Federal Style, Mahogany, Ladder Back, Set Of 8	1100.00
Furniture, Chair, Dining, Federal Style, Mahogany, Pierced Splat, Set Of 8	300.00
Furniture, Chair, Dining, Federal, Mahogany, Carved, Set Of 3	700.00
Furniture, Chair, Dining, Federal, Mahogany, Carved, Concave Crest, Set Of 8	2100.00
Furniture, Chair, Dining, Federal, Mahogany, Ladder Back, Set Of 8	850.00
Furniture, Chair, Dining, George III, Mahogany, Shield Back, Set Of 12	3000.00
Furniture, Chair, Dining, Mahogany, Ladder Back, Pierced Crest, Set Of 4	375.00
Furniture, Chair, Doctor's, Examining, Cast Iron, Padded Arms & Headrest	250.00
Furniture, Chair, Invalid, Windsor, Continuous Arms, 9 Spindles	440.00
Furniture, Chair, Lolling, Martha Washington Style, Serpentine Crest, Pair	175.00
Furniture, Chair, Lolling, Martha Washington, Mass., C.1800, Mahogany	1400.00
Furniture, Chair, New England, C.1810, Painted, Yellow, Decorated, Set Of 6	1050.00
Furniture, Chair, New England, C.1825, Rush Seat, Shaped Crest & Splat	112.50
Furniture, Chair, New England, C.1840, Rush Seat, Yellow Paint, Decorated, 6	1200.00
Furniture, Chair, New England, 1810, Bamboo Turned, Yellow *Illus*	150.00
Furniture, Chair, New York, C.1815, Curly Maple, Horseshoe Seat, Set Of 4	400.00
Furniture, Chair, New York, 1825, Late Federal *Illus*	160.00
Furniture, Chair, Painted, Decorated, Cane Seat, C.1810, Set Of 4	200.00
Furniture, Chair, Painted, Decorated, X Back Support, C.1820, Pair	110.00
Furniture, Chair, Painted, Green, Decorated, Cane Seat, C.1830, Set Of 7	275.00
Furniture, Chair, Papier-Mache, C.1890 *Illus*	750.00
Furniture, Chair, Plank Bottom, Set Of 6	350.00
Furniture, Chair, Potty, Child's, Pennsylvania, Color Stencil, C.1820	85.00
Furniture, Chair, Potty, Child's, Shaker, Watervliet, Gray, Potty	105.00
Furniture, Chair, Reclining, Mahogany, C.1850 *Illus*	950.00
Furniture, Chair, Shaker, Ladder Back *Illus*	525.00
Furniture, Chair, Shaker, 35 X 17 X 13 1/2 In., Set Of 5	350.00
Furniture, Chair, Side, American, C.1850, Rosewood, Cabriole Legs, Set Of 8	2600.00
Furniture, Chair, Side, American, C.1850, Rosewood, Pierced Back, Set Of 3	2300.00
Furniture, Chair, Side, Applewood, Curved Crest Rail, Pierced Splat, C.1760	350.00
Furniture, Chair, Side, Art Nouveau, Cane Seat, Carved Knees, C.1900, Set Of 6	700.00
Furniture, Chair, Side, Art Nouveau, Gilt Wood, Pair	800.00
Furniture, Chair, Side, Art Nouveau, Gilt Wood, Pierced Backrest, C.1895	142.00
Furniture, Chair, Side, Baltimore, C.1790, Mahogany, Carved, Shield Back, Pair	2600.00
Furniture, Chair, Side, Bird's-Eye Maple, Cane Seat, Vase Splat, C.1815	50.00
Furniture, Chair, Side, Camel Back, Mahogany, Pierced Slats, C.1790, Pair	350.00
Furniture, Chair, Side, Charles II, Walnut, Pierced Top Rail, Set Of 6	850.00
Furniture, Chair, Side, Child's, Maple, Brown Paint, Decorated, Arrowback, 1800	125.00
Furniture, Chair, Side, Chinese, Hardwood, Set Of 8 *Illus*	750.00
Furniture, Chair, Side, Chippendale Style, Mahogany, Ladder Back, Pair	150.00
Furniture, Chair, Side, Chippendale, Mahogany, Carved, Cupid's Bow Crest	750.00
Furniture, Chair, Side, Chippendale, Walnut, Carved, Vase Splat	1200.00
Furniture, Chair, Side, Connecticut, C.1725, Maple, Painted, Turned	1900.00
Furniture, Chair, Side, Connecticut, C.1780, Walnut, Cupid's Bow Crest, Pair	950.00
Furniture, Chair, Side, Curly Maple, Vase Splat, Crest Rail, C.1825	56.50
Furniture, Chair, Side, Dutch, C.1790, Marquetry, Spoon Backrest, Pair	525.00
Furniture, Chair, Side, Gaines, N.H., C.1720, Birch, Painted, Spoon Back	3800.00
Furniture, Chair, Side, George II, Mahogany, Carved Top Rail, Set Of 4	1200.00

Furniture, Chair, New England, 1810,
Bamboo Turned, Yellow
(See Page 203)

Furniture, Chair, Reclining, Mahogany, C.1850
(See Page 203)

Furniture, Chair, New York,
1825, Late Federal
(See Page 203)

Furniture, Chair, Side, Chinese,
Hardwood, Set Of 8
(See Page 203)

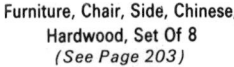

Furniture, Chair,
Papier-Mache, C.1890
(See Page 203)

Furniture, Chair, Side, Walnut
(See Page 205)

Furniture, Chair,
Shaker, Ladder Back
(See Page 203)

Furniture, Chair, Side, George III Style, Mahogany, Serpentine Top Rail		250.00
Furniture, Chair, Side, George III Style, Prince Of Wales Plumes, C.1850		150.00
Furniture, Chair, Side, Hitchcock, Pillow Back, Rush Seat		50.00
Furniture, Chair, Side, Mahogany, Carved Knees, Saber Legs, C.1890, Pair		300.00
Furniture, Chair, Side, Mahogany, Carved, Saber Legs, C.1820, Set Of 4		1000.00
Furniture, Chair, Side, Mahogany, Carved, Scroll Back, N.Y., C.1825, Pair		350.00
Furniture, Chair, Side, Mahogany, Carved, 3 Vertical Slats, C.1800, Set Of 6		3100.00
Furniture, Chair, Side, Mahogany, Leaf Carved Splat, Block Toes, C.1790, Pair		1400.00
Furniture, Chair, Side, Mahogany, Paneled Backrest, C.1930, Set Of 12		650.00
Furniture, Chair, Side, Mahogany, Serpentine Top Rail, Pierced Splat, C.1790		225.00
Furniture, Chair, Side, Mass., C.1740, Walnut, Balloon Seat, Vase Splat		3500.00
Furniture, Chair, Side, New England, C.1760, Cherry, Vase Splat		500.00
Furniture, Chair, Side, New England, C.1810, Bamboo Turned, Painted Yellow		150.00
Furniture, Chair, Side, New England, C.1830, Plank Seat, Crest Rail, Set Of 6		850.00
Furniture, Chair, Side, New York, C.1765, Mahogany, Carved, Cupid's Bow Crest		5500.00
Furniture, Chair, Side, New York, C.1790, Mahogany, Carved, Heart Back, Pair		1600.00
Furniture, Chair, Side, New York, C.1790, Mahogany, Carved, Shield Back, Pair		5500.00
Furniture, Chair, Side, New York, C.1810, Mauve Paint, Decorated, Set Of 4		350.00
Furniture, Chair, Side, Oak, Cane Seat, Set Of 5		48.00
Furniture, Chair, Side, Pennsylvania, C.1815, Painted, Stenciled, Arrow Back		160.50
Furniture, Chair, Side, Phila., C.1760, Mahogany, Carved, Vase Splat		9000.00
Furniture, Chair, Side, Queen Anne, Maple, Rush Seat, Serpentine Crest Rail		325.00
Furniture, Chair, Side, Queen Anne, Maple, Spoon Back, Yoke Crest, Rush Seat		300.00
Furniture, Chair, Side, Rhode Island, C.1760, Mahogany, Cupid's Bow Crest		425.00
Furniture, Chair, Side, Rosewood, Laminated, Pierced, Needlepoint, C.1860		325.00
Furniture, Chair, Side, Shaker, Mushroom Tilting Devices On Legs, Red, Yellow		375.00
Furniture, Chair, Side, Victorian, Mahogany, Fiddleback		23.50
Furniture, Chair, Side, Victorian, Walnut, French Legs		16.50
Furniture, Chair, Side, Walnut	Illus	1200.00
Furniture, Chair, Side, Walnut, Balloon Seat, Pierced Splat, C.1750		2100.00
Furniture, Chair, Side, Walnut, Pierced Top Rail, Cane Seat, C.1690, Pair		525.00
Furniture, Chair, Side, Windsor, Birdcage, C.1750		195.00
Furniture, Chair, Side, Windsor, Connecticut, C.1800, Crest Rail, Pair		850.00
Furniture, Chair, Side, Windsor, Continuous Arms, Legs Come Through Seat		440.00
Furniture, Chair, Side, Windsor, Fanback, 7 Spindles, C.1780		300.00
Furniture, Chair, Side, Windsor, N.E., C.1780, Brace Back, Cupid's Bow Crest		5000.00
Furniture, Chair, Side, Windsor, New England, C.1810, Bamboo Turned, Painted		142.00
Furniture, Chair, Side, Windsor, New England, C.1820, Painted, Decorated		43.50
Furniture, Chair, Side, Windsor, Rhode Island, C.1780, Brace Back		525.00
Furniture, Chair, Side, Windsor, Rhode Island, C.1780, Fanback, Vase Stiles		375.00
Furniture, Chair, Side, Windsor, Step Down, Pair		240.00
Furniture, Chair, Tilt, Shaker, Canterbury, Red Paint Removed, 32 1/4 In.		170.00
Furniture, Chair, Turned Stiles, Cane Seat, Painted, Decorated, C.1810		50.00
Furniture, Chair, Vasiform Splat, Painted, Stenciled, C.1820, Set Of 3		400.00
Furniture, Chair, Wagon, Split Wood Seat, Red Finish, C.1700, 34 X 31 In.		600.00
Furniture, Chair, Walnut, Turned, Brass Fittings, C.1850	Illus	725.00
Furniture, Chair, Windsor, Bow Back, Signed, C.1760, Set Of 5		2500.00
Furniture, Chair, Windsor, Fanback, C.1750, Pair		695.00
Furniture, Chair, Windsor, Fanback, C.1750, 9 Spindles		250.00
Furniture, Chair, Windsor, Invalid, 9 Spindles		440.00
Furniture, Chair, Windsor, Pennsylvania, C.1800, Bamboo Turned, Black Paint		375.00
Furniture, Chair, Windsor, Rhode Island, C.1810, Arrow Back, Painted		200.00
Furniture, Chair, Windsor, Saddle Seat		150.00
Furniture, Chair, Writing Arm, New England, 1815	Illus	250.00
Furniture, Chaise Longue, Charles II, Walnut, Scrolled Top Rail, 5 Ft.		675.00
Furniture, Chaise Longue, Le Corbusier, C.1930, Stainless Steel, 5 Ft.		1100.00
Furniture, Chest-On-Chest, Curly Maple & Birch, 2 Parts, C.1770, 6 1/2 Ft.		3000.00
Furniture, Chest-On-Chest, Mahogany, Secretaire Drawer, C.1790, 6 Ft.		1500.00
Furniture, Chest-On-Chest, New York, C.1760, Cherry, Carved, 2 Parts, 6 Ft.		6500.00
Furniture, Chest-On-Chest, Oak, Bracket Feet, 5 Drawer, C.1790, 69 In.		500.00
Furniture, Chest-On-Chest, Virginia, C.1800, Walnut, Inlaid, 3 Part, 8 Ft.		3200.00
Furniture, Chest On Stand, Mulberry, 7 Drawer, Brass Handles, C.1650, 5 Ft.		800.00
Furniture, Chest, Apothecary, New England, C.1800, Pine, 13 Drawer, 38 1/4 In.		800.00
Furniture, Chest, Apothecary, Pine, 3 Tiers Of 9 Drawers, Wood Knobs, C.1800		175.00
Furniture, Chest, Blanket, Conn., C.1800, Pine, Painted, Bracket Feet, 24 In.		100.00
Furniture, Chest, Blanket, Lift Top, Blue Paint, Miniature		80.00

Furniture, Chair,
Walnut, Turned,
Brass Fittings, C.1850
(See Page 205)

Furniture, Chair,
Writing Arm,
New England, 1815
(See Page 205)

Furniture, Chest, Dower, Pennsylvania, 1795, Painted
(See Page 207)

Furniture, Chest, Blanket,
Shaker, Canterbury

Furniture, Chest, Blanket, Miniature, Pine, New England, 6 Plank, 7 X 5 In.	29.00
Furniture, Chest, Blanket, New England, C.1720, Pine, 2 Drawer, 42 In.	650.00
Furniture, Chest, Blanket, New England, C.1750, Pine, Hinged, 49 X 25 In.	100.00
Furniture, Chest, Blanket, New England, C.1770, Pine, Bracket Feet, 11 In.	225.00
Furniture, Chest, Blanket, New England, C.1800, Pine, Hinged Lid, Bracket Feet	350.00
Furniture, Chest, Blanket, New England, C.1815, Pine, Painted, 37 X 21 In.	225.00
Furniture, Chest, Blanket, North Shore, Mass., 2 Bottom Drawers	550.00
Furniture, Chest, Blanket, Pennsylvania, C.1790, Pine, Painted, 23 In.	2500.00
Furniture, Chest, Blanket, Pennsylvania, C.1800, Pine, Painted, Decorated	650.00
Furniture, Chest, Blanket, Pennsylvania, 1782, Pine, Painted, 23 1/2 In.	700.00
Furniture, Chest, Blanket, Pilgrim Century, Oak, Hinged, Carved, C.1700, 44 In.	1000.00
Furniture, Chest, Blanket, Pilgrim Century, Pine, Carved, Hinged, 26 In.	450.00
Furniture, Chest, Blanket, Pine, Blue Paint, Bracket Feet, C.1770, 22 1/2 In.	300.00
Furniture, Chest, Blanket, Pine, Wide Board, 1 Drawer	114.50
Furniture, Chest, Blanket, Red Paint, Brasses, 2 Drawer	200.00
Furniture, Chest, Blanket, Rhode Island, C.1720, Pine, 2 Drawer, 39 In.	600.00
Furniture, Chest, Blanket, Rhode Island, C.1720, Pine, 2 Drawer, 44 In.	750.00
Furniture, Chest, Blanket, Shaker, Canterbury .... *Illus*	475.00
Furniture, Chest, Blanket, Shaker, Groveland, Walnut, Screw-In Feet, 4 Ft.	525.00
Furniture, Chest, Blanket, Sheraton, Crotch Curly Maple	1300.00
Furniture, Chest, Blanket, Walnut, Inlaid, 2 Drawers In Base, C.1780, 32 In.	600.00
Furniture, Chest, Boudoir, Chinese Chippendale, Pine, Mirror	175.00
Furniture, Chest, Bowfront, Green Paint, 17 X 14 X 12 In.	135.00
Furniture, Chest, Bowfront, Hepplewhite, Splayed Feet, Beaded Drawers	850.00

Furniture, Chest, Bowfront, 4 Graduated Drawers, Bracket Feet, C.1790, 34 In. 400.00
Furniture, Chest, Campaign, Mahogany, 5 Drawer, Brass Fittings, C.1890, 39 In. 400.00
Furniture, Chest, Carved, 4 Drawer, 9 X 8 In. 35.00
Furniture, Chest, Charles II, Oak, 4 Drawer, Bun Feet, 36 In. 675.00
Furniture, Chest, Child's, Pine, 4 Drawer, C.1850, 40 1/2 In. 200.00
Furniture, Chest, Chippendale Style, Mahogany, 3 Drawer, 4 In. 100.00
Furniture, Chest, Chippendale, Cherry, 5 Drawer, Ogee Feet, 42 In. 600.00
Furniture, Chest, Chippendale, Mahogany, Carved, 4 Drawer, 36 1/2 In. 550.00
Furniture, Chest, Dower, Pennsylvania Dutch, C.1830 .... 1600.00
Furniture, Chest, Dower, Pennsylvania, 1795, Painted .... *Illus* 5500.00
Furniture, Chest, Dower, Virginia, 1809, Walnut, Inlaid, Base Drawers, 31 In. 2000.00
Furniture, Chest, Dutch, C.1820, Mahogany, Convex Frieze, 6 Drawer, 5 Ft. 750.00
Furniture, Chest, Elm, 3 Drawers In Frieze, 2 Rows Of 5 Below, C.1750, 43 In. 300.00
Furniture, Chest, Federal Style, Mahogany, Inlaid, 4 Drawer, French Feet 150.00
Furniture, Chest, Federal, Cherry, Inlaid, 4 Graduated Drawers, 34 3/4 In. 850.00
Furniture, Chest, Federal, Inlaid Mahogany, Bowfront, Bracket Feet, 37 In. 1600.00
Furniture, Chest, Federal, Mahogany & Maple, Bowfront, 2 Drawer, 42 In. 1100.00
Furniture, Chest, Federal, Mahogany, Bowfront, 4 Graduated Drawers, 32 In. 1400.00
Furniture, Chest, Federal, Maple, Serpentine Front, 4 Graduated Drawers 800.00
Furniture, Chest, Fruitwood, 4 Beaded & Graduated Drawers, 14 1/4 In. 100.00
Furniture, Chest, George I, Burr Walnut, Bracket Feet, 5 Drawer, 29 1/4 In. 800.00
Furniture, Chest, George I, Burr Walnut, Bracket, 4 Graduated Drawers, 36 In. 1000.00
Furniture, Chest, George I, Burr Walnut, 5 Drawer, Bracket Feet, 33 1/4 In. 800.00
Furniture, Chest, George I, Walnut & Oak, Bracket Feet, 5 Drawer, 33 1/2 In. 450.00
Furniture, Chest, George II, Mahogany, Serpentine Front, 4 Drawer, 33 In. 1300.00
Furniture, Chest, George III Style, Mahogany, Serpentine Front, 34 1/4 In. 1650.00
Furniture, Chest, Green Paint, Decorated, 4 Drawer, C.1820, 20 1/2 In. 400.00
Furniture, Chest, Japanned, Hunting Scenes, 4 Drawer, C.1700, 35 1/2 In. 1200.00
Furniture, Chest, Mahogany, Bowfront, Bracket Feet, 5 Drawer, C.1820, 44 In. 300.00
Furniture, Chest, Mahogany, Bowfront, Carved, 5 Drawer, C.1790, 42 In. 175.00
Furniture, Chest, Mahogany, Bowfront, Inlaid, 5 Drawer, C.1800, 41 In. 350.00
Furniture, Chest, Mahogany, Bowfront, 3 Graduated Drawers, C.1790, 35 In. 300.00
Furniture, Chest, Mahogany, Bowfront, 4 Drawer, Ring Turned Legs, C.1810 .... 400.00
Furniture, Chest, Mahogany, Bowfront, 4 Graduated Drawers, C.1770, 32 In. 1500.00
Furniture, Chest, Mahogany, Bowfront, 4 Graduated Drawers, C.1770, 34 In. 1800.00
Furniture, Chest, Mahogany, Bowfront, 5 Drawer, Bracket Feet, C.1790, 41 In. 250.00
Furniture, Chest, Mahogany, Fruitwood Inlay, Serpentine Front, C.1790, 39 In. 1000.00
Furniture, Chest, Mahogany, Inlaid, 3 Graduated Drawers, C.1800, 33 1/2 In. 250.00
Furniture, Chest, Mahogany, Inlaid, 4 Drawer, Tapering Feet, C.1830, 50 In. 125.00
Furniture, Chest, Mahogany, 4 Drawer, Bracket Base, C.1830, 43 In. 250.00
Furniture, Chest, Massachusetts, C.1790, Mahogany, Inlaid, Bowfront, 37 In. 700.00
Furniture, Chest, Massachusetts, C.1810, Mahogany, Bowfront, 4 Drawer, 38 In. 400.00
Furniture, Chest, Massachusetts, C.1800, Mahogany, Inlaid, Bowfront, 4 Drawer 1000.00
Furniture, Chest, Massachusetts, C.1865, Pilgrim, Oak, Carved, 2 Drawer, Paint 2750.00
Furniture, Chest, New England, C.1790, Cherry, Inlaid, 4 Drawer, 17 1/2 In. 800.00
Furniture, Chest, New England, C.1790, Cherry, 4 Graduated Drawers, 34 In. 325.00
Furniture, Chest, New England, C.1800, Cherry, 4 Graduated Drawers, 39 In. 100.00
Furniture, Chest, New England, C.1830, Mahogany, Carved, 4 Drawer, 43 1/2 In. 175.00
Furniture, Chest, New England, C.1830, Pine, Painted, Grained, 9 X 12 In. 300.00
Furniture, Chest, New Hampshire, C.1790, Birch, Inlaid, 4 Drawer, 37 In. 750.00
Furniture, Chest, New York, C.1690, Pilgrim, Walnut, 2 Part, 42 In. 3500.00
Furniture, Chest, New York, C.1800, Mahogany, Bowfront, 4 Graduated Drawers 550.00
Furniture, Chest, New York, C.1800, Mahogany, Inlaid, 4 Drawer, 43 1/4 In. 700.00
Furniture, Chest, New York, C.1800, Mahogany, Inlaid, 4 Graduated Drawers 325.00
Furniture, Chest, Newport, C.1760, Curly Maple, 4 Drawer, Bracket Feet, 32 In. 2000.00
Furniture, Chest, Pennsylvania, C.1760, Walnut, Coved Cornice, 9 Drawer, 5 Ft. 1400.00
Furniture, Chest, Pennsylvania, C.1780, Coved Cornice, 9 Drawer, 5 Ft.4 In. 1600.00
Furniture, Chest, Pennsylvania, C.1810, Curly Maple, 4 Drawer, 37 3/4 In. 400.00
Furniture, Chest, Pilgrim Century, White Oak, 4 Drawer, Bun Feet, 39 3/4 In. 600.00
Furniture, Chest, Pine, 3 Drawer, Arcaded Skirt, C.1830, 14 In. 50.00
Furniture, Chest, Rawson, R.I., 1803, Mahogany, Inlaid, Serpentine Front 8500.00
Furniture, Chest, Rhode Island, C.1760, Curly Maple, 5 Drawer, 41 3/4 In. 1700.00
Furniture, Chest, Rhode Island, C.1760, Curly Maple, 6 Graduated Drawers 3200.00
Furniture, Chest, Shaker, Alfred, Maine, 2 Graduated Drawers 450.00
Furniture, Chest, Shaker, Six Board, Key, 10 X 10 In. 145.00
Furniture, Chest, Southern, 1830, Cherry, 4 Drawer .... *Illus* 450.00

Furniture, Chest, Spice, Pine, Cornice Top, 7 Drawer, Brass Pulls, 1850, 12 In. 60.00
Furniture, Chest, Spice, Pine, 2 Small & 3 Long Drawers, Button Feet, 16 In. 200.00
Furniture, Chest, Storage, Shaker, Children's House, Canterbury, 60 In., Pair 1500.00
Furniture, Chest, Virginia, C.1790, Walnut, Inlaid, 6 Drawer, 4 Ft. 1/4 In. 850.00
Furniture, Chest, Walnut, 3 Drawer, Carved Pulls, 30 In. 395.00
Furniture, Closet, China, Victorian, Walnut, 5 Shelves, 50 X 64 In. 265.00
Furniture, Commode, George III, Mahogany, Chinese Export Bidet, 18 1/2 In. 1600.00
Furniture, Commode, Louis XV Style, Mahogany, Kingwood, 2 Drawer, C.1890 .... 325.00
Furniture, Commode, Louis XV Style, Marquetry, Ormolu, Marble, C.1890 .... 2500.00
Furniture, Commode, Louis XV Style, Parquetry, Ormolu, C.1850, 36 3/4 In. 1000.00
Furniture, Console, American, C.1850, Rosewood, Cabriole Legs, Carved, 41 In. 450.00
Furniture, Console, Biedermeier, Elm, Semicircular Top, 31 In. 90.00
Furniture, Console, Louis XV Style, Carved, Marble Top, 32 In. 90.00
Furniture, Cooler On Stand, Wine, Mahogany, Inlaid, Brasses, C.1790, 29 In. 250.00
Furniture, Cradle, American, C.1850 ....*Illus* 150.00
Furniture, Cupboard, American, C.1850, Pine, Carved, Bracket Feet, 4 1/2 Ft. 650.00
Furniture, Cupboard, Barbershop, Hanging, Maple, Glass Door, 23 X 37 In. 59.00
Furniture, Cupboard, Child's, Pine, Double Doors, C.1860, 46 In. 225.00
Furniture, Cupboard, Corner, Cherry, C.1840 .... 1400.00
Furniture, Cupboard, Corner, Chippendale Style, Pine, 10 In. 75.00
Furniture, Cupboard, Corner, Hanging, New England, C.1750, Pine, 4 Ft. 700.00
Furniture, Cupboard, Corner, Mahogany, 2 Parts, Doors, Glass Panels, 6 1/2 Ft. 700.00
Furniture, Cupboard, Corner, New England, C.1800, Pine, Paneled Door, 5 Ft. 400.00
Furniture, Cupboard, Corner, Pennsylvania, C.1720, Pine, Red Stain, 8 Ft. 1800.00
Furniture, Cupboard, Corner, Pine & Tulip Poplar, Door, C.1800, 6 Ft. 900.00
Furniture, Cupboard, Corner, Virginia, C.1790, Walnut, Inlaid, Bowfront, 10 Ft. 2100.00
Furniture, Cupboard, Corner, Virginia, C.1790, Walnut, Inlaid, 2 Part, 8 Ft. 600.00
Furniture, Cupboard, Hanging, Corner, Oak, 2 Door, C.1750, 40 1/2 In. 100.00
Furniture, Cupboard, Hanging, Oak, 13 X 19 In. 17.50
Furniture, Cupboard, Pennsylvania, C.1850, Pine, 6 Ft. ....*Illus* 1400.00
Furniture, Cupboard, Pewter, Pine, Scalloped Frieze, 6 Ft.8 3/4 In. 525.00
Furniture, Cupboard, Pie, Bottom Drawer, Tin Sides, 56 In. High 175.00
Furniture, Cupboard, Wall, Delaware River Valley, C.1820, Pine, 2 Parts 1300.00
Furniture, Cupboard, Wall, New England, 1841, Pine, Painted, Red, 22 X 16 In. 150.00
Furniture, Cupboard, Wall, Pine, 2 Doors, C.1800, 6 Ft.8 In. High 325.00
Furniture, Cupboard, Wall, Walnut, Molded Cornice, Glass Door, 30 In. 150.00
Furniture, Desk & Bookcase, Lady's, Massachusetts, C.1790, Mahogany, Inlaid 3500.00
Furniture, Desk & Chair, Child's, Oak, Roll Top, C.1890, 33 In. 200.00
Furniture, Desk On Frame, Counting House, Massachusetts, C.1790, Pine 250.00
Furniture, Desk, Butler's, C.1830 .... 195.00
Furniture, Desk, Butler's, N.Y., C.1810, Mahogany, French Bracket Feet, 45 In. 900.00
Furniture, Desk, Captain's, Burl Walnut, Brass Corners & Nameplate, 18 In. 149.00
Furniture, Desk, Captain's, Mahogany, C.1810, 34 In. ....*Illus* 550.00
Furniture, Desk, Child's, Rhode Island, C.1760, Maple, Slant Front, 24 1/2 In. 2500.00
Furniture, Desk, Chippendale Style, Maple, Slant Front, Hinged Lid, 41 In. 350.00
Furniture, Desk, Chippendale Style, Walnut, Carved, Slant Front, 27 In. 325.00
Furniture, Desk, Chippendale, Mahogany, Blockfront, Hinged Lid, 43 1/2 In. 2700.00
Furniture, Desk, Chippendale, Mahogany, Blockfront, Slant Lid, 44 In. 7250.00
Furniture, Desk, Chippendale, Mahogany, Blockfront, 4 Drawer, 44 1/2 In. 8000.00
Furniture, Desk, Counting House, Henry B.May, 1838, Tulip Poplar, 18 In. 100.00
Furniture, Desk, Counting House, Pine, Painted, 2 Parts, 6 Ft. 275.00
Furniture, Desk, Cylinder, Victorian, Walnut, Drawers 395.00
Furniture, Desk, English, C.1775, Mahogany, Roll Top ....*Illus* 900.00
Furniture, Desk, Federal, Bird's-Eye Maple ....*Illus* 1500.00
Furniture, Desk, G.John, Pa., C.1760, Walnut, Slant Front, Bracket Feet, 16 In. 7600.00
Furniture, Desk, Howard & Company, C.1850, Edwardian Style, Bamboo, Ebonized 700.00
Furniture, Desk, Lady's, Art Nouveau, Marquetry, Floral, C.1900, 3 Ft.9 In. 350.00
Furniture, Desk, Lap, Burl Walnut, Brassbound Corners, 15 X 9 X 6 In. 140.00
Furniture, Desk, Lap, Ivory & Abalone Inlay, Floral Design On Top 30.00
Furniture, Desk, Lap, Mahogany, Inlaid Brass Cartouche, C.1900, 8 X 12 In. 65.00
Furniture, Desk, Lap, Near Eastern, Wood, Ivory Inlaid, 6 X 15 1/2 In. 125.00
Furniture, Desk, Lap, Oak, 18 X 13 1/2 In. .... 26.00 To 40.00
Furniture, Desk, Lap, Painted & Grained, Hinged Slant Lid, C.1750, 14 In. 110.00
Furniture, Desk, Lap, Papier-Mache, Mother-Of-Pearl, Reverse Painting, C.1890 .... 80.00
Furniture, Desk, Lap, Shaker, Canterbury 140.00
Furniture, Desk, Lap, Victorian, Papier-Mache, Black, Mother-Of-Pearl Floral 110.00

Furniture, Chest, Southern, 1830,
Cherry, 4 Drawer
(See Page 207)

Furniture, Desk, Federal, Bird's-Eye Maple
(See Page 208)

Furniture, Cupboard, Pennsylvania,
C.1850, Pine, 6 Ft.
(See Page 208)

Furniture, Desk, English, C.1775,
Mahogany, Rolltop
(See Page 208)

Furniture, Desk, Captain's, Mahogany, C.1810, 34 In.
(See Page 208)

Furniture, Cradle, American, C.1850
(See Page 208)

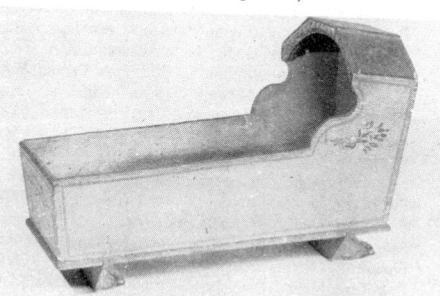

Furniture, Desk, Lap, Walnut, Felt Inside, 2 Inks, Pens, Paper, 11 X 8 1/2 In. 45.00
Furniture, Desk, Lawyer's, Victorian, Walnut, Bethel, Me. 265.00
Furniture, Desk, Lawyer's, Victorian, Walnut, Bethel, Me. 500.00
Furniture, Desk, Massachusetts, C.1800, Mahogany, Inlaid, 2 Parts, 5 Drawer 1350.00
Furniture, Desk, New England, Maple & Curly Maple, Slant Top, C.1750 .... 800.00
Furniture, Desk, New York, C.1800, Mahogany, Inlaid, Butler's Drawer, 44 In. 1750.00
Furniture, Desk, Painted To Simulate Oak, Fall Front, C.1750, 38 In. 2000.00
Furniture, Desk, Pennsylvania, C.1725, Walnut, Slant Front, 43 In. .... *Illus* 1600.00
Furniture, Desk, Pennsylvania, C.1760, Curly Maple 2300.00
Furniture, Desk, Pennsylvania, C.1780, Walnut, Slant Front, Brass Handles 1700.00
Furniture, Desk, Pennsylvania, C.1780, Walnut, Slant Front, 45 1/2 In. 1325.00
Furniture, Desk, Postmaster's, Walnut, 2 Piece, C.1850 .... 250.00
Furniture, Desk, Queen Anne, Burr Walnut, 2 Drawers, Shelves, 36 X 12 In. 2500.00
Furniture, Desk, Rhode Island, C.1760, Birch, Slant Front, 41 3/4 In. 1900.00
Furniture, Desk, Rhode Island, C.1760, Curly Maple, Slant Front, 42 In. 295.00
Furniture, Desk, Roll Top, Oak, 36 In. 1600.00
Furniture, Desk, Wooten Patent, C.1890, Mahogany, Galleried Top, 5 1/2 Ft. 4500.00
Furniture, Desk, Wooten, Indianapolis, 1874, 67 X 40 X 29 In. 140.00
Furniture, Dresser, Chippendale Style, Mahogany, 10 1/4 In. 225.00
Furniture, Dresser, Chippendale Style, Pine, Double Doors, 10 1/2 In. 1100.00
Furniture, Dresser, Elm, Pierced Heart & Scroll Apron, C.1790, 31 In. 99.00
Furniture, Dresser, Victorian, Decorated, Walnut Fruit Pulls, Mirror 150.00
Furniture, Dressing Glass, Federal, Inlaid Mahogany, Brass Finials, 23 In. 700.00
Furniture, Fauteuil A La Reine, Regence Style, Parcel Gilt, Carved, Pair 650.00
Furniture, Fauteuil De Cabinet, Louis XV Style, Caned Seat, C.1890 .... 150.00
Furniture, Fauteuil En Cabriolet, Louis XVI Style, Cabriole Legs, C.1890 .... 125.00
Furniture, Fauteuil, Black Paint, White Outlined Scrolls, C.1820 .... 75.00
Furniture, Footstool, Chestnut, Needlework Top, C.1800, 10 1/4 In., Pair 375.00
Furniture, Footstool, Chippendale Style, Mahogany, Carved, Blue Damask 22.50
Furniture, Footstool, New England, Pine, Cutout Feet, Scalloped Sides 45.00
Furniture, Footstool, Shaker, Green Cushion, 7 X 13 In. 110.00
Furniture, Footstool, Shaker, Mount Lebanon, Plush Cover, Ecru Initials 18.00
Furniture, Footstool, Walnut, Caned Top, 13 X 10 In. 19.75
Furniture, Frame, Easel, Art Nouveau Woman On Side, 10 1/2 X 7 1/2 In. 15.00
Furniture, Frame, Picture, Embossed Gilt, Deep, 13 X 15 In. 30.00
Furniture, Frame, Walnut, 14 X 16 In. 850.00
Furniture, Gueridon, Empire Style, Ormolu Mounted, Onyx Top, 30 In. 325.00
Furniture, Gueridon, Louis XV Style, Ormolu Mounted, Marble Top, 29 In. 800.00
Furniture, Gueridon, Ormolu Mounted, Fleur De Peche Marble Top, C.1890 .... 20.00
Furniture, Hat Rack, Hanging, 4 Iron Hooks, Patent 1862, 26 1/4 X 5 In. 650.00
Furniture, Highboy Base, Cherry, Frieze Drawer, C.1750, 34 In. 750.00
Furniture, Highboy Base, New England, C.1740, Cherry, Carved, Fan Drawer 4900.00
Furniture, Highboy, Connecticut, C.1740, Cherry, Carved, Flat Top, 5 Ft.7 In. 900.00
Furniture, Highboy, Connecticut, C.1750, Cherry, Fan Carved Drawer, 30 In. 3600.00
Furniture, Highboy, Connecticut, C.1750, Maple, Carved, Flat Top, 5 Ft.2 In. 1900.00
Furniture, Highboy, Mass., C.1740, Burl Walnut & Maple, 3 Drawer, 28 3/4 In. 3600.00
Furniture, Highboy, New Hampshire, C.1770, Maple, Flat To .... *Illus* 6000.00
Furniture, Highboy, Newport, C.1740, Curly Maple, Flat Top, 2 Part, 6 Ft. 3000.00
Furniture, Highboy, Queen Anne, Cherry, Bonnet Top, 2 Parts, 6 Ft.7 In. 250.00
Furniture, Highchair, Child's, American, C.1850, Painted, Decorated, 35 In. 100.00
Furniture, Highchair, Child's, Cherry, Slat Back, C.1800, Leather Seat 400.00
Furniture, Kas, N.Y., C.1750, Pine, Painted, 2 Paneled Doors, 6 Ft.3 In. 800.00
Furniture, Lectern, George II, Mahogany, 3 Graduated Shelves, 44 In. 1100.00
Furniture, Love Seat, Empire, American, Carved, Rolled Arms 725.00
Furniture, Lowboy, Chippendale Style, Mahogany, Carved, Ball & Claw Feet 1400.00
Furniture, Lowboy, Queen Anne, Walnut, Oblong Top, Ball Feet, 30 1/2 In. 700.00
Furniture, Mantel, Virginia, C.1800, Pine, Carved, Painted, 5 X 6 1/2 Ft. .... *Illus* 85.00
Furniture, Mirror On Stand, C.1820, 12 In. 38.50
Furniture, Mirror, Art Nouveau, Cast Iron, Gilded, 14 X 9 1/2 In. 3750.00
Furniture, Mirror, Chippendale, Mahogany, Carved, Parcel Gilt, Phoenix, 47 In. 3750.00
Furniture, Mirror, Chippendale, Walnut & Parcel Gilt, Phoenix Crest, 6 Ft. 350.00
Furniture, Mirror, Convex, Eagle Top, Round, C.1820, 37 1/2 In. 550.00
Furniture, Mirror, Courting, Painted Wood, Eglomise Panels, C.1750, 16 In. 35.00
Furniture, Mirror, Dressing Table, Victorian, Oak, Folding, 3 Part, 10 In. 90.00
Furniture, Mirror, Dressing, Federal, Mahogany, Inlaid, Drawer In Base, 18 In. 60.00
Furniture, Mirror, Dressing, Federal, Mahogany, 2 Drawer Case, Brass Finials 150.00
Furniture, Mirror, Dressing, Mahogany, Bowfront 3 Drawer Base, C.1790 ....

Furniture, Desk,
Pennsylvania,
C.1760, Curly Maple
(See Page 210)

Furniture, Highboy,
New Hampshire,
C.1770, Maple,
Flat Top
(See Page 210)

Furniture, Mirror On Stand, C.1820, 12 In.
(See Page 210)

Furniture, Mirror, Philadelphia, C.1820, Gilt Wood & Gesso
(See Page 212)

Furniture, Mirror, Dressing, Mahogany, Inlaid, 3 Drawers, 21 In.	110.00
Furniture, Mirror, Dressing, Mahogany, Ring Turned Supports, Drawers, C.1800	100.00
Furniture, Mirror, English Regency, Bronze, Slate Base, C.1810, 15 In.	250.00
Furniture, Mirror, Federal, Gilt & Gesso, Acanthus & Parasol Crest, 47 In.	700.00
Furniture, Mirror, Federal, Inlaid Mahogany & Parcel Gilt, Swan Crest, 5 Ft.	5500.00
Furniture, Mirror, Federal, Inlaid Mahogany, Carved & Scrolled Crest, 40 In.	700.00
Furniture, Mirror, Federal, Inlaid Mahogany, Cheval, Brass Candle Arms, 5 Ft.	1200.00
Furniture, Mirror, Federal, Mahogany & Parcel Gilt, Eagle & Crest, 37 In.	140.00
Furniture, Mirror, George II Style, Gilt Wood, Chinaman Crest, 6 Ft.10 In.	2100.00
Furniture, Mirror, George II Style, Gilt Wood, Ho-Ho Birds, 6 1/2 Ft., Pair	2200.00
Furniture, Mirror, George II, Carved Gilt Wood, Ho-Ho Birds, 7 Ft.8 In.	1300.00
Furniture, Mirror, George III Style, Carved Gilt Wood, C Scrolls, 6 Ft.	250.00
Furniture, Mirror, George III Style, Carved Gilt Wood, Oval Plate, 4 Ft.	800.00
Furniture, Mirror, George III Style, Carved Gilt Wood, Urn Top, 4 Ft.2 In.	250.00
Furniture, Mirror, Gilt Wood, Carved Leaf Tips & Ribbon Twist, 4 Ft.4 In.	40.00
Furniture, Mirror, Girandole, Gilt & Gesso, C.1820, Vase Finial, 38 1/2 In.	300.00
Furniture, Mirror, Girandole, Gilt & Gesso, Carved Eagle, C.1850, 44 In.	300.00
Furniture, Mirror, Italian, Parcel Gilt, Maroon Paint, Carved, 30 1/4 In.	80.00
Furniture, Mirror, Mahogany, Eglomise Panel, C.1810, 39 X 21 In.	200.00
Furniture, Mirror, Mahogany, Parcel Gilt, Floral Basket Crest, 48 In.	2100.00
Furniture, Mirror, Mass., C.1820, Girandole, Parcel Gilt, Round, 25 1/2 In.	400.00
Furniture, Mirror, New England, C.1810, Gilt & Gesso, Eglomise Panel, 28 In.	425.00
Furniture, Mirror, New England, C.1815, Gilt Wood & Gesso, Painting, 15 In.	350.00
Furniture, Mirror, New York, C.1810, Gilt & Gesso, Eglomise Painting, 43 In.	1000.00

Furniture, Mirror, New York, C.1825, Gilt & Gesso, Carved, 49 1/2 X 27 In. 175.00
Furniture, Mirror, Philadelphia, C.1820, Gilt Wood & Gesso .... *Illus* 500.00
Furniture, Mirror, Pennsylvania, C.1825, Mahogany, Carved, 31 X 16 In. 50.00
Furniture, Mirror, Philadelphia, C.1830, Curly Maple, 30 X 20 3/4 In. 300.00
Furniture, Mirror, Philadelphia, C.1835, Mahogany, Carved, Eglomise, 35 In. 225.00
Furniture, Mirror, Pier, George III Style, Carved Gilt Wood, 6 Ft.10 In. 500.00
Furniture, Mirror, Plateau, Gilt & Silver, Scroll & Flower Feet, 10 In. 25.00
Furniture, Mirror, Plateau, Silver Metal, Floral Edges, Fancy Feet, 10 In. 15.00
Furniture, Mirror, Queen Anne, Carved & Parcel Gilt, Pierced Crest, 37 In. 450.00
Furniture, Mirror, Queen Anne, Japanned, Tortoiseshell, 2 Parts, 5 Ft. 2250.00
Furniture, Mirror, Queen Anne, Walnut & Parcel Gilt, Carved, 43 X 18 In. 475.00
Furniture, Mirror, Queen Anne, Walnut & Parcel Gilt, Scrolled Crest, 22 In. 350.00
Furniture, Mirror, Queen Anne, Walnut, 2 Part Beveled Glass, 52 In. 575.00
Furniture, Mirror, Shaving, Victorian, Light Wood, On Stand, Adjustable 55.00
Furniture, Mirror, Shaving, Victorian, Walnut, Swing Mirror, 15 X 10 In. 45.00
Furniture, Mirror, Standard, Hand-Carved, Inlaid Mother-Of-Pearl, 9 X 16 In. 85.00
Furniture, Mirror, Toilet, Mahogany, Drawer, Brass Urn Finials, C.1820, 22 In. 600.00
Furniture, Mirror, Toilet, Queen Anne Style, Red Lacquer, Gold Trim, 30 In. 150.00
Furniture, Mirror, Victorian, Oak, Folding, 3 Section, Brass Feet, 30 In. 35.00
Furniture, Mirror, Wall, Chippendale, Mahogany, Scrolled Crest, 36 1/4 In. 250.00
Furniture, Mirror, Walnut, Oval, Gilt Wood Border, 12 X 10 In. 20.00
Furniture, Mirror, Whaling Ship Picture At Top, Black & Gold Wood, 18 In. 29.00
Furniture, Nest Of Tables, Galle, Seashore Motif, 4 .... 1250.00
Furniture, Pail, Plate, Mahogany, Brass Band & 2 Ring Handles, C.1790, 14 In. 350.00
Furniture, Pew, Church, Oak 35.00
Furniture, Pie Safe, Walnut, 2 Drawers At Top, Tin 5.95
Furniture, Press, Linen, New Jersey, 1790, Cherry & Pine .... *Illus* 1200.00
Furniture, Queen Anne, Mahogany, Drop Leaf, Pad Feet, 27 1/4 In. 1000.00
Furniture, Rack, Hat, Victorian, Walnut, Accordion Style, White Enamel Pegs 22.00
Furniture, Rack, Magazine, Wall, Oak, Oil Painting Center, 18 X 16 In. 22.00
Furniture, Rack, Spoon, R.H., 1852, Pine, Carved, Painted, Red, 21 1/2 X 10 In. 1800.00
Furniture, Rack, Towel, Walnut, 2 Bars, Cut Leaf Corners, 23 In. 55.00
Furniture, Rocker, Child's, Wicker, Heywood Bros., Dated 1871 .... 75.00
Furniture, Rocker, New England, C.1815, Arm, Painted, Grained, Yellow Ocher 175.00
Furniture, Rocker, Shaker, Hancock, C.1800, 43 1/2 X 24 X 15 In. 450.00
Furniture, Rocker, Shaker, Label No.7, Mushroom Knuckles, Tapes, 41 1/2 In. 350.00
Furniture, Rocker, Shaker, Marked Number 3, Red & Cream Tapes, 35 X 19 In. 240.00
Furniture, Rocker, Windsor, New England, C.1810, Painted, Red, Crest Rail 140.00
Furniture, Rocker, Windsor, Rhode Island, C.1810, Bamboo Turned 250.00
Furniture, Rod, Towel, Oak Rod, Brass Ends & Chain, 3 Oak Rings, 22 In. 19.50
Furniture, Screen, Color & Gold On Paper, Battle, Tosa, 6 Fold, C.1790, 12 Ft. 1000.00
Furniture, Screen, Color On Gold Paper, Cranes, Dorin, 6 Fold, C.1850, 12 Ft. 1400.00
Furniture, Screen, Color On Gold Paper, Pine & Birds, 6 Fold, C.1850, 12 Ft. 350.00
Furniture, Screen, Ink On Gold Paper, Monogotari, 6 Fold, C.1790, 12 Ft. 950.00
Furniture, Screen, Ivory & Shibayama, 2 Fold, Silver Fittings, C.1790, 8 In. 2250.00
Furniture, Screen, Japanese, Embroidered, Painted, 6 Fold, 18 In. 55.00
Furniture, Screen, Korean, 6 Wooden Panels, Openwork Carving, 18 X 66 In. 45.00
Furniture, Screen, Sumi, Gofun, & Color On Paper, Bridge, 4 Fold, C.1850, 8 Ft. 475.00
Furniture, Screen, Sumi, Gofun, & Color On Paper, C.1790, 6 Fold, 11 Ft.10 In. 2200.00
Furniture, Screen, Sumi, Gofun, & Color On Silver Paper, Egrets, 4 Fold, 5 Ft. 500.00
Furniture, Screen, Sumi, Gofun, & Gold On Paper, Tosa, C.1790, 6 Fold, 12 Ft. 1700.00
Furniture, Screen, Table, Arita, Blue & White, Flying Chidori, 5 In. 125.00
Furniture, Screen, Table, Chinese Export, Blue & White, Scene, C.1850, 17 In. 150.00
Furniture, Seat, Hall, Pine, 2 Hinged Seat Lids, C.1800, 5 Ft.10 In. 425.00
Furniture, Seat, Wagon, New England, C.1800, Maple & Ash, Turned, 34 1/2 In. 270.00
Furniture, Seat, Wagon, New England, C.1835, Pine & Maple, Scrolled Arms 150.00
Furniture, Seat, Window, George III Style, Mahogany, Cabriole Legs, 39 In. 350.00
Furniture, Secretaire, C.H.& J.F.White, C.1825, Mahogany, Fall Front, 5 Ft. 1800.00
Furniture, Secretaire, Mahogany, Fall Front Drawer, C.1790, 45 In. 450.00
Furniture, Secretary Bookcase, Federal, Inlaid Mahogany, 2 Parts, 8 Ft. 1200.00
Furniture, Secretary Bookcase, Federal, Walnut, 2 Parts, Hinged Flap, 6 Ft. 500.00
Furniture, Secretary Bookcase, Virginia, C.1790, Walnut, Inlaid Eagle, 9 Ft. 4250.00
Furniture, Secretary, N.Y., C.1800, Inlaid Mahogany, Butler's Drawer, 45 In. 600.00
Furniture, Settee, American, C.1850, Rosewood, Cabriole Legs, 5 1/2 Ft., Pair 3000.00
Furniture, Settee, Art Deco, Inscrolled Armrest, C.1930, 7 Ft. 400.00
Furniture, Settee, Art Nouveau, Gilt Wood, Pierced Backrest, C.1895, 5 Ft. 1200.00

Furniture, Settee, Art Nouveau, Stained Oak, 2 Chair Back, C.1900, 4 Ft.	400.00
Furniture, Settee, George III Style, Painted, Serpentine Top Rail, 7 Ft.	425.00
Furniture, Settee, Mahogany, Arched Upholstered Backrest, C.1790, 6 Ft.5 In.	800.00
Furniture, Settee, Mahogany, Art Nouveau	*Illus* 750.00
Furniture, Settee, Mahogany, C.1775, 5 Ft.7 1/4 In.	*Illus* 1500.00
Furniture, Settee, Mahogany, Carved, C.1840, Ormolu Mounts, 4 Ft.8 In.	250.00
Furniture, Settee, Mahogany, Carved, Square Back, C.1815, Green Leather, 6 Ft.	500.00
Furniture, Settee, Massachusetts, C.1825, Mahogany, Carved, Reeded Turnings	575.00
Furniture, Settee, New England, C.1820, Painted, Stenciled, 5 Ft.11 1/2 In.	275.00
Furniture, Settee, Oak, Raked Backrest, Cabriole Legs, Pad Feet, C.1750, 6 Ft.	200.00
Furniture, Settee, Pennsylvania, C.1810, Pine, Painted, Decorated, 7 Ft.	475.00
Furniture, Settee, Pennsylvania, C.1810, Pine, Painted, Green, Decorated, 6 Ft.	300.00
Furniture, Settee, Pennsylvania, C.1810, Pine, Painted, Olive, Decorated, 6 Ft.	650.00
Furniture, Settee, Pennsylvania, C.1815, Curly Maple, Cabriole Legs, 42 In.	800.00
Furniture, Settee, Pennsylvania, Maple & Pine	*Illus* 1300.00
Furniture, Settee, Tub-Shaped Back, Carved Gilt Wood, 4 1/2 Ft., Pair	475.00
Furniture, Shelf, Corner, Victorian, 3 Shelves, Amber Stained Glass	35.00
Furniture, Shelf, Pantry, Child's, Wooden, C.1900, 11 1/2 X 8 1/2 In.	22.00
Furniture, Shelf, Wall, Walnut, 27 X 29 1/2 In., Set Of 3	65.00
Furniture, Sideboard, Boston, C.1810, Mahogany, Carved, Hollow Front, 35 In.	2750.00
Furniture, Sideboard, Federal Style, Mahogany, Inlaid, Frieze Drawers, 40 In.	700.00
Furniture, Sideboard, Federal Style, Mahogany, Inlaid, Serpentine, 40 In.	800.00
Furniture, Sideboard, Federal Style, Mahogany, Inlaid, Serpentine, 41 In.	1300.00
Furniture, Sideboard, Federal, Mahogany, Inlaid, Grass Gallery, 44 3/4 In.	550.00
Furniture, Sideboard, Federal, Mahogany, Inlaid, Serpentine Front, 42 In.	350.00
Furniture, Sideboard, Federal, Mahogany, Inlaid, 5 Frieze Drawers, 42 In.	425.00
Furniture, Sideboard, Haines-Connelly, Phila., C.1790, Mahogany, Inlaid	3600.00
Furniture, Sideboard, Mahogany, Bowfront, Arched Kneehole, C.1790, 37 In.	1100.00
Furniture, Sideboard, Mahogany, Bowfront, Kneehole Front, C.1790, 36 In.	2200.00
Furniture, Sideboard, Mahogany, Inlaid, Serpentine Front, C.1790, 42 In.	2000.00
Furniture, Sideboard, Mahogany, Kneehole Front, Square Legs, C.1790, 36 In.	800.00
Furniture, Sideboard, Mahogany, Marquetry Inlays, Serpentine, C.1790, 36 In.	2000.00
Furniture, Sideboard, Mahogany, Serpentine Front, Square Legs, C.1790, 39 In.	900.00
Furniture, Sideboard, New York, C.1790, Mahogany, Inlaid, 5 Ft. X 43 In.	3000.00
Furniture, Sideboard, New York, C.1840, Mahogany, Carved, Milk Glass Pulls	200.00
Furniture, Sideboard, Oak, 3 Drawer, Pad Feet, Rectangular, C.1790, 31 3/4 In.	950.00
Furniture, Sideboard, Tambour, Mahogany, Inlaid, Ball Feet, C.1810, 43 In.	650.00
Furniture, Sofa, Duncan Phyfe, C.1820, Mahogany, Carved Crest Rail, 7 1/2 Ft.	5750.00
Furniture, Sofa, Federal Style, Mahogany, Carved, Brass Feet, 7 Ft.3 In.	500.00
Furniture, Sofa, Federal Style, Mahogany, Carved, Reeded Crest, 6 Ft.	325.00
Furniture, Sofa, Mahogany, C.1825	*Illus* 725.00
Furniture, Sofa, Mahogany, Camel Back, Blue Silk Damask, C.1790, 7 Ft.	3500.00
Furniture, Sofa, Mahogany, Carved, Camel Back, Crewelwork, C.1760, 5 Ft.2 In.	2600.00
Furniture, Sofa, Mahogany, Carved, Round Crest, Scrolled Arms, 7 Ft.	500.00
Furniture, Sofa, Massachusetts, C.1800, Mahogany, Carved, Square Back, 6 Ft.	1000.00
Furniture, Sofa, New York, C.1825, Carved	*Illus* 650.00
Furniture, Sofa, Philadelphia, C.1790, Mahogany, Carved, Cabriole, 5 Ft.10 In.	2100.00
Furniture, Sofa, Recamier, Mahogany, Carved, Green Striped Silk, C.1825, 6 Ft.	725.00
Furniture, Sofa, Salem Style, Mahogany, Carved, Blue Silk Damask, 6 Ft.	750.00
Furniture, Sofa, William Lescaze, C.1935, Wooden Frame, Silk & Wool, 6 Ft.	80.00
Furniture, Stand, Basin, Federal, Inlaid Mahogany, Corner, Drawer, 37 1/2 In.	375.00
Furniture, Stand, Cherry, Green Paint, Stenciled, 2 Drawer, 29 In.	125.00
Furniture, Stand, Liqueur, George III Style, Mahogany, Pierced Brackets	425.00
Furniture, Stand, Plant, Galle, Marquetry Of Leaves, 2 Tiers, 44 1/2 In.	1750.00
Furniture, Stand, Sewing, Shaker, Drawer, 5 3/4 X 7 X 5 In.	70.00
Furniture, Stand, Sewing, Shaker, 6 1/2 X 6 1/2 X 5 In.	85.00
Furniture, Stand, Sewing, Victorian, Bamboo Legs & Trim, Hinged, 30 In.	35.00
Furniture, Stand, Shaving, Mahogany, Bowfront, Inlaid Drawer, Glass	95.00
Furniture, Stool, Cobbler's, 3 Hickory Legs, 13 X 16 1/2 In.	110.00
Furniture, Stool, George I Style, Walnut, Cabriole Legs, Pad Feet, 15 In.	625.00
Furniture, Stool, Mahogany, Rectangular Upholstered Seat, C.1790, 18 In.	75.00
Furniture, Stool, Milk, Oak, 3 Legs Go Through To Top, 10 1/2 In.	10.00
Furniture, Stool, Milking, 3 Legs	18.00
Furniture, Stool, Pennsylvania, C.1800, Pine, Painted, Decorated, 5 3/4 In.	450.00
Furniture, Stool, Piano, Adjustable, Glass Ball & Claw Feet	43.00

Furniture, Press, Linen,
New Jersey, 1790, Cherry & Pine
(See Page 212)

Furniture, Settee, Mahogany, Art Nouveau
(See Page 213)

Furniture, Settee, Mahogany, C.1775, 5 Ft.7 1/4 In.
(See Page 213)

Furniture, Settee, Pennsylvania, Maple & Pine
(See Page 213)

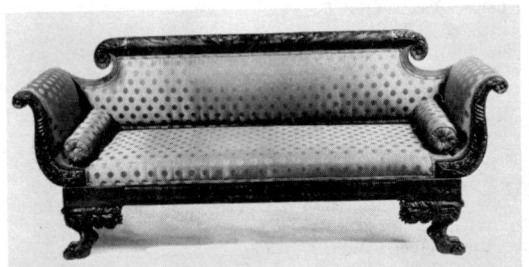

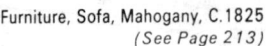

Furniture, Sofa, New York, C.1825, Carved
(See Page 213)

Furniture, Sofa, Mahogany, C.1825
(See Page 213)

Furniture, Stool, Piano, Boston, C.1825, Mahogany, Carved, Backrest, 32 In. 400.00
Furniture, Stool, Piano, Duncan Phyfe, N.Y., C.1825, Carved Mahogany 700.00
Furniture, Stool, Shaker, Mount Lebanon Decal On Leg, Taped Seat, 16 In. 205.00
Furniture, Stool, 3 Legs Come Through Seat, 18 In. 20.00
Furniture, Table A Ecrire, Parquetry, Ormolu Mounted, C.1850, 26 In. 500.00
Furniture, Table De Milieu, Gilt Wood, Carved, Marble Top, C.1890, 30 In. 275.00
Furniture, Table En Chiffonniere, Louis XVI Style, Parquetry, 29 In. 250.00
Furniture, Table En Rognon, Louis XVI Style, Mahogany, Ormolu, C.1890 .... 700.00
Furniture, Table En Rognon, Louis XVI Style, Ormolu, Kidney Top, 32 In. 350.00
Furniture, Table Stool, Massachusetts, C.1730, Maple, Turned, Oblong, 23 In. 750.00
Furniture, Table, Banquet, Rosewood, Carved, 3 Leaves .... *Illus* 4000.00
Furniture, Table, Bedside, Curly Maple & Cherry, Drawer, C.1790, 27 3/4 In. 425.00
Furniture, Table, Bedside, Mahogany, Drawer, Reeded Tapering Legs, C.1810 .... 175.00
Furniture, Table, Bedside, Massachusetts, C.1810, Cherry & Curly Maple 300.00
Furniture, Table, Bedside, New England, C.1800, Maple, Oblong, Drawer, 28 In. 250.00
Furniture, Table, Bedside, Walnut, Inlaid, Cupboard Door, C.1800, 35 In. 175.00
Furniture, Table, Birdcage, Georgian, Mahogany, Piecrust Edge, English, C.1850 .... 325.00
Furniture, Table, Breakfast, Mahogany, Drop Leaf, Ball Feet, C.1800, 28 In. 275.00
Furniture, Table, Breakfast, Mahogany, Drop Leaf, C.1740, 26 1/2 X 36 In. 2000.00
Furniture, Table, Breakfast, Mahogany, Inlaid, Drop Leaf, C.1790, 28 1/2 In. 850.00
Furniture, Table, Breakfast, New England, C.1800, Cherry, Oblong, 28 1/2 In. 275.00
Furniture, Table, Breakfast, New York, C.1820, Mahogany .... *Illus* 150.00
Furniture, Table, Breakfast, Philadelphia, C.1830, Mahogany, Drop Leaf, 29 In. 600.00
Furniture, Table, Card, Boston, C.1810, Mahogany, Inlaid, Serpentine, Hinged 1000.00
Furniture, Table, Card, Chippendale, Mahogany, Hinged Top, 29 1/4 In. 450.00
Furniture, Table, Card, Empire, Mahogany, Lyre Base, Serpentine Top 45.00
Furniture, Table, Card, Federal Style, Mahogany, Inlaid, Serpentine, 31 In. 400.00
Furniture, Table, Card, Federal, Mahogany, Eagle Inlays, Oblong, 29 1/4 In. 9000.00
Furniture, Table, Card, Hepplewhite, Tilt Top, Undecorated 150.00
Furniture, Table, Card, Inlaid Mahogany, Hinged Demilune Top, C.1810, 29 In. 350.00
Furniture, Table, Card, Lyre Base, C.1830 .... 225.00
Furniture, Table, Card, Mahogany, Carved, Hinged Oblong Top, C.1825, 29 In. 275.00
Furniture, Table, Card, Mahogany, Carved, Triple Top, Hinged, C.1760, 29 In. 1200.00
Furniture, Table, Card, Mahogany, Inlaid, Lyre Base, Hinged, C.1810, 28 In. 1200.00
Furniture, Table, Card, Massachusetts, C.1800, Mahogany, Inlaid, Serpentine, ... 1250.00
Furniture, Table, Card, Philadelphia, C.1820, Mahogany, Carved, Hinged, 27 In. 225.00
Furniture, Table, Card, Rigby, Phila., C.1780, Walnut, Hinged, Gate Support 2200.00
Furniture, Table, Center, Art Nouveau, Mahogany, Pierced Scrolls, C.1895 .... 325.00
Furniture, Table, Center, Mahogany, Inlaid, Carved Legs, C.1815, 28 1/2 In. 500.00
Furniture, Table, Center, Mahogany, Round Divided Top, Leaf, C.1790, 29 In. 475.00
Furniture, Table, Cherry, Drop Leaf, Drawer, Ball Feet, C.1815, 11 1/2 In. 275.00
Furniture, Table, Cherry, Tilt Top, Carved Shell Edge, C.1770, 29 In. 1900.00
Furniture, Table, Chester County, Pa., C.1720, Walnut, Gateleg, 29 In. 3400.00
Furniture, Table, Chinese Black Lacquer Top, River Scene In Gold 250.00
Furniture, Table, Chippendale, Mahogany, Tilt Top, Round Dished Top, 28 In. 900.00
Furniture, Table, Coffee, French, C.1930, Fruitwood, Mother-Of-Pearl Tiles 125.00
Furniture, Table, Connecticut, C.1760, Cherry, Tilt Top, Birdcage, 26 1/2 In. 1500.00
Furniture, Table, Console, George I Style, Mahogany, D Top, Pad Feet, 29 In. 125.00
Furniture, Table, Console, George III Style, Satinwood, Marquetry, 29 In. 800.00
Furniture, Table, Console, Graham & Banks, Satinwood, Marquetry, 32 In., Pair 1900.00
Furniture, Table, Console, Ormolu & Painted Metal, Marble Top, C.1890, Pair 1800.00
Furniture, Table, Console, Papier-Mache, Mother-Of-Pearl, D Top, C.1850, Pair 800.00
Furniture, Table, Console, Steel & Ormolu, Marble Top, C.1890, 31 In. 1400.00
Furniture, Table, Corner, Rounded Top, Shelf, Painted, 22 X 22 X 30 In. 25.00
Furniture, Table, Cricket, George II, Oak, Round, Platform Shelf, 30 In. 125.00
Furniture, Table, Dining, Carved Mahogany, Arched Legs, C.1840, 29 1/2 In. 150.00
Furniture, Table, Dining, Connecticut, C.1740, Cherry, Drop Leaf, 27 1/2 In. 1600.00
Furniture, Table, Dining, Faded Rosewood, Stepped Plinths, C.1930, 28 In. 300.00
Furniture, Table, Dining, Federal Style, Mahogany, 2 Part, Carved, 30 In. 300.00
Furniture, Table, Dining, Federal, Mahogany, Carved, 3 Pedestal, 29 In. 2000.00
Furniture, Table, Dining, Federal, Mahogany, 3 Part, Brass Feet, 30 In. 550.00
Furniture, Table, Dining, Federal, Mahogany, 3 Part, D Shaped Ends, 29 In. 1500.00
Furniture, Table, Dining, Federal, Mahogany, 3 Part, Molded Apron, 6 Ft. 550.00
Furniture, Table, Dining, George III, Mahogany, 2 Pedestal, 28 In. 1300.00
Furniture, Table, Dining, Mahogany, Carved, 4 Pedestal, C.1810, 14 Ft. 2700.00

Furniture, Table, Dining, Mahogany, 3 Part

Furniture, Table, Globe,
Boston, 1844

Furniture, Table, Banquet, Rosewood, Carved, 3 Leaves
(See Page 215)

Furniture, Table, Breakfast, New York,
C.1820, Mahogany
(See Page 215)

Furniture, Table, Dining, Mahogany, Swivel Top, 2 Part, C.1820, 8 Ft.1 In.	1050.00
Furniture, Table, Dining, Mahogany, 3 Part .... *Illus*	1000.00
Furniture, Table, Dining, New England, C.1820, Cherry, Drop Leaf, 29 3/4 In.	300.00
Furniture, Table, Dining, Philadelphia, C.1750, Walnut, Drop Leaf, 29 In.	2900.00
Furniture, Table, Dining, Philadelphia, C.1760, Walnut, Carved, Drop Leaf	1500.00
Furniture, Table, Dining, Victorian, Walnut, Drop Leaf, Oval, 39 In.	69.00
Furniture, Table, Dining, Virginia, C.1790, Walnut, Inlaid, 3 Part, 29 1/2 In.	2200.00
Furniture, Table, Dining, Virginia, C.1800, Walnut, Drop Leaf, 27 1/2 In.	475.00
Furniture, Table, Dining, Virginia, C.1800, Walnut, Drop Leaf, 29 In.	600.00
Furniture, Table, Dressing, Federal, Inlaid Mahogany, Mirror, 4 Ft.5 1/4 In.	100.00
Furniture, Table, Dressing, Galle, Marquetry, Hinged Top, Floral, C.1900	450.00
Furniture, Table, Dressing, Marquetry, Galle Style, Hinged Top, Floral, C.1900	400.00
Furniture, Table, Dressing, Oak, 2 Drawers In Frieze, Pad Feet, C.1720, 28 In.	400.00
Furniture, Table, Drop Leaf, Queen Anne, Fruitwood, 47 1/2 In.	1200.00
Furniture, Table, Galle, Inlaid Wooded Scene, Art Nouveau Legs, Single Tier	395.00
Furniture, Table, Game, Dutch, C.1820, Rosewood, Parquetry, Drop Leaf, 29 In.	1900.00
Furniture, Table, Game, George II, Mahogany, Carved Knees, Oblong, 29 In.	900.00
Furniture, Table, Game, George III, Mahogany, Hinged Swivel Top, 32 In.	150.00
Furniture, Table, Game, Mahogany, Folding Swivel Top, Lion's Paw Feet, C.1890	100.00
Furniture, Table, Game, Mahogany, Hinged Top, Frieze Drawer, C.1790, 29 In.	250.00
Furniture, Table, Game, Marquetry, Hinged Swivel Top, C.1890, 31 1/2 In.	650.00
Furniture, Table, Game, Moroccan, Ivory, Mother-Of-Pearl, Parquetry, 29 In.	600.00
Furniture, Table, Game, Queen Anne, Tongue Carved Knees, American	975.00
Furniture, Table, Game, Rosewood, Hinged Swivel Top, C.1820, 28 3/4 In.	225.00
Furniture, Table, Game, Satinwood, Folding D Top, Purple Wood Banding, C.1790	1300.00
Furniture, Table, Game, Satinwood, Mahogany Inlay, D Top, C.1790, 37 In.	475.00
Furniture, Table, Game, Satinwood, Marquetry, Hinged D Top, C.1790, 42 In.	650.00
Furniture, Table, George II, Mahogany, Gateleg, Pad Feet, Oblong, 27 In.	275.00
Furniture, Table, Globe, Boston, 1844 .... *Illus*	425.00

Furniture, Table,
Papier-Mache, 26 1/2 In.
(See Page 218)

Furniture, Table,
Mahogany, Tripod,
C.1775, 29 In.

Furniture, Table, Pembroke,
New England, 1825, Cherry
(See Page 218)

Furniture, Table, Rhode Island,
C.1740, Drop Leaf, 28 In.
(See Page 218)

Furniture, Table, Hunt, Mahogany, Demilune, Removable Center, C.1825, 29 In.	1500.00
Furniture, Table, Hunt, Virginia, C.1770, Walnut, 2 Drawers, 4 Ft.10 1/2 In.	6000.00
Furniture, Table, Hutch, Chippendale, Pine & Maple, 5 Feet	395.00
Furniture, Table, Library, Mahogany, Cupboard Pedestal, Leather Top, C.1790	1700.00
Furniture, Table, Library, Mahogany, Lions' Heads & Claw Feet, 2 Drawer	950.00
Furniture, Table, Library, Oak, With Shelf, 23 X 23 X 23 In.	45.00
Furniture, Table, Library, Pennsylvania, C.1720, Walnut, Turned, Drawer, 30 In.	2700.00
Furniture, Table, Mahogany, Drop Leaf, Drawer, Spiral Legs, C.1825, 29 In.	225.00
Furniture, Table, Mahogany, Gateleg, Frieze Drawer, Pad Feet, C.1720, 29 In.	325.00
Furniture, Table, Mahogany, Tilt Top, Birdcage, Carved, Round, C.1750, 28 In.	350.00
Furniture, Table, Mahogany, Tilt Top, Tripod, Pierced Gallery, C.1790, 28 In.	900.00
Furniture, Table, Mahogany, Tripod, C.1775, 29 In.	*Illus* 550.00
Furniture, Table, Majorelle, Marquetry, Mahogany, 2 Tier, C.1900, 31 3/4 In.	450.00
Furniture, Table, Majorelle, 2 Tier, Marquetry, Bronze Handles, 31 In.	1000.00
Furniture, Table, Marble Specimens Top, Carved Base, 30 In.	1100.00
Furniture, Table, Massachusetts, C.1720, Maple & Cherry, Gateleg, Drawers	800.00
Furniture, Table, New England, C.1750, Maple, Drop Leaf, Cabriole Legs, 27 In.	1600.00
Furniture, Table, New England, C.1800, Pine, Trestle, 29 In.	200.00
Furniture, Table, New England, C.1820, Mahogany, Drop Leaf, Oblong, 29 1/4 In.	150.00
Furniture, Table, Occasional, Louis XV Style, Ormolu Mounted, 24 3/4 In.	200.00
Furniture, Table, Occasional, Louis XVI Style, Marble Chessboard Top	200.00
Furniture, Table, Occasional, Mahogany, Carved, Hinged Top, C.1810, 31 3/4 In.	400.00
Furniture, Table, Occasional, Marquetry, Galle Style, Floral, C.1890, 29 In.	170.00

Furniture, Table, Occasional, Massachusetts, C.1820, Mahogany & Maple 600.00
Furniture, Table, Occasional, N.E., C.1800, Curly Maple, Square, Shelf, 30 In. 500.00
Furniture, Table, Occasional, New York, C.1810, Cherry, Drop Leaf, 27 In. 325.00
Furniture, Table, Occasional, Papier-Mache, Mother-Of-Pearl, C.1850, 30 In. 250.00
Furniture, Table, Occasional, Pine, Square Top, C.1800, 25 In. 225.00
Furniture, Table, Papier-Mache, 26 1/2 In. .... *Illus* 400.00
Furniture, Table, Parcel Gilt, Satinwood Top, Mahogany, Inlaid, C.1790, 30 In. 600.00
Furniture, Table, Pembroke, Baltimore, C.1790, Mahogany, Inlaid, Oval, 29 In. 2200.00
Furniture, Table, Pembroke, Connecticut, C.1790, Cherry, Oblong, 28 In. 150.00
Furniture, Table, Pembroke, Federal, Inlaid Mahogany, Oblong, D Ends, 28 In. 850.00
Furniture, Table, Pembroke, Mahogany, D Drop Leaves, C.1790, 28 In. 150.00
Furniture, Table, Pembroke, Mahogany, Drop Leaf, Drawer, C.1790, 28 1/2 In. 600.00
Furniture, Table, Pembroke, Mahogany, Frieze Drawer, Serpentine Ends, C.1790 .... 200.00
Furniture, Table, Pembroke, N.E., C.1825, Cherry, Oblong, Drop Leaf, 28 1/2 In. 200.00
Furniture, Table, Pembroke, New England, 1825, Cherry .... *Illus* 225.00
Furniture, Table, Pembroke, Walnut, Oval Top, Drop Leaf, C.1790, 28 In. 400.00
Furniture, Table, Pier, Mahogany, Inlaid, Marble Top, Gilt Bronze, C.1810 .... 600.00
Furniture, Table, Pier, New York, C.1810, Painted, Stenciled, Marble Top 8500.00
Furniture, Table, Pier, New York, C.1820, Mahogany, Inlaid, Stenciled, 37 In. 1300.00
Furniture, Table, Pine, Trestle, Breadboard Ends, 29 In. 475.00
Furniture, Table, Pool, Brunswick Amaranth, Inlaid Woods, C.1880 .... 5000.00
Furniture, Table, Regency Style, Mahogany, Simulated Bamboo, Nest Of 3 .... 159.00
Furniture, Table, Rent, Mahogany, Revolving Top, 8 Drawers, C.1850, 6 Ft. 1600.00
Furniture, Table, Rhode Island, C.1740, Drop Leaf, 28 In. .... *Illus* 900.00
Furniture, Table, Rosewood, Simulated Bamboo Supports, C.1820, Nest Of 4 .... 250.00
Furniture, Table, Sawbuck, Pine, New York State, C.1750, 48 1/2 X 28 1/2 In. 825.00
Furniture, Table, Serving, Galle, Floral Design, Handles, Oval, 27 X 26 In. 750.00
Furniture, Table, Shaker, Mount Lebanon, 30 1/2 X 44 X 32 In. 380.00
Furniture, Table, Shaker, 2 Drawers 425.00
Furniture, Table, Sheraton, Inlaid Mahogany, Nest Of 3 .... 295.00
Furniture, Table, Side, Charles II, Oak, Frieze Drawer, Rectangular, 26 In. 150.00
Furniture, Table, Side, Galle, Marquetry, Daffodils, C.1900, 29 1/2 In. 350.00
Furniture, Table, Side, Galle, Marquetry, Shield-Shaped Top, C.1900, 16 In. 175.00
Furniture, Table, Side, George I, Walnut, Frieze Drawer, Oblong, 27 1/2 In. 650.00
Furniture, Table, Side, George II, Mahogany, Carved Floral & Ribbon, 36 In. 650.00
Furniture, Table, Side, George II, Mahogany, Carved Knees, Pad Feet, 30 In. 575.00
Furniture, Table, Side, Oak, Frieze Drawer, Square Tapered Legs, C.1790, 27 In 150.00
Furniture, Table, Side, Oak, 2 Drawers Above Apron, C.1690, 28 1/4 In. 300.00
Furniture, Table, Side, Rosewood & Ebonized Wood, 2 Stools Inside, C.1932 .... 200.00
Furniture, Table, Silver, Mahogany, Pierced Gallery & Legs, C.1790, 28 In. 2000.00
Furniture, Table, Slate Picture Frame Top, Tripod 150.00
Furniture, Table, Sofa, Mahogany, Drop Leaves, Frieze Drawers, C.1830, 29 In. 150.00
Furniture, Table, Sofa, Mahogany, Inlaid, Oblong Top, Reeded Edge, 28 In. 225.00
Furniture, Table, Sofa, Mahogany, Satinwood Inlay, Drop Leaf, C.1820, 28 In. 675.00
Furniture, Table, Sofa, Rosewood, Gilt Metal Mounts, Drop Leaf, C.1820, 29 In. 550.00
Furniture, Table, Tavern, Pennsylvania, C.1720, Curly Walnut, 3 Drawer, 29 In. 5000.00
Furniture, Table, Tavern, Pennsylvania, C.1750, Pine & Curly Walnut, 26 In. 1100.00
Furniture, Table, Tea, Conn., C.1780, Cherry, Square, Tripod, 26 In. 800.00
Furniture, Table, Tea, Conn., C.1780, Maple, Tilt Top, Tripod, 27 1/4 In. 600.00
Furniture, Table, Tea, Galle, 2 Tier, Iris Inlay, 29 1/2 In. 850.00
Furniture, Table, Tea, Maple, Porringer Top, Painted, Gilding, C.1750, 26 In. 3700.00
Furniture, Table, Tea, Massachusetts, C.1720, Lignum Vitae, Drop Leaf, Oval 5500.00
Furniture, Table, Tea, Massachusetts, C.1730, Walnut, Drop Leaf, Oval 5800.00
Furniture, Table, Tea, Massachusetts, C.1735, Walnut, Drop Leaf, Oval, Pad Feet 8000.00
Furniture, Table, Tea, Queen Anne, Curly Maple, Serpentine Top, 29 In. 400.00
Furniture, Table, Tea, Virginia, C.1750, Walnut, Tray Top, 26 In. 3100.00
Furniture, Table, Tea, Virginia, C.1780, Pine & Cherry, Tilt Top, 27 1/4 In. 425.00
Furniture, Table, Tilt Top, Dish Top, Pedestal Vase, Pad Feet, R.I., 1750 .... 1500.00
Furniture, Table, Tortoiseshell & Porcelain Plaques Top, C.1890, 18 In. 1300.00
Furniture, Table, Urn, George III, Mahogany, Brass Gallery, 26 In., Pair 375.00
Furniture, Table, Vitrine, George III Style, Mahogany, Hinged Case, 33 In. 700.00
Furniture, Table, William & Mary, Pine, Gateleg, Frieze Drawer, 28 1/4 In. 350.00
Furniture, Table, Windsor, New England, C.1800, Pine & Turned Maple, Drawer 325.00
Furniture, Table, Work, Boston, C.1790, Burl Walnut & Bird's-Eye Maple 850.00
Furniture, Table, Work, Federal, C.1810, Mahogany, Astragal Ends, 45 1/2 In. 1700.00
Furniture, Table, Work, George III, Mahogany, Hinged Octagonal Top, 30 In. 125.00

Furniture, Table, Work, Mahogany & Rosewood, Hinged Octagonal Top, C.1810	300.00
Furniture, Table, Work, Massachusetts, C.1780, Mahogany, 2 Drawers, 30 In.	1400.00
Furniture, Table, Work, Massachusetts, C.1800, Mahogany, Inlaid, 28 3/4 In.	500.00
Furniture, Table, Work, Massachusette, C.1810, Mahogany, Inlaid, Square, Drawer	700.00
Furniture, Table, Work, Massachusetts, C.1815, Maple & Inlaid Mahogany	200.00
Furniture, Table, Work, Phila., C.1810, Mahogany & Curly Maple, 29 3/4 In.	850.00
Furniture, Table, Work, Sheraton, Tiger Maple, 1 Drawer	65.00
Furniture, Table, Writing, George II, Lacquer, Black, Chinoiserie, 31 In.	1300.00
Furniture, Table, Writing, George III, Mahogany, Pedestal, Leather, 31 In.	500.00
Furniture, Table, Writing, Gold Lacquer, Silver Mounted, C.1850, 24 In.	1000.00
Furniture, Table, Writing, Mahogany, Frieze Drawer, Tapered Legs, C.1790, Pair	1200.00
Furniture, Table, Writing, Mahogany, Hinged Checkerboard Top, C.1790, 32 In.	800.00
Furniture, Table, Writing, Mahogany, Pedestal, Leather Top, C.1790, 31 In.	1600.00
Furniture, Table, Writing, Regency Style, Mahogany, Pedestal, 4 X 7 In.	120.00
Furniture, Tea Caddy, Mahogany, Hinged, Cut Glass Bowl Center, C.1820	300.00
Furniture, Tea Caddy, Quillwork, Silver Pull, Octagonal, C.1790, 5 3/8 In.	235.00
Furniture, Tea Caddy, Rosewood, Brass Stringing, Hinged, C.1820, 6 3/4 In.	80.00
Furniture, Tea Caddy, Rosewood, Hinged Stepped Top, Mushroom Finial, C.1820	90.00
Furniture, Tea Cart, Walnut, Wood & Glass Tray Top, C.1900	150.00
Furniture, Torchere, James Wyatt, Parcel Gilt & Paint, C.1790, 5 Ft., Pair	1600.00
Furniture, Tray, Butler's, Mahogany, Pierced Trellis Gallery, C.1790, 24 In.	150.00
Furniture, Tray, Butler's, Regency Style, Mahogany, 4 Hinged Flaps, 23 In.	225.00
Furniture, Urn, Knife, Mahogany, Inlaid Boxwood & Ebony, C.1790, 27 In., Pair	600.00
Furniture, Vitrine, Louis XV-XVI Style, Rosewood, Marble Top, 44 In.	450.00
Furniture, Vitrine, Louis XVI Style, Gilt Metal Gallery, 4 Ft.6 1/2 In.	950.00
Furniture, Washstand & Desk, Walnut, Built-In Bowl, Compartments, Doors	850.00
Furniture, Washstand, George III Style, Mahogany, Corner, 2 Doors, 33 In.	125.00
Furniture, Washstand, George III, Mahogany, Center Drawer, 34 In.	100.00
Furniture, Washstand, Shaker, Signed Abil Hull	350.00
Furniture, Whatnot, Mahogany, 4 Shelves, 2 Drawers At Base, C.1790, 43 In.	325.00
G.Argy-Rousseau, Bowl, Pate De Verre, Grapevine & Leaf On Gray, 3 1/2 In.	325.00
G.Argy-Rousseau, Box, Pate De Verre, Violets, Round, 3 X 3 In.	950.00
G.Argy-Rousseau, Lamp Base, Pate De Verre, Gray & Lilac, C.1920, 21 In.	300.00
G.Argy-Rousseau, Lamp, Pate De Verre & Wrought Iron, Blue, C.1920, 7 In.	660.00
G.Argy-Rousseau, Lamp, Pate De Verre & Wrought Iron, Yellow, 1925, 6 In.	400.00
G.Argy-Rousseau, Tray, Pate De Cristal, Yellow, Jaguar, Cobra, C.1930, 7 In.	800.00

galle Galle glass was made by the Galle Factory founded by Emile Galle of France. The firm made cameo glass, furniture, and other Art Nouveau items, including some pottery, from 1879 to 1905.

Galle Pottery, Candlestick, Heraldic Lion & Castle, C.1879, 15 1/2 In., Pair	100.00
Galle Pottery, Inkstand, Seashell Covers, Harbor Scene, 6 1/2 X 15 In.	475.00
Galle Pottery, Jardiniere, Buff, Grasshoppers & Beetles, C.1900, 10 In.	150.00
Galle Pottery, Vase, Chrysanthemums, C.1895, 16 In. .... Illus	475.00
Galle, Atomizer, Perfume, Landscape, Purple, Brown, Green, & White	450.00
Galle, Atomizer, Red Poppies On Yellow, Metal Mounts, Ovoid, 8 3/4 In.	200.00
Galle, Bottle, Scent, Wick Assembly, Brass Filigree Top, Amber, Green, 8 In.	450.00
Galle, Bowl, Boat Shape, Purple & Lavender Flowers, Frosted, 11 X 4 In.	290.00
Galle, Bowl, Shell Finial, Faience, Shell Shape, Painted Floral, C.1880, 6 In.	90.00
Galle, Box, Powder, Covered, Blue, Violet, Pink, & Green Floral, 5 In.	450.00
Galle, Box, Powder, Oval, Covered, Blue, Pink, Violet, Green On White, 5 In.	595.00
Galle, Decanter, Lavender, Blown-Out Leaves, 10 In. .... Illus	675.00
Galle, Dish, Candy, Triangular, Grays, Cameo, Signed, 5 X 1 1/2 In.	129.00
Galle, Liqueur Set, Amber, Rope Band Neck & Handle, Enameled, 6 Piece	750.00
Galle, Mug, Enameled Bugs & Flora, Intaglio Stars, Applied Handle	395.00
Galle, Night-Light, 3 Butterflies Carved On Top, Metal Base, 4 1/2 In.	225.00
Galle, Pitcher, Water, Pink & Lavender Enamel Floral On Amber, Signed	350.00
Galle, Rose Bowl, Pale Blue Floral On Tangerine & Camphor Ground, 7 In.	495.00
Galle, Shade, Caramel, Columbine Flowers, 5 In.	230.00
Galle, Shot Glass, Ribbed, Enameled, Signed E.Galle	50.00
Galle, Toothpick, White Enamel Cross Of Lorraine & Floral Spray, 2 In.High	200.00
Galle, Tray, Water, Pink & Lavender Enamel Floral On Amber, Signed	95.00
Galle, Tray, Wooden, People In Rowboat On Water, Birds, 16 X 12 In.	250.00
Galle, Tumbler, Inverted Thumbprint, Swirl, Vaseline Ground, Leaves, 4 In.	115.00
Galle, Tumbler, Oval Shape, Acid Cutback, Purple To Clear Frosted, Cameo	285.00
Galle, Tumbler, Pink & Lavender Enamel Floral On Amber, Signed	225.00

Galle, Vase, Art Nouveau Design In Violet & Blue, Pedestal, 9 In.High	575.00
Galle, Vase, Banjo, Flared Base, Orange & Yellow, 4 3/4 In.	245.00
Galle, Vase, Banjo, White, Pink, & Brown, 6 3/4 In.	365.00
Galle, Vase, Berry & Leaf On Vine, Lemon Yellow & Deep Pink, 3 1/2 In.	210.00
Galle, Vase, Brown & Ocher Landscape On Mustard Gray, C.1900, 16 3/4 In.	475.00
Galle, Vase, Brown Flowers & Leaves On Gray Ground, 5 In.High	250.00
Galle, Vase, Brown Over Yellow, 11 In.	275.00
Galle, Vase, Brown To Gold Pine Branches & Cones On Frosted, 6 In.	450.00
Galle, Vase, Brown, Green, & Pink, Seed Pods & Vines, Signed, 9 1/2 In.	375.00
Galle, Vase, Bud, Blossoms On Gray Purple Peach, C.1900, 11 3/4 In.	275.00
Galle, Vase, Bud, Lilacs On Gray, Flattened Spherical, C.1900, 6 1/2 In.	200.00
Galle, Vase, Bud, 5 Colors, 4 1/2 In.	268.00
Galle, Vase, Bulbous Top, Fern & Parsley In Brown, Tan, & Camphor, 11 In.	480.00
Galle, Vase, Bulbous, Purple & Pink Floral On Gold, 8 X 25 In.	685.00
Galle, Vase, Bullet Shape, Red Cherries On Frosted To Orange, 7 In.	270.00
Galle, Vase, Cabinet, Purple Berries On Lavender, 3 In.High	160.00
Galle, Vase, Cameo, Signed, 10 1/2 X 4 In.	395.00
Galle, Vase, Camphor, Green Ivy & Fern, 5 1/2 In.	235.00
Galle, Vase, Chartreuse & Moss Green, Pink On Frosted, 9 In.	375.00
Galle, Vase, Chartreuse & Moss Green, Pink On Frosted, 15 In.	495.00
Galle, Vase, Enamel Dragon, Applied Amethyst Teardrops, C.1890, 4 3/4 In.	350.00
Galle, Vase, Enameled Lilylike Floral On Translucent Amber, 13 1/2 In.	325.00
Galle, Vase, Floral, Pink, Blue, & Green, 21 In.High	595.00
Galle, Vase, Gray, Salmon Orange Peonies, C.1900, 4 In.	200.00
Galle, Vase, Green Floral & Berries On Pink & Green, 3 7/8 In.	195.00
Galle, Vase, Green Leaf & Berries On Frosted White, Green Base, 3 In.	200.00
Galle, Vase, Green Leaves & Vines On Frosted, 2 3/4 X 2 In.	85.00
Galle, Vase, Green, Purple, Pink & White Floral Design, 17 In.High	395.00
Galle, Vase, Heart Shape, Purple Floral, 3 Color, Signed, 13 In.	490.00
Galle, Vase, Intaglio Fronds & Pods On Mottled Green Clear, C.1890, 4 In.	350.00
Galle, Vase, Inverted Bell Shape, 4 To 5 Colors, 4 1/2 In.	248.00
Galle, Vase, Leaves & Berries, 5 Colors, 4 Cuttings, 3 1/2 In.	350.00
Galle, Vase, Louchet Silver Gilt Mounts, Cherries On Green, C.1895, 10 In.	1200.00
Galle, Vase, Maroon Over Blue, 6 In.	650.00
Galle, Vase, Mold Blown, Plums, C.1895, 15 1/2 In. .... *Illus*	3100.00
Galle, Vase, Orange Flower & Leaf On Frosted Yellow, 4 In.	200.00
Galle, Vase, Orange Red Blossoms On Mustard, C.1900, 23 3/4 In.	900.00

Galle, Decanter, Lavender, Blown-Out Leaves, 10 In.
(See Page 219)

Galle Pottery, Vase,
Chrysanthemums, C.1895, 16 In.
(See Page 219)

Galle, Vase, Mold Blown,
Plums, C.1895, 15 1/2 In.

Galle, Vase, Orchid Leaves & Vines On Frosted & Violet, 4 In.	200.00
Galle, Vase, Pale Salmon To Gray, Lavender & Green Floral, C.1900, 18 In.	300.00
Galle, Vase, Pale Yellow To Mauve, Floral & Leaf, Satin Finish, C.1904, 4 In.	210.00
Galle, Vase, Pansies, 3 Footed, Signed E.Galle, Nancy, 3 3/4 In.	175.00
Galle, Vase, Pink Berry On Vine & Leaf On Frosted Yellow, 3 1/2 In.	210.00
Galle, Vase, Purple Brown Floral With Pink & Green On Frosted, 11 In.	325.00
Galle, Vase, Purple Enamel On Deep Amber, 7 1/2 In.	495.00
Galle, Vase, Purple Floral & Leaves On White, Pink, & Lavender, 15 In.	350.00
Galle, Vase, Purple Florals, 5 1/4 X 2 1/4 In.	200.00
Galle, Vase, Purple Iris On Frosted, Wheel Cut Floral, 8 In.	350.00
Galle, Vase, Purple Orchids & Grasses On Yellow, C.1900, 11 3/4 In.	375.00
Galle, Vase, Purple Wine Lilies & Leaves On Frosted, 3 In.	195.00
Galle, Vase, Red Roses On Yellow, Signed, 11 In.	675.00
Galle, Vase, Red, Landscape, Trees On Lake, Pedestal, 16 In.High	790.00
Galle, Vase, Reds & Yellows, Cameo, Signed, 10 In.	475.00
Galle, Vase, Scenic, Banjo Shape, Trees, Water, Birds, Greens & Brown, 7 In.	235.00
Galle, Vase, Spanish Oak Leaves & Acorns, 5 Colors, 23 In.	950.00
Galle, Vase, Squat, Olive Green Leaves, Berries, & Vines On Frosted, 4 In.	195.00
Galle, Vase, Stick, Nasturtiums On Cinnamon, Signed, 23 1/2 In.	450.00
Galle, Vase, Stick, White Frosted, Floral, 2 Shades Of Green & Pink, 13 In.	395.00
Galle, Vase, Tangerine Flower On Frosted, 12 In.	395.00
Galle, Vase, Three Acid Cuttings, 5 3/4 In.	300.00
Galle, Vase, Tree Scene, Brown On Orange Ground, 9 1/2 In.High	495.00
Galle, Vase, Trefoil Lip, Starlike Floral On Green & Pink, 15 In.	350.00
Galle, Vase, Trumpet, Brown Iris & Leaves On Mustard, C.1900, 5 1/8 In.	175.00
Galle, Vase, Urn Shape, Green Thistles On Lighter Green, Cameo, 3 In.	185.00
Galle, Vase, Violets On Yellow To Frosted, 3 1/2 In.	235.00
Galle, Vase, Wheel Cut Blue & Purple Floral, 4 Layers, 10 In.	695.00
Galle, Vase, White Ground, Sky Blue Flowers, Dark Centers, 10 In.High	795.00
Galle, Vase, 2 Color, Wheel Cutting & Polishing, 4 In.	290.00
Galle, Vase, 2 Shades Of Red Flowers On Yellow, Cameo, 9 In.	395.00
Galle, Vase, 3 Color, Cut Floral & Leaves, 3 1/2 In.	300.00
Galle, Vase, 4 Layer, 3 Color, Yellow On Clear Base, Floral, 8 In.	750.00
Galle, Water Set, Amber Ground, Pink & Lavender Enamel Flowers, 5 Piece	1195.00
Game Plate, Birds In Meadow, Flower Border, P.K, Silesia, 8 1/2 In.	26.50
Game, see also Disneyana, Game, Hopalong Cassidy, Game, Lindbergh, Game, Lone Ranger, Game, Orphan Annie, Game, Popeye, Game	
Game, Airways, Marble, Metal, Lindstron Tool & Toy Co.	8.50
Game, Bagley's, Tin	65.00
Game, Beatles, Flip Your Wig	10.00
Game, Bezique, Card Game, 1917, Spin Boards, Instructions	9.00
Game, Bingo, Child's, Milton Bradley, C.1930, Original Box	5.00
Game, Bingo, Dick Tracy, C.1935, 5 X 3 1/2 In.	7.50
Game, Boy Scouts, Milton Bradley, C.1910	18.00
Game, Checkers, Occupied Japan, Wooden, In Box	1.00
Game, Chess Set, see also Wedgwood, Chess Set	
Game, Chess Set, Lowe, 1959	9.50
Game, Chinese Checkers, Wooden Frame, Akro Agate Marbles	12.00
Game, Ching Gond, Oriental Checkers, Wooden Board & Checkers	14.00
Game, Cribbage Board, Handmade, Wooden, C.1910, 12 X 3 5/8 In.	4.00
Game, Cribbage Board, Victorian, Brass, Footed	16.50
Game, Cribbage Board, Walnut, Brass Inlay & Pegs	15.00
Game, Dominoes, Bone & Ebony, Set Of 28	25.00
Game, Dominoes, Carved Bone, 2 X 3/4 In. Pieces	1.50
Game, Dominoes, Checkers, & Dice, Ivory & Wood, Checkerboard On Box, 6 In.	25.00
Game, Dominoes, Checkers, & Dice, Ivory & Wood, Checkerboard On Box, 8 In.	35.00
Game, Dominoes, Checkers, & Dice, Ivory, Checkerboard On Box, 2 X 2 X 1/2 In.	50.00
Game, Dominoes, Dark Wood & Ivory, Wooden Box With Sliding Cover	65.00
Game, Dominoes, Embossed Railroad Engine, Wooden Box	10.00
Game, Dominoes, Embossed Woolworth Building	8.00
Game, Dominoes, Ivory Covered Wood, Doll Size, Maple Box	15.00
Game, Dominoes, Ivory, Wood Box, Slide Cover, 2 X 2 1/2 In.	50.00
Game, Dominoes, Teak & Ivory, Brass Rivets, Set Of 28 In Box	25.00
Game, Fish Pond, Patent 1890	12.00
Game, Jack Straws, Parker Bros., C.1900	5.00

Game, Little Mother Goose	5.95
Game, Lotto, 1895	15.00
Game, Mah-Jongg Set, Bone, Bamboo Pieces, Oak Box	35.00
Game, Mah-Jongg Set, Ivory & Bamboo, 1920s, Case	30.00
Game, Mah-Jongg, 1923, Wood Sticks, Tiles, Dice	35.00
Game, Modern Authors, Milton Bradley, C.1900	5.00
Game, Peg, Wooden, Handmade, 1 Piece, 8 Pegs, 5 1/2 In. Square	14.00
Game, Peppy Parlor Pranks, Punchboard	6.00
Game, Pilgrim's Progress, McLoughlin, 1875	35.00
Game, Pin The Tail On Buster Brown, Original Box	50.00
Game, Pit Game, Parker Bros.	6.00 To 10.00
Game, Puzzle, see also Store, Puzzle	
Game, Punchboard, Uncle Sam, World War II, 5 Cents	35.00
Game, Puzzle, Bringing Up Father, Saalfield, 1932, 8 X 10 In. Box	7.50
Game, Puzzle, Jigsaw, Lamb, Wooden, 11 In.	5.00
Game, Puzzle, Jigsaw, Rooster, Wooden, 11 In.	5.00
Game, Puzzle, Jigsaw, Woodburner Locomotive, McLoughlin Bros., C.1880	35.00
Game, Puzzle, Li'l Abner & Daisy Mae, Pair	5.00
Game, Puzzle, Picture, Ed Wynn Fire Alarm, No.2	8.00
Game, Seal Hunting In Alaska, Chaffee & Selchow, 1898, 22 X 13 In.	25.00
Game, Siege, Milton Bradley, C.1910	28.00
Game, Sliced Nations, Selchow & Righter, Copyright 1881	7.00
Game, Solider Nine Pins, Parker Bros.	6.00
Game, Solitaire, Victorian, Mahogany Board & Box, Marbles, 7 In.	45.00
Game, Spoof, Milton Bradley	6.00
Game, The Game Of Letters, McLoughlin Bros., C.1890	15.00
Game, The Peppy Card Game, 1926, Gene Byrnes, Wooden Jelly Beans	18.50
Game, Tiddley Winks, Martin	8.00
Game, Tiddley Winks, Milton Bradley, No.4517	5.50
Game, Touring, Automobile, Card, Parker Bros., 1926	11.00
Game, Tru Scale, Wood Candlepins, 9 Steel Balls, Keystone	18.00
Game, Winko, Baseball, Milton Bradley, 1945, Boxed	6.00
Game, Zorro Bean Bag Dart, 1950s	6.50

*The Gardner porcelain works was founded in Verbilki, outside Moscow, by
the English-born Francis Gardner in 1766. Gardner made porcelain
tablewares, figurines, and faience.*

Gardner, Bowl, Basket Form, Order Of St.George, Reticulated, C.1790, 13 In.	700.00
Gardner, Bowl, Basket Shape, Order Of St.George, Reticulated, C.1790, 14 In.	800.00
Gardner, Bowl, Floral On White, Gold Design Inside, C.1860, 7 In.	62.50
Gardner, Bowl, Flying Birds & Magenta Floral On White, 9 In.	125.00
Gardner, Bowl, Green & Red Floral On Green, C.1860, 6 1/2 In.	60.00
Gardner, Bowl, Marigold Luster, Red, Yellow, & Blue Floral, C.1860, 5 In.	60.00
Gardner, Charger, Floral On White Center, Blue Glaze, 13 1/2 In.	175.00
Gardner, Cup, Ice, Domed Cover, Order Of St.Alexander Nevski, C.1790	425.00
Gardner, Cup, Ice, Domed Cover, Order Of St.Vladimir, C.1790, Scroll Handle	425.00
Gardner, Cup, Ice, Order Of St.George, C Scroll Branch Handle, C.1790	90.00
Gardner, Dish, Basket Shape, Order Of St.Andrew, Reticulated, C.1790, 13 In.	1400.00
Gardner, Dish, Leaf Shape, Order Of St.Alexander Nevski, C.1790, 10 1/8 In.	800.00
Gardner, Dish, Leaf Shape, Order Of St.Alexander Nevski, C.1790, 11 1/2 In.	750.00
Gardner, Dish, Leaf Shape, Order Of St.George, , Branch Handle, C.1790, 10 In.	1000.00
Gardner, Dish, Leaf Shape, Order Of St.George, Handle, Oval, C.1790, 9 1/8 In.	950.00
Gardner, Dish, Leaf Shape, Order Of St.George, Pierced, Handle, C.1790, 10 In.	800.00
Gardner, Dish, Leaf Shape, Order Of St.Vladimir, C.1790, 11 1/4 In.	800.00
Gardner, Dish, Leaf Shape, Order Of St.Vladimir, C.1790, 11 1/2 In.	700.00
Gardner, Dish, Leaf Shape, Order Of St.Vladimir, Pierced, C.1790, 10 1/4 In.	750.00
Gardner, Figurine, Coachman, Grassy Base, C.1850, 7 1/2 In.	300.00
Gardner, Figurine, Cobbler, Lavender Tunic, Bisque, Seated, C.1890, 5 1/4 In.	425.00
Gardner, Figurine, Cobbler, Seated, Bearded, Bisque, C.1890, 4 7/8 In.	150.00
Gardner, Figurine, Cossack Woman, Gilt Kokoshnik, C.1850, 6 3/4 In.	300.00
Gardner, Figurine, Dancing Coachman, C.1850 .... *Illus*	475.00
Gardner, Figurine, Jewish Man, C.1850 .... *Illus*	625.00
Gardner, Figurine, Old Man, C.1850, 6 1/4 In. .... *Illus*	500.00
Gardner, Figurine, Woodsman, Leaning On Stump, Bisque, Glazed, C.1850, 5 In.	475.00
Gardner, Plate, Order Of St.Alexander Nevski, C.1790, 9 1/4 In., Pair	450.00
Gardner, Plate, Order Of St.Andrew, C.1790, 9 3/4 In., Pair	1200.00

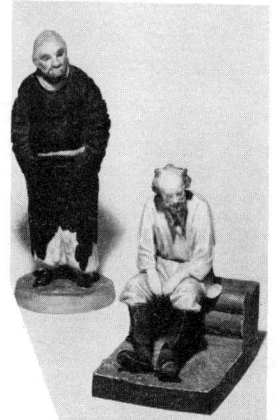

Gardner, Figurine, Jewish Man, C.1850
(See Page 222)

Gardner, Figurine, Old Man,
C.1850, 6 1/4 In.
(See Page 222)

Gardner, Figurine,
Dancing Coachman, C.1850
(See Page 222)

Gaudy Dutch, Plate,
Carnation, 9 1/4 In.

Gardner, Plate, Soup, Order Of St.Alexander Nevski, C.1790, 8 7/8 In., Pair	400.00
Gardner, Plate, Soup, Order Of St.Vladimir, C.1790, 8 7/8 In., Pair	350.00
Gardner, Teacup & Saucer, Gentlewoman Medallion On Stippled, C.1890	31.65
Gardner, Teapot, Pink & White Floral On Pale Blue, C.1880, 5 In.	120.00

*Gaudy Dutch pottery was made in England for America from about 1810 to
1820. It is a white earthenware with Imari style decorations of red, blue,
green, yellow, and black. Only sixteen patterns of Gaudy Dutch were made:
Butterfly, Carnation, Dahlia, Double Rose, Dove, Grape, Leaf,
Oyster, Primrose, Single Rose, Strawflower, Sunflower, Urn,
War Bonnet, Zinnia, and No Name. Other similar wares are called
Soft Paste, Gaudy Ironstone, or Gaudy Welsh.*

Gaudy Dutch, Cup & Saucer, Double Rose		525.00
Gaudy Dutch, Plate, Butterfly, 8 1/4 In.		600.00
Gaudy Dutch, Plate, Carnation, 9 1/4 In.	*Illus*	700.00
Gaudy Dutch, Plate, Single Rose, 6 3/4 In.		510.00
Gaudy Dutch, Saucer, Oyster, C.1820, 5 1/2 In.		120.00
Gaudy Ironstone, Pitcher, Milk, Wadenheath, England		42.00
Gaudy Ironstone, Plate, Blackberry, 8 1/2 In.		44.00
Gaudy Ironstone, Plate, Davenport, 9 1/2 In.		38.00
Gaudy Ironstone, Plate, Double Handled, C.1830, 10 7/8 X 9 3/4 In.		48.00
Gaudy Ironstone, Plate, Double Handled, C.1830, 11 1/2 X 9 In.		48.00
Gaudy Ironstone, Plate, Green Bible, Orange & Blue, Masons, 10 1/2 In.		38.00
Gaudy Ironstone, Plate, Soup, Urn & Flowers, Mason's, 9 3/4 In.		40.00
Gaudy Ironstone, Plate, Soup, 10 1/2 In.		19.00
Gaudy Ironstone, Plate, Strawberry, 7 5/8 In.		66.50
Gaudy Ironstone, Plate, Wedge Shape, Handled, C.1830		48.00
Gaudy Ironstone, Plate, Well & Tree, Vesper, 10 In.		25.00
Gaudy Ironstone, Platter, Well & Tree, 17 X 21 In.		150.00

*Gaudy Welsh is an Imari decorated earthenware with red, blue, green, and
gold decorations. It was made after 1820.*

Gaudy Welsh, Barrel, Biscuit, Silver Plate Fittings, Marked Fenton	75.00
Gaudy Welsh, Bowl, Oyster, C.1850, 8 X 4 1/4 In.	80.00
Gaudy Welsh, Creamer, Oyster	40.00
Gaudy Welsh, Creamer, Stylized Floral, 3 1/4 In.	38.00
Gaudy Welsh, Cup & Saucer, Demitasse	45.00
Gaudy Welsh, Cup & Saucer, Imari Pattern	28.00
Gaudy Welsh, Cup & Saucer, Oyster	22.00
Gaudy Welsh, Cup & Saucer, Wagon Wheel, Blue	56.00
Gaudy Welsh, Dish, Sweetmeat, Imari Type Decoration, Signed, Dated 1880	18.00
Gaudy Welsh, Flower Arranger, Covered, Cobalt, Russet, & Gold, C.1860	85.00
Gaudy Welsh, Pitcher, Dark Blue, Burnt Orange, Green, & Copper, C.1850, 5 In.	35.00

Gaudy Welsh, Pitcher, Oyster, 5 In.	85.00
Gaudy Welsh, Plate, Wagon Wheel, 7 1/2 In.	30.00
Gaudy Welsh, Teapot, Oyster Decoration	60.00
Gaudy Welsh, Teapot, Trivet, Milk Pitcher, & Creamer, Pewter Lid	95.00
Gaudy Welsh, Vase, Urn Type, Handle, 7 In., Pair	125.00
Gene Autry, Book, Gene Autry & Arapaho War Drums, Hard Cover	4.50
Gene Autry, Book, The Bandits Of Silver Tip, Better Little Books, 1949	4.75
Gene Autry, Button, Picture, Pinback	2.00
Gene Autry, Gun, Cap, Kenton, Caps, 2 In Original Box	35.00
Gene Autry, Gun, Cap, Kenton, White Handled, Cast Iron, 8 1/2 In.	20.00
Gene Autry, Gun, Cap, Plastic Grips	9.00
Gene Autry, Gun, Cap, Red Handles, Cast Iron, 6 1/2 In.	12.50
Gene Autry, Program, Rodeo, Boston Gardens, 1943	8.00
Gene Autry, Watch, Wrist, Animated Gun, 1948	45.00

Gibson Girl plates were made in the early 1900s by the Royal Doulton Pottery at Lambeth, England. There are twenty-four different plates featuring a picture of the Gibson Girl by the artist Charles Dana Gibson.

Gibson Girl, Plate, Failing To Find Rest & Quiet In The Country, 10 In.	48.00
Gibson Girl, Plate, She Decides To Die In Spite Of Dr.Bottles, 10 In.	68.00
Gibson Girl, Plate, She Goes Into Retreat, 10 In.	50.00
Gibson Girl, Plate, She Looks For Relief Among The Old Ones, 10 In.	48.00
Gibson Girl, Plate, They All Go Skating, Royal Doulton, 10 1/2 In.	42.00

GILLINDER *Gillinder pressed glass was first made by William T.Gillinder of Philadelphia in 1863. Many pressed glass items were made for the Centennial.*

Gillinder, Muffineer, Melon Ribbed, Satin Opalescent, Floral Enamel	110.00
Gillinder, Muffineer, Satin Finish, Melon, Blue & White Floral	95.00
Gillinder, Muffineer, Satin Glass, Painted Flowers	120.00
Gillinder, Muffineer, Satin, Blue & White Floral	95.00
Gillinder, Paperweight, Buddha, Amber, 6 In.	40.00 To 50.00
Gillinder, Paperweight, Crouching Lion	85.00
Gillinder, Paperweight, Frosted Lion, Centennial, Signed	115.00
Gillinder, Paperweight, Memorial Hall, Dated 1776, Frosted & Clear	200.00
Gillinder, Plate, Bread, Centennial, Frosted Polar Bear, Round	125.00
Gillinder, Vase, Hand With Torch, Frosted, Dated 1876, 7 In.	45.00
Girandole Set, Brass, Indians, Frontiersman, Marble Bases, Prisms, 3 Piece	250.00
Girandole, George III, Gilt Wood, 2 Arms, Brass Fittings, 45 In., Pair	800.00
Glasses, Coin Silver, E.E.Bailey, Portland, Me., C.1825	14.75
Glasses, Granny, Gold Filled	3.75
Glasses, Granny, Nose Clip	3.50
Glasses, Lorgnette Type, Push Lenses Together To Close, Brass Frame	15.00
Glove Stretcher, see Ivory, Glove Stretcher, Silver Plate,	
Glove Stretcher, Silver, Sterling, Glove Stretcher, Store,	
Glove Stretcher	
Gold, Box, Flat Top, Engraved, Ring Attached, Gorham, C.1885, 1 1/2 In.	175.00
Gold, Case, Cigarette, Cabochon Thumbpiece, Fedotov, C.1900	1000.00
Gold, Case, Cigarette, Russian, Garnet Thumbpiece, Basket Weave, B.F., C.1850	1200.00
Gold, Cigar Cutter, Engine Turned, Flat, Monogrammed	50.00
Gold, Cigar Cutter, On Gold Chain, English	140.00
Gold, Snuffbox, En Grisaille Bacchanal Procession In Lid, Strachan, 1815	625.00
Gold, Snuffbox, Engine Turned, 2 Color, Chased Foliage, C.1820, 3 In.	750.00
Gold, Tea Set, 18K, Openwork Harp-Shaped Handles, 3 Piece	3300.00
Gold, Vinaigrette, Agate Inset In Cover & Base, C.1820, 1 1/2 In.	425.00
Gold, Vinaigrette, Basket Of Flowers, 18K, Mills, 1835, 1 3/8 In.	700.00
Gold, Vinaigrette, Crystal Body, Diamond Faceting, Pierced Grill, C.1800	550.00
Gold, Vinaigrette, Crystal Body, Diamond Pattern, Continental, C.1850, 1 In.	125.00
Gonder, Cornucopia, Gray, Pink Interior, Marked, 8 In.	2.50
Gonder, Cornucopia, Gray, Pink Interior, Marked, 9 In.	2.50
Gonder, Planter, Swan, High Gloss Pearly Blue, Marked, 5 1/2 In.	9.00
Gonder, Vase, Brown Lavender, Leaflike Design, 6 1/2 In.	4.50
Gonder, Vase, Fan, Scrolls On Green & Brown, Footed Base, Peach In, 7 In.	4.50
Gonder, Vase, Green & Brown, Scrolls At Base, Pink Interior, 9 1/2 In.	7.00
Gonder, Vase, Light Blue Mottled Lined In Pink, Handled, 9 In.	8.50

Gonder, Vase, Medium Blue High Glaze, Flower At Base, Palm Leaf, 11 In.	8.00
Gonder, Vase, Pink, Marked, 7 In.	2.50
Gonder, Vase, Turquoise & Brown, Indented Middle, 4 Pointed Top, 8 1/2 In.	7.50

Goofus glass was made from about 1900 to 1920 by many American factories. It was originally painted gold, red, green, bronze, pink, purple, and other bright colors.

Goofus Glass, Bowl, Berry, Gold, Red Florals, 6 1/2 In.	4.50
Goofus Glass, Bowl, Birds & Berries, Painted, 10 In.	12.00
Goofus Glass, Bowl, Gold & Red Mums, Painted, 9 In.	11.00
Goofus Glass, Bowl, Leaf & Fleur-De-Lis, Gilded, 5 Red Poppies, 9 1/4 In.	30.00
Goofus Glass, Plate, Bread, Last Supper, Painted	25.00
Goofus Glass, Plate, Red Strawberries, 10 In.	10.00
Goofus Glass, Plate, Stranahan's Candies, 6 In.	10.00
Goofus Glass, Salad Set, Three Colored Fruits, 6 Piece	50.00
Goofus Glass, Vase, Embossed Red Rose, 7 In.	8.00
Goofus Glass, Vase, Red & Gold Roses, Painted, 5 In.	10.00

Goss china has been made since 1858. English potter William Henry Goss first made it at the Falcon Pottery in Stoke-on-Trent. In 1934 the factory name was changed to Goss China Company when it was taken over by Cauldon Potteries. Goss china resembles Irish Belleek in both body and glaze. The company also made popular souvenir china.

Goss Type, Vase, Egyptian, Armorial Crest, Crafton, England, 2 In.	5.25
Goss, Bust, Shakespeare, Parian, Colored, 3 X 4 In.	22.00
Goss, Creamer, Henry VIII On Crest, 2 In.	14.50
Goss, Cup & Saucer, Heraldic	10.00
Goss, Cup, 3 Handled, Seal Of Chichester, 1 1/2 In.	8.00
Goss, Egg, Henry VIII On Crest, 2 In.	12.50
Goss, Ewer, Miniature, Moon & Star Crest, Southsea, 3 In.	8.00
Goss, Mug, Henry VIII On Crest, 3 Handles, 2 1/2 X 2 1/4 In.	17.50
Goss, Vase, Arms Of Huntingdon, Tree, Deer, Dogs, Man, 3 X 2 In.	10.00
Goss, Vase, Henry VIII On Crest, Miniature	6.00

Gouda is a district in Holland famous for tin-glazed pottery and tiles. Gouda pottery has been made by many factories in the district since the seventeenth century and is still being made. Most of the pieces found today are from the nineteenth and twentieth centuries.

Gouda, Ashtray, Dutch Shoe, Floral, 7 In.	26.00
Gouda, Basket, Art Nouveau Decoration, 5 In.Diameter	48.00
Gouda, Basket, Royal Plazuid, 5 In.	38.00
Gouda, Bowl & Underplate, Gold Trim, Peacocks' Feathers, 7 In.	125.00
Gouda, Bowl Vase, Black & White Art Deco On Brown, Rolf, Handled, 8 1/2 In.	35.00
Gouda, Bowl, Black Matte, Colored Leaf, Emerance & Plazuid, 5 1/2 In.	50.00
Gouda, Bowl, Black Matte, Multicolor Decoration, Bacalar & Plazuid, 10 In.	65.00
Gouda, Bowl, Cratera, Floral On Gray, Orange Rim, Deep, 10 In.	62.00
Gouda, Bowl, Green Matte, Stylized Leaf, Flaring, Candia, 7 1/2 X 3 1/2 In.	48.00
Gouda, Bowl, Green, Orange, Blue, & White, Gouda, Holland, Pizo, 12 In.	110.00
Gouda, Bowl, Massa, Blues, Greens, & Yellows, Oval, 8 X 5 1/4 In.	35.00
Gouda, Butter Pat, Tobris, Stylized Florals	16.00
Gouda, Candlestick, Green, Browns, & Rusts, Curved Handle, 12 In.	115.00
Gouda, Candlestick, House Mark, 6 In., Pair	80.00
Gouda, Charger, Palzuel, Holland House Mark, 14 In.	145.00
Gouda, Compote, Lavender, Green, & Orange Flowers, 3 Knob Legs, 8 In.	42.00
Gouda, Ewer, Art Deco Design, 8 1/2 X 6 In.	155.50
Gouda, Jug, Candia, Matte Finish, Handled, Initial K, 7 1/2 In.	70.00
Gouda, Jug, Wine, House & Tree, Royal Blue, Turquoise, 8 In., Pair	195.00
Gouda, Lamp Base, Futurist Pattern, 13 X 12 1/2 In.	130.00
Gouda, Match Holder, Footed	22.50
Gouda, Pitcher, Aero, Floral On Gray, Green Inside, 5 In.	58.00
Gouda, Pitcher, Brown, Turquoise, Plum & Gold, High Glaze, 8 In.	80.00
Gouda, Pitcher, Bulbous, Purple, Yellow & Orange Floral, 7 In.	75.00
Gouda, Pitcher, Dark Green Matte, Art Nouveau Design, 8 1/2 In.	85.00
Gouda, Pitcher, Deep Red High Glaze, Black Abstract Drawing, 4 1/2 In.	60.00
Gouda, Pitcher, Floral Design On Mottled Gray, Green Lining, Strap Handle	45.00

Gouda, Pitcher, Floral, Browns, Orange, Black, & Off-White, 10 In. 90.00
Gouda, Pitcher, Irene, White Floral On Beige, Yellow Interior, 3 In. 45.00
Gouda, Pitcher, Regina, Royal Blue, Black Handle & Base, Designs, 3 5/8 In. 45.00
Gouda, Pitcher, Zenith, Maniy, Brown Handle, Wine, Blue, & Yellow, 3 1/8 In. 45.00
Gouda, Plaque, Swirled Floral, Glazed Finish, 12 In. 140.00
Gouda, Plate, High Glaze, Pansies Decoration, 7 In. 55.00
Gouda, Plate, Mona, Plum & Apple On Yellow, 7 5/8 In. 28.00
Gouda, Pot, Rodian, Dark Green, Blue, Yellow, & Brick Red Designs, 2 1/2 In. 50.00
Gouda, Shoe, Windmill & Village Scene, High Glaze, 7 1/2 In. 100.00
Gouda, Tile, Girl & Boy At Dock, High Glaze, Square, 6 In. 50.00
Gouda, Tray, Flambe, Black Ground, Holland House Mark, 17 X 12 1/2 In. 145.00
Gouda, Urn, Art Deco Floral, Double Handled, Orel, 9 X 7 1/2 In. 75.00
Gouda, Vase, Black Matte, Red Flowers, Green, Blue, Gold, 3 1/2 In. 28.00
Gouda, Vase, Blue Matte, Green Base & Handles, Leaves, Bloeman, 9 1/4 In. 188.00
Gouda, Vase, Bulbous Base, Slender Neck, 7 1/2 In. 35.00
Gouda, Vase, Bulbous, Green, Blue, Brown, Cream, & Black, Signed Flora, 5 In. 25.00
Gouda, Vase, Corset Shape, Gray & Green, Yellow, Orange, & Brown, Leaves, 7 In. 40.00
Gouda, Vase, Floral & Geometrics, Art Nouveau Style, House Mark, 5 In. 27.00
Gouda, Vase, Floral, Art Nouveau Style, House Mark, 7 In. 37.00
Gouda, Vase, Geometric, Two Handles, Signed Mero, Gouda, 13 1/2 In.High 65.00
Gouda, Vase, Handled, Royal Zuid, 3 In. 22.00
Gouda, Vase, Isolde, Art Deco, Arnheim Holland Mark, 10 In. 85.00
Gouda, Vase, Olive, Beige, & Blue, Art Nouveau Tulip Medallion, 12 In., Pair 235.00
Gouda, Vase, Orange & Black, Royal Gouda, 9 In.High, 7 1/2 In.Diameter 75.00
Gouda, Vase, Orange, Blue, & White, Black Trim, Plazuid & House, 6 3/4 In. 75.00
Gouda, Vase, Plazuid, 3 In. 28.00
Gouda, Vase, Plum & Lilac Floral On Turquoise, High Glaze, Zuid, 9 1/4 In. 90.00
Gouda, Vase, Ramid, Floral On Beige, Green Interior, Bulbous, 3 In. 45.00
Gouda, Vase, Regina, Matte Finish, Olympics Of 1928, 3 In., Pair 75.00
Gouda, Vase, Regina, 6 In. 30.00
Gouda, Vase, Shiny Glaze, 10 1/2 In. 150.00
Gouda, Vase, Signed Paris & Marks, 8 In. 65.00
Goupy, Vase, Art Deco, Pear Shape, Enamel Pussy Willows On Clear, 6 In. 140.00

Graniteware is an enameled tinware that has been used in the kitchen from the late nineteenth century to the present. Earlier graniteware was green or turquoise blue, with white spatters. The later ware was gray with white spatters. Reproductions are being made in all colors.

Graniteware, Coffeepot, Blue & White 10.00
Graniteware, Coffeepot, Gray Speckled, Wooden Handle, C.1900, 4 Quart 15.00
Graniteware, Coffeepot, Red With White, Original Label 5.00
Graniteware, Coffeepot, Wooden Handle, Original Label, 12 In. 15.00
Graniteware, Coffeepot, 2 Part, Original Label 7.00
Graniteware, Colander, Gray, Footed 7.50
Graniteware, Cup, Green & White 3.00
Graniteware, Dipper, Purple & White 6.00
Graniteware, Dish, Soap, Hanging, Blue Splatter 20.00
Graniteware, Double Boiler, Gray, Tin Lid 8.00
Graniteware, Kettle, Bail Handle, C.1900 .... 8.00
Graniteware, Lunch Pail, Round, Gray, Lid & Bail 12.50
Graniteware, Measure, Gray, Quart, 5 In. 7.00
Graniteware, Mug, Child's, Blue, "Mary Had A Little Lamb" 8.50
Graniteware, Mug, Coffee 1.50
Graniteware, Pan, Blue & White, 11 X 3 In. 6.00
Graniteware, Pan, Pie, Gray, Deep 5.00
Graniteware, Pan, Pie, Shallow 3.50
Graniteware, Pitcher, Gray, Very Large Opening, 11 In. 15.00
Graniteware, Plate, Pie, Gray, Granite Iron Ware, '76 & '77, 8 In. 2.00
Graniteware, Potty, Blue 4.00
Graniteware, Spoon, Gray With White, 13 In. 5.00
Graniteware, Teakettle, Black With White, Wooden Handle 7.50
Graniteware, Teapot, Gray 12.00
Graniteware, Teapot, Gray, Pewter Top & Fittings, C.1880 .... 95.00
Graniteware, Teapot, Individual, Aqua Splatter 20.00
Graniteware, Tub, Foot, Gray, Dated 1912 .... 25.00

Greentown glass was made by the Indiana Tumbler and Goblet Company of Greentown, Indiana, from 1894 to 1903. In 1899, the factory name was changed to National Glass Company. A variety of pressed, milk, and chocolate glass was made.

Greentown, see also Milk Glass, Pressed Glass, Slag, Caramel

Greentown, Bowl, Geneva, Oval, Footed, 8 1/4 In.	45.00
Greentown, Bowl, Leaf & Bracket, 8 In.	20.00
Greentown, Bowl, Master Berry, Cord Drapery	19.50
Greentown, Compote, Covered, Pleat Band, 11 X 9 In.	30.00
Greentown, Creamer, Cord Drape, Clear	19.00
Greentown, Creamer, Dewey	65.00
Greentown, Creamer, Masonic	32.50
Greentown, Creamer, Overall Lattice	18.50
Greentown, Creamer, Swirl, Miniature	15.00
Greentown, Dish, Chicken Cover, Green, Nest Base	65.00
Greentown, Dish, Rabbit Cover, Green	100.00
Greentown, Mug, Blue, Elves	40.00
Greentown, Mug, Blue, Embossed Characters	16.50
Greentown, Mug, Blue, Serenade	12.00 To 38.00
Greentown, Mug, Green	90.00
Greentown, Mug, Opaque Blue	75.00
Greentown, Mug, Opaque Blue, Knights	65.00
Greentown, Mug, Opaque Green, Knights	70.00
Greentown, Relish, Leaf Bracket	24.50
Greentown, Sugar & Creamer, Austrian	45.00
Greentown, Tumbler, Blue, Teardrop & Tassel	40.00
Greentown, Tumbler, Frosted, Wild Rose & Bowknot	17.50 To 18.50
Greentown, Tumbler, Uneeda Milk Biscuit, Golden Agate	285.00

Grueby Faience Company of Boston, Massachusetts, was incorporated in 1897 by William H. Grueby. Garden statuary, art pottery, and architectural tiles were made until 1920.

Grueby, Scarab, Brown Variegated Tints, 3 In.	185.00
Grueby, Vase, Opaque Cucumber Green Glaze, Trumpet Neck, W.Post, 1891, 12 In.	300.00
Grueby, Vase, Pitted Green Glaze, Black Splashes, C.1891, 8 In.	200.00
Grueby, Vase, Sea Green, Molded Fiddlebacks, Elongated Ovoid, C.1891, 7 In.	200.00

Gun, see Weapon, Gun

Gunderson glass was made at the Gunderson Pairpoint Works of New Bedford, Massachusetts, from 1952 to 1957. Gunderson Peachblow is especially famous.

Gunderson, Burmese, Basket, Acorn Knobs, 7 In.High	45.00
Gunderson, Burmese, Fairy Lite, Crimped Edge On Shade, 6 In.High	225.00
Gunderson, Burmese, Rose Bowl, Crimped Edge, 3 In.	124.00
Gunderson, Burmese, Vase, Acid Finish, 10 In.	175.00
Gunderson, Peachblow, Bowl, 3 Applied Leaflike Feet, Prunt On Pontil, 7 In.	195.00
Gunderson, Peachblow, Toothpick, Embossed Silver Holder, C.1890	85.00
Gunderson, Peachblow, Vase, 7 In.	200.00

Hampshire pottery was made in Keene, New Hampshire, between 1871 and 1923. Hampshire developed a popular line of colored glazed works as early as 1883, which included a Royal Worcester-type pink, olive green, blue, and mahogany.

Gutta-Percha, see Album, Photography

Hampshire, Bowl, Natural Bridge, W.Va., Oblong, 6 X 4 1/2 In.	25.00
Hampshire, Bowl, Waterlilies & Leaves, 10 X 3 In.	35.00
Hampshire, Creamer, Matte Green, 4 In.	40.00
Hampshire, Ewer, Matte Green, 6 1/2 In.	38.00
Hampshire, Mug, High Glaze Black, 5 In.High	30.00
Hampshire, Pitcher, Congregational Church & Manse, 5 1/4 In.	37.50
Hampshire, Pitcher, Green, 8 1/4 In.	35.00
Hampshire, Pitcher, Old Man Of The Mountain, Souvenir, 3 1/4 In.	25.00
Hampshire, Vase, Bowl Type, Brown High Glaze, Wide Ribbing, 3 1/2 In.	17.50
Hampshire, Vase, Bowl Type, Matte Green, Molded Design, 4 1/2 In.	20.00
Hampshire, Vase, Cobalt Shiny Glaze, Decorated, 3 X 5 1/2 In.	20.00
Hampshire, Vase, Green Matte Finish, Lotus Leaf Decoration, 6 1/4 In.	40.00
Hampshire, Vase, Matte Green, Carafe Shape, 5 In.	34.00

Hampshire, Vase, Matte Green, Cylindrical Neck, 2 Handles, 4 5/8 In.High	39.00
Hampshire, Vase, Matte Green, Double Handles On Neck, 4 5/8 In.	30.00 To 33.00
Hampshire, Vase, Matte Green, Lily Pad, 8 X 5 In.	55.00
Hampshire, Vase, Matte Green, MO Cypher, 7 In.	25.00
Hampshire, Vase, Two Tone Green, Artist Signed, 7 1/2 In.	11.50

Philip Handel worked in Meriden, Connecticut, about 1885 and in New York City from about 1900 to the 1930s. His firm made art glass and other types of lamps.

Handel, Humidor, Painting	195.00
Handel, Lamp, Amber, Green Ferns On Base, Signed 3 Places, 18 In.	675.00
Handel, Lamp, Bronze Base, Enameled Glass, 23 In. *Illus*	1000.00
Handel, Lamp, Bronze Base, Red Cattails On White Shade, C.1893, 23 1/2 In.	850.00
Handel, Lamp, Bronze Petal-Shaped Base, 2-Light, 20 In.	65.00
Handel, Lamp, Bronze, Bird Of Paradise On Cased Glass Shade, 18 In.	775.00
Handel, Lamp, Bronze, Pink Flowers & Green On Leaded Caramel Shade, 18 In.	1475.00
Handel, Lamp, Floor, Mosserine	395.00
Handel, Lamp, Leaded Shade, Red Floral On Green, Uneven Border, 13 In.	115.00
Handel, Lamp, Leaded, Green Leaves, Pink Flowers, Bronze Base, 18 In.Diameter	1300.00
Handel, Lamp, Mica Shade, 21 In.	200.00
Handel, Lamp, Parrots On Shade, Signed Base, 18 In.Shade	525.00
Handel, Lamp, Pine Forest Scene, Orange Ground, 18 In.Shade, Base	495.00
Handel, Lamp, Red & Pink Flowers, Blue & Green Leaves, 9 1/2 In.Shade	295.00
Handel, Lamp, Reverse Painted, Oak Leaves & Acorns, 20 1/2 In.	625.00
Handel, Lamp, Reverse Painting Of Meadow, Tree Trunk Base, Miniature	595.00
Handel, Lamp, Table, Lily Pod, Green, Signed, 3 Ft.	1450.00
Handel, Lamp, Table, Scenic Shade, Moon On Orange Ground, 16 In.	650.00
Handel, Lamp, Table, 14 In. Orange Art Glass Shade With Shamrock Border	495.00
Handel, Lamp, Windmills & Landscape On Orange, Palmer, 14 In. Shade	575.00
Handel, Shade, Hanging, Acorn Motif, Leaded, Amber, Blue, Green, & White, 20 In.	975.00
Handel, Shade, Tan & Green Marbleized, Bronze Honeycomb, Pagoda Shape, 9 In.	160.00
Handel, Vase, Autumn Painted Scene, Snowflake Ground, Artist Signed, 4 In.	225.00
Handel, Vase, Signed Teroma Handel, 11 1/2 In.	350.00

Handel, Lamp, Bronze Base, Enameled Glass, 23 In.

Harlequin dinnerware was produced by the Homer Laughlin Company at East Liverpool, Ohio. The rings on Harlequin Ware are evenly spaced. The pieces are usually unmarked.

Harlequin Ware, Bowl, Cream Soup, Maroon, Handled	3.00
Harlequin Ware, Bowl, Cream Soup, Yellow	3.00
Harlequin Ware, Bowl, Cream Soup, Yellow, Handled	3.00
Harlequin Ware, Bowl, Fruit, Turquoise, Flared, 5 1/2 In.	1.50
Harlequin Ware, Bowl, Light Green, Flared Sides, 8 3/4 In.	3.50
Harlequin Ware, Bowl, Light Green, Straight Sided, 7 1/4 In.	2.75
Harlequin Ware, Bowl, Serving, Maroon	4.00
Harlequin Ware, Creamer, Gray	2.00
Harlequin Ware, Cup & Saucer, Demitasse, Maroon	6.00

Harlequin Ware, Cup & Saucer, Green 4.00
Harlequin Ware, Cup & Saucer, Rose 2.75
Harlequin Ware, Cup & Saucer, Turquoise .... 2.75 To 4.00
Harlequin Ware, Cup & Saucer, Yellow .... 2.75 To 3.75
Harlequin Ware, Cup, Blue 2.50
Harlequin Ware, Cup, Green 2.50
Harlequin Ware, Cup, Maroon 2.50
Harlequin Ware, Cup, Rose 2.50
Harlequin Ware, Cup, Yellow 2.50
Harlequin Ware, Eggcup, Maroon 3.50
Harlequin Ware, Eggcup, Rose 4.00
Harlequin Ware, Eggcup, Turquoise 3.50
Harlequin Ware, Eggcup, Yellow .... 3.00 To 3.50
Harlequin Ware, Gravy Boat, Rose .... 2.50 To 3.00
Harlequin Ware, Gravy Boat, Turquoise 5.00
Harlequin Ware, Gravy Boat, Yellow .... 2.50 To 3.00
Harlequin Ware, Pitcher, Water, Maroon, Ice Lip 8.50
Harlequin Ware, Plate, Dessert, Maroon, 6 In. 1.00
Harlequin Ware, Plate, Dessert, Medium Blue, 6 In. 1.00
Harlequin Ware, Plate, Dessert, Rose, 6 In. 1.00
Harlequin Ware, Plate, Dinner, Blue 2.00
Harlequin Ware, Plate, Dinner, Spruce, 10 In. 2.00
Harlequin Ware, Plate, Dinner, Yellow 2.00
Harlequin Ware, Plate, Luncheon, Yellow, 9 In. 1.50
Harlequin Ware, Platter, Spruce, Oval, 11 1/2 In. 3.00
Harlequin Ware, Platter, Yellow, Oval, 11 1/2 In. 3.00
Harlequin Ware, Saucer, Rose 1.00
Harlequin Ware, Sugar, Dark Green 2.00
Harlequin Ware, Sugar, Medium Blue 2.00
Harlequin Ware, Sugar, Rose 2.00
Harlequin Ware, Sugar, Turquoise 2.00
Harlequin Ware, Teapot, Turquoise 7.50
Hatpin Holder, Bavarian, Roses 23.00
Hatpin Holder, Dripping Candle Shape, Green & Yellow Luster 15.00
Hatpin Holder, Hand-Painted Silver Floral Sprays, 5 In. 15.00
Hatpin Holder, Multicolor Floral, Devonshire Pottery 11.00
Hatpin Holder, Pink Flowers, Green Leaves, Beading 13.00
Hatpin Holder, White, Gold Top, Green Ferns, Royal Austria 15.00
Hatpin, Amber Glass, Thimble Stone, Silver Base 12.00
Hatpin, Art Nouveau, Powder Blue, Silver Floral Design 25.00
Hatpin, Gold Filled, 11 In. 15.00
Hatpin, Gold, Oval Top, Scrolled Base 10.00
Hatpin, Jet Black, Hat With Beaded Brim 4.00
Hatpin, Jet, Round, 1 5/8 In. Diameter 15.00
Hatpin, Opaline, Oval, Blue, Orange Tones 7.00
   Hatpin Holder, see also Porcelain and various porcelain categories

Haviland & Co.
Limoges

Haviland china has been made in Limoges, France, since 1846. The factory
was started by the Haviland Brothers of New York City. Other
factories worked in the town of Limoges making a similar chinaware.

H&Cº
DEPOSE

Haviland, see also Moss Rose
Haviland, Bowl, Cereal, Cornflower, 6 In. 12.00
Haviland, Bowl, Floral Spray, Handled, Limoges, 8 1/4 In. 18.00
Haviland, Bowl, Fruit, Frontenac 4.00
Haviland, Bowl, Fruit, No.32, Blank 12 .... 4.00
Haviland, Bowl, Fruit, Poppies, "The Belmont, New York," 10 In. 25.00
Haviland, Bowl, Holly, Shallow, 8 1/2 In. 17.50
Haviland, Bowl, No.101, Handled, Round, 9 In. 7.50
Haviland, Bowl, Serving, No.101, 2 Handled, 10 In. 8.00
Haviland, Bowl, Serving, Pale Blue Flowers, Green Leaves, Gold Trim, 11 In. ... 25.00
Haviland, Bowl, Soup, Drop Rose, No.55G 12.00
Haviland, Bowl, Soup, No.101, 7 1/2 In. 4.50
Haviland, Bowl, Soup, Silver Pattern 9.00
Haviland, Bowl, Vegetable, Cornflower, Oval 16.00
Haviland, Bowl, Vegetable, Covered, Gold & Floral, Lattice, H&Co., 1877 ... 45.00
Haviland, Bowl, Vegetable, Covered, No.15583, Oval, Handled, 8 1/2 In. ... 35.00

Haviland, Bowl, Vegetable, Covered, Oval, Pink Roses, Green Leaves, Limoges	29.00
Haviland, Bowl, Vegetable, Covered, Silver Pattern, Round	35.00
Haviland, Bowl, Vegetable, Limoges, Covered, Handled, Roses, Ivy, Gold, 8 In.	20.00
Haviland, Bowl, Vegetable, Nut Finial, White, Holly, H&Co., C.1880, 12 1/2 In	39.50
Haviland, Bowl, Vegetable, Pink Flowers, Green Leaves, Limoges, 7 1/2 In.	5.00
Haviland, Bowl, Vegetable, Red Flowers, Green Leaves, Gold, 10 X 8 In.	16.50
Haviland, Bowl, Vegetable, Silver Pattern, Oval	16.00
Haviland, Bowl, Vegetable, Silver Pattern, Round	16.00
Haviland, Butter Pat, American Beauty Roses, Gold Edge	8.00
Haviland, Butter Pat, Cerise & Blue Floral, Scalloped, Square, Limoges	.35
Haviland, Butter Pat, Cornflower	8.00
Haviland, Butter Pat, Gold Band	5.00
Haviland, Butter Pat, No.24	3.00
Haviland, Butter Pat, No.32, Blank 5	4.50
Haviland, Butter Pat, No.86	5.00
Haviland, Butter Pat, No.124, White, Theo. Haviland	4.00
Haviland, Butter, Covered, Pink & Violet Sprays, Floral, Gold, GDM, France	25.00
Haviland, Butter, Covered, Pink, Blue & White Flowers, 3 Piece	35.00
Haviland, Butter, White, Pink Roses, Gold Finial, Limoges	18.00
Haviland, Cake Stand, Pink Morning Glories, Gold, Limoges, Footed, 9 In.	35.00
Haviland, Celery, Gold Handles, Limoges, 12 X 5 1/2 In.	20.00
Haviland, Celery, No.57-A	32.50
Haviland, Chocolate Pot, Pink Roses, Cobalt & Gold Scrolls, Gold Handle	45.00
Haviland, Chocolate Set, Limoges, Pastel Floral Garlands, 13 Piece	90.00
Haviland, Coffeepot, Drop Rose, Pink & White, 8 In.	125.00
Haviland, Coffeepot, Square, White, Gold D Monogram, Green Mark, H & Co.	47.00
Haviland, Creamer, Frontenac, 4 In.	15.00
Haviland, Creamer, Pink & Blue Floral Garland, Gold Handles, Elite, Limoges	25.00
Haviland, Creamer, Red Clover	19.00
Haviland, Cup & Saucer, Autumn Leaf	16.00
Haviland, Cup & Saucer, Bouillon, Clover	12.50
Haviland, Cup & Saucer, Bouillon, Covered, Apple Blossoms On White	15.00
Haviland, Cup & Saucer, Bouillon, No.142a	8.50
Haviland, Cup & Saucer, Bouillon, White, Gold Trim	8.25
Haviland, Cup & Saucer, Clover	12.50
Haviland, Cup & Saucer, Coffee, No.567a	15.00
Haviland, Cup & Saucer, Coffee, Silver Anniversary	17.00
Haviland, Cup & Saucer, Coffee, White, No.9	14.00
Haviland, Cup & Saucer, Coin Gold Drip Edge & Handle, Melon Ribbed, Limoges	11.50
Haviland, Cup & Saucer, Demitasse, Balloonists, Limoges	25.00
Haviland, Cup & Saucer, Demitasse, Blue Forget-Me-Nots, Metal Stand, 1882	13.50
Haviland, Cup & Saucer, Demitasse, C.F.H., GDA Limoges	7.00
Haviland, Cup & Saucer, Demitasse, No.420, Gold Trim	15.00
Haviland, Cup & Saucer, Demitasse, Paisley	7.00
Haviland, Cup & Saucer, Frontenac	15.00
Haviland, Cup & Saucer, No.32, Blank 12	15.00
Haviland, Cup & Saucer, No.98, Cloverleaf, Limoges	15.00
Haviland, Cup & Saucer, No.98b	15.00
Haviland, Cup & Saucer, No.269	15.00
Haviland, Cup & Saucer, No.271	15.00
Haviland, Cup & Saucer, No.510b	15.00
Haviland, Cup & Saucer, No.560	15.00
Haviland, Cup & Saucer, Pale Blue Flowers, Green Leaves, Gold Trim	11.00
Haviland, Cup & Saucer, Silver Pattern, Gold & White	16.00
Haviland, Cup & Saucer, White	2.50
Haviland, Cup, American Beauty Roses, Gold Edge	16.00
Haviland, Cup, Demitasse, Monaco	5.00
Haviland, Cup, No.122	8.00
Haviland, Cup, Nut, Hand-Painted, Gold Edge, Footed	8.50
Haviland, Cup, Pink & Blue Floral Garland, Gold, Elite, Limoges	9.50
Haviland, Cup, Soup, Garland	10.00
Haviland, Dish, Bone, Blue Forget-Me-Nots, Green Tracery, Limoges	8.00
Haviland, Dish, Bone, Cerise & Blue Floral, Scalloped, Limoges	9.00
Haviland, Dish, Bone, Cerise & Blue Shaggy Floral, Scalloped Edge	9.00
Haviland, Dish, Bone, Cherbourg, Limoges	8.00
Haviland, Dish, Bone, Limoges, H & Co., Depose	9.50

Haviland, Dish, Bone, No.12	10.00
Haviland, Dish, Bone, No.315 A	8.50
Haviland, Dish, Bone, No.798, Gold Edge, Yellow, Black, Limoges	8.00
Haviland, Dish, Bone, Pink & Blue Floral Garland, Gold, Elite, Limoges	15.00
Haviland, Dish, Bone, Pink Flowers, Green Leaves	8.00
Haviland, Dish, Bone, Silver Pattern	14.00
Haviland, Eggcup, Floral Spray, Limoges	14.00
Haviland, Gravy Boat & Attached Underplate, American Beauty Roses, Gold	28.00
Haviland, Gravy Boat & Attached Underplate, Cornflower	28.00
Haviland, Gravy Boat & Attached Underplate, Floral, 2 Handles, 1926	18.50
Haviland, Gravy Boat & Attached Underplate, Gold, Yellow, Black, Limoges	19.50
Haviland, Gravy Boat & Attached Underplate, No.865A, Pink Roses, Gold	29.00
Haviland, Gravy Boat & Underplate, No.57c	32.50
Haviland, Gravy Boat & Underplate, No.101	12.50
Haviland, Gravy Boat, Covered, White, Gold Trim	28.00
Haviland, Gravy Boat, No.32, Blank 12	17.00
Haviland, Gravy Boat, No.122, Gold, Roses, Blue Ribbons, Theo. Haviland	16.00
Haviland, Gravy Boat, Pink Roses, Green Gray Foliage, Limoges	15.00
Haviland, Luncheon Set, No.118, 18 Piece	150.00
Haviland, Mug, Friendship, 3 Handles, Small Blue Flowers On White, 6 In.	90.00
Haviland, Pitcher, Gold Trim, Marked H & Co., 5 1/2 In.	10.00
Haviland, Plate, American Beauty Roses, Gold Edge, 7 1/2 In.	7.50
Haviland, Plate, American Beauty Roses, Gold Edge, 8 1/2 In.	8.50
Haviland, Plate, Blue Forget-Me-Nots, 8 1/2 In.	12.50
Haviland, Plate, Bread & Butter, Frontenac	5.00
Haviland, Plate, Bread & Butter, Pink & Blue Floral Garland, Gold, Limoges	8.00
Haviland, Plate, Cake, Wedding Band	15.00
Haviland, Plate, Chop, Lavender Asters, H & Co., France, 13 1/2 In.	27.50
Haviland, Plate, Cornflower, 6 In.	7.50
Haviland, Plate, Cornflower, 8 1/2 In.	8.50
Haviland, Plate, Cornflower, 9 In.	7.50
Haviland, Plate, Dessert, Autumn Leaf, 8 1/2 In.	6.50
Haviland, Plate, Dessert, Clover, No.98, 8 1/2 In.	8.00
Haviland, Plate, Dessert, Frontenac, 8 1/2 In.	6.50
Haviland, Plate, Dessert, Gold Trim & Center, Scalloped Edge, Limoges	5.00
Haviland, Plate, Dinner, No.39e	10.00
Haviland, Plate, Dinner, White, No.9, 9 3/4 In.	7.00
Haviland, Plate, Drop Rose, Red, 6 In.	15.00
Haviland, Plate, Gold Trim, 6 In.	4.00
Haviland, Plate, Gold Trim, 8 1/2 In.	7.00
Haviland, Plate, Green With Gold, 7 1/2 In.	7.00
Haviland, Plate, Hand-Painted Flower Center, C.1870, 9 In.	21.00
Haviland, Plate, Limoges, Floral Festoon, 6 1/4 In.	3.00
Haviland, Plate, No.32, Blank 12, 8 1/2 In.	6.00
Haviland, Plate, No.142a, 6 1/4 In.	5.00
Haviland, Plate, No.142a, 7 3/4 In.	6.00
Haviland, Plate, Oyster, Lavender Floral With Gold	25.00
Haviland, Plate, Oyster, Limoges, 5 Indents, Cream, Fish & Seaweed, Gold, 9 In.	45.00
Haviland, Plate, Oyster, No.32c, Blank 1	22.00
Haviland, Plate, Oyster, White, Feathery Gold Edge & Band, 9 In.	18.50
Haviland, Plate, Oyster, 6 Shell Indentations, Gold Trim, C.1880, 9 In.	35.00
Haviland, Plate, Pink Moss Roses & Green Fern Leaves, 8 In.	6.00
Haviland, Plate, Ransom, 9 1/2 In.	7.50
Haviland, Plate, Roses In Full Bloom, Gold Trim, Artist Signed, 8 1/2 In.	24.00
Haviland, Plate, Shamrock, 9 1/2 In.	12.50
Haviland, Plate, Silver Pattern, 6 In.	7.50
Haviland, Plate, Silver Pattern, 7 1/2 In.	7.50
Haviland, Plate, Silver Pattern, 8 1/2 In.	8.50
Haviland, Plate, Silver Pattern, 9 1/2 In.	10.00
Haviland, Plate, Soup, No.222	5.00
Haviland, Plate, Soup, Various Floral Centers, Set Of 12	225.00
Haviland, Plate, Soup, Violets & White Roses, 9 In.	7.00
Haviland, Plate, Wedding Band, 7 1/2 In.	7.50
Haviland, Plate, White, No.9, 8 1/2 In.	6.00
Haviland, Platter, Blue Cornflowers & Wheat, 12 1/2 X 8 1/4 In.	19.50
Haviland, Platter, Fish, No.418, 24 In.	30.00

Haviland, Platter, Frontenac, 16 In.	18.00
Haviland, Platter, Garland, 15 In.	35.00
Haviland, Platter, Geese Center, Pink Roses, Gold, Limoges, 13 X 18 In.	55.00
Haviland, Platter, Meat, Ransom, 2 Wells, 18 In.	25.00
Haviland, Platter, No.32, Blank 12, 16 In.	18.00
Haviland, Platter, No.101, 11 1/2 X 8 1/2 In.	12.50
Haviland, Platter, No.101, 16 X 12 In.	15.00
Haviland, Platter, Roses, Gold, Limoges, Oval, 19 In.	42.00
Haviland, Platter, Silver Pattern, 12 In.	17.00
Haviland, Platter, Silver Pattern, 16 In.	24.00
Haviland, Ramekin & Saucer, No.142a	8.50
Haviland, Ramekin & Underplate, No.296	12.00
Haviland, Ramekin & Underplate, Roses, Signed	7.50
Haviland, Ramekin, Green & Lavender Foliage	8.00
Haviland, Relish, Cornflower	10.00
Haviland, Relish, No.101, 8 X 5 In.	5.50
Haviland, Relish, Red Outlined Blue Floral, Green Foliage, 8 X 4 1/2 In.	9.50
Haviland, Sauce, American Beauty Roses, Gold Edge	7.50
Haviland, Sauce, Cornflower, 5 In.	7.00
Haviland, Sauce, No.101, 5 1/2 In.	3.00
Haviland, Sauce, No.69	3.00
Haviland, Sauce, Silver Anniversary, 5 In.	6.00
Haviland, Saucer, Gold Band	1.00
Haviland, Saucer, Louis XV, No.122	8.00
Haviland, Saucer, No.122	8.00
Haviland, Saucer, Pink & Blue Floral Garland, Gold, Elite, Limoges	6.00
Haviland, Saucer, Pink Roses, Theodore Haviland	8.00
Haviland, Saucer, Silver Pattern, Gold & White	2.00
Haviland, Sugar & Creamer, Covered, No.101	15.00
Haviland, Sugar & Creamer, Gold Handles & Lid, Floral, Limoges	25.00
Haviland, Sugar & Creamer, Silver Pattern, Gold & White	30.00
Haviland, Sugar, Covered, Frontenac	16.00
Haviland, Sugar, Covered, Pink & Blue Floral Garland, Gold, Elite, Limoges	30.00
Haviland, Sugar, Raised Gold Leaves On Lid & At Handles, Gold Band, 8 In.	30.00
Haviland, Sugar, White With Gold Trim, Square, Finial, 7 In.High	40.00
Haviland, Tea Set, Medallions, Pink & Green Ribbons, Gold, Limoges, 8 Piece	110.00
Haviland, Tea Set, No.4300, 3 Piece	97.50
Haviland, Teacup & Saucer, Silver Anniversary	17.00
Haviland, Teacup, Cornflower	17.50
Haviland, Tray, Dresser, Limoges, Pink & White Roses, Gold, Scalloped, 11 In.	28.00
Haviland, Tray, Fancy Gold Edge, Blue Green Dutch Center, Square, 10 In.	20.00
Haviland, Tray, Fancy Gold Handles, Pink, 15 In.	40.00
Haviland, Tray, Gold Edge, Pink & Blue Flowers, Oval, 9 X 11 1/2 In.	26.00
Haviland, Tray, Pickle, Blue Floral, Green & Brown Foliage, 8 X 4 1/2 In.	9.50
Haviland, Tray, Pin, Autumn Leaves, Artist Signed	12.00
Haviland, Tureen & Attached Underplate, Gravy, White, Limoges, 9 1/2 In.	27.50
Haviland, Tureen, Soup, Gold Finial & Scroll Handles, Roses, Pinkish	65.00
Haviland, Tureen, Vegetable, Covered, Forget-Me-Not, 8 In.	20.00
Haviland, Tureen, Vegetable, Covered, No.142a, Round	16.50
Haviland, Warmer, Pancake, Pastels, Gold	60.00

T.G.Hawkes & Company of Corning, New York, was founded in 1880. The firm cut glass made at other firms until 1962. Many pieces are marked with the trademark, a trefoil ring enclosing a fleur-de-lis and two hawks.

Hawkes, see also Cut Glass

Hawkes, Antalus Set, 2 Cut Glass, Bottles, Silver Holder & Lock	250.00
Hawkes, Goblet, Etched	8.25
Hawkes, Syrup, Etched, Sterling Silver Knob On Glass Lid	40.00
Hawkes, Vase, Etching, Footed, 8 In.	57.50
Hawkes, Vase, Sapphire Blue, Engraved Flower Garland, 10 In.	85.00
Hawkes, Vase, Sapphire, Cutback Floral Garland, Silver Overlay, 8 1/4 In.	85.00

Heisey glass was made from 1895 to 1958 in Newark, Ohio, by A.H. Heisey and Co., Inc.

Heisey, see also Custard Glass

Heisey, Ashtray, Narrow Flute	6.50

Heisey, Ashtray, Nude Lady	5.00
Heisey, Banana Boat, Amber Panel Design On Sides, Star Base, Oval, 12 In.	43.50
Heisey, Basket, Flower, Apple Green, 6 Sided Shape, Rayed, 7 1/4 X 4 1/2 In.	20.00
Heisey, Basket, Pink Paneled, 8 1/2 X 6 In.	35.00
Heisey, Bonbon, Marigold, Twist, Handled	30.00
Heisey, Bowl & Stand, Punch, Fancy Loop	125.00
Heisey, Bowl & Underplate, Whipped Cream, Crystal, Silver Leaf Decoration	36.00
Heisey, Bowl Set, Jam & Relish, Oval Thumbprint, Silver Plate Holder	65.00
Heisey, Bowl, Banana, Pineapple & Fan, Oval, Sawtooth Rim, 10 1/4 X 5 1/4 In.	28.00
Heisey, Bowl, Berry, Alexandrite, Footed, 4 In.	50.00
Heisey, Bowl, Berry, Master, Ruby Stained, Beaded Swag	45.00
Heisey, Bowl, Berry, Opal, Beaded Swag, Gold Trim	35.00
Heisey, Bowl, Console, Dolphin Footed, Marked	25.00
Heisey, Bowl, Crystal, 2 Mock Handles, Signed, 6 In.	8.00
Heisey, Bowl, Crystolite, Glass Flower On Chrome Lid, 6 In.	38.00
Heisey, Bowl, Diamonds, Marked, 10 X 5 In.	35.00
Heisey, Bowl, Fandango, 9 In.	12.00
Heisey, Bowl, Finger, Puritan, Flared, Signed	6.00
Heisey, Bowl, Floral, Sahara, No.135, Footed, 12 1/2 In.	27.50
Heisey, Bowl, Greek Key, Marked, 8 1/2 In.	24.00
Heisey, Bowl, Green, Swirled, Signed, 9 In.	25.00
Heisey, Bowl, Jelly, Saturn, 4 3/4 X 3 In.	5.50
Heisey, Bowl, Moongleam, Empress, Dolphin Footed, Floral, 11 In.	35.00
Heisey, Bowl, New Era, Oval, Shallow, 8 In.	5.00
Heisey, Bowl, Opaque White, Bead Swag, Silver Plated Base, 5 In.	18.00
Heisey, Bowl, Pink, Etched, Signed, 8 In.	22.00
Heisey, Bowl, Pinwheel & Fan, C.1908, 7 In.	39.50
Heisey, Bowl, Punch, Fancy Loop, Serrated Edge, 11 X 5 1/2 In.	85.00
Heisey, Bowl, Punch, Punty & Diamond Point, Patent 1889, 42 X 8 In.	135.00
Heisey, Bowl, Queen Anne, Handled, Footed, 8 1/2 In.	23.00
Heisey, Bowl, Ray, 4 Sections, 2 Square Handles, H In Diamond Mark, 8 In.	20.00
Heisey, Bowl, Sahara, Queen Anne, 3 Dolphin Feet, 8 X 5 1/2 In.	28.50
Heisey, Bowl, Shallow, Narrow Flute, Patent 6/20/16	12.50
Heisey, Bowl, Soup, Marigold, Twist, Handled	13.00
Heisey, Bowl, Swirl, Oval, 10 In.	20.00
Heisey, Bowl, Wedding Band, Marked, 9 In.	15.00
Heisey, Bowl, Zircon, Ridgeleigh, Oval, 12 In.	48.00
Heisey, Box, Cigarette, Crystal, Horse's Head Finial, 3 X 4 In.	27.50
Heisey, Box, Puff, Pinwheel & Fan, Silver Plate Cover, Marked	22.00
Heisey, Bucket, Ice, Crystolite	20.00
Heisey, Butter Pat, Old Sandwich	4.00
Heisey, Butter, Colonial	35.00
Heisey, Butter, Covered, Colonial	35.00
Heisey, Butter, Rose, Etched, Sea Horse Finial	50.00
Heisey, Cake Stand, Locket On Chair, 9 1/2 In.	68.00
Heisey, Candleholder, Cornucopia, Old Williamsburg, 2 1/2 In., Pair	28.00
Heisey, Candleholder, Scrolled Cups With Bull's-Eye, Triple, 7 1/2 In., Pair	48.50
Heisey, Candlestick, Crystal, Grape, Marked, 10 In.	25.00
Heisey, Candlestick, Crystal, 8 In., Pair	65.00
Heisey, Candlestick, Crystolite, Bobeches, 10 Prisms, 10 In., Pair	130.00
Heisey, Candlestick, Marked, 4 1/2 In., Pair	35.00
Heisey, Candlestick, Marked, 6 In., Pair	45.00
Heisey, Candlestick, Thumbprint, Scalloped, Marked, 6 1/2 In., Pair	40.00
Heisey, Celery, Amber, Coarse Rib, 12 In.	28.50
Heisey, Celery, Block, Star Rayed Bottom, 5 X 12 In.	14.00
Heisey, Celery, Etched Flowers, Rayed Base, Scalloped Edge, 11 1/2 In.	21.00
Heisey, Celery, Flamingo, Yeoman, 12 In.	18.00
Heisey, Celery, Gold Flashed, Fancy Loops	25.00
Heisey, Celery, Marigold, Twist, 13 In.	21.00
Heisey, Celery, Minuet	37.50
Heisey, Celery, Moon Gleam, Twist, 10 In.	13.00
Heisey, Celery, Ridgeleigh, Marked, 12 In.	25.00
Heisey, Celery, Ridgeleigh, 10 In.	14.00
Heisey, Champagne, Diamond Optic, Alexandrite, Set Of 6	60.00
Heisey, Claret, Victorian	4.00
Heisey, Coaster, Sahara, Ridgeleigh, 4 In.	4.75

Heisey, Coaster, Star Cut Base	4.00
Heisey, Cocktail Shaker, Figural, Rooster's Head, Stopper, Pourer Insert	35.00
Heisey, Compact, Locket On Chain	75.00
Heisey, Compact, Pillows	65.00
Heisey, Compote, Beaded Panel & Sunburst, 7 In.	35.00
Heisey, Compote, Covered, Pink Ribbing, Signed H In Diamond, 9 X 4 In.	30.00
Heisey, Compote, Etched Floral, Signed, 4 1/4 X 7 1/2 In.	22.00
Heisey, Compote, Moongleam, Queen Anne, 6 1/4 In.	18.50
Heisey, Compote, Scalloped Edge, Footed, Marked, 5 X 7 1/2 In.	25.00
Heisey, Compote, Silver Overlay Rim & Base, Etched Scepter, 1913, 4 3/4 In.	12.50
Heisey, Console Set, Grape Cluster, 3 Piece	105.00
Heisey, Console Set, Lariat, Low Candleholders, Unsigned, 3 Piece	36.00
Heisey, Console Set, Oval Footed Bowl, 13 In., 3 Piece	45.00
Heisey, Cordial, Colonial, Stemmed, Signed, 10 3/4 In.	6.50
Heisey, Cornucopia, Crystal, Warwick, Signed, 7 In.	25.00
Heisey, Creamer, Etched, 2 X 2 In.	20.00
Heisey, Creamer, Fancy Loop, Miniature	22.50
Heisey, Creamer, Individual, Colonial Flute	9.50
Heisey, Creamer, Individual, Paneled, Signed, 2 3/4 In.	4.00
Heisey, Creamer, Moongleam, Coarse Rib, No.406	11.00
Heisey, Creamer, Moongleam, Colonial, No.354	12.50
Heisey, Creamer, Paneled, Signed	19.00
Heisey, Creamer, Provincial, Clear, Signed	8.00
Heisey, Creamer, Ridgeleigh	6.00
Heisey, Creamer, Sahara, Ribbed Octagon	12.50
Heisey, Creamer, Whirlpool, Signed	12.50
Heisey, Cup & Saucer, Flamingo, Diamond Optic, Signed	7.50
Heisey, Cup & Saucer, Green, Diamond Optic, Signed	10.00
Heisey, Cup & Saucer, Queen Anne, Signed	10.00
Heisey, Cup & Underplate, Nut, Embossed Diamonds, Marked, Set Of 6	58.00
Heisey, Cup, Bouillon, Sahara, Yeoman, Empress Etching, Footed	20.00
Heisey, Cup, Punch, Beaded Panel & Sunburst	7.00
Heisey, Cup, Punch, Coarse Rib, Flared	7.00
Heisey, Cup, Punch, Colonial, Star Base, Flared Top	3.25 To 5.00
Heisey, Cup, Punch, Fancy Loop	7.00
Heisey, Cup, Punch, Prison Stripe	15.00
Heisey, Cup, Punch, Question Mark Handle, Marked	3.50
Heisey, Cup, Sandwich, Marked	3.75
Heisey, Decanter, Ridgeleigh, 11 1/2 In.	70.00
Heisey, Dish, Banana Split, Greek Key, 7 1/2 In.	25.50
Heisey, Dish, Candy, Covered, Clear & Green, Spire Top	40.00
Heisey, Dish, Candy, Covered, Zodiac, Footed	12.75
Heisey, Dish, Candy, Crystolite, Covered	21.90
Heisey, Dish, Candy, Etched Random Lines, Gilt Border, 6 In.Diameter	35.00
Heisey, Dish, Candy, Fluted Sides, 40 Point Star Base, Divided, Oval, 7 In.	9.50
Heisey, Dish, Candy, Lariat	40.00
Heisey, Dish, Candy, Marigold, Triangular, 3 Handled, 7 1/2 In.	12.50
Heisey, Dish, Candy, Yellow, Covered, Pedestal	30.00
Heisey, Dish, Cheese, Ridgeleigh, Double Handled, 6 1/2 In.	8.50
Heisey, Dish, Honey, Diamond Point, Signed	8.75
Heisey, Dish, Honey, Flamingo	9.00
Heisey, Dish, Honey, Green, Open Handles, Ornate Shape	5.50
Heisey, Dish, Jelly, Ridgeleigh, Double Handled, 5 1/2 In.	8.50
Heisey, Dish, Mint, Flamingo, Empress, Etched	15.00
Heisey, Dish, Nut, Flamingo, Flared, Signed, 2/22/16	8.50
Heisey, Dish, Nut, Individual, Green, Octagonal, Handle, Signed	2.00
Heisey, Dish, Nut, Master, Swan, 7 In.	20.00
Heisey, Dish, Nut, Swan, Small	9.00
Heisey, Dish, Salmon Pink, Fan Handles, 3 Sections, 9 X 9 1/2 In.	29.00
Heisey, Dish, Sundae, Sahara, Sandwich	9.00
Heisey, Eggcup, Continental	14.00
Heisey, Ewer, "Oxford, Wisc.," Marked, 4 1/2 In.	34.00
Heisey, Figurine, Pony, Standing, 5 In.	38.50
Heisey, Figurine, Rooster, 6 In.	38.00
Heisey, Figurine, Rooster, 8 In.	74.00
Heisey, Glass, Juice, Pigeon Blood, Thumbprint	55.00

Heisey, Glass, Shot, Colonial, 2 1/2 In.	5.00
Heisey, Goblet, Amber, Cube Block	19.00
Heisey, Goblet, Amber, Victorian	19.00
Heisey, Goblet, Arcadia, No.1025, 10 Ozs.	10.00
Heisey, Goblet, Cobalt, Spanish Stem	50.00
Heisey, Goblet, Cocktail, Arcadia, No.1025, 3 1/2 Ozs.	8.00
Heisey, Goblet, Cocktail, Arcadia, 3 1/2 In.	8.00
Heisey, Goblet, Cocktail, Rooster's Head	18.00
Heisey, Goblet, Colonial	7.00 To 8.00
Heisey, Goblet, Double Knopped Stem, Signed, 6 In.	8.00
Heisey, Goblet, Etched Orchid	15.00
Heisey, Goblet, Paneled Band	10.00
Heisey, Goblet, Pink, Shawl Girl Dancing, Crystal Stem	8.75
Heisey, Goblet, Ridgeleigh	10.00
Heisey, Goblet, Ridgeleigh, Pink Stripe On Frosted	13.00
Heisey, Goblet, Sahara, Diamond Optic	20.00
Heisey, Goblet, Waffle, Victorian	12.00
Heisey, Goblet, Wedding Band, Marked	10.00
Heisey, Goblet, Whirlpool, Stemmed, 10 Ozs.	6.85
Heisey, Hair Receiver, Pinwheel & Fan, Silver Plate Cover, Marked	25.00
Heisey, Jam Set, Punty Band, Amber Rims, E.P.N.S. Holder, 2 4 1/2 In. Bowls	75.00
Heisey, Jar & Underplate, Jam, Covered, Etched Flowers & Leaves	42.50
Heisey, Jar, Candy, Dolphin Handles, 9 In.	27.50
Heisey, Jar, Candy, Green Flashed, Gold Trim, Signed, 8 In.	41.00
Heisey, Jar, Marmalade, Chrome Lid & Spoon, Victorian	11.50
Heisey, Jar, Mustard, Covered, Amber, Coarse Rib	40.00
Heisey, Jar, Powder, Silver Lid, Thumbprints & Prisms	35.00
Heisey, Jar, Silver Cover, Man Holding Fish & Bucket, Signed	55.00
Heisey, Jug, Molasses, Paneled, Metal Top Patent May 15, 1910, Signed	23.00
Heisey, Knife Rest, Flat Panel	10.00
Heisey, Lemonade Set, Flamingo, Diamond Optic, 7 Piece	90.00
Heisey, Match Holder, Sawtooth Band, Souvenir	25.00
Heisey, Mayonnaise Set, 3 Beads At Intervals, Scalloped, 3 Piece	35.00
Heisey, Muffineer, Punty & Diamond Point	45.00
Heisey, Mug, Beer, Old Sandwich, Large	35.00
Heisey, Mug, Green, Pineapple & Fan, Souvenir, 1900, 4 In.	21.50 To 30.00
Heisey, Mug, Red Flashed, Beaded Swag, Marked Joe 1907, Signed	30.00
Heisey, Mug, Red Flashed, Punty Band, Souvenir, Lamberton, Minn.	22.00
Heisey, Nappy, Pink, 2 Handles	10.00
Heisey, Nut Set, Swan, 7 Piece	65.00
Heisey, Pepper Shaker, Waverly, Sterling Top	10.00
Heisey, Pitcher, Crossline Flute, 7 1/2 In.High	47.50
Heisey, Pitcher, Greek Key, 6 X 5 1/2 In.	45.00
Heisey, Pitcher, Greek Key, 6 1/4 In.	55.00
Heisey, Pitcher, Sahara, Old Sandwich, 2 Quart	35.00 To 40.00
Heisey, Pitcher, Squatty, 6 In.	40.00
Heisey, Pitcher, Water, Colonial, 1 1/2 Quart	18.00
Heisey, Pitcher, Water, Greek Key, 6 1/2 In.	90.00
Heisey, Pitcher, Water, Sahara, Sandwich	36.50
Heisey, Pitcher, Wedding Band, Marked, 6 In.	24.00
Heisey, Planter, Pink, Signed, 8 X 3 X 4 In.	22.00
Heisey, Plate, Cake, Crystolite	15.00
Heisey, Plate, Cake, Marked, 13 In.	10.00
Heisey, Plate, Colonial, 12 In.	12.00
Heisey, Plate, Cracker, Crystal, Rococo, Marked, 12 In.	18.00
Heisey, Plate, Diamonds, Scalloped, Marked, 14 In.	35.00
Heisey, Plate, Diana, 6 1/4 In.	6.00
Heisey, Plate, Fancy Loop, 8 In.	20.00
Heisey, Plate, Flamingo, Coarse Rib, Signed, 6 In.	5.25
Heisey, Plate, Flamingo, Coarse Rib, Signed, 7 In.	6.25
Heisey, Plate, Flamingo, Paneled, Star Bottom, Signed, 7 1/4 In.	5.00
Heisey, Plate, Green, Twist, Signed, 7 In.	6.00
Heisey, Plate, Green, Twist, Signed, 8 In.	8.00
Heisey, Plate, Green, Twist, Signed, 9 In.	10.00
Heisey, Plate, Honey	2.50
Heisey, Plate, Intercepted Flute, 9 In.	8.75

Heisey, Plate, Luncheon, Etched	5.00
Heisey, Plate, Marigold, Twist, Marked, 8 In.	32.00
Heisey, Plate, Marigold, Twist, 7 In.	12.00
Heisey, Plate, Moongleam, Coarse Rib, 7 1/2 In.	8.25
Heisey, Plate, Moongleam, Pleat & Panel, 7 In.	5.00
Heisey, Plate, Narrow Flute, Signed, 6 3/4 In.	6.00
Heisey, Plate, Old Williamsburg, 4 1/2 In.	4.00
Heisey, Plate, Orchid, 7 1/4 In.	7.50
Heisey, Plate, Pink, Ribbed Edge, Signed, 8 1/4 In.	8.00
Heisey, Plate, Queen Anne, Square, 7 1/4 In.	4.50
Heisey, Plate, Sahara, Sandwich, Square, 8 In.	10.00
Heisey, Plate, Sahara, Square, Signed, 8 1/2 In.	10.00
Heisey, Plate, Sandwich, Moongleam, Queen Anne, Handled, 15 In.	32.50
Heisey, Plate, Whirlpool, 8 1/2 In.	4.50
Heisey, Platter, Green, Etched Floral, Silver Overlay Border, Oval, 12 In.	25.00
Heisey, Punch Set, Colonial, 14 Piece	100.00
Heisey, Relish, Crystolite, 3 Sections, 12 1/2 In.	20.00
Heisey, Relish, Flamingo, Oceanic, Signed	20.00
Heisey, Relish, Green, Divided, Center Handle, 10 In.	22.50
Heisey, Relish, Lariat, 3 Sections, 10 In.	15.00
Heisey, Relish, Old Williamsburg, 3 Sections, Oval, 10 In.	13.00
Heisey, Relish, Queen Anne	18.00
Heisey, Relish, Ridgeleigh, Silver Overlay, 3 Sections, Signed, 11 In.	27.50
Heisey, Relish, Ridgeleigh, Star, 5 Compartments	18.00
Heisey, Relish, Sahara, 4 Compartments	17.50
Heisey, Rose Bowl, Fancy Loops, 4 In.	20.00
Heisey, Salt & Pepper, Pineapple & Fan	40.00
Heisey, Salt & Pepper, Plantation	18.00
Heisey, Salt, Fancy Loop	6.00
Heisey, Salt, Flamingo, Octagon, 2 Handled	14.00
Heisey, Salt, Roman Key, Footed	9.00
Heisey, Salt, Square, Signed	8.00
Heisey, Salt, Tub	12.50
Heisey, Salver, Punty & Diamond Point, 9 1/2 In.	45.00
Heisey, Sauce, Colonial, 4 3/4 X 2 In.	4.50
Heisey, Sauce, Moongleam, Queen Anne	5.00
Heisey, Saucer, Lariat	1.95
Heisey, Saucer, Sahara, Signed	4.50
Heisey, Sherbet, Greek Key, Marked, 3 In.	12.00
Heisey, Sherbet, Greek Key, 4 1/2 In.High	8.50
Heisey, Sherbet, Narrow Flute, Low Footed, Marked	5.00
Heisey, Sherbet, Pink, Diana, 5 In.	6.50
Heisey, Sherbet, Provincial With Lariat	4.50
Heisey, Sherbet, Thumbprint, Stemmed, Signed	3.35
Heisey, Sherbet, Wedding Band	5.00
Heisey, Shot Glass, Colonial, Signed, 2 1/2 In.	1.95
Heisey, Smoking Set, Ridgeleigh, Signed, Covered Box & 4 Ashtrays	16.95
Heisey, Spooner, Colonial	12.00
Heisey, Spooner, Fancy Loop, Ruby Flashed	55.00
Heisey, Spooner, Prince Of Wales's Plumes, Gold, Signed	38.00
Heisey, Sugar & Creamer On Tray, Individual, Ribbed Panel, Oval Tray	29.50
Heisey, Sugar & Creamer, Amethyst, Bull's-Eye	35.00
Heisey, Sugar & Creamer, Block, Marked 1912, 9 In.	55.00
Heisey, Sugar & Creamer, Child's, Pink, Flute, Signed	20.00
Heisey, Sugar & Creamer, Colonial	25.00
Heisey, Sugar & Creamer, Crystal, Etched Floral, Footed	15.00
Heisey, Sugar & Creamer, Crystolite, Signed	15.00
Heisey, Sugar & Creamer, Deep Amethyst, Thumbprint	35.00
Heisey, Sugar & Creamer, Emerald Green, Pineapple & Fan, Hotel	75.00
Heisey, Sugar & Creamer, Etched Daisy, Marked	45.00
Heisey, Sugar & Creamer, Flamingo, Stacked	28.00
Heisey, Sugar & Creamer, Flute	35.00
Heisey, Sugar & Creamer, Greek Key, Round	38.00
Heisey, Sugar & Creamer, Green, Square	27.00
Heisey, Sugar & Creamer, Individual, Orchid, Etched, Pedestal	22.00
Heisey, Sugar & Creamer, Ipswich	20.00

Heisey, Sugar & Creamer, Narrow Flute	18.50
Heisey, Sugar & Creamer, Panel & Floral, Pedestal	30.00
Heisey, Sugar & Creamer, Pink, Hotel	18.00
Heisey, Sugar & Creamer, Plantation	25.00
Heisey, Sugar & Creamer, Ridgleigh, Pink Stripe On Frosted	22.00
Heisey, Sugar & Creamer, Sahara	28.00
Heisey, Sugar & Creamer, Sahara, Quator, No.355, Footed	35.00
Heisey, Sugar & Creamer, Sahara, Queen Anne	32.50
Heisey, Sugar & Creamer, Silver Morning Glory Overlay	52.00
Heisey, Sugar, Colonial, Signed, 3 1/4 In.	9.50
Heisey, Sugar, Covered, Sunburst, Signed	38.00
Heisey, Sugar, Flamingo, Flute, Domino, Signed, 8 1/4 In.	22.00
Heisey, Sugar, Flute, Marked	12.50
Heisey, Sugar, Moongleam, Hotel, No.479	6.50
Heisey, Sugar, Moongleam, Quator, No.355	16.50
Heisey, Sugar, Open, Minuet, Dolphin Foot	17.50
Heisey, Sugar, Punty & Diamond Point	25.00
Heisey, Sugar, Sahara, Sandwich	12.00
Heisey, Syrup, Dated 1919	27.50
Heisey, Syrup, Etched Floral, Spring Hinged Top, Applied Handle, 4 1/2 In.	19.50
Heisey, Table Set, White Opaque, Beaded Swag, Roses Decoration, 4 Piece	375.00
Heisey, Toothpick, Opal, Beaded Swag	58.00
Heisey, Toothpick, Red Stained, Beaded Swag	32.00
Heisey, Toothpick, Red Stained, Beaded Swag, Souvenir	28.00
Heisey, Toothpick, Red Stained, Beaded Swag, Souvenir, Niagara Falls, 1903	25.00
Heisey, Toothpick, Red Stained, Heisey Co. Founded 1896	6.50
Heisey, Toothpick, Strawberry	15.00
Heisey, Toothpick, 12 Panels, Marked	12.00
Heisey, Tray, Sugar Cube, Moongleam	18.00
Heisey, Tub, Lemon, Covered, Pink, Diamond Optic	7.50
Heisey, Tub, Lemon, Narrow Flute, Tab Handled	9.50
Heisey, Tumbler, Crystal, Colonial, Marked	7.50
Heisey, Tumbler, Diamond Optic, Flamingo, Footed, 12 Oz.	4.50
Heisey, Tumbler, Etched Monticello	2.65
Heisey, Tumbler, Iced Tea, Whirlpool, Footed, 12 Ozs.	7.50
Heisey, Tumbler, Juice, Arcadia, No.1025, Footed, 5 Ozs.	6.00
Heisey, Tumbler, Juice, Wedding Band, Marked	7.00
Heisey, Tumbler, Old Sandwich, Sahara	13.00
Heisey, Tumbler, Provincial, Cobalt	22.00
Heisey, Tumbler, Rib & Panel, Clear	5.00
Heisey, Tumbler, Soda, Victoria, Footed	7.00
Heisey, Tumbler, Tally Ho	25.00
Heisey, Tumbler, Whirlpool, Signed	8.50
Heisey, Urn, Gold Overlay On Handles & Rim & Base, 3 3/4 In.	12.00
Heisey, Vase, Cobalt, Lily Type, Footed, Marked, 9 In.	150.00
Heisey, Vase, Fancy Loop, 9 1/2 In.High	30.00
Heisey, Vase, Horn Of Plenty, 7 1/2 In.	17.00
Heisey, Vase, Paneled, Floral & Scroll Silver Overlay, 8 3/4 In.	64.95
Heisey, Vase, Trumpet, Pineapple & Fan, No.1255, 10 1/4 In.	16.00
Heisey, Vase, Whirlpool, 5 1/2 In.	12.00
Heisey, Wine, Wedding Band, Marked	10.00
Herend, see Fischer	
Heubach, Figurine, Hound Dog, Sitting, Gray, Blue, & White, Fan Mark, 5 In.	35.00
Heubach, Figurine, Schnauzer, Sitting On Haunches, Parian, 5 In.	55.00
Heubach, Group, 3 Naked Children In Barrel Of Water, Bisque, 3 In.	85.00
Heubach, Vase, Jasperware, Green, White Greek Figure & Birds, 5 1/2 In.	50.00
Heubach, Vase, Quail In Winter Scene, Grays & White, 7 In.	75.00

Higbee glass was made by the J.B.Higbee Company of Bridgeville, Pennsylvania, about 1900.

(H I G)

Higbee, see also Amberina

Higbee, Bowl, Berry, Hawaiian Lei, Signed, 8 In.	12.50
Higbee, Bowl, Floral Ovals, Rectangular, Bee Mark, 7 1/4 X 5 1/2 In.	12.50
Higbee, Bowl, Hawaiian Lei, Scalloped, Signed, 9 In.	10.00
Higbee, Bowl, Hawaiian Lei, Scalloped, 7 1/2 In.	7.00
Higbee, Bowl, Irregular Scallops, Allover Pressed Design, Footed, 6 In.	12.00

Higbee, Bowl, Paneled Thistle, Bee Mark, 9 In.	16.00
Higbee, Bowl, Perkins, 5 In.	5.00
Higbee, Bowl, Perkins, 6 1/2 In.	7.00
Higbee, Bowl, 3 Footed, Bee Mark, 6 X 2 1/2 In.	28.00
Higbee, Cake Stand, Pineapple, C.1860	28.00
Higbee, Compote, Hawaiian Lei, Footed, 7 1/2 X 8 In.	15.00
Higbee, Compote, Perkins, 7 In.	20.00
Higbee, Dish, Honey, Covered, Paneled Thistle, Square, Bee Mark	32.50
Higbee, Dish, Pickle, Paneled Thistle, Bee Mark	16.50
Higbee, Plate, Bread, Elaine, 101 Border, Iowa City, Handled, 8 In.	68.00
Higbee, Sugar, Colonial, 2 Handles	10.00
Higbee, Vase, Crystal, Signed, 16 In.	15.00
Higbee, Vase, Hat Shape, Flaring Top, Bee Mark, 5 1/2 X 6 3/4 In.	12.75
Higbee, Vase, Paneled, Scalloped Flaring Edge, Bee Mark, 8 In.	11.95
Higbee, Wine, Hawaiian Lei, 4 1/2 In.	9.50

Historic Blue, see Adams, Clews, Staffordshire

Hobnail glass is a pattern of pressed glass with bumps in an allover pattern.
Dozens of hobnail patterns and variants have been made. Reproductions of
many types of hobnail glass can be found.

Hobnail, see also Francisware

Hobnail, Bowl, Amber Square Top, Long Hobs, 8 1/2 In.	85.00
Hobnail, Bowl, Opalescent, Ruffled Crimped Top, 6 1/4 In.	27.50
Hobnail, Bowl, Punch, Child's, Footed, 4 In.	18.00
Hobnail, Cup & Saucer, Opalescent	20.00
Hobnail, Dish, Candy, Covered, Opalescent	22.50
Hobnail, Goblet, Opalescent	12.00
Hobnail, Mug, Blue, Decorated Top	44.00
Hobnail, Mug, Dark Blue, Pointed Hobs, Rope Handle	20.00
Hobnail, Pitcher, Water, Opalescent, Canary Yellow, Square Top, 8 In.	265.00
Hobnail, Pitcher, Water, Yellow Opalescent	165.00
Hobnail, Plate, Opalescent, 8 1/2 In.	10.00
Hobnail, Salt & Pepper, Silver Tops	10.00
Hobnail, Sugar & Creamer, Opalescent	39.50
Hobnail, Toothpick, Blue, Flattened Hobs, 3 Footed	22.00
Hobnail, Tumbler, Amber, 5 Rows Hobs	10.00
Hobnail, Tumbler, Blue	50.00
Hobnail, Tumbler, 9 Rows Of Opalescent Hobs	12.50
Hobnail, Vase, Fan, Opalescent Blue, 6 In.	15.00
Hobnail, Wine, Amber, 4 In.	16.50

Hochst, or Hoechst, porcelain was made in Germany from 1746 to 1796. It
was marked with a six-spoke wheel.

Hochst, Cup & Saucer, Gold Decoration, C.1790	200.00
Hochst, Figurine, Boy With Dog, 6 In.	350.00
Hochst, Figurine, Woodsman Leaning On Stump, Axe In Hand, 6 In.High	145.00

Holly amber, or golden agate, glass was made by the Indiana Tumbler and
Goblet Company from January 1, 1903, to June 13, 1903. It is a pressed
glass pattern featuring holly leaves in the amber shaded glass.

Holly Amber, Bowl, 8 In.	675.00
Holly Amber, Butter, Covered	950.00 To 1100.00
Holly Amber, Butter, Covered, Beaded, Scalloped, 5 3/4 X 7 1/4 In.	595.00
Holly Amber, Creamer, Mold Roughness At Spout, 4 1/2 In.	490.00
Holly Amber, Sauce	235.00
Holly Amber, Saucer	200.00
Holly Amber, Sugar	450.00
Holly Amber, Syrup	725.00
Holly Amber, Syrup, Original Lid	850.00
Holly Amber, Tray, Water, Square, 7 1/2 In.	400.00
Holly Amber, Tumbler	395.00
Honesdale Type, Vase, Emerald Green, Gold Floral, Cream Enamel, 7 In.	60.00
Honesdale, Vase, Crystal, Green Cased, Trefoil Devices, Gilt, C.1904, 11 In.	150.00
Honesdale, Vase, Gold Encased Green Leaves, Poppies, Gold Beaded Trim, 9 In.	45.00
Honesdale, Vase, Opalescent, Enamel Floral, Gilt, C.1920, 5 3/4 In.	100.00
Hopalong Cassidy, Album, 2 Records	10.00

Hopalong Cassidy, Bank, Signed	6.50
Hopalong Cassidy, Banner, Hoppy & Topper, Black Felt, 20 In.	2.75 To 3.75
Hopalong Cassidy, Banner, Hoppy & Topper, Black Felt, 29 In.	5.00
Hopalong Cassidy, Blotter, Hoppy & Gabby Hayes, C.1950, 4 X 10 In.	4.00
Hopalong Cassidy, Book, Comic, March, 1955	1.50
Hopalong Cassidy, Bottle, Hair Lotion	10.00
Hopalong Cassidy, Box, Candy, Cardboard, C.1950	7.00
Hopalong Cassidy, Button, Picture, Embossed Tin Boot Attached, 2 1/2 In.	2.75
Hopalong Cassidy, Button, Pinback, Picture	3.50
Hopalong Cassidy, Can, Popcorn, Tin, C.1950	8.00
Hopalong Cassidy, Cowboy Outfit, Boy's, 1950	15.00
Hopalong Cassidy, Fork	4.50
Hopalong Cassidy, Game, Chinese Checkers, 1950, Boxed	7.50
Hopalong Cassidy, Knife, Fork, & Spoon,	25.00
Hopalong Cassidy, Knife, Pocket, Arm & Hammer, 3 Blades, Picture Of Hoppy	8.50
Hopalong Cassidy, Lunch Box, Red Metal, Picture Of Hoppy	7.50
Hopalong Cassidy, Movie Film, Bar 20 Rides Again, C.1949, 16 Mm.	10.00
Hopalong Cassidy, Mug	5.00 To 6.00
Hopalong Cassidy, Penknife	10.00
Hopalong Cassidy, Pinback	3.50
Hopalong Cassidy, Ring, Hoppy & Bar 20, Tin, C.1940	4.50
Hopalong Cassidy, Ring, Nickel Plated Brass, Cereal Premium	5.00
Hopalong Cassidy, Theater, Gun, 7 Rolls Of Film, Boxed	22.50
Hopalong Cassidy, Thermos	4.00
Hopalong Cassidy, Tin, Popcorn, C.1947, Picture Of Hoppy, 6 In.	4.50
Hopalong Cassidy, Tumbler, Milk White	4.00
Hopalong Cassidy, Viewer, Keychain, Miniature	3.00
Hopalong Cassidy, Watch, Wrist, Strap	30.00
Hopalong Cassidy, Writing Paper, Picture, Package Of 50 Sheets	2.50
Horn, Drawer Pull, Deerhorn, Pair	4.00
Horn, Snuffbox, C.1840	50.00
Horn, Tumbler, Inlaid Letters IMT, 5 1/4 In.	28.00
Horn, Tumbler, 5 1/2 In.	28.00
Howdy Doody, Beanie Kit, Leather, Boxed	6.00
Howdy Doody, Bib, National Broadcasting Co.	8.00
Howdy Doody, Camera, Sunray	8.00
Howdy Doody, Doll, Marionette, 15 In.	18.50
Howdy Doody, Hat, Sailor, White Cotton	3.75
Howdy Doody, Magic Slate, 11 X 10 In.	2.25
Howdy Doody, Playsuit, Child's, Cloth, 1950s	9.50

*Hull pottery is made in Crooksville, Ohio. The factory started in 1903
as the Acme Pottery Company. Art pottery was first made in 1917.*

Hull, Ashtray, Butterfly Line, Heart Shape, Marked Hull USA- B8 '56	7.50
Hull, Ashtray, Heart Shape, Butterflies On Yellow, Pink & Blue Daisies	17.50
Hull, Basket, Bow On Top, Raised Flowers, 7 In.	15.00
Hull, Basket, Ebb Tide, Shrimp, & Turquoise, Hull USA E11, 16 1/2 In.	35.00
Hull, Basket, Regal, Pink, Green Inside, Marked Hull USA 56, 9 In.	10.00
Hull, Basket, Tokay Line, Marked Hull USA, 8 In.	12.00
Hull, Basket, Woodland Line, Pink Floral On Pink & Yellow, W-9, 8 1/4 In.	10.00
Hull, Basket, Woodland, Green & Pink, W 22, 10 1/2 X 12 In.	25.00
Hull, Basket, Woodland, 2 Tone, Marked W9, 8 3/4 In.	20.00
Hull, Bowl, Centerpiece, Woodland, Marked W 29, 15 In.	20.00
Hull, Bowl, Console, Magnolia, Pink, Yellow, Green Floral On Cream, 13 1/2 In.	12.00
Hull, Bowl, Iris, Pink & Green Blue, Handled, Oval, Hull USA 409, 12 In.	14.00
Hull, Bowl, Pale Green, Scalloped, Hull USA 154, Oval, 8 1/2 In.	7.00
Hull, Bowl, Pink, Oval, Satin Finish, Scalloped, 10 X 6 X 3 1/2 In.	7.50
Hull, Bowl, Woodland Line, Blue Green, Pink Floral, USA W-7, 5 1/2 In.	7.50
Hull, Candleholder, Pink & White Wild Flowers, H On Base, 2 3/4 In.	5.00
Hull, Candlestick, Woodland, Marked W 30, 3 1/4 In., Pair	10.00
Hull, Compote, Glossy Dark Green, Scalloped Edges, 4 In.	2.50
Hull, Cornucopia, Speckled Turquoise, High Gloss, Handled, W 10, 11 In.	8.00
Hull, Cornucopia, Woodland Line, Blue Gray, Pink Floral, Green, 5 1/2 In.	7.00
Hull, Cornucopia, Woodland Line, Chartreuse, Marked USA, W-2, 5 1/4 IN.	7.50
Hull, Cornucopia, Woodland Line, Chartreuse, Pink Floral & Base, 5 1/2 In.	7.00
Hull, Cornucopia, Woodland, Dark Green To Brown To White To Blue, 5 In.	10.00

Hull, Cornucopia, Yellow & Pink Floral On Brown To Yellow, Signed, 9 In.	12.00
Hull, Creamer, Open Rose, Marked 111-5	5.00
Hull, Ewer, Rosella, Pink Wild Roses On Glossy White, 6 1/2 In., Pair	17.50
Hull, Pitcher Vase, Camellia Line, Pink & Blue, Hull Art USA 14, 4 1/2 In.	12.50
Hull, Pitcher, Pink & Yellow Floral On Blue, White, & Pink Ground, 7 In.	12.00
Hull, Pitcher, Woodland Line, Chartreuse, Marked USA W-3, 5 1/4 In.	7.50
Hull, Planter, Chartreuse Goose With Dark Green Head On White, 6 In.	10.00
Hull, Planter, Compote Shape, Speckled Pink & White, Scalloped, 6 In.	10.00
Hull, Planter, Dark & Light Green, Ribbed, Rectangular, 7 1/2 X 4 1/2 In.	3.50
Hull, Planter, Duck, White, 10 In.	6.50
Hull, Planter, Duck, White, 11 X 8 In.	10.00
Hull, Planter, Green & Wine, Flared, Marked Hull 124 USA, 10 X 7 In.	8.00
Hull, Planter, Leaf Shape, Stem Handle, Gray Pink, 3 X 11 In.	15.00
Hull, Planter, Mother Goose, 6 1/2 X 7 In.	7.50
Hull, Planter, Mottled Pink Lined In Mottled Blue, Marked USA 65, 6 In.	5.00
Hull, Planter, Parrot Pulling Floriform Planter, Blossom Wheels, 6 In.	25.00
Hull, Planter, Shell, Ivory, 5 X 8 In.	6.00
Hull, Planter, White, Pedestal, Octagonal, 4 X 3 1/2 In.	3.00
Hull, Planter, Wild Flowers On Blue To Cream To Pink, Open Handles, 3 In.	10.00
Hull, Pocket, Wall, Woodland Line, Pink Floral On Blue Gray, W-13, 7 1/2 In.	7.50
Hull, Sugar & Creamer, Ebb Tide, Marked Hull USA E-15 & E-16	12.00
Hull, Sugar & Creamer, Woodland Pink Flower, Twig Handle	9.00
Hull, Sugar, Magnolia On Blue To Cream To Pink, Marked 25, 3 1/4 In.	5.00
Hull, Teapot, Parchment & Pine	30.00
Hull, Teapot, Woodland	25.00
Hull, Teapot, Woodland, Green, Marked Hull USA W 26	30.00
Hull, Vase, Blue Floral On White, 2 Gold Handles, Signed, 9 In.	12.00
Hull, Vase, Blue To White To Pink Floral, 8 In., Pair	12.00
Hull, Vase, Butterfly, 10 X 6 In.	20.00
Hull, Vase, Camellia, Marked Hull USA 123, 6 1/2 In.	10.00
Hull, Vase, Cornucopia Shape, Wild Flowers On Light Blue To Pink, 7 In.	12.00
Hull, Vase, Cornucopia Shape, Woodland, White, Pink Flower, Gold, 5 1/2 In.	10.00
Hull, Vase, Cornucopia Shape, Woodland, 2 Tone, Marked W10, 11 In.	15.00
Hull, Vase, Dark Pink Flowers & Green Leaves On Pink, High Gloss, 5 1/2 In.	3.50
Hull, Vase, Deer, Pink & Green, 2 Deer, Marked Hull 62 USA, 11 1/4 In.	18.00
Hull, Vase, Double Cornucopia, Floral, Pink & Blue, B 13, 13 In.	19.00
Hull, Vase, Fan, Glossy White, Pedestal, Deer & Foliage On Deep Rose, 9 In.	20.00
Hull, Vase, Floral On Blue To Rose, Open Wing Handles, Pedestal, 6 1/2 In.	5.50
Hull, Vase, Floral On Pink, White, & Blue Ground, 2 Handled, 8 In.	13.00
Hull, Vase, Giraffe & Foliage, Green, Signed, 8 In.	5.00
Hull, Vase, Handled, 11 In.	8.50
Hull, Vase, Iris, Yellow & Rose, Handled, Marked No.302, 10 1/2 In.	23.00
Hull, Vase, Line No.2, Blue Flowers Each Side, 6 1/2 In.	6.50
Hull, Vase, Magnolia On Blue To Cream To Pink Top, 9 In.	15.00
Hull, Vase, Magnolia, Pink, High Glaze, Gold Handled, 8 1/2 In.	15.00
Hull, Vase, Magnolias On Pink To Yellow, Open Handles, 4 1/2 In., Pair	10.00
Hull, Vase, Open Rose, Pink To Cream To Blue, Leaf-Shaped Handles, 7 In.	21.00
Hull, Vase, Pale & Dark Green, Hull USA 110, 9 1/4 In.	10.00
Hull, Vase, Pink & Blue Flowers, Double Handles, 9 In.	8.00
Hull, Vase, Pink Bowknot Joins Square Base, Green, Blue, & Cream, 8 1/2 In.	17.50
Hull, Vase, Pink, Wild Flower Design, Handled, 8 In., Pair	12.00
Hull, Vase, Pitcher Shape, Wild Flowers On Blue To Beige To Pink, 4 In.	12.50
Hull, Vase, Rosella, Heart Shape, Square Base, Pink Roses On White, 6 1/2 In.	15.00
Hull, Vase, Rosella, Squarish Shape, White Floral On Pink, 6 1/2 In.	20.00
Hull, Vase, Speckled Pink & White, Gray Speckled Open Handles, 10 3/4 In.	25.00
Hull, Vase, Square, Leaves At Top, Dark Green To Pink Red To White, 6 In.	10.00
Hull, Vase, Wall, Flying Goose On Brown To Yellow, Goldlike Finish, 6 In.	15.00
Hull, Vase, Wall, Woodland, Pink Flower On Blue To White, 7 1/2 In.	17.50
Hull, Vase, Water Lily On Green To Beige To Pink Top, 6 1/2 In.	12.50
Hull, Vase, White Water Lily & Green Pads On Brown To Beige, 5 1/2 In.	12.00
Hull, Vase, Wild Flower Line, Blue To Cream To Pink, Open Handled, 7 1/2 In.	14.00
Hull, Vase, Wild Flower Line, Marked W8, 7 1/2 In.	12.00
Hull, Vase, Wild Flower Line, Marked 9, 10 1/2 In.	22.50
Hull, Vase, Wild Flower Line, Pink & Blue Matte Glaze, Marked W 8, 7 1/2 In.	12.50
Hull, Vase, Wild Flower Line, Pink & Blue, Incised K, Hull Art W 3, 5 1/2 In.	10.00
Hull, Vase, Wild Flower Line, Pink & Blue, 2 Handled, Hull Art W 1, 5 1/2 In.	8.00

Hull, Vase, Wild Flower Line, Pink & Blue, 2 Handled, Hull Art W 4, 6 1/2 In.	10.00
Hull, Vase, Wild Flower Line, Pink & Blue, 2 Handled, Hull Art W 5, 6 1/2 In.	10.00
Hull, Vase, Wild Flower Line, Pink & Yellow, Hull Art W 5, 6 1/2 In.	12.00
Hull, Vase, Wild Flower Line, Yellow, Marked Hull Art USA W-1, 5 1/2 In.	8.00
Hull, Vase, Woodland Line, Chartreuse, Pink Base & Flowers, W-8, 7 1/2 In.	12.50

Hummel figurines, based on the drawings of Berta Hummel, are made by the W.Goebel Porzellanfabrik of Oeslau, Germany. They were first made in 1934.

Hummel, Ashtray, Happy Pastime, V & Bee, Germany In Black	65.00
Hummel, Candleholder, Angel, Goebel, 1937 Mark, 2 1/2 In.	18.00
Hummel, Figurine, Angel With Bird Holy Water Font, Blue Mark, 4 In.	15.00
Hummel, Figurine, Apple Tree Girl, 1935, 6 In.	90.00
Hummel, Figurine, Boy On Fence With Duck, 1948, 4 In.	35.00
Hummel, Figurine, Chimney Sweep, Black Mark, 4 1/8 In.	50.00
Hummel, Figurine, Friends, 11 In.High	215.00
Hummel, Figurine, Goose Girl, 4 In.	32.00
Hummel, Figurine, Home From Market, Dated 1948, 5 In.	35.00
Hummel, Figurine, Joyful, Bee Mark, West Germany, 4 1/4 In.	35.00
Hummel, Figurine, Just Resting, 3 3/4 In.	30.00
Hummel, Figurine, Little Gardener, 1933, Incised Mark, 4 1/4 In.	52.00
Hummel, Figurine, Little Girl Holding Flower, 1945, 5 In.	18.00
Hummel, Figurine, Little Girl With Angel's Wings, Goebel, 3 1/2 In.	4.00
Hummel, Figurine, Madonna, Colored, 11 In.	50.00
Hummel, Figurine, Meditation, Girl, Envelope & Basket, Black Mark, 6 In.	80.00
Hummel, Figurine, Orchestra Leader, Black Mark, 5 3/8 In.	55.00
Hummel, Figurine, Playmates, V & Bee, Germany, 4 1/4 In.	57.50
Hummel, Figurine, Sensitive Hunter, Boy & Begging Rabbit, Black Mark, 5 In.	60.00
Hummel, Figurine, She Loves Me, Black Mark, 4 7/8 In.	35.00
Hummel, Figurine, Signs Of Spring, West Germany In Black Print, 4 In.	55.00
Hummel, Figurine, Soldier Boy, 1957, 6 In.	25.00
Hummel, Figurine, Spring Cheer, 5 In.	36.00
Hummel, Figurine, St.Francis Holding Infant, Goebel, 7 In.	13.50
Hummel, Figurine, Wayside Harmony, Black Mark, 6 In.	65.00
Hummel, Figurine, White Flower Madonna, 11 In.	55.00
Hummel, Group, Angel Trio, 1967, 2 1/2 In.	32.00
Hummel, Group, Girl & Boy Standing Under Umbrella, 6 1/2 In.	95.00
Hummel, Group, Girl Holding Basket & Boy, 4 1/2 In.	45.00
Hummel, Group, Mother Embracing Child, Goebel, 9 In.	25.00
Hummel, Lamp, To Market, White Silk Shade, V & Bee, Germany, 12 In.	145.00
Hummel, Salt & Pepper Shakers, Pigs, Early Mark, Pair	40.00
Hutschenreuther, Figurine, Bison, Standing, 2 1/2 In.	39.00
Hutschenreuther, Figurine, Blue Jay, Granget, Flying, 7 X 9 In.	175.00
Hutschenreuther, Figurine, Butterfly, Decorated Swallowtail, 2 1/4 In.	32.00
Hutschenreuther, Figurine, Canary, Singing, Yellow, On Branch, 5 1/2 In.	48.00
Hutschenreuther, Figurine, Chihuahua, Standing, 4 X 4 In.	42.00 To 45.00
Hutschenreuther, Figurine, Collie, Standing, Decorated, 4 X 7 In.	53.00
Hutschenreuther, Figurine, Dolphin, Dranget, 4 In.	66.00
Hutschenreuther, Figurine, Donkey, Lying, 3 1/4 X 4 In.	30.00
Hutschenreuther, Figurine, Donkey, Standing, 5 X 4 In.	40.00
Hutschenreuther, Figurine, Dragonfly, Luster, Wings Outstretched, 3 X 4 In.	31.00
Hutschenreuther, Figurine, Hummingbird, On Blooming Dogwood, 4 1/4 In.	46.00
Hutschenreuther, Figurine, Rainbow Trout, Granget, 2 3/4 X 4 3/4 In.	55.00
Hutschenreuther, Figurine, Rhinoceros, Standing, 4 1/2 X 2 In.	38.00
Hutschenreuther, Figurine, Standing Rhinoceros, 2 X 4 1/2 In.	37.00
Hutschenreuther, Figurine, Yellow Perch, Granget, 4 1/2 In.	47.00
Hutschenreuther, Plate, Bust Of Princess, Gros Bleu Border, C.1890, 10 In.	225.00
Icon, Greek, Martyred Saint, C.1850, 31 X 21 3/4 In.	450.00
Icon, Greek, St.Gerasimos, Repousse Silver Riza, C.1850, 14 1/4 X 8 3/8 In.	575.00
Icon, Greek, St.Minas, C.1750, 20 3/4 X 4 5/8 In.	500.00
Icon, Greek, St.Thomas, C.1850, 35 3/4 X 27 In.	2400.00
Icon, Russian, Our Lady Kazanaskaya, Repousse Gilt Silver, C.1890, 4 1/2 In.	275.00
Icon, Russian, Our Lady Kazanaskaya, Repousse Silver, Enamel, C.1890, 10 In.	2100.00
Icon, Russian, St.Kiril & St.Mefodi, Enamel, Gilt Silver, C.1890, 10 X 8 In.	1600.00
Icon, Russian, Vernicle, Gilt Silver, C.1890, 10 1/2 X 8 3/4 In.	1700.00

Imari patterns are named for the Japanese ware decorated with orange and blue stylized flowers. The design on the Japanese ware became so characteristic that the name Imari has come to mean any pattern of this type. It was copied by the European factories of the eighteenth and early nineteenth centuries.

Imari, Beaker, Flying Phoenix Birds & Oriental Floral, C.1750, 8 3/4 In.	200.00
Imari, Berry Set, 7 Piece	225.00
Imari, Bowl, Armorial, Corbeau Family, Octagonal, C.1790, 11 1/2 In., Pair	1250.00
Imari, Bowl, Blue & White Center, Blue Panels, Reddish Medallions, 6 In.	85.00
Imari, Bowl, Blue Flowerhead, Stylized Roundels, 8 5/8 In., Pair	35.00
Imari, Bowl, Blue, Flower & Leaf, Gold Trim, Touches Of Rust Red, 8 1/2 In.	45.00
Imari, Bowl, Carp In Waterfall, Floral, Diaper Designs, 7 1/2 In.	50.00
Imari, Bowl, Floral, Blue, Rouge-De-Fer, & Gilt, C.1690, 11 1/4 In., Pair	450.00
Imari, Bowl, Green, Red, Blue, & Gold, Floral, Scalloped Edges, 5 1/2 In.	35.00
Imari, Bowl, Kiku Roundel, Diaper & Brocade Designs, 10 1/8 In.	100.00
Imari, Bowl, Oriental Flowers, Blue Rockwork, C.1750, 9 1/8 In.	200.00
Imari, Bowl, Ormolu Mounted, Flowering Shrubbery, Gilding, C.1720, 9 1/2 In.	850.00
Imari, Bowl, Pine & Plum Trees, Pomegranate Medallion, Footed, 9 1/2 In.	55.00
Imari, Bowl, Rabbit In Flowering Shrubs, Square, 5 1/2 In., Set Of 6	140.00
Imari, Bowl, Red, Blue, Gold, & Green, 5 7/8 In.	20.00
Imari, Bowl, Scalloped Edge, 8 1/2 In.	80.00
Imari, Charger, Blue, Red, & Green, 6 Panels, Scalloped, 12 1/2 In.	100.00
Imari, Charger, 15 In.	90.00
Imari, Cup & Saucer, Brocade Type, 5 Colors	22.50
Imari, Jar, Ginger, Covered, 14 In.	160.00
Imari, Jar, Ginger, Urn Type, Covered, 13 1/2 In.	175.00
Imari, Jar, Tear Finial, Reserve Panels On Blue, C.1750, 11 3/8 In., Pair	225.00
Imari, Plaque, Fujiyama Mountain & Geese Scene, 18 In., Pair	900.00
Imari, Plate, Basket Of Flowers, Polychrome, 8 In.	35.00
Imari, Plate, Birds & Flowering Shrubs Central Medallion, C.1750, 9 In.	43.75
Imari, Plate, Blue & White, Flower Border, 6 5/8 In.	23.50
Imari, Plate, Central Flowering Sprigs Medallion, C.1750, 9 In., Pair	90.00
Imari, Plate, Chop, Plum Blossoms & Tree Of Life Medallions, 13 In.	125.00
Imari, Plate, Copeland Spode, Gold Decoration, C.1870, 6 3/4 In.	48.00
Imari, Plate, Flower Filled Vases On Tables, C.1750, 11 1/2 In., Pair	275.00
Imari, Plate, Fruit & Floral, Iron Red Trellis Border, C.1750, 9 In., Pair	140.00
Imari, Plate, Ironstone, A.J.Wilkinson, 9 In.	15.00
Imari, Plate, Panels Of Orange & Dark Blue With Floral On White, 8 1/2 In.	25.00
Imari, Plate, Peony Tree Central Medallion, Rockwork, C.1750, 10 3/8 In.	175.00
Imari, Plate, Scalloped Edge, 8 1/4 In.	70.00
Imari, Plate, Scalloped, Bright Red, Dark Blue, Jardiniere Center, 8 1/2 In.	30.00
Imari, Plate, Soup, Floral & Fruit, Rockwork, C.1750, 9 In., Pair	140.00
Imari, Plate, 6 Panels, 12 In.	90.00
Imari, Tea Caddy, Lotus Blossoms & Ju-I Heads, Oblong, C.1720, 4 1/8 In.	100.00
Imari, Tea Caddy, Walled Town & Pagodas Scene, Octagonal, C.1720, 4 In.	100.00
Imari, Vase, Cylindrical, Flaring Top, 10 X 4 In., Pair	135.00
Imperial Austria, Jar & Underplate, Jam, Covered, White, Gold Medallions	45.00
Imperial Austria, Plate, Spring Scene, Lady & 3 Cherubs, 9 3/8 In.	31.50
Imperial Austria, Plate, 3 Ladies In Colorful Robes, 9 1/2 In.	27.50

Imperial Glass Corporation was founded in Bellaire, Ohio, in 1902. Stretch glass and art glass are two of the many kinds of glass made.

Imperial, Bowl, Bead & Panel, Crossmark, 7 1/2 In.	12.00
Imperial, Bowl, Jewels, Rolled In Rim, Blue, 10 1/2 In.	25.00
Imperial, Bowl, Mayonnaise, Pink, Colonial, 5 In.	12.50
Imperial, Bowl, Orange, Upside-Down Top Hat Shape, Blue Borders, 8 1/2 In.	95.00
Imperial, Bowl, Salad, Marigold, Beaded Band & Panel, 8 In.	15.00
Imperial, Candleholder, Maiden Servant, Signed Evans, 9 1/2 In., Pair	65.00
Imperial, Compote, Jelly, No.1	10.00
Imperial, Compote, Stretch Glass, Purple, Lid, 6 In.	27.50
Imperial, Creamer, Amberina, Pedestal	48.00
Imperial, Dish, Candy, Imperial Jewels, Rainbow Iridescent, 6 1/2 In.	40.00
Imperial, Goblet, Stemmed, Paneled, Clear, 7 1/4 In.	9.00
Imperial, Luncheon Set, Pink, Molly, 16 Piece	28.00
Imperial, Nappy, Nucut, Crystal Handled	10.00
Imperial, Relish, Amberina Color, Handled, Crossmark Signed	32.50

Imperial, Saucer, Aqua, Imperial Jewels	10.00
Imperial, Sherbet, Colonial, Crossmark	4.80
Imperial, Vase, Deep Purple, Signed, 5 1/2 In. Top Opening, 4 1/2 In.	55.00
Imperial, Vase, Free-Blown, Gold Threading On Orange Luster, 7 In.	155.00
Imperial, Vase, Free-Blown, Orange Luster, 9 3/4 In.	100.00
Imperial, Vase, Gold Iridescent, Imperial Jewels, 5 1/2 X 4 5/8 In.	55.00
Imperial, Vase, Jack-In-Pulpit, Opal With Blue Loopings, Blue Inside, 11 In.	225.00
Imperial, Vase, Opaque Apricot, Flared, Ribbed Interior, Crossmark, 8 3/4 In.	85.00
Imperial, Vase, Orange Luster, Cobalt Rim & Foot, 11 In.	215.00
Imperial, Vase, Orange Luster, Trailing Vines & Hearts, 7 In.	175.00
Imperial, Vase, Purple Iridescent, 5 1/2 In. Flared Top Opening, 4 1/2 In.	55.00

*Indian Tree is a china pattern that was popular during the last half of the
nineteenth century. It was copied from earlier patterns of English china
that were very similar. The pattern includes the crooked branch of a tree and
a partial landscape with exotic flowers and leaves. It is colored green, blue,
pink, and orange. King's Rose pattern of soft paste Staffordshire was made
in England from about 1820 to 1830. It was decorated in pink, red, yellow, and
green. The pattern featured a large roselike flower.*

Indian Tree, Bowl, Cream Soup, Burslem, England	7.00
Indian Tree, Bowl, Oval, Johnson Bros., England, 9 In.	11.00
Indian Tree, Bowl, Vegetable, Covered, Handled, Coalport, 1855, 10 In.	100.00
Indian Tree, Bowl, Vegetable, Johnson Bros., England, 8 1/2 In.	12.50
Indian Tree, Compote, Footed, Copeland, C.1860, 7 1/2 X 2 3/4 In.	25.00
Indian Tree, Cup & Saucer, Sipping Saucer, Burgess & Leigh, England, C.1867	15.00
Indian Tree, Plate, Burgess & Leigh, England, C.1867, 9 3/4 In.	12.00
Indian Tree, Plate, Burgess & Leigh, England, C.1876, 8 3/4 In.	10.00
Indian Tree, Plate, Dessert, Minton, Pastel Colors, Raised Design, 7 1/2 In.	5.50
Indian Tree, Plate, Gold Luster, Copeland & Sons, C.1847, 10 In.	15.00
Indian Tree, Plate, Johnson Bros., England, 10 In.	12.50
Indian Tree, Plate, Luncheon, Square, Johnson Bros., England, 7 3/4 In.	7.50
Indian Tree, Plate, T.B.& Co., 1868-72, 9 In.	11.50
Indian Tree, Plate, Wedgwood & Co., 10 1/2 In.	7.50
Indian Tree, Platter, Oval, Johnson Bros., England, 12 In.	17.50
Indian Tree, Platter, Staffordshire, 14 1/2 X 11 In.	24.00
Indian Tree, Sugar & Creamer, Johnson Bros., England	30.00
Indian Tree, Teapot, Demitasse, Staffordshire, 7 X 6 1/2 In.	20.00
Indian Tree, Teapot, Sadler	35.00
Indian Tree, Tureen & Underplate, Gravy, Handled, Coalport, 1855, 6 In.	100.00

*Indian art from North America has attracted the collector for many years.
Each tribe has its own distinctive designs and techniques. Baskets, jewelry,
and leatherwork are of greatest collector interest.*

Indian, Arrow, Sioux, Stone Point, Wavy Blood Groove Shaft, Sinew Wrapped	20.00
Indian, Arrowhead, Northern Mexico	.25
Indian, Bag, Pipe, Sioux, 1860s, Quilted Fringe, Beads, 5 1/2 In.	375.00
Indian, Basket, California Mission, Geometric Design Cover, 8 1/2 X 8 In.	115.00
Indian, Basket, Makah, Geometrics, 3 1/2 X 2 1/2 In.	45.00
Indian, Basket, Pomo, Feathered, 5 In. *Illus*	400.00
Indian, Basket, Walapai, Twined, Vegetable Dyes, 7 1/4 In.	60.00
Indian, Belt, Navajo, Sandcast, 15 Conchas, Turquoise, Stone In Buckle	425.00
Indian, Bolo Tie, Zuni, Sunface Inlay	195.00
Indian, Bonnet, Menominee, Turkey Feather	95.00
Indian, Bowl, Pottery, Black On Black, San Ildefonso, Geometric, 3 X 4 1/2 In.	30.00
Indian, Bowl, Southwest, Redware, Black Design, 4 1/2 In.	30.00
Indian, Box, Silver, Eagles, Arrows, Swastika, Oval, 3 1/2 In.	100.00
Indian, Bracelet, Navajo, Lady's, 3 Blue Stones With Matrix, Silver	175.00
Indian, Bracelet, Navajo, Turquoise, Cabochon, Silver	35.00
Indian, Bracelet, Navajo, Turquoise, Coral, Gold Nugget, Silver Rattlesnake	425.00
Indian, Bracelet, Navajo, 1 Turquoise, 2 Coral Stones, 3 Silver Bands	160.00
Indian, Bracelet, Navajo, 5 Turquoise Stones	110.00
Indian, Bracelet, Zuni, Petit Point, 41 Turquoise Stones, C.1940, Silver	400.00
Indian, Bracelet, Zuni, Signed Paqua, Blue Nuggets, Silver	400.00
Indian, Bracelet, Zuni, Silver, 7 Turquoise Stones, Pair	100.00
Indian, Bracelet, Zuni, 41 Blue Gem Stones	395.00
Indian, Bracelet, Zuni, 73 Turquoise Stones In Cluster	750.00

Indian, Coat, Hide, 45 1/8 In.

Indian, Basket, Pomo, Feathered, 5 In.
(See Page 243)

Indian, **Buckle**, Belt, Navajo, Man's, Oval, Sterling, Blue Turquoise	145.00
Indian, **Button**, Navajo, Buffalo Nickel	2.00
Indian, **Button**, Navajo, Liberty Head Dime	2.00
Indian, **Club**, War, Mohawk Region, Stone Head, Skin Wrapped, 19 1/2 In.	45.00
Indian, **Club**, War, New York State, Wooden, Carved, 15 In. Long	55.00
Indian, **Coat**, Hide, 45 1/8 In. *Illus*	850.00
Indian, **Doll**, Kachina, Wooden, 10 In.	65.00
Indian, **Doll**, Leather, Painted Face, Horsehair Braids, C.1900, 13 1/2 In.	35.00
Indian, **Doll**, Navajo, Beadwork, C.1920, 6 In., Pair	25.00
Indian, **Doll**, Navajo, Drawn Face, C.1920, 5 3/4 In., Pair	45.00
Indian, **Drum**, Sioux, Buckskin, Painting Of Thunderbird, 10 1/4 X 15 In.	145.00
Indian, **Earrings**, Zuni, Badger's Paw, 1 Turquoise Stone, Pair	35.00
Indian, **Earrings**, Zuni, Button, Pierced, 4 Turquoise Stones, Pair	25.00
Indian, **Earrings**, Zuni, Pierced, Silver Tortoise, Turquoise Stone, Pair	28.00
Indian, **Knife Sheath**, Sioux, Beaded, Tin Danglers, Color Hackle Feathers	65.00
Indian, **Necklace & Earrings**, Zuni, Squash Blossom, Needlepoint	1200.00
Indian, **Necklace**, Fetish, Santo Domingo, N.M., Birds & Turtles	350.00
Indian, **Necklace**, Navajo, Choker, Black Heische Shell, Silver	100.00
Indian, **Necklace**, Navajo, Choker, Heische Shell, 13 Blue Nuggets	100.00
Indian, **Necklace**, Navajo, Choker, Silver Beads, 6 Turquoise Stones, Naja	595.00
Indian, **Necklace**, Navajo, Choker, Silver, 7 Coral Stones	200.00
Indian, **Necklace**, Navajo, Choker, 3 Turquoise Stones, Silver Leaf	50.00
Indian, **Necklace**, Navajo, Choker, 4 Turquoise Stones, Silver Shadowboxes	375.00
Indian, **Necklace**, Navajo, Man's, Squash Blossom, 72 Turquoise Stones	950.00
Indian, **Necklace**, Navajo, Silver Tubing, Tumbled Turquoise Nuggets, 15 In.	17.50
Indian, **Necklace**, Navajo, Squash Blossom, Double Naja, 10 Turquoise Stones	950.00
Indian, **Necklace**, Navajo, Squash Blossom, Naja, Shadowbox Stones	750.00
Indian, **Necklace**, Navajo, Squash Blossom, Shadowboxes, Turquoise, Silver	600.00
Indian, **Necklace**, Navajo, Squash Blossom, 17 Turquoise Stones	155.00
Indian, **Necklace**, Navajo, Squash Blossom, 6 Turquoise, 4 In Double Naja	950.00
Indian, **Necklace**, Navajo, Squaw, 77 Blue Nuggets, Silver	800.00
Indian, **Necklace**, Navajo, Turquoise Disc Beads, Silver Inserts & Closure	125.00
Indian, **Necklace**, Navajo, Turquoise Nuggets	200.00
Indian, **Necklace**, Navajo, Turquoise Nuggets & Olive Shell Heische	60.00
Indian, **Necklace**, Navajo, 28 In. *Illus*	900.00
Indian, **Necklace**, Santo Domingo Indian, Fetish, Heische Shell, Silver	450.00
Indian, **Necklace**, Santo Domingo Indian, Fetish, 38 Figures	500.00
Indian, **Necklace**, Sioux, Horse Bone & Brass Beads, C.1850	95.00
Indian, **Necklace**, Tennessee, Various Hard Berries, 22 In.	22.50
Indian, **Necklace**, Zuni, Bird Fetish, Tortoiseshell, Silver, 48 Figures	1500.00
Indian, **Necklace**, Zuni, Channel, 5 Tortoiseshell Owls, Coral, Jet, Pearl	950.00
Indian, **Necklace**, Zuni, Choker, Turquoise, Heische, Silver	200.00
Indian, **Necklace**, Zuni, Fetish, Heische Shell, Turquoise, Coral, & Rose Quartz	500.00
Indian, **Necklace**, Zuni, Fetish, Peyote Birds, Coral & Turquoise	950.00

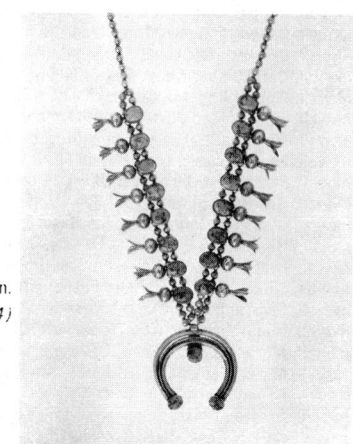

Indian, Necklace, Navajo, 28 In.
(See Page 244)

Indian, Necklace, Zuni, Fetish, Red Coral Birds, Turquoise & Coral Beads	600.00
Indian, Necklace, Zuni, Fetish, 76 Turquoise, Pearl, & Serpentine Birds	1200.00
Indian Necklace, Zuni, Heische, Turquoise, Silver Clasp	495.00
Indian, Necklace, Zuni, Mother-Of-Pearl, Bird Fetish	400.00
Indian, Pendant On Chain, Zuni, Badger's Paw, Center Turquoise Stone	25.00
Indian, Pendant On Chain, Zuni, Peyote Bird, Coral & Turquoise Wings, Silver	32.00
Indian, Pendant, Navajo, Blue Diamond Turquoise, Silver Leaves	375.00
Indian, Pendant, Navajo, Linda Arrowsmith, Turquoise, Silver, Copper Matrix	625.00
Indian, Pendant, Navajo, Morning Star, Turquoise, Tom Bahe	245.00
Indian, Pouch, Tuscarora, Drawstring, Beaded	125.00
Indian, Purse, Lady's, Crow, Rattlesnake, Billings, Mont.	5.00
Indian, Rattle, Haida, Wooden, Hand-Carved, Beach Pebbles	85.00
Indian, Rattle, Hopi, Kachina, Earth Colors	65.00
Indian, Ring, Navajo, Lady's, Turquoise Cluster, Size 6	50.00
Indian, Ring, Zuni, Badger's Paw, 1 Turquoise Stone	38.00
Indian, Ring, Zuni, Coral Cluster, 10 Oxblood Coral Stones, Lady's, Size 8	60.00
Indian, Ring, Zuni, Owl, Mother-Of-Pearl, Jet Coral & Turquoise	89.00
Indian, Ring, Zuni, Snoopy Dog, Silver, Turquoise Eye	60.00
Indian, Ring, Zuni, Sun God, Jet, Mother-Of-Pearl, Coral, & Turquoise, Size 11	90.00
Indian, Ring, Zuni, Sun God, Turquoise, Mother-Of-Pearl, Jet, & Coral	75.00
Indian, Ring, Zuni, Wedding, Lady's & Man's, Turquoise Stones, Silver, Pair	135.00
Indian, Rug, Navajo, Geometrics, 26 X 56 In.	65.00
Indian, Rug, Navajo, Pictorial, 41 X 48 In.	1295.00
Indian, Rug, Navajo, Wool, Browns, Crystal Area, 32 X 68 In.	225.00
Indian, Rug, Navajo, Wool, Red, White, & Black On Gray, Steppes & Storm, 7 Ft.	400.00
Indian, Rug, Navajo, 2 Gray Hills, C.1940, 4 Ft.1 1/2 In. X 2 Ft.6 1/2 In.	150.00
Indian, Spear, Comanche, Stone Point, Hide Wrapped Shaft, 54 1/2 In.	225.00
Indian, Stick, Digging, Eastern, Shell Blade, Vine Lashing	20.00
Indian, Tie, Bola, Man's, Zuni, Apache Ghost Dancer, Cross Of Lorraine	600.00
Indian, Totem Pole, Haida, Carved, Bear, Frog, & 3 Figures, 11 In.	300.00
Indian, Whistle, Grave, Dakota, Bone, Carved Designs, 4 In.	17.50
Inkstand, Brass & Beaten Copper, Repousse Owls & Pinecones, 9 1/2 In.	62.00
Inkstand, Continental Silver, Handled Clover Shape, Crystal Well, Hinged	75.00

The McK numbers refer to the book 'American Glass' by George and Helen McKearin.

Inkwell, see also Brass, Inkwell, Pewter, Inkwell, and various porcelain categories

Inkwell, A.Bossu, Double, Metal, Brass Collar, Dog On Top, 4 Footed, 6 In.	120.00
Inkwell, Amber, Cut Glass	45.00
Inkwell, Bakelite, The Davis Pat.1889, Clear Glass Holder, 2 1/2 In.	9.75
Inkwell, Blue & White, Sailboat, Windmill, Marked D., Square, 2 1/2 In.	28.00
Inkwell, Bronze Eagle, Chiseled Marble Base, Brass Well, American, C.1850	225.00
Inkwell, Bronze, Amethyst Glass Insert, Masked Handles, Domed Cover, 12 In.	65.00

Inkwell, Copper, Owl With Green Glass Eyes, Seated On Book, 8 1/2 X 4 In.	50.00
Inkwell, Coventry, Blown, Three Mold, McK G II-18, Deep Amber	110.00
Inkwell, Crystal, Reticulated Sterling Cage, Silver Lid, Beveled, 2 1/2 In.	45.00
Inkwell, Dark Amber Glass, Coventry, Ringed Base, 2 9/16 In.Diameter	135.00
Inkwell, Figural Angel In Center, Swirled Glass, Victorian, 7 In.	65.00
Inkwell, Figural, Man Seated Cross Legged, Germany, Carter's Ink, 3 1/2 In.	38.00
Inkwell, Flint Glass, Pewter, Kenny Bros. & Wolkins, Boston	18.00
Inkwell, For Lap Desk, Square, Gold Finish Cover, 1 1/2 In.	2.95
Inkwell, France, Art Deco, Bust Of Girl In Leopard Coat, Quill Hole	68.00
Inkwell, Girl Golfer, Well Is Golf Ball, Painted, C.1900	32.00
Inkwell, Glass On Carved Wooden Base, 3 X 3 In.	20.00
Inkwell, Hinged Lid, Silver Plate Fittings, Scene Under Glass, 2 1/2 In.	32.00
Inkwell, Leaf Shape, Art Nouveau, Cast Brass, Hinged Lid, China Liner	15.00
Inkwell, Loetz Type Glass, Brass Leaf-Shaped Lid	65.00
Inkwell, Manzanita Root, 3 1/2 In.	10.00
Inkwell, Metal Kitty By Tree Trunk, Porcelain Insert	15.00
Inkwell, Metal, Le Sacre Coeur Cathedral Shape, 5 X 5 3/8 In.	7.75
Inkwell, Metal, Neptune's Face Base, Crown Slides To Cover Well, 1911	25.00
Inkwell, Paperweight Type, Crystal, Raised Flowers	35.00
Inkwell, Pressed Glass, American, Patent 1907, Screw-On Composition Top	12.00
Inkwell, School Desk, Black Bakelite Top	2.75 To 2.95
Inkwell, Seashell, Hinged, "The Hub, Chicago 1900"	25.00
Inkwell, Silver Plate, Deer's Head On Cover, Long Antlers To Hold Pens	95.00
Inkwell, Tiffany, see Tiffany, Inkwell	
Inkwell, Traveler's, Shaped Like Leather Satchel, Leather, Blown Well	55.00
Inkwell, Traveling, Au Cadeau Bijouterie, Secret Button	50.00
Inkwell, Traveling, Blown Bottle In Screw Top, Wooden Case, C.1860, 2 In.	47.50
Inkwell, Traveling, Vest Pocket, Silver Metal, Penholder	60.00
Inkwell, Walnut Base, 2 Bottles In Clear Glass, 1916, Hinged Lid, 10 X 5 In.	55.00

Insulators of glass or pottery have been made for use on telegraph or telephone poles since 1844.

Insulator, Agee, Bell, Purple	16.00
Insulator, Am.Ins.Co., CD 134, Aqua	22.00
Insulator, American Insulator Co., CD 156	35.00
Insulator, Armstrong, Root Beer Amber	4.00
Insulator, B.& C., Diamond Front & Back, Purple	8.00
Insulator, B.E.L.Co., CD 185, Aqua	88.00
Insulator, B.G.M., Iridized	50.00
Insulator, B.T.Co. Of Canada, Amber	5.00
Insulator, Beehive, Blue Green	1.50
Insulator, Beehive, Double B, Blue Green	1.50
Insulator, Beehive, Single B, Blue Green	1.50
Insulator, Brookfield, CD 101, Aqua	2.00
Insulator, Brookfield, CD 102, Dark Aqua	1.00
Insulator, Brookfield, CD 102, Light Aqua	1.00
Insulator, Brookfield, CD 126, Aqua	20.00
Insulator, Brookfield, Light Aqua	2.00
Insulator, Brookfield, M, CD 731, Baby Spiral, Threadless Tillotson	150.00
Insulator, Brookfield, New York, CD 126, Aqua	2.00
Insulator, Brookfield, Patent Dates	4.00
Insulator, C.E.L., CD 134, Unembossed, Light Green	8.00
Insulator, C.E.L.Co., CD 134	35.00
Insulator, CD 121, Pleated Skirt, Aqua	8.00
Insulator, CD 121, Pleated Skirt, Green	12.00
Insulator, Cable, No.3	15.00
Insulator, Cable, No.4, Aqua	125.00
Insulator, California, CD 112, Purple	20.00
Insulator, California, CD 121, Purple	14.00
Insulator, California, CD 166, Purple	7.00 To 8.00
Insulator, California, CD 166, Straight Sides, Sage Green	9.00
Insulator, California, CD 178, Aqua	15.00
Insulator, Canadian Pacific Railroad Co., CD 143, Ice Blue	2.00
Insulator, Canadian Pacific, Beehive	3.00
Insulator, Carnival Glass, Sage Green	10.00
Insulator, Columbia, Lid	3.50

Insulator, **Corkscrew,** CD 410	90.00
Insulator, **Corning,** Carnival Glass, Orange	8.00
Insulator, **Cutter,** Coffin Bottom, Aqua	110.00
Insulator, **Cutter,** Porcelain, Brown	25.00
Insulator, **Danish,** Iron Hook	12.50
Insulator, **Diamond,** CD 102, Embossed, Purple	5.00
Insulator, **Dominion**	4.50
Insulator, **Edison,** CD 285	30.00
Insulator, **ESS,** Cable, No.401, Aqua	70.00
Insulator, **Fire Plug,** No.1001	20.00
Insulator, **Fire Plug,** No.1002	10.00
Insulator, **Folenbray's**	25.00
Insulator, **Foster Brothers,** St.John, C.E., 1858, CD 740, Black Amethyst	700.00
Insulator, **Fred M.Locke,** Patent May 22, 1884, CD 289, Aqua	86.00
Insulator, **G.T.P.,** CD 145, Light Green	5.00
Insulator, **GNW,** Beehive, Aqua	3.00
Insulator, **H.G.Co.,** CD 145, Amber	45.00
Insulator, **H.G.Co.,** Nat.Co., CD 152, Cobalt	60.00
Insulator, **H.G.Co.,** Petticoat	8.00
Insulator, **Hawley,** CD 164	48.00
Insulator, **Hawley,** Pa., Light Aqua	8.00
Insulator, **Hemingray,** Blue	10.00
Insulator, **Hemingray,** CD 106, Emerald Green	5.00
Insulator, **Hemingray,** Columbia, Helmet, Patent May 12, 1891	60.00
Insulator, **Hemingray,** No.D-510, Green	4.00
Insulator, **Hemingray,** No.3, Cable, Drips, Aqua	20.00
Insulator, **Hemingray,** No.16, CD 122, Emerald Green	6.00
Insulator, **Hemingray,** No.23, Amber	25.00
Insulator, **Hemingray,** No.25, Aqua	10.00
Insulator, **Hemingray,** No.38, CD 157, Aqua	5.00
Insulator, **Hemingray,** No.38, CD 157, Teepee, Aqua	10.00
Insulator, **Hemingray,** No.42, Blue Green	1.00
Insulator, **Hemingray,** No.43, Seven Up Green	8.00
Insulator, **Hemingray,** No.53, CD 202, Aqua	7.00
Insulator, **Hemingray,** No.55, Aqua	3.00
Insulator, **Hemingray,** No.55, CD 205, Blue	4.00
Insulator, **Hemingray,** No.72, CD 295, Drip Points, Aqua	9.00
Insulator, **Hemingray,** No.205, CD 55, Blue	4.00
Insulator, **Hemingray,** No.661, CD 216, Honey Amber	20.00
Insulator, **Hemingray,** No.720, CD 237	3.00
Insulator, **Imperial Porcelain Works,** Trenton, N.J., No.U-208, N.N.	10.00
Insulator, **Imperial Porcelain Works,** Trenton, N.J., No.U-239, Brown	12.00
Insulator, **Imperial Porcelain Works,** Trenton, N.J., No.U-241, Red Brown	35.00
Insulator, **Imperial Porcelain Works,** Trenton, N.J., No.U-294, Brown	15.00
Insulator, **Imperial Porcelain Works,** Trenton, N.J., No.U-746	35.00
Insulator, **Imperial Porcelain Works,** Trenton, N.J., No.U-958, Brown	20.00
Insulator, **Johns Manville,** No.U-241, Red Brown	35.00
Insulator, **Jos.Middleby,** Lid, Sun Colored Amethyst	2.00
Insulator, **KCGW,** CD 162, Green	10.00
Insulator, **Kimble,** No.231.5, CD 820	3.00
Insulator, **Kimble,** No.231, CD 820	3.00
Insulator, **Kimble,** No.820, CD 231	3.00
Insulator, **Kimble,** No.820, CD 231.5	3.00
Insulator, **Knowles,** CD 190-1	48.00
Insulator, **Lynchburg,** No.43-L, CD 145, Aqua	10.00
Insulator, **Lynchburg,** No.145, CD 43-L, Aqua	10.00
Insulator, **M.T.Co.,** CD 742, Aqua	180.00
Insulator, **Manhattan,** CD 256, Dated, Blue	25.00
Insulator, **Manhattan,** Dated, Green	35.00
Insulator, **Maydwell,** CD 122, Light Purple	7.00
Insulator, **Maydwell,** CD 154, Light Purple	8.00
Insulator, **Maydwell,** CD 164, Milk Glass, White	6.00
Insulator, **Maydwell,** Milk Glass	5.00 To 6.00
Insulator, **Maydwell,** No.20, Milk Glass	5.00 To 6.00
Insulator, **Maydwell,** White	10.00
Insulator, **McLaughlin,** Black Glass	6.00

Insulator, McLaughlin, CD 121, Black Amethyst	5.00
Insulator, McLaughlin, CD 121, Emerald Green	7.00
Insulator, McLaughlin, CD 122, Lime Green	6.00
Insulator, McLaughlin, CD 164, Emerald Green	5.00
Insulator, McLaughlin, No.16, Black Amethyst	6.00
Insulator, McLaughlin, No.16, CD 122, Light Green	500.00
Insulator, McLaughlin, No.16, Lime Green	5.00
Insulator, Mickey Mouse	6.00
Insulator, Mickey Mouse, Dated	8.00
Insulator, Minnie Mouse, No.25, Cutter	25.00
Insulator, N.N., CD 731, Threadless, Light Aqua	100.00
Insulator, N.N., Light Blue Lavender	10.00
Insulator, N.N., No.U-958, Brown	20.00
Insulator, N.N., Transposition, No.U-208	10.00
Insulator, N.N., 1/2 In. Bar Front & Back, Purple	8.00
Insulator, No.20, CD 133, Light Blue	3.00
Insulator, No.20, CD 133, Light Green	3.00
Insulator, No.72, CD 295, Drip Points	9.00
Insulator, O.V.G.Co., Petticoat, CD 164, Sterling, Aqua	25.00
Insulator, Ohio Brass, Cobalt Blue	4.00
Insulator, P.R.R., CD 162, Aqua	3.50
Insulator, PSSA, No.9, Green	8.00
Insulator, Patent Dec.19, 1871, CD 134, Aqua	2.00
Insulator, Patent Dec.19, 1871, CD 433, Aqua	4.00
Insulator, Pennsylvania Railroad, No.162.5, Aqua	3.50
Insulator, Porcelain Signal, Cobalt Blue	3.00
Insulator, Pyrex, No.662, Deep Carnival	8.00
Insulator, Pyrex, Sombrero, Dark Rainbow Carnival, 10 In.	12.00
Insulator, Pyrex, Sombrero, Light Rainbow Carnival, 10 In.	8.00
Insulator, Pyrex, Sombrero, Medium Rainbow Carnival, 10 In.	10.00
Insulator, Pyrex, Sombrero, No Metal, Dark Carnival Rainbow Color, 10 In.	12.00
Insulator, Pyrex, Sombrero, No Metal, Light Carnival Rainbow Color, 10 In.	8.00
Insulator, Pyrex, Sombrero, No Metal, Medium Carnival Rainbow Color, 10 In.	10.00
Insulator, S.S.& Co., CD 162	65.00
Insulator, San Francisco, CD 102, Aqua	3.00
Insulator, San Francisco, CD 102, Yellow Green	5.00
Insulator, San Francisco, California, CD 102, Aqua	3.00
Insulator, San Francisco, California, CD 102, Yellow Green	5.00
Insulator, San Francisco, California, Yellow	5.00
Insulator, Santa Ana, California, Aqua	15.00
Insulator, Santa Ana, California, CD 178, Purple	40.00
Insulator, Signal, Porcelain, Baby Blue	3.00
Insulator, Signal, Porcelain, Cobalt Blue	3.00
Insulator, Signal, Porcelain, Turquoise	3.00
Insulator, Telegraph, Similar To Hemingray, No.43, Amber	25.00
Insulator, Thomas, No.U-239, Embossed, Brown	12.00
Insulator, Thomas, No.U-294, Embossed, Brown	15.00
Insulator, Threadless, CD 744, Dark Green	375.00
Insulator, U, No.210, Transposition	8.00
Insulator, U, No.857, Fog Bell	15.00
Insulator, V.V.V.N.M., CD 1001, Cutter, Aqua	125.00
Insulator, W.E.Mfg.Co., Dec.19, 1871	20.00
Insulator, Whitall Tatum, Amber	5.00
Insulator, Whitall Tatum, No.1, CD 154, Purple	4.00
Insulator, Whitall Tatum, No.1, Purple	10.00
Insulator, Whitall Tatum, No.511a, Root Beer Amber	4.00
Insulator, Whitall Tatum, Purple	4.00
Iron, see also Kitchen, Tool, Store	
Iron, Aquarium, American, C.1840, Octagonal, Baluster Stand, 41 In.	100.00
Iron, Bookend, Buccaneer, Pirate Holds Cutlass, 7 X 4 In.	14.00
Iron, Bookend, Bust Of Abraham Lincoln, Copyright 1930, 6 X 5 3/8 In., Pair	8.95
Iron, Bookend, Shape Of Fox Terrier, 4 1/2 In., Pair	12.75
Iron, Bootjack, Beetle, Brown Color, Pair Of Feelers, Green Wings, 12 In.	25.00
Iron, Bootjack, Beetle, Eyes On Top Of Head	50.00
Iron, Bootjack, Design, Handmade, Round, 13 In.	35.00
Iron, Bootjack, Double End, 4 Triangles, 2 Footed, 13 In.	25.00

Iron, Bootjack, Downs & Co., Design On Each Side, 13 In.	25.00
Iron, Bootjack, Heart, Tip Toward Prongs, 13 In.	35.00
Iron, Bootjack, Long Single End, 3 Ribs, 14 1/2 In.	25.00
Iron, Bootjack, Naughty Nellie, Red With Gilt	25.00
Iron, Bootjack, Open Design In Middle, 11 In.	25.00
Iron, Bootjack, Pitts Novelty Works, Buggy Wrench At 1 End, 13 In.	50.00
Iron, Bootjack, Shoe Outlined, Brass Tips, Wooden Base, 1855, 14 In.	25.00
Iron, Bootjack, 2 Prongs, Slides Up & Down, Design On Sides, 5 In.	25.00
Iron, Bottle Opener, Rooster, Painted	12.00
Iron, Bracket, Shelf, Lacy, 5 1/4 X 4 1/4 In., Pair	4.95 To 5.95
Iron, Bracket, Shelf, Lacy, 9 X 7 In., Pair	5.95
Iron, Bracket, Shelf, Lacy, 9 1/4 X 6 3/4 In.	5.95
Iron, Branding Iron, CA, Hand-Forged	15.00
Iron, Branding Iron, HQ, Hand-Forged	15.00
Iron, Branding Iron, Hand-Forged, Socket End Type Handle	4.50 To 6.50
Iron, Branding Iron, JA, Hand-Forged	15.00
Iron, Branding Iron, Letter G	5.00
Iron, Branding Iron, YT, Hand-Forged	15.00
Iron, Broom Holder, Floor, Round, Casters	85.00
Iron, Candelabra, 3 Arm, C.1840, 8 In. Wide	20.00
Iron, Candleholder, Flemish, 12 In.	225.00
Iron, Candlesnuffer, Hand-Forged Iron, Scissors Type	14.75
Iron, Candlesnuffer, Scissor Shape, Legs	12.50
Iron, Candlestand, Floor, 2 Adjustable Scrolling Arms, C.1790, 27 3/4 In.	400.00
Iron, Candlestick, Hog Scraper, Push-Up, C.1780	20.00
Iron, Clip, Bill, Dated 1874	10.00
Iron, Clip, Bill, Wall, Patent 1885-1894, 3 X 4 3/4 In.	5.95
Iron, Coffee Grinder, see Coffee Grinder	
Iron, Collar, Stovepipe, Ornate	3.50
Iron, Cork Roller	35.00
Iron, Curler, Hair, Handwrought Iron, Scissor Type, C.1750, 10 In.	20.00
Iron, Door Knocker, Hand Holding Ball, 4 In.	21.75
Iron, Door Knocker, Hand Holding Ball, 5 In.	21.75
Iron, Door Knocker, Woman's Hand Holding Ball, Ruffled Sleeve	39.00
Iron, Door Knocker, Woman's Hand Holding Ball, Victorian, 5 1/2 X 2 1/2 In.	25.00

Iron doorstops have been made in all types of designs. The vast majority of the doorstops sold today are cast iron and were made from about 1890 to 1930. Most of them are shaped like people, animals, flowers, or ships.

Iron, Doorstop, Basket Of Flowers, Hubley, 7 1/2 In.	7.95
Iron, Doorstop, Boston Bulldog, 9 1/2 In.	20.00 To 45.00
Iron, Doorstop, Cat Reclining, Black, Dark Green Round Base, 7 1/4 In.	21.50
Iron, Doorstop, Coach With Driver, Bugler, & 2 Horses	50.00
Iron, Doorstop, Cockatoo Standing On Tree Stump, 7 In.	18.00
Iron, Doorstop, Cottage, Painted	9.00
Iron, Doorstop, Elephant, Trunk Up, 6 X 3 1/2 In.	10.00
Iron, Doorstop, Elephant, 8 1/4 X 5 1/4 In.	11.75
Iron, Doorstop, Fisherman, 6 In.	12.00
Iron, Doorstop, Frog	16.00
Iron, Doorstop, German Shepherd Dog, Red, Wedges, 12 X 12 In.	20.00
Iron, Doorstop, Hawk On Stump, 6 In.High	12.00
Iron, Doorstop, Heron, Standing, Folded Neck, Painted, 7 1/2 In.High	22.00
Iron, Doorstop, Horse, Saddle, Head Down, Bronzed, 10 X 9 In.	22.50
Iron, Doorstop, Lady In Bonnet, 4 3/4 In.	5.00
Iron, Doorstop, Pair Of Standing Kittens, 7 1/2 In.	35.00
Iron, Doorstop, Reclining Black Cat, Circular Front Base, 7 1/4 X 6 2/3 In.	22.00
Iron, Doorstop, Rigged Schooner, Brown Sails, Blue Sea, 5 3/4 X 9 In.	22.00
Iron, Doorstop, Sitting Kitten, Ribbon Around Neck, 8 In.	11.75
Iron, Doorstop, Sunbonnet Sue, Negro	35.00
Iron, Doorstop, Wire Haired Fox Terrier, 8 X 9 1/2 In.	27.50
Iron, Dryer, Corn, Indiana, Cast Iron	10.00
Iron, Figure, Horse's Head, For Hitching Post	35.00
Iron, Figurine, Bulldog, English, 2 1/2 In.	7.00
Iron, Figurine, Elephant, Trunk Up, 6 X 3 1/2 In.	9.95
Iron, Figurine, English Setter On The Point, 5 X 2 3/4 In.	7.50
Iron, Figurine, Rooster, Painted Black, C.1850, 21 1/2 In.	600.00

Iron, **Figurine**, Scottie Dog, Cast, 4 In.	8.00
Iron, **Flowers In Pot**, Enameled, 10 X 7 In.	10.00
Iron, **Frame**, Easel Type, War Eagle At Top, Battleships, Flags, Bugles, 12 In.	16.00
Iron, **Frame**, Easel, Open Scrollwork, Gold Finish, 12 X 8 3/4 In.	16.75
Iron, **Frame**, Easel, Ornate, Gold Finish, Scrollwork Border, 12 X 9 In.	17.95
Iron, **Frame**, Easel, Victorian, Oval, Cherubs & Flowers, 11 X 9 In.	16.75
Iron, **Frame**, Girl With Flowing Gown, & Cherub, 12 X 9 1/2 In.	38.00
Iron, **Frame**, Lacy, Black, Oval, Chain, 11 X 8 In.	17.50
Iron, **Frame**, Lacy, Black, Rectangular, Stand, 11 X 8 In.	17.50
Iron, **Hinge**, Strap, Heart Finial, 22 In., Pair	12.00
Iron, **Hitching Post**, Horse's Head, Black Paint, 10 1/2 In.	150.00
Iron, **Holder**, Receipt, Hanging, Dated 1889	5.00
Iron, **Hook**, Ceiling, Ornate Design, 10 In.Long	3.00
Iron, **Hook**, Ceiling, Ornate, Screw-In, For Hall Lanterns, 11 In.	3.95
Iron, **Hook**, Ceiling, Ornate, Screw-In, 11 In.	2.95
Iron, **Hook**, Meat, Handwrought, Ring Handle, 4 Hooks, 24 In.	60.00
Iron, **Hook**, Wall Bracket, Ornate, Screw-In, Extends 9 In. From Wall	3.75
Iron, **Hook**, Wall Bracket, Screw-In Type, Extends 8 In. From Wall	2.95
Iron, **Inkwell**, Pen Holder, Art Deco	25.00
Iron, **Inkwell**, 4 Leaf Clover Shape, Bonnet Head Lady Lid, Gold, Green, 6 In.	45.00
Iron, **Kettle**, W.Bullock & Co., Size 3	90.00
Iron, **Key**, Chest, Italian Palace, C.1790, 3 3/4 In.	7.00
Iron, **Key**, Chest, Italian Palace, 1820, 4 3/4 In.	8.00
Iron, **Key**, Jail, 5 In.	2.25
Iron, **Key**, Jail, 7 In.	2.25
Iron, **Key**, Ranch, 5 In.	2.25
Iron, **Key**, Ranch, 7 In.	2.25
Iron, **Ladle**, Candle Wax Pouring, 4 X 5 In.	12.50
Iron, **Last**, Shoe, Floor Type, 3 Sizes	15.00
Iron, **Leg Iron**, Hand-Forged, Midwest Area, C.1850, Pair	40.00
Iron, **Mailbox**, Victorian, Barnes Mfg.Co., No.1, Phoenix	15.00
Iron, **Match Container**, Dog On Lift-Up Cover, Standing, Used Matches, 3 In.	14.75
Iron, **Match Container**, Wall, Hinged Cover, D.M.& Co., New Haven, 1864, 4 In.	16.75
Iron, **Match Container**, Wall, Open Vines, Leaves, & Flowers, 7 X 5 3/8 In.	16.75
Iron, **Match Holder**, see also Match Holder	
Iron, **Match Holder**, American Fusee Co., Erie, Pa., Scrolls, Female Bust	20.00
Iron, **Match Holder**, Boxer Dog With Paw On Rat's Tail, Basket, 6 1/2 In.	55.00
Iron, **Match Holder**, Wall, Double, Dated 1867, Striker	20.00
Iron, **Match Holder**, Wall, Fireplace Shape	37.50
Iron, **Match Holder**, 2 Part, V Shaped, Paneled, 7 X 4 3/4 In.	18.00
Iron, **Match Safe**, Bird Picks Up Match	26.00
Iron, **Match Safe**, Half Circle, Hanging, Open, 5 1/2 X 2 1/2 X 1 In.	24.00
Iron, **Match Safe**, Shape Of Two Leather Boots, Square Base	9.00
Iron, **Match Safe**, Wall Type, Hinged Cover, Ornate, 6 3/4 In.High	20.00
Iron, **Mold**, Cork, Victorian, 8 1/4 In.Long	24.00
Iron, **Mold**, Lamb, Handles, 2 Piece, 10 1/2 In.	15.00
Iron, **Mortar & Pestle**, Pedestal Base, 3 1/2 X 4 In.	10.00
Iron, **Mortar & Pestle**, Urn Shape, 5 5/8 X 5 3/8 In.	18.75
Iron, **Mudscraper**, T Shape, Ram's Head Curl, Handwrought	65.00
Iron, **Nutcracker**, Alligator, 10 X 3 1/2 In.	15.00
Iron, **Nutcracker**, Dog, 12 X 5 In.	15.00
Iron, **Nutcracker**, Nutshell Shape	12.00
Iron, **Nutcracker**, Squirrel, Silver Paint, Mounted On Wood, 8 3/4 In.	40.00
Iron, **Opener**, Can, Keen Kutter	3.50
Iron, **Plaque**, Farmyard Scene, Painted, Repousse, C.1850, 14 1/4 X 9 In.	150.00
Iron, **Pot**, Bean, Rings, Legs	16.00
Iron, **Pot**, Movable Bail, 3 Legs, 6 X 5 1/2 In.	35.00
Iron, **Pot**, Spider Legs, Handle, 5 1/2 In.	30.00
Iron, **Pull**, Door, Junge's Bread, 18 In.	18.00
Iron, **Ratchet**, Betty Holder, Handwrought, 8 1/2 In.	165.00
Iron, **Ratchet**, Betty Holder, Handwrought, 13 In.	180.00
Iron, **Ring**, Bull's Nose Lead	2.00
Iron, **Rushlight Holder**, 10 1/2 In. *Illus*	185.00
Iron, **Rushlight**, Crown-Shaped Head On Arm, Tripod Base, C.1750, 9 In.	175.00
Iron, **Safe**, Combination, Cast Iron, Painted, 12 X 12 In.	135.00
Iron, **Scraper**, Foot, For Outside Steps	7.95

Iron, Rushlight Holder, 10 1/2 In.
(See Page 250)

Iron, Snow Eagle, 5 In.

Iron, Shoe, Mannequin, Left Foot, 10 X 9 In.	38.00
Iron, Skillet, Spider Legs, Handle, 8 In.	30.00
Iron, Snow Eagle, 5 In. _Illus_	15.00
Iron, Spittoon, White Porcelain Rim, 8 In.	15.00
Iron, Spur, European, C.1650, Pierced Fleur-De-Lis, 6 Pointed Rowel	64.50
Iron, Spur, Spanish, 3 In. Rowels	2.25
Iron, Stamp, Frog, Hinged Top, 3 3/4 X 3 In.	10.00
Iron, Stirrup, U.S.Cavalry, Stamped, Pair	10.00
Iron, String Holder, Screws On Table Top, Ball Of String	15.00
Iron, Taper Holder, Double, Handwrought Iron, Tripod Base, 11 1/2 In.	205.00
Iron, Trammel, 4 Adjustments For Fireplace Kettle	38.00
Iron, Weaner, Calf, Spikes	3.50

*Ironstone china was first made in 1813. It gained its greatest popularity
during the mid-nineteenth century. The heavy, durable, off-white pottery was
made in white or was colored with any of hundreds of patterns. Much flow blue
pottery was made of ironstone. Some of the pieces had raised decorations.*

Ironstone, see also Chelsea Grape, Gaudy Ironstone, Moss Rose

Ironstone, Bowl & Ladle, Soup, White, Elliot & Son, C.1864	10.00
Ironstone, Bowl & Plate, Nursery Rhymes, Wood & Sons, England, 6 & 8 In.	12.00
Ironstone, Bowl, Fruit, Mandarin, 2 Handled, Mason's, 9 1/2 In.	87.50
Ironstone, Bowl, Parakeet, Octagonal, Johnson Bros., 9 In.	9.00
Ironstone, Bowl, Salad, 12 Sided, Alcock, 10 In.	13.50
Ironstone, Bowl, Scalloped, 10 In.	25.00
Ironstone, Bowl, Serving, Apple Finial, White, Wooliscroft, 1855, 10 In.	55.00
Ironstone, Bowl, Vegetable, Apple Finial, White, Wollison, 1855, Pedestal	55.00
Ironstone, Bowl, Vegetable, Covered, Applied Handle, Johnson Bros., 11 In.	30.00
Ironstone, Bowl, Vegetable, Covered, Scenic, Sepia, Alcock, C.1830, 12 In.	75.00
Ironstone, Bowl, Vegetable, Vista, Mulberry, Mason's Patent	11.00
Ironstone, Butter Pat, Blue Flowers, Gold, J.G.Meakin, England	2.50
Ironstone, Butter Pat, Floral Center, Wreath Border, Round, Grindley	1.50
Ironstone, Butter Pat, White, Bees & Flowers, Square	3.50
Ironstone, Butter Pat, White, J.& G. Meakin, Hanley, England, Set Of 6	17.50
Ironstone, Compote, Oyster Color, Mason's, 8 1/2 In.	65.00
Ironstone, Creamer, Mandarin, Hand-Painted, Mason's, 4 1/2 In.	25.00
Ironstone, Creamer, Temple, Mulberry	24.75
Ironstone, Cup & Saucer, Demitasse, Pink Vista, Mason's, Set Of 6	25.00
Ironstone, Cup & Saucer, Handleless, Eon, Blue & White, 10 Sided, Wooliscroft	22.50
Ironstone, Cup, Coddle, Covered, White	4.00
Ironstone, Cup, Handleless, White, Flower & Vine At Rim	6.00
Ironstone, Cup, Lady's Spit, White, Goodwin Bros., 3 3/8 In.	27.25
Ironstone, Demitasse Set, Medway, Alfred Meakin, 13 Piece	48.00

Ironstone, Dish, Cheese, Covered, Square, Mason's Patent	40.00
Ironstone, Dish, Soap, Drain, 4 1/2 In.	2.50
Ironstone, Dish, Sweetmeat, Mason's	125.00
Ironstone, Eggcup, Gold Rim	4.00 To 5.50
Ironstone, Gravy Boat, Blue & White, Diaper & Bead Festoons, Leaf Handle	18.00
Ironstone, Jar, Black & Ocher Boar Hunt Scene, Blue Glaze, Eng., 4 In.	28.00
Ironstone, Jar, Cracker, Oriental Design, Silver Bail & Lid, Mason's	67.50
Ironstone, Jug, Pink Flowers, Green Leaves, Maddox & Sons, 7 In.	12.00
Ironstone, Match Holder, Table Type, White, Flower & Vine At Rim, 5 In.	5.00
Ironstone, Mug & Bowl, Child's, Rose, Girl & Boy Scenes, Meakin, 3 & 6 In.	8.00
Ironstone, Pitcher, Brown Floral On White Tiger Banner, 8 1/4 In.	16.00
Ironstone, Pitcher, Imari Colors, Dolphin Handle, Octagon Top, Mason's, 7 In.	65.00
Ironstone, Pitcher, Mason's, 7 X 5 1/2 In.	55.00
Ironstone, Pitcher, Sheaf Of Wheat, Johnson's, 6 In.	15.00
Ironstone, Pitcher, Six Sided, Oriental Scene, Red, Green, Cobalt, Gold	125.00
Ironstone, Pitcher, T & R Boote, 1883, Brown Transfer Prints, 7 3/4 In.	18.00
Ironstone, Pitcher, Tan, Cattails Allover, Boy & Girl, 8 X 23 In.Diameter	26.50
Ironstone, Pitcher, Washstand, Gloxinia, TG & FB England	10.00
Ironstone, Pitcher, White, Wheat, Elsnore N.Forster, 13 In.	29.50
Ironstone, Plate, Ardennes, Pink, E.Challinor, 8 1/2 In.	10.00
Ironstone, Plate, Canova, Mayer, C.1836, 9 1/2 In.	15.00
Ironstone, Plate, Chang, E.Malkins, 7 1/2 In.	18.00
Ironstone, Plate, Corean, Mulberry, 10 In.	22.50
Ironstone, Plate, Dark Blue Serpent On Light Blue, Mason's, 9 1/4 In.	18.00
Ironstone, Plate, Dominion Of Canada, Mason's, 10 3/4 In.	25.00
Ironstone, Plate, Flowers On Border, Square, Mason's, 9 In.	15.00
Ironstone, Plate, Hand-Painted, Bluebells On White, C.1820, 8 3/4 In., Pair	22.00
Ironstone, Plate, Man On Horseback, Purple Luster, C.1853, E.& F., 9 1/2 In.	16.50
Ironstone, Plate, Pelew, Mulberry, 10 In.	22.50
Ironstone, Plate, Persiana, Blue, Yellow, & Oranges, Mason's, 8 In.	13.50
Ironstone, Plate, Rhone Scenery, Mulberry, 8 3/4 In.	12.50
Ironstone, Plate, Vincennes, Mulberry, 10 In.	22.50
Ironstone, Platter, A.Meakin, 10 X 18 In.	23.00
Ironstone, Platter, Corean, 16 X 12 In.	50.00
Ironstone, Platter, White, Oval, Mercer Pottery Co., 18 In.	12.00
Ironstone, Potty, Child's, Covered, White, Cartwright Bros.	19.50
Ironstone, Salt Dip, Rectangular, Rust & Blue, Mason's	8.50
Ironstone, Sauceboat & Attached Underplate, Brown Transfer, Imperial Stone	18.00
Ironstone, Saucer, Orange & Blue Pattern, Mason's	10.00
Ironstone, Server, Vegetable, Geneva, Blue, Octagonal, J.Heath	25.00
Ironstone, Sugar & Creamer, Chelsea	50.00
Ironstone, Sugar & Creamer, White, Miniature	12.00
Ironstone, Tea Leaf, Bowl, Soup, 9 In.	15.00
Ironstone, Tea Leaf, Bowl, Square, Meakin, 7 In.	20.00 To 22.00
Ironstone, Tea Leaf, Bowl, Square, Meakin, 8 In.	37.50
Ironstone, Tea Leaf, Bowl, Vegetable	16.50
Ironstone, Tea Leaf, Bowl, Vegetable, Covered, Oblong, Alfred Meakin	27.00
Ironstone, Tea Leaf, Butter Pat, Rectangular	6.00
Ironstone, Tea Leaf, Butter Pat, Round	5.00
Ironstone, Tea Leaf, Butter Pat, Square, Meakin	7.50
Ironstone, Tea Leaf, Chamberpot, Grindley	45.00
Ironstone, Tea Leaf, Cup & Saucer, Copper Luster Trim	20.00
Ironstone, Tea Leaf, Cup & Saucer, Meakin	32.00
Ironstone, Tea Leaf, Cup & Saucer, Powell & Bishop	34.00
Ironstone, Tea Leaf, Dish, Bone, A.Meakin	21.50
Ironstone, Tea Leaf, Dish, Pickle, Handled	25.00
Ironstone, Tea Leaf, Dish, Vegetable, Covered, 2 Handles, 10 1/4 X 5 3/4 In.	40.00
Ironstone, Tea Leaf, Gravy Boat, Powell & Bishop	18.00
Ironstone, Tea Leaf, Pitcher & Bowl, Alfred Meakin, 12 In.High	150.00
Ironstone, Tea Leaf, Pitcher, Meakin, 5 1/2 In.	20.00
Ironstone, Tea Leaf, Pitcher, Milk, Lily-Of-The-Valley, A.Shaw, 5 1/2 In.	47.50
Ironstone, Tea Leaf, Plate, Alfred Meakin, 10 In.	15.00
Ironstone, Tea Leaf, Plate, Copper Luster Trim, 7 1/2 In.	6.50
Ironstone, Tea Leaf, Plate, Meakin, 8 3/4 In.	9.00 To 9.50
Ironstone, Tea Leaf, Plate, Soup, T.Furnival	14.00
Ironstone, Tea Leaf, Plate, Wedgwood & Co., England, 8 1/2 In.	8.00

Ironstone, Tea Leaf, Plate, 8 In.	9.00
Ironstone, Tea Leaf, Plate, 9 1/2 In.	14.00
Ironstone, Tea Leaf, Platter, Alfred Meakin, 10 1/2 X 7 1/2 In.	18.00
Ironstone, Tea Leaf, Platter, Alfred Meakin, 14 X 10 In.	22.50
Ironstone, Tea Leaf, Platter, Alfred Meakin, 16 X 11 In.	25.00
Ironstone, Tea Leaf, Platter, Meakin, 14 X 10 In.	38.00
Ironstone, Tea Leaf, Platter, Oval, Thos.Furnival & Sons, Eng., 12 X 17 In.	32.00
Ironstone, Tea Leaf, Platter, Wedgwood & Co., England, 13 In.	20.00
Ironstone, Tea Leaf, Platter, 13 In.	22.00
Ironstone, Tea Leaf, Sugar & Creamer, Cover	95.00
Ironstone, Tea Leaf, Sugar, Covered, Meakin	45.00
Ironstone, Tea Leaf, Sugar, Covered, Wilkinson, Royal Ironstone China	40.00
Ironstone, Tea Leaf, Sugar, Portland Shape, Funstall, 8 In.	50.00
Ironstone, Teapot, Corn Pattern, Wedgwood	45.00
Ironstone, Teapot, Gold, Red, & Blue Oriental Design, Mason's, C.1825, 6 In.	240.00
Ironstone, Teapot, White, Rope Finial, T.& R.Boote, Eng., 8 In.	20.00
Ironstone, Toothbrush Holder, Drain Bottom, John Edwards	24.00
Ironstone, Tureen & Attached Underplate, California, F.M.& Co., 7 1/2 In.	42.00
Ironstone, Tureen & Underplate, Gravy, Blue & White	25.00
Ironstone, Tureen & Underplate, Gravy, Covered, White, Floral, Handled, Meakin	23.00
Ironstone, Tureen, Covered, Cyprus, Brown, 7 1/4 In. Long	9.50 To 25.00
Ironstone, Tureen, Covered, Gray Transfer Print, Octagonal, 11 3/4 In.	90.00
Ironstone, Tureen, Soup, Blackberry, Meakin	50.00
Ironstone, Tureen, Underplate, & Ladle, Scenic, Sepia, Alcock, C.1830, 11 In.	175.00
Ironstone, Tureen, Vegetable, Covered, Blue & White, Cyprus Banner, 12 In.	55.00
Ironstone, Vase, Urn Shape, Castles, Blues, Handled, Mayer, 12 In., Pair	125.00
Ironstone, Washstand Set, Oriental Scenes, 16 Sided, Mason's, 2 Piece	150.00
Ironstone, Washstand Set, Rainbow Effect, Gold, Meakin, 2 Piece	95.00
Ironstone, Washstand Set, Red Poppies, Johnson Bros., 3 Piece	95.00
Ironstone, Washstand Set, White, Ribbed, 3 X 3 In., 2 Piece	15.00
Ivory, see also Bottle, Snuff, Netsuke	
Ivory, Back Scratcher, Carved Bone Hand, Wooden Handle, 13 In.	10.00
Ivory, Back Scratcher, Inlaid Coral Studs, Gold Band, 13 In.	80.00
Ivory, Bookmark, Japanese, Carved, Cord With Ojimes & Ivory Cat	45.00
Ivory, Bottle, Snuff, Carved Foo Dog, Polychromed, 2 1/2 In.	92.00
Ivory, Box, Covered, Carved, Round, 4 X 3 1/4 In.	195.00
Ivory, Box, Phoenix In Bamboo Grove On Lid, Dragons, Round, 2 In.	40.00
Ivory, Box, Trinket, Miniature Portrait On Lid, Round, 2 1/2 In.	75.00
Ivory, Brush, Barber's, Hand-Carved	10.00
Ivory, Burner, Incense, Dragons, Grotesque Mask Feet, Foo Dogs, 14 1/4 In.	550.00
Ivory, Candlestick, Russian, Carved Polar Bears, 7 In., Pair	165.00
Ivory, Case, Needle, In Form Of Umbrella	45.00
Ivory, Cigarette Holder, Carved Lioness, 3 1/2 In.	5.00
Ivory, Cigarette Holder, Hand-Carved Dragons, 7 In.	15.00
Ivory, Comb, Brilliants	5.50
Ivory, Corkscrew, Whale's Tooth, Sterling Silver Fitting At Top	35.00
Ivory, Doll, Doctor's, Carved, Teakwood Base, 9 In.	75.00
Ivory, Figurine, Chinese Sage With Walking Stick, 5 In.	400.00
Ivory, Figurine, China Wiseman, Staff In Hand & Fruit, 3 3/4 X 1 1/4 In.	70.00
Ivory, Figurine, Crab, Hinged Legs & Claws, Fan-Shaped Shell, C.1850, 8 In.	400.00
Ivory, Figurine, Elephant, Jewellike Stones, Ebony Wood Base, 1 1/2 In.	100.00
Ivory, Figurine, Elephant, 2 In.	8.50
Ivory, Figurine, Farmer, Standing, Grasping Sea Eagle, C.1850, 8 3/4 In.	275.00
Ivory, Figurine, Four Seasons, French, C.1850, 9 3/8 In., Set Of 4	1700.00
Ivory, Figurine, God Of Contentment, C.1821, 4 In.	125.00
Ivory, Figurine, Guard Dogs, Carved, 6 In., Pair	410.00
Ivory, Figurine, Hotie, 7 In.	138.75
Ivory, Figurine, Kwannon, Pierced Nimbus With Dragon, C.1850, 10 In.	375.00
Ivory, Figurine, Man Holding Broom On Basket With Sleeping Cat, 1 3/4 In.	100.00
Ivory, Figurine, Old Man With Staff, Oriental, Signed, 7 In.	100.00
Ivory, Figurine, Oriental Lady Holding Rose, Hand-Carved, 8 In.	35.00
Ivory, Figurine, Rabbit, Red Eyes, 1 1/2 In.	85.00
Ivory, Figurine, St.George On Horse Slaying Dragon, C.1925, 6 In.	150.00
Ivory, Figurine, Temple Dog, Carved, Chinese, 6 In., Pair	395.00
Ivory, Figurine, Woman With Musical Instrument, Carved, Signed, 7 In.	100.00
Ivory, Frame, Picture, Floral Carving, Oval, 3 3/4 X 3 In.	18.50

Ivory, Glove Stretcher, 8 In.	10.00
Ivory, Group, Chinese General, Woman Seated, 6 1/2 In.	160.00
Ivory, Group, Courtesan Offering Tray To Benten, 4 In.	700.00
Ivory, Group, Courtesan, Elderly Priest At Her Feet, 3 5/8 In.	700.00
Ivory, Group, Elephant Bridge, 7 Elephants, Wooden Base, 17 In.	138.00 To 145.00
Ivory, Group, Farmer Holding Pole, Small Boy, 7 3/8 In.	275.00
Ivory, Group, Japanese Woman, Holding Son, C.1890, 7 1/2 In.	175.00
Ivory, Group, Nessus & Dejanira On Centaur, French, C.1850, 8 7/8 In.	1100.00
Ivory, Group, Rabbit & Baby Rabbit, Red Eyes, 2 In.	100.00
Ivory, Group, Samurai Warrior & 2 Children, Teak Stand, 7 1/2 In.	500.00
Ivory, Group, Three Ruffians Bullying Another Man, 5 3/8 In.	475.00
Ivory, Hairpin, Leather Box, 5 1/2 In., Pair	25.00
Ivory, Holder, Watch, Carved, 11 In. *Illus*	265.00

Ivory, Holder, Watch,
Carved, 11 In.

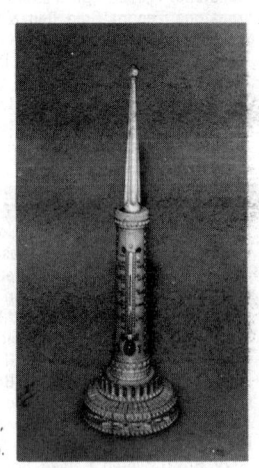

Ivory, Thermometer,
1865, 9 In.

Ivory, Knife, Paper, Japanese, Inlaid Mother-Of-Pearl & Stones, C.1885	38.00
Ivory, Letter Opener & Pen, Carved, 3 Screw-Together Sections, 9 In.	35.00
Ivory, Letter Opener, 16 Carved Elephants	7.50
Ivory, Necklace, White & Purple Beads, 48 In. Long	10.00
Ivory, Pin, Carved 2 Deer In Forest, 1 1/2 In.	20.00
Ivory, Plaque, Shibayama, Bird & Floral, Pearl & Tortoiseshell, C.1850, 8 In.	300.00
Ivory, Seal, Wax Holder, Pagoda Form, Floral, 2 Piece, 2 3/4 X 1 1/4 In.	85.00
Ivory, Snuffbox, Gold Mounted, Gouache Miniature On Lid, C.1780, 3 7/8 In.	250.00
Ivory, Snuffbox, Mauet, Paris, Lady & Gentleman In Garden, Gold Fittings	175.00
Ivory, Tankard, Equestrian Battle, Repousse Silver Mounted, C.1850, 13 In.	1300.00
Ivory, Thermometer, 1865, 9 In. *Illus*	55.00
Ivory, Toothpick, Folding, Carved, C.1850, 4 In.	15.00
Ivory, Tusk, Elephant, Carved, Silver Mounts At End, 29 In.Long, C.1800	300.00

*Jack-In-The-Pulpit vases were named for their odd trumpetlike shape
that resembles the wild plant called jack-in-the-pulpit. The design
originated in the late Victorian years.*

Jack-In-The-Pulpit, Vase, Amberina Swirl, Applied Amber Foot & Top, 12 In.	165.00
Jack-In-The-Pulpit, Vase, Blue & Opalescent, Crimped Top, 5 1/2 In.High	27.50
Jack-In-The-Pulpit, Vase, Blue With Opalescent Trim, 7 In.	35.00
Jack-In-The-Pulpit, Vase, Czechoslovakia, White Jade, 10 In.	35.00
Jack-In-The-Pulpit, Vase, Fiery Opalescent Petals, Clear Veins, 11 1/2 In.	95.00
Jack-In-The-Pulpit, Vase, Green, Fluted & Crimped, Milk Glass Base, 6 In.	50.00
Jack-In-The-Pulpit, Vase, Green, Spiral Fluted, Milk Glass, Base, 6 3/4 In.	50.00
Jack-In-The-Pulpit, Vase, Light To Opalescent, Crimped, 7 In., Pair	60.00
Jack-In-The-Pulpit, Vase, Opalescent Blue Lattice, Hobnail, Fluted, 9 In.	72.50
Jack-In-The-Pulpit, Vase, Opalescent Swirls, 10 In.	55.00
Jack-In-The-Pulpit, Vase, Red To Light Red Band, Waffle Base, 7 1/2 In.	65.00
Jack-In-The-Pulpit, Vase, Red To White, Clear Threading, Green Top, 12 In.	75.00
Jack-In-The-Pulpit, Vase, White, Pink Lining, 9 In.	20.00

Jackfield ware was originally a black glazed pottery made in Jackfield, England, since 1630. A yellow glazed ware has also been called Jackfield ware. Most of the pieces referred to as Jackfield are black pieces made during the Victorian era.

Jackfield, Creamer, Cow, Black Glaze	42.00
Jackfield, Creamer, Cow, Covered, Shiny Black, Gold Trim, 4 3/4 In. High	75.00
Jackfield, Creamer, Eagle Handle, C.1850, 3 In.	35.00
Jackfield, Tea Set, Blue Enamel Flowers, 3 Piece	150.00
Jackfield, Teabowl & Saucer, Black Glaze, Fruiting Vines, Gilding, C.1765	50.00
Jackfield, Teapot, Black, Floral & Birds, Bird's Head Spout, 4 In.	55.00
Jacob Petit, Bottle, Scent, Raised Flowers, 6 In.	75.00
Jacob Petit, Toby Mug, Portly Gentleman, Tricorner Hat, C.1850, 9 1/2 In.	110.00
Jade, Buckle, Carved Dragon, White, 3 1/4 In.	150.00
Jade, Cup, Mutton Fat, White	35.00
Jade, Figurine, Fantail Goldfish, Apple Green, Wood Base, 3 In.	90.00 To 145.00
Jade, Figurine, Foo Dog, Sitting, Winged, Green, Carved, 3 1/2 X 5 1/2 In.	200.00
Jade, Figurine, Lion, Roaring, Green, Wooden Stand, 2 1/2 X 3 In., Pair	115.00
Jade, Figurine, Rabbit, Oriental, Tail Up, 2 3/4 In.	65.00
Jade, Frame, Mutton Fat, Carved, 12 X 15 In.	200.00
Jade, Saucer, Snuff, Liver, Turquoise Rooster Sitting On Side	45.00

Jasperware is a fine-grained pottery developed by Josiah Wedgwood in 1755. The jasper was made in many colors including the most famous, a light blue. It is still being made.

Jasperware, see also Wedgwood

Jasperware, Box, Germany, Blue, Heart Shape, White Classical Figures, 3 In.	20.00
Jasperware, Box, Green, Queen Louise On Lid, Heart Shape, Floral, 5 In.	85.00
Jasperware, Creamer, Light Brown, White Grapes & Leaves, 3 1/4 In.	32.00
Jasperware, Pitcher, Dark Blue, Classical Medallions, 4 1/2 In.	35.00
Jasperware, Plaque, Green, White Girl On Tree Stump & Cupid, 5 1/2 In.	45.00
Jasperware, Plaque, Light Blue, White Classical Lady & Harp, 3 1/2 In.	35.00
Jasperware, Spoon & Fork, Salad, Blue, 11 In.	125.00

Jewelry, see also Coronation, Faberge

Jewelry, Bangle, 14K Gold, Turquoise Studded Anchor, Victorian	325.00
Jewelry, Beads, Flapper, Iridescent Red, 45 In.	8.00
Jewelry, Beads, Flapper, 1920s, Glass & Wood, Orange Tassel, 50 In.	27.50

Jewelery, Bracelet, see also Orphan Annie, Bracelet

Jewelry, Bracelet, Bangle, Six Garnets, 14K Gold	110.00
Jewelry, Bracelet, Century Of Progress, 1933, Copper	5.00
Jewelry, Bracelet, Gold Plated, Victorian, Engraved	30.00
Jewelry, Bracelet, World's Fair, 1939, Penny	12.00
Jewelry, Bracelet, 14K White Gold, 3 Topaz, 2 Diamonds, C.1920	175.00
Jewelry, Brooch & Earrings, Cameo, Garnet, Pearls ....Illus	600.00
Jewelry, Brooch, Enamel, Lady With Book, Gold Frame	275.00
Jewelry, Brooch, Limoges Enamel, Lovely Woman, Sterling Frame	65.00
Jewelry, Brooch, Russian Imperial Crown, Gold, Enamel, Jeweled, C.1890, 2 In.	800.00
Jewelry, Brooch, Russian Imperial Eagle, Gold, Diamonds, C.1890, 1 3/8 In.	575.00

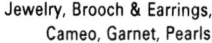

Jewelry, Brooch & Earrings,
Cameo, Garnet, Pearls

Jewelry, Brooch, Silver, Turquoise Flower Centers, Square, 1 1/8 In.	50.00
Jewelry, Brooch, Sterling Oval, Onyx & Mosaic, Italy, C.1860	105.00
Jewelry, Brooch, Sterling Silver, Victorian	5.00
Jewelry, Brooch, 18K Gold, 5 Raised Hearts & Floral, C.Civil War	385.00
Jewelry, Cameo, Victorian, Lady's Bust, Diamond In Hair, Coral, 14K Gold	125.00
Jewelry, Charm, Knight Of Columbus, 14K Gold, Enameled, C.1920, 2 In.	150.00
Jewelry, Charm, Poodle, Gold, 1/2 In.	20.00
Jewelry, Charm, Rabbit, Platinum, Diamond, Ruby Eyes, 1/2 In.	225.00
Jewelry, Chatelaine, English Sterling, Ivory Inserts, C.1850	450.00
Jewelry, Cross & Chain, 18K Gold, C.1850, Applied Pink Gold Flowers	795.00
Jewelry, Earrings, Georgian Silver, Rose Diamonds, Pierced, Teardrop, Pair	185.00
Jewelry, Earrings, Gold Orchids, Pearl, Panama, 1920s, Pair	100.00
Jewelry, Earrings, Pierced, 18K Yellow Gold Hoop, Rock Crystal, C.1850	110.00
Jewelry, Earrings, Sapphire, 18K Gold Wires, Victorian	35.00
Jewelry, Indian, see Indian	
Jewelry, Lavaliere, Art Nouveau Silver, Turquoise, 3 Segments, Filigree	85.00
Jewelry, Lavaliere, 10K Yellow Gold Chain & Drop, Amethyst, C.1890	120.00
Jewelry, Locket, Heart, 14K Gold, Turquoise & Rose Diamonds, Victorian	145.00
Jewelry, Locket, Mourning, Gold, Oval, Glass Back, Dated 1815, 2 1/2 In.	55.00
Jewelry, Locket, Victorian, Double, Seed Pearls, Enameled, Hallmarked	65.00
Jewelry, Necklace, Diamond Paste, Hallmarked France, 1840	100.00
Jewelry, Necklace, Pollera, 24K Gold, Handmade, C.1850, 60 In.	550.00
Jewelry, Pendant, Art Deco, Marcasite, Rhinestones Center, C.1928, 2 1/4 In.	12.50
Jewelry, Pendant, Victorian, Diamond Shape, 300 Seed Pearls On Horsehair	30.00
Jewelry, Pin With Pendant, Victorian, Diamond, Locket Back, 15K Gold	75.00
Jewelry, Pin, Art Nouveau Lady In Profile, Metal, 2 3/4 X 2 1/4 In.	35.00
Jewelry, Pin, Cameo, Queen Victoria Jubilee, Onyx, White Face, Sterling Set	28.00
Jewelry, Pin, Centennial, 1776-1876, Red Glass, Memorial Hall, 1 1/2 In.	55.00
Jewelry, Pin, Crescent, 29 Graduated Cultured Pearls, C.1890, 2 1/4 In.	85.00
Jewelry, Pin, Gold Flower Form, Pearl Bud, Enameled Tulip, 1 In.	55.00
Jewelry, Pin, Gold, Enamel Woman's Portrait, F.Vernon, C.1900	250.00
Jewelry, Pin, Lapel, Man's, 3 Owls On Branch, 1900, Lodge & Name	6.00
Jewelry, Pin, Mother-Of-Pearl, Victorian, Oval, 2 1/4 X 1 1/2 In.	15.00
Jewelry, Pin, Mourning, Black Enamel, 15 K Gold, Dated, 1870	100.00
Jewelry, Pin, Scarf Holder, 14K Gold, Victorian, C.1870	38.00
Jewelry, Pin, Scarf, Victorian, Gold, Turquoise & Diamond	65.00
Jewelry, Pin, Solid Gold Bar, Civil War Era, Applied Hearts & Flowers	350.00
Jewelry, Pin, Victorian, Gold Filled, Purple Stone In Middle, 2 In.	25.00
Jewelry, Pin, Watch, Art Nouveau, 2 Girls & Grass, Gold Filled, 1903	24.00
Jewelry, Ring, see also Disneyana, Ring, Hopalong Cassidy, Ring, Shirley Temple, Ring	
Jewelry, Ring, Black Onyx, 14K Gold Dancing Girl, Art Deco	65.00
Jewelry, Ring, Cocktail, 3 Diamonds & 6 Rubies In 14K Gold, 1930s	60.00
Jewelry, Ring, Krazy Kat, Goldstone & Composition	8.50
Jewelry, Ring, Lalique Type Crystal & Diamond In 14K Gold, Victorian	42.00
Jewelry, Ring, Lapis Lazuli Cameo, Art Nouveau Gold Setting	195.00
Jewelry, Ring, Remembrance, Swivel, Silver Flower, Diamonds, 14K Gold, 1839	197.00
Jewelry, Ring, Turquoise, 14K Gold Setting, Victorian	135.00
Jewelry, Ring, Wedding Band, Victorian, 18K Gold, Raised Leaf, Size 6 1/2	35.00
Jewelry, Ring, 14K Yellow Gold, Opal, U.S.A., C.1900	115.00
Jewelry, Ring, 18K Yellow Gold, 2 Garnets & Emeralds, France, C.1870	95.00
Jewelry, Ring, 2 Pearls & 3 Rubies In 15K Yellow Gold, Chester, Eng., 1885	100.00
Jewelry, Ring, 7 Diamonds In 14K Gold Victorian Openwork Setting	85.00
Jewelry, Scarab, Egyptian, Iridescent, Mounted	37.50
Jewelry, Stickpin, Bust Of Satan Holding Pearl	175.00
Jewelry, Stickpin, Garnet, Square Stone, 10 K White Gold	30.00
Jewelry, Stickpin, Great Seal of the U.S., Sterling	5.00
Jewelry, Stickpin, Pan American Exposition, Frypan Shape	5.50
Jewelry, Stickpin, White Gold Filigree, Diamond, Sapphire, U.S.A., C.1890	67.00
Jewelry, Stickpin, 18K Yellow Gold, Ruby, France, C.1870	53.00
Jewelry, Tie Clasp, World War II Tank, Fort Campbell	3.00
Jewelry, Watch, see Watch	

John Rogers statues were made from 1859 to 1892. The originals were bronze, but the thousands of copies made by the Rogers Factory were of painted plaster. Eighty different figures were made.

John Rogers, Group, Campfire, Painted, Signed	1100.00
John Rogers, Group, Council Of War, Painted, Signed	750.00
John Rogers, Group, Parting Promise, Signed	335.00
Judaica, Amulet, Cast Silver, Hexagonal, Hebrew Inscription, 2 1/2 In.	40.00
Judaica, Amulet, Mideast, Silver, Gilt, Copper Bands, 12 In.	300.00
Judaica, Amulet, Vienna, C.1833, Silver, Filigree, Medallion Center	350.00
Judaica, Ark, Torah, Mideast, Bronze, Hinged Door, Star Of David, 16 In.	450.00
Judaica, Ark, Torah, Wooden, 3 Tiers, Metal Appliques, 13 1/2 In.	750.00
Judaica, Basket, Fruit, Jerusalem, Silver, Ivory, Green Stones, 10 In.	600.00
Judaica, Belt, Marriage, Persian, Silver, Oval Medallion	275.00
Judaica, Belt, Marriage, Russian, C.1850, Silver, Gilt, Filigree	400.00
Judaica, Book, Bible & Grammar, Lipsiae, 1733, Vellum Jacket	100.00
Judaica, Book, Hebrew-Latin Dictionary, Basel, 1631, Vellum Jacket	130.00
Judaica, Book, Passover Haggadah, Amsterdam, 1695, Leather Jacket	2200.00
Judaica, Book, Prayer, Amsterdam, 1740, Fabric Binding	100.00
Judaica, Book, Prayer, French, C.1850, Silver Repousse Jacket	100.00
Judaica, Book, Prayer, High Holiday, Florence, 1735, Leather, Gilt, Silver	125.00
Judaica, Book, Prayer, Italian, C.1750, Leather, Silver Medallion	1700.00
Judaica, Book, Prayer, Livorno, 1854, Silver Jacket, Aaron & Moses	200.00
Judaica, Book, Prayer, London, 1916, Silver Jacket, Ivory Inlays	350.00
Judaica, Book, Psalms, Repousse Silver Jacket & Clasp	600.00
Judaica, Book, Works Of Flavius Josephus, Birmingham, 1770	170.00
Judaica, Box, Alms, Silver, C.1900, Tankard Shape, Repousse, 5 3/4 In.	675.00
Judaica, Box, Circumcision, Mohel, Carved Wood, 10 Commandments, 3 3/4 In.	60.00
Judaica, Box, Ethrog, Fruit Shape, Silver Plate, 6 1/2 In.	125.00
Judaica, Candlestick, Continental, Silver, Lion Mounts, 13 5/8 In., Pair	800.00
Judaica, Carrier, Water, Mediterranean, C.1850, Brass, Hebraic Inscription	170.00
Judaica, Case, Amulet, Silver, Chased Foliage, Heart Center, 4 In.	90.00
Judaica, Case, Amulet, Silver, Filigree, Blue Stones, 3 In.	70.00
Judaica, Case, Megillah, European, C.1900, Esther, King, & 2 Guards, 19 In.	650.00
Judaica, Case, Mezzuzah, Copper, Metal Foliate Mounts, Stones, 13 In.	275.00
Judaica, Case, Torah, Eastern, Silver, Stylized Floral, Glass Panels, 35 In.	1500.00
Judaica, Case, Torah, Silver Filigree, C.1850, Hinged Door, 5 In.	275.00
Judaica, Case, Torah, Silver Plate, Hebraic Inscriptions, Stones, 5 1/4 In.	175.00
Judaica, Circumcision Set, Silver, Agate Handle, C.1700, 2 Piece	250.00
Judaica, Circumcision Set, Sterling Silver, Chased Foliage, 4 Piece	250.00
Judaica, Container, Spice, Austria, C.1890, Silver, Tower Shape, 6 In.	150.00
Judaica, Container, Spice, Continental, C.1890, Silver, Basket, Filigree, 2 In.	225.00
Judaica, Container, Spice, Continental, C.1890, Silver, Flower & Fruit Shape	550.00
Judaica, Container, Spice, Continental, C.1890, Silver, Flower Shape, Filigree	375.00
Judaica, Container, Spice, Continental, C.1890, Silver, Tower Shape, 17 In.	600.00
Judaica, Container, Spice, German, C.1930, Silver Plate, Tower Shape, 4 In.	60.00
Judaica, Container, Spice, Palestinian, Silver, Ram Shape, 8 In.	850.00
Judaica, Container, Spice, Pewter, C.1750, Sliding Top Panel, Footed, 3 1/4 In	230.00
Judaica, Container, Spice, Pewter, Flared Foot, Detachable Cap, 5 In.	70.00
Judaica, Container, Spice, Russian, 1872, Tower Shape, Silver, Hinged, 9 In.	300.00
Judaica, Container, Spice, Silver, Bird Shape, C.1900, Detachable Head, 3 In.	200.00
Judaica, Container, Spice, Silver, Filigree, Amphora Shape, 5 In.	150.00
Judaica, Container, Spice, Silver, Mule Shape, Detachable Head, 3 In.	275.00
Judaica, Container, Spice, Silver, Parcel Gilt, Fish Shape, C.1890, 5 1/4 In.	300.00
Judaica, Container, Spice, Silver, Tower Shape, Hinged Door, 6 In.	200.00
Judaica, Container, Spice, Silver, Tower Shape, Hinged Door, 7 1/4 In.	250.00
Judaica, Container, Spice, Silver, Tower Shape, Ivory Inlay, 12 In.	300.00
Judaica, Container, Spice, South America, Gourd, Silver Mounts, Gold Cup	175.00
Judaica, Container, Spice, Sterling Silver, Scalloped Form, Chased, 2 1/4 In.	80.00
Judaica, Crown, Torah, Silver, Eastern Europe, Double Tiered, 19 In.	1800.00
Judaica, Cup, Ceremonial, Silver, 3 Handles, Chased, Hebrew Inscription	325.00
Judaica, Cup, Funeral, Copper, 2 Handled, Lion & Menorah Applique, 5 In.	350.00
Judaica, Cup, Kiddush, Berlin, C.1850, Silver, Molded Foot, 5 3/4 In.	375.00
Judaica, Cup, Kiddush, Chinese, C.1900, Silver, Scroll Handle, 3 3/4 In.	375.00
Judaica, Cup, Kiddush, Continental, C.1900, Silver, Repousse, 7 1/8 In.	275.00
Judaica, Cup, Kiddush, Palestinian, Silver, Hebraic Inscription, Footed, 4 In.	250.00
Judaica, Cup, Kiddush, Silver, Presentation, 1860, Scroll Handle, 4 1/8 In.	300.00
Judaica, Gavel, Continental, Ivory, Judgment Of Solomon & Babel	250.00
Judaica, Globe, Scholar's, Brass, Arabic & Hebrew Inscriptions, 6 3/4 In.	325.00
Judaica, Goblet & Stand, Wine, Vienna, 1857, Silver, Covered, 10 5/8 In.	800.00

Judaica, Goblet, Silver, Foliate Design, Knopped Stem, 5 In.	300.00
Judaica, Goblet, Wine, Ivory, Hebraic Inscription, Knopped Stem, 7 3/8 In.	325.00
Judaica, Habdulah Spice Container, Silver, C.1890, 4 Twisted Columns, 7 In.	450.00
Judaica, Habdulah, European, C.1850, Silver, Lions & Grapevines, 6 In.	450.00
Judaica, Habdulah, Moscow, 1864, Silver, Gilt, Bone Plaques, Wine Cup	850.00
Judaica, Headdress, Bride's, Yemenite, Silver, Blue Stones, Gilt	400.00
Judaica, Headpiece, Marriage, Yemenite, C.1850, Central Medallion	1100.00
Judaica, Headpiece, Torah, Brass, Mideast, Knop Finial, 12 1/4 In., Pair	175.00
Judaica, Headpiece, Torah, Mediterranean, C.1800, Silver, Flag Top, 9 In., Pair	375.00
Judaica, Headpiece, Torah, Mediterranean, C.1850, Silver, 9 In., Pair	400.00
Judaica, Headpiece, Torah, Silver Plate, Lion & Shield Top, 11 3/4 In., Pair	130.00
Judaica, Headpiece, Torah, Silver, Austrian, C.1900, Pierced Floral, 12 In.	300.00
Judaica, Headpiece, Torah, Silver, Blue Stone Top, Mideast, C.1890, Pair	275.00
Judaica, Headpiece, Torah, Silver, Eagle End, C.1900, 16 1/4 In., Pair	375.00
Judaica, Headpiece, Torah, Silver, Eastern Europe, C.1900, Eagle On Orb, Pair	650.00
Judaica, Headpiece, Torah, Silver, Eastern Mediterranean, 12 In., Pair	250.00
Judaica, Headpiece, Torah, Silver, Hebraic Inscription, C.1830, 12 In., Pair	850.00
Judaica, Headpiece, Torah, Silver, Mideast, C.1850, Star Finial, 11 In., Pair	750.00
Judaica, Headpiece, Torah, Silver, Turquoise, Carnelian, & Stones, Pair	200.00
Judaica, Knife, Circumcision, Silver, Binding Of Isaac On Handle, 5 In.	90.00
Judaica, Knife, Circumcision, Silver, Mother-Of-Pearl, 1854, 7 1/2 In.	225.00
Judaica, Lamp, Hanging, Brass, Dome, Openwork Grill, 6 In.	130.00
Judaica, Lamp, Hanukkah, American, C.1890, Hammered Tin, 8 Wells, 7 1/4 In.	175.00
Judaica, Lamp, Hanukkah, Europe, C.1850, Brass, 2 Candle Socles, 4 1/4 In.	120.00
Judaica, Lamp, Hanukkah, Franz Fornier, 1852, Silver, Binding Of Isaac, 7 In.	750.00
Judaica, Lamp, Hanukkah, Oil, German, Silver, C.1900, 12 1/2 In.	2700.00
Judaica, Lamp, Hanukkah, Polish, C.1850, Silver, Menorah & Lion, 8 1/4 In.	425.00
Judaica, Lamp, Memorial, Hanging, Turkish, Scroll Bracket, 21 In.	130.00
Judaica, Lamp, Oil, Brass, 4 Light, Loop & Branch Finial, 8 7/8 In.	110.00
Judaica, Lamp, Oil, Italian, C.1750, Brass, Baluster Shaft, 23 1/2 In.	175.00
Judaica, Lamp, Oil, Moscow, 1850, Suspended By Chains, 3 1/4 In. Diameter	275.00
Judaica, Lamp, Sabbath & Festival, Brass, C.1850, 6 Oil Reserves, 13 1/2 In.	300.00
Judaica, Lamp, Sabbath & Festival, Brass, 8 Oil Reserves, 23 In.	450.00
Judaica, Marriage Contract, Moshe Ben Abraham & Rachael Bat Ezekiel, 1860	130.00
Judaica, Marriage Contract, Shalom Ben Mier & Sarah Bat Jokotiel, 1740	300.00
Judaica, Megillah, Continental, C.1830, Silver, Gilt, Scroll, Book Of Esther	1600.00
Judaica, Megillah, Ivory, Scroll, Book Of Esther, 7 1/8 In.	350.00
Judaica, Megillah, Mediterranean, C.1850, Brass & Copper, Silver Plaques	600.00
Judaica, Megillah, Mediterranean, Silver, Ivory, Scroll, Book Of Esther	475.00
Judaica, Megillah, Mideast, C.1850, Silver, Gilt, Scroll, Book Of Esther	325.00
Judaica, Megillah, Silver, Moscow, 1874, Illuminated Scroll, Esther	800.00
Judaica, Megillah, Silver, Scroll, Book Of Esther, 10 In.	525.00
Judaica, Menorah, Hanukkah, 4 Branches Of 8 Socles, Center Socle, 18 In.	400.00
Judaica, Mezzuzah, Silver, Pierced, Sliding Top, 6 1/2 In.	125.00
Judaica, Mezzuzah, Silver, Repousse, Hinged Cap, Stones, 9 1/2 In.	225.00
Judaica, Mezzuzah, Silver, Repousse, Pierced, Hinged Cap, 9 1/2 In.	300.00
Judaica, Necklace, Persian, C.1890, Gold, Pendant, Hebraic Inscription	650.00
Judaica, Necklace, Persian, Silver, Pendant, Hebraic Inscription	250.00
Judaica, Necklace, Silver, Amulet, Chainwork, Bells	125.00
Judaica, Noisemaker, Purim, Silver, Mordecai & Haman, 5 In.	425.00
Judaica, Noisemaker, Purim, Wooden, Baluster-Shaped Handle, 8 1/2 In.	130.00
Judaica, Noisemaker, Purim, Wooden, Turn Handle, 11 1/2 In.	100.00
Judaica, Noisemaker, Purim, Wooden, Turn Handle, 6 In.	110.00
Judaica, Picture, On Leather, Haman, King, & Esther, Mideast, 8 1/4 In.	90.00
Judaica, Pitcher, Passover, Continental, C.1850, Pewter, Hinged Cap, 11 In.	550.00
Judaica, Plaque, Adoration Of The Torah, Ivory, 6 3/4 X 5 1/2 In.	170.00
Judaica, Plate, Copper, Binding Of Isaac, Abraham Center, 10 1/8 In.	100.00
Judaica, Plate, Mideast, Copper, Benjamin Scenes, 15 3/8 In.	50.00
Judaica, Plate, Mideast, Copper, Silver Wash, Judgment Of Solomon, 19 In.	225.00
Judaica, Plate, Passover, Brass, Etched Designs, 15 3/4 In.	50.00
Judaica, Plate, Passover, Continental, C.1900, Silver, Scenes, 18 7/8 In.	575.00
Judaica, Plate, Passover, Dutch, Pewter, 11 1/8 In.	225.00
Judaica, Plate, Passover, Europe, C.1900, Silver, Exodus, 11 7/8 In.	700.00
Judaica, Plate, Passover, Mediterranean, Copper, Silver Wash, 18 5/8 In.	175.00
Judaica, Plate, Seder, Judgment Of Solomon, 13 1/2 In.	300.00
Judaica, Poem, Marriage, Joseph Cohen Moden & Esther, On Silk	550.00

Judaica, Pointer, Continental, Ivory, Twisted Center, 11 3/4 In.	200.00
Judaica, Pointer, Torah, Continental, C.1850, Silver, Crown Top, 8 In.	300.00
Judaica, Pointer, Torah, Continental, C.1890, Silver, Flat Knop, 10 1/4 In.	250.00
Judaica, Pointer, Torah, Continental, C.1890, Silver, Gilt, Ball Loop, 6 In.	150.00
Judaica, Pointer, Torah, Continental, C.1890, Silver, Gilt, Pierced Crown	300.00
Judaica, Pointer, Torah, Continental, C.1890, Silver, Hand With Cuff, 18 In.	275.00
Judaica, Pointer, Torah, Israeli, Silver, Half-Ball Finial & Loop, 12 In.	150.00
Judaica, Pointer, Torah, Italian, Silver, Ball Finial, 6 3/4 In.	150.00
Judaica, Pointer, Torah, Mideast, Brass, Chain End, 10 1/4 In.	90.00
Judaica, Pointer, Torah, Mideast, Silver, Stone & Medallion, 9 In.	125.00
Judaica, Pointer, Torah, Silver Filigree, C.1890, Fish End, 21 In.	275.00
Judaica, Pointer, Torah, Silver, Ball Finial, 21 In.	125.00
Judaica, Pointer, Torah, Silver, C.1850, Hebraic Inscription, 11 1/2 In.	150.00
Judaica, Pointer, Torah, Silver, C.1890, Hand & Sleeve, 12 1/4 In.	175.00
Judaica, Pointer, Torah, Silver, Foliate Knops & Finial, 11 3/4 In.	150.00
Judaica, Pointer, Torah, Silver, Hinged Spice Box Dome, 17 In.	250.00
Judaica, Pointer, Torah, Silver, Ivory Rod, Dragon & Serpent, 9 3/4 In.	325.00
Judaica, Pointer, Torah, Silver, Ivory Spice Box Top, C.1850, 18 1/4 In.	350.00
Judaica, Ring, Marriage, Gold, C.1750, 2 Story Synagogue	1500.00
Judaica, Ring, Marriage, Gold, Hinged House, Blue Stone	550.00
Judaica, Ring, Marriage, Silver, C.1720, Hinged Synagogue	1100.00
Judaica, Ring, Marriage, Silver, C.1820, Openwork Dome	300.00
Judaica, Ring, Marriage, Silver, C.1850, Openwork Synagogue	850.00
Judaica, Ring, Signet, Silver, Hebraic Inscription	60.00
Judaica, Scroll, Book Of Esther, Leather, Wooden Handles, 15 In.	750.00
Judaica, Scroll, Torah, Parchment, Silver Roller, Embroidered Cover, 13 In.	300.00
Judaica, Sheet, Prayer, Bible Scenes, C.1850, 20 X 17 1/4 In.	350.00
Judaica, Sheet, Study, Parchment, Anniversary Of The Dead, 14 X 10 5/8 In.	50.00
Judaica, Shofar, Ram's Horn, Curved, Flat, Scalloped End, 8 3/4 In.	50.00
Judaica, Shofar, Ram's Horn, Hebraic Inscriptions & Foliate, 14 1/2 In.	90.00
Judaica, Shofar, Ram's Horn, Hebraic Inscriptions, 10 1/2 In.	175.00
Judaica, Shofar, Ram's Horn, Silver Foliate Band, Cutouts, 17 In.	250.00
Judaica, Shofar, Ram's Horn, Twisted, 7 3/4 In.	90.00
Judaica, Shofar, Ram's Horn, Twisted, 19 In.	110.00
Judaica, Shofar, Yemenite, Ram's Horn, Twisted, 33 In.	225.00
Judaica, Snuffbox, Silver, C.1820, Star Of David, 2 3/4 In.	120.00
Judaica, Tifillin, Leather, Metal Case, 4 X 2 1/2 In.	40.00
Judaica, Torah Breastplate, German, C.1900, Silver, Parcel Gilt, 12 1/2 In.	900.00
Judaica, Torah Breastplate, Russian, 1900 .... Illus	1200.00
Judaica, Torah Breastplate, Silver Plate, 10 Commandments, 12 In., Pair	425.00
Jugtown, Bowl Vase, Blue Green & Red Purple Top, Red Brown Base, 3 1/2 In.	15.00
Jugtown, Bowl, Mottled Brown, Lift-Up Handles, Covered, 6 1/4 X 4 In.	35.00

Kate Greenaway, who was a famous illustrator of children's books, drew pictures of children in high-waisted Empire dresses. She lived from about 1846 to 1901. Her designs appear on china, glass, and other pieces.

Judaica, Torah Breastplate, Russian, 1900

Kate Greenaway, see also Napkin Ring

Kate Greenaway, Almanac, 1884	75.00
Kate Greenaway, Book, Alphabet	20.00
Kate Greenaway, Book, Birthday	40.00
Kate Greenaway, Book, Mother Goose	40.00
Kate Greenaway, Button, Sterling, "Pussycat, Pussycat, Where Have You Been"	15.00
Kate Greenaway, Cup & Saucer, Child's, Girl & Sled, Germany	32.00
Kate Greenaway, Dish, Child's, This Is The House That Jack Built, 6 1/2 In.	40.00
Kate Greenaway, Dish, Child's, This Is The Maiden All Forlorn, 6 1/2 In.	40.00
Kate Greenaway, Dish, Feeding, 7 Scenes, 8 1/4 In.	42.00
Kate Greenaway, Mug, Cream, Sarreguemines, Children, 3 1/4 In.	15.00
Kate Greenaway, Napkin Ring, 2 Small Boys, Middletown Silver Co.	85.00
Kate Greenaway, Paperweight, Kate With Umbrella & Butterfly, Tuft's, 9 In.	125.00
Kate Greenaway, Parasol, Pink Silk, 72 Children Playing, Bamboo Handle	42.00
Kate Greenaway, Salt & Pepper, Boy & Girl, Pair	55.00
Kate Greenaway, Salt & Pepper, Boy & Girl, Sailor Outfit	75.00
Kate Greenaway, Salt & Pepper, Girl & Boy	50.00
Kate Greenaway, Saltshaker, Britannia Type Metal, Girl With Bonnet & Muff	30.00
Kate Greenaway, Toothpick, Girl, Cape & Bonnet, Meriden, No.47	85.00
Kate Greenaway, Vase, Dark Green To Ivory, 2 Children, Sterling Rim, 5 In.	49.00
Kate Greenaway, Vase, Emerald Green, 2 Girls, Silver Band On Rim, 4 In.	60.00
Kate Greenaway, Vase, Porcelain, Hand-Painted, 3 3/4 In.High	35.00
Kate Greenaway, Whistle, Porcelain	6.50

Kauffmann refers to the type work done by Angelica Kauffmann, a painter and decorative artist for Adam Brothers in England between 1766 and 1781. She designed small-scale pictorial subjects in the neoclassic manner. Most porcelains signed Kauffmann were made in the nineteenth century.

Kauffmann Type, Dish, Crescent, Classical Medallion Center, Gold, 7 In.	10.00
Kauffmann, Bowl, Cupid & 3 Nymphs, Gold, Ivory, & Wine Border, 9 1/2 In.	65.00
Kauffmann, Bowl, Fruit, Classical Figures, Green Ground, Gold Snowflakes	20.00
Kauffmann, Candlestick, Gold Leaves, Classical Scene, 5 1/2 In., Pair	95.00
Kauffmann, Plate, Classical Scene, Green Border, Russet Medallions, 9 In.	50.00
Kauffmann, Plate, Draped Maidens, Cherubs, Roses Border, 9 1/2 In.	18.00
Kauffmann, Plate, Figural Medallion, Green Border, Scalloped, 8 1/2 In.	35.00
Kauffmann, Plate, Jeweled Border, Classic Scene, 9 1/2 In.	40.00
Kauffmann, Plate, Maiden & Sleeping Warrior, Green & Gilt Border, 9 1/4 In.	26.00
Kauffmann, Plate, Portrait, Woman & Cupid On Landscape, Stoke-On-Trent, 9 In	25.00
Kauffmann, Plate, Portrait, Young Girl & Man Holding Flowers, 7 1/2 In.	38.00
Kauffmann, Tea Set, Scenic Medallions, 8 Piece	165.00
Kauffmann, Urn, Crimson, 10 1/2 In.	60.00
Kauffmann, Vase, Egg Shape, 3 Feet, Ladies In Classical Dress, Cobalt, 4 In.	38.00
Kauffmann, Vase, Medallion Of Young Couple On Maroon, 2 Handled, 11 In.	35.00

Kaziun, see Paperweight, Kaziun

KELVA *Kelva glassware was made by the C.F.Monroe Company of Meriden, Connecticut, about 1904. It is a pale pastel painted glass decorated with flowers, designs, or scenes.*

Kelva, Box, Hexagon, Mottled Raspberry, Signed	235.00
Kelva, Box, Mottled Green & Silver	200.00
Kelva, Box, Oak Leaf Decoration, 4 1/2 In.Square	215.00
Kelva, Box, Orange Oak Leaf On Hinged Lid, Mottled Green, Square, 4 1/2 In.	185.00
Kelva, Box, Pink Floral On Green Lid, Silver Plate Base, 5 X 5 In.	175.00
Kelva, Humidor, Cigar, Cylindrical, Blue & White, Wild Roses, 3 7/8 In.Diam.	250.00
Kelva, Vase, Burnt Orange Carnation On Peach, Silver Rim, 8 In.	165.00
Kelva, Vase, Ormolu Trim, Signed, 14 In.	275.00
Kemple, Cruet, Intaglio, Opalescent, Clear Stopper	60.00
Kemple, Toothpick, Indian's Head, Blue	10.00

Kew Blas is the name used by the Union Glass Company of Somerville, Massachusetts. The name refers to an iridescent golden glass made from the 1890s to 1924.

Kew Blas, Bowl, 4 In. Across	145.00
Kew Blas, Vase, Blue Opalescent, Pulled-Up Opalescent Loopings, 6 1/2 In.	235.00
Kew Blas, Vase, Dark Blue, Light Blue Loopings, 6 1/2 In.	235.00
Kew Blas, Vase, Elongated, Green Feathers On Gold Iridescent, 10 In.	675.00

Kew Blas, Vase, Gold Iridescent, Vertical Ribs, Footed, 3 1/2 X 3 In.	155.00
Kew Blas, Vase, Green, Green Spirals, Blue Swags, Scalloped Top, 6 In.	475.00
Kew Blas, Vase, Lily, Gold, Signed, 10 In.	300.00
Kew Blas, Vase, Opalescent Blue Luster, Pulled-Up Loopings, 6 1/2 In.	200.00

*Kewpies were first pictured in the "Ladies' Home Journal" by Rose
O'Neill. The pixielike figures became an immediate success, and Kewpie
dolls started appearing in 1911. Kewpie pictures and other items soon
followed.*

Kewpie, Bag, Lingerie, 4 Rose O'Neill Kewpies, 13 X 12 In.	20.00
Kewpie, Ball, Foam, Pink Ribbon To Hang, 3 In.	2.00
Kewpie, Bank, Plaster, 8 In.	15.00
Kewpie, Bank, Wings, 10 In.	22.00
Kewpie, Book, "The Kewpies, Their Book, " C.1913, 80 Pages	75.00
Kewpie, Bowl, Soup, Rose O'Neill, Royal Rudolstadt	35.00
Kewpie, Bowl, Soup, Signed Rose O'Neill	60.00
Kewpie, Box, Trinket, Bisque, Kewpie On Lid	10.00
Kewpie, Camera, Box	20.00
Kewpie, Candy Container, Kewpie At Barrel	37.50
Kewpie, Candy Container, Plastic, Removable Head, 7 In. High	4.00
Kewpie, Card, Valentine, Signed Rose O'Neill	10.00
Kewpie, Clock, Blue Jasperware, Signed	195.00
Kewpie, Container, Cake, Covered, Tin, Kewpies Frolicking	20.00
Kewpie, Creamer, Blue Jasperware, 7 White Kewpies, Signed, 2 1/2 In.High	100.00
Kewpie, Creamer, Rose O'Neill, Jasperware, Germany, Green, 7 Kewpies	106.00
Kewpie, Creamer, Wilson, Signed Rose O'Neill	80.00
Kewpie, Cup & Saucer, Rose O'Neill, Pink & Green, Miniature	18.00
Kewpie, Cup & Saucer, Rose O'Neill, Pink, Germany, Miniature	43.50
Kewpie, Cup & Saucer, Signed Rose O'Neill Wilson	65.00
Kewpie, Dish, Feeding, O'Neill, On Tightrope & On Lawn	125.00
Kewpie, Dish, Feeding, Rose O'Neill Wilson, Milk Glass, 1930, 8 1/2 In.	65.00
Kewpie, Doll, Baby, 18 In.	30.00
Kewpie, Doll, Bisque, Lying On Tummy, Marked KW228, 4 1/2 In.	18.00
Kewpie, Doll, Bisque, Movable Arms, Blue Wings, 5 In.	60.00
Kewpie, Doll, Bisque, Movable Arms, Rose O'Neill, 5 In.	65.00
Kewpie, Doll, Bisque, Movable Arms, Signed, 4 1/2 In.	65.00
Kewpie, Doll, Bisque, Standing On Round Wood Base, 4 5/8 In.	42.00
Kewpie, Doll, Bride & Groom, Wedding Cake, Celluloid, C.1900, 4 In., Pair	15.00
Kewpie, Doll, Cameo, Vinyl, Dressed, 27 In.	28.50
Kewpie, Doll, Cameo, Vinyl, 11 In.	7.00
Kewpie, Doll, Cameo, 1965, Vinyl, 14 In.	12.00
Kewpie, Doll, Cameo, 1966, Movable Limbs, Dressed, 27 In.	25.00 To 35.00
Kewpie, Doll, Cameo, 1967, Movable Limbs, Dressed, 16 In.	14.00
Kewpie, Doll, Cameo, 8 In.	8.00
Kewpie, Doll, Celluloid, Movable Arms, Heart On Chest Reads Kewpie, 4 In.	18.00
Kewpie, Doll, Composition, Jointed Arms, Blue Wings, Heart On Chest, 12 In.	80.00
Kewpie, Doll, Hard Celluloid, Rose O'Neill, Dressed, 8 1/2 In.	55.00
Kewpie, Doll, Kewpie Gal, Vinyl, Cameo, 9 In.	7.75
Kewpie, Doll, Kewpie Germany, Jointed Hips, 6 In.	175.00
Kewpie, Doll, Kewpie Kin, Rubber, 4 1/2 In.	11.00
Kewpie, Doll, Knickerbocker, Vinyl Face, Cloth, 15 In.	3.00
Kewpie, Doll, Kuddly, Nightgown, 16 In.	9.95
Kewpie, Doll, Kuddly, Yellow, Green, & Lavender Dress, 16 In.	9.95
Kewpie, Doll, Kuddly, 3 Outfits, 14 In.	8.50
Kewpie, Doll, Negro, Bisque, Movable Arms, 6 1/2 In.	10.00
Kewpie, Doll, O'Neill Impressed On Feet, Bisque, 5 1/2 In.	65.00
Kewpie, Doll, O'Neill On Foot, Bisque, Jointed Shoulders, 6 3/4 In.	95.00
Kewpie, Doll, O'Neill On Foot, The Gardner, Bisque, 4 In.	185.00
Kewpie, Doll, Pair, Embracing, 3 3/8 In.	35.00
Kewpie, Doll, Paper, Clothes, Pair	15.00
Kewpie, Doll, Plaster, 12 In.	22.50
Kewpie, Doll, Rose O'Neill Sticker On Back, Bisque, Hands Out, 1 3/4 In.	55.00
Kewpie, Doll, Rose O'Neill, Bisque, Movable Arms, 4 3/8 In.	43.00
Kewpie, Doll, Rose O'Neill, Composition, 11 1/4 In.	50.00
Kewpie, Doll, Santa Claus Outfit, Bisque, 4 1/2 In.	95.00
Kewpie, Doll, Signed Rose O'Neill, 4 1/4 In.	70.00

Kewpie, Doll, The Thinker, Cameo, Rose O'Neill, 4 In.	4.00
Kewpie, Doll, The Thinker, Chalk, Signed Rose O'Neill, 1913, 6 In.	10.00
Kewpie, Doll, Vinyl Face & Hands, Stuffed Body, Snow Suit, 8 In.	7.75
Kewpie, Egg, Foam, Pink Ribbon To Hang, 3 In.	2.00
Kewpie, Figurine, Chalk, Hands On Stomach, Wings, 13 In.High, 1930s	22.50
Kewpie, Flannel, Rose O'Neill, 1914	12.00
Kewpie, Hatpin, Carpenter, 6 In. Long	35.00
Kewpie, Match Holder, Clear, Bubble In Base	16.00
Kewpie, Match Holder, Pewter, Basket	16.00
Kewpie, Match Holder, Pewter, Marked	15.00
Kewpie, Match Holder, Signed Rose O'Neill, Pewter	15.00
Kewpie, Mold, Ice Cream, Pewter, Dated 1913	43.00
Kewpie, Mug, Rose O'Neill, Yellow, C.1920, Miniature	20.00
Kewpie, Napkin Ring, Back To Ring, Paye & Barker Mfg.Co., Mass.	75.00
Kewpie, Napkin Ring, Rose O'Neill, Sterling Silver	45.00
Kewpie, Paperweight, Round	6.00
Kewpie, Pendant, Sterling Silver, Marked, Ring For Chain, 1 In.	14.50
Kewpie, Picture, Rose O'Neill, Jell-O Ad, Framed, 14 X 11 In.	6.00
Kewpie, Pitcher, Playing Leapfrog, Rose O'Neill, 3 In.	60.00
Kewpie, Planter, High Glaze White Pottery, Seated Kewpie Thinker, 6 1/4 In.	27.00
Kewpie, Planter, Seated Kewpie Alongside Tree Bark Container, Pink, 6 In.	29.00
Kewpie, Planter, White Pottery, Seated Kewpie Near Tree, 6 1/4 In.	27.00
Kewpie, Plate, Rose O'Neill Wilson, 7 Action Kewpies, Rudolstadt, 7 In.	85.00
Kewpie, Plate, Rose O'Neill, Germany, 4 Action Kewpies, Pink, Green, 7 In.	48.00
Kewpie, Plate, Rose O'Neill, 6 Kewpies, Rudolstadt, 7 In.	50.00
Kewpie, Plate, 6 Action Kewpies, Royal Rudolstadt, 6 In.	75.00
Kewpie, Postcard, Gartner & Bender, Sitting On Mailbox	7.50
Kewpie, Postcard, Signed	10.00
Kewpie, Saucer, Action Kewpies, Porcelain	15.00
Kewpie, Saucer, Rose O'Neill, Yellow, C.1920, Miniature	7.00
Kewpie, Seal, Silver Plate, London, 2 5/8 In.	25.00
Kewpie, Sugar & Creamer, Cover, Rose O'Neill, 6 Action Kewpies	150.00
Kewpie, Sugar & Creamer, Covered, Signed	160.00
Kewpie, Sugar & Creamer, Pearlized, Signed	103.50
Kewpie, Toothpick, Crystal	8.50
Kewpie, Tray, Ice Cream, Rose O'Neill, 11 Kewpies Making Lemonade, Tin	28.00
Kewpie, Tray, Ice Cream, Rose O'Neill, 13 In.	45.00
Kimball, see also Cluthra	
Kimball, Vase, Cluthra, Blue, 10 X 9 In.	350.00
Kimball, Vase, Cluthra, Green, 8 X 8 In.	300.00
Kimball, Vase, Cluthra, Ovoid, White, 6 1/2 In.	110.00
Kimball, Vase, Sky Blue Cluthra, Urn Shape, Lemon Yellow Veins, 8 1/4 In.	350.00
King's Rose, see Soft Paste	
Kitchen, see also Iron, Store, Tool, Wooden	
Kitchen, Apple & Peach Peeler, Sinclair Scot Co.	22.50
Kitchen, Apple Peeler & Corer, Institutional, Patent 1889, 30 X 15 In.	32.50
Kitchen, Apple Peeler & Corer, Iron, Dated 1885	22.00
Kitchen, Apple Peeler, Little Star, Patent 1885, Iron	12.00
Kitchen, Apple Peeler, Reading, Pa., 1868, Iron, 2 Gears, Clamp On	25.00
Kitchen, Apple Peeler, Sinclair Scot Co., Baltimore, Iron	22.50
Kitchen, Apple Peeler, Tin, T Shaped, C.1856	5.00
Kitchen, Apple Peeler, Wood & Hand-Forged Iron, Red, Pulley, 24 In.	150.00
Kitchen, Basket, Picnic, Woven Cane, Metal Liner	5.50
Kitchen, Beater, Chocolate, Wooden, 11 1/2 In.	15.00
Kitchen, Blender, Hand, Green Glass, Wooden Top	12.00
Kitchen, Board, Bread, Carved Hex Sign, 8 X 11 In.	55.00
Kitchen, Boiler, Washing Machine, Happy Hour, Fits On Stove, Hand Crank	85.00
Kitchen, Bowl, Butter, Wood, 18 In.Diameter	75.00
Kitchen, Bowl, Chopping, Wooden, 15 In.	17.00
Kitchen, Bowl, Hazel Atlas, Pair, 6 & 7 In.	3.50
Kitchen, Bowl, Maple Burl, 9 1/4 X 3 1/2 In.	160.00
Kitchen, Box, Knife Cleaning, Pine, Square Nails, Rectangular, 12 X 8 In.	25.00
Kitchen, Box, Spice, Blue, Red Eagle Stencil On Lid, Round, 8 In.	95.00
Kitchen, Box, Spice, Old Judge	2.00
Kitchen, Bread Mixer, St.Louis Exposition, 1904, Metal	30.00
Kitchen, Butter Stamp, Pineapple Design, 4 In.Diameter	20.00

Kitchen, Chopper

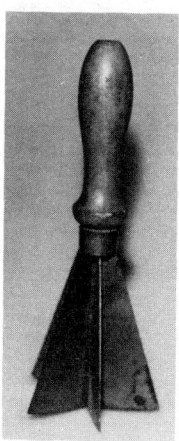

Kitchen, Cooler, Butter,
John Roberts Patent,
Red Clay

Kitchen, Cabinet, Bread & Cake, Home Comfort, Tin, 12 X 24 X 15 In.	40.00
Kitchen, Carving Set, Bone Handles, Herndon, Phila., Steel Blade & Tines	35.00
Kitchen, Carving Set, Ivory Type Handles, 3 Piece	5.00
Kitchen, Carving Set, Personna, Stainless Steel, Wooden Holder, 3 Piece	5.00
Kitchen, Carving Set, Pressed Glass Handles, 1904, 2 Piece	12.50
Kitchen, Cast, Muffin, Iron, Porcelain Glazed Molds, F & Crown Mark	14.00
Kitchen, Cherry Pitter, Enterprise, Cast Iron, 13 In.	25.00
Kitchen, Cherry Seeder, Cast Iron, 4 Legs	19.00
Kitchen, Cherry Seeder, Enterprise, Iron, Patent 1903, 12 In.	14.50
Kitchen, Cherry Seeder, Rollman Mfg.Co., Mount Joy, Pa.	12.50
Kitchen, Chopper *Illus*	10.00
Kitchen, Chopper, Food, Handwrought, Handle Is Metal Wrapped Around Dowel	12.00
Kitchen, Chopper, Food, Keen Kutter	7.50
Kitchen, Chopper, Food, Wooden Side Handle, Brass Ferrule, 11 1/2 In.	15.00
Kitchen, Chopper, Meat, Dated 1873, Cast Iron, 2 Rows Of Knives	22.50
Kitchen, Chopper, Vegetable, Wrought Iron, Wooden Handle	15.00
Kitchen, Churn, see also Shaker, Churn	
Kitchen, Churn, Butter, Wooden, Triangular, Bird's-Eye Roller, 53 In.	125.00
Kitchen, Churn, Dazey, Glass	12.50
Kitchen, Churn, Dazey, No.40, Patent Feb.14, 1922	12.00
Kitchen, Cleaner, Glass Chimney, Wire & Wood, 16 In.	12.00
Kitchen, Coffee Grinder, see Coffee Grinder	
Kitchen, Colander, Bowl Shaped, 2 Handles	3.00
Kitchen, Colander, Pierced Tin, Footed	150.00
Kitchen, Colander, Rolled Handles, Pedestal	2.50
Kitchen, Colander, Tin, Dated 1888, 11 1/2 X 2 1/2 In.	10.00
Kitchen, Cookie Board, Pennsylvania Dutch, Gingerbread Lady & Man, Pair	35.00
Kitchen, Cookie Roller, Child's, Wooden, Ridges, 12 In.	15.00
Kitchen, Cookie Roller, Corrugated, Wooden	16.00
Kitchen, Cooler, Butter, John Roberts Patent, Red Clay *Illus.*	75.00
Kitchen, Corn Sheller, Wood, Iron Handles, Set On Plank, 41 X 16 X 1 1/2 In.	25.00
Kitchen, Curd Cutter, Steel, Brass, & Wood, 3 Blades, D.C.Young, Cedarville	20.00
Kitchen, Cutter, Biscuit, Cottolene, Ring Handle	4.00
Kitchen, Cutter, Cookie, see also Disneyana, Cookie Cutter	
Kitchen, Cutter, Cookie, Adams Home, Tenn., Wooden, 1 Piece	35.00
Kitchen, Cutter, Cookie, Eagle, Tin, 6 1/4 X 4 1/2 In.	40.00
Kitchen, Cutter, Cookie, Heart, Tin, 2 1/4 X 3 1/2 In.	20.00
Kitchen, Cutter, Cookie, Lion, Tin, Handle, 3 1/2 X 2 1/4 In.	12.00
Kitchen, Cutter, Cookie, Rocking Horse, Tin, 14 X 10 In.	75.00
Kitchen, Cutter, Doughnut, Rumford	4.00
Kitchen, Cutter, Doughnut, Tin	2.00
Kitchen, Cutter, Kraut, Board	8.00
Kitchen, Cutter, Kraut, Wall, Pine, Marked 1898, 30 In.	24.00
Kitchen, Cutter, Kraut, Wooden, Cabbage Box, 9 X 26 In.	27.50

Kitchen, Decorator, Cake, Pewter, 10 1/2 In. 30.00
Kitchen, Dipper, Apple Butter, Copper, Iron & Wooden Handle 15.00
Kitchen, Dipper, Brass, Iron Handle, Scrolled Hook, 19 In.Long 65.00
Kitchen, Dish, Soap, Covered, Blue Windmill Pattern 29.50
Kitchen, Double Boiler, Blue Agate Tin, Covered, 8 1/2 X 8 In. 25.00
Kitchen, Dough Kneader, J.I.C.Nafe, Winchester, Ky., Iron Handle & Clamp 85.00
Kitchen, Douser, Pewter, Brass Spray Face, 18 In. 35.00
Kitchen, Dustpan, Tin, Rolled Edges, Braced Handle, 15 1/2 X 8 1/2 In. 20.00
Kitchen, Egg Poacher, Copper, Brass Handle, Tin Interior, 7 Eggs, 10 In. 20.00
Kitchen, Eggbeater, Cast Iron, Double Tooth Gear, 1903 .... 12.50
Kitchen, Eggbeater, Cast Iron, 1903, 10 1/2 In. 7.00
Kitchen, Eggbeater, Glass Bowl, Wheel On Top, Pierced Disc Beater, 4 In. 8.00
Kitchen, Eggbeater, Opaque Glass, Beater In Lid 5.00
Kitchen, Firkin, Wooden, 14 In. High 20.00
Kitchen, Flatiron, Child's, Dover No.12 Sadiron In Relief, Wood Handle 20.00
Kitchen, Flatiron, Child's, Iron, 2 1/2 X 3 1/2 In. 20.00
Kitchen, Flatiron, Child's, Victorian, Cast Iron, Pointed At 1 End 7.50
Kitchen, Flatiron, The Gem, Wooden Handle, 4 In. 15.00
Kitchen, Fork, Meat, Winchester, 13 In. 20.00
Kitchen, Fork, Toasting, Hand-Forged Iron, Ring Handle, C.1750, 20 In. 28.00
Kitchen, Frypan, Copper, Brass & Wood Handle, Tin Lined 12.50
Kitchen, Funnel, Canning Jar, Glass 2.00
Kitchen, Grater, Nutmeg, Lid, Tin, 5 In. Long .... 4.00 To 20.00
Kitchen, Grater, Nutmeg, Tin, Swing Action 22.00
Kitchen, Grater, Nutmeg, 2 Handled 15.00
Kitchen, Griddle, Iron, Stamp Decorated Handle 150.00
Kitchen, Grinder, Food, Child's, Rollmar Mfg.Co., 7 In. 8.00
Kitchen, Grinder, Sausage, Cast Iron, Bolt-Down Type 9.50
Kitchen, Hook, Jam, Brass 32.00
Kitchen, Hook, Kettle Lifting, Twisted Shaft, Wooden Handle, 5 X 4 1/2 In. 50.00
Kitchen, Ice Shaver, Logan & Strobridge Iron Co., Cast 8.50
Kitchen, Icebox, Oak, White Porcelain 265.00
Kitchen, Iron & Trivet, Twined Heart, 2 3/4 In. 25.00
Kitchen, Iron, Charcoal, Chinese 38.50
Kitchen, Iron, Charcoal, Dolphins Form Part Of Handle .... 25.00 To 52.00
Kitchen, Iron, Charcoal, Kaiser Wilhelm's Head For Opener 45.00
Kitchen, Iron, Coleman, Gasoline 10.50
Kitchen, Iron, Coleman, Gasoline, No.609A, Brass Pump, Stand, Filler Can 30.00
Kitchen, Iron, Fluting, Dated 1874 .... 28.00
Kitchen, Iron, Fluting, Embossed The Best, Rocker Style 17.50
Kitchen, Iron, Fluting, Geneva, Dated 1866 .... 25.00
Kitchen, Iron, Fluting, Roller, Heater, Patent 1880 On Handle 22.00
Kitchen, Iron, Fluting, The Best, C.W.Whitfield, Syracuse, N.Y., 2 Part 18.00
Kitchen, Iron, Mandarin, Canton, Enamel, Pastel Floral, 6 X 1 1/2 In. 70.00
Kitchen, Iron, Sleeve, Fylk & Co., N.Y. 12.00
Kitchen, Iron, Sleeve, Grand Union Tea Co., Detachable Handle 4.95
Kitchen, Jar, Measuring, Lightning Dasher Eggbeater Co., O., 1888, Quart 17.00
    Kitchen, Juicer, see also Silver Plate, Juicer
Kitchen, Juicer, Garlic, Marked Mrs.Danar, Made In Italy 6.00
Kitchen, Juicer, Green Opaque Glass .... 6.50 To 8.50
Kitchen, Juicer, Porcelain, Pouring Pitcher 7.00
Kitchen, Juicer, Sunkist, Green, McKee 8.00
Kitchen, Kettle, Jelly, Brass, Wrought Iron Handle, 11 1/2 In.Diameter 60.00
Kitchen, Knife & Fork, 2 Tines, Bone Handles, Cast Iron 5.00
Kitchen, Knife & Fork, 2 Tines, Bone Handles, Steel 5.00
Kitchen, Knife Cleaning Board, Made From Red & White Sign, Nails, 13 In. 19.00
Kitchen, Knife, Child's, Pine, Gray Weathered, 1 In. 10.00
Kitchen, Knife, Chopping, Marked Double Action, Patent 1892, Cast Steel 7.50
Kitchen, Knife, Swingling, For Flax Breaking, Wooden, 22 1/2 In. 18.00
Kitchen, Ladder, Cheese, Mortised Hickory, Pegged, C.1750, 8 X 13 In. 25.00
Kitchen, Ladder, Cheese, Pine, Two Rung, Mortised & Pegged, 29 1/2 In.Long ... 23.00
Kitchen, Ladle, Brass, Strainer Lip, Iron Handle, 18 1/2 In.Long 165.00
Kitchen, Ladle, Tasting, Iron, Initials On Handle, C.1750, 16 In. 22.50
Kitchen, Maker, Sauerkraut, Movable Box 8.00
Kitchen, Masher, Bird's-Eye & Curly Maple, Turned, 11 1/2 In. 12.00
Kitchen, Masher, Potato, Wooden, 10 In. 6.00

Kitchen, Measure, Turned Maple, Double Sided, 5 1/4 In. High 35.00
Kitchen, Meat Grinder, Table Model, Clamp, Crank Handle, Iron, Wooden, 12 In. 18.00
Kitchen, Mill, Sausage, Winchester Arms Co., Embossed, Cast Iron 22.50
Kitchen, Mixer, Green Glass, Wooden Handle 15.00
Kitchen, Mixer, Kraft Malted Milk, Glass Container, Metal Lid & Mixer 5.00
   Kitchen, Mold, see also Pewter, Mold, Tin, Mold
Kitchen, Mold, Butter, Acorn, 1 1/2 In.Diameter 10.00
Kitchen, Mold, Butter, Deep Cut Flower, Pewter Band 95.00
Kitchen, Mold, Butter, Fern Leaves, Wooden, Round 22.00
Kitchen, Mold, Butter, Initial Y & Leaf, Plunger, Round, 3 3/4 In. 30.00
Kitchen, Mold, Butter, Leaf & Acorn, Plunger, Dovetailed, Oblong, 6 X 4 In. 24.00
Kitchen, Mold, Butter, Leaf, Handle 35.00
Kitchen, Mold, Butter, Pineapple, Pound 28.00
Kitchen, Mold, Butter, Pineapple, Wooden, Plunger, Dated 1866, Pound 50.00
Kitchen, Mold, Butter, Pineapple, Wooden, 4 X 4 X 6 3/4 In. 50.00
Kitchen, Mold, Butter, Pineapple, 3 In. 50.00
Kitchen, Mold, Butter, Pineapple, 4 In.Diameter 25.00
Kitchen, Mold, Butter, Sheaf Of Wheat, Plunger, Wooden, Dated 1866, Pound 50.00
Kitchen, Mold, Butter, Sheaf Of Wheat, Plunger, Wooden, 1/2 Pound 35.00
Kitchen, Mold, Butter, Sheaf Of Wheat, Wooden, 4 In. 30.00
Kitchen, Mold, Butter, Sheaf Of Wheat, Wooden, 4 1/4 In. 50.00
Kitchen, Mold, Butter, Star, Pine, 6 X 5 X 2 1/2 In. 10.00
Kitchen, Mold, Butter, Star, Wooden, 3 1/2 X 1 3/4 In. 10.00
Kitchen, Mold, Butter, Strawberry & Flower, Wooden, Plunger, Dated 1866, Pound 50.00
Kitchen, Mold, Butter, Swan, Wooden, 3 1/2 In. Diameter 35.00
Kitchen, Mold, Butter, 2 Maple Imprints, Rectangular, Plunger, Pound 58.00
Kitchen, Mold, Butter, 5 Pointed Star, Plunger, Wooden, 1/2 Pound 35.00
   Kitchen, Mold, Candle, see also Tin, Mold, Candle
Kitchen, Mold, Candle, 4 Tube, Silver Paint 20.00
Kitchen, Mold, Candle, 6 Tube 25.00
Kitchen, Mold, Candle, 8 Tube, Tin .... 18.00 To 35.00
Kitchen, Mold, Candle, 12 Tube 40.00
Kitchen, Mold, Candle, 24 Tube, Tin 110.00
Kitchen, Mold, Cookie, Scrimshaw & Carved Wood, Rolling Pin Form, C.1850 .... 200.00
Kitchen, Mold, Food, Fluted Sides, Oval, Clear Glass, Anchor, 5 1/4 In. 28.00
Kitchen, Mold, Food, Lamb, Iron 32.50
Kitchen, Mold, Food, Oval, Fluted, Anchor On Top, Glass, 5 1/4 In. 30.00
Kitchen, Mold, Foot, Bird Shape, Metal, Hinged Base 12.00
Kitchen, Mold, Fruit, Grape Cluster & 2 Strawberries, Cover, Tin, 6 In. 20.00
Kitchen, Mold, Gothic Pattern With Pig In Base, Pottery, 7 In.Wide 185.00
Kitchen, Mold, Jell-O, Marked, 10 In. 8.00
Kitchen, Mold, Jelly, Amber, Oval, Flett's Fresh Fruit Jellies, 2 1/2 Cups 35.50
Kitchen, Mold, Melon, Kreamer, Tin 8.50
Kitchen, Mortar & Pestle, Child's 18.00
Kitchen, Nutcracker, Hand-Carved Wood, Figure Of Old Man In Stocking Cap 25.00
Kitchen, Nutcracker, Squirrel, Cast Iron 18.00
Kitchen, Opener, Can, Kutz Ezy 2.25
   Kitchen, Opener, Jar, see Disneyana, Jar Opener
Kitchen, Paddle, Apple Butter, 5 In. 12.00
Kitchen, Paddle, Butter, Wooden, Hand, Curved 8.50
Kitchen, Paddle, Lard, Wooden 3.50
Kitchen, Pan, Baking, Calumet Baking Powder, Tin, 11 X 7 X 1 1/2 In. 10.00
Kitchen, Pan, Baking, Snowking Baking Powder, 7 1/2 X 7 1/2 X 1 1/2 In. 10.00
Kitchen, Pan, Bread, Copper, 18 X 12 In. 35.00
Kitchen, Pan, Cake, Angel Food, Patent Date 3.00
Kitchen, Pan, Cake, Swans Down Angel Food, Embossed Lettering 4.50
Kitchen, Pan, Dough, Hand-Forged Iron, 20 In. 70.00
Kitchen, Pan, Muffin, Fruits, Iron, 8 Muffins 75.00
Kitchen, Pan, Muffin, Iron, Patent April 5, 1859, 12 Cups, Handled, 10 3/4 In. 16.50
Kitchen, Pastry Jigger, Iron, Crimped Wheel, Wooden Handle, 6 1/2 In. 29.00
Kitchen, Pastry Wheel, Victorian, Cast Brass, 6 In.Long 15.00
Kitchen, Peel, Bread, One Piece Pine, Chamfered Back, 31 X 13 1/2 In. 55.00
Kitchen, Pie Crimper & Pastry Jigger, Iron, 4 In. 20.00
Kitchen, Pie Crimper, Brass Wheel & Ferrule, Wooden Handle, V Groove 12.00
Kitchen, Pie Crimper, Wood, Brass, & Bone 29.00
Kitchen, Pie Lifter, Marked 1875, Cast Iron, 15 In. 40.00

Kitchen, Pie Lifter, Wire, Turned Wooden Handle, C.1830, 19 1/2 In. 20.00
Kitchen, Pie Lifter, 2 Pronged, Wooden Handle 3.95
Kitchen, Pie Lifter, 2 Tines, Wooden Handle, 20 In. 12.00
Kitchen, Popper, Corn, Tin 17.00
Kitchen, Pot Lifter, Hand-Forged Iron, Twisted, C.1750, 6 1/2 In. 25.00
Kitchen, Pot, Bean, Cast Iron, Bail Handle, 3 Legs 17.50
Kitchen, Pot, Bean, Covered, Brown & White, 3 Quart 18.00
Kitchen, Pot, Bean, Tole-Painted, Legs 17.50
Kitchen, Press, Cookie, Tin & Wood 5.00
Kitchen, Pressure Cooker, Kook-Kwick 6.50
Kitchen, Rack, Clothes, Perfection Clothes Drier, 8 Arms, Patent 8/30/87 .... 12.00
Kitchen, Reamer, Juice, Catching Pitcher, Porcelain 6.00
Kitchen, Rolling Pin, Blown Glass, Hole For Filling, 15 In. 20.00
Kitchen, Rolling Pin, Blown Olive Green Glass, Knobbed Ends, 11 3/4 In. 55.00
Kitchen, Rolling Pin, Blown, Dark Amber 50.00
Kitchen, Rolling Pin, Bristol Glass 27.50
Kitchen, Rolling Pin, Child's, Lockport Color, 4 In. 150.00
Kitchen, Rolling Pin, Clear Glass 6.00
Kitchen, Rolling Pin, Curly Tiger Maple, 17 In. 16.00
Kitchen, Rolling Pin, Glass, Bottle Type, Screw Cap 8.50
Kitchen, Rolling Pin, Lignum Vitae, 1 Piece, 15 1/2 In. 28.00
Kitchen, Rolling Pin, Maple, 22 In. Long .... 11.00 To 20.00
Kitchen, Rolling Pin, Milk Glass, Wooden Handles, Cambridge, O., 1921 .... 22.50
Kitchen, Rolling Pin, Milk Glass, Wooden Handles, Patent 6-26-1921 .... 21.50
Kitchen, Rolling Pin, Nailsea Glass Type, Knobbed End, Clear, Cobalt Loops 55.00
Kitchen, Rolling Pin, Nailsea, Blue & White Swirl 120.00
Kitchen, Rolling Pin, Nailsea, Cranberry & White Loopings, Blown, 9 In. 55.00
Kitchen, Rolling Pin, Nailsea, Red, White, & Clear 50.00
Kitchen, Rolling Pin, Porcelain, Black Picture On Cream, Loop To Hang 15.00
Kitchen, Sadiron & Trivet, Child's, Swan 22.00
Kitchen, Sadiron & Trivet, Child's, 1 5/8 X 3 In. 10.00
Kitchen, Sadiron, Box, Cast Iron, Wooden Handle 19.50
Kitchen, Sadiron, Charcoal, Brass 18.00
Kitchen, Sadiron, Child's, Dover 5.00
Kitchen, Sadiron, Colebrookdale, Pottstown, Pa., Double Pointed 4.75
Kitchen, Sadiron, Fluting, Embossed, 2 Piece 25.00
Kitchen, Sadiron, Ober, Chagrin Falls, Ohio 4.95
Kitchen, Scoop, Butter, Maple, Ring For Hanging, 7 X 12 In. 32.00
Kitchen, Scoop, Marrow, Cherry, 14 In. 25.00
Kitchen, Scraper, Pots & Pans, Red Wing Milling Co. 10.00
    Kitchen, Sieve, see also Shaker, Sieve
Kitchen, Sieve, Tin, 12 In. 2.00
Kitchen, Sieve, Winnowing, N.H., Patent 1878, Wooden, Folding, 19 X 18 1/2 In. 40.00
    Kitchen, Sifter, see also Shaker, Sifter
Kitchen, Sifter, Flour, Fairy, Tin 3.50
Kitchen, Sifter, Flour, Triple, Indented Wooden Handle 6.00
Kitchen, Sifter, Wooden, Round, 18 In. 7.00
Kitchen, Skillet, Child's, Iron, 3 Legged, Long Handle, 4 3/4 In. 5.00
Kitchen, Skillet, Hand-Forged Iron, Ring Handle, Rivets, C.1750, 12 In. 28.00
Kitchen, Skimmer, Brass, Iron Ring Handle, Round, Punched, 26 In. 55.00
Kitchen, Skimmer, Cast Aluminum, Hook Handle, 15 In. 4.00
Kitchen, Skimmer, Cream, Hammered Copper, Oval, 4 X 4 1/2 In. 35.00
Kitchen, Skimmer, Cream, Tin 2.50
Kitchen, Skimmer, Cream, Wooden, Hook On Handle 10.00
Kitchen, Skimmer, Pierced Brass, Iron Handle, 8 In.Long 50.00
Kitchen, Slicer, Cabbage, Pennsylvania Dutch, Wooden, Hanging Piece, 18 In. 45.00
Kitchen, Spatula, Hand-Forged Iron, 15 3/4 In. 28.00
Kitchen, Spatula, Iron 8.00
Kitchen, Spatula, Wrought Iron, 13 In. 18.00
Kitchen, Spice Set, Japanned, 6 Round Boxes, Decorated Handled Tray 25.00
    Kitchen, Spinning Wheel, see Tool, Spinning Wheel
Kitchen, Spoon, Bone, Narrow Bowl, 6 1/2 In. 5.00
Kitchen, Spoon, Tasting, Wrought Iron, 13 In. 18.00
Kitchen, Squeezer, Lemon, Cherry, 10 1/2 In. 28.00
Kitchen, Squeezer, Lemon, Clown 8.00
Kitchen, Squeezer, Lemon, Maple, Hinged, 2 Handled 22.00

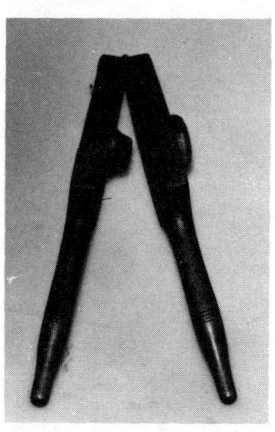

Kitchen, Squeezer,
Lemon, Wooden

Kitchen, Stamp, Butter,
Wheat, Wooden

Kitchen, **Squeezer**, Lemon, Ornate Cast Iron, Milk Glass Bottom, Wood Plunger	13.75
Kitchen, **Squeezer**, Lemon, Wooden .... *Illus*	21.00
Kitchen, **Stamp**, Butter, Tulip, Pennsylvania, Chamfered Back	70.00
Kitchen, **Stamp**, Butter, Wheat, Wooden .... *Illus*	22.00
Kitchen, **Stamp**, Butter, 4 Petaled Flower, Wooden	13.00
Kitchen, **Strainer**, Tea, Ivorene Handle	4.00
Kitchen, **Sweeper**, Carpet, Bissel's, The Ward, Wooden	6.00
Kitchen, **Tin**, Angel Food Cake, Swans Down	4.00
Kitchen, **Toaster**, Iron	170.00
Kitchen, **Toaster**, Westinghouse, Turnover, 1914	2.50
Kitchen, **Tongs**, Potato, Bronze, Scissors Type, 9 1/2 In.	11.00
Kitchen, **Tool**, 5 Way, Sifter, Cutter, Corer, & Pitter, Tin, 3 In. Diameter	13.00
Kitchen, **Tray Dish**, Deep, Sloping Sides, Patent On Bottom, 8 X 11 X 3 In.	6.00
Kitchen, **Tray**, Bread, Wooden, 21 1/2 X 11 In.	47.50
Kitchen, **Tray**, Wicker, Seashell Design Center, Southern Glass Works, 12 In.	7.50
Kitchen, **Trencher**, Iron, Scalloped, Deep, 9 1/2 In.	165.00
Kitchen, **Turner**, Pancake, Cast Iron, Round End	20.00
Kitchen, **Turner**, Pancake, FA Wenrich, Cast Iron, Rattail	70.00
Kitchen, **Waffle Iron**, Flipover, Bail Handle, 4 In. Base	12.50
Kitchen, **Waffle Iron**, Gridwold	12.50
Kitchen, **Waffle Iron**, Iron	20.00
Kitchen, **Waffle Iron**, Wagner's, Sidney, O., 1910, Salesman's Sample	20.00
Kitchen, **Waffle Iron**, Wrought Iron, Long Handled	45.00
Kitchen, **Waffle Iron**, 4 Different Designs	90.00
Kitchen, **Waffle Maker**, Wrought Iron, Handle	135.00
Kitchen, **Washboard**, Cast Iron, Pine Frame, Square Nails, Dated 1861, 23 In.	35.00
Kitchen, **Washboard**, Square Wooden Rollers	15.00
Kitchen, **Washboard**, Wire & Wood, Handmade	12.00
Kitchen, **Washboard**, Wooden, Handmade	48.00
Kitchen, **Washboard**, Wooden, Pegged, Mortised, 12 1/2 X 33 In.	25.00
Kitchen, **Whipper**, Cream, Embossed Jar, Patent Date 1915, Tin Lid, Metal Mixer	6.00
Knowles, Taylor & Knowles, see KTK, Lotus Ware	
Koch, **Cake Set**, Purple & Green Grapes, Gold Scalloped, 7 Piece	135.00
Koch, **Plate**, Apples On Beige & White, J & C Bavaria, 6 In.	6.45
Koch, **Plate**, Apples On Dark Green, Louise, Bavaria, 8 1/2 In.	32.50
Koch, **Plate**, Apples, Signed, 7 7/8 In.	25.00
Koch, **Plate**, Cake, Apples, Open Handles, 11 In.	39.00
Koch, **Plate**, Cake, Grapes, Open Handle	30.00
Koch, **Plate**, Cake, Tinted Peaches, Open Handled, Signed	36.00
Koch, **Plate**, Fruit, Grapes, Green & Rose, J.& C.Louise, Bavaria, 8 1/2 In.	32.50
Koch, **Plate**, Fruit, Strawberries, Irregular Edge, 8 5/8 In.	25.00
Koch, **Plate**, Grapes On Beige & White, J & C Bavaria, 6 In.	6.45
Koch, **Plate**, Grapes, Signed Louis, 8 1/2 In.	25.00
Koch, **Plate**, Grapes, White, Bavarian, 9 1/2 In.	35.00
Koch, **Plate**, Grapes, 8 1/2 In.	38.00

Koch, Plate, Peaches, Signed, 7 7/8 In.	25.00
Koch, Plate, Plums On Beige & White, J & C Bavaria, 6 In.	6.45
Koch, Plate, Purple & Green Grapes On White, Yellow, & Brown, 7 1/2 In.	20.00
Koch, Plate, Strawberries, 8 1/2 In.	38.00
Koch, Sauce, Apple, Gold Scalloped Edge, 5 3/4 In.	18.00
Kosta, Vase, Etched Arcade & 3 Saints On Clear, C.1935, 15 1/2 In.	90.00

K. P.M

KPM is part of one of the marks used about 1723 by the Meissen Factory Konigliche Porzellan Manufaktur. Other firms using the letters include the Royal Manufactory of Berlin, Germany, that worked from 1832 to 1847. A factory in Scheibe, Germany, used the mark in 1928. The mark was also used in Waldenburg, Germany, and other German cities during the twentieth century.

KPM, Bowl, Gold Tracery, Cream & Pink Feathers, Scalloped, 9 1/2 In.	15.00
KPM, Bowl, Handled, 2 Part, Pink Edge & Flowers, 9 X 12 In.	35.00
KPM, Bowl, Mashed Potatoes, Floral On White, Blue Edge Inside, 10 X 8 In.	66.00
KPM, Cachepot, Winter Scene, Hunter, Dog, Ducks, 6 In.High, Pair	295.00
KPM, Cake Set, Violets With Green On White, Soft Pastels, Gold, 7 Piece	79.95
KPM, Chocolate Pot, Rose Floral Stencil & Hand-Painted	68.00
KPM, Coffeepot, Blue & Orange Flowers On White, Marked Crown & KPM	10.00
KPM, Coffeepot, White, Twig Handle, Blossom Finial, Blue & Gilt, 10 In.	75.00
KPM, Cup & Saucer, Child's Portrait & Flowers, Raised Gold, 6 Feet	65.00
KPM, Cup & Saucer, Coffee, Floral & Gold Filigree On White	45.00
KPM, Cup & Saucer, Dresden Pattern	25.00
KPM, Cup & Saucer, Raised Gold, Hand-Painted	95.00
KPM, Dish, Leaf Shape, Center Handle, Divided, Floral & Gold, 12 X 9 X 4 In.	38.00
KPM, Group, Bacchus & Putto, 2 Sections, C.1850, 9 1/2 In.	275.00
KPM, Lamp, Fairy, Three Face, Bulldog, Cat, & Owl, Glass Eyes	250.00
KPM, Painting, Austrian Baron, Oval, 6 1/2 X 9 In.	450.00
KPM, Painting, Cleopatra Holding Asp, Oval, 6 X 4 1/2 In.	525.00
KPM, Painting, Madonna Of The Chair, Framed, 8 X 6 1/4 In.	650.00
KPM, Painting, Mother & Child, A.E.Eckardt, 12 X 10 In.	1200.00
KPM, Painting, Mother Showing Her Son The World Outside, 7 1/4 X 5 1/4 In.	395.00
KPM, Painting, Woman, Framed, Oval, 7 X 5 In.	750.00
KPM, Plaque, Die Trauernde Magdalene, H.Stadler, C.1850, 13 X 11 In.	1500.00
KPM, Plaque, Jesus Talking To The Elders In Temple, C.1850, 12 X 15 In.	2300.00
KPM, Plaque, Mideastern Young Girl, Tasseled Hat, Oval, 6 1/2 X 4 1/2 In.	875.00
KPM, Plate, Christmas, 1930, Flight Into Egypt, 9 In.	65.00
KPM, Plate, Clover, Daisies, Bachelor Buttons, Gold Tracery Border, 8 In.	18.50
KPM, Plate, Fruit, Open Handles, 10 1/2 In.	12.50
KPM, Plate, Multicolored Floral Center, 7 1/2 In.	6.00
KPM, Plate, Sneaky Looking Mice On A Rope, M.Darge, 7 In.	16.00
KPM, Plate, Two Bunches Grapes & Leaf In Center, Cream Border, 8 1/2 In.	11.00
KPM, Platter, White, Yellow & Pink Roses In Center, 15 X 9 In.	65.00
KPM, Pot, Chocolate, Garlands Of Roses	29.00
KPM, Vase, Portrait, Gold & Blue Beading, 10 1/2 In.	375.00

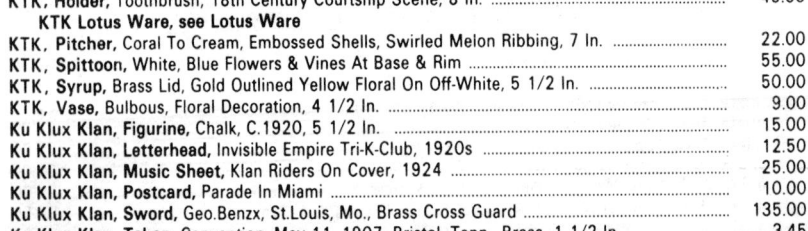

KTK.
CHINA

KTK are the initials of the Knowles, Taylor and Knowles Company of East Liverpool, Ohio, founded by Isaac W.Knowles in 1853. The company is still working. They made Lotus Ware.

KTK, Holder, Toothbrush, 18th Century Courtship Scene, 8 In.	45.00
KTK Lotus Ware, see Lotus Ware	
KTK, Pitcher, Coral To Cream, Embossed Shells, Swirled Melon Ribbing, 7 In.	22.00
KTK, Spittoon, White, Blue Flowers & Vines At Base & Rim	55.00
KTK, Syrup, Brass Lid, Gold Outlined Yellow Floral On Off-White, 5 1/2 In.	50.00
KTK, Vase, Bulbous, Floral Decoration, 4 1/2 In.	9.00
Ku Klux Klan, Figurine, Chalk, C.1920, 5 1/2 In.	15.00
Ku Klux Klan, Letterhead, Invisible Empire Tri-K-Club, 1920s	12.50
Ku Klux Klan, Music Sheet, Klan Riders On Cover, 1924	25.00
Ku Klux Klan, Postcard, Parade In Miami	10.00
Ku Klux Klan, Sword, Geo.Benzx, St.Louis, Mo., Brass Cross Guard	135.00
Ku Klux Klan, Token, Convention, May 11, 1907, Bristol, Tenn., Brass, 1 1/2 In.	3.45

Kutani ware is a Japanese porcelain made after the mid-seventeenth century. Most of the pieces found today are nineteenth century.

Kutani, Berry Set, Orange Red & Gold Band, Japanese Ladies, 5 Piece	58.00

Kutani, Bowl, Bird & Cherry Blossom Design, 6 In.	15.50
Kutani, Bowl, Lotus Form, Ring Foot, Morning Glories, C.1850, 5 1/2 In.	375.00
Kutani, Bowl, Two Samurai Warriors On Horses, 12 In.	195.00
Kutani, Cup & Saucer, Demitasse, Scenic	4.00
Kutani, Cup & Saucer, Mustache, Melon Ribbed, Scalloped Saucer, Scenic, Gold	40.00
Kutani, Cup & Saucer, Pagodas	15.00
Kutani, Figurine, Empress, Hooded Cape, 12 In.	55.00
Kutani, Hair Receiver, Human Figures, Oranges With Gold, 3 1/4 In.	42.00
Kutani, Jar, Powder, Figures, Gold	25.00
Kutani, Jar, Tea, Foo Dog On Inner Lid, Floral & Figures On Rust, 7 1/4 In.	70.00
Kutani, Tea Set, Garden Scenes, Rust Borders, Red Mark, C.1890, 3 Piece	38.00
Kutani, Tray, Old Man, Child, & Deer, Gold, 6 1/2 X 4 1/2 In.	25.00
Kutani, Vase, Birds & Flowers, Burnt Orange, Yellows, White, & Gold, 6 1/4 In.	48.00
Kutani, Vase, Double Gourd Shape, Chinese Boys, C.1850, 13 1/2 In., Pair	375.00
Lacquer, Bowl, Roiro, Flowers & Birds, Signed Seika, 8 1/8 In.	65.00
Lacquer, Bowl, Roiro, Seika, Floral & Birds, 8 1/8 In., Set Of 10	250.00
Lacquer, Box, Chinese Scenes, Octagonal, 15 X 15 1/2 In.	50.00
Lacquer, Box, Covered, Black, Flowers, Orange, Gold, Gray, & Green, 10 X 11 In.	150.00
Lacquer, Box, Covered, Floral & Diamond On Gold, C.1850, 7 1/4 X 3 In.	250.00
Lacquer, Box, Document, Mottled Cover, Tsuba & A Kozuka, C.1850, 10 3/4 In.	150.00
Lacquer, Box, Gold Top, Pink Floral & Bird, 7 X 5 3/4 In.	15.00
Lacquer, Box, Gold, Dome Lid, Edged In Pewter, C.1790, 6 7/8 X 4 1/4 In.	100.00
Lacquer, Box, Gyobu Ground, Floral, 6 Legs, 8 1/2 X 6 1/2 In.	125.00
Lacquer, Box, Laque Burgautee, Covered, Chinese Landscapes, C.1850, 19 In.	200.00
Lacquer, Box, Mandarin Drake Shape, Gold, Color Plumage, C.1850, 4 In.	300.00
Lacquer, Box, Netsuke & 2 Inro On Lid, Nashiji Ground, C.1850, 5 1/4 In.	825.00
Lacquer, Box, On Wood, Buddhistic Symbols, C.1850, 12 3/4 X 6 1/4 In.	200.00
Lacquer, Box, Ono No Komachi On Fitted Lid, Scenic, C.1850, 7 X 6 In.	225.00
Lacquer, Box, Oriental, Lift-Off Lid, Scallops Form Sides, Black, Gold, 11 In.	18.00
Lacquer, Box, Shigeaki Saku, C.1850, Peacock Shape, Gold, Pearl, 4 3/8 In.	175.00
Lacquer, Box, Toilet, Turtles In Waves, 2 Drawers, C.1850, 11 X 9 In.	275.00
Lacquer, Case, Carrying, Chinese, C.1850, Red, Landscape, Brass Handles, 25 In.	200.00
Lacquer, Chest, Storage, Gold, Foliage, Brass Mounts, C.1850, 23 X 16 In.	1100.00
Lacquer, Chest, Storage, Gold, 2 Drawers, C.1850, 12 1/4 X 10 1/4 In.	300.00
Lacquer, Chest, Storage, The Three Friends In Winter, Brass Mounts, 24 In.	1600.00
Lacquer, Figurine, Buddha, On Vahna, Gilt, C.1790, 10 7/8 In.	900.00
Lacquer, Figurine, Monkey, Glass Eyes, Gilt Muzzle, C.1850, 9 1/4 In.	400.00
Lacquer, French, Box, Powder, Gold Mounted, Tortoiseshell Lined, C.1780	100.00
Lacquer, Inro, 4 Compartments, Eagle On Side, Floral, 2 7/8 X 1 7/8 In.	225.00
Lacquer, Jubako, Red, Floral, Carrying Handle, 4 Trays, 8 3/4 In. High	200.00
Lacquer, Jubako, Sage Scene, 2 Pewter Sake Bottles, 12 X 11 3/4 In.	825.00
Lacquer, Plaque, Black, Mother-Of-Pearl Floral Carving, C.1895, 18 In., Pair	70.00
Lacquer, Plate, Russian, Religious Scene, 6 In.	125.00
Lacquer, Plate, Russian, Scene Of Kremlin, 5 3/4 In.	125.00
Lacquer, Shrine, Kwannon, Red, Gilt Mounts, C.1850, 15 3/4 In.	150.00
Lacquer, Shrine, Portable, Buddha, Gold, Copper Mounts, 6 3/4 In.	425.00
Lacquer, Snuffbox, Commander Oliver Perry Esq. On Lid, C.1850, 3 1/4 In.	150.00
Lacquer, Tray, Serving, Musicians, Tradesmen, & A Sarumawashi, C.1850, 13 In.	250.00
Lacquer, Tray, Serving, Wildflowers Beside Stream, C.1850, 13 1/8 In.	325.00
Lacquer, Tray, Victorian, Mother-Of-Pearl Inlay, Harbor Scene, 31 In.	100.00

*Lalique glass was made by Rene Lalique's factory in Paris, France, from
1860 to 1945. The glass was molded, pressed, and engraved. Many of the most
familiar designs were clear or with a bluish-tinged glass molded into birds,
animals, or foliage.*

Lalique, Atomizer, Nude Females, Gilded Top, Light Amber Base, 5 1/2 In.	125.00
Lalique, Bottle, Perfume, Charcoal Branches On Clear, C.1930, 4 1/2 In.	70.00
Lalique, Bottle, Perfume, Frosted, Art Deco Black Enamel Hobs, 5 1/4 In.	115.00
Lalique, Bottle, Perfume, Frosted, Kissing Doves, 4 In.	70.00
Lalique, Bottle, Perfume, Mauve, Sculptured, 3 1/2 In., Pair	68.50
Lalique, Bottle, Snail Design, Ribbed, Nude Kneeling Girl Stopper, 4 In.	235.00
Lalique, Bowl & Underplate, Finger, Frosted Pine Trees Pattern, Signed	49.50
Lalique, Bowl, Border Of Frosted Sparrows, Script Signed, 3 1/2 In.	40.00
Lalique, Bowl, Frosted, Floral, 4 Lions' Paws Base, Signed, 13 In.	65.00
Lalique, Bowl, Mistletoe, Brown Toning, Signed, 8 In.	115.00
Lalique, Bowl, Silver Overlay, Clear & Frosted, C.1920, 8 In.	80.00

Lalique, Vase,
Blue Green,
Molded, 11 In.

Lamp,
Adams & Westlake Co.,
Patent 1890,
Brass, Wall
(See Page 271)

Lalique, **Bowl,** Yellow, Raised Lily Pads, 8 1/2 In.	95.00
Lalique, **Box,** Covered, Round, Children Around Perimeter, 4 1/4 In.Diameter	120.00
Lalique, **Box,** Embossed Dragonflies On Cover, Round, 3 1/2 In.	65.00
Lalique, **Box,** Female Nudes On Lid, Leaf Border, Satin Finish, Round, 3 5/8 In	58.00
Lalique, **Box,** Frosted Blossoms On Lid, Vertical Herringbone, 4 1/4 In.	85.00
Lalique, **Box,** Powder, Art Deco Cherubs Encircle Box, Signed	100.00
Lalique, **Box,** Powder, Three Dancing Girls In Relief, Leaf Border, 3 1/2 In.	58.00
Lalique, **Box,** Powder, Three Nude Dancing Girls, 3 5/8 X 1 1/2 In.	68.00
Lalique, **Figurine,** Fish, Round Base, 4 In.	27.00
Lalique, **Figurine,** Quail On Saucer, Signed, 3 1/2 X 2 In.	40.00
Lalique, **Figurine,** Rooster, Clear, Molded Feathers, C.1930, 8 In.	500.00
Lalique, **Figurine,** Rooster, Frosted Body & Feathers, Signed, 8 In.	80.00
Lalique, **Flacon,** Clear, Circular Domed Marble Base, C.1930, 6 1/2 In.	425.00
Lalique, **Globe,** Fiery Opalescent, Notched Swirled Ribbing, 10 1/2 X 7 In.	250.00
Lalique, **Globe,** Hanging, Opalescent, Swirled, Notched, 9 X 7 1/2 In.	250.00
Lalique, **Globe,** Torch, Swirled & Notched, Fiery Iridescent, 10 X 7 1/2 In.	250.00
Lalique, **Goblet,** Frosted, Blue Grapevines & Leaves Stem, C.1935	32.50
Lalique, **Goblet,** Ribbed Bowl & Foot, Moldwork Stem, Signed	35.00
Lalique, **Knife Rest,** Camphor Satin Baby Heads At End, 3 1/2 In.Long	35.00
Lalique, **Pitcher,** Amber, Molded & Cut Berries & Leaves, 10 In.	165.00
Lalique, **Piaque,** Raised Head Of Louis Pasteur, 4 In.Diameter	105.00
Lalique, **Plate,** Black, Embossed Tree, Signed, 8 In.	32.00
Lalique, **Plate,** Frosted Floral, 8 1/4 In.	25.00
Lalique, **Plate,** Green, Wheat Pattern, Signed Rene Lalique, 10 1/2 In.	40.00
Lalique, **Plate,** Radiating Concentric Circles, C.1930, 11 In.	34.50
Lalique, **Plate,** Sailboats, Signed, 8 1/2 In.	37.50
Lalique, **Shade,** Fiery Opalescent, 9 X 7 1/2 In.	250.00
Lalique, **Shade,** Lamp, Opalescent Swirled & Notched Ribs, 6 X 10 In.	250.00
Lalique, **Sherbet,** Blue Grapevines & Leaves Stem, C.1935	16.00
Lalique, **Shot Glass,** Art Deco Pattern, Black Enameled Flowers, 2 In.	30.00
Lalique, **Shot Glass,** Cherubs At Each Side, Berries, Pink Tones, Set Of 4	150.00
Lalique, **Toothpick,** Raised Frosted Cherubs	55.00
Lalique, **Tumbler,** Light Amber, Fluted, Thorny Outline, Set Of 4	220.00
Lalique, **Vase,** Allover Leaf & Vine, Frosted & Clear, 6 1/2 In.	80.00
Lalique, **Vase,** Blue Green, Molded, 11 In. .... *Illus*	400.00
Lalique, **Vase,** Carved Frosted & Clear Leaves & Vines, Signed, 6 1/2 In.	85.00
Lalique, **Vase,** Ferns & Leaves On Iridescent, R.Lalique, 7 In.	115.00
Lalique, **Vase,** Ferns, Flared, Footed, 6 In.	145.00
Lalique, **Vase,** Frosted Ground, 8 Panels Of Clear Mimosa Leaves, 4 3/4 In.	68.00
Lalique, **Vase,** Frosted Scalloped Layers, Flared, Footed, 5 In. .... 60.00 To 85.00	
Lalique, **Vase,** Frosted, Lovebirds In Foliage, 4 Handles, C.1935, 10 1/4 In.	250.00
Lalique, **Vase,** Iridescent, Leaf-Decorated, 7 In.	125.00
Lalique, **Vase,** Opalescent Cased, Blown, Thistles, 8 1/2 In.	500.00
Lalique, **Vase,** Overlapping Scallop Shells, Wide Mouth, Short Neck, 7 1/2 In.	140.00
Lalique, **Vase,** Ribbed, Fernery Decoration, Bulbous, 7 In.	100.00
Lalique, **Vase,** Scallop Shells Design, Straight Sides, Short Neck, 7 1/2 In.	140.00
Lalique, **Vase,** Smoky Gray, Interlocking Feathers, C.1925, 9 In.	110.00
Lalique, **Vase,** Tinted Gray, 3 Rows Of Raised Cones, C.1925, 7 1/2 In.	350.00

Lalique, Vase, Tobacco Leaves In High Relief, 5 In.High	35.00
Lalique, Vase, Twelve Birds, Foliage, Frosted, 6 7/8 In.High	125.00
Lalique, Vase, 12 Birds In Floral Niches, Signed, 7 In.	175.00
Lalique, Vase, 2 Bands Of Antelopes Leaping Over Bushes, Signed, 7 In.	195.00
Lalique, Wine, Red Grapevines & Leaves Stem, C.1935	25.00
Lalique, Wine, Ribbed Bowl & Foot, Moldwork On Stem, Signed	25.00
Lalique, Wine, Ribbed, Molded Stem, Script Signature	20.00
Lalique, Wine, Rooster Stem, Frosted Lines, Signed, 6 In.	45.00
Lalique, Wine, White Grapevines & Leaves Stem, C.1935	15.75
Lambeth, Bowl, Silicon, Scroll Legs, Blue & White Apples, 6 In.	70.00
Lamp, see also Baccarat, Lamp, D'Argental, Lamp, Daum Nancy,	
Lamp, Fulper, Lamp, Hummel, Lamp, Mary Gregory, Lamp,	
Mt. Washington, Lamp, Muller Freres, Lamp, Nippon, Lamp,	
Owens, Lamp, Patte de Verre, Lamp, Quezel, Lamp, Tiffany,	
Lamp, Van Briggle, Lamp, Webb, Lamp, Weller, Lamp	
Lamp, Acorn Burner, Cased, Pink, Melon Ribbed, Swirl Chimney, Miniature	55.00
Lamp, Adams & Westlake Co., Patent 1890, Brass, Wall *Illus*	130.00
Lamp, Aladdin Majestic, Green Moonstone Bowl, Silver Plated Base, 15 In.	22.50
Lamp, Aladdin, Alacite, Art Deco Style, Footed Base, 22 In.	32.00
Lamp, Aladdin, Alacite, Bracket	55.00
Lamp, Aladdin, Alacite, Gold & Pink Base, Feathers On Green Ribbed, 16 In.	26.00
Lamp, Aladdin, Amber Base	42.00
Lamp, Aladdin, Art Deco, Urn Type, Scroll Handles, Harp, 10 In.	20.00
Lamp, Aladdin, B26	235.00
Lamp, Aladdin, B28	75.00
Lamp, Aladdin, B30	50.00
Lamp, Aladdin, B41	55.00
Lamp, Aladdin, B47	65.00
Lamp, Aladdin, B48	75.00 To 80.00
Lamp, Aladdin, B51	50.00
Lamp, Aladdin, B53	27.50 To 32.00
Lamp, Aladdin, B53X	47.50
Lamp, Aladdin, B53, Crow's-Foot	35.00
Lamp, Aladdin, B53, Washington Drape	25.00
Lamp, Aladdin, B53, Zigzag	35.00
Lamp, Aladdin, B55	40.00
Lamp, Aladdin, B61	1000.00
Lamp, Aladdin, B75	45.00 To 65.00
Lamp, Aladdin, B76A	150.00
Lamp, Aladdin, B77, Ruby, Lincoln Drape	220.00 To 275.00
Lamp, Aladdin, B80	35.00 To 40.00
Lamp, Aladdin, B80, Beehive Beta Crystal	25.00
Lamp, Aladdin, B82	55.00 To 75.00
Lamp, Aladdin, B83	185.00
Lamp, Aladdin, B83, Beehive Amber Beta Crystal	45.00
Lamp, Aladdin, B83, Beehive Ruby Beta Crystal	175.00
Lamp, Aladdin, B85, Diamond-Quilted, White Moonstone	75.00
Lamp, Aladdin, B87	120.00 To 125.00
Lamp, Aladdin, B88, Yellow	225.00
Lamp, Aladdin, B91	80.00
Lamp, Aladdin, B92	120.00
Lamp, Aladdin, B93	385.00
Lamp, Aladdin, B95, Queen, White Moonstone, Bronze Base	55.00
Lamp, Aladdin, B97	80.00
Lamp, Aladdin, B102	40.00
Lamp, Aladdin, B104	40.00
Lamp, Aladdin, B110	110.00
Lamp, Aladdin, B111	85.00
Lamp, Aladdin, B112	125.00
Lamp, Aladdin, B114	75.00
Lamp, Aladdin, B116	60.00
Lamp, Aladdin, B200, Hanging, 216 Shade	150.00
Lamp, Aladdin, Kerosene, Nickel Plated	35.00
Lamp, Aladdin, Lincoln Drape, Near White, 10 1/4 In.	75.00
Lamp, Aladdin, Model B, Table, Milk Glass Shade	55.00
Lamp, Aladdin, No.6 Burner, Table, Nickel, 10 In. Shade	40.00

Lamp, Aladdin, No.6, Hanging, White Shade 110.00
Lamp, Alcohol, Tin, 3 1/4 In. 7.00
Lamp, Argand, Brass & Cut Glass, C.1810, Pair .... *Illus* 650.00
Lamp, Argand, Bronze, Overlay Glass Shade, C.1815, 17 1/2 In., Pair 275.00
Lamp, Argand, Gilt Bronze, Dolphin Support, Urn Font, C.1815, 21 In., Pair 650.00
Lamp, Argand, J.& I.Cox, N.Y., C.1815, Double, Bronze, Cut Glass, 22 In., Pair 1100.00
Lamp, Art Deco Nude & Afghan Hound, Metal, Hobnail Glass Shade, 8 3/4 In. 47.00
Lamp, Art Deco Nude Lady, Pond, 4 Swans, Metal, 9 1/2 X 8 1/2 In. 49.00
Lamp, Art Deco Nude, Metal, Holding Ashtray, Red Finish, 17 In. 40.00
Lamp, Art Deco, Marble, Seductive Girl, Onyx Base, Fan Shade, 15 X 13 In. 245.00
Lamp, Art Glass, Boudoir, Reverse Painting, Sunset Scene, Orange, 16 In. 90.00
Lamp, Art Nouveau, Bronzed Metal, Stained Glass Tiles Shade, C.1910, 22 In. 700.00
Lamp, Art Nouveau, Metallic Red Shade, Acorn Shape, Vined Bronze Base, 16 In 175.00
Lamp, Art Nouveau, Red Luster Glass, Bronze Flowers & Vines Holder, 16 In. 186.00
Lamp, Art Nouveau, Table, Draped Nude, Black Amethyst Top, 14 In., Pair 150.00
Lamp, Banquet, Brass And Pewter, White Ball Shade, 23 In. 250.00
Lamp, Banquet, Brass, Shade Light Blue Satin Glass With Opaque Draping 200.00
Lamp, Banquet, Figural Stem, Cherub Playing Flute, Embossed Base 65.00
Lamp, Banquet, Figural Stem, Revolutionary Soldier, 22 In. 45.00
Lamp, Belgium, Art Deco, Boch, Crackle, Sun Motif, Yellow & Aqua, 14 In. 50.00
Lamp, Betty, American, Wrought Iron, C.1750, 3 3/4 In. 95.00
Lamp, Betty, Hinged Top, 5 In. 35.00
Lamp, Betty, Sliding Cover, Wrought Iron, 4 In.Hanger 45.00
Lamp, Betty, Tin, Hanger 35.00
Lamp, Bicycle Light, Carbide, C.1905 .... 15.00
Lamp, Blown, Blue, Pedestal Base, 5 In. High To Burner 40.00
Lamp, Bohemian Cut Glass, 9 In. 140.00
Lamp, Boudoir, Brass, Woven, 14 In. 50.00
Lamp, Boudoir, Lady Sitting With Dog, German, Luster, Pair 50.00
Lamp, Boudoir, Occupied Japan, Bisque, Free Trunk, Rail Fence, Boy, 12 In. 30.00
Lamp, Boudoir, Six Cream Colored Glass Panels, Birds, 15 1/2 In.High 60.00
Lamp, Bracket, Aladdin, Nickel, 9 1/2 In. 70.00
Lamp, Bracket, Cast Iron, L Shaped, Clear Glass Font, 19 X 13 In., Pair 90.00
     Lamp, Bradley & Hubbard, see Bradley & Hubbard, Lamp
Lamp, Brass Base, Yellow Flowers & Green On White Leaded Shade, 18 In. 850.00
Lamp, Brass Standard, Curved Arm Holds Art Glass Shade, 19 1/2 In. 95.00
Lamp, Brass, Spout, 4 In. 47.50
Lamp, Brass, 3 Legged, Shade 10 In.Ball, Frosted, Embossed Gold 360.00
Lamp, Bronze Base, Red Poppies On Green Leaded Shade, 6 Panels, 21 In. 750.00
Lamp, Bronze, Art Deco Dancing Girl On Marble, Brass Shade, 23 1/2 In.High 340.00
Lamp, Bronze, Vienna, Rider On Elephant, Palm Tree, 21 In. 475.00
Lamp, Bulbous 8 Section China Font, Floral, Handle, 8 In. 75.00
Lamp, Bull's-Eye, Amber, Ruby Flashed Chimney, Dated 1877, 10 1/2 In. 40.00
Lamp, Cambridge, Crown Tuscan, Nautilus, Footed, Gold Lace Decoration, 12 In. 195.00
Lamp, Camphene, American, Pewter, 9 1/2 In. 295.00
Lamp, Camphene, Pewter, Handled, 4 1/2 In. 150.00
Lamp, Camphene, Sellew Type, Pewter, American, Handled, 8 In. 250.00
Lamp, Camphor Glass, Art Nouveau Girl, Cone Shade, 10 In. 42.50
Lamp, Candlestick, Depression Glass, English Hobnail, Electric, 9 In., Pair 40.00
Lamp, Carriage, Beveled Lenses, 15 In., Pair 100.00
Lamp, Carriage, Candle, Tin & Brass 22.00
Lamp, Carriage, Square & Oval Beveled Glass, 16 In., Pair 150.00
Lamp, Carvel, Tole, Painted, Etched Pyriform Shade, Brass Stem, C.1850, 30 In. 250.00
Lamp, Ceiling Dome, Frosted White, Man In The Mountain, 16 In.Diameter 27.50
Lamp, Ceiling Fixture, Gas, Brass, 31 1/2 In. 8.00
Lamp, Chamber, Cranberry Glass, 11 In. 60.00
     Lamp, Chandelier, see also Steuben, Chandelier, Tiffany, Chandelier
Lamp, Chandelier, Continental, C.1850, Brass, 6 Scrolling Arms, 19 1/2 In. 500.00
Lamp, Chandelier, Copper & Brass, Blown-Out Fruit & Nuts, 3 Half-Moon Drops 250.00
Lamp, Chandelier, Cut Glass, Louis XV Style, 3 Arm, 34 In. 275.00
Lamp, Chandelier, Hand-Carved Wood, East Lake Style, Victorian, 4 Arm, 3 Ft. 250.00
Lamp, China, Floral Font, 2 Handles, 6 In. 60.00
Lamp, Christmas Tree, Miniature 175.00
Lamp, Composite, Clear Glass Font & Stem, 6 Panel, Edged Cable & Fan, 8 In. 35.00
     Lamp, Cosmos, see Cosmos, Lamp
Lamp, Cranberry Glass & Gilt Metal, Oil, Cut Glass Font, C.1850, 25 In. 60.00

Lamp, Cranberry Glass, Spiral Relief Beaded Columns, 9 1/2 In. 100.00
Lamp, Cranberry Pear Shade Font & Umbrella Shade, Thumbprint, Brass, 23 In. 200.00
Lamp, Cresolene, Miniature, Milk Glass Shade, Cast Iron Stand 24.00
Lamp, Crystal, Applied Handle, 4 X 2 In. 24.00
Lamp, Cut Glass, American, Harvard & Floral, Prisms, 29 In. 200.00
Lamp, Cut Glass, Dorflinger, Pointed Top, Metal Ring, Prisms, 24 In. 795.00
Lamp, Cut Glass, Harvard, Russian, Cane, Cut Prisms, 28 1/2 In. 1100.00
Lamp, Cut Glass, Hawkes, Sheridan Variation, Crosscut Diamonds, 14 In. 675.00
Lamp, Cut Glass, Libbey, Star & Fan, Spear Prisms, 18 In. 550.00
Lamp, Cut Glass, Mushroom Dome Shade, Intaglio, White Rose, 15 In. 190.00
Lamp, Cut Glass, Prisms, 21 In. 1100.00
Lamp, DeVilbiss, Gold Washed Base, Glass Shade, Art Nouveau, 7 1/2 In. 45.00
Lamp, Depression Glass, English Hobnail, Pink, Miniature 35.00
Lamp, Desk, Double, Fostoria, Pink Satin Glass Tulip Shades 125.00
Lamp, Double Cruisie, Wrought Iron, 6 In.Hanger, 12 1/2 In. 30.00
Lamp, Eagle Mfg.Co., U.S.A., Oil, 1870 Embossed On Base, Blown, Handle, 11 In. 55.00
Lamp, Embossed Brass Font, Iron Frame, White Bristol Shade, 14 In. 185.00
Lamp, English Hobnail, 9 1/4 In. 27.50
Lamp, Fairy, Brass, Jeweled Shade, 4 1/2 In. 95.00
Lamp, Fairy, Brown Pottery Owl, Indented Space For Candle, 4 1/2 In. 85.00
    Lamp, Fairy, Burmese, see Burmese , Lamp, Fairy
Lamp, Fairy, Clarke, Cranberry Overshot Dome Shade, Clear Base, 3 1/2 In. 110.00
Lamp, Fairy, Clarke, Decorated Burmese Shade, Unfired, 4 In. 265.00
Lamp, Fairy, Clarke, Webb Burmese Dome Shade, Green Ivy Leaves, 3 3/4 In. 195.00
Lamp, Fairy, Frog Figure, Green Bisque, Brown Glass Eyes, 4 1/2 In. 125.00
Lamp, Fairy, George Davidson, 1867, England, Ruby Diamond Point, 5 1/8 In. 15.00
Lamp, Fairy, Nailsea, Clarke Base, White & Blue Loopings On Blue, 4 1/2 In. 75.00
Lamp, Fairy, Nailsea, Clarke Base, 3 Color Loopings On Pink Satin, 4 1/2 In. 75.00
Lamp, Fairy, Nailsea, Cranberry & White, Ruffled Tricorn Shape, 8 In.High 395.00
Lamp, Fairy, Nailsea, Ruffled Base, Clarke Holder, 5 1/2 In.High 285.00
Lamp, Fairy, S.Clarke, Pyramid, Amber, Diamond Point, 3 3/4 In. 37.50
Lamp, Fairy, Sapphire Blue, Applied Rigaree, Clarke Base 75.00
Lamp, Fairy, Satin Cranberry Shade, Clarke Base 65.00
Lamp, Fairy, Teapot, White, Red Roses, Gilded Trim, 8 In. 200.00
Lamp, Fairy, 4 Children's Faces, Apple Green Shade, 5 In. 75.00
Lamp, Fat, Tin, 2 X 1 1/2 In. 40.00
Lamp, Figural Stem, Indian, Black Marble Base, Pink, Gold, Ivy Font, 12 In. 47.50
Lamp, Figural, Girl With Dog & Puppy, Brass Top, Frosted Font, 12 In. 45.00
Lamp, Findlay, Pressed Glass, Currier & Ives, 9 1/2 In. 75.00
Lamp, Finger, Coolidge Drape Pattern, Light Green, Applied Handle, Ruffled 63.00
Lamp, Finger, Cranberry, Clear Handle, Beveled Sides, 3 1/2 In. 95.00
Lamp, Finger, Moon & Star Pattern, Brass Collar, 4 In.High 85.00
Lamp, Fixture, Brass, Gas & Electric, 4 Frosted Cut Shades, 34 In. 150.00
Lamp, Flemish, Spout, Copper, 9 1/2 In. 40.00
Lamp, Flint Glass, Whale Oil, Excelsior & Maltese Cross, 11 1/4 In., Pair 195.00

Lamp, Argand, Brass & Cut Glass,   Lamp, Headlight, Wood-   Lamp, Student, Cobalt Font,
C.1810, Pair   Burning Steam Engine, 23 In.   8 In. Milk Glass Shade
(See Page 272)   (See Page 274)   (See Page 276)

Lamp, Flint, Harp Font, Brass Column, Leaf Stem, Marble Base, 9 In.	87.50
Lamp, Flint, Moon & Star, Opal Baroque Base, 15 In.	135.00
Lamp, Fluid, American, Brass, Bell Shape, C.1860, 3 In. Diameter	18.00
Lamp, Fluid, Horn Of Plenty Font, Hexagonal Standard, C.1835, 10 In., Pair	100.00
Lamp, France, China Cherub Playing Accordion, Bronze Base, Marble, 11 In.	195.00
Lamp, French, Crystal, Ormolu, Porcelain Medallions, 14 In., Pair	100.00
Lamp, Frosted Pink Glass, Hand-Painted Shade, 9 In.	78.00
Lamp, George Duncan, 1891, Honey Amber, Narrow Swirl, 12 In.	85.00
Lamp, Glo, Dated Aug.27, 1885, Ribbed Base, Frosted Shade, Miniature	60.00
Lamp, Glow Lamp, Milk Glass Shade, Clear Base, Miniature	50.00
Lamp, Gone With The Wind, Brass Finish, Chrysanthemums, 26 In.	165.00
Lamp, Gone With The Wind, Brass Foot, Orchids On Pink To White, 19 1/2 In.	175.00
Lamp, Gone With The Wind, Lions' Heads, Desert Scenes On Green, 23 In.	500.00
Lamp, Gone With The Wind, Miniature, Cranberry Swirl, 9 In.	125.00
Lamp, Gone With The Wind, Multicolor Floral On White, 25 In.	225.00
Lamp, Gone With The Wind, Pink & Red Roses On Green, Wired, 20 1/2 In.	225.00
Lamp, Gone With The Wind, Porcelain, Pink Floral On Green To Purple, 26 In.	195.00
Lamp, Gone With The Wind, Red Satin Glass, Iris, 23 In.	390.00
Lamp, Gone With The Wind, Red Satin, Raised Design, 11 In.	135.00
Lamp, Gone With The Wind, Rose Colored Blossoms On Shaded Yellow, 22 In.	200.00
Lamp, Gone With The Wind, Roses On Shades Of Blue, Electrified, 19 In.	67.50
Lamp, Gorham, Table, Sterling, Signed, Copper Wheel Etching, 9 In.	60.00
Lamp, Hall, Hanging, Cranberry Swirl, Brass Fittings, 8 In.Shade	250.00
Lamp, Hall, Hanging, Pink Oval Hobnail, Brass Fittings, 6 1/2 In. Shade	185.00
Lamp, Hand, Badger Brass Mfg.Co., Kenosha, Wis., Patent 1896-99, Solar, 12 In.	52.50
Lamp, Hand, Brass, Embossed Handle, 5 X 4 1/2 In.	17.50 To 20.00
Lamp, Hand, Clear Glass, Applied Handle, 2 3/4 In.	19.00 To 22.50
Lamp, Hand, Clear Glass, Bull's-Eye Pattern, 8 In.	25.00
Lamp, Hand, Clear Glass, Peanut Font, 5 In.	21.00
Lamp, Hand, Clear Glass, 8 Paneled Front, 8 In.	15.00
Lamp, Hand, Clear Glass, 9 Sided Block Paneled Font, 5 In.	22.00
Lamp, Hand, Glass, Attached Match Holder, Basket Weave Pattern, 8 In.	100.00
Lamp, Hand, Glass, Marigold, Paneled Block Font, Height 3 3/4 In.	30.00
Lamp, Hand, John A.Hurley Inc., 1902, Tin, 7 X 3 1/2 In.	16.00
Lamp, Hand, Kerosene, 4 Mold, Pedestal Base, Handle, 4 1/2 In. To Burner	20.00
Lamp, Hand, Pressed Glass, Roman Key, Square Base, 9 3/4 In.	28.00
Lamp, Hand, Roman Sandal, Bronze, 7 In.	300.00
Lamp, Hand, Vaseline Glass, 8 1/2 In.	60.00
Lamp, Hand, Whale Oil Burner, Brass, 4 1/2 In.	17.50
Lamp, Handel, see Handel, Lamp	
Lamp, Hanging, Brass Frame, Prisms, Sailing Ship On 14 In. Shade	395.00
Lamp, Hanging, Brass, Green Shade, 10 In., Prisms	160.00
Lamp, Hanging, Brass, Patented 1881, Clear Glass Font, 8 In. Ball Shade	80.00
Lamp, Hanging, Brass, Signed Beacon Home Supply Co., 14 In.	80.00
Lamp, Hanging, Brass, Smoke Bell, 14 In. Diameter Shade, Prisms	160.00
Lamp, Hanging, Brass, 15 In.Shade, Electrified, Prisms	260.00
Lamp, Hanging, Cottage, Brass Frame, 14 In. Shade, Frosted Dotted Domino	100.00
Lamp, Hanging, Cottage, Iron, Frosted Star Font, 10 1/2 In.Shade	90.00
Lamp, Hanging, Cranberry Swirl, Brass Fittings, 8 X 22 In.	185.00
Lamp, Hanging, Cranberry, Hobnail, Prisms, Wired, 14 In. Shade	375.00
Lamp, Hanging, Iron, 3 Chains, Gilded Milk Glass Smoke Bell, C Shade, 11 In.	140.00
Lamp, Hanging, 14 In.Shade, Maple Leaf	230.00
Lamp, Headlight, Wood-Burning Steam Engine, 23 In. .... *Illus*	180.00
Lamp, Heileman's Brewery, Table, 14 In. Shade, Pair	15.00
Lamp, Hitchcock, Key-Wind Mechanism, Height 1i 1/2 In.	100.00
Lamp, Honey Amber, Narrow Swirl, George Duncan, 1891, 12 In.	85.00
Lamp, Hurricane, Brass, Glass Shade, 20 In.	18.00
Lamp, Inspector's Mine, 10 In.	20.00
Lamp, James How & Co., London, Microscope, Kerosene, Iron, Brass, 11 In.	135.00
Lamp, Juno, Oil, Brass, White Opalescent Mushroom Shade, 19 In., Pair	85.00
Lamp, Kerosene, Cranberry Glass, Shade, Base, & Chimney, 15 1/2 In.High	210.00
Lamp, Kerosene, Glass, Wall Bracket Style, Handled, 4 In. Base, 14 In.	12.00
Lamp, Kerosene, Hand, Round, 8 1/2 In.	40.00
Lamp, Kerosene, Milk Glass Base, Opalescent Font, 9 1/2 In.	50.00
Lamp, Kerosene, Milk Glass Base, Pressed Font, Pedestal, 9 1/2 In.	50.00

Lamp, Kerosene, Table, Glass, 6 In. Base, 18 In.	15.00
Lamp, Kosmos-Brenner, Oil, Swirled Blue Green Glass, 12 In.	70.00
Lamp, Light Fixture, Brass, Ornate, 10 X 6 Ft.	1200.00
Lamp, Loetz & Gurschner, C.1900, Iridescent Glass & Gilt Metal, 21 In.	4900.00
Lamp, Marriage, Twin Font, Match Holder Between, Clambroth Base, Ripley	475.00
Lamp, Metal, Seated Nude Beside 5 In. Satin Amber Globe	30.00
Lamp, Milk Glass, Flint, Oil, Blackberry, Brass Fittings, Pressed Font, 11 In.	47.50
Lamp, Milk Glass, Floral, Milk Glass Chimney, Miniature	40.00
Lamp, Milk Glass, Nutmeg, Miniature	45.00
Lamp, Milk Glass, Oil, Translucent, 21 In.	20.00
Lamp, Milk Glass, Painted Flower, Dated 1867, Miniature	49.00
Lamp, Milk Glass, Pedestal Foot, Octagonal, Gilt Panels, 6 1/4 In.	135.00
Lamp, Milk Glass, Pewter Base & Fitting, 6 In.	80.00
Lamp, Miller, Metal Base & Frame, 4 Green Slag Panels, Openwork, 20 In.	155.00
Lamp, Miner's, Liberty, Tin	17.50
Lamp, Miner's, Tallow	12.00
Lamp, Mission, Milk Glass, Miniature	72.00
Lamp, Morey & Ober, Whale Oil, Pewter, 6 3/4 In.	395.00
Lamp, Mt.Washington, see Mt.Washington, Lamp	
Lamp, Night-Light, see Galle, Night-Light	
Lamp, Nutmeg, Green, Brass Band, Miniature	55.00
Lamp, Nutmeg, Miniature	28.50
Lamp, Nutmeg, Oil, Cobalt Blue, Pewter Handle, Miniature	45.00
Lamp, Oak, Hand-Carved, Electric	9.50
Lamp, Occupied Japan, Man In Colonial Costume, 7 In.	34.00
Lamp, Occupied Japan, Woman In Colonial Costume, 7 In.	34.00
Lamp, Oil, Cranberry Glass, Molded Out Bottom, Miniature	45.00
Lamp, Oil, Gilt Bronze, Enameled Green Glass, Hurricane Shade, C.1890, 18 In.	130.00
Lamp, Oil, Glass, Metal Holder, 5 7/8 In., Pair	68.00
Lamp, Oil, Green Satin Glass, Dot Design, Squatty Shape, 5 1/4 X 4 3/4 In.	150.00
Lamp, Oil, Hand, Waisted Loop, Sandwich, Clambroth	65.00
Lamp, Oil, Handwrought Iron, 4 Channeled, Crown Base, 14 1/2 In.	95.00
Lamp, Oil, Hobnail, Applied Curled Handle, Miniature	60.00
Lamp, Oil, Imperial Font, Blue, Grape Leaf, Nutmeg Burner, Miniature	75.00
Lamp, Oil, Milk Glass, Feather Pattern, Acorn Burner, Miniature, 6 1/2 In.	32.50
Lamp, Oil, Pressed Glass, Blue, 14 In.	45.00
Lamp, Oil, Pressed Glass, Embossed Design, Ceramic Stem, Slate Base, 20 In.	30.00
Lamp, Oil, Pressed Glass, Embossed Double Chicken Tracks On Font, 15 In.	23.00
Lamp, Oil, Pressed Glass, Embossed Panels On Font Base, 14 In.	23.00
Lamp, Oil, Pressed Glass, Paneled Wheat, Round, 15 In.	30.00
Lamp, Oil, Pressed Glass, Ribbed, 15 In.	23.00
Lamp, Oil, Pressed Glass, Turkey Foot On Base & Font, 17 In.	30.00
Lamp, Oil, Red Goofus Glass Font, Brass Connector, White Footed Base, 17 In.	90.00
Lamp, Oriental, Carved Teakwood God Holds Leaded Globe, 37 In.	450.00
Lamp, P&A Mfg.Co. Victor, Oil, Brass, Fluted Acid Etched Shade, 13 1/2 In.	125.00
Lamp, Pairpoint, see Pairpoint, Lamp	
Lamp, Parrot, Orange, Ebony Base, 13 1/4 In.High	55.00
Lamp, Peg, Brass Candleholder, Hand Held, Clear Font, 4 3/4 In.	47.50
Lamp, Peg, Candlestick, Brass, Double Wick Burner, 19 1/4 In.	45.00
Lamp, Peg, Tin Candleholder, Clear Font, 4 3/4 In.	47.50
Lamp, Perfection Student Lamp, Patent 1881, 8 In.Milk Glass Shade	390.00
Lamp, Pewter, see Pewter, Lamp	
Lamp, Photographer's Developing, Tin With Red Globe, Height 9 3/4 In.	17.00
Lamp, Porter, Alcohol, Amber, 2 In.	22.00
Lamp, Pressed Glass, Acanthus Leaf, Blue, Fluid, C.1840, 12 1/2 In., Pair	475.00
Lamp, Pressed Glass, Beaded Panel, Blue, Miniature	175.00
Lamp, Pressed Glass, Bellflower, Brass Center, Opalescent Base, 9 In.	150.00
Lamp, Pressed Glass, Bellflower, 7 1/2 In., Pair	300.00
Lamp, Pressed Glass, Block & Dot, Half Shade, Miniature	85.00
Lamp, Pressed Glass, Dakota, 10 In.	45.00
Lamp, Pressed Glass, Fleur-De-Lis & Chain, Amber, 2 1/2 In.	30.00
Lamp, Pressed Glass, Flint, Bull's-Eye & Fleur-De-Lis, 9 1/2 In., Pair	200.00
Lamp, Pressed Glass, Flint, Coolidge Drape, 15 In.	60.00
Lamp, Pressed Glass, Fluid, Baluster Standard, C.1835, 9 1/2 In., Pair	100.00
Lamp, Pressed Glass, Fluid, Blown & Cut Font, C.1825, 9 1/2 In., Pair	140.00
Lamp, Pressed Glass, Fluid, Trumpet Form Font, C.1825, 12 1/2 In., Pair	325.00

Lamp, Pressed Glass, Greek Key, Miniature	49.00
Lamp, Pressed Glass, Halley's Comet, Fluid, C.1835, 11 1/2 In., Pair	210.00
Lamp, Pressed Glass, Lincoln Drape Font & Shade, Miniature	47.50 To 50.00
Lamp, Pressed Glass, Lincoln Drape, Frosted & Clear, Miniature	60.00
Lamp, Pressed Glass, Loop, Fluid, Brass Standard, Marble, C.1840, 12 In., Pair	130.00
Lamp, Pressed Glass, Loop, Fluid, Reeded Standard, C.1840, 12 In., Pair	175.00
Lamp, Pressed Glass, Moon & Star, Stem Base, Miniature	45.00
Lamp, Pressed Glass, Oil, Bearded Man, 7 1/4 In.	125.00
Lamp, Pressed Glass, Peacock's Feather, 8 1/4 In.	30.00
Lamp, Pressed Glass, Peacock's Feather, 8 1/2 In.	29.50
Lamp, Pressed Glass, Petal & Loop, Brass Standard, C.1840, 25 In., Pair	275.00
Lamp, Pressed Glass, Roman Key, Miniature	22.00 To 30.00
Lamp, Pressed Glass, Swirl, Miniature	22.00
Lamp, Pressed Glass, Swirl, Mushroom Type, 8 In.	47.50
Lamp, Pressed Glass, Torpedo, Pedestal, 7 1/2 In.	32.50
Lamp, Pressed Glass, Tulip, Applied Handle, 3 1/2 In.	35.00
Lamp, Pressed Glass, Waffle, Fluid, Brass Standard, C.1840, 10 1/2 In., Pair	125.00
Lamp, Pressed, Heart, Miniature	24.00
Lamp, Rayo, Green Satin Shade, 18 1/2 In.High	139.00
Lamp, Rayo, Nickel, White Lilies On Yellow 10 In. Shade	45.00
Lamp, Ripley, Marriage, Blue Twin Font, Clambroth Match Holder, 13 1/2 In.	550.00
Lamp, Ripley, Marriage, Twin Font, Match Holder, Blue, Clambroth, 1870, 14 In.	475.00
Lamp, Rogers Type Statue, Country Girl & Boy, Ivory Finish, 28 In., Pair	75.00
Lamp, Ruby Flashed Bull's-Eye & Loop, 9 In., Pair	80.00
Lamp, Russian, Oil, Brass, Glass Shade, Turkish Market, C.1890, 21 In., Pair	125.00
Lamp, Sabatier, Parcel Gilt Bronze Woman, Marble Base, C.1900, 13 1/2 In.	175.00
Lamp, Sandwich Glass, Acanthus Leaf, White, Fluid, C.1840, 11 3/4 In., Pair	400.00
Lamp, Sandwich Glass, Cobalt Blue, Handled, 5 X 3 In.	60.00
Lamp, Sandwich Glass, Flint, Green Font, Clambroth Baroque Base, 12 1/2 In.	200.00
Lamp, Sandwich Glass, Flint, Oil, Opalescent Dot, 7 1/2 In.	55.00
Lamp, Sandwich Glass, Flint, Oil, Overlay, Blue To Clear Stem, 10 In.	120.00
Lamp, Sandwich Glass, Flint, Oil, Overlay, Ruby To Clear Font, 18 In.	105.00
Lamp, Sandwich Glass, Flint, Overlay Blue To Clear Stem, 9 3/4 In.	120.00
Lamp, Sandwich Glass, Flint, Overlay, Ruby To Clear, 18 In.	105.00
Lamp, Sandwich Glass, Flint, Petal, Scalloped Base, Brass Collar, 9 In.	50.00
Lamp, Sandwich Glass, Flint, Whale Oil, Blown, Frosted Font, 10 1/2 In., Pair	220.00
Lamp, Sandwich Glass, Flint, Whale Oil, Frosted Pear Font, 10 1/2 In., Pair	220.00
Lamp, Sandwich Glass, Flint, Whale Oil, Onion Font, Rough Pontil, 6 1/4 In.	35.00
Lamp, Sandwich Glass, Washington, Brass Stem, Marble Base, 18 1/2 In.	90.00
Lamp, Sandwich Glass, Whale Oil, Emerald Green, C.1840, 12 In.	550.00
Lamp, Sandwich Glass, Whale Oil, Mold Blown, Pressed Stem & Base, 9 1/4 In.	65.00
Lamp, Satin Glass, see Satin Glass, Lamp	
Lamp, Skater's, Tin, Bail Handle, 6 1/2 In.	18.00
Lamp, Sparking, Blown, Enameling, 5 In.	48.00
Lamp, Sparking, Camphene, American Pewter, 6 In.	125.00
Lamp, Sparking, Camphene, Pewter, Handled, 3 1/2 In.	125.00
Lamp, Sparking, Whale Oil, Pewter, American, 4 3/4 In.	175.00
Lamp, Stove, No.712 B, Two Double Wick Burners	70.00
Lamp, Student, American, 3 Fonts, 2 Clear Hurricane Shades, C.1890, 26 In.	375.00
Lamp, Student, Cobalt Font, 8 In. Milk Glass Shade *Illus*	390.00
Lamp, Swirl Squeeze Base, Chimney, Miniature	15.00
Lamp, Table, Amber Glass, Dotted Diamond Font, 7 3/4 In.	45.00
Lamp, Table, Aladdin Model 12, Brass, Satin Glass Shade	65.00
Lamp, Table, Amber Glass, Dotted Diamond Font, 7 3/4 In.	45.00
Lamp, Table, Amber Glass, Hobnail Font, 5 1/4 In.	27.50
Lamp, Table, Amber Glass, Stem Raised Flute Pattern, 9 In.	30.00
Lamp, Table, Atterbury, Clear Glass, Drip Catcher, Patent 1876, 10 In.	37.50
Lamp, Table, Brass Stem, Candle Shape, Painted Cream, 7 1/2 In.	25.00
Lamp, Table, Brass Stem, Candle Shape, 7 1/2 In.	17.50
Lamp, Table, Brass Stem, Marble Base, Buckle Font, 8 In.	25.00
Lamp, Table, Brass Stem, Marble Base, Clear Glass Font, 9 In.High	50.00
Lamp, Table, Brass Stem, Marble Base, Clear Glass Font, 9 1/4 In.	22.50
Lamp, Table, Brass Stem, Marble Base, Frosted Font, 5 1/4 In. Frosted Shade	47.50
Lamp, Table, Embossed Nickel, Signed 1892, Green, 10 In.	100.00
Lamp, Table, Figural, Cherub And Goat, Cast Iron, Frosted Font, 11 In.	40.00
Lamp, Table, George II Style, Mahogany, Brass Finial, Tripod, 47 In.	400.00

Lamp, Table, Glass, Clear Ball Font, 5 In.	13.00
Lamp, Table, Glass, Clear Bull's-Eye Font, 10 In.	25.00
Lamp, Table, Glass, Clear Beaded Font, 10 In.	16.00
Lamp, Table, Glass, Clear Copper Wheel Etched Font, 5 In.	15.00
Lamp, Table, Glass, Clear Font, Drip Catcher, 8 In.	30.00
Lamp, Table, Glass, Clear Font, Peanut On Base & Font, 11 X 7 In.	27.50
Lamp, Table, Glass, Clear Princess Feather, 12 In.	22.50
Lamp, Table, Glass, Embossed Clear Cosmos Font, 8 1/2 In.	25.00
Lamp, Table, Glass, Fluted Chimney, Milk Glass Font, 7 1/2 In.	35.00
Lamp, Table, Glass, Milk Glass Base & Stem, White Petticoat Shade, 12 In.	45.00
Lamp, Table, Glass, Milk Glass Base & Stem, 9 3/4 In.	42.50
Lamp, Table, Glass, Milk Glass Shade & Font, Painted Town Scene, 25 1/2 In.	80.00
Lamp, Table, Glass, Swirl Stem, Clear Font, 10 In.	16.00
Lamp, Table, Holmes Booth And Haydens, Pat.1860, China	65.00
Lamp, Table, Imperial Glass, Carnival Glass, Purple, 10 In.	27.50
Lamp, Table, Milk Glass, Clear Glass Font, Diamond-Quilted, 13 In.	30.00
Lamp, Table, Milk Glass, Hand-Painted, Embossed Scrollwork, 9 1/4 In.	45.00
Lamp, Table, Nickel, Rayo 7 Frosted Ball Shade With Poppies & Stars	55.00
Lamp, Table, Opalescent Glass, 6 In.	20.00
Lamp, Table, Whale-Oil Burner, Brass Stem, Marble Base, Height 8 3/4 In.	55.00
Lamp, Teapot On Top, Porcelain, Coral Flowers, Bird Form Spout, 8 1/4 In.	220.00
Lamp, The New Juno No.2, Rayo Type, Nickel On Brass, Dome Shade, 17 In.	80.00
Lamp, Tiffany, see Tiffany, Lamp	
Lamp, Vaporizer, Simplex Lamp Company, Tin, 7 1/2 In.	20.00
Lamp, Venus, 1867, Metal Base, Etched Scalloped Glass Shade, 19 In.	60.00
Lamp, Wall, Ditmar, Tin Bracket, Cobalt Blue Front, 4 1/2 In.	40.00
Lamp, Wall, Hanging, Coin Spot Cranberry Shade, Oil	135.00
Lamp, Weighted Brass, 20 Matador Burner, 13 1/2 In.	45.00
Lamp, Whale Oil, Bell Shape, Handle, 4 1/4 In.	168.00
Lamp, Whale Oil, Boiler Inspector's, Tin, 2 Tube, Wire Bail, 4 1/2 In.	38.00
Lamp, Whale Oil, Brass, Single Burner, Oil Cap, 7 1/2 In.	86.00
Lamp, Whale Oil, Brass, Single Burner, Oil Cap, 8 1/2 In.	90.00
Lamp, Whale Oil, Cut Glass, Miniature	75.00
Lamp, Whale Oil, Excelsior, Maltese Cross, Flint, 9 3/4 In.High, Pair	195.00
Lamp, Whale Oil, Finger, Applied Crimped Handle, 5 1/4 In.High	140.00
Lamp, Whale Oil, Flint, Brass & Marble Base, 9 1/2 In.	110.00
Lamp, Whale Oil, Flint, Sawtooth On Hexagonal Base, 2 Brass Burners, 10 In.	84.00
Lamp, Whale Oil, Gilt On Brass, 8 In. *Illus*	95.00
Lamp, Whale Oil, Gothic Windows Font & Base, Pewter Collar, 10 In.	90.00
Lamp, Whale Oil, Green Glass, 6 Sided Tapered Font, C.1840, 8 3/4 In.	80.00
Lamp, Whale Oil, Heart & Thumbprint, Pedestal, 8 1/2 In.	125.00
Lamp, Whale Oil, Horn Of Plenty, Brass Burner, 10 1/2 In.	175.00
Lamp, Whale Oil, Miniature, Flint	85.00
Lamp, Whale Oil, Pewter Burner, 9 1/4 In.	80.00
Lamp, Whale Oil, Pewter, American, Handled, 6 3/4 In.	275.00
Lamp, Whale Oil, Pewter, Cape Cod, Spout, 9 1/2 In.	285.00
Lamp, Whale Oil, Pewter, Domed Hinged Lid, Ball Finial, C.1825, 11 In.	375.00
Lamp, Whale Oil, Pewter, R.Gleason, 5 1/2 In.	450.00
Lamp, Whale Oil, Pewter, 7 1/2 In.	210.00
Lamp, Whale Oil, Sandwich Glass, Flint, Peg, Swirled Onion Font, 3 3/4 In.	26.00
Lamp, Whale Oil, Sandwich Glass, Pewter Rim, 9 In.	75.00
Lamp, Whale Oil, Sandwich, Flint, Heart, 2 Pronged Burner, 11 1/2 In., Pair	185.00
Lamp, Whale Oil, Sweetheart, 8 In., Pair	180.00
Lamp, Whale Oil, Waisted Loop, Hand, Clambroth, Sandwich	165.00
Lamp, Wide Awake, 1876, Finger, Cobalt Blue, Miniature	75.00
Lamp, Wire Bracket, Tin Reflector, Clear Font, 5 In.	17.50
Lamp, Woman Standing, Pewter & Brass, Clear Glass Font, 11 In.High	27.50
Lampshade, Gas, Lightolier Co., Marigold, Frosted, Glossy Inside, 5 In.	25.00
Lampshade, Hanging, Tiffany Type, Fruit Border, Caramel Fish Scale, 20 In.	850.00
Lantern, see also Railroad, Lantern, Silver, Sheffield, Lantern	
Lantern, Buggy, Whale Oil	34.00
Lantern, Buoy, Mohawk, N.Y.S. Canal System, Iron, Brass, Kerosene, Red, 23 In.	275.00
Lantern, Carriage, City Of Boston, Beveled Glass, C.1880, 20 In., Pair	45.00
Lantern, Child's, Red	11.00
Lantern, Civil War Portable Field Tent, Lancaster's Patent Ruby Lamp, Tole	97.50
Lantern, Dietz, Comet, Marked Syracuse, N.Y., U.S.A.	12.00

Lamp, Whale Oil,
Gilt On Brass, 8 In.
(See Page 277)

Lantern, Paul Revere, Tin, 15 In.

Lantern, Whale Oil, Tin & Glass, 19 In.

Lantern, Dietz, King, Fire Department, Brass	85.00
Lantern, Dietz, King, Fire Department, Copper	85.00
Lantern, Farm, Red Globe	6.50 To 7.50
Lantern, Flashing Signal, Tin, Double Wick Burner, 3 1/4 X 6 1/2 In.	25.00
Lantern, Hall, Brass, Etched Pyriform Globe, Candle Socket, C.1825, 28 In.	650.00
Lantern, Hall, Brass, Etched Pyriform Globe, Candle Socket, C.1825, 29 In.	375.00
Lantern, Hall, Brass, Etched Waisted Globe, Candle Socket, C.1825, 21 In.	170.00
Lantern, Hanging, Tiffany Style, Gothic Arches, Glass, Bronze, C.1900, 13 In.	1000.00
Lantern, Miniature, Tin, 6 1/2 In.	18.00
Lantern, Moroccan Garde, 6 Panels Colored Glass, 34 In.	40.00
Lantern, Paul Revere, Tin, 15 In. ....*Illus*	40.00
Lantern, Post & Co., Cincinnati, Ohio, Brass, Plated	150.00
Lantern, Railroad, see, Railroad, Lantern	
Lantern, Signal Boat, Keystoneware, 8 1/2 X 3 1/2 In.	20.00
Lantern, Skater's, Brass	22.00
Lantern, Skater's, Copper	34.00
Lantern, Skater's, Whale Oil	80.00
Lantern, Tin, Signed Perko Wonder Junior, Top Signed Jewel, 6 3/4 In.	15.00
Lantern, Whale Oil Burner, Tin, Early Glass Globe, 19 In.	125.00
Lantern, Whale Oil Burner, Tin, Tradesman, 9 1/2 In.	60.00
Lantern, Whale Oil, Tin & Glass, 19 In. ....*Illus*	125.00
Lapis Lazuli, Bottle, Snuff, Chinese, Carved, 2 1/2 In.	125.00

*Le Gras glass was made by August J.F.Le Gras in Saint-Denis,
France, between 1864 and 1914. Cameo, acid cut, and enameled glass were made.*

Le Gras, Bowl, Flower, Art Deco, Maroon Scrolls On Frosted Pink, 4 In.	120.00
Le Gras, Rose Bowl, Cloverleaf Opening, Cameo Cut, Signed, 7 X 6 In.	225.00
Le Gras, Vase, Acid Cut, Brown Leaves On Gray, 7 In.	245.00
Le Gras, Vase, Blue Enamel Branches On Gray, Ovoid Base, 14 In.	168.00
Le Gras, Vase, Blue Enamel Peacock & Flowers On Orange Mottled, 8 In.	115.00
Le Gras, Vase, Blue Stylized Twigs & Floral On Gray, 14 In.	175.00
Le Gras, Vase, Butterflies & Floral On Blue Opaque, Enameled, 13 In.	110.00
Le Gras, Vase, Cut & Enamel Grapes & Black Geometrics On Grayish, 8 In.	235.00
Le Gras, Vase, Dragonfly, Butterfly, & Water Lilies On Oranges, 11 In.	312.50
Le Gras, Vase, Enameled Butterflies, Signed, 12 In., Pair	180.00
Le Gras, Vase, Enameled, Leaf & Vine, 4 Colors, 5 X 4 1/2 In.	75.00
Le Gras, Vase, Green Ships & River Scene On Ocher, C.1900, 2 1/2 In.	250.00
Le Gras, Vase, Heart-Shaped Top, Woman In Winter Forest On Orange, 16 In.	125.00
Le Gras, Vase, Mold Blown, Pink, Majorelle, Signed, 10 1/2 In.	275.00
Le Gras, Vase, Winter Scene, Enamel On Orange, 14 In., Pair	300.00

*Le Verre Francais cameo glass was made in Paris during the late
nineteenth and early twentieth centuries. The glass is mottled and usually
decorated with floral designs.*

Le Verre Francais, Bowl, Charder, Orange Fish On Gray Blue, C.1930, 6 In.	350.00

Le Verre Francais, Bowl, Geometrics On Yellow Mottled, 8 1/4 In.	140.00
Le Verre Francais, Bowl, Magenta Floral, Pedestal, Signed, 9 X 4 In.	215.00
Le Verre Francais, Bowl, Oblong, Footed, Blue On Mottled Orange, 7 In.	135.00
Le Verre Francais, Plate, Cameo, Red & Orange Art Nouveau Pattern, 12 In.	225.00
Le Verre Francais, Vase, Art Deco, Cameo, 8 X 5 In.	295.00
Le Verre Francais, Vase, Art Deco, Orange, Red, Blue, & Yellow, Cameo, 10 In.	250.00
Le Verre Francais, Vase, Art Nouveau Florals On Orange, Cameo, 13 In.	350.00
Le Verre Francais, Vase, Cameo, Pink & Purple, 12 In.High	225.00
Le Verre Francais, Vase, Carved Tortoiseshell Foliage On Oranges, 12 In.	350.00
Le Verre Francais, Vase, Orange Base, Tortoiseshell Top, Footed, 4 1/2 In.	375.00
Le Verre Francais, Vase, Orange Bell-Shaped Flowers On Pink White, 10 In.	180.00
Le Verre Francais, Vase, Orange Flowers, Blue Berries, 15 1/2 In.High	285.00
Le Verre Francais, Vase, Yellow & Brown, Flying Geese, Satin Finish, 12 In.	225.00
Lead, Figurine, Buffalo, Germany, 4 In.	8.00
Lead, Figurine, Elephant, Painted, Britain, 1 3/4 In.	2.50
Lead, Figurine, Johnnie Walker, England, Painted, 1 1/4 In.	2.00
Leaded Glass, Plate, Tulip & Leaves, Scalloped Rim, 12 In.	120.00
Leather, Handbag, Gray Lizard Grained, Side Opening, 8 X 6 1/2 In.	37.50
Leather, Purse, Shape Of Chauffeur's Cap, Brown, Metal, Auto Scene	13.50
Leather, Rein, Pony, Woven Rawhide, 36 In., Pair	3.00
Leather, Saddle, Cowboy's, Brown, Hand Tooled, Iron Pommel, Hooded Stirrups	110.00
Leather, Saddlebag, Marked U.S.Cavalry	7.50
Leather, Shoe, Infant's, Patent, High Button, Pair	3.50
Leather, Shoe, Lady's, High Top, Pair	8.50
Leather, Wallet, U.S.Naval Officer's, C.1800, Presentation Inscription	74.50
Leeds Type, Plate, Pearlware, Blue Chinoiserie, Lobed Rim, C.1780, 9 1/2 In.	85.00
Leeds Type, Tea Set, Lavender Scenes, Miniature, 15 Piece	95.00

Leeds pottery was made at Leeds, Yorkshire, England, from 1774 to 1878.
Most Leeds ware was not marked. Early Leeds pieces had distinctive
twisted handles with a greenish glaze on part of the creamy ware. Later ware
often had blue borders on the creamy pottery.

Leeds, Bowl, Creamware, Pierced Lacework Band, Fluted, C.1790, 10 3/4 In.	40.00
Leeds, Coffeepot, Creamware, Pear Shape, Entwined Rope Handle, C.1785	100.00
Leeds, Coffeepot, Creamware, Pear Shape, Tear Finial, C.1750, 4 5/8 In.	80.00
Leeds, Cup & Saucer, Handleless, Brick Red Rose, Green Leaves, Blue Flowers	178.00
Leeds, Figurine, Sheep, Creamware, Reclining, Curly Coat, C.1790, 4 1/2 In.	100.00
Leeds, Jug, Creamware, Figures, Italianate Scape, Black Transfer, 1777, 12 In.	250.00
Leeds, Jug, Creamware, Virgin & Child, Dutch Decorated, C.1780, 5 1/4 In.	250.00
Leeds, Jug, Puzzle, Silver Resist, 1814 .... *Illus*	575.00
Leeds, Muffineer, Green	95.00
Leeds, Mug, Creamware, Entwined Strap Handle, C.1790, 3 1/4 In., Pair	75.00
Leeds, Patch Stand, Creamware, Waisted Foot, C.1790, 3 1/8 In.	75.00
Leeds, Plate, Creamware, Pierced Lacework Rim, C.1790, 10 In.	25.00
Leeds, Plate, Feather Edge, 8 3/4 In.	7.95
Leeds, Plate, White, Green Combed Edge, Scalloped, 10 In.	30.00
Leeds, Platter, Blue Feather Edge, 13 X 10 In.	12.00
Leeds, Platter, Blue, Combed Edge, 16 1/2 In.	50.00
Leeds, Pot, Bough, Silver Resist & Polychrome, 7 Holes In Top, 9 In.High	525.00
Leeds, Sauceboat, Creamware, Entwined Strap Handle, Molded Floral, C.1785	50.00
Leeds, Stirrup Cup, Creamware, Stag's Head, Mauve, Red, & Black, C.1790	450.00
Leeds, Strainer, Cheese, Creamware, Oblong Octagonal, Pierced, C.1790, 6 In.	90.00
Leeds, Sugar, Creamware, Pierced Cover, Waisted Foot, C.1785, 5 1/2 In.	100.00
Leeds, Teakettle, Creamware, Globular, Strap Handle, C.1790, 4 In.	70.00
Leeds, Teapot, Creamware, Enamel Florettes, Strap Handle, C.1775, 4 1/2 In.	150.00
Leeds, Teapot, Creamware, Floral Knop, Gilding, Rope Handle, C.1790	40.00
Leeds, Tub, Butter, Creamware, Pierced Cover, Upright Handles, C.1785, Pair	250.00
Leeds, Tureen, Creamware, Covered, Pierced Lacework Band, C.1790, 8 1/2 In.	100.00

Lenox china was made in Trenton, New Jersey, after 1906. The firm also
makes a porcelain similar to Belleek.

Lenox, Ashtray, Individual, Scallop Shape, 3 1/2 In.	3.50
Lenox, Bowl, Ivory, Floriform, 8 In.	14.50
Lenox, Bowl, Ivory, Gold Scalloped Rim, Green Wreath Mark, 6 1/4 In.	25.00
Lenox, Bowl, Nautilus Shape, Coin Gold Drip Edge, Beading, Green Mark, 6 In.	22.00
Lenox, Bowl, Washington's Tomb, Sepia, Gold, Patchin, C.1933, Handled, 4 In.	40.00

Lenox, Candlestick, Belleek, Ivory, Black Mark, 8 In., Pair	37.00
Lenox, Candlestick, Dusty Pink, Gold Rim, Round Base, 4 In., Pair	35.00
Lenox, Candlestick, Hexagonal, Ivory, Gold Bands, 8 1/4 In., Pair	135.00
Lenox, Chocolate Pot, Ming	65.00
Lenox, Chocolate Set, Gold Handles & Trim, Pedestal Pot, 17 Piece	150.00
Lenox, Coffeepot, Post Office, New York, 1830, Sepia, Gold, Patchin, C.1933	85.00
Lenox, Compote, Gold Trim, 6 X 3 1/2 In.	32.00
Lenox, Cornucopia, Lenox Rose, Green Wreath Mark, 5 In.	16.00
Lenox, Creamer, Covered Wagon, Nevada, Sepia, Gold, Patchin, C.1933, 4 In.	40.00
Lenox, Creamer, Silver Overlay	38.00
Lenox, Cup & Saucer, Bouillon, Embossed Gold Borders, 2 Handled	8.35
Lenox, Cup & Saucer, Coffee, Rutledge	15.00
Lenox, Cup & Saucer, Demitasse, Cobalt & Basket Of Fruit Panels, Gold	16.65
Lenox, Cup & Saucer, Demitasse, Cream, Gold Rim & Band, Sterling Holder	24.00
Lenox, Cup & Saucer, Demitasse, Golden Gate, Black Wreath Mark	15.00 To 18.50
Lenox, Cup & Saucer, Demitasse, Greek Key Handle, Green Wreath Mark	7.50
Lenox, Cup & Saucer, Demitasse, Rutledge	10.00
Lenox, Cup & Saucer, Demitasse, Sterling Silver Holder	20.00 To 20.50
Lenox, Cup & Saucer, Demitasse, Wide Gold Border	9.35
Lenox, Cup & Saucer, Wide Embossed Gold Border, 2 Handled, Bulbous	15.00
Lenox, Cup, Bouillon, Green & Gold Garlands, Sterling 2 Handled Holder	15.00
Lenox, Cup, Bouillon, Silver Holder & Saucer, Scroll Handled, C.1900	25.50
Lenox, Cup, Chocolate, Gold Trim & Handle, Pedestal, For Tiffany & Co., N.Y.	22.00
Lenox, Cup, Gold Gilding At Handle & Base, Green Wreath Mark	12.50
Lenox, Cup, Nut, Footed, White, Gold Trim, 3 1/4 In.Diameter	12.00
Lenox, Cup, Nut, Pedestal, White, Gold Trim, Green Wreath Mark	7.50
Lenox, Dish, Scallop Shell Shape, White, Green Mark, 7 3/4 In.	35.00
Lenox, Dish, Shell, Pink Outside, 6 X 2 In.	30.00
Lenox, Figurine, Bird, Blue Mark, 3 In.	10.00
Lenox, Figurine, Bird, White, Head Down, Tail Up, Green Wreath Mark, 3 3/4 In.	12.50
Lenox, Figurine, Head Of Woman, Art Deco Style, White, Green Mark, 4 In.	40.00
Lenox, Jar, Cracker, Covered, Ribbed Design, Green Leaf Mark	30.00
Lenox, Lamp Base, Art Deco Enamel On Ecru, 14 In.	92.00
Lenox, Mug, Monk Drinking Scene, Silver Rim, 1898	95.00
Lenox, Mug, Old Fort Dearborn, 1857, Sepia, Gold, Patchin, C.1933, Green Mark	35.00
Lenox, Mug, Old Spanish Courthouse, New Orleans, Sepia, Gold, Patchin, C.1933	35.00
Lenox, Mug, Santa Barbara Mission, Sepia, Gold, Patchin, C.1933, Green Mark	35.00
Lenox, Mug, Saratoga Springs, N.Y., 1831, Sepia, Gold, Patchin, C.1933	35.00
Lenox, Mug, Statehouse, Montpelier, Vt., Sepia, Gold, Patchin, C.1933	35.00
Lenox, Mug, Tammany Hall, N.Y., 1830, Sepia, Gold, Patchin, C.1933, Green Mark	35.00
Lenox, Penholder, Pink Round Base, White Ruffled Top, 4 X 2 In.	32.50
Lenox, Pitcher, Cider, Belleek, Red Cherries On Mocha, Palette Mark, 6 In.	75.00
Lenox, Pitcher, Urn In Blue Oval, Gold Handle & Rims, Bands, 6 3/4 In.	125.00
Lenox, Plate, Dinner, Virginian, Hand-Painted Borders, Set Of 12	295.00
Lenox, Plate, Dutch People & Boats, Tiffany & Co., Wood Frame, 5 1/2 In.	35.00
Lenox, Plate, Game, Birds Flying, Winter Scene, Gold Rim, Belleek, 9 In.	25.00
Lenox, Plate, Game, Birds, Habitat, Winter Scene, Gold Rim, Belleek, 9 In.	25.00
Lenox, Plate, Game, Birds, Nesting, Winter Scene, Gold Rim, Belleek, 9 In.	25.00
Lenox, Plate, Luncheon, Pink Primroses Center, No.2021/C.352, Green Mark	7.25
Lenox, Plate, Ming, 9 In.	6.50
Lenox, Plate, Octagonal, Mauve Woman's Bust Facing Left, Palette, 7 1/4 In.	12.50
Lenox, Plate, Octagonal, Mauve Woman's Bust Facing Right, Palette, 7 1/4 In.	12.50
Lenox, Plate, Rutledge, 6 1/4 In.	6.00
Lenox, Plate, Turquoise Jewels, Gold Bands & Ovals, Green Wreath Mark, 9 In.	32.50
Lenox, Salt, Belleek, Gold Decoration, Round	10.00
Lenox, Salt, Belleek, Green, Hand-Painted Flower, Green Inside, Pair	12.50
Lenox, Salt, Belleek, Hand-Painted Roses	5.40
Lenox, Salt, Belleek, Pink, Gold Rim, Hand-Painted Rose Inside, Pair	12.50
Lenox, Salt, Floral & Gilt	9.00
Lenox, Salt, Floral Sprays On Ivory, Cylindrical, Spoon	10.00
Lenox, Salt, Hand-Painted Floral, Belleek, Palette Mark	4.00
Lenox, Salt, Individual, Belleek, Pink Roses, Blue Forget-Me-Nots, Gold	8.00
Lenox, Salt, Master, Swan, Cream, Pair	22.00
Lenox, Salt, Scallop Shell Shape, Coral Design, Green Mark	10.00
Lenox, Salt, Sterling Silver Overlay, Green Wreath Mark	9.00

Lenox, **Salt**, Round, Gold Decoration, Belleek 10.00
Lenox, **Sugar & Creamer**, Rutledge 18.00
Lenox, **Sugar**, Covered, Cobalt Blue, Silver Overlay, Black Wreath L Mark 50.00
Lenox, **Sugar**, Covered, Silver Overlay, 2 Handled 52.00
Lenox, **Swan**, White, Gold Brushed Wings, Green Wreath Mark, 4 1/2 In. 10.00
Lenox, **Tea Set**, Art Nouveau, Silver Overlay On Cream Porcelain, 3 Piece 160.00
Lenox, **Tea Set**, Eagle & Stars, Scenes, Patchin, 1933, Green Mark, 10 Piece 225.00
Lenox, **Teacup & Saucer**, Shreve & Co. Sterling Holder 45.00
Lenox, **Teapot**, Belleek, Green & Tan, Art Nouveau Designs, 10 1/2 In. 65.00
Lenox, **Teapot**, Brown Ware, Sterling Overlay 42.50
Lenox, **Toby Mug**, Belleek, William Penn, Indian Head Handle, 6 1/2 In. 160.00
Lenox, **Toby Mug**, William Penn, Indian Head Handle, 6 1/2 In.High 95.00
Lenox, **Toby Mug**, William Penn, White, Green Wreath L Mark, 7 In. 115.00
Lenox, **Toby Mug**, William Penn, White Indian Head Handle, 12 In. 70.00
Lenox, **Tray**, Pin, Gold Edge 30.00
Lenox, **Urn**, Green, White Swans On Sides, Pedestal, Green Mark, 8 1/2 In. 58.00
Lenox, **Vase**, Belleek, Cream To Beige, 3 Purple Iris, 10 1/2 In. 135.00
Lenox, **Vase**, Belleek, Mother Cuddling Baby, Palette Mark, 16 X 5 In. 250.00
Lenox, **Vase**, Belleek, Orange Poppies On Burnt Orange, 14 7/8 In. 175.00
Lenox, **Vase**, Belleek, Pearl Luster, Women With Butterfly Wings, Keith, 11 In. 125.00
Lenox, **Vase**, Belleek, Trees & Black On Lemon Yellow, 12 In. 160.00
Lenox, **Vase**, Belleek, Trumpet, Etched Silver Overlay, Pink Roses, 8 1/2 In. 120.00
Lenox, **Vase**, Blue Green To Ivory, Poppies & Green Leaves, Palette, 5 In. 57.00
Lenox, **Vase**, Cornucopia, Green Wreath Mark, 4 1/2 In., Pair 22.00
Lenox, **Vase**, Double, Half-Moon Shape, Center Ring Handle, Green Mark, 7 In. 22.00
Lenox, **Vase**, Fluted, White On Rose-Colored Base, Green Wreath Mark, 8 1/2 In 45.00
Lenox, **Vase**, Trumpet, Footed, Fluted, Cream & Gold, 8 1/2 In., Pair 65.00
Lenox, **Vase**, White Wheat On Soft Green, Embossed, Green Wreath Mark, 10 In. 45.00
Libbey, **Champagne**, Silhouette, Squirrel Base 95.00
Libbey, **Goblet**, Silhouette, Cat Base .... 95.00 To 110.00
Libbey, **Liqueur**, Silhouette, Monkey Base 95.00
Libbey, **Wine**, Kangaroo Silhouette, Opalescent, Signed 85.00
   Lighting Devices, see Candleholder, Candlestick, Lamp, etc.

   Lightning rod balls are collected for their variety of shape and color.
   These glass balls were at the center of the rod that was attached to the
   roof of a house or barn to avoid lightning damage.
Lightning Rod, **Ball**, Milk Glass 10.00
Lightning Rod, **Ball**, RHF, Milk Glass, White 10.00
Lightning Rod, **Blue Ornate Balls** 17.00
Lightning Rod, **Globe**, Milk Glass 4.00
Lightning Rod, **Globe**, Milk Glass, Blue 4.00
Lightning Rod, **Globe**, Milk Glass, Orange, 4 1/2 In. 30.00

   Limoges porcelain has been made in Limoges, France, since the
   mid-nineteenth century. Fine porcelains were made by many factories,
   including Haviland, Ahrenfeldt, Guerin, Pouyat, Elite, and others.
   Limoges, see also Haviland
Limoges, **Basket**, Sculptured Handle, Roses & Foliage, Gold, 9 X 5 In. 35.00
Limoges, **Bell**, Dinner, Hand-Painted Roses 30.00
Limoges, **Bowl**, Berry, Gold Edge, Berries & Leaves, J.P., 1906, 3 1/2 In. 15.50
Limoges, **Bowl**, Bouillon, La Cloche, Gold Eared Handles 15.00
Limoges, **Bowl**, Man's Portrait, Pegasus & Muses In Landscape, C.1890, 16 In. 500.00
Limoges, **Bowl**, Oval, Green With Brown, 8 1/2 X 5 1/2 In. 6.00
Limoges, **Bowl**, Pink Florals, Gold Trim, Scalloped, A.Lanternier, 9 1/2 In. 14.00
Limoges, **Bowl**, Pink Roses & Green Leaves, Gold Scalloped, J.P., 9 1/2 In. 9.25
Limoges, **Bowl**, Pink Roses, Gold Trim, Artist Signed, 11 1/2 X 8 In. 37.50
Limoges, **Bowl**, Punch, Pedestal, Grapes & Leaves, T&V, 14 In. 185.00
Limoges, **Bowl**, Ruffled, Pink & Green Floral, Footed, Gold, J.Pouyat, 7 In. 45.00
Limoges, **Box**, Collar Button, T.V.Limoges 11.50
Limoges, **Box**, Powder, Gold Border, Scene, French Blue, Signed Joel, 7 In. 6500.00
Limoges, **Butter Pat**, Green Olives Center, 3 1/4 In., Set Of 6 .... 21.00
Limoges, **Butter Pat**, Pink Roses, Gold Edge, GDA 3.35
Limoges, **Cake Set**, Peach To Cream, White & Orchid Floral, Gold, 7 Piece 75.00
Limoges, **Candlestick**, Cream & Blue, Roses, Gold, W.G.& Co., 7 1/2 In., Pair 45.00
Limoges, **Celery**, Gold On Raised Ivory Plumes, Blue Floral On Cream 22.50
Limoges, **Celery**, Plume Border, Soft Tan, Blue Flowers, 12 1/4 In. 22.50

Limoges, Celery, White Roses & Green Leaves On White, Gold, 13 1/2 X 6 In.	37.00
Limoges, Charger, Game, Two Pheasants In Bush, J.Marsay, 13 3/4 In.	145.00
Limoges, Chocolate Pot, Country Scene, Gold Bordered, 8 In.High	30.00
Limoges, Chocolate Pot, White With Gold, 8 X 8 1/2 In.	35.00
Limoges, Chocolate Set, Gold Leaves & Flowers On Buff, 25 Piece	225.00
Limoges, Coffee Set, Rose Garlands, Gold Decoration, G.D.& C.G., 3 Piece	90.00
Limoges, Console Set, Orchids, Covered Pot, A.Lanternier, 3 Piece	15.00
Limoges, Creamer, Yellow Roses & Violets, Gold Trim, Fleur-De-Lis & Shield	3.00
Limoges, Cup & Saucer, Chocolate, Floral & Gold On Beige	8.00
Limoges, Cup & Saucer, Demitasse, Blue Forget-Me-Nots On White, Gilt Trim	13.00
Limoges, Cup & Saucer, Demitasse, Blue To White, Gold Floral & Flecks	7.50
Limoges, Cup & Saucer, Demitasse, Pale Blue, Gold Handle & Feet	10.00
Limoges, Cup & Saucer, 2 Handled, Engraved Gold Band, Red Band, Soyer	17.50
Limoges, Dish, Candy, Ruffled, Elite	15.00
Limoges, Dish, Nut, Heart Shape, Forget-Me-Nots, Blue, 2 1/2 In., Pair	16.00
Limoges, Dish, Shell, Feather Edge, Orchid With Floral Sprays, 5 1/2 In.	12.00
Limoges, Dresser Set, Violet Decoration, 5 Pieces	100.00
Limoges, Dresser Set, Violets On Pastel Shaded Ground, Dated 1909, 3 Piece	85.00
Limoges, Fish Set, Fishnet, Pale Blue Center, Light Beige Border, 13 Piece	395.00
Limoges, Fish Set, Gold Speckled Swimming Fish, Scalloped, 13 Piece	160.00
Limoges, Game Set, Pheasants, 12 Piece	265.00
Limoges, Gravy Boat & Attached Tray, Pink Dianthus, Gold Traces, 9 In.	15.00
Limoges, Hair Receiver, Floral & Fish Scale, Gold, T & V, 1900	30.00
Limoges, Hair Receiver, Pink Roses On Pale Blue, Artist Signed	17.50
Limoges, Hatpin Holder, Pink Roses On Shaded Ground, Gold Top, J.P.Limoges	25.00
Limoges, Humidor, Indian Brave Smoking Peace Pipe, Yellow Ground, 5 In.	75.00
Limoges, Inkwell & Attached Tray, Pink Floral On Blue, Insert, 8 X 5 In.	50.00
Limoges, Jar & Underplate, Jam, Covered, Currants, Gold Band, Handled	42.50
Limoges, Jar, Cracker, Dark Red Roses, Signed Rene	42.00
Limoges, Jar, Cracker, Pink, Red Berries, Leaves, T&V, 1902	58.00
Limoges, Jar, Cracker, Swirled, Floral, Gold, M.Redon, 7 In.	42.50
Limoges, Jar, Powder & Hair Receiver, Cobalt Cornflowers, Gilbert	48.00
Limoges, Jar, Powder, White To Pastel, Roses, Gold Finial, 5 In.	36.00
Limoges, Lemonade Set, Pale Green Ground, Grapes & Leaves, Gold, 6 Pieces	195.00
Limoges, Mug, Beer, Grapes On The Vine, 6 In.	45.00
Limoges, Mug, Dutch Girls & Boys, J.Rankin, 4 1/2 In.	65.00
Limoges, Mug, Fruit & Leaves, Gold, JPL	60.00
Limoges, Mug, Tankard, Purple & Green Grapes On Green & Gold, 6 1/2 In.	75.00
Limoges, Nappy, Blue & Green Forget-Me-Nots, Gold Trim, T & V	25.00
Limoges, Oyster Set, Hand-Painted, J.P.L., France, T & V, 9 Piece	900.00
Limoges, Pitcher, Apples On Yellow & Green, Bulbous, J.P., 5 In.	34.00
Limoges, Pitcher, Cider, Berries & Floral On Cream To Brown, Guerin, 10 In.	45.00
Limoges, Pitcher, Cider, Bulbous, Apples, Green Handle, Gold Edge, 3 Quart	50.00
Limoges, Pitcher, Claret, Hand-Painted, Multicolor, 11 1/4 In.	225.00
Limoges, Pitcher, Diamond Shape, Orange & Blue Floral Bands On Cream, 7 In.	32.00
Limoges, Pitcher, Hand-Painted Apples, Green Handle, 3 Quart	65.00
Limoges, Pitcher, Milk, Apple Blossoms	85.00
Limoges, Pitcher, Tankard Type, Currants, Leaves, Turquoise Ground, 12 1/2 In	140.00
Limoges, Plaque, Apples, Signed, 16 In.	200.00
Limoges, Plaque, Bird Dog & Swan, Gold Rococo Border, Artist Signed, 10 In.	145.00
Limoges, Plaque, Indian, Decal & Hand-Painted, 11 1/2 X 8 1/2 In.	385.00
Limoges, Plaque, Roses, Signed, 16 In.	200.00
Limoges, Plate, Apples & Blossoms On Yellow, Gold, Elite, 10 1/2 In.	32.00
Limoges, Plate, Apples On White, Coin Gold Rim, Sena, 8 3/4 In.	45.00
Limoges, Plate, Apples, Artist Signed, 12 In.	50.00
Limoges, Plate, Asparagus, Green & Gold, 10 In.	30.85
Limoges, Plate, Bird, Lavender Geometric Border, Elite, CEC, 8 1/2 In.	11.00
Limoges, Plate, Butterfly & Flower Center, Gold Band, A.Seynu, 9 1/4 In.	32.50
Limoges, Plate, Cake, Gold Outlined Tiger Lilies & Green, 1893, 10 In.	19.50
Limoges, Plate, Cake, Open Gold Handles, Floral, T.& V., 11 In.	18.00
Limoges, Plate, Cavalier Sitting On Bench, Coronet, 10 In.	65.00 To 135.00
Limoges, Plate, Chop, Apple Blossoms, Scalloped Edge, 14 In.	85.00
Limoges, Plate, Chop, Peacocks In Medallions Border, 13 3/8 In.	85.00
Limoges, Plate, Chop, Pink & Purple Sweetpeas, Gold Scalloped, D & C, 12 In.	55.00
Limoges, Plate, Chop, Pink Roses, Elite, 12 In.	20.00
Limoges, Plate, Cows, Gold Border, Leona, 10 In.	95.00

Limoges, Plate, Dessert, White, Gold, G.D.A.	20.00
Limoges, Plate, Dog Portrait, Gold Rococo Rim, Coronet, Coudert, 10 In.	85.00
Limoges, Plate, Ducks, Gold Rococo Border, Scalloped, 10 1/2 In.	60.00
Limoges, Plate, Fish, Ivory Ground, Gold Fish, Shell, Scalloped, 8 1/2 In.	35.00
Limoges, Plate, Fish, Reddish Brown & Blue Flowers, Trout In Center, 9 In.	18.50
Limoges, Plate, Fish, Ribboned Edge, Gold Trim, Artist Signed, 9 In.	20.00
Limoges, Plate, Fish, Swimming Under Water, Scalloped, 7 1/2 In.	10.00
Limoges, Plate, Fish, Swimming, Scalloped Embossed Border, 9 1/2 In.	22.00
Limoges, Plate, Floral Garland, Gold Circle, White, T & V, 9 1/4 In.	22.50
Limoges, Plate, Floral, Gold, 5 In.	3.00
Limoges, Plate, Game Bird, Ducks, Landing & On Water, Coudert, 10 3/4 In.	97.00
Limoges, Plate, Game Bird, Purple Ground, Rococo Gold Scalloped, 9 1/2 In.	50.00
Limoges, Plate, Game Bird, Rococo Border, 9 7/8 In.	55.00
Limoges, Plate, Game Bird, Rococo Gold Border, Coronet, 10 1/2 In.	85.00
Limoges, Plate, Game Birds, Gold Rim, 10 1/4 In.	37.00
Limoges, Plate, Game, Bird Standing, Nesting, Gold Border, 9 1/2 In.	51.00
Limoges, Plate, Game, Deer, Pradet, Gold Rococo Edge, Coronet, 10 In.	85.00
Limoges, Plate, Game, Duck, Blue Purple Ground, Rococo Gold, Coronet, 10 In.	157.00
Limoges, Plate, Game, Two Ducks Feeding, Leaves, Gold Rim, 10 In.	75.00
Limoges, Plate, Game, Wild Boars, Artist Signed, Coronet, 10 In.	58.00
Limoges, Plate, Game, 2 Trout, Gold Rim, 8 In.	35.00
Limoges, Plate, Gold Outlined Floral & Tropical Fish, Scalloped, 9 1/4 In.	35.00
Limoges, Plate, Grapes, Gold Border, T.Colse, 8 3/4 In.	15.00
Limoges, Plate, Green & Red Holly, Scalloped, T & V France, 8 1/4 In.	15.85
Limoges, Plate, Hand-Painted Lilies Of The Valley, 8 In.	12.00
Limoges, Plate, Hand-Painted, Signed McKee, 10 1/2 In.	20.00
Limoges, Plate, Irises, Signed Billy, 12 1/2 In.	60.00
Limoges, Plate, Large Fish Swimming Among Tiny Fish, Blue Ground, 9 In.	15.00
Limoges, Plate, Lavender Floral, Green & Tan Leaves, Gold, Elite, 8 1/2 In.	17.00
Limoges, Plate, Pastoral Scene, Gold Rococo Edge, Alanchor, 1891, 8 In.	25.00
Limoges, Plate, Peasants At Fireside, Octagonal, GB France, 8 In.	22.00
Limoges, Plate, Peasants On Bench, Octagonal, GB France, 8 In.	22.00
Limoges, Plate, Pink & Red Roses On Pastel Peach To White, Vogt, 10 1/4 In.	38.00
Limoges, Plate, Poppies On Yellow & Cream, Scalloped, Artist Signed, 12 In.	55.00
Limoges, Plate, Portrait, Art Nouveau Woman's Bust, Imperial Crown, 11 In.	48.00
Limoges, Plate, Portrait, Gainsboro Lady, Gold Rococo Rim, 8 1/2 In.	35.00
Limoges, Plate, Red Poppies, Gold Border, J.P.L., France, Stouffer, 8 3/4 In.	14.00
Limoges, Plate, Red, Pink, & Purple Poppies On Tans, Scalloped, 12 In.	45.00
Limoges, Plate, Roses & Violets, Gold Leaf Rim, Losinslay, TV, 9 1/4 In.	25.00
Limoges, Plate, Roses On Turquoise, Gold Edge, Duval, Coronet, 9 In., Pair	45.00
Limoges, Plate, Rust & Yellow Rose & Buds, Gold, La Mour, Coronet, 9 In.	22.50
Limoges, Plate, Scalloped Rim, Pink Poppy, 10 In.	4.75
Limoges, Plate, Seacoast Scene, Gold Rim, Hanging, 11 3/4 In.	85.00
Limoges, Plate, Strawberries & White Floral On Pastel, 7 1/2 In.	15.00
Limoges, Plate, Sunburst Center, Scalloped, Gold Scrolls, Daisies, 12 1/4 In.	85.00
Limoges, Plate, Swimming Fish, Gold Scalloped Edge, T.& V., 9 In.	16.50
Limoges, Plate, Thistles, Lavender, Gold Trim, 9 In.	17.00
Limoges, Plate, Tropical Bird On Colorful Background, Coronet, Max, 9 1/2 In	35.00
Limoges, Plate, Violets, 8 1/2 In.	18.50
Limoges, Plate, Wall, Lady Near Footbridge, Gold Rococo Rim, 12 5/8 In.	165.00
Limoges, Plate, Wall, Lady Near Lake, Gold Rococo Rim, 12 5/8 In.	165.00
Limoges, Plate, White, Gold Border, A.Lanternier, 6 1/4 In.	2.00
Limoges, Platter, Game, Hand-Painted, 13 X 21 In.Long	95.00
Limoges, Ramekin & Underplate, Pink Rosebuds, Gold Trim, C & A	14.00
Limoges, Relish, Quail, Gold, Coronet	35.00
Limoges, Salt & Underplate, Master, Ahrenfeldt	10.00
Limoges, Salt, Irregular Shape, Hand Decorated, J.P.L., France	12.00
Limoges, Sherbet Set, Berries, Green, Pedestaled Dishes, Tray, 9 Piece	275.00
Limoges, Slipper, Pink, 2 1/2 In.	8.00
Limoges, Sugar & Creamer, Eagle Design, T & V Limoges, U.S.A.	22.00
Limoges, Sugar & Creamer, Pancake Shape, Forget-Me-Nots, Gold	46.00
Limoges, Tankard Set, Grapes On Tankard, Different Berries On Mugs, 7 Piece	400.00
Limoges, Tankard, Monk With Cigar & Stein, Brown To Peach, Worth, 15 In.	225.00
Limoges, Tankard, Tall Monk Toasting Short Monk, J.P., 1906, 12 In.	225.00
Limoges, Tea Set, Blue Forget-Me-Nots, Gold Finials, J.P., 3 Piece	38.00
Limoges, Tea Set, Florence, Patent Oct.2, 1890, T & V, 3 Piece	55.00

Limoges, Tea Strainer & Bowl, Wild Roses On Blue, Gold	29.00
Limoges, Teapot, Pink Roses, Gold Beading, 8 In.	45.00
Limoges, Tile, Tea, Purple Violets, Green, Round, 7 1/8 In.	35.00
Limoges, Toothpick, Laydown, High Gloss, 4 In.	15.00
Limoges, Tray, Bisque Bottom, Handled, Floral, Gold Scalloped, 12 X 9 1/2 In.	19.00
Limoges, Tray, Comb, Pink & Blue Flowers, Gold Edges, Handled, J.P.L., 10 In.	12.00
Limoges, Tray, Dresser, Green Bows & Pink Flowers, Gold Trim, T & V	28.50
Limoges, Tray, Dresser, Wild Pink Roses On Green, T & V, 1912, 11 X 7 1/2 In.	22.00
Limoges, Tray, Palette Shape, Pansies, 12 X 10 In.	40.00
Limoges, Tray, Perfume, Kidney Shape, Purple & Blue Floral, 17 X 10 In.	45.00
Limoges, Tray, Pin, George & Martha Washington, Mt.Vernon	9.00
Limoges, Tray, Pin, Yellow Roses On Beige, Gold Rim	10.00
Limoges, Tray, Red & White Roses, Irregular Gold Edge, T & V, 11 X 7 1/2 In.	25.00
Limoges, Tray, 5 Swans On Blue Water, Gold Trim, T.& V., 1917, 17 In.	19.00
Limoges, Tureen, Rust & Blue Flowers, Blue Ground, Gold Trim, 3 Quart Size	75.00
Limoges, Urn, Hand-Painted Roses, 3 Footed, 3 1/2 In.	15.00
Limoges, Vase, Boat Scene, 4 Gold Feet, 12 1/4 In.	95.00
Limoges, Vase, Cobalt, Gold Trim, Colonial Scenes, Pairpoint, 13 1/2 In.	125.00
Limoges, Vase, Nude Blonde Woman Putting Hands In Pond, Swans, Gold, 14 In.	1200.00
Limoges, Vase, Roses On Beige To Pink, Gold Trim, B & C Limoges, 12 In.	195.00
Limoges, Vase, Scenic, Browns & Oranges, T & V, 10 In.	75.00
Limoges, Vase, 2 Unrelated Floral Paintings On Each Side, JPL, 13 In.	250.00
Lindbergh, Bust, Bronze, Lindy Incised On Jacket, 6 X 4 1/2 In.	10.50
Lindbergh, Game, Card, 1927	16.00
Lindbergh, Matches, 1927 Dinner In New York	7.00
Lindbergh, Paperweight, Bronzed	28.00
Lindbergh, Photograph, Testifying In Congress On Airmail Legislation	8.50
Lindbergh, Plate, 1927, Commemorative, Yellow, Square, 8 1/4 In.	10.00
Lindbergh, Tapestry, 53 X 19 In.	75.00
Lindbergh, Ticket, Baltimore Celebration, 1927	8.00

Lithophanes are porcelain pictures made by casting clay in layers of various thicknesses. When a piece is held to the light, a picture of light and shadow is seen through it. Most lithophanes date from the 1825 to 1875 period. A few are still being made.

Lithophane, Mug, Child's, Floral, 2 1/2 In.	35.00
Lithophane, Panel Set, Ruby Glass, Leaded, 7 X 7 1/2 In.	49.50
Lithophane, Plaque, Girl & Boy Ringing Bell, 7 X 5 In.	55.00
Lithophane, Plaque, People & Woodlands Panels, Brass Hanger, 4 1/4 X 4 In.	40.00
Lithophane, Tea Warmer, Animals & Hunters, Feet With Gargoyles' Heads	95.00
Lithophane, Tea Warmer, Four Scenic Lithophanes In Holder, Burner	120.00
Lithophane, Tea Warmer, Scenic, Footed Nickel Plate Holder, Round, 4 In.	125.00

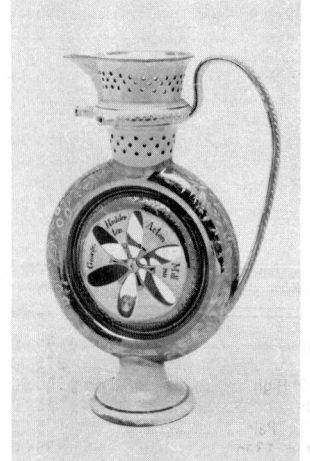

Leeds, Jug, Puzzle,
Silver Resist, 1814
(See Page 279)

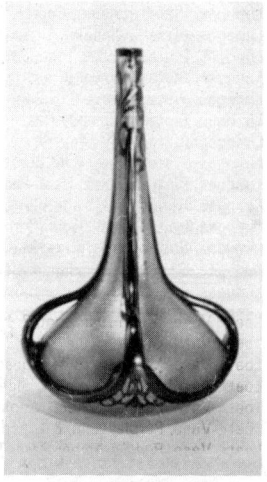

Loetz, Vase, Silver Mounts,
Signed, C.1900, 12 In.
(See Page 286)

Lithophane, Tea Warmer, Scenic, Footed Nickel Plate Holder, Square, 5 In.	125.00
Lithophane, Tea Warmer, 4 Scenes Of Animals In Forest, Silver Holder	95.00
Lithophane, Tea Warmer, 4 Scenic Panels, Ball Handle, Oil Burner	145.00
Lithophane, View Of Heidelberg, Pierced, 4 X 4 1/2 In.	45.00

Liverpool, England, has been the site of several pottery and porcelain factories from 1716 to 1785. Some earthenware was made with transfer decorations. Sadler and Green made print-decorated wares from 1756. Many of the pieces were made for the American market and featured patriotic emblems such as eagles, flags, and other special-interest motifs.

Liverpool, Creamer, Black Transfer, Pink Luster Rim	42.00
Liverpool, Jar, Cracker, Leaf Finial, Pink Floral, Green Leaves, 5 1/2 In.	25.00
Liverpool, Jug, Creamware, Annette & Lubin, Brown Transfer, 1797, 6 3/4 In.	70.00
Liverpool, Jug, Creamware, Benjamin Burton, Black Transfer, C.1800, 9 In.	175.00
Liverpool, Jug, Creamware, Farmer's Arms, Black Transfer, C.1800, 9 1/8 In.	350.00
Liverpool, Jug, Creamware, George Washington, Black Transfer, C.1800, 9 In.	875.00
Liverpool, Jug, Creamware, James McDonald, Black Transfer, 1800, 8 3/4 In.	900.00
Liverpool, Jug, Creamware, Washington & Franklin, Black Print, 1800, 10 In.	950.00
Liverpool, Jug, Creamware, Washington Portrait, Black Transfer, C.1800, 9 In.	225.00
Liverpool, Jug, White, Black Transfer, State Names, Peace & Prosperity, 8 In.	150.00
Liverpool, Mug, Creamware, Herculaneum, Washington Memorial, C.1800, 9 In.	225.00
Liverpool, Mug, Creamware, Washington Memorial, Black Transfer, 1800, 9 In.	525.00
Liverpool, Plate, Creamware, British Ship, Black Transfer, C.1825, 9 5/8 In.	50.00
Liverpool, Teapot, Oriental Figures, Finial, C.1765, 7 1/2 In.High	500.00
Locke Art, Goblet, Engraved Grapes & Leaves, Footed, Signed	105.00
Locke Art, Goblet, Engraved Grapes & Leaves, Signed	85.00
Locke Art, Sherbet, Etched Butterflies & Wheat, Fluted, 6 In.	150.00

Loetz glass was made in Austria in the late nineteenth century. Many pieces are signed Loetz, Loetz-Austria, or Austria, and a pair of crossed arrows in a circle. Some unsigned pieces are confused with Tiffany glass.

Loetz, Berry Set, Red To Mottled Green, Ruffled, Rainbow Iridescent, 7 Piece	395.00
Loetz, Bowl Vase, Silverized Iridescence, Threading, Sterling Collar, 11 In.	425.00
Loetz, Bowl, Crimped Top, Green Iridescent, 6 X 3 1/2 In.	85.00
Loetz, Bowl, Fruit, Iridescent Green, Orange Enameling, Silver Base	175.00
Loetz, Bowl, King Tut, Green Aqua On Amber, Pinched Sides, 7 In.	275.00
Loetz, Bowl, Salmon Iridescent, Amber Snake Forms Handle, C.1900, 3 1/4 In.	400.00
Loetz, Box, Covered, Green With Red, Gold & Yellow Enamel Floral, 2 X 4 In.	90.00
Loetz, Compote, Green Blue Iridescent, Metal Base, 8 In.	100.00
Loetz, Inkwell, Blue, Green, & Purple, Iridescent, Embossed Brass Top	135.00
Loetz, Inkwell, Splatter Design, Green & Purple Iridescent, Square, 3 In.	115.00
Loetz, Jar, Pickle, Blue & Purple, Threading, Silver Fittings, 7 In.	275.00
Loetz, Jug, Claret, Dark On Light Green, 5 3/4 In.High	75.00
Loetz, Pitcher, Milk, Red, Applied Clear Handle, Grecian Scene, 10 In.	195.00
Loetz, Tumbler, Iridescent Green, Veined Design	50.00
Loetz, Vase, Amber Iridescent, Amber Blue Splotches, C.1900, 9 1/4 In.	300.00
Loetz, Vase, Amber Iridescent, Silver Blue Droppings, Footed, C.1900, 9 In.	1000.00
Loetz, Vase, Blue Over Damascene, Red Base, 8 1/2 In.	550.00
Loetz, Vase, Burgundy Red, Bronze Vines & Leaves, 12 1/2 In.High, Pair	550.00
Loetz, Vase, Corset Shaped, Gold Ground, Enamel Decoration, Unsigned, 10 In.	125.00
Loetz, Vase, Cranberry Spatter, Blue Feathers, 10 1/2 In.	120.00
Loetz, Vase, Elephant Ear, Applied Leaf At Base, Iridescent, 12 In.	595.00
Loetz, Vase, Emerald Green & Blue, Gold Iridescent, Scalloped Rim, 11 In.	350.00
Loetz, Vase, Flower Form, Green Iridescent To Cranberry, Silver Holder	125.00
Loetz, Vase, Gold Iridescent, Gold Scrolls, 9 1/2 In.	85.00
Loetz, Vase, Gold, Blue Iridescence, Pinched Top, Signed, 5 1/2 In.	160.00
Loetz, Vase, Gold, Iridescent, Signed, 8 In.	65.00
Loetz, Vase, Green Iridescent, 12 X 12 In.	145.00
Loetz, Vase, Green Iridescent, 7 1/4 In.	65.00
Loetz, Vase, Green Purple, 5 In.	45.00
Loetz, Vase, Miniature, Blue Iridescent, 9 1/2 In.	275.00
Loetz, Vase, Peacock Feather, Blue Ground, Blue, Gold, Silver, 13 In.High	750.00
Loetz, Vase, Purple & Green, Applied Silver Waves & Fish, 6 3/4 In.	45.00
Loetz, Vase, Purple, Gold, & Green Iridescent, Bulbous, Flared, 11 In., Pair	175.00
Loetz, Vase, Red To Amber Base, Twisted & Perforated, Coin Spot In, 13 In.	335.00
Loetz, Vase, Red, Blue, Purple, & Gold, Blown-Out Geometrics, 7 1/2 In.	150.00

Loetz, Vase, Red, Blue, Purple, & Gold, Geometrical Design, 7 1/2 In.High 150.00
Loetz, Vase, Silver Feather Design, Signed, 6 1/2 X 4 In. 150.00
Loetz, Vase, Silver Iridescent, 5 In. 85.00
Loetz, Vase, Silver Mounts, Signed, C.1900, 12 In. .... Illus 1000.00
Loetz, Vase, 5 Finger, Metallic Blue Mottled, Red Interior, 6 In. 385.00
Lone Ranger, Book, Lone Ranger On Powder Horn Trail, Striker, 1949 .... 6.00
Lone Ranger, Card, Penny Arcade, Set Of 10 .... 2.50
Lone Ranger, Flashlight, Signal Siren, Lithographed, Tin, 7 In. 11.00
Lone Ranger, Game Board, Target, Tin 13.00
Lone Ranger, Game, Board, Milton Bradley, 1938 .... 11.00
Lone Ranger, Harmonica, Magnus, Gold Color, Metal, 1950 .... 9.25 To 10.50
Lone Ranger, Holder, Toothbrush, 1938, Syroco Wood 15.00
Lone Ranger, Holster Set, Leather, Tooled, Nailheads, 1947, 3 Piece 15.00
Lone Ranger, Holster Set, Leather, 2 On Belt 10.00
Lone Ranger, Key, Jail, Metal, Silver Bullet Key Ring 12.50
Lone Ranger, Knife 12.00
Lone Ranger, Movie Still, Color, 1956 .... 8.00
Lone Ranger, Pedometer 12.00
Lone Ranger, Ranch, Lithographed, Tin, Rubber Figures, Marx 15.00
Longwy, Plaque, House Picture, Belgium, C.1900, 14 1/2 In. 165.00

Lonhuda Pottery Company of Steubenville, Ohio, was organized in 1892 by
William Long, W. H. Hunter and Alfred Day. Brown underglaze
slip decorated pottery was made. The firm closed in 1896.
Lonhuda Pottery, Vase, Bowl Type, Two Fish Decoration, 3 Feet 445.00

Lotus ware was made by the Knowles, Taylor & Knowles Company of East
Liverpool, Ohio, from 1890 to 1900.
Lotus Ware, Bonbon, Shell Shape, White, Joshua Poole, K.T.K., 5 1/2 X 5 In. 135.00
Lotus Ware, Bonbon, Twig Design & 4 Twig Feet, 5 1/2 X 4 In. 75.00
Lotus Ware, Bowl, Boat Shape, Pink & Gold Openwork, A.L., 1895, K.T.K., 8 In. 350.00
Lotus Ware, Creamer, Purple Violets, Gold Handle 150.00
Lotus Ware, Dish, Shell, White, 5 In. 85.00
Lotus Ware, Jar, Biscuit, Fishnet Patterned Panels 550.00
Lotus Ware, Pitcher, Bulbous, Gold Fishnet & Apple Blossoms, 3 1/2 In. 165.00
Lotus Ware, Rose Bowl, Gold Apple Blossoms, Green Fish Scale, K.T.K., 5 In. 500.00
Lotus Ware, Teapot, K.T.K., Embossed Flowers On White 125.00
Lotus Ware, Vase, Olive Green, Scroll Handle, White Flowers, 8 1/2 In.High 285.00

Low art tiles were made by the J. and J.G. Low Art Tile Works
of Chelsea, Massachusetts, from 1877 to 1902. A variety of art and other
tiles were made.
Low, Tile, Benjamin Franklin, Glossy Shaded Brown, 6 In.Square 85.00
Low, Tile, Embossed Woman's Head On Blue, Marked J.& J.G., Square, 4 3/8 In. 25.00
Low, Tile, Nude Boys With Grapes & Ribbons, Teal Blue, 4 1/2 In.Square 32.00
Low, Tile, Portrait Of Grecian Woman, Olive Green, 6 In.Square 45.00

The Lowestoft factory in Suffolk, England, worked from 1757 to 1802.
They made many commemorative gift pieces and small dated, inscribed pieces of
soft paste porcelain.
Lowestoft, see also Chinese Export
Lowestoft, Bowl, Blue Swags, Rose Garlands, English, 10 1/2 In. 95.00
Ludwigsburg, Group, Bacchic, 2 Nude Children, Dog, Birds, C.1890, 8 1/2 In. 110.00

Lusterware was meant to resemble copper, silver, or gold. It has been used
since the sixteenth century. Most of the luster found today was made during
the nineteenth century.
Luster, Copper, Bowl, Blue Band With Raised Enamel Design, Pedestal, 5 In. 58.00
Luster, Copper, Bowl, Oblong, 6 In. 22.50
Luster, Copper, Creamer, Blue Band 35.00
Luster, Copper, Creamer, Double Bands, Beading, 3 In.High 18.00
Luster, Copper, Creamer, Tan Band, 4 In. 35.00
Luster, Copper, Cup & Saucer, Demitasse 25.00
Luster, Copper, Cup & Saucer, Flowers, Elsmore & Sons, Tunstall 45.00
Luster, Copper, Goblet, Cream Band, Green & Pink Luster Vines, 4 1/2 In. 50.00
Luster, Copper, Goblet, Floral Enamel Decoration, 4 3/4 In.High 69.00

Luster, Copper, Goblet, Purple Luster Resist Band On White, C.1820	70.00
Luster, Copper, Goblet, White Resist Leaf On Purple Luster Band, C.1825	70.00
Luster, Copper, Jug, Blue Rim Band, Flowers, C.1820, 6 1/4 In.	115.00
Luster, Copper, Jug, Wine, Bulbous, Carter, Poole, 14 1/2 In.	125.00
Luster, Copper, Jug, Yellow Reserve Scenic Band, C.1830, 6 5/8 In.	50.00
Luster, Copper, Mug, Child's, Wide Yellow Band	25.00
Luster, Copper, Mug, Cream Band With Floral, Pink Luster Rim, 3 In.	30.00
Luster, Copper, Mug, Off-White Sanded Band, English, C.1820, 2 1/4 In.	28.00
Luster, Copper, Mug, Pink Luster Rim, Copper Flowers On Cream Band, 3 In.	30.00
Luster, Copper, Mug, Scored Banding & Beading, White Lining, Applied Handle	36.00
Luster, Copper, Mug, Squiggly Design On Yellow Gold Band, 3 In.	21.75
Luster, Copper, Mug, Sunderland Band, Applied Handle	42.00
Luster, Copper, Mug, Wide Yellow Band, 2 1/2 In.	25.00
Luster, Copper, Mug, Yellow Gold Band At Center, 3 In.	21.75
Luster, Copper, Pitcher, Beige Band, Allerton, England, 4 1/2 In.High	32.50
Luster, Copper, Pitcher, Blue Band, Beading, 4 1/2 In.	55.00
Luster, Copper, Pitcher, Blue Band, Luster Design At Neck, 4 1/2 In.	22.50
Luster, Copper, Pitcher, Blue Band, Raised Designs, 3 1/2 In.	25.00
Luster, Copper, Pitcher, Dancing Girls, Blue Decoration, 6 In.	45.00
Luster, Copper, Pitcher, Embossed & Painted On Each Side, 2 3/4 In.	15.00
Luster, Copper, Pitcher, Helmet, Green Trim, Dancing Couple, C.1884, 7 1/2 In.	35.00
Luster, Copper, Pitcher, Mask Spout, Beading, Blue Band Of Floral, 6 In.	65.00
Luster, Copper, Pitcher, Milk, Melon Ribbed, Roses	62.50
Luster, Copper, Pitcher, Painted Flowers, C.1800, 6 In.	58.00
Luster, Copper, Pitcher, Raised Cherubs & Flowers, 7 1/2 In.	65.00
Luster, Copper, Pitcher, Raised Dots Around Body, 3 1/4 In.	17.00
Luster, Copper, Pitcher, Relief Of Woman & Dogs, Blue Band, C.1820, 5 In.	45.00
Luster, Copper, Pitcher, Sanded Band, 2 1/4 In.	28.00
Luster, Copper, Pitcher, Strawberries & White Floral Bands, 6 In.	90.00
Luster, Copper, Pitcher, Yellow Band With Blue Dots, Allerton, 2 1/2 In.	25.00
Luster, Copper, Pitcher, Yellow Band With Design Around Body, 7 1/2 In.	125.00
Luster, Copper, Pitcher, Yellow Band With House Design, 4 1/4 In.	57.50
Luster, Copper, Pitcher, Yellow Band, 5 In.	70.00
Luster, Copper, Pitcher, Yellow Handle & Flowers, Red Rose, C.1850, 5 1/2 In.	55.00
Luster, Copper, Plate, Flowers, Elsmore & Sons, Tunstall, 7 In.	10.00
Luster, Copper, Pot, Pepper, Blue Band	45.00
Luster, Copper, Salt, Master, Floral Band, Footed	35.00
Luster, Copper, Salt, Master, Sanded Band, Pedestal	30.00
Luster, Copper, Salt, Pedestal, Enameled Flowers On Band	45.00
Luster, Copper, Tea Leaf, see Ironstone, Tea Leaf	
Luster, Copper, Vase, Angel & Lamb, Open Handled, 7 In.High	35.00
Luster, Fairyland, see Wedgwood, Fairyland Luster	
Luster, Pink, Bowl, Soft Paste, Black Floral, 6 1/2 In.	75.00
Luster, Pink, Bowl, Waste, House, Decoration On Both Sides, 6 In.	45.00
Luster, Pink, Creamer, Floral & Green Leaves, Staffordshire, 5 In.	32.50
Luster, Pink, Creamer, Flowers & Leaves On Cream	18.00
Luster, Pink, Creamer, House, Boat Shape	45.00
Luster, Pink, Cup & Saucer, Allerton	41.00
Luster, Pink, Cup & Saucer, Applied White & Gold Relief	15.00
Luster, Pink, Cup & Saucer, Castle	35.00
Luster, Pink, Cup & Saucer, Cats Playing Cards Medallion, Gold, Miniature	18.00
Luster, Pink, Cup & Saucer, Dahlia	48.00
Luster, Pink, Cup & Saucer, Daisy	48.00
Luster, Pink, Cup & Saucer, Faith, Hope, & Charity, Hand-Painted, C.1850	40.00
Luster, Pink, Cup & Saucer, Floral Decoration, Wishbone Handle	25.00
Luster, Pink, Cup & Saucer, Handleless	32.00
Luster, Pink, Cup & Saucer, Handleless, Lady, Man, Child, & Sheep In House	35.00
Luster, Pink, Cup & Saucer, House Pattern, C.1820	58.00
Luster, Pink, Cup & Saucer, Picket Fence, Wishbone Handle, C.1820	25.00
Luster, Pink, Cup & Saucer, Rose Band, Germany	10.00
Luster, Pink, Cup & Saucer, Roses & Grapes In 1 In. Band	30.00
Luster, Pink, Cup & Saucer, Schoolhouse	35.00
Luster, Pink, Dessert Set, Branches & Floral Sprays, 13 Piece	225.00
Luster, Pink, Gravy Boat, 5 1/8 X 5 1/2 In.	68.00
Luster, Pink, Jug, Band Of Strawberries & Fruits, C.1820, 5 1/2 In.	60.00
Luster, Pink, Jug, Black Transfer Birds & Floral, C.1850, 7 1/8 In.	30.00

Luster, Pink, Jug, Floral Medallions, Molded Floral Rim, C.1820, 5 1/8 In.	40.00
Luster, Pink, Jug, Green Fruiting Vines & Herringbone Edge, C.1820, 6 In.	70.00
Luster, Pink, Jug, Hunting Dogs, Strawberry Band Rim, C.1825, 5 In.	70.00
Luster, Pink, Jug, Hunting Scene, Fruiting Vine Border, C.1820, 6 In.	70.00
Luster, Pink, Jug, Molded Stag, Doe, & Fawn, Scroll Handle, C.1815, 6 3/8 In.	80.00
Luster, Pink, Plate, Pagoda, 10 1/2 In.	18.00
Luster, Pink, Plate, Rust Color Dahlia In Center, 7 1/2 In.	50.00
Luster, Pink, Plate, Serving, Floral Center, 10 1/2 In.	18.00
Luster, Pink, Saucer, Mottled, Allerton	15.00
Luster, Pink, Saucer, Schoolhouse	15.00
Luster, Pink, Teapot, White Flowers, Gold Decoration	22.00
Luster, Pink, Teapot, 6 In. Diameter At Top, 4 In.	68.00
Luster, Silver, Box, Trinket, Covered, 1 X 2 X 2 3/4 In.	12.00
Luster, Silver, Creamer	30.00
Luster, Silver, Jug, C.1810, 5 In.	28.00
Luster, Silver, Jug, Mask, Gray Beard, Potato Shape, C.1815, 4 1/2 In.	70.00
Luster, Silver, Jug, Mask, 3 Color Masks, Potato Shape, C.1815, 5 In.	125.00
Luster, Silver, Jug, Resist, Chinoiserie, Transfer Printed, C.1815, 5 1/2 In.	175.00
Luster, Silver, Jug, Resist, Fruiting Vines, Zigzag Rim, C.1815, 4 1/4 In.	125.00
Luster, Silver, Jug, Satyr Mask, Dark Brown Body, C.1815, 4 5/8 In.	175.00
Luster, Silver, Mug, Purple Luster Lining, C.1820	90.00
Luster, Silver, Mug, Wade, England, C.1830, 4 1/2 In.High	57.50
Luster, Silver, Pitcher, Raised Resist On Floral, Footed, 4 3/4 In.	120.00
Luster, Silver, Pitcher, Resist, Poles With Ribbon Garlands, C.1825, 5 In.	100.00
Luster, Silver, Salt, Master, Scalloped Top, 3 1/2 In.	20.00
Luster, Silver, Server, Lump Sugar, Handled, Scalloped Feet, Gold Lining	15.00
Luster, Silver, Sugar & Creamer, Cover, Georgian Pattern, No Handle On Sugar	125.00
Luster, Silver, Tea & Coffee Set, Spiral Gadroons, C.1820, 3 Piece	50.00
Luster, Silver, Tea Set, Molded Bands Of Foliage, Gadrooning, C.1820, 3 Piece	20.00
Luster, Silver, Tea Set, Spiral & Vertical Gadroons, C.1820, 5 Piece	70.00
Luster, Silver, Tea Set, 9 In.High Pot, 4 Piece	350.00
Luster, Silver, Teapot, Ribbed Lid & Body, C.1820, 5 1/2 In.High	85.00

Lustre Art Glass Company was founded in Long Island, New York, in 1920 by Conrad Vahlsing and Paul Frank. The company made lampshades and globes that are almost indistinguishable from those made by Quezal.

Lustre Art, Vase, Blue Iridescent, Bulbous Shape, Short Collar, 4 3/4 In.	375.00

Lustres are mantel decorations, or pedestal vases, with many hanging glass prisms. The name really refers to the prisms, and it is proper to refer to a single glass prism as a lustre. Either spelling, luster or lustre, is correct.

Lustres, Cranberry, Gold Floral, 2 Rows Of 7 In. Prisms, 14 1/2 In., Pair	335.00
Lustres, Cut Glass, 9 Prisms On Sunburst Base, C.1850, 9 In., Pair	90.00
Lustres, Etched Amber Glass, Floral & Leaf, Victorian, 13 1/4 In., Pair	275.00
Lustres, Hungarian, Cranberry, Overlay, 14 In., Pair	500.00
Lustres, Milk Glass, Gold Trimmed, 12 In., Pair	80.00
Lustres, Overlay, White Cut To Clear, Gold Trim, Cut Pendants, 13 In.	135.00
Lustres, Pressed Glass, White Enamel, Gold Trim, 13 Cut Prisms, 22 In., Pair	90.00
Lustres, Ruby Glass, Enameled, 14 Double Row Prisms, 14 In., Pair	425.00
Lustres, Ruby, Double Row Of Gilded Lustres, 14 In., Pair	325.00
Lustres, Waterford Crystal, Double Row Of Prisms, 14 In., Pair	450.00
Lutz Type, Bowl & Underplate, Finger, Amber, Threaded, Fluted Bowl	75.00

Lutz glass was made in the 1870s by Nicholas Lutz at the Boston and Sandwich Company. He made a delicate and intricate threaded glass of several colors. Other similar wares are referred to as Lutz.

Lutz, Ewer, Blue & White Ribbon Between Layers, Handle, Spout, Jeweled, 5 In.	395.00
Lutz, Tumbler, Lemonade, Canary	40.00
Lutz, Tumbler, Liqueur, White, Stripes Of Yellow, Goldstone On Clear	75.00
Lutz, Tumbler, Pink, White, & Blue Ribbon Between Layers, Stemmed, Jeweled	125.00
Lutz, Vase, Stick, Striped Panels, Pink & Blue Spirals, Goldstone, 5 In.	200.00
M.Z.Austria, Bowl & Underplate, Soup, Floral Edge	15.00
M.Z.Austria, Dish, Pin, Signed, 6 In.	6.00
M.Z.Austria, Mug, Art Nouveau, Three Owls On Green, 1914	28.00
M.Z.Austria, Plate, Cake, Pastel Floral, Shell Scallops, 11 In.	42.50
M.Z.Austria, Plate, Royal Junsbruck, Roses, Water Lilies, 7 In.	15.00
M.Z.Austria, Ramekin, White, Pink Floral, Green Leaves, Irregular Rim	1.65

M.Z.Austria, Sugar & Creamer, Gold Trim	15.00
Maastricht, Plate, Cobalt & White, Abbey, 9 1/4 In.	6.25
Maastricht, Plate, Pompeii, 8 1/2 In.	6.00
Maastricht, Plate, Royal Sphinx, Delft, Holland, 10 In.	30.00

Maize glass, sold by the W.L.Libbey & Son Company of Toledo, Ohio, was made by Joseph Locke in 1889. It is pressed glass formed like an ear of corn. Most pieces were made for household use.

Maize, Celery, Libbey, Ivory, Green Leaves, 6 1/2 In.	95.00 To 135.00
Maize, Muffineer, Libbey, Decorated	138.00
Maize, Saltshaker	55.00
Maize, Tumbler, Custard, Blue Leaves, Libbey	120.00
Maize, Vase, Locke, 6 1/2 In. .... *Illus*	110.00

Maize, Vase, Locke, 6 1/2 In.

Majolica is any pottery glazed with a tin enamel. Most of the majolica found today is decorated with leaves, shells, branches, and other natural shapes and in natural colors. It was a popular nineteenth-century product.

Majolica, see also Wedgwood

Majolica, Barrel, Biscuit, Green Medallions, Blue, Brass Fitting	95.00 To 110.00
Majolica, Bottle, Cucumber Shape, Green & Tan, 5 In.High	28.50
Majolica, Butter Pat, Fern Rose	4.50
Majolica, Cake Stand, Etruscan, Maple Leaves On Top, Tree Base, 9 X 5 In.	50.00
Majolica, Compote, Tree Trunk Standard, Cobalt Center, Begonias, 10 In.	35.00
Majolica, Creamer, Blackberry, Turquoise Lining, Barrel Shape	19.00
Majolica, Creamer, Cobalt, Brown & Ivory Fan, Bird & Roses, 6 3/8 In.	25.00
Majolica, Creamer, Ear Of Corn, Pink Lining, 4 In.	12.00
Majolica, Creamer, Etruscan, GHS, Butterfly Spout, Basket Weave	35.00
Majolica, Cup & Saucer, GHS, Shell & Seaweed	75.00
Majolica, Dish, Beehive, George Jones, Covered, Simulated Wood, 1872, 13 In.	200.00
Majolica, Dish, Candy, Blois, Dragon Center Handle, Gold Trim, 14 X 15 In.	210.00
Majolica, Dish, Leaf Shape, Brown & Yellows, 6 X 9 In.	12.50
Majolica, Dish, Leaf Shape, Etruscan, Multicolored, 9 1/4 In.	38.00
Majolica, Figurine, Parrot, 15 In.High	95.00
Majolica, Humidor, Figural Cigars Tied In Middle With Bow, 6 1/2 In.High	35.00
Majolica, Humidor, Figural Indian's Head, Headdress, 5 In.High	50.00
Majolica, Jardiniere, Green, Raised Cabbage Leaf Pattern, 9 1/2 X 6 3/4 In.	27.50
Majolica, Jug, Beige, Tree Bark, Wild Roses, Green Lining, 7 1/4 In.	32.50
Majolica, Pitcher, Cobalt, Floral & Leaf, Yellow Rims, Bark Handle, 8 1/4 In.	55.00
Majolica, Pitcher, Ear Of Corn Shape, Yellow & Green, 4 1/2 In.	25.00
Majolica, Pitcher, English, Orchid Ground, Embossed Daisies, C.1842, 6 In.	45.00
Majolica, Pitcher, Etruscan, Butterfly Spout, Basket Weave, 8 In.	52.00
Majolica, Pitcher, Etruscan, Butterfly Spout, Yellow Floral, GHS, 8 In.	52.00
Majolica, Pitcher, Fish, Green, White Belly, Rose Lining, 10 In.	55.00
Majolica, Pitcher, Green, Tree Branch Handle, Lavender Interior, 5 1/2 In.	25.00
Majolica, Pitcher, Milk, Cobalt, Brown & Ivory, Fan, Bird & Roses, 6 7/8 In.	35.00

Majolica, Pitcher, Milk, Raised Wild Rose & Green Leaves On Beige	30.00
Majolica, Pitcher, Shell & Seaweed, Etruscan, 5 1/2 X 5 3/4 In.	110.00
Majolica, Pitcher, Water, Cobalt, Brown & Ivory Fan, Bird & Roses, 7 3/8 In.	45.00
Majolica, Planter, Art Nouveau Floral Projections At Top, 13 X 5 In.	48.00
Majolica, Plaque, Red Snapper Fish, 17 1/2 In.	125.00
Majolica, Plate, Bread, Stem Form Handles, Leaves & Floral, 11 1/2 X 8 In.	28.00
Majolica, Plate, Brown Basketweave Ground, Yellow & Brown Floral, 8 1/4 In.	15.00
Majolica, Plate, Brown Stag & Dog On Yellow, Tortoiseshell Back, 8 1/4 In.	14.00
Majolica, Plate, Cake, Green, Raised White Lily Center, Legs, 9 In.	50.00
Majolica, Plate, Closed Branch Handles, Beige Leaf, Green Acorns, 11 In.	15.00
Majolica, Plate, Etruscan, Cauliflower, 6 In.	15.00
Majolica, Plate, Pink Flowers & Green Leaves, Cobalt Center, Browns, 9 In.	30.00
Majolica, Plate, Three Leaf Pattern, Green, 8 In.	7.50
Majolica, Saucer, Etruscan, Shell & Seaweed	20.00
Majolica, Smoking Set, Negro Man Strumming Guitar, Basket Each Side	48.00
Majolica, Sugar, Etruscan, Covered, Daisies On Cream, Green Basket Weave	22.00
Majolica, Sugar, Owls, Tricornered	28.00
Majolica, Syrup, Fern & Leaf Design, Lavender Inside, Hinged Cover, C.1870	49.00
Majolica, Syrup, Pink Bow, Yellow & Green Floral, Pewter Lid, 1872, 8 1/4 In.	70.00
Majolica, Teapot, Dancing Frogs On Green, Raffia Handle, Squatty	40.00
Majolica, Teapot, Pear Design, Pear Finial	35.00
Majolica, Teapot, Penguin Shaped, Fish For Tail, England	35.00
Majolica, Teapot, Shell, Seaweed, Coral, Shell Finial, Etruscan	125.00
Majolica, Tray, Leaf, Four Colors, 9 X 7 In.	10.00
Majolica, Vase, Frog Musician, 6 In.	35.00

Marbles of glass were made during the nineteenth century. Venetian swirl, clear glass, sulfides, and marbles with frosted white animal figures embedded in the glass were popular. Handmade clay marbles were made in many places, but most of them came from the pottery factories of Ohio and Pennsylvania. Occasionally, real stone marbles of onyx, carnelian, or jasper can be found.

Marble, Akro Agate, Tri-Agates O, Box Of 100	10.00
Marble, Candle Swirl, 1/2 In.	3.00
Marble, Candy Stripe, 1 3/4 In.	27.50
Marble, Candy Stripe, 1 5/8 In.	29.00
Marble, Candy Stripe, 2 In.	27.50
Marble, Candy Swirl, Blues, Pinks, Black, & White, 7 1/4 In.	40.00
Marble, Hand-Blown, Mexico, Multicolor Twist, Pontil Scar, 1 In.	.15
Marble, Spiral Type, 2 In.	20.00
Marble, Sulfide, Buffalo, 6 1/2 In.	135.00
Marble, Sulfide, Polar Bear	20.00 To 40.00
Marble, Sulfide, Rooster, 5 In. Circumference	55.00
Marble, Swirl, Colored, 1 3/4 In.	60.00
Marble, Swirl, Sandwich	9.00
Marble, Swirl, 1 1/2 In.	45.00
Marble, Swirl, 1 3/4 In.	45.00

The Marblehead Pottery was founded in 1905 as a rehabilitative program for the patients of a Marblehead, Mass., sanitarium by Dr. J. Hall. Two years later it was separated from the sanitarium, and it continued operations until 1936. Many of the pieces were decorated with marine motifs.

Marblehead, Rose Bowl, Green, Brown Inside, 3 In.	55.00
Marblehead, Vase, Blue, Baluster Shape, Flaring Rim, 6 1/4 In.	50.00
Marblehead, Vase, Brown, 3 1/2 In.	35.00
Marblehead, Vase, Dark Blue, Bulbous, Marked, 5 In.	35.00
Marblehead, Vase, Dark Blue, 4 In.	32.00
Marblehead, Vase, Green, Bronze Inside, Marked, 4 1/2 In.	55.00
Marblehead, Vase, Lilac, 3 1/4 In.	35.00
Marblehead, Vase, Lilac, 3 1/2 In.	35.00
Marilyn Monroe, Calendar, C.1954, Golden Dreams, 12 X 16 In.	12.50

Mary Gregory glass is identified by a characteristic white figure painted on dark glass. It was made from 1870 to 1910. The name refers to any glass decorated with a white silhouette figure and not just the Sandwich glass originally painted by Miss Mary Gregory.

Mary Gregory, **Bottle,** Perfume, Green, Girl On Swing, 10 In. High 105.00
Mary Gregory, **Bottle,** Perfume, 3 1/2 In. 50.00
Mary Gregory, **Bowl,** Cranberry, Girl Blowing Bubbles, 5 In. Diameter 85.00
Mary Gregory, **Box,** Black Amethyst, Girl Feeding Bird, Hinged, 4 1/2 In. 155.00
Mary Gregory, **Box,** Round, Black, Girl & Bird, 2 1/2 X 4 1/2 In. 138.00
Mary Gregory, **Box,** Sapphire Blue, Girl With Kite, 4 X 2 1/2 X 3 1/2 In. 195.00
Mary Gregory, **Butter,** Covered 75.00
Mary Gregory, **Creamer,** Emerald, White Girl & Foliage, Applied Handle 85.00
Mary Gregory, **Cruet,** Vinegar, Lime Green, Boy & Cane, Ball Stopper, 8 1/2 In. 125.00
Mary Gregory, **Decanter,** Clear, Trees, Little Girl, 6 1/4 In. High 34.00
Mary Gregory, **Flagon,** Clear, White Boy & Girl, Flowers, Tinted, 13 In., Pair 97.50
Mary Gregory, **Glass,** Ale, Amber, Boy, 6 1/2 In. High 35.00
Mary Gregory, **Glass,** Green, White Girl Holding Flower, 7 1/4 In. High 65.00
Mary Gregory, **Jar,** Biscuit, Cranberry, Cherub, Clear Finial, 7 In. High 135.00
Mary Gregory, **Jar,** Biscuit, Green, Cherub & Floral, Blown, 8 In. 80.00
Mary Gregory, **Jar,** Biscuit, Sapphire Blue, Cherub, 5 X 3 1/2 In. 85.00
Mary Gregory, **Lamp,** Black Amethyst, White Boy With Whip, 12 In. 240.00
Mary Gregory, **Lamp,** Black, White Figures, Bronze Base, 29 In. High 200.00
Mary Gregory, **Lamp,** Rubena, Boy & Butterfly, 2 In. 125.00
Mary Gregory, **Lamp,** Smoky Beige, Bristol Porcelain, 21 In., Pair 500.00
Mary Gregory, **Liqueur Set,** Clear, Girl, 5 Piece 125.00
Mary Gregory, **Mug,** Cranberry, Boy, Clear Handle, 3 1/2 In. High 45.00
Mary Gregory, **Pitcher,** Amber, 13 In. High 90.00
Mary Gregory, **Pitcher,** Blue Green, Girl & Basket, Ribbed, 6 In. 95.00
Mary Gregory, **Pitcher,** Blue, Boy In Forest, Applied Handle, 14 In. 165.00
Mary Gregory, **Pitcher,** Crystal, Girl, Tinted Face, Gold Top Rim, 11 1/2 In. 125.00
Mary Gregory, **Pitcher,** Emerald Green, Costumed Figure, Village Scene, 13 In. 250.00
Mary Gregory, **Pitcher,** Green, Cupid & Trumpet Flying Over Cattails, 6 In. 85.00
Mary Gregory, **Pitcher,** Green, Girl With Basket, 6 In. High 100.00
Mary Gregory, **Pitcher,** Olive Amber, Boy, Inverted Thumbprint, Flint, 12 In. 195.00
Mary Gregory, **Pitcher,** Water, Clear, Girl Holding Flowers 95.00
Mary Gregory, **Pitcher,** Water, Golden Brown, White Girl, Blown 150.00
Mary Gregory, **Pitcher,** Water, Green, Girl & Foliage, Long Lip, Pedestal, 11 In 165.00
Mary Gregory, **Pitcher,** Water, Lady In Garden, 14 In. High 150.00
Mary Gregory, **Pitcher,** Water, Mother & 2 Girls, Reeded Handle, Fluted Top 65.00
Mary Gregory, **Pitcher,** Water, Sapphire Blue, Girl & Roses, Applied Handle 135.00
Mary Gregory, **Rose Bowl,** Lime Green, Little Girl, 2 1/2 In. High 76.00
Mary Gregory, **Sherbet,** Amber, Crackle, Girl, Blue Trim On White 55.00
Mary Gregory, **Stein,** Blue, White Figure 125.00
Mary Gregory, **Tankard,** Cranberry, Girl & Balloon, Inverted Thumbprint, 6 In. 235.00
Mary Gregory, **Tankard,** Sapphire Blue, Girl & Birds, Blue Handle, 12 1/2 In. 175.00
Mary Gregory, **Tray,** Pin, Cranberry, 5 In. Long 135.00
Mary Gregory, **Tumble-Up,** Emerald Green, Girl & Boy, 8 1/2 In. 205.00
Mary Gregory, **Tumbler,** Amber, White Girl, 3 3/4 In. High 65.00
Mary Gregory, **Tumbler,** Blue, White Enamel Girl 42.00
Mary Gregory, **Tumbler,** Cranberry, Boy & Floral, 3 3/4 In. 45.00
Mary Gregory, **Tumbler,** Cranberry, Girl & Flowers, 3 3/4 In. 45.00
Mary Gregory, **Tumbler,** Cranberry, White Enamel Child, Paneled 37.50
Mary Gregory, **Tumbler,** Green, Boy, Corset Shape, 3 1/4 In. 30.00
Mary Gregory, **Tumbler,** Green, Cupid, Barrel Shape, 3 1/4 In. 30.00
Mary Gregory, **Tumbler,** Hand-Blown, Boy & Foliage 25.00
Mary Gregory, **Tumbler,** Hand-Blown, Girl & Foliage 25.00
Mary Gregory, **Tumbler,** Juice, Boy, Tinted Face 47.00
Mary Gregory, **Tumbler,** Juice, Girl, Tinted Face 47.00
Mary Gregory, **Tumbler,** Juice, Light Blue, Boy, 3 3/4 In. 30.00
Mary Gregory, **Tumbler,** Olive Amber, Boy, Paneled, Footed, Flint 50.00
Mary Gregory, **Tumbler,** Pilsner, White Enamel Cherub & Flowers 25.00
Mary Gregory, **Tumbler,** Sapphire Blue, Girl & Boy, Pair 95.00
Mary Gregory, **Tumbler,** Water, Clear, Boy 28.00
Mary Gregory, **Vase,** Amber, Boy Among Ferns, Flaring, 5 3/8 In. 75.00
Mary Gregory, **Vase,** Amethyst, White Girl, Inverted Thumbprint, 5 3/4 In. 145.00
Mary Gregory, **Vase,** Black Amethyst, Girl & Boy, Butterfly, 11 1/2 In., Pair 100.00
Mary Gregory, **Vase,** Blue, Narrow Neck, Bulbous Base, 7 In. 75.00
Mary Gregory, **Vase,** Bud, Boy Carrying Flowers, Tinted Face, 6 1/2 In. 75.00
Mary Gregory, **Vase,** Bud, Cranberry, 6 In. 40.00
Mary Gregory, **Vase,** Bud, Turquoise, White Girl, Gilt Band, 6 3/4 In. 22.00

Mary Gregory, Vase, Chartreuse, White Girl & Boy, 4 1/2 In., Pair	185.00
Mary Gregory, Vase, Cobalt Blue, Tricorn Shape, Girl & Flowers, 7 In.	65.00
Mary Gregory, Vase, Cranberry, Boy & Girl Figures, 9 In.High, Pair	285.00
Mary Gregory, Vase, Garniture, Medium Green, Girls, 17 In.High, Pair	395.00
Mary Gregory, Vase, Green Blue, Child Angel & Flowers, Ruffled, 7 1/2 In.	75.00
Mary Gregory, Vase, Green Blue, Ruffled Rim, Angel & Flowers, 7 1/2 In.	78.00
Mary Gregory, Vase, Green Satin, Girl & Boy, White Beaded Top, 12 In., Pair	150.00
Mary Gregory, Vase, Ice Blue, White Figure, Blown, 12 In.	115.00
Mary Gregory, Vase, Navy Blue, Girl & Bubbles, Boy & Ball, 9 3/4 In., Pair	265.00
Mary Gregory, Warmer, Tea, Lavender, Three Figures	325.00
Mary Gregory, Water Set, Clear, 3 Boys, 3 Girls, 7 Piece	250.00

Masonic Shrine glassware was made from 1893 to 1917. It is occasionally
called Syrian Temple Shrine glassware. Most pieces are dated.

Masonic, Ashtray, Shriner, 1922	8.00
Masonic, Bookend, Minneapolis, 1917, Syria Shrine, Milk Glass, 4 X 4 In., Pair	50.00
Masonic, Bookmark, Dieu Le Veut, KT 45, Wilkes-Barre, 1924, Metal	5.00
Masonic, Chain, Watch, 32nd Degree, Gold Fob, Gold, Double	575.00
Masonic, Chalice, Pittsburgh, Pa., 1899, Lion, Green	100.00
Masonic, Chalice, San Francisco, 1902, Syria Shrine, Bear, Glass	60.00
Masonic, Chalice, St.Paul, 1908, Red Bowl, Black Foot	70.00
Masonic, Chalice, Washington, D.C., 1900, Syria Shrine, Glass	60.00 To 65.00
Masonic, Champagne, Louisville, 1909, Syria Shrine, Tobacco Leaf	55.00 To 60.00
Masonic, Champagne, New Orleans, 1910, Syria Shrine, Alligators	55.00 To 60.00
Masonic, Champagne, Pittsburgh, Pa., 1910, Syria Shrine *Illus*	45.00
Masonic, Champagne, Rochester, N.Y., 1911, Camera, Iridescent	55.00 To 60.00
Masonic, Cup, Loving, Niagara Falls, 4 In. *Illus*	55.00
Masonic, Cup, Loving, Pittsburgh, 1905, Syria Shrine, 3 Handled	50.00
Masonic, Cup, 96th American Conclave, June, 1909, 3 Handled, Porcelain	22.50
Masonic, Goblet, Los Angeles, 1907, Syria Shrine, Etched, Footed	60.00 To 65.00
Masonic, Goblet, 1900, Washington, D.C., Frosted, Syria	60.00
Masonic, Knife, Pocket, Damascus Temple, Rochester, N.Y., Silver, 2 Blades	10.00
Masonic, Matchbox Holder & Attached Ashtray, Aleppo Temple, Boston, 1911	12.00
Masonic, Mug, Alchymia Temple, Memphis, Rochester, 1911, Ceramic, White, 5 In.	15.00
Masonic, Mug, Atlantic City, 1904, Syria Shrine, Fish Handle, Gir	55.00 To 60.00
Masonic, Mug, Monk Eating, Edgewater Lodge, Brown & Tan, Germany	40.00
Masonic, Mug, Niagara Falls, 1905, Syria Shrine, 3 Handled, 3 Scenes, Glass	50.00
Masonic, Mug, Pittsburgh, 1903, Syria Shrine, Indian Head	38.00
Masonic, Mug, Saratoga, 1903, Syria Shrine, Indian In Regalia	60.00 To 65.00
Masonic, Mug, Shaving, Master Mason Emblem & Name, Incised Germany	48.50
Masonic, Paperweight, Emblem, 1915, Metal, 5 In.	15.00
Masonic, Paperweight, Keystone Royal Arch, 75th Anniversary, 1928, Bronze	25.00

Masonic, Cup, Loving, Niagara Falls, 4 In.

Masonic, Champagne, Pittsburgh, Pa.,
1910, Syria Shrine

Masonic, Pin, Lady's, Gold Bar, Shrine	7.50
Masonic, Pin, Lapel, Man's, Osman Temple Enameled	7.50
Masonic, Pitcher, Black & White Transfer, Camden Lodge, 1911, Silver Gilding	78.00
Masonic, Plaque, Shriners, 1923, Capitol Building, Metal, Round, 5 1/2 In.	15.00
Masonic, Plate, Albert Pike Memorial Temple, Gold Border, 8 In.	10.00
Masonic, Plate, Marietta, Ohio, Knights Templar, 8 1/2 In.	30.00
Masonic, Plate, Stichter Lodge 254, 1851-1911, Blue & White, Gold, 8 3/4 In.	12.75
Masonic, Spoon, Demitasse, Masonic Temple, Chicago, Ornate	7.50
Masonic, Sword & Scabbard, Knight Templar, York Rite, Red Enamel Crosses	65.00
Masonic, Tankard, A.F.& A.M. In Gold, Green Acacia Branches, 4 1/4 In.	12.75
Masonic, Tumbler, Juice, Dallas, 1898, Shriner On Steer, 6 In.	100.00
Masonic, Tumbler, Shriner's Convention, Seattle, 1915, Carnation Milk	25.00
Masonic, Watch Fob & Chain, Gold, Masonic Seal Pendant	10.00
Masonic, Watch, Howard Movement	130.00
Masonic, Wine, San Francisco, 1902, Syria Shrine	55.00
Masonic, Wine, Washington, 1900, Syria Shrine	55.00
Massier, Vase, Free Form, Pinched Sides, Purple & Blue Luster, 3 In.High	140.00
Massier, Vase, Luster, Floral, Silver Rim, 3 3/4 In.	110.00
Match Holder, see also Iron, Match Holder, Staffordshire, Match Holder, Store, Match Holder	
Match Holder, Bisque, German Boy, World War I Uniform, 6 In.	40.00
Match Holder, Dog, Amber Glass, Victorian	55.00
Match Holder, Figural Shoe On Stand, Amber Glass	34.00
Match Holder, Open Brick Chimney Base, Brown & White Dog	13.00
Match Safe, see also Silver Plate, Match Safe, Silver, Sterling, Match Safe	
Match Safe, Brass, Two Birds Fighting In Bamboo Jungle	60.00
Match Safe, Burled Wood, Double Compartments, 8 1/2 In.High	60.00
Match Safe, Gold, Plain, Small Ruby Set Into One Side	225.00
Match Safe, Iron, Alligator Shape, Cast Iron Tinning Co., 9 In.Long	20.00
Match Safe, Iron, Wall, Hinged Cover, Patented 1869, D.M.& Co., 4 X 2 1/2 In.	16.75
Match Safe, Pocket, English, Inlaid Design Of Matches On Side	7.95
Match Safe, Pocket, Sterling Silver, Engraved Lee	15.00
Match Safe, Silver Plate, Mother-Of-Pearl Inserts Of Dog & Moose	35.00
Match Safe, Silver, Coin Section, 1846	47.50
Match Safe, Sterling Silver, Raised Water Nymph And Cupids	52.50
Match Safe, Sterling, Allover Design Of Leaves & Flowers	12.75
Match Safe, Sterling, Ornate Sunflower Repousse	37.50
Match Safe, Tin, Wall Type, Green, 3 1/2 X 2 X 1 1/2 In.	10.00
Match Safe, Unger Bros. Silver, 2 Cherubs Building Fire, 3 1/2 In.	65.00
Matchbox Holder, Dog Finial On Lid, 2 Compartments, Metal, Square, 3 1/2 In.	12.00
Matt Morgan, Jug, Honey, Aqua Glaze, Red Clay, Incised Flowers, 4 In.	170.00
Matt Morgan, Vase, Gilt & Painted Moresque Scene On Salmon, C.1883, 15 In.	225.00

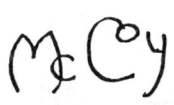

McCoy pottery is made in Roseville, Ohio. The J.W.McCoy Pottery was founded in 1899. It became the Brush McCoy Pottery Company in 1911. The name changed to the Brush Pottery in 1925. The Nelson McCoy Sanitary and Stoneware Company was founded in Roseville, Ohio, in 1910. This firm made art pottery after 1926. In 1933 it became the Nelson McCoy Pottery. Pieces marked McCoy were made by the Nelson McCoy Company.

McCoy, Basket, Hanging, Green, 6 X 4 1/4 In.	10.00
McCoy, Bowl, Black Gloss, McCoy U S A In Relief, 5 1/2 In.	3.00
McCoy, Bowl, Sylvan, Brush, 2 1/2 X 5 1/4 In.	7.00
McCoy, Creamer, Brown & Green Ivy On Ivory, 3 In.	8.00
McCoy, Flower Holder, Under The Spreading Chestnut Tree	3.00
McCoy, Jar, Cookie, Clown	12.00
McCoy, Jar, Cookie, Dog In Basket	15.00
McCoy, Jar, Cookie, Honey Bear	15.00
McCoy, Jar, Cookie, Kookie Kettle, Black, Metal Handles	17.00 To 20.00
McCoy, Jar, Cookie, Mammy, Cream, Black Face, Red Scarf, Green	16.00 To 18.00
McCoy, Jar, Cookie, Stove	12.00
McCoy, Jardiniere, Green Flying Birds On Brown Swirled, C.1930, 8 1/2 In.	6.00
McCoy, Jardiniere, Pinecone Line, Brown & Green, 6 1/2 In.	6.50
McCoy, Pitcher, Butterfly In White, Marked NM, 10 In.	10.00
McCoy, Pitcher, Green Stoneware, 2 Fish, 6 In.	12.50

McCoy, Pitcher, Water, Blue, Three Fish	20.00
McCoy, Planter, Cowboy Hat Shape, 8 X 5 1/2 In.	6.75
McCoy, Planter, Dogwood, Pink, 6 3/4 In.	5.00
McCoy, Planter, Embossed Flowers, 6 Legs, 4 1/2 X 10 In.	16.00
McCoy, Planter, Green, Abstract Relief Flower, 8 In.	14.50
McCoy, Planter, Quail Family, 8 1/2 X 7 In.High	14.00
McCoy, Shoe, Baby's, White, Laced, Marked Nelson McCoy, 5 In.	3.00
McCoy, Tea Set, Brown Pinecones On Light Green, 3 Piece	17.50
McCoy, Tea Set, Pinecone, 3 Piece	16.00
McCoy, Teapot, Pinecone, Green & Brown	7.50
McCoy, Vase, Blossomtime, 6 1/4 In.	8.00
McCoy, Vase, Cascade Line, 5 X 7 In.	12.50
McCoy, Vase, Cascade Line, 9 X 5 In.	12.50
McCoy, Vase, Flower, Dark Green, Oblong, 7 In.	3.50
McCoy, Vase, Flowers, Signed Green Turtle, 8 In.	10.00
McCoy, Vase, Hyacinth, Blue, 8 In.High	9.00
McCoy, Vase, Marbleized Brush Brown, 10 In.High	10.00
McCoy, Vase, Peach Color, Swirl Design, Openwork Sides, 9 In.	12.50
McCoy, Vase, Peacock, Green, Open Handles, 8 1/4 In.	7.00
McCoy, Vase, Spring Wood Line, 9 1/4 In.	10.00
McCoy, Vase, Spring Wood, Green, Square Top, Round Bottom, 7 1/4 In.	8.00
McCoy, Vase, Three Lily, 6 In.	10.50
McCoy, Vase, Yellow, Sculptured, Relief Floral, 2 Handled, 7 1/2 In.	11.50
McKee, Berry Set, Colonial, 13 Piece	30.00
McKee, Glass, Whiskey, Rainbow	7.50
McKee, Mug, Tom & Jerry, Custard	3.50
McKee, Pitcher, Water, Rock Crystal, 9 In.	25.00
McKee, Punch Set, Tom & Jerry, White, Red, 7 Piece	12.00
McKee, Relish, Fentec	6.00
McKee, Spooner, Sunburst	9.00
McKee, Tray, Celery, Masonic	27.50
McKee, Tray, Wine, Rainbow, 10 1/4 In.Diameter	12.50
McKee, Tumbler, Bottoms Up, Frosted	18.50
McKee, Vase, Vulcan, Ground Pontil, 11 1/2 In.High	18.00
Mechanical Bank, see Bank, Mechanical	

Meerschaum pipes and other carved pieces of meerschaum date from the nineteenth century to the present time.

Meerschaum, Holder, Cigar, Dog, Case	32.00
Meerschaum, Holder, Cigarette, Carved Dog, 4 In.	20.00
Meerschaum, Holder, Cigarette, Etched Sterling Silver Design	25.00
Meerschaum, Pipe Bowl, Carved Castle Wall & Running Stag	50.00
Meerschaum, Pipe, Bearded Man's Face, Hand-Carved, Leather Case	12.50
Meerschaum, Pipe, Perched Rabbit, 3 1/2 In.	57.50

Meissen is a town in Germany where porcelain has been made since 1710. Any china made in that town can be called Meissen, although the famous Meissen Factory made the finest porcelains of the area.

Meissen, see also Dresden, Onion	
Meissen, Basket, Openwork, Applied Floral, Stalk Handle, C.1890, 10 In., Pair	190.00
Meissen, Bowl, Centerpiece, Floral, Latticework Border, 18 In.	225.00
Meissen, Bowl, Condiment, Leaf Shape, Carving Spoon, India Flowers, C.1845	95.00
Meissen, Bowl, Hand-Painted Millefleur, Square, Crossed Swords, 8 1/2 In.	45.00
Meissen, Bowl, Shallow, Cobalt Border, 3 Panels Flowers, 11 In.	90.00
Meissen, Box, Covered, Green Dragons Chasing Orange Pearls, Gilding, 6 In.	42.00
Meissen, Bust, Child, C.1755, 6 1/8 In. ....*Illus*	700.00
Meissen, Butter, Covered	85.00
Meissen, Chamber Stick, Pinlike Handle, About 1840, 2 1/2 In.High	125.00
Meissen, Coffee Service, Puce Floral, Gilding, Crossed Swords, 22 Piece	275.00
Meissen, Cup & Saucer, Bouquets, Twig Handles, Flowers In Relief	50.00
Meissen, Cup & Saucer, Demitasse, Blue & Purple, Raised Gold, C.1880	38.00
Meissen, Cup & Saucer, Floral, Gold Rimmed	39.50
Meissen, Cup & Saucer, Hand-Painted Pastoral Scene On Purple, Marked	115.00
Meissen, Cup & Saucer, Lass & Lad In Pastoral Landscape, C.1890	80.00
Meissen, Cup & Saucer, Scalloped Rims, Deutschesche Blumen, C.1845	45.00
Meissen, Figurine, Astrological, Capricorn, Little Girl & Goat, 5 1/2 In.	225.00

Meissen, Bust, Child,
C.1755, 6 1/8 In.
(See Page 294)

Meissen, Group,
Allegorical,
C.1850, 13 In.

Meissen, Figurine, Astrological, Sagittarius, 5 1/4 In.High	210.00
Meissen, Figurine, Farm Girl, 9 1/2 In.	325.00
Meissen, Figurine, Hunting Dog, Miniature, Tan & White, Lying, 1 X 3 In.	75.00
Meissen, Figurine, Juno, Seated On Clouds, C.1890, 7 7/8 In.	250.00
Meissen, Figurine, Peasant Girl, Standing, Basket In Arms, C.1850, 5 In.	150.00
Meissen, Figurine, Pug, Lying, Tan, 1 X 3 In.	88.00
Meissen, Figurine, Putto Fishing, Nude, Puce Drapery, C.1850, 4 7/8 In.	175.00
Meissen, Group, Allegorical, C.1850, 13 In. ....*Illus*	900.00
Meissen, Group, Leopard Battling Boa Constrictor, W.SRB, C.1920, 10 In.	225.00
Meissen, Inkwell, Multicolor Floral On White, Crossed Swords Mark, 2 In.	14.00
Meissen, Knife Rest, Floral & Gold On White, Angularly Faceted, 4 In.	38.00
Meissen, Pin Holder, British Isles Globe On Figural Tripod Stand, C.1850	225.00
Meissen, Plate, Cobalt Berry Center, Triple Layer Gold, Marked, 7 1/4 In.	85.00
Meissen, Plate, Embossed Green & Gold Leaves, Scalloped, 10 In.	135.00
Meissen, Plate, Floral Latticework Border, 3 Flying Birds, C.1880, 10 In.	135.00
Meissen, Plate, Lovers On Swing, Gold Tracery Border, 10 In.	100.00
Meissen, Plate, Rose Center, Buds Around Scalloped Edge, 7 In.	20.00
Meissen, Ramekin, Floral	12.50
Meissen, Rose Bowl, Guelder Rose, C.1750, Miniature	40.00
Meissen, Salt, Square, Blue & White, Crossed Swords Mark	14.00
Meissen, Slipper, Pink, Floral Medallion On Toe, Rundown Heel, 6 1/2 In.	75.00
Meissen, Tea Set, Small Flowers On Blue, Crossed Swords, 15 Piece	300.00
Meissen, Teapot, Melon Shape, Floral & Insects, Gold Gilding, 5 In.	135.00
Meissen, Teapot, Round Melon Shape, Flowers & Insects, Floral Finial, 4 In.	135.00
Meissen, Urn, Pate Sur Pate, Cobalt Ground, White Figure, Handles, 12 In.	450.00
Meissen, Vase, Ormolu Mounts, Gros Bleu, Floral Reserves, C.1850, 26 In.	850.00
Meissen, Vase, Woman & Man In Scene, Crossed Swords Mark, 3 3/4 In.	25.00

*Mercury, or silvered, glass was first made in the 1850s. It lost favor for a
while but became popular again about 1910. It looks like a piece of silver.*

Mercury Glass, Bowl, Grape Design, Pedestal Base, 6 X 6 In.	30.00
Mercury Glass, Box, Powder, Covered	27.00
Mercury Glass, Candlestick, 4 In., Pair	15.00
Mercury Glass, Doorknob, Crystal Outside, Metal Shaft, Brass Cap	10.00
Mercury Glass, Inkwell, Lund, London, Green Cut To Silver, Silver Band, 4 In.	285.00
Mercury Glass, Muffineer, Pear Shape, Raised Floral & Leaf, Pewter Top	45.00
Mercury Glass, Salt, Footed	22.50
Mercury Glass, Salt, Master	17.50
Mercury Glass, Tieback, Curtain, Pair	30.00
Mercury Glass, Tieback, Etched Design, Pair	18.00
Mercury Glass, Tieback, Pewter Stem, Pair	15.00
Mercury Glass, Vase, Flowers, 11 In.	28.00
Mercury Glass, Wig Stand	50.00

*Mettlach, Germany, is a city where the Villeroy and Boch factories
worked. Steins from the firm are known as Mettlach steins. They date from
about 1842. PUG means painted under glaze.*

Mettlach, Beaker, No.1095, 1/4 Liter, 5 In.	65.00
Mettlach, Beaker, No.1137, 1/4 Liter, Series No.2327	65.00
Mettlach, Beaker, No.1176, 1/4 Liter, Series 2327	65.00
Mettlach, Beaker, No.1232, 1/4 Liter, Series 2327	65.00
Mettlach, Beaker, No.1233, 1/4 Liter, Series 2327	65.00
Mettlach, Beaker, No.1234, 1/4 Liter, Series 2327	65.00
Mettlach, Beaker, No.3237/1025, 1/4 Liter, Serving Girl, Mercury Mark	38.00
Mettlach, Bowl & Underplate, Punch, No.2602	525.00
Mettlach, Coaster, No.1032, PUG	45.00
Mettlach, Coaster, No.2819, Etched	100.00
Mettlach, Coaster, No.2822, Etched	100.00
Mettlach, Mug, B.P.O.E., 1897	40.00
Mettlach, Mug, Beer, 4/10 Liter, B.P.O.E., Minneapolis, Minn., 1897	45.00
Mettlach, Pitcher, Cream Color, Villeroy & Boch, 4 Liter	45.00
Mettlach, Pitcher, No.1492, Pedestal Base, Floral Pattern, 15 In.High	250.00
Mettlach, Pitcher, No.2183	475.00
Mettlach, Planter, No.1556, Hanging, 5 1/2 X 6 In.	115.00
Mettlach, Plaque, Jason & Argonauts, Pate-Sur-Pate, Stahl, 1898, 18 3/8 In.	525.00
Mettlach, Plaque, No.1044, Roses, Fruit, Butterfly, Gold Border, 17 In.	200.00
Mettlach, Plaque, No.1108	650.00
Mettlach, Plaque, No.1384 & 1385, Land Knight, Castles, Pair	895.00
Mettlach, Plaque, No.2070 & 2071, Hunting Scene, Pair	1075.00
Mettlach, Plaque, No.2113, Dwarf, Gold Leafed Edges	725.00
Mettlach, Plaque, No.2287, Etched, 17 In.	795.00
Mettlach, Plaque, No.2322 & 2323, Pair	1100.00
Mettlach, Plaque, No.2323, Etched, 14 1/2 In.	650.00
Mettlach, Plaque, No.2362, Castle Mark, 17 In.	470.00
Mettlach, Plaque, No.2444, Cameo, 3 Children Playing Music, 10 In.	500.00
Mettlach, Plaque, No.2517	625.00
Mettlach, Plaque, No.2533	700.00
Mettlach, Plaque, No.2534, Ruined Castle, 18 In.	495.00
Mettlach, Plaque, No.2549, 18 In.	395.00
Mettlach, Plaque, No.2750, Etched, 20 In.	950.00
Mettlach, Plaque, No.2898, 17 1/2 In.	600.00
Mettlach, Plaque, No.3112, Green, 18 In.	675.00
Mettlach, Plaque, No.3321, Castle Mark, 12 In.	150.00
Mettlach, Plaque, Nuremberg Castle, PUG, 12 1/4 In.	150.00
Mettlach, Plate, Faenza, Cherubs & Shield On Blue, Villeroy & Boch, 9 In.	30.00
Mettlach, Plate, No.3096, Octagon Shape, Art Nouveau, Blue, Cream, Tan	65.00
Mettlach, Stein, No.1163, 1/2 Liter, 4 Musicians & Instruments, Warth	345.00
Mettlach, Stein, No.1164, 1/2 Liter, Etched, Warth	345.00
Mettlach, Stein, No.1284, Blue, Brown, & Beige Mosaic, V & B, Castle Mark	178.00
Mettlach, Stein, No.1325, 1/2 Liter, Etched	400.00
Mettlach, Stein, No.1394, 1/2 Liter	385.00
Mettlach, Stein, No.1395, 1/2 Liter	325.00
Mettlach, Stein, No.1396, 1/2 Liter, Etched, Pewter Lid	325.00 To 400.00
Mettlach, Stein, No.1397, 1/4 Liter, Etched, Inlaid Lid	350.00
Mettlach, Stein.No.1397, 1/2 Liter, Etched, Inlaid Lid	325.00
Mettlach, Stein, No.1431, 1/4 Liter, Pewter Lid Engraved 1885-86	65.00
Mettlach, Stein, No.1453, 1/2 Liter, Etched	400.00
Mettlach, Stein, No.1476, 1/2 Liter, Etched Dwarfs	375.00 To 400.00
Mettlach, Stein, No.1508, 1/2 Liter, Etched	390.00
Mettlach, Stein, No.1526, 1/4 Liter	165.00
Mettlach, Stein, No.1526, 1/2 Liter	100.00
Mettlach, Stein, No.1526, Liter, PUG, Cavalier, German Writing, Pewter Top	195.00
Mettlach, Stein, No.1533, Liter, Gray, Man Drinking Beer, Pewter	300.00 To 325.00
Mettlach, Stein, No.1566, 1/2 Liter, Man On Highwheel Bicycle, Silver Lid	450.00
Mettlach, Stein, No.1645, 1/2 Liter	290.00
Mettlach, Stein, No.1654, 1/4 Liter, Green Mosaic On Lid, V & B	105.00
Mettlach, Stein, No.1675, 1/2 Liter	375.00
Mettlach, Stein, No.171, 3/10 Liter, Inlaid Lid, White Figures On Blue	120.00
Mettlach, Stein, No.171, 1/2 Liter	165.00
Mettlach, Stein, No.171, 3 Liter	350.00
Mettlach, Stein, No.485, Liter, Cream Relief Figures On Blue Green	295.00
Mettlach, Stein, No.953, Brown & Blue, Pewter Top, 4 1/2 In.	45.00
Mettlach, Stein, No.1725, 1/2 Liter	325.00

Mettlach, Stein, No.1742, 1/2 Liter, Gottington 475.00
Mettlach, Stein, No.1796, 1/2 Liter, Etched, Warth 345.00
Mettlach, Stein, No.1896, 1/4 Liter, Cream, Relief 175.00
Mettlach, Stein, No.1909, 4/10 Liter 75.00
Mettlach, Stein, No.1909, 1/2 Liter, Geschutz Mark 110.00
Mettlach, Stein, No.1949, 3 Liter, Etched, Inlaid Lid 825.00
Mettlach, Stein, No.1995, 1/2 Liter 350.00
Mettlach, Stein, No.1997, 1/2 Liter 250.00
Mettlach, Stein, No.2001-B, Book 345.00
Mettlach, Stein, No.2001-I, Book 345.00
Mettlach, Stein, No.2002, 1/2 Liter 350.00
Mettlach, Stein, No.2005, 1/2 Liter, Inlaid Lid 375.00
Mettlach, Stein, No.2008, 1/2 Liter, Etched 390.00
Mettlach, Stein, No.2025, 1/2 Liter, Inlaid Lid, Nude Cherubs 395.00
Mettlach, Stein, No.2028, 1/2 Liter 445.00
Mettlach, Stein, No.2035, Liter 425.00
Mettlach, Stein, No.2051, 1/2 Liter, Inlaid Lid 425.00
Mettlach, Stein, No.2054, 1/2 Liter 475.00
Mettlach, Stein, No.2057, 3/10 Liter 185.00
Mettlach, Stein, No.2076, 3 Liter, Blue & Gray Relief, Pewter Lid 275.00
Mettlach, Stein, No.2077, 3/10 Liter, Blue & Gray 125.00
Mettlach, Stein, No.2085, 3 1/2 Liter 375.00
Mettlach, Stein, No.2090, 1/2 Liter, Inlaid Lid, Club Stein 400.00
Mettlach, Stein, No.2099, 3/10 Liter, Floral, Bulbous .... 145.00 To 195.00
Mettlach, Stein, No.2140, 1/2 Liter, PUG, Chicken .... 198.00 To 225.00
Mettlach, Stein, No.2176-954, 3 Liter, PUG 495.00
Mettlach, Stein, No.2177, 1/4 Liter 115.00
Mettlach, Stein, No.2235, 1/2 Liter 450.00
Mettlach, Stein, No.2243, 3/10 Liter 195.00
Mettlach, Stein, No.2246, Relief Peasant On Gray Blue Ground 185.00
Mettlach, Stein, No.2307, Los Angeles Brewing Co., Beige, 9 In. 100.00
Mettlach, Stein, No.2324, 1/2 Liter, Pewter Lid, Football Stein 495.00
Mettlach, Stein, No.2332, 3 Liter 250.00
Mettlach, Stein, No.2373, 1/2 Liter, Etched Inlaid Lid .... 100.00 To 425.00
Mettlach, Stein, No.2501, 1/2 Liter 450.00
Mettlach, Stein, No.2640, 1/2 Liter, Engraved 375.00
Mettlach, Stein, No.2762, 2 Liter, Cameo 500.00
Mettlach, Stein, No.2791, 1/2 Liter, PUG .... 275.00 To 295.00
Mettlach, Stein, No.2797, 5 Liter, Wagner, Etched 550.00
Mettlach, Stein, No.2813, 1/2 Liter, Etched, St.Hubert .... 375.00 To 425.00
Mettlach, Stein, No.2880, 1/2 Liter, Etched .... 280.00 To 455.00
Mettlach, Stein, No.2886, 1/2 Liter 465.00
Mettlach, Stein, No.2893/1197, 3 Liter, Painted Under Glaze 325.00
Mettlach, Stein, No.2893, 3 Liter, Fisherman & Lady, PUG .... 175.00 To 425.00
Mettlach, Stein, No.2893, 3 Liter, Pewter Top & Thumblift 175.00
Mettlach, Stein, No.2931, 1/2 Liter 250.00
Mettlach, Stein, No.2934, 1/4 Liter, Mosaic 215.00
Mettlach, Stein, No.2989, 1/2 Liter 435.00
Mettlach, Stein, No.3004, 1/2 Liter, Castle Mark 265.00
Mettlach, Stein, No.3219, 1/2 Liter 465.00
Mettlach, Tea Set, Blue, Brown, & Cream Colors, Castle Mark, 15 Piece 275.00
Mettlach, Tumbler, No.1024, Villeroy & Boch 38.00
Mettlach, Tumbler, No.2327, Stadt Munchen On Top 42.00
Mettlach, Tumbler, State Symbol Of Colorado, Denver Souvenir, 5 In. 24.00
Mettlach, Tureen, Wine, No.2339, Men Making Wine, Castle Mark, 15 X 15 In. 500.00
Mettlach, Urn, Blue Jewellike Drops On Red, 15 X 7 1/2 In. 450.00
Mettlach, Vase, Art Deco, Gold Baskets Of Flowers On Cream, 9 In. 45.00
Mettlach, Vase, Green, Cream, & Red, Gold Trim, 6 Sided, 6 In. 35.00
Mettlach, Vase, No.1326, High Glaze, Jeweled Colors, 11 1/2 In. 185.00
Mettlach, Vase, No.1336, Beige Ground, Floral & Geometric Design, 11 In.Pair 295.00
Mettlach, Vase, No.2187, Rose, Raised Medallion, 7 1/2 In. 50.00
Mettlach, Vase, No.2252, Incised Figure Of Maiden, Black Matte Body, 13 In. 325.00
Mettlach, Vase, Sgraffito, To Work & To Play, Castle Mark, 15 In. 450.00
Michel, Bowl, Canoe Shape, Red Sailboat Scene On Yellow, C.1910, 7 In. 350.00
Michel, Lamp Base, Cameo, Scenic, Black, Green, & Yellow, 8 1/2 X 5 In. 350.00
Michel, Vase, Cameo, Scenic, Square Neck, 6 1/2 X 4 In. 375.00

Mickey Mouse, see Disneyana

Milk glass was named for its milky white color. It was first made in England during the 1700s. The height of its popularity in the United States was from 1870 to 1880. It is now correct to refer to some colored glass as blue milk glass, black milk glass, etc. The letters B-xx refer to the book "Milk Glass" by E.Belknap.

Milk Glass, see also Cosmos

Milk Glass, **Bathtub**, Blue Flowers, Footed, 5 1/4 In.	8.00
Milk Glass, **Bell**, Smoke, Opalescent, 7 In.	10.00
Milk Glass, **Bell**, Smoke, Ruffled Ruby Edge, 7 1/2 X 5 1/2 In.	52.00
Milk Glass, **Boot With Spur**, Black, Opaque, 3 1/4 In.	34.00
Milk Glass, **Bottle**, Dresser, Actress, Painted Decoration, 11 In.	40.00 To 75.00
Milk Glass, **Bottle**, Dresser, Hand-Painted Roses, 9 In.High, Pair	70.00
Milk Glass, **Bottle**, Figural, Sitting Bear, Black, 11 In., B-242	95.00 To 110.00
Milk Glass, **Bottle**, Perfume, Figural Milk Bottles In Basket	55.00
Milk Glass, **Bottle**, Trylon & Perisphere, N.Y., 1939, 9 In.	9.50 To 30.00
Milk Glass, **Bowl**, Basket Weave, Lacy, Footed, Oblong, 10 In.	45.00
Milk Glass, **Bowl**, Beaded Rib, Oval, Flint, 12 In., B-125-113A	78.00
Milk Glass, **Bowl**, Berry, Master, Single Rose, 8 In.	14.00
Milk Glass, **Bowl**, Blackberry, Oval, 8 1/4 X 5 1/2 In.	30.00
Milk Glass, **Bowl**, Blackberry, Oval, 9 1/4 X 6 In.	35.00
Milk Glass, **Bowl**, Blue, Acanthus Leaf, 9 In., B-110c	85.00
Milk Glass, **Bowl**, Blue, Marbleized, Lattice Edge, 7 In.	25.00
Milk Glass, **Bowl**, Blue, Scroll With Eye, 7 In.	25.00
Milk Glass, **Bowl**, Covered, Blackberry, 7 In.	75.00
Milk Glass, **Bowl**, Crossed Ferns, Collared, 8 1/4 In.	30.00
Milk Glass, **Bowl**, Daisy & Button, Flint, 9 In.	34.00
Milk Glass, **Bowl**, Floral, 4 Row Lattice Border, Atterbury, 8 1/2 In.	45.00
Milk Glass, **Bowl**, Fluted, Cranberry Fluted Inside Overlay, 11 1/4 In.	50.00
Milk Glass, **Bowl**, Fruit, Clear Overlay Ruffled Edge, Fenton, 12 In.	17.50
Milk Glass, **Bowl**, Green, Pedestal, Paint, Square, 5 In.	20.00
Milk Glass, **Bowl**, Lacy Edge, Painted, B-122	65.00
Milk Glass, **Bowl**, Lacy Rim, 7 In., B-141	30.00
Milk Glass, **Bowl**, Lattice Edge, Apple Blossom Center, 9 In.	28.00
Milk Glass, **Bowl**, Lattice Edge, Trumpet Vine Decoration, Atterbury, 9 In.	55.00
Milk Glass, **Bowl**, Lustre Rose, 3 Footed, Imperial, C.1910, 7 3/4 In.	22.00
Milk Glass, **Bowl**, Punch, Child's, Nursery Rhyme	125.00
Milk Glass, **Bowl**, Shallow, Wicket, 8 In.	30.00
Milk Glass, **Bowl**, Shell Finials, Shells, 3 Dolphin Feet, Vallerystahl, 7 In.	25.00
Milk Glass, **Bowl**, Trurnpet Vines, Lattice Edge, Atterbury, 9 In.	65.00
Milk Glass, **Bowl**, 1 1/2 In. Lace, 8 In.	35.00
Milk Glass, **Box**, Covered, Actress, Footed, Oval, 6 X 2 1/2 In.	45.00
Milk Glass, **Box**, Dresser, Beaded, Doeskin Finish, Marked S In Diamond	18.00
Milk Glass, **Box**, Dresser, Covered, Needlepoint, 5 1/2 X 4 In.	35.00
Milk Glass, **Box**, Hairpin, Covered, Actress, 5 X 2 1/4 In.	24.50
Milk Glass, **Box**, Pink, Opalescent, Scalloped Sides, Slant Cover, 5 1/4 In.	28.00
Milk Glass, **Box**, Powder, Blue, Drum Base, Seated Cat, Portieux	60.00
Milk Glass, **Box**, Red Rose On Lid, Gold Edge, 4 1/2 X 3 In.	10.00
Milk Glass, **Box**, Ring, Gold Edged Scalloped	15.00
Milk Glass, **Butter**, Child's, Dome Top, Flattened Diamond	22.50
Milk Glass, **Butter**, Covered, Chartreuse, Scroll	135.00
Milk Glass, **Butter**, Covered, Daisy & Tree Of Life On Panels, Flint	110.00
Milk Glass, **Butter**, Melon With Leaf, Footed, Patent Date, Atterbury	45.00
Milk Glass, **Butter**, Spiraled Triangle	20.00
Milk Glass, **Cake Stand**, Bellflower, 9 In.	20.00
Milk Glass, **Cake Stand**, Mixed Flowers, 9 In.	20.00
Milk Glass, **Cake Stand**, Pink Trumpet Vine Center, 9 X 6 In.	35.00
Milk Glass, **Cake Stand**, Ringed Foot, On Standard, Hand-Painted Flowers, 9 In	28.00
Milk Glass, **Cake Stand**, Trumpet Vine, 9 In.	20.00
Milk Glass, **Cake Stand**, Waffle, Opaque Green, Atterbury	90.00
Milk Glass, **Candleholder**, Dolphin Stem, Octagonal Base, 4 In., Pair	35.00
Milk Glass, **Candlestick**, Blue, Heavy, 10 In.High, Pair	90.00
Milk Glass, **Candlestick**, Crucifix, 9 1/2 In., Pair	55.00
Milk Glass, **Candlestick**, Crucifix, 10 In., Pair	55.00
Milk Glass, **Candlestick**, Dolphin, 4 1/2 In.High, Pair	10.00
Milk Glass, **Candlestick**, Swirl, 3 1/2 In., Pair	12.50

Milk Glass, Celery, Blackberry	175.00
Milk Glass, Celery, Blue, Jewel, B-187	58.00 To 100.00
Milk Glass, Compote, Atlas, Scalloped, B-103	144.00
Milk Glass, Compote, Blue, Twig & Bell Stem, 8 1/2 X 8 In., B-261	39.00
Milk Glass, Compote, Chartreuse, Scroll Footed, 8 X 7 1/2 In., B-127	135.00
Milk Glass, Compote, Covered, Blackberry, 8 In.	150.00
Milk Glass, Compote, Covered, Sawtooth, C.1860, 7 3/4 X 4 In.	59.00
Milk Glass, Compote, Covered, Strawberry, Low Standard, 8 1/4 In.	55.00
Milk Glass, Compote, Floral Inside, 7 1/4 In.	45.00
Milk Glass, Compote, Open Edge, Trumpet Vine Decoration, Atterbury, 9 In.	90.00
Milk Glass, Compote, Open Edge, Waffle Stem, Flint, 10 In.	80.00
Milk Glass, Condiment Set, Cloverleaf Gray, Wreath, Floral, 4 Piece	49.00
Milk Glass, Condiment Set, Forget-Me-Not, Cloverleaf Tray, 4 Piece	70.00
Milk Glass, Creamer, Blackberry, Dated, B-119	20.00 To 35.00
Milk Glass, Creamer, Blue, Owl, Menagerie, Miniature	35.00
Milk Glass, Creamer, Child's, Blue, Menagerie	50.00
Milk Glass, Creamer, Covered, Basket Weave, Atterbury	16.50
Milk Glass, Creamer, Covered, Blue, Feather	17.00
Milk Glass, Creamer, Grape, B-85c	28.00
Milk Glass, Creamer, Owl, Original Eyes	42.50
Milk Glass, Creamer, Strawberry, Applied Handle	35.00
Milk Glass, Creamer, Swan	16.00
Milk Glass, Creamer, Water Lily, Painted, 5 In.	27.50
Milk Glass, Cruet, English Hobnail	1.00
Milk Glass, Cruet, Tree Of Life	55.00
Milk Glass, Cruet, Tree Of Life, Green	40.00
Milk Glass, Cup, Little Red Riding Hood, Miniature	27.50
Milk Glass, Cup, Punch, Little Red Riding Hood	25.00
Milk Glass, Cup, Punch, Nursery Rhyme	18.00
Milk Glass, Dish, American Hen Cover, B-176	40.00 To 50.00
Milk Glass, Dish, Battleship Cover, Marked Maine, B-176	45.00 To 56.00
Milk Glass, Dish, Battleship Cover, Marked S.S.Wheeling, B-198	18.00
Milk Glass, Dish, Black Hen Cover, White Head	70.00
Milk Glass, Dish, Boar's Head Cover, Original Eyes	450.00
Milk Glass, Dish, British Lion Cover	55.00 To 60.00
Milk Glass, Dish, Cabbage Shape, Covered, Portieux, France	37.50
Milk Glass, Dish, Candy, Blue, Dolphin With Seashells, Covered, 3 Footed	75.00
Milk Glass, Dish, Cat Cover, Blue, Drum Base, Portieux	45.00 To 60.00
Milk Glass, Dish, Chick & Eggs Cover, Atterbury	150.00
Milk Glass, Dish, Chick Cover, Sleigh Base	55.00
Milk Glass, Dish, Chick Emerging From Egg Cover, Sleigh Base	42.00 To 65.00
Milk Glass, Dish, Chicken Cover, Hazel Atlas	6.50
Milk Glass, Dish, Chicken Cover, Weed Base, 5 In.	50.00
Milk Glass, Dish, Closed Neck Swan Cover	29.00
Milk Glass, Dish, Cruiser Ship Cover	50.00
Milk Glass, Dish, Deer Cover, Fallen Tree Base, Open Bubbles, B-174	165.00
Milk Glass, Dish, Deer Cover, Fallen Tree Base, Signed Flaccus	125.00
Milk Glass, Dish, Dog Cover *Illus*	37.50

Milk Glass, Dish, Dog Cover

Milk Glass, Dish, Dog Cover, Blue, White Head, Ribbed Base .... 55.00 To 65.00
Milk Glass, Dish, Dog Cover, Wide Ribbed Base, B-179A 30.00
Milk Glass, Dish, Double Chicks' Heads Cover, McKee 275.00
Milk Glass, Dish, Dove Cover, Basket Weave Base, Opalescent 250.00
Milk Glass, Dish, Duck Cover, Amethyst Head, Patent March 15, 1887, B-152c 285.00
Milk Glass, Dish, Duck Cover, Eyes, Ribbed Base 76.00
Milk Glass, Dish, Duck Cover, Grass Base .... 50.00 To 55.00
Milk Glass, Dish, Duck Cover, Wavy Base, B-164 .... 60.00 To 85.00
Milk Glass, Dish, Eagle Cover, Nest Base, B-162h .... 45.00 To 55.00
Milk Glass, Dish, Eagle Cover, Three Baby Eagles Looking Up, 8 X 8 In. 75.00
Milk Glass, Dish, Entwined Fish Cover, Atterbury, B-163a 150.00
Milk Glass, Dish, Entwined Fish Cover, Eyes, Patent Aug.1889, B-177 .... 132.00
Milk Glass, Dish, Fish Cover, Flanged Base, Tail Handle, 8 1/2 X 4 3/4 In. 145.00
Milk Glass, Dish, Fish Cover, Skiff Base .... 30.00 To 40.00
Milk Glass, Dish, Flat Earred Rabbit Cover, Split Rib Base 65.00
Milk Glass, Dish, Hand & Dove Cover, Lace Border Base, Atterbur .... 115.00 To 130.00
Milk Glass, Dish, Hand & Dove Cover, Lacy Base, Stone Eye & Rin .... 59.00 To 97.50
Milk Glass, Dish, Hen Cover, Basket Weave Base, Lavender Head, 7 1/2 In. 175.00
Milk Glass, Dish, Hen Cover, Basket Weave Base, Turned Head, 7 1/2 In. 48.00
Milk Glass, Dish, Hen Cover, Black, White Head, Basket Weave Nest, 5 1/2 In. 115.00
Milk Glass, Dish, Hen Cover, Blue Head, Darker Blue Ribbed Base 40.00
Milk Glass, Dish, Hen Cover, Blue Head, 5 1/2 In. 45.00
Milk Glass, Dish, Hen Cover, Blue, Basket Weave Base, White Head 52.50
Milk Glass, Dish, Hen Cover, Blue, Lacy Base, Marbleized 130.00
Milk Glass, Dish, Hen Cover, Blue, Nest Base, 5 3/4 In. 38.00
Milk Glass, Dish, Hen Cover, Blue, Turned White Head, 7 In. 35.00
Milk Glass, Dish, Hen Cover, Blue, White Head, 5 1/2 In. 45.00
Milk Glass, Dish, Hen Cover, Nest Base, Black Eyes 40.00
Milk Glass, Dish, Honey, Blue, Beehive, Footed 24.50
Milk Glass, Dish, Honey, Robin's-Egg Blue, Basket Weave, 1 7/8 X 1 1/8 In. 7.00
Milk Glass, Dish, Lamb Cover, Picket Base 45.00
Milk Glass, Dish, Lion Cover, Amber, Kemple Label 40.00
Milk Glass, Dish, Lion Cover, Blue, Picket Base, White Head 65.00
Milk Glass, Dish, Lion Cover, British, B-165d 59.00
Milk Glass, Dish, Lion Cover, Lacy Base, Ribbed Lion, Dated, Atterbury 82.50
Milk Glass, Dish, Lion Cover, Picket Base 45.00
Milk Glass, Dish, Lion Cover, Ribbed Base, Atterbury, Dated, B-167c 145.00
Milk Glass, Dish, Lion Cover, Scroll Base, B-181 .... 45.00
Milk Glass, Dish, Mule Eared Rabbit Cover .... 35.00 To 45.00
Milk Glass, Dish, Mustard, Covered, Bull's Head, Atterbury 80.00
Milk Glass, Dish, Pekingese Dog Cover 185.00
Milk Glass, Dish, Pickle, Blackberry 50.00
Milk Glass, Dish, Pickle, Fish, Dated 1870, B-210 .... 27.00
Milk Glass, Dish, Quail Cover, 6 1/2 X 4 1/2 In., B-179b 55.00
Milk Glass, Dish, Rabbit Cover, Atterbury, Mar.9, 1886, 9 1/4 In. .... 145.00 To 185.00
Milk Glass, Dish, Rabbit Cover, Egg Base, Portieux, 5 In. 30.00
Milk Glass, Dish, Rabbit Cover, Greentown 110.00
Milk Glass, Dish, Rabbit Emerging From Egg Cover, Herringbone Base, 5 In. 65.00
Milk Glass, Dish, Resting Camel Cover, B-183a .... 59.00 To 65.00
Milk Glass, Dish, Ribbed Lion Cover, Lacy Base, Atterbury, Dated .... 45.00 To 95.00
Milk Glass, Dish, Robin Cover, Blue, Nest Base, Stem, Vallerystahl .... 55.00 To 65.00
Milk Glass, Dish, Rooster Cover, Blue Head, 6 In. 49.00
Milk Glass, Dish, Rooster Cover, B-140 .... 55.00 To 85.00
Milk Glass, Dish, Rooster Cover, Black Head 45.00
Milk Glass, Dish, Rooster Cover, Blue, Wide Ribbed Base 40.00
Milk Glass, Dish, Rooster Cover, Wide Ribbed Base .... 25.00 To 60.00
Milk Glass, Dish, Setter Dog Cover, Blue, Carpet Base, Vallerystahl 65.00
Milk Glass, Dish, Setter Dog Cover, Turquoise, B-173 .... 90.00
Milk Glass, Dish, Snail Cover, Strawberry Base, Vallerystahl 60.00
Milk Glass, Dish, Snare, Drum, & Cannon Cover, B-206 .... 55.00
Milk Glass, Dish, Stagecoach Cover 65.00
Milk Glass, Dish, Swan Cover, B-179 .... 55.00
Milk Glass, Dish, Swan Cover, Black, Atterbury, B-186 .... 175.00
Milk Glass, Dish, Swan Cover, Blue, Vallerystahl 59.00
Milk Glass, Dish, Swan Cover, Raised Wings, B-153 .... 136.00
Milk Glass, Dish, Swan Cover, Square Block 250.00

Milk Glass, Dish, Swan Cover, Vallerystahl, B-183c 50.00
Milk Glass, Dish, Swan, Black, Hand Made Glass Ware, L.E.Smith Co., 9 In. 35.00
Milk Glass, Dish, Swimming Duck Cover 20.00
Milk Glass, Dish, Swimming Duck Cover, Blue, Oval Base, 5 In. 30.00
Milk Glass, Dish, Trinket, Scrolled, Open Handled, Painted, 4 1/2 X 4 In. 9.00
Milk Glass, Dish, Turtle Cover .... 75.00 To 96.00
Milk Glass, Dish, 3 Frosted Apples Cover, Basket Weave Base, Paint, 4 In. 22.00
Milk Glass, Dish, 4 Chicks' Heads Cover, Oblong Basket Base 225.00
Milk Glass, Egg, Blown, Raised Basket, Egg, & Easter, Gold Trim, 4 3/4 In. 17.50
Milk Glass, Eggcup, Basket Weave, Dated 1874 .... 14.00
Milk Glass, Eggcup, Basket Weave, Double, Atterbury 23.00
Milk Glass, Eggcup, Birch Leaf, Flint 22.00
Milk Glass, Eggcup, Blackberry .... 15.00 To 18.00
Milk Glass, Eggcup, Blackberry, Double 15.00
Milk Glass, Eggcup, Blue, Chick, Signed Portieux 14.00
Milk Glass, Eggcup, Blue, Chick, Signed Vallerystahl .... 15.00 To 35.00
Milk Glass, Eggcup, Blue, Single At One End, Double At The Other 35.00
Milk Glass, Eggcup, Chartreuse, Double 29.50
Milk Glass, Eggcup, Strawberry 15.00
Milk Glass, Eggcup, Vallerystahl 14.00
Milk Glass, Epergne, Pink, 3 Lily, Hobnail 75.00
Milk Glass, Epergne, Sapphire Blue Edges, 4 Arms, Crystal, Metal, 12 In. 275.00
Milk Glass, Fernery, Wreath, 4 Scrolled Feet, 7 1/2 In. 35.00
Milk Glass, Figurine, Rooster, Red Comb, Yellow Feet, 9 In. 26.40
Milk Glass, Goblet, Blackberry 25.00
Milk Glass, Goblet, Blackberry, C.1940, 6 In. 5.00
Milk Glass, Goblet, Blackberry, Dated 1870 .... 30.00
Milk Glass, Goblet, Paneled Grape 20.00
Milk Glass, Goblet, Strawberry 35.00
Milk Glass, Gravy Boat, Dolphin, Covered 35.00
Milk Glass, Hat, Blue, Flared, Raised Dogwood Flower, Gilt, 3 1/2 In. 75.00
Milk Glass, Hatchet, Souvenir Of Wellsburg, Pa., 6 In. 9.50
Milk Glass, Holder, Card Case 22.00
Milk Glass, Humidor, Mahogany Case 47.50
Milk Glass, Jar, Covered, Blue, Ovoid, Atterbury, 6 In. 35.00
Milk Glass, Jar, Covered, Eagle, B-78a 95.00
Milk Glass, Jar, Jam, Figural Apple, Realistic Color 5.00
Milk Glass, Jar, Jam, Figural Strawberry, Realistic Color 5.00
Milk Glass, Jar, Metal Lid, 1880, 2 1/2 In. 6.00
Milk Glass, Jar, Owl, Atterbury, B-182 .... 135.00
Milk Glass, Jar, Pickle, Heavy Rose, B-264, 7 X 4 1/2 In. 16.00
Milk Glass, Jar, Powder, Covered, Scrolls & Fans 7.00
Milk Glass, Jar, Tobacco, Dog's Head Smoking Pipe, Green Hat With Feather 35.00
Milk Glass, Jar, Tobacco, Three Kittens On Cover 45.00
Milk Glass, Lamp Base, Miniature, Maltese Cross 38.00
Milk Glass, Lamp Base, Oil, Beading & Floral, Blue Bands, 1877, 4 1/2 In. 35.00
Milk Glass, Lamp, see Lamp, Milk Glass
Milk Glass, Lemonade Set, Ice Lip, Grapes, Footed, 9 Piece 32.00
Milk Glass, Match Holder, Basket Weave 25.00
Milk Glass, Match Holder, Frosted, "Matches" 14.00
Milk Glass, Match Holder, Hand & Fan 22.50
Milk Glass, Match Holder, Hanging, Kettle Shape, Embossed Grapes, Leaves 28.00
Milk Glass, Matchbox, Striker Inside Lift-Off Lid, 4 Scroll Feet, 3 1/4 In. 18.00
Milk Glass, Muffineer, Blue, Plain & Floral Paneled 55.00
Milk Glass, Muffineer, Blue, Waffle, Tin Cap, 6 1/2 In. 30.00
Milk Glass, Muffineer, Melon Ribbed, Forget-Me-Nots 43.50
Milk Glass, Muffineer, Royal Oak, Pink & Green Leaves On Net .... 44.00 To 75.00
Milk Glass, Muffineer, Royal Oak, Waffle Mold 53.00
Milk Glass, Muffineer, Swirl, Pink & Yellow Transfer Decoration, 3 3/4 In. 35.00
Milk Glass, Muffineer, Swirled, Pink & Yellow Transfer Decoration 32.00
Milk Glass, Muffineer, Yellow & Blue Enameled Daisies, 5 1/2 In.High 28.00
Milk Glass, Mug, Burred Hobnail 22.50
Milk Glass, Mug, Chef's 24.00
Milk Glass, Mug, Child's, Bopeep & Her Sheep 6.00
Milk Glass, Paperweight, Hatchet, "Redwood, N.Y.," C.1893, 6 In. 25.00
Milk Glass, Perfumer, G.W.Laird, N.Y., 4 1/2 In. 15.00

Milk Glass, Pitcher, Water, Blackberry, Applied Handle	500.00
Milk Glass, Planter, Dancing Nudes, Signed Smith, 3 1/2 X 7 1/4 In.	20.00
Milk Glass, Plate, Angel & Harp, 7 1/4 In.	12.00
Milk Glass, Plate, Angel With Lute & Clouds, 7 In.	16.50
Milk Glass, Plate, Angel, Marked Kemple, 8 In.	25.00
Milk Glass, Plate, Angel's Head Border, 9 In.	25.00
Milk Glass, Plate, Angel's Head, Gilded, Hand-Painted Flowers, 9 In.	20.00
Milk Glass, Plate, Angel's Head, Handled, 9 In., B-7f	15.00
Milk Glass, Plate, Arch Border, 8 In.	16.00
Milk Glass, Plate, Backward C, Opalescent, Square, 8 In.	35.00
Milk Glass, Plate, Battleship Maine, Shell & Club Rim, 7 In.	12.00
Milk Glass, Plate, Beaded & Scroll, Piecrust Rim, 8 In., Pair	15.00 To 25.00
Milk Glass, Plate, Black, Gothic, Handled, 8 In., B-9b	15.00
Milk Glass, Plate, Blue, Angel's Head, 9 In.	25.00
Milk Glass, Plate, Blue, Keyhole Border, 7 1/2 In., B-11e	22.00
Milk Glass, Plate, Bread, Basket Weave	65.00
Milk Glass, Plate, Bread, Columbus	29.00
Milk Glass, Plate, Bread, Fleur De Lis, Flag, Eagle Border	14.00
Milk Glass, Plate, Bread, Hare & Clover	39.00
Milk Glass, Plate, Bread, Retriever	65.00 To 85.00
Milk Glass, Plate, Bread, Rock Of Ages, Blue, Clear Handles, Atterbury	175.00
Milk Glass, Plate, Chartreuse, Open Edge, English, 8 In.	55.00
Milk Glass, Plate, Child's, Little Bopeep On Cobalt, Vitrock, 3 Sections	15.00
Milk Glass, Plate, Closed Lattice, Red Rose Center, 10 In.	35.00
Milk Glass, Plate, Club & Shell, Handled, 9 1/2 In., B-11f	11.00
Milk Glass, Plate, Club & Shell, Waffle Center, 9 1/2 In., B-11f	15.00 To 17.00
Milk Glass, Plate, Columbus, Club & Shell Border, 9 1/2 In.	20.00
Milk Glass, Plate, Contrary Mule, 7 In.	15.00
Milk Glass, Plate, Crown Border, 7 1/2 In.	12.00
Milk Glass, Plate, Cupid & Psyche, 7 1/2 In.	18.00
Milk Glass, Plate, Daisy, Open Border, 7 1/2 In.	24.00
Milk Glass, Plate, Dart Border, 7 1/4 In.	9.00
Milk Glass, Plate, Diamond & Shell Border, 7 1/4 In.	16.00
Milk Glass, Plate, Dog, Cat, & Three Puppies, Open Leaf Border, B-24	95.00
Milk Glass, Plate, Easter Chicks, Painted, 4 1/4 In.	15.00
Milk Glass, Plate, Easter Opening, 6 3/4 In., B-7d	39.00
Milk Glass, Plate, Flag With Star Border, 7 1/2 In.	15.00
Milk Glass, Plate, Floral Center, Lattice Border, 10 In.	35.00
Milk Glass, Plate, Floral, Open Lattice Border, 11 In.	45.00
Milk Glass, Plate, Flower In Square, Square, 8 In.	12.00
Milk Glass, Plate, Forget-Me-Not Border, 8 1/2 In.	12.50
Milk Glass, Plate, Forget-Me-Not, 7 In.	9.00
Milk Glass, Plate, Gothic, 8 1/2 In.	12.00 To 15.00
Milk Glass, Plate, Gothic, 9 In.	12.00
Milk Glass, Plate, Gothic, 9 1/4 In.	15.00
Milk Glass, Plate, Grill, Diamond, Give Us This Day Around Border	35.00
Milk Glass, Plate, Hare & Clover, 7 1/2 In., B-6e	39.00
Milk Glass, Plate, Heart Border, 6 In.	12.00
Milk Glass, Plate, Heart Shaped, Lacy Edge, Plain Center, 7 1/2 In.	9.50
Milk Glass, Plate, Indian Head Center, Beaded Loop Border	25.00
Milk Glass, Plate, Indian's Head, Beaded Loop, 7 1/2 In., B-8	20.00 To 40.00
Milk Glass, Plate, Lattice Edge, Hand-Painted Flowers, 2 In. Deep, 9 In.	45.00
Milk Glass, Plate, Leaf, 6 In.	5.00
Milk Glass, Plate, No Easter Without Us, 6 1/2 In., B-3e	14.00 To 32.00
Milk Glass, Plate, Open Edge, 10 In.	35.00 To 70.00
Milk Glass, Plate, Open Lattice Border, 11 In.	40.00
Milk Glass, Plate, Open Lattice, Floral Patterned Center, 11 In.	38.00
Milk Glass, Plate, Openwork Border, Fruit Transfer, Kemple, 7 1/4 In.	22.50
Milk Glass, Plate, Owls Lovers, B-117b	25.00 To 39.00
Milk Glass, Plate, Painted Flag, Eagle & Fleur-De-Lis Border, 1903, 7 In.	12.00
Milk Glass, Plate, Painted Strawberries Center, Lacy Edge, 7 1/2 In., B-6	14.00
Milk Glass, Plate, Pinwheel, 8 1/2 In.	18.00
Milk Glass, Plate, Psyche & Cupid, 7 1/2 In., B-6b	26.00
Milk Glass, Plate, Rear Admiral George Dewey, Open Edge, 7 1/4 In.	25.00
Milk Glass, Plate, S Border, Square, 7 1/2 In.	12.00
Milk Glass, Plate, Sailboat & Anchor, Chain Border, 7 3/8 In.	25.00

Milk Glass, Plate, Scroll & Eye, Latticework, Hand-Painted Floral, 10 In.	37.50
Milk Glass, Plate, Scroll & Eye, Open Edge, Black, 9 In.	24.00
Milk Glass, Plate, Scroll & Eye, 7 In.	15.00
Milk Glass, Plate, Scroll & Eye, 8 In.	13.00 To 14.00
Milk Glass, Plate, Serenade, 6 1/2 In., B-9e	20.00 To 30.00
Milk Glass, Plate, Single Forget-Me-Not, 7 1/4 In.	12.00
Milk Glass, Plate, Spring Meets Winter, 7 1/4 In.	27.00
Milk Glass, Plate, Three Kittens, Painted, 8 In.	15.00
Milk Glass, Plate, Three Owls, 7 In.	12.00
Milk Glass, Plate, Triple Forget-Me-Not, 7 1/4 In.	12.00
Milk Glass, Plate, Trumpet Vine, Lattice Edge, Atterbury, 11 In.	20.00 To 65.00
Milk Glass, Plate, Two Chicks Eating Corn, Open Leaf & Scroll, 7 1/2 In.	13.75
Milk Glass, Plate, Waffle, Club & Shell Border, 9 1/2 In.	17.00
Milk Glass, Plate, Wicket Border, 9 In.	9.00
Milk Glass, Plate, Wicket, 8 1/2 In.	14.00
Milk Glass, Plate, Wild Rose Floral Center, Lattice, 10 1/4 In.	38.00
Milk Glass, Plate, Woof-Woof, B-17	25.00
Milk Glass, Plate, 101 Border, 5 1/4 In.	13.50
Milk Glass, Plate, 101 Border, 7 1/4 In.	15.00
Milk Glass, Plate, 101 Border, 8 1/2 In.	14.00
Milk Glass, Plate, 101, 8 3/4 In.	16.50
Milk Glass, Platter, Liberty Bell, John Hancock, Shell Handled, 11 1/4 In.	295.00
Milk Glass, Platter, Retriever, B-53	75.00 To 138.00
Milk Glass, Pot, Mustard, Blue, Decorated, Wooden Spoon, 3 3/4 In.	26.00
Milk Glass, Pot, Mustard, Bull's Head, Atterbury	85.00
Milk Glass, Rack, Towel, Free-Blown, 30 In.	33.00
Milk Glass, Reamer, Green, Sunkist	7.00
Milk Glass, Reamer, Sunkist	4.50
Milk Glass, Relish, Blackberry, 9 1/2 In.	35.00
Milk Glass, Relish, Pale Pink, Beaded Edge, Divided, 12 1/2 In.	40.00 To 65.00
Milk Glass, Rose Bowl, Blue, Raised Calla Lily, Gilt, 3 1/4 In.	75.00
Milk Glass, Rose Bowl, Shell & Scroll, Footed, 5 In.	22.00

The numbers P-xx refer to the books '333 Glass Saltshakers' and 'Glass Saltshakers, 1, 000 Patterns' by Arthur Peterson.

Milk Glass, Salt & Pepper, Aqua Fish	38.00
Milk Glass, Salt & Pepper, Embossed & Painted Apple Blossoms	35.00
Milk Glass, Salt & Pepper, Embossed, Metal Lids, 5 1/2 X 3 In.	19.00
Milk Glass, Salt & Pepper, Figural, Carved Women, Painted Trim	45.00
Milk Glass, Salt & Pepper, G.E.Monitor Top Refrigerator	9.95 To 15.00
Milk Glass, Salt & Pepper, Grape, Bulbous Base, 3 1/2 In., Pair	12.00
Milk Glass, Salt & Pepper, Owl, Metal Tops, 6 In.	250.00
Milk Glass, Salt & Pepper, Paisley & Scroll, Bulbous Base, 3 1/2 In., Pair	12.00
Milk Glass, Salt & Pepper, Robbins, Findlay	22.00
Milk Glass, Salt & Pepper, St.Pauls & Trafalgar Square, Brass Tops	6.00
Milk Glass, Salt & Pepper, Torch & Wreath, Blue	45.00
Milk Glass, Salt Dip, Basket Weave, Pedestal, Side Handle, 1874	18.00
Milk Glass, Salt Dip, Black, Honeycomb, Flint	18.00
Milk Glass, Salt Dip, Blackberry	23.00 To 26.00
Milk Glass, Salt Dip, Blackberry, Pedestal	20.00
Milk Glass, Salt Dip, Corn Husk	17.00
Milk Glass, Salt Dip, Dewdrop Star, Footed	10.00
Milk Glass, Salt Dip, Master, Atterbury, Dated	25.00
Milk Glass, Salt Dip, Master, Blackberry, Footed	15.00
Milk Glass, Salt Dip, Master, Strawberry	15.00
Milk Glass, Salt Dip, Sawtooth, Acorn Finial	85.00
Milk Glass, Salt Dip, Sawtooth, Flint	65.00
Milk Glass, Salt Dip, Sawtooth, Footed, Flint	65.00
Milk Glass, Salt Dip, Stippled Leaf	26.00
Milk Glass, Salt Dip, Swimming Duck	12.50
Milk Glass, Salt Dip, Swirl	18.50
Milk Glass, Salt Dip, Turtle	17.50
Milk Glass, Saltshaker, Beehive	16.00
Milk Glass, Saltshaker, Blue, Columbian Exposition, 1893, Egg On End	48.00
Milk Glass, Saltshaker, Blue, Floral	9.50
Milk Glass, Saltshaker, Blue, Paneled Scroll	18.00

Milk Glass, **Saltshaker**, Blue, Rosette Sides, Beaded Corners, Squatty	12.50
Milk Glass, **Saltshaker**, Blue, Tassel	8.00
Milk Glass, **Saltshaker**, Butterfly, Pewter Top	7.50
Milk Glass, **Saltshaker**, Creased Neck, Iris Decoration	20.00
Milk Glass, **Saltshaker**, Double Cord & Tassel, P-19e	12.00
Milk Glass, **Saltshaker**, Draped Beads, Fostoria	14.00
Milk Glass, **Saltshaker**, Ear Of Corn	10.00
Milk Glass, **Saltshaker**, Embossed Rabbits	30.00 To 35.00
Milk Glass, **Saltshaker**, Embossed Rabbits & Hen	35.00
Milk Glass, **Saltshaker**, Fan With Double Band	8.00
Milk Glass, **Saltshaker**, Fan, Beaded	8.50
Milk Glass, **Saltshaker**, Feather Panel	8.00
Milk Glass, **Saltshaker**, Floral, Brass Top	9.00
Milk Glass, **Saltshaker**, Green, Guttate, Pewter Top	20.00
Milk Glass, **Saltshaker**, John Bull, P-31	55.00
Milk Glass, **Saltshaker**, Pink, Scroll In Scroll	22.00
Milk Glass, **Saltshaker**, Single Rose	9.00
Milk Glass, **Saltshaker**, Square	5.00
Milk Glass, **Saltshaker**, Torch & Wreath	8.00
Milk Glass, **Sauce**, Blackberry, Ribbed Top	6.00
Milk Glass, **Sauce**, Paneled Wheat, 4 In.	14.00
Milk Glass, **Sauce**, Strawberry	6.00
Milk Glass, **Spill**, Black, Schoolboys & Arithmetic Numbers, Sowerby	45.00
Milk Glass, **Spill**, Blue, Old Man Bowing To Lady, Sowerby, 4 In.	32.00
Milk Glass, **Spooner**, Birch Leaf	26.00
Milk Glass, **Spooner**, Blackberry	12.50 To 22.00
Milk Glass, **Spooner**, Ceres	35.00
Milk Glass, **Spooner**, Crossed Fern, Ball Feet	30.00
Milk Glass, **Spooner**, Strawberry	15.00
Milk Glass, **Spooner**, Two Panel	15.00
Milk Glass, **Spooner**, Wheat, Milled Edge, B-64b	30.00
Milk Glass, **Sugar & Creamer**, Blackberry	80.00
Milk Glass, **Sugar & Creamer**, Blue, Paneled Shell	40.00
Milk Glass, **Sugar & Creamer**, Blue, Yutec, Marked Kemple	20.00
Milk Glass, **Sugar & Creamer**, Flower Rim	10.00
Milk Glass, **Sugar & Creamer**, Helmet Shape, English	39.50
Milk Glass, **Sugar & Creamer**, Hobnail, Star-Shaped Ruffled Tops	12.00
Milk Glass, **Sugar & Creamer**, Ivory, Peacock & Rib, Patent Queens Ivory Ware	75.00
Milk Glass, **Sugar & Creamer**, Pink	12.50
Milk Glass, **Sugar & Creamer**, Sunflower	68.00 To 80.00
Milk Glass, **Sugar & Creamer**, 12 Panels, Scalloped Rim & Foot	20.00
Milk Glass, **Sugar & Creamer**, 4 Legs, Painted Flower, Sowerby, Dec.2, 1879	75.00
Milk Glass, **Sugar**, Basket Finial, Basket Weave, Footed, Atterbury, 1874-1875	65.00
Milk Glass, **Sugar**, Birch Leaf, Flint	45.00
Milk Glass, **Sugar**, Blackberry	12.50
Milk Glass, **Sugar**, Blue, Painted Cosmos & Leaves, 2 1/2 In.	25.00
Milk Glass, **Sugar**, Cathedral	35.00
Milk Glass, **Sugar**, Cherry, Twig Finial, Vallerystahl	60.00
Milk Glass, **Sugar**, Covered, Bakewell Pears, Rochelle, Fiery Opalescent	85.00
Milk Glass, **Sugar**, Covered, Blackberry	38.00 To 55.00
Milk Glass, **Sugar**, Covered, Blackberry, Oval	375.00
Milk Glass, **Sugar**, Covered, Blue, Gold Chrysanthemum Sprig	125.00
Milk Glass, **Sugar**, Covered, Double Loop	82.50
Milk Glass, **Sugar**, Covered, Forget-Me-Not, Gilt Trim	12.50
Milk Glass, **Sugar**, Covered, Geometric	85.00
Milk Glass, **Sugar**, Covered, Gothic Windows	15.00
Milk Glass, **Sugar**, Covered, Viking	20.00
Milk Glass, **Sugar**, Royal Oak, Lattice	50.00
Milk Glass, **Swan**, Open Neck	65.00
Milk Glass, **Syrup**, Beehive, Applied Handle, Pewter Top, Patent 1869, B-80	82.75
Milk Glass, **Syrup**, Blackberry, Applied Handle	175.00
Milk Glass, **Syrup**, Bunch Of Grapes, Painted, Tin Top	45.00
Milk Glass, **Syrup**, Coreopsis	75.00
Milk Glass, **Syrup**, Embossed Beads & Panels, Tin Top, Flint	21.00
Milk Glass, **Syrup**, Embossed Flower	45.00
Milk Glass, **Syrup**, Green, Applied Handle, Hand-Painted, Top Patent 1884	48.00

Milk Glass, Syrup, Painted Blue Morning Glories, Oval Shape	26.00
Milk Glass, Syrup, Palmette, Pewter Top, Applied Handle, B-83	74.25
Milk Glass, Syrup, Swirled, Embossed Floral, Tin Top	35.00
Milk Glass, Syrup, Tree Of Life, Metal Lid, Dated 1871	45.00
Milk Glass, Table Set, Blackberry, 4 Piece	160.00
Milk Glass, Table Set, Child's, Diamond & Sunburst, 3 Piece	70.00
Milk Glass, Table Set, Flattened Diamond & Sunburst, Miniature, 3 Piece	49.00
Milk Glass, Table Set, Roman Cross, 4 Piece, B-213	85.00
Milk Glass, Tankard, Water, Beaded Circle, B-90a	32.00
Milk Glass, Tom & Jerry Set, Red Scrolls, McKee, 13 Piece	23.50
Milk Glass, Tom & Jerry Set, Winter Scene With People, McKee, 6 Piece	65.00
Milk Glass, Toothpick, Basket Weave, Basket Shape, 2 Handles	11.00 To 12.00
Milk Glass, Toothpick, Blue, Boy Playing Marbles, Holder On His Back	22.00
Milk Glass, Toothpick, Blue, Bulging Petal	35.00
Milk Glass, Toothpick, Cherubs Holding Barrel	20.00
Milk Glass, Toothpick, Diamond Point Heart	5.00
Milk Glass, Toothpick, Forget-Me-Not, Squat	20.00
Milk Glass, Toothpick, Green, Bulging Loop	35.00
Milk Glass, Toothpick, Green, Shell & Seaweed	35.00
Milk Glass, Toothpick, Minstrel Boy	40.00
Milk Glass, Toothpick, Nile Green, 101	40.00
Milk Glass, Toothpick, Pink & Yellow, Gold Spatter	10.00
Milk Glass, Toothpick, Raised Petal Waist, Hand-Painted Floral	22.00
Milk Glass, Tray, Actress, Painted, 6 X 3 1/2 In.	10.00
Milk Glass, Tray, Actress, 11 X 7 1/2 In.	40.00
Milk Glass, Tray, Bison's Head, Bison's Head On Each End, 11 In.	28.00
Milk Glass, Tray, Bisons' Heads At Each End, Scrolls, 11 1/2 X 7 1/2 In.	29.00
Milk Glass, Tray, Dresser, Scroll Edge, Signed McKee, Pair	30.00
Milk Glass, Tray, Pickle, Blackberry	28.00
Milk Glass, Tray, Pin, Delaware	14.00
Milk Glass, Tray, Pin, Gilded, Signed McKee	20.00
Milk Glass, Tray, Pin, Monkey's Face	16.00
Milk Glass, Tray, Pin, World's Fair, St.Louis, 1904, Gold Trim, 4 1/2 X 8 In.	17.00
Milk Glass, Tray, Ribbed Border, Waffle Pattern Underside, Blue, 13 X 9 In.	35.00
Milk Glass, Tray, Rose Garland, Oval, 9 1/2 In.	22.00
Milk Glass, Tumbler, Apple Blossom	35.00 To 38.00
Milk Glass, Tumbler, Apple Blossom, Blue Band	35.00
Milk Glass, Tumbler, Blue, Dart Bar, Footed	25.00
Milk Glass, Tumbler, Paneled Daisy & Tree Of Life, Barrel Shape	20.00
Milk Glass, Tumbler, Single Rose	12.50
Milk Glass, Tumbler, St.Louis Exposition	10.00 To 13.50
Milk Glass, Tumbler, Thumbprint, Bakewell Pears	18.00
Milk Glass, Tumbler, Versailles, Pink & Green	12.50
Milk Glass, Vase, Baluster Shape, Hand-Painted Roses, 6 In.High	22.00
Milk Glass, Vase, Black, Square, Sowerby, 5 In.	22.00
Milk Glass, Vase, Blue, Hand, Blown, 8 1/2 In.	20.00
Milk Glass, Vase, Blue, Hand, Jack-In-The-Pulpit, Blown, Pink Trim, 10 5/8 In.	32.00
Milk Glass, Vase, Blue, Old King Cole, Rectangular, 3 1/4 X 5 In.	75.00
Milk Glass, Vase, Blue, Old Man & Lady, Little Girl & Bird, Sowerby, 4 In.	62.00
Milk Glass, Vase, Blue, Old Woman Drinking Tea, Square, Sowerby, 4 In.	65.00
Milk Glass, Vase, Blue, Raised Wild Rose, Ruffled, Gilt, 8 3/4 In.	55.00
Milk Glass, Vase, Blue, Triple, 3 Handles, Sowerby, 3 1/2 In.	30.00
Milk Glass, Vase, Cylindrical, Faint Gold Trim, 8 In.	10.00
Milk Glass, Vase, Deep Blue Ruffled Edge, Opalescent, 4 In., Pair	25.00
Milk Glass, Vase, Indian Chief Under Tan & Brown Glaze, 5 X 5 In.	25.00
Milk Glass, Vase, Opalescent Coin Spot, Ruffled Top, 6 1/4 In.	25.00
Milk Glass, Vase, Orange, Swamp Bird Decoration, Black Base, 9 In.	45.00

*Millefiori means many flowers. It is a type of glasswork popular in
paperweights. Many small flowerlike pieces of glass are grouped together to
form a design.*

Millefiori, see also Paperweight

Millefiori, Cruet, Bulbous, 4 In.	65.00
Millefiori, Cup & Saucer, Demitasse, Footed	78.00
Millefiori, Sugar & Creamer, Blown, Candy Stripe Handle On Creamer	195.00
Millefiori, Toothpick	55.00

Millefiori, Tumbler, 4 In.	85.00
Millefiori, Vase, Lavender, Green, & White Canes, Handled, 3 1/2 In.	37.00
Millefiori, Vase, Lily, 10 1/2 In.	350.00
Millefiori, Vase, Miniature, Brown & Blue Pulled Canes On White, 2 In.	37.00
Miniature, Beaker, Dutch Silver, C.1760, 1 5/8 In. .... *Illus*	400.00
Miniature, Bowl, Brandy, Dutch Silver, 2 1/2 In. .... *Illus*	325.00
Miniature, Chair, Silver, 2 1/8 In.High, Ornate, Pair	75.00
Miniature, Distaff, English Silver, David Clayton, C.172 .... *Illus*	350.00
Miniature, Tea Set, Silver, 6 Piece, Tray 4 In.Long	75.00
Miniature, Teakettle, Dutch Silver, Van Strant, 1738 .... *Illus*	300.00
Miniature, Urn, Coffee, Dutch Silver, Van Geffen, 1762 .... *Illus*	425.00
Miniature, Urn, Coffee, Dutch Silver, Van Strant, 1738 .... *Illus*	475.00

Miniature, Urn, Coffee, Dutch Silver, Van Strant, 1738

Miniature, Distaff, English Silver, David Clayton, C.1725

Miniature, Urn, Coffee, Dutch Silver, Van Geffen, 1762

Miniature, Beaker, Dutch Silver, C.1760, 1 5/8 In.

Miniature, Bowl, Brandy, Dutch Silver, 2 1/2 In.

Miniature, Teakettle, Dutch Silver, Van Strant, 1738

Minton china has been made in England from 1793 to the present time.

Minton, Bowl, Cabbage, Green & Ivory, 10 X 3 In.	69.00
Minton, Bowl, Medium Blue, 15 1/2 In.	78.00
Minton, Bowl, Pedestal, Fruit Medallion, Turquoise, C.1912, 11 1/4 In.	135.00
Minton, Bowl, Punch, Footed, Cobalt, Orange, & Green, Luster Decoration, 6 In.	175.00
Minton, Bowl, Waste, White With Green & Gold, 3 1/4 X 5 3/4 In.	38.00
Minton, Butter, Handled Dome Cover, Floral Festoons, Jeweled	45.00
Minton, Compote, Powder Blue Border, Enamel Roses, 8 1/2 X 3 3/4 In.	33.50
Minton, Creamer, White With Green & Gold, 5 In.	28.00
Minton, Cup & Saucer, Butterfly Handle, Floral On White, Gold, 1869	50.00
Minton, Cup, Demitasse, Ivory Ground, Wreath Decoration, Gold Rim, 4 1/2 In.	25.00
Minton, Dessert Set, Pink Roses, Green Border, 7 Piece	40.00
Minton, Figurine, Parrot, Majolica, Perching On Stump, 1928, 12 1/4 In.	120.00
Minton, Jug, Covered, Blue & White, Grapes, Branch Handle, C.1846, 9 1/2 In.	175.00
Minton, Pitcher, Majolica, Cobalt, Yellow Mask Spout & Floral, C.1867, 8 In.	100.00

Minton, Plate, Floral Wreath, Turquoise Jeweled Border, Scalloped, 8 In.	17.50
Minton, Plate, Ganges, White, Brown Trim, 9 In.	25.00
Minton, Plate, Gold Butterflies & Floral On Mazarin Blue, C.1875, 9 In.	42.00
Minton, Plate, Hot, Blue & White, Brass Corners, Ball Feet, Wood Frame, 8 In.	12.50
Minton, Plate, Majolica, Green & Pink, 8 In.	20.00
Minton, Plate, Oyster, Majolica, 9 X 7 1/2 In.	38.00
Minton, Plate, Portrait Bust Of Prince Albert, Green Mark, 8 3/4 In.	55.00
Minton, Plate, Roses On White, Aqua Border, 9 In.	6.00
Minton, Plate, Service, White, Gold Design, Cream Band, C.1920	150.00
Minton, Plate, Soup, White, Green & Gold On Cream Rim, 9 In.	5.00
Minton, Plate, Wreaths, Rose Sprays, & Blue Floral Garlands, Gold, 10 In.	4.00
Minton, Platter, White, Translucent, Signed, 15 X 12 In.	15.00
Minton, Saltshaker, Yellow Sanded Band, Blue, White Floral Bands, Blue Mark	18.00
Minton, Sugar, Covered, White With Green & Gold, Double Handled, 4 1/2 In.	38.00
Minton, Tile, Boston Statehouse, 1818, Black Print, Footed Iron Frame, 6 In.	18.00
Minton, Tile, Plymouth Rock, Square, 6 In.	20.00
Minton, Tile, Scenes Of Children, Black & White	18.00
Minton, Tile, Tea, Hancock House, 6 X 6 In.	25.00
Minton, Tile, 2 Women Raking Hay, Black Transfer, Footed Iron Frame, 6 In.	25.00
Minton, Toby Mug, Female, Majolica, 1865, 11 1/2 In.	225.00
Minton, Tray, Chop, Decorated, Signed, Round, 37 In.	38.00
Minton, Vase, Birds, Floral, & Insects On Cream, Jeweled, 8 1/2 In.	215.00
Minton, Vase, White & Green Art Nouveau Floral On Red Enamel, 8 In.	200.00
Minton, Wash Basin Set, Green & Orange Art Nouveau Design, 5 Piece	500.00

Mirror, see Furniture, Mirror

Mocha ware is an English-made product that was sold in America during the early 1800s. It is a heavy pottery with pale coffee and cream coloring. Designs of blue, brown, green, orange, or black or white were added to the pottery.

Mocha, Bowl, Beige Band, Green Seaweed, C.1875, 10 1/4 X 4 1/2 In.	58.00
Mocha, Bowl, Yellow, Design, Large Lip, 12 X 5 1/2 In.	110.00
Mocha, Jug, Applied Leaf Handle, Banded Blue & Green, C.1850, 7 In.	65.00
Mocha, Mug, Yellow, Brown & White Bands, Applied Handle, C.1845, 2 3/4 In.	43.00

Mold, Bullet, see Weapon, Mold, Bullet
Mold, Candle, see Kitchen, Mold, Candle, Tin, Mold, Candle
Mold, Ice Cream, see Pewter, Mold, Ice Cream

Monart, Bowl, Blue, Pink, Green, & Gold, Swirled, 3 1/4 X 1 1/4 In.	52.00
Monart, Vase, Mottled Tortoiseshell To Burnt Orange, 10 In.	160.00

Mont Joye, see Mt.Joye

Moorcroft Pottery was founded in Burslem, England, in 1914 by William Moorcroft. The earlier wares are similar to those made today, but color and marking will help indicate the age.

Moorcroft, Bowl, Blue, Purple Pansy Inside, C.1915, 1 1/2 X 4 1/2 In.	62.00
Moorcroft, Bowl, Cobalt, Floral Interior, Paper Label, 4 In.	22.00
Moorcroft, Bowl, Cobalt, Pansies Interior, Script Signature, 11 In.	90.00
Moorcroft, Bowl, Coronation, Edward VIII, 1937, White, 8 1/4 In.	250.00
Moorcroft, Bowl, Florian Ware, Blue Poppies On Dark Blue, Macintyre, 4 In.	85.00
Moorcroft, Bowl, Florian Ware, Macintyre, Cobalt, Blue & White, 3 In.	125.00
Moorcroft, Bowl, Flowers Inside, 5 1/2 In.	20.00
Moorcroft, Bowl, Footed, Green Ground, Multifloral Decoration, 3 X 3 In.	32.00
Moorcroft, Bowl, Fruit On Blue, Signed W.M., C.1925, 7 1/2 In.	88.00
Moorcroft, Bowl, Green, Multicolor Floral, Footed, 3 X 3 In.	30.00
Moorcroft, Bowl, Irises, Signed, 3 In.	22.50
Moorcroft, Bowl, Leaves & Berries, Green Script Signed, 7 X 3 1/4 In.	95.00
Moorcroft, Bowl, Red & Yellow Floral On Green, 9 In.Diameter	45.00
Moorcroft, Box, Covered, Floral Design, Rose Colors, 3 X 5 In.	80.00
Moorcroft, Candleholder, Poppies On Cobalt, W.M., C.1925, 3 1/2 In., Pair	125.00
Moorcroft, Chalice, Macintyre, Tan, Floral, Cobalt Handles & Lining, 8 In.	225.00
Moorcroft, Cup & Saucer, Blue Shaded, Floral, Incised Script Signature	35.00
Moorcroft, Cup & Saucer, Green Shaded, Floral, Incised Script Signature	35.00
Moorcroft, Cup & Saucer, Yellow, Red, & Purple Fruit On Blue, C.1925	68.00
Moorcroft, Eggcup, Green Iridescent, Block Signature	85.00
Moorcroft, Fernery, Oval, Purple Flowers, 6 1/2 X 3 1/2 In.	45.00
Moorcroft, Inkwell, Blue Ground, Floral Decoration, 3 In.Square	62.00

Moorcroft, Jug, Slip Outlined Blue Roses On White, MacIntyre, 4 1/2 In. 245.00
Moorcroft, Lamp Base, Flowers, Mushrooms, Red, Blue, Green Ground, 29 In. 225.00
Moorcroft, Lamp, Vase Base, Orchid Type Floral On Cobalt, 27 In. 95.00
Moorcroft, Plate, Yellow, Purple, & Red Orchids, 6 3/4 In. 35.00
Moorcroft, Potpourri, Flamminian, Pierced Cover, Foliate Panels, 5 In. 125.00
Moorcroft, Rose Jar, Lavender Orchids On Blue Green Ground, 12 In. 275.00
Moorcroft, Sugar & Creamer, Blue 45.00
Moorcroft, Teapot, Green, Pomegranates, Signed, 7 X 7 In. 95.00
Moorcroft, Vase, Blue & Green, Flowers, 2 In. 12.00
Moorcroft, Vase, Blue Violets On Pale Blue, MacIntyre, 2 3/4 In. 135.00
Moorcroft, Vase, Cobalt Blue Ground, Orchids, 4 In.High 35.00
Moorcroft, Vase, Cobalt With Pomegranate, WM In Blue Script, 4 1/4 In. 75.00
Moorcroft, Vase, Cream & Green, Pansies, Rose & Lemon, 4 1/2 In. 16.50
Moorcroft, Vase, Flambe Coloring, Bulbous, Script Signed, 8 1/2 In. 125.00
Moorcroft, Vase, Flambe Slip Floral & Fruit On Flambe, Green, 5 1/2 In. 88.00
Moorcroft, Vase, Flamminian Ware, 3 White Slip Medallions, C.1900, 4 3/4 In. 55.00
Moorcroft, Vase, Floral Decoration On Cobalt Ground, 4 1/2 In. 32.00
Moorcroft, Vase, Floral On Cobalt, Blue Script Signed, 10 In. 80.00
Moorcroft, Vase, Flowers, 12 1/2 In. 185.00
Moorcroft, Vase, Grapes & Leaves On Shaded Green, Artist Signed, 9 In. 65.00
Moorcroft, Vase, Irregular Rim, Purple & Yellow Pansies, C.1914, 3 1/2 In. 60.00
Moorcroft, Vase, Mountains, Blue & Green Slip, Sgraffito, MacIntyre, 7 In. 265.00
Moorcroft, Vase, Orchids, Script Signature, 6 1/4 In. 55.00
Moorcroft, Vase, Pansies On White & Gray Green, C.1915, 6 3/4 In. 325.00
Moorcroft, Vase, Pomegranate On Mottled Cobalt Blue, 4 3/4 In. 38.00
Moorcroft, Vase, Pomegranate, Signature In Green, Burslem, Eng., 9 1/4 In. 75.00
Moorcroft, Vase, Poppies On Blue, Bulbous, 3 X 3 In. 18.00
Moorcroft, Vase, Purple & Red Berries & Gold & Green Leaves, 7 1/4 In. 75.00
Moorcroft, Vase, Rose, Lemon Pansy, Creamware Ground, 4 1/2 In. 16.50
Moorcroft, Vase, Scenic, Trees & Mountains, Abstract Style, 7 1/2 In. 185.00

Moriaga is used to identify Japanese pottery to which a raised overglaze decoration has been added. This relief ornamentation may be elaborate. The term applies to the style or technique.

Moriaga, Box, Powder, Hinged, Purple Roses, White & Green 90.00
Moriaga, Candlestick, Green, Purple, & Yellow Grapes, 12 In.High, Pair 45.00
Moriaga, Dish, Dresser, Covered, Green, Marbleized, Pinched-In 60.00
Moriaga, Plate, Long-Tail Bird, 7 In. 45.00
Moriaga, Sugar & Creamer, Signed 39.00
Moriaga, Tankard, Nippon, 13 1/2 In. 190.00
Moriaga, Teapot, Pastel Floral Medallions On Lavender, Raised Design 75.00
Moriaga, Vase, Gray, Floral, Ornate Handles, 8 In. 90.00
Moriaga, Vase, Gray, Pink Flowers, White Vines, Flared Top, 4 3/4 In. 80.00
Moriaga, Vase, Peacock & Flowers, 2 Handled, 15 In. 125.00
Moriaga, Vase, Pink Floral & Scrolls On Green, 2 Handled, Bulbous, 7 In. 145.00
Moriaga, Vase, Tan, Pink & Lavender Floral, Green Wreath Mark, 9 In. 35.00

Mosaic Tile Company of Zanesville, Ohio, was started by Karl Langenbeck and Herman Mueller in 1894. Many types of plain and ornamental tiles were made until 1959. The company closed in 1967.

Mosaic Tile Co., Ashtray, Dog, Marked, 7 1/2 X 5 1/2 In. 65.00
Mosaic Tile Co., Box, Cigarette, Dog On Cover, Green, 8 1/2 X 4 In. 62.50
Mosaic Tile Co., Box, Dog Cover, Marked, 8 In. 50.00
Mosaic Tile Co., Box, Turtle Cover, Tan, Marked, 4 1/2 In. 35.00
Mosaic Tile Co., Figurine, Standing Bear, Black Semigloss Glaze, 6 In. 95.00
Mosaic Tile Co., Plaque, Lincoln's Head, Matte Blue, Hexagonal, 3 In. 22.00
Mosaic Tile Co., Tile Paperweight, A.Lincoln, White On Blue, 6 Sided, 4 In. 55.00
Mosaic Tile Co., Tile, Incised Cat, Hand-Painted, Marked, Square, 4 In. 15.00
Mosaic Tile Co., Tile, Pershing's Head On Blue Jasperware, Oblong, 3 X 5 In 30.00
Mosaic Tile Co., Tile, Rabbit On Green & Brick Red, Square, 6 In. 65.00
Mosaic Tile Co., Tile, Woodrow Wilson, White On Blue Jasperware, 3 In. 45.00
Mosaic Tile Co., Tile, 3 Gray Birds On Cream, Mottled, Square, 6 In. 25.00
Mosaic Tile Co., Tile, 3 Tiger Lilies On Cream, Square, 6 In. 19.50
Mosaic, Obelisk, Onyx, French, Flower On Square Base, 17 1/2 In. 95.00
Mosaic, Plaque, Ruins Of Pompeii, Oval, Framed, 10 X 7 1/2 In. 850.00

Moser glass was made by Kolomon Moser in the early 1900s. The Art Nouveau type glassware had detailed exotic enamel designs.

Moser, Atomizer, Gold Encrusted, Graphic Flowers & Birds, 9 1/2 In.	85.00
Moser, Bottle, Perfume, Cherry Red, Intaglio Floral, 4 Sided	125.00
Moser, Bowl & Underplate, Mayonnaise, Gold Engraved Bands, Signed	125.00
Moser, Bowl, Amber Crackle, Two Fish, Gold Lily Pads, Seaweed, 7 X 7 In.	350.00
Moser, Bowl, Finger, Pale Orchid, 14 1/2 X 4 In.	100.00
Moser, Cup & Saucer, Amber, Enamel Floral & Gold & Maroon Bands	195.00
Moser, Cup & Saucer, Demitasse, Green To Clear With Gold Trim	125.00
Moser, Dish, Jam, Green & Crystal, Silver & Gold Enamel, Gold Handle	80.00
Moser, Eggcup, Inverted Baby Thumbprint, Enamel Oak Leaves & Gold Seaweed	195.00
Moser, Ewer, Cranberry, Gold Enamel, Enamel Floral, 4 In.	55.00
Moser, Goblet, Amber, Intaglio Deer, 5 In.	60.00
Moser, Goblet, Tulip, Green Stem, Signed, 7 1/2 In.	55.00
Moser, Goblet, Wine, Cranberry To Clear, Applied Swirling, 9 In.High	85.00
Moser, Pitcher, Amberina, Diamond-Quilted, Oak Leaves, 10 Acorns, 4 1/2 In.	875.00
Moser, Pitcher, Green, Acorn & Enamel Decoration, Paperweight Base, 17 In.	295.00
Moser, Plaque, Sapphire Blue, Butterfly Center, Floral, Berries, Square, 7 In.	225.00
Moser, Pot, Jam, Transparent Green, Gold & Silver Foliage, Gold Handle	85.00
Moser, Punch Set, Cranberry, Gold Decoration, Signed, 15 Piece	490.00
Moser, Tumbler, Amber, Gold At Top & Stem	7.00
Moser, Tumbler, Green, Intaglio Flowers, 4 1/2 In.	65.00
Moser, Tumbler, Green, White Caramel Effect, Silver Gilt Beading, 4 In.	110.00
Moser, Tumbler, Juice, Amethyst, Enamel Floral & Birds, Gold Leaves	95.00
Moser, Tumbler, Purple, Intaglio Flowers, 4 1/2 In.	65.00
Moser, Tumbler, Translucent Green, Gold Filigree, Enamel Floral, 4 In.	38.00
Moser, Vase, Alexandrite, Footed, 12 Panels Deep Cut Blocks, 10 1/4 In.High	325.00
Moser, Vase, Amber, Cameo, Elephants & Palm Trees, Signed, 13 In.	595.00
Moser, Vase, Amber, Covered, Cut Glass, Signed, 11 1/2 In.	100.00
Moser, Vase, Amber, Warrior Band, Signed, 9 1/2 In.	150.00
Moser, Vase, Amber, Yellow, & Clear, Intaglio, Applied Cameo Flower, 11 In.	475.00
Moser, Vase, Amethyst Ground, Enameled Decoration, 16 In.High	175.00
Moser, Vase, Amethyst, Applied Bees, 11 1/2 In.	135.00
Moser, Vase, Amethyst, Jack-In-The-Pulpit, Enameled, Signed, 19 In.	225.00
Moser, Vase, Amethyst, Warrior Band, Signed, 4 In.	85.00
Moser, Vase, Blue, Enameled Fish, Seaweed, & Plants, 12 In.	225.00
Moser, Vase, Blue, Enameled Leaves & Bees, 10 1/2 In., Pair	95.00
Moser, Vase, Brown Ground, Enameled Flowers, Ribbed, 9 1/2 In.High	85.00
Moser, Vase, Bud, Cranberry, Gilded White Enamel Decoration, 6 1/2 In.	92.00
Moser, Vase, Bud, Dolphin Feet, White & Gold Enamel, 6 1/2 In.	105.00
Moser, Vase, Cranberry, Gold Enamel, Yellow Fernery, 4 1/2 In.	68.00
Moser, Vase, Cranberry, White & Gold Enamel Trim, 9 1/2 In.	50.00
Moser, Vase, Cranberry, Yellow & Blue Floral, Sea Dragons, 8 1/2 In.	265.00
Moser, Vase, Elephants & Palm Trees In Gold On Cobalt, 7 In.High	350.00
Moser, Vase, Emerald Green, Gold Warrior Band, Signed, 8 In.	95.00
Moser, Vase, Flower Form, Alexandrite, 9 In.High	100.00
Moser, Vase, Green To Clear, Intaglio Cut Iris, 13 In.	80.00
Moser, Vase, Jade Green, Malachite, Art Deco Nudes, Green Floral, 5 In.	58.00
Moser, Vase, Lemon To Blue Gray, Thorn Handles, Floral, 6 1/2 In., Pair	325.00
Moser, Vase, Opaque Yellow, Enameled, 10 In., Pair	220.00
Moser, Vase, Pilgrim, Cranberry, Blue & Yellow Flowers, Sea Serpent, 8 In.	275.00
Moser, Vase, Purple, Enamel & Bees Decoration, Ruffled Top, 12 X 15 In.	175.00
Moser, Vase, Royal Blue, Oriental Design Enameling, Signed, 14 In., Pair	195.00
Moser, Vase, Rubena, Intaglio Cut Lilies, Panels, 7 1/2 In.High, Pair	130.00
Moser, Vase, Tumbler Shape, Green Cased Glass, Cameo Forest Scene, 6 In.	135.00
Moser, Vase, Warrior Band, 10 Panel Shape, Deep Amethyst, 9 3/4 In.	125.00
Moser, Wine, Rhine, Cranberry, Oak Leaves, 2 Beetles & 6 Acorns Applied	395.00

Moss rose china was made by many firms from 1808 to 1900. It refers to any china decorated with the moss rose flower.

Moss Rose, Bowl, Vegetable, Covered, Gold Band, Haviland, 1880, 8 X 5 1/2 In.	50.00
Moss Rose, Bowl, 6 1/4 In.	28.00
Moss Rose, Chamberstick, White, 5 1/4 In., Pair	17.50
Moss Rose, Dinner Set, Child's, 25 Piece	14.00
Moss Rose, Pitcher, Hand-Painted, 5 In.	7.50
Moss Rose, Pitcher, 12 In.	45.00

Moss Rose, Plate, H.& Co., 7 1/2 In.	8.00
Moss Rose, Plate, Signed J.F.& Co., 7 In.	12.00
Moss Rose, Platter, Ironstone, 13 In.	18.00
Moss Rose, Platter, Meat, Gold Band, CFH, C.1880, Oval, 15 1/4 X 10 3/8 In.	50.00
Moss Rose, Saucer, Deep, Ironstone, Meakin	2.00
Moss Rose, Sugar, Covered, H.& Co.	22.00
Moss Rose, Tea Set, Demitasse, Butterfly Handles, 21 Piece	225.00
Moss Rose, Tea Set, Haviland, 27 Piece	185.00
Moss Rose, Teapot, H.& Co.	45.00

Mother-of-pearl glass, or pearl satin glass, was first made in the 1850s in England and in Massachusetts. It was a special type of mold-blown satin glass with air bubbles in the glass, giving it a pearlized color.

Mother-of-Pearl, Satin Glass, see also Satin Glass, Smith Brothers, Tiffany, etc.

Mother-Of-Pearl Glass, Bride's Basket, Pink, Quilted, Tufts Frame, 10 In.	575.00
Mother-Of-Pearl Glass, Creamer, Pink, Diamond-Quilted, Camphor Handle	45.00
Mother-Of-Pearl Glass, Creamer, Rose To Pink, Herringbone, Square Mouth	165.00
Mother-Of-Pearl Glass, Ewer, Rose To Pink To White, Heringbone, 8 3/4 In.	350.00
Mother-Of-Pearl Glass, Pitcher, Coin Spot, Rainbow, Frosted Handle, 10 In.	540.00
Mother-Of-Pearl Glass, Pitcher, Water, Pink, Frosted Handle, Square	450.00
Mother-Of-Pearl Glass, Pitcher, Water, Rainbow, Burnt Gold, Peach, & White	675.00
Mother-Of-Pearl Glass, Tumbler, Pink, Diamond-Quilted	65.00
Mother-Of-Pearl Glass, Tumbler, Yellow To White, Herringbone	150.00
Mother-Of-Pearl Glass, Vase, Apricot, Herringbone Pattern, 6 3/4 In.High	95.00
Mother-Of-Pearl Glass, Vase, Blue, Diamond-Quilted, Bulbous Base, 9 In.	95.00
Mother-Of-Pearl Glass, Vase, Blue, Quilted, Pedestal, Ruffle Trim, 8 In.	110.00
Mother-Of-Pearl Glass, Vase, Diamond-Quilted, Vaseline, Ruffled Top, 5 In.	195.00
Mother-Of-Pearl Glass, Vase, Tan To Brown, Diamond-Quilted, 7 In.	175.00
Mother-Of-Pearl Glass, Vase, White To Raspberry Top, Raindrop, 12 In.	250.00
Mother-Of-Pearl Glass, Vase, Yellow & White, 14 In.	195.00

Mother-of-Pearl, see Pearl
Moustache Cup, see Mustache Cup

Mont Joye is an enameled cameo glass made in the late nineteenth and the twentieth centuries by Saint-Hilaire Touvior de Varraux and Co.of Pantin, France. This same company produced De Vez glass.

Mt.Joye, Vase, Acid Cut, Enameled Pansies, Gold Rococo Design, 6 1/2 In.	162.50
Mt.Joye, Vase, Frosted Green Iridescent Ground, Enameled Flowers, 8 In.	285.00
Mt.Joye, Vase, Green Frosted, Enamel Violets, Gold Leaves & Vines, 6 1/2 In.	140.00

Mt.Washington Glass was made at the Mt.Washington Glass Co. located in New Bedford, Massachusetts. Many types of art glass were made there from 1850 to the 1890s.

Mt.Washington, see also Burmese, Crown Milano

Mt.Washington, Barrel, Biscuit, Square Body, Floral, Turquoise, 9 In.High	275.00
Mt.Washington, Basket, Satin, Blue To Pink, Meriden Footed Frame, 11 In.	475.00
Mt.Washington, Bowl, Bride's, Light Blue Satin, Pink Roses, Gold, 12 In.	250.00
Mt.Washington, Box, Collar & Cuff, Cuff Shape, Lusterless White, Lilacs, 5 In	80.75
Mt.Washington, Castor, Pickle, Red, Enameled	150.00
Mt.Washington, Creamer, Pink Flowers, Silver Trim	55.00
Mt.Washington, Dish, Candy, Green & White, Red Holly Berries, 4 1/2 In.	75.00
Mt.Washington, Ewer Vase, Blue Satin, Frosted Thorn Handle, Ribbed, 9 In.	175.00
Mt.Washington, Hat, Diamond-Quilted, Blue Threading, Polished Pontil	38.00
Mt.Washington, Hatpin Holder, Albertine, Mushroom, White To Blue, Enamel	125.00
Mt.Washington, Jar, Biscuit, Opaline	175.00
Mt.Washington, Jar, Biscuit, White, Ribbed, Floral, Silver Fittings, 8 1/2 In.	225.00
Mt.Washington, Jar, Cookie, Pairpoint, Pagoda, Yellow, Enameled, Silver Lid	250.00
Mt.Washington, Jar, Cracker, Lusterless Satin, Red & Wild Pink Roses	135.00
Mt.Washington, Jar, Cracker, Melon Ribbed, Opaque, Enameled, Silver Fittings	85.00
Mt.Washington, Jar, Cracker, Opalware, Yellow To Ivory, Metal Fittings	125.00
Mt.Washington, Jar, Mustard, Mint Green To White, Raised Pink Flowers, Rib	80.00
Mt.Washington, Jar, Pickle, Yellow To White, Pink Flowers, 6 5/8 In.High	120.00
Mt.Washington, Jar, Sweetmeat, Chrysanthemums On Green, Metal Rope Handle	245.00
Mt.Washington, Lamp, Burmese Shadings, Floral & Vine, 18 In.	375.00
Mt.Washington, Muffineer, Egg Shape, Pastel Violets & Leaves	125.00

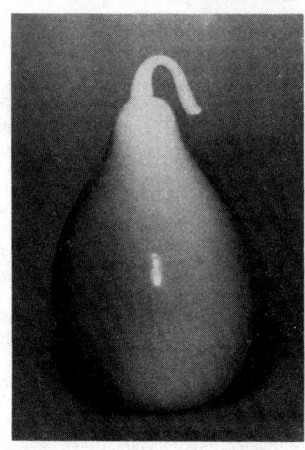

Mt.Washington, Pear

Mt.Washington, Muffineer, Egg Shape, Pink Flowers	125.00
Mt.Washington, Muffineer, Egg Shape, White Satin, Strawberries & Leaves	175.00
Mt.Washington, Muffineer, Melon Shape, Pansies	165.00
Mt.Washington, Muffineer, Satin Glass, Pink & Blue Dot Flowers, 4 In.	125.00
Mt.Washington, Pear *Illus*	450.00
Mt.Washington, Plate, Hand-Painted Yellow Roses, 15 In.	55.00
Mt.Washington, Plate, Lusterless White, Bronze, Pink, Spider Mums, 12 In.	37.50
Mt.Washington, Plate, Portrait, Artist Signed & Dated '99, 8 In.	24.00
Mt.Washington, Plate, White Lusterless, Hand-Painted Pansies, Folded Edge	20.00
Mt.Washington, Plate, White Satin, Painted Flowers, 6 1/4 In.	12.00
Mt.Washington, Plate, White Satin, Painted Flowers, 10 1/2 In.	25.00
Mt.Washington, Plate, White Satin, Painted Flowers, 17 1/4 In.	50.00
Mt.Washington, Pot, Mustard, Silver Plate Top, Shiny Yellow To White, Floral	25.00
Mt.Washington, Potpourri, Prunt On Cover, Inner Lid, Lusterless White, 6 In.	78.00
Mt.Washington, Rose Bowl, Pink Satin, Enameled Flowers, Silver Rim, 4 3/4 In	78.00
Mt.Washington, Rose Bowl, White Acid Finish, Ruffled Top, 6 In.	52.00
Mt.Washington, Rose Bowl, Yellow, Pansy Decoration, 4 1/2 In.High	175.00
Mt.Washington, Salt & Pepper, Blue Satin Glass, Diamond-Quilted, Pair	195.00
Mt.Washington, Salt & Pepper, Egg Shape, Columbian Exposition 1893 In Gold	85.00
Mt.Washington, Salt & Pepper, Egg Shape, Violets	85.00
Mt.Washington, Salt & Pepper, Figs, Floral Decoration, White & Beige	195.00
Mt.Washington, Salt & Pepper, Pink To White, Blue Enamel Flowers, Pair	85.00
Mt.Washington, Salt & Pepper, Tomato, Floral On Burmese & Violets On White	70.00
Mt.Washington, Salt & Pepper, Tomatoes, Ivy, Pink Carnations, Pewter Tops	135.00
Mt.Washington, Saltshaker, Blue, Melon Ribbed, Decorated	45.00
Mt.Washington, Saltshaker, Egg Shape, Pink Beige Satin, Yellow Floral	32.00
Mt.Washington, Saltshaker, Egg Shape, White Satin, Ivy Decoration	32.00
Mt.Washington, Saltshaker, Egg Shape, White, Pansies, "Cottage City"	30.00
Mt.Washington, Saltshaker, Egg, Pairpoint, Boat & Windmill, Pair	135.00
Mt.Washington, Saltshaker, Egg, Palmer Cox Brownie Decoration	70.00
Mt.Washington, Saltshaker, Egg, Violet Decoration, Metal Top	35.00
Mt.Washington, Saltshaker, Indio, Pansies	42.00
Mt.Washington, Saltshaker, Laydown Egg, Pansy Decoration	38.50
Mt.Washington, Saltshaker, Little Apple, Butterscotch, Leaf & Blue Dots	45.00
Mt.Washington, Saltshaker, Melon Rib, Green With Enameled Flowers	65.00
Mt.Washington, Saltshaker, Melon Rib, Squatty, Berry Lid, Floral	30.00
Mt.Washington, Saltshaker, Melon, Pansy Decoration	28.00
Mt.Washington, Saltshaker, Pink To White, Melon Ribbed, Daisies	35.00
Mt.Washington, Saltshaker, Tomato Shape, Melon Ribbed, Blue Flowers, Pink	75.00
Mt.Washington, Saltshaker, Tomato Shape, Pansies	38.00
Mt.Washington, Saltshaker, Tulip, Decorated	24.00
Mt.Washington, Saltshaker, Yellow, Melon Ribbed, Decorated	45.00
Mt.Washington, Toothpick, Yellow, Satin, Melon, Enamel Ferns & Berries	190.00
Mt.Washington, Vase, Amber & Blue Ribbon Glass, Floriform, Ruffled, 8 In.	100.00
Mt.Washington, Vase, Deep Amethyst To Clear Satin, Enamel Daisies, 11 In.	135.00

Mt.Washington, Vase, Flask Shape, Brown Yellow, Mums, Gold, C.1880, 10 In. 145.00
Mt.Washington, Vase, Jack-In-The-Pulpit, White, Hand-Painted Floral, 9 In. 110.00
Mt.Washington, Vase, Lavender Satin, Amethyst Neck, Daisies, 11 1/2 In. 135.00
Mt.Washington, Vase, Satin, Pink Blossoms, 2 1/2 X 3 1/2 In. 65.00
Mt.Washington, Vase, Verona Glass, Enamel Iris, Gold Trim, 8 In. 65.00
Mueller Mosaic, Tile, Nude Riding Dolphin, Bright Blues & Greens, 6 In. 55.00
Muffineer, Apple Blossom, Netted Ground With Pink Flowers 78.00
Muffineer, Aqua To Opalescent, Ribbed 45.00
Muffineer, Beatty Rib, Blue Opalescent 65.00
Muffineer, Blue Opaque, Clear Cased, Silver Plate Domed Lid, 6 In. 49.00
Muffineer, Cased Glass, Pink, Cone 65.00
Muffineer, Clear & Frosted, Royal Ivy, Pewter Type Top, 4 1/4 In. 65.00
Muffineer, Clear Ribbed Glass, Openwork Top, 5 1/2 In.High 22.00
Muffineer, Daisy Decoration, Footed 35.00
Muffineer, Dark Green Glass, 10 Panels, Domed Top 30.00
Muffineer, Hand-Painted Pink & Red High Relief Florals, Bulbous 55.00
Muffineer, Opalescent Feather 45.00
Muffineer, Opaque Blue, Florette Pattern 55.00
Muffineer, Oriental Porcelain, Birds & Flowers, Slotted Top 30.00
Muffineer, Pineapple Cone, Pink Cased Glass 52.00
Muffineer, Pink Flowers, Green Leaves, Enameled, Beaded, Japan 25.00
Muffineer, Porcelain, Hand-Painted Violets, Gold Top 16.00
Muffineer, Porcelain, Pale Green, Lavender & Yellow Flowers, Gold Top 30.00
Muffineer, Purple Pansies, Gold Top & 4 Feet 29.00
Muffineer, Ribbed, Opalescent Crisscross 35.00
Muffineer, Zipper Pattern, Silver Plate Top, C.1890 .... 20.00

Muller Freres, French for Muller Brothers, made cameo and other art
glass from the early 1900s to the late 1930s. Their factory was first located
in Luneville and later moved to Croismaire, France.

Muller Freres, Lamp, Forest Scene, Browns On Orange, 13 In. 1150.00
Muller Freres, Shade, Art Deco, Camphor Smoke Color 30.00
Muller Freres, Shade, Purple To Frosted Top, 6 In. 65.00
Muller Freres, Vase, Acid Cut Back, Scenic, 14 In. 395.00
Muller Freres, Vase, Cameo, Scenic, Woman, Yellow Ground To Dark Green, 12 In 308.00
Muller Freres, Vase, End-Of-Day Spatter, Brown & Orange, 9 1/2 In. 135.00
Muller Freres, Vase, Forest Scene On Yellow, Purple, & Frosted, 3 In. 235.00
Muller Freres, Vase, Gourd, Trees, Mountains, Lake, Green, Orange, Purple, 11 In 825.00
Muller Freres, Vase, Mottled Blue To Gray, Pink & Brown, Ovoid, 6 In. 105.00
Muller Freres, Vase, Ocher & Purple, Shepherdess & Flock, C.1900, 11 3/8 In. 400.00
Muller Freres, Vase, Peonies On Cream, Green, & Red, C.1900, 15 1/2 In. 850.00
Muller Freres, Vase, Purple & Orange, 5 X 5 In. 110.00
Muller Freres, Vase, Scenic, Blue With Orange, 11 1/2 In.High 375.00
Muller Freres, Vase, Scenic, Cameo, 10 X 5 In. 375.00
Muller Freres, Vase, Scenic, Cameo, 14 In. 350.00
Music, Album, see Hopalong Cassidy
Music, Book, Mutt & Jeff In The Wild & Wooley West, 1916 .... 5.00
Music, Box, see also Popeye, Music Box
Music, Box, Adler, Disc, 7 In. 300.00
Music, Box, B.A.Bremond, Switzerland, Cylinder, 8 Tune, 20 X 8 1/2 X 6 In. 895.00
Music, Box, Bremond, Inlaid Walnut Case, Orchestral, 6 Cylinders, 44 In. 3250.00
Music, Box, Calliope, Bells, 21 In. 1750.00
Music, Box, Columbia, Swiss, Inlaid Rosewood, Zither Attachment, 12 Tunes 600.00
Music, Box, Empress, Mira, Parlor, Grand, Claw Feet, 25 Discs 1650.00
Music, Box, Fabrique De Geneve, Rosewood Case, Marquetry, C.1850, 22 X 6 In. 300.00
Music, Box, French, Leather-Covered Writing Case 18.00
Music, Box, Harp-Piccolo, Inlaid Floral On Lid, 8 Classical Tunes, 22 In. 675.00
Music, Box, Mermod Freres, 11 1/2 In. Nickeled Cylinder, Inlaid Case, 8 Tune 695.00
Music, Box, Ohio Art, Hand Crank, Lithographed, Tin, 5 In. 8.00
Music, Box, Polyphon, Upright, 15 1/2 In. 1795.00
Music, Box, Polyphon, Upright, 19 5/8 In. .... 1695.00 To 1795.00
Music, Box, Regina, Double, Oak Case, 6 Tune, 15 1/2 In. 1000.00
Music, Box, Regina, Oak Case, 8 8-In. Discs 395.00
Music, Box, Regina, Oak Case, 12 In. Discs 900.00
Music, Box, Regina, Oak Case, 12 X 10 In. 425.00
Music, Box, Regina, Style 14, Coin Operated, Single Comb, Oak Case, 16 In. 1395.00

Music, Box, Regina, Style 14, Single Comb, 15 1/2 In. Disc, 8 Discs	750.00
Music, Box, Regina, Style 14, 15 1/2 In.	750.00
Music, Box, Regina, Style 34, Automatic Changer, Disc, Oak Case, 27 In.	5395.00
Music, Box, Regina, Table Model, Disc, 11 In.	795.00
Music, Box, Sankyo Echigo Jishi, Jpaanese Dancers On Top, C.1940, 8 In.	30.00
Music, Box, Stella, Disc, Oak Case, 15 1/2 In.	1500.00
Music, Box, Sublime Harmonie, Paneled Walnut & Tulip Case, 8 Tunes, C.1850	575.00
Music, Box, Swiss, Cylinder, 6 Tune, Inlaid Top, 25 X 8 X 10 1/2 In.	695.00
Music, Box, Swiss, Cylinder, 8 Tune, Religious Tunes, 17 1/2 X 8 1/4 In.	395.00
Music, Box, Swiss, Grand Piano, C.1880, 2 Tunes	125.00
Music, Box, Swiss, Light Wood Case, 11 In. Cylinder, 8 Tunes, 21 In.	375.00
Music, Box, Swiss, Walnut Case, Outside Handle Wind, 8 Tunes, 23 In.	375.00
Music, Box, Symphonion, Carved Rococo Case, Double Comb, 11 3/4 In. Discs	1750.00
Music, Box, Thorens, Carved Wood, Child With Basket Of Chicks, Fawn, Bird	35.00
Music, Bugle, Hunting, Charing Cross, London, Brass & Copper	50.00
Music, Bugle, Style Used By British In India, Brass	19.50
Music, Bugle, U.S.Regulation, Brass	22.50
Music, Calliope, Steam, Circus, Brass Whistles & Keys, Rubber Wheels	4500.00
Music, Calliope, Tangley, 44 Note, Roll Or Manual Operated, Gas Engine	5500.00
Music, Disc, Music Box, Metal, Dated 1897, 17 In.	3.50
Music, Drum, Civil War Period, Roped, Bird's-Eye Body, Red Paint	100.00
Music, Drum, Roped, Dictator On Metal Plate, 1888, Metal Hooks	55.00
Music, Flute, Wooden Case, C.1850	30.00
Music, Gramophone, C.1894, Case .... *Illus*	450.00
Music, Gramophone, Thorens, Excelda, Camera Shape, Portable, 12 In. Discs	37.50
Music, Guitar, see Disneyana, Guitar	
Music, Harmonica, see also Lone Ranger, Harmonica	
Music, Harmonica, M.Hohner, Marine Band, No.1896	9.00
Music, Harmonica, M.Hohner, 1881	6.00
Music, Horn, Child's, U.S.Mfg.Co., Red, White, & Blue, Statue Of Liberty, Tin	4.50
Music, Jukebox, A.M.I., C.1940, 78 RPM Records	495.00
Music, Jukebox, Colorama Theatres, 16 Mm. Color Film, 25 Cent Slot	695.00
Music, Jukebox, Mills Novelty Co., 1935	150.00
Music, Jukebox, Mills, Color Expressors, 78 RPM	450.00
Music, Jukebox, Wurlitzer, Wooden, Plays 78 RPM Records, C.1947	595.00
Music, Jukebox, Wurlitzer, 1938, 2 Piece Wooden Top, 5, 10, & 25 Cents	425.00
Music, Mandolin, Tortoiseshell, Inlaid Mother-Of-Pearl & Silver, 4 In.	15.00
Music, Nickelodeon, Singing Tower	40.00
Music, Orchestrelle, Solo, Style F, 116 Note Rolls	6000.00
Music, Orchestrion, Popper & Co., Jazz Band, 5 Ft.2 In. X 7 Ft.5 In.	3550.00
Music, Organ Orchestrion, Bursens, Antwerp, Dance, Roll Operated, C.1925	6000.00
Music, Organ, Arburo, Dance Hall, Accordion, Book Operated, 10 Ft.	5000.00
Music, Organ, Band, Wurlitzer Style, 103, 3 Rolls, 44 X 37 In.	3895.00
Music, Organ, Barrel, 10 Tune, Motor Or Hand Crank, 7 Ft.6 In. X 3 Ft.6 In.	4295.00
Music, Organ, Bijou Orchestrone, Munroe Organ Reed Co., Hand Roller	200.00
Music, Organ, Burssens, Dance, Book Operated, 97 Key, 10 X 10 Ft.	6000.00
Music, Organ, Burssens, Dance, Continuous Loop	9750.00
Music, Organ, Concert, Roller, 15 Rolls	250.00
Music, Organ, Crown, Oak, Geo.Bent Mfg.Co.	250.00
Music, Organ, Henri Camerlynck, Antwerp, Roll Operated, 11 Rank, 8 X 7 Ft.	1550.00
Music, Organ, Monkey, Portable, Europe, Hand Cranked, 18 X 10 X 12 In.	395.00
Music, Organ, Regal, Artisan, 5 Rank, Electronic Sound	4300.00
Music, Organ, Wicks, 3 Rank, Console Separate From Chest, 6 X 8 X 2 Ft.	1200.00
Music, Organ, Wilcox & White, Player, Electric, 43 Rolls	1895.00

The Phonograph, invented by Thomas Edison in the 1880s, has been made by many firms.

    Music, Phonograph, see also Disneyana, Phonograph

Music, Phonograph, Amberola 6	250.00
Music, Phonograph, Brunswick, Acoustic, Panatrope, Walnut Case	250.00
Music, Phonograph, Brunswick, Panatrope, Radiola, Walnut Case, Electric	275.00
Music, Phonograph, Busy Bee, Table Model, Brass Horn	200.00
Music, Phonograph, Columbia, Grafonola Regent, Desk, Oak, 46 X 30 X 29 In.	350.00
Music, Phonograph, Columbia, Grafonola, Baby Grand Piano Shape, Patent 1896	600.00
Music, Phonograph, Columbia, Grafonola, 78 RPM	65.00 To 175.00

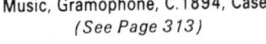

Music, Gramophone, C.1894, Case
(See Page 313)

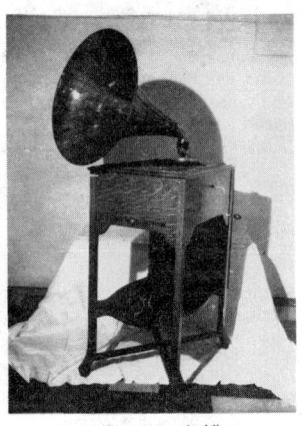

Music, Phonograph, Victor,
School Model, Oak,
Wooden Horn

Music, Phonograph, Edison Cylinder, Morning Glory Horn	385.00
Music, Phonograph, Edison, Amberola, Table Model, 4-Minute Cylinders	225.00
Music, Phonograph, Edison, Amberola, 4-Minute Blue Amberola Cylinders	250.00
Music, Phonograph, Edison, Diamond Disc, Floor Model, Oak Case, 50 Records	395.00
Music, Phonograph, Edison, Gem, Table Model, Horn	225.00
Music, Phonograph, Edison, Home Model, 1898	250.00
Music, Phonograph, Edison, Home, Table Model, Morning Glory Horn	475.00
Music, Phonograph, Edison, Morning Glory Horn, 2 Minute Cylinde	225.00 To 295.00
Music, Phonograph, Edison, Small Horn, 10 Records	225.00
Music, Phonograph, Edison, Standard, Morning Glory Horn	249.00 To 295.00
Music, Phonograph, Edison, Triumph	325.00
Music, Phonograph, Magnavox, Gooseneck Horn	25.00
Music, Phonograph, Outing, Carrying Case	150.00
Music, Phonograph, Pathe, L.Van Goitsenhoven, Brussels, Cylinder	395.00
Music, Phonograph, Phonocraft Corp., Jackson, Michigan, C.1928, Coin Operated	450.00
Music, Phonograph, Schoolhouse Model	675.00
Music, Phonograph, Sonora, Table Model, 78 RPM	54.00
Music, Phonograph, Standard, A, Table Model, Morning Glory Horn	175.00
Music, Phonograph, Standard, Disc, Blue Morning Glory Horn	200.00
Music, Phonograph, Victor, D	425.00
Music, Phonograph, Victor, E, Morning Glory Horn, Table Model	300.00
Music, Phonograph, Victor, E, Rear Mount, Small Elbow	250.00
Music, Phonograph, Victor, M, Front Mount	260.00
Music, Phonograph, Victor, R, Front Mount, Zinc Horn	265.00
Music, Phonograph, Victor, School Model, Oak, Wooden Horn .... *Illus*	800.00
Music, Phonograph, Victor, Style XVI, Floor Model, Mahogany Vase, Records	249.00
Music, Phonograph, Victor, VVIV, Table Model, 2 Doors In Front	70.00
Music, Phonograph, Victor, VVVI, Table Model, 2 Doors In Front	60.00
Music, Phonograph, Victrola, 78 RPM	80.00
Music, Piano, Ampico, Model B, Marshall & Wendell, Art Case, 1929, Bench	4750.00
Music, Piano, English, Barrel, 48 X 28 In.	1195.00
Music, Piano, Europe, Black Keys, White Sharps, Oil Painting, 6 Ft.9 In.	4500.00
Music, Piano, Grand, Square, Metropolitan, C.1830	2700.00
Music, Piano, Harrington, Grand, Player, 88 Note, Mahogany Finish, 5 Ft.	1395.00
Music, Piano, Metropolitan Of New York, C.1800, Square Grand	2700.00
Music, Piano, Piere Eich, 25 Rolls	3750.00
Music, Piano, Steinway & Sons, Grand, Square, 1877	1650.00
Music, Piano, Symphonique, Grand, Red Mahogany, Ampico Mechanism, 5 Ft.	2400.00
Music, Piano, Wurlitzer, Baby Grand, Player, Rolls, Bench	3000.00
Music, Pianoforte, Adam Ault, Pa., C.1785, Mahogany & Satinwood, Inlaid, 5 Ft.	750.00
Music, Player Pipe Organ, Marie Antoinette Cabinet	6500.00

Music, Sheet, see also Charlie Chaplin, Music Sheet, Disneyana,

Music Sheet, Elvis Presley, Music Sheet, Shirley Temple, Music Sheet

Music, Sheet, Al Jolson In Bombo, 1923, 11 X 14 In.	3.00
Music, Sheet, And They Called It Dixie Land, 1906, Negro Mammy & Girl	3.00
Music, Sheet, Chariot Race Of Ben Hur, E.T.Paull, 1894	3.50
Music, Sheet, Ching Ching Chinaman, 1923, Lon Chaney Picture, 11 X 14 In.	10.00
Music, Sheet, Come Josephine In My Flying Machine, 1910, 11 X 14 In.	4.00
Music, Sheet, Conqueror March, E.T.Paull, C.1897, 11 X 14 In.	5.00
Music, Sheet, Cotton, 1907, Black Dancers Picture	4.00
Music, Sheet, Daddy Longlegs, 1909, Mary Pickford Picture, 11 X 14 In.	6.00
Music, Sheet, Don't Blame The Germans, 1915, Pro-German, 11 X 14 In.	4.00
Music, Sheet, Don't Take A Chance, Take A Checker Cab, 1925, 11 X 14 In.	5.00
Music, Sheet, Everybody Rag With Me, Al Jolson, 1914	4.00
Music, Sheet, Everybody Shimmies Now, Mae West, 1918	5.00
Music, Sheet, Franklin Hose Song, Fire, 1940s, 10 X 6 In.	9.00
Music, Sheet, Gold Diggers, Lullaby Of Broadway, 1935	5.00
Music, Sheet, Great American, 1918, Theodore Roosevelt, 1919, 11 X 14 In.	4.00
Music, Sheet, Gregorian Chant, 1541, Handmade Linen Paper, 15 X 11 In.	30.00
Music, Sheet, I Love The U.S.A., 1914	4.00
Music, Sheet, It's A Smart Little Feller Who Stocked Up His Celler, 1920	7.50
Music, Sheet, Magnus, Union Forever, 1864, Hand-Tinted Woodcut At Top	12.00
Music, Sheet, Nigger Toe Rag, 1913, 14 X 11 In.	9.00
Music, Sheet, Ninth Regiment, N.Y., March, C.1870, 11 X 14 In.	5.00
Music, Sheet, Nobody Knows Where John Brown Went, Negro Man, 1909	4.00
Music, Sheet, Over There, 1918, Norman Rockwell Cover, 11 X 14 In.	10.00
Music, Sheet, Pershing's Crusaders, E.T.Paull, World War I, 14 X 11 In.	9.50
Music, Sheet, Plantation Medley, 1905	3.00
Music, Sheet, Ragtime Goblin Man, Devil Picture, 11 X 14 In.	3.50
Music, Sheet, Rally Cry Of Freedom, 1864, Hand-Tinted Woodcut At Top	12.00
Music, Sheet, Remember Pearl Harbor, 1942, 11 X 14 In.	2.50
Music, Sheet, Sergeant Mike O'Leary, 1918, 11 X 14 In.	3.00
Music, Sheet, So This Is College, 1929, John Held Cover	5.00
Music, Sheet, Suzy, Jean Harlow, 1936	3.00
Music, Sheet, Tenting On The Old Camp Ground, Kittredge, 1898	2.95
Music, Sheet, The Palmetto State Song, C.1860, Geo.O.Robinson	125.00
Music, Sheet, Tickled To Death, 3 Picaninnies On Cover, 1899	3.00
Music, Sheet, Tiptoe Through The Tulips With Me, 1929	8.00
Music, Sheet, Turn Back The Universe & Give Me Yesterday, 1916	4.00
Music, Sheet, Uncle Sammy March, 1904, 11 X 14 In.	3.50
Music, Sheet, When Yankee Doodle Learns To Parlez Vous Francais, 1917	2.95
Music, Sheet, Wreck Of The Titanic, 1912, 11 X 14 In.	4.50
Music, Sheet, Yankee Doodle Blues, Gershwin, 1917	3.50
Music, Sheet, Yankee Doodle Dandy, Cagney, 1932	3.50
Music, Sheet, You Will Miss The Colored Soldiers, Dabney, Ohio, 1907	50.00
Music, Trombone, Brass, Case	18.00
Music, Trumpet, Tibetan, C.1850, Thigh Bone, Silver & Brass Fittings, 12 In.	50.00
Music, Ukelele, Martin & Co., Canvas Case	45.00
Music, Violin, Antonius Stradivarius, Copy, Germany, Wood Case	75.00
Music, Zither, Metal	15.00

Mustache cups were popular from 1850 to 1900. A ledge of china or silver held the hair out of the liquid in the cup.

Mustache Cup, see also Coronation

Mustache Cup & Saucer, Austria, Yellow Roses On Brown & Green	25.00
Mustache Cup & Saucer, Austrian, Strawberries & Floral Sprays	25.00
Mustache Cup & Saucer, C.T.Germany, Pastel Flowers, Gold Trim	30.00
Mustache Cup & Saucer, Chocolate Size, White, Gold Decoration	35.00
Mustache Cup & Saucer, Elaborate Gold Decoration	32.00
Mustache Cup & Saucer, Embossed Floral & Scroll, Coffee Size, Pairpoint	51.50
Mustache Cup & Saucer, Floral	26.00
Mustache Cup & Saucer, Floral, Blue, Wine, & Salmon, Gold	18.00
Mustache Cup & Saucer, German Porcelain, Green Floral, Rococo Shape	42.00
Mustache Cup & Saucer, German, Pink Luster, Gold Beading, Leaf Panels	38.00
Mustache Cup & Saucer, Germany, Love The Giver In Gold, Floral	38.00
Mustache Cup & Saucer, Germany, Medallion Of Lady On Pink	35.00
Mustache Cup & Saucer, Haviland, Limoges, Pink Carnation, Gold Trim	35.00
Mustache Cup & Saucer, Kutani, Reserves Scenes, Gold, Melon Ribbed, C.1850	40.00

Mustache Cup & Saucer, Nippon, Blue Maple Leaf Mark, Lavender & Gold 85.00
Mustache Cup & Saucer, Orange Floral, Brownfield & Son 28.00
Mustache Cup & Saucer, "Papa, " Ornate 36.50
Mustache Cup & Saucer, RS Germany, Pastel Floral 29.00
Mustache Cup & Saucer, RS Prussia, White Floral On Green, Red Mark 60.00
Mustache Cup & Saucer, Silver Plate, Pairpoint 58.00
Mustache Cup & Saucer, Weimar, Germany, Pink Flowers On Ivory 18.00
Mustache Cup & Saucer, White & Pink Luster Porcelain 25.00
Mustache Cup & Saucer, White, Pink Roses, Gold Bows & Trim 26.00
 Mustache Cup, see also Coronation
Mustache Cup, Asymmetrical Whimsy, Floral, Twisted Openwork Handle 23.00
Mustache Cup, Floral Decoration, German Poem 25.00
Mustache Cup, Gilt Husband On Bright Blue, Gold Floral, 3 1/2 In. 32.50
Mustache Cup, Hand-Painted Red Flower 16.00
Mustache Cup, Nippon, Pink & Red Roses, Blue & Gold 35.00
Mustache Cup, Rosenthal, Hydrangeas, Gold Decoration, Artist Signed 20.00
Mustache Cup, Violets 12.00

Nailsea glass was made in the Bristol District in England from 1788 to 1873. Many pieces were made with loopings of colored glass as decorations.
 Nailsea, see also Kitchen Rolling Pin, Lamp
Nailsea, Cruet, Blue & White, 8 In. 90.00
Nailsea, Flask, Amber With White Loops, C.1800, 7 1/2 In.High 300.00
Nailsea, Flask, Perfume, Gold & Orange Loopings On Blue, 2 1/2 In. 40.00
Nailsea, Flask, Reclining, White Loopings & Red Stripes, 7 In. 85.00
Nailsea, Flask, White, Blue & Purple Loops, 7 1/4 In. 65.00
Nailsea, Gemel, White & Clear With Blue Rim, 7 1/2 In. 105.00
Nailsea, Perfume, Laydown, Pink & White Swirls, Red & Mica Overlay, 3 In. 15.00
Nailsea, Pitcher, White Loopings, 13 In. 129.00
Nailsea, Vase, Green Opalescent, Wide Ruffled Top, 7 X 10 In. 65.00

Nakara is a trade name for a white glassware made around 1900 that was decorated in pastel colors. It was made by the C.F.Monroe Company of Meriden, Connecticut.
Nakara, Box, Blonde Woman's Portrait On Lid, Aqua, Enamel, 4 In. 300.00
Nakara, Box, Cigars, Moss Green, Pink Floral On Lid & Base 350.00
Nakara, Box, Crown Mold, Deep Green, Pink Mums, Round, 8 In. 485.00
Nakara, Box, Crown Mold, Moss Green To Mauve, Pink & Purple Mums, 8 In. 500.00
Nakara, Box, Enameled Pink Flowers On Green, 4 In.Wide 225.00
Nakara, Box, Hinged Lid, Pale Blue, Raised Enamel Floral, Round, 2 In. 55.00
Nakara, Box, Portrait, 4 3/4 In.Diameter 275.00
Nakara, Humidor, Tobacco, Indian Chief Portrait 278.00
Nakara, Inkwell, Pink To Yellow, Brass Top, 4 X 4 In. 155.00
Nakara, Jar, Silver Plate Lid, Butterscotch, Floral, 4 3/4 X 7 In. 200.00

Nanking china is a blue-and-white porcelain made in China for export during the eighteenth century.
Nanking, Bowl, Blue & White, Scalloped, 9 In. 295.00
Nanking, Bowl, Blue & White, Shallow, 10 In. 30.00
Nanking, Bowl, Tea Slop, Blue & White, 6 X 3 In. 115.00
Nanking, Box, Brush, Covered, Blue & White, Rectangular, 7 X 3 1/2 In. 695.00
Nanking, Box, Covered, Blue & White, Round, 2 1/2 In. 145.00
Nanking, Cup & Saucer, Blue & White, Handleless, Gold Trim 59.00
Nanking, Flagon, Foo Dog Cover, Blue & White, Orange Peel, 11 1/2 In. 925.00
Nanking, Gravy Boat, Blue & White, Gold Trim, Twist Handle, 7 1/2 X 3 In. 165.00
Nanking, Mug, Blue & White, Chicken Skin, 1 1/2 Quart, 6 In. 625.00
Nanking, Platter, Blue & White, Octagon, 13 X 16 In. 145.00
Nanking, Platter, Willow, Orange, C.1810 ....*Illus* 750.00
Nanking, Tea Caddy, Blue & White, Gold Trim, 5 In. 375.00
Nanking, Tray, Spoon, Oval, Scalloped, 4 7/8 In. 75.00

Napkin rings were popular from 1869 to about 1900.
 Napkin Ring, see also Kate Greenaway, Napkin Ring, Kewpie,
 Napkin Ring, Satsuma, Napkin Ring, Tiffany Silver,
 Napkin Ring
Napkin Ring, Applied Wishbone, Silver Plate 10.50

Nanking, Platter, Willow, Orange, C.1810
(See Page 316)

Napkin Ring, Figural, Boy & Dog, Aurora

Napkin Ring, **Band On Leaf Shape Base,** Raised Buds	34.00
Napkin Ring, **Bone,** Openwork	7.50
Napkin Ring, **Brass,** Enameled, Cutout Floral & Scrolls	25.00
Napkin Ring, **Cloisonne,** Floral	25.00
Napkin Ring, **Cloisonne,** Geometric Pattern, Blue	12.00
Napkin Ring, **Coin Silver,** Engraved Jan.1, 1851 E.B.To E.G.F.C.	9.75
Napkin Ring, **Coin Silver,** Initials E.F.C., C.1850	8.75
Napkin Ring, **Cut Glass,** Blue To Clear, Oval, 2 1/4 In.	30.00
Napkin Ring, **Cut Glass,** Zipper, 8 Sided, 2 In.	30.00
Napkin Ring, **Dresden Type,** Applied Flowers	5.00
Napkin Ring, **Figural,** Acorn	60.00
Napkin Ring, **Figural,** Alligator, Silver Plate	110.00
Napkin Ring, **Figural,** Angel	38.00
Napkin Ring, **Figural,** Angel Hiding From Large Butterfly, Silver Plate	95.00
Napkin Ring, **Figural,** Antelope	65.00
Napkin Ring, **Figural,** Antlered Reindeer, Footed Base, Derby Silver Co.	60.00
Napkin Ring, **Figural,** Attached Horseshoe, Silver Plate	25.00
Napkin Ring, **Figural,** Barrel On Logs & Leaf, Mouse	85.00
Napkin Ring, **Figural,** Billy Goat, Rectangular Base, Meriden	120.00
Napkin Ring, **Figural,** Bird & Wishbone, "Best Wishes, " Derby, Quadruple	45.00
Napkin Ring, **Figural,** Bird On Branch Resting On Backs Of Two Boys	95.00
Napkin Ring, **Figural,** Bird On Leaf Base, Wing On Ring, Toronto 1142	85.00
Napkin Ring, **Figural,** Bird On Looped Perch, Double Leaf Base, Silver Plate	60.00
Napkin Ring, **Figural,** Bird With Fan	90.00
Napkin Ring, **Figural,** Bird With Ring On Tail, Derby Silver Co.	65.00
Napkin Ring, **Figural,** Bird With Wings Spread, Silver Plate	45.00 To 75.00
Napkin Ring, **Figural,** Bow & Quiver Of Arrows, Pedestal, Derby, No.316	70.00
Napkin Ring, **Figural,** Boy & Dog, Aurora	*Illus* 125.00
Napkin Ring, **Figural,** Boy Dressed For Work, Pushes Hoop, Silver Plate	110.00
Napkin Ring, **Figural,** Boy Feeding Dog	85.00
Napkin Ring, **Figural,** Boy Holding Ring On Head, Meriden	75.00
Napkin Ring, **Figural,** Boy Kneeling With Bowl Of Eggs, Meriden, No.269	50.00
Napkin Ring, **Figural,** Boy With Wings Holding Pair Of Bottles, Sled	95.00
Napkin Ring, **Figural,** Boys With Arms Outstretched, Silver Plate	65.00
Napkin Ring, **Figural,** Bud Vase, Spout & Flower, Ring On Top, Reed & Barton	75.00
Napkin Ring, **Figural,** Bunch Of Grapes, Silver Plate, Toronto, No.730	75.00
Napkin Ring, **Figural,** Butterfly & 2 Fans, Square Base, Rogers	45.00 To 65.00
Napkin Ring, **Figural,** Camel, Engraved Olive, Rogers Bros. Silver Plate	70.00
Napkin Ring, **Figural,** Cannon, Embossed Flowers & Leaves, Silver Plate	60.00
Napkin Ring, **Figural,** Cat & Dog, Ornate Oval Base, Meriden	150.00
Napkin Ring, **Figural,** Cat On Ring	65.00
Napkin Ring, **Figural,** Chair Made From Tree Limbs, Silver	55.00 To 75.00
Napkin Ring, **Figural,** Cherries & Leaf, Ring On Pedestal, Barbour Silver	49.50
Napkin Ring, **Figural,** Cherub Blowing Horn, Standing, Flowers	210.00

Napkin Ring, Figural, Cherub Pulls Sled That Holds Ring, Meriden 95.00
Napkin Ring, Figural, Cherub Wearing Sport Cap Holds Fish 60.00
Napkin Ring, Figural, Cherub, Silver Plate 85.00
Napkin Ring, Figural, Cherubs, Seated, Holding Barrel, Meriden, No.147 .... 75.00
Napkin Ring, Figural, Cherubs, Winged, Stepped Octagonal Base, Derby 65.00
Napkin Ring, Figural, Chick Looking Over Ring, Silver Plate 85.00
Napkin Ring, Figural, Chick On Wishbone, "Best Wishes, " Derby .... 35.00 To 65.00
Napkin Ring, Figural, Chicken & Rake, Webster Bros., N.Y. .... 47.50 To 95.00
Napkin Ring, Figural, Chicken & Wishbone & Egg, Derby Silver Plate 58.00
Napkin Ring, Figural, Chicken, Meriden 86.00
Napkin Ring, Figural, Child With Ring On Back 82.00
Napkin Ring, Figural, Circular Base Holds Ring, Acorn At Side, Meriden 35.00
Napkin Ring, Figural, Closed Bud On Leaf, Meriden, No.4404 .... 68.50
Napkin Ring, Figural, Cupid Hiding From Butterfly Perched On Ring 90.00
Napkin Ring, Figural, Cupid On Sled, Silver Plate 110.00
Napkin Ring, Figural, Cupid With Trumpet, Floral, Simpson Hall 150.00
Napkin Ring, Figural, Cupid, Simpson, Hall, Miller, Silver 80.00
Napkin Ring, Figural, Cupids Holding Ring 95.00
Napkin Ring, Figural, Dachshund With Ring On Back 65.00
Napkin Ring, Figural, Dog & Ring On Round Base, Tufts, Quadruple 40.00
Napkin Ring, Figural, Dog Chasing Cat 112.00
Napkin Ring, Figural, Dog In Doghouse On Each Side, Meriden 90.00
Napkin Ring, Figural, Dog, Glass Eyes 98.00
Napkin Ring, Figural, Dog, Sitting 32.00
Napkin Ring, Figural, Eagle Each Side, Meriden .... 48.50 To 60.00
Napkin Ring, Figural, Eagles, Rogers Silver Plate 40.00
Napkin Ring, Figural, Fan On Footed Base 85.00
Napkin Ring, Figural, Fox On Fancy Base, Derby Plate 47.50
Napkin Ring, Figural, Fox Sitting On Round Base, Rockford Silver Co. 31.00
Napkin Ring, Figural, Foxes Crouching, Ring Between Them 95.00
Napkin Ring, Figural, Girl With Ring On Back, Silver Plate 104.00
Napkin Ring, Figural, Greek Barrel Man, Tufts 225.00
Napkin Ring, Figural, High Collar With Bow Tie, Sterling Silver 30.00
Napkin Ring, Figural, Hooded Girl On Toboggan, Rogers 165.00
Napkin Ring, Figural, Horse With Ring On Back 45.00
Napkin Ring, Figural, Horseshoe .... 46.00 To 75.00
Napkin Ring, Figural, Horseshoe Leans Against Ring 48.00
Napkin Ring, Figural, Horseshoe, Ring On Footed Base, Tufts, 1881 .... 90.00
Napkin Ring, Figural, Kangaroo & Kiwi Bird, Australia, Silver 50.00
Napkin Ring, Figural, Kate Greenaway Bonnet Girl & 2 Geese, Silver 35.00
Napkin Ring, Figural, Kate Greenaway Girl As Soldier 150.00
Napkin Ring, Figural, Kate Greenaway Child Playing With Dog .... 85.00 To 125.00
Napkin Ring, Figural, Kate Greenaway Girl Playing Drum 165.00
Napkin Ring, Figural, Kitten 35.00
Napkin Ring, Figural, Knights With Armor, Silver Plate 75.00
Napkin Ring, Figural, Leaf Base, Pond Lily, Engraved, Meriden 39.50
Napkin Ring, Figural, Leaf Base, Strawberry On Double Ring 42.00
Napkin Ring, Figural, Lion With Ring On Back, Rogers Silver Plate 79.00
Napkin Ring, Figural, Llama On One Side, Peruvian Silver, 1 1/2 X 1 1/4 In. 37.50
Napkin Ring, Figural, Log & Leaf 50.00
Napkin Ring, Figural, Longtailed Peacock 64.00
Napkin Ring, Figural, Man With Rabbit Face, Tricorn Hat, 4 In.High 150.00
Napkin Ring, Figural, Mother Bird & Baby Birds, Silver Plate 100.00
Napkin Ring, Figural, Nest With 4 Eggs On Branches, Mother Bird Perched 65.00
Napkin Ring, Figural, Pair Of Seated Cherubs, Hall, Elton & Co. Plate 75.00
Napkin Ring, Figural, Parrot On Branch, Silver Plate 93.00
Napkin Ring, Figural, Parrot On Perch, Double Leaf Base, Silver Plate 59.00
Napkin Ring, Figural, Parrot Sitting On Open Fretwork Ring 45.00
Napkin Ring, Figural, Pheasants On Footed Plate, Aurora S.P.Co. 75.00
Napkin Ring, Figural, Pheasants, One On Each Side, Ornate Circular Base 130.00
Napkin Ring, Figural, Pond Lily Leaves, Frog On Each Side, Meriden 95.00
Napkin Ring, Figural, Porcelain, Baby Boy & Girl On Each Side 45.00
Napkin Ring, Figural, Prancing Horse Pulling Ring On Wheels, Silver 80.00
Napkin Ring, Figural, Prancing Horse Pulling Sulky, Rogers 115.00
Napkin Ring, Figural, Rabbit, Celluloid 5.50
Napkin Ring, Figural, Resting On Leaf, Silver Plate, Middletown Co. 47.50

Napkin Ring, Figural, Squirrel, Meriden

Napkin Ring, Figural, Robin, Engraved Ring, Oval Footed Base, Meriden, No.222	120.00
Napkin Ring, Figural, Satchel	49.00
Napkin Ring, Figural, Schoolboy Standing Next To Ring	95.00
Napkin Ring, Figural, Scottie Dog With Doghouse, Rogers Silver Plate	77.00
Napkin Ring, Figural, Sphinx, Fluted Ring On Back, Meriden	70.00
Napkin Ring, Figural, Sphinx, Ring On Back, 3 In.	98.00
Napkin Ring, Figural, Spread Winged Bird, Leaf, Oval Chased Ring	95.00
Napkin Ring, Figural, Squirrel Eating Nut, Floral, Rogers	80.00
Napkin Ring, Figural, Squirrel With Nut, Simpson, Hall, & Miller Silver	55.00
Napkin Ring, Figural, Squirrel, Meriden *Illus*	85.00
Napkin Ring, Figural, Stag With Antlers, Ring On Back, Meriden, N.H.	100.00
Napkin Ring, Figural, Thistle On Mound, Filigree Ring, Meriden	65.00
Napkin Ring, Figural, Tree Limb Chair	65.00
Napkin Ring, Figural, Tulip With Stem Next To Ring, Heart Base, Meriden	54.00
Napkin Ring, Figural, Turkish Dancers, Pelton Bros.	40.00
Napkin Ring, Figural, Viking	53.00
Napkin Ring, Figural, Winged Figures, Springfield Silver Plate Co.	45.00
Napkin Ring, Ivory, Carved Elephant In Relief	15.00
Napkin Ring, Ivory, Carved Snake	20.00
Napkin Ring, Ivory, Chinese Buddhas, Openwork	30.00
Napkin Ring, Nippon, Winter Scene	28.00
Napkin Ring, Noritake, Hand-Painted Floral, Half-Moon	10.00
Napkin Ring, Noritake, Hand-Painted Yellow Roses, Green Wreath Mark	10.00
Napkin Ring, Open Band, E.P.N.S.	7.00
Napkin Ring, Pewter, Hammered, 1/2 In. Colored Glass Setting	11.00
Napkin Ring, Plastic, Scenes On London In Black, Box Of 6	20.00
Napkin Ring, Russian Enamel, Gilt Silver, Semenova, C.1900, Pair	475.00
Napkin Ring, Russian Silver, Cutout, Bright Cut	48.00
Napkin Ring, Russian Silver, Floral Design, 1 3/8 In.	25.00
Napkin Ring, Russian Silver, Gold Washed, Bright Cut, Pair	98.00
Napkin Ring, Sheffield Silver, Hi Diddle Diddle, Child's	20.00
Napkin Ring, Silver Plate, Engraved Flowers & Berries, Victorian, Pair	19.00
Napkin Ring, Silver Plate, Mr.Fox Offering Miss Mole A Bouquet, Victorian	12.00
Napkin Ring, Silver Plate, The Big Bad Wolf, Child's, E.P.N.S.	20.00
Napkin Ring, Silver, Etched Kate Greenaway Girl Feeding A Yearling	55.00
Napkin Ring, Silver, Fly Mounted Upon Engraving, Coin	70.00
Napkin Ring, Sterling Silver, Beading, "Dorothy"	10.00
Napkin Ring, Sterling Silver, Chased, Victorian	8.00
Napkin Ring, Sterling Silver, French Mark, Decorated	15.00
Napkin Ring, Sterling Silver, Initial M, Flowers & Leaves	7.95
Napkin Ring, Sterling Silver, Initials S.E.G., Dec.25, 1916, Floral	7.95
Napkin Ring, Sterling Silver, Pierced, Victorian	8.00
Napkin Ring, Tortoiseshell, Laced With Ribbon, Gold Leaves	15.00
Napkin Ring, Wedgwood, Strawberries	8.00

Nash glass was made in Corona, New York, by Arthur Nash and his sons
after 1919. He worked at the Webb Factory in England and for the
Tiffany Glassworks in the United States.

Nash, Bowl, Gold Luster, Optic Rib, 16 In.Diameter	1250.00
Nash, Bowl, Punch, Chintz	480.00
Nash, Candlestick, Green Chintz Top, Clear Stem, Prisms, 11 3/4 In., Pair	225.00
Nash, Plate, Chintz, Clear With Orchid & Green Spirals, 6 1/2 In.	80.00
Nash, Plate, Chintz, Green & Blue Radials, 10 Sided, 8 5/8 In.	65.00
Nash, Plate, Chintz, Mottled Green, Blue Radials, 10 Sided, 8 In.	65.00
Nash, Plate, Chintz, Orange Iridescent, 8 1/2 In.Diameter	110.00
Nash, Plate, Chintz, 10 Sided, Mottled Green, Blue Radials, 8 5/8 In.	65.00
Nash, Tumbler, Blue & Green Iridescent, Chintz, Footed, 4 In.	110.00
Nash, Vase, Bowl Type, Buried Blue Lattice, 6 In.High	675.00
Nash, Vase, Bubbly Glass, Mottled Purple, Blue, & Ruby, Opaline Body, 10 In.	650.00
Nash, Vase, Chintz, Orange, Red Zipper, 6 1/2 In.	350.00
Nash, Vase, Chintz, Trumpet Shape, Footed, Blue Stripes, 6 1/4 In.High	150.00
Nash, Vase, Red & Silver Chintz, 19 In.High	2500.00
Nash, Vase, Trumpet, Chintz, Footed, Blue Stripes, 6 1/4 In.	150.00
Navarre, Vase, Black Bubbles, Aquamarine Overlay, Latticework, C.1930, 6 In.	700.00
Needlework, see Textile, Picture, Textile, Sampler	
Negro, Book, Comical Coons, Kemble, 1898	75.00
Negro, Potholder, Wall Type	5.00
Negro, Salt & Pepper, Aunt Jemima, 3 In.	6.50
Negro, Salt & Pepper, Aunt Jemima, 5 In.	6.50
Negro, Salt & Pepper, Brayton, Calif., 5 1/2 In.	4.50
Negro, Salt & Pepper, Topsy, 5 In.	8.50
Negro, Salt & Pepper, Topsy, 5 1/2 In.	6.50
Negro, Spooner, Boy	12.50

Netsuke are small ivory, wood, metal, or porcelain pieces used as the button on
the end of a cord holding a Japanese money pouch. The earliest date from
the sixteenth century.

Netsuke, Actor Dressed As Demon, Ivory, 2 3/4 In.	26.00
Netsuke, Actor With Monkey On Shoulder, Ivory, 2 1/2 In.	38.00
Netsuke, Bamboo Shoot, Stagshorn, C.1790	60.00
Netsuke, Double Gourd, Loose Ring At Waist, Ivory	325.00
Netsuke, Foo Dog, Paws Resting On Ball, Ivory, 1 1/4 X 1 3/8 In.	75.00
Netsuke, Fukurokuju, Standing, Laughing, Ivory, C.1850, Inscribed Kaigyokusai	700.00
Netsuke, Green Lacquer Mask, From Gigaku Drama, Wooden, C.1850	110.00
Netsuke, Head Of A Horse, Seal Form, Ivory, C.1750	875.00
Netsuke, Horse, Head Bent To Ground, Ivory, C.1750	225.00
Nestuke, Lotus Pod, Ripe, Moveable Seeds, Wooden, C.1850	240.00
Nestuke, Manju Type, Pierced Panels, Rooftops & Trees, Ivory, C.1850	200.00
Nestuke, Monkey On Straw Mat, Ivory, 2 X 7/8 In.	150.00
Netsuke, Man On A Carp, Ivory, Signed	147.00
Netsuke, Man, Sitting, Fan In Hand, Basket, 2 Masks, Ivory, Polychromed, 3 In.	48.00
Netsuke, Manju, Samurai, Seated, Nine Tail Fox, Ivory, C.1850	100.00
Netsuke, Mongoose Attacking 2 Cobras, Ivory	55.00
Netsuke, Monkey Group, Female & 2 Young, Stagshorn	150.00
Netsuke, No Mask, Deme Style, Boxwood, Inscribed Gyokosai	120.00
Netsuke, Oni, Clings To Side Of Rice Cauldron, Wooden, Horn Eyes, C.1850	425.00
Netsuke, Oriental Seated Lady Holding Plaque, Polychrome	20.00
Netsuke, Ox, Legs Folded Underneath, Ivory, Inscribed Masanao	325.00
Netsuke, Revolving Face, Sad To Happy, Ivory, 2 In.	28.00 To 39.00
Netsuke, Sage, Wrapping Himself In Robes, Ivory, C.1750	120.00
Netsuke, Sashi, Sea Dragon, Wooden, C.1850	175.00
Netsuke, Sashi, Wasp Alighted, Stagshorn, C.1790	350.00
Netsuke, Seated Man, Cloth Around Shoulders, Ivory, 1 1/2 X 1 3/8 In.	90.00
Netsuke, Sennin, Standing On Right Foot, Holding Double Gourd, Ivory, C.1750	100.00
Netsuke, Sennin, Standing, Gourd On Shoulder, Ivory, C.1750	150.00
Netsuke, Sennin, Standing, Leafy Cape & Skirt, Holding Fan, Ivory, C.1850	100.00
Netsuke, Sashi, Seated Beast, Wooden, C.1850, Inscribed Tomotada	350.00
Netsuke, Sitting Cat, Wooden, Artist Signed, 2 In.High	67.50
Netsuke, Temple Dog, Ivory, 2 In.	24.00
Netsuke, Turtle With Baby Turtle On Back, Carved Ivory, 2 In.	42.00
Netsuke, Two Frogs Sitting On A Log, Carved Ivory, 2 In.	42.00

Netsuke, Wasp & Pomegranate, Ivory, Inscribed Tomoyuki 275.00
New Jersey Pottery, Plate, James Garfield Picture, 1880, 8 1/4 In. 20.00

(N)   Newcomb Pottery was founded by Ellsworth and William Woodward at
      Sophie Newcomb College, New Orleans, Lousiana, in 1896. The work
      continued through the 1940s. Pieces of this art pottery are marked with the
      letter N inside the letter C.

Newcomb, Planter, Floral On Cream, 3 Ball Feet, 9 1/4 In. 135.00
Newcomb, Plate, White, Black, & Grays Pinwheel, Pierced, 7 3/4 In. 67.50
Newcomb, Vase, Beehive Shape, Matte Green, Horizontal Ribbing, 3 In. 115.00
Newcomb, Vase, Begonia Blossoms On Blue, 5 In. 175.00
Newcomb, Vase, Blue & Pink Flowers & Leaves, 7 3/4 In.High 125.00
Newcomb, Vase, Blue & Violet Matte, Abstract Floral Neck, CMC, 7 1/4 In. 185.00
Newcomb, Vase, Blue, Pink Flowers, 2 3/4 In. 125.00
Newcomb, Vase, Matte Blue, Stylized Leaves & Flowers, 2 3/8 In. 74.00
Newcomb, Vase, Matte Yellow, Horizontal Lines, Wide Mouth, 4 1/2 In. 115.00
Newcomb, Vase, Moon Through Spanish Moss, Blue, A.F., 5 In. 200.00
Newcomb, Vase, Moon Through Spanish Moss, Signed, 8 X 3 1/4 In. 265.00
Newcomb, Vase, Pink Morning Glories On Slate Blue, Bailey, 8 1/2 In. 185.00
Newcomb, Vase, Raised Cream Begonias On Blue, 6 In. 175.00
Newcomb, Vase, Wide Mouth, Bulbous, Horizontal Encircling Lines, JM, 4 In. 35.00

Newhall Porcelain Manufactory was started at Newhall, Shelton,
Staffordshire, England, in 1782. Simple decorated wares were made.
Between 1810 and 1825, the factory made a glassy bone porcelain marked with
the factory name.

Newhall, Bowl, Pearlware, Window Pattern, Transfer Printed, C.1790, 9 3/4 In. 110.00
Newhall, Cup & Saucer, Open Window 68.00
Newhall, Cup & Saucer, Oriental Figures 70.00
Newhall, Teabowl & Saucer, Enamel Floral & Ribbon, C.1800 .... 45.00

NILOAK   Niloak Pottery (Kaolin spelled backwards) was made at the Hyten
         Brothers Pottery in Bremen, Arkansas, between 1909 and 1946. Although
         the factory did make cast and molded wares, collectors are most interested in
         the marbleized art pottery line.

Niloak, Bowl, Miniature, Rose Shading, 3 In.Diameter 12.00
Niloak, Bowl, Swirl, Art Letter Marking, 10 5/8 X 3 In. 37.50
Niloak, Ewer, Ivory, 7 In. 7.00
Niloak, Ewer, Mottled Pastel Green, 7 3/4 In. 3.50
Niloak, Figurine, Dog, Brown, Original Label, 3 In. 15.00
Niloak, Figurine, Hen, Dark Brown Glaze, Marked Niloak, 6 1/2 In. 9.50
Niloak, Figurine, Rooster, Dark Brown Glaze, Marked Niloak, 8 1/2 In. 9.50
Niloak, Lamp Base, Signed 40.00
Niloak, Pitcher, Ivory, 4 3/4 In. 7.00
Niloak, Pitcher, Spherical, Lavender, 5 In. 7.00
Niloak, Planter, Elephant, Medium Blue, High Glaze, 7 In.Long 11.00
Niloak, Planter, Pink Elephant Standing On A Drum, 6 In. 5.00
Niloak, Planter, Swan, Blue, 5 In. 7.00
Niloak, Pocket, Wall, Swirl, 4 1/2 In. 22.50
Niloak, Shoe, Dutch, Blue, 4 3/4 In. 7.00
Niloak, Urn, Classic Shape, Rolled Out Top, Marbleized, 8 In. 40.00
Niloak, Vase, Baluster, Marbleized, 6 1/4 In.High 35.00
Niloak, Vase, Marbleized Swirls, Brown, Aqua, Cream, 4 1/2 In. 20.00
Niloak, Vase, Marbleized, Signed, 8 X 5 In. 35.00
Niloak, Vase, Plum Matte, Shells, 4 Openings, 7 In. 15.00
Niloak, Vase, Rose Color, Pedestal, Semicircular Cuts On Rim, 6 1/2 In. 16.00
Niloak, Vase, Shell, Plum Matte, 5 Openings, 7 In. 10.00
Niloak, Vase, Swirl, Blue & Brown, Ivory Inside, 8 In. 25.00
Niloak, Vase, Swirl, Blue, Gray, White, & Brown, Impressed Mark, 10 1/2 In. 30.00
Niloak, Vase, Swirl, Paper Label, 4 1/2 In. 17.00
Niloak, Vase, Swirl, 6 1/2 In. 14.00
Niloak, Vase, Swirl, 8 In. .... Illus 14.00

Nippon-marked porcelain was made in Japan after 1891.

Nippon, Ashtray, Cigar, Cigar & Matches On Brown, Marked 30.00
Nippon, Ashtray, Dutch Water Scene 23.00

Niloak, Vase, Swirl, 8 In.
(See Page 321)

Nippon, Ashtray, Floral Decoration	28.00
Nippon, Ashtray, Lavender Floral On Yellow, Triangular, Green M Mark, 16 In.	30.00
Nippon, Ashtray, Sailing Ship Decoration, Square, 4 1/4 In.	37.50
Nippon, Ashtray, Scenic, Brown & Black Trim, Wreath Mark	42.00
Nippon, Ashtray, Scenic, 4 Holders, Beading, Green M Mark, Square, 16 In.	25.00
Nippon, Ashtray, Ships, Jeweled, Square, Green Wreath Mark, 5 In.	45.00
Nippon, Ashtray, Sunset Scene, Turquoise Beading, Green M Mark, 16 In.	25.00
Nippon, Ashtray, Triangular, Art Nouveau Pattern, Palm Scene Inside	30.00
Nippon, Ashtray, Triangular, Horse's Head In Bottom, Geometrics, 5 In.	32.00
Nippon, Ashtray, 4 Lips, Round, 6 In.	28.00
Nippon, Barrel, Cracker, Finial On Lid, Green M Mark, 8 1/2 In.	90.00
Nippon, Barrel, Cracker, Pink Dragon On Charcoal, 3 Footed, 9 In.	80.00
Nippon, Basket, Black, Diamond Shape Floral Medallions, Gold Handle, 7 In.	42.50
Nippon, Basket, Pink Rose In Cameos, Gold, Blue Trim, 4 In.	12.00
Nippon, Basket, Serving, Pink & Blue Floral, Gold Concentrics, 9 1/2 X 7 In.	32.00
Nippon, Berry Set, Butterflies & Floral On White, C.1800, 7 Piece	45.00
Nippon, Berry Set, Pyramid Scene, Palm Trees, Green & Black, 8 Sided, 7 Piece	95.00
Nippon, Berry Set, Sunset Lake Scene, Gold Rim, Green Wreath, 6 Piece	90.00
Nippon, Berry Set, Violets, Openwork Handles, Gold, Half Sun Mark, 7 Piece	45.00
Nippon, Bonbon, Gold Decoration, Handled	20.00
Nippon, Bonbon, Scenic, Black & White, Gold Trim, Green M Mark, 8 1/2 In.	15.00
Nippon, Bottle, Cologne, Bulbous, Floral, Gold Beading, Cobalt Trim	45.00
Nippon, Bottle, Cologne, Pink Roses & Geometrics, Gold Band, 4 3/4 In.	65.00
Nippon, Bottle, Cologne, Raised Gold Floral, Pink, Blue, 5 1/2 In.	55.00
Nippon, Bottle, Perfume, Cobalt & Gold Lforal & Scrolls, 5 In.	70.00
Nippon, Bottle, Perfume, Gold Floral Stopper, Gold, Beading, 4 In., Pair	60.00
Nippon, Bottle, Perfume, Green, Gold Beading, Roses, Metro Mark, 4 In.	22.00
Nippon, Bottle, Perfume, Violets On Pastel Green, Gold Lattice, 5 In.	48.00
Nippon, Bowl & Ladle, Mayonnaise, Lavender & Gold Floral, Gold Lattice	35.00
Nippon, Bowl & Underplate, Cucumber, Pink & Gold Border Inside Rim, 7 In.	42.50
Nippon, Bowl & Underplate, Cucumber, Pink Roses, Green Ferns, 7 1/4 In.	65.00
Nippon, Bowl & Underplate, Floral, Jeweled, Gold, Perforated, Blue Mark, 8 In.	30.00
Nippon, Bowl & Underplate, Strawberry, Perforated, Roses, Gold, 7 1/2 In.	48.00
Nippon, Bowl, Azalea Border, Gold, Scalloped, 2 Incised Handled, Oval, 6 In.	8.50
Nippon, Bowl, Bisque Finish, House & Lake Scene, Jeweled Rim, Fluted, 7 In.	24.00
Nippon, Bowl, Blown-Out Acorns & Leaves, 6 1/2 In.	55.00
Nippon, Bowl, Blown-Out Black Walnuts, Basket Weave, Leaf Inside, 7 1/2 In.	85.00
Nippon, Bowl, Blown-Out Peanuts, Basket Weave, Leaf Inside, 7 1/2 In.	85.00
Nippon, Bowl, Blown-Out Pecans, Basket Weave, Leaf Inside, 7 1/2 In.	85.00
Nippon, Bowl, Blue, Swimming Swans, Ruffled, Elite, 7 1/4 In.	65.00 To 75.00
Nippon, Bowl, Cobalt Floral Medallions, Light Blue, Green M Mark, 9 In.	80.00
Nippon, Bowl, Cobalt, Rouge, & Gold, 6 1/2 In.	18.50
Nippon, Bowl, Cracker & Dip, Covered, Floral Lei, Gold Roping, 9 1/2 In.	32.00
Nippon, Bowl, Cutout Cobalt Handles, Pink Floral, Gold, Scalloped, 10 In.	45.00
Nippon, Bowl, Cutout Handle, Bird With Roses, Signed, 7 3/4 In.	8.00
Nippon, Bowl, Deer On Lakeshore, Sunset, 4 Sides, Green Mark, 7 1/4 In.	48.00

Nippon, Bowl, Eagles & Floral On Blue, Gold Handles, Green M Mark, 9 1/2 In. 78.00
Nippon, Bowl, Floral, Gold, Gold Handles, 4 Sections, Green Mark, 10 In. 25.00
Nippon, Bowl, Footed, Oval, Castle Scene, Matte, Green Mark, 8 1/2 In. 42.00
Nippon, Bowl, Fruit, Tree Trunk & Forest Design, Gold Feet, Grapes, 11 In. 58.00
Nippon, Bowl, Fruits, Nuts, & Leaves In Autumn Coloring, Fluted, 7 1/4 In. 22.00
Nippon, Bowl, Gold Beading, Feet, & Panels, Pastel Floral, 7 1/2 In. 48.00
Nippon, Bowl, Gold Eagles & Shields, Blue Edge, Handled, Wreath Mark, 10 In. 22.00
Nippon, Bowl, Gold Geometrics & Beading, Pink & Red Roses, 9 In. 85.00
Nippon, Bowl, Gold Outlined Floral, Black Trim, Green Maple Leaf Mark, 8 In. 75.00
Nippon, Bowl, Greek Key Border, 6 Sections Of Roses, Gold Trim, 9 X 8 In. 20.00
Nippon, Bowl, Nut, Blown-Out Nuts, Leaves, Satin Finish, 8 In. Diameter 45.00
Nippon, Bowl, Nut, Chestnuts 17.00
Nippon, Bowl, Nut, Marsh Scene, Jeweled 28.50
Nippon, Bowl, Nuts & Leaves, Footed, Textured Basket Weave, 8 1/2 In. 38.00
Nippon, Bowl, On Pedestal, Bowl Form Lid, 3 Footed, Floral, Blue Band, 10 In. 88.00
Nippon, Bowl, Open Handled, Grapes, Roses, & Gold Floral, Blue Mark, 10 In. 40.00
Nippon, Bowl, Painted Windmill Inside, Jeweled, 2 Handles, 6 X 2 1/2 In. 19.00
Nippon, Bowl, Pink & Red Rose Medallions, Gold Feet & Beads, 7 1/4 In. 90.00
Nippon, Bowl, Pink & White Floral On Browns, Gold Beading, 9 1/2 X 3 In. 45.00
Nippon, Bowl, Pink Floral On Blue, Gold Trim, Pierced Handle, 5 1/2 In. 8.00
Nippon, Bowl, Pink Floral, Octagonal, Rising Sun Mark, 10 In. 28.00
Nippon, Bowl, Pink, Red, & Yellow Roses, Gold Dots, Footed, 7 1/2 In. 28.00
Nippon, Bowl, Red & Pink Roses, Cobalt & Gold Design, 9 X 3 In. 45.00
Nippon, Bowl, Red & White Cherry Blossoms, Pedestal, 9 1/2 X 3 In. 30.00
Nippon, Bowl, Rice, Pedestal, Floral, Gold, Marked 10.00
Nippon, Bowl, Ruffled, Limb Handles, Blossoms Around Edge, 7 In.Diameter 55.00
Nippon, Bowl, Scenic, Black & White, Gold Handles & Trim, 10 1/2 In. 35.00
Nippon, Bowl, Soup, Pink Floral, Green Trim 12.00
Nippon, Bowl, Square, Trees, Swan On Lake, Gold Trim, 5 3/4 In.Diameter 22.50
Nippon, Bowl, Sunshine Scene, Fruit, Gold Handles & Trim, 8 In.Diameter 36.00
Nippon, Bowl, Tapestry, Lovers Scene, Claw Feet, Rising Sun Mark, 6 1/2 In. 155.00
Nippon, Bowl, Triangular, Landscape, Beaded Folded Rim, Green Mark, 7 1/2 In. 65.00
Nippon, Bowl, Yellow Flowers, Blue, Green, & Gold, Handled, 5 1/4 In. 7.50
Nippon, Bowl, 4 Floral Medallions, Roses Center, Gold Handles, 9 1/2 In. 45.00
Nippon, Bowl, 4 Scenic Medallions, Gold Handles, Green M Mark, 8 1/2 In. 20.00
Nippon, Box, Collar Button, Collar Button Shape Lid, Floral 15.00
Nippon, Box, Covered, Scenic Decoration, Gold Enameling, 4 1/2 X 3 1/2 In. 65.00
Nippon, Box, Hairpin, Covered, Orange Poppies, Gold Trim, Marked 12.00
Nippon, Box, Powder, Blue Floral, Cobalt Jewel On Each Flower, Yellow 15.00
Nippon, Box, Stamp, Rooster On Lid, Cloud Form Base, Slant Top, Double Bin 45.00
Nippon, Box, Stamp, Slanted Top, Art Nouveau Rooster, Double Holder Inside 25.00
Nippon, Box, Trinket, Gold Swirled Lid, 2 White Flying Geese, 4 X 3 In. 28.00
Nippon, Box, Trinket, Indian Maiden On Lid, Green M Mark, 4 1/2 X 3 1/4 In. 65.00
Nippon, Box, Trinket, Kidney Shape, Light Blue, Grapes, Gold Beads, 6 X 4 In. 45.00
Nippon, Box, Trinket, Scene On Cover, Quilted Design, Square, 2 1/2 In. 35.00
Nippon, Bread & Butter Set, Round Floral Tray, Pierced Handles, 7 Piece 55.00
Nippon, Bridge Set, Scenic Centers, Morieye, 4 Piece 30.00
Nippon, Butter Pat, Gold, Floral, Green Mark 2.50
Nippon, Butter Pat, Open Handle, Roses On Raised Green, Yellow Border 5.00
Nippon, Butter Pat, Pink Flowers, Gold 5.00
Nippon, Butter, Covered, Green & Pink Floral, Beading, Blue M Mark, 7 3/4 In. 45.00
Nippon, Butter, Covered, Liner 53.00
Nippon, Cake Set, Artist Signed, Marked, 5 Piece 60.00
Nippon, Cake Set, Bird With Spread Wings, Floral, 7 Piece 60.00
Nippon, Cake Set, Gold Decoration, Green Mark, 7 Piece 28.00
Nippon, Cake Set, Lavender & Pink Flowers, Butterlies, & Birds, 5 Piece 32.00
Nippon, Cake Set, Pink Flying Dragon On Charcoal, Marked TT, 5 Piece 58.00
Nippon, Cake Set, Roses Center, Floral & Gold Border, 5 Piece 20.00
Nippon, Cake Set, Violets, Gold, Handled Plate, 7 Piece 55.00
Nippon, Candleholder, Black & Gold, Maroon Cat On Tiered Base, 10 In., Pair 135.00
Nippon, Candleholder, Diamond Shape Floral Medallions On Black, 6 1/4 In. 35.00
Nippon, Candleholder, Geometrics On Beige & White Squares, Gold, 5 1/2 In. 20.00
Nippon, Candleholder, Red Poppies, Rising Sun Mark, 7 1/2 In., Pair 38.00
Nippon, Candleholder, Scenic, Black & White, Gold Trim, 6 In., Pair 40.00
Nippon, Candleholder, Tan 5-Petaled Flowers, Black Geometrics, Gold, 8 In. 38.00
Nippon, Candleholder, White Floral On Light Blue, Greek Key, 8 In., Pair 100.00

Nippon, Candlestick, Rosettes On Green, Gold Bands, Brown, Green Mark, 8 In.	20.00
Nippon, Casserole, Covered, Cobalt Floral, Royal Sometuke, 8 In.	22.50
Nippon, Celery Set, Canoe Shape, Egyptian Style, Green M Mark, 7 Piece	70.00
Nippon, Celery Set, Floral & Lattice, Black & White, Gold Trim, 7 Piece	40.00
Nippon, Celery Set, Pastel Block Panels & Black Stripes, 5 Piece	16.00
Nippon, Celery, Lake Scene, Green & Orange	23.00
Nippon, Celery, Pink Roses On Yellow, Gold, Open Handles, 12 X 5 1/2 In.	24.00
Nippon, Celery, Pink, White, & Red Roses, Gold Bands, 11 3/4 X 5 1/2 In.	58.00
Nippon, Celery, Raised Designs, Flowers, & Dots, Maple Leaf Mark, 11 7/8 In.	20.00
Nippon, Chalice, Royal Blue, Gold Band, Egyptian Figures, Handled, 9 In.	175.00
Nippon, Chocolate Pot, Floral & Gold, Gold Handle, 8 1/2 In.	65.00
Nippon, Chocolate Pot, Geisha Girls Scene On Light Blue, Gold At Top	32.50
Nippon, Chocolate Pot, Gilt Berries & Leaves, Gold Handle & Lid, 9 In.	85.00
Nippon, Chocolate Pot, Gold, Pastels, Jewels, Orchids, Blue Mark, 10 1/2 In.	50.00
Nippon, Chocolate Pot, Ribbed, Chrysanthemums, Raised Gold, 10 1/4 In.	60.00
Nippon, Chocolate Pot, Scalloped Base & Top, Raised Gold, Cobalt, Blue Mark	55.00
Nippon, Chocolate Pot, Slip Medallions, Roses, Gold Finial	50.00
Nippon, Chocolate Pot, Yellow Roses On Red Pink, Gold Trim	78.00
Nippon, Chocolate Pot, Yellow, 4 Floral & Geometric Medallions On Black	38.00
Nippon, Chocolate Set, Black, 4 Diamond Shape Floral Medallions, 11 Piece	135.00
Nippon, Chocolate Set, Cobalt & Orange On White, People, Flowers, 9 Piece	45.00
Nippon, Chocolate Set, Dragons, 13 Piece	90.00
Nippon, Chocolate Set, Floral, Black Branches, Gold Handles, 13 Piece	125.00
Nippon, Chocolate Set, Floral, Green M In Wreath Mark, 13 Piece	65.00
Nippon, Chocolate Set, Geese In Flight On Aqua, Gold, Beading, 14 Piece	125.00
Nippon, Chocolate Set, Geisha Girls Scene, Gold & Red Trim, 13 Piece	90.00
Nippon, Chocolate Set, Geometric & Floral, Black & White, Gold, 13 Piece	85.00
Nippon, Chocolate Set, Gold Beading & Encrusted Border, 13 Piece	60.00
Nippon, Chocolate Set, Gold Flowers & Ferns, 7 Piece	45.00
Nippon, Chocolate Set, Gold Flowers & Stems On Cobalt Ground, 4 Piece	150.00
Nippon, Chocolate Set, Gold On White, Turquoise & Coral Jewels, 9 Piece	200.00
Nippon, Chocolate Set, Green Bisque, Fox Hunt Scene, Gold, 13 Piece	180.00
Nippon, Chocolate Set, Pagoda Type House Scene, People In Windows, 11 Piece	95.00
Nippon, Chocolate Set, Pink Flowers, Brown Trim, 9 Piece	45.00
Nippon, Chocolate Set, Pink Roses, Cobalt Blue Trim, 9 Piece	50.00
Nippon, Chocolate Set, Pink, Lavender, & Yellow Flowers, 11 Piece	55.00
Nippon, Chocolate Set, Raspberries, Gold, Maple Leaf Mark, 5 Piece	65.00
Nippon, Chocolate Set, Robin's-Egg Blue, Flying Geese, 5 Piece	85.00
Nippon, Chocolate Set, Scenic, Enamel & Etched, Green Mark, 9 Piece	325.00
Nippon, Chocolate Set, Scenic, Gold Trim, Green Wreath Mark, 13 Piece	150.00
Nippon, Chocolate Set, White & Red Roses, Gold, 12 In. Tray, 10 Piece	85.00
Nippon, Chocolate Set, White Herons On Light Blue, 12 Piece	65.00
Nippon, Chocolate Set, Yellow & Pink Roses, Black & Gold Bands, 9 Piece	45.00
Nippon, Coaster, Sailboats On Ocean, Satin Finish	10.00
Nippon, Coffeepot, Raised White Dragon On Dark Gray, Jewel Eyes	35.00
Nippon, Compote, Covered, Miniature, Pink Wild Roses, Gilt, 2 In. High	15.00
Nippon, Compote, Geisha Girls Scene, Gold & Red Trim, 9 In.	45.00
Nippon, Compote, Gold Handles, Scenic, On Standard, 5 X 8 In.	40.00
Nippon, Compote, Hand-Painted Flowers & Leaves, Red Rust, 3 Feet, 6 1/2 In.	7.50
Nippon, Compote, Scenic, Black & White, Gold Trim, Green M Mark, 7 In.	18.00
Nippon, Condiment Set, Blue, Pink, & Yellow, Floral Bouquest, 4 Piece	30.00
Nippon, Condiment Set, Sailboat Scene, Blue, Rising Sun Mark, 4 Piece	38.00
Nippon, Condiment Set, Scenic, Autumn Colors, Rising Sun Mark, 4 Piece	29.00
Nippon, Condiment Set, Scenic, Green Wreath Mark, 6 Piece	22.00
Nippon, Condiment Set, White, Raised Gold Border With Beading, 5 Piece	45.00
Nippon, Container, Condensed Milk, Pink Roses Encased With Black	30.00
Nippon, Container, Marked Talc, Bluebird & Flowers	25.00
Nippon, Creamer, Babydoll Face, Blown-Out, Green Mark, 3 1/4 In.	55.00
Nippon, Creamer, Covered, Scenic, Jeweled Finial & Handle	15.00
Nippon, Creamer, Figural Duck, Hand-Painted, 6 In.	9.00
Nippon, Creamer, Figural, Elephant, Tusk Forms Handle, Mark 31	40.00
Nippon, Creamer, Hand-Painted Red Roses, Gold Trim	13.00
Nippon, Creamer, Orange & Green Flowers, 3 Gold Feet, Raised Beading	10.00
Nippon, Creamer, Pink Roses	6.00
Nippon, Creamer, Scenic, Beaded Handle, Blue M Mark, 2 1/4 In.	5.00
Nippon, Cup & Saucer, Blue & Pink Floral On Cream, Gold Handle & Rims	28.00

Nippon, Cup & Saucer, Demitasse, Floral, Gold 7.00
Nippon, Cup & Saucer, Gold & White, M Mark 10.00
Nippon, Cup & Saucer, Green, Gold, Floral, Rising Sun Mark 3.00
Nippon, Cup & Saucer, Hand-Painted 5.00
Nippon, Cup & Saucer, Light Aqua, Blue & Pink Jewels On Rim 38.00
Nippon, Cup & Saucer, Pedestal, Raised Gold Floral On Cobalt, Gold Lined 16.00
Nippon, Cup & Saucer, Pink Floral, Green Leaves, Gold Beading, Green Crown 5.50
Nippon, Cup & Saucer, Pink Roses & Cobalt 8.00
Nippon, Cup & Saucer, Scenic, Art Nouveau Style, Green Wreath Mark 20.00
Nippon, Cup & Saucer, Scenic, Rising Sun Mark 6.75
Nippon, Cup, Handleless, White, Blue Teahouse Scene Border 5.00
Nippon, Cup, Lemonade, Pink Roses, Gold Trim, 4 In. 7.00
Nippon, Cup, Lemonade, Purple Violets, Green Leaves & Vines 5.00
Nippon, Cup, Nut, Picture Of Capitol Building, Marked 5.00
Nippon, Cup, Scenic, Hand-Painted 2.45
Nippon, Demitasse Set, Scenic, Black & White, Gold Trim, 15 Piece 165.00
Nippon, Demitasse Set, Scenic, Lavender, Green, & Red, E-Oh Mark, 9 Piece ... 40.00
Nippon, Demitasse Set, White, Black With Gold Borders, Green Mark, 13 Piece . 65.00
Nippon, Dish & Underplate, Cheese, Slanting, Eagles & Floral On Blue, Gold 68.00
Nippon, Dish & Underplate, Cheese, Slanting, Pink Roses Medallions 38.00
Nippon, Dish & Underplate, Sardine, Coral, Shells, & Fish, Sardine Finial 95.00
Nippon, Dish, Baby Feeding, Decals Decoration 12.00
Nippon, Dish, Basket, Floral & Geometrics, Gold Handle, Green M Mark, 7 In. 12.00
Nippon, Dish, Basket, Gold & Floral, Gold Handle, Green M Mark, 7 5/8 In. 25.00
Nippon, Dish, Boat Shape, Hand-Painted 6.50
Nippon, Dish, Candy, Covered, Floral On Black, 3 Gold Feet, 17 1/2 In. 75.00
Nippon, Dish, Candy, Covered, Pink & Red Roses, Gold Edges, 2 Handled 13.00
Nippon, Dish, Candy, Covered, The Hunt, Landscape Setting, 9 1/2 X 3 In. 135.00
Nippon, Dish, Candy, Footed, Pink Roses On Pastel, Blue Maple Leaf Mark 15.00
Nippon, Dish, Candy, Handled, Roses & Leaves, Gold Trim, Green Mark 12.50
Nippon, Dish, Candy, Heart Shape, Handle, Pink & Yellow Clover, Blue Mark 8.50
Nippon, Dish, Candy, Pagodas Scene, Birds, Green M Mark, 7 In. 28.00
Nippon, Dish, Candy, Pierced Jeweled Floral Handles, Scenic 12.50
Nippon, Dish, Candy, Pink & Purple Roses In Panels, Octagonal, 8 1/2 In. 18.00
Nippon, Dish, Candy, Purple Thistles On Tan & Cream, Green Wreath Mark 15.00
Nippon, Dish, Cheese & Cracker, Covered, Scenic, Black & White, Gold Trim 22.50
Nippon, Dish, Cheese & Cracker, Red Roses On Lid, Panels Of Pink, 9 1/4 In. 20.00
Nippon, Dish, Cheese & Cracker, 9 1/2 In. 18.00
Nippon, Dish, Cheese, Covered, Floral & Gold, Marked 20.00
Nippon, Dish, Cheese, Covered, Yellow Blocks, Floral, White Ground, 8 In. 25.00
Nippon, Dish, Cucumber, Poppies, Gold Beading, 2 Piece, Leaf Mark 16.00
Nippon, Dish, Dip, Yellow Geometric Medallions, Gold Vines, Cream Bands 12.50
Nippon, Dish, Mint, Spray Of Violets, Gold Trim, 7 1/2 X 5 In. 10.00
Nippon, Dish, Nut, Blown-Out Peanuts, Handled 38.00
Nippon, Dish, Nut, Pink Floral, Gold Beading, Blue Mark, 2 X 5 1/2 In. 10.00
Nippon, Dish, Peanut, Blown-Out, Marked 35.00
Nippon, Dish, Pickle, Oval, Hand-Painted Water Scene, Flowered Border 8.50
Nippon, Dish, Pin, Pink Flowers, Round, 4 In. 15.00
Nippon, Dish, Powder, Gold, Pink Roses, 3 Footed 37.50
Nippon, Dresser Set, Child's, Gold Outlined Bees & Roses, 3 Piece 18.50
Nippon, Dresser Set, Footed, Octagonal, Floral, Gold Beading, 3 Piece 40.00
Nippon, Dresser Set, Pink Apple Blossoms On White, Gold Beading, 5 Piece 150.00
Nippon, Dresser Set, Pink Flowers, Red, Green, & Gray Design, 4 Piece 80.00
Nippon, Dresser Set, Pink With Blues, 3 Piece 28.00
Nippon, Dresser Set, Roses, Green, Maroon, & Gold, 5 Piece 48.00
Nippon, Dresser Set, Square Hair Receiver, Green Wreath Mark, 4 Piece 85.00
Nippon, Eggcup, Floral, Green & Gold Trim, Marked 12.00
Nippon, Ewer, Purple Orchids & Gold, Cobalt & Gold Handle, 7 1/2 In. 90.00
Nippon, Ewer, Violets, Gold Handle & At Top, Green Maple Leaf Mark, 9 In. 58.00
Nippon, Ewer, White Beading Outlined Pink Roses On Dark Green, 7 1/2 In. 125.00
Nippon, Fernery, Floral & 5 Butterflies, Gold Feet, Square, 5 1/2 In. 30.00
Nippon, Fernery, Scenic, Pink Cherry Blossoms, Footed, Beading, 5 1/2 In. 48.00
Nippon, Fernery, Square, Gold Beading, Roses Medallions, Footed, 5 In. 40.00
Nippon, Figurine, Bird On Log, Blue Head, White, 4 In. 20.00
Nippon, Flowerpot, Hanging, 4 Applied Rams' Heads, Palm Tree Scene 105.00
Nippon, Gravy Boat & Underplate, Floral, Black, & Gold Decoration, Marked 25.00

Nippon, Hair Receiver & Powder Jar, Snow Scene, Gold Beading 30.00
Nippon, Hair Receiver, Cobalt & Gold Floral & Scrolls 49.00
Nippon, Hair Receiver, Floral & Gold Beading, Kinran 15.50
Nippon, Hair Receiver, Footed, Violets, Gold Beading 17.50
Nippon, Hair Receiver, Gold Scrolls On White, Cobalt Border, White Beads 40.00
Nippon, Hair Receiver, Multicolor Floral, Cobalt & Gold, Maple Leaf Mark 30.00
Nippon, Hair Receiver, Oriental Poppies, Green Leaves, Gold Trim 25.00
Nippon, Hair Receiver, Pink, Red & Yellow Roses On Green, Gold Beading 18.50
Nippon, Hair Receiver, Red Oval Panels, Gold 20.00
Nippon, Hair Receiver, Scenic Sunset Sky, White Geese In Marsh 11.00
Nippon, Hatpin Holder, Apricot, Yellow, & Gold Floral On White 19.00
Nippon, Hatpin Holder, Floral, Gold, 12 Holes On Top, Green Maple Leaf Mark 39.00
Nippon, Hatpin Holder, Floral, Green Wreath Mark 22.00
Nippon, Hatpin Holder, Hand-Painted, 4 1/2 In. 13.00
Nippon, Hatpin Holder, House By Lake Scene, Peach, Blue Maple Leaf Mark 33.00
Nippon, Hatpin Holder, Pink & Cerise Roses, Green Beading, Gold Trim 29.00
Nippon, Hatpin Holder, Pink Floral, Green & Brown Geometrics, Gold Beading 19.00
Nippon, Hatpin Holder, Pink Flying Dragon On Charcoal, Green M Mark, 5 In. 58.00
Nippon, Hatpin Holder, Scene On White, Lima Mark, 6 1/2 In. 3.00
Nippon, Humidor, Bisque, Desert Island Scene, Jeweled, Beaded, Green Mark 78.50
Nippon, Humidor, Blown-Out Acorns, Moriye On Handle 110.00
Nippon, Humidor, Brown Knob, Island Scene, 5 1/2 In. 42.00
Nippon, Humidor, Brown, Orange, Yellow & Green Sunlit Forest Scene 145.00
Nippon, Humidor, Cigar, Cigarette, Pipe, & Matches On 6 Sides, Signed 85.00
Nippon, Humidor, Dog In Relief, Blown-Out, Sunset Colors, 5 In. 150.00
Nippon, Humidor, Egyptian Motifs, Bronze Coloring, Green M Mark, 6 1/2 In. 135.00
Nippon, Humidor, Green, Red, White, Brown, & Blue Design, 6 In. 90.00
Nippon, Humidor, Hunt Scene, Red Coated Riders, Green Bisque, 7 In.High 175.00
Nippon, Humidor, Indian & Canoe On Lake, Green & Yellow, Knob Top 175.00
Nippon, Humidor, Lion In Jungle 80.00
Nippon, Humidor, Monk Playing Fiddle, Painted Wooden Lid 80.00
Nippon, Humidor, Mythological Birds On Sand Ground 35.00
Nippon, Humidor, Poppies On Shaded Brown, 6 Sided, Marked 38 Lima, 6 3/4 In. 55.00
Nippon, Humidor, Square Base, Dragon On Front, Raised Work, 5 1/2 In. 48.00
Nippon, Humidor, Squat, Sunset Coloring & Scene, Green Mark 49.00
Nippon, Humidor, Tobacco, Deer In Woodland Scene, Green Mark 95.00
Nippon, Ice Cream Set, Gold Band & Beading, Floral, Blue M Mark, 7 Piece 140.00
Nippon, Ice Cream Set, Heavy Gold Trim, 14 X 8 1/2 In. Platter, 5 Piece 19.00
Nippon, Incense Burner, Embossed, Color Accent Areas, Footed, 3 1/2 In. 35.00
Nippon, Inkwell, Geometrics, Pink Roses, Yellow Stripes, Gold Beading 55.00
Nippon, Inkwell, Pink & Yellow Flowers On Pastel Ground, Gold Knob Top 50.00
Nippon, Inkwell, Pyramids At Top, Owl With Wings Spread, Green M Mark, 4 In. 78.00
Nippon, Inkwell, Tan & Green Geometrics, Gold Outlined, Green M Mark 58.00
Nippon, Jar & Attached Underplate, Honey, Covered, Roses, Gold, 4 1/2 In. 18.50
Nippon, Jar & Plate, Cracker, Melon Shape, Cabriole Legs, Red Roses, 9 3/4 In 110.00
Nippon, Jar & Underplate, Jam, Covered, Floral, Gold Geometrics, Handled 45.00
Nippon, Jar, Biscuit, Footed, Melon Shape, Beading, Roses Panels 69.50
Nippon, Jar, Condensed Milk, Floral & Gold, Marked 25.00
Nippon, Jar, Condiment, Indian Teepees, River, Spreading Tree, 4 In. 27.50
Nippon, Jar, Cookie, Oval Scenic Panels, 3 Gold Feet, Green Mark, 7 In. 95.00
Nippon, Jar, Cracker, Black & White Flowers, Geometric Gold Pattern 40.00
Nippon, Jar, Cracker, Covered, Landscape, Gold Feet & Finial 110.00
Nippon, Jar, Cracker, Dainty Roses, Heavy Gold, 6 X 5 1/2 In. 95.00
Nippon, Jar, Cracker, Gold Beading With Floral, Yellow, Wreath Mark 42.00
Nippon, Jar, Cracker, Pink Roses & Gold, 4 1/2 X 8 1/2 In. 40.00
Nippon, Jar, Cracker, Purple Flowers, Gold Trim, 2 Handled, Leaf Mark 27.00
Nippon, Jar, Cricket, Floral & Gold Decoration, Marked 25.00
Nippon, Jar, Cricket, Multicolored Floral, Light & Dark Blue, Spoke Mark 35.00
Nippon, Jar, Floral & Gold, 3 Toed, Green Wreath Mark, 4 In. 11.50
Nippon, Jar, Rose, Scenic, Black & White, Gold Trim, Green Mark, 5 In. 38.50
Nippon, Jar, Rose, Yellow Butterfly & Pink Roses, Green M Mark, 5 In. 28.00
Nippon, Jar, Tobacco, Figural Head Of Girl 30.00
Nippon, Jelly Set, Roses On Gold, Green Band, 9 Piece 15.00
Nippon, Jug, Bottle Type, Indian Warrior On Tan, White Beaded Handle, 5 In. 45.00
Nippon, Lamp, Handled, Cherry Blossoms On Shaded, 10 In. 70.00
Nippon, Lamp, Ribbon Handles, Brass Base, Poinsettias, 14 In. 85.00

Nippon, Lazy Susan, Scenic, E-Oh Mark, 7 Pieces	45.00
Nippon, Lazy Susan, Scenic, 6 Dishes Around Center Dish, Lacquer Box, 12 In.	148.00
Nippon, Lemonade Set, Pink Roses Trimmed In Gold, Gold Beading, 7 Piece	62.00
Nippon, Lemonade Set, Scenic On Yellow, Marked 37 Lima, 6 Piece	120.00
Nippon, Lemonade Set, Scenic, Turquoise Jewels, 6 Piece	30.00
Nippon, Lemonade Set, Violets, Marked, 5 Piece	65.00
Nippon, Luncheon Set, Geisha Girls Scene, Gray Border, Florals, 5 Piece	45.00
Nippon, Match Holder & Attached Ashtray, Scenic	38.00
Nippon, Match Holder & Attached Tray, Owl On Limb, Dark Blue, Green Mark	85.00
Nippon, Match Holder & Attached Underplate, Warrior On Horse	33.00
Nippon, Match Holder, Brown & Yellow Country House On Lake, Bisque Type	36.00
Nippon, Match Holder, Covered, Cigar & Match Decoration, 3 1/2 In.	27.50
Nippon, Match Holder, Wall, Double, Pink Roses, Cobalt & Gold Trim	65.00
Nippon, Match Holder, Wall, Pink & Orange Floral On White, Gold, 5 1/2 In.	35.00
Nippon, Match Holder, Wall, Sailing Ships Scene, Marked	48.50
Nippon, Match Striker, Egyptian Boat & Sunset Scene, Enamel Rim, 3 1/2 In.	40.00
Nippon, Mayonnaise Set, Floral On Tan, Mother-Of-Pearl, 3 Piece	12.50
Nippon, Mayonnaise Set, Gold Floral Decoration, 3 Piece	20.00
Nippon, Mayonnaise Set, Grapes On White, Gold, Pedestal Bowl, 3 Piece	26.00
Nippon, Mayonnaise Set, Scalloped, Diamond, Pink Roses On Blue, 3 Piece	24.00
Nippon, Mayonnaise Set, Small Blue Flowers, Gold Rim, 3 Piece	18.00
Nippon, Muffineer, Cobalt With Roses & Heavy Gold, 6 Sided	38.50
Nippon, Muffineer, Floral & Gold, Marked	25.00
Nippon, Muffineer, Floral Medallions, Gold Encrusted, M In Wreath Mark	40.00
Nippon, Muffineer, Handled, Pink, Green, Brown, & Blue, 5 1/4 In.High	30.00
Nippon, Muffineer, Ornate Shape, Roses, Gold, Jeweled	22.00
Nippon, Muffineer, Pink & Red Rose Medallions, Black Panels, Gold, 4 In.	32.50
Nippon, Muffineer, Raised Pink Floral, Cerise, & Ivory, Blue Mark	29.00
Nippon, Muffineer, Violets, Gold	19.00
Nippon, Muffineer, White, Gold Floral & Trim, Side Handle, Green Wreath Mark	28.00
Nippon, Mug, Blown-Out Child's Face	22.00
Nippon, Mug, Blown-Out Stag In Forest, Antler Handle, Green M Mark, 5 In.	225.00
Nippon, Mug, Deer In Forest, Jeweled & Beaded Handle, Geometric Border	95.00
Nippon, Mug, Gold Handle, Green M Mark	75.00
Nippon, Mug, Owl, 5 In.	25.00
Nippon, Mustard Set, Gold Handle & Ladle, Gold Floral, Pastels, 3 Piece	65.00
Nippon, Mustard Set, Hand-Painted, Covered Pot, 2 Piece	10.00
Nippon, Nappy, Heart Shape, Loop Handle, Floral, Gold, Raisedwork, 7 1/2 In.	41.00
Nippon, Nappy, Triangular, Floral Spray, Gold Trim, Marked	10.00
Nippon, Nut Set, Acorn Pattern, Beaded Edges, 7 Piece	75.00
Nippon, Nut Set, Gold, Pink Roses, Scalloped, Footed Bowl, Green Mark, 4 Piece	18.00
Nippon, Nut Set, Gold, Violets, Blue Maple Leaf Mark, 6 Piece	90.00
Nippon, Nut Set, Pink Floral, Gold, Footed, 7 Piece	50.00
Nippon, Nut Set, Purple & Gold Floral On Yellow & Gold, Footed, 7 Piece	42.00
Nippon, Nut Set, Raised Daisies, Gold Footed, Metro Mark, 5 Piece	20.00
Nippon, Pitcher, Corset Shape, Coin Gold, Green & Black, 5 1/2 In.	75.00
Nippon, Pitcher, Covered, House, Trees, Jeweled Lid, Handle	32.50
Nippon, Pitcher, Lemonade, Red Roses, Gold Bow & Streamers, Geometrics	28.00
Nippon, Pitcher, Lemonade, Squatty Type, Continous Scene, E-Oh	35.00
Nippon, Pitcher, Milk, Covered, Scenic, Gold Overlay Roses	70.00
Nippon, Pitcher, Milk, Geisha Girls Scene, 4 1/2 In.	15.00
Nippon, Pitcher, Milk, Six-Sided, Gold & Wisteria	65.00
Nippon, Pitcher, Milk, 6 Sided, Gold Outlined Floral & Handle, Green Mark	49.00
Nippon, Pitcher, Tapestry, Jeweled, Roses, Gold Handle & Trim, 7 In.	250.00
Nippon, Planter, Continuous Scene, Cobalt & Gold Geometrics, 25 1/2 In.	40.00
Nippon, Planter, Frog, Salmon Color, White Blue Dragon, 7 In.	45.00
Nippon, Planter, Ships, Jeweled, Footed, Liner, Green Mark, Square, 7 1/4 In.	95.00
Nippon, Plaque, Autumn Scene, 9 1/2 In.Diameter	34.00
Nippon, Plaque, Black Stallion's Head On Light Blue, Blown-Out, 10 In.	295.00
Nippon, Plaque, Egyptian Nile Scene, Gold Border, Beading & Jewels, 10 In.	38.00
Nippon, Plaque, English Hunt Scene, Dog In Front, Green Wreath, 9 In.	55.00
Nippon, Plaque, Indian Hunting Wild Game In Landscape, Blown-Out, 10 In.	295.00
Nippon, Plaque, Indian On Horseback On Beige, Blown-Out, 10 In.	295.00
Nippon, Plaque, Indian, Blown-Out, 10 In.	225.00
Nippon, Plaque, Landscape, Green Wreath Mark, 9 In.	65.00
Nippon, Plaque, Lion & Lioness On Mountain Ledge, Green Wreath Mark, 10 In.	295.00

Nippon, Plaque, Lioness & Lion, Blown-Out, Green M Mark, 10 1/2 In. 350.00
Nippon, Plaque, Roses On Black, Striped Border, Signed, 12 In. 35.00
Nippon, Plaque, Sailing Boats & Windmill, Gold Border, 10 1/2 In. 150.00
Nippon, Plaque, Scenic Hills, House, & Tree, Greek Key Border, 10 In. 30.00
Nippon, Plaque, Stag In Forest On Cream, Blown-Out, Green M Mark, 10 In. 295.00
Nippon, Plaque, Steeplechase, Greek Key Rim, Leaf Mark, 9 1/2 In. 45.00
Nippon, Plaque, Windmill & Lake Scene, Browns & Greens, 10 In. 60.00
Nippon, Plaque, Windmill Scene, Bisque, Brown Rim, 10 1/4 In. 45.00
Nippon, Plate, Black, Diamond Shape Floral Medallions, Gold Handles, 9 In. 35.00
Nippon, Plate, Blown-Out Child's Face, Heart Shape, 5 1/2 In. 28.00
Nippon, Plate, Blue & White Floral, Raised Gold, Tapestrylike, 10 In. 45.00
Nippon, Plate, Cake, Gold Butterflies & Floral On Pink, Jeweled, 9 3/4 In. 70.00
Nippon, Plate, Cake, Gold Outlined Daisies, Incised Handled, 10 3/4 In. 15.00
Nippon, Plate, Cake, Green, Gold Outlined White Daisies, Handled 14.00
Nippon, Plate, Cake, Pink Roses Medallions, Gold, Jeweled, 10 In. 70.00
Nippon, Plate, Cake, Pink Roses, Blue Forget-Me-Nots, Gold, Open Handled 10.50
Nippon, Plate, Cake, Scenic, Black & White, Gold Handles & Trim, 9 1/2 In. 18.00
Nippon, Plate, Center Handle, Marked, 6 In. 20.00
Nippon, Plate, Geisha Girls Scene On Pastel Blue, 7 In. 7.00
Nippon, Plate, Geisha Girls Scene, Red Poppies, 7 1/2 In. 8.50
Nippon, Plate, Geisha Girls Scenes, Gold Beading, 9 1/2 In. 14.00
Nippon, Plate, Gold Open Handles, Pink Floral, Black & White, 7 1/2 In. 11.00
Nippon, Plate, Gold People & Pagodas, 8 1/2 In. 25.00
Nippon, Plate, Gold Scroll In Panels, Pink Roses, Green Foliage, 8 1/2 In. 70.00
Nippon, Plate, Japanese Women Scene, Cherry Blossoms, Satsuma Colors, 6 In. 4.00
Nippon, Plate, Luncheon, Oyster Pattern 8.50
Nippon, Plate, Luncheon, Pink Roses, Gold Beading & Trim 5.75
Nippon, Plate, Man On Camel Scene, Marked, 6 1/2 In. 15.00
Nippon, Plate, Peacock, Fruits, & Flowers, Black, 7 1/4 In. 30.00
Nippon, Plate, Peacocks & Flowers, Red Mark, 9 1/2 In. 65.00
Nippon, Plate, Peonies, Gold, Jeweled, Maple Leaf Mark, 8 3/4 In. 50.00
Nippon, Plate, Pink Blossoms, Green Wreath Mark, 6 1/4 In. 6.00
Nippon, Plate, Pink Corsage On Gold Beaded Garlands, Handles, 10 1/4 In. 15.00
Nippon, Plate, Pink Floral, Green Leaves, Raised Gold, Green Mark, 6 1/4 In. 7.00
Nippon, Plate, Pink Roses On Pastel Blue Center, Cobalt & Gold, 11 In. 30.00
Nippon, Plate, Purple Blossoms On Gold Vine, Gold Border, 7 In.Diameter, 6 .... 32.50
Nippon, Plate, Purple Bluebells, Sunset Scene, 8 1/2 In. 9.00
Nippon, Plate, Raised Gold Floral, Yellow Border, Green Mark, 6 1/4 In. 3.50
Nippon, Plate, Red & White Roses, Maroon & Gold Border, 9 In. 35.00
Nippon, Plate, Red Roses, Narrow Green Border, Gold Loops, 10 In. 15.00
Nippon, Plate, Roses, Turquoise Jewels, Cobalt & Gold Border, 7 1/2 In. 30.00
Nippon, Plate, Scenic, Black & White, Gold Trim, 7 In. 12.00
Nippon, Plate, Scenic, Farmhouse & Pastures, Gold Rim, 10 In. 75.00
Nippon, Plate, Serving, Palm Tree Scene, Applied Slipwork, 10 In. 55.00
Nippon, Plate, Serving, Scenic, Black & White, Gold Trim, Gold Handles, 8 In. 13.50
Nippon, Plate, Snow Covered Foot Bridge & Sunset Scene, Marked, 8 In. 15.00
Nippon, Plate, Swans On Lake, Mountain & Forest, T.S. In Diamond, 6 1/4 In. 6.50
Nippon, Plate, Windmill Scene, 6 In. 10.00
Nippon, Plate, Winter Scene Of Mt.Fugi, Marked, 6 In. 5.00
Nippon, Plate, Yellow & Pink Roses, Gold Beading, 6 1/4 In. 17.00
Nippon, Plate, Yellow Flowers, Orange & Black Jeweled Border, 10 In. 55.00
Nippon, Plate, Yellow, Pink, & White Rose Medallions, Gold Border, 9 3/4 In. 25.00
Nippon, Pot & Ladle, Relish, Pastel Roses, Gold Trim, 4 In. 37.00
Nippon, Pot, Mustard, Gold Trim, 2 Handled, Green Mark 15.00
Nippon, Relish Set, Cutout Handles, White & Pink Floral, 7 Piece 25.00
Nippon, Relish Set, Indian In Canoe Shooting At Deer, Canoe Celery, 6 Piece 85.00
Nippon, Relish, Divided, Gold Trim, 9 In. 10.00
Nippon, Relish, Floral, Gold, 2 Handled 14.00
Nippon, Relish, Gold American Eagles & Crest On Blue Band, Cutout Handles 19.00
Nippon, Relish, Raised Gold & Violets 27.50
Nippon, Ring Tree, Gold Fingers, Light Blue Wrist, E-OH Mark 15.00
Nippon, Ring Tree, Gold Hand On White 6 Sided Base, Floral, Gold 35.00
Nippon, Ring Tree, Hand & Colored Flowers 15.00
Nippon, Ring Tree, Violets & Gold On Cobalt 25.00
Nippon, Rose Bowl, Pink, White, & Red Roses, Gold Bands, 18 X 4 1/2 In. 58.00
Nippon, Salt & Pepper, Dark Blue, Roses, Gold, M & Leaf Mark 28.00

Nippon, Salt & Pepper, Floral, Gold Trim	6.50
Nippon, Salt & Pepper, Handled, Raised Gold Beading	12.00
Nippon, Salt & Pepper, Japanese Children Scene, Pinwheels On Green	50.00
Nippon, Salt & Pepper, Lighthouse Type, Island & Palm Trees Scene	12.00
Nippon, Salt & Pepper, Oriental Children, Raised Gold, Cork Closures	45.00
Nippon, Salt & Pepper, Roses, Blue Band, 3 In.	9.00
Nippon, Salt & Pepper, Water Buffalo Scene, 8 Sided, Pair	18.00
Nippon, Salt Dip, Floral, Gold, Oval, 3 1/2 In.	4.00
Nippon, Salt Dip, Floral, Round, Footed	5.00
Nippon, Salt Dip, Geometric Ovals	4.00
Nippon, Salt Dip, Master, Floral, Gold	6.25
Nippon, Salt Dip, Tub Shape, Handled, Floral	6.50
Nippon, Salt Dip, Tub Shape, Handled, Hand-Painted, 6 Sided	4.00
Nippon, Salt Dip, White, Gold, Footed	2.35
Nippon, Saltshaker, Pink & Red Roses, Yellow Ground, C.1890, Artist Signed	8.00
Nippon, Separator & Underplate, Egg, Black Candy Stripes On Light Blue	15.00
Nippon, Server, Gold Center Handle, Black & Gold Geometrics, Floral	50.00
Nippon, Server, Gold Center Handle, Black, Diamond Shape Medallions, 9 In.	50.00
Nippon, Shoe, Clog, Pastel Green, Pink & Yellow Floral, Green M Mark, 3 In.	12.00
Nippon, Smoking Set, Art Nouveau, Tan, Scenic Medallion, Green M, 3 Piece	70.00
Nippon, Smoking Set, Cigar, Matches, & Pipe Decoration, 3 Piece	100.00
Nippon, Spittoon, Raised Flowers & Enamel, Ruffled Top, 7 1/2 In.	78.00
Nippon, Spooner, Bluebirds, Gold Trim, Marked	35.00
Nippon, Spooner, Double, Floral & Gold, Marked	17.50
Nippon, Stein, Castle Scene & Geese, Greek Key Border, Beaded Handle, 6 In.	100.00
Nippon, Stein, Dutch Windmill Scene, Geometrics, Beaded Handle, 5 3/4 In.	100.00
Nippon, Stein, Gold Geometrics & Handle, Red On Greens, 5 1/2 In.	120.00
Nippon, Stein, Gold Leaf & Beading, Wisteria On Pastel, Gold Handle, 7 In.	150.00
Nippon, Stein, Landscape Scene, Beaded Handle, 7 In.	95.00
Nippon, Stein, Scenic, Black & White, Gold Trim, 6 In.	90.00
Nippon, Stein, Stag In Forest, Sunset Sky, Gold Handle, Green M Mark, 6 In.	100.00
Nippon, Stickpin Holder, Orange Floral On Blue & Black, Gold, Green Mark	58.00
Nippon, Stickpin Holder, Pink Floral, Blue & Yellow Shading, Gold Trim	70.00
Nippon, Stickpin Holder, Violets, White Dots	36.00
Nippon, Sugar & Creamer, Black Dragon On Yellow, Beaded Eyes, Gold	29.00
Nippon, Sugar & Creamer, Butterflies, Gold Trim	12.50
Nippon, Sugar & Creamer, Cover, Floral, Gold Design & Rim	15.00
Nippon, Sugar & Creamer, Cover, Japanese Lords & Empress's Head	50.00
Nippon, Sugar & Creamer, Cover, Sailboats & Trees, Violet Shading	16.50
Nippon, Sugar & Creamer, Covered, Pastel Flowers, Gold Outlines, Beaded	22.50
Nippon, Sugar & Creamer, Floral, Beading, M In Wreath Mark	13.00
Nippon, Sugar & Creamer, Floral, Hand-Painted	18.00
Nippon, Sugar & Creamer, Gold Handles, Black & Gold Geometrics, Floral	60.00
Nippon, Sugar & Creamer, Grapes & Leaves On White, Gold, Green Wreath Mark	38.00
Nippon, Sugar & Creamer, Paneled Geometrics, Gold Handles, Blue Maple Leaf	60.00
Nippon, Sugar & Creamer, Pastel Floral & Leaf On White, Raised Gold	30.00
Nippon, Sugar & Creamer, Pink Blossoms & Green Leaves On White, Small	11.50
Nippon, Sugar & Creamer, Pink Floral On White	16.00
Nippon, Sugar & Creamer, Pink Roses Medallions, Gold, Jeweled, RC Mark	100.00
Nippon, Sugar & Creamer, Pink Roses, Gold Trim, Miniature	15.00
Nippon, Sugar & Creamer, Portrait Of Girl, Gold & Jeweling, 3 Feet	110.00
Nippon, Sugar & Creamer, Purple Floral On White	16.00
Nippon, Sugar & Creamer, Sailing Ships, Gold Beading, Handles, & Finial	38.50
Nippon, Sugar & Creamer, Scenic, Black & White, Gold Trim	33.00
Nippon, Sugar, Azalea, Rising Sun Mark	12.00
Nippon, Sugar, Covered, Blues, Browns, & Greens, 2 Handles, Raised Floral	12.00
Nippon, Sugar, Covered, Scenic, Black Beading	7.50
Nippon, Sugar, Cube Holder, Scenic, Marked	25.00
Nippon, Sugar, Large Pink Blossoms, & Raised Gold, Wreath Mark	10.00
Nippon, Syrup & Underplate, Cobalt Bands, Gold Floral & Handle, 5 In.	50.00
Nippon, Syrup & Underplate, Floral Bands, Raised Gold, Wreath Mark	18.00
Nippon, Syrup & Underplate, Gold Flowers & Bluebirds	20.00
Nippon, Syrup, Roses & Gold Beading	15.00
Nippon, Tankard, Bisque Finish, Violet Color Blossoms, Gold Beading, 10 In.	115.00
Nippon, Tankard, Scenic, Encrusted, Blue Maple Leaf Mark, 5 1/2 In.	95.00
Nippon, Tea & Cake Set, Cream Color, Bluebirds On Branch, 15 Piece	70.00

Nippon, Tea & Cake Set, Yellow, Blue Bird Of Paradise, Gold, 15 Piece	175.00
Nippon, Tea Set, Allover Floral & Geometric, Raised Gold, 11 Piece	75.00
Nippon, Tea Set, Azalea, Creamer, Sugar, 4 Cup & Saucers, 4 Plates	55.00
Nippon, Tea Set, Cobalt Blue, Roses, Gold Beading, 11 Piece	60.00
Nippon, Tea Set, Dragon Pattern, Moriye, 18 Piece	95.00
Nippon, Tea Set, Dragons, 21 Piece	100.00
Nippon, Tea Set, Floral & Gold, Marked, 19 Piece	65.00
Nippon, Tea Set, Gold Overlay Applied, 3 Piece	45.00
Nippon, Tea Set, Japanese Figures, Gold Finials, Royal Naga, 11 Piece	69.50
Nippon, Tea Set, Pink Flying Dragon On Charcoal, Brown Trim, 11 Piece	65.00
Nippon, Tea Set, Pink, Gold, & Green Flowers On Cream, Gold Trim, 15 Piece	75.00
Nippon, Tea Strainer, Gold Encrusted Cerise Band, Gold Feet & Beading	29.00
Nippon, Tea Strainer, Pastel Floral, Gold Trim, Lima Mark	19.00
Nippon, Tea Strainer, Yellow & Red Flowers, Gold Beading	14.50
Nippon, Teapot, Bluebirds, Roses, Raised Gold Flower Sprays	35.00
Nippon, Teapot, Butterflies & Pink Flowers, Gold Trim, Wreath Mark	15.00
Nippon, Teapot, Figural Elephant, 10 1/2 In.	29.00
Nippon, Teapot, Geisha Girls, Butterflies, & Floral On Green, 9 In.	25.00
Nippon, Teapot, Gold Outlined Floral, Raised Gold, Laurel Mark	27.00
Nippon, Teapot, Metal Lid With Chained Teaball, Floral On White	29.00
Nippon, Teapot, Pagodas, Boats, Bridges, & Trees On Orange, C.1920, 7 In.	28.50
Nippon, Teapot, Red Berries, Dark Green Leaves, Gold Trim, 5 In.	18.00
Nippon, Teapot, Square, Hod Spout, Blue Enamel Florals, 4 1/2 In.	9.50
Nippon, Teapot, White, Green Trim, Bands Of Roses & Gold	19.50
Nippon, Tobacco Set, Camel Design On White, Sunset Scene, 5 Piece	175.00
Nippon, Toothpick, Boats & Sunset, 2 1/4 In.	6.50
Nippon, Toothpick, Continuous Lake Scene, 3 Handled, Blue Maple Leaf Mark	32.50
Nippon, Toothpick, Green, Gold Bands, Flowers, 2 Handled	13.00
Nippon, Toothpick, Hexagonal, Footed, Green Wreath Mark	17.50
Nippon, Toothpick, Red, Gold, & Green Geometrics, 3 Gold Handles	28.00
Nippon, Tray, Desert Scene, Man On Camel, Bisque Finish, 11 X 7 1/2 In.	55.00
Nippon, Tray, Dresser, Colonial Woman & Man Center, Floral, 9 1/2 X 7 In.	29.00
Nippon, Tray, Dresser, White, Brown Enamel Flowers, 8 1/8 X 5 3/4 In.	8.00
Nippon, Tray, Floral, Gold & Turquoise Beading, Marked, 8 1/2 X 4 In.	12.00
Nippon, Tray, Lazy Susan, Bird Of Paradise & Floral, 7 Sections, C.1890	55.00
Nippon, Tray, Octagon, Island & Ocean Scene, Blue, Black, Green, & White, 12 In	85.00
Nippon, Tray, Parrot On Tree Limb & Floral On Yellow, Handled, 9 1/2 In.	55.00
Nippon, Tray, Purple Bluebells & Green Leaves, Sunset Scene, 10 In.	12.00
Nippon, Tray, Red Coated Fox Hunter On Horse, Foxhound, 8 3/4 X 3 3/4 In.	38.00
Nippon, Tray, Red Roses Medallions & 6 White Medallions, 9 X 6 3/4 In.	50.00
Nippon, Tray, Sunset, Swans On Water By Bridge, Raised Gold, 12 In.	125.00
Nippon, Tray, Water, Trees, Swans On Lake, 9 X 6 1/4 In.	12.00
Nippon, Tray, Yellow, Parrot On Tree Limb, 2 Handled, Square, 9 1/4 In.	55.00
Nippon, Tub, Butter, Covered, Lavender, Blue, & White Floral, Gold, 2 1/4 In.	49.00
Nippon, Tub, Butter, Insert, Lavender Floral, Gold Handles, Border & Trim	20.00
Nippon, Tumbler, Flowers, Gold Trim, Marked	12.00
Nippon, Urn, Muted Roses, Cobalt Band, Gold Beading, White, Yellows, 3 In.	15.00
Nippon, Urn, Two Handles, Egyptian River Scene, Palms, Blue Flowers, 12 In.	75.00
Nippon, Vase, Arab On Camel, Hexagonal, Satin Finish, 9 In.	78.00
Nippon, Vase, Art Deco Style, Egyptian Scenic, Palms, Triangles, 12 1/2 In.	225.00
Nippon, Vase, Art Nouveau Type Florals, 2 Handles, Blue Mark, 7 In.	42.00
Nippon, Vase, Autumn Scene Panels, Gold Elephants' Heads Handles, 11 In.	50.00
Nippon, Vase, Bands & Ovals Of Roses, Gold, Handled, Moriye, 5 In.	50.00
Nippon, Vase, Beaded Pink Dragon On Gray, Bulbous, 8 In.	48.00
Nippon, Vase, Bird & Tapestry In Center, 12 In.	185.00
Nippon, Vase, Birds, Tree Branches, & Berries, Handled, Green M Mark, 7 In.	135.00
Nippon, Vase, Bisque, Beige, Rust, White, Blues, Green, Brown, & Black, 9 1/4 In.	55.00
Nippon, Vase, Black, Panels, Floral Border, Handled, Green Mark, 10 1/4 In.	58.00
Nippon, Vase, Blue Jasper Ground, Flowers & Leaves, 2 Handles, 11 In.High	65.00
Nippon, Vase, Blue, Floral, 2 Handled, 9 3/4 In.	65.00
Nippon, Vase, Blue, White Band With Scenes On Upper Middle, 5 In.	9.00
Nippon, Vase, Cobalt & Gold, Handled, Ostriches, Sunset Scene, 8 In.	80.00
Nippon, Vase, Conical, Poppies On Cream, 2 Gold Handles, Beading, 5 1/2 In.	18.00
Nippon, Vase, Coralene, Pink Roses On Shaded, Gold Trim, 5 1/2 In.	115.00
Nippon, Vase, Cottage Scene, Trees, Gray Ground, Gold Handles, 10 In.	55.00
Nippon, Vase, Deep Blue, Hand-Painted, Green M Mark, C.1880, 10 In.	65.00

Nippon, Vase, Desert Scene, 3 Gold Handles, M In Wreath Mark, 10 In. 95.00
Nippon, Vase, Ewer Type, Roses Medallions, Gold Overlay, 7 1/4 X 6 In. 58.00
Nippon, Vase, Ewer, Countryside Scene In Green & Blue Pastels, 11 In.High 120.00
Nippon, Vase, Floral & Leaf On Green & Stippled Gold, 2 Handled, 8 1/2 In. 45.00
Nippon, Vase, Floral On Cream, Bird Of Paradise On Branch, 8 In. 35.00
Nippon, Vase, Floral On Orange, Gold Handles, Bisque Finish, 10 In., Pair 95.00
Nippon, Vase, Game, Handles, Raised Leaves, Moose In Forest Setting, 7 1/2 In 95.00
Nippon, Vase, Gold Handles & Bands At Top In Bottom, Pink Roses, 9 1/2 In. 32.00
Nippon, Vase, Gold Handles & Beaded Checkerboard Trim, Orchids, 9 In. 48.00
Nippon, Vase, Gold Handles, Black & Gold Geometrics, Floral, 8 1/2 In. 60.00
Nippon, Vase, Gold Long-Stemmed Roses On Beige, Gold Handles, 13 1/4 In. 50.00
Nippon, Vase, Gold Outlined Iris, 2 Handled, Green Wreath Mark, 7 1/2 In. 55.00
Nippon, Vase, Handled, Roses, White Beading On Blue, Gold, 9 In., Pair 95.00
Nippon, Vase, Handled, 2 Seminole Type Indians, Palm Tree, River, 8 1/2 In. 125.00
Nippon, Vase, High-Relief Acorn & Leaves, 5 1/2 In. 80.00
Nippon, Vase, House, Trees & Water Scene, Handled, Footed, Green Mark, 10 In. 45.00
Nippon, Vase, Indian In Canoe Shooting Deer Scene, Green M Mark, 7 In. 130.00
Nippon, Vase, Indian On White Horse In Landscape, Imperial Mark, 12 1/2 In. 75.00
Nippon, Vase, Indian Pattern, Thunderbird, 7 1/4 X 4 1/2 In. 69.00
Nippon, Vase, Japanese Coralene, Cobalt, Green, & Gold, Scenic, 12 In.High 125.00
Nippon, Vase, Jewels On Scenic Band, 2 Handled, 6 In. 24.50
Nippon, Vase, Moriye White Birds On Blue Gray, Maple Leaf Mark, 9 1/4 In. 120.00
Nippon, Vase, Ostriches In Medallion, Palms, Sunset, Handles, 8 1/4 In.High 125.00
Nippon, Vase, Ovoid, Lion Feet, Shore Scene, Figure, Black & Gold, 6 1/2 In. 50.00
Nippon, Vase, Paneled Seascape, Jeweled Handles, 9 In. 75.00
Nippon, Vase, Panels, Raised Gold Beading, Handled, 4 Footed, 7 In. 50.00
Nippon, Vase, Pastel Floral & Leaf, Gold Veining, 2 Handled, 11 1/2 In. 65.00
Nippon, Vase, Pastel Floral On Soft Brown, Geometrics, Gold Beading, 10 In. 70.00
Nippon, Vase, Pink & Red Roses, Black & Gold, Maple Leaf Mark, 11 In. 85.00
Nippon, Vase, Pink Chrysanthemums, Gold, 11 In., Pair 165.00
Nippon, Vase, Pitcher, Red & Pink Roses, Gold & Cobalt Trim, Footed, 10 In. 65.00
Nippon, Vase, Pitcher, Victorian Ladies Medallion On Gold, Footed, 10 In. 65.00
Nippon, Vase, Rams' Heads Handles, Enameled, 12 In. 45.00
Nippon, Vase, Red Floral On Blue, Gold Trim, 10 3/4 In. 50.00
Nippon, Vase, Red Roses On Cream, Green Panels, Gold, Handled, 8 3/8 In. 55.00
Nippon, Vase, Rose Cameos, Floral, Gold, Handled, Green Mark, 11 1/2 In. 65.00
Nippon, Vase, Roses On Yellow, Gold Beading & Trim, 2 Handles, 7 1/2 In. 18.00
Nippon, Vase, Roses, Green Foliage, Noritake Bone China, 8 1/2 In., Pair 85.00
Nippon, Vase, Scenic Panels, Figures, Gold Trim, Green M Mark, 11 In. 48.00
Nippon, Vase, Scenic, Birds, Gold Beads, Gilt Handles, Royal Nishiki, 12 In. 60.00
Nippon, Vase, Scenic, Handled, Brown & White, Gold Beading, 13 In. 75.00
Nippon, Vase, Six Sided, Desert Ruin Scene, Beaded Gold Border, 13 1/2 In. 110.00
Nippon, Vase, Stick, 6 Geometric Panels, Gold Beading & Greek Key, 10 In. 42.50
Nippon, Vase, Swans On Lake, Cobalt & Gold Collar, Gold Handles, 12 In. 65.00
Nippon, Vase, Tapestry, Mountain Scene & Owl, Double Handles, 12 In., Pair 200.00
Nippon, Vase, Tapestry, Scenic, Jeweled Collar & Base, 12 In. 325.00
Nippon, Vase, Tapestry, Squat Shape, Grapes & Leaves, Gold Dripping 265.00
Nippon, Vase, Three Handled, Cabbage Rose, Violets, Gold Trim, 6 1/2 In. 48.00
Nippon, Vase, Truncated Pyramid Shape, Pansies & Gold, Handles, 9 In., Pair 70.00
Nippon, Vase, Urn Shape, Scrolled Handles, Black Trim, Scenic, 6 In. 18.00
Nippon, Vase, Urn Shaped, Violets & Leaves, Gold Trim, 5 1/2 In.High 20.00
Nippon, Vase, Urn Type, Cobalt, Country Scenes, Square, 6 In. 35.00
Nippon, Vase, Violets On Tinted, Handled, Squatty, 6 1/2 In. 75.00
Nippon, Vase, Water Scene, House, Trees, 8 In.High 38.50
Nippon, Vase, Water Scenes On Blue Gray, 2 Handled, Jeweled, Gold, 12 In. 50.00
Nippon, Vase, Wedgwood Blue, Rams' Heads Handles, Scenic Medallion, 10 In. 155.00
Nippon, Vase, White & Gold, Jeweled, Gold Handles At Mouth, 11 1/4 In. 60.00
Nippon, Vase, White Cherry Blossoms On Black, Green M Mark, 8 3/4 In. 40.00
Nippon, Vase, White Egrets In Water, Pink Water Lily, Birds, Handled, 10 In. 125.00
Nippon, Vase, White Flying Dragon On Green & Blue, Handled, 9 In. 65.00
Nippon, Vase, White Roses, 2 Gold Rams' Heads & Cording, 8 3/4 In., Pair 150.00

Nodders or nodding figures, or pagods, are porcelain figures with heads and hands that are attached to wires. Any slight movement causes the parts to move up and down. They were made in many countries during the eighteenth and nineteenth centuries.

Nodder, Bisque, Hand-Painted, Grass Skirt, Flowers, 5 In. 25.00
Nodder, Boy Clown, Gold Trim, Staffordshire, 7 In. 70.00
Nodder, Boy Wearing Glasses, Blue Victorian Attire, 6 1/2 In. 55.00
Nodder, Genie, Bisque German, 3 In. 20.00
Nodder, Girl In Cape & Bonnet, Holding Basket, 7 In. 52.00
Nodder, Goose, Tin, White, Orange Bill & Feet, 3 3/4 In. 20.00
Nodder, Goose, Tin, 2 X 4 1/2 In. 16.00
Nodder, Lady, Blue Cape Over Pink Dress, 5 1/2 In. 68.50
Nodder, Male & Female Orientals, Bisque, Pair 78.00
Nodder, Moon Mullins, Bisque 25.00
Nodder, Negro Child, Head Wags Between Arms, Yellow Polka Dot Pants 65.00
Nodder, Oriental Girl With Fan, Bisque, Marked Germany, 3 In. 25.00
Nodder, Seated Japanese Woman, Bisque, Hand-Painted, Gold Beading 100.00
Nodder, Woman In Blue & White Costume, Staffordshire, 6 1/2 In.High 65.00
Nodder, Woman, Blue Coat, Tan Trousers, 5 In. 68.50
Nodder, Woman, Little Boy, Staffordshire, 8 In., Pair 150.00

Noritake-marked porcelain was made in Japan after
1904 by Nippon Toki Kaisha.

Noritake, Basket, Scene In Purple On Chartreuse, 6 In. 15.00
Noritake, Bowl & Underplate, Jelly, Mountains, Water, & Sailboats, Footed 30.00
Noritake, Bowl, Blown-Out, Peanuts, Dark Tones, 7 In. 35.00
Noritake, Bowl, Blue Ground, 2 In.Figural Bird On Side, 7 3/4 X 6 3/4 In. 25.00
Noritake, Bowl, Boat Shape, Swan On Lake, Pastels, 7 In. 8.00
Noritake, Bowl, Cereal, Azalea 10.00
Noritake, Bowl, Dessert, Azalea 4.75
Noritake, Bowl, Nut, Blown-Out, 2 Handles, Green Mark 40.00
Noritake, Bowl, Open Handles, Gold Enamel, Blue & Red Floral, 7 In. 6.00
Noritake, Bowl, Soup, Azalea 10.00
Noritake, Bowl, Soup, Baskets Of Flowers, Gold Trim, 8 1/4 In. 6.00
Noritake, Bowl, Swan Scene, Open Handles, 10 1/2 In. 16.00
Noritake, Bowl, Vegetable, Azalea, Oval .... 22.50 To 24.00
Noritake, Bowl, Vegetable, Baskets Of Flowers, Gold Trim, Oval, 10 1/2 In. 12.00
Noritake, Bowl, Vegetable, Covered, Handled, Baskets Of Flowers, Gold, 11 In. 20.00
Noritake, Bowl, Vegetable, Covered, La Salle 9.50
Noritake, Box, Pin, Covered, Allover Gold, Dancing Girl On Lid, Round, 4 In. 10.00
Noritake, Bread & Butter Set, Handled Plate, Gold, Roses, 7 Piece 25.00
Noritake, Butter Pat, Azalea 18.50
Noritake, Cake Set, Beige, Blue, Purple, & Black Geometrics, 7 Piece 25.00
Noritake, Cake Set, Open Handled Plate, Pink & Yellow Daffodils, 7 Piece 19.50
Noritake, Celery Set, Gold Outlined Floral Medallions, 7 Piece 52.00
Noritake, Celery Set, Gold Outlined Yellow Floral, Open Handled, 7 Piece 20.00
Noritake, Celery, Scenic, Red Mark 12.50
Noritake, Chocolate Pot, Trees, Mountains, Water, & Sailboats, Green M Mark 58.00
Noritake, Chocolate Set, Scenic, Heavy Gold, 3 Piece 35.00
Noritake, Chocolate Set, Windmill Scene, 11 Piece 68.00
Noritake, Compote, Gold & Blue Decoration, 2 Piece, 9 1/4 X 7 In. 75.00
Noritake, Condiment Set, Azalea, No.19322, Green Mark, 6 Piece 14.00
Noritake, Condiment Set, Azalea, 5 Piece 20.00
Noritake, Condiment Set, Hear, Speak, & See No Evil Monkeys, Tray, 3 Piece 12.00
Noritake, Creamer, Azalea 8.50
Noritake, Creamer, Fruit Flowers, 3 1/2 In. 6.50
Noritake, Cup & Saucer, Anaconda 9.00
Noritake, Cup & Saucer, Azalea .... 7.50 To 8.00
Noritake, Cup & Saucer, Azalea, Set Of 6 .... 35.00
Noritake, Cup & Saucer, Bancroft 9.00
Noritake, Cup & Saucer, Castella 9.00
Noritake, Cup & Saucer, Coffee, Pattern No.16034 .... 12.50
Noritake, Cup & Saucer, Demitasse, Gold Rims, Nippon Toki Kasha Signed 4.50
Noritake, Cup & Saucer, Demitasse, Orange & Blue Flowers 10.00
Noritake, Cup & Saucer, Demitasse, Pedestal Cup, Black 3.00
Noritake, Cup & Saucer, Demitasse, Pedestal Cup, Light Blue 3.00
Noritake, Cup & Saucer, Demitasse, Pedestal Cup, Yellow 3.00
Noritake, Cup & Saucer, Demitasse, Pedestal Cup, Maroon 3.00
Noritake, Cup & Saucer, Glennis 9.00
Noritake, Cup & Saucer, Mariana 9.00

Noritake, Cup & Saucer, Paisley	9.00
Noritake, Cup & Saucer, Pheasant	9.00
Noritake, Cup & Saucer, Tarantella	9.00
Noritake, Cup & Saucer, Tree In The Meadow	6.00
Noritake, Cup, Baskets Of Flowers, Gold Trim	3.00
Noritake, Cup, Bouillon, Azalea	14.50
Noritake, Cup, Malvern	3.50
Noritake, Dish, Boat Shape, Orange & White, Gold Trim, 9 In.	10.00
Noritake, Dish, Candy, Azalea, Scalloped, 2 Sections	12.50
Noritake, Dish, Candy, Center Handled	8.50
Noritake, Eggcup, Azalea	18.50
Noritake, Gravy Boat & Attached Underplate, Baskets Of Flowers, Gold Trim	12.00
Noritake, Gravy Boat & Underplate, Sailboat Scene	15.00
Noritake, Gravy Boat, Azalea	22.00 To 24.00
Noritake, Gravy Boat, La Salle	6.50
Noritake, Humidor, 6 Scenic Panels, Scenic Lid Blends In, Green Mark, 6 In.	70.00
Noritake, Jar, Honey, Red Bird Finial, Black Nymphet Silhouettes, 5 In.	20.00
Noritake, Jar, Tobacco, Applied Pipe On Lid, Red & Black Scene, 3 1/2 In.	18.00
Noritake, Jar, Tobacco, Forest Scene With Crane, Ornate Shape	37.50
Noritake, Mayonnaise Set, Azalea, Footed Bowl, 3 Piece	17.00 To 22.00
Noritake, Muffineer & Creamer, Scenic, Autumn Shades	24.00
Noritake, Muffineer & Creamer, Tree In The Meadow	25.00
Noritake, Napkin Holder, Hand-Painted	18.00
Noritake, Nappy, Azalea, Handled	8.50
Noritake, Pancake Set, Azalea, 2 Piece	34.00
Noritake, Pitcher, Gold Encrusted, Green & Black Accents, Nippon, 7 In.	75.00
Noritake, Plate, Azalea, 10 In.	8.00
Noritake, Plate, Bread & Butter, Azalea	4.75
Noritake, Plate, Bread & Butter, Pattern No.16034, 6 1/2 In.	3.00
Noritake, Plate, Cake, Azalea, Open End, 9 1/2 In.	15.00
Noritake, Plate, Canary Yellow, White Pinstripes, Green M Mark, 7 1/2 In.	24.00
Noritake, Plate, Dessert, Baskets Of Flowers, Gold Trim, 6 1/2 In.	5.00
Noritake, Plate, Dinner, Allure	2.50
Noritake, Plate, Dinner, Azalea	7.50
Noritake, Plate, Dinner, Baskets Of Flowers, Gold Trim, 10 In.	8.00
Noritake, Plate, Dinner, Century Pattern, 1900	6.00
Noritake, Plate, Dinner, Corinthia	3.50
Noritake, Plate, Gold, 7 In.	4.50
Noritake, Plate, Goldena, Gold Band, 7 1/2 In.	1.00
Noritake, Plate, Luncheon, Baskets Of Flowers, Gold Trim, 7 3/4 In.	5.50
Noritake, Plate, The Flamingo, 8 1/2 In.	30.00
Noritake, Plate, Tree In The Meadow, 7 3/4 In.	3.50
Noritake, Platter, Azalea, Oval, 14 In.	18.00 To 35.00
Noritake, Platter, Azalea, 12 In.	20.00
Noritake, Platter, Baskets Of Flowers, Gold Trim, 16 1/4 In.	25.00
Noritake, Platter, Meat, Pattern No.16034, Oval, 14 In.	25.00
Noritake, Platter, White & Gold, Oval, M Mark, 10 In.	9.00
Noritake, Pot & Ladle, Mustard, Green Wreath M	15.00
Noritake, Pot, Underplate, & Spoon, Marmalade, Azalea	20.00
Noritake, Ring Tree, Gold Hand, Pink Roses, Navy Stripes, Blue Mark	15.00
Noritake, Salt & Pepper, Azalea, 3 1/2 In.	18.00
Noritake, Salt & Pepper, Figural, Clowns	8.50
Noritake, Salt & Pepper, Pink Floral & Green Leaves On Blue, Gold Tops	8.00
Noritake, Salt & Pepper, Yellow Roses	6.00
Noritake, Saltshaker, Pattern No.16034	3.00
Noritake, Sauce, Azalea	4.75
Noritake, Sauce, Baskets Of Flowers, Gold Trim, 5 3/4 In.	3.50
Noritake, Saucer, Baskets Of Flowers, Gold Trim	3.00
Noritake, Saucer, Goldena, Gold Band	1.00
Noritake, Spooner, Florals, Pale Blue, Black, & Gold, 8 In.	30.00
Noritake, Spooner, Flowers On Blue	22.00
Noritake, Spooner, Spoon Shape, Floral, 2 Handles	6.50
Noritake, Spooner, Stack Type, 2 Handles, Hand-Painted, Marked	40.00
Noritake, Sugar & Creamer, Aldine Pattern	28.75
Noritake, Sugar & Creamer, Azalea	13.50 To 42.50
Noritake, Sugar & Creamer, Azalea, Tall Creamer	28.00

Noritake, Sugar & Creamer, Beige & Gold With Ivory Floral, Gold Handles	22.50
Noritake, Sugar & Creamer, Cover, Copper Color Luster, Pearl Luster Knob	15.00
Noritake, Sugar, Azalea	5.00
Noritake, Sugar, Covered, Pattern No.16034	10.00
Noritake, Tea Set, Child's, White, Gold Bands & Trim, Green Mark, 13 Piece	95.00
Noritake, Tea Set, Flowerbaskets On Orange, 14 Piece	65.00
Noritake, Tea Set, Mandarin Red, Black, & Gold, Geometrics, 3 Piece	25.00
Noritake, Tea Set, Mother-Of-Pearl, Blue Rims, 13 Piece	13.00
Noritake, Teapot, Iridescent Blue, Raised Floral, Gold Rim	27.50
Noritake, Teapot, Tree In The Meadow, 4 1/2 X 4 1/2 In.	15.00
Noritake, Tray & Cup, Snack, Azalea	18.00
Noritake, Tub, Butter, Azalea	19.00 To 25.00
Noritake, Vase, Flambe, Artist Signed, 6 3/4 In.	45.00
Noritake, Vase, Hand-Painted, Handled, 6 In. Across Mouth, 6 In.	22.00
Noritake, Vase, Urn Shape, 2 Gold Handled, Bird & Floral, 14 In.	65.00
Noritake, Vase, Urn Shape, 2 Handles, Bird & Pastel Flowers, 14 In.High	65.00
Noritake, Watermelon Set, Iris On Cream To Blue, Gold Edge, 7 Piece	30.00

Northwood Glass Company worked in Martins Ferry, Ohio, in the 1880s. They marked some pieces with the letter N in a circle. Many pieces of carnival glass were made by this company.

N

Northwood, see also Carnival Glass, Custard Glass, Pressed Glass, Rubena, Vaseline Glass

Northwood, Berry Set, Cherry & Plum, Gold & Red Trim, 7 Piece	125.00
Northwood, Berry Set, Cherry Thumbprint, Gold Trim, 7 Piece	135.00
Northwood, Berry Set, Paneled Cherry, 7 Piece	140.00
Northwood, Berry Set, Ruby, Paneled Cherry, Gold, 7 Piece	130.00
Northwood, Bowl, Berry, Green Opalescent, Regal, Signed N	65.00
Northwood, Bowl, Berry, Green, Inverted Fan & Feather, Grape & Lattice In	175.00
Northwood, Bowl, Berry, Master, Stained, Cherry & Thumbprint	30.00
Northwood, Bowl, Berry, Opalescent, Jeweled Heart, Beaded & Ruffled Rim, 1900	36.50
Northwood, Bowl, Berry, Stained, Cherry & Thumbprint	14.00
Northwood, Bowl, Blue, Meander, Footed, 6 1/2 X 4 In.	35.75
Northwood, Bowl, Blue, Ruffles & Rings, Opalescent, 8 1/2 In.	28.00
Northwood, Bowl, Deep Green, Fluted Scrolls, Fan Edge, 7 In.	25.00
Northwood, Bowl, Fluted Scrolls, Deep Green, Footed, 7 In.	25.00
Northwood, Bowl, Fruit, Green, Intaglio, Pedestal, Gold, 9 In.	95.00
Northwood, Bowl, Grape, Fluted, Custard, 7 In.	30.00
Northwood, Bowl, Master Berry, Holly, Colored Berries, Gold Trim, Marked N	49.50
Northwood, Bowl, Opalescent, Meander, Footed, 6 1/2 X 4 In.	35.00
Northwood, Bowl, Opalescent, Rings & Ruffled, Crimped Edge, Footed, 9 In.	29.50
Northwood, Bowl, Opalescent, Rings & Ruffles, Footed, 8 3/4 In.	28.50
Northwood, Butter, Covered, Cherry Thumbprint	75.00
Northwood, Butter, Covered, Cherry, Gold Trim	55.00
Northwood, Butter, Covered, Fluted Scrolls, White Opalescent	448.00
Northwood, Butter, Covered, Frosted, Royal Oak	95.00
Northwood, Butter, Covered, Green, Memphis	70.00
Northwood, Butter, Covered, Paneled Cherry, Clear Thumbprint With Red	65.00
Northwood, Butter, Covered, Paneled Cherry, Cranberry On Fruit, Gold	54.50
Northwood, Butter, Covered, Regal, Gold Trim	75.00
Northwood, Butter, White Opalescent, Covered, Fluted Scrolls	45.00
Northwood, Card Receiver, Vaseline, Fluted Scroll, Shell Edge, Scroll Feet	26.50
Northwood, Celery, Canary, Block	35.00
Northwood, Celery, Cherry Thumbprint, Signed N	85.00
Northwood, Celery, Paneled Cherry, Cranberry On Fruit, Gold & Foliage	39.50
Northwood, Compote, Dark Green, Purple Highlights, Signed N, 5 1/2 In.	32.50
Northwood, Compote, Jelly, Blue Opalescent, Maple Leaf	48.00
Northwood, Compote, Jelly, Intaglio Opal	15.00
Northwood, Creamer, Amethyst, Leaf Medallion	95.00
Northwood, Creamer, Blue To Opalescent, Intaglio	34.00
Northwood, Creamer, Cherry & Plum, Gold Trim	65.00
Northwood, Creamer, Cherry Thumbprint	45.00
Northwood, Creamer, Deep Rose, Pull-Ups Of Maroon, Yellow, Amber, & White	385.00
Northwood, Creamer, Opalescent, Drapery, Signed	28.00
Northwood, Cruet, Cobalt, Leaf Medallion, Canary Stopper	135.00
Northwood, Cruet, Intaglio, White Opalescent	58.00

Northwood, Cruet, White Opalescent, Argonaut Shell	68.00
Northwood, Humidor, Blue, Grape & Cable, Iridescent	125.00
Northwood, Muffineer, Cranberry, Leaf Umbrella	125.00
Northwood, Muffineer, Frosted & Clear, Royal Ivy	75.00
Northwood, Muffineer, Yellow Cased, Umbrella	120.00
Northwood, Pitcher, Hand-Painted Fruit, Gold Number On Bottom, 12 In.	45.00
Northwood, Pitcher, Water, Cherry Cable, Signed N, 8 In.	85.00
Northwood, Pitcher, Water, Chrysanthemum Sprig, Blue, Signed	400.00
Northwood, Pitcher, Water, Emerald Green, Leaf Medallion, Gold Trim	125.00
Northwood, Pitcher, Water, Frosted, Royal Ivy	95.00
Northwood, Pitcher, Water, Green, Geneva, Gold Trim	125.00
Northwood, Pitcher, Water, Leaf Mold, Pink & White Spatter Handle, 8 In.	145.00
Northwood, Pitcher, Water, Royal Oak	138.00
Northwood, Pitcher, Water, Yellow Cased, Leaf Umbrella	195.00
Northwood, Rose Bowl, Blue Opalescent, Wide Panel, Knob Stem, 5 In.	23.50
Northwood, Salt & Pepper, Emerald Green, Near Cut	35.00
Northwood, Saltshaker, Alaska, Opalescent Vaseline	28.00
Northwood, Saltshaker, Cranberry & Frosted, Royal Ivy	32.00
Northwood, Saltshaker, Cranberry Splash, Leaf Umbrella	35.00
Northwood, Saltshaker, Cranberry To Frosted To Clear, Royal Oak	50.00
Northwood, Saltshaker, Rubena, Royal Ivy	32.00
Northwood, Saltshaker, White Opalescent, Everglades	28.00
Northwood, Sauce, Cherry & Thumbprint	16.00
Northwood, Sauce, Green Opalescent, Jeweled Heart, 5 1/2 In.	22.00
Northwood, Sauce, Holly, Colored Berries, Gold Trim, Marked N	9.00
Northwood, Sauce, Jewel, Clear & Frosted, 3 1/2 In., Set Of 5	30.00
Northwood, Sauce, Lattice With Cherries, Gold Band, Cranberry Fruit	7.00
Northwood, Sauce, Vaseline, Intaglio, Footed, 1890	26.00
Northwood, Spooner, Amethyst, Regent	75.00
Northwood, Spooner, Blue Opalescent, Alaska	45.00
Northwood, Spooner, Blue Opalescent, Drapery, Signed N	40.00
Northwood, Spooner, Blue Opalescent, Intaglio	85.00
Northwood, Spooner, Blue, Everglades	26.00
Northwood, Spooner, Chrysanthemum Sprig, Blue, Script	240.00
Northwood, Spooner, Drapery, Clear & Opalescent, Signed	45.00
Northwood, Spooner, White Opalescent, Alaska	15.00 To 18.75
Northwood, Sugar & Creamer, Cherry, Gold Trim	87.50
Northwood, Sugar & Creamer, Emerald Green, Gold Bands, Marked N	42.00
Northwood, Sugar & Creamer, Open, Cherry & Plum, Gold Flashed	45.00
Northwood, Sugar, Covered, Opalescent, Drapery, Signed	28.00
Northwood, Syrup, Frosted & Clear, Royal Ivy	75.00
Northwood, Syrup, Frosted & Clear, Royal Ivy, Spring Lid	78.00
Northwood, Table Set, Cherry & Plum, Gold Trim, 4 Piece	250.00
Northwood, Table Set, Green, Near Cut, Gold Trim, Signed N, 4 Piece	175.00
Northwood, Table Set, Opalescent Drape, Gold Trim, 4 Piece	210.00
Northwood, Toothpick, Chrysanthemum Sprig, Blue, Signed Script	250.00
Northwood, Toothpick, Cranberry To Clear, Royal Ivy	65.00
Northwood, Tumbler, Blue Opalescent, Drape, Signed	50.00
Northwood, Tumbler, Blue Opalescent, Inverted Feather & Fan, Signed	80.00
Northwood, Tumbler, Blue, Oriental Poppy, Gold Trim	22.00
Northwood, Tumbler, Cherry & Plum, Gold Trim	22.00
Northwood, Tumbler, Chrysanthemum Sprig, Blue, Unsigned	105.00
Northwood, Tumbler, Frosted Rainbow Crackle, Royal Ivy	100.00
Northwood, Tumbler, Green, Cherry	25.00
Northwood, Tumbler, Green, Oriental Poppy, Gold, Signed With Circle	25.00
Northwood, Tumbler, Green, Poppy, Gold Trim	25.00
Northwood, Tumbler, Pressed Plums, Signed	17.50
Northwood, Tumbler, Swag, Opaline, Gold Flash	22.00
Northwood, Tumbler, Teal Blue, Grape, Signed N	18.00
Northwood, Tumbler, White Opalescent, Wild Bouquet	16.00
Northwood, Tumbler, White, Yellow Cased, Leaf Umbrella	22.00
Northwood, Vase, Amethyst, Rustic, Signed, 9 In.	22.00
Northwood, Vase, Fluted, Green, 10 In.	14.00
Northwood, Vase, Green, Fine Rib, Marigold Iridescent, Signed, 10 In.	15.00
Northwood, Vase, Ivory, Brown Pull-Up, Robin's-Egg Blue Interior, 4 1/2 In.	850.00
Northwood, Vase, Opalescent White, Clear Diamond Point, Marked N, 9 In.	16.00

Northwood, Water Set, Blue Opalescent, Drapery, 7 Piece 350.00
Northwood, Water Set, Deep Blue, Enamel Floral 5 Piece 135.00
Northwood, Water Set, Green Opalescent, Regal, Signed, 5 Piece 265.00
Northwood, Water Set, Green, Oriental Poppy, Gold Trim, 7 Piece 450.00
Northwood, Water Set, Green, Peach, Gold Trim, Signed N, 7 Piece 240.00
Northwood, Water Set, Opalescent, Everglades, Raised Gold, 7 Piece 225.00
Northwood, Water Set, Paneled Cherry, 9 Piece 200.00
Nuart, Globe, Gas, Fishscale Pattern, Iridescent Interior, 4 1/2 X 5 In. 15.00

Nymphenburg, a German porcelain factory, was established at Neudeck-ob-der-Au in 1753 and moved to Nymphenburg in 1761. The company is still in existence. Modern marks include a shield superseded by a star or crown, and a crowned CT with a checkered shield.

Nymphenburg, Cup & Saucer, Cupids At Hunt, Stag, Scenery, Gold Engraved 95.00
Nymphenburg, Cup & Saucer, Demitasse, Hand-Painted Flowers, Gold Scalloped 37.50
Nymphenburg, Cup & Saucer, Demitasse, Ribbed, Scalloped Gold Rim Saucer 37.00
Nymphenburg, Figurine, Toy Terrier, Sitting On Haunches, 10 In.High 135.00

Occupied Japan is the mark used on pieces of pottery and porcelain made during the American occupation of Japan after World War II. Collectors are now buying these pieces. The items were made for export to the United States.

Occupied Japan, see also Silver Plate, Salt & Pepper
Occupied Japan, Ashtray, Metal, Leaf 1.50
Occupied Japan, Ashtray, Metal, Rose 1.50
Occupied Japan, Bowl, Floral Center, Open Beneath Scalloped Rim, Gold, 8 In. 12.00
Occupied Japan, Bowl, Fruit, Maruni Lacquerware, Openwork, Metal Base, 15 In. 25.00
Occupied Japan, Bowl, Pastels, Meito, 7 1/2 In. 5.00
Occupied Japan, Chocolate Set, Victorian Style Floral, 13 Piece 35.00
Occupied Japan, Condiment Set, Dog Shapes, 4 Piece 14.00
Occupied Japan, Creamer, Figural, Standing Cow, Black & White 8.50
Occupied Japan, Cup & Saucer, Floral, 3 1/2 In. 5.00
Occupied Japan, Cup & Saucer, Geisha Girl In Cup Bottom, Dragons 15.50
Occupied Japan, Cup & Saucer, Pastel Floral On Ivory, Gold Trim 6.00
Occupied Japan, Cup & Saucer, Rose 15.00
Occupied Japan, Cup & Saucer, Tulips 6.50
Occupied Japan, Demitasse Set, White & Eggshell, Roses Medallions, 9 Piece 15.00
Occupied Japan, Dish, Candy, Dresden Type, Square, 5 In. 8.50
Occupied Japan, Dish, Candy, Petaled Leaf Form, Raised Flowers, Signed 12.00
Occupied Japan, Figurine, Autumn, Cherub, Bisque, 7 1/2 In. 6.00
Occupied Japan, Figurine, Colonial Lady & Gentleman, 5 1/2 In., Pair 12.00
Occupied Japan, Figurine, Colonial Lady & Gentleman, 6 In., Pair 10.00
Occupied Japan, Figurine, Colonial Lady & Gentleman, 8 1/4 In., Pair 15.00
Occupied Japan, Figurine, Little Girl Playing Yellow Accordion, 4 In. 6.00
Occupied Japan, Figurine, Organ Grinder & Monkey, 6 In. 8.00
Occupied Japan, Figurine, Pony & Cart, Cowgirl Finial On Lid, 8 In. 6.00
Occupied Japan, Figurine, Victorian Lady, 8 In. 8.50
Occupied Japan, Figurine, Victorian Man, 8 In. 8.50
Occupied Japan, Group, Boy & Girl Musicians, 4 1/4 In. 4.00
Occupied Japan, Group, Wise Monkeys, 3 In. 3.50
Occupied Japan, Humidor, Covered, Rust Color, Mums, Foo Dog Finial 25.00
Occupied Japan, Lighter, Gun Shape 5.00
Occupied Japan, Mug, Lady In Sedan Chair, Gold & Enamel 20.00
Occupied Japan, Mug, Men Parading, Gold & Enamel 20.00
Occupied Japan, Planter, Boy Carrying Buckets, 5 In. 4.50
Occupied Japan, Planter, Girl Musician, 4 In. 4.50
Occupied Japan, Planter, Goose In Front, 3 X 2 1/2 In. 6.00
Occupied Japan, Planter, Lady, 6 In. 7.50
Occupied Japan, Planter, Poodle, 6 In. 8.50
Occupied Japan, Planter, Swan, 6 1/2 In. .... 6.00 To 7.50
Occupied Japan, Plate, Ardalt, Hand-Painted, 5 1/2 In. 9.00
Occupied Japan, Salt & Pepper, Gondola 8.50
Occupied Japan, Salt & Pepper, 2 Baby Birds In Nest 4.00
Occupied Japan, Salt, Individual, Marked O.J. 1.90
Occupied Japan, Sharpener, Pencil, Pistol, Metal, 1 1/4 In. 1.50
Occupied Japan, Shoe, Baby's, 5 3/4 In. .... 7.00 To 9.00

Occupied Japan, Spoon Rest, Blue & Green Seascape 3.50
Occupied Japan, String Of Ivory Colored Elephants 8.50
Occupied Japan, Tea Set, Doll's, Porcelain, Hand-Painted, 3 Piece 10.00
Occupied Japan, Tea Set, Doll's, Porcelain, Hand-Painted, 10 Piece 20.00
Occupied Japan, Tea Set, Fall Leaves, Pink Glaze, 3 In. Tray, 8 Piece 15.00
Occupied Japan, Tea Set, Floral, 3 In. Oblong Tray, 8 Piece 14.00
Occupied Japan, Tea Set, Gold Border, 4 3/4 In. Tray, 8 Piece 20.00
Occupied Japan, Tea Set, Hiro, Floral, 3 3/4 In. Tray, 8 Piece 17.00
Occupied Japan, Teapot, Porcelain, Hand-Painted, 1 1/2 In. 1.75
Occupied Japan, Toby Mug, Lord With Glasses On 9.50
Occupied Japan, Toothpick, Indian With Bow, Tree Stump, 3 In. 4.00
Occupied Japan, Tray, Fruit, Lacquer Ware 47.50
Occupied Japan, Vase, Stump, Girl With Umbrella, 6 1/2 In. 9.00
Occupied Japan, Vase, Stump, Girl, Blue Shorts, Yellow Jacket, 6 1/2 In. 8.50

G. E. OHR, BILOXI. *Ohr pottery was made by George E.Ohr in Biloxi, Mississippi, between 1883 and 1918. The pieces were made of very thin clay and were twisted, folded and dented into odd, graceful shapes.*

Ohr, Candleholder, Blue Eggshell Glaze, 5 1/2 In. ....
Ohr, Mug, Puzzle, Iridescent Glaze 95.00
Ohr, Mug, Puzzle, Signed 95.00
Ohr, Mug, Sleeve Cuff With Button Shape, Brown Glaze, Signed, 3 1/2 In. 90.00
Ohr, Vase, Black Metallic Glaze, Impressed G.E.Ohr Biloxi Miss., 3 1/2 In. 95.00
Ohr, Vase, Glossy Brown Glaze, Crinkled Handles, 4 1/2 In.High 75.00
Ohr, Vase, Green Tan Speckled Glaze, Crumpled Style, 4 In. 75.00
Ohr, Vase, Orange With Black High Glaze, Pinched In Sides, 5 1/2 In. 115.00
Ohr, Vase, Pinch, Dark Iridescent, Biloxi, Miss., 3 In. 125.00
Ohr, Vase, Fluted, Ruffled Shape, Metallic Brown, 3 1/4 In. 125.00
Ohr, Vase, Pot Shaped, Orange & Brown, 3 1/2 In. 65.00
.... 150.00

Old ivory china was made in Silesia, Germany, at the end of the nineteenth century. It is often marked with a crown and the word Silesia. The pattern numbers appear on the base of each piece.

Old Ivory, Bowl, Berry, No.16, Silesia, 5 In. 14.00
Old Ivory, Bowl, Berry, No.84, 9 1/2 In. 39.00
Old Ivory, Bowl, No.28, 10 In. 60.00
Old Ivory, Bowl, Waste, No.16, Silesia, 5 In. 40.00
Old Ivory, Cake Set, No.10, 6 Piece 95.00
Old Ivory, Celery, No.15 .... 55.00
Old Ivory, Chocolate Set, No.16, 7 Piece 300.00
Old Ivory, Creamer, No.16, Yellow Roses, Brown Trim, Clarion Mark 28.00
Old Ivory, Creamer, Silesia 25.00
Old Ivory, Cup & Saucer, Demitasse, Birds & Flowers, Syracuse, Set Of 6 .... 50.00
Old Ivory, Cup & Saucer, No.16, Silesia .... 24.00 To 35.00
Old Ivory, Cup & Saucer, No.28 .... 33.00
Old Ivory, Cup & Saucer, No.200 .... 35.00
Old Ivory, Dish, Candy, Handle, Clarion & Silesia Mark, 7 In. 22.00
Old Ivory, Dish, Candy, No.16, Silesia, Oval, 7 In. 20.00
Old Ivory, Hair Receiver, Roses, Fleur-De-Lis 35.00
Old Ivory, Jar, Cracker, No.16, Silesia 100.00
Old Ivory, Nappy, No.16, Handle On Top, 6 In. 29.00
Old Ivory, Plate, Cake, No.16, Pierced Handles, Silesia, 10 In. 35.00
Old Ivory, Plate, Chop, Chantilly, Pink & Yellow Roses, 12 In. 24.00
Old Ivory, Plate, Dessert, No.16, 7 3/4 In. 18.00
Old Ivory, Plate, Holly, No.22, 6 In. 30.00
Old Ivory, Plate, Holly, 7 1/2 In. 28.00
Old Ivory, Plate, No.16, Silesia, 6 1/2 In. 15.00
Old Ivory, Plate, No.16, Silesia, 7 1/2 In. 16.00
Old Ivory, Plate, No.16, Silesia, 9 In. 18.00
Old Ivory, Plate, No.84, 6 1/4 In. 13.00
Old Ivory, Plate, No.200, 6 1/4 In. 16.00
Old Ivory, Plate, No.200, 7 1/2 In. 18.00
Old Ivory, Plate, No.202, 8 1/2 In. 22.50
Old Ivory, Plate, Scalloped, Pink & White Roses, Gold, Germany, 8 1/4 In. 18.00
Old Ivory, Platter, No.16, Silesia, Oval, 13 1/2 In. 40.00
Old Ivory, Sauceboat & Underplate, Apricot Floral, Silesia, Green Mark 58.00

Old Ivory, Saucer, No.16	5.00
Old Ivory, Sugar & Creamer, No.11	65.00
Old Ivory, Sugar & Creamer, No.16, Silesia	75.00
Old Ivory, Sugar & Creamer, No.200	100.00
Old Ivory, Sugar, No.200	30.00
Old Ivory, Teapot, No.16, Silesia, 7 In.	75.00

Onion, originally named 'Bulb Pattern,' is a white ware decorated with cobalt blue. Although it is commonly associated with Meissen, other companies made the pattern in the latter part of the nineteenth century.

Onion, Bowl, Center, Blue On White, Bisque Foot & Rim, Meissen, 9 1/2 In.	45.00
Onion, Bowl, Curved Divider, Meissen, 14 In.	85.00
Onion, Butter, 3 Piece, English Mark	38.00
Onion, Chamberstick, Meissen, C.1840, Pinlike Handle, 2 1/2 In.	125.00
Onion, Coffee Pot, Rosebud Finial, Meissen, 10 In.	110.00
Onion, Creamer, Germany, Blue, 5 In.	15.00
Onion, Creamer, Meissen, Crossed Swords Mark, 3 1/2 In.	32.00
Onion, Creamer, 3 In.	36.00
Onion, Cup & Saucer, Demitasse	15.00
Onion, Cup & Saucer, Meissen, Crossed Swords Mark	16.00
Onion, Cup & Saucer, Meissen, Extra Large	58.00
Onion, Cup & Saucer, Royal Copenhagen	12.50
Onion, Cup & Saucer, Scalloped Edges, Meissen In Oval Mark	22.50
Onion, Cup, Nut, Footed, Meissen, Crossed Swords Mark	45.00
Onion, Dish, Leaf, Meissen, Crossed Swords Mark, 7 1/2 In.	35.00
Onion, Eggcup, Meissen, Crossed Swords Mark	12.00 To 15.00
Onion, Gravyboat & Attached Tray, Meissen	30.00
Onion, Mustard Set, Handled, Spoon, Germany, 2 Piece	11.95
Onion, Plate, Gold Decoration, Meissen, 9 1/2 In.	50.00
Onion, Plate, Meissen, Crossed Swords Mark, 9 In.	29.00
Onion, Platter, Meissen, Crossed Swords Under Glaze, 13 1/2 In.	34.00
Onion, Stein, Meissen, Lithophane, 1/2 Liter	200.00
Onion, Sugar, Rosebud Finial, Meissen	35.00 To 48.50
Onion, Teapot, Rosebud Finial, Meissen	75.00

Opalescent glass is translucent glass that has the bluish-white tones of the opal gemstone. It is often found in pressed glassware made in Victorian times. Some dealers use the terms opaline and opalescent for any of the bluish-white translucent wares.

Opalescent, Berry Set, Swag With Bracket, Green, 7 Piece	160.00
Opalescent, Bowl, Banana, Shell, Rolled Sides	38.00
Opalescent, Bowl, Berry, Blue, Idyll, 4 1/2 In.Diameter	15.00
Opalescent, Bowl, Blue, Scalloped Loop Variant, Fluted Rim, 8 1/2 In.	27.00
Opalescent, Bowl, Fiery Clear & Pulled, Striped, Clear Scalloped Edge, 6 In.	8.00
Opalescent, Bowl, Green, Spatula Feet, 9 In.	21.00
Opalescent, Bowl, Green, 8 3/4 In.	45.00
Opalescent, Bowl, Round, Fan Design, Scalloped Edge, Green, 8 In.	23.00
Opalescent, Bowl, Strawberry & Honeycomb, Green, 9 In.	27.50
Opalescent, Bowl, Swirled, 8 X 3 1/2 In.	24.00
Opalescent, Bowl, White To Blue, Ruffled, Hand-Painted, 7 X 5 1/4 In.	75.00
Opalescent, Bride's Bowl, Pastel Green, Flowers & Leaves, Crimped, 8 1/8 In.	16.00
Opalescent, Cake Stand, Sapphire Blue, Ruffled Edge, 4 X 8 1/2 In.	28.00
Opalescent, Celery, Blue, Beatty Rib	45.00
Opalescent, Compote, Jelly, Intaglio	19.50
Opalescent, Creamer, Beatty, Ribbed	45.00
Opalescent, Creamer, Cherry, Vasleine Wreathed	20.00
Opalescent, Creamer, Crisscross Ribbing	49.00
Opalescent, Creamer, Paneled Holly, Red Berries, Green Leaves	49.50
Opalescent, Creamer, Tokyo, Green	40.00 To 45.00
Opalescent, Cruet, Blue, Handles, Raised Leaf Decoration, Pair	95.00
Opalescent, Cruet, Blue, Leaf Spray, Blue Stopper	110.00
Opalescent, Dish, Banana, Shell & Seaweed, Footed, Blue, Small	20.00
Opalescent, Dish, Candy, Blue, 3 Tree Trunks On Shell Base	35.00
Opalescent, Dish, Santa Cover, Blue, Sleigh Base, 5 1/4 In.	7.50
Opalescent, Epergne, Three Lily, Opalescent To Lime Green, Hobs, 10 In.	110.00
Opalescent, Jar, Biscuit, A.J.Hall, Hand-Painted Floral, Silver Fittings	139.00

Opalescent, Muffineer, Blue, Crisscross	65.00
Opalescent, Muffineer, Blue, Ribbed Sides	38.00
Opalescent, Muffineer, Blue, Spot Resist Ribbed Swirl, Collared	110.00
Opalescent, Mug, Beatty Honeycomb	20.00
Opalescent, Pitcher, Blue, Swirl, 10 In.High	75.00
Opalescent, Pitcher, Rose To Yellow Green, Hobnail, Square, 8 In.High	245.00
Opalescent, Pitcher, Water, Beatty, Swirl	75.00
Opalescent, Pitcher, Water, Green, Coin Spot, Turned-In Sides On Spout	58.00
Opalescent, Rose Bowl, Clear To Blue, Owl On Feet, Acanthus Leaves, 4 1/2 In	37.50
Opalescent, Salt & Pepper, Yellow, Ribbon Diagonal	45.00
Opalescent, Sauce, Lions Leg, Yellow	18.50
Opalescent, Spooner, Blue, Ribbed Swirl, Miniature	45.00
Opalescent, Spooner, Everglades	20.00 To 30.00
Opalescent, Spooner, Hobnail	12.50
Opalescent, Spooner, Hobnail, Miniature	15.00
Opalescent, Spooner, Horses' Heads Handles	8.50
Opalescent, Spooner, Wreath & Shell, Footed	32.50
Opalescent, Sugar & Creamer, Hobnail, 3 1/4 In.	14.00
Opalescent, Sugar, Covered, Blue, Palm Beach, Twig Handles, Grapes Finial	85.00
Opalescent, Sugar, Covered, Swirled Rib, Opalescent & Clear	25.00
Opalescent, Syrup, Blue, Coin Spot	85.00
Opalescent, Syrup, Coin Spot, Bulbous	49.00
Opalescent, Syrup, Coin Spot, Nickel Top	42.00
Opalescent, Syrup, Coin Spot, Tapered	49.00
Opalescent, Syrup, Crisscross Ribbing	69.00
Opalescent, Syrup, Lattice	79.00
Opalescent, Syrup, Reverse Swirled Rib, Collared	69.00
Opalescent, Syrup, Reversed Swirled Rib	79.00
Opalescent, Syrup, Striped, Rose Colored Flowers, Dated Lid	75.00
Opalescent, Syrup, Swirl & Coin Dot	55.00 To 60.00
Opalescent, Table Set, Swag With Bracket, Green	185.00
Opalescent, Toothpick, Beatty Ribbed	23.00
Opalescent, Toothpick, Blue, Hobnail, 3 Feet	25.00
Opalescent, Toothpick, Blue, Ribbed, Square	28.00
Opalescent, Toothpick, Frosted Ribbed Swirl, Overshot	28.00
Opalescent, Toothpick, Green, Swag With Brackets	38.00
Opalescent, Toothpick, Hobnail, Footed	12.50
Opalescent, Toothpick, Iris Meander, Blue	48.00
Opalescent, Toothpick, White, Ribbed	15.00
Opalescent, Tumbler, Blue & Clear, Diagonal Stripes & Ribs, C.1900	17.00
Opalescent, Tumbler, Blue & Clear, Fine Rib With Diamonds & Flowers, C.1900	17.00
Opalescent, Tumbler, Blue & Clear, Fine Rib With Zigzag, C.1900	17.00
Opalescent, Tumbler, Blue, Hobnail, Ground Pontil	25.00
Opalescent, Tumbler, Blue, Vertical Stripes, C.1900	17.00
Opalescent, Tumbler, Buttons & Braid, Clear	18.50
Opalescent, Tumbler, Coin Spot, Ribbed Sides & Top Band	50.00
Opalescent, Tumbler, Everglades, Blue	35.00
Opalescent, Tumbler, Geometric Decoration, Gold Floral, Footed, Flint	35.00
Opalescent, Tumbler, Green, Spanish Lace Type, 3 1/2 In.	18.00
Opalescent, Tumbler, Green, Swag With Brackets	12.50
Opalescent, Tumbler, White, Pointed Hobnail	15.00
Opalescent, Water Set, Herringbone, Applied Handle, 9 In.Pitcher, Set Of 6	145.00
Opalescent, Water Set, Rose, Hobnail, Barrel Tumblers, 5 Piece	250.00

Opaline glass, or opal glass, was made in white, apple green, and other colors. The glass had a matte surface and a lack of transparency. It was often gilded or painted. It was a popular mid-nineteenth-century European glassware.

Opaline, Bowl, Hat Shaped, Blue, White Enamel Bowl, 3 1/2 In.High	27.50
Opaline, Epergne, Rose Color, Ruffled Center Horn & Base Edge, 12 In.	85.00
Opaline, Hat, Swirl Striped, 6 1/2 X 11 1/2 X 9 1/2 In.	69.00
Opaline, Saltshaker, Florals In Low Relief, White, Pewter Top	12.50
Opaline, Sugar & Creamer, Gold Trim	17.50
Opaline, Toothpick, Hand-Painted Pug Dog, Ormolu Rim, Signed Bauer	30.00
Opaline, Toothpick, Touring Car	25.00
Opaline, Tumble-Up, Blue, French	145.00

Opaline, Tumbler, White, Picture Of Kitten With Ball, 4 In.	7.50
Opaline, Vase, Blue, Melon Shape Bowl, Flared Ruffled Top, 8 In.	35.00
Opaline, Vase, Deep Blue, Fluted, White Enamel Flowers, 6 1/2 In.	25.00
Opaline, Vase, French, White, Floriform, Blue Stem, Double Wafer, C.1820, 8 In.	95.00
Opera Glasses, Art Nouveau, Lady's Head Profile, Red & Green Flowers	175.00
Opera Glasses, French, Ivory	18.50
Opera Glasses, French, Pearl, Handled	33.00
Opera Glasses, Mother-Of-Pearl, Velvet Bag	30.00
Opera Glasses, Paris, Mother-Of-Pearl	25.00
Organ, see Music, Organ	
Ormolu, Candelabra, Foliate Branch, 5 Arm, C.1850, 25 1/2 In., Pair	325.00
Ormolu, Candelabra, Louis XV Style, Lelievre, 4 Arm, C.1890, 22 In., Pair	1000.00
Ormolu, Candelabra, Louis Philippe, Female Figure, Marble Base, 25 In., Pair	375.00
Ormolu, Figurine, Seminude Man, Basket On His Back, C.1890, 4 Ft.8 In.	120.00
Orphan Annie, Ashtray, Bisque, Annie & Sandy	30.00
Orphan Annie, Book, About Dogs, 1936, Radio Premium	30.00
Orphan Annie, Book, Little Orphan Annie & Chizzler, 1933, Big Little Books	12.50
Orphan Annie, Book, Pop-Up	50.00
Orphan Annie, Bracelet, I.D.	11.00 To 20.00
Orphan Annie, Coin, Good Luck, Secret Society, Radio	9.50
Orphan Annie, Decoder, 1936	18.00 To 20.00
Orphan Annie, Dog, Sandy, Suitcase	125.00
Orphan Annie, Doll, Composition, Dressed, 13 In.	75.00
Orphan Annie, Doll, Composition, 14 In.	65.00
Orphan Annie, Doll, Stuffed Felt, Painted Features, Red Dress, 22 In.	12.00
Orphan Annie, Game, Treasure Hunt, 1933	15.00 To 18.00
Orphan Annie, Map, Simmons Corners, 1939 Radio Premium	40.00
Orphan Annie, Mug	10.00 To 30.00
Orphan Annie, Mug, Ovaltine, Beetleware	12.00 To 19.00
Orphan Annie, Mug, Shake-Up, Game, Instructions	15.00 To 17.00
Orphan Annie, Stove, Green	17.00 To 22.00
Orphan Annie, Stove, Red	15.00 To 22.00
Orphan Annie, Toy, Sandy, Mechanical, Tin	85.00
Orphan Annie, Tumbler, Ovaltine	10.00

Orrefors Glassworks, located in the Swedish Province of Smaland, was established in 1916.

Orrefors, Vase, Gourd Shape, Clear Casing, Violet Stripes, Ariel, 1936, 4 In.	250.00
Ott & Brewer, Cup & Saucer, Belleek, Tridacna, Pink Inside	90.00
Ott & Brewer, Cup & Saucer, Demitasse, Gold Wishbone Handle, White, Pink	75.00
Ott & Brewer, Cup, Demitasse, Belleek, Tridacna, Gold	65.00
Ott & Brewer, Sugar & Creamer, Belleek, Yellow Shading, Draped Pattern	85.00

OWENS UTOPIAN

Owens Pottery was made in Zanesville, Ohio, from 1891 to 1928. The first art pottery was made after 1896. Utopian Ware, Cyrano, Navarre, Feroza, and Henri Deux were made. Pieces were usually marked with a form of the name Owens. About 1907 the firm began to make tile and gave up the art pottery wares.

Owens, Creamer, Utopian, Brown With Leaf & Berry, Plated Handle	50.00
Owens, Lamp Base, Opalesce, Crinkled Blue, Lessell Luster Floral, 8 In.	250.00
Owens, Lamp, Lessell Ware, Lasa Type, Double Socket Fittings, 14 In.	275.00
Owens, Lamp, Lessell Ware, Trees, Mountains, & Lake On Blue, 14 In.	275.00
Owens, Lamp, Soudanese, Gloss Black, 11 In.	65.00
Owens, Mug, Owensart Matt Green 1212, Trees With Fruit, 4 1/2 In.	125.00
Owens, Mug, Utopian, Brown Glaze, Cherries, 5 1/4 In.	65.00
Owens, Mug, Utopian, Brown Glaze, Leaves & Berries, 4 1/2 In.	75.00
Owens, Mug, Utopian, Cherry, Artist Signed	75.00
Owens, Mug, Utopian, Left Handed, Berry & Leaf, Artist Signed	120.00
Owens, Tankard, Utopian, Standard Brown Glaze, Left Handed, Florals, 5 In.	60.00
Owens, Vase, Brown & Yellow, Floral, Footed, 8 In.	55.00
Owens, Vase, Bud, Clewell, Raised Floral, Marked Owens, 5 In.	150.00
Owens, Vase, Buff To Blue, Daisy Decoration, 7 In.High	32.00
Owens, Vase, Clover, 13 X 5 In.	40.00
Owens, Vase, Henri Deux, Goldwork, 11 In.	375.00
Owens, Vase, Henri Deux, Marked Owens 2 Henri Deux 1306, 8 1/2 In.	425.00
Owens, Vase, Navarre, Green, Green Stamp Mark, 9 In.	175.00

Owens, Vase, Opalesce Inlaid, Iridescent Copper, Floral, Gold, Black, 12 In. 100.00
Owens, Vase, Opalesce Utopian, Gold, Yellow Rose, White Beads, 13 1/4 In. 235.00
Owens, Vase, Opalesce, Inlaid, Copper, Black Outlined Floral, Handled, 12 In. 225.00
Owens, Vase, Pitcher, Utopian, Glossy Brown To Green, Painted Floral, 5 In. 56.00
Owens, Vase, Utopian, Autumn Leaves, 6 In. 95.00
Owens, Vase, Utopian, Brown Glaze, Floral Decoration, 4 In.High 90.00
Owens, Vase, Utopian, Brown Glaze, Floral, E.B., 7 In. 60.00
Owens, Vase, Utopian, Brown, Orange Flowers, Green Leaves, T.S., 6 1/2 In. 75.00
Owens, Vase, Utopian, Dark Brown, Orange Flower, Yellow Green Leaves, 8 In. 45.00
Owens, Vase, Utopian, Deep Brown, Yellow & Brown Roses, Green Leaves, 8 In. 85.00
Owens, Vase, Utopian, Drilled For Lamp, Marked J.B.Owens, 12 In. 75.00
Owens, Vase, Utopian, Opalesce, Floral, Marked Owens, 11 1/4 In. 350.00
Owens, Vase, Utopian, Pansy Decoration, Swirled Rib, 4 In.High 65.00
Owens, Vase, Utopian, Pine Branches On Dark To Light Brown To Green, 4 In. 80.00
Owens, Vase, Utopian, Red & Yellow Floral On Brown & Green, 8 1/2 In. 65.00
Owens, Vase, Utopian, Twisted Body, Pansy Decoration, Artist Signed, 3 3/4 In 75.00
Owens, Vase, Utopian, Yellow Daisies On Yellow, Gold, & Brown, 11 In. 120.00
Owens, Vase, Venetian, Metallic Luster Over Yellow, 2 Handled, 11 X 4 In. 195.00
Oyster Plate, French, Green Sprays On Pink & Green, Gold 25.00
Oyster Plate, French, White, Beige Outlined Oysters 22.50
Oyster Plate, French, White, Sterling Overlay, Scalloped 20.00
Oyster Plate, German, White, 5 Indentations, Floral, Gold, 11 In. 30.00
Painting, see also Store, Painting
Painting, Diorama, Birds & Rodents, Mahogany, Glass Paneled, 25 X 4 Ft. 275.00
Painting, Diorama, Mounted Sailing Vessels Scene, Wm.Peters, C.1850, 29 In. 225.00
Painting, Diorama, Ship, Merrill, Carved & Painted Wood, C.1850, 27 1/2 In. 70.00
Painting, Fraktur, Anna Margaret Beirle, Maryland, 1815, 14 1/2 X 12 In. 10.00
Painting, Fraktur, Berks County, Pa., 1788, 14 1/2 X 12 1/2 In. 900.00
Painting, Fraktur, Charlotta Meier, Maryland, 1783, 16 1/2 X 13 3/4 In. 1700.00
Painting, Fraktur, Gebrust Und Taufschein Of Limen Koehl, Pa., 1837, 16 In. 180.00
Painting, Fraktur, Maria Heilman, Pa., 1812, 14 1/2 X 12 1/2 In. 1500.00
Painting, Fraktur, Montgomery County, Pa., 1789, Floral, Birds, 16 X 13 In. 375.00
Painting, Fraktur, Pennsylvania, 1828, Birds & Floral, 9 X 7 In. 150.00
Painting, Fraktur, Susan Prutzman, Pa., 1873, 16 X 13 In. 80.00
Painting, Fraktur, Two Soldiers, Drawn Swords, C.1850, 7 X 6 In. 300.00
Painting, Miniature On Ivory, Lady, Ornate Frame 48.00
Painting, Miniature On Ivory, Lord Nelson, Ivory Frame 135.00
Painting, Miniature On Ivory, Young Woman, Regina Daxemberger, C.1830 .... 125.00
Painting, Miniature, Colonel Archibald Cary, Virginia, Oval, 1 3/4 In. 300.00
Painting, Miniature, Daniel Gadson, American, Gold Frame, Oval, 2 3/4 In. 300.00
Painting, Miniature, Gentleman, Black Coat, American, Oval, 2 1/2 In. 150.00
Painting, Miniature, Richard Earl Hower, Oval, 3 In. 225.00
Painting, Miniature, Samuel Adams, C.1785, Gold Frame, Oval, 2 5/8 In. 375.00
Painting, Miniature, 18th Century Cavalier, Oval, Frame, 5 1/4 In. 75.00
Painting, Oil On Artist Board, Blonde Victorian Child, 1850, 13 1/2 In. 45.00
Painting, Oil On Artist Board, 2 Vessels Under Sail, C.1870, 15 3/4 In. 35.00
Painting, Oil On Canvas, Two Young Children, American School, C.1850, 36 In. 2700.00
Painting, Oil On Composition Board, Boy Scouts, Motto, C.1915, 22 X 16 In. 100.00
Painting, Oil On Leather, Lady With Harp, European School, C.1850, 24 In. 500.00
Painting, Oil On Velvet, Bald Eagle With American Flag, C.1850, 29 X 21 In. 750.00
Painting, Oil On Velvet, Woman & Man On Palace Balcony, C.1910, 3 Ft. 400.00
Painting, Oil, Outdoor Cottage Scene, Spinning Wheel, 8 1/4 X 5 1/4 In. 10.50
Painting, Oil, Sea Captain, Chinese Artist, C.1850, 36 X 24 In. 200.00
Painting, Oil, The Hunter, C.1850, 29 X 24 In. 750.00
Painting, On Ivory, After Tintoretto, Frame, 4 1/2 X 6 1/2 In. 275.00
Painting, On Ivory, Napoleon As Young Man, Peler, 3 1/4 X 2 3/4 In. 125.00
Painting, On Ivory, Portrait, Young Woman, C.1790, Framed, 2 X 3 In. 65.00
Painting, On Porcelain, Alexander I, Bisque, Blue & White, C.1820, 3 1/4 In. 210.00
Painting, On Porcelain, Amour Scene, Gilt Frame, 10 1/2 X 8 1/2 In. 40.00
Painting, On Porcelain, Dark Haired Girl, Gold Leaf Frame, 13 X 15 In. 275.00
Painting, On Porcelain, Girl & Basket Of Flowers, French, Oval, 3 In. 240.00
Painting, On Porcelain, Girl On Pillow, Art Nouveau Type, Frame, 4 X 5 In. 250.00
Painting, On Porcelain, Lady With Long Hair, Gold Jewelry, 5 1/4 X 8 In. 375.00
Painting, On Porcelain, Napoleon & Josephine, 3 1/2 In.Long, Pair 225.00
Painting, On Porcelain, Old Woman Reading, Brass Frame, 5 3/4 X 4 1/2 In. 250.00
Painting, On Porcelain, Orpheus & Eurydice, Framed, 8 1/2 X 5 1/2 In. 450.00

Painting, On Porcelain, Psyche, Gold Leaf Frame, 6 1/4 X 4 1/4 In.	190.00
Painting, On Porcelain, Two Lovers, Framed, 5 1/4 X 7 1/4 In.	550.00
Painting, On Porcelain, Victorian Lady, Ribbons In Hair, Oval, 5 1/2 In.	125.00
Painting, On Porcelain, Young Girl On Beach, Gold Frame, 3 X 2 1/2 In.	110.00
Painting, On Porcelain, Young Man & Lady, Old Man, Small Boy, Crown, 4 X 5 In	125.00
Painting, On Velvet, River, Bridge, Mountain Landscape, 22 X 24 In.	45.00
Painting, Portrait On Ivory, Bust Of Woman, Oval Frame, 2 X 1 5/8 In.	45.00
Painting, Portrait On Ivory, Lady & Man, Oval, Framed, 2 X 2 1/2 In., Pair	275.00
Painting, Portrait On Ivory, Lady Hamilton, Bronze Frame, 3 1/2 X 3 In.	175.00
Painting, Portrait On Ivory, Lady, Holding Rose, Bronze Frame, 4 X 4 3/4 In.	160.00
Painting, Portrait On Ivory, Marquis De Brincourt, Frame, 2 1/2 X 3 1/2 In.	120.00
Painting, Portrait On Ivory, Woman, Dated 1830, Framed, 2 X 2 In.	75.00
Painting, Reverse On Glass, General Lafayette, C.1825, 12 1/2 X 9 3/4 In.	325.00
Painting, Reverse On Glass, General Lafayette, C.1850, 8 1/2 X 6 In.	325.00
Painting, Reverse On Glass, George & Martha Washington, 5 1/4 X 6 In., Pair	28.00
Painting, Reverse On Glass, George Washington, C.1850, 19 3/4 X 15 1/2 In.	150.00
Painting, Reverse On Glass, George Washington, C.1850, 23 1/4 X 19 1/2 In.	190.00
Painting, Reverse On Glass, The Death, Framed, 10 X 13 In.	125.00
Painting, Theorem On Velvet, Basket Of Flowers & Fruit, C.1850, 16 X 13 In.	225.00
Painting, Theorem On Velvet, Fruit Filled Basket, C.1850, 19 1/2 X 15 In.	350.00
Painting, Watercolor & Embroidery On Silk, C.1850, Feast, 21 X 29 In.	400.00
Painting, Watercolor & Featherwork, Bluejay, C.1850, 12 3/4 X 10 In.	200.00
Painting, Watercolor & Ink, Portrait Of A Child, Framed, 10 X 8 In.	29.50
Painting, Watercolor, Castle Ruins, Figures, C.1850, 16 1/2 X 13 1/2 In.	70.00
Painting, Watercolor, Clusters Of Garden Flowers, C.1850, 11 X 9 In., Pair	100.00
Painting, Watercolor, Falls Of The Passaic, C.1850, 13 1/2 X 10 3/4 In.	600.00
Painting, Watercolor, Family Register, Noah L, Peck Family, 1847, 20 In.	250.00
Painting, Watercolor, Flower-Filled Bowl, C.1850, 21 1/4 X 15 1/2 In.	250.00
Painting, Watercolor, Seated Gentleman, Jacob Mantael, C.1835, 5 1/2 In.	500.00
Painting, Watercolor, Square Rigged Naval Frigate, C.1870, 7 X 11 In.	97.50
Painting, Watercolor, Woman & Man Dancing, Art Deco, 12 X 7 In.	18.00

Pairpoint Corporation was a silver and glass firm founded in New Bedford, Massachusetts, in 1880.

Pairpoint, Basket, Cake, Silver Plate, Four Feet, Flowers & Parrots, 10 In.	45.00
Pairpoint, Bottle, Cologne, Paperweight, Finial Stopper, Controlled Bubble	58.00
Pairpoint, Bottle, Perfume, Bubble Ball Base, 4 Crystal Leaves, 7 1/4 In.	75.00
Pairpoint, Bottle, Perfume, Controlled Bubbles, 6 1/2 In.	65.00
Pairpoint, Bowl, Icy Blue, Clear Ball Stem, 9 In.Diameter, 6 In.High	45.00
Pairpoint, Box, Trinket, Hinged, Gold Floral & Scrolls, White, 6 1/2 X 5 In.	175.00
Pairpoint, Box, Yellow & Orange Ground, Floral, Covered, Loop Handles, 7 In.	250.00
Pairpoint, Caddy, Tea, Delft Decoration, Crown Pairpoint Ware	65.00
Pairpoint, Candlestick, Amber, Clear Ball, 12 In., Pair	120.00
Pairpoint, Candlestick, Cobalt, Vintage Engraving, 10 In., Pair	140.00
Pairpoint, Candlestick, Paperweight Type, Deep Amethyst, 4 1/2 In.	22.00
Pairpoint, Castor, Sugar, Carved Floral & Leaves Insert, Floral Top	69.00
Pairpoint, Compote, Butterly & Flower, Etched, 10 1/2 In.	40.00
Pairpoint, Compote, Paperweight Base, Controlled Bubbles, 9 X 7 In.	60.00
Pairpoint, Compote, Vaseline, Blown, Engraved, Tendrils, 4 1/4 In.	38.00
Pairpoint, Console Set, Cobalt, Bubble Ball Stem, 4 In. Candles, 3 Piece	160.00
Pairpoint, Console Set, Cut Glass, Royal Blue, 12 In. Candlesticks, 3 Piece	450.00
Pairpoint, Console Set, Wickham, Etching, 16 In. Candles, 3 Piece	175.00
Pairpoint, Cornucopia, Gold Ruby, Bubble Ball, Ruffled Top, 6 In., Pair	95.00
Pairpoint, Cruet, Butterfly & Flower, Etched, Stopper	42.00
Pairpoint, Dish, Candy, Peachblow, Pairpoint Bryden Signed	35.00
Pairpoint, Jar, Cookie, Lilacs On Pale Green, Silver Plate Fittings	185.00
Pairpoint, Jar, Cracker, Butterscotch, Blossom Decoration, 6 1/2 In.	75.00
Pairpoint, Jar, Cracker, Yellow, Floral, Blown-Out Panels, 7 In.	350.00
Pairpoint, Lamp, Boudoir, Scenic, Orange, Brown, & Green, 3 Candle Light, 27 In	690.00
Pairpoint, Lamp, Bronze Base, White Basket Weave Shade, Floral, 10 In.	250.00
Pairpoint, Lamp, Bronze Base, Wooded Scenes, Artist W.Macy, 20 In.	875.00
Pairpoint, Lamp, Polished Wood Base, Ambero Shade With Grapes, 20 1/2 In.	165.00
Pairpoint, Lamp, Puffy, Miniature, Pair	375.00
Pairpoint, Lamp, Table, Purple, Pink Flower, Irises, Gold, Pedestal, 20 In.	495.00
Pairpoint, Lamp, Table, Tivoli Mushroom Shade, Reverse Painting, 14 In.	975.00
Pairpoint, Lustre, Amber, Clear Bubble Ball Base, 6 In.Prisms, 11 In., Pair	195.00

Pairpoint, Night-Light, Yellow & Pink Roses & Butterflies On Black, 9 In. 1500.00
Pairpoint, Paperweight, Air Trap In Lemon Yellow 85.00
Pairpoint, Pitcher, Milk, Opaline Colored, Striped 16.50
Pairpoint, Pitcher, Water, Silver Plate, 6 1/2 In.High 35.00
Pairpoint, Plate, Vintage Engraving, 8 1/2 In. 12.00
Pairpoint, Salt & Pepper, Blue Delft, Boat, Windmill 135.00
Pairpoint, Tazza, Green, Vintage, 6 X 4 In.High 25.00
Pairpoint, Urn, Brown Metal, Pewter Handles, Carved Lions' Heads, 11 1/2 In. 95.00
Pairpoint, Vase, Amethyst, Flared, Clear Ball Stem, Controlled Bubble, 12 In. 175.00
Pairpoint, Vase, Amethyst, Paperweight Base, Bubbles, 8 1/2 In. 35.00
Pairpoint, Vase, Black & Red, Double Hand, Flambe, 5 In. 65.00
Pairpoint, Vase, Cranberry, Horn Shape, Controlled Bubbles, Footed, 9 3/4 In. 95.00
Pairpoint, Vase, Delft, Melon Ribbed, White, Windmill & Sailboat, 3 1/2 In. 185.00
Pairpoint, Vase, Emerald Green, Flared, Bubble Ball, 12 In. 80.00
Pairpoint, Vase, Red & Black Flambe, Hand, 5 In. 55.00
Pairpoint, Vase, Rosano, Diamond-Quilted, Wafer Connection, 8 1/2 In. 75.00
Pantin, Salt, Pink Stripes, Gold Interior, Monot Stumpf 30.00
Pantin, Vase, Acid Cut Red Poppies & Butterfly On Green, Pear Shape, 6 In. 245.00
Pantin, Vase, Floral & Butterflies, Deep Aqua, 16 In. 475.00
Pantin, Vase, Pear Shape, Red Poppies & Butterfly On Gray, Cameo, 6 In. 245.00
Pantin, Vase, Tricolored Enameled Iris, Buds, & Leaves, Dragonfly, 11 1/2 In. 235.00
    Paper, Almanac, see also Shaker, Almanac
Paper, Almanac, Ayer's American, 1884-1913, Each 3.00
Paper, Almanac, Ayer's, 1876-1889, Each 5.00
Paper, Almanac, Columbian, 1859 .... 10.00
Paper, Almanac, D.M.Ferry & Co., 1909 .... 3.00
Paper, Almanac, Dr.Jayne's, 1884-1904, Each 5.00
Paper, Almanac, Dr.Miles', 1922-1923-1928-1929-1930-1931-1932-1934, Each 2.50
Paper, Almanac, Dr.Pierce's, 1928 .... 3.00
Paper, Almanac, Franklin, The, 1848 .... 10.00
Paper, Almanac, Greenes Diary, 1883-84 .... 4.00
Paper, Almanac, Herrick's, 1894-1896-1897-1898-1900, Each 3.00
Paper, Almanac, Hostetter's Bitters, 1884 .... 5.00
Paper, Almanac, Hostetter's, 1894-1898-1900, Each 3.00
Paper, Almanac, Kickapoo Indian Remedies, 1886 .... 27.00
Paper, Almanac, Merchant's Gargling Oil, 1886, Dream & Fate 10.00
Paper, Almanac, Morrow's, 1929 .... 12.50
Paper, Almanac, Mutual Baseball, 1955 .... 4.50
Paper, Almanac, New Orleans Picayune, The, 1886 .... 10.00
Paper, Almanac, New York, The, 1888-1889, Each 2.50
Paper, Almanac, Pennsylvania Dutch, 1787 .... 12.00
Paper, Almanac, Peruna, The, 1897 .... 3.00
Paper, Almanac, Radway's, 1889 .... 2.50
Paper, Almanac, Thedford's, 1936 .... 3.00
Paper, Apprentice Indenture, Warren Co., Ky., 1847, Negro Girl, 6 Years Old 22.50
    Paper, Book, see also Charlie Chaplin, Book, Coronation, Book,
    Dick, Tracy, Book, Dionne Quintuplet, Book, Disneyana, Book,
    Gene Autry, Book, Book, Kate Greenaway, Book, Kewpie, Book,
    Lone Ranger, Book, Orphan Annie, Book, Shaker, Book, Store,
    Book, Sunbonnet Babies, Book, Toy, Book, World's Fair, Book
Paper, Book, A Child's Garden Of Verses, Jump-Ups, McLoughlin Bros., 1946 .... 5.00
Paper, Book, Blondie & Dagwood, Paste 2.00
Paper, Book, Buck Jones & The Night Riders, Big Big Book, Whitman, 1937 .... 7.50
Paper, Book, Charlie Chan, Big Little Book 3.50
Paper, Book, Chester Gump, Big Little Book 3.00
Paper, Book, Child's Garden Of Verses, McLaughlin Jolly Jump Up, 1940s 5.00
Paper, Book, Children Of Autumn, Maude Humphrey, 1888, Stokes & Bro. 50.00
Paper, Book, Coloring, Katzenjammer Kids, Saalfield, 1917 .... 9.00
Paper, Book, Coloring, Mr.Peanut, Saalfield 4.00
Paper, Book, Coloring, Three Little Kittens, Saalfield 1.50
Paper, Book, Comic, Barney Google, 1923 .... 15.00
Paper, Book, Comic, Foky Grampa, Bunny Schultze, 1905 .... 35.00
Paper, Book, Comic, Kellogg's Funny Jungleland Moving Pictures, 1909 .... 25.00
Paper, Book, Comic, Mutt & Jeff, Winter Issue, 1945 .... 10.00
Paper, Book, Comic, Tom Mix, British, 1951 .... 4.00
Paper, Book, Comic, Wally, C.1917, Hard Cover, 52 Pages 22.00

Paper, Book, Cowboy Millionaire, Big Little Book	6.00
Paper, Book, Dumbo, The Flying Elephant, 1941	12.00
Paper, Book, Floppsie Bunnies, Beatrix Potter, 1909	19.50
Paper, Book, Katzenjammer Kids Story Book, 1937	18.00
Paper, Book, Li'l Abner, Big Little Book	4.00
Paper, Book, Raggedy Ann Coloring, Dated 1945	1.45
Paper, Book, The Teddy Beard, Sutton, 1907	8.50
Paper, Book, Tom Mix, Big Little Book	6.00
Paper, Book, Tom Sawyer, Big Little Book	3.00
Paper, Book, Will Rogers, Big Little Book	10.00
Paper, Book, Wizard Of Oz, Coloring, 1939	1.50
Paper, Catalogue, Annin Co., 1931	10.00
Paper, Catalogue, Artificial Lighting, Nagel-Chase Co., 1914-15	7.50
Paper, Catalogue, Butler Brothers, 1916	35.00
Paper, Catalogue, Chicago Mail Order Clothing, 1913	2.00
Paper, Catalogue, Corticelli Home Needlework, 1898	2.00
Paper, Catalogue, Daniel, Law & Co., Jewelers & Silversmiths, 1929	4.00
Paper, Catalogue, Dr.Miles' Nervine, C.1900	3.00
Paper, Catalogue, Edison Dealers' Supplement, 1929	2.50
Paper, Catalogue, Edison, Records, The New Phonogram, Jan.1909	22.50
Paper, Catalogue, Folding Saw Machine Co., 1895	7.00
Paper, Catalogue, Gleeson Jewelry Co., 1937	12.00
Paper, Catalogue, Harrington & Richardson Pistols, 1906	12.00
Paper, Catalogue, Iver Johnson Canoes & Boats, 1929	5.50
Paper, Catalogue, John Smyth Mdse.1913	2.00
Paper, Catalogue, John Wanamaker, 1911	20.00
Paper, Catalogue, Johnson Outboard Motors, C.1930	3.00
Paper, Catalogue, Johnson-Smith, 1937, Toys	7.00
Paper, Catalogue, Kalamazoo Stove, 1934	10.00
Paper, Catalogue, Lionel Trains, 1936	10.00
Paper, Catalogue, Lionel Trains, 1939	10.00
Paper, Catalogue, Montgomery Ward, Sale Supplement, 1930	6.00
Paper, Catalogue, Montgomery Ward, Spring & Summer, 1936	7.50
Paper, Catalogue, Montgomery Ward, 1894	8.00
Paper, Catalogue, National Cloak & Suit Co., Fall & Winter, 1926-27	18.00
Paper, Catalogue, National Cloak & Suit Co., 1925-26	10.00
Paper, Catalogue, New Home Sewing Machines, 1889	10.00
Paper, Catalogue, Philipsborn Garment, 1915	2.00
Paper, Catalogue, Rochester Cycle Mfg.Co., 1898	12.00
Paper, Catalogue, Schmidt Co. Whiskeys, 1900	7.00
Paper, Catalogue, Scott's Standard, Stamp, 1944	120.00
Paper, Catalogue, Sears Roebuck, Bargain Bulletin, 1926	5.00
Paper, Catalogue, Sears Roebuck, 1900	2.95
Paper, Catalogue, Sears Roebuck, 1908	3.49
Paper, Catalogue, Sears Roebuck, 1923	2.95
Paper, Catalogue, Sears Roebuck, 1947	5.00
Paper, Catalogue, Standard Mail Order, 1913	2.00
Paper, Catalogue, Star Brand Shoes, 1930	2.00
Paper, Catalogue, Star, Best Clothing, 1914	2.00
Paper, Catalogue, Starrett Tools, 1935	5.00
Paper, Catalogue, Victor Records, January, 1906	7.50
Paper, Catalogue, Victor Records, October, 1906	8.50
Paper, Catalogue, Victor Records, September, 1905	8.50
Paper, Catalogue, Victor Records, 1920	22.50
Paper, Catalogue, Victor Records, 1922	22.50
Paper, Catalogue, Ward's, 1913, Sale	2.00
Paper, Catalogue, Ward's, 1947, Midsummer	2.00
Paper, Certificate, Slavery, Lancaster County, Pa., 1788, Baby Girl & Boy	50.00
Paper, Doll, see also Coronation, Disneyana, Kewpie	
Paper, Doll, Ann Sothern, Wardrobe	8.00
Paper, Doll, Betsy McCall, Clothes, Dynel Wigs, 2 10 In. Dolls	8.75
Paper, Doll, Betty Grable	12.00
Paper, Doll, Blondie, Uncut, Dated 1952	8.00
Paper, Doll, Chatty Baby, Stand-Up, 14 Outfits, 1961	10.00
Paper, Doll, College Set, 1950, Cut	5.00
Paper, Doll, Connie Francis	2.00

Paper, Doll, Dennis The Menace, Uncut	5.50
Paper, Doll, Dodie	1.50
Paper, Doll, Donna Reed, 1959, Uncut	7.50 To 8.00
Paper, Doll, Dottie Darling, Christmas, 1934	8.50
Paper, Doll, Eddie Albert, Uncut	5.50
Paper, Doll, Eva Gabor, Uncut	5.50
Paper, Doll, Eve Arden, 1956, Uncut	7.00
Paper, Doll, Flying Nun	1.50
Paper, Doll, Four Lane Sisters, Cutouts, 1930s, 43 Outfits	6.00
Paper, Doll, Four Sisters, 1943, Uncut	5.00
Paper, Doll, Greer Garson	10.00
Paper, Doll, Growing Up, 1930s, Clothes, Cut	4.50
Paper, Doll, Joanne Woodward, Uncut	8.00
Paper, Doll, Judy Holliday, Uncut	7.00
Paper, Doll, Julia Batman	1.50
Paper, Doll, June Allyson, Watkins, Uncut	6.50
Paper, Doll, Junior Miss, 1942, Uncut	5.25
Paper, Doll, Lettie Lane, 1909, Dresses	7.50
Paper, Doll, Little Orphan Annie Dress-Up Kit, Sandy, Dated 1968, Boxed	12.50
Paper, Doll, Marlo Thomas, Book Of Uncut	4.75
Paper, Doll, Patti Page, Uncut	5.00
Paper, Doll, Patty Duke, Uncut	5.75 To 7.50
Paper, Doll, Pebbles & Bambam	4.00
Paper, Doll, Pinn Family, Uncut	6.00
Paper, Doll, Playmate Pam, Clothes, Uncut	5.00
Paper, Doll, Polly & Peter Perkins At Circus, 1933	8.50
Paper, Doll, Polly Bergen, Uncut	8.00
Paper, Doll, Quiz Kids, Uncut, 1942, Outfits	18.00
Paper, Doll, Raggedy Ann	5.00
Paper, Doll, Raphael Tuck, Series VII, 3 Dressed	35.00
Paper, Doll, Rhonda Fleming, Uncut	6.50
Paper, Doll, Ricky Nelson, 1959, Uncut	5.00
Paper, Doll, Rita Hayworth	3.50
Paper, Doll, Rock Hudson, 1957, Uncut	5.00
Paper, Doll, Rosemary Clooney, Abott, 1959, Uncut	5.50
Paper, Doll, Sandra Dee, Uncut, Boxed Set	5.75 To 8.00
Paper, Doll, Sparkle Plenty, Uncut	6.00
Paper, Doll, Strawberry Sue, Uncut	4.00
Paper, Doll, The Young Set, Uncut	4.00
Paper, Doll, Tillie The Toiler	10.00
Paper, Doll, Tricia Nixon, Cut	5.00
Paper, Doll, Tricia Nixon, Uncut	8.50
Paper, Magazine, Harper's, May 26, June 23, Aug.25, Sept.8, 1900, Each	4.00
Paper, Scrapbook, see also Elvis Presley, Scrapbook	
Paper, Scrapbook, Embossed Gold Front, 1876, Advertising Cards, Prints, Etc.	15.00
Paper, Scrapbook, 1900s Car Ads From Magazines	25.00
Paperweight, see also Baccarat, Paperweight, Coca-Cola, Paperweight, Gillinder, Paperweight, Kate Greenaway, Paperweight, Lindbergh, Paperweight, Masonic, Paperweight, Milk Glass, Paperweight, Rookwood, Paperweight, Store, Paperweight, Sunbonnet Babies, Paperweight	
Paperweight, Admiral Dewey, Photograph, Painted Border, Clear Glass, 3 In.	12.00
Paperweight, Atlas Crystal Works, Snow, Person In Parka With Dog	10.00
Paperweight, Atlas Crystal Works, Snow, Saluting Soldier	10.00
Paperweight, Attalla Pipe & Fdy Co., Cast Iron, 5 In.	5.00
Paperweight, Baccarat, see Baccarat, Paperweight	
Paperweight, Banford, Green Lizard Over Red Rosette On Blue, Gold Mica	105.00
Paperweight, Banford, Pink Roses & Green Foliage On Gold Foil Ground	130.00
Paperweight, Banford, Striped Snake On Orange Yellow Pebbled	45.00 To 49.00
Paperweight, Barker, Blue & White Primrose On Clear Ground, Signed	95.00
Paperweight, Bristol, Steeple Shape, Opaque Multicolored Glass, 10 3/4 In.	100.00
Paperweight, Bronze, Hand, Ring On Forefinger, Brass Cuff	35.00
Paperweight, Brown Wright, N.Y., Amber Red & Clear, 3 In. Diameter	20.00
Paperweight, Buddha, Amber, Gillinder, 6 In.	50.00
Paperweight, Buffalo, Crystal, Signed	25.00
Paperweight, Cambridge Glass Co., Dahlia Type Flower, 3 5/8 In.	45.00

Paperweight, Capitol, Washington, D.C., Glass, Rectangular, 4 X 2 3/4 In.	4.95
Paperweight, Choco, Green Lizard On Yellow, Goldstone	200.00
Paperweight, Coin, Shakespeare, Anniversary, Stratford, Ontario, 1964	5.00
Paperweight, Cut Glass, Facet Cut, 2 1/4 In.	6.50
Paperweight, D'Albret, Audubon, Sulfide	68.00
Paperweight, D'Albret, Da Vinci, Overlay	160.00
Paperweight, D'Albret, Da Vinci, Sulfide	62.00
Paperweight, D'Albret, Hemingway, Overlay	160.00
Paperweight, D'Albret, Hemingway, Sulfide	62.00
Paperweight, D'Albret, Kennedy, Jacqueline, Sulfide	62.00
Paperweight, D'Albret, Kennedy, John F., Sulfide	62.00
Paperweight, D'Albret, Lind, Jenny, Overlay	160.00
Paperweight, D'Albret, Lind, Jenny, Sulfide	68.00
Paperweight, D'Albret, MacArthur, Overlay	160.00
Paperweight, D'Albret, MacArthur, Sulfide	62.00
Paperweight, D'Albret, Revere, Paul, Overlay	160.00
Paperweight, D'Albret, Revere, Paul, Sulfide	62.00
Paperweight, D'Albret, Roosevelt, F.D., Overlay	160.00
Paperweight, D'Albret, Roosevelt, F.D., Sulfide	62.00
Paperweight, D'Albret, Schweitzer, Albert, Sulfide	62.00
Paperweight, Dome Island At Bolton, Lake George, N.Y., Glass, 4 1/4 In.	5.95
Paperweight, Duck, Iron, Painted, 3 1/2 In.	7.00
Paperweight, End-Of-Day Glass, Souvenir World's Columbian Exposition	65.00
Paperweight, End-Of-Day, Mushroom Type, Domed, 3 In.	45.00
Paperweight, English, Colored Sand Glass, Thermometer, 5 In.	12.00
Paperweight, Figural, Baby, Silver Plate	38.00
Paperweight, Ford, Kansas City Aircraft Plant, Aluminum, 1st Shipment, 1953	22.50
Paperweight, Frosted Hand Holding Clear Fish Bowl With Turtle, Gillinder	200.00
Paperweight, Frosted Lion, Pressed Glass	75.00
Paperweight, G.A.R. Encampment, 1892, Washington, D.C., Glass, 4 In.	9.95
Paperweight, Glass, Capitol, Albany, N.Y., Rectangular, C.1890, 4 X 2 1/2 In.	5.00
Paperweight, Glass, Photograph Of 1895 Street Scene, Oblong, 4 X 2 1/2 In.	15.00
Paperweight, Guinness Stout Ale, Bottom Embossed	12.00
Paperweight, Hacker, 2 Ladybugs In Different Colors Eating Leaf, Signed	145.00
Paperweight, Hansen, Pink & Blue Flower On Cobalt, Faceted, 2 In.	225.00

Kaziun glass has been made by Charles Kaziun since 1942. His paperweights have been gaining fame steadily. Most of his glass and all of the paperweights are signed with A K designed cane worked into the design. He makes buttons, earrings, perfume bottles, and paperweights.

Paperweight, Kaziun, Blue Flowers On Pink, Signed	175.00
Paperweight, Kaziun, Blue Rose	275.00
Paperweight, Kaziun, Lily & 4 Green Leaves On Gold Flecked, Pedestal, 2 In.	245.00
Paperweight, Kaziun, Lily & 4 Green Leaves On Mica Flecked, 2 In.	200.00
Paperweight, Kaziun, Millefiori, Flat	445.00
Paperweight, Kaziun, Red Lily On Gold Flecked Turquoise, 2 In.	190.00
Paperweight, Kaziun, Rose In Clear Glass	650.00
Paperweight, Kossuth, Sulfide, Dated 1851	300.00
Paperweight, Labino, Flower On Lavender	165.00
Paperweight, Lew Kaines, Pink Dahlia On Yellow, Faceted, 2 In.	85.00
Paperweight, Liberty Bell, Metal	5.00
Paperweight, Lincoln, Glass, Gillinder, 3 X 4 1/2 In.	115.00
Paperweight, Lion, Gillinder	15.00
Paperweight, Marine National Bank, Glass, Rectangular	20.00
Paperweight, McMahan, Horem & Nusey, Ala., Gold Money Form, Metal, 6 In.	5.00
Paperweight, Memorial Hall 1776-1876, Frosted & Clear	195.00 To 285.00
Paperweight, Millefiori, Peacock	10.00
Paperweight, Millville, New Jersey Rose, Oscar Skip Woods, 3 1/4 X 4 In.	300.00
Paperweight, Mormon Tabernacle Choir, Glass	14.00
Paperweight, Mosaic, Black Basalt, Inlays Of Ancient Rome, C.1800, 6 In.	285.00
Paperweight, Moses In Bulrushes, Frosted & Clear, Oval	50.00
Paperweight, Mutt & Jeff, Iron, Painted	25.00
Paperweight, Nailsea, Magnum, Bottle Green, Controlled Bubbles, 4 1/2 In.	65.00
Paperweight, Ohio Valley, Green & Pink Pebbled Ground, 4 Air Traps, 3 In.	42.00

Paperweight, Ohio Valley, Pink & Green Spatter, Blue Floral, 4 Air Traps	45.00
Paperweight, Old Hickory, Bust Of Pres.Jackson, Babbit Metal, Dated 1891	22.00
Paperweight, Old Stone Mill, Newport, R.I., Glass, Rectangular, 4 In.	5.95
Paperweight, Pairpoint, see Pairpoint, Paperweight	
Paperweight, Perthshire, Canes On Dark Ground	8.00
Paperweight, Perthshire, Peach Color Flower, Faceted, 2 In.	90.00
Paperweight, Perthshire, Scattered On Blue, Pastry Mold Canes, 2 3/4 In.	85.00
Paperweight, Planter's Peanut, Glass	20.00
Paperweight, Plymouth Rock, Inscribed	50.00
Paperweight, Pressed Glass, Dewey, Rectangular, Picture, "Hero Of Manila"	18.00
Paperweight, Russian, Malachite, Asymmetrical Concave Panels, 6 X 4 In.	225.00
Paperweight, Souvenir, Laconia, N.H.Railroad Depot, Flat Glass	29.00
Paperweight, Spaniel On Cushion, Salt Glaze Stoneware, C.1825, 3 1/2 In.	88.00
Paperweight, St.Louis, King Of France Commemorative, Sulfide, Faceted	250.00
Paperweight, Steamer Hendrick Hudson, Metal, 3 In.	3.00
Paperweight, Strathearn, Egg Shape, Blue Flower On Goldstone	50.00
Paperweight, Strathearn, Magnum, Flower, Latticinio, Blue Green	50.00
Paperweight, Texas Centennial, Lone Star Shape, Glass, 1836-1936	27.50
Paperweight, The Franklin Press, Miami, Fla., Glass, Oval, 4 1/2 In.	8.00
Paperweight, Tiger On Rock, Kelly Is. Line & Transport, Cleveland, O., Metal	9.00
Paperweight, Union Glass, Spatter, Mushroom Flower	29.00
Paperweight, Ward's Orange Crush, 1924	16.00
Paperweight, West Virginia Centennial	40.00
Paperweight, Whittemore, Colorado State Flower	350.00
Paperweight, Whittemore, Dogwood On Green, 2 In.	350.00
Paperweight, Whittemore, Minnesota State Flower	350.00
Paperweight, Whittemore, North Carolina State Flower	350.00
Paperweight, Whittemore, Partridge In A Pear Tree	300.00
Paperweight, Whittemore, Purple & Yellow Pansy On Cobalt, 2 1/2 In.	300.00
Paperweight, Whittemore, Red Camellia, Green Leaves, Signed	125.00
Paperweight, Whittemore, South Carolina State Flower	350.00
Paperweight, Whittemore, White Rose On 4 Green Leaves, Pedestal, 2 3/4 In.	145.00
Paperweight, Wild Rose Brand Table Syrup, Glass, Rectangular, 4 1/4 In.	5.95
Paperweight, Winchester, 1910, Flat Glass	22.50
Paperweight, Women's Pavilion, Inscribed 1776-1876, Oval, 3 3/8 X 4 7/8 In.	145.00
Paperweight, World War I German Aviator's, Brass, Bomb Shape, 2 In. Long	39.00
Paperweight, Ysart, Dragonfly, Blue & White Jasper	180.00
Paperweight, Ysart, Millefiori, White Cushion, Latticinio	130.00
Paperweight, Ysart, 10 Petal Red & Goldstone Flower On Latticinio	190.00

Papier-mache is a decorative form made from paper mixed with glue, chalk, and other ingredients, then molded and baked. It becomes very hard and can be decorated. Boxes, trays, and furniture were made of papier-mache. Some of the early nineteenth-century pieces were decorated with mother-of-pearl.

Papier-Mache, see also Doll, Furniture

Papier-Mache, Box, Black Lacquer, Landscape On Lid, Feodoskino, C.1890, 4 In.	100.00
Papier-Mache, Box, Covered, Birds & Floral On Gold, Round, 3 1/2 In.	45.00
Papier-Mache, Box, Pink Rose Buds, 3 Girls In Color, Satin Lined, 4 X 2 In.	15.00
Papier-Mache, Candy Container, Hen On Nest, 7 In.	15.00
Papier-Mache, Case, Eyeglasses, Clipper Ship In Harbor Scene	75.00
Papier-Mache, Case, For Folding Glasses, Valvet Linin	
Papier-Mache, Egg, Easter, Lacquer, Christ & Angel, Palekh, C.1850, 3 1/4 In.	350.00
Papier-Mache, Egg, Easter, Lacquer, Christ Rising, Lukutin, C.1820, 3 1/2 In.	275.00
Papier-Mache, Egg, Easter, Lacquer, Christ Scenes, Palekh, C.1850, 6 1/4 In.	900.00
Papier-Mache, Egg, Easter, Lacquer, Kremlin Bell Tower, Lukutin, C.1820, 4 In.	325.00
Papier-Mache, Egg, Easter, Lacquer, St.Alexandra, Kremlin, C.1850, 3 1/4 In.	250.00
Papier-Mache, Figurine, Santa Claus, 10 In.	7.25
Papier-Mache, Folder, Artist's, Mother-Of-Pearl, Hand-Painted, Gilded, 12 In.	100.00
Papier-Mache, Plate, New York Lake & Mountain Scene, 1880, 8 1/2 In., Pair	35.00
Papier-Mache, Snuffbox, Floral On Red On Lid, C.1750, Round, 3 In.	14.00
Papier-Mache, Snuffbox, Mother-Of-Pearl Mosaic On Hinged Lid, 1 1/2 In.	28.00
Papier-Mache, Tray, Black, Gold Foliage, Pierced Handles, 11 3/4 In., Pair	70.00
Papier-Mache, Tray, Grape, Handled, 12 X 10 In.	125.00
Papier-Mache, Tray, On Tilt-Top Stand, Summer Flowers, C.1850, 32 1/4 In.	75.00

Papier-Mache, Tray, Scalloped, Ornate Design, Oriental, 8 1/2 X 12 In. 10.00

Parian is a fine-grained, hard-paste porcelain named for the marble it resembles. It was first made in England in 1846 and gained in favor in the United States about 1860. Figures, tea sets, vases, and other items were made of Parian at many English and American factories.

Parian, Bottle, Figural, Venus Di Milo, Love Goddess Of Liquers, 13 In.	65.00
Parian, Box, Trinket, Oval, Heavy Relief Grapes & Foliage, 3 X 4 1/2 In.	27.00
Parian, Bust, Alexandre, Princess Of Denmark, Copeland, 12 In.High	275.00
Parian, Bust, Cromwell, Marked P.& L., 8 In.	30.00
Parian, Bust, Edward VII, Marked P.& L., 7 1/4 In.	28.00
Parian, Bust, Garfield, 12 In.	85.00
Parian, Bust, Longfellow, Pedestal, 5 In.	38.00
Parian, Bust, Princess Louise, Art Union Of London, Thornycroft, 1871, 15 In.	185.00
Parian, Bust, Robert Burns, Copeland, 7 In.High	50.00
Parian, Bust, Robert Burns, 5 In.	35.00
Parian, Bust, Thomas Sampson, Spanish American War Hero, 5 1/4 In.	32.00
Parian, Bust, Venus, 6 In.Including Pedestal .... *Illus*	35.00
Parian, Bust, 7 1/2 In.	50.00
Parian, Creamer, Dolphin, 3 In.	10.00
Parian, Figurine, Art Nouveau Woman, Bare Breasted, Drunot, 14 In.	145.00
Parian, Figurine, Child's Hand, White Beaded Cuff At Wrist, 4 In.	55.00
Parian, Figurine, Classic Nude, 22 In. .... 195.00 To	200.00
Parian, Figurine, Girl Knitting & Reading, 16 In.High	145.00
Parian, Figurine, Grecian Woman Carrying Urn, 13 In.	65.00
Parian, Figurine, Hermione, Greek Classic, Copeland, 1860, 17 In.High	135.00
Parian, Figurine, Joan Of Arc, John Ball, 1848, 13 In.	160.00
Parian, Figurine, Nude, Greenery, 22 In.	195.00
Parian, Figurine, Praying Girl On Pillow, 9 In.High	45.00
Parian, Figurine, Ruth, White, Oval Base, 13 In.	65.00
Parian, Figurine, Semidraped Kneeling Woman With Lyre, 5 1/4 In.	38.00
Parian, Figurine, Shakespeare, Standing, Oval Base, 9 In.	45.00
Parian, Group, Ewe With Lamb, 5 X 4 1/2 In.	45.00
Parian, Jug, Green Ground, Classical Figures, Molded, 1863, 7 In.High	85.00
Parian, Pitcher, Blue & White, 6 1/2 In.	30.00
Parian, Plate, Blue & White, Grapes & Strawberries, Mayer, C.1847, 8 1/2 In.	48.50
Parian, Plate, Bread, Give Us This Day, Wheat Handles, Basket Weave, 13 In.	75.00
Parian, Plate, Grapes, Strawberries, & Leaves, 8 1/2 In.	30.00
Parian, Plate, White, Relief Water Lilies On Border, 8 1/4 In.	32.00
Parian, Vase, Vintage, Cream Color, Bulbous, 10 In.	175.00
Parian, Vase, White, T.J.& J. Mayer, 1850, 4 In.	30.00
Paris, Box, Hinged Lid, Ormolu Trim, Floral, 1850, HL, 2 X 6 X 3 1/2 In.	58.00
Paris, Box, Lass & Lad On Lid, Bottles On Ends, C.1850, 16 1/4 In.	225.00
Paris, Cup & Saucer, Bust Of Josephine On Green, Footed Cup	45.00
Paris, Cup & Saucer, Raised Design On White, Gilt Trim, 2 Cup Size	20.00
Paris, Dessert Set, Pierced Bowls, Blue Bands, Floral, C.1850, 25 Piece	300.00
Paris, Inkwell, Petite Beurre, Fool-The-Eye Style, C.1840, 3 1/2 In.	65.00
Paris, Plate, En Grisaille American Flag Center, Gilt, C.1820, 9 1/4 In.	200.00
Paris, Vase, Armorial, Unicorn & Lion, Floral, White, 13 1/2 In., Pair	390.00
Paris, Vase, Boutonniere, Faun Holding Pipes Of Pan, C.1845, 5 X 6 In.	75.00
Paris, Vase, Pierced Rim, Floral Cartouches, C.1850, 12 1/2 In., Pair	160.00
Paris, Vase, Washington Decoration, C.1810 .... *Illus*	350.00
Paris, Vielleuse, Blossoms, Gilding, C.1850, 10 7/8 In.	150.00

Pate de verre is an ancient technique in which glass is made by blending and refining powdered glass of different colors into molds. The process was revived by French glassmakers, especially Galle, around the end of the nineteenth century.

Pate De Verre, Bowl, A.Walter Nancy, Blue Green, Crocus, C.1910, 5 5/8 In.	350.00
Pate De Verre, Bowl, Crab & Seaweed In Bottom, A.Walter & Berge, 9 1/2 In.	550.00
Pate De Verre, Bowl, Decorchemont, Ocher, Purple, & Clear, C.1925, 3 1/4 In.	475.00
Pate De Verre, Bowl, Queen Bee Finial, A.Walter, Nancy, Yellow, 1910, 4 In.	1300.00
Pate De Verre, Dish, Leaf Shaped, Blue & Green, A.Walter Nancy, 5 X 2 In.	450.00
Pate De Verre, Inkwell, Tree Trunk, Bee, Berries, A.Walter, 1 X 1 1/2 In.	525.00
Pate De Verre, Lamp, A.Walter, C.1915, Iron, 5 In. .... *Illus*	400.00
Pate De Verre, Lamp, G.Argy-Rousseau, Signed, 8 1/2 In.	675.00

Paris, Vase, Washington Decoration,
C.1810
(See Page 348)

Parian, Bust, 7 1/2 In.
(See Page 348)

Pate De Verre, Lamp, A.Walter,
C.1915, Iron, 5 in.
(See Page 348)

Pate De Verre, **Plaque,** Christ's Head, J.D.3 3/4 In.	335.00
Pate De Verre, **Plaque,** Jewelry, Yellow Daisy, Silk Cord, A.W., 2 In.	150.00
Pate De Verre, **Tray,** A.Walter, Nancy, Yellow To Blue Green, C.1910, 13 In.	1500.00

*Pate-sur-pate means paste on paste. The design was made by painting layers
of slip(which see) on the piece until a relief decoration was formed. The
method was developed at the Sevres factory in France about 1850. It
became even more famous at the English Minton factory about 1870.*

Pate-Sur-Pate, **Cup & Saucer,** 2 Cupids & Nude, Gold Interior	350.00
Pate-Sur-Pate, **Stein,** Cavalier Serenading Lady, Green, 8 1/4 In.	165.00
Pate-Sur-Pate, **Vase,** Marbleized Metallic Green, Lizard On Shoulder, 9 In.	150.00
Pate-Sur-Pate, **Vase,** Panel Of Children Playing, Celadon Green, 5 In.	110.00
Paul Revere, **Bowl Vase,** Saturday Evening Girls, Green, TM, 4 1/2 In.	43.00
Paul Revere, **Bowl,** Saturday Evening Girls, Yellow, Signed, 8 1/2 In.	40.00
Paul Revere, **Bowl,** Yellow, Low, Signed, 5 In.	25.00
Paul Revere, **Candlestick,** Saturday Evening Girls, Deep Blue, 7 3/4 In., Pair	95.00
Paul Revere, **Console Set,** Blue & Green Decorated, 10 1/4 In. Bowl, 3 Piece	90.00
Paul Revere, **Console Set,** Floral, Blue & Green, 10 In. Bowl, 3 Piece	90.00
Paul Revere, **Creamer,** Blue, Signed, 3 1/4 In.	30.00
Paul Revere, **Pitcher,** Matte Pink, Marked, 3 1/4 In.	43.00
Paul Revere, **Plate,** Yellow, Signed, 8 1/4 In.	25.00
Paul Revere, **Vase,** Saturday Evening Girls, Yellow, Signed, 3 1/2 In.	35.00

*Peachblow glass orginated about 1883 at Hobbs, Brockunier and Company of
Wheeling, West Virginia. It is a glass that shades from yellow to peach.
It was lined in white. New England peachblow is a one-layer glass with a*

lining shading from red to white. Mt.Washington peachblow shades from pink to blue. Reproductions of peachblow have been made, but they are of a poor quality and can be detected.

Peachblow, see also Gunderson, Peachblow, Webb, Peachblow

Peachblow, Bowl, New England, Acid, 10 Scalloped Flaring Rim, 4 1/2 X 3 In.	595.00
Peachblow, Bowl, New Martinsville, Ribbed, Ruffled Edge, Sun Gold, 10 1/2 In.	125.00
Peachblow, Bowl, Sunglow, Caramel & Yellow, New Martinsville, 4 7/8 In.	85.00
Peachblow, Creamer, Wheeling, Applied Amber Handle, Square Top, 5 1/4 In.	795.00
Peachblow, Cruet, Webb	475.00
Peachblow, Cup, Punch, Wheeling, Applied Amber Handle, White Lining	255.00
Peachblow, Cup, Punch, World's Fair 1893, Libbey	300.00
Peachblow, Darner, New England, Shiny Finish	95.00
Peachblow, Dish, Sweetmeat, Pairpoint Bryden, Fluted, 6 In.	35.00 To 45.00
Peachblow, Ewer, Webb, Applied Amber Thorn Handle, Ruffled, 12 In., Pair	400.00
Peachblow, Goblet, Gunderson, Light To Dark Pink, 6 1/2 In.	155.50
Peachblow, Gunderson, see Gunderson, Peachblow	
Peachblow, Muffineer, Wheeling, Acid Finish, 5 1/2 In.	495.00
Peachblow, Pear, Open End Stem, New England	250.00
Peachblow, Pitcher, Applied Amber Handle, White Lining, Shiny, 5 1/2 In.	250.00
Peachblow, Pitcher, Cream, Sandwich, 5 1/2 In.High	265.00
Peachblow, Pot, Mustard, Wheeling, Covered, Mahogany To Yellow, Opal Lined	237.50
Peachblow, Saltshaker, Glossy Pink & White	65.00
Peachblow, Saltshaker, New England, Shiny Finish	165.00
Peachblow, Sugar & Creamer, New England, "World's Fair 1893"	450.00
Peachblow, Syrup, Pewter Lid, 6 In.	575.00
Peachblow, Toothpick, New England, Acorn Shape, Raised Gold & Pink Floral	45.00
Peachblow, Toothpick, New England, Square Top, Glossy, 2 1/4 In.	250.00
Peachblow, Tumbler, New England	240.00
Peachblow, Tumbler, New England, Coloring Halfway Down, Glossy	275.00
Peachblow, Tumbler, New England, Glossy	275.00 To 450.00
Peachblow, Tumbler, Wheeling	450.00
Peachblow, Tumbler, Wheeling, 4 In.	120.00
Peachblow, Vase, Bryden Pairpoint, Enamel Sprig Of Flowers, 5 In.	38.00
Peachblow, Vase, Fan Shape, Dolphin Handles, 6 In.	20.00
Peachblow, Vase, New England, Pear Shape, White Inside, Bulbous, 9 In.	295.00
Peachblow, Vase, New England, Raspberry Jack Top, Applied White Base, 8 In.	395.00
Peachblow, Vase, New England, Square Mouth, Pinched Corners, 5 3/4 In.High	350.00
Peachblow, Vase, New England, 3 Petal Lily, Raspberry To White, 7 3/4 In.	475.00
Peachblow, Vase, Pairpoint, 5 In.	90.00
Peachblow, Vase, Pink To Raspberry, White & Gold Enamel Design, Webb, 5 In.	195.00
Peachblow, Vase, Sandwich, Pink To Cream, Twisted Ribbing At Neck, 9 1/2 In.	285.00
Peachblow, Vase, Stick, Wheeling, Glossy, Mahogany To Fuchsia To Yellow, 9 In	595.00
Peachblow, Vase, Three Petal Lily, Acid, Raspberry To Pink To White, 8 In.	475.00
Peachblow, Vase, Webb, Gold & Pewter Leaves & Flowers, 5 In.High	195.00
Peachblow, Vase, Webb, Gold Prunus Blossoms & Leaves, 6 3/4 In.	550.00
Peachblow, Vase, Webb, Signed, 9 In.	450.00
Peachblow, Vase, Yellow Seaweed Coralene, Double Lip, White Lined, 6 1/2 In.	245.00
Peachblow, Whimsey, New England, Pear, Curved Stem, 5 X 3 In.	135.00
Peahcblow, Bowl, New England, Raspberry To White Base, 5 1/2 In. Wide	495.00
Pearl, Carving Set, Sterling Ferrules, 3 Piece	35.00
Pearl, Case, Business Card, Engraved R.A.Webster	20.00
Pearl, Case, Calling Card, Hinged, Diamond Designs, Silver Inlay	38.00
Pearl, Case, Calling Card, White	30.00
Pearl, Case, Card, Engraved Diamond Shape Section	45.00
Pearl, Fork, Cold Meat, Patent '97	25.00
Pearl, Fork, Fish, Engraved Fish On Sterling Ferules	12.00
Pearl, Fork, Serving, Silver Ferrules, 3 Tines, 5 3/4 In.	10.00
Pearl, Fork, Sterling Bands, 7 3/8 In.	25.00
Pearl, Holder, Pen, Case	12.50
Pearl, Knife & Fork, A.S.World Brand, Silver, Set Of 12	80.00
Pearl, Knife & Fork, E.P.N.S. Silver, Embossed, Set Of 12 In Case	67.00
Pearl, Knife, Butter, Carved Handle, 1824 Hallmarked Silver Blade	20.00
Pearl, Knife, Butter, Coin Silver Blade, Stephen Hardy	35.00
Pearl, Knife, Columbia Cutlery, Silver Blade & Fittings, 7 7/8 In.	4.15
Pearl, Knife, Dinner, Gorham Mfg.Co., Sterling Fittings, 8 In.	7.50
Pearl, Knife, Dinner, Sterling Bands	15.00

Pearl, Knife, Dinner, Sterling Ferrules, Dated 1855, Set Of 12	75.00
Pearl, Knife, Embossed Wide Sterling Ferrules, 7 7/8 In., Set Of 6	30.00
Pearl, Knife, Fruit, Sterling Ferrules, Set Of 6	22.50
Pearl, Knife, Fruit, Wm.Rogers, 6 In., Set Of 6	40.00
Pearl, Knife, Luncheon, Coin Silver Blade, Hardy, N.H., C.1840, Set Of 8	120.00
Pearl, Knife, Luncheon, Sterling Ferrules, Set Of 6	35.00
Pearl, Knife, Master Butter, Engraved Blade	10.00
Pearl, Ladle, Berry, Silver Ferrules, 7 1/4 In.	9.00
Pearl, Lighter, Cigarette, Signed France, 4 In.	26.00
Pearl, Manicure Set, Green Velvet Lined Case, 13 Piece	14.00
Pearl, Opera Glasses, see Opera Glasses	
Pearl, Pen, Gold Base & Tip	12.00
Pearl, Pen, Twisted Stem	10.00
Pearl, Pick, Nut, Sterling Ferrules, Set Of 6	17.50
Pearl, Salt Dip, Shell Shape, Footed, 12 In Oriental Lacquer Box	35.00
Pearl, Spreader, Butter, Sterling Bands, Silver Plate Blade, Set Of 6	45.00
Pearl, Spreader, Butter, Sterling Ferrule, Engraved Plated Blade, Set Of 6	60.00
Pearl, Tea Strainer & Sugar Spoon, Marked Sterling, Pair	18.00

Peking glass is a Chinese cameo glass of the eighteenth and nineteenth centuries.

Peking Glass, Beads, Pink	6.00
Peking Glass, Bottle, Prunus, Pink, 4 Seasons, Kang-Hsi, 9 In.	3500.00
Peking Glass, Bottle, Snuff, Blue Overlay, Horse Under Trees, 3 In.	85.00
Peking Glass, Bottle, Snuff, Cameo Cut Garden Scene, C.1920	45.00
Peking Glass, Bottle, Snuff, Carved, Imperial Yellow, 2 3/4 In.	100.00
Peking Glass, Bowl, Ruby, Carved Floral & Rockwork, 6 1/4 In.	175.00
Peking Glass, Bowl, White, Bluebirds & Lotus, 6 In.	210.00
Peking Glass, Bowl, Yellow, Floral & Bamboo, C.1850, Square, 6 In., Pair	225.00
Peking Glass, Cup & Saucer	65.00
Peking Glass, Plate, Deep Purple, Ribbed, 7 In., Pair	100.00
Peking Glass, Plate, Sky Blue, 7 1/2 In.	35.00
Peking Glass, Vase, Flowers & Dragon, Red To Canary, Cameo, C.1800, 5 3/4 In.	390.00
Peking Glass, Vase, Red Over Yellow, Leopards, Floral, C.1800, 5 3/4 In.	390.00
Peking Glass, Vase, White Body, Green Leaves, Blue & Red Flowers, 7 In.High	550.00
Peloton, Pitcher, Green, Overthreadings, Iridescent, 8 In.	95.00

Peloton glass is European glass with small threads of colored glass rolled onto the surface of clear or colored glass. It is sometimes called spaghetti, or shredded coconut, glass.

Peloton, Pitcher, Green, Overthreadings, Iridescent, 8 In.	95.00
Peloton, Vase, Fan Shaped, Cased, Rose To White, Ruffled, 4 3/4 In.High	395.00
Peloton, Vase, Rose To White, Cased, Ribbed, Fan Top, Applied Filaments, 5 In.	395.00
Peloton, Vase, Urn Shape, Cobalt Spaghetti Threading, Gold Edge, 4 1/4 In.	75.00
Pen, see Store, Pen	
Pencil, see Store, Pencil	

Peters and Reed Pottery Company of Zanesville, Ohio, was founded by John D. Peters and Adam Reed in 1897. Chromal, Landsun, Montene, Pereco, and Persian are some of the art lines that were made until the company closed in 1920.

    Peters & Reed, see also Zane

Peters & Reed, Bowl, Red, Green, 2 1/2 X 4 In.	12.50
Peters & Reed, Console Set, Abbington, Pink, 3 Piece	15.00
Peters & Reed, Tile, Mosaic, Reclining Dog, Blue, 3 1/2 X 8 In.	30.00
Peters & Reed, Vase, Aztec Moss, 8 In.	19.00
Peters & Reed, Vase, Red, Green, 7 3/4 X 3 3/4 In.	30.00
Peters & Reed, Vase, Sheenware, 4 In.	7.50
Peters & Reed, Vase, Wall, Brown, Brushed On Green, Grapes, Ferrell, 8 1/2 In.	27.50
Pewabic, Vase, White Pebbly, Green Gold Luster Interior, Bulbous, 3 1/2 In.	85.00

Pewter is a metal alloy of tin and lead. Some of the pewter made after about 1840 has a slightly different composition and is called Britannia metal.

Pewter, Apothecary's Display Piece, Double Handles, 14 X 8 1/4 In.	228.00
Pewter, Ashtray, Art Nouveau Woman, Copper Painted Edges, 9 In.	18.00
Pewter, Beaker, Kayserzinn, Embossed Hops & Grapes, Ergo-Bibamus	45.00

Pewter, Basket, Kayserzinn, Heart Shape, Orchid, Stem & Leaf Handle, 10 In.	68.00
Pewter, Bowl, Covered, Round, 4 1/2 X 3 1/2 In.	25.00
Pewter, Bowl, Nekrassoff, Hand Hammered, 2 Flower & Stem Handles, 7 1/4 In.	10.75
Pewter, Bowl, Nekrassoff, Hand Hammered, 2 Flower Shape Handles, 6 In.	9.95
Pewter, Bowl, Nekrassoff, Hand Hammered, 2 Leaf & Berry Handles, 10 In.	14.75
Pewter, Bowl, Samuel Danforth, Hartford, Deep, C.1795, 11 1/8 In.	325.00
Pewter, Bowl, Tudric, Pierced Sides, Handled, Enameled, C.1900, 11 In.	125.00
Pewter, Bowl, Vegetable, Covered, Queen City Silver Co., 10 1/4 In.	35.00
Pewter, Bowl, Wallace, 8 In.	9.00
Pewter, Box, Jewel, Art Nouveau, 5 X 7 X 3 1/4 In.	75.00
Pewter, Butter, Covered, Richfield Plate Co., 5 3/4 In.	15.00
Pewter, Butter, Whippet Dog Cover, Insert	40.00
Pewter, Candle Snuffer, Chinese, Two Stones, Twist Handle	16.00
Pewter, Candleholder, Reed & Barton, Inverted Geometric Steps, 8 In., Pair	105.00
Pewter, Candlestick, Art Nouveau Female Figure, 5 1/2 In., Pair	105.00
Pewter, Candlestick, C.1840, 1 In.	95.00
Pewter, Candlestick, Continental, 1793, Pricket, Tripod Base, 22 In., Pair	300.00
Pewter, Candlestick, Flagg & Homan, 3 1/8 In.	50.00
Pewter, Candlestick, Push-Up, Bulbous Turned, 9 In., Pair	250.00
Pewter, Candlestick, Sellew Type, 9 3/4 In., Pair	225.00
Pewter, Chalice, Boardman & Co., 7 1/2 In.High	250.00
Pewter, Charger, Deep Dish, 13 In.	175.00
Pewter, Charger, Deep Dish, 14 1/2 In.	195.00
Pewter, Charger, Flagg & Homan, 14 1/8 In.	95.00
Pewter, Charger, Gershom Jones, R.I., C.1785, Molded Rim, 13 1/2 In.	1100.00
Pewter, Charger, Gershom Jones, R.I., C.1790, Deep Bouge, 15 In.	225.00
Pewter, Charger, Molded Rim, Deep Cavetto, C.1850, 14 In.	120.00
Pewter, Charger, Richard Austin, Boston, Massachusetts Arms, 15 In.	1500.00
Pewter, Charger, Townsend & Giffin, London, C.1750, Deep Bouge, 14 3/4 In.	70.00
Pewter, Cocktail Set, Footed Covered Shaker, C.1920, 6 Piece	30.00
Pewter, Coffeepot, Boardman & Co., C.1830, Acorn Finial, Scroll Handle	225.00
Pewter, Coffeepot, Demitasse, Reed & Barton	24.75
Pewter, Coffeepot, F.Porter, Westbrook, Ebony Handle	200.00
Pewter, Coffeepot, J.Dixon	95.00
Pewter, Coffeepot, James Dixon & Son, Wooden Handle & Finial, 8 In.	88.00
Pewter, Coffeepot, James Dixon & Sons, Sheffield, Footed, Melon Shape, 11 In.	65.00
Pewter, Coffeepot, James Dixon, 12 In.	150.00
Pewter, Coffeepot, Reed & Barton, 10 1/2 In.	185.00
Pewter, Coffeepot, Smith & Co., Boston, C.1847, Acorn Finial, Black Handle	140.00
Pewter, Coffeepot, Wooden Handle & Finial, James Dixon & Son, 8 In.	70.00
Pewter, Commode, Samuel Kilbourn, Baltimore, C.1814, Handle, 17 In.	225.00
Pewter, Compote, Flagg & Hoffman, 6 X 3 1/4 In.	25.00
Pewter, Condiment Set, Child's, 4 Bottles	45.00
Pewter, Cooler, Water, Germany, Spigot, Miniature	8.00
Pewter, Cover, Dish, Shaw & Fisher, England, 1845, Ring Handle, 10 1/4 In.	29.75
Pewter, Creamer & Sugar, Standish	75.00
Pewter, Creamer, J.Dixon & Sons	8.00
Pewter, Cup, James Dixon & Son, 2 Handled	49.00
Pewter, Dish, Soap, Ashbil Griswold, Meriden, Hinged, Divided Well, C.1830	425.00
Pewter, Flagon, S With 3 Touchmarks, 1776, Dome Lid, Thumblift, 9 In.	187.50
Pewter, Flask, England, Marked W In Diamond, Screw On Cap, C.1915, 6 Ozs.	15.00
Pewter, Goblet, Reed & Barton	23.00
Pewter, Goblet, Woodbury Pewterers	8.00
Pewter, Inkstand, Davenport, Fort Pitt, 1761, Double Hinged Lid, 8 1/2 In.	375.00
Pewter, Inkwell, Cowlishaw, Boston, Quill Holes, Insert	40.00
Pewter, Inkwell, Insert, 3 1/4 In.	45.00
Pewter, Inkwell, Whitcomb, School	72.00
Pewter, Jug, Yeast, 6 Sided, Covered, Swinging Handle, 11 In.	135.00
Pewter, Knife Rest, Kayserzinn, Figural, Panther, 4 3/4 In.	45.00
Pewter, Ladle, James Dixon, 12 In.	36.00
Pewter, Lamp, Sparking, 5 1/8 X 1 1/2 In.	95.00
Pewter, Lamp, Whale Oil, Hand, Double Wick Threaded Burner, 6 1/2 In.	120.00
Pewter, Measure, James Yates, 1/2 Pint	88.00
Pewter, Measure, 1/4 Gill	28.00
Pewter, Mold, Chocolate, Turkey, 8 In.	7.50
Pewter, Mold, Ice Cream, Airplane	40.00

Pewter, Mold, Ice Cream,
American Flag,
Capitol, 6 In.

Pewter, Mold, Ice Cream,
George Washington, 5 In.

Pewter, Mold, Ice Cream, American Flag, Capitol, 6 In. ....*Illus* 75.00
Pewter, Mold, Ice Cream, Art Nouveau 28.50
Pewter, Mold, Ice Cream, Banana, 5 3/4 In.Long 15.00
Pewter, Mold, Ice Cream, Basket, No Handle 45.00
Pewter, Mold, Ice Cream, Berry, Double 16.00
Pewter, Mold, Ice Cream, Berry, Triple 18.00
Pewter, Mold, Ice Cream, Caveman Figure 22.50
Pewter, Mold, Ice Cream, Chicken, Large 55.00
Pewter, Mold, Ice Cream, Christopher Columbus 30.00
Pewter, Mold, Ice Cream, Dahlia, 3 3/4 In.Diameter 30.00
Pewter, Mold, Ice Cream, Donkey 22.00
Pewter, Mold, Ice Cream, Father Christmas, Large 65.00
Pewter, Mold, Ice Cream, Fruit 8.00
Pewter, Mold, Ice Cream, George Washington, 5 In. ....*Illus* 40.00
Pewter, Mold, Ice Cream, Gladiola 22.50
Pewter, Mold, Ice Cream, Grape Cluster 15.00
Pewter, Mold, Ice Cream, Kewpie Doll 40.00
Pewter, Mold, Ice Cream, Kiwanis 18.00
Pewter, Mold, Ice Cream, Lamb 22.00
Pewter, Mold, Ice Cream, Lily 18.00
Pewter, Mold, Ice Cream, Lily In 3 Sections 25.00
Pewter, Mold, Ice Cream, Lovebirds 25.00
Pewter, Mold, Ice Cream, Maltese Cross 18.00
Pewter, Mold, Ice Cream, Mason Symbol 22.50
Pewter, Mold, Ice Cream, Mason, Master 18.00
Pewter, Mold, Ice Cream, Orange 18.00
Pewter, Mold, Ice Cream, Piece Of Pie 18.00
Pewter, Mold, Ice Cream, Pretzel 18.00
Pewter, Mold, Ice Cream, Pumpkin, Large 40.00
Pewter, Mold, Ice Cream, Purse, Heart Center 18.00
Pewter, Mold, Ice Cream, Rabbit 22.50
Pewter, Mold, Ice Cream, Rabbit, Large 55.00
Pewter, Mold, Ice Cream, Rose, Hinged, E. & C., N.Y. 16.50
Pewter, Mold, Ice Cream, Rotary 18.00
Pewter, Mold, Ice Cream, Rowboat, 6 In.Long 16.00
Pewter, Mold, Ice Cream, Shoe & Hat Top 20.00
Pewter, Mold, Ice Cream, Slipper 22.50
Pewter, Mold, Ice Cream, Star .... 15.00 To 18.00
Pewter, Mold, Ice Cream, Stetson Hat 18.00
Pewter, Mold, Ice Cream, Stork 28.50
Pewter, Mold, Ice Cream, Stork With Baby 20.00
Pewter, Mold, Ice Cream, Suitcase 18.00
Pewter, Mold, Ice Cream, Swan 25.00
Pewter, Mold, Ice Cream, Tennis Racket 40.00
Pewter, Mold, Ice Cream, Turkey, Cooked 22.50
Pewter, Mold, Ice Cream, Turkey, E & Co., N.Y., 3 3/4 In.Long 32.00

Pewter, Mold, Ice Cream, Turkey, Large 55.00
Pewter, Mold, Ice Cream, Turkey, Small 18.00
Pewter, Mold, Ice Cream, W.C.Fields 35.00
Pewter, Mold, Ice Cream, Wishbone 18.00
Pewter, Mold, Ice Cream, Wolf 22.50
    Pewter, Mold, Ice Cream, see also Kewpie, Mold, Ice Cream
Pewter, Mug, Child's, English, C.1850, 3 1/4 In. 32.00
Pewter, Mug, English, Marked E5RF, Lord Nelson Etched On Side, 1/2 Pint 62.00
Pewter, Mug, Roundhead, England, Hammered, Crest, 1934, 3 1/2 In. 18.00
Pewter, Mug, 1/2 Pint, 3 1/2 In. 65.00
Pewter, Pitcher, American, Ornate Handle, Bulbous, 7 1/4 In. 12.50
Pewter, Pitcher, Homan & Co., Ohio, C.1850, Covered, Acorn Finial, 12 1/4 In. 110.00
Pewter, Pitcher, Kayserzinn, Devil's Head, 14 In. 85.00
Pewter, Pitcher, Queen Art Pewter, Wicker Covered Handle, 7 1/2 In. 23.00
Pewter, Pitcher, Robins, Cherries, & Trees, Embossed, Kayserzinn 75.00
Pewter, Pitcher, Water, Nekrassoff, Art Nouveau Style, Handmade, 8 1/2 In. 75.00
Pewter, Plaque, Napoleon, Oval, 6 X 5 In. 65.00
Pewter, Plate, Bread, Flagg & Homan, 13 In. 13.75
Pewter, Plate, Bread, 6 1/2 X 12 1/2 In. 22.00
Pewter, Plate, Crown & Rose Touchmark, 9 1/2 In. 108.00
Pewter, Plate, Hot Water, Parks Boyd, Phila., C.1795, Bail Handles, 9 1/4 In. 150.00
Pewter, Plate, Samuel Ellis, Initialed L.B., C.1750, 9 1/4 In. 225.00
Pewter, Plate, Soup, Schroeder Feinzinn Justice, 8 3/4 In. 50.00
Pewter, Plate, Thomas Danforth, Phila., C.1777, 7 5/8 In. 275.00
Pewter, Platter, Kayserzinn, Oval, Water Lilies Border, Bee, 16 1/2 X 12 In. 50.00
Pewter, Platter, Robert Palethorpe, Phila., C.1822, Molded Rim, 13 1/2 In. 300.00
Pewter, Porringer, Flagg & Homan, Handle, 3 1/8 In. 85.00
Pewter, Porringer, Laughlin, N.E., C.1800, Crown Handle, 5 1/2 In. 325.00
Pewter, Porringer, Nekrassoff, Hand-Hammered, Flower Handle, 3 5/8 In. 9.95
Pewter, Porringer, New England, C.1800, Pierced Scrolling Handle, 5 In. 110.00
Pewter, Porringer, R.I., C.1790, Flowered Handle, 3 1/4 In. 375.00
Pewter, Porringer, Thomas Melville, R.I., C.1790, Trefoil Handle, 5 3/8 In. 650.00
Pewter, Porringer, Thomas Melville, R.I., C.1795, Trefoil Handle, 5 1/2 In. 1200.00
Pewter, Pot, Short, R.Dunham, Westbrooke, Me., C.1830, 7 1/2 In.High 325.00
Pewter, Potpouri, Reed & Barton, Legs 48.75
Pewter, Salt & Pepper, L.B.Smith Co., Boston, 3 In. 27.50
Pewter, Salt & Pepper, Sheffield 12.00
Pewter, Salt, Master, James Dixon, Low Foot 55.00
Pewter, Saltshaker, Signed By Quaker, Bell Finial, Side Handle 15.00
Pewter, Spoon, Soup, Rattail 15.00
Pewter, Stein, German, Guild, C.1680, 15 1/2 In. 1250.00
Pewter, Sugar & Creamer, Benedict Pewter 14.75
Pewter, Sugar & Creamer, Leonard, Reed & Barton, C.1830, 8 In. 225.00
Pewter, Sugar, Covered, E-A-P, Double Handle, 4 In. 18.00
Pewter, Sugar, Manning & Bowman, 2 3/4 In. 25.00
Pewter, Syrup, Nut Finial 40.00
Pewter, Tankard, Beer, Portrait George V, 1910-1935, 4 3/4 In. 110.00
Pewter, Tankard, Manning Bowman & Co., Middletown Ct., C.1865, 8 1/2 In. 350.00
Pewter, Tankard, Stieff, Glass Bottom, 5 In. 20.00
Pewter, Tankard, Two Handled, Clear Glass Bottom, 1904, James Dixon 85.00
Pewter, Tankard, 6 X 4 1/2 In. 40.00
Pewter, Tazza, Tudric, Liberty, 10 In. 200.00
Pewter, Tea Set, Child's, American, Art Nouveau, C.1800, 9 Piece 100.00
Pewter, Tea Set, James Dixon & Son, 5 Piece 650.00
Pewter, Tea Set, Kayserzinn, Raised Iris & Poppy, 4 Piece 125.00
Pewter, Tea Set, Stacked In 1 Piece, C.1900, 3 Piece 25.00
Pewter, Tea Set, Tudric, Liberty, 3 Piece 150.00
Pewter, Teapot, Acorn Finial, Paneled, Footed, Dated 1867 .... 75.00
Pewter, Teapot, Boardman & Co., N.Y., C.1830, Black Double Scroll Handle 375.00
Pewter, Teapot, C.1900, 3 Pieces Stacked In One 38.00
Pewter, Teapot, Chinese Scenes & Writing, 7 In. 27.50
Pewter, Teapot, Copper Bottom, C.1860, 7 1/2 In. 49.75
Pewter, Teapot, Crescent Pewter, Pear Shape, Melon Ribbed, Bakelite Knob 48.00
Pewter, Teapot, Dixon & Sons, Wooden Handle 75.00
Pewter, Teapot, Flagg & Homan 60.00
Pewter, Teapot, George Richardson, C.1830, 8 1/4 In. .... Illus 350.00

Pewter, Teapot, George Richardson, C.1830, 8 1/4 In.
(See Page 354)

Pewter, Urn, Coffee, Japanned,
C.1800, 14 1/2 In.

Pewter, Teapot, James Dixon & Son, Fluted, Oak Leaves & Acorns Band	230.00
Pewter, Teapot, James Dixon & Sons, 5 X 9 1/2 In.	35.00
Pewter, Teapot, James Dixon, 8 In.	85.00
Pewter, Teapot, Melon Ribbed	18.00
Pewter, Teapot, P.Ashberry & Sons	65.00
Pewter, Teapot, Patent June 5, 1863, 9 3/4 In.	49.75
Pewter, Teapot, Pear Shape, 6 In.	185.00
Pewter, Teapot, Reed & Barton, Footed, Wooden Handle	75.00
Pewter, Token Communion, 1770	45.00
Pewter, Token Communion, 1827	45.00
Pewter, Toothpick, Bird, Wishbone, & Egg	15.00
Pewter, Toothpick, Sheffield, England, Handled Stein, Silver Plated	22.00
Pewter, Tray, Lilies & Pads, Kayserzinn, 12 1/4 In.Long	65.00
Pewter, Tumbler, C.1820, 1/2 Pint	31.35
Pewter, Tureen, Kayserzinn, Covered, Footed, Floral, 2 Handled, 7 In.	65.00
Pewter, Urn, Coffee, Japanned, C.1800, 14 1/2 In. .... Illus	110.00
Pewter, Urn, Domed Lid, Continental, C.1800, Scroll Handles, Footed, 19 In.	80.00
Pewter, Vase, Baluster Shape, Double Scroll Handles, C.1825, 6 In., Pair	175.00
Pewter, Vase, Carnation Design, Kayserzinn, 6 3/4 In.	55.00
Pewter, Vase, Crescent, Trumpet Style, 10 In.	20.00
Pewter, Vase, J.Garnier, C.1900, 3 D Handles, Winged Females, 15 In., Pair	80.00
Pewter, Vase, Kayserzinn, Embossed Grapes & Leaves, 11 1/2 In.	45.00
Pewter, Vase, Liberty & Co., Signed Tudric, 10 In., Pair	600.00
Pewter, Warmer, Foot, American, Oval, 11 X 7 In.	125.00
Pewter, Warmer, Foot, James Dixon & Son, Sheffield, Holds 64 Ozs.	125.00
Pewter, Whistle, Bird	6.50

Phoenix Glass Company was founded in 1880 in Pennsylvania. The firm made commercial products such as lampshades, bottles, glassware. Collectors today are interested in the sculptured glassware made by the company from the 1930s until the mid-1950s.

Phoenix Type, Bowl, Opaque, Clear Floral, Bulbous, Art Deco Shape, 7 In.	35.00
Phoenix, Bowl, Blue, Diving Girl, Oval, 14 In.	60.00
Phoenix, Box, Powder, Green, Hummingbirds	38.00
Phoenix, Lamp Base, Bittersweet & Aqua Leaves On White, 11 In.	30.00
Phoenix, Lamp, Dresser, Relief Nudes, Camphor, Pair	138.00
Phoenix, Plate, Green, Clear, & Frosted, 7 Dancing Nymphs, 17 1/2 In.	95.00
Phoenix, Shade, Chandelier, Bluebirds On Cream, 4 Panels, 5 1/4 In., Set Of 4	100.00
Phoenix, Shade, Tulip Design, Frosted & Clear, Small	20.00
Phoenix, Vase, Aqua Poppies In Relief, 12 In.High	38.00
Phoenix, Vase, Aqua, Ferns, Label, 7 In.	42.00
Phoenix, Vase, Blue Birds, Tan Tree Branches, White Flowers, 9 3/4 In.High	90.00

Phoenix, Vase, Blue, Geese In Flight, Satin Finish, 10 In. 85.00
Phoenix, Vase, Brown Cattails, Green Dragonflies, & Leaves On Cream, 9 In. 45.00
Phoenix, Vase, Clear & Opaque, Art Deco, 7 X 8 In. 35.00
Phoenix, Vase, Coral Goldfish On Sea Green Ground, 3 X 8 X 3 In.High 65.00
Phoenix, Vase, Diving Nude, Frosted, Pink Ground, 13 1/2 X 4 1/2 In. 65.00
Phoenix, Vase, Dragonflies & Leaves, 6 In., Pair 85.00
Phoenix, Vase, Fan, White Freesia On Pale Blue, Satin Finish, 8 1/4 In. 53.00
Phoenix, Vase, Flying Geese, White On Blue, 11 X 9 In. 95.00
Phoenix, Vase, Frosted & Clear, Sculptured Dogwood, 10 In. 37.50
Phoenix, Vase, Grasshopper, Opaque Brown, 7 1/4 In.High 48.00
Phoenix, Vase, Madonna, White On Gray Ground, 10 In.High 62.00
Phoenix, Vase, Milk White Opaque, Sculptured Flowers, 12 1/4 In. 42.00
Phoenix, Vase, Opalescent White, Flying Blue Swallows, 11 1/2 In. 95.00
Phoenix, Vase, Orange Bittersweet, Aqua Leaves On White, 10 In. 50.00
Phoenix, Vase, Persimmon Color, Iridescent Madonna Profile, 10 In. 85.00
Phoenix, Vase, Philodendron, Label, 10 1/2 In. .... 52.00 To 75.00
Phoenix, Vase, Pink & White Trumpet Flowers, White Interior, 8 1/4 In.High 65.00
Phoenix, Vase, Praying Mantis, Fan Shaped, Clear On Green, 8 3/4 In.High 55.00
Phoenix, Vase, Rose Bowl Type, White Cameo Floral On Green, 6 1/2 In. 35.00
Phoenix, Vase, Sculptured Fern, 7 In. 45.00
Phoenix, Vase, Smoked Glass, Art Deco, Multiple Planes, 6 In. 38.00
Phoenix, Vase, White Floral On Pearlized, 7 In. 38.00
Phoenix, Vase, White, Blue Berries, Vines, & Leaves, 9 1/2 In. 60.00
Phoenix, Vase, White, Flared, 8 1/2 X 8 In. 75.00
Phoenix, Vase, White, Yellow Flowers & Green Leaves, 6 1/2 In. 35.00
Phoenix, Vase, Yellow & Clear, Cosmos, Sculptures, 7 1/2 In. 58.00
Phonograph, see Music, Phonograph
Photography, Album, British Military, Tooled & Embossed Leather, 9 X 12 In. 135.00
Photography, Album, Carte De Visite, Civil War Generals, 5 1/2 X 4 1/2 In. 100.00
Photography, Album, Oval Prints, Crockett Name, 1862 On, 5 X 8 In. 14.00
Photography, Album, Scandinavian & Russian Cruise, 1936, 7 X 5 In. 8.00
Photography, Album, Tintypes, Abraham Lincoln & 10 Soldiers 1150.00
Photography, Album, Tintypes, Celluloid, Dutch Mill & House, 8 X 11 In. 22.50
Photography, Album, Tooled Leather, Brass Straps, C.1870, Pictures 35.00
Photography, Album, 55 Railroad Photographs, C.1850 .... 150.00
Photography, Ambrotype Case, Quarter Plate, Leather, Hinged 65.00
Photography, Ambrotype, Boy With Dog 40.00
Photography, Ambrotype, Civil War Soldier Holding Cup In Hand 30.00
Photography, Ambrotype, Horse In Cabbage Patch 50.00
Photography, Ambrotype, Man & 2 Oxen, Sixth Plate, Plastic Case 35.00
Photography, Ambrotype, Quarter Plate, Governor & U.S.Senator, Mass. 460.00
Photography, Ambrotype, Quarter Plate, Scientist & Microscope 175.00
Photography, Ambrotype, Sixth Plate, Young Man With Violin, Leather Case 35.00
Photography, Ambrotype, Transfiguration Painting, 4 3/4 X 6 1/2 In. 50.00
Photography, Ambrotype, Young Civilian Man, Leather Case, Gilt Frame 22.50
Photography, Calotype, Bust Of Greco-Roman Figure, 11 1/2 X 15 In. 58.00
Photography, Calotype, Female Bust 58.00
Photography, Camera, see also Disneyana, Camera, Howdy Doody,
Camera, Kewpie, Camera
Photography, Camera, Ansco, Buster Brown, No.3A, Folding, Wood, Leather 25.00
Photography, Camera, Ansco, Studio, Paragon Anastigmat Lens, Wooden 100.00
Photography, Camera, Baby Brownie, 1935, Plastic, 127 Film 4.00
Photography, Camera, Brownie Special 25.00
Photography, Camera, Conley, Kewpie, Box, No.2 .... 10.50
Photography, Camera, Conley, 1907, Full Plate, Mahogany, Leather 115.00
Photography, Camera, E.& H.T.Anthony, Dry Plate, 188 Model, Wood Case 120.00
Photography, Camera, Eastman Kodak, CINE Model B 40.00
Photography, Camera, Eastman Kodak, 50th Anniversary, 1880-1930 .... 20.00
Photography, Camera, Fallowfield, C.1880, Mahogany, Brass, & Leather 230.00
Photography, Camera, Gundlach, Manhattan Optical Co., N.Y., C.1890 .... 110.00
Photography, Camera, Houghton-Butcher Mfg.Co., London, C.1920, Roll Film 265.00
Photography, Camera, Kodak, Autographic Jr., Model A, Folding, Case 12.00
Photography, Camera, Kodak, Autographic, 3-A, Folding 15.00
Photography, Camera, Kodak, Eastman, C.1890, Round Pictures 600.00
Photography, Camera, Kodak, Eureka No.4, 1899 .... 40.00
Photography, Camera, Kodak, Kodomatic, 3A, 1917, Autographic, Model B 75.00

Photography, Camera, Kodak, No.2, Folding, Automatic Brownie 8.00
Photography, Camera, Kodak, Pocket Series II, Folding, Case 14.00
Photography, Camera, Kodak, Pocket, Model 1898, Box, 127 Film 50.00
Photography, Camera, Kodak, S-16, C.1935, K.A.F6.3 Lens In Dakor Shutter 12.00
Photography, Camera, Kodak, Stereo, No.1, Anastigmat 7.7 Lens 150.00
Photography, Camera, Kodak, Target, Hawk Eye, Box 6.00
Photography, Camera, Kodak, 3-A, Autographic, Brownie, 1908 .... 13.95
Photography, Camera, Korona, Special, Folding, Wood, Black Leather 40.00
Photography, Camera, Leica, C, No.39913, C.1929, Leitz Elmar 50 Mm. Lens 200.00
Photography, Camera, Minox B, World War II German Espionage, Leather Case 75.00
Photography, Camera, Perkin & Son, London, C.1890, Optimus, Brass, Leather 120.00
Photography, Camera, Remington 10.00
Photography, Camera, Rival 35, German, Retina Copy F3.5, Enna Lens, C.1950 .... 14.00
Photography, Camera, Simon Wing, Repeating, 6 Lenses, 5 X 8 In. View 1200.00
Photography, Camera, Super Ikonta B-C, 1938, Single Window View, 120 Film 72.00
Photography, Camera, The Junior Sanderson, G.H.& S., London, C.1900 .... 195.00
Photography, Camera, U.S.Army Air Corps, Movie, Heavy Duty 22.50
Photography, Carte De Visite, Abraham Lincoln, Bearded 20.00
Photography, Carte De Visite, Civil War Soldier, Rome, N.Y. 8.00
Photography, Carte De Visite, Col. Tom Thumb & Wife, C.1860 .... 10.00 To 15.00
Photography, Carte De Visite, Commodore Mutt & Minnie Warren, Midgets 10.00
Photography, Carte De Visite, General Braxton Bragg, Florida Studio 20.00
Photography, Carte De Visite, George Armstrong Custer, C.1862, 3/4 Angle 28.00
Photography, Carte De Visite, John Wilkes Booth, C.1861, Sepia, 4 X 2 1/2 In 38.00
Photography, Carte De Visite, Lieutenant General U.S.Grant, Mouring Dress 45.00
Photography, Carte De Visite, Lincoln & His Cabinet 20.00
Photography, Carte De Visite, Lincoln, Peck Bros. 10.00
Photography, Carte De Visite, Masaachusetts Fireman, C.1870 .... 3.50
Photography, Carte De Visite, Old Abe, The Live Wisconsin War Eagle, 1876 .... 15.00
Photography, Carte De Visite, Ulysses S.Grant Bust, Sepia 5.00
Photography, Carte De Visite, Union Soldier Leaning On His Rifle 15.00
Photography, Carte De Visite, Young Wench In Afro Hairdo, C.1870 .... 5.00
Photography, Carte De Visite, 6 Men In Women's Apparel, C.1850 .... 17.00
Photography, Daguerreotype Case, Brass Frame Signed Holmes Booth & Hayden 50.00
Photography, Daguerreotype Case, Concentrics, Embossed Leather, Tintype 28.00
Photography, Daguerreotype Case, Gentleman On Rock, Rose Color, Oval 12.00
Photography, Daguerreotype Case, Gutta-Percha, Apple Picker 52.00
Photography, Daguerreotype Case, Gutta-Percha, Beehive, 1/16 Plate Size 60.00
Photography, Daguerreotype Case, Gutta-Percha, Bobby Shafto 75.00
Photography, Daguerreotype Case, Gutta-Percha, Brown, Woman, 3 X 2 In. 22.75
Photography, Daguerreotype Case, Gutta-Percha, Brown, 3 3/4 X 3 1/4 In. 22.75
Photography, Daguerreotype Case, Gutta-Percha, Civil War Soldiers 42.00
Photography, Daguerreotype Case, Gutta-Percha, Cupid & Stag 55.00
Photography, Daguerreotype Case, Gutta-Percha, Flower Bier, The, 6 In. 100.00
Photography, Daguerreotype Case, Gutta-Percha, Fruit & Floral Urn, 2 In. 22.50
Photography, Daguerreotype Case, Gutta-Percha, Girl Riding Horse, 5 In. 30.00
Photography, Daguerreotype Case, Gutta-Percha, Goblet & Flowers, 3 In. 48.00
Photography, Daguerreotype Case, Gutta-Percha, Horn Of Plenty, 3 3/4 In. 40.00
Photography, Daguerreotype Case, Gutta-Percha, Little Girl In Fire Hat 45.00
Photography, Daguerreotype Case, Gutta-Percha, Lord's Prayer, 5 In. 85.00
Photography, Daguerreotype Case, Gutta-Percha, Mary & Her Lamb 55.00
Photography, Daguerreotype Case, Gutta-Percha, Medallions, Floral, Scrolls 45.00
Photography, Daguerreotype Case, Gutta-Percha, Patent Oct.14, 1856 .... 30.00
Photography, Daguerreotype Case, Gutta-Percha, Patriotic, A.Shaefer 260.00
Photography, Daguerreotype Case, Gutta-Percha, Scottish Highlander 70.00
Photography, Daguerreotype Case, Gutta-Percha, Scroll & Flower, 3 In. 18.00
Photography, Daguerreotype Case, Gutta-Percha, Shield & Shells, 3 3/4 In. 45.00
Photography, Daguerreotype Case, Gutta-Percha, Union & Constitution 38.00
Photography, Daguerreotype Case, Gutta-Percha, Wheat Sheaves .... 38.00 To 60.00
Photography, Daguerreotype Case, Gutta-Percha, Young Man, 2 In. 18.00
Photography, Daguerreotype, Dog On Chair, Sixth Plate 65.00
Photography, Daguerreotype, Father In Boston Rocker Holding Dead Infant 45.00
Photography, Daguerreotype, Half Plate, Couple, Oval Mat 30.00
Photography, Daguerreotype, Half Plate, Gentleman, Leather Case 45.00
Photography, Daguerreotype, Half Plate, Girl With Dog, Leather Case 135.00
Photography, Daguerreotype, Man, Signed Cooley, Springfield 22.50

Photography, Daguerreotype, Ninth Plate, Young Boy, Boston	10.00
Photography, Daguerreotype, Old Lady In Cap, Velvet Lined Case	13.00
Photography, Daguerreotype, Sixth Plate, Gentleman, Leather Case	30.00
Photography, Daguerreotype, Sixth Plate, Old Gentleman, Leather Case	40.00
Photography, Daguerreotype, Sixth Plate, Young Man In Odd Fellows Dress	70.00
Photography, Daguerreotype, Sixth Plate, Young Woman, Whipple, Leather Case	50.00
Photography, Daguerreotype, Sixth Plate, 10 Year Old Boy, Anthony Style	35.00
Photography, Daguerreotype, Sixth Plate, 2 Black Women, Tinted	85.00
Photography, Daguerreotype, Woman Wearing Paisley Shawl, Full Plate	300.00
Photography, Daguerreotype, Young Boy In Uniform, Embossed Leather	12.00
Photography, Daguerreotype, Young Couple, Brass Matted & Frames	27.00
Photography, Daguerreotype, Young Woman, Half Case, 3 1/2 In.	15.00
Photography, Duoscope	495.00
Photography, Ferrotype, Prince Napoleon	15.00
Photography, Ferrotype, Secretary Of State Seward, 1860s	20.00
Photography, Frame, Wooden, Dated 1880, 8 1/2 X 6 1/4 In.	15.00
Photography, Glass Slide, 2 Men & 2 Women With Cameras, English, 1905	15.00
Photography, Lantern, Developing, Kodak, Red Amber Lens	18.00
Photography, Lens, Adams & Co., London, C.1885, Aluminum, Pinhole	85.00
Photography, Lens, Daguerreotype, Lerebours Et Secretan A Paris, 1850, Brass	275.00
Photography, Lucida, Camera, Cary, London, C.1890, Brass, 14 In.	110.00
Photography, Magic Lantern, Kerosene Burner, Tin & Brass On Wood, 1880s	79.00
Photography, Magic Lantern, Laterna Magica, Cosmos, C.1890, Slides, Case	160.00
Photography, Magic Lantern, Radiopticon, 2 Heat Vents	59.00
Photography, Mutoscope, Aluminum Case	995.00
Photography, Mutoscope, Tin Case	495.00
Photography, Photograph, see also Charlie Chaplin, Photograph, Lindbergh, Photograph, Shirley Temple, Photograph	
Photography, Photograph, Alan Todd, 1947	7.00
Photography, Photograph, August A.Busch & Family, Brewers, 1929, 8 X 10 In.	25.00
Photography, Photograph, Buckingham Fountain, Chicago, 5 3/4 X 4 In.	25.00
Photography, Photograph, Cabinet, Soldier, C.1885, Hulten, Ill.	25.00
Photography, Photograph, Captain Hickey, U.S.Infantry, 1917, 47 In.	9.50
Photography, Photograph, Col. W.F. Cody, 8 1/2 X 6 1/2 In.	4.95
Photography, Photograph, Confirmation Of Sioux, 1860, Peavey & Peterson	5.00
Photography, Photograph, Esther Williams, Autographed, C.1953, 8 X 10 In.	5.50
Photography, Photograph, Fire Engine, 2 Horse, Fireman, Dog, 4 1/2 X 8 In.	25.00
Photography, Photograph, Franklin D.Roosevelt, Sepia, Bust, 1936, 10 In.	75.00
Photography, Photograph, German Army & Dog Team, C.1916, 5 X 7 In.	4.00
Photography, Photograph, High Ranking Mason In Robes, Case & Getchell	4.00
Photography, Photograph, Indian & Pony, Fort Apache, Arizona, Randall, 1884	15.00
Photography, Photograph, King Faisal, Black & White, Signed, 7 X 10 In.	20.00
Photography, Photograph, Life Motion, Farmer, 2 Pieces Of Celluloid, C.1910	5.00
Photography, Photograph, Life Motion, Girl, 2 Pieces Of Celluloid, 4 X 5 In.	4.00
Photography, Photograph, Man & Woman, Oval Porcelain, Civil War Era, Pair	150.00
Photography, Photograph, Massachusetts Hurricane, 1939	3.00
Photography, Photograph, Mohave Tribe At Home, Parker, 4 1/2 X 7 1/2 In.	17.50
Photography, Photograph, Motion, Man Batting Ball, Muybridge, 1887, 24 In.	70.00
Photography, Photograph, Motion, Man Picking Up Ball, Muybridge, 1887, 24 In.	65.00
Photography, Photograph, Mourning Card, Mike O'Conner, Cuba, 1898, Sepia	4.00
Photography, Photograph, Nicholas, Alexandra, & 3 Children, 4 X 2 1/2 In.	10.00
Photography, Photograph, Nikolai Alexandrovich, 1920, 12 1/4 X 8 1/4 In.	100.00
Photography, Photograph, Nude Woman Sewing Indian Dress, Sepia, 1916	8.00
Photography, Photograph, Providence Baseball Team, 1904, Sepia, 13 X 16 In.	23.00
Photography, Photograph, Sculptor, C.Dimitriedy, Athens, 1930, 7 X 9 In.	40.00
Photography, Photograph, Sitting Bull, Portrait, Barry *Illus*	150.00
Photography, Photograph, Tobacco Society, Crow, Montana, 3 1/2 X 2 1/2 In.	29.50
Photography, Photograph, U.S.Grant As 4 Star General, Whipple	10.00
Photography, Photograph, Vermont Flood, 1927, 8 X 10 In.	1.20
Photography, Photograph, 4 Union Officers, 1863, 3 1/4 X 4 In.	20.00
Photography, Projector, see also Disneyana, Projector	
Photography, Projector, Glass Slide, Bausch & Lomb, 1911, 75 Slides	100.00
Photography, Projector, Movie Film, Hand Crank, Black Metal, 11 X 9 In.	75.00
Photography, Projector, Tin, Glass, Kerosene, 2 Lenses, 8 1/2 X 14 In.	100.00
Photography, Sensitivity Tester, Sanger Shepherd & Co., London, C.1901	185.00
Photography, Slide, Glass, La Taxiphoto, New England Scenes, 25	32.50

Photography, Photograph, Sitting Bull, Portrait, Barry
(See Page 358)

Photography, Slide, Lantern, Boss Charging Candidate, C.& I., 1880, Pair	35.00
Photography, Slide, Lantern, Luncheon Wheels, Prospectown, N.J., 1906, Glass	5.50
Photography, Slide, Magic Lantern, Santa, 9	12.00
Photography, Slide, Magic Lantern, Spanish American War, 12	20.00
Photography, Stereo, see Stereo	
Photography, Tintype, Baby Sitting Among Ruffled Covers, Half Case, 3 In.	10.00
Photography, Tintype, Barbara Frietchie With Flag, 8 1/2 X 6 1/2 In.	85.00
Photography, Tintype, Bearded Man, Visored Cap, C.1850, Gilt Frame, N.H.	27.50
Photography, Tintype, Civil War Soldier, Seated, Leather Case, 3 5/8 In.	20.00
Photography, Tintype, Dragoon Soldier, C.1850, Tinted, Gilt Frame, 3 1/4 In.	44.50
Photography, Tintype, Elderly Couple, Color, Walnut Frame, 9 X 7 In.	30.00
Photography, Tintype, Girl With Cat & Dog, 4 X 6 In.	22.50
Photography, Tintype, Group Of 4, Negro Man Standing, 4 X 2 1/2 In.	10.00
Photography, Tintype, Horse & Buggy	8.00
Photography, Tintype, Infantryman, Frock Coat, Gilt Frame, 2 X 3 In.	32.50
Photography, Tintype, Little Girl With China Doll	3.50
Photography, Tintype, Negress, Plaid Dress, 2 X 3 In.	15.00
Photography, Tintype, Negro Baby	10.00
Photography, Tintype, Portrait Of Sea Captain, C.1870, 7 X 9 In.	15.00
Photography, Tintype, Seated Soldier, C.1840, Leather Case, 2 X 2 1/2 In.	25.00
Photography, Tintype, Sixth Plate, Civil War Soldier, Leather Case	27.00
Photography, Tintype, Sixth Plate, Infant Postmortem	17.00
Photography, Tintype, Sixth Plate, Union Soldiers, Leather Case, Va., 1863	110.00
Photography, Tintype, U.S.Artillery Sergeant, Gilt Frame, 3 1/4 X 2 3/4 In.	32.50
Photography, Tintype, Union Army Captain, Tinted, Gilt Frame, 2 1/2 X 2 In.	27.50
Photography, Tintype, Union Army Infantry, Grizzled, Gilt Frame, 3 X 4 In.	39.50
Photography, Tintype, Union Cavalry Soldier, Tinted, Gilt Frame, 2 1/2 In.	29.50
Photography, Tintype, Union Civil War Soldier	10.00
Photography, Tintype, Union Infantryman, Gilt Frame, 3 1/4 X 3 In.	34.50
Photography, Tintype, Union Soldier, Gun & Bayonet	22.50
Photography, Tintype, Union Soldier, Tinted, Gilt Frame, 2 X 2 1/2 In.	27.50
Photography, Tintype, White Woman With Negro Child, Leather Case	15.00
Photography, Tintype, Woman, Horse & Buggy, Dirt Road, 5 X 8 In.	44.50
Photography, Tintype, Yankee Soldier, 2 X 1 In.	10.00
Photography, Tintype, 3 Civil War Soldiers, Tinted, Gilt Frame, 4 X 3 In.	54.50
Photography, Zoogroscope, For Steel Engraving, C.1790	195.00
Piano Baby, Baby On Stomach, Bisque, White Dress, Pink Bow, Dimples, 10 In.	125.00

Piano Baby, Baby, Crawling On Stomach, Bisque, Hand On Chest, 5 In.	30.00
Piano Baby, Baby, Hands Behind On Floor, 1 Leg Raised, Glazed China, 7 In.	50.00
Piano Baby, Baby, Sitting, Surprise Pose, Bisque, 6 In.	45.00
Piano Baby, Boy, Gun, Dog At Side, Bisque, 8 In.	42.50
Piano Baby, Crawling Baby, Miniature, Victorian	25.00
Piano Baby, Crawling On Stomach, 1 Leg In Air, Open Gown, Heubach, 8 In.	175.00
Piano Baby, Girl Lying On Pillow, Heubach	195.00
Piano Baby, Girl On Stomach, Bisque, Yellow Dress, Blue Bow, 10 In.	125.00
Piano Baby, Girl, On Stomach, Ball In Hand, Bisque, Gold Beading, 6 1/2 In.	40.00
Piano Baby, Girl, Bisque, 5 In.	35.00
Piano Baby, Girl, Sitting, Reading Book, Bisque, Finger Pointing, 4 1/2 In.	30.00
Piano Baby, On Stomach, Blue Pillow, Puppy, Heubach, 8 In., Pair	175.00
Piano Baby, On Tummy, Bisque, 12 In.	68.00
Piano Baby, Pulling On Toes, Pale Green Nightshirt, Kestner, 12 In.	365.00
Piano Baby, Reclining, Wearing Bonnet, Lacy Trim, Bisque, 5 In.	34.00
Piano Baby, Right Leg & Arm In Air, Heubach, 5 In.	37.50
Piano Baby, Sitting On Pillow, Pulling On Sock, Heubach, 13 In.	345.00

Piano, see Music, Piano

Pickard china was started in 1898 by Wilder Pickard. Hand-painted china was a featured product. The firm is still working in Antioch, Illinois.

Pickard, Bowl, Daisy Medallions, Gold Handles & Interior, Oblong, 7 1/2 In.	39.00
Pickard, Bowl, Gold Floral & Wheat On White Donatello Blank, Handled, 7 In.	25.00
Pickard, Bowl, Pastel Floral, Gold Border, Handled, 1910, 7 In.	55.00
Pickard, Bowl, Pastel Scene Of Autumn Trees & Hills, Marked Nippon, 8 In.	65.00
Pickard, Bowl, Pink & White Roses, Artist Signed, 9 X 3 In.	45.00
Pickard, Candlestick, Etched Gold Floral, Square Base, 9 In.High, Pair	28.00
Pickard, Creamer, Red Poinsettias, Gold Trim	35.00
Pickard, Cup & Saucer, Bouillon, Gold Rims & Bands, Black Geometrics	12.00
Pickard, Cup & Saucer, Bouillon, 2 Handled, Wild Roses, Gold Trim, Leach	48.00
Pickard, Cup & Saucer, Nasturtiums	35.00
Pickard, Dish, Candy, Pierced Handled, Green, Gold, Leaf On Sides, 5 1/2 In.	18.00
Pickard, Dish, Candy, Scalloped, Red Poppies, Cream To Coral, 7 1/4 In.	55.00
Pickard, Dish, Leaf Shape, Gold Etched, 6 In.	12.00
Pickard, Dish, Olive, Pink, Blue, & Gold, Hand-Painted	13.00
Pickard, Hatpin Holder, Allover Gold Etched Florals	29.50
Pickard, Jar & Underplate, Marmalade, Covered, Blackberries, Gold Trim, 6 In.	85.00
Pickard, Jug, Gold Grapes & Leaves, Signed Keen, 6 1/2 In.	130.00
Pickard, Mug, Green, Gold, Orange Luster Leaves, Signed Lind, 7 In.	95.00
Pickard, Pitcher, Ivory, Art Nouveau Silver & Gold, C.1905, 6 1/2 In.	285.00
Pickard, Pitcher, Milk, Poppies, 1905-10	68.00
Pickard, Plate, Art Nouveau Design, Gold Border, Green Flowers, 8 1/2 In.	22.00
Pickard, Plate, Art Nouveau, Green Flowers, Gold Border, 8 1/2 In.	22.00
Pickard, Plate, Blue Floral, Stylized Gilt On White, Gold Border, 8 5/8 In.	17.50
Pickard, Plate, Bowleg Bill, The Seafaring Cowboy, 11 In.	65.00
Pickard, Plate, Bread, Floral, Wide Gold Edge, 14 In.	25.00
Pickard, Plate, Cherries & Gooseberries, Gold Border, Signed, 8 1/2 In.	25.00
Pickard, Plate, Greek Ruins & Gardens, Handled, C.Marker, 8 In.	155.00
Pickard, Plate, Open Gold Handles, Bands, & Rim, Black Geometrics, 10 3/4 In.	22.00
Pickard, Plate, Orchids, Signed, 9 In.	25.00
Pickard, Plate, Raised Gold Poppies, Artist Signed, 6 In.	11.50
Pickard, Plate, Roses, Scalloped, Artist Signed, Early Mark, 8 1/2 In.	44.00
Pickard, Plate, Strawberries & Blossoms, C.1905, 8 1/2 In.	35.00
Pickard, Plate, White Flowers, Red & Yellow Centers, Green Ground, 8 1/2 In.	22.50
Pickard, Plate, White, Art Deco Decoration, Hand-Painted, 8 3/4 In.	25.00
Pickard, Relish, White, Gold, Signed A.Richter	75.00
Pickard, Salt & Pepper, Gold Etched	12.00
Pickard, Salt & Pepper, Gold, Incised Pattern, 2 In.	7.50
Pickard, Salt & Pepper, Gold, Signed, 3 1/2 In.	12.00
Pickard, Salt & Pepper, Individual, Etched Gold, 1 5/8 In.	10.00
Pickard, Sugar & Creamer, Art Deco Violets, Green Leaves, Gondola Shape	75.00
Pickard, Sugar & Creamer, Cover, Art Deco Floral, Circle Mark	65.00
Pickard, Sugar & Creamer, Cover, Diamond Shape, Gold & Silver Floral	75.00
Pickard, Sugar & Creamer, Cover, Floral, Gold, & Silver, Furlys & Fallon	65.00
Pickard, Sugar & Creamer, Cover, Footed, Gold, Daisies	55.00
Pickard, Sugar & Creamer, Cover, Gold, Footed, Ornate Handles	65.00

Pickard, Sugar & Creamer, Gold, No.511 .... 18.00
Pickard, Sugar & Creamer, Metallic Grapes On Green Ground, F.H., 3 In. 65.00
Pickard, Sugar & Creamer, No.598, Gold 18.00
Pickard, Sugar, Pink & Green Floral, Nippon Blank 19.00
Pickard, Tea Set, Art Nouveau Scenic Decoration, Gold & Platinum, 3 Piece 400.00
Pickard, Tea Set, Embossed Florals, Signed, 3 Piece 80.00
Pickard, Tea Set, Gold Floral On Thomas Bavarian Blanks, C.1825, 4 Piece 145.00
Pickard, Teapot, Allover Gold, Ginori, Italy Mark, 8 In. 20.00
Pickard, Tray, Dresser, Poppies, Gold, Artist Signed 49.00
Pickard, Tray, Handled, Gold & Red Art Deco Design, 1912, 14 X 5 In. 35.00
Pickard, Tray, Leaf Shape, Handled, Rose & Daisy, 6 In. 12.00
Pickard, Tray, Sugar Cube, Band & Ellipses, Gold Leaves, 7 3/4 In.Long 19.50
Pickard, Vase, Cream To Orange, Violets, Gold, R.C.Bavaria, 7 X 13 In. 35.00
Pickard, Vase, Gold Outlined Poinsettias On Cream & Peach, Gasper, 15 In. 195.00
Pickard, Vase, Lake & Woods Scene, 3 Legs, Challinor, C.1938, 5 1/2 In. 65.00
Pickard, Vase, Poinsettias, Gold Trim & Outlining, Gasper, 15 In. 195.00
Pickard, Vase, Portrait, Young Lady, Gold Floral On Green, 9 1/4 In. 150.00
    Picture, see also Painting, Print
Picture, Carved & Painted Wood, Red Jacket Off Cape Horn, 20 X 12 In. 150.00
Picture, Cross-Stitch On Linen, Washington Silhouette, Framed, 7 1/2 In. 8.00
Picture, Family Register, Wescott Family, Conn., C.1850, 23 X 17 In. 70.00
    Picture Frame, see Furniture, Frame
Picture, Hair Wreath, New England, C.1860, Brass Frame, 20 X 14 In. 125.00
Picture, Ink Drawing, Clipper Ship, Gordon Grant, 12 X 9 In. 250.00
Picture, Needlework, Biblical, 3 Scenes, Gilt Frame, C.1620, 23 X 19 In. 500.00
Picture, Needlework, Punch & Judy, B.1750, Maple Frame, 14 X 18 In., Pair 295.00
Picture, Needlework, Sovereign Gazing To Eternal Glory, C.1620, 14 X 19 In. 700.00
Picture, Pen, Penmanship, American Eagle With Pen In Beak, C.1850, 10 In. 160.00
Picture, Penmanship, Bird On Flowering Spray, C.1850, 14 X 11 In. 70.00
Picture, Silhouette, Profile Busts Colonial Woman & Man, C.1790, 7 In., Pair 65.00
Picture, Silhouette, Rev.Jonas Clarke, Mass., C.1800, To Left, 14 X 9 In. 350.00
Picture, Silk & Chenille Embroidery, Ruth & Naomi, Drew, N.E., 1850, 30 In. 225.00
Picture, Silk Embroidery, Maiden Leaning On An Anchor, C.1850, 12 1/4 In. 100.00
Picture, Silk Embroidery, Young Lady & Dog, Painted, C.1850, 9 X 8 In. 70.00
Picture, Tinsel, Floral, C.1850, 17 1/2 X 11 In. 130.00
Picture, Tinsel, Red Flowers & Buds, Silver Leaves, Black, 11 X 9 In. 28.00
Picture, Wax Silhouette, Colonial Gentleman, Frame, 6 X 5 In. .... 65.00 To 75.00
Picture, Wool Embroidery, British Ships, G.Fuller, C.1850, 26 X 13 In. 425.00
Picture, Woven Silk, Centennial Independence Memento Souvenir, 6 X 10 In. 127.50
    Pigeon Blood, see Cranberry Glass, Ruby Glass
Pigeon Forge, Figurine, Bear, Black, Marked, 4 1/4 In. 10.00
Pilkington, Vase, Sunstone Glaze, Flared, Dated 1907, 5 1/4 In. 85.00
    Pink Slag, see Slag, Pink
    Pinocchio, see Disneyana
Pipe, Bowl, Clay, Henry Clay Figure Head 6.50
Pipe, Carved Horn, Hand-Painted Bowl, 32 In. 50.00
Pipe, Clay Bowl, Wooden Stem, 6 In. 10.00
Pipe, Clay, Incised Bowl 18.00
Pipe, Imperial German Soldier's, Porcelain Bowl, Hand-Painted Scene 195.00
Pipe, Imperial German Soldier's, Porcelain Bowl, Helmet Lid, 1904 .... 235.00
Pipe, Imperial German Soldier's, Porcelain Bowl, Mounted Dragoon, 1898 .... 185.00
Pipe, Kaywoodie, Briar, Velvet Presentation Box, 2 In. 25.00
    Pipe, Meerschaum, see Meerschaum, Pipe
Pipe, Opium, Brass Bowl & Stem 10.00
Pipe, Porcelain, Wooden Stem, Deer Decoration, 9 1/2 In. 30.00
Pipe, Soap Bubble, Redwood Bowl, Double Metal Stems 4.00
Pipe, Turkish Hookah, Cranberry Glass, Hand-Cut Decoration 32.50
Pipe, Water, Cloisonne, On Brass, Insects 175.00
Pipe, Wood & Brass, Ivory Ojime, Umimatsu Holder, Ashinaga, C.1850 .... 200.00
    Pipe, see also Cloisonne, Pipe

    Pisgah pottery pieces that are marked Pisgah Forest Pottery were made
    from 1926 until the present. Vases, teapots, jugs, candlesticks, and many other
    items were made.
Pisgah Forest, Jar, Covered, Green, Pink Interior, Signed, 3 In. 15.00
Pisgah Forest, Vase, White Relief Wagon Train, Stephen, 1951, 4 In. 90.00

Plate, see under special types such as ABC, Calendar, Christmas

Plated Amberina, Pitcher, 3 Scallops At Top, 6 3/4 In.	4000.00
Plated Amberina, Tumbler	1000.00 To 1500.00

Plated Silver, see Silver Plate

Plique a jour is an enameling process. The enamel was laid between thin
raised metal lines and heated. The finished piece has transparent enamel held
between the thin metal wires.

Plique A Jour, Bowl, Goldfish Swimming On Green, 5 In.	200.00
Plique A Jour, Bowl, Pastel Green, Prunus Tree, Yellow Blossoms, 5 1/4 In.	275.00
Plique A Jour, Bowl, Silver Metal Outlined Floral, 3 Footed, 4 1/4 In.	350.00
Plique A Jour, Bowl, 3 Orange Fantail Gold Fish Swimming On Green, 5 In.	285.00
Plique A Jour, Mint Green Ground, Prunus Trees, Yellow Blossoms, 5 1/4 In.	230.00
Plique A Jour, Spoon, Gold Washed Sterling, Red, Green, & Clear, 4 In.	45.00
Plique A Jour, Vase, Ball Shape, Mums & Dahlias On Green, 5 X 4 1/2 In.	295.00
Plique A Jour, Vase, Orange Fantailed Goldfish & Water Plants, 6 In.	290.00
Plique A Jour, Vase, Pink Cherry Blossoms On Tree On Green, 5 3/4 In.	265.00
Political Campaign, Badge & Inauguration Ribbon, 1973	6.50
Political Campaign, Badge, Bell, Ambrotype, Oval	300.00 To 400.00
Political Campaign, Badge, Breckenridge, Ambrotype, Oval	300.00 To 400.00
Political Campaign, Badge, Douglas, Ambrotype, Oval	300.00 To 400.00
Political Campaign, Badge, Garfield, Portrait & Shell, Brass Frame, 30 Mm.	100.00
Political Campaign, Badge, Greeley, Tintype	85.00
Political Campaign, Badge, Hancock, Tintype	75.00
Political Campaign, Badge, Horace Greeley, Cardboard	75.00
Political Campaign, Badge, Horace Greeley, Tintype	75.00
Political Campaign, Badge, Humphrey & Muskie	4.00
Political Campaign, Badge, J.F.K., Inaugural, Blue Ribbon, 1961	22.00
Political Campaign, Badge, J.F.Kennedy, 1960, Cardboard, Floral	25.00
Political Campaign, Badge, Johnson & Humphrey	4.00
Political Campaign, Badge, Lincoln, Ambrotype, Oval	300.00 To 400.00
Political Campaign, Badge, McClellan, Tintype	50.00
Political Campaign, Badge, McKinley, Brass, 5 In.	75.00
Political Campaign, Badge, Willkie & McNary	4.00
Political Campaign, Ballot, Sample, Cleveland Hendricks, 1844	15.00
Political Campaign, Ballot, Sample, McKinley & Hobart, 1896, Silk	18.00
Political Campaign, Ballot, Sample, Richmond, 1956	5.00
Political Campaign, Ballot, Sample, 1928 Presidential Election, 17 X 11 In.	10.00
Political Campaign, Bandana, Benjamin Harrison, 1888, Silk, 20 In.	50.00
Political Campaign, Bandana, Bryan, Silk, 17 1/2 In.	50.00
Political Campaign, Bandana, Harrison & Morton Portraits	55.00
Political Campaign, Bandana, Ike For President, Linen, 25 In.	20.00
Political Campaign, Bandana, Ike In Blue On Red, Flag, Square, 27 In.	20.00
Political Campaign, Bandana, Willkie, Square, 20 1/2 In.	27.00
Political Campaign, Banner, Polk & Clay, American Eagle, C.1850, 45 In.	750.00
Political Campaign, Book, Democratic, 1906	4.00
Political Campaign, Book, Hoover & Curtis, 1928, Ohio	9.00
Political Campaign, Book, National Democratic Convention, 1928	20.00
Political Campaign, Booklet, National Democratic Committee, 1860, Slaves	12.00
Political Campaign, Bookmark, Ike, Stevenson, 1956, Woven Silk	19.00
Political Campaign, Bookmark, Lincoln, Paterson, N.H., Picture, 11 In.	85.00
Political Campaign, Bowtie, J.F.Kennedy, Metallic Letters On Gray	17.00
Political Campaign, Box, Collar, Chester A.Arthur, Celluloid, 4 X 3 In.	100.00
Political Campaign, Box, Thread, Adams	400.00
Political Campaign, Box, Thread, Jackson	400.00
Political Campaign, Broadside, Roosevelt, A Gallant Leader, C.1945, 12 In.	6.00
Political Campaign, Broadside, Whig Party, San Francisco, 1852, 9 X 12 In.	175.00
Political Campaign, Brochure, Anti-Buchanan, 1856	10.00
Political Campaign, Brochure, Anti-McClellan	20.00
Political Campaign, Bug, McKinley & Hobart, Gold, Mechanical	100.00
Political Campaign, Button & Pocket Tag, John F.Kennedy, 1960, Blue, White	2.00
Political Campaign, Button, Every Buddy For Willkie	3.50
Political Campaign, Button, General Douglas MacArthur, Pinback, Ribbon	2.00
Political Campaign, Button, Herbert Hoover For President, Picture	25.00
Political Campaign, Button, I Like Ike	1.00
Political Campaign, Button, Ike, Pinback, C.1957, 1 3/4 In.	2.50

Political Campaign, Button, Kennedy & Johnson	1.00
Political Campaign, Button, McGovern, Photograph, 3 In.	1.50
Political Campaign, Button, McKinley, Picture, Pinback	12.50
Political Campaign, Button, Nixon & Lodge	1.00
Political Campaign, Button, Nixon, Photograph	4.00
Political Campaign, Button, Our Next President, Nixon, Ribbon, Pinback	6.00
Political Campaign, Button, Robert Kennedy For President, Picture, 5 In.	1.50
Political Campaign, Button, Shamrock, Democracy, People, Republic, Bimetalism	15.00
Political Campaign, Button, Taft, 1909, Eagle & Shield, 1 1/4 In.	22.00
Political Campaign, Button, Truman, Celluloid, Hanging, Stand-Up, 9 In.	35.00
Political Campaign, Button, Van Buren, Gilt Brass, 20 Mm.	250.00
Political Campaign, Button, William J.Bryan, Pinback, Picture	11.00
Political Campaign, Button, Willkie & McNary, Red, White, & Blue	2.50
Political Campaign, Cane, Wm.J.Bryan, Pewter Head Of Bryan, 35 In.	100.00
Political Campaign, Card, Anti-Grover Cleveland, British Flag	5.50
Political Campaign, Card, Benjamin Harrison & J.G.Blaine, American Flag	6.00
Political Campaign, Card, Blaine & Logan, Ho For Salt River, 4 1/4 In.	5.00
Political Campaign, Card, Cleveland & Stevenson, Picture, Sepia	18.00
Political Campaign, Card, Lincoln & Johnson, Prang	75.00
Political Campaign, Card, Logan, Our Next Vice President, Picture, Brown	5.00
Political Campaign, Card, Richard Nixon, 1968, Signed, 7 X 5 In.	85.00
Political Campaign, Card, Trade, Allen Thurman Picture, Vaseline Ad Back	6.00
Political Campaign, Card, Trade, Blaine For President, Vaseline Ad Back	6.50
Political Campaign, Card, Trade, Garfield For President, Vaseline Ad Back	9.00
Political Campaign, Card, Trade, Grover Cleveland Picture, Vaseline Ad Back	7.50
Political Campaign, Cards, Playing, J.K.Kennedy	15.00
Political Campaign, Cards, Playing, Nixon, "The Spirit Of '76"	55.00
Political Campaign, Cigar, Bill Taft, In Glass Tube	15.00
Political Campaign, Coaster, Willkie, Tin, 3 1/4 In. Diameter	5.00
Political Campaign, Coin, Lucky Tillicum, F.D.R., Bronze, 1 1/4 In.	4.00
Political Campaign, Compact, F.D.R., Mirror, Brass, Volupe, 3 In.	25.00
Political Campaign, Cuff Links, Nixon & Agnew Inaugural	10.00
Political Campaign, Cup, Munroe, Staffordshire	300.00
Political Campaign, Cup, Wm.Jennings Bryan, Covered, Glass	45.00
Political Campaign, Earrings, Ike, Gold Metal, Pair	7.00
Political Campaign, Emblem, License Plate, Win With Willkie, 3 X 5 In.	8.50
Political Campaign, Ferrotype, Breckinridge & Lane, Brass Frame	125.00
Political Campaign, Ferrotype, Fremont, 1864, Metallic Frame, Brass Shell	250.00
Political Campaign, Ferrotype, H.Greeley, 1872-26, Brass Shell, 24 Mm.	75.00
Political Campaign, Ferrotype, J.C.Breckinridge, 1860-24, Brass Shell	150.00
Political Campaign, Ferrotype, Lincoln, 1860, Beardless, Metallic Frame	300.00
Political Campaign, Ferrotype, Lincoln, 1860, Brass, 24 Mm.	200.00
Political Campaign, Ferrotype, R.B.Hayes, On 6 Pointed Star	75.00
Political Campaign, Figurine, John F.Kennedy In Rocking Chair, Plastic	3.75
Political Campaign, Flag, Clay	300.00
Political Campaign, Flag, Lincoln	300.00
Political Campaign, Flag, Polk	300.00
Political Campaign, Flyer, Republican Campaign, 1875, Reform Candidates	8.00
Political Campaign, Folder, Richard Nixon, Signed, Picture	65.00
Political Campaign, Frame Of Stickers, Socialist Workers, 1968	4.50
Political Campaign, Frame Of Stickers, Willkie, 1940	6.00
Political Campaign, Game Board, Nomination, 1889, Lithographed, 18 1/2 In.	16.00
Political Campaign, Guide, 1973 Inaugural, Pictures	3.00
Political Campaign, Handbill, Hoover, 1928	4.00
Political Campaign, Handkerchief, Cleveland & Thurman, 1888, Linen, 20 In.	32.00
Political Campaign, Handkerchief, Harrison-Morton, Industry, 18 X 20 In.	34.00
Political Campaign, Invitation, Eisenhower & Nixon Inaugural, 1953	20.00
Political Campaign, Invitation, Hoover & Curtis Inaugural, 1929, Photos	22.00
Political Campaign, Invitation, J.F.Kennedy Inaugural, Photographs	22.50
Political Campaign, Invitation, Johnson & Humphrey Inaugural, 1965	18.00
Political Campaign, Invitation, Lincoln Inaugural Ball, 10 1/2 X 7 1/2 In.	150.00
Political Campaign, Invitation, Lincoln Inaugural Ball, 1865, 12 X 9 In.	125.00
Political Campaign, Invitation, Roosevelt Garner Inaugural, 1937, Photos	25.00
Political Campaign, Invitation, Wilson Inaugural, 1913	35.00
Political Campaign, Jug, Cleveland & Stevenson, Ceramic, Paper Label	35.00
Political Campaign, Jugate, Bryan & Kern, Our Choice, 1908, Brass	35.00

Political Campaign, Jugate, Bryan & Stevenson, Blue Ribbon, 1 3/4 In.	45.00
Political Campaign, Jugate, Bryan & Sulzer, Silver Border, 1 1/4 In.	45.00
Political Campaign, Jugate, Bryan & Watson, 1896, Populist Party	175.00
Political Campaign, Jugate, Cleveland & Stevenson, 1892, White Metal	50.00
Political Campaign, Jugate, Cleveland & Thurman, 1888	40.00
Political Campaign, Jugate, Davis & Bryan, Paper Stamp Type, 1 1/2 In.	85.00
Political Campaign, Jugate, F.D.R. & Garner, Lithograph, 7/8 In.	85.00
Political Campaign, Jugate, Hughes & Fairbanks, 1916, Celluloid	400.00
Political Campaign, Jugate, Landon & Knox, Lithograph, Beige, 13/16 In.	115.00
Political Campaign, Jugate, McKinley & Roosevelt, Pinback	14.00
Political Campaign, Jugate, McKinley & Teddy Roosevelt, Sepia, 2 In.	150.00
Political Campaign, Jugate, Nixon & Agnew, 3 1/2 In.	2.00
Political Campaign, Jugate, Taft & Sherman, Our Choice, Brass	25.00
Political Campaign, Jugate, Teddy Roosevelt, A Full Dinner Bucket	20.00
Political Campaign, Kerchief, Silk, McKinley Hobart, Battleship Maine	49.00
Political Campaign, Key Chain, Eisenhower, Brass, Picture, 1953	1.75
Political Campaign, Knife, Pocket, Wilson, Inaugural	215.00
Political Campaign, Lantern, Parade, Harrison & Morton, 1888, Paper	100.00
Political Campaign, License Plate Attachment, Willkie & McNary	14.00
Political Campaign, Locket, Cleveland, White Metal	45.00
Political Campaign, Locket, Thurman	75.00
Political Campaign, Match Holder, Wall, Horace Greeley, Cast Iron	75.00
Political Campaign, Match Safe, Bust Of McKinley	175.00
Political Campaign, Medal, Coolidge Inauguration, Bronze, Darrel Crain	350.00
Political Campaign, Medallion, George Washington, C.1800, Pewter Frame	150.00
Political Campaign, Mug, Al Smith, Syracuse China, 7 In.	40.00
Political Campaign, Mug, Eisenhower, 7 In.	35.00
Political Campaign, Mug, McKinley, Stippled, Crystal, 3 3/4 In.	20.00
Political Campaign, Music Broadside, No Nothing Political Party, C.1840	10.00
Political Campaign, Necktie, Landon, Deep Blue	25.00
Political Campaign, Paperweight, F.D.Roosevelt, 1933, Seashell	25.00
Political Campaign, Paperweight, McKinley, Sepia Portrait, Star, Glass	37.50
Political Campaign, Paperweight, Roosevelt & Fairbanks, Graeser, Pa., Glass	35.00
Political Campaign, Paperweight, Watergate Circus	10.00
Political Campaign, Penknife, McGovern & Eagleton, Pictures	4.00
Political Campaign, Pennant, Al Smith, 1928	10.00
Political Campaign, Pennant, Hoover, 1928	10.00
Political Campaign, Pennant, Thomas E.Dewey, 1948, Presidential Election	12.00
Political Campaign, Penny, Teddy Roosevelt For President, Picture	50.00
Political Campaign, Photograph, Dwight D.Eisenhower, On Silk, Bachrach	35.00
Political Campaign, Photograph, McKinley & Roosevelt In Boat	17.00
Political Campaign, Photograph, Nixon & Agnew	9.00
Political Campaign, Photograph, President William Taft, Tintype Case	20.00
Political Campaign, Picture, Nixon, On Plastic	3.00
Political Campaign, Pin, American Party, 1916, I Am For Sulzer	300.00
Political Campaign, Pin, Bryan, Anti-Trust, Rebus, Gold Bug	75.00
Political Campaign, Pin, General MacArthur, Photograph	8.00
Political Campaign, Pin, John W.Davis, Black & White Bust, 7/8 In.	85.00
Political Campaign, Pin, John W.Davis, Picture, 1 1/4 In.	175.00
Political Campaign, Pin, La Follette & Wheeler, Bronze	30.00
Political Campaign, Pin, McKinley & Roosevelt, Bug Shape, Folding Wings	38.00
Political Campaign, Pin, Ribbon, & Medal, Truman Inauguration	8.00
Political Campaign, Pin, Roosevelt, Donkey	6.50
Political Campaign, Pin, Single Tax Party, 1920, White On Blue, 7/8 In.	150.00
Political Campaign, Pin, Stevenson, Shoe, Red, White, & Blue, 3 1/2 In.	12.00
Political Campaign, Pin, Teddy Roosevelt, Coaxing Taft, 1 1/4 In.	125.00
Political Campaign, Pin, Wage Earners Club, 1908, 7/8 In.	100.00
Political Campaign, Pin, Willkie, Mother-Of-Pearl	6.50
Political Campaign, Pipe Bowl, Taft, 1908, Figural, Clay	42.00
Political Campaign, Plaque, Ben Butler Bust, Lead, Amew Sword Co., 3 In.	150.00
Political Campaign, Plaque, Car, Willkie	14.50
Political Campaign, Plate, James Blaine, 1884, Black & White, 8 In.	40.00
Political Campaign, Plate, President Taft, Our Choice, 1908, 8 3/4 In.	36.00
Political Campaign, Plate, William J.Bryan, Sepia Bust, Dresden, 7 1/2 In.	15.00
Political Campaign, Plate, Wm.H.Taft, President Luncheon, 1911, 10 In.	38.50
Political Campaign, Postcard, I'm For Bill, 1908	10.00

Political Campaign, Postcard, Taft & Sherman, Jugate	5.00
Political Campaign, Postcard, Wilson, 1910	10.00
Political Campaign, Poster, Adlai Stevenson, Danger Ahead, 8 1/2 X 13 In.	45.00
Political Campaign, Poster, Eugene McCarthy, Political Cabaret, 22 In.	25.00
Political Campaign, Poster, Eugene McCarthy, 1968, Ben Shahn, 40 X 28 In.	30.00
Political Campaign, Poster, F.D.Roosevelt, 11 X 4 1/2 In.	10.00
Political Campaign, Poster, Herbert Hoover, 16 X 22 In.	17.50
Political Campaign, Poster, Lincoln & Johnson, 1864, 19 X 24 In.	300.00
Political Campaign, Poster, President McKinley, Omaha Exposition, C.1898	92.50
Political Campaign, Poster, Teddy Roosevelt & Johnson, 18 1/2 X 22 3/4 In.	49.00
Political Campaign, Poster, Teddy Roosevelt & Johnson, 1912, 25 X 18 In.	35.00
Political Campaign, Poster, Willkie & McNary, 22 X 16 In.	22.50
Political Campaign, Ribbon, Andrew Jackson, Memorial, Silk, 3 X 8 In.	85.00
Political Campaign, Ribbon, Blaine & Logan, Leather, 4 In.	65.00
Political Campaign, Ribbon, Bryan & Sewall, Pictures	15.00
Political Campaign, Ribbon, Cleveland & Hendricks, Inaugural, Gold, Red	85.00
Political Campaign, Ribbon, Cleveland, Silk, Jacquard, Bust, 4 1/2 X 2 In.	15.00
Political Campaign, Ribbon, David B.Hill, Favorite Son, 1892, Silk, 7 In.	25.00
Political Campaign, Ribbon, Flag, Harrison & Morton, Silk, 2 1/2 X 4 In.	22.00
Political Campaign, Ribbon, Garfield & Arthur	5.00
Political Campaign, Ribbon, George Washington, Silk, 1847, 7 1/2 In.	110.00
Political Campaign, Ribbon, Harrison, 1892, Celluloid Portrait	35.00
Political Campaign, Ribbon, Johnson's Inauguration, 1965	1.00
Political Campaign, Ribbon, McKinley & Hobart	25.00
Political Campaign, Ribbon, McKinley, Cloth, War Veterans, 1896	15.00
Political Campaign, Ribbon, McKinley, 1896, Yellow, Black Letters	20.00
Political Campaign, Ribbon, Nixon, 1960, Label, Silk, 6 In.	8.00
Political Campaign, Ribbon, Teddy Roosevelt, 1904, Silk, 5 1/4 In.	45.00
Political Campaign, Ring, Al Smith For President, 1928, Porcelain & Metal	22.00
Political Campaign, Sewing Needle Packet, Hoover & Curtis, 1926	10.00
Political Campaign, Sheet Music, Horace Greeley's March, Waters, 1872	25.00
Political Campaign, Sheet Music, We're All For Eisenhower, 1952	8.50
Political Campaign, Sheet Music, 1888 Candidate's Songs, Pair	45.00
Political Campaign, Shell, Cleveland, 1888, Moonstone Portrait, Brass	125.00
Political Campaign, Snuffbox, Clay, Papier-Mache	150.00 To 250.00
Political Campaign, Snuffbox, Taylor, Papier-Mache	150.00 To 250.00
Political Campaign, Snuffbox, Van Buren, Papier-Mache	175.00 To 250.00
Political Campaign, Songster, Grant & Colfax, Beadle & Co., 1868	50.00
Political Campaign, Spoon, J.F.K.	2.00
Political Campaign, Stationery, Kennedy For President, Picture J.F.K.	4.00
Political Campaign, Sticker, Window, Nixon & Lodge, 1960, Blue & White, 7 In.	42.00
Political Campaign, Stickpin, Cleveland, Rooster, 1/2 X 5/8 In.	25.00
Political Campaign, Stickpin, Wilson, Pink Cameo, Brass Frame	55.00
Political Campaign, Stud, Harding, Running Elephant, Pewter, 1 In.	6.50
Political Campaign, Stud, Harrison, Enamel	25.00
Political Campaign, Thimble, Coolidge & Dawes	4.00 To 6.00
Political Campaign, Thimble, Hoover	4.00 To 6.00
Political Campaign, Thimble, Nixon & Agnew, 1972, Yellow Plastic	3.00
Political Campaign, Ticket, Electoral, Weaver & Chambers, 1880, 3rd Party	20.00
Political Campaign, Ticket, Inaugural Ball, 1973	3.00
Political Campaign, Ticket, Inauguration, 1965	3.00
Political Campaign, Ticket, Johnson Impeachment, April 1868, 3 X 3 1/2 In.	65.00
Political Campaign, Ticket, McKinley, 1912, National Convention	3.50
Political Campaign, Ticket, Republican National Convention, 1932	5.00
Political Campaign, Ticket, Republican 100 Dollar A Plate Dinner, 1968	3.50
Political Campaign, Ticket, Wilson, Democratic National Convention, 1920	15.00
Political Campaign, Tile, Portrait W.Wilson, Glazed, 5 3/4 X 8 1/2 In.	45.00
Political Campaign, Token, Al Smith, 1928	20.00
Political Campaign, Token, Cleveland For President, 1888, Picture	12.00
Political Campaign, Token, General Winfield Scott, Picture, Battles	10.00
Political Campaign, Token, H.Clay, DeWitt, 1840-1, Brass, 28 Mm.	20.00
Political Campaign, Token, Harrison's Inauguration, Picture, Gold Color	16.00
Political Campaign, Token, Maj.General W.H.Harrison, 1840, Brass, 1 In.	34.50
Political Campaign, Token, People's Choice, William Harrison, 1840, Picture	8.50
Political Campaign, Token, W.H.Harrison, DeWitt, 1849-9, White Metal	15.00
Political Campaign, Tray, Keep Roosevelt In The White House	30.00

Political Campaign, Tray, McKinley & Teddy Roosevelt, Tin, Oval, 16 In.	65.00
Political Campaign, Watch Fob, Harding, Brass	65.00
Political Campaign, Watch Fob, James A.Garfield, Mechanical, Gold Finish	350.00
Political Campaign, Watch Fob, Roosevelt & Fairbanks, 1904, Brass	10.00
Political Campaign, Watch Fob, Wm.H.Taft, Embossed Bust, White Metal	18.00

Pomona glass is clear with a soft amber border decorated with pale blue or rose-colored flowers and leaves. The colors are very, very pale. The background of the glass is covered with a network of fine lines. It was made from 1885 to 1888 by the New England Glass Company.

Pomona, Bowl & Underplate, Finger, Midwestern, Decorated	100.00
Pomona, Bowl, Ruffled Rim, First Grind, 2 1/4 X 5 In.	150.00
Pomona, Castor, Pickle, Clear Cornflower Band, Meriden Holder	185.00
Pomona, Celery, Blue Cornflower, 2nd Grind	110.00
Pomona, Celery, Inverted Thumbprint, Amber Fluted Rim, Footed, 1st Grind	125.00
Pomona, Creamer, Blueberry Sprays, Applied Spout & Handle, Footed, 2nd Grind	425.00
Pomona, Cup, Punch, Cornflowers, Applied Loop Handle, 1st Grind, C.1900	58.50
Pomona, Cup, Punch, Diamond-Quilted, 1st Grind	85.00
Pomona, Cup, Punch, Thumbprint, First Grind	70.00
Pomona, Pitcher, Inverted Thumbprint, Honey Amber, Gold Handle, 7 1/2 In.	285.00
Pomona, Pitcher, Water, Etched Bluebirds, Floral, & Vine, 2nd Grind, 8 In.	225.00
Pomona, Pitcher, Water, Inverted Thumbprint, Amber Band & Handle, 7 1/2 In.	155.00
Pomona, Rose Bowl, Lilac & Amber Clematis Vine, Frosted Center, 4 X 4 In.	65.00
Pomona, Salt & Pepper, Amber, Blue Cornflowers, Silver Tops	235.00
Pomona, Sugar, Acorn Finial, Floral, Yellow Green Foliage, Silvered Handles	215.00
Pomona, Toothpick, Mt.Washington	150.00
Pomona, Toothpick, New England, Amber, Tricorner, 2nd Grind	100.00
Pomona, Tumbler, Iced Tea, Cornflower, Inverted Thumbprint, 1st Grind	150.00
Pomona, Tumbler, Inverted Thumbprint, Acorn Decoration	95.00
Pomona, Tumbler, New England, Cornflower, 1st Grind	110.00 To 130.00
Pomona, Tumbler, New England, Diamond-Quilted, Pansy & Butterfly, 2nd Grind	175.00
Pomona, Tumbler, 1st Grind	70.00
Pomona, Vase, Fan, Miniature, Ruffled Top, First Ground, 2 1/2 In.High	125.00
Pomona, Vase, New England, Cornflowers, Diamond-Quilted, 2nd Grind, 5 1/2 In.	375.00
Pomona, Vase, Rose Bowl Type, Cornflowers, Diamond-Qulted, 2nd Grind, 5 In.	275.00
Pomona, Vase, Rose Bowl Type, Cornflowers, 2nd Grind, 5 1/2 In.High	375.00
Pontypool, see Tole	
Popeye, Button	5.00
Popeye, Doll, Rubber, 1935, 7 In.	35.00
Popeye, Figurine, Plaster, 21 In.	35.00
Popeye, Film, Train Busters, 1935, 16mm.	15.00
Popeye, Game, Funny Face	10.00
Popeye, Music Box	15.00
Porcelain, see also Copeland, Nippon, R.S.Prussia, etc.	
Porcelain, Barrel, Biscuit, Victoria, Floral On White, Silver Fittings, 6 In.	72.00
Porcelain, Basket, Applied Roses, Leaves, & Buds, Gold Trim, German, 7 1/2 In.	32.00
Porcelain, Basket, Czechoslovakia, Gold Etched, 4 X 4 In.	15.00
Porcelain, Basket, Germany, Forget-Me-Nots & Pink Rose, Green Handle, 3 In.	10.00
Porcelain, Berry Set, Germany, Pink Roses, Lilacs, & Grapes, 5 Piece	35.00
Porcelain, Berry Set, Japanese, Red & Gold, Scenic Medallions, 7 Piece	85.00
Porcelain, Bonbon, C.Tielsch, Altwasser, Pierced Handle, Shell Shape, 12 In.	35.00
Porcelain, Boot, German, Picture Of Washington On Toe, 2 1/2 In.	3.00
Porcelain, Bowl, Austria, Alhambra, Footed, Geometrics, Gold Trim, 9 X 8 In.	40.00
Porcelain, Bowl, Baby's, Czechoslovakian, Decals	15.00
Porcelain, Bowl, Condiment, Chinese, Floral On Celadon Green, 8 In.	30.00
Porcelain, Bowl, Czechoslovakia, Covered, Red Lobster, 3 1/2 In.	5.00
Porcelain, Bowl, English, 3 Section, Floral, Gold Trim, Handle, 11 1/2 In.	22.50
Porcelain, Bowl, English, 3 Sections, White Crackle, Gold Trim, Handle, 12 In.	17.50
Porcelain, Bowl, Germany, Flower Center, White Grapes, Gold, 11 In.	55.00
Porcelain, Bowl, Karmlow Bros., Russia, Signed J.H.V., 6 1/2 In.	28.00
Porcelain, Bowl, Russian, Covered, Royal, 6 1/4 In., Pair *Illus*	1600.00
Porcelain, Bowl, Russian, Reticulated Basket, Branch Handles, C.1825, 14 In.	350.00
Porcelain, Bowl, Saxony, Altenberg, Cameolike Cupids & Lovers, 10 In.	57.00
Porcelain, Bowl, Serving, Schwartzburg, Tricornered, Gold On White, 7 X 6 In.	23.00
Porcelain, Bowl, Sponge, English, White, Gold, Yellow Bow, 7 1/2 In.	28.00
Porcelain, Bowl, Vegetable, England, Covered, Cobalt Trim, Spoon Hole	25.00

Porcelain, Bowl, Russian,
Covered, Royal, 6 1/4 In., Pair
(See Page 366)

Porcelain, Plate, Russian, Royal, 8 3/4 In.
(See Page 370)

Porcelain, Bowl, W.T.English, I.R.& Co., Covered, Birds, Blue, Gilt, 5 1/2 In.	65.00
Porcelain, Box, French, Rose Camaieu, Ship, Silver Gilt Mounts, 2 5/8 In.	65.00
Porcelain, Box, Powder, Oscar Schlegelmilch, Rust Trim, Gold	24.00
Porcelain, Box, Powder, Victoria, Austria, Blue Bird Lid, 4 In.	20.00
Porcelain, Box, Stamp, Austria, Blue Floral, 2 1/2 X 3 1/2 In.	10.00
Porcelain, Butter Pat, Saxony With Crown, Band Of Pink Roses, Gold Edge	3.25
Porcelain, Cereal Set, Child's, Jackson Vitrified China, Pa., Floral, 2 Piece	8.50
Porcelain, Chamber Pot, English, White, Gold, Yellow Bow	28.00
Porcelain, Chamberstick, Monkey Sitting On Blue Book, German, 6 1/2 In.	70.00
Porcelain, Chocolate Pot, Austrian, Floral, Scrolls, & Gold On White	29.00
Porcelain, Chocolate Pot, Eleanor, Austria, Green Gold Bands & Roses	42.00
Porcelain, Chocolate Pot, FHN, Victoria Austria, Seminude, 8 In.	25.00
Porcelain, Chocolate Pot, G.M.M.Z., Austria, Pink Carnations, Green Leaves	60.00
Porcelain, Chocolate Pot, Germany, Blue, Green, Red, & Gold, Artist Signed	27.00
Porcelain, Chocolate Pot, Germany, Green, Gold, Pink Roses, Domed Top	45.00
Porcelain, Chocolate Pot, Germany, Roses Decoration, 9 In.	33.00
Porcelain, Chocolate Set, Child's, Germany, Red & White Roses, 13 Piece	48.00
Porcelain, Chocolate Set, Garden Scene, Cobalt, Beaded, Japanese, 13 Piece	70.00
Porcelain, Chocolate Set, Germany, Roses On Green To White, Gilt, 13 Piece	87.50
Porcelain, Chocolate Set, Hand-Painted Flowers, Gold & Cobalt, 13 Piece	175.00
Porcelain, Chocolate Set, Japan, Figures On White, Domed Cover, 13 Piece	45.00
Porcelain, Chocolate Set, Prussia, Signed With Dragon, Pink & Gold, 13 Piece	75.00
Porcelain, Chocolate Set, Roses & Leaves, Gold At Top & Handles, 9 Piece	125.00
Porcelain, Cider Set, Castle Scene On Cream, Tankard, German, 7 Piece	45.00
Porcelain, Coffee Set, Iridescent Blue, Silesia, 13 Piece	45.00
Porcelain, Coffeepot, French, Gold Handle & Spout, Yellow, Roses & Lattice	75.00
Porcelain, Compote, French, Enamel Fierce Looking Bird & Floral, 9 3/4 In.	65.00
Porcelain, Compote, Russian, Grand Duke Paul Alexandrovitch, C.1890, 9 In.	325.00
Porcelain, Creamer, Austria, Elk's Head, 4 1/2 In.	22.00
Porcelain, Creamer, Austrian, Moose, 4 In.	18.50
Porcelain, Creamer, B.B.K., Pineapple Shape, Leaf Handle	12.00
Porcelain, Creamer, Czechoslovakia, Bird	12.50
Porcelain, Creamer, Czechoslovakia, Cow	12.50
Porcelain, Creamer, Czechoslovakia, Moose	12.50
Porcelain, Creamer, Czechoslovakia, Sitting Cow, Brown & White	7.00
Porcelain, Creamer, Foley, England, Floral Panels, Gold, Twisted Handle	13.50
Porcelain, Creamer, German, Cow With Crumpled Horn	15.00
Porcelain, Creamer, German, Cow, Black & Brown On White	18.00
Porcelain, Creamer, German, Cow, Standing, Brown, 7 In.	12.50
Porcelain, Creamer, German, Fat Monk, Brown Robe, Hat, 4 1/2 In.	25.00
Porcelain, Creamer, German, Lobster Forms Handle Of Shell, Pearlized	35.00
Porcelain, Creamer, German, Reclining Cow, Light Gold & Beige	15.00
Porcelain, Creamer, Germany, Brown Standing Cow, 6 1/2 In.	16.50
Porcelain, Creamer, Germany, Dutch Girl & Windmills	10.00
Porcelain, Creamer, Germany, Parrot, Green & Orange	8.50
Porcelain, Creamer, Japanese, Birds, Lilac Luster Top, Tan Luster Interior	6.00

Porcelain, **Creamer**, Prussian, Purple & Pink Flowers, Gold Edge	16.50
Porcelain, **Creamer**, Prussian, Relief Panels, 4 Footed	16.50
Porcelain, **Cup & Sacuer**, Demitasse, Pink Floral, Baroda Pattern, Johnson	3.50
Porcelain, **Cup & Saucer**, C.T., Altwasser, Germany, Pink & White Roses	5.00
Porcelain, **Cup & Saucer**, Coffee, Russian, Raphael, 1895, Pair	750.00
Porcelain, **Cup & Saucer**, Demitasse, Booths' Silicon China, Wreath Pattern	4.00
Porcelain, **Cup & Saucer**, Demitasse, Russian, Scene & Gilt Eagle, C.1796	300.00
Porcelain, **Cup & Saucer**, Gardner, Mass.Railroad Station	7.50
Porcelain, **Cup & Saucer**, German, Purple & Green, Gold Think Of Me	18.00
Porcelain, **Cup & Saucer**, Germany, Green & Gold, "Remember Me"	8.50 To 16.00
Porcelain, **Cup & Saucer**, Hand-Painted Flowers, Gold, Maroon, Leonard, Austria	18.00
Porcelain, **Cup & Saucer**, Napoleonic, Green, Raised Gold, Portrait	50.00
Porcelain, **Cup & Saucer**, Victoria, Czechoslovakia, Turquoise	3.00
Porcelain, **Cup & Saucer**, Vienna, Salem Witch, Tea Leaf Reading Symbols	85.00
Porcelain, **Decanter**, Austrian, Lilac, Green, Open Webbed Handles, 9 1/2 In.	20.00
Porcelain, **Dessert Set**, Austria, Wild Roses, Vines, Burnt Orange, 8 Piece	65.00
Porcelain, **Dish**, Bone, Fleurette, England, Blue Garlands, Gold Scalloped Rim	3.00
Porcelain, **Dish**, Cheese, Covered, Pink Roses Blue Flowers, Winton	35.00
Porcelain, **Dish**, Cheese, English, C.1850, Yellow Glazed, Square Cover	25.00
Porcelain, **Dish**, Hen Cover, Western Germany, Nest Base, Yellow, 7 1/2 In.	7.00
Porcelain, **Dish**, Nut, Japanese, Lavender Blue, Gold Interior, Footed	1.50
Porcelain, **Dish**, Ram Cover, Kuznetsov, Black & White, Gold, C.1900, 7 In.	180.00
Porcelain, **Dish**, Refrigerator, Covered, Blue, White, Hall China Co.	5.00
Porcelain, **Dish**, St.Bernard On Pale Green Ground, German, 4 In.Square	11.00
Porcelain, **Dish**, Sweetmeat, Japanese, Fan Shape, 8 Compartments, 10 In.	15.00
Porcelain, **Dresser Set**, Czechoslovakian, Rose Color Marble Effect, 6 Piece	55.00
Porcelain, **Dresser Set**, English, Oriental Pattern, 6 Piece	45.00
Porcelain, **Dresser Set**, Lavender Ground, Purple Violets, Gold 3 Piece	55.00
Porcelain, **Dresser Set**, Roses & Pansies On White, 7 Piece	75.00
Porcelain, **Egg**, Easter, Russian, Alexandra Feodorovna Monogram, C.1790, 4 In.	325.00
Porcelain, **Egg**, Easter, Russian, Alexandra Feodorovna Monogram, C.1820, 3 In.	250.00
Porcelain, **Egg**, Easter, Russian, Alexandra Feodorovna Monogram, C.1850, 3 In.	225.00
Porcelain, **Egg**, Easter, Russian, Alexandra Feodorovna Monogram, C.1890, 4 In.	400.00
Porcelain, **Egg**, Easter, Russian, Alexandra Feodorovna Monogram, C.1890, 4 In.	850.00
Porcelain, **Egg**, Easter, Russian, Alexei Nikolaevitch Monogram, C.1920, 3 In.	400.00
Porcelain, **Egg**, Easter, Russian, Christ & Crown Of Thorns, C.1850, 4 1/2 In.	800.00
Porcelain, **Egg**, Easter, Russian, Christ Rising From Tomb, C.1850, 3 1/2 In.	325.00
Porcelain, **Egg**, Easter, Russian, Figure Of St.Michael Tverskoi, C.1850, 5 In.	550.00
Porcelain, **Egg**, Easter, Russian, Figure Of St.Olga & Christ, C.1850, 4 In.	550.00
Porcelain, **Egg**, Easter, Russian, Lilacs & Christ Is Risen, C.1850, 5 1/2 In.	475.00
Porcelain, **Egg**, Easter, Russian, Maria Feodorovna Monogram, C.1890, 4 In.	800.00
Porcelain, **Egg**, Easter, Russian, Maria Feodorovna Monogram, 1917, 2 1/2 In.	350.00
Porcelain, **Egg**, Easter, Russian, Maria Nikolaevna Monogram, C.1890, 2 1/2 In.	375.00
Porcelain, **Egg**, Easter, Russian, Mark The Evangelist, C.1850, 4 3/4 In.	850.00
Porcelain, **Egg**, Easter, Russian, Morning Glories On Pale Green, C.1850, 4 In.	325.00
Porcelain, **Egg**, Easter, Russian, Nicholas II Monogram, C.1890, 2 1/2 In.	375.00
Porcelain, **Egg**, Easter, Russian, Nicholas II Monogram, C.1890, 3 3/4 In.	450.00
Porcelain, **Egg**, Easter, Russian, Pink & White Floral On Gray, C.1850, 4 In.	175.00
Porcelain, **Egg**, Easter, Russian, Portrait Of St.Peter, C.1850, 3 In.	800.00
Porcelain, **Egg**, Easter, Russian, St.Basil The Great, C.1850, 4 1/2 In.	550.00
Porcelain, **Egg**, Easter, Russian, St.Catherine, Signed E.D., C.1850, 4 1/2 In.	800.00
Porcelain, **Egg**, Easter, Russian, St.Dmitri, Half Portrait, C.1850, 4 1/4 In.	525.00
Porcelain, **Egg**, Easter, Russian, St.Sergei Radonezhsky, C.1850, 3 3/4 In.	450.00
Porcelain, **Egg**, Easter, Russian, Virgin On Blue, Gilt, C.1850, 4 1/4 In.	550.00
Porcelain, **Etui**, Thuringian, Gold Mounts, Floral, C.1820, 4 1/2 In.	250.00
Porcelain, **Ewer**, Crane & Rushes, Royal Leicester, 8 1/2 In.	28.00
Porcelain, **Ewer**, Russian, Gray Blue, Enamel, Handled, Covered, 12 In.	75.00
Porcelain, **Feeder**, Invalid, White With Blue Decoration	15.00
Porcelain, **Figurine**, Annie Oakley, Japan, Painted, 5 In.	13.00
Porcelain, **Figurine**, Ballet Dancer, White, Iridescent Costume, Russian, 5 In.	65.00
Porcelain, **Figurine**, Bulldog, Brown & White, 7 In.Long	18.00
Porcelain, **Figurine**, Cobbler, Russian, C.1850 *Illus*	425.00
Porcelain, **Figurine**, Dancing Woman, Russian, Popov, C.1820, 7 In.	325.00
Porcelain, **Figurine**, Dog, Blue Green, Yellow Stand, 2 In.	3.00
Porcelain, **Figurine**, Girl & Bouquet, Boy & Shovel, Germany, 3 1/2 In., Pair	6.00
Porcelain, **Figurine**, Long Hair Pointer, Vienna, White, Tan Spots, 7 X 3 In.	38.00

Porcelain, Figurine, Man,
Russian, C.1890, 9 In.

Porcelain, Figurine,
Cobbler, Russian, C.1850
(See Page 368)

Porcelain, Figurine, Man By Tree Stump Feeding Dog, Blanc De Chine, 5 In.	70.00
Porcelain, Figurine, Man, Russian, C.1890, 9 In. .... *Illus*	450.00
Porcelain, Figurine, Nude, Seated, Metzler & Orlaff, Germany, 8 In.	32.50
Porcelain, Figurine, Peasant Girl, Gemschultz-Bergmann, Sepia, 6 In.	30.00
Porcelain, Figurine, Potentate, English, Seated, Crimson Turban, C.1840, 5 In.	30.00
Porcelain, Figurine, Pug Dog, Bisque Finish, Whimsical Look On Face, 5 In.	23.00
Porcelain, Figurine, Winter, Russian, Allegorical, Bearded Man, C.1750, 7 In.	800.00
Porcelain, Figurine, Woman Washing Clothes On Seacoast, Orlov, 10 In.	65.00
Porcelain, Figurine, Wooden Shoe, Pink To White, Openwork Panel, 4 1/2 In.	14.50
Porcelain, Figurine, Young Man Petting Pony, S.Orlov, 7 In.	55.00
Porcelain, Fish Set, Imperial Crown Vienna, Underwater Scenes, 15 Piece	375.00
Porcelain, Flask, Tea, Oriental, White, Scenes, Brass Neck, 6 1/2 In.	70.00
Porcelain, Game Set, Ducks, Turkey, Pheasant, Gold Edged, Blue, Set Of 6	150.00
Porcelain, Gravy Boat, Gien, France, Blue & Orange Floral	10.00
Porcelain, Group, Russian, Cobbler Mending Soldier's Boot, C.1850, 7 1/4 In.	800.00
Porcelain, Group, Russian, War, Allegorical, Mars & Venus, C.1762, 6 In.	600.00
Porcelain, Hair Receiver, French, Hand-Painted Violets	7.00
Porcelain, Handle, Umbrella, Gold On Blue Flowers, White Ground	27.50
Porcelain, Hat, Czechoslovakian, Derby, White, Gold Band, 2 In.	7.00
Porcelain, Hatpin Holder, Germany, No.178, White, Pink & White Roses	16.00
Porcelain, Hatpin Holder, Hand-Painted Blue & White Violets	12.50
Porcelain, Humidor, Shaped & Textured Like Burlap Sack, 9 X 6 In.	40.00
Porcelain, Ice Cream Set, C.T.Germany, White, Amethyst Floral, Brown, 9 Piece	68.00
Porcelain, Invalid Feeder, Stoke-On-Trent, White	14.00
Porcelain, Jar & Spoon, Jam, Japanese, Pagoda Shape, Cream, Color	7.00
Porcelain, Jar, Biscuit, Germany, 2 Medallions Of Lovers, Bouquets	35.00
Porcelain, Jar, Cookie, Prussia, Cabbage Shape, Bowknot On Lid	35.00
Porcelain, Jar, Cracker, Eleanor China, Austria, Medallions On Green, Handled	37.00
Porcelain, Jar, Cracker, Green & White, Pink Flowers, Silver Lid & Bail	35.00
Porcelain, Jar, Cracker, J.S.V.Germany, Poppies, 6 Sided, Gold Handles	38.00
Porcelain, Jar, Cracker, Japan, Water Lilies On Blue, Gold, Embossed, 6 In.	39.00
Porcelain, Jar, Cracker, Japanese, Geisha Designs, 5 In.	22.00
Porcelain, Jar, Cracker, Leucht-Enburg, Woman & 2 Children, Gold Trim	60.00
Porcelain, Jar, Ovoid, Floral, Birds, Japanese, 4 3/4 In.High	35.00
Porcelain, Jar, Powder, E.S.Germany, Roses	15.00
Porcelain, Jar, Powder, Germany, Figural, Lady In Green Gown	12.00
Porcelain, Kitchen Appliance Set, Japan, White, 1930s, Miniature, 3 Piece	32.00
Porcelain, Ladle, China, Gold Edged, Oriental Designs, 6 In.	28.00
Porcelain, Letter Holder, Pink Roses & Blue Forget-Me-Nots, 3 Tier	35.00
Porcelain, Match Holder, Germany, Dog & Doghouse, Striker	8.50
Porcelain, Mug, Austria, Elk, Brown Luster On Cream, 6 In.	16.50
Porcelain, Mug, Child's, Birds Dressed As Gendarmes, Gray & Blue, Scrolled	30.00
Porcelain, Mug, Child's, English, Floral On Claret, Gilding, C.1830	25.00
Porcelain, Mug, German, 2 Girls Blowing Bubbles	15.00
Porcelain, Mug, Germany, St.Bernard Dog Picture	15.00
Porcelain, Mug, Gibson Girl & Gentleman, Beige & Brown Ground, France, 5 In.	35.00
Porcelain, Mug, Vienna, Austria, Snowballs & Leaves On Dark Green To Blue	20.00

Porcelain, Napkin Ring, see Napkin Ring

Porcelain, **Nappy,** CT Germany, Leaf Shape, Lavender & Pink Floral, 9 In.	35.00
Porcelain, **Pitcher,** Austria, Elk, 4 1/2 X 6 In.	38.50
Porcelain, **Pitcher,** Cider, French, Hand-Painted Yellow Apples On Dark	55.00
Porcelain, **Pitcher,** Czechoslovakia, Checkerboard, 4 In.	15.00
Porcelain, **Pitcher,** Czechoslovakia, Figural, Parrot, 4 1/2 In.	4.50
Porcelain, **Pitcher,** Figural Fish, Blue & White, Tail Forms Handle, 3 In.	36.50
Porcelain, **Place Card Holder,** Germany, Rosebuds, Set Of 10	38.00
Porcelain, **Planter,** Germany, Felix The Cat, 2 3/4 In.	5.00
Porcelain, **Plaque,** German, Young Lady Holding Vase Of Flowers, C.1890, 5 In.	275.00
Porcelain, **Plaque,** German, Young Lady, Loose Gown, C.1890, 5 X 4 In.	175.00
Porcelain, **Plate,** Austria, Roses, Fancy Border, 8 In.	8.00
Porcelain, **Plate,** Awakening Of Fatima, Blue Border, Gold, 7 1/4 In.	22.50
Porcelain, **Plate,** Baby's, Germany, Baby Bunting, 7 In.	15.00
Porcelain, **Plate,** Baby's, Germany, Children Feeding Parrot, 8 In.	20.00
Porcelain, **Plate,** Bruder Schwalb Carlsbad, Hand-Painted Fruit, 8 1/2 In.	5.00
Porcelain, **Plate,** C.P.Co., Dixie, Hand-Painted Fruit, 10 In.	18.00
Porcelain, **Plate,** Child's, Germany, Little Jack Horner & Verse, 6 1/4 In.	5.00
Porcelain, **Plate,** Child's, Germany, This Is The Maiden All Forlorn, 7 In.	10.00
Porcelain, **Plate,** Child's, Octagon, Boy, Poodle, Animals, 6 In.	45.00
Porcelain, **Plate,** Crown Saxe, Red Maine Lobster On White, Green, 8 1/2 In.	12.50
Porcelain, **Plate,** Dessert, Russian, Raphael, 1894, 8 1/2 In.	400.00
Porcelain, **Plate,** Dinner, Chateau China, Czechoslovakia, Floral, 10 1/2 In.	36.65
Porcelain, **Plate,** Dinner, Chateau China, Czechoslovakia, Roses, Garnet, 10 In.	12.50
Porcelain, **Plate,** Dinner, Russian, Raphael, 1903, 9 1/2 In.	450.00
Porcelain, **Plate,** Dinner, Victoria, Czechoslovakia, Maroon	4.00
Porcelain, **Plate,** England, Cobalt & Gold, C.1900, 6 In.	11.00
Porcelain, **Plate,** French, Floral Center, Gold Scalloped Rococo Rim, 10 In.	27.00
Porcelain, **Plate,** Germany, Game, Buck & Doe, Gold Border, 11 3/4 In.	35.00
Porcelain, **Plate,** Germany, Hand-Painted Cherries & Leaves, 13 In.	25.00
Porcelain, **Plate,** Germany, Mauve, Cream Rim, Pink & White Roses, 8 1/4 In.	12.50
Porcelain, **Plate,** Germany, Portrait, Napoleon & Josephine, 10 In., Pair	62.00
Porcelain, **Plate,** Hot, M.A.& Co., Blue & White, Brass Feet, Wood Frame, 8 In.	12.50
Porcelain, **Plate,** Japan, Cat Portrait, Floral Border, 9 3/4 In.	22.00
Porcelain, **Plate,** Japan, Geisha Girls, Cobalt & Gold Border, 8 1/2 In.	7.50
Porcelain, **Plate,** Japanese, Blue & Tan Luster, Jeweled, Floral, 7 1/4 In.	2.00
Porcelain, **Plate,** Japanese, Flying Phoenix, Blue & White, 6 1/2 In.	3.50
Porcelain, **Plate,** M.B.Austria, Pink & Blue Forget-Me-Nots, Gold, 9 In.	12.00
Porcelain, **Plate,** Medallions, Four Horses Heads, Beading, 7 1/2 In.	125.00
Porcelain, **Plate,** Nursery, Children, Blue, White, & Charcoal, French, 12	135.00
Porcelain, **Plate,** Pink Roses, Pierced Handles, 10 1/2 In.	6.50
Porcelain, **Plate,** Royal York, Hohenberg, Germany, Christmas Tree, 10 1/4 In.	35.00
Porcelain, **Plate,** Russian, Kornilov, Imperial Eagle Medallion, C.1900, 8 In.	250.00
Porcelain, **Plate,** Russian, Military Painting, French Title, 1829, 9 3/8 In.	850.00
Porcelain, **Plate,** Russian, Military Painting, Morosov, C, 1855, 9 3/4 In.	750.00
Porcelain, **Plate,** Russian, Military Painting, Semenov, 1840, 9 1/2 In.	650.00
Porcelain, **Plate,** Russian, Military Painting, Trachkov, 1878, 8 5/8 In.	550.00
Porcelain, **Plate,** Russian, Nicholas I Inscription & Eagle, C.1825, 8 3/4 In.	375.00
Porcelain, **Plate,** Russian, Royal, 8 3/4 In. *Illus*	350.00
Porcelain, **Plate,** Service, Crescent & Sons, England, Embossed Gold Border	45.00
Porcelain, **Plate,** Soup, Russian, Monograms Of Alexander I & II, C.1855	87.50
Porcelain, **Plate,** Soup, Russian, Orders Of Sts.George & Andrew, C.1855	425.00
Porcelain, **Plate,** Spanish Dancing Girl, Pink Border, German, 9 1/2 In.	18.00
Porcelain, **Plate,** Terripan, Moore Bros., C.1890, Set Of 6	175.00
Porcelain, **Plate,** Victoria China, Sepia Prints Of 1st 27 Presidents, 11 In.	35.00
Porcelain, **Plate,** Zell, Germany, Plums & Vines, 8 1/4 In.	8.50
Porcelain, **Plate,** 3 Crown, Plums, Magenta Border, Gold Edge, 8 In.	9.50
Porcelain, **Ring Tree,** Pink & White, Flowers	16.00
Porcelain, **Salt Dip,** Austria, Roses, Heavy Gold	4.50
Porcelain, **Salt Dip,** France, White, Gold Edge	1.85
Porcelain, **Salt,** Vienna, Gold Interior	15.00
Porcelain, **Slipper,** France, Rose On Toe, 1 1/2 In., Pair	10.00
Porcelain, **Slipper,** Hand-Painted Floral, Gold Scrolls, Marked Westley China	12.00
Porcelain, **Spice Set,** German, Pink & Blue Floral, Black Lettering, 7 Piece	80.00
Porcelain, **Squeezer,** Lemon, Japan, Clown	15.00
Porcelain, **Stickpin Holder,** French, Pink Roses, 6 Sided	20.00

Porcelain, Sugar & Creamer, Austria, Pink Roses	15.00
Porcelain, Sugar & Creamer, G.Wiegand, Germany, Luster, Roses, Footed	25.00
Porcelain, Sugar & Creamer, Germany, Cover, Card Suits & 4 Leaf Clovers	25.00
Porcelain, Sugar & Creamer, Weimar, Peacocks, Pastel Green & White	30.00
Porcelain, Syrup, German, 3 Crown, Pink Roses On Green & White	6.50
Porcelain, Tankard, Monk In Wine Cellar, Cream To Brown, Gold, 14 1/2 In.	135.00
Porcelain, Tea Caddy, Gorham, Boston Tea Party, Indians	15.00
Porcelain, Tea Set, Child's, Beston, Japan, Dragon & Beading, 11 Piece	25.00
Porcelain, Tea Set, Child's, Japan, Beige, 7 Piece	5.00
Porcelain, Tea Set, Child's, Japan, Colorful, 17 Piece	14.00
Porcelain, Tea Set, Child's, Japan, Musical Teapot, Roses, 15 Piece	39.00
Porcelain, Tea Set, Child's, Japan, Red Floral & Green On Tan, 11 Piece	15.00
Porcelain, Tea Set, Child's, 1935, Musical Teapot, 13 Piece	39.00
Porcelain, Tea Set, Germany, Miniature, 10 Piece	9.50
Porcelain, Tea Set, Hirade, Japan, Red, Blue, & Yellow Floral, 11 Piece	25.00
Porcelain, Tea Set, Japan, Blue & White, Windmill Design, 3 Piece	12.00
Porcelain, Tea Set, Japan, Gold Glaze, Miniature, 8 Piece	25.00
Porcelain, Tea Set, Japanese, Geisha, Handleless Cups With Lids, 6 Piece	36.00
Porcelain, Teacup & Saucer, Russian, Raphael, 1894	375.00
Porcelain, Teapot, G.Phillips, Longport, C.1830, Individual, Blue Floral	36.00
Porcelain, Toast Rack, German, Black & White Decoration	32.00
Porcelain, Toothpick, Vienna, Violets, 3 Handled, Artist Signed	28.00
Porcelain, Tray, Dresser, Austria, Alhambra, Roses & Leaves, Gold Trim, 11 In.	25.00
Porcelain, Tray, Dresser, France, Blue, Reserve Floral Panels, Gold, Round	45.00
Porcelain, Tray, Dresser, Yellow & Pink Roses On Pastel, Kidney Shape, 12 In	32.00
Porcelain, Tray, Germany, Artist Clarion, Closed Handles, Roses, 11 X 8 In.	25.00
Porcelain, Tray, Italy, Triangular, Handle, Bird On Branch, Insects, 10 In.	35.00
Porcelain, Tray, Jewel, D.& C. France, Floral, Jeweled, Irregular Edge, 9 In.	20.00
Porcelain, Tray, Pin, French, 2 Cupids On Lid, Pink, Gold Trim, 8 X 6 In.	10.00
Porcelain, Tray, RW Germany, Kidney Shape, Hand-Painted, 7 X 8 In.	35.00
Porcelain, Tray, Tea, English, Grecian, Blue, Scalloped Gold Rim, 1892, 15 In.	40.00
Porcelain, Tray, Tea, English, White, Blue Greek Pattern, 1892, 14 1/2 In.	32.00
Porcelain, Tureen, Sauce, Kuznetsov, C.1900, Pear Shape, 4 3/4 In.	175.00
Porcelain, Vase, C.T.Altwasser, Pink & White Roses On Green, 6 In.	20.00
Porcelain, Vase, China, Decorated, C.1915, 11 In.	89.00
Porcelain, Vase, China, Hand-Painted Chinese Floral, 2 In.	20.00
Porcelain, Vase, English, Portrait, 3 Ladies, Cobalt, Gold Trim, 9 In.	45.00
Porcelain, Vase, French, Painted Flowers, 13 In.	50.00
Porcelain, Vase, German, Portrait, Art Nouveau Style, Gold Handles, 3 1/2 In.	56.00
Porcelain, Vase, German, Portrait, Peasant Girl, Sheaf Of Wheat, Gagel, 10 In.	300.00
Porcelain, Vase, German, Portrait, Woman & Child, 7 In.	25.00
Porcelain, Vase, Marldbough Artware, England, Portrait, 14 In., Pair	100.00
Porcelain, Vase, Paragon China, Turquoise Dots On Cream, 2 1/2 In., Pair	55.00
Porcelain, Vase, Paragon, Turquoise Dots On Cream, 2 1/2 In., Pair	55.00
Porcelain, Vase, Russian, Hussars Hunting, Mironov, 1875, 13 1/2 In., Pair	900.00
Porcelain, Vase, Sidney T.Callowhill, Gold, 8 X 12 In.	65.00
Porcelain, Water Set, Monk, Dog Handled Mugs & Pitcher, 7 Piece	150.00
Portrait, Goblet, Green Glass, Gold Filigree, Porcelain Plaque Of Girl, 4 In	105.00
Portrait, Pitcher, Tankard Type, Queen Louise, Full Length, 13 In.High	120.00
Portrait, Pitcher, Woman On One Side, Woman & Child On Other, 4 1/2 In.High	20.00
Portrait, Plate, John Dewey, Cobalt Rim, 7 In.	18.00
Portrait, Plate, Lady With Plumed Hat, Green & Gold Border, 9 1/2 In.	35.00
Portrait, Plate, Lady With Plumed Hat, Maroon & Gold Border, 10 In.	25.00
Portrait, Plate, Maroon & Gold Border, C.T.Germany, 9 1/2 In.	33.00
Portrait, Plate, Queen Louise, Head & Shoulder, Gold Tracery, 7 1/2 In.	17.00
Portrait, Plate, Queen Louise, Scalloped, Gold Tracery, White Ground, 9 In.	18.50
Portrait, Plate, Short Haired Lady, Floral Ground, Turquoise & Gold, 9 In.	40.00
Portrait, Plate, The Fruit Sellers, Murillo, 10 In.	65.00
Portrait, Plate, Victoria, Carlsbad, Austria, 9 In.	28.00
Portrait, Vase, Bust Of Lady With Holly Wreath In Hair, Chartreuse, 10 In.	75.00
Portrait, Vase, Men & Child Warming Hands, Gold Trim, Silesia, 8 1/4 In.	65.00

Postcards were first legally permitted in Austria on October 1, 1869.
The United States passed postal regulations allowing the card in 1873.
Most of the picture postcards collected today date from 1910.
Postcard, see also Kewpie, Postcard

Postcard, Album, C.1900, 200 Cards	45.00
Postcard, Album, C.1900, 82 Cards	17.50
Postcard, Album, Pictorial & Seasonal Greeting, 1907-11, 53 Cards	21.00
Postcard, Album, World War I Sailor's, 232 Cards	30.00
Postcard, Album, 200 C.1910 Postcards	200.00
Postcard, Album, 200 Cards	25.00
Postcard, Anheuser Busch, Beer Wagon	3.00
Postcard, Annie Oakley, Picture	3.00
Postcard, B.P.O.E., 1909	5.00
Postcard, Battle Of The Somme, 1917, Set Of 20	10.00
Postcard, Buffalo Bill, Picture	3.00
Postcard, Campbell Kids Type, Bathing, S.S.Porter	7.50
Postcard, Canoemates, Howard Chandler Christy	4.00
Postcard, Chicago World's Fair, 1933, 27	22.00
Postcard, Doll, 2 Cats, & Dutch Girl, Ullman, 1905	12.00
Postcard, Firehouse, 1911	2.00
Postcard, First Pony Express Ride, 1860, St.Joseph, Mo.	4.50
Postcard, Five Senses, Bessie Pease Gutmann, 5 In One Frame	45.00
Postcard, Garden Truck, Lemon & Peach, Tuck	5.00
Postcard, George Washington, Patriotic, Embossed	1.35
Postcard, Germany, Child With A Turkey, Embossed	5.00
Postcard, Girl & Her Doll, 1904	2.00
Postcard, Great Britain, Stamp, C.1900	4.00
Postcard, Halloween, Owl Moon, Tuck	5.00
Postcard, Happy Hooligan, Opper	7.50
Postcard, Harry Langdon, Picture	3.00
Postcard, International Art Co., Germany, Boy In Blue Suit	6.00
Postcard, Italy, Stamp, C.1900	4.00
Postcard, James A Garfield, Written Message, Mentor, Ohio	40.00
Postcard, Japan, Gold Coins, C.1900	6.00
Postcard, Korn Kinks	3.00
Postcard, Kornelia Kinks	7.50
Postcard, Leap Year Calendar Card, 1912	5.00
Postcard, Leather	1.00
Postcard, Lincoln Centennial Souvenir	3.00
Postcard, Lincoln The Candidate	3.00
Postcard, Lincoln's Birthday, Emancipation, Tuck	10.00
Postcard, Lincoln, Patriotic, Embossed	2.00
Postcard, Lindbergh In Front Of Spirit Of St.Louis, 1927	5.00
Postcard, Little Girl With Real Hair	7.50
Postcard, Man On Trapeze On Head Spinning Barrel With Feet	5.00
Postcard, Musical, Prohibition Song, 1914	6.00
Postcard, Netherlands Indies, Silver & Gold Coins, C.1900	6.00
Postcard, Photograph Of 1920s Football Team, Sepia	2.00
Postcard, Picture Puzzle, Cutout, 50 Pieces, 1909	10.00
Postcard, Pope Pius X, 1937, Color	2.00
Postcard, President Coolidge	1.00
Postcard, President Theodore Roosevelt	1.00
Postcard, Princess Wee Wee	2.00
Postcard, Prohibition	1.50
Postcard, Quiz Kids, Alka Seltzer, 1930s	2.50
Postcard, Red Cross Shoes	4.50
Postcard, Red Riding Hood, White Border	7.50
Postcard, Ruins Of Verdun, 1918, Set Of 20	10.00
Postcard, Santa Receiving Letter From Child, Clapsaddle	7.50
Postcard, Squeaker, Cat With Eyes	10.00
Postcard, St.Louis Fair, 1904, Hold To Light	8.00
Postcard, Suffragette, 1909	3.00
Postcard, Sunbonnet Babies, Christmas, 1911	12.00
Postcard, Switzerland, Stamp, C.1900	4.00
Postcard, Teddy Roosevelt With Family	4.00
Postcard, The Doctor & The Doll, Norman Rockwell, Color, Signed	15.00
Postcard, The Socialist Woman, 1908	5.00
Postcard, Tom Mix, 1929	4.00
Postcard, Tough Pull Olive 77 Tractor, 1949	3.50
Postcard, U.S.S. Georgia, 1918, Cancellation	5.00

Postcard, Ullman, Coney Island, Gold Border	.50
Postcard, Ullman, Luna Park, Gold Border	.50
Postcard, Unused Motorcycle Equipment Co., C.1909	3.00
Postcard, World's Fair, 1964	.25

Poster, see Political Campaign, Poster, Store, Poster,
World War I, Poster, World War II, Poster
Potlid, see Pratt
Pottery, see also Buffalo Pottery, Staffordshire, Wedgwood, etc.

Pottery, Bank, Pig, Hand-Painted, Cream, Green, & Russet Scroddle, 6 X 4 In.	65.00
Pottery, Bottle, Carpenter & Son, Olive Brown, Pint	11.00
Pottery, Bottle, Figural, Cucumber, Green With Tan, 5 In.	32.50
Pottery, Bottle, Figural, Cucumber, Green With Yellow, 6 In.	27.50
Pottery, Bottle, Ink, Pennsylvania, Funnel Type, Brown Glaze, 10 Panel, C-1363	40.00
Pottery, Bottle, Korean, White, Red Pine Branches Underglaze, C.1790, 8 In.	275.00
Pottery, Bottle, Myer's Made By E.H.Merril Co., Akron, O., 10 1/2 In.	17.50
Pottery, Bowl, Apricot, Blue & White, 9 1/2 In.	22.50
Pottery, Bowl, Butter, Covered, Embossed Butterflies, Blue & White, 6 1/2 In.	23.00
Pottery, Bowl, English, Cobalt Blue Glaze, Gilt Letters, C.1850, 10 In.	60.00
Pottery, Bowl, Korean, C.1850, Blue & White, Cranes & Clouds, Ring Foot, 4 In.	50.00
Pottery, Bowl, Mixing, Zigzag, Blue & White, 10 1/2 In.	15.00
Pottery, Bowl, Pudding, Brown, White Inside, Fraunfelter, Ohio, C.1939, 8 In.	3.50
Pottery, Bowl, Wedding Band, Blue & White, 8 1/2 In.	22.50
Pottery, Bust, General Grant, Gaaltan Bros., Conn., 1885, 8 In.	75.00
Pottery, Canteen, 26th Annual, GAR, June 12-13-14, 1900, 1/4 Pint	40.00
Pottery, Crock, Blue & Gray, Embossed Fruit & Leaves, 5 X 9 1/2 In.	54.00
Pottery, Crock, Butter & 2 Stripes In Blue On Gray, Covered, 6 1/2 In.	25.00
Pottery, Cruet Set, English, Salt, Pepper, & Mustard, E.P.N.S. Tray & Tops	25.00
Pottery, Dish, Bone, Marked Anchor Pottery	6.00
Pottery, Figurine, Leprechaun Seated On Frog, Ardalt Japan 6189, 4 1/2 In.	12.50
Pottery, Figurine, Spaniel, Seated, Buff, Mottled Brown, Ohio, C.1850, 11 In.	100.00
Pottery, Holder, Napkin, Dancing Ballerina Beside Drum, Blue, 8 In.	4.00
Pottery, Jar, Korean, Blue & White, Flared Mouth, Peonies, C.1750, 4 3/4 In.	75.00
Pottery, Jar, Tobacco, Devil's Head	85.00
Pottery, Jug, Milk, Cobalt With Gold Tracery, New England Pottery Co.	38.00
Pottery, Jug, Sample, Continental, Brown & White Glaze	15.00
Pottery, Medallion, Profile Of Woman, Olive Green, Trenton, 4 In.Diameter	52.00
Pottery, Mold, Turk's Head, Light Brown Glaze, 9 In.	24.50
Pottery, Mug, Gray Glaze Outside & Inside, 3 Blue Flowers, 3 In.	20.00
Pottery, Mug, M.I.T. Alumni Day, 1953, Picture Of Henry Smith Pritchett	8.00
Pottery, Mug, Remember The Maine, Transfer Design, 4 1/2 In.	34.50
Pottery, Mug, Swan, Brown, Beaded Ring Handle, 2 1/2 In.	18.00
Pottery, Mug, Uncle Wiggily, Dated 1924	22.00
Pottery, Pitcher, Admiral Dewey, Flagship, Eagle Spout, Cook Pottery, 4 In.	85.00
Pottery, Pitcher, Bathroom, Rose & Fish Scale, Blue & White, 10 In.	45.00
Pottery, Stirrup Cup, Fox's Head, Grapes Decoration	48.00
Pottery, Teapot, White, Purple Luster & Orange Design, Gray's Pottery, 5 In.	25.00
Pottery, Tom & Jerry Set, Homer Laughlin, Cream, Gold Band, 7 Piece	9.50
Pottery, Vase, Art Deco Pink With Raised Birds & Flowers, Longwy, 9 In.	30.00
Pottery, Vase, Blue Metallic Luster, Porcelain Oval Woman's Head, 8 In.	110.00
Pottery, Vase, Czechoslovakia, Cream, Green, Orange & Black Design, 7 In.	12.00
Pottery, Vase, English, Blue, Applied Floral, Ormolu Fittings, C.1890, 21 In.	70.00
Pottery, Vase, English, Cream, Applied Gilt Rams' Heads, C.1890, 30 1/2 In.	150.00
Pottery, Vase, French, Peacock Blue, The Reapers Porcelain Medallion, 5 In.	88.00
Pottery, Vase, Frog Shaped, Turquoise Glaze, Burmantofts, C.1885, 5 In.High	65.00
Pottery, Vase, Mermaid In Sea, Fish Around Top, Marked B B, 10 In.	110.00

Powder Horn, see Weapon, Powder Horn

PRATT
FENTON.
   Pratt ware means two different things. It was an early Staffordshire pottery, cream-colored with colored decorations, made by Felix Pratt during the late eighteenth century. There was also Pratt ware made with transfer designs during the mid-nineteenth century.

Pratt, Bottle, Snuff, Blue, Hunting Scene	20.00
Pratt, Creamer, Basalt, Black, Grecian Figures, 3 In.	35.00
Pratt, Figurine, Cockerel, Standing, Brown, Ocher, & Yellow, C.1790, 9 1/8 In.	900.00
Pratt, Figurine, Man, White Pantaloons, Green Overgarment, 3 1/2 In.	40.00
Pratt, Goblet, Satyr Mask, Handled, Ocher Frog Inside, Spreading Foot, 5 In.	140.00

Pratt, Jar, Black & Yellow Hunt Scene, Blue Ground, 4 In.	24.50
Pratt, Jar, Jam, Village Wedding On Lid, Dated Jan.15, 1857	80.00
Pratt, Jar, Snuff, Blue, Boar Hunt Scene	24.00
Pratt, Jar, Snuff, Blue, Tan & Black Transfer Of Men & Animals, 4 In.	30.00
Pratt, Jardiniere, White Greek Scene On Black, Greek Key Border, 5 In.	75.00
Pratt, Jug, Continuous Fox Hunting Scene, Scroll Handle, C.1810, 6 In.	250.00
Pratt, Jug, Duke Of York & Prince Cobourg On Horseback, C.1810, 6 In.	150.00
Pratt, Jug, Hunter, 2 Gardeners & Brown Spotted Dogs, C.1810, 7 1/4 In.	150.00
Pratt, Jug, Hunters In Blue Coats & Dogs, C.1810, 6 In.	75.00
Pratt, Jug, Lord Jarvis, Scroll Handle, Ocher & Blue Rim, C.1810, 7 1/2 In.	250.00
Pratt, Jug, Luster, Dogs In Relief, Green & Pink, 4 1/2 In.	110.00
Pratt, Jug, Medallions Of English Admiral & 3 Females, C.1810, 4 1/2 In.	75.00
Pratt, Jug, Oval Peafowl Medallions, Strap Handle, C.1810, 5 3/4 In.	225.00
Pratt, Jug, Sailor's Farewell, Figures On Grassy Mounds, C.1810, 6 In.	140.00
Pratt, Jug, Snuff Taker In Ocher Coat, Strap Handle, C.1810, 5 3/8 In.	150.00
Pratt, Mug, Bacchus Mask, Yellow Frog Inside, C.1810, 4 In.	275.00
Pratt, Plaque, Queen Charlotte, Putto & Dancing Man, C.1800, 8 7/8 In.	400.00
Pratt, Plate, Dessert, Landscapes & Ruins, Gold Edge, Baroque Handle, 9 In.	50.00
Pratt, Plate, Orange, Gold, White, Greek Key Band, Scenic Center, 7 1/4 In.	65.00
Pratt, Plate, Transfer, Apple Green Border, C.1830, 7 In.	68.00 To 78.00
Pratt, Plate, Transfer, C.1840, 9 1/4 In., Pair	138.00
Pratt, Plate, Transfer, Gold Border, 9 1/4 In.	168.00
Pratt, Plate, Transfer, Pale Yellow With Ocher, C.1840, Pair	125.00
Pratt, Pot, Shakespeare's House On Lid, Henley St., Stratford On Avon	60.00
Pratt, Potlid, Albert, Prince Consort	37.50
Pratt, Potlid, Cherry Tooth Paste, Patronized By The Queen, 3 1/4 In.	45.00
Pratt, Potlid, Doc. Johnson	37.50 To 50.00
Pratt, Potlid, Herring Fishing	37.50
Pratt, Potlid, Landing The Fare Pegwell Bay, Framed	50.00
Pratt, Potlid, Room Where Shakespeare Was Born, Framed	58.00
Pratt, Potlid, Shakespeare's House, Henley St., With Pot	60.00
Pratt, Potlid, The Game Bag, Including Pot	65.00
Pratt, Potlid, The Late Prince Consort	85.00
Pratt, Potlid, Trafalgar Square	58.00
Pratt, Tankard, Basket Of Flowers, Strap Handle, C.1800, 4 5/8 In.	150.00
Pratt, Tankard, Children Playing, Blue & Ocher Clothes, C.1810, 5 7/8 In.	50.00
Pratt, Toby Mug, Admiral Nelson, En Queue, Hair Forms Handle, C.1800, 6 In.	475.00
Pratt, Toby Mug, C.1790 Illus	550.00
Presidential China, Fish Set, Rutherford B.Hayes, Haviland, C.1880, 13 Piece	3700.00
Presidential China, Plate, Breakfast, Benjamin Harrison, Limoges, C.1892	1300.00
Presidential China, Plate, Cake, Benjamin Harrison, Limoges, C.1892, 7 In.	292.00
Presidential China, Plate, Dessert, Benjamin Harrison, Limoges, C.1892, 9 In.	625.00
Presidential China, Plate, Dinner, Benjamin Harrison, Limoges, C.1892, 10 In.	708.50
Presidential China, Plate, Dinner, Franklin Delano Roosevelt, Lenox, 1932	283.50
Presidential China, Plate, Franklin Pierce, C.1853, 7 1/4 In.	400.00
Presidential China, Plate, George Augustine Washington, Paris, C.1785, 9 In.	5000.00
Presidential China, Platter, Abraham Lincoln, C.1860, 15 3/4 In.	1900.00

Pratt, Toby Mug, C.1790

Presidential China, Plate,
Lincoln, Limoges, C.1876

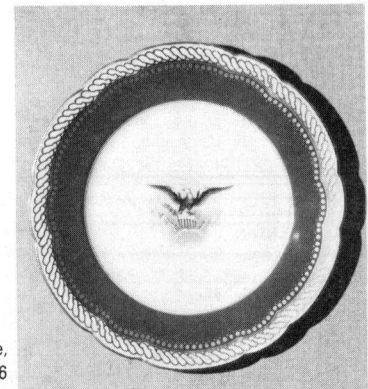

Pressed glass was first made in the United States in the 1820s after the invention of pressed-glass machines. Hundreds of patterns of pressed glass were made in complete table settings. Although the Boston and Sandwich Works was the most famous of the pressed glass factories, there were about sixteen other factories making pressed glass from 1830 to 1850, and still more from 1850 to 1900, when pressed glass reached its greatest popularity. It is now being widely reproduced.

Pressed Glass, see also Vaseline Glass

Pressed Glass, A Good Boy With Floral Wreaths, Mug, Amber, 3 1/2 In. 30.00
Pressed Glass, Aberdeen, Goblet 11.50
Acanthus, see Ribbed Palm
Acme, see Butterfly & Spray
Pressed Glass, Acorn, Goblet .... 14.00 To 22.50
Pressed Glass, Acorn, Spooner, Footed 8.50
Pressed Glass, Actress, Bowl, Maud Granger, Rounded Corners, 9 X 5 3/4 In. 35.00
Pressed Glass, Actress, Butter 44.00
Pressed Glass, Actress, Celery, H.M.S.Pinafore Scenes, Footed, Scalloped 110.00
Pressed Glass, Actress, Compote, Covered, High Standard, 14 1/2 In. 85.00
Pressed Glass, Actress, Compote, Covered, Low Standard, 12 In. .... 90.00 To 125.00
Pressed Glass, Actress, Creamer 65.00

Pressed Glass, Actress, Creamer

Pressed Glass,
Arched Fleur-De-Lis, Sugar

Pressed Glass, Actress, Dish, Cheese, Covered, Two Dromios, Clear Base 165.00
Pressed Glass, Actress, Dish, Cheese, Covered, Two Dromios, Frosted Base 175.00
Pressed Glass, Actress, Dish, Pickle, Kate Claxton Picture, Motto 24.50
Pressed Glass, Actress, Goblet, Lotta Crabtree & Kate Claxton .... 42.00 To 68.00
Pressed Glass, Actress, Mug 25.00
Pressed Glass, Actress, Plate, Bread, Miss Neilsen Center 46.00
Pressed Glass, Actress, Plate, Bread, Pinafore 46.00
Pressed Glass, Actress, Saltshaker, Pewter Lid 32.00
Pressed Glass, Actress, Sauce 18.00
Pressed Glass, Actress, Sauce, Footed .... 10.50 To 23.00
Pressed Glass, Actress, Spooner, Mary Anderson & Maud Granger .... 45.00 To 58.00
Pressed Glass, Admiral Dewey, Pitcher, Water .... 35.00 To 65.00
Pressed Glass, Admiral Dewey, Pitcher, Water, Gridley 67.50
Pressed Glass, Admiral Dewey, Plate, 5 1/2 In. 18.00
Pressed Glass, Admiral Dewey, Tumbler, Wreath & Eagle .... 28.00 To 34.00
Pressed Glass, Admiral Dewey, Tumbler, 3 3/4 In. 25.00
Pressed Glass, Adonis, Compote, Jelly, Footed 15.00
Pressed Glass, Adonis, Pitcher, Milk, Green 20.00
Pressed Glass, Akron Block, Celery .... 10.00 To 13.75
Pressed Glass, Alabama, Cake Stand, 9 In. 30.00
Pressed Glass, Alabama, Compote, Covered, 9 1/4 In.High 30.00
Pressed Glass, Alabama, Dish, Honey 75.00
Pressed Glass, Alabama, Spooner .... 12.00 To 24.50

Pressed Glass, Alabama, Toothpick .... 19.00 To 20.00
Pressed Glass, Alabama, Water Set, Gold On Beads, 7 Piece 190.00
Pressed Glass, Alaska, Bowl, Berry, Green .... 20.00 To 32.00
Pressed Glass, Alaska, Bowl, Berry, Opalescent 24.00
Pressed Glass, Alaska, Bowl, Green, Enamel Decoration, Square, 8 In. 65.00
Pressed Glass, Alaska, Creamer, Blue, Flowers 48.00
Pressed Glass, Alaska, Creamer, Blue, Opalescent .... 42.00 To 52.00
Pressed Glass, Alaska, Creamer, Child's 60.00
Pressed Glass, Alaska, Creamer, White, Opalescent 20.00
Pressed Glass, Alaska, Creamer, Yellow 35.00
Pressed Glass, Alaska, Dish, Candy, Green 42.00
Pressed Glass, Alaska, Salt & Pepper, Blue, Decorated 35.00
Pressed Glass, Alaska, Sauce, Green, Square .... 17.00 To 22.00
Pressed Glass, Alaska, Sauce, Green, 3 3/4 In. 22.50
Pressed Glass, Alaska, Sauce, Yellow 20.00
Pressed Glass, Alaska, Spooner, Flint 20.00
Pressed Glass, Alaska, Spooner, White, Opalescent 18.50
Pressed Glass, Alhambra, Tureen, Deep Blue, Covered, 7 X 10 In. 38.00
Pressed Glass, Alligator Scales, Goblet, Flint .... 17.00 To 28.00
Pressed Glass, Alligator, Goblet .... 30.00 To 42.50
Pressed Glass, Almond Thumbprint, Celery 28.00
Pressed Glass, Almond Thumbprint, Celery, Amethestine 42.00
Pressed Glass, Almond Thumbprint, Compote, Jelly, 6 X 5 3/4 In.High 35.00
Pressed Glass, Almond Thumbprint, Goblet .... 10.00 To 15.00
Pressed Glass, Almond Thumbprint, Salt, Master, Flint 16.00
Pressed Glass, Almond Thumbprint, Salt, Master, Flint, Pair 14.00
Pressed Glass, Almond Thumbprint, Sugar, Flint 30.00
Pressed Glass, Almond Thumbprint, Tumbler, Flint 25.00
Pressed Glass, Almond Thumbprint, Wine 14.00
Pressed Glass, Amazon, Compote, Covered, 4 3/4 In. 35.00
Pressed Glass, Amazon, Compote, Scalloped, 10 In. 55.00
Pressed Glass, Amazon, Creamer .... 20.00 To 28.00
Pressed Glass, Amazon, Creamer, Miniature .... 15.00 To 23.00
Pressed Glass, Amazon, Spooner, Miniature .... 15.00 To 23.00
Pressed Glass, Amazon, Sugar, Child's 24.00
Pressed Glass, Amazon, Sugar, Child's, Covered 35.00
 Amberette, see Klondike
Pressed Glass, Amberino, Goblet, Flint 7.50
Pressed Glass, American Beauty, Tumbler, Green, Gold Roses, Marked Near-Cut 16.00
Pressed Glass, American Coin, Celery, Frosted 235.00
Pressed Glass, American Coin, Spooner, Frosted 145.00
Pressed Glass, Amulet, Goblet .... 9.00 To 9.50
Pressed Glass, Amulet, Goblet, Gilt Band 20.00
Pressed Glass, Amulet, Goblet, Gold Trim 9.50
Pressed Glass, Amulet, Wine 25.00
Pressed Glass, Angora, Goblet .... 11.00 To 22.50
Pressed Glass, Anthemion, Bowl, Berry, Round, 8 In. 15.00
Pressed Glass, Anthemion, Bowl, Berry, Square, 7 In. 21.50
Pressed Glass, Anthemion, Bowl, Berry, Square, 7 1/2 In. 15.00
Pressed Glass, Anthemion, Butter 25.00
Pressed Glass, Anthemion, Cake Stand, 9 1/4 In. 18.00
Pressed Glass, Anthemion, Creamer 19.00
Pressed Glass, Anthemion, Pitcher, Water .... 22.00 To 37.50
Pressed Glass, Anthemion, Plate, Dinner, 10 In. 17.00
Pressed Glass, Anthemion, Plate, Ruffled Edge, 9 1/2 In. 20.00
Pressed Glass, Anthemion, Sugar 24.00
Pressed Glass, Anthemion, Sugar, Covered 30.00
Pressed Glass, Anthemion, Tumbler 11.00
Pressed Glass, Anthemion, Tumbler, Amber, Albany 16.50
Pressed Glass, Anvil, Goblet 7.50
Pressed Glass, Anvil, Salt, Master, Patent Applied For 19.50
Pressed Glass, Anvil, Toothpick .... 10.00 To 15.00
Pressed Glass, Apollo, Compote, Low Standard, 8 In. 18.00
Pressed Glass, Apollo, Creamer, Pedestal Base 15.00
Pressed Glass, Apollo, Plate, Frosted, Square, 9 3/4 In. 18.75
Pressed Glass, Apollo, Plate, Frosted, 9 3/4 In. 15.00

Pressed Glass, Apollo, Sauce	12.00
Pressed Glass, Apollo, Spooner, Etched	25.00
Pressed Glass, Apollo, Syrup, Etched	25.00
Pressed Glass, Apollo, Tumbler, Frosted	15.00
Pressed Glass, Aquarium, Pitcher, Water	150.00
Pressed Glass, Arch Band, Spill, Flint	40.00
Pressed Glass, Arch Band, Spooner	40.00
Pressed Glass, Arch Band, Spooner, Flint	40.00
Pressed Glass, Arched Fleur-De-Lis, Cake Stand	13.50
Pressed Glass, Arched Fleur-De-Lis, Celery, Higbee	20.00
Pressed Glass, Arched Grape, Goblet	16.50
Pressed Glass, Arched Grape, Tumbler	15.00
Pressed Glass, Arched Ovals, Butter, Covered, Purple Flashing	35.00
Pressed Glass, Arched Ovals, Goblet	14.50
Pressed Glass, Arched Ovals, Toothpick, Gold Band	12.50
Pressed Glass, Arched Panels, Sauce, Footed, 3 1/4 In.	4.00
Pressed Glass, Arched Tripod, Creamer	25.00
Pressed Glass, Argosy, Goblet, Flint	24.00
Pressed Glass, Argus, Barrel, Goblet, Flint	37.50
Pressed Glass, Argus, Celery, Flint	100.00
Pressed Glass, Argus, Celery, Fluted	100.00
Pressed Glass, Argus, Champagne, Flint	25.00 To 48.00
Pressed Glass, Argus, Creamer, Flint	125.00 To 150.00
Pressed Glass, Argus, Eggcup, Flint	14.00 To 40.00
Pressed Glass, Argus, Goblet, Barrel, Flint	35.00
Pressed Glass, Argus, Goblet, Five Rows, Flint	45.00 To 60.00
Pressed Glass, Argus, Goblet, Flint	21.00 To 50.00
Pressed Glass, Argus, Goblet, Hotel, Flint	32.50
Pressed Glass, Argus, Goblet, Master, Flint	45.00 To 57.50
Pressed Glass, Argus, Salt, Master	35.00
Pressed Glass, Argus, Spill, Flint	35.00
Pressed Glass, Argus, Spooner, Flint	35.00 To 40.00
Pressed Glass, Argus, Sugar, Covered, Flint	60.00 To 65.00
Pressed Glass, Argus, Tumble-Up, Five Row, Flint	125.00
Pressed Glass, Argus, Tumbler, Flint	60.00 To 70.00
Pressed Glass, Argus, Tumbler, Footed, Flint	30.00 To 50.00
Pressed Glass, Argus, Tumbler, Whiskey, Flint	40.00
Pressed Glass, Argus, Tumbler, Whiskey, Handled, Flint	55.00
Pressed Glass, Argus, Wine	45.00
Pressed Glass, Armorial, Spill	50.00
Pressed Glass, Armorial, Spooner	50.00
Pressed Glass, Arrowhead In Oval, Butter, Child's	26.00
Pressed Glass, Arrowhead In Oval, Creamer	20.00
Pressed Glass, Arrowhead In Oval, Creamer, Child's	16.00
Pressed Glass, Arrowhead In Oval, Sugar, Child's, Covered	18.00
Pressed Glass, Art Nouveau, Sauce, Ruby & Clear	12.50

Pressed Glass,
Arched Grape, Goblet

Pressed Glass,
Ashburton, Champagne,
Presentation Piece

Pressed Glass, Art, Bowl, Square, 8 1/4 In. 22.00
Pressed Glass, Art, Cake Stand, High Standard, 9 In. 35.00
Pressed Glass, Art, Celery .... 16.00 To 18.00
Pressed Glass, Art, Spooner .... 14.00 To 27.50
Pressed Glass, Art, Sugar 11.00
Pressed Glass, Art, Sugar, Covered 25.00
Pressed Glass, Artichoke, Bowl, 8 In. 10.00
Pressed Glass, Artichoke, Celery .... 12.50 To 14.50
Pressed Glass, Artichoke, Sauce, Frosted 19.50
Pressed Glass, Artichoke, Sugar, Frosted, Covered 72.00
Pressed Glass, Artichoke, Tankard, Water, Frosted 75.00
Pressed Glass, Artichoke, Tumbler, Frosted 45.00
Pressed Glass, Artichoke, Water Set, Frosted, 7 Piece 140.00
Pressed Glass, Ashburton, Bottle, Bar, Flint, Quart 40.00
Pressed Glass, Ashburton, Celery, Flint .... 58.00 To 85.00
Pressed Glass, Ashburton, Celery, Scalloped Top .... 100.00 To 125.00
Pressed Glass, Ashburton, Champagne, Flint .... 30.00 To 62.50
Pressed Glass, Ashburton, Claret 20.00
Pressed Glass, Ashburton, Claret, Flint 50.00
Pressed Glass, Ashburton, Decanter, Bar Lip, Flint, 3/4 Pint 25.00
Pressed Glass, Ashburton, Decanter, Flint, Pint .... 100.00 To 125.00
Pressed Glass, Ashburton, Decanter, Flint, Quart .... 45.00 To 55.00
Pressed Glass, Ashburton, Dish, Honey, Flint .... 4.00 To 7.00
Pressed Glass, Ashburton, Eggcup, Flint .... 15.00 To 40.00
Pressed Glass, Ashburton, Goblet, Barrel, Flint .... 30.00 To 35.00
Pressed Glass, Ashburton, Goblet, Flared Top, Flint .... 30.00 To 42.00
Pressed Glass, Ashburton, Goblet, Flint .... 23.00 To 60.00
Pressed Glass, Ashburton, Goblet, Semisquared, Flint 28.00
Pressed Glass, Ashburton, Sauce, Flint, 4 1/4 In. .... 4.00 To 12.00
Pressed Glass, Ashburton, Sugar, Covered, Flint .... 75.00 To 85.00
Pressed Glass, Ashburton, Sugar, Flint .... 28.00 To 30.00
Pressed Glass, Ashburton, Tumbler, Ale, Flint 70.00
Pressed Glass, Ashburton, Tumbler, Bar, Flint 55.00
Pressed Glass, Ashburton, Tumbler, Flint .... 48.00 To 50.00
Pressed Glass, Ashburton, Tumbler, Footed, Flint .... 70.00 To 75.00
Pressed Glass, Ashburton, Tumbler, Handled 75.00
Pressed Glass, Ashburton, Tumbler, Whiskey, Flint .... 15.00 To 70.00
Pressed Glass, Ashburton, Tumbler, Whiskey, Handled, Flint 75.00
Pressed Glass, Ashburton, Wine, Flint, 5 In. .... 16.00 To 30.00
Pressed Glass, Ashland, Goblet 14.50
Pressed Glass, Ashman, Basket, Cake, Etched, Metal Handle, 10 In. 37.00
Pressed Glass, Ashman, Basket, Cake, Oblong, Silver Handle .... 37.00 To 47.50
Pressed Glass, Ashman, Butter, Covered 23.75
Pressed Glass, Ashman, Celery .... 23.50 To 28.75
Pressed Glass, Ashman, Goblet .... 17.50 To 25.00
Pressed Glass, Ashman, Sauce 4.50
Pressed Glass, Ashman, Sauce, Footed, 3 5/8 In. 6.00
Pressed Glass, Ashman, Sauce, Footed, 4 1/2 In. 4.00
Pressed Glass, Atlanta, Butter, Covered .... 45.00 To 48.00
Pressed Glass, Atlanta, Compote, Covered, 6 In. 39.50
Pressed Glass, Atlanta, Goblet 8.00
Pressed Glass, Atlanta, Saltshaker 23.00
Pressed Glass, Atlas, Butter, Cannonball Cover 28.00
Pressed Glass, Atlas, Cake Stand, 9 1/2 In. 24.00
Pressed Glass, Atlas, Cake Stand, 10 In. 21.00
Pressed Glass, Atlas, Celery 20.00
Pressed Glass, Atlas, Champagne 26.50
Pressed Glass, Atlas, Compote, Jelly, 4 X 4 1/2 In. 12.50
Pressed Glass, Atlas, Cordial .... 16.00 To 30.00
Pressed Glass, Atlas, Pitcher, Water, Tankard Type 25.00
Pressed Glass, Atlas, Relish 5.00
Pressed Glass, Atlas, Sauce, Footed 8.75
Pressed Glass, Atlas, Sauce, Large 4.50
Pressed Glass, Atlas, Spooner .... 9.50 To 13.75
Pressed Glass, Atlas, Sugar 12.00
Pressed Glass, Atlas, Tankard, 9 1/2 In. 22.00

Pressed Glass, Atlas, Toothpick 15.00
Pressed Glass, Atlas, Wine .... 18.50 To 25.00
Pressed Glass, Aurora, Goblet 10.00
Pressed Glass, Aurora, Wine Set, Ruby Stained, 6 Piece 29.00
Pressed Glass, Aurora, Wine, 3 3/4 In. .... 9.00 To 15.00
Pressed Glass, Austrian, Creamer .... 10.00 To 45.00
Pressed Glass, Austrian, Goblet, Gold Flashed 20.00
Pressed Glass, Austrian, Goblet 25.00
Pressed Glass, Austrian, Mug 13.50
Pressed Glass, Austrian, Nappy, Covered, 2 Handled 18.00
Pressed Glass, Austrian, Saltshaker, Tin Top 18.50
Pressed Glass, Austrian, Sauce 12.50
Pressed Glass, Austrian, Spooner, Child's .... 40.00 To 45.00
Pressed Glass, Austrian, Spooner, 4 3/4 In. 18.00
Pressed Glass, Austrian, Sugar & Creamer, Child's 24.00
Pressed Glass, Austrian, Sugar & Creamer, Cover 32.00
Pressed Glass, Austrian, Sugar, Covered 13.00
Pressed Glass, Austrian, Tumbler .... 14.00 To 15.00
Pressed Glass, Austrian, Wine .... 12.50 To 27.50
Pressed Glass, Aztec, Cup, Punch, Signed McKee 5.00
Pressed Glass, Aztec, Sauce 3.00
Pressed Glass, Baby Face, Spooner 55.00
Pressed Glass, Baby Lion, Celery 38.00
Pressed Glass, Baby Lion, Jar, Jam, Covered 45.00
Pressed Glass, Baby Lion, Sugar 45.00
 Baby Thumbprint, see Dakota
Pressed Glass, Baby's Head, Knife Rest 35.00
Pressed Glass, Bakewell Block, Celery 65.00
Pressed Glass, Bakewell Block, Celery, Flint 48.00
Pressed Glass, Bakewell Block, Goblet, Flint 90.00
Pressed Glass, Bakewell Block, Sugar, Covered, Flint 85.00
Pressed Glass, Balder, Bowl, Berry, Gold, 9 In. 29.50
Pressed Glass, Balder, Butter, Covered 21.50
Pressed Glass, Balder, Creamer, Gold Trim 8.50
Pressed Glass, Balder, Cup, Punch .... 5.00 To 9.00
Pressed Glass, Balder, Goblet .... 8.00 To 15.00
Pressed Glass, Balder, Goblet, Gold Band 15.00
Pressed Glass, Balder, Tumbler, Juice 8.50
Pressed Glass, Balder, Tumbler, Whiskey 9.75
Pressed Glass, Balder, Wine .... 10.00 To 18.50
Pressed Glass, Balder, Wine, Barrel Shape 9.50
 Balky Mule, see Currier & Ives
Pressed Glass, Ball & Swirl, Creamer .... 7.00 To 18.00
Pressed Glass, Ball & Swirl, Goblet 18.50
Pressed Glass, Ball & Swirl, Mug 10.00
Pressed Glass, Ball & Swirl, Sauce 17.50
Pressed Glass, Ball & Swirl, Sauce, Footed 6.00
Pressed Glass, Ball & Swirl, Sugar, Covered 32.50
Pressed Glass, Ball & Swirl, Tankard, Water 57.50
Pressed Glass, Balloon, Creamer, Flint 140.00
Pressed Glass, Balloon, Sugar, Covered, Flint 130.00
Pressed Glass, Baltimore Pear, Cake Stand 28.00
Pressed Glass, Baltimore Pear, Creamer .... 10.00 To 30.00
Pressed Glass, Baltimore Pear, Goblet .... 8.50 To 35.00
Pressed Glass, Baltimore Pear, Pitcher, Water 57.50
Pressed Glass, Baltimore Pear, Relish, 8 1/4 In.Long 12.00
Pressed Glass, Baltimore Pear, Sugar, Covered .... 10.00 To 40.00
 Bamboo, see Broken Column
 Banded Beaded Grape Medallion, see Beaded Grape Medallion,
 Banded
Pressed Glass, Banded Buckle, Bowl, Oval, 8 1/4 X 5 1/4 In. 12.50
Pressed Glass, Banded Buckle, Creamer, Applied Handle .... 30.00 To 42.00
Pressed Glass, Banded Buckle, Goblet, Buttermilk, Flint 30.00
Pressed Glass, Banded Buckle, Pitcher, Water 95.00
Pressed Glass, Banded Buckle, Spooner .... 10.00 To 16.75
Pressed Glass, Banded Buckle, Spooner, Flint 42.50

Pressed Glass, Barberry, Celery

Pressed Glass, Balder, Goblet

Pressed Glass, Barberry,
Covered Sugar Bowl

Pressed Glass, Banded Buckle, Sugar	12.50 To 14.50
Pressed Glass, Banded Buckle, Sugar, Flint	25.00
Pressed Glass, Banded Buckle, Tumbler	32.50
Pressed Glass, Banded Buckle, Tumbler, Bar	35.00
Pressed Glass, Banded Portland, Butter, Maiden Blush, Covered	165.00
Pressed Glass, Banded Portland, Carafe	27.00
Pressed Glass, Banded Portland, Celery	22.45 To 24.50
Pressed Glass, Banded Portland, Compote, 7 1/2 X 9 1/2 In.	35.00
Pressed Glass, Banded Portland, Creamer, Gold Trim	12.00
Pressed Glass, Banded Portland, Goblet	27.00 To 30.00
Pressed Glass, Banded Portland, Goblet, Ruby Stained	35.00
Pressed Glass, Banded Portland, Muffineer	30.00 To 39.00
Pressed Glass, Banded Portland, Relish, Ruby Stained	20.00
Pressed Glass, Banded Portland, Saltshaker	10.00
Pressed Glass, Banded Portland, Sauce	2.50 To 12.00
Pressed Glass, Banded Portland, Sauce, Maiden Blush, Boat Shape, Gold Trim	35.00
Pressed Glass, Banded Portland, Sauce, Maiden Blush, Round	18.00
Pressed Glass, Banded Portland, Sauce, Oval	10.00
Pressed Glass, Banded Portland, Sugar & Creamer	17.00
Pressed Glass, Banded Portland, Toothpick	8.00
Pressed Glass, Banded Portland, Toothpick, Gold Trim	25.00
Pressed Glass, Banded Portland, Tumbler	17.00
Pressed Glass, Banded Portland, Vase, Bud, Gold Trim	19.50
Pressed Glass, Banded Portland, Vase, Flared, 6 In.	12.50
Pressed Glass, Banded Portland, Vase, Tapered, 6 In.	12.50
Pressed Glass, Banded Portland, Vase, 6 In.	12.50
Pressed Glass, Banded Portland, Wine, Gold Trim	23.00
Pressed Glass, Banded Prism Bar, Goblet	7.50
Pressed Glass, Banded Prisms, Salt, Master	14.00
Pressed Glass, Banded Star, Creamer, Legs	26.00
Pressed Glass, Banded Star, Sauce	5.00 To 6.50
Pressed Glass, Banded Star, Sauce, Footed, 4 In.	8.00
Other "Banded" patterns, see under name of basic pattern. Eg: Banded Honeycomb, see Honeycomb, Banded	
Pressed Glass, Banner, Butter, Blue, Covered	66.00
Pressed Glass, Banner, Butter, Blue	75.00 To 85.00
Pressed Glass, Bar & Block, Tankard, 10 In.	10.00
Bar & Diamond, see Kokomo	
Pressed Glass, Bar & Finecut, Goblet	7.00 To 11.00
Pressed Glass, Barberry, Box, Dresser	10.00
Pressed Glass, Barberry, Butter, Covered	26.00
Pressed Glass, Barberry, Cake Stand, 10 1/2 In.	35.00 To 37.50
Pressed Glass, Barberry, Celery	18.50 To 20.00
Pressed Glass, Barberry, Compote, Covered, Low Standard, Flint, 8 1/2 In.	45.00

Pressed Glass, Barberry, Compote, Shell Finial, Oval Berries, 8 1/2 In.	30.00
Pressed Glass, Barberry, Eggcup	16.50
Pressed Glass, Barberry, Goblet	10.00 To 17.50
Pressed Glass, Barberry, Pitcher, Water, Applied Handle	48.00 To 55.00
Pressed Glass, Barberry, Plate, 6 In.	12.50 To 25.00
Pressed Glass, Barberry, Sauce	4.50 To 12.00
Pressed Glass, Barberry, Sauce, Footed	6.00 To 9.00
Pressed Glass, Barberry, Spooner	20.00
Pressed Glass, Barberry, Sugar, Shell Finial	32.00
Pressed Glass, Barberry, Wine	15.00 To 22.50
Pressed Glass, Barley, Butter	23.00 To 30.00
Pressed Glass, Barley, Butter, Covered	23.00 To 25.00
Pressed Glass, Barley, Cake Stand, 9 1/2 In.	20.00
Pressed Glass, Barley, Cordial	14.00
Pressed Glass, Barley, Creamer	15.00
Pressed Glass, Barley, Goblet	15.00 To 22.00
Pressed Glass, Barley, Pitcher, Water	18.00 To 25.00
Pressed Glass, Barley, Plate, Bread, Oval, Deep	18.00
Pressed Glass, Barley, Platter, 11 1/2 X 9 1/2 In.	20.00
Pressed Glass, Barley, Relish, Oval	9.00
Pressed Glass, Barley, Salt, Wheelbarrow	35.00
Pressed Glass, Barley, Sauce	6.00
Pressed Glass, Barley, Sauce, Footed, Scalloped Edge, 4 1/4 In.	8.50
Pressed Glass, Barley, Sauce, Footed, 3 3/4 In.	7.50
Pressed Glass, Barley, Sauce, Footed, 4 1/4 In.	8.50
Pressed Glass, Barley, Sugar	27.50
Pressed Glass, Barley, Wine	18.00 To 25.00
Pressed Glass, Baroque, Salt	42.50
Pressed Glass, Barred Forget-Me-Not, Cake Stand, 8 1/4 In.	18.00
Pressed Glass, Barred Forget-Me-Not, Cake Stand, 10 1/2 In.	23.00
Pressed Glass, Barred Forget-Me-Not, Compote, Covered, 9 1/2 X 7 In.	32.50
Pressed Glass, Barred Forget-Me-Not, Goblet	15.00 To 17.50
Pressed Glass, Barred Forget-Me-Not, Pitcher, Water	23.00
Pressed Glass, Barred Forget-Me-Not, Plate, Handled, 9 In.	13.00
Pressed Glass, Barred Forget-Me-Not, Plate, 9 In.	12.00
Pressed Glass, Barred Forget-Me-Not, Spooner, 2 Handles	14.00
Pressed Glass, Barred Forget-Me-Not, Wine	22.00
Pressed Glass, Barred Hobnail, Compote, 8 1/2 In.	11.00
Pressed Glass, Barred Hobnail, Goblet	20.00 To 25.00
Pressed Glass, Barred Hobnail, Mug	11.00
Pressed Glass, Barred Hobnail, Pitcher, Water	15.00
Pressed Glass, Barred Hobnail, Tumbler	11.00
Pressed Glass, Barred Hobnail, Tumbler, Ruby Stained, Greensburg	22.50
Barred Ovals, see Banded Portland	
Pressed Glass, Barred Star, Goblet	7.00 To 12.00
Barrel, see Argus, Barrel, Honeycomb, Barrel, etc.	
Barreled Block, see Red Block	
Bartlett Pear, see Pear	
Pressed Glass, Basket Weave With Cable, Cup & Saucer, Amber	22.00
Pressed Glass, Basket Weave & Frosted Leaf, Butter	45.00
Pressed Glass, Basket Weave, Cup & Saucer, Amber	20.00 To 22.00
Pressed Glass, Basket Weave, Cup & Saucer, Blue	18.50
Pressed Glass, Basket Weave, Goblet, Amber	14.00 To 16.00
Pressed Glass, Basket Weave, Goblet, Blue	14.00 To 15.00
Pressed Glass, Basket Weave, Goblet, Blue, Knob Stem	15.00
Pressed Glass, Basket Weave, Goblet, Yellow	20.00
Pressed Glass, Basket Weave, Pitcher, Blue, 8 In.	37.50
Pressed Glass, Basket Weave, Pitcher, Milk, Yellow	18.00
Pressed Glass, Basket Weave, Pitcher, Water, Amber	24.00 To 35.00
Pressed Glass, Basket Weave, Plate, Handled, 8 3/4 In.	11.00 To 13.50
Pressed Glass, Basket Weave, Plate, 8 3/4 In.	11.00
Pressed Glass, Basket Weave, Sauce, Footed	5.00 To 6.50
Pressed Glass, Basket Weave, Spooner, Opalescent & Clear	25.00
Pressed Glass, Basket Weave, Sugar, Yellow	12.00
Pressed Glass, Basket Weave, Toothpick	12.50
Pressed Glass, Basket Weave, Toothpick, Handled	5.00

Pressed Glass, Basket Weave, Tray, Water, Amber 25.00
Pressed Glass, Bates, Plate, 7 3/4 In. 65.00
Pressed Glass, Battleship Maine, Plate, Green, 101 Border, 5 1/2 In. 18.50
Pressed Glass, Battleship Maine, Tumbler, Gold Rim, 3 1/2 In. 25.00
Pressed Glass, Beacon Thumbprint, Goblet .... 5.00 To 6.00
Pressed Glass, Bead Swag, Spooner, Opalescent, Interior Stress Marks 15.00
Pressed Glass, Bead Swag, Butter, Ruby Stained 70.00
Pressed Glass, Beaded Acanthus, Pitcher, Milk, 9 In. 18.50
Pressed Glass, Beaded Acorn Medallion, Champagne 35.00
Pressed Glass, Beaded Acorn Medallion, Eggcup 24.00
Pressed Glass, Beaded Acorn Medallion, Goblet .... 14.50 To 15.00
Pressed Glass, Beaded Acorn Medallion, Plate, 6 In. 15.00
Pressed Glass, Beaded Band, Butter, Covered 18.75
Pressed Glass, Beaded Band, Compote, Covered, High Standard, 7 In. 38.00
Pressed Glass, Beaded Band, Goblet .... 7.50 To 20.00
Pressed Glass, Beaded Band, Pitcher, Water .... 27.50 To 55.00
Pressed Glass, Beaded Band, Relish .... 7.50 To 8.00
Pressed Glass, Beaded Band, Spooner 8.00
Pressed Glass, Beaded Band, Sugar 15.00
Pressed Glass, Beaded Band, Syrup 30.00
Pressed Glass, Beaded Band, Syrup, Tin Lid 26.00
Pressed Glass, Beaded Band, Wine .... 12.50 To 20.00
Pressed Glass, Beaded Cable, Bowl, Green, Opalescent, Footed, 7 3/4 In. 18.50
Pressed Glass, Beaded Cable, Relish 5.50
Pressed Glass, Beaded Chain, Goblet .... 11.50 To 13.50
Pressed Glass, Beaded Chain, Plate, 6 1/4 In. 8.50
Pressed Glass, Beaded Circle, Spooner 22.00
Pressed Glass, Beaded Coarse Bars, Goblet 12.50
Pressed Glass, Beaded Dart Band, Goblet 10.50
Pressed Glass, Beaded Dart Band, Goblet, Ruby Stained 25.00
Pressed Glass, Beaded Dewdrop, Bowl, Berry, 8 1/4 In. 23.00
Pressed Glass, Beaded Dewdrop, Cake Stand, 8 1/2 In. 25.00
Pressed Glass, Beaded Dewdrop, Celery .... 18.00 To 35.00
Pressed Glass, Beaded Dewdrop, Pitcher, Water 28.00
Pressed Glass, Beaded Dewdrop, Plate, Square, 6 3/4 In. 15.00
Pressed Glass, Beaded Dewdrop, Spooner .... 18.50 To 18.75
Pressed Glass, Beaded Dewdrop, Sugar, Individual 11.00
Pressed Glass, Beaded Dewdrop, Wine .... 28.50 To 37.50
Pressed Glass, Beaded Ellipse, Relish 4.00
Pressed Glass, Beaded Eye & Scale, Sauce, 4 1/2 In. 35.00
Pressed Glass, Beaded Fan, Butter, Covered .... 16.00 To 17.00
Pressed Glass, Beaded Fan, Creamer 12.50
Pressed Glass, Beaded Finecut, Creamer .... 15.50 To 18.00
Pressed Glass, Beaded Finecut, Creamer, Findlay .... 15.00 To 16.00
Pressed Glass, Beaded Finecut, Sugar & Creamer 45.00
Pressed Glass, Beaded Grape Medallion, Banded, Spooner .... 17.50 To 35.00
Pressed Glass, Beaded Grape Medallion, Banded, Tumbler, Footed 15.00
Pressed Glass, Beaded Grape Medallion, Butter 45.00
Pressed Glass, Beaded Grape Medallion, Butter, Covered .... 27.50 To 28.75
Pressed Glass, Beaded Grape Medallion, Creamer 18.00
Pressed Glass, Beaded Grape Medallion, Creamer, Applied Handle 30.00
Pressed Glass, Beaded Grape Medallion, Eggcup .... 22.00 To 45.00
Pressed Glass, Beaded Grape Medallion, Goblet .... 12.00 To 15.00
Pressed Glass, Beaded Grape Medallion, Salt Dip 8.50
Pressed Glass, Beaded Grape Medallion, Sauce, 4 In. 6.00
Pressed Glass, Beaded Grape Medallion, Spooner .... 10.00 To 15.00
Pressed Glass, Beaded Grape, Bowl, Green, Rectangular, 8 3/8 X 6 1/8 In. 27.50
Pressed Glass, Beaded Grape, Bowl, Rectangular, 7 1/8 X 4 1/4 In. 12.50
Pressed Glass, Beaded Grape, Bowl, Rectangular, 8 3/8 X 6 1/8 In. 22.50
Pressed Glass, Beaded Grape, Bowl, Rectangular, 8 1/2 X 6 1/4 In. 32.50
Pressed Glass, Beaded Grape, Bowl, Rectangular, 10 1/4 X 5 In. 22.50
Pressed Glass, Beaded Grape, Bowl, Rectangular, 10 3/8 X 7 1/4 In. 30.00
Pressed Glass, Beaded Grape, Bowl, Square, 3 1/2 In. 6.00
Pressed Glass, Beaded Grape, Bowl, Square, 3 7/8 In. 6.00
Pressed Glass, Beaded Grape, Bowl, Square, 4 1/4 In. 7.50
Pressed Glass, Beaded Grape, Bowl, Square, 5 3/8 In. 15.00

Pressed Glass, Beaded Grape, Bowl, Square, 5 1/4 In.	14.00
Pressed Glass, Beaded Grape, Bowl, Square, 6 3/8 In.	10.00
Pressed Glass, Beaded Grape, Bowl, Square, 7 3/8 In.	12.50
Pressed Glass, Beaded Grape, Bowl, Square, 8 1/4 In.	18.00
Pressed Glass, Beaded Grape, Bowl, Square, 8 1/2 In.	28.00
Pressed Glass, Beaded Grape, Bowl, 8 1/4 In. Diameter	18.00
Pressed Glass, Beaded Grape, Butter, Covered	40.00
Pressed Glass, Beaded Grape, Butter, Green, Square	38.00
Pressed Glass, Beaded Grape, Cake Stand, High Standard, 9 In.	50.00
Pressed Glass, Beaded Grape, Celery	25.00
Pressed Glass, Beaded Grape, Celery, Green	28.00 To 35.00
Pressed Glass, Beaded Grape, Compote, Covered, High Standard, 6 In.	65.00
Pressed Glass, Beaded Grape, Compote, Green, High Standard, 8 1/4 In.	55.00
Pressed Glass, Beaded Grape, Compote, High Standard, 6 1/4 In.	22.50
Pressed Glass, Beaded Grape, Compote, Jelly	20.00
Pressed Glass, Beaded Grape, Compote, Jelly, Square	16.50
Pressed Glass, Beaded Grape, Creamer	30.00
Pressed Glass, Beaded Grape, Creamer, Green	35.00 To 36.00
Pressed Glass, Beaded Grape, Goblet	22.00 To 45.00
Pressed Glass, Beaded Grape, Pitcher, Milk, 5 3/4 In.	65.00
Pressed Glass, Beaded Grape, Pitcher, Water	38.00
Pressed Glass, Beaded Grape, Pitcher, Water, Green	95.00
Pressed Glass, Beaded Grape, Plate, Green, Square, 8 In.	37.50
Pressed Glass, Beaded Grape, Plate, Square, 8 In.	30.00
Pressed Glass, Beaded Grape, Plate, Square, 8 1/4 In.	22.00
Pressed Glass, Beaded Grape, Relish, 7 X 4 In.	6.00 To 18.00
Pressed Glass, Beaded Grape, Salt & Pepper	30.00
Pressed Glass, Beaded Grape, Sauce, Green, Gold Trim, Square, 3 3/4 In.	10.00
Pressed Glass, Beaded Grape, Sauce, Green, Handled	17.50
Pressed Glass, Beaded Grape, Sauce, Green, 5 3/8 In.	20.00
Pressed Glass, Beaded Grape, Sauce, Handled	12.50
Pressed Glass, Beaded Grape, Sauce, Square, 3 3/4 In.	10.00
Pressed Glass, Beaded Grape, Spooner	19.50
Pressed Glass, Beaded Grape, Spooner, Green	37.50
Pressed Glass, Beaded Grape, Sugar, Covered	32.50
Pressed Glass, Beaded Grape, Toothpick	30.00
Pressed Glass, Beaded Grape, Tumbler	30.00
Pressed Glass, Beaded Grape, Wine	25.00 To 30.00
Beaded Jewel, see Lacy Dewdrop	
Pressed Glass, Beaded Loop, Bowl, Berry, Low, 8 In.	7.50
Pressed Glass, Beaded Loop, Bowl, Berry, Ruby Stained	30.00
Pressed Glass, Beaded Loop, Butter, Covered, Ruby Stained	40.00
Pressed Glass, Beaded Loop, Cake Stand, 7 3/4 In.	20.00
Pressed Glass, Beaded Loop, Cake Stand, 9 In.	26.00
Pressed Glass, Beaded Loop, Cake Stand, 9 1/2 In.	26.00
Pressed Glass, Beaded Loop, Carafe, Whiskey	18.00
Pressed Glass, Beaded Loop, Celery	14.00
Pressed Glass, Beaded Loop, Compote, 7 1/2 X 5 1/4 In.	18.00
Pressed Glass, Beaded Loop, Compote, 9 X 7 1/4 In.	17.00
Pressed Glass, Beaded Loop, Cookie Stand, 8 X 5 In.	20.00
Pressed Glass, Beaded Loop, Creamer, Flat Base	12.00
Pressed Glass, Beaded Loop, Creamer, Ruby Stained	30.00
Pressed Glass, Beaded Loop, Dish, Pickle	7.00
Pressed Glass, Beaded Loop, Goblet	10.50 To 20.00
Pressed Glass, Beaded Loop, Pitcher, Milk	20.00
Pressed Glass, Beaded Loop, Plate, Bread, 11 1/4 X 7 3/4 In.	15.00 To 23.50
Pressed Glass, Beaded Loop, Sauce	5.00 To 7.50
Pressed Glass, Beaded Loop, Sauce, Footed	7.00
Pressed Glass, Beaded Loop, Spooner	13.50
Pressed Glass, Beaded Loop, Spooner, Ruby Stained	22.50
Pressed Glass, Beaded Loop, Sugar, Covered	36.00
Pressed Glass, Beaded Loop, Sugar, Covered, Ruby Stained	35.00
Pressed Glass, Beaded Loop, Syrup	22.50
Pressed Glass, Beaded Loop, Tumbler, Ruby Stained	30.00
Pressed Glass, Beaded Loop, Wine	18.00
Beaded Medallion, see Beaded Mirror	

Pressed Glass, Beaded Mirror, Eggcup	45.00
Pressed Glass, Beaded Mirror, Eggcup, Flint	40.00
Pressed Glass, Beaded Mirror, Goblet	28.00
Pressed Glass, Beaded Mirror, Goblet, Flint	22.00
Pressed Glass, Beaded Mirror, Plate, Bread	19.50 To 21.50
Pressed Glass, Beaded Mirror, Spill, Flint	35.00
Pressed Glass, Beaded Mirror, Spooner	35.00
Pressed Glass, Beaded Mirror, Spooner, Flint	18.00 To 35.00
Pressed Glass, Beaded Oval & Scroll, Berry Set, Green, Gold Trim, 6 Piece	95.00
Pressed Glass, Beaded Oval & Scroll, Butter, Covered	22.00 To 25.00
Pressed Glass, Beaded Oval & Scroll, Creamer	15.00
Pressed Glass, Beaded Oval & Scroll, Goblet	20.00
Pressed Glass, Beaded Oval Window, Creamer, Blue	27.00
Pressed Glass, Beaded Oval Window, Goblet, Amber	18.00
Pressed Glass, Beaded Ovals, Butter, Covered	25.00
Pressed Glass, Beaded Ovals, Goblet, Buttermilk	9.00
Pressed Glass, Beaded Ovals, Plate, Bread	22.00
Pressed Glass, Beaded Ovals, Spooner	15.50 To 25.00
Pressed Glass, Beaded Ovals, Sugar	9.00
Pressed Glass, Beaded Panel, Sauce, Greentown	14.50
Pressed Glass, Beaded Rosette, Goblet	18.50
Pressed Glass, Beaded Scroll, Sauce, Footed, Flared	6.50
Pressed Glass, Beaded Scroll, Tray, Pin, Ruby Stained	12.00
Pressed Glass, Beaded Star, Bowl, Green, Opalescent, 8 X 1 1/2 In.	22.00
Pressed Glass, Beaded Star, Compote, Blue, Opalescent, Footed, 6 1/2 In.	24.00
Pressed Glass, Beaded Swirl With Disc Band, Cup & Saucer	16.00
Pressed Glass, Beaded Swirl With Disc Band, Pitcher, Milk	18.00
Pressed Glass, Beaded Swirl With Disc Band, Pitcher, Water	10.00
Pressed Glass, Beaded Swirl, Cake Stand, Child's	20.00 To 28.00
Pressed Glass, Beaded Swirl, Cordial	7.00
Pressed Glass, Beaded Swirl, Creamer, Amber Stained Lenses	24.00
Pressed Glass, Beaded Swirl, Creamer, Emerald Green & Gold	30.00
Pressed Glass, Beaded Swirl, Mug, Blue, Gold Trim	15.00
Pressed Glass, Beaded Swirl, Tumbler, Green With Gold	18.00
Pressed Glass, Beaded Swirl, Tumbler, Ruby Stained	18.00
Pressed Glass, Beaded Swirl, Wine	10.00 To 17.00
Pressed Glass, Beaded Tulip, Creamer	21.50
Pressed Glass, Beaded Tulip, Goblet	17.50 To 22.00
Pressed Glass, Beaded Tulip, Pitcher, Milk	47.50 To 62.50
Pressed Glass, Beaded Tulip, Pitcher, Water	30.00 To 45.00
Pressed Glass, Beaded Tulip, Sauce	5.50
Pressed Glass, Beaded Tulip, Wine	32.00
Pressed Glass, Bear Climber, Goblet	42.50
Bearded Man, see Viking	
Pressed Glass, Beatrice, Goblet	7.50
Pressed Glass, Beatrice, Goblet, 6 In.	15.00
Pressed Glass, Beatty Rib, Berry Set, Opalescent, 7 Piece	85.00
Pressed Glass, Beatty Rib, Berry Set, 7 Piece	95.00
Pressed Glass, Beatty Rib, Bowl, Berry, Opalescent, 9 In.	22.50
Pressed Glass, Beatty Rib, Butter, Blue, Opalescent, Covered	55.00
Pressed Glass, Beatty Rib, Creamer	28.75 To 30.00
Pressed Glass, Beatty Rib, Creamer, Lavender Tint	12.00
Pressed Glass, Beatty Rib, Creamer, Opalescent	25.00
Pressed Glass, Beatty Rib, Mug	20.00
Pressed Glass, Beatty Rib, Pitcher, Water, Blue	95.00
Pressed Glass, Beatty Rib, Spooner	20.00
Pressed Glass, Beatty Rib, Spooner, Lavender Tint	15.50
Pressed Glass, Beatty Rib, Taster, Whiskey	15.00
Pressed Glass, Beatty Rib, Taster, Whiskey, Blue, Opalescent	20.00
Pressed Glass, Beatty Rib, Toothpick, Blue	27.50
Pressed Glass, Beatty Rib, Toothpick, Opalescent	13.00 To 15.00
Pressed Glass, Beaumont, Goblet	6.50
Pressed Glass, Beehive, Goblet	12.00
Pressed Glass, Beetle Band, Bowl, Blue, 10 In.	45.00
Pressed Glass, Beetle Band, Spooner, Blue	18.00
Pressed Glass, Belcher Loop, Goblet	9.50 To 15.00

Pressed Glass, Beaded Grape Medallion, Covered Dish

Pressed Glass, Bellflower, Celery Vase

Pressed Glass, Bellflower, Compote

Pressed Glass, Belfast, Goblet	9.00
Pressed Glass, Bellflower & Coarse Rib, Goblet, Flint	35.00
Pressed Glass, Bellflower & Coarse Rib, Sauce	6.00
Pressed Glass, Bellflower & Fine Rib, Celery	195.00
Pressed Glass, Bellflower & Fine Rib, Eggcup	30.00
Pressed Glass, Bellflower & Fine Rib, Goblet, Knob Stem, Flint	16.00
Pressed Glass, Bellflower & Fine Rib, Spooner, C.1840	45.00
Pressed Glass, Bellflower & Fine Rib, Spooner, Flint	28.00
Pressed Glass, Bellflower & Fine Rib, Tumbler, 3 1/4 In.	59.50
Pressed Glass, Bellflower, Banded, Tumbler	65.00
Pressed Glass, Bellflower, Butter, Covered	40.00
Pressed Glass, Bellflower, Butter, Covered, Flint	68.00
Pressed Glass, Bellflower, Celery	130.00
Pressed Glass, Bellflower, Champagne	90.00
Pressed Glass, Bellflower, Champagne, Flint	85.00
Pressed Glass, Bellflower, Compote, Excelsior Standard, Flint, 8 In.	92.00
Pressed Glass, Bellflower, Compote, Fluted Stem, Flint, 9 In.	87.50
Pressed Glass, Bellflower, Compote, Flint, 8 1/4 In.	65.00
Pressed Glass, Bellflower, Compote, Low Standard, 8 In.	45.00
Pressed Glass, Bellflower, Compote, Scalloped Top, Flint, 8 X 8 1/2 In.	92.00
Pressed Glass, Bellflower, Cordial, Barrel Shape, Knob Stem, Flint	125.00
Pressed Glass, Bellflower, Creamer	130.00
Pressed Glass, Bellflower, Creamer, Flint	130.00
Pressed Glass, Bellflower, Dish, Honey	16.00
Pressed Glass, Bellflower, Dish, Honey, Flint, 3 In.	22.00 To 30.00
Pressed Glass, Bellflower, Double Vine, Creamer, Flint	125.00
Pressed Glass, Bellflower, Double Vine, Creamer, 7 In.	135.00
Pressed Glass, Bellflower, Double Vine, Fine Rib, Goblet, Flint, C.1840	250.00
Pressed Glass, Bellflower, Double Vine, Fine Rib, Tumbler, Flint	250.00
Pressed Glass, Bellflower, Double Vine, Pitcher, Milk, Flint	450.00
Pressed Glass, Bellflower, Double Vine, Pitcher, Water	210.00
Pressed Glass, Bellflower, Double Vine, Pitcher, Water, Flint	220.00
Pressed Glass, Bellflower, Double Vine, Pitcher, 8 In.	325.00
Pressed Glass, Bellflower, Double Vine, Plate, Bread	28.00
Pressed Glass, Bellflower, Double Vine, Plate, 10 5/8 In.	20.00
Pressed Glass, Bellflower, Double Vine, Plate, 10 3/4 In.	16.50
Pressed Glass, Bellflower, Double Vine, Spill, Flint	25.00
Pressed Glass, Bellflower, Double Vine, Spooner, Flint	25.00 To 30.00

Pressed Glass, Bellflower, Double Vine, Sugar 35.00
Pressed Glass, Bellflower, Eggcup .... 20.00 To 30.00
Pressed Glass, Bellflower, Eggcup, Flint .... 20.00 To 35.00
Pressed Glass, Bellflower, Goblet .... 21.00 To 25.00
Pressed Glass, Bellflower, Goblet, Barrel, Flint .... 26.00 To 28.00
Pressed Glass, Bellflower, Goblet, Flint .... 20.00 To 35.00
Pressed Glass, Bellflower, Goblet, Knob Stem 23.00
Pressed Glass, Bellflower, Goblet, Knob Stem, Flint 22.00
Pressed Glass, Bellflower, Goblet, Rayed Base, Flint 36.00
Pressed Glass, Bellflower, Mug 16.00
Pressed Glass, Bellflower, Salt, Footed, Flint 30.00
Pressed Glass, Bellflower, Salt, Master 40.00
Pressed Glass, Bellflower, Salt, Master, Flint .... 25.00 To 28.00
Pressed Glass, Bellflower, Salt, Master, Footed, Flint 35.00
Pressed Glass, Bellflower, Salt, Master, Scalloped, Flint 35.00
Pressed Glass, Bellflower, Sauce 12.00
Pressed Glass, Bellflower, Sauce, Flint .... 9.50 To 12.50
Pressed Glass, Bellflower, Spill .... 15.00 To 37.50
Pressed Glass, Bellflower, Spill, Flint .... 20.00 To 30.00
Pressed Glass, Bellflower, Spooner .... 15.00 To 37.50
Pressed Glass, Bellflower, Spooner, Flint .... 20.00 To 45.00
Pressed Glass, Bellflower, Spooner, High Footed 41.50
Pressed Glass, Bellflower, Spooner, Scalloped Rim 30.00
Pressed Glass, Bellflower, Spooner, Scalloped Rim, Flint 80.00
Pressed Glass, Bellflower, Sugar, Covered, Flint .... 55.00 To 80.00
Pressed Glass, Bellflower, Sugar 28.50
Pressed Glass, Bellflower, Sugar, Covered 65.00
Pressed Glass, Bellflower, Sugar, Extra Leaf, Flint 35.00
Pressed Glass, Bellflower, Sugar, Flint .... 28.00 To 35.00
Pressed Glass, Bellflower, Tumbler 55.00
Pressed Glass, Bellflower, Tumbler, Flint 125.00
Pressed Glass, Bellflower, Tumbler, Whiskey 35.00
Pressed Glass, Bellflower, Wine 75.20
Pressed Glass, Bellflower, Wine, Flint, 3 3/4 In. 85.00
    Belted Icicle, see Icicle, Belted
    Belted Worcester, see Worcester, Belted
Pressed Glass, Bent Buckle, Bowl, Berry, Maiden Blush, 5 1/4 In. 6.00
Pressed Glass, Berlin, Creamer 10.00
Pressed Glass, Berlin, Jar, Cracker, Covered 45.00
Pressed Glass, Berry Cluster, Butter, Covered 35.00
Pressed Glass, Bessemer Flute, Goblet 12.00
Pressed Glass, Bessemer Flute, Goblet, Flint .... 18.00 To 18.50
Pressed Glass, Bessemer Flute, Goblet, Knob Stem, Flint 25.00
Pressed Glass, Bethlehem Star, Berry Set, 7 Piece 17.50
Pressed Glass, Bethlehem Star, Creamer 12.00
Pressed Glass, Bethlehem Star, Pitcher, Water, 9 In. .... 18.00 To 27.50
Pressed Glass, Bethlehem Star, Sherbet, Footed, 3 1/2 In. 2.25
Pressed Glass, Beveled Diamond & Star, Cake Stand 10.00
Pressed Glass, Beveled Diamond & Star, Compote, 8 1/4 In. .... 18.00 To 20.00
Pressed Glass, Beveled Diamond & Star, Jar, Cracker .... 18.50 To 32.00
Pressed Glass, Beveled Diamond & Star, Pitcher, Water 30.00
Pressed Glass, Beveled Diamond & Star, Relish 12.50
Pressed Glass, Beveled Diamond & Star, Sauce, Scalloped Edge, 5 In. 6.50
Pressed Glass, Beveled Diamond & Star, Spooner .... 10.00 To 12.50
Pressed Glass, Beveled Diamond & Star, Sugar 8.00
Pressed Glass, Beveled Diamond & Star, Tray, Water, 9 3/4 In. 12.00
Pressed Glass, Beveled Diamond & Star, Wine, Ruby Stained 25.00
Pressed Glass, Beveled Star, Sauce, Individual 6.00
Pressed Glass, Beveled Star, Spooner, Emerald Green 35.00
Pressed Glass, Bible, Match Holder 24.00
Pressed Glass, Bible, Plate, Bread, Open Bible Center 45.00
Pressed Glass, Big Button, Bowl, Finger 5.00
Pressed Glass, Big Button, Celery 18.00
Pressed Glass, Big Button, Sauce, Oval 8.50
Pressed Glass, Bigler, Celery 75.00
Pressed Glass, Bigler, Celery, Flint 65.00

Pressed Glass, Bigler, Champagne	60.00
Pressed Glass, Bigler, Champagne, Flint	54.00
Pressed Glass, Bigler, Creamer, Flint	55.00
Pressed Glass, Bigler, Creamer, Footed, Scalloped Rim, High Handle, Flint	52.00
Pressed Glass, Bigler, Cup Plate	8.50
Pressed Glass, Bigler, Goblet	31.00 To 55.00
Pressed Glass, Bigler, Goblet, Flint	21.00 To 35.00
Pressed Glass, Bigler, Grooved, Goblet, Flint	29.50
Pressed Glass, Bigler, Muffineer	9.00
Pressed Glass, Bigler, Sauce Set, C.1830, 7 Piece	47.50
Pressed Glass, Bigler, Tumbler, Ale, Flint	18.00 To 40.00
Pressed Glass, Bigler, Wine	16.00
Pressed Glass, Birch Leaf, Goblet	11.50 To 14.00
Pressed Glass, Birch Leaf, Plate, 9 1/4 In.	13.00
Pressed Glass, Birch Leaf, Sauce, Amber, Footed	12.50
Pressed Glass, Birch Leaf, Sauce, Yellow	9.50
Pressed Glass, Bird & Harp, Mug, 3 1/4 In.	16.50
Pressed Glass, Bird & Strawberry, Bowl, Oval, Footed, 9 1/2 X 6 In.	22.50
Pressed Glass, Bird & Strawberry, Bowl, Ruffled & Scalloped, 10 In.	28.00
Pressed Glass, Bird & Strawberry, Bowl, 10 In.	22.00
Pressed Glass, Bird & Strawberry, Butter	85.00
Pressed Glass, Bird & Strawberry, Cake Stand, 9 In.	35.00
Pressed Glass, Bird & Strawberry, Compote, Fluted, 8 X 6 1/2 In.	48.00
Pressed Glass, Bird & Strawberry, Compote, Jelly, Covered	85.00
Pressed Glass, Bird & Strawberry, Compote, Ruffled & Scalloped, 6 1/4 In.	40.00
Pressed Glass, Bird & Strawberry, Creamer	25.00 To 40.00
Pressed Glass, Bird & Strawberry, Cup, Punch	10.00
Pressed Glass, Bird & Strawberry, Dish, Candy, Heart Shape	35.00
Pressed Glass, Bird & Strawberry, Pitcher, Water	100.00
Pressed Glass, Bird & Strawberry, Sauce	8.00
Pressed Glass, Bird & Strawberry, Sugar	45.00
Pressed Glass, Bird & Strawberry, Sugar, Two Handles, 4 In.	35.00
Pressed Glass, Bird & Strawberry, Table Set, 3 Piece	100.00
Pressed Glass, Bird & Strawberry, Tumbler	25.00
Pressed Glass, Bird & Strawberry, Water Set, Painted, 7 Piece	385.00
Pressed Glass, Birds & Roses, Jigger, Whiskey, Frosted	5.00
Pressed Glass, Birds & Wheat, Mug	21.50
Pressed Glass, Birds In Swamp, Goblet	28.00 To 33.00
Pressed Glass, Bismarck Star, Bowl, Berry, 10 In.	6.00
Pressed Glass, Bismarck Star, Goblet	9.00 To 12.50
Pressed Glass, Bismarck Star, Goblet	9.00
Pressed Glass, Bissing, Goblet	5.00
Pressed Glass, Blackberry, Bowl, Oval, 8 1/4 X 5 1/2 In.	15.00
Pressed Glass, Blackberry, Celery	25.00
Pressed Glass, Blackberry, Compote, Low Standard, 7 1/2 In.	22.50
Pressed Glass, Blackberry, Creamer	15.00
Pressed Glass, Blackberry, Eggcup	12.50
Pressed Glass, Blackberry, Eggcup, Double	12.50
Pressed Glass, Blackberry, Goblet	15.00 To 17.00
Pressed Glass, Blackberry, Naturalistic, Goblet	20.00 To 27.50
Pressed Glass, Blackberry, Plate, 3 Compartments, 8 1/2 In.	5.00
Pressed Glass, Blackberry, Relish	12.50
Pressed Glass, Blackberry, Salt, Double	45.00
Pressed Glass, Blackberry, Salt, Footed	25.75
Pressed Glass, Blackberry, Spooner	12.40
Pressed Glass, Blackberry, Spooner, Footed	18.50
Pressed Glass, Blaze, Butter, Covered	45.00
Pressed Glass, Blaze, Celery	60.00
Pressed Glass, Blaze, Celery, Flint	48.00
Pressed Glass, Blaze, Champagne	45.00
Pressed Glass, Blaze, Eggcup	38.00
Pressed Glass, Blaze, Goblet	30.00
Pressed Glass, Blaze, Spill, Flint	35.00
Pressed Glass, Blaze, Spooner	45.00
Pressed Glass, Blaze, Spooner, Flint	35.00
Pressed Glass, Blaze, Sugar, Covered	75.00

Pressed Glass, **Blaze,** Sugar, Covered, Flint 70.00
Pressed Glass, **Bleeding Heart,** Bowl, Bleeding Heart Finial, 7 In. 68.00
Pressed Glass, **Bleeding Heart,** Bowl, Oval, 8 1/4 X 5 3/4 In. 20.00
Pressed Glass, **Bleeding Heart,** Butter, Covered .... 50.00 To 60.00
Pressed Glass, **Bleeding Heart,** Cake Stand, 9 In. 25.00
Pressed Glass, **Bleeding Heart,** Cake Stand, 10 In. .... 30.00 To 47.50
Pressed Glass, **Bleeding Heart,** Compote, Covered, Low Standard, 8 In. 55.00
Pressed Glass, **Bleeding Heart,** Compote, 8 1/2 X 4 1/4 In. 24.00
Pressed Glass, **Bleeding Heart,** Creamer, Applied Handle 47.50
Pressed Glass, **Bleeding Heart,** Dish, Honey, 3 1/2 In. 12.50
Pressed Glass, **Bleeding Heart,** Eggcup 30.00
Pressed Glass, **Bleeding Heart,** Goblet .... 20.00 To 28.00
Pressed Glass, **Bleeding Heart,** Goblet, Knob Stem .... 20.00 To 29.50
Pressed Glass, **Bleeding Heart,** Sauce .... 7.00 To 22.00
Pressed Glass, **Bleeding Heart,** Spooner .... 16.50 To 30.00
Pressed Glass, **Bleeding Heart,** Sugar .... 20.00 To 27.50
Pressed Glass, **Bleeding Heart,** Wine 60.00
Pressed Glass, **Block & Bar,** Creamer 75.00
Pressed Glass, **Block & Bar,** Creamer, Flint .... 65.00 To 85.00
Pressed Glass, **Block & Circle,** Goblet 12.50
Pressed Glass, **Block & Circle,** Goblet, Patterned Foot 13.00
Pressed Glass, **Block & Circle,** Spooner 35.00
Pressed Glass, **Block & Circle,** Wine 12.00
Pressed Glass, **Block & Double Bar,** Tumbler, Ruby Stained 22.00
Pressed Glass, **Block & Fan,** Bowl, Ice, 7 X 5 1/2 In. 35.00
Pressed Glass, **Block & Fan,** Bowl, 10 In. 30.00
Pressed Glass, **Block & Fan,** Cake Stand 38.00

Pressed Glass,
Bellflower, Goblet

Pressed Glass,
Bleeding Heart, Goblet

Pressed Glass, **Block & Fan,** Celery, 7 In. 8.50
Pressed Glass, **Block & Fan,** Compote, High Standard, 8 In. 38.00
Pressed Glass, **Block & Fan,** Creamer .... 19.00 To 30.00
Pressed Glass, **Block & Fan,** Goblet .... 9.00 To 15.00
Pressed Glass, **Block & Fan,** Goblet, Milk White 12.50
Pressed Glass, **Block & Fan,** Jar, Cracker 35.00
Pressed Glass, **Block & Fan,** Muffineer 18.00
Pressed Glass, **Block & Fan,** Pitcher, Milk 25.00
Pressed Glass, **Block & Fan,** Pitcher, Water 25.00
Pressed Glass, **Block & Fan,** Pitcher, Water, Ruby 58.75
Pressed Glass, **Block & Fan,** Plate, 9 1/4 In. 20.00
Pressed Glass, **Block & Fan,** Plate, 10 In. 28.50
Pressed Glass, **Block & Fan,** Relish 16.50
Pressed Glass, **Block & Fan,** Relish, Oblong 90.00
Pressed Glass, **Block & Fan,** Salt & Pepper 20.00
Pressed Glass, **Block & Fan,** Saltshaker .... 8.00 To 12.50
Pressed Glass, **Block & Fan,** Sauce 6.50
Pressed Glass, **Block & Fan,** Sauce, Footed .... 3.50 To 7.00
Pressed Glass, **Block & Fan,** Wine .... 28.00 To 32.50

Block & Finecut, see Finecut & Block

Pressed Glass, Block & Lattice, Bowl, Berry, Ruby Stained	45.00
Pressed Glass, Block & Lattice, Butter, Covered, Amber & Clear	95.00
Pressed Glass, Block & Lattice, Creamer, Yellow & Clear	55.00
Pressed Glass, Block & Lattice, Pitcher, Water, Ruby Stained, Large	85.00
Pressed Glass, Block & Lattice, Pitcher, Water, Ruby Stained, Small	65.00
Pressed Glass, Block & Lattice, Spooner, Ruby Stained	30.00
Pressed Glass, Block & Lattice, Sugar, Covered, Ruby Stained	45.00
Pressed Glass, Block & Lattice, Water Set, Ruby Stained, Etched, 5 Piece	175.00

Block & Star, see Valencia Waffle

Pressed Glass, Block & Thumbprint, Celery	21.50 To 75.00
Pressed Glass, Block & Thumbprint, Goblet	12.50
Pressed Glass, Block & Thumbprint, Salt, Flint	20.00
Pressed Glass, Block & Thumbprint, Salt, Footed, Flint	20.00
Pressed Glass, Block & Thumbprint, Salt, Master, Footed, Flint	20.00
Pressed Glass, Block & Thumbprint, Tumbler, Footed, Flint	25.00
Pressed Glass, Block On Stilts, Goblet	16.00
Pressed Glass, Block With Fringe, Goblet	10.00
Pressed Glass, Block With Sawtooth Band, Goblet	13.00
Pressed Glass, Block With Sawtooth Band, Wine	8.00

Block with Stars, see Hanover
Blockade, see Diamond Block with Fan

Pressed Glass, Blocked Arches, Syrup, Lid	20.00

Blockhouse, see Hanover
Bluebird, see Bird & Strawberry

Pressed Glass, Bordered Ellipse, Butter, Covered, Ruby Stained	45.00
Pressed Glass, Bordered Ellipse, Goblet	5.00
Pressed Glass, Bordered Ellipse, Mug, Ruby Stained	17.50

Boswell, see Seashell

Pressed Glass, Bosworth, Goblet	6.00
Pressed Glass, Bosworth, Pitcher, Water, Applied Handle	30.00
Pressed Glass, Bouquet, Butter, Covered	20.00
Pressed Glass, Bouquet, Goblet	9.00 To 22.00
Pressed Glass, Bowtie, Compote, High Standard, 8 In.	45.00
Pressed Glass, Bowtie, Creamer	28.00
Pressed Glass, Bowtie, Jar, Jam, Covered	32.00 To 35.00
Pressed Glass, Bowtie, Spooner	13.00 To 15.00
Pressed Glass, Box In Box, Tumbler, Ruby Stained	20.00
Pressed Glass, Boy & Girl, Mug, Amber, Findlay	35.00
Pressed Glass, Boy With Goose, Cake Stand	155.00
Pressed Glass, Bracket With Swag, Berry Set, Green, 7 Piece	185.00
Pressed Glass, Bracket With Swag, Spooner, Green, Footed	28.50
Pressed Glass, Bracket With Swag, Sugar, Green, Footed	35.00

Bradford Blackberry, see Bradford Grape

Pressed Glass, Bradford Grape, Goblet	50.00
Pressed Glass, Bradford Grape, Goblet, Flint	45.00 To 60.00
Pressed Glass, Bradford Grape, Wine	45.00
Pressed Glass, Bradford Grape, Wine, Flint	40.00
Pressed Glass, Branches, Pitcher, Water	46.00
Pressed Glass, Brazen Shield, Goblet	12.50
Pressed Glass, Brazen Shield, Sugar, Cobalt, Covered, Greentown	45.00
Pressed Glass, Brazen Shield, Tumbler, Blue, Greentown	40.00
Pressed Glass, Brickwork, Creamer	10.50
Pressed Glass, Bridle Rosettes, Butter, Covered	35.00
Pressed Glass, Bridle Rosettes, Wine	11.00
Pressed Glass, Brilliant, Goblet	50.00
Pressed Glass, Brilliant, Goblet, Flint	30.00 To 37.50
Pressed Glass, Britannic, Mug, Ruby Stained, Etched	18.00
Pressed Glass, Broad Flute, Compote, Low Standard, Flint, 8 X 3 In.	20.00
Pressed Glass, Broken Column With Red Dots, Butter, Covered, Ruby Stained	75.00
Pressed Glass, Broken Column With Red Dots, Celery, Ruby Stained	50.00
Pressed Glass, Broken Column With Red Dots, Saucer	22.50
Pressed Glass, Broken Column, Banana Stand	78.50
Pressed Glass, Broken Column, Bowl, 7 1/4 In.	26.50
Pressed Glass, Broken Column, Cake Stand	55.00 To 67.50
Pressed Glass, Broken Column, Cake Stand, Ruby & Clear, 9 5/8 In.	65.00

Pressed Glass, Broken Column, Carafe, Water 38.00
Pressed Glass, Broken Column, Celery 18.50
Pressed Glass, Broken Column, Champagne .... 37.50 To 48.50
Pressed Glass, Broken Column, Compote, Covered, 8 X 11 In. 85.00
Pressed Glass, Broken Column, Compote, Jelly 39.50
Pressed Glass, Broken Column, Compote, 6 In. 29.00
Pressed Glass, Broken Column, Compote, 7 In. 42.50
Pressed Glass, Broken Column, Creamer .... 22.50 To 30.00
Pressed Glass, Broken Column, Cup, Punch, Blue 40.00
Pressed Glass, Broken Column, Goblet, Lady's 32.50
Pressed Glass, Broken Column, Jar, Cracker .... 47.50 To 55.00
Pressed Glass, Broken Column, Plate, 5 In. 22.00
Pressed Glass, Broken Column, Plate, 8 1/4 In. 18.00
Pressed Glass, Broken Column, Spooner .... 16.00 To 36.00
Pressed Glass, Broken Column, Sugar, Covered .... 35.00 To 40.00
Pressed Glass, Broken Column, Toothpick 20.00
Pressed Glass, Broken Column, Tumbler .... 25.00 To 30.00
Pressed Glass, Brooklyn Flute, Goblet, Flint 16.00
Pressed Glass, Brooklyn, Ale Glass 52.50
Pressed Glass, Brooklyn, Goblet, Flint 30.00
Pressed Glass, Brooklyn, Sugar, Flint 35.00
Pressed Glass, Broughton, Goblet 7.50
Pressed Glass, Broughton, Goblet, Amethyst, Gold Flashed 19.00
Pressed Glass, Bryan, Mug, Covered 41.00
   Bryce, see Ribbon Candy
Pressed Glass, Buckingham, Sugar, Covered 18.00
Pressed Glass, Buckle & Shield, Goblet 15.00
Pressed Glass, Buckle & Star, Butter, Covered 15.00
Pressed Glass, Buckle & Star, Creamer, Footed 12.50
Pressed Glass, Buckle & Star, Dish, Pickle 8.50
Pressed Glass, Buckle & Star, Goblet 16.00
Pressed Glass, Buckle & Star, Goblet, Buttermilk, Pedestal Base 15.00
Pressed Glass, Buckle & Star, Salt, Master 16.00
Pressed Glass, Buckle & Star, Sauce, Footed 7.00
Pressed Glass, Buckle With Diamond Band, Goblet 15.00
Pressed Glass, Buckle With Diamond Band, Goblet, Flint 35.00
Pressed Glass, Buckle With Diamond Band, Sauce 4.50
Pressed Glass, Buckle With English Hobnail, Bowl, 7 In. 8.50
Pressed Glass, Buckle, Cake Stand, 10 In. 15.00
Pressed Glass, Buckle, Champagne 65.00
Pressed Glass, Buckle, Compote, Low Standard, Flint, 8 In. 35.00
Pressed Glass, Buckle, Compote, Low Standard, 8 In. 22.50
Pressed Glass, Buckle, Compote, Scalloped Edge, High Standard, 10 In. 45.00
Pressed Glass, Buckle, Compote, 12 In. 36.00
Pressed Glass, Buckle, Creamer .... 15.00 To 85.00
Pressed Glass, Buckle, Creamer, Applied Handle 45.00
Pressed Glass, Buckle, Creamer, Flint 75.00
Pressed Glass, Buckle, Dish, Pickle 5.00
Pressed Glass, Buckle, Eggcup .... 10.00 To 35.00
Pressed Glass, Buckle, Eggcup, Flint 35.00
Pressed Glass, Buckle, Goblet .... 15.00 To 35.00
Pressed Glass, Buckle, Goblet, Flint .... 18.00 To 30.00
Pressed Glass, Buckle, Relish 9.00
Pressed Glass, Buckle, Relish, Amber 15.00
Pressed Glass, Buckle, Salt, Master 16.50
Pressed Glass, Buckle, Salt, Master, Footed, Scalloped Rim, Flint 28.00
Pressed Glass, Buckle, Sauce .... 5.00 To 7.50
Pressed Glass, Buckle, Sauce, Flint 7.50
Pressed Glass, Buckle, Sauce, Footed 7.00
Pressed Glass, Buckle, Spill, Flint 25.00
Pressed Glass, Buckle, Spooner .... 10.00 To 32.00
Pressed Glass, Buckle, Spooner, Flint .... 18.00 To 25.00
Pressed Glass, Buckle, Sugar, Covered .... 25.00 To 75.00
Pressed Glass, Buckle, Sugar, Covered, Flint .... 35.00 To 75.00
Pressed Glass, Buckle, Sugar, Flint 47.00
Pressed Glass, Buckle, Wine 45.00

Pressed Glass, Broken Column, Goblet

Pressed Glass, Buckle, Goblet

Pressed Glass,
Bull's-Eye With Diamond Point, Goblet

Pressed Glass, Buckle, Wine, Flint	40.00
Pressed Glass, Budded Ivy, Butter, Covered	18.75
Pressed Glass, Budded Ivy, Sauce	3.50
Pressed Glass, Budded Ivy, Spooner	18.00
Pressed Glass, Bull's-Eye & Bar, Champagne	125.00
Pressed Glass, Bull's-Eye & Bar, Eggcup	110.00
Pressed Glass, Bull's-Eye & Bar, Eggcup, Flint	80.00 To 110.00
Pressed Glass, Bull's-Eye & Bar, Goblet	90.00
Pressed Glass, Bull's-Eye & Bar, Goblet, Flint	90.00 To 150.00
Pressed Glass, Bull's-Eye & Bar, Wine	125.00
Pressed Glass, Bull's-Eye & Broken Column, Goblet, Flint	58.00
Pressed Glass, Bull's-Eye & Broken Column, Tumbler, Footed, Flint	35.00
Pressed Glass, Bull's-Eye & Daisy, Berry Set, Gold Eyes, 6 Piece	28.00
Pressed Glass, Bull's-Eye & Daisy, Goblet, Purple Eyes	14.00
Pressed Glass, Bull's-Eye & Daisy, Goblet, Purple Eyes, Gold Trim	10.00
Pressed Glass, Bull's-Eye & Daisy, Nappy, Amethyst Eyes, Gold Trim	16.00
Pressed Glass, Bull's-Eye & Daisy, Spooner, Amethyst, Gold Trim, 2 Handled	37.00
Pressed Glass, Bull's-Eye & Daisy, Tumbler	3.00
Pressed Glass, Bull's-Eye & Diamond Panels, Goblet	7.00 To 13.50
Pressed Glass, Bull's-Eye & Diamond Point, Celery	115.00 To 125.00
Pressed Glass, Bull's-Eye & Diamond Point, Celery, Flint	110.00 To 125.00
Pressed Glass, Bull's-Eye & Diamond Point, Creamer	225.00
Pressed Glass, Bull's-Eye & Diamond Point, Creamer, Flint	200.00
Pressed Glass, Bull's-Eye & Diamond Point, Decanter, Bar, Quart	95.00 To 97.50
Pressed Glass, Bull's-Eye & Diamond Point, Decanter, Quart	95.00
Pressed Glass, Bull's-Eye & Diamond Point, Dish, Honey, 3 In.	10.00
Pressed Glass, Bull's-Eye & Diamond Point, Eggcup, Flint	125.00
Pressed Glass, Bull's-Eye & Diamond Point, Goblet, Flint	80.00 To 95.00
Pressed Glass, Bull's-Eye & Diamond Point, Sauce	15.00
Pressed Glass, Bull's-Eye & Diamond Point, Sauce, Flint	18.50
Pressed Glass, Bull's-Eye & Diamond Point, Spill, Flint	55.00
Pressed Glass, Bull's-Eye & Diamond Point, Spooner	60.00
Pressed Glass, Bull's-Eye & Diamond Point, Spooner, Flint	55.00
Pressed Glass, Bull's-Eye & Diamond Point, Spooner, Handled, Flint	225.00

Pressed Glass, Bull's-Eye & Diamond Point, Sugar, Covered	125.00
Pressed Glass, Bull's-Eye & Diamond Point, Tumbler	100.00
Pressed Glass, Bull's-Eye & Diamond Point, Wine	130.00
Pressed Glass, Bull's-Eye & Diamond Point, Wine, Flint	130.00
Bull's-Eye & Fan, see Daisies in Oval Panels	
Pressed Glass, Bull's-Eye & Rosette, Tumbler, Flint	75.00
Pressed Glass, Bull's-Eye & Spearhead, Goblet	15.00
Pressed Glass, Bull's-Eye & Sunburst, Plate, Toddy, Flint, 5 In.	12.00
Bull's-Eye Band, see Reverse Torpedo	
Bull's-Eye Variant, see Texas Bull's-Eye	
Pressed Glass, Bull's-Eye With Fleur-De-Lis, Celery	100.00
Pressed Glass, Bull's-Eye With Fleur-De-Lis, Compote, Flint, 7 1/2 In.	41.00
Pressed Glass, Bull's-Eye With Fleur-De-Lis, Goblet	45.00
Pressed Glass, Bull's-Eye With Fleur-De-Lis, Goblet, Flint	55.00 To 60.00
Pressed Glass, Bull's-Eye With Fleur-De-Lis, Sugar, Covered	115.00
Pressed Glass, Bull's-Eye With Fleur-De-Lis, Sugar, Flint	30.00
Pressed Glass, Bull's-Eye, Bottle, Oil, Findlay	15.00
Pressed Glass, Bull's-Eye, Celery	90.00
Pressed Glass, Bull's-Eye, Celery, Flint	90.00
Pressed Glass, Bull's-Eye, Claret, Flint	70.00
Pressed Glass, Bull's-Eye, Cordial, Flint	90.00
Pressed Glass, Bull's-Eye, Creamer	125.00

Pressed Glass, Bull's Eye, Creamer

Pressed Glass, Cabbage Rose, Handled Mug

Pressed Glass, Bull's-Eye, Eggcup	25.00 To 38.50
Pressed Glass, Bull's-Eye, Goblet	42.00
Pressed Glass, Bull's-Eye, Goblet, Flint	20.00 To 60.00
Pressed Glass, Bull's-Eye, Salt, Flint	30.00
Pressed Glass, Bull's-Eye, Salt, Master, Flint	40.00 To 45.00
Pressed Glass, Bull's-Eye, Salt, Master, Rectangular, Flint	45.00
Pressed Glass, Bull's-Eye, Spill, Flint	50.00
Pressed Glass, Bull's-Eye, Spooner, Flint	45.00 T3 50.00
Pressed Glass, Bull's-Eye, Sugar, Covered	110.00
Pressed Glass, Bull's-Eye, Toothpick, Ruby Stained, Souvenir, Luverne, Minn.	17.00
Pressed Glass, Bull's-Eye, Tumbler	80.00
Pressed Glass, Bull's-Eye, Tumbler, Flint	45.00 To 75.00
Pressed Glass, Bull's-Eye, Tumbler, Footed, Flint	60.00
Pressed Glass, Bull's-Eye, Tumbler, Whiskey, Flint	90.00
Pressed Glass, Bull's-Eye, Wine	35.00 To 38.50
Pressed Glass, Bull's-Eye, Wine, Flint	30.00 To 55.00
Pressed Glass, Bull's-Eye, Wine, Ruby Stained	15.00
Pressed Glass, Bullet Emblem, Mug	95.00
Pressed Glass, Bullet Emblem, Relish	27.00
Pressed Glass, Bumper To The Flag, Tumbler, Whiskey, Flint	75.00 To 85.00
Pressed Glass, Bungalow, Goblet	11.00 To 12.00

Pressed Glass, Bungalow, Tumbler 15.00
Pressed Glass, Bunker Hill, Plate, Bread .... 42.00 To 55.00
Pressed Glass, Butterfly & Fan, Celery 28.75
Pressed Glass, Butterfly & Fan, Creamer 14.50
Pressed Glass, Butterfly & Fan, Tumbler .... 12.50 To 25.00
Pressed Glass, Butterfly & Spray, Creamer 20.00
Pressed Glass, Butterfly & Spray, Goblet 12.50
Pressed Glass, Butterfly & Spray, Mug, Child's, Amber 15.00
Pressed Glass, Butterfly & Spray, Mug, Child's, 2 1/2 In. 22.00
Pressed Glass, Butterfly & Spray, Sugar, Covered 20.00
Pressed Glass, Butterfly Handles, Creamer 28.75
Pressed Glass, Butterfly On Stump, Mug 18.00
Pressed Glass, Button & Fan, Bowl, 9 In. 16.00
Pressed Glass, Button Arches, Butter, Bell Shaped Lid, Ruby Stained 48.50
Pressed Glass, Button Arches, Cake Stand, Gold Rim, 9 1/2 In. 27.50
Pressed Glass, Button Arches, Cup, Punch, Ruby Stained 12.50
Pressed Glass, Button Arches, Goblet 12.50
Pressed Glass, Button Arches, Goblet, Clambroth, Gold Striping 26.50
Pressed Glass, Button Arches, Mug, Deep Ruby Top, 3 1/4 In. 15.00
Pressed Glass, Button Arches, Mug, Pink Enamel Flowers, 2 1/4 In. 6.00
Pressed Glass, Button Arches, Mug, Ruby Stained 18.00
Pressed Glass, Button Arches, Pitcher, Water 18.00
Pressed Glass, Button Arches, Pitcher, Water, Ruby & Clear 50.00
Pressed Glass, Button Arches, Pitcher, Water, Tankard Type, Ruby Stained .. 35.00
Pressed Glass, Button Arches, Saltshaker 8.00
Pressed Glass, Button Arches, Sauce, Ruby Stain, Frosted Band 10.00
Pressed Glass, Button Arches, Spooner, Ruby & Clear 25.00
Pressed Glass, Button Arches, Sugar & Creamer, Frosted Band, Ruby Stained . 25.00
Pressed Glass, Button Arches, Sugar & Creamer, Red Stained, 4 In. 48.50
Pressed Glass, Button Arches, Sugar, Individual, Open, Ruby Stained 12.50
Pressed Glass, Button Arches, Sugar, 4 X 3 1/2 In. 7.50
Pressed Glass, Button Arches, Toothpick 10.00
Pressed Glass, Button Arches, Toothpick, Ruby Stained 10.00
Pressed Glass, Button Arches, Tumbler 14.00
Pressed Glass, Button Arches, Tumbler, Etched 7.00
Pressed Glass, Button Arches, Tumbler, Ruby Stained .... 15.00 To 25.00
Pressed Glass, Button Arches, Wine 24.50
Pressed Glass, Button Arches, Wine, Ruby Stained .... 20.00 To 24.50
Pressed Glass, Button Band, Bowl, 14 Feet, 8 In. 22.00
Pressed Glass, Button Band, Compote, Jelly, Etched, High Standard 21.50
Pressed Glass, Button Band, Creamer, Etched Leaves Upper Portion 15.00
Pressed Glass, Button Band, Salt, Master .... 17.50 To 18.50
Pressed Glass, Button Band, Saltshaker, Flower Etching 16.00
Pressed Glass, Button Band, Sauce, Etched, 4 3/8 In. 7.50
Pressed Glass, Button Band, Sauce, Etched, 4 3/4 In. 7.50
Pressed Glass, Button Band, Sauce, 3 1/2 In. 5.50
Pressed Glass, Button Band, Spooner, Etched 12.50
Pressed Glass, Button Band, Tumbler 15.00
Pressed Glass, Button Panel, Cup, Punch, Handled 6.00
Pressed Glass, Button With Braid, Pitcher, Water, Green, Opalescent 75.00
Pressed Glass, Buzz Star, Goblet 8.00
Pressed Glass, Cabbage Leaf, Creamer, Frosted, Footed 32.50
Pressed Glass, Cabbage Rose, Cake Stand, 9 1/2 In. .... 20.00 To 30.00
Pressed Glass, Cabbage Rose, Champagne 48.50
Pressed Glass, Cabbage Rose, Compote, Covered, 8 In. 65.00
Pressed Glass, Cabbage Rose, Creamer, 5 1/4 In. 75.00
Pressed Glass, Cabbage Rose, Goblet .... 20.00 To 22.50
Pressed Glass, Cabbage Rose, Spooner .... 14.00 To 18.00
Pressed Glass, Cabbage Rose, Sugar 25.00
Pressed Glass, Cabbage Rose, Wine .... 9.50 To 38.00
Pressed Glass, Cable & Fan, Spooner, Flint .... 25.00 To 35.00
Pressed Glass, Cable & Fan, Sugar 35.00
Pressed Glass, Cable & Fan, Sugar, Flint .... 30.00 To 35.00
Pressed Glass, Cable With Rings, Sugar & Creamer, Applied Handle, Flint .. 160.00
Pressed Glass, Cable With Rings, Sugar & Creamer, Cover 230.00
Pressed Glass, Cable With Rings, Sugar, Covered, Flint .... 72.50 To 77.50

Pressed Glass, Cable & Ring, Footed Bowl

Pressed Glass, Canadian, Compote

Pressed Glass, **Cable With Rings,** Sugar, Flint	27.80
Pressed Glass, **Cable,** Bowl, Footed, Flint, 7 In.	33.00
Pressed Glass, **Cable,** Butter	57.00
Pressed Glass, **Cable,** Butter, Covered	57.00 To 65.00
Pressed Glass, **Cable,** Butter, Covered, Flint	60.00
Pressed Glass, **Cable,** Celery	95.00
Pressed Glass, **Cable,** Celery, Flint	95.00
Pressed Glass, **Cable,** Champagne	110.00
Pressed Glass, **Cable,** Compote, Flint, 7 In.	32.00
Pressed Glass, **Cable,** Compote, Flint, 8 In.	34.00
Pressed Glass, **Cable,** Compote, 7 In.	35.00
Pressed Glass, **Cable,** Compote, 8 In.	38.00
Pressed Glass, **Cable,** Creamer	30.00
Pressed Glass, **Cable,** Decanter, Quart	95.00
Pressed Glass, **Cable,** Dish, Honey	8.50
Pressed Glass, **Cable,** Dish, Honey, Flint * 6.50 To	12.50
Pressed Glass, **Cable,** Eggcup	30.00 To 38.00
Pressed Glass, **Cable,** Eggcup, Flint	30.00 To 38.00
Pressed Glass, **Cable,** Goblet	60.00 To 65.00
Pressed Glass, **Cable,** Goblet, Flint	45.00 To 55.00
Pressed Glass, **Cable,** Goblet, Lady's, Flint	57.50 To 80.00
Pressed Glass, **Cable,** Pitcher, Water, Flint	275.00
Pressed Glass, **Cable,** Sauce	7.00
Pressed Glass, **Cable,** Spill	22.00
Pressed Glass, **Cable,** Spill, Flint	25.00 To 30.00
Pressed Glass, **Cable,** Spooner	15.00 To 35.00
Pressed Glass, **Cable,** Spooner, Flint	16.50 To 30.00
Pressed Glass, **Cable,** Sugar, Covered	95.00
Pressed Glass, **Cable,** Sugar, Covered, Flint	90.00
Pressed Glass, **Cable,** Tumbler, Footed	68.00
Pressed Glass, **Cable,** Wine	175.00
Pressed Glass, **Cable,** Wine, Flint	165.00
Pressed Glass, **Cadmus,** Toothpick	9.50
Pressed Glass, **Camel Caravan,** Goblet	35.00 To 55.00
Pressed Glass, **Camel Caravan,** Goblet, Etched	55.00
Cameo, see Ceres	
Canadian Drape, see Garfield Drape	
Pressed Glass, **Canadian Victoria,** Sauce, Footed	7.50
Pressed Glass, **Canadian,** Celery, Pedestal	43.50
Pressed Glass, **Canadian,** Compote, Covered, Low Standard, 7 In.	53.00
Pressed Glass, **Canadian,** Compote, 8 In.	35.00
Pressed Glass, **Canadian,** Creamer	20.00 To 38.00
Pressed Glass, **Canadian,** Goblet	20.00 To 25.00

Pressed Glass, Canadian, Pitcher, Milk	59.50
Pressed Glass, Canadian, Pitcher, Water	50.00
Pressed Glass, Canadian, Plate, Cake, Handled, 12 In.	26.00
Pressed Glass, Canadian, Plate, Cake, 12 In.	21.00
Pressed Glass, Canadian, Plate, Two Handles, 7 In.	23.50
Pressed Glass, Canadian, Plate, 7 In.	15.00 To 18.50
Pressed Glass, Canadian, Plate, 7 1/2 In.	19.50
Pressed Glass, Canadian, Plate, 8 In.	15.00 To 28.00
Pressed Glass, Canadian, Plate, 9 In.	18.00
Pressed Glass, Canadian, Plate, 10 In.	22.50
Pressed Glass, Canadian, Plate, 12 In.	21.00
Pressed Glass, Canadian, Sauce, 4 In.	9.50
Pressed Glass, Canadian, Sugar, Covered, 9 X 4 1/4 In.	45.00
Pressed Glass, Canadian, Wine	15.00 To 27.50
Pressed Glass, Candlewick, Pitcher, Water	20.00
Pressed Glass, Candlewick, Plate, 8 1/2 X 7 1/2 In.	7.50
Pressed Glass, Candlewick, Saucer	5.00
Candy Ribbon, see Ribbon Candy	
Pressed Glass, Cane & Pinwheel, Tray, Red Flashed Spokes, 10 In.	25.00
Pressed Glass, Cane & Rosette, Butter, Green, Gold Trim	50.00
Pressed Glass, Cane & Rosette, Celery	18.50
Pressed Glass, Cane & Rosette, Creamer, Purple Petals	22.50
Pressed Glass, Cane & Rosette, Goblet	15.00
Pressed Glass, Cane & Rosette, Mug	8.00 To 12.50
Pressed Glass, Cane & Rosette, Tumbler, Gold Trim	16.00
Pressed Glass, Cane & Rosette, Wine	14.50
Pressed Glass, Cane & Star Medallion, Goblet	16.00
Pressed Glass, Cane & Star Medallion, Goblet, Gilt	12.50
Pressed Glass, Cane Medallion, Creamer, Apple Green	29.50
Pressed Glass, Cane, Bowl, Waste, Canary	20.00
Pressed Glass, Cane, Creamer, Blue	28.00
Pressed Glass, Cane, Creamer, Canary	24.00
Pressed Glass, Cane, Goblet	12.00 To 14.50
Pressed Glass, Cane, Goblet, Amber	20.00 To 25.00
Pressed Glass, Cane, Goblet, Blue	32.00
Pressed Glass, Cane, Pitcher, Water	24.00 To 32.50
Pressed Glass, Cane, Pitcher, Water, Amber	30.00 To 52.00
Pressed Glass, Cane, Pitcher, Water, Apple Green	40.00
Pressed Glass, Cane, Pitcher, Water, Blue	46.00
Pressed Glass, Cane, Pitcher, Water, Green	50.00
Pressed Glass, Cane, Plate, Toddy, Amber	14.00
Pressed Glass, Cane, Plate, Toddy, Blue	15.00
Pressed Glass, Cane, Plate, Toddy, Green	14.00
Pressed Glass, Cane, Plate, Toddy, Handled, 4 1/2 In.	4.00
Pressed Glass, Cane, Relish, Blue, Oval	15.00
Pressed Glass, Cane, Salt	.35
Pressed Glass, Cane, Slipper, Amber, 6 In.	37.00
Pressed Glass, Cane, Sugar, Amber, Covered	32.00
Pressed Glass, Cane, Toothpick, Amber, Gypsy Kettle	20.00
Pressed Glass, Cane, Toothpick, Gypsy Kettle	12.00
Pressed Glass, Cane, Tray, Water	8.50
Pressed Glass, Cane, Tray, Water, Amber	32.00
Pressed Glass, Cane, Tray, 9 X 12 In.	20.00
Pressed Glass, Cannonball, Wine	20.00
Pressed Glass, Cape Cod, Goblet	20.00 To 30.00
Pressed Glass, Cape Cod, Pitcher, Water	34.00
Pressed Glass, Cape Cod, Plate, Bread	30.00
Pressed Glass, Cape Cod, Plate, 6 In.	17.50
Pressed Glass, Cape Cod, Sugar & Creamer	12.50
Pressed Glass, Capitol Building, Goblet	16.00 To 40.00
Pressed Glass, Capitol Building, Wine	28.00
Pressed Glass, Cardinal Bird, Creamer	25.00 To 35.00
Pressed Glass, Cardinal Bird, Goblet	25.00 To 35.00
Pressed Glass, Cardinal Bird, Sauce	12.50
Pressed Glass, Cardinal Bird, Spooner	22.50 To 30.00
Pressed Glass, Cardinal Bird, Sugar, Covered	45.00

Pressed Glass, Cardinal Bird, Spooner

Pressed Glass, Cathedral, Compote

Pressed Glass, Chain & Shell, Pitcher

Pressed Glass, Centennial, Butter, Covered

Carmen, see Paneled Diamond & Finecut
Pressed Glass, Carolina, Goblet 14.50
Pressed Glass, Cart, Salt 20.00
Pressed Glass, Cat In Basket & Dog On Drum, Mug .... 20.00 To 24.00
Pressed Glass, Cat In Basket & Dog On Drum, Mug, Child's, 3 In. .... 18.00 To 30.00
Pressed Glass, Cathedral, Cake Stand, Amber .... 40.00 To 45.00
Pressed Glass, Cathedral, Compote, Amber, Flared Rim, 9 X 6 1/2 In. 28.00
Pressed Glass, Cathedral, Creamer 35.00
Pressed Glass, Cathedral, Sauce, Footed 9.75
Pressed Glass, Cathedral, Spooner .... 15.00 To 24.00
Pressed Glass, Cathedral, Sugar, Covered .... 22.00 To 45.00
Pressed Glass, Cathedral, Wine 18.00
Pressed Glass, Cattails & Ferns, Goblet .... 14.00 To 22.00
Pressed Glass, Cavitt, Celery 10.00
Pressed Glass, Cayuga, Tumbler 20.00
Pressed Glass, Celtic, Celery .... 18.75 To 20.00
Pressed Glass, Celtic, Goblet 11.00
Pressed Glass, Celtic, Wine 8.50
Centennial, see also Liberty Bell
Pressed Glass, Centennial, Pittsburgh, Tumbler, Ale, 7 In. 30.00
Pressed Glass, Center Medallion, Sauce 5.00
Pressed Glass, Ceres, Creamer .... 12.50 To 20.00
Pressed Glass, Ceres, Mug 14.00
Pressed Glass, Ceres, Spooner 27.50
Pressed Glass, Ceres, Sugar 25.00
Pressed Glass, Ceres, Sugar & Creamer 36.00
Pressed Glass, Chain & Shield, Creamer .... 12.50 To 17.00
Pressed Glass, Chain & Shield, Goblet 14.00

Pressed Glass, Chain & Shield, Pitcher, Water 48.00
Pressed Glass, Chain & Shield, Plate, Bread .... 15.00 To 26.50
Pressed Glass, Chain & Shield, Wine 15.00
Pressed Glass, Chain & Star Band, Goblet 9.50
Pressed Glass, Chain & Star, Goblet .... 12.50 To 21.00
Pressed Glass, Chain & Star, Plate, 7 3/8 In. 15.00
Pressed Glass, Chain & Star, Relish 3.00
Pressed Glass, Chain & Star, Sauce, Footed, 4 1/4 In. 5.50
Pressed Glass, Chain & Star, Spooner 12.50
Pressed Glass, Chain & Star, Wine 10.00
Pressed Glass, Chain, Creamer 20.00
Pressed Glass, Chain, Goblet .... 12.00 To 21.00
Pressed Glass, Chain, Plate, Bread, Amber 20.00
Pressed Glass, Chain, Sauce 4.50
Pressed Glass, Chain, Sauce, Footed, 4 1/2 In. 7.50
Pressed Glass, Chain, Wine .... 10.00 To 14.50
Pressed Glass, Champion, Toothpick, Gold Trim 17.50
Pressed Glass, Champion, Wine 19.00
Pressed Glass, Champion, Wine, 3 1/2 In. 9.50
Pressed Glass, Chandelier, Celery .... 12.50 To 24.50
Pressed Glass, Chandelier, Creamer 18.50
Pressed Glass, Chandelier, Creamer, Etched 35.00
Pressed Glass, Chandelier, Goblet .... 22.00 To 38.00
Pressed Glass, Chandelier, Pitcher, Water .... 37.50 To 45.00
Pressed Glass, Chandelier, Spooner 16.50
Pressed Glass, Chandelier, Tumbler .... 12.50 To 25.00
Pressed Glass, Charleston, Goblet 8.00
Pressed Glass, Checker With Rib Band, Goblet 10.00
Pressed Glass, Checkerboard, Butter, Covered .... 15.00 To 37.50
Pressed Glass, Checkerboard, Creamer 22.50
Pressed Glass, Checkerboard, Cup, Punch 4.00
Pressed Glass, Checkerboard, Plate, 10 In. 10.00
Pressed Glass, Checkerboard, Tumbler 12.50
Pressed Glass, Checkerboard, Tumbler, 5 In. 12.00
Pressed Glass, Checkered Diamonds, Goblet 9.50
Pressed Glass, Cherry & Cable, Table Set, Marked N, 3 Piece 100.00
Pressed Glass, Cherry & Fig, Creamer 21.00
Pressed Glass, Cherry & Fig, Pitcher, Milk 18.00
Pressed Glass, Cherry Lattice, Sugar, Covered 20.00
Pressed Glass, Cherry, Butter, Amber 40.00
Pressed Glass, Cherry, Creamer, Applied Handle .... 28.50 To 30.00
Pressed Glass, Chesterfield, Goblet 12.50
Pressed Glass, Chestnut Oak, Creamer, Applied Handle 30.00
Pressed Glass, Chestnut Oak, Sugar 23.00
Pressed Glass, Chestnut, Butter, Covered 22.50
Pressed Glass, Chestnut, Goblet 12.00
Pressed Glass, Chicken, Pitcher, Water 31.00
Pressed Glass, Chicken's-Foot, Eggcup 22.50
Pressed Glass, Chilson, Goblet .... 115.00 To 125.00
Pressed Glass, Chilson, Goblet, Flint 110.00
Pressed Glass, Chimo, Goblet 5.00
Pressed Glass, Chrysanthemum Base, Celery, White Opalescent 30.00
Pressed Glass, Chrysanthemum Leaf, Creamer 25.00
Pressed Glass, Chrysanthemum Leaf, Toothpick, Gold Decoration 55.00
Pressed Glass, Chrysanthemum Leaf, Tumbler 20.00
Pressed Glass, Churchill, Goblet .... 11.00 To 20.00
Pressed Glass, Circle Scroll, Sauce, Opalescent 14.00
Pressed Glass, Circular Saw, Celery, Oblong 6.50
Pressed Glass, Circular Saw, Cup, Punch .... 2.50 To 4.50
Pressed Glass, Classic Medallion, Spooner 20.00
Pressed Glass, Classic, Bowl, Berry, Open Log Feet, 8 In. 85.00
Pressed Glass, Classic, Butter, Covered, Open Feet, 5 1/2 In. Diameter 135.00
Pressed Glass, Classic, Celery, Open Log Feet 110.00
Pressed Glass, Classic, Compote, Covered, Log Feet, 10 X 8 1/4 In. 225.00
Pressed Glass, Classic, Compote, Covered, Open Feet, 7 1/2 In. 165.00
Pressed Glass, Classic, Compote, Covered, 9 1/2 In.High 150.00

Pressed Glass, Classic, Compote, Covered

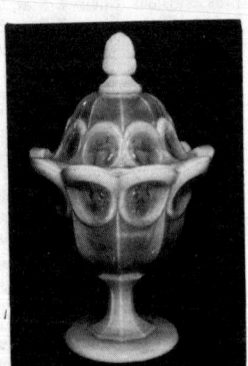

Pressed Glass, Colonial,
Goblet, Jefferson

Pressed Glass, Colonial,
Covered Sugar Bowl, Opalescent

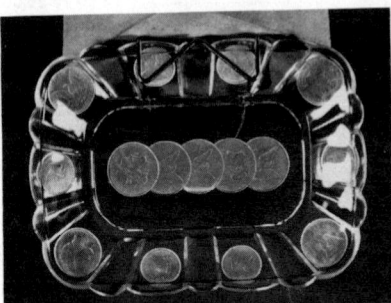

Pressed Glass, Coin, Bread Tray

Pressed Glass, Clover, Creamer, 3 1/2 In.

Pressed Glass, **Classic**, Goblet	145.00 To 150.00
Pressed Glass, **Classic**, Sauce, Branch Feet	20.00
Pressed Glass, **Classic**, Sauce, Open Log Feet	38.50
Pressed Glass, **Classic**, Spooner	75.00
Pressed Glass, **Classic**, Spooner, Open Log Feet	60.00 To 80.00
Pressed Glass, **Classic**, Sugar	40.00
Pressed Glass, **Classic**, Sugar, Footed	55.00
Pressed Glass, **Clear Block**, Bowl, Berry, 8 In.	7.00
Pressed Glass, **Clear Block**, Wine	8.50
Pressed Glass, **Clear Circle**, Muffineer	20.00
Pressed Glass, **Clear Circle**, Tumbler, Juice	17.50
Pressed Glass, **Clear Diagonal Band**, Butter, Covered	15.00
Pressed Glass, **Clear Diagonal Band**, Creamer	16.00
Pressed Glass, **Clear Diagonal Band**, Goblet	12.00
Pressed Glass, **Clear Diagonal Band**, Sauce	3.75
Pressed Glass, **Clear Diagonal Band**, Sauce, Footed, 3 5/8 In.	6.50
Pressed Glass, **Clear Diagonal Band**, Wine	15.00
Pressed Glass, **Clear Dot**, Compote, 7 X 5 1/2 In.	55.00
Pressed Glass, **Clear Dot**, Tumbler	22.50
Pressed Glass, **Clear Panels With Cord Band**, Butter, Covered	23.75
Pressed Glass, **Clear Panels With Cord Band**, Cake Stand, 11 In.	18.00
Pressed Glass, **Clear Panels With Cord Band**, Goblet	11.50
Pressed Glass, **Clear Panels With Cord Band**, Plate, 7 1/4 In.	12.50

Pressed Glass, Clear Panels With Cord Band, Sauce, Footed, 3 1/2 In. 5.00
Pressed Glass, Clear Ribbon, Sauce, Footed, 3 1/2 In. 7.00
Pressed Glass, Clear Ribbon, Spooner 16.00
Pressed Glass, Cleat, Decanter, Quart 95.00
Pressed Glass, Cleat, Pitcher, Milk, Flint 75.00
Pressed Glass, Cleat, Pitcher, Water .... 125.00 To 145.00
Pressed Glass, Cleat, Pitcher, 9 In. 75.00
Pressed Glass, Clematis, Goblet .... 15.00 To 20.00
Pressed Glass, Cleopatra, Plate, Bread 65.00
Pressed Glass, Cleopatra, Platter, Blue, Hexagonal, 17 X 13 1/2 In. 65.00
Pressed Glass, Cleopatra, Spooner, Heads On Each Side 22.00
Pressed Glass, Climbing Ivy, Spill 40.00
Pressed Glass, Climbing Ivy, Spill, Color Decoration 50.00
Pressed Glass, Climbing Ivy, Spill, Flint 40.00
Pressed Glass, Climbing Ivy, Spooner 40.00
Pressed Glass, Climbing Ivy, Spooner, Color Decoration 50.00
Pressed Glass, Climbing Ivy, Spooner, Flint 40.00
Pressed Glass, Clio, Cake Stand, 10 In. 35.00
Pressed Glass, Clock, Butter, Covered 75.00
Pressed Glass, Clover, Creamer 10.00
Pressed Glass, Coachman's Cape, Goblet 10.50
Pressed Glass, Coachman's Cape, Goblet, Findlay 12.00
Pressed Glass, Coarse Rib, Eggcup, Flint 28.00
Pressed Glass, Coarse Zigzag, Compote, Stemmed, 8 X 7 In. 15.00
Pressed Glass, Coarse Zigzag, Creamer, Footed 6.50
Pressed Glass, Coin & Dewdrop, Goblet 5.00
Pressed Glass, Coin & Dewdrop, Pitcher, Water 12.50
Pressed Glass, Coin Dot, Tumbler, Milky Blue 22.50
Pressed Glass, Coin Spot, Muffineer, Blue 52.50
Pressed Glass, Colonial, Celery 70.00
Pressed Glass, Colonial, Celery, Flint 65.00
Pressed Glass, Colonial, Champagne 60.00
Pressed Glass, Colonial, Champagne, Flint .... 50.00 To 55.00
Pressed Glass, Colonial, Cordial 5.00
Pressed Glass, Colonial, Eggcup .... 4.00 To 5.00
Pressed Glass, Colonial, Goblet 38.00
Pressed Glass, Colonial, Goblet, Flint .... 26.00 To 38.00
Pressed Glass, Colonial, Goblet, Knob Stem, Flint 37.00
Pressed Glass, Colonial, Slipper, Frosted, 6 In. 32.50
Pressed Glass, Colonial, Tumbler 52.00
Pressed Glass, Colonial, Tumbler, Footed, Flint 30.00
Pressed Glass, Colonial, Water Set, Miniature, 7 Piece 28.50
Pressed Glass, Colonial, Whiskey Taster, Footed, Flint 10.00
Pressed Glass, Colonial, Wine .... 5.00 To 50.00
Pressed Glass, Colonial, Wine, Flint 45.00
Pressed Glass, Colorado, Berry Set, 5 Piece 45.00
Pressed Glass, Colorado, Bowl, Berry, Green, Beaded Edge, 4 3/4 In. 13.50
Pressed Glass, Colorado, Bowl, Blue, Boat Shape, 6 1/2 In. 38.00
Pressed Glass, Colorado, Bowl, Blue, Crimped Edge, 5 In. 22.00
Pressed Glass, Colorado, Bowl, Fruit, Green, Pedestal Foot, Ruffled, 9 1/2 In. 37.50
Pressed Glass, Colorado, Bowl, Green, Fluted, Footed, 10 In. 30.00
Pressed Glass, Colorado, Bowl, Green, Gold Trim, Ruffled, 5 1/2 In. 30.00
Pressed Glass, Colorado, Bowl, Green, Gold, Footed, Tricornered, 6 1/2 In. 24.00
Pressed Glass, Colorado, Bowl, Shallow, 6 1/2 In. 10.00
Pressed Glass, Colorado, Bowl, 6 In. 8.00
Pressed Glass, Colorado, Butter, Footed 25.00
Pressed Glass, Colorado, Creamer, Blue, Gold Trim 35.00
Pressed Glass, Colorado, Creamer, Etched Stars 30.00
Pressed Glass, Colorado, Creamer, Master, Green, Gold Trim 50.00
Pressed Glass, Colorado, Dish, Mint, Footed 10.00
Pressed Glass, Colorado, Mug, Ruby Stained 20.00
Pressed Glass, Colorado, Plate, Green, Gold Edge, 8 In. 25.00
Pressed Glass, Colorado, Sauce, Blue, Gold Trim, Crimped 30.00
Pressed Glass, Colorado, Table Set, Green, Gold Trim, 3 Piece 195.00
Pressed Glass, Colorado, Table Set, Green, 4 Piece 375.00
Pressed Glass, Colorado, Toothpick, Blue, Gold Feet 27.00

Pressed Glass, Colorado, Toothpick, Blue, Rose Bowl Shape, Gold Trim, 3 In. 30.00
Pressed Glass, Colorado, Toothpick, Emerald Green 18.00
Pressed Glass, Colorado, Toothpick, Green, Gold Trim .... 25.00 To 29.50
Pressed Glass, Colorado, Toothpick, Ruby Stained 17.50
Pressed Glass, Colorado, Wine, Ruby Stained 20.00
Pressed Glass, Colossus, Cake Stand, 10 In. 17.00
Pressed Glass, Colossus, Goblet .... 16.00 To 25.00
Pressed Glass, Colossus, Sugar, Covered 25.00
Pressed Glass, Columbian Coin, Butter, Coin Finial, 1492-1892, Square 135.00
Pressed Glass, Columbian Coin, Butter, Silver Lid, Gold Coins 49.50
Pressed Glass, Columbian Coin, Compote, Covered, Etched Berry & Leaf, 11 In. 18.00
Pressed Glass, Columbian Coin, Dish, Pickle 85.00
Pressed Glass, Columbian Coin, Inkwell, Double, C.1860, Iron Base 55.00
Pressed Glass, Columbian Coin, Mug, 2 3/4 X 4 3/4 In. 45.00
Pressed Glass, Columbian Coin, Pitcher, Frosted Collar, 10 In. 95.00
Pressed Glass, Columbian Coin, Sugar, Covered, Gold Coins 125.00
Pressed Glass, Columbian Coin, Toothpick 49.00
Pressed Glass, Columbian Coin, Tumbler 72.00
Pressed Glass, Columbian Exposition, Goblet .... 12.50 To 15.00
Pressed Glass, Columbus & Santa Maria, Mug, 1893 Exposition 75.00
Pressed Glass, Comet, Goblet .... 8.00 To 65.00
Pressed Glass, Comet, Goblet, Flint .... 52.50 To 70.00
Pressed Glass, Comet, Tumbler 100.00
Pressed Glass, Comet, Tumbler, Flint 90.00
Pressed Glass, Comet, Tumbler, Whiskey, Flint 80.00
Compact, see Snail
Pressed Glass, Connecticut Flute, Goblet, Flint 14.00
Pressed Glass, Connecticut Flute, Wine 6.00
Pressed Glass, Constitution, Plate, Bread, "Give Us This Day-, " 12 3/4 In. 60.00
Pressed Glass, Conventional Band, Goblet, Frosted & Clear 10.00
Pressed Glass, Coral Gables, Goblet 9.00
Pressed Glass, Corcoran, Goblet 12.50
Pressed Glass, Cord & Tassel, Cake Stand, High Standard, 10 In. 45.00
Pressed Glass, Cord & Tassel, Goblet .... 12.00 To 15.00
Pressed Glass, Cord & Tassel, Goblet, Gentleman's 18.50
Pressed Glass, Cord & Tassel, Goblet, Lady's 17.50
Pressed Glass, Cord & Tassel, Saltshaker, Frosted 8.00
Pressed Glass, Cord & Tassel, Saltshaker, Green, Double, Satin Finish 21.00
Pressed Glass, Cord & Tassel, Saltshaker, Pink, Double, Satin Finish 21.00
Pressed Glass, Cord & Tassel, Spooner 30.00
Pressed Glass, Cord & Tassel, Sugar 35.00
Pressed Glass, Cord & Tassel, Tumbler, Bar .... 30.00 To 45.00
Pressed Glass, Cord & Tassel, Wine 15.00
Pressed Glass, Cord Drapery, Berry Set, 5 Piece .... 30.00 To 65.00
Pressed Glass, Cord Drapery, Bowl, Footed, Shallow, 10 In. 8.00
Pressed Glass, Cord Drapery, Cake Stand, 9 In. 35.00
Pressed Glass, Cord Drapery, Pitcher, Water .... 35.00 To 55.00
Pressed Glass, Cord Drapery, Pitcher, 8 In. 25.00
Pressed Glass, Cord Drapery, Plate, Cake 20.00
Pressed Glass, Cord Drapery, Plate, Cake, Amber, Greentown 100.00
Pressed Glass, Cord Drapery, Sauce .... 5.50 To 10.00
Pressed Glass, Cord Drapery, Sauce, Greentown 7.50
Pressed Glass, Cord Drapery, Tumbler, Amber 75.00
Pressed Glass, Cord Rosette, Goblet 18.50
Pressed Glass, Cordova, Bottle, Dresser 20.00
Pressed Glass, Cordova, Creamer 12.00
Pressed Glass, Cordova, Cup, Punch 7.00
Pressed Glass, Cordova, Pitcher, Water, 9 1/2 In. 30.00
Pressed Glass, Cordova, Spooner 12.50
Pressed Glass, Cordova, Toothpick .... 8.50 To 14.50
Pressed Glass, Cornucopia, Pitcher, Water .... 35.00 To 65.00
Pressed Glass, Cornucopia, Tumbler 10.00
Pressed Glass, Cornucopia, Vase, C.1920, 5 In. 3.00
Pressed Glass, Cornucopia, Wine 13.00
Pressed Glass, Corrigan, Compote, High Standard, Ruffled, Findlay, 8 In. 45.00
Pressed Glass, Cottage, Butter, Covered .... 27.50 To 35.00

Pressed Glass, Cottage, Butter, Covered, Footed	20.00
Pressed Glass, Cottage, Cake Stand, 9 In.	20.00
Pressed Glass, Cottage, Compote, Jelly	5.00
Pressed Glass, Cottage, Creamer	12.50 To 15.00
Pressed Glass, Cottage, Goblet	15.00 To 18.50
Pressed Glass, Cottage, Pitcher, Water	34.00
Pressed Glass, Cottage, Pitcher, Water, Hand Forms Handle, C.1890	20.00
Pressed Glass, Cottage, Sugar & Creamer, Cover	35.00
Pressed Glass, Cradled Prisms, Creamer	10.00 To 15.00
Crane, see Stork	
Pressed Glass, Crane's-Bill, Creamer	12.50
Pressed Glass, Crazy Patch, Goblet	11.00
Pressed Glass, Creased Ashburton, Champagne	30.00
Pressed Glass, Creased Ashburton, Champagne, Flint	30.00
Pressed Glass, Creased Ashburton, Goblet	32.00
Pressed Glass, Creased Ashburton, Goblet, Flint	35.00
Pressed Glass, Crisscross, Cake Stand, Child's	26.00
Pressed Glass, Crisscross, Creamer	19.00
Pressed Glass, Crisscross, Spooner, Child's	20.00
Pressed Glass, Crisscross, Sugar, Covered	22.50
Pressed Glass, Crochet Band, Goblet	3.75 To 8.00
Crossbar & Finecut, see Ashman	
Pressed Glass, Crossed Pressed Leaf, Goblet	24.00
Pressed Glass, Crossed Shield, Sugar, Covered	25.00
Pressed Glass, Crow's-Foot, Butter, Covered	22.00
Pressed Glass, Crow's-Foot, Cake Stand	35.00
Pressed Glass, Crow's-Foot, Compote, 8 X 6 3/4 In.	26.00
Pressed Glass, Crow's-Foot, Creamer	10.50 To 25.00
Pressed Glass, Crow's-Foot, Goblet	28.50
Pressed Glass, Crow's-Foot, Sauce, Footed	5.00
Pressed Glass, Crow's-Foot, Sauce, 5 In.	5.00
Pressed Glass, Crow's-Foot, Sauce, 5 1/2 In.	7.50
Pressed Glass, Crow's-Foot, Spooner	10.50 To 20.00
Pressed Glass, Cryptic, Compote, Covered, Low, Collared Base, 8 In.	45.00
Pressed Glass, Cryptic, Goblet	18.00 To 20.00
Pressed Glass, Cryptic, Saltshaker	6.00
Pressed Glass, Crystal Band, Goblet	8.75
Pressed Glass, Crystal Wedding, Banana Stand	60.00
Pressed Glass, Crystal Wedding, Cake Stand, 10 In.	45.00
Pressed Glass, Crystal Wedding, Creamer, Ruby Stained	25.00 To 85.00
Pressed Glass, Crystal Wedding, Dish, Pickle, Rectangular, 7 1/2 X 4 In.	15.00
Pressed Glass, Crystal Wedding, Goblet	40.00
Pressed Glass, Crystal Wedding, Spooner, Ruby Stained	25.00
Pressed Glass, Crystal Wedding, Sugar, Covered, Ruby Stained	40.00 To 90.00
Pressed Glass, Crystal Wedding, Tumbler, Frosted	28.75
Pressed Glass, Crystal Wedding, Tumbler, Red Stained	38.00
Pressed Glass, Crystal, Banded, Goblet, Lady's, Knob Stem	16.50

Pressed Glass, Columbian Coin, Salt & Pepper

Pressed Glass, Cupid & Venus, Bread Plate

Pressed Glass, Crystal, Celery	30.00
Pressed Glass, Crystal, Celery, Flint	15.00
Pressed Glass, Crystal, Champagne	3.00
Pressed Glass, Crystal, Champagne, Flint	19.50
Pressed Glass, Crystal, Creamer	7.00
Pressed Glass, Crystal, Creamer, Knob Stem	39.00
Pressed Glass, Crystal, Eggcup, Flint	35.00
Pressed Glass, Crystal, Goblet	5.00 To 8.00
Pressed Glass, Crystal, Goblet, Flint	16.00 To 18.00
Pressed Glass, Crystal, Tumbler, Footed, Flint	18.00
Pressed Glass, Crystal, Wine, Flint	19.00 To 25.00
Cube & Diamond, see Milton	
Pressed Glass, Cube & Double Fan, Sauce	4.50
Cube & Fan, see Pineapple & Fan	
Pressed Glass, Cube, Butter, Covered, Square Stem	15.00
Pressed Glass, Cube, Celery	18.00
Pressed Glass, Cube, Goblet	4.50 To 15.00
Pressed Glass, Cube, Goblet, Amethestine, Etched, Square Stem	24.00
Pressed Glass, Cube, Goblet, Purple Hue, Etched, Square Stem	28.00
Pressed Glass, Cube, Rose Bowl, 7 In.	20.00
Pressed Glass, Cube, Wine	6.00
Pressed Glass, Cupid & Venus, Celery, 8 1/2 In.	30.00
Pressed Glass, Cupid & Venus, Compote, Scalloped Edge, 8 3/4 In.	27.50
Pressed Glass, Cupid & Venus, Cordial	60.00
Pressed Glass, Cupid & Venus, Creamer	31.50
Pressed Glass, Cupid & Venus, Jar, Jam	45.00
Pressed Glass, Cupid & Venus, Jar, Marmalade	45.00
Pressed Glass, Cupid & Venus, Mug, 3 1/2 In.	16.50
Pressed Glass, Cupid & Venus, Pitcher, Milk	35.00 To 45.00
Pressed Glass, Cupid & Venus, Pitcher, Water	32.00 To 75.00
Pressed Glass, Cupid & Venus, Pitcher, 7 1/2 In.	30.00
Pressed Glass, Cupid & Venus, Plate, Bread	20.00 To 25.00
Pressed Glass, Cupid & Venus, Plate, Bread, Round	25.00
Pressed Glass, Cupid & Venus, Plate, Cake	33.00
Pressed Glass, Cupid & Venus, Plate, 10 1/2 In.	26.00
Pressed Glass, Cupid & Venus, Salt, Individual, Amethyst	7.00
Pressed Glass, Cupid & Venus, Sauce, Footed, 3 1/2 In.	3.00 To 8.00
Pressed Glass, Cupid & Venus, Sauce, Footed, 3 3/4 In.	6.00
Pressed Glass, Cupid & Venus, Sauce, Footed, 4 In.	7.50
Pressed Glass, Cupid & Venus, Sauce, Footed, 4 1/2 In.	5.00
Pressed Glass, Cupid & Venus, Sauce, 3 1/2 In.	5.00
Pressed Glass, Cupid & Venus, Sauce, 4 1/2 In.	6.00
Pressed Glass, Cupid & Venus, Spooner	20.00 To 40.00
Pressed Glass, Cupid & Venus, Spooner, Scalloped Rim	35.00
Pressed Glass, Cupid & Venus, Sugar	18.00
Pressed Glass, Cupid & Venus, Wine	35.00 To 55.00
Pressed Glass, Cupid's Hunt, Butter, Covered, Etched	24.00
Pressed Glass, Cupid's Hunt, Compote, 7 X 5 In.	25.00
Pressed Glass, Cupid's Hunt, Compote, 7 3/4 X 5 In.	24.50
Pressed Glass, Cupid's Hunt, Plate, Bread	35.00
Pressed Glass, Cupid's Hunt, Relish	18.50
Pressed Glass, Cupid's Hunt, Relish, Oval	16.00
Pressed Glass, Cupid's Hunt, Sauce, Footed, 4 In.	10.00
Pressed Glass, Curled Leaf, Spooner	16.50
Pressed Glass, Currant, Celery	23.00 To 25.00
Pressed Glass, Currant, Compote, Tree-Branch Finial, 8 In.	45.00
Pressed Glass, Currant, Eggcup	12.00 To 18.00
Pressed Glass, Currant, Goblet	20.00
Pressed Glass, Currant, Goblet, Double Row	18.00
Pressed Glass, Currant, Sauce, Footed	13.00
Pressed Glass, Currant, Spooner	18.00
Pressed Glass, Currant, Wine	20.00 To 22.00
Pressed Glass, Currier & Ives, Bowl, Berry, Oval	29.50
Pressed Glass, Currier & Ives, Bowl, Boat Shape, 10 X 5 In.	27.00
Pressed Glass, Currier & Ives, Bowl, Boat Shape, 10 X 5 3/4 In.	28.00

Pressed Glass, Currier & Ives, Decanter, Wine, Faceted Stopper	35.00
Pressed Glass, Currier & Ives, Goblet	15.00
Pressed Glass, Currier & Ives, Plate, Bread, Balky Mule	37.50
Pressed Glass, Currier & Ives, Plate, Bread, Dog & Rabbit	40.00
Pressed Glass, Currier & Ives, Relish	14.50
Pressed Glass, Currier & Ives, Syrup	28.00 To 37.50
Pressed Glass, Currier & Ives, Tray, Water, Blue, Balky Mule, 12 In.	65.00
Pressed Glass, Currier & Ives, Tray, Water, Blue, Basket Weave, 12 1/2 In.	49.00
Pressed Glass, Currier & Ives, Tray, Water, Blue, Frontier Scene, 12 1/2 In.	49.00
Pressed Glass, Currier & Ives, Wine	12.50 To 20.00
Pressed Glass, Curtain Tieback, Goblet	9.00 To 14.50
Pressed Glass, Curtain Tieback, Goblet, Round Base	15.00
Pressed Glass, Curtain Tieback, Pitcher, Water	20.00
Pressed Glass, Curtain Tieback, Saucer, Green	6.00
Pressed Glass, Curtain Tieback, Sugar, Covered	30.00
Pressed Glass, Curtain, Celery	14.00
Pressed Glass, Curtain, Creamer, 4 1/2 In.	15.00
Pressed Glass, Curtain, Goblet, Flint	33.00
Pressed Glass, Curtain, Saltshaker	5.00
Pressed Glass, Curtain, Sauce, Footed, 4 1/2 In.	5.00
Pressed Glass, Curtain, Sugar & Creamer, Pedestal	25.00
Pressed Glass, Curtain, Vase, 9 In., Pair	35.00
Pressed Glass, Cut Log, Celery	17.50 To 27.50
Pressed Glass, Cut Log, Compote, Covered, 8 In.	52.50
Pressed Glass, Cut Log, Compote, Jelly	12.50
Pressed Glass, Cut Log, Compote, 8 In.	28.50
Pressed Glass, Cut Log, Creamer, Individual	12.00 To 12.50
Pressed Glass, Cut Log, Creamer, 5 In.	15.00
Pressed Glass, Cut Log, Doughnut Stand, 9 X 6 In.	35.00
Pressed Glass, Cut Log, Goblet	16.50 To 28.50
Pressed Glass, Cut Log, Mug, 3 1/4 In.	13.00 To 18.00
Pressed Glass, Cut Log, Pitcher, Water	59.50
Pressed Glass, Cut Log, Relish, Footed, 5 In.	13.50
Pressed Glass, Cut Log, Sauce, Large	18.50
Pressed Glass, Cut Log, Spooner	14.50
Pressed Glass, Cut Log, Sugar, Covered	38.00
Pressed Glass, Cut Log, Tumbler	22.00
Pressed Glass, Cut Log, Wine	12.00 To 25.00
Pressed Glass, Cut Mirror, Champagne, Flint	35.00
Pressed Glass, Cyclone, Goblet, Etched	15.00
Pressed Glass, Cyclone, Tumbler	7.50
Czarina, see Diamond Point & Fan	
Pressed Glass, Dahlia With Petal, Tumbler, Green, Gold Trim	23.50
Pressed Glass, Dahlia With Petal, Wine, Green, Gold Trim	20.00
Pressed Glass, Dahlia, Bowl, Banana, Green, Gold, 12 1/2 In.	25.00
Pressed Glass, Dahlia, Compote, Footed, 4 X 6 In.	12.50
Pressed Glass, Dahlia, Creamer	10.00 To 20.00
Pressed Glass, Dahlia, Eggcup, Double	45.00

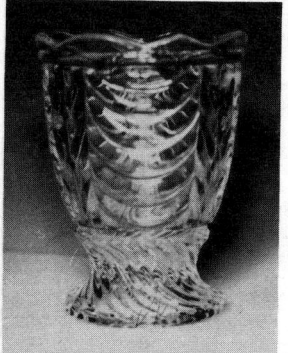

Pressed Glass,
Curtain, Spooner

Pressed Glass, Daisy Whorl
With Diamond Band, Goblet

Pressed Glass, Dahlia, Goblet .... 25.00 To 27.50
Pressed Glass, Dahlia, Mug .... 19.00 To 24.50
Pressed Glass, Dahlia, Mug, Child's, Apple Green, 2 3/4 In. 20.00
Pressed Glass, Dahlia, Mug, Miniature 25.00
Pressed Glass, Dahlia, Pitcher, Milk, 1 1/2 Quart 30.00
Pressed Glass, Dahlia, Pitcher, Water .... 20.00 To 25.00
Pressed Glass, Dahlia, Pitcher, 8 3/4 In. 16.00
Pressed Glass, Dahlia, Plate, Cake, Closed Handles, 9 In. 20.00
Pressed Glass, Dahlia, Plate, Cake, Handled, 9 In. .... 13.50 To 22.50
Pressed Glass, Dahlia, Plate, Handled, 9 In. 12.50
Pressed Glass, Dahlia, Plate, Handled, 10 In. 18.00
Pressed Glass, Dahlia, Saltshaker, Green Opaque, Beaded 18.50
Pressed Glass, Dahlia, Sauce, Amber 16.00
Pressed Glass, Dahlia, Sauce, Footed 8.00
Pressed Glass, Dahlia, Sauce, 4 1/2 In. 5.00
Pressed Glass, Dahlia, Spooner .... 9.00 To 14.00
Pressed Glass, Dahlia, Wine 22.00
Pressed Glass, Daisies In Oval Panels, Bowl, Berry, Green Eyes, 8 In. 20.00
Pressed Glass, Daisies In Oval Panels, Bowl, 8 1/4 In. 11.50
Pressed Glass, Daisies In Oval Panels, Cake Stand, 9 In. 23.50
Pressed Glass, Daisies In Oval Panels, Creamer, 3 1/2 In. 17.00
Pressed Glass, Daisies In Oval Panels, Goblet .... 7.00 To 14.50
Pressed Glass, Daisies In Oval Panels, Goblet, Gold Trim 18.00
Pressed Glass, Daisies In Oval Panels, Mug 9.50
Pressed Glass, Daisies In Oval Panels, Pitcher, Milk, 8 1/2 In. .... 24.00 To 35.00
Pressed Glass, Daisies In Oval Panels, Pitcher, 8 1/2 In. 24.00
Pressed Glass, Daisies In Oval Panels, Sauce 4.00
Pressed Glass, Daisies In Oval Panels, Toothpick 12.50
Pressed Glass, Daisies In Oval Panels, Tumbler 5.00
Pressed Glass, Daisies In Oval Panels, Tumbler, Lemonade, Handled 7.50
Pressed Glass, Daisies In Oval Panels, Vase, 4 1/4 In. 9.50
Pressed Glass, Daisy & Block, Goblet .... 4.00 To 13.00
Pressed Glass, Daisy & Block, Tumbler, Blue Blocks 27.50
Pressed Glass, Daisy & Button Star Block, Spooner 24.00
Pressed Glass, Daisy & Button With Almond Band, Butter, Covered 35.00
Pressed Glass, Daisy & Button With Almond Band, Pitcher, 7 In. 25.00
Pressed Glass, Daisy & Button With Amber Panels, Creamer, Applied Handle 85.00
Pressed Glass, Daisy & Button With Amber Panels, Sugar, Covered 80.00
Pressed Glass, Daisy & Button With Crossbar, Bowl, Amber, Collared, 8 In. 45.00
Pressed Glass, Daisy & Button With Crossbar, Bowl, Blue, Rectangular, 9 In. 24.50
Pressed Glass, Daisy & Button With Crossbar, Celery 16.00
Pressed Glass, Daisy & Button With Crossbar, Celery, Amber 24.50
Pressed Glass, Daisy & Button With Crossbar, Celery, Blue 26.00
Pressed Glass, Daisy & Button With Crossbar, Creamer, Individual, Amber 22.50
Pressed Glass, Daisy & Button With Crossbar, Goblet 18.50
Pressed Glass, Daisy & Button With Crossbar, Goblet, Amber 35.00
Pressed Glass, Daisy & Button With Crossbar, Pitcher, Amber, 8 In. 45.00
Pressed Glass, Daisy & Button With Crossbar, Pitcher, Milk, Amber, Pedestal 45.00
Pressed Glass, Daisy & Button With Crossbar, Pitcher, Water, Amber 32.00
Pressed Glass, Daisy & Button With Crossbar, Plate, Bread, 7 X 10 In. 12.00
Pressed Glass, Daisy & Button With Crossbar, Sauce, Amber, Footed 12.00
Pressed Glass, Daisy & Button With Crossbar, Tumbler, Amber 30.00
Pressed Glass, Daisy & Button With Finecut Panels, Pitcher, Water 40.00
Pressed Glass, Daisy & Button With Narcissus, Decanter, Wine 50.00
Pressed Glass, Daisy & Button With Narcissus, Goblet 18.00
Pressed Glass, Daisy & Button With Narcissus, Tray, 10 1/2 In. 23.00
Pressed Glass, Daisy & Button With Narcissus, Wine 8.50
    Daisy & Button With Oval Panels, see Hartley
Pressed Glass, Daisy & Button With Pointed Panel, Goblet, Amber 20.00
Pressed Glass, Daisy & Button With Scroll Panel, Goblet 10.00
Pressed Glass, Daisy & Button With Thumbprint, Cake Stand, Amber, 11 In. 80.00
Pressed Glass, Daisy & Button With Thumbprint, Goblet, Amber 23.00
Pressed Glass, Daisy & Button With Thumbprint, Sauce, Blue Prints, Footed 8.75
Pressed Glass, Daisy & Button With Thumbprint, Tumbler 14.00
Pressed Glass, Daisy & Button With V Ornament, Butter Pat 8.50
Pressed Glass, Daisy & Button With V Ornament, Celery .... 13.50 To 18.00

Pressed Glass, Daisy & Button With V Ornament, Celery, Crimped Top	25.00
Pressed Glass, Daisy & Button With V Ornament, Pitcher, Water	32.00
Pressed Glass, Daisy & Button With V Ornament, Salt, Blue, Top	25.00
Pressed Glass, Daisy & Button With V Ornament, Sauce	4.00 To 5.00
Pressed Glass, Daisy & Button With V Ornament, Spooner	24.00
Pressed Glass, Daisy & Button With V Ornament, Spooner, Amber, 4 1/2 In.	35.00
Pressed Glass, Daisy & Button With V Ornament, Toothpick	14.50
Pressed Glass, Daisy & Button With V Ornament, Toothpick, Amber	25.00
Daisy & Button, see also Paneled Daisy & Button	
Pressed Glass, Daisy & Button, Bottle, Cologne, Square, 8 In., Pair	37.50
Pressed Glass, Daisy & Button, Bowl & Stand, Single Panel, Amber, 11 In.	145.00
Pressed Glass, Daisy & Button, Bowl, Amber, Oval, 7 X 12 In.	28.00
Pressed Glass, Daisy & Button, Bowl, Amber, 8 Sided, Scalloped, 9 1/2 In.	40.00
Pressed Glass, Daisy & Button, Bowl, Berry, Amber, Square, C.1850, 4 1/2 In.	15.00
Pressed Glass, Daisy & Button, Bowl, Berry, Amber, Square, C.1850, 8 1/2 In.	39.00
Pressed Glass, Daisy & Button, Bowl, Blue, Oval, 9 X 12 X 6 In.	95.00
Pressed Glass, Daisy & Button, Bowl, Canary, Boat Shape, 10 In.	28.00
Pressed Glass, Daisy & Button, Bowl, Dark Blue, Oval, 5 In.	18.00
Pressed Glass, Daisy & Button, Bowl, Emerald Green, 12 In.	37.50
Pressed Glass, Daisy & Button, Bowl, Finger	9.00
Pressed Glass, Daisy & Button, Bowl, 5 X 3 1/2 In.	9.00
Pressed Glass, Daisy & Button, Bowl, 6 1/4 X 4 1/4 In.	9.00
Pressed Glass, Daisy & Button, Bowl, 9 In.	22.50
Pressed Glass, Daisy & Button, Bowl, 9 3/4 In.	14.00
Pressed Glass, Daisy & Button, Butter Pat, Blue	8.00
Pressed Glass, Daisy & Button, Butter Pat, Triangular	5.00
Pressed Glass, Daisy & Button, Butter, Amber, Covered, Stove	46.00
Pressed Glass, Daisy & Button, Celery	17.50
Pressed Glass, Daisy & Button, Celery, Amber, Boat Shape	45.00
Pressed Glass, Daisy & Button, Compote, Amber, Pedestal, 10 In.	67.50
Pressed Glass, Daisy & Button, Condiment Set, Glass Holder, 3 Piece	47.50
Pressed Glass, Daisy & Button, Creamer, Amber, Applied Air Twist Handle	150.00
Pressed Glass, Daisy & Button, Creamer, Green, Miniature	12.00
Pressed Glass, Daisy & Button, Dish, Bone, Amber	15.00
Pressed Glass, Daisy & Button, Dish, Ice Cream, Amber Daisies	15.00
Pressed Glass, Daisy & Button, Jar, Powder, Covered	15.00
Pressed Glass, Daisy & Button, Pen & Pencil Holder, 8 1/2 X 2 3/4 In.	35.00

Pressed Glass, Daisies In Oval, Goblet

Pressed Glass, Daisy & Button
With Thumbprint, Goblet

Pressed Glass,
Deer & Dog, Goblet

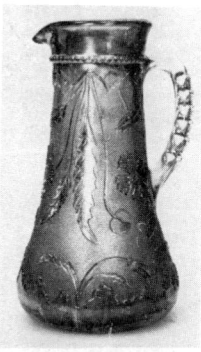

Pressed Glass,
Daisy & Button
With Crossbar, Goblet

Pressed Glass,
Delaware, Pitcher,
Rose Color, 9 1/2 In.

Pressed Glass, Daisy & Button, Pitcher, Golden Amber, 9 In.High 72.50
Pressed Glass, Daisy & Button, Plate, Bread, Amber, Open Handles, 13 X 9 In. 24.00
Pressed Glass, Daisy & Button, Relish, Amber, Boat Shape, C.1850, 9 1/2 In. 29.00
Pressed Glass, Daisy & Button, Salt & Pepper, Sapphire Blue, Peg Bases 20.00
Pressed Glass, Daisy & Button, Salt, Amber 6.50
Pressed Glass, Daisy & Button, Salt, Amber, Footed, Pair 21.50
Pressed Glass, Daisy & Button, Salt, Blue, Anvil Shape 55.00
Pressed Glass, Daisy & Button, Salt, Blue, Hat Shape 13.50
Pressed Glass, Daisy & Button, Sauce, Amber 10.00
Pressed Glass, Daisy & Button, Sauce, Triangular 4.00
Pressed Glass, Daisy & Button, Slipper, Amber, Patent 1886, 4 1/2 In. 16.00
Pressed Glass, Daisy & Button, Slipper, Blue, Bow, 5 1/2 In. 48.00
Pressed Glass, Daisy & Button, Slipper, Blue, Bow, 5 3/4 In. 55.00
Pressed Glass, Daisy & Button, Slipper, Blue, Cat's Head, 5 In. 16.00
Pressed Glass, Daisy & Button, Slipper, Blue, 3 1/4 In. 30.00
Pressed Glass, Daisy & Button, Slipper, Deep Blue, Dated, 7 In. 30.00
Pressed Glass, Daisy & Button, Slipper, 5 1/2 In. 16.00
Pressed Glass, Daisy & Button, Spooner, Amber, Scalloped Top, C.1850 .... 32.00
Pressed Glass, Daisy & Button, Spooner, Blue 39.50
Pressed Glass, Daisy & Button, Sugar, Sapphire Blue, Covered, Barrel Shape 35.00
Pressed Glass, Daisy & Button, Sugar, 4 X 3 In. 18.00
Pressed Glass, Daisy & Button, Syrup, Blue 59.00
Pressed Glass, Daisy & Button, Tankard, Golden Amber, Applied Handle, 9 In. 72.50
Pressed Glass, Daisy & Button, Toothpick, Amber, Hat Shape, C.1850 .... 18.00
Pressed Glass, Daisy & Button, Toothpick, Amber, Hat Shape, 2 1/2 In. 25.00
Pressed Glass, Daisy & Button, Toothpick, Amber, Hat Shape, 3 3/4 In. 40.00
Pressed Glass, Daisy & Button, Toothpick, Blue, Hat Shape .... 12.50 To 18.00
Pressed Glass, Daisy & Button, Toothpick, Blue, Slipper Shape, 4 1/2 In. 30.00
Pressed Glass, Daisy & Button, Toothpick, Cobalt 20.00
Pressed Glass, Daisy & Button, Toothpick, Hat Shape, 2 1/2 In. 12.00
Pressed Glass, Daisy & Button, Toothpick, Red Stained Buttons, Scalloped 35.00
Pressed Glass, Daisy & Button, Toothpick, Ruby Stained 35.00
Pressed Glass, Daisy & Button, Tray, Sky Blue, 11 X 8 In. 27.50
Pressed Glass, Daisy & Button, Tray, Water, Canary, Handled, 12 1/2 In. 45.00
Pressed Glass, Daisy & Button, Tumbler, Juice, Amber, 4 In. 13.50
Pressed Glass, Daisy & Diamond, Compote, Fruit, Gold Flashing, 5 In. 25.00
Pressed Glass, Daisy & Stripe, Goblet 7.50
Pressed Glass, Daisy & Stripe, Wine 22.00
Pressed Glass, Daisy Block, Goblet 9.00
Pressed Glass, Daisy In Diamond, Creamer, Miniature 9.30
Pressed Glass, Daisy In Diamond, Pitcher, Water 28.50
Pressed Glass, Daisy In Diamond, Saltshaker 12.50
Pressed Glass, Daisy, Barred, Goblet .... 10.00 To 15.00
Pressed Glass, Dakota, Bowl, Ice Cream, Etched 16.00
Pressed Glass, Dakota, Butter 38.50
Pressed Glass, Dakota, Butter, Covered .... 29.00 To 30.00
Pressed Glass, Dakota, Butter, Covered, Etched 45.00
Pressed Glass, Dakota, Butter, Etched 30.00
Pressed Glass, Dakota, Cake Stand, 7 X 10 1/2 In. 28.00
Pressed Glass, Dakota, Cake Stand, 8 In. 24.00
Pressed Glass, Dakota, Celery .... 24.00 To 25.00
Pressed Glass, Dakota, Celery, Etched Bird On Cherry Branch .... 30.00 To 45.00
Pressed Glass, Dakota, Celery, Etched Swan 36.00
Pressed Glass, Dakota, Celery, Etched, Pedestal 32.00
Pressed Glass, Dakota, Celery, Scalloped Rim, 8 1/2 In. 14.50
Pressed Glass, Dakota, Compote, Etched, 5 In. 18.50
Pressed Glass, Dakota, Compote, Etched, 7 In. 35.00
Pressed Glass, Dakota, Compote, High Standard, 6 1/2 In. 30.00
Pressed Glass, Dakota, Compote, Jelly, Etched Fern & Berry, Covered 55.00
Pressed Glass, Dakota, Compote, 7 In. .... 24.50 To 35.00
Pressed Glass, Dakota, Creamer, Etched 55.00
Pressed Glass, Dakota, Goblet .... 15.00 To 27.00
Pressed Glass, Dakota, Goblet, Etched Fern & Berry .... 28.00 To 32.00
Pressed Glass, Dakota, Goblet, Etched Floral & Leaf 15.00
Pressed Glass, Dakota, Goblet, Etched Leaf, Ruby Stained 75.00
Pressed Glass, Dakota, Goblet, Etched Ruby Top .... 35.00 To 37.50

Pressed Glass, Dakota, Goblet, Ruby Stained 30.00
Pressed Glass, Dakota, Pitcher, Milk, Etched, 7 1/4 In. 55.00
Pressed Glass, Dakota, Pitcher, Water, Etched Floral & Leaf 32.50
Pressed Glass, Dakota, Pitcher, Wine, Etched Fern & Berry, 9 X 3 In. 65.00
Pressed Glass, Dakota, Pitcher, Wine, 2 3/4 In. Top Diameter, 7 1/2 In. 55.00
Pressed Glass, Dakota, Salt 6.50
Pressed Glass, Dakota, Salt, Amber 16.50
Pressed Glass, Dakota, Salt, Green 16.50
Pressed Glass, Dakota, Sauce, Footed, 3 3/4 In. 7.50
Pressed Glass, Dakota, Sherbet, Footed 6.00
Pressed Glass, Dakota, Spooner, Pedestal 19.50
Pressed Glass, Dakota, Sugar, Etched Fern & Berry 25.00
Pressed Glass, Dakota, Sugar, Etched, Covered, 9 1/2 In. 30.00
Pressed Glass, Dakota, Tankard, Etched Oak Leaf, Quart 50.00
Pressed Glass, Dakota, Tumbler .... 28.00 To 35.00
Pressed Glass, Dakota, Tumbler, Etched .... 38.00 To 38.50
Pressed Glass, Dakota, Tumbler, Ruby Stained .... 22.00 To 35.00
Pressed Glass, Dakota, Vase, F.& B., 7 In. 22.50
Pressed Glass, Dakota, Wine .... 11.00 To 22.50
Pressed Glass, Dakota, Wine, Etched Maple Leaf .... 27.50 To 30.00
Pressed Glass, Dancing Girl, Cordial, Pedestal 6.50
Pressed Glass, Dart, Compote, Covered, High Standard, 8 1/2 In. 45.00
Pressed Glass, Dart, Sauce, Footed 2.00
Pressed Glass, Dart, Sugar, Covered 25.00
Pressed Glass, Deep Star, Tumbler, Child's 8.00
Pressed Glass, Deer & Dog, Goblet .... 55.00 To 62.00
Pressed Glass, Deer & Dog, Goblet, Etched 75.00
Pressed Glass, Deer & Dog, Mug, Child's 50.00
Pressed Glass, Deer & Dog, Pitcher, Water 75.00
Pressed Glass, Deer & Dog, Pitcher, Water, Applied Reeded Handle 55.00
Pressed Glass, Deer & Dog, Sauce, Footed 15.00
Pressed Glass, Deer & Dog, Sauce, Footed, Etched, 4 In. 12.00
Pressed Glass, Deer & Dog, Sugar, Setter Finial 65.00
Pressed Glass, Deer & Dog, Table Set, 3 Piece 95.00
Pressed Glass, Deer & Lily Of The Valley, Goblet 47.50
Pressed Glass, Deer & Oak Tree, Pitcher, Water .... 68.00 To 95.00
Pressed Glass, Deer & Oak Tree, Pitcher, Water, Findlay 65.00
Pressed Glass, Deer & Pine Tree, Butter, Covered 65.00
Pressed Glass, Deer & Pine Tree, Cake Stand, 10 In. 37.00
Pressed Glass, Deer & Pine Tree, Compote, High Standard, 8 In. 22.50
Pressed Glass, Deer & Pine Tree, Goblet .... 33.00 To 35.00
Pressed Glass, Deer & Pine Tree, Mug .... 25.00 To 30.00
Pressed Glass, Deer & Pine Tree, Mug, Blue 35.00
Pressed Glass, Deer & Pine Tree, Mug, Green 15.00
Pressed Glass, Deer & Pine Tree, Pitcher, Water .... 35.00 To 60.00
Pressed Glass, Deer & Pine Tree, Plate, Bread .... 22.50 To 28.50
Pressed Glass, Deer & Pine Tree, Plate, Bread, Amber, 13 X 8 In. 35.00
Pressed Glass, Deer & Pine Tree, Plate, Bread, Amber, 13 X 9 In. 48.50
Pressed Glass, Deer & Pine Tree, Plate, Bread, Green 42.00
Pressed Glass, Deer & Pine Tree, Relish 23.00
Pressed Glass, Deer & Pine Tree, Sauce 10.00
Pressed Glass, Deer & Pine Tree, Sauce, Footed 17.50
Pressed Glass, Deer & Pine Tree, Spooner 25.00
Pressed Glass, Deer & Pine Tree, Tray, Water, 15 X 9 In. 75.00
Pressed Glass, Delaware, Banana Boat, Cranberry, 12 X 5 In. 60.00
Pressed Glass, Delaware, Banana Boat, Green, Gilt 68.50
Pressed Glass, Delaware, Banana Boat, Rose, Gilt .... 45.00 To 100.00
Pressed Glass, Delaware, Bowl, Berry, Green, Gold, 8 In. .... 30.00 To 32.50
Pressed Glass, Delaware, Bowl, Berry, Green, Ruffled Edge, 9 In. 22.50
Pressed Glass, Delaware, Bowl, Berry, Rose, Gold, Round 55.00
Pressed Glass, Delaware, Bowl, Green & Gold, 7 1/2 In. 38.50
Pressed Glass, Delaware, Bowl, Green, Gold Trim, Curved In, 8 In. 45.00
Pressed Glass, Delaware, Bowl, Green, Gold Trim, 8 In. 32.50
Pressed Glass, Delaware, Bowl, Green, Gold Trim, 8 1/2 In. .... 45.00 To 47.50
Pressed Glass, Delaware, Bowl, Oval, 5 1/4 X 3 1/4 In. 8.00
Pressed Glass, Delaware, Bowl, Red Stained, Gilt Trim, 8 1/4 In. 29.50

Pressed Glass, Delaware, Bowl, Rose, Gold Trim, 8 In. .... 32.00 To 67.50
Pressed Glass, Delaware, Bowl, Rose, Oval, 12 X 7 In. 50.00
Pressed Glass, Delaware, Box, Powder, Cranberry 145.00
Pressed Glass, Delaware, Butter, Green, Covered 55.00
Pressed Glass, Delaware, Butter, Rose, Covered 50.00
Pressed Glass, Delaware, Celery 30.00
Pressed Glass, Delaware, Celery, Green, Gold Trim 52.50
Pressed Glass, Delaware, Creamer, Gold 7.00
Pressed Glass, Delaware, Creamer, Green, Gold 30.00
Pressed Glass, Delaware, Creamer, Green, 4 In.High 48.00
Pressed Glass, Delaware, Cup, Punch, Cranberry .... 30.00 To 35.00
Pressed Glass, Delaware, Cup, Punch, Cranberry, Gold Trim 17.50
Pressed Glass, Delaware, Cup, Punch, Gold Trim 25.00
Pressed Glass, Delaware, Cup, Punch, Rose 25.00
Pressed Glass, Delaware, Cup, Punch, Rose, Gold Trim 25.00
Pressed Glass, Delaware, Dish, Sweetmeat, Cranberry, Boat Shape, Silver Frame 65.00
Pressed Glass, Delaware, Pitcher, Green, Bulbous, 7 X 5 In. 90.00
Pressed Glass, Delaware, Pitcher, Water, Green, Bulbous 95.00
Pressed Glass, Delaware, Pitcher, Water, Green, Gold Trim, 7 In. 85.00
Pressed Glass, Delaware, Pitcher, Water, Rose, Gold Trim .... 50.00 To 80.00
Pressed Glass, Delaware, Sauce 4.00
Pressed Glass, Delaware, Sauce, Boat Shape 10.00
Pressed Glass, Delaware, Sauce, Cranberry Flowers, Gold Trim 25.00
Pressed Glass, Delaware, Sauce, Green, Gold, 4 In. 25.00
Pressed Glass, Delaware, Sauce, Rose & Gold Trim 15.00
Pressed Glass, Delaware, Spooner, Cranberry Flowers, Gold Trim 42.00
Pressed Glass, Delaware, Sugar & Creamer, Green 125.00
Pressed Glass, Delaware, Sugar & Creamer, Green, Gold Trim 75.00
Pressed Glass, Delaware, Toothpick, Cranberry, Gold Trim 85.00
Pressed Glass, Delaware, Toothpick, Green 65.00
Pressed Glass, Delaware, Toothpick, Green, Gold 30.00
Pressed Glass, Delaware, Toothpick, Rose 75.00
Pressed Glass, Delaware, Tray, Dresser, Rose, Gold Trim 75.00
Pressed Glass, Delaware, Tumbler 20.00
Pressed Glass, Delaware, Tumbler, Cranberry 38.00
Pressed Glass, Delaware, Tumbler, Green 40.00
Pressed Glass, Delaware, Tumbler, Green, Gold Trim .... 25.00 To 35.00
Pressed Glass, Delaware, Tumbler, Rose, Barrel 42.00
Pressed Glass, Delaware, Tumbler, Rose, Gold Trim 30.00
Pressed Glass, Delaware, Tumbler, Ruby Stained 40.00
Pressed Glass, Delaware, Vase, Green, Gold Trim, Octagonal Top, 9 In. 110.00
Pressed Glass, Delaware, Vase, Green, Gold, 8 In., Pair 15.00
Pressed Glass, Delaware, Water Set, Green, Set Of 6 .... 195.00
Pressed Glass, Della Robbia, Sugar & Creamer, Flashed 20.00
Pressed Glass, Derigo Pear, Sauce 7.00
Pressed Glass, Dew & Raindrop, Bowl, Berry, Ruby Stained 50.00
Pressed Glass, Dew & Raindrop, Bowl, Berry, 8 1/4 In. 19.50
Pressed Glass, Dew & Raindrop, Cordial .... 5.50 To 9.00
Pressed Glass, Dew & Raindrop, Sauce 3.00
Pressed Glass, Dew & Raindrop, Spooner 25.00
Pressed Glass, Dew & Raindrop, Wine, 3 In. 25.00
Pressed Glass, Dewdrop & Coin, Goblet 17.00
Pressed Glass, Dewdrop Band, Goblet .... 5.00 To 12.50
Pressed Glass, Dewdrop Drapery, Goblet 11.00
Pressed Glass, Dewdrop In Points, Cake Stand, 10 1/4 In. 28.50
Pressed Glass, Dewdrop In Points, Pitcher, Water 22.50
Pressed Glass, Dewdrop In Points, Plate, Bread .... 13.00 To 19.50
Pressed Glass, Dewdrop In Points, Plate, Bread, Round, Handled 15.00
Pressed Glass, Dewdrop In Points, Plate, Vine Border, 9 In. 18.00
Pressed Glass, Dewdrop In Points, Plate, 8 3/4 In. 14.00
Pressed Glass, Dewdrop In Points, Plate, 9 In. 15.00
Pressed Glass, Dewdrop With Fan, Creamer 12.50
Pressed Glass, Dewdrop With Inverted Thumbprint, Goblet 11.00
Pressed Glass, Dewdrop With Sheaf Of Wheat, Plate, Bread 32.00
Pressed Glass, Dewdrop With Small Star, Goblet 13.00
Pressed Glass, Dewdrop With Star, Butter, Covered 28.00

Pressed Glass, Dewdrop With Star, Cake Stand, 8 1/2 In.	25.00
Pressed Glass, Dewdrop With Star, Creamer	35.00
Pressed Glass, Dewdrop With Star, Plate, 6 1/4 In.	8.50
Pressed Glass, Dewdrop With Star, Plate, 7 1/4 In.	7.50
Pressed Glass, Dewdrop With Star, Plate, 8 1/4 In.	11.00 To 12.50
Pressed Glass, Dewdrop With Star, Salt, Master	12.00
Pressed Glass, Dewdrop With Star, Salt, 3 In. Diameter At Base, 3 In., Pair	20.00
Pressed Glass, Dewdrop With Star, Sauce, 4 In.	3.00
Pressed Glass, Dewdrop, Butter	40.00
Pressed Glass, Dewdrop, Butter, Covered	23.75
Pressed Glass, Dewdrop, Cake Stand, 9 3/4 In.	35.00
Pressed Glass, Dewdrop, Goblet	14.00
Pressed Glass, Dewdrop, Goblet, Etched	13.00
Dewey, see also Admiral Dewey	
Pressed Glass, Dewey, Butter, Amber	80.00
Pressed Glass, Dewey, Butter, Amber, Covered	87.50
Pressed Glass, Dewey, Creamer, Amber	35.00 To 39.50
Pressed Glass, Dewey, Mug	14.00
Pressed Glass, Dewey, Pitcher, Water	45.00 To 50.00
Pressed Glass, Dewey, Pitcher, Water, Cannonballs, Cannon, & Ship, 9 In.	60.00
Pressed Glass, Dewey, Pitcher, 4 Stacks Cannonballs, 9 1/4 In.	35.00
Pressed Glass, Dewey, Plate, 6 In.	15.00
Pressed Glass, Dewey, Relish, Amber, Serpentine	40.00
Pressed Glass, Dewey, Sauce, Green, Greentown	10.00
Pressed Glass, Dewey, Sauce, Green, 4 1/2 In.	23.00
Pressed Glass, Dewey, Sugar, 3 1/2 In.	12.00
Pressed Glass, Dewey, Table Set, Canary, 4 Piece	225.00
Pressed Glass, Dewey, Tumbler	7.50 To 47.50
Pressed Glass, Dewey, Tumbler, Amber	30.00
Pressed Glass, Dewey, Tumbler, Green	21.00
Pressed Glass, Diagonal Band & Fan, Champagne	17.50 To 18.50
Pressed Glass, Diagonal Band & Fan, Compote, Low Standard, 7 In.	9.00
Pressed Glass, Diagonal Band & Fan, Creamer	19.00
Pressed Glass, Diagonal Band & Fan, Pitcher, Milk, 7 1/2 In.	25.00
Pressed Glass, Diagonal Band & Fan, Plate, Handled, 6 In.	5.00
Pressed Glass, Diagonal Band & Fan, Plate, Handled, 7 In.	6.00
Pressed Glass, Diagonal Band & Fan, Plate, Handled, 8 In.	9.00
Pressed Glass, Diagonal Band & Fan, Plate, 6 In.	7.00 To 12.00
Pressed Glass, Diagonal Band & Fan, Plate, 7 In.	7.50 To 12.75
Pressed Glass, Diagonal Band & Fan, Plate, 8 In.	8.00 To 8.75
Pressed Glass, Diagonal Band & Fan, Sauce, Footed, 4 In.	5.00
Pressed Glass, Diagonal Band & Fan, Spooner	16.50 To 24.00
Pressed Glass, Diagonal Band & Fan, Sugar	15.00 To 25.00
Pressed Glass, Diagonal Band & Fan, Wine	20.00
Pressed Glass, Diagonal Band, Cake Stand, 9 In.	25.00
Pressed Glass, Diagonal Band, Celery	15.00
Pressed Glass, Diagonal Band, Goblet	12.00 To 16.50
Pressed Glass, Diagonal Band, Relish, Oblong	9.00
Pressed Glass, Diagonal Band, Salt, Footed	8.00

Pressed Glass,
Delaware,
Salt & Pepper, Green

Pressed Glass,
Diagonal Band,
Creamer

Pressed Glass,
Diagonal Band, Goblet

Pressed Glass,
Diamond Cut With Leaf, Plate

Pressed Glass,
Diamond Point,
Claret Glass

Pressed Glass, Diagonal Band, Salt, Individual, Footed	8.00
Pressed Glass, Diagonal Basket Weave, Salt & Pepper, Tin Tops, In Basket	25.00
Pressed Glass, Diagonal Sawtooth Band, Wine, Flint	22.00 To 28.00
Pressed Glass, Diamonds & Crossbars, Creamer	50.00
Pressed Glass, Diamond & Dewdrops, Goblet	7.00 To 10.00
Diamond & Sunburst, see also Flattened Diamond & Sunburst	
Pressed Glass, Diamond & Sunburst, Butter, Covered	20.00
Pressed Glass, Diamond & Sunburst, Goblet	10.00 To 16.00
Pressed Glass, Diamond & Sunburst, Spooner	9.00
Pressed Glass, Diamond & Sunburst, Sugar, Ruby Stained	15.00
Pressed Glass, Diamond & Sunburst, Tumbler, Bar Type	15.00
Pressed Glass, Diamond & Sunburst, Tumbler, Ruby Stained	12.00 To 22.00
Pressed Glass, Diamond & Sunburst, Wine	15.00
Pressed Glass, Diamond Band, Goblet	10.00 To 11.00
Pressed Glass, Diamond Band, Sugar	9.00
Pressed Glass, Diamond Band, Tumbler	20.00
Pressed Glass, Diamond Block With Fan, Bowl, Berry, 8 1/2 In.	27.00
Pressed Glass, Diamond Block With Fan, Celery	22.00
Pressed Glass, Diamond Block With Fan, Muffineer	18.00
Pressed Glass, Diamond Block With Fan, Punch Set, Miniature, 7 Piece	68.00
Pressed Glass, Diamond Block With Fan, Spooner	18.00
Pressed Glass, Diamond Block With Fan, Spooner, Pedestal	16.00
Pressed Glass, Diamond Block With Fan, Sugar, Standard	10.00
Pressed Glass, Diamond Block, Salt, Canary & Blue, Pair	8.00
Pressed Glass, Diamond Cut With Leaf, Goblet	12.50 To 18.00
Pressed Glass, Diamond Cut With Leaf, Plate, 9 1/4 In.	22.00
Pressed Glass, Diamond Cut With Leaf, Wine	15.00
Diamond Horseshoe, see Aurora	
Pressed Glass, Diamond In Diamond, Goblet	10.00 To 14.00
Pressed Glass, Diamond In Diamond, Pitcher, Water, Bulbous, Applied Handle	28.50
Pressed Glass, Diamond In Diamond, Spooner	9.50 To 22.00
Pressed Glass, Diamond Medallion, Butter, Covered	18.75
Pressed Glass, Diamond Medallion, Cake Stand, 8 1/2 In.	16.50
Pressed Glass, Diamond Medallion, Cake Stand, 10 1/4 In.	22.00
Pressed Glass, Diamond Medallion, Celery, 7 1/2 In.	15.00
Pressed Glass, Diamond Medallion, Compote, Covered, 7 In.	28.00 To 32.00
Pressed Glass, Diamond Medallion, Creamer	9.00 To 12.00
Pressed Glass, Diamond Medallion, Goblet	11.00 To 15.50
Pressed Glass, Diamond Medallion, Pitcher, Water, 9 In.	22.00
Pressed Glass, Diamond Medallion, Plate, 10 In.	12.50
Pressed Glass, Diamond Medallion, Sauce	3.75
Pressed Glass, Diamond Medallion, Spooner	1.90 To 14.00
Pressed Glass, Diamond Medallion, Sugar, Covered	18.00
Pressed Glass, Diamond Medallion, Wine	12.00

Pressed Glass, Diamond Mirror, Creamer	15.00
Pressed Glass, Diamond Panel Fruits, Goblet	13.75
Pressed Glass, Diamond Point & Fan, Celery	14.00
Pressed Glass, Diamond Point & Fan, Rose Bowl, 4 1/4 In.	11.00
Pressed Glass, Diamond Point Band, Sauce, Footed, 3 1/2 In.	4.50
Pressed Glass, Diamond Point Band, Shade, Gas, Red Flashed, 4 1/4 X 2 In.	35.00
Pressed Glass, Diamond Point Band, Spooner	12.00
Diamond Point Discs, see Eyewinker	
Pressed Glass, Diamond Point Heart, Toothpick	5.00
Pressed Glass, Diamond Point Loop, Celery, Amber	35.00
Pressed Glass, Diamond Point Loop, Creamer, Amber	29.50
Pressed Glass, Diamond Point Loop, Sauce, Blue	8.50
Pressed Glass, Diamond Point Loop, Sauce, Blue, Square, 4 In.	9.50
Pressed Glass, Diamond Point Loop, Sauce, Green	5.85
Pressed Glass, Diamond Point Loop, Spooner, Amber	29.50
Pressed Glass, Diamond Point Loop, Spooner, Blue	32.50
Pressed Glass, Diamond Point Loop, Sugar & Creamer, Blue, Cover	95.00
Pressed Glass, Diamond Point Loop, Sugar, Apple Green, Covered, Ball Feet	35.00
Pressed Glass, Diamond Point With Flute, Celery, Flint	40.00
Pressed Glass, Diamond Point With Flute, Wine	5.50
Diamond Point with Panels, see Hinoto	
Pressed Glass, Diamond Point With Ring, Sauce, Flint	6.00
Pressed Glass, Diamond Point, Bottle, Dresser	20.00
Pressed Glass, Diamond Point, Butter, Flint	45.00
Pressed Glass, Diamond Point, Celery	54.00 To 55.00
Pressed Glass, Diamond Point, Celery, Flint	43.00 To 55.00
Pressed Glass, Diamond Point, Celery, Footed, Flint	60.00
Pressed Glass, Diamond Point, Celery, Scallop & Point Rim	50.00
Pressed Glass, Diamond Point, Champagne	60.00 To 65.00
Pressed Glass, Diamond Point, Champagne, Flint	55.00 To 63.00
Pressed Glass, Diamond Point, Claret, Flint	70.00
Pressed Glass, Diamond Point, Compote, Covered, 9 1/2 X 12 In.	75.00
Pressed Glass, Diamond Point, Compote, Flint, 10 In.	80.00
Pressed Glass, Diamond Point, Compote, High Standard, Flint, 7 1/2 In.	47.50
Pressed Glass, Diamond Point, Compote, High Standard, Flint, 8 In.	47.00
Pressed Glass, Diamond Point, Compote, 10 In.Diameter	110.00
Pressed Glass, Diamond Point, Creamer	125.00
Pressed Glass, Diamond Point, Creamer, Flint	85.00 To 100.00
Pressed Glass, Diamond Point, Decanter, Flint, Quart, Pair	90.00
Pressed Glass, Diamond Point, Decanter, Quart	95.00
Pressed Glass, Diamond Point, Eggcup	30.00 To 45.00
Pressed Glass, Diamond Point, Eggcup, Blue, Covered, Flint	350.00
Pressed Glass, Diamond Point, Eggcup, Flint	25.00 To 38.00
Pressed Glass, Diamond Point, Goblet	7.00 To 55.00
Pressed Glass, Diamond Point, Goblet, Flint	25.00 To 50.00
Pressed Glass, Diamond Point, Mug	35.00
Pressed Glass, Diamond Point, Pitcher, Water	45.00
Pressed Glass, Diamond Point, Pitcher, Water, Applied Handle	55.00
Pressed Glass, Diamond Point, Pitcher, Water, Bulbous, Flint	55.00
Pressed Glass, Diamond Point, Pitcher, Water, Flint	200.00
Pressed Glass, Diamond Point, Plate, 6 In.	16.50
Pressed Glass, Diamond Point, Salt Dip, 2 1/2 In.	4.00
Pressed Glass, Diamond Point, Salt, Master, Flint	30.00
Pressed Glass, Diamond Point, Sauce, Flint	5.00
Pressed Glass, Diamond Point, Spill, Flint	30.00 To 50.00
Pressed Glass, Diamond Point, Spill, Knob Stem	20.00
Pressed Glass, Diamond Point, Spooner	22.00 To 50.00
Pressed Glass, Diamond Point, Spooner, Flint	22.00 To 50.00
Pressed Glass, Diamond Point, Spooner, Knob Stem	20.00
Pressed Glass, Diamond Point, Sugar	15.00
Pressed Glass, Diamond Point, Sugar, Covered	65.00
Pressed Glass, Diamond Point, Sugar, Covered, Flint	38.00 To 65.00
Pressed Glass, Diamond Point, Sugar, Flint	20.00
Pressed Glass, Diamond Point, Sugar, Pedestal Foot, Flint	22.00
Pressed Glass, Diamond Point, Table Set, Child's, Turning Purple, 3 Piece	37.50
Pressed Glass, Diamond Point, Toothpick, Anvil	22.50

Pressed Glass, Diamond Point, Tumbler	12.00 To 55.00
Pressed Glass, Diamond Point, Tumbler, Flint	50.00
Pressed Glass, Diamond Point, Tumbler, Whiskey, Flint	60.00
Pressed Glass, Diamond Point, Tumbler, Whiskey, Handled	55.00
Pressed Glass, Diamond Point, Tumbler, Whiskey, Handled, Flint	75.00 To 85.00
Pressed Glass, Diamond Point, Wine	65.00
Pressed Glass, Diamond Point, Wine, Flint	50.00 To 60.00
Pressed Glass, Diamond Prisms, Spooner, Footed	12.00
Pressed Glass, Diamond Ridge, Jar, Cracker	35.00
Pressed Glass, Diamond Rosette, Dish, Honey	12.00
Pressed Glass, Diamond Rosette, Goblet	12.00
Pressed Glass, Diamond Shield, Goblet	12.00
Pressed Glass, Diamond Splendor, Goblet	12.50
Pressed Glass, Diamond Thumbprint, Bowl, Footed, Flint, 8 X 3 In.	40.00
Pressed Glass, Diamond Thumbprint, Cake Stand, Flint, 8 In.	200.00
Pressed Glass, Diamond Thumbprint, Cake Stand, Flint, 12 In.	600.00
Pressed Glass, Diamond Thumbprint, Celery	130.00
Pressed Glass, Diamond Thumbprint, Celery, Flint	120.00
Pressed Glass, Diamond Thumbprint, Champagne	200.00
Pressed Glass, Diamond Thumbprint, Champagne, Flint	190.00
Pressed Glass, Diamond Thumbprint, Compote, Flint, 7 X 4 1/2 In.	55.00
Pressed Glass, Diamond Thumbprint, Compote, Flint, 8 1/2 X 6 In.	75.00
Pressed Glass, Diamond Thumbprint, Compote, Low Standard, Flint, 7 3/4 In.	75.00
Pressed Glass, Diamond Thumbprint, Compote, Low Standard, Flint, 8 In.	65.00
Pressed Glass, Diamond Thumbprint, Compote, Low Standard, 8 In.	47.00
Pressed Glass, Diamond Thumbprint, Compote, Scalloped, Flint, 8 In.	50.00
Pressed Glass, Diamond Thumbprint, Compote, Scalloped, Pointed, Flint, 8 In.	35.00
Pressed Glass, Diamond Thumbprint, Compote, 10 X 8 In.	150.00
Pressed Glass, Diamond Thumbprint, Compote, 11 In.	130.00
Pressed Glass, Diamond Thumbprint, Creamer, Applied Handle	185.00
Pressed Glass, Diamond Thumbprint, Decanter, Pewter & Cork Cap, Flint, Quart	125.00
Pressed Glass, Diamond Thumbprint, Dish, Honey, Flint	12.00 To 14.50
Pressed Glass, Diamond Thumbprint, Goblet, Square Base	2.00
Pressed Glass, Diamond Thumbprint, Pitcher, Milk	350.00
Pressed Glass, Diamond Thumbprint, Pitcher, Milk, Flint	325.00
Pressed Glass, Diamond Thumbprint, Pitcher, Water, Applied Handle	375.00
Pressed Glass, Diamond Thumbprint, Sauce	10.00 To 12.50
Pressed Glass, Diamond Thumbprint, Sauce, Flint	12.00 To 14.00
Pressed Glass, Diamond Thumbprint, Spooner	52.50
Pressed Glass, Diamond Thumbprint, Spooner, Flint	38.00 To 41.50
Pressed Glass, Diamond Thumbprint, Sugar, Covered	125.00 To 175.00
Pressed Glass, Diamond Thumbprint, Sugar, Covered, Flint	110.00 To 150.00
Pressed Glass, Diamond Thumbprint, Sugar, Covered, Petal Base, Flint	125.00
Pressed Glass, Diamond Thumbprint, Tumbler	85.00 To 100.00
Pressed Glass, Diamond Thumbprint, Tumbler, Flint	90.00

Pressed Glass, Diamond
Thumbprint, Decanter

Pressed Glass, Dolphin,
Compote, Pittsburgh, 8 In.

Pressed Glass,
Egg & Sand, Goblet

Pressed Glass, Diamond Thumbprint, Wine	175.00
Pressed Glass, Diamond Thumbprint, Wine, Flint	165.00
Pressed Glass, Diamond With Almond Thumbprint, Barrel, Goblet	6.50
Pressed Glass, Diamond With Double Fan, Goblet, Red Top	14.00
Pressed Glass, Diamond-Quilted, Celery, Blue, Pedestal Base	35.00
Pressed Glass, Diamond-Quilted, Compote, Low Standard, 9 1/4 In.	20.00
Pressed Glass, Diamond-Quilted, Goblet, Amber, Short Stem	25.00
Pressed Glass, Diamond-Quilted, Goblet, Blue	28.00
Pressed Glass, Diamond-Quilted, Mug, Canary	20.00
Pressed Glass, Diamond-Quilted, Sauce, Amethyst	15.00
Pressed Glass, Diamond-Quilted, Sauce, Amethyst, Footed	15.00
Pressed Glass, Diamond-Quilted, Sauce, Yellow, Footed	10.00
Pressed Glass, Diamond-Quilted, Spooner, Blue	28.50
Pressed Glass, Diamond-Quilted, Wine, Amber	23.75
Pressed Glass, Diamond-Quilted, Wine, Blue	11.00 To 23.00
Pressed Glass, Diamonds In Ovals, Goblet	10.00 To 25.00
Pressed Glass, Dickerson, Goblet, Flint	28.00 To 35.00
Pressed Glass, Dickory Dock, Goblet	7.00
Pressed Glass, Dickory Dock, Goblet, Flint	32.00
Pressed Glass, Dickinson, Sugar, Flint	35.00
Pressed Glass, Divided Block With Sunburst, Creamer, Scalloped	10.00
Pressed Glass, Divided Block With Sunburst, Cup, Punch	5.00
Pressed Glass, Divided Diamonds, Goblet, Flint	45.00
Pressed Glass, Divided Hearts, Eggcup	35.00
Pressed Glass, Divided Hearts, Eggcup, Flint	32.00
Pressed Glass, Divided Hearts, Goblet	70.00
Pressed Glass, Divided Hearts, Goblet, Flint	60.00
Pressed Glass, Divided Hearts, Spill, Flint	35.00
Pressed Glass, Divided Hearts, Spooner	45.00
Pressed Glass, Divided Hearts, Spooner, Flint	35.00
Pressed Glass, Divided Squares, Dish, Sweetmeat, Covered, Flint	48.00
Pressed Glass, Doderly Thumbprint, Goblet	8.50
Pressed Glass, Dodo, Goblet, Flint	28.00
Pressed Glass, Dog & Bird, Mug, 2 3/4 In.	12.00
Pressed Glass, Dog & Rabbit, Plate, Bread, Frosted	40.00
Dog on Drum, see Cat in Basket & Dog on Drum	
Pressed Glass, Dogwood, Bowl, Banana, Emerald Green, Gold Flashing	25.00
Pressed Glass, Dogwood, Butter, Covered, Cranberry Flashed, Gold	48.00
Pressed Glass, Dogwood, Pitcher, Water, Ruby Stained, Gold Floral & Leaf	75.00
Pressed Glass, Dogwood, Sugar, Ruby Stained, Covered, Gold Trim	55.00
Pressed Glass, Dolphin, Compote, Frosted, 8 In.	57.50
Pressed Glass, Dolphin, Compote, Frosted, 8 1/2 In.	55.00
Pressed Glass, Dolphin, Creamer	47.50 To 50.00
Pressed Glass, Dolphin, Creamer, Frosted	67.50
Pressed Glass, Dolphin, Creamer, Stemmed	45.00
Pressed Glass, Dolphin, Pitcher, Water, Frosted, 10 In.	95.00
Pressed Glass, Domino, Toothpick	22.50
Doric, see Feather	
Pressed Glass, Dots & Dashes, Goblet	12.00 To 14.00
Pressed Glass, Dots & Dashes, Spooner	15.00 To 22.00
Pressed Glass, Dotted Loop, Creamer	10.00
Pressed Glass, Double Arch, Cake Stand	22.50
Pressed Glass, Double Arch, Goblet	12.50
Pressed Glass, Double Arch, Sauce	3.75
Pressed Glass, Double Arch, Tumbler	10.50
Pressed Glass, Double Band Forget-Me-Not, Wine	18.50
Pressed Glass, Double Beetle Band, Goblet	9.50 To 11.00
Pressed Glass, Double Beetle Band, Wine, Blue	22.50
Pressed Glass, Double Circle, Goblet, Flint	125.00
Pressed Glass, Double Circle, Spill, Flint	35.00
Pressed Glass, Double Circle, Spooner	50.00
Pressed Glass, Double Circle, Spooner, Flint	35.00
Pressed Glass, Double Cord & Tassel, Salt & Pepper, Opaque Blue	45.00
Double Daisy, see Rosette Band	
Pressed Glass, Double Disc Prism, Goblet, Flint	90.00
Pressed Glass, Double Eye Hobnail, Creamer	19.50 To 21.50

Pressed Glass, **Double Fleur-De-Lis**, Compote, Low Standard, 8 1/4 In.	85.00
Pressed Glass, **Double Frosted Ribbon**, Sauce	5.00
Pressed Glass, **Double Leaf & Dart**, Goblet	11.00
Pressed Glass, **Double Loop & Dart**, Goblet	12.00
Pressed Glass, **Double Loop & Dart**, Spooner	35.00
Pressed Glass, **Double Loop & Dart**, Wine	28.00
Double Loop, see Double Loop & Dart	
Pressed Glass, **Double Petal Tulip**, Butter, Covered, Flint	32.00
Pressed Glass, **Double Red Block**, Goblet, Ruby & Clear	40.00
Pressed Glass, **Double Ribbon**, Goblet, Frosted	15.00 To 16.50
Pressed Glass, **Double Ribbon**, Goblet, Frosted, Knob Stem	11.00
Pressed Glass, **Double Ribbon**, Plate, Bread, Frosted	19.00
Pressed Glass, **Double Ribbon**, Platter, Frosted, 13 X 9 In.	25.00
Pressed Glass, **Double Ribbon**, Salt, Master, Frosted, Rectangular	18.00 To 18.50
Pressed Glass, **Double Scroll**, Tumbler	10.00
Pressed Glass, **Double Spear**, Goblet	12.50
Pressed Glass, **Double Spear**, Pitcher, Water	20.00
Pressed Glass, **Double Spear**, Sauce	3.75
Pressed Glass, **Double Spear**, Spooner	11.50
Pressed Glass, **Double Spear**, Sugar & Creamer	50.00
Pressed Glass, **Double Spear**, Sugar, Covered	25.00
Pressed Glass, **Double Tub**, Salt, Spoons	25.00
Double Vine, see Bellflower, Double Vine	
Pressed Glass, **Double Wafer**, Wine, Stem Turned Base, Flint	25.00
Pressed Glass, **Double Wedding Ring**, Goblet, Flint	50.00
Pressed Glass, **Draped Fan**, Goblet	9.50
Pressed Glass, **Draped Jewel**, Sauce	6.50
Draped Top, see Draped Red Top	
Pressed Glass, **Draped Red Top**, Berry Set, Ruby Stained, 9 Piece	150.00
Pressed Glass, **Draped Red Top**, Bowl, Ruby Stained, 7 In.	20.00
Pressed Glass, **Draped Red Top**, Creamer, Ruby Stained	37.50
Pressed Glass, **Draped Red Top**, Goblet, Ruby Stained	35.00
Pressed Glass, **Draped Red Top**, Pitcher, Water, Ruby Stained, Bulbous	70.00
Pressed Glass, **Draped Red Top**, Spooner, Ruby Stained	22.50 To 30.00
Pressed Glass, **Draped Red Top**, Sugar, Ruby Stained, Covered	45.00
Pressed Glass, **Draped Window**, Mug, Blue	25.00
Pressed Glass, **Drapery Band With Stars**, Goblet	8.50 To 13.50
Pressed Glass, **Drapery**, Cake Stand, 12 In.	22.00
Pressed Glass, **Drapery**, Creamer	18.00
Pressed Glass, **Drapery**, Goblet	12.00 To 24.00
Pressed Glass, **Drapery**, Plate, 6 1/4 In.	12.50
Pressed Glass, **Drapery**, Sauce	5.00 To 7.00
Pressed Glass, **Drapery**, Spooner	18.75 To 30.00
Pressed Glass, **Drapery**, Spooner, Pedestal	17.00
Pressed Glass, **Droplet Band**, Goblet	9.00
Pressed Glass, **Drum With Eagle**, Mug, Child's, Gold Trim	9.00 To 16.00
Pressed Glass, **Drum**, Creamer, Child's	20.00 To 42.00
Pressed Glass, **Drum**, Mug, Gold Trim	15.00 To 20.00
Pressed Glass, **Drum**, Spooner	30.00
Pressed Glass, **Drum**, Sugar, Child's, Blue, Covered	42.00
Pressed Glass, **Drum**, Table Set, Child's, 4 Piece	125.00
Pressed Glass, **Duchess Loop**, Goblet, Flint	15.00
Pressed Glass, **Duck Cover**, Dish, Frosted, 8 1/2 In.	70.00
Pressed Glass, **Duke**, Goblet	9.50 To 11.50
Pressed Glass, **Dunkirk Swirl**, Mug, 3 1/4 In.	15.00
Pressed Glass, **Duquesne**, Goblet	11.00 To 20.00
Dynast, see Radiant	
Pressed Glass, **Eagle**, Mug, Gold Trim	12.00 To 15.00
Eal, see Spirea Band	
Pressed Glass, **Eastern Star**, Goblet	10.00
Pressed Glass, **Edgerton**, Spooner, Ruby Stained	39.00
Pressed Glass, **Edgerton**, Sugar	10.00
Pressed Glass, **Effulgent Star**, Goblet	15.00
Pressed Glass, **Egg In Sand**, Goblet	20.00 To 24.50
Pressed Glass, **Egg In Sand**, Pitcher, Milk	34.50
Pressed Glass, **Egg In Sand**, Pitcher, Water	37.50

Pressed Glass, Egg In Sand, Pitcher, 7 In.	25.00
Pressed Glass, Egg In Sand, Plate, Bread, 13 X 8 In.	16.00
Pressed Glass, Egg In Sand, Spooner	17.50 To 30.00
Pressed Glass, Egg In Sand, Sugar, Covered	38.00
Pressed Glass, Egg In Sand, Tray, 12 1/2 In. X 8 In.	15.00
Pressed Glass, Egyptain, Celery, Footed	45.00
Pressed Glass, Egyptian, Compote, Covered, Sphinx On Base, 11 In. High	110.00
Pressed Glass, Egyptian, Compote, Sphinx Base, 7 1/4 In.	45.00
Pressed Glass, Egyptian, Creamer	20.00 To 37.50
Pressed Glass, Egyptian, Creamer, Master	20.00
Pressed Glass, Egyptian, Dish, Pickle	9.00
Pressed Glass, Egyptian, Goblet	16.00 To 30.00
Pressed Glass, Egyptian, Plate, Bread	47.50
Pressed Glass, Egyptian, Plate, Bread, Cleopatra	25.00 To 39.50
Pressed Glass, Egyptian, Relish	12.50
Pressed Glass, Egyptian, Sauce	6.00
Pressed Glass, Egyptian, Sauce, On Base	15.00
Pressed Glass, Egyptian, Sherbet	12.00
Pressed Glass, Egyptian, Spooner	17.50
Pressed Glass, Eight Panel, Wine, Flint	7.50
Pressed Glass, Electric, Spooner	13.00
Pressed Glass, Electric, Syrup	22.50 To 29.50
Pressed Glass, Elegant, Goblet, Flint	15.00
Pressed Glass, Elephant, Goblet	42.50
Pressed Glass, Elk & Doe, Jar, Jam, Owl In Circle Finial On Cover	35.00
Pressed Glass, Emblem, Dish, Pickle, American Shields On Ends	24.00 To 37.50
Pressed Glass, Emblem, Plate, Bread, Eagle Center	75.00
Pressed Glass, Empress, Bowl, Fruit	20.00
Pressed Glass, Empress, Butter, Covered, Green	90.00 To 95.00
Pressed Glass, Empress, Creamer, Green	75.00
Pressed Glass, Empress, Salt Dip, Emerald Green	28.00
Pressed Glass, Empress, Saltshaker, Gold Decoration	12.00
Pressed Glass, Empress, Spooner, Green, Gold Trim	35.00
Pressed Glass, English Hobnail, Printed, Goblet	110.00
Pressed Glass, English Hobnail With Thumbprint, Bowl, Banana, Flat Base	10.00
Pressed Glass, English Hobnail With Thumbprint, Plate, 10 1/2 In.	12.50
Pressed Glass, English Hobnail, Cruet, Child's	16.50
English Hobnail Cross, see Klondike	
Pressed Glass, Esther, Bowl, Berry, 4 In.	18.00
Pressed Glass, Esther, Bowl, Green, Footed, Shallow, 11 In.	39.00
Pressed Glass, Esther, Butter, Covered	42.00
Pressed Glass, Esther, Cake Stand, 3/4 In. Amber Band, 10 1/2 In.	35.00
Pressed Glass, Esther, Celery, Emerald Green, Gold, 11 X 6 In.	35.00
Pressed Glass, Esther, Celery, Etched	17.00
Pressed Glass, Esther, Celery, Green	78.00
Pressed Glass, Esther, Compote, 5 In.	12.00
Pressed Glass, Esther, Creamer, Ruby Stained, Small	17.50
Pressed Glass, Esther, Dish, Pickle, Amber Stained	19.00
Pressed Glass, Esther, Pitcher, Water, Amber, Enamel Floral	135.00
Pressed Glass, Esther, Relish, Emerald Green, Gold, 8 1/2 X 4 1/2 In.	25.00
Pressed Glass, Esther, Spooner	24.00
Pressed Glass, Esther, Spooner, Green, Gold Trim	25.00
Pressed Glass, Esther, Sugar, Emerald Green, Covered, Gold	55.00
Pressed Glass, Esther, Toothpick, Amber Band, Enamel Decoration	30.00
Pressed Glass, Esther, Toothpick, Amber Stained	45.00
Pressed Glass, Esther, Tumbler	14.50
Pressed Glass, Esther, Tumbler, Amber Flashed	28.75
Pressed Glass, Esther, Tumbler, Green, Gold Trim	37.50
Pressed Glass, Esther, Tumbler, Yellow Flashed, Enameled Flowers	35.00
Pressed Glass, Esther, Wine, Etched Amber Band	30.00 To 32.50
Etched Band, see Dakota	
Etched Dakota, see Dakota	
Etched Fern, see Ashman	
Pressed Glass, Etched Grape, Tumbler, 4 In.	3.00
Etched patterns, see under main pattern, e.g. Etched Dakota, see Dakota	
Pressed Glass, Etched Lion With Cable, Sugar	18.50

Pressed Glass, Etruscan, Goblet, Flint	30.00
Pressed Glass, Eugenie, Bowl, Oval, Flint, 9 In.	28.50
Pressed Glass, Eugenie, Celery	60.00
Pressed Glass, Eugenie, Celery, Flint	35.00 To 55.00
Pressed Glass, Eugenie, Champagne, Flint	34.50
Pressed Glass, Eugenie, Eggcup	38.00
Pressed Glass, Eugenie, Eggcup, Flint	34.00
Pressed Glass, Eugenie, Goblet, Flint	42.50
Pressed Glass, Eugenie, Sugar, Dolphin Finial, Flint	135.00
Pressed Glass, Eugenie, Wine	40.00
Pressed Glass, Eureka, Berry Set, Ruby Flashed, National, 7 Piece	58.00
Pressed Glass, Eureka, Butter, Flint	40.00
Pressed Glass, Eureka, Champagne	38.00
Pressed Glass, Eureka, Champagne, Flint	34.00
Pressed Glass, Eureka, Cordial, Flint	35.00
Pressed Glass, Eureka, Creamer	75.00
Pressed Glass, Eureka, Creamer, Flint	65.00
Pressed Glass, Eureka, Eggcup	30.00
Pressed Glass, Eureka, Eggcup, Flint	28.00
Pressed Glass, Eureka, Goblet	10.00 To 34.00
Pressed Glass, Eureka, Goblet, Flint	20.00 To 38.00
Pressed Glass, Eureka, Goblet, Flint, Short Stem	24.00
Pressed Glass, Eureka, Plate, Bread	22.00 To 30.00
Pressed Glass, Eureka, Spill, Flint	35.00
Pressed Glass, Eureka, Spooner	40.00
Pressed Glass, Eureka, Spooner, Flint	35.00
Pressed Glass, Eureka, Sugar, Flint	20.00 To 25.00
Pressed Glass, Eureka, Wine	35.00
Pressed Glass, Eureka, Wine, Flint	30.00
Pressed Glass, Excelsior Variant, Sugar, Covered	75.00
Pressed Glass, Excelsior With Maltese Cross, Creamer, Small	44.00
Pressed Glass, Excelsior With Maltese Cross, Goblet, Flint	45.00
Pressed Glass, Excelsior With Maltese Cross, Tumbler, Bar, 2 1/2 In.	80.00

Pressed Glass, Egyptian,
Goblet

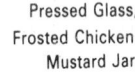

Pressed Glass,
Frosted Chicken,
Mustard Jar

Pressed Glass,
Fern Burst, Goblet

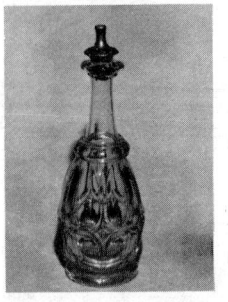

Pressed Glass, Egyptian,
Compote, 7 1/2 In.

Pressed Glass,
Excelsior, Bitters

Pressed Glass, Excelsior With Maltese Cross, Tumbler, Flint, 3 In.	70.00
Pressed Glass, Excelsior, Celery	70.00
Pressed Glass, Excelsior, Celery, Flint	55.00
Pressed Glass, Excelsior, Champagne	40.00
Pressed Glass, Excelsior, Champagne, Flint	35.00
Pressed Glass, Excelsior, Creamer	75.00
Pressed Glass, Excelsior, Eggcup	22.50 To 40.00
Pressed Glass, Excelsior, Eggcup, Double, Flint	31.00
Pressed Glass, Excelsior, Eggcup, Flint	18.00 To 30.00
Pressed Glass, Excelsior, Goblet, Flint	30.00 To 35.00
Pressed Glass, Excelsior, Pitcher, Water, Flint	250.00
Pressed Glass, Excelsior, Spill, Flint	30.00 To 35.00
Pressed Glass, Excelsior, Spooner	45.00
Pressed Glass, Excelsior, Spooner, Flint	35.00
Pressed Glass, Excelsior, Sugar, Covered	80.00
Pressed Glass, Excelsior, Sugar, Covered, Flint	60.00 To 75.00
Pressed Glass, Excelsior, Sugar, Thistle Finial, Flint	95.00
Pressed Glass, Excelsior, Tumbler	65.00
Pressed Glass, Excelsior, Tumbler, Ale	45.00
Pressed Glass, Excelsior, Tumbler, Flint, 3 In.	65.00
Pressed Glass, Excelsior, Tumbler, Footed	30.00 To 50.00
Pressed Glass, Excelsior, Tumbler, Footed, Flint	25.00
Pressed Glass, Excelsior, Tumbler, Whiskey, Flint	45.00
Pressed Glass, Excelsior, Wine, Flint	33.00
Pressed Glass, Eyewinker, Bowl, Banana	38.50
Pressed Glass, Eyewinker, Bowl, 8 X 3 1/2 In.	45.00
Pressed Glass, Eyewinker, Butter, Covered	45.00
Pressed Glass, Eyewinker, Butter, Covered, Flared Base	85.00
Pressed Glass, Eyewinker, Cake Stand, 8 In.	21.50
Pressed Glass, Eyewinker, Celery	35.00
Pressed Glass, Eyewinker, Compote, Covered, 6 1/2 In.	69.50
Pressed Glass, Eyewinker, Compote, Covered, 12 X 7 In.	85.00
Pressed Glass, Eyewinker, Compote, Fruit, On Standard, 4 1/2 X 8 In.	45.00
Pressed Glass, Eyewinker, Compote, Jelly	37.50
Pressed Glass, Eyewinker, Compote, 5 In.	16.00
Pressed Glass, Eyewinker, Compote, 8 1/2 X 7 1/2 In.	75.00
Pressed Glass, Eyewinker, Doughnut Stand	45.00
Pressed Glass, Eyewinker, Plate, Bread	45.00
Pressed Glass, Eyewinker, Plate, Turned Sides, 7 3/4 In.	27.50
Pressed Glass, Eyewinker, Plate, 8 In.	27.50
Pressed Glass, Eyewinker, Plate, 8 3/4 In.	32.50
Pressed Glass, Eyewinker, Sauce	13.00
Pressed Glass, Eyewinker, Sauce, Footed, 4 In.	6.50
Pressed Glass, Eyewinker, Spooner	35.00
Pressed Glass, Eyewinker, Sugar, Covered	45.00
Pressed Glass, Eyewinker, Syrup	75.00
Pressed Glass, Eyewinker, Wine	16.00
Fagot, see Vera	
Pressed Glass, Falmouth Strawberry, Goblet	35.00
Pressed Glass, Fan & Flute, Celery	9.00
Pressed Glass, Fan & Flute, Creamer, Ruby Stained	25.00
Pressed Glass, Fan & Flute, Pitcher, Water, Etched, Ruby Stained	40.00
Pressed Glass, Fan & Flute, Sauce, Ruby Stained	5.00
Pressed Glass, Fan Band, Pitcher, Water	19.00
Pressed Glass, Fan Band, Sauce, Footed, 4 In.	6.50
Pressed Glass, Fan With Diamond, Goblet	9.00 To 10.00
Pressed Glass, Fan With Diamond, Spooner	9.50 To 12.50
Pressed Glass, Fan, Banana Stand, High	24.50
Pressed Glass, Fan, Match Holder, Amber	14.50
Fan, see also Butterfly & Fan	
Pressed Glass, Fancy Cut, Creamer	32.00
Pressed Glass, Fancy Cut, Creamer, Child's	25.00 To 26.00
Pressed Glass, Fancy Cut, Table Set, Child's, 3 Piece	70.00
Pressed Glass, Fancy Loop, Sauce, Square	6.00
Pressed Glass, Fancy Loop, Toothpick, Green	58.00 To 75.00
Pressed Glass, Fandango, Bowl, Ruffled, 9 1/2 In.	37.50

Pressed Glass, Fandango, Cup, Punch	4.00
Pressed Glass, Fans With Baby Breath Band, Goblet	11.00
Pressed Glass, Fans With Crossbar, Celery, Ruby Stained	48.00
Pressed Glass, Fans With Crossbar, Goblet, Ruby Stained	35.00
Pressed Glass, Fans With Crossbar, Sugar, Ruby Stained	20.00
Pressed Glass, Feather Band, Tumbler, 5 In., Set Of 4	42.50
Pressed Glass, Feather Duster, Cake Stand	12.00
Pressed Glass, Feather Duster, Celery	12.00
Pressed Glass, Feather Duster, Pitcher, Water	19.00
Pressed Glass, Feather Duster, Plate, Bread	23.50
Pressed Glass, Feather Duster, Tumbler, Green	17.50
Pressed Glass, Feather, Bowl, 8 In.	12.00
Pressed Glass, Feather, Butter, Covered	35.00
Pressed Glass, Feather, Butter, Dome Cover	37.50
Pressed Glass, Feather, Cake Stand, Emerald Green	98.00
Pressed Glass, Feather, Cake Stand, 8 In.	17.50 To 21.00
Pressed Glass, Feather, Cake Stand, 8 1/4 In.	18.50
Pressed Glass, Feather, Cake Stand, 8 1/2 In.	26.00
Pressed Glass, Feather, Cake Stand, 9 3/4 In.	37.50
Pressed Glass, Feather, Compote, Jelly	12.50 To 18.00
Pressed Glass, Feather, Compote, Jelly, Amber & Clear	47.50
Pressed Glass, Feather, Compote, Low Standard, 7 1/2 In.	18.00
Pressed Glass, Feather, Compote, 8 In.	20.00 To 28.00
Pressed Glass, Feather, Creamer	15.00
Pressed Glass, Feather, Creamer, Green	48.75
Pressed Glass, Feather, Dish, Pickle	10.00
Pressed Glass, Feather, Goblet	15.00 To 32.00
Pressed Glass, Feather, Pitcher, Water	19.00 To 37.50
Pressed Glass, Feather, Pitcher, Water, Greentown	30.00
Pressed Glass, Feather, Plate, Cake, Footed, 8 1/2 In.	23.00
Pressed Glass, Feather, Plate, 7 3/4 In.	50.00
Pressed Glass, Feather, Plate, 10 In.	18.75
Pressed Glass, Feather, Relish	12.50
Pressed Glass, Feather, Relish, Oval	19.00
Pressed Glass, Feather, Saltshaker, Squat	26.50
Pressed Glass, Feather, Sauce	6.25 To 6.50
Pressed Glass, Feather, Spooner	10.00 To 25.00
Pressed Glass, Feather, Spooner, Flared Top	15.00
Pressed Glass, Feather, Sugar	9.50 To 15.00
Pressed Glass, Feather, Sugar, Covered	18.00 To 25.00
Pressed Glass, Feather, Table Set, 4 Piece	125.00
Pressed Glass, Feather, Toothpick	28.00
Pressed Glass, Feather, Tumbler	15.00
Pressed Glass, Feather, Tumbler, Green	32.00
Pressed Glass, Feather, Wine	25.00
Pressed Glass, Feathers With Arches, Bowl, Punch	15.00
Pressed Glass, Feathers With Arches, Bowl, Punch, Pink, Miniature	25.00
Pressed Glass, Fedora, Tumbler, Flint	30.00
Pressed Glass, Fern & Berry, Goblet	6.50
Pressed Glass, Fern Burst, Goblet	10.00
Pressed Glass, Fern Sprig, Goblet	18.50
Pressed Glass, Fern With Lily Of The Valley, Goblet	17.50
Pressed Glass, Fernland, Butter	32.50
Pressed Glass, Fernland, Butter, Covered, Child's	20.00 To 25.00
Pressed Glass, Fernland, Creamer	25.00
Pressed Glass, Fernland, Creamer, Child's	16.00 To 21.00
Pressed Glass, Fernland, Creamer, Child's, Blue	35.00
Pressed Glass, Fernland, Creamer, Child's, Green	30.00
Pressed Glass, Ferris Wheel, Goblet, 6 1/2 In.	11.00
Pressed Glass, Festoon, Bowl, Berry, 4 1/2 In.	5.50
Pressed Glass, Festoon, Bowl, Berry, 9 In.	33.00
Pressed Glass, Festoon, Bowl, Berry, 9 1/2 In.	15.00
Pressed Glass, Festoon, Bowl, 9 In.	20.00
Pressed Glass, Festoon, Cake Stand, 9 In.	17.00
Pressed Glass, Festoon, Cake Stand, 10 In.	19.00 To 25.00
Pressed Glass, Festoon, Creamer	16.50 To 25.00

Pressed Glass, Festoon, Pitcher, Water .... 27.50 To 45.00
Pressed Glass, Festoon, Plate, 7 1/4 In. 32.50
Pressed Glass, Festoon, Sauce .... 4.50 To 6.00
Pressed Glass, Festoon, Sugar, Covered .... 29.50 To 45.00
Pressed Glass, Festoon, Tray, Water .... 15.00 To 30.00
Pressed Glass, Festoon, Tumbler, 4 In. 14.00
Pressed Glass, Fighting Cats, Mug, Miniature 22.00
Pressed Glass, Fine Diamond Point, Butter, Covered 70.00
Pressed Glass, Fine Diamond Point, Butter, Covered, Flint 45.00
Pressed Glass, Fine Diamond Point, Eggcup 34.00
Pressed Glass, Fine Diamond Point, Eggcup, Flint 25.00
Pressed Glass, Fine Diamond Point, Goblet 35.00
Pressed Glass, Fine Diamond Point, Goblet, Flint 30.00
Pressed Glass, Fine Diamond Point, Spill, Flint 28.00
Pressed Glass, Fine Diamond Point, Spooner 35.00
Pressed Glass, Fine Diamond Point, Spooner, Flint 28.00
Pressed Glass, Fine Pleat, Goblet 8.50
Pressed Glass, Fine Prism, Champagne 42.50
Pressed Glass, Fine Prism, Champagne, Flint 42.50
Pressed Glass, Fine Prism, Goblet, Flint .... 20.00 To 25.00
Pressed Glass, Fine Prism, Goblet, Straight Top, Flint 24.00
Pressed Glass, Fine Prism, Sauce, Flint 10.00
Pressed Glass, Fine Prism, Sugar, Covered, Flint 51.50
Pressed Glass, Fine Prism, Whiskey Taster, Flint 38.00
Pressed Glass, Fine Prism, Wine, Flint 34.50
Pressed Glass, Fine Rib With Cut Ovals, Celery 160.00
Pressed Glass, Fine Rib With Cut Ovals, Celery, Flint 150.00
Pressed Glass, Fine Rib With Cut Ovals, Champagne, Flint 190.00
Pressed Glass, Fine Rib With Cut Ovals, Eggcup, Flint 125.00
Pressed Glass, Fine Rib With Cut Ovals, Sugar 65.00
Pressed Glass, Fine Rib With Cut Ovals, Tumbler 140.00
Pressed Glass, Fine Rib With Cut Ovals, Tumbler, Flint 125.00
Pressed Glass, Fine Rib With Cut Ovals, Wine 140.00
Pressed Glass, Fine Rib With Cut Ovals, Wine, Flint 130.00
Pressed Glass, Fine Rib With Plain Band, Champagne, Flint 36.00
Pressed Glass, Fine Rib With Plain Band, Goblet, Flint 40.00
Pressed Glass, Fine Rib With Plain Band, Sugar, Flint 16.00
Pressed Glass, Fine Rib, Celery .... 60.00 To 70.00
Pressed Glass, Fine Rib, Celery, Flint 50.00
Pressed Glass, Fine Rib, Champagne 60.00
Pressed Glass, Fine Rib, Champagne, Flint 55.00
Pressed Glass, Fine Rib, Claret, Flint 100.00
Pressed Glass, Fine Rib, Compote, 7 In. 35.00
Pressed Glass, Fine Rib, Cordial, Flint 90.00
Pressed Glass, Fine Rib, Creamer, Flint 150.00
Pressed Glass, Fine Rib, Decanter, Bar Lip, Quart 58.00
Pressed Glass, Fine Rib, Eggcup .... 24.00 To 42.00
Pressed Glass, Fine Rib, Eggcup, Flint 40.00
Pressed Glass, Fine Rib, Goblet 62.00
Pressed Glass, Fine Rib, Goblet, Flint .... 52.00 To 59.50
Pressed Glass, Fine Rib, Mug, Applied Handle, Flint 15.00
Pressed Glass, Fine Rib, Mug, Applied Handle, Ground Pontil, Flint, 2 3/4 In. 15.00
Pressed Glass, Fine Rib, Pitcher, Water, Flint 175.00
Pressed Glass, Fine Rib, Salt Dip 10.50
Pressed Glass, Fine Rib, Salt, Master, Pedestal, Flint .... 15.00 To 25.00
Pressed Glass, Fine Rib, Sauce, 3 1/2 In. 6.00
Pressed Glass, Fine Rib, Shot Glass 22.00
Pressed Glass, Fine Rib, Sugar, Covered 95.00
Pressed Glass, Fine Rib, Sugar, Covered, Flint 85.00
Pressed Glass, Fine Rib, Tumbler .... 45.00 To 50.00
Pressed Glass, Fine Rib, Tumbler, Flint .... 45.00 To 50.00
Pressed Glass, Fine Rib, Tumbler, Whiskey, Handled, Flint .... 60.00 To 85.00
Pressed Glass, Fine Rib, Whiskey Measure, Flint 10.00
Pressed Glass, Fine Rib, Whiskey Taster, Flint 10.00
Pressed Glass, Fine Rib, Wine .... 25.00 To 55.00
Pressed Glass, Fine Rib, Wine, Flint 50.00

Pressed Glass, Finecut & Block, Celery, Amber Blocks	52.50
Pressed Glass, Finecut & Block, Celery, Pink Blocks, Oblong, Pointed Edges	75.00
Pressed Glass, Finecut & Block, Eggcup	16.50 To 19.50
Pressed Glass, Finecut & Block, Eggcup, Blue Blocks	37.00
Pressed Glass, Finecut & Block, Eggcup, Footed	15.00
Pressed Glass, Finecut & Block, Eggcup, Pink Blocks	37.00
Pressed Glass, Finecut & Block, Eggcup, Yellow Blocks	37.00
Pressed Glass, Finecut & Block, Goblet	15.00
Pressed Glass, Finecut & Block, Pitcher, Water, Amber	75.00
Pressed Glass, Finecut & Block, Plate, Blue Blocks, 10 1/2 In.	50.00
Pressed Glass, Finecut & Block, Salt, Amber	15.00
Pressed Glass, Finecut & Block, Spooner, Amber Blocks, Scalloped Rim	45.00
Pressed Glass, Finecut & Block, Spooner, Yellow Blocks, Pointed Rim	38.00
Pressed Glass, Finecut & Block, Sugar, Amber	30.00
Pressed Glass, Finecut & Block, Sugar, Yellow Blocks	52.50
Pressed Glass, Finecut & Block, Tumbler	16.50
Pressed Glass, Finecut & Block, Wine	30.00
Pressed Glass, Finecut & Fan, Cake Stand, Child's	28.50
Pressed Glass, Finecut & Panel, Goblet	15.00 To 50.00
Pressed Glass, Finecut & Panel, Goblet, Blue	26.00
Pressed Glass, Finecut & Panel, Plate, Bread	32.00
Pressed Glass, Finecut & Panel, Wine	12.50
Pressed Glass, Finecut & Panel, Wine, Canary	16.75
Pressed Glass, Finecut Band, Goblet	71.50
Pressed Glass, Finecut Bar, Cordial	12.00
Pressed Glass, Finecut Medallion, Jar, Cracker, 9 X 7 In.	65.00
Pressed Glass, Finecut With Leaf, Goblet	15.00
Pressed Glass, Finecut With Leaf, Tumbler	15.00
Pressed Glass, Finecut, Bowl, Waste, Footed	16.50
Pressed Glass, Finecut, Butter, Miniature	15.00
Pressed Glass, Finecut, Castor, Pickle, Blue, Dog Finial	100.00
Pressed Glass, Finecut, Goblet	15.00 To 22.50
Pressed Glass, Finecut, Pitcher, Water	28.50 To 30.00
Pressed Glass, Finecut, Plate, Bread, Cornflower Blue, 22 1/2 X 8 1/2 In.	40.00
Pressed Glass, Finecut, Plate, Bread, 7 1/4 In.	12.00
Pressed Glass, Finecut, Plate, 7 1/4 In.	9.00
Pressed Glass, Finecut, Saltshaker, Amber	15.00
Pressed Glass, Finecut, Tray, Water, Yellow	45.00
Pressed Glass, Fishbone, Goblet	8.00 To 10.00
Pressed Glass, Fishscale, Cake Stand, 8 3/4 In.	20.00
Pressed Glass, Fishscale, Cake Stand, 9 In.	22.50
Pressed Glass, Fishscale, Cake Stand, 10 1/4 In.	26.00
Pressed Glass, Fishscale, Celery	22.50 To 27.50
Pressed Glass, Fishscale, Compote, Jelly, High Standard, 4 1/2 In.	18.00
Pressed Glass, Fishscale, Compote, Jelly, 4 1/2 In.	18.00
Pressed Glass, Fishscale, Goblet	22.50 To 24.50
Pressed Glass, Fishscale, Pitcher, Milk, 8 In.	22.00
Pressed Glass, Fishscale, Pitcher, Quart Size	18.00
Pressed Glass, Fishscale, Pitcher, Water	30.00
Pressed Glass, Fishscale, Plate, 7 1/4 In.	10.00
Pressed Glass, Fishscale, Saltshaker, Hand Holding Shaker	24.00
Pressed Glass, Fishscale, Sauce	4.00 To 8.50
Pressed Glass, Fishscale, Spooner	15.00
Pressed Glass, Flack, Goblet	8.50
Pressed Glass, Flamboyant, Goblet	10.00
Pressed Glass, Flaming Sword, Bowl, Sapphire Blue, 10 X 4 1/4 In.	75.00
Pressed Glass, Flamingo Habitat, Dish, Cheese, Covered, Burst Bubble On Lid	65.00
Pressed Glass, Flamingo Habitat, Goblet, Etched	32.00 To 35.00
Pressed Glass, Flamingo Habitat, Wine	25.00
Pressed Glass, Flamingo, Compote, Etched, 6 1/4 X 4 1/4 In.	15.00
Pressed Glass, Flamingo, Plate, Bread	45.00
Pressed Glass, Flamingo, Sugar, Covered, Star In Circle Finial	45.00
Pressed Glass, Flange, Sauce	10.00
Pressed Glass, Flat Diamond, Decanter, Quart	65.00
Pressed Glass, Flat Diamond, Goblet	11.00 To 15.00
Pressed Glass, Flat Diamond, Spooner	11.50

Pressed Glass, Flat Diamond, Wine 6.00
Pressed Glass, Flat Panel, Bowl, Berry, Ruby Stained, 8 In. 20.00
Pressed Glass, Flat Panel, Bowl, Ruby Stained, Oval, 9 X 6 In. 20.00
Pressed Glass, Flat Panel, Spooner, Ruby Stained 20.00
Pressed Glass, Flat Panel, Table Set, Ruby Stained, 4 Piece 110.00
Pressed Glass, Flat Panel, Tankard, Water, Ruby Stained 45.00
Pressed Glass, Flat Panel, Toothpick, Ruby Stained 18.50
Pressed Glass, Flat Prisms, Goblet 6.00
Pressed Glass, Flatiron, Butter, Blue 65.00
Pressed Glass, Flattened Diamond & Sunburst, Bowl, Punch, Miniature 18.00
Pressed Glass, Flattened Diamond & Sunburst, Butter, Miniature 35.00
Pressed Glass, Flattened Diamond & Sunburst, Creamer, Miniature ... 9.50 To 21.00
Pressed Glass, Flattened Diamond & Sunburst, Cup, Miniature 12.50
Pressed Glass, Flattened Diamond & Sunburst, Cup, Punch, Miniature 7.50
Pressed Glass, Flattened Diamond & Sunburst, Punch Set, Child's, 7 Piece ... 85.00
Pressed Glass, Flattened Diamond & Sunburst, Punch Set, Miniature, 9 Piece ... 80.00
Pressed Glass, Flattened Diamond & Sunburst, Spooner, Miniatur ... 17.00 To 21.00
Pressed Glass, Flattened Diamond & Sunburst, Sugar, Miniature 23.00
Pressed Glass, Flattened Diamond & Sunburst, Table Set, Child's, 3 Piece ... 50.00
Pressed Glass, Flattened Diamond & Sunburst, Table Set, Miniature, 4 Piece ... 60.00
Pressed Glass, Flattened Hobnail, Goblet .... 7.50 To 12.50
Pressed Glass, Flattened Hobnail, Tumbler, 2 3/4 In. 6.00
Pressed Glass, Flattened Sawtooth, Goblet 8.00
Pressed Glass, Flattened Sawtooth, Salt, Master, Flint 20.00
Pressed Glass, Flattened Sawtooth, Spill 16.50
Pressed Glass, Flattened Sawtooth, Spill, Flint 24.00
Pressed Glass, Flattened Sawtooth, Spooner 16.50
Pressed Glass, Flattened Sawtooth, Sugar, Flint 25.00
Pressed Glass, Flattened Sawtooth, Tumbler, Footed, Flint 20.00
Pressed Glass, Fleur-De-Lis & Drape, Cake Stand 38.00
Pressed Glass, Fleur-De-Lis & Drape, Compote, Covered, 5 In. 32.00
Pressed Glass, Fleur-De-Lis & Drape, Compote, Green, 5 1/4 In. 15.00
Pressed Glass, Fleur-De-Lis & Drape, Compote, Jelly 8.00
Pressed Glass, Fleur-De-Lis & Drape, Creamer .... 14.00 To 16.75
Pressed Glass, Fleur-De-Lis & Drape, Creamer, Emerald Green 20.00
Pressed Glass, Fleur-De-Lis & Drape, Pitcher, Milk 23.50
Pressed Glass, Fleur-De-Lis & Drape, Pitcher, Water 19.00
Pressed Glass, Fleur-De-Lis & Drape, Plate, 10 1/4 In. 8.75
Pressed Glass, Fleur-De-Lis & Drape, Relish 8.00
Pressed Glass, Fleur-De-Lis & Drape, Relish, Rectangular 7.00
Pressed Glass, Fleur-De-Lis & Drape, Spooner 16.00
Pressed Glass, Fleur-De-Lis & Drape, Sugar, Covered .... 18.50 To 20.00
Pressed Glass, Fleur-De-Lis, Banded, Compote, Jelly 12.00
Pressed Glass, Fleur-De-Lis, Celery 16.50
Pressed Glass, Fleur-De-Lis, Celery, Green 25.00
Pressed Glass, Fleur-De-Lis, Cup Plate, Flint 8.00
Pressed Glass, Fleur-De-Lis, Mug, Ruby Stained 25.00
Pressed Glass, Fleur-De-Lis, Nappy, Greentown 14.50
Pressed Glass, Fleur-De-Lis, Pitcher, Water, Ruby Stained 45.00
Pressed Glass, Fleur-De-Lis, Plate, Cake, 10 In. 8.00
Pressed Glass, Fleur-De-Lis, Saltshaker 9.00
Pressed Glass, Fleur-De-Lis, Spooner, Ruby Stained 22.50
Pressed Glass, Fleur-De-Lis, Sugar & Creamer, Ruby Stained 40.00
Pressed Glass, Fleur-De-Lis, Sugar, Covered, Flint 80.00
Pressed Glass, Fleur-De-Lis, Toothpick .... 10.00 To 12.00
Pressed Glass, Fleur-De-Lis, Tumbler, Ruby Stained 18.00
Pressed Glass, Fleur-De-Lis, Vase, Ruby Stained, 11 In. 30.00
Pressed Glass, Floradora, Bottle, Cologne, Green, Gold, Footed 58.00
Pressed Glass, Floradora, Creamer, Green, Gold Trim, 4 Footed, 3 1/4 In. ... 22.50
Pressed Glass, Floradora, Spooner, Green, Gold 45.00
Pressed Glass, Floradora, Sugar, Rose, Covered, Gold Trim 50.00
Pressed Glass, Floradora, Toothpick, Rose, Gold Decoration 80.00
Pressed Glass, Floral Diamond, Cup, Punch 5.00
Pressed Glass, Floral, Bowl, Oval, Deep, 6 3/4 In. 18.00
Pressed Glass, Florida Palm, Creamer 22.50
Pressed Glass, Florida Palm, Goblet .... 15.00 To 18.00

Pressed Glass, Florida Palm, Plate, 9 1/4 In. 8.75
Pressed Glass, Florida Palm, Relish 3.75
Pressed Glass, Florida Palm, Tumbler 7.50
   Florida, see Herringbone
Pressed Glass, Flower Band, Celery, Frosted .... 42.00 To 48.75
Pressed Glass, Flower Band, Celery, Frosted, 2 Handles 45.00
Pressed Glass, Flower Band, Creamer, Frosted 35.00
Pressed Glass, Flower Band, Goblet, Frosted 35.00
Pressed Glass, Flower Band, Pitcher, Milk, Frosted 50.00
Pressed Glass, Flower Band, Sauce, Frosted, Footed, 4 In. 6.00
Pressed Glass, Flower Band, Sugar 16.50
Pressed Glass, Flower Band, Sugar, Frosted, Lovebirds Finial 85.00
Pressed Glass, Flower Medallion, Goblet 30.00
Pressed Glass, Flower Medallion, Goblet, Flint 28.00
   Flower Paneled Cane, see Cane & Rosette
   Flower with Cane, see Cane & Rosette
Pressed Glass, Flowerpot, Butter, Covered 20.00
Pressed Glass, Flowerpot, Pitcher, Milk 24.00
Pressed Glass, Flowerpot, Sauce, Amber, Footed, Square, 4 In. 14.00
Pressed Glass, Flowerpot, Sauce, Footed 5.50
Pressed Glass, Flowerpot, Sauce, Footed, 2 Handles 5.50
Pressed Glass, Flowerpot, Spooner 13.75
Pressed Glass, Flowerpot, Sugar 12.50
Pressed Glass, Flute, Berry Set, Miniature, 7 Piece 65.00
Pressed Glass, Flute, Butter, Domed Lid, Scalloped Base 22.50
Pressed Glass, Flute, Eggcup 15.00
Pressed Glass, Flute, Eggcup, Double, Flint .... 17.00 To 25.00
Pressed Glass, Flute, Eggcup, Flint 16.00
Pressed Glass, Flute, Goblet .... 9.50 To 15.00
Pressed Glass, Flute, Goblet, Flared Top, Flint 18.00
Pressed Glass, Flute, Goblet, Flint .... 16.00 To 20.00
Pressed Glass, Flute, Goblet, Flint, Pittsburgh 30.00
Pressed Glass, Flute, Goblet, Knob Stem, Flint 23.00
Pressed Glass, Flute, Hat, From Tumbler Mold, Flint, 3 X 5 In. 58.00
Pressed Glass, Flute, Mug, Applied Handle, Flint .... 12.00 To 36.00
Pressed Glass, Flute, Mug, Applied Handle, Ground Pontil, Flint, 2 3/4 In. 12.00
Pressed Glass, Flute, Spooner, Miniature 9.00
Pressed Glass, Flute, Tumbler, Bar, Flint 15.00
Pressed Glass, Flute, Tumbler, Child's 3.75
Pressed Glass, Flute, Tumbler, Flint 20.00
Pressed Glass, Flute, Tumbler, Whiskey, Flint 22.00
Pressed Glass, Flute, Water Set, Miniature, 7 Piece 45.00
Pressed Glass, Flute, Whiskey Taster, Footed, Flint 10.00
Pressed Glass, Flute, Wine 12.00
Pressed Glass, Flute, Wine, Flint 24.00
Pressed Glass, Flute, Wine, Rayed Base, Flint 7.50
Pressed Glass, Flute, Wine, Reeded Stem 12.00
Pressed Glass, Fluted Icicle, Goblet 15.00
Pressed Glass, Fluted Scroll, Bowl, Blue, Opalescent, Signed N, 7 In. 37.00
Pressed Glass, Fluted Scroll, Butter, Canary, Covered 85.00
Pressed Glass, Fluted Scroll, Butter, Canary, Opalescent 72.50
Pressed Glass, Fluted Scroll, Butter, Covered 25.00
Pressed Glass, Fluted Scroll, Creamer, Canary, Opalescent .... 55.00 To 65.00
Pressed Glass, Fluted Scroll, Dish, Candy, Blue, Opalescent 18.00
Pressed Glass, Fluted Scroll, Spooner, Opalescent 15.00
Pressed Glass, Fluted Scroll, Sugar, Canary, Covered 72.50
Pressed Glass, Fluted Scroll, Tray, Card, Emerald Green 14.00
   Flying Robin, see Hummingbird
Pressed Glass, Forget-Me-Not In Scroll, Butter, Covered 15.00
Pressed Glass, Forget-Me-Not In Scroll, Goblet .... 10.50 To 13.00
Pressed Glass, Forget-Me-Not In Scroll, Spooner 25.00
   Forget-Me-Not in Snow, see Stippled Forget-Me-Not
Pressed Glass, Forget-Me-Not, Muffineer, Green Opaque 78.00
Pressed Glass, Forget-Me-Not, Plate, World's Fair 1904, 7 1/2 In. 25.00
Pressed Glass, Forget-Me-Not, Relish 14.00
Pressed Glass, Four Panel, Sugar 12.50

Pressed Glass, Four Petal, Creamer	100.00
Pressed Glass, Four Petal, Creamer, Flint	80.00
Pressed Glass, Four Petal, Sugar & Creamer, Cover, Applied Handles, Flint	140.00
Pressed Glass, Four Petal, Sugar & Creamer, Cover, Flint	165.00
Pressed Glass, Four Petal, Sugar, Applied Handles, Flint	35.00
Pressed Glass, Four Petal, Sugar, Covered, Applied Handles, Flint	65.00
Pressed Glass, Four Petal, Sugar, Covered	60.00
Pressed Glass, Four Petal, Sugar, Covered, Flint	55.00 To 65.00
Pressed Glass, Four Petal, Sugar, Flint	35.00 To 55.00
Pressed Glass, Four Petal, Sugar, Pagoda Cover, Flint	72.50
Pressed Glass, Fox & Crow, Pitcher, Water	125.00
Pressed Glass, Frazier, Butter, Covered, Cranberry Flashed, Enamel Floral	38.00
Pressed Glass, Frazier, Sugar, Covered, Cranberry Flashed, Enamel Floral	28.00
Pressed Glass, French Drape, Tumbler, 6 Footed	30.00
Pressed Glass, Fringed Drape, Creamer, Ruby Stained	20.00
Pressed Glass, Fringed Drape, Salt & Pepper	16.50
Pressed Glass, Frost Crystal, Pitcher, Water, Ruby Stained	40.00
Pressed Glass, Frost Crystal, Table Set, Ruby Stained, 4 Piece	85.00
Pressed Glass, Frost Crystal, Tumbler, Ruby Stained	20.00
Pressed Glass, Frosted Artichoke, Plate, 6 In.	12.00
Pressed Glass, Frosted Artichoke, Sauce	6.25
Pressed Glass, Frosted Artichoke, Sauce, Large	8.50
Pressed Glass, Frosted Circle, Compote, Covered, High Standard, 7 X 12 In.	65.00
Pressed Glass, Frosted Circle, Compote, 7 X 7 In.	32.00
Pressed Glass, Frosted Circle, Compote, 10 In.	27.50
Pressed Glass, Frosted Circle, Cup & Saucer	40.00
Pressed Glass, Frosted Circle, Saltshaker	22.50
Pressed Glass, Frosted Circle, Sugar, Covered	40.00 To 50.00
Pressed Glass, Frosted Circle, Tumbler	20.00
Frosted Crane, see Frosted Stork	
Pressed Glass, Frosted Eagle, Compote, Covered, High Standard, 8 In.	145.00
Pressed Glass, Frosted Eagle, Compote, Covered, 8 In.	145.00
Pressed Glass, Frosted Eagle, Compote, Etched Leaf Lid, 13 In.	150.00
Pressed Glass, Frosted Eagle, Compote, 8 In.	150.00
Pressed Glass, Frosted Eagle, Creamer	11.00
Pressed Glass, Frosted Eagle, Salt, Individual	22.50
Frosted Festal Band, see Shield Band	
Frosted Flower Band, see Flower Band	
Pressed Glass, Frosted Leaf, Celery	150.00
Pressed Glass, Frosted Leaf, Celery, Flint	120.00
Pressed Glass, Frosted Leaf, Eggcup	130.00
Pressed Glass, Frosted Leaf, Eggcup, Flint	65.00
Pressed Glass, Frosted Leaf, Goblet	75.00
Pressed Glass, Frosted Leaf, Goblet, Buttermilk, Flint	18.00
Pressed Glass, Frosted Leaf, Goblet, Lady's, Flint	65.00
Pressed Glass, Frosted Leaf, Sauce	15.00
Pressed Glass, Frosted Leaf, Sauce, Flint	12.00
Pressed Glass, Frosted Lion, Butter, Etched Rampant Lion	125.00
Pressed Glass, Frosted Lion, Celery	55.00 To 68.00
Pressed Glass, Frosted Lion, Compote, Covered, High Standard, 7 In.	65.00
Pressed Glass, Frosted Lion, Compote, Covered, Low Standard, 8 In.	50.00
Pressed Glass, Frosted Lion, Compote, Covered, Oval, Low Standard, 7 In.	55.00
Pressed Glass, Frosted Lion, Compote, Covered, 8 In.	75.00 To 80.00
Pressed Glass, Frosted Lion, Compote, Frosted Lion's Head Finial, 8 In.	75.00
Pressed Glass, Frosted Lion, Compote, 7 In.	33.00
Pressed Glass, Frosted Lion, Compote, 9 1/2 In.High	85.00
Pressed Glass, Frosted Lion, Creamer	45.00 To 50.00
Pressed Glass, Frosted Lion, Dish, Cheese, Covered	275.00
Pressed Glass, Frosted Lion, Eggcup	47.50
Pressed Glass, Frosted Lion, Goblet	32.50 To 65.00
Pressed Glass, Frosted Lion, Jar, Jam	65.00
Pressed Glass, Frosted Lion, Jar, Marmalade	45.22
Pressed Glass, Frosted Lion, Pitcher, Water	225.00
Pressed Glass, Frosted Lion, Pitcher, Water, Applied Handle	145.00
Pressed Glass, Frosted Lion, Plate, Bread	55.00
Pressed Glass, Frosted Lion, Plate, Bread, Lion Handles, Etched Ferns, C.1870	55.00

Pressed Glass, Frosted Lion, Plate, Bread, Rope Edge, 12 In. 45.00
Pressed Glass, Frosted Lion, Plate, Bread, Round 35.00
Pressed Glass, Frosted Lion, Relish, Handled 35.00
Pressed Glass, Frosted Lion, Salt, Master 125.00
Pressed Glass, Frosted Lion, Sauce, Footed, 4 In. .... 14.00 To 15.00
Pressed Glass, Frosted Lion, Spooner 38.00
Pressed Glass, Frosted Lion, Sugar, Covered 85.00
Pressed Glass, Frosted Lion, Sugar, Covered, Etched 95.00
Pressed Glass, Frosted Lion, Sugar, Covered, Etched Rampant Lion 95.00
Pressed Glass, Frosted Ribbon, Bowl, Waste 38.00
Pressed Glass, Frosted Ribbon, Celery 45.00
Pressed Glass, Frosted Ribbon, Compote, Low Standard, 8 In. 45.00
Pressed Glass, Frosted Ribbon, Creamer .... 20.00 To 38.00
Pressed Glass, Frosted Ribbon, Goblet .... 12.50 To 22.50
Pressed Glass, Frosted Ribbon, Pitcher, Water 30.00
Pressed Glass, Frosted Ribbon, Sauce, Handled, Scalloped Top 5.00
Pressed Glass, Frosted Ribbon, Spooner 12.00
Pressed Glass, Frosted Ribbon, Table Set, 4 Piece 135.00
Pressed Glass, Frosted Roman Key, Celery 85.00
Pressed Glass, Frosted Roman Key, Celery, Flint 70.00
Pressed Glass, Frosted Roman Key, Champagne 58.00
Pressed Glass, Frosted Roman Key, Champagne, Flint 50.00
Pressed Glass, Frosted Roman Key, Eggcup 35.00
Pressed Glass, Frosted Roman Key, Eggcup, Flint .... 32.00 To 35.00
Pressed Glass, Frosted Roman Key, Goblet 40.00
Pressed Glass, Frosted Roman Key, Goblet, Flint .... 30.00 To 45.00
Pressed Glass, Frosted Roman Key, Salt, Master 35.00
Pressed Glass, Frosted Roman Key, Spill, Flint 35.00
Pressed Glass, Frosted Roman Key, Spooner 40.00
Pressed Glass, Frosted Roman Key, Spooner, Flint 35.00
Pressed Glass, Frosted Roman Key, Sugar, Covered .... 55.00 To 95.00
Pressed Glass, Frosted Roman Key, Sugar, Covered, Flint 85.00
Pressed Glass, Frosted Roman Key, Tumbler 90.00
Pressed Glass, Frosted Roman Key, Tumbler, Flint 85.00
Pressed Glass, Frosted Roman Key, Wine 60.00
Pressed Glass, Frosted Roman Key, Wine, Flint 55.00
Pressed Glass, Frosted Stork, Creamer 45.00
Pressed Glass, Frosted Stork, Goblet .... 30.00 To 45.00
Pressed Glass, Frosted Stork, Jar, Pickle, Silver Plate Frame, Stork On Lid 95.00
Pressed Glass, Frosted Stork, Pitcher, Water 55.00
Pressed Glass, Frosted Stork, Plate, Bread 75.00
Pressed Glass, Frosted Stork, Plate, Bread, 101 Border .... 43.00 To 55.00

Pressed Glass,
Frosted Eagle, Compote

Pressed Glass, Frosted Lion,
Open Compote

Pressed Glass,
Frosted Dolphin, Pitcher

Pressed Glass, Frosted Stork, Plate, 101 Border, Iowa City, Handled, 9 In.	68.00
Pressed Glass, Frosted Stork, Platter, 101 Border, Iowa City, 11 3/4 X 8 In.	65.00
Pressed Glass, Frosted Stork, Sauce	12.50
Pressed Glass, Frosted Swirl, Butter	38.00
Pressed Glass, Frosted Swirl, Creamer	27.50
Pressed Glass, Frosted Swirl, Spooner	25.00
Pressed Glass, Frosted Swirl, Sugar, Covered	38.00
Frosted Waffle, see Hidalgo	
Frosted patterns, see under name of main pattern	
Pressed Glass, Fruit Panels, Goblet	15.00 To 18.50
Pressed Glass, G.A.R., Goblet	60.00
Pressed Glass, Gaelic, Cake Stand, 10 1/2 In.	26.00
Pressed Glass, Gaelic, Goblet	7.00
Pressed Glass, Gaelic, Spooner	15.00
Pressed Glass, Galloway, Bowl, Berry, Gold Edge	18.00
Pressed Glass, Galloway, Bowl, Vegetable, Oval	22.00
Pressed Glass, Galloway, Bowl, 9 3/4 In.	30.00
Pressed Glass, Galloway, Cake Stand	35.00
Pressed Glass, Galloway, Compote, Jelly, 6 X 4 In.	28.00
Pressed Glass, Galloway, Compote, 4 X 6 1/2 In.	28.00
Pressed Glass, Galloway, Cruet, Vinegar	25.00 To 27.50
Pressed Glass, Galloway, Cup, Punch	12.50
Pressed Glass, Galloway, Pitcher, Water	17.50
Pressed Glass, Galloway, Plate, 6 In.	9.00
Pressed Glass, Galloway, Salt & Pepper	15.00 To 19.50
Pressed Glass, Galloway, Salt & Pepper, Aluminum Tops	12.50
Pressed Glass, Galloway, Salt, Pink	10.00
Pressed Glass, Galloway, Saltshaker	8.00
Pressed Glass, Galloway, Sauce, Footed	5.75 To 8.00
Pressed Glass, Galloway, Sherbet, 4 In. Diameter	6.00
Pressed Glass, Galloway, Spooner	25.00
Pressed Glass, Galloway, Sugar & Creamer, Etched, McKee	35.00
Pressed Glass, Galloway, Sugar, Covered	45.00
Pressed Glass, Galloway, Syrup	24.00 To 38.00
Pressed Glass, Galloway, Toothpick	10.00 To 22.00
Pressed Glass, Galloway, Tumbler	12.00 To 20.00
Pressed Glass, Galloway, Tumbler, Gold Trim	20.00
Pressed Glass, Galloway, Vase, 11 In.	10.00
Pressed Glass, Galloway, Vase, 12 In.	15.00
Pressed Glass, Galloway, Vase, 14 In.	15.00
Pressed Glass, Galloway, Vase, 20 In.	20.00
Pressed Glass, Galloway, Water Set, Miniature, 5 Piece	40.00
Pressed Glass, Galloway, Wine	15.00 To 25.00
Pressed Glass, Garden Fern, Goblet	16.00
Pressed Glass, Garden Fruits, Compote, Jelly	15.00
Pressed Glass, Garden Fruits, Goblet	14.00
Garden of Eden, see Lotus & Serpent	
Pressed Glass, Garfield Drape, Celery	18.00
Pressed Glass, Garfield Drape, Creamer	20.00 To 32.50
Pressed Glass, Garfield Drape, Goblet	25.00 To 54.50
Pressed Glass, Garfield Drape, Goblet, Large Size	24.50
Pressed Glass, Garfield Drape, Pitcher, Water	40.00
Pressed Glass, Garfield Drape, Pitcher, Water, Bulbous, Applied Handle	55.00
Pressed Glass, Garfield Drape, Plate, Bread	30.00 To 55.00
Pressed Glass, Garfield Drape, Plate, Bread, Round	36.00
Pressed Glass, Garfield Drape, Plate, Star Base, 11 1/4 In.	24.50
Pressed Glass, Garfield Drape, Spooner	17.50 To 22.00
Pressed Glass, Garfield Memorial, Mug	30.00
Pressed Glass, Garfield Memorial, Plate, Scalloped Edge, 10 In.	34.00
Pressed Glass, Garfield Memorial, Plate, 10 In.	23.50 To 35.00
Pressed Glass, Garfield Memorial, Plate, 12 In.	25.00
Pressed Glass, Garfield Star, Plate, Frosted, 6 In.	14.00 To 18.00
Pressed Glass, Garfield, Cup Plate, Frosted Bust In Base	35.00
Pressed Glass, Garfield, Plate, Frosted, 6 In.	18.50
Pressed Glass, Garfield, Tumbler, Wreath In Base	28.75
Pressed Glass, Gathered Knot, Wine	10.00

Pressed Glass, Geneva, Pitcher, Water, Green, Gold Trim 125.00
Pressed Glass, Geneva, Saltshaker 35.00
Pressed Glass, Georgia Belle, Goblet 18.00
Pressed Glass, Giant Bull's-Eye, Goblet, Flint .... 65.00 To 70.00
Pressed Glass, Giant Bull's-Eye, Wine, Findlay .... 19.00 To 19.50
Pressed Glass, Giant Prism With Thumbprint Band, Celery 125.00
Pressed Glass, Giant Prism With Thumbprint Band, Goblet, Flint 85.00
Pressed Glass, Giant Prism With Thumbprint Band, Spill, Flint 30.00
Pressed Glass, Giant Prism With Thumbprint Band, Spooner 35.00
Pressed Glass, Giant Prism With Thumbprint Band, Spooner, Flint 30.00
Pressed Glass, Giant Prism With Thumbprint Band, Tumbler, Flint 50.00
Pressed Glass, Giant Prism, Champagne 25.00
Pressed Glass, Giant Prism, Champagne, Flint 20.00
Pressed Glass, Giant Prism, Compote, Covered, Flint, 6 In.Diameter 65.00
Pressed Glass, Giant Prism, Goblet 50.00
Pressed Glass, Giant Prism, Tumbler, Bar, Flint 25.00
Pressed Glass, Giant Sawtooth, Eggcup 35.00
Pressed Glass, Giant Sawtooth, Goblet, Flint .... 35.00 To 85.00
Pressed Glass, Giant Sawtooth, Salt, Master 11.00
Pressed Glass, Giant Sawtooth, Salt, Master, Flint 13.50
Pressed Glass, Giant Sawtooth, Spooner, Flint 25.00
Pressed Glass, Giant Sawtooth, Tumbler 95.00
Pressed Glass, Giant Sawtooth, Tumbler, Flint 70.00
Pressed Glass, Giant Thumbprint, Tumbler, Flint 30.00
Pressed Glass, Girl With Fan, Goblet .... 20.00 To 40.00
Pressed Glass, Girl With Parrot, Plate, 10 In. 75.00
Pressed Glass, Goat's Head, Compote, Low Standard, Oval, 9 In. 45.00
Pressed Glass, Goat's Head, Creamer .... 40.00 To 55.00
Pressed Glass, Goat's Head, Spooner 35.00
    Good Luck, see Horseshoe
Pressed Glass, Gooseberry, Creamer .... 19.50 To 27.50
Pressed Glass, Gooseberry, Mug 16.00
Pressed Glass, Gooseberry, Tumbler 13.00
Pressed Glass, Gooseberry, Tumbler, Handled 35.00
Pressed Glass, Gormand, Goblet, Inverted Thumbprint 12.50
Pressed Glass, Gothic Arch, Eggcup 30.00
Pressed Glass, Gothic Arch, Sugar, Covered 77.50
Pressed Glass, Gothic Arch, Sugar, Covered, Flint 110.00
Pressed Glass, Gothic Arch, Sugar, Flint 95.00
Pressed Glass, Gothic Windows, Creamer 5.00
Pressed Glass, Gothic, Bowl, Oblong, 7 X 5 1/4 In. 55.00
Pressed Glass, Gothic, Celery 125.00
Pressed Glass, Gothic, Champagne 90.00
Pressed Glass, Gothic, Champagne, Flint 80.00
Pressed Glass, Gothic, Creamer, Flint 62.50
Pressed Glass, Gothic, Eggcup .... 27.50 To 30.00
Pressed Glass, Gothic, Eggcup, Flint 42.00
Pressed Glass, Gothic, Goblet 36.00
Pressed Glass, Gothic, Goblet, Flint .... 40.00 To 45.00
Pressed Glass, Gothic, Sauce, Flint 10.00
Pressed Glass, Gothic, Spill, Flint 30.00
Pressed Glass, Gothic, Spooner 40.00
Pressed Glass, Gothic, Spooner, Flint 30.00
Pressed Glass, Gothic, Sugar 25.00
Pressed Glass, Gothic, Sugar, Covered .... 60.00 To 70.00
Pressed Glass, Gothic, Sugar, Covered, Flint 65.00
Pressed Glass, Gothic, Wine 75.00
    Grace, see Butterfly & Fan
Pressed Glass, Graduated Diamonds, Goblet 18.00
    Grand Army of the Republic, see G.A.R.
Pressed Glass, Grand Inverted Thumbprint, Goblet, Light Amber 14.00
    Grand, see Diamond Medallion
Pressed Glass, Grant, Plate, Patriot & Soldier, Square, 9 1/2 In. 45.00
Pressed Glass, Grape & Festoon With Shield, Mug 16.00
Pressed Glass, Grape & Festoon With Clear Leaf, Goblet 17.50
Pressed Glass, Grape & Festoon With Shield, Mug, Child's .... 12.00 To 18.00

Pressed Glass, Garfield Drape, Water Pitcher

Pressed Glass,
Sandwich Loop,
Eggcup, Opalescent

Pressed Glass,
Grape & Festoon With Shield,
Goblet

Pressed Glass,
Grape & Festoon, Cup

Pressed Glass, Grape & Festoon With Shield, Sauce	5.00
Pressed Glass, Grape & Festoon With Stippled Leaf, Creamer	16.50 To 18.00
Pressed Glass, Grape & Festoon With Stippled Leaf, Goblet	14.50 To 17.00
Pressed Glass, Grape & Festoon With Stippled Leaf, Goblet, Buttermilk, 1870	14.00
Pressed Glass, Grape & Festoon, Eggcup	13.00 To 16.00
Pressed Glass, Grape & Festoon, Goblet	12.50 To 16.00
Pressed Glass, Grape & Festoon, Relish, Oval, 8 1/2 In.	9.50
Pressed Glass, Grape & Festoon, Spooner	28.00
Pressed Glass, Grape & Festoon, Sugar, Amber, Grape Finial, Footed	35.00
Pressed Glass, Grape & Fig, Pitcher, Milk	38.00
Pressed Glass, Grape & Leaf, Cake Stand	12.50
Pressed Glass, Grape & Thumbprint Band, Bowl, Berry, Covered	30.00
Pressed Glass, Grape & Thumbprint Band, Goblet	9.00
Pressed Glass, Grape Band, Butter, Covered	26.50
Pressed Glass, Grape Band, Creamer, Pedestal Base	25.00
Pressed Glass, Grape Band, Goblet	13.00 To 16.00
Pressed Glass, Grape Band, Sauce	3.75
Pressed Glass, Grape Band, Tumbler, Bar Type	15.00
Pressed Glass, Grape Bunch, Eggcup	12.00
Pressed Glass, Grape Vintage, Plate, Bread	22.50
Pressed Glass, Grape With Scroll Medallion, Butter, Covered	22.50
Pressed Glass, Grape With Scroll Medallion, Mug, Miniature	12.00 To 14.00
Pressed Glass, Grape With Vine, Butter	22.00
Pressed Glass, Grape With Vine, Butter, Covered	22.50
Pressed Glass, Grape With Vine, Creamer	12.50 To 14.00
Pressed Glass, Grape, Eggcup	22.50
Pressed Glass, Grape, Pitcher, Water, Applied Handle, McKee	65.00
Pressed Glass, Grape, Sugar, Covered, 6 1/2 In.	10.00

Grape, see also Beaded Grape, Beaded Grape Medallion, Magnet &
Grape, Magnet & Grape with Frosted Leaf, Paneled Grape, Paneled
Grape Band

Pressed Glass, Grapevine In Ovals, Creamer, Amber, Miniature	40.00
Pressed Glass, Grapevine In Ovals, Spooner, Oval, Miniature	25.00
Pressed Glass, Grasshopper With Insect, Celery	38.00
Pressed Glass, Grasshopper With Insect, Sugar, Covered	64.00

Pressed Glass, Grasshopper, Bowl, Footed, Round, 10 In.	15.00
Pressed Glass, Grasshopper, Bowl, Shallow, 10 In.	15.00
Pressed Glass, Grasshopper, Butter	45.00
Pressed Glass, Grasshopper, Pitcher, Water, 9 In.	45.00
Pressed Glass, Grasshopper, Sugar & Creamer, Insect On Sugar	60.00
Pressed Glass, Greek Cross, Goblet	20.00
Pressed Glass, Greek Key, Celery, 9 In.	48.00
Pressed Glass, Greek Key, Goblet, Frosted, Flint	40.00
Pressed Glass, Greek Key, Sugar, Flint	28.00
Pressed Glass, Greek Key, Sugar, U.S.Glass Co.	8.00
Pressed Glass, Greek Key, Tumbler, Red Flashed Strawberries, Gold, Paneled	15.00
Pressed Glass, Greek Key, Wine	12.00
Pressed Glass, Grenada, Celery	12.50
Pressed Glass, Gridley, Pitcher, Water	47.50 To 85.00
Pressed Glass, Grogan, Goblet	12.00
Pressed Glass, Group Thumbprint, Goblet	8.50
Gypsy, see Baltimore Pear	
Pressed Glass, Gyro, Sauce, Green	12.00
Pressed Glass, Hairpin & Diamond Diapering, Compote, Flint, 6 1/2 In.	190.00
Pressed Glass, Hairpin With Thumbprint, Cordial, Flint	52.00
Pressed Glass, Hairpin With Thumbprint, Goblet, Flint	32.00 To 38.00
Pressed Glass, Hairpin With Thumbprint, Spill, Flint	35.00
Pressed Glass, Hairpin With Thumbprint, Spooner	40.00
Pressed Glass, Hairpin With Thumbprint, Spooner, Flint	35.00
Pressed Glass, Hairpin, Celery, Flint	45.00
Pressed Glass, Hairpin, Celery, Scalloped Rim, 8 1/4 In.	30.00
Pressed Glass, Hairpin, Champagne, Flint	35.00 To 40.00
Pressed Glass, Hairpin, Compote, Scalloped Rim, C.1850, 11 1/4 X 8 1/2 In.	120.00
Pressed Glass, Hairpin, Creamer	80.00
Pressed Glass, Hairpin, Creamer, Flint	65.00
Pressed Glass, Hairpin, Eggcup	17.50
Pressed Glass, Hairpin, Eggcup, Flint	15.00 To 20.00
Pressed Glass, Hairpin, Goblet	32.00
Pressed Glass, Hairpin, Goblet, Flint	20.00 To 26.00
Pressed Glass, Hairpin, Sauce, Flint, 4 In.	6.00
Pressed Glass, Hairpin, Sugar, Covered, Flint	60.00
Pressed Glass, Hairpin, Sugar, Flint	26.00
Pressed Glass, Hairpin, Tumbler, Whiskey, Handled, Flint	40.00
Pressed Glass, Hairpin, Wine, Flint	30.00 To 35.00
Pressed Glass, Half Flute, Wine, Etched	12.00
Pressed Glass, Halley's Comet, Goblet	16.50 To 25.00
Pressed Glass, Halley's Comet, Goblet, Findlay	15.00
Pressed Glass, Halley's Comet, Spooner, Findlay	17.50
Pressed Glass, Halley's Comet, Sugar, Findlay	14.00
Pressed Glass, Halley's Comet, Tumbler	12.00
Pressed Glass, Halley's Comet, Tumbler, Etched	15.00
Pressed Glass, Halley's Comet, Wine	10.00 To 18.50
Hamilton with Clear Leaf, see Hamilton with Leaf	
Pressed Glass, Hamilton With Frosted Leaf, Butter, Covered	75.00
Pressed Glass, Hamilton With Frosted Leaf, Creamer	60.00
Pressed Glass, Hamilton With Frosted Leaf, Goblet, Flint	55.00 To 60.00
Pressed Glass, Hamilton With Frosted Leaf, Sugar, Covered	80.00
Pressed Glass, Hamilton With Frosted Leaf, Sugar, Covered, Flint	75.00
Pressed Glass, Hamilton With Leaf, Creamer, Flint	35.00
Pressed Glass, Hamilton With Leaf, Eggcup	25.00 To 40.00
Pressed Glass, Hamilton With Leaf, Eggcup, Flint	38.00
Pressed Glass, Hamilton With Leaf, Goblet	45.00 To 58.00
Pressed Glass, Hamilton With Leaf, Goblet, Flint	28.00 To 48.00
Pressed Glass, Hamilton With Leaf, Wine	50.00
Pressed Glass, Hamilton, Butter, Covered	65.00
Pressed Glass, Hamilton, Butter, Covered, Flint	65.00
Pressed Glass, Hamilton, Compote, Flint, 7 In.	30.00
Pressed Glass, Hamilton, Compote, Flint, 8 In.	32.00
Pressed Glass, Hamilton, Compote, Scalloped, Raised Foot, Flint, 7 3/4 In.	55.00
Pressed Glass, Hamilton, Compote, 8 In.	32.00
Pressed Glass, Hamilton, Creamer	12.00

Pressed Glass, Hairpin, Goblet, Rayed Base

Pressed Glass, Hamilton, Compote

Pressed Glass, Harp, Spill Holder

Pressed Glass, Hamilton, Eggcup	22.50 To 35.00
Pressed Glass, Hamilton, Eggcup, Flint	26.00 To 28.00
Pressed Glass, Hamilton, Goblet	25.00 To 35.00
Pressed Glass, Hamilton, Goblet, Flint	30.00 To 48.00
Pressed Glass, Hamilton, Sauce	8.50
Pressed Glass, Hamilton, Sauce, Scalloped Rim	10.00
Pressed Glass, Hamilton, Sauce, Scalloped Rim, Flint, 4 In.	10.00
Pressed Glass, Hamilton, Spill, Flint	25.00
Pressed Glass, Hamilton, Spooner	25.00 To 32.00
Pressed Glass, Hamilton, Spooner, Flint	18.50 To 25.00
Pressed Glass, Hamilton, Sugar, Flint	20.00 To 29.00
Pressed Glass, Hamilton, Tumbler	85.00
Pressed Glass, Hamilton, Tumbler, Whiskey, Flint	70.00
Pressed Glass, Hamilton, Wine	55.00
Hand, see Pennsylvania	
Pressed Glass, Hanover, Cake Stand, Amber	45.00
Pressed Glass, Hanover, Celery	18.00
Pressed Glass, Hanover, Goblet	14.75 To 16.00
Pressed Glass, Hanover, Plate, 10 1/2 In.	10.00
Pressed Glass, Harp, Dish, Sweetmeat, Covered, Flint	110.00
Pressed Glass, Harp, Spill	37.00 To 45.00
Pressed Glass, Harp, Spill, Flint	37.00 To 65.00
Pressed Glass, Harp, Spooner	35.00 To 45.00
Pressed Glass, Harp, Spooner, Flint	40.00
Pressed Glass, Hartford, Goblet	5.00
Pressed Glass, Hartley, Celery	12.00 To 18.00
Pressed Glass, Hartley, Creamer	15.00 To 18.50
Pressed Glass, Hartley, Goblet	15.00 To 17.50
Pressed Glass, Hawaiian Lei, Bowl, 8 In.	7.00
Pressed Glass, Hawaiian Lei, Celery, 2 Handled	21.00
Pressed Glass, Hawaiian Lei, Champagne	13.50
Pressed Glass, Hawaiian Lei, Compote, Jelly	8.00
Pressed Glass, Hawaiian Lei, Creamer, Miniature	15.00 To 23.00
Pressed Glass, Hawaiian Lei, Pitcher, Milk, 5 1/2 In.	17.00
Pressed Glass, Hawaiian Lei, Sauce	3.75
Pressed Glass, Hawaiian Lei, Spooner, Miniature	22.00
Pressed Glass, Hawaiian Lei, Sugar & Creamer	20.00
Pressed Glass, Hawaiian Lei, Table Set, Miniature, 4 Piece	105.00
Pressed Glass, Hawaiian Lei, Wine	7.50 To 12.50
Pressed Glass, Hawaiian Pineapple, Goblet, Flint	50.00
Pressed Glass, Hawaiian Pineapple, Tumbler	80.00
Pressed Glass, Heart & Thumbprint, Bowl, Berry, Gold, 9 In.	16.50
Pressed Glass, Heart & Thumbprint, Bowl, Fruit, 9 In.	38.00
Pressed Glass, Heart & Thumbprint, Bowl, 8 1/2 In.	27.50
Pressed Glass, Heart & Thumbprint, Bucket, Ice	29.00
Pressed Glass, Heart & Thumbprint, Celery	25.00

Pressed Glass, Heart & Thumbprint, Cordial 45.00
Pressed Glass, Heart & Thumbprint, Creamer 32.00
Pressed Glass, Heart & Thumbprint, Creamer, Child's 8.00
Pressed Glass, Heart & Thumbprint, Cruet, Faceted Stopper 45.00
Pressed Glass, Heart & Thumbprint, Cup, Punch .... 6.00 To 12.00
Pressed Glass, Heart & Thumbprint, Goblet .... 28.00 To 34.00
Pressed Glass, Heart & Thumbprint, Goblet, Gold Trim .... 19.00 To 32.00
Pressed Glass, Heart & Thumbprint, Jar, Powder 22.50
Pressed Glass, Heart & Thumbprint, Plate, Cake, 10 In. 35.00
Pressed Glass, Heart & Thumbprint, Plate, Gold, 9 In. 18.00
Pressed Glass, Heart & Thumbprint, Sugar, Gold Flashing 16.00
Pressed Glass, Heart & Thumbprint, Sugar, Individual 9.00
Pressed Glass, Heart & Thumbprint, Syrup, Pewter Lid, 6 In.High 38.00
Pressed Glass, Heart & Thumbprint, Tray, Card 18.00
Pressed Glass, Heart & Thumbprint, Tray, Gold Flashing, 6 In. 18.00
Pressed Glass, Heart & Thumbprint, Tray, Card, Gold Trim, Turned Up Sides 15.00
Pressed Glass, Heart & Thumbprint, Tumbler 20.00
Pressed Glass, Heart & Thumbprint, Vase, Gold Trim, 6 In. 13.50
Pressed Glass, Heart & Thumbprint, Vase, 6 In. 22.00
Pressed Glass, Heart & Thumbprint, Wine .... 20.00 To 35.00
Pressed Glass, Heart & Thumbprint, Wine, Gold Trim 29.00
Pressed Glass, Heart Band, Creamer, Ruby Stained 12.50
Pressed Glass, Heart Band, Mug, Ruby Stained, Large 15.00
Pressed Glass, Heart Band, Mug, Ruby Stained, Small 10.00
Pressed Glass, Heart Band, Sugar & Creamer, Ruby Stained 20.00
Pressed Glass, Heart Band, Tumbler, Ruby Stained 15.00
Pressed Glass, Heart Plume, Dish, Candy, Heart Shape 10.00
Pressed Glass, Heart Plume, Nappy, Gold Trim, Heart Shape 10.00
Pressed Glass, Heart Stem, Table Set, 3 Piece 100.00
Pressed Glass, Heart, Eggcup 20.00
Pressed Glass, Heart, Goblet .... 15.00 To 16.50
Pressed Glass, Heart, Match Holder, Green, Wall 12.00
    Hearts of Loch Laven, see Shuttle
Pressed Glass, Heavy Diamond, Creamer .... 9.50 To 10.00
Pressed Glass, Heavy New York, Goblet 6.00
    Heavy Paneled Finecut, see Paneled Diamond Cross
Pressed Glass, Heavy Thumbprint, Goblet, 3 Rows 7.50
Pressed Glass, Hen Cover, Dish, Deep Blue Frosted, Basket Weave Base, 6 In. 65.00
Pressed Glass, Hen Cover, Dish, Feathers & Basket Weave Base, Oval 25.00
Pressed Glass, Henrietta, Bowl, Berry, Ruby Stained 35.00
Pressed Glass, Henrietta, Butter, Covered, Ruby Stained 35.00
Pressed Glass, Henrietta, Celery 20.00
Pressed Glass, Henrietta, Creamer, Ruby Stained 30.00
Pressed Glass, Henrietta, Cup, Punch, Etched, Ruby Stained 29.00
Pressed Glass, Henrietta, Pitcher, Water, Tankard Type, Ruby Stained 55.00
Pressed Glass, Henrietta, Spooner, Ruby Stained 25.00
Pressed Glass, Henrietta, Sugar, Covered, Ruby Stained 35.00
Pressed Glass, Henrietta, Tumbler, Ruby Stained, Etched 25.00
Pressed Glass, Hercules' Pillar, Claret, Flint 55.00
Pressed Glass, Hercules' Pillar, Eggcup, Double, Flint 30.00
Pressed Glass, Hercules' Pillar, Sugar, Flint 30.00
Pressed Glass, Hercules' Pillar, Tumbler, Footed, Flint 30.00
Pressed Glass, Heron With Fish Base, Eggcup 37.50
Pressed Glass, Heron, Creamer 18.00
Pressed Glass, Heron, Jar, Jam 17.00
Pressed Glass, Herringbone Band, Goblet 5.00
Pressed Glass, Herringbone Band, Sugar 9.50
Pressed Glass, Herringbone Band, Wine 6.00
Pressed Glass, Herringbone, Bowl, Berry, Emerald Green, 9 In. 28.00
Pressed Glass, Herringbone, Bowl, Ruby Stained, Square, 7 In. 15.00
Pressed Glass, Herringbone, Bowl, Ruby Stained, 7 In. 15.00
Pressed Glass, Herringbone, Butter, Covered, 5 X 6 In. 25.00
Pressed Glass, Herringbone, Butter, Green, Covered 37.50
Pressed Glass, Herringbone, Creamer 17.50
Pressed Glass, Herringbone, Creamer, Green 25.00
Pressed Glass, Herringbone, Creamer, Ruby Stained, Gold Flower 48.00

Pressed Glass, Herringbone, Goblet .... 9.00 To 13.00
Pressed Glass, Herringbone, Pitcher, Water, Emerald Green .... 40.00 To 55.00
Pressed Glass, Herringbone, Relish, Ruby Stained, Oval 39.00
Pressed Glass, Herringbone, Sauce, Emerald Green .... 5.00 To 8.00
Pressed Glass, Herringbone, Sauce, Green, Square, 8 In. 5.00
Pressed Glass, Herringbone, Sauce, Ruby Stained 5.00
Pressed Glass, Herringbone, Spooner 15.00
Pressed Glass, Herringbone, Sugar, Green 20.00
Pressed Glass, Herringbone, Wine 15.00
Pressed Glass, Hexagon Block, Bowl, Berry, Ruby Stained, Scalloped, 6 3/4 In. 25.00
Pressed Glass, Hexagon Block, Cake Stand, Findlay, 9 In. 27.50
Pressed Glass, Hexagon Block, Cake Stand, 9 In. 27.00
Pressed Glass, Hexagonal Bull's-Eye, Spooner 18.00
Pressed Glass, Hexagonal Bull's-Eye, Spooner, Findlay 13.00
Pressed Glass, Hickman, Bowl & Base, Punch, 16 In. 125.00
Pressed Glass, Hickman, Butter, Covered, Pedestal 27.00
Pressed Glass, Hickman, Compote, Candy 12.50
Pressed Glass, Hickman, Compote, Tall Foot, 7 1/2 X 5 1/2 In. 28.00
Pressed Glass, Hickman, Condiment Set, Child's, 4 Piece .... 30.00 To 40.00
Pressed Glass, Hickman, Goblet .... 14.50 To 21.50
Pressed Glass, Hidalgo, Celery 10.00
Pressed Glass, Hidalgo, Celery, Frosted, Boat Shape 37.50
Pressed Glass, Hidalgo, Goblet 18.00
Pressed Glass, Hidalgo, Goblet, Etched .... 12.00 To 15.00
Pressed Glass, Hidalgo, Goblet, Frosted 13.50
Pressed Glass, Hidalgo, Goblet, Ruby Stained 22.50
Pressed Glass, Hidalgo, Muffineer, Frosted 20.00
Pressed Glass, Hidalgo, Plate, Square, 10 1/2 In. 8.75
Pressed Glass, Hidalgo, Plate, 10 1/2 In. 5.00
Pressed Glass, Hidalgo, Sauce, Frosted 4.50
Pressed Glass, High Hob, Plate, Round, 10 1/4 In. 12.50
Pressed Glass, High Hob, Wine 9.75
Pressed Glass, Hinoto, Celery 125.00
Pressed Glass, Hinoto, Celery, Flint 100.00
Pressed Glass, Hinoto, Champagne 55.00
Pressed Glass, Hinoto, Creamer, Flint 70.00
Pressed Glass, Hinoto, Salt 15.00
Pressed Glass, Hinoto, Spill, Flint 30.00
Pressed Glass, Hinoto, Spooner 40.00
Pressed Glass, Hinoto, Spooner, Flint 30.00
Pressed Glass, Hinoto, Sugar, Covered .... 70.00 To 75.00
Pressed Glass, Hinoto, Sugar, Covered, Flint .... 65.00 To 75.00
Pressed Glass, Hinoto, Tumbler, Footed 60.00
Pressed Glass, Hinoto, Tumbler, Footed, Flint .... 25.00 To 45.00
Pressed Glass, Hinoto, Tumbler, Whiskey, Flint 40.00
Pressed Glass, Hinoto, Tumbler, Whiskey, Handled, Flint .... 45.00 To 50.00
Pressed Glass, Hinoto, Wine 65.00
Pressed Glass, Hinoto, Wine, Flint 60.00
Pressed Glass, Hobnail In Square, Mug 6.00
Pressed Glass, Hobnail With Fan, Bowl, Berry 5.00
Pressed Glass, Hobnail With Fan, Goblet 18.50
Pressed Glass, Hobnail With Fan, Sauce, Amber 14.00
Pressed Glass, Hobnail With Fan, Sauce, Blue 11.00
Pressed Glass, Hobnail With Ornamental Band, Pitcher, Footed, 5 1/2 In. 17.50
Pressed Glass, Hobnail With Thumbprint Base, Creamer, Child's 12.00
Pressed Glass, Hobnail With Thumbprint Base, Pitcher, Milk, Ruby Stained 30.00
Pressed Glass, Hobnail With Thumbprint Base, Pitcher, Ruby Top, 7 In. 45.00
Pressed Glass, Hobnail, Dish, Candy, Green Opalescent, Ruffled, 6 In. 20.00
Pressed Glass, Hobnail, Goblet, Printed Square Base 16.00
Pressed Glass, Hobnail, Mug 5.50
Pressed Glass, Hobnail, Salt, Blue 7.00
Pressed Glass, Hobnail, Salt, Green 7.00
Pressed Glass, Hobnail, Salt, Master, Blue, Square 10.00
Pressed Glass, Hobnail, Sauce 5.50
Pressed Glass, Hobnail, Tumbler 15.00
Pressed Glass, Hobnail, Tumbler, Amber Band 30.00

Pressed Glass, **Hobnail**, Tumbler, Blue	27.50
Pressed Glass, **Hobnail**, Twine Holder, 5 1/2 X 4 In.	22.50
Pressed Glass, **Hobnail**, Wine	9.50
Pressed Glass, **Hobstar**, Cup, Punch	2.00
Pressed Glass, **Hobstar**, Knife Rest, Press Cut, 4 1/2 In.	12.50
Pressed Glass, **Holland**, Butter, Covered	18.50
Pressed Glass, **Holly Band**, Celery	18.50 To 30.00
Pressed Glass, **Holly Leaves**, Goblet	12.50
Pressed Glass, **Holly**, Salt, Pedestal	27.50
Pressed Glass, **Home**, Pitcher, Milk	22.50
Pressed Glass, **Honeycomb & Clover**, Boat, Opalescent, 8 In.	22.00
Pressed Glass, **Honeycomb Band**, Goblet	7.00
Pressed Glass, **Honeycomb Band**, Syrup, Pewter Lid	25.00
Pressed Glass, **Honeycomb With Diamonds**, Eggcup	35.00
Pressed Glass, **Honeycomb With Diamonds**, Eggcup, Flint	30.00
Pressed Glass, **Honeycomb With Diamonds**, Goblet	5.00 To 22.00
Pressed Glass, **Honeycomb With Diamonds**, Goblet, Flint	8.00 To 22.00
Pressed Glass, **Honeycomb With Flower Rim**, Toothpick	12.00
Pressed Glass, **Honeycomb With Flower Rim**, Toothpick, Green, Gilt Buttress	39.00
Pressed Glass, **Honeycomb With Flower Rim**, Vase, 6 1/2 In.	12.50
Pressed Glass, **Honeycomb With Ovals**, Eggcup, Engraved, Flint	27.00
Pressed Glass, **Honeycomb With Panels**, Eggcup	35.00
Pressed Glass, **Honeycomb With Panels**, Eggcup, Flint	30.00
Pressed Glass, **Honeycomb With Panels**, Goblet	26.00
Pressed Glass, **Honeycomb With Panels**, Goblet, Flint	18.00
Pressed Glass, **Honeycomb With Panels**, Sugar, Covered	75.00
Pressed Glass, **Honeycomb With Panels**, Sugar, Covered, Flint	60.00
Pressed Glass, **Honeycomb With Star**, Goblet, Flint	17.00
Pressed Glass, **Honeycomb**, Barrel, Goblet, Flint	12.00 To 24.00
Pressed Glass, **Honeycomb**, Celery	22.00 To 75.00
Pressed Glass, **Honeycomb**, Celery, Flint, 10 X 5 In.	65.00
Pressed Glass, **Honeycomb**, Celery, Scalloped Top	20.00
Pressed Glass, **Honeycomb**, Champagne	25.00
Pressed Glass, **Honeycomb**, Champagne, Flint	20.00 To 35.00
Pressed Glass, **Honeycomb**, Compote, Etched, High Standard, 8 In.	95.00
Pressed Glass, **Honeycomb**, Compote, Flint, 8 X 5 1/2 In.	32.50 To 35.00
Pressed Glass, **Honeycomb**, Cordial, 3 1/8 In.	9.00
Pressed Glass, **Honeycomb**, Creamer	65.00
Pressed Glass, **Honeycomb**, Creamer, Applied Handle	20.00
Pressed Glass, **Honeycomb**, Creamer, Flint	55.00
Pressed Glass, **Honeycomb**, Creamer, Gillinder	55.00
Pressed Glass, **Honeycomb**, Dish, Honey, Flint	8.25
Pressed Glass, **Honeycomb**, Eggcup	6.50 To 30.00
Pressed Glass, **Honeycomb**, Eggcup, Flint	28.00 To 35.00
Pressed Glass, **Honeycomb**, Eggcup, Straight Sides, Flint	20.00
Pressed Glass, **Honeycomb**, Goblet	6.50 To 19.00
Pressed Glass, **Honeycomb**, Goblet, Amethestine	19.00
Pressed Glass, **Honeycomb**, Goblet, Ball Knob Stem, Flint	23.00
Pressed Glass, **Honeycomb**, Goblet, Flint	10.00 To 32.00
Pressed Glass, **Honeycomb**, Goblet, Flint, Engraved Roses	40.00
Pressed Glass, **Honeycomb**, Goblet, 4 Rows	15.00
Pressed Glass, **Honeycomb**, Goblet, 4 Rows, Flint	15.00
Pressed Glass, **Honeycomb**, Pitcher, Water	62.50
Pressed Glass, **Honeycomb**, Pitcher, Water, Amber	38.00
Pressed Glass, **Honeycomb**, Pitcher, Water, Anchor Hocking	47.00
Pressed Glass, **Honeycomb**, Pitcher, Water, Applied Handle	55.00
Pressed Glass, **Honeycomb**, Pitcher, Water, Dated Under Handle	85.00
Pressed Glass, **Honeycomb**, Salt	18.00
Pressed Glass, **Honeycomb**, Shot Glass	8.00
Pressed Glass, **Honeycomb**, Spooner	25.00
Pressed Glass, **Honeycomb**, Spooner, Etched, Flint	18.50
Pressed Glass, **Honeycomb**, Spooner, Flint	15.00
Pressed Glass, **Honeycomb**, Spooner, Scalloped Top, Flint	22.00
Pressed Glass, **Honeycomb**, Sugar, Flint	17.00 To 20.00
Pressed Glass, **Honeycomb**, Tumbler, Amber	12.00
Pressed Glass, **Honeycomb**, Tumbler, Footed, Flint, 3 1/2 In.	12.00

Pressed Glass, Holly Band, Celery

Pressed Glass, Honeycomb, Goblet, Flint, Pittsburgh

Pressed Glass,
Horseshoe, Covered
Stemmed Bowl

Pressed Glass, Horn
Of Plenty, Whiskey

Pressed Glass,
Honeycomb, Bottle

Pressed Glass, Holly, Compote

Pressed Glass, Horn Of Plenty, Low Dish

Pressed Glass, **Honeycomb,** Whiskey Taster, Flint	10.00
Pressed Glass, **Honeycomb,** Wine	7.00 To 18.50
Pressed Glass, **Honeycomb,** Wine, Flint	18.50
Honeycomb, see also Laredo Honeycomb, Loop & Honeycomb, Vernon Honeycomb	
Pressed Glass, **Hooks & Eyes,** Goblet	12.50 To 30.00
Pressed Glass, **Hops Band,** Creamer	16.50 To 20.00
Pressed Glass, **Hops Band,** Dish, Pickle	7.50
Pressed Glass, **Hops Band,** Goblet	8.50 To 20.00
Pressed Glass, **Hops Band,** Pitcher, Water, Applied Handle	24.00
Pressed Glass, **Hops Band,** Spooner	12.00
Pressed Glass, **Hops Band,** Tumbler, Footed	17.50
Pressed Glass, **Horizontal Rib,** Bowl, Pink, Handled, 5 In.	6.00
Pressed Glass, **Horn Of Plenty,** Candleholder, 5 Prisms, 9 In., Pair	25.00
Pressed Glass, **Horn Of Plenty,** Celery	75.00
Pressed Glass, **Horn Of Plenty,** Celery, Flint	75.00 To 120.00
Pressed Glass, **Horn Of Plenty,** Champagne	85.00
Pressed Glass, **Horn Of Plenty,** Compote, Flint, 8 In.	85.00
Pressed Glass, **Horn Of Plenty,** Compote, Low Standard, Flint, 8 In.	85.00
Pressed Glass, **Horn Of Plenty,** Compote, 6 3/4 X 5 1/2 In.	95.00
Pressed Glass, **Horn Of Plenty,** Compote, 7 1/2 X 7 In.	95.00
Pressed Glass, **Horn Of Plenty,** Compote, 8 In.	85.00 To 95.00
Pressed Glass, **Horn Of Plenty,** Creamer, 7 In.High	70.00
Pressed Glass, **Horn Of Plenty,** Decanter, Pint	55.00
Pressed Glass, **Horn Of Plenty,** Dish, Honey	10.00
Pressed Glass, **Horn Of Plenty,** Dish, Honey, Flint, 3 1/4 In.	13.00
Pressed Glass, **Horn Of Plenty,** Eggcup, Flint	30.00 To 40.00

	75.00
Pressed Glass, Horn Of Plenty, Goblet	30.00 To 65.00
Pressed Glass, Horn Of Plenty, Goblet, Flint	45.00 To 65.00
Pressed Glass, Horn Of Plenty, Goblet, Knob Stem, Flint	47.50
Pressed Glass, Horn Of Plenty, Plate, Flint, 6 In.	60.00
Pressed Glass, Horn Of Plenty, Plate, Tea, Flint, 6 In.	10.00 To 20.00
Pressed Glass, Horn Of Plenty, Sauce	12.50 To 15.00
Pressed Glass, Horn Of Plenty, Sauce, Flint	28.00 To 37.50
Pressed Glass, Horn Of Plenty, Spill, Flint	28.00 To 35.00
Pressed Glass, Horn Of Plenty, Spooner, Flint	52.00
Pressed Glass, Horn Of Plenty, Sugar	75.00
Pressed Glass, Horn Of Plenty, Sugar, Covered	75.00
Pressed Glass, Horn Of Plenty, Sugar, Covered, Flint	40.00 To 52.00
Pressed Glass, Horn Of Plenty, Sugar, Flint	330.00
Pressed Glass, Horn Of Plenty, Table Set, Flint, 4 Piece	75.00
Pressed Glass, Horn Of Plenty, Tumbler	60.00 To 65.00
Pressed Glass, Horn Of Plenty, Tumbler, Flint	85.00
Pressed Glass, Horn Of Plenty, Tumbler, Whiskey, Flint	75.00
Pressed Glass, Horn Of Plenty, Wine, Small	150.00
Pressed Glass, Horse, Cat, & Rabbit, Goblet	27.50
Pressed Glass, Horsehead Medallion, Celery	18.00
Pressed Glass, Horsemint, Cake Stand	12.00 To 16.00
Pressed Glass, Horsemint, Goblet	25.00
Pressed Glass, Horseshoe, Bowl, Footed, 7 In.	65.00
Pressed Glass, Horseshoe, Bowl, Waste	55.00
Pressed Glass, Horseshoe, Butter	58.00
Pressed Glass, Horseshoe, Butter, Covered	25.00
Pressed Glass, Horseshoe, Cake Stand, 8 1/2 In.	26.00
Pressed Glass, Horseshoe, Cake Stand, 9 In.	10.00 To 45.00
Pressed Glass, Horseshoe, Cake Stand, 10 In.	28.00 To 35.00
Pressed Glass, Horseshoe, Celery	30.00
Pressed Glass, Horseshoe, Celery, Stemmed	52.00
Pressed Glass, Horseshoe, Compote, Covered, 8 In.	25.00
Pressed Glass, Horseshoe, Compote, High Standard, 6 In.	88.00
Pressed Glass, Horseshoe, Compote, 11 In.	32.00 To 35.00
Pressed Glass, Horseshoe, Creamer	16.00
Pressed Glass, Horseshoe, Creamer, Knob Stem	45.00
Pressed Glass, Horseshoe, Creamer, Stemmed	165.00
Pressed Glass, Horseshoe, Dish, Cheese, Covered	9.00
Pressed Glass, Horseshoe, Dish, Pickle	15.00
Pressed Glass, Horseshoe, Dish, Pickle, Closed Handles, 9 1/2 In.	12.00 To 30.00
Pressed Glass, Horseshoe, Goblet	35.00
Pressed Glass, Horseshoe, Goblet, Knob Stem	35.00 To 55.00
Pressed Glass, Horseshoe, Muffineer, Amber	17.00
Pressed Glass, Horseshoe, Mug	32.50 To 52.50
Pressed Glass, Horseshoe, Pitcher, Water	42.00 To 50.00
Pressed Glass, Horseshoe, Plate, Bread	42.50
Pressed Glass, Horseshoe, Plate, Bread, Double Handled	20.00 To 47.50
Pressed Glass, Horseshoe, Plate, 7 In.	30.00
Pressed Glass, Horseshoe, Plate, 7 1/4 In.	10.00 To 57.50
Pressed Glass, Horseshoe, Plate, 10 In.	17.50
Pressed Glass, Horseshoe, Relish	22.50
Pressed Glass, Horseshoe, Relish, 2 Handled, 9 X 5 1/4 In.	35.00 To 49.00
Pressed Glass, Horseshoe, Salt & Pepper, Amber	6.50
Pressed Glass, Horseshoe, Sauce	6.00 To 7.50
Pressed Glass, Horseshoe, Sauce, Footed, 4 In.	8.50
Pressed Glass, Horseshoe, Sauce, Footed, 4 1/2 In.	11.25
Pressed Glass, Horseshoe, Sauce, Footed, 5 In.	4.50
Pressed Glass, Horseshoe, Sauce, 4 In.	18.50 To 35.00
Pressed Glass, Horseshoe, Spooner	15.00
Pressed Glass, Horseshoe, Sugar	5.00
Pressed Glass, Horseshoe, Tumbler, 3 3/4 In.	27.00
Pressed Glass, Hotel Argus, Goblet	20.00 To 40.00
Pressed Glass, Hotel Argus, Goblet, Flint	22.00
Pressed Glass, Hotel Argus, Wine	5.00
Pressed Glass, Hotel Thumbprint, Goblet	80.00
Pressed Glass, Hourglass, Creamer	

Pressed Glass, Hourglass, Creamer, Flint	70.00
Pressed Glass, Hourglass, Eggcup	38.00
Pressed Glass, Hourglass, Eggcup, Flint	32.00
Pressed Glass, Hourglass, Tumbler, Footed	50.00
Pressed Glass, Hourglass, Tumbler, Footed, Flint	40.00
Pressed Glass, Hourglass, Wine	12.50 To 40.00
Pressed Glass, Hourglass, Wine, Flint	35.00
Pressed Glass, Hoyt, Goblet	8.50
Pressed Glass, Huber, Celery	35.00
Pressed Glass, Huber, Celery, Flint	25.00
Pressed Glass, Huber, Champagne	3.00 To 25.00
Pressed Glass, Huber, Champagne, Barrel, Flint	22.00
Pressed Glass, Huber, Champagne, Flint	20.00 To 24.50
Pressed Glass, Huber, Cordial, Flint	20.00
Pressed Glass, Huber, Eggcup	18.50
Pressed Glass, Huber, Eggcup, Barrel	22.50
Pressed Glass, Huber, Eggcup, Flint	8.00 To 19.00
Pressed Glass, Huber, Goblet	6.00
Pressed Glass, Huber, Goblet, Barrel	6.50
Pressed Glass, Huber, Goblet, Barrel, Flint	8.50 To 18.00
Pressed Glass, Huber, Goblet, Buttermilk	12.00
Pressed Glass, Huber, Goblet, Flaring	7.00
Pressed Glass, Huber, Goblet, Flint	10.00
Pressed Glass, Huber, Goblet, Lady's	12.50
Pressed Glass, Huber, Mug, Applied Handle, Flint	15.00
Pressed Glass, Huber, Mug, Applied Handle, Ground Pontil, Flint, 2 3/4 In.	15.00
Pressed Glass, Huber, Spill	6.00
Pressed Glass, Huber, Spooner	6.00
Pressed Glass, Huber, Tumbler, Bar, Flint	15.00
Pressed Glass, Huber, Tumbler, Footed, Flint	30.00
Pressed Glass, Huber, Tumbler, Whiskey, Handled, 3 In.	20.00
Pressed Glass, Huber, Wine, Flint	14.00
Pressed Glass, Huber, Wine, Knob Stem	12.50
Huckle, see Feather Duster	
Pressed Glass, Hummingbird, Celery	18.00
Pressed Glass, Hummingbird, Creamer	35.00 To 37.50
Pressed Glass, Hummingbird, Goblet	15.00 To 35.00
Pressed Glass, Hummingbird, Pitcher, Milk	65.00
Pressed Glass, Hummingbird, Pitcher, Water	65.00
Pressed Glass, Hummingbird, Tumbler, Blue	65.00
Pressed Glass, Hummingbird, Wine	24.00 To 45.00
Pressed Glass, Humpty-Dumpty, Mug	18.00 To 23.00
Pressed Glass, Humpty-Dumpty, Mug, Pink	18.00
Hundred-Eye, see 100-Eye	
Hundred-Leaved Ivy, see 100-Leaved Ivy	
Hundred-Leaved Rose, see 100-Leaved Rose	
Pressed Glass, I.O.U., Salt & Pepper, Emerald Green	59.00
Pressed Glass, Icicle With Chain Band, Goblet, Flint	18.00
Pressed Glass, Icicle With Chain Band, Goblet, Frosted, Flint	50.00
Pressed Glass, Icicle With Diamond Bowl, Goblet, Flint	20.00
Pressed Glass, Icicle With Loops, Goblet	20.00
Pressed Glass, Icicle With Loops, Goblet, Flint	20.00 To 25.00
Pressed Glass, Icicle With Panels, Goblet, Flint	45.00 To 60.00
Pressed Glass, Icicle, Belted, Goblet	7.50
Pressed Glass, Iconoclast, Goblet, Flint	30.00 To 35.00
Ida, see Sheraton	
Pressed Glass, Idyll, Sauce	21.00
Pressed Glass, Idyll, Spooner, Green, Gold Trim, Jefferson	38.00
Pressed Glass, Illinois, Creamer	12.50
Pressed Glass, Illinois, Dish, Olive	5.00
Pressed Glass, Illinois, Toothpick	18.00
Pressed Glass, Illinois, Vase, Green, 9 1/2 In.	39.50
Pressed Glass, Imperial Jewel, Compote, Candy, Covered, Yellow, 10 1/2 In.	28.50
Pressed Glass, Indian Head, Sauce, Footed	8.75
Indian Tree, see Sprig	
Indiana Swirl, see Feather	

Pressed Glass, Intaglio, Creamer, Blue Opalescent	38.00
Pressed Glass, Intaglio, Salt, Amber, Oblong	6.00
Pressed Glass, Intaglio, Salt, Oblong	5.00
Pressed Glass, Interlocked Hearts, Creamer	10.00
Pressed Glass, Interlocked Hearts, Syrup	17.00
Interlocking Crescents, see Double Arch	
Pressed Glass, Inverness, Goblet	5.00
Pressed Glass, Inverted Baby Thumbprint, Pitcher, Water, Ruby Stained	97.00
Pressed Glass, Inverted Diamond Point & Bull's-Eye, Spill	20.00
Pressed Glass, Inverted Diamond Point & Bull's-Eye, Spooner	20.00
Pressed Glass, Inverted Diamond, Goblet, Flint	26.00
Pressed Glass, Inverted Fan & Feather, Creamer, Emerald Green, Gold Trim	48.00
Pressed Glass, Inverted Fern, Butter, Covered	55.00 To 65.00
Pressed Glass, Inverted Fern, Butter, Covered, Flint	50.00
Pressed Glass, Inverted Fern, Dish, Honey, Flint	8.00
Pressed Glass, Inverted Fern, Eggcup	18.50 To 45.00
Pressed Glass, Inverted Fern, Eggcup, Flint	18.00 To 28.00
Pressed Glass, Inverted Fern, Goblet	12.00 To 35.00
Pressed Glass, Inverted Fern, Goblet, Flint	22.50 To 32.00
Pressed Glass, Inverted Fern, Salt, Master	35.00
Pressed Glass, Inverted Fern, Sauce	12.00
Pressed Glass, Inverted Fern, Spill, Flint	30.00
Pressed Glass, Inverted Fern, Spooner	28.00 To 35.00
Pressed Glass, Inverted Fern, Spooner, Flint	25.00 To 30.00
Pressed Glass, Inverted Fern, Sugar	24.50 To 35.00
Pressed Glass, Inverted Fern, Sugar, Covered	55.00 To 75.00
Pressed Glass, Inverted Fern, Sugar, Covered, Flint	50.00 To 58.00
Pressed Glass, Inverted Fern, Sugar, Flint, 5 1/4 In.	55.00
Pressed Glass, Inverted Hearts, Sauce, Flint	6.00
Pressed Glass, Inverted Hearts, Sugar, Ruby Stained, Handled	15.00
Pressed Glass, Inverted Hobnail Arches, Mug	16.00
Pressed Glass, Inverted Hobnail Arches, Mug, Findlay	21.50
Pressed Glass, Inverted Loops & Fan, Goblet	12.00
Pressed Glass, Inverted Prism, Goblet, Blue	15.00
Pressed Glass, Inverted Prism, Goblet, Etched	6.00 To 12.00
Pressed Glass, Inverted Sawtooth, Wine	45.00
Pressed Glass, Inverted Strawberry, Amethyst	15.00
Pressed Glass, Inverted Strawberry, Bowl, Berry, Child's, Master	45.00
Pressed Glass, Inverted Strawberry, Compote, Jelly, 5 X 3 1/2 In.	45.00
Pressed Glass, Inverted Strawberry, Creamer	22.50
Pressed Glass, Inverted Strawberry, Toothpick, Marked Near Cut	40.00
Pressed Glass, Inverted Strawberry, Tumbler	6.50
Pressed Glass, Inverted Strawberry, Tumbler, Amethyst, Gold Trim	18.00
Pressed Glass, Inverted Strawberry, Tumbler, Ruby Stained	25.00
	20.00

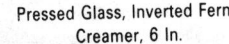

Pressed Glass, Iconoclast, Goblet

Pressed Glass, Inverted Fern,
Creamer, 6 In.

Pressed Glass,
Jacob's Ladder, Compote

Pressed Glass, Inverted Thistle, Cake Stand, 6 3/4 X 10 3/4 In. 45.00
Pressed Glass, Inverted Thumbprint With Daisy Band, Toothpick 34.00
Pressed Glass, Inverted Thumbprint, Berry Set, Gold Trim, 7 Piece 30.00
Pressed Glass, Inverted Thumbprint, Bowl, Berry, Apple Green, 9 In. 15.00
Pressed Glass, Inverted Thumbprint, Bowl, Finger, Amber, 5 1/4 In. 30.00
Pressed Glass, Inverted Thumbprint, Creamer, Amber, Reeded Handle & Feet 25.00
Pressed Glass, Inverted Thumbprint, Cup, Punch, Amber .... 9.00 To 15.00
Pressed Glass, Inverted Thumbprint, Cup, Punch, Medium Blue 90.00
Pressed Glass, Inverted Thumbprint, Goblet, Amber, Ferguson 14.00
Pressed Glass, Inverted Thumbprint, Goblet, Amber, Knob Stem, 5 3/4 In. 12.00
Pressed Glass, Inverted Thumbprint, Goblet, Bennington 7.00
Pressed Glass, Inverted Thumbprint, Muffineer, Amber 36.00
Pressed Glass, Inverted Thumbprint, Pitcher, Blue, Applied Handle, 5 In. 65.00
Pressed Glass, Inverted Thumbprint, Pitcher, Sapphire Blue, 4 In. 42.00
Pressed Glass, Inverted Thumbprint, Pitcher, Water, Amber, Pleated Top 45.00
Pressed Glass, Inverted Thumbprint, Pitcher, Water, Red, Reeded Handle 87.50
Pressed Glass, Inverted Thumbprint, Sauce, Canary, Footed 8.00
Pressed Glass, Inverted Thumbprint, Sugar, Amber, Covered, Footed, Ferguson 30.00
Pressed Glass, Inverted Thumbprint, Syrup, Amber 48.00
Pressed Glass, Inverted Thumbprint, Syrup, Amber, Hinged Tin Lid, 1882 .... 65.00
Pressed Glass, Inverted Thumbprint, Syrup, Amber, On Standard 49.00
Pressed Glass, Inverted Thumbprint, Tumbler, Amber 16.50
Pressed Glass, Inverted Thumbprint, Tumbler, Blue 20.00
Pressed Glass, Inverted Thumbprint, Tumbler, Purple, C.1900 .... 17.00
Pressed Glass, Inverted Thumbprint, Wine, Apple Green 15.00
Pressed Glass, Inverted Thumbprint, Wine, Tegman 10.00
Pressed Glass, Ionia, Goblet .... 9.00 To 15.00
Pressed Glass, Iowa City, Mug, Lambs With Bell 30.00
Pressed Glass, Iowa City, Plate, "Be True, " 7 3/4 In. 50.00
Pressed Glass, Iowa City, Wine, Greentown 22.00
Pressed Glass, Iowa, Saltshaker, Gold Trim 10.00
Pressed Glass, Iris & Herringbone, Bowl, Ruffled, 9 In. 6.00
Pressed Glass, Iris & Herringbone, Butter 15.00
Pressed Glass, Iris & Herringbone, Water Set, 9 Piece 55.00
Pressed Glass, Iris Meander, Plate, Green Opalescent, 7 In. 25.00
Pressed Glass, Iris Meander, Toothpick, Blue Opalescent 32.00
Pressed Glass, Iris Meander, Toothpick, Opalescent & Clear 20.00
Pressed Glass, Iris Meander, Tumbler, Blue Opalescent, Gold Trim 65.00
Pressed Glass, Iris, Celery 7.00
Pressed Glass, Isis, Goblet .... 9.00 To 14.50
Pressed Glass, Isis, Tumbler 7.50
Pressed Glass, Ivanhoe, Plate, Findlay, 8 In. 10.00
Pressed Glass, Ivy Band, Sauce, Footed, 3 1/2 In. 4.50
Pressed Glass, Ivy In Snow, Cake Stand, 10 In. 21.00
Pressed Glass, Ivy In Snow, Celery .... 20.00 To 25.00
Pressed Glass, Ivy In Snow, Creamer 16.50
Pressed Glass, Ivy In Snow, Dish, Pickle 8.00
Pressed Glass, Ivy In Snow, Dish, Pickle Relish 12.50
Pressed Glass, Ivy In Snow, Plate, 10 In. .... 12.50 To 13.75
Pressed Glass, Ivy In Snow, Relish 8.00
Pressed Glass, Ivy In Snow, Sauce, Ruby Stained 18.00
Pressed Glass, Ivy In Snow, Spooner 30.00
Pressed Glass, Ivy Leaves, Cup & Saucer, Findlay 30.00
Pressed Glass, Ivy Leaves, Saucer, Findlay 9.75
Pressed Glass, Jack Rabbit Cover, Dish 47.50
Pressed Glass, Jacob's Coat, Sauce 9.00
Pressed Glass, Jacob's Ladder, Bowl, Flat, 7 1/2 In. 10.50
Pressed Glass, Jacob's Ladder, Bowl, Oval, 7 3/4 In. 10.50
Pressed Glass, Jacob's Ladder, Bowl, Oval, 8 1/2 In. 13.50
Pressed Glass, Jacob's Ladder, Bowl, 6 In. 14.00
Pressed Glass, Jacob's Ladder, Bowl, 10 In. 14.50
Pressed Glass, Jacob's Ladder, Celery .... 19.00 To 20.00
Pressed Glass, Jacob's Ladder, Compote, Covered, 7 1/4 In. 58.00
Pressed Glass, Jacob's Ladder, Compote, 7 1/2 In. 30.00
Pressed Glass, Jacob's Ladder, Compote, 9 In. 35.00
Pressed Glass, Jacob's Ladder, Creamer .... 18.50 To 26.50

Pressed Glass, Jacob's Ladder, Creamer, Pedestal 24.50
Pressed Glass, Jacob's Ladder, Goblet .... 30.00 To 45.00
Pressed Glass, Jacob's Ladder, Jar, Jam, Rose Base 18.50
Pressed Glass, Jacob's Ladder, Pitcher, Milk 30.00
Pressed Glass, Jacob's Ladder, Plate, 6 In. .... 18.00 To 28.00
Pressed Glass, Jacob's Ladder, Plate, 6 1/2 In. .... 14.50 To 25.00
Pressed Glass, Jacob's Ladder, Relish 8.75
Pressed Glass, Jacob's Ladder, Relish, Handled, 10 In. 15.00
Pressed Glass, Jacob's Ladder, Relish, Maltese Cross Handles 12.50
Pressed Glass, Jacob's Ladder, Relish, Oval, 10 X 6 In. 8.00
Pressed Glass, Jacob's Ladder, Salt, Master .... 16.00 To 18.00
Pressed Glass, Jacob's Ladder, Sauce .... 5.00 To 7.00
Pressed Glass, Jacob's Ladder, Sauce, Footed 9.50
Pressed Glass, Jacob's Ladder, Spooner .... 15.00 To 18.00
Pressed Glass, Jacob's Ladder, Sugar 20.00
Pressed Glass, Jacob's Ladder, Sugar, Covered 32.50
Pressed Glass, Jacob's Ladder, Syrup .... 35.00 To 58.00
Pressed Glass, Jacob's Ladder, Wine .... 24.50 To 30.00
Pressed Glass, Janssen, Goblet, Buttermilk 9.00
Pressed Glass, Japanese Iris, Tumbler, Ruby With Gold 37.50
Pressed Glass, Jardiniere, Creamer 19.75
   Jasper, see Late Buckle
Pressed Glass, Jefferson, Sauce, Apple Green, Gold Trim, 4 1/2 In. 15.00
Pressed Glass, Jefferson, Toothpick, Blue 40.00
Pressed Glass, Jefferson, Tumbler, Gold Band Top 16.00
Pressed Glass, Jenny Lind, Compote, Frosted Figure, 9 X 7 In. 85.00
Pressed Glass, Jenny Lind, Compote, 8 1/2 X 8 1/2 In. 80.00
Pressed Glass, Jenny Lind, Match Holder, Hanging, June 13, 1876 .... 48.00 To 50.00
Pressed Glass, Jersey Swirl, Celery, Pedestal 29.50
Pressed Glass, Jersey Swirl, Creamer 12.00
Pressed Glass, Jersey Swirl, Goblet 15.00
Pressed Glass, Jersey Swirl, Goblet, Buttermilk 12.00
Pressed Glass, Jersey Swirl, Plate, Amber, 6 1/4 In. 20.00
Pressed Glass, Jersey Swirl, Plate, 6 In. 10.00
Pressed Glass, Jersey Swirl, Spooner, Blue 35.00
Pressed Glass, Jersey Swirl, Sugar, Blue, Covered 85.00
Pressed Glass, Jersey Swirl, Tumbler 22.50
Pressed Glass, Jersey Swirl, Tumbler, Etched 12.50
Pressed Glass, Jersey, Creamer 9.00
Pressed Glass, Jersey, Sauce, Footed, 3 1/2 In. 7.50
Pressed Glass, Jewel & Dewdrop, Bowl, Vegetable, 8 1/2 X 6 1/4 In. 13.50
Pressed Glass, Jewel & Dewdrop, Bowl, 7 1/2 X 3 In. 15.00
Pressed Glass, Jewel & Dewdrop, Bowl, 8 1/2 X 6 1/4 X 2 1/4 In. 15.00
Pressed Glass, Jewel & Dewdrop, Cookie Stand 35.00
Pressed Glass, Jewel & Dewdrop, Cup, Whiskey, Handled 6.50
Pressed Glass, Jewel & Dewdrop, Dish, Honey 6.00
Pressed Glass, Jewel & Dewdrop, Goblet 26.50
Pressed Glass, Jewel & Dewdrop, Mug .... 8.00 To 9.50
Pressed Glass, Jewel & Dewdrop, Mug, 4 In. 4.50
Pressed Glass, Jewel & Dewdrop, Mug, Blue 22.50
Pressed Glass, Jewel & Dewdrop, Mug, Child's, Toddy, 3 1/2 X 3 In. 35.00
Pressed Glass, Jewel & Dewdrop, Mug, Child's, 3 1/2 In. 35.00
Pressed Glass, Jewel & Dewdrop, Pickle 19.50
Pressed Glass, Jewel & Dewdrop, Pitcher, Water .... 25.00 To 40.00
Pressed Glass, Jewel & Dewdrop, Relish .... 11.00 To 15.00
Pressed Glass, Jewel & Dewdrop, Sauce .... 5.50 To 9.00
Pressed Glass, Jewel & Dewdrop, Tumbler, Juice, Handled .... 2.50 To 8.50
Pressed Glass, Jewel & Festoon, Bottle, Dresser, 6 1/2 In. 37.50
Pressed Glass, Jewel & Festoon, Bowl, Berry, 8 In. 7.00
Pressed Glass, Jewel & Flower, Creamer, Yellow Opalescent 35.00
   Jewel Band, see Scalloped Tape
Pressed Glass, Jeweled Drapery, Champagne 14.00
Pressed Glass, Jeweled Drapery, Goblet 7.50
Pressed Glass, Jeweled Heart, Berry Set, Opalescent, 7 Piece 95.00
Pressed Glass, Jeweled Heart, Creamer 26.50
Pressed Glass, Jeweled Heart, Spooner 24.00

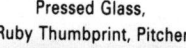

Pressed Glass, Leaf & Dart, Goblet

Pressed Glass,
Ruby Thumbprint, Pitcher

Pressed Glass,
Jumbo, Jar, Marmalade

Pressed Glass, Jeweled Moon & Star, Carafe, Water	35.00
Pressed Glass, Jeweled Moon & Star, Celery	14.50
Pressed Glass, Jeweled Moon & Star, Compote, 8 In.	25.00
Pressed Glass, Jeweled Moon & Star, Goblet	22.50
Pressed Glass, Jeweled Moon & Star, Sauce, Amber & Blue	27.00
Pressed Glass, Jeweled Moon & Star, Tumbler	20.00
Pressed Glass, Jeweled Moon & Star, Tumbler, Gold Trim	15.00
Pressed Glass, Jeweled Pendants, Creamer	13.00
Job's Tears, see Art	
Jubilee, see Hickman	
Pressed Glass, Jumbo, Compote, Covered, 12 X 7 In.	235.00
Pressed Glass, Jumbo, Dish, Candy, Covered	185.00
Pressed Glass, Kalbach, Goblet	14.00
Pressed Glass, Kalbach, Goblet, 6 Rows	5.00
Kamoni, see Balder	
Kansan, see Jewel & Dewdrop	
Pressed Glass, Kellogg, Creamer	8.00
Pressed Glass, Kentucky, Plate, Square, 10 In.	15.00
Pressed Glass, Kentucky, Saltshaker	13.50
Pressed Glass, Kentucky, Sauce	4.00 To 5.00
Pressed Glass, Kentucky, Sauce, Footed	6.75
Pressed Glass, Keystone Grape, Goblet	10.00 To 15.00
Pressed Glass, Keystone Grape, Goblet, Flint	16.00
Pressed Glass, King's Crown, Bowl, Berry, 8 In.	39.00
Pressed Glass, King's Crown, Bowl, 6 1/2 In.	30.00
Pressed Glass, King's Crown, Butter, Covered	33.00
Pressed Glass, King's Crown, Celery, Ruby Stained	32.00
Pressed Glass, King's Crown, Compote, 8 X 8 In.	125.00
Pressed Glass, King's Crown, Creamer, Bulbous, 7 1/2 In.	85.00
Pressed Glass, King's Crown, Creamer, Ruby Stained	23.00
Pressed Glass, King's Crown, Creamer, 3 In.	25.00
Pressed Glass, King's Crown, Cup & Saucer	45.00
Pressed Glass, King's Crown, Goblet	12.00 To 15.00
Pressed Glass, King's Crown, Goblet, Amethyst Thumbprints, Gilt Top	15.00
Pressed Glass, King's Crown, Pitcher, Water, Bulbous, 8 In.	125.00
Pressed Glass, King's Crown, Plate, Serving, Square, 8 In.	28.00
Pressed Glass, King's Crown, Relish	18.75
Pressed Glass, King's Crown, Salt & Pepper	35.00
Pressed Glass, King's Crown, Sauce, Oval, Ruby Top	10.00
Pressed Glass, King's Crown, Spooner	6.00 To 25.00
Pressed Glass, King's Crown, Sugar & Creamer	52.50
Pressed Glass, King's Crown, Tankard, Water, 8 In.	55.00
Pressed Glass, King's Crown, Toothpick	15.00

Item	Price
Pressed Glass, King's Crown, Tumbler	25.00
Pressed Glass, King's Crown, Tumbler, Ruby Stained	35.00
Pressed Glass, King's Crown, Wine	6.00 To 22.00
Pressed Glass, King's Crown, Wine, Amethyst Thumbprints	12.00
Pressed Glass, King's Crown, Wine, Three Mold	6.00
Pressed Glass, King's Curtain, Goblet	10.00 To 14.00
Pressed Glass, Kirkland, Bowl, Berry, Scalloped Top, 6 In.	8.50
Pressed Glass, Kitten On Pillow, Toothpick	27.00
Pressed Glass, Klondike, Butter	285.00
Pressed Glass, Klondike, Butter, Gold Flash, Frosted	285.00
Pressed Glass, Klondike, Cup, Punch	165.00
Pressed Glass, Klondike, Salt, Pepper, & Toothpick	150.00
Pressed Glass, Klondike, Sauce	110.00
Pressed Glass, Klondike, Spooner	225.00
Pressed Glass, Klondike, Sugar	225.00
Pressed Glass, Klondike, Tumbler	150.00
Pressed Glass, Klondike, Tumbler, Gold Trim	115.00
Pressed Glass, Knights Of Labor, Mug	20.00 To 30.00
Pressed Glass, Knives & Forks, Goblet, Banded	6.00
Pressed Glass, Knives & Forks, Goblet, Flint	12.00
Pressed Glass, Knobby Bull's-Eye, Creamer	12.50
Pressed Glass, Knobby Bull's-Eye, Goblet, Amethyst Eyes	12.50
Pressed Glass, Knobby Bull's-Eye, Sugar & Creamer	16.00
Pressed Glass, Kokomo, Berry Set, Footed, 7 Piece	50.00
Pressed Glass, Kokomo, Celery	20.00
Pressed Glass, Kokomo, Compote, Covered, High Standard, 7 1/2 In.	45.00
Pressed Glass, Kokomo, Compote, Covered, 8 In.	25.00
Pressed Glass, Kokomo, Pitcher, Water	24.50 To 16.00
Pressed Glass, Kokomo, Pitcher, Water, Etched	45.00
Pressed Glass, Kokomo, Spooner, Ruby Stained	30.00
Pressed Glass, Kokomo, Tumbler, Ruby Stained	30.00
Pressed Glass, Kokomo, Wine	13.50 To 15.00
Pressed Glass, Kokomo, Wine, Etched	13.00
Pressed Glass, Krom, Goblet, Flint	65.00
Pressed Glass, Lace Band, Sauce	3.75
Lace, see Drapery	
Pressed Glass, Lacy Daisy, Berry Set, Miniature, 5 Piece	24.50
Pressed Glass, Lacy Daisy, Berry Set, Miniature, 6 Piece	65.00
Pressed Glass, Lacy Daisy, Berry Set, Miniature, 7 Piece	55.00
Pressed Glass, Lacy Daisy, Bowl, Berry, Child's, Blue	12.00
Pressed Glass, Lacy Daisy, Bowl, 4 In.	6.00
Pressed Glass, Lacy Daisy, Butter, Covered	27.50
Pressed Glass, Lacy Daisy, Creamer	23.00
Pressed Glass, Lacy Daisy, Plate, Bread, Round, 10 In.	11.00
Pressed Glass, Lacy Daisy, Spooner	7.50 To 20.00
Pressed Glass, Lacy Daisy, Sugar & Creamer	27.50 To 38.00
Pressed Glass, Lacy Daisy, Sugar, Covered	25.00
Pressed Glass, Lacy Daisy, Sugar, Scalloped	7.50
Pressed Glass, Lacy Dewdrop, Mug, Amber	16.00
Pressed Glass, Lacy Dewdrop, Pitcher, Water	20.00
Pressed Glass, Lacy Floral, Sauce	3.50
Pressed Glass, Lacy Floral, Syrup, Tin Lid	35.00
Pressed Glass, Lacy Gothic Arch, Sugar, Covered, Flint	90.00
Pressed Glass, Lacy Lane, Bowl, Berry, Small, Miniature	7.50
Pressed Glass, Lacy Medallion, Creamer, Green	25.00
Pressed Glass, Lacy Medallion, Cup, Green, Gold Trim	12.00
Pressed Glass, Lacy Medallion, Toothpick, Green	20.00
Pressed Glass, Lacy Medallion, Tumbler, Amethyst Eye, Gold Trim, Handled	22.50
Pressed Glass, Lacy Medallion, Tumbler, Blue, Gold Trim	35.00
Pressed Glass, Lacy Medallion, Wine, Green	22.00
Pressed Glass, Lacy Oak, Sauce	10.00
Pressed Glass, Lacy Peacock's-Eye, Sauce	10.00
Lacy Spiral, see Colossus	
Pressed Glass, Lacy Sunburst, Sauce	10.00
Pressed Glass, Ladder With Diamond, Celery	19.00
Pressed Glass, Ladder With Diamond, Goblet, Gold Band	16.50

Pressed Glass, Ladder With Diamond, Tumbler	7.50
Pressed Glass, Ladder, Goblet	7.00
Pressed Glass, Lady With Fan, Goblet	32.00
Pressed Glass, Lakewood, Goblet	8.50 To 10.50
Pressed Glass, Laminated Petals, Champagne	65.00
Pressed Glass, Laminated Petals, Champagne, Flint	60.00
Pressed Glass, Laminated Petals, Claret, Flint	60.00
Pressed Glass, Laminated Petals, Goblet, Flint	38.00 To 50.00
Pressed Glass, Laredo Honeycomb, Goblet	4.50 To 20.00
Pressed Glass, Late Block, Creamer, Ruby Stained, Applied Handle, 3 1/4 In.	15.00
Pressed Glass, Late Block, Muffineer, Ruby Stained	55.00
Pressed Glass, Late Block, Mug, Ruby Stained	15.00
Pressed Glass, Late Block, Pitcher, Water, Bulbous, Ruby Stained	65.00
Pressed Glass, Late Block, Tumbler, Ruby Stained	25.00
Pressed Glass, Late Buckle, Cake Stand, 10 In.	15.00
Pressed Glass, Lattice & Oval Panels, Pitcher, Water, Flint	200.00
Pressed Glass, Lattice & Oval Panels, Wine	40.00
Pressed Glass, Lattice Medallion, Bowl, Opalescent, 8 In.	26.00
Pressed Glass, Lattice, Butter, Covered	18.75
Pressed Glass, Lattice, Goblet	12.00 To 18.50
Pressed Glass, Lattice, Mug, Child's	5.00
Pressed Glass, Lattice, Pitcher, Milk	30.00
Pressed Glass, Lattice, Plate, Bread, "Waste Not, Want Not"	35.00
Pressed Glass, Lattice, Plate, 6 In.	7.00
Pressed Glass, Lattice, Sauce, Footed	5.00
Pressed Glass, Lattice, Syrup	39.50 To 42.50
Pressed Glass, Lattice, Wine	14.50
Pressed Glass, Leaf & Beads, Dish, Candy, Blue & Opalescent, Twig Feet	25.00
Pressed Glass, Leaf & Dart, Celery	14.00 To 16.50
Pressed Glass, Leaf & Dart, Celery, Pedestal	22.50
Pressed Glass, Leaf & Dart, Creamer, Applied Handle	25.00 To 32.50
Pressed Glass, Leaf & Dart, Dish, Pickle	12.50
Pressed Glass, Leaf & Dart, Eggcup	22.50
Pressed Glass, Leaf & Dart, Goblet	12.00 To 18.50
Pressed Glass, Leaf & Dart, Goblet, Buttermilk	9.00
Pressed Glass, Leaf & Dart, Relish	12.50
Pressed Glass, Leaf & Dart, Salt	14.50 To 15.00
Pressed Glass, Leaf & Dart, Spooner	15.00 To 18.00
Pressed Glass, Leaf & Dart, Sugar	9.00 To 12.50
Pressed Glass, Leaf & Dart, Sugar, Covered	34.50
Pressed Glass, Leaf & Dart, Tumbler, Footed	18.50 To 19.50
Pressed Glass, Leaf & Dart, Wine	12.50 To 20.00
Pressed Glass, Leaf & Flower, Butter, Amber	70.00
Pressed Glass, Leaf & Flower, Creamer, Amber	45.00
Pressed Glass, Leaf & Flower, Sauce, Frosted	4.50
Pressed Glass, Leaf & Flower, Sugar, Amber, Covered	55.00
Pressed Glass, Leaf & Flower, Syrup, Amber & Clear	65.00
Pressed Glass, Leaf & Flower, Tankard, Water, Amber & Clear	70.00 To 75.00
Pressed Glass, Leaf & Flower, Tumbler, Amber	20.00
Pressed Glass, Leaf & Flower, Tumbler, Frosted	15.00
Pressed Glass, Leaf & Star, Butter, Covered	25.00 To 38.00
Pressed Glass, Leaf & Star, Creamer	9.00
Pressed Glass, Leaf & Star, Pitcher, Water, Ice Lip	28.50
Pressed Glass, Leaf & Star, Pitcher, Water, Smoky, Marked N M	30.00
Pressed Glass, Leaf & Star, Table Set, 4 Piece	90.00
Pressed Glass, Leaf Medallion, Berry Set, Cobalt, 7 Piece	250.00
Pressed Glass, Leaf Medallion, Bowl, Berry, Purple	70.00
Pressed Glass, Leaf Medallion, Creamer, Green	65.00
Pressed Glass, Leaf Medallion, Sugar, Covered, Amethyst	18.00
Pressed Glass, Leaf Medallion, Sugar, Covered, Green	15.00
Pressed Glass, Leaf Medallion, Tumbler, Purple	30.00
Pressed Glass, Leaf Medallion, Water Set, Emerald Green, 5 Piece	125.00
Pressed Glass, Leaflets, Creamer, Footed	12.00
Pressed Glass, Lee, Celery	130.00
Pressed Glass, Lee, Sugar, Covered	110.00
Pressed Glass, Lee, Wine	125.00

Pressed Glass, Lee, Wine, Flint 110.00
Pressed Glass, Lennox, Bowl, Berry, Child's .... 8.00 To 9.00
Pressed Glass, Lennox, Spooner, Child's 9.00
   Lens & Star, see Star & Oval
   Leverne, see Star in Honeycomb
Pressed Glass, Liberty Bell, Bowl, Master Berry, Footed, 8 In. 110.00
Pressed Glass, Liberty Bell, Butter, Covered .... 85.00 To 110.00
Pressed Glass, Liberty Bell, Butter, Covered, Child's .... 95.00 To 125.00
Pressed Glass, Liberty Bell, Compote, Low Standard, 8 In. 95.00
Pressed Glass, Liberty Bell, Creamer 90.00
Pressed Glass, Liberty Bell, Creamer, Applied Handle .... 85.00 To 95.00
Pressed Glass, Liberty Bell, Creamer, Applied Reeded Handle .... 65.00 To 95.00
Pressed Glass, Liberty Bell, Creamer, Applied Ribbed Handle 85.00
Pressed Glass, Liberty Bell, Creamer, Miniature 95.00
Pressed Glass, Liberty Bell, Goblet .... 18.50 To 45.00
Pressed Glass, Liberty Bell, Goblet, Dated 1876 .... 40.00
Pressed Glass, Liberty Bell, Goblet, Knob Stem .... 38.00 To 40.00
Pressed Glass, Liberty Bell, Mug, " E Pluribus Unum, " 13 Stars Banner .. 55.00
Pressed Glass, Liberty Bell, Mug, Fiery Opalescent, 2 In. 165.00
Pressed Glass, Liberty Bell, Mug, Snake Handle 295.00
Pressed Glass, Liberty Bell, Pitcher, Water 650.00
   Liberty Bell, Plate, Bread, Signers, see under Bread Plate
Pressed Glass, Liberty Bell, Plate, Dated, 6 In. 55.00
Pressed Glass, Liberty Bell, Plate, States, 6 In. 75.00
Pressed Glass, Liberty Bell, Plate, States, 8 In. 67.50
Pressed Glass, Liberty Bell, Plate, 6 In. 60.00
Pressed Glass, Liberty Bell Plate, 6 1/4 In. 52.00
Pressed Glass, Liberty Bell, Plate, 6 1/2 In. 45.00
Pressed Glass, Liberty Bell, Plate, 8 In. .... 55.00 To 75.00
Pressed Glass, Liberty Bell, Plate, 10 In. 75.00
   Liberty Bell, Platter, Shell Handles, see Bread Plate
Pressed Glass, Liberty Bell, Relish 35.00
Pressed Glass, Liberty Bell, Relish, Signers 50.00
Pressed Glass, Liberty Bell, Salt & Pepper 200.00
Pressed Glass, Liberty Bell, Salt, Individual 28.50
Pressed Glass, Liberty Bell, Salt, Oval, 2 1/4 In., Pair 40.00
Pressed Glass, Liberty Bell, Saltshaker, "Proclaim Liberty Through Land" . 55.00
Pressed Glass, Liberty Bell, Saltshaker, 3 1/4 In. 90.00
Pressed Glass, Liberty Bell, Sauce, Footed .... 24.00 To 25.00
Pressed Glass, Liberty Bell, Sauce, Scalloped Edges 22.00
Pressed Glass, Liberty Bell, Sauce, 4 1/8 In. 21.00
Pressed Glass, Liberty Bell, Spooner .... 65.00 To 68.00
Pressed Glass, Liberty Bell, Spooner, Scalloped 45.00
Pressed Glass, Liberty Bell, Sugar 45.00
Pressed Glass, Liberty Bell, Sugar, Covered .... 65.00 To 95.00
Pressed Glass, Liberty Bell, Tumbler, Ale 55.00
Pressed Glass, Liberty, Creamer 18.00
Pressed Glass, Liberty, Wine 12.00
Pressed Glass, Lightning, Tankard, Water, Applied Handle 45.00
Pressed Glass, Lily Of The Valley, Bowl, Oval, 4 1/2 X 7 In. 13.50
Pressed Glass, Lily Of The Valley, Bowl, Oval, 5 1/4 X 8 In. 13.50
Pressed Glass, Lily Of The Valley, Butter 15.00
Pressed Glass, Lily Of The Valley, Butter, Covered 45.00
Pressed Glass, Lily Of The Valley, Celery .... 27.50 To 38.50
Pressed Glass, Lily Of The Valley, Compote, Covered, High Standard, 8 1/4 In .. 70.00
Pressed Glass, Lily Of The Valley, Creamer, Applied Handle .... 37.50 To 45.00
Pressed Glass, Lily Of The Valley, Creamer, Three-Legged Base .... 32.50 To 45.00
Pressed Glass, Lily Of The Valley, Eggcup .... 30.00 To 48.50
Pressed Glass, Lily Of The Valley, Goblet .... 30.00 To 45.00
Pressed Glass, Lily Of The Valley, Goblet, Etched .... 12.50 To 15.00
Pressed Glass, Lily Of The Valley, Pitcher, Milk 57.50
Pressed Glass, Lily Of The Valley, Pitcher, Milk, Applied Handle 57.50
Pressed Glass, Lily Of The Valley, Pitcher, Water 65.00
Pressed Glass, Lily Of The Valley, Pitcher, Water, Applied Handle 65.00
Pressed Glass, Lily Of The Valley, Pitcher, Water, Applied Reeded Handle .. 35.00
Pressed Glass, Lily Of The Valley, Relish, Eggplant Shape 5.50

Pressed Glass, Liberty Bell, Goblet

Pressed Glass, Lincoln Drape,
Syrup Pitcher, Opalescent

Pressed Glass, Lincoln Drape,
Compote, 8 In.

Pressed Glass, Liberty Bell,
Bread Tray

Pressed Glass, Lily Of The Valley, Salt, Covered	38.00
Pressed Glass, Lily Of The Valley, Salt, Master	15.00
Pressed Glass, Lily Of The Valley, Sauce	7.50
Pressed Glass, Lily Of The Valley, Spooner	16.50 To 22.50
Pressed Glass, Lily Of The Valley, Sugar, Covered	45.00
Pressed Glass, Lily Of The Valley, Wine	37.50 To 45.00
Pressed Glass, Lincoln Drape, Butter, Covered	60.00
Pressed Glass, Lincoln Drape, Compote, Low Standard, Flint, 8 In.	52.50
Pressed Glass, Lincoln Drape, Compote, Rope Edge, Flint, 8 In.	75.00
Pressed Glass, Lincoln Drape, Eggcup	45.00
Pressed Glass, Lincoln Drape, Eggcup, Flint	32.00 To 38.00
Pressed Glass, Lincoln Drape, Goblet, Flint	65.00 To 72.00
Pressed Glass, Lincoln Drape, Salt	22.00
Pressed Glass, Lincoln Drape, Syrup, Applied Handle	80.00
Pressed Glass, Lincoln Drape, Syrup, Applied Handle, Pewter Top	79.50
Pressed Glass, Lincoln Drape, Syrup, Applied Handle, Tin Lid & Thumbpiece	80.00
Pressed Glass, Lincoln Drape, Syrup, Crimped Handle, Metal Stopper, Flint	95.00
Pressed Glass, Lined Rib, Cordial, Findlay, 3 3/4 X 1 3/4 In.	15.00
Pressed Glass, Lined Smocking, Goblet, Flint	45.00
Pressed Glass, Lion & Baboon, Butter, Frosted & Clear, Covered	95.00
Pressed Glass, Lion & Baboon, Sauce	12.50
Pressed Glass, Lion Cover, Dish, Amber, Dated 1889	75.00
Pressed Glass, Lion, Bowl, Covered, 6 X 6 In.	65.00
Pressed Glass, Lion, Butter, Miniature	75.00
Pressed Glass, Lion, Celery	32.50
Pressed Glass, Lion, Celery, Frosted	65.00 To 68.00
Pressed Glass, Lion, Compote, Covered, 11 X 9 In.	100.00
Pressed Glass, Lion, Compote, Frosted, Covered, Flint, 12 In.	85.00
Pressed Glass, Lion, Compote, Lion's Head Cover, Crouching Lions Base, 7 In.	65.00
Pressed Glass, Lion, Creamer	19.50

Pressed Glass, Lion, Jar, Jam, Frosted, Crouched Lion Finial 65.00
Pressed Glass, Lion, Plate, Bread, Frosted .... 38.00 To 53.00
Pressed Glass, Lion, Plate, Bread, Frosted, Handled, Motto, 10 In. 48.00
Pressed Glass, Lion, Plate, Bread, Handled, Rope Edge, 12 In. 47.50
Pressed Glass, Lion, Plate, Bread, Standing Lion 48.00
Pressed Glass, Lion, Salt, Frosted, Rectangular 15.00
Pressed Glass, Lion, Sauce, Frosted, Footed 15.00
Pressed Glass, Lion, Sauce, Square 12.50
Pressed Glass, Lion, Spooner 16.00
Pressed Glass, Lion, Spooner, Miniature 65.00
Pressed Glass, Lion, Sugar, Miniature 75.00
Pressed Glass, Lion, Table Set, Miniature, 4 Piece 200.00
Pressed Glass, Lion, Toothpick, Sterling Ring On Top 13.50
Pressed Glass, Lion, Tumbler 24.00
Lion's Leg, see Alaska
Lippman, see Flat Diamond
Pressed Glass, Little Bopeep, Plate, Etched, 5 1/4 In. 10.00
Pressed Glass, Little Bopeep, Plate, 6 1/2 In. 10.00
Pressed Glass, Little Bullet, Goblet 13.50
Pressed Glass, Little Bullet, Goblet, Findlay 9.00
Pressed Glass, Little Bullet, Tumbler 7.50
Pressed Glass, Little Lamb, Creamer, Miniature .... 33.00 To 48.00
Pressed Glass, Little May, Creamer, Blue 16.00
Pressed Glass, Little Miss Muffet, Plate, Etched, 5 In. 18.00
Pressed Glass, Log & Star, Cordial, Dark Blue 22.50
Pressed Glass, Log & Star, Mug, Amber, 2 1/4 In. 15.00
Pressed Glass, Log & Star, Mug, Blue 18.50
Pressed Glass, Log & Star, Pitcher, Lemonade, Findlay 35.00
Pressed Glass, Log Cabin, Creamer 75.00
Pressed Glass, Loganberry & Grape, Pitcher, Milk 32.50
Pressed Glass, Long Bowl, Goblet .... 8.00 To 9.00
Pressed Glass, Loop & Argus, Goblet 10.00
Pressed Glass, Loop & Argus, Goblet, Pale Lavender 12.50
Pressed Glass, Loop & Block, Table Set, Ruby Stained, 4 Piece 285.00
Pressed Glass, Loop & Block, Wine .... 9.00 To 10.00
Pressed Glass, Loop & Crystal, Champagne, Flint 25.50
Pressed Glass, Loop & Crystal, Goblet, Flint 20.00
Pressed Glass, Loop & Crystal, Tumbler, Bar, Flint 15.00
Pressed Glass, Loop & Crystal, Tumbler, Flint .... 20.00 To 25.00
Pressed Glass, Loop & Crystal, Tumbler, Whiskey, Flint 30.00
Pressed Glass, Loop & Dart With Daisy Ornament, Eggcup 13.50
Pressed Glass, Loop & Dart With Daisy Ornament, Sugar, Covered 28.00
Pressed Glass, Loop & Dart With Daisy Ornament, Tumbler 24.50
Pressed Glass, Loop & Dart With Diamond Ornament, Creamer 20.00
Pressed Glass, Loop & Dart With Diamond Ornament, Eggcup .... 10.50 To 13.50
Pressed Glass, Loop & Dart With Diamond Ornament, Goblet 12.50
Pressed Glass, Loop & Dart With Diamond Ornament, Spooner 30.00
Pressed Glass, Loop & Dart With Diamond Ornament, Sugar, Covered 18.50
Pressed Glass, Loop & Dart With Round Ornament, Butter Pat 10.00
Pressed Glass, Loop & Dart With Round Ornament, Champagne 22.50
Pressed Glass, Loop & Dart With Round Ornament, Cup Plate, 3 1/8 In. 18.00
Pressed Glass, Loop & Dart With Round Ornament, Dish, Vegetable, Oval 14.50
Pressed Glass, Loop & Dart With Round Ornament, Eggcup 13.50
Pressed Glass, Loop & Dart With Round Ornament, Goblet .... 15.00 To 19.00
Pressed Glass, Loop & Dart With Round Ornament Goblet, Flint 20.00
Pressed Glass, Loop & Dart With Round Ornament, Spooner .... 14.00 To 30.00
Pressed Glass, Loop & Dart, Creamer .... 20.00 To 23.00
Pressed Glass, Loop & Dart, Goblet 10.00
Pressed Glass, Loop & Dart, Goblet, Buttermilk 9.00
Pressed Glass, Loop & Dart, Sauce 5.00
Pressed Glass, Loop & Dart, Spooner 18.00
Pressed Glass, Loop & Dart, Sugar .... 9.00 To 22.50
Pressed Glass, Loop & Dart, Sugar, Covered 27.00
Pressed Glass, Loop & Dart, Wine 18.00
Pressed Glass, Loop & Dewdrop, Creamer .... 15.00 To 20.00
Pressed Glass, Loop & Dewdrop, Goblet 16.00

Pressed Glass, Loop & Dewdrop, Mug	18.00
Pressed Glass, Loop & Dewdrop, Sugar, Covered	16.00
Pressed Glass, Loop & Fans, Celery	19.50
Pressed Glass, Loop & Fans, Pitcher, Milk	24.50
Pressed Glass, Loop & Hairpin, Eggcup, Sandwich	24.50
Pressed Glass, Loop & Honeycomb, Goblet	5.00 To 10.00
Pressed Glass, Loop & Jewel, Pitcher, Water	65.00
Pressed Glass, Loop & Jewel, Syrup, Metal Spring Lid	38.00
Pressed Glass, Loop & Moose Eye, Goblet, Flint	27.50 To 32.00
Pressed Glass, Loop & Moose Eye, Tumbler, Flint	25.00
Pressed Glass, Loop & Moose Eye, Tumbler, Whiskey	20.00
Pressed Glass, Loop & Ovals, Goblet, Flint	15.00 To 23.00
Pressed Glass, Loop & Petals, Goblet, Flint	26.00 To 30.00
Pressed Glass, Loop & Petals, Salt, Master	19.75
Pressed Glass, Loop & Pillar, Bowl, Berry, 8 In.	9.50
Pressed Glass, Loop & Pillar, Goblet	15.00
Pressed Glass, Loop & Pillar, Toothpick	8.50
Pressed Glass, Loop & Pyramid, Goblet	12.50
Pressed Glass, Loop With Fisheye, Goblet	17.00 To 17.50
Pressed Glass, Loop With Garter Band, Goblet	8.00
Loop with Stippled Panels, see Texas	
Loop, see Seneca Loop, Yuma Loop	
Pressed Glass, Lorne, Butter, Covered	18.50
Pressed Glass, Lotus & Serpent, Mug	19.50 To 35.00
Pressed Glass, Lotus & Serpent, Plate, Bread	35.00
Pressed Glass, Lotus & Serpent, Pitcher, Water	40.00 To 65.00
Pressed Glass, Lotus & Serpent, Plate, Bread	35.00
Pressed Glass, Lotus, Bowl, Handled, 6 1/2 In.	10.00
Pressed Glass, Lotus, Creamer, Individual, 3 3/8 In.	14.00
Pressed Glass, Lotus, Dish, Pickle	7.00
Pressed Glass, Lotus, Nappy, Handled, 6 1/4 In.	9.50
Pressed Glass, Lotus, Plate, Bread	35.00
Pressed Glass, Lotus, Plate, Bread, Motto	28.00
Pressed Glass, Lotus, Plate, Handled, 6 1/2 In.	20.00
Pressed Glass, Lotus, Plate, 6 1/2 In.	15.00
Pressed Glass, Lotus, Relish, Oval	7.50
Pressed Glass, Lotus, Sauce, 4 In.	8.00
Pressed Glass, Lotus, Tray, Ice Cream	22.00
Pressed Glass, Louis XV, Spooner, Green	55.00
Pressed Glass, Louise, Compote, Jelly, 4 3/4 In.Diamter	12.00
Pressed Glass, Louise, Sauce	5.00
Pressed Glass, Louisiana, Butter, Covered	26.00
Pressed Glass, Louisiana, Cake Stand, 9 1/2 In.	27.00
Pressed Glass, Louisiana, Compote, Jelly, 4 1/4 In.	13.00 To 17.00
Pressed Glass, Louisiana, Goblet	22.50
Pressed Glass, Louisiana, Pitcher, Water	32.50
Pressed Glass, Lustre Rose, Creamer, Green & Gold	45.00
Pressed Glass, Lyre & Grapevine, Plate, Toddy, 4 3/8 In.	15.00
Pressed Glass, Madison, Creamer	90.00
Pressed Glass, Madison, Creamer, Flint	75.00
Pressed Glass, Madison, Spill, Flint	30.00
Pressed Glass, Madison, Spooner	40.00
Pressed Glass, Madison, Spooner, Flint	30.00
Pressed Glass, Madison, Sugar, Covered	85.00
Pressed Glass, Madison, Sugar, Covered, Flint	70.00
Pressed Glass, Magnet & Grape With Frosted Leaf, Bottle, Castor, Shaker Top	19.00
Pressed Glass, Magnet & Grape With Frosted Leaf, Butter, Covered	95.00
Pressed Glass, Magnet & Grape With Frosted Leaf, Celery	90.00 To 185.00
Pressed Glass, Magnet & Grape With Frosted Leaf, Champagne	90.00
Pressed Glass, Magnet & Grape With Frosted Leaf, Champagne, Flint	85.00
Pressed Glass, Magnet & Grape With Frosted Leaf, Compote, 7 In.	75.00
Pressed Glass, Magnet & Grape With Frosted Leaf, Creamer	135.00
Pressed Glass, Magnet & Grape With Frosted Leaf, Creamer, Flint	125.00
Pressed Glass, Magnet & Grape With Frosted Leaf, Decanter, Wine	500.00
Pressed Glass, Magnet & Grape With Frosted Leaf, Eggcup	110.00
Pressed Glass, Magnet & Grape With Frosted Leaf, Eggcup, Flint	90.00

Pressed Glass,
Loop With Fisheye, Goblet

Pressed Glass, Magnet & Grape,
Stippled Leaf, Goblet

Pressed Glass, Magnet & Grape With Frosted Leaf, Goblet	35.00 To 50.00
Pressed Glass, Magnet & Grape With Frosted Leaf, Goblet, Flint	42.50 To 65.00
Pressed Glass, Magnet & Grape With Frosted Leaf, Goblet, Knob Stem, Flint	38.00
Pressed Glass, Magnet & Grape With Frosted Leaf, Sugar	22.50
Pressed Glass, Magnet & Grape With Frosted Leaf, Sugar, Covered	95.00
Pressed Glass, Magnet & Grape With Frosted Leaf, Tumbler	125.00
Pressed Glass, Magnet & Grape With Frosted Leaf, Wine	90.00
Pressed Glass, Magnet & Grape With Frosted Leaf, Wine, Flint	85.00
Pressed Glass, Magnet & Grape With Stippled Leaf, Goblet	8.50 To 9.50
Pressed Glass, Magnet & Grape, Eggcup	19.00
Pressed Glass, Magnet & Grape, Goblet	18.00
Pressed Glass, Magnet & Grape, Goblet, Flint	22.00
Pressed Glass, Magnet & Grape, Spooner	14.00
Pressed Glass, Magnet & Grape, Sugar, Covered	45.00
Pressed Glass, Magnet & Grape, Wine	16.00
Pressed Glass, Maiden's Blush, Creamer	22.00 To 36.50
Pressed Glass, Maiden's Blush, Creamer, Tankard Type	25.00
Pressed Glass, Maiden's Blush, Pitcher, Etched Name & 1901, 9 1/4 In.	125.00
Pressed Glass, Maiden's Blush, Relish, Green	23.00
Pressed Glass, Maiden's Blush, Tumbler, Pink	40.00
Pressed Glass, Maine, Butter, Covered	26.00
Pressed Glass, Maine, Cake Stand, 8 3/4 In.	25.00
Pressed Glass, Maine, Compote, 5 In.	18.00
Pressed Glass, Maine, Celery	22.00
Pressed Glass, Maine, Creamer	12.00
Pressed Glass, Maine, Goblet	12.00 To 22.50
Pressed Glass, Maine, Spooner	14.00
Pressed Glass, Maine, Relish	32.50
Pressed Glass, Maine, Syrup, Tin Top	25.00
Pressed Glass, Maine, Wine	28.50
Majestic, see Puritan	
Pressed Glass, Maltese Cross, Sauce	6.00
Pressed Glass, Man's Head, Creamer	20.00 To 24.50
Pressed Glass, Manhattan, Cake Stand, 10 In.	30.00
Pressed Glass, Manhattan, Creamer	4.00 To 9.50
Pressed Glass, Manhattan, Goblet	13.50
Pressed Glass, Manhattan, Relish, Gold	6.00
Pressed Glass, Manhattan, Toothpick	12.00 To 20.00
Pressed Glass, Manhattan, Tumbler, 2 In.	10.00
Pressed Glass, Manting, Champagne	38.00
Pressed Glass, Manting, Champagne, Flint	35.00
Pressed Glass, Manting, Goblet, Flint	20.00
Pressed Glass, Many Loops, Bowl, Blue & Opalescent, Fluted, 8 1/4 In.	27.50
Pressed Glass, Many Loops, Bowl, Green, 8 1/2 In.	16.00
Pressed Glass, Maple Leaf, Band, Goblet	21.50
Pressed Glass, Maple Leaf, Berry Set, Frosted, Footed Bowl, 11 Piece	65.00
Pressed Glass, Maple Leaf, Bowl, Frosted, Oval, 6 X 4 1/2 In.	25.00
Pressed Glass, Maple Leaf, Bowl, Waste, Frosted	29.50
Pressed Glass, Maple Leaf, Compote, Green, 3 Twigs Form Stem, 5 In.	20.00

Pressed Glass, Maple Leaf, Cup Plate, Opalescent	37.50
Pressed Glass, Maple Leaf, Goblet	35.00 To 85.00
Pressed Glass, Maple Leaf, Goblet, Etched Band	35.00
Pressed Glass, Maple Leaf, Pitcher, Milk, Frosted, 4 Footed	40.00
Pressed Glass, Maple Leaf, Pitcher, Water	65.00
Pressed Glass, Maple Leaf, Plate, Bread, Frosted & Clear, 13 1/2 In.	28.50
Pressed Glass, Maple Leaf, Plate, Dark Blue, 11 In.	45.00
Pressed Glass, Maple Leaf, Sauce	6.00 To 14.00
Pressed Glass, Maple Leaf, Sauce, Frosted	4.50 To 10.00
Pressed Glass, Maple Leaf, Spooner, Frosted	21.50
Pressed Glass, Maple Leaf, Spooner, Frosted, 4 Log Feet	22.50
Pressed Glass, Maple Leaf, Tumbler, Frosted	18.00
Pressed Glass, Mario, Tumbler, Ruby Stained	25.00
Pressed Glass, Marquisette, Celery, Pair	27.50
Pressed Glass, Marquisette, Champagne	19.00
Pressed Glass, Marquisette, Compote, 8 1/4 X 7 3/4 In.	25.00
Pressed Glass, Marquisette, Goblet	18.00
Pressed Glass, Marquisette, Sugar	10.00
Pressed Glass, Marsh Fern, Celery, Etched	20.00
Pressed Glass, Marsh Fern, Compote, 8 1/2 X 7 In.	14.00
Pressed Glass, Marsh Fern, Tumbler, Etched	12.50
Pressed Glass, Marsh Pink, Butter, Covered	25.00
Pressed Glass, Marsh Pink, Cake Stand	29.50
Pressed Glass, Marsh Pink, Creamer	16.00 To 17.50
Pressed Glass, Marsh Pink, Creamer, Square	25.00
Pressed Glass, Marsh Pink, Pitcher, Water	23.00
Pressed Glass, Marsh Pink, Plate, Handled, Square, 10 In.	18.00
Pressed Glass, Marsh Pink, Plate, Octagonal, 10 In.	20.00
Pressed Glass, Marsh Pink, Plate, Square, 10 In.	18.00 To 20.00
Pressed Glass, Marsh Pink, Plate, 10 In.	22.00
Pressed Glass, Marsh Pink, Relish	8.50 To 10.00
Pressed Glass, Marsh Pink, Relish, Rectangular	7.00
Pressed Glass, Marsh Pink, Salt	17.50
Pressed Glass, Marsh Pink, Saltshaker	15.00 To 17.50
Pressed Glass, Marsh Pink, Sauce, Footed, 2 Handled, 4 In.	12.50
Pressed Glass, Marsh Pink, Sauce, 2 Handled, 4 In.	9.50
Pressed Glass, Marsh Pink, Sugar, Covered	24.00
Pressed Glass, Martha's Tears, Goblet	12.00
Pressed Glass, Martha's Tears, Wine	17.50
Pressed Glass, Maryland, Pitcher, Milk	25.00
Pressed Glass, Maryland, Pitcher, Water	32.50
Pressed Glass, Maryland, Plate, 7 In.	4.00 To 9.00
Pressed Glass, Maryland, Sugar, Covered	20.00
Pressed Glass, Maryland, Tumbler, Ruby Stained	25.00
Pressed Glass, Mascotte, Butter, Etched	26.00
Pressed Glass, Mascotte, Butter, Etched, Covered	25.00 To 35.00
Pressed Glass, Mascotte, Celery	20.00 To 22.50
Pressed Glass, Mascotte, Creamer	19.00 To 20.00
Pressed Glass, Mascotte, Creamer, Applied Handle	18.00
Pressed Glass, Mascotte, Creamer, Etched	18.00
Pressed Glass, Mascotte, Jar, Covered, Patent May 20, 1873, 8 X 4 1/2 In.	38.00
Pressed Glass, Mascotte, Spooner, Etched	16.50
Pressed Glass, Mascotte, Sugar, Covered	20.00
Pressed Glass, Mascotte, Sugar, Etched, Covered	26.00
Pressed Glass, Mascotte, Tumbler, Etched	20.00
Pressed Glass, Mascotte, Wine	15.00 To 15.50
Pressed Glass, Masonic, Creamer, Greentown	32.50
Pressed Glass, Massachusetts, Butter, Covered	35.00
Pressed Glass, Massachusetts, Creamer	11.50
Pressed Glass, Massachusetts, Decanter, 23 Oz.	65.00
Pressed Glass, Massachusetts, Goblet, Gold	18.50
Pressed Glass, Massachusetts, Jug, Rum, 5 3/8 In.	45.00
Pressed Glass, Massachusetts, Mug	12.00
Pressed Glass, Massachusetts, Mug, Gold Trim	14.00
Pressed Glass, Massachusetts, Relish	12.50

Pressed Glass, Massachusetts, Sugar, 2 Handled	12.00
Pressed Glass, Massachusetts, Vase, Green, 9 3/4 In.	27.50
Pressed Glass, Massachusetts, Wine	28.00
Pressed Glass, McKinley, Figurine, Opaque White, 5 In.	130.00
Pressed Glass, McKinley, Mug, Covered, "Protection & Plenty"	30.00 To 50.00
Pressed Glass, McKinley, Plate, Frosted, "Protection & Plenty, " 7 In.	20.00
Pressed Glass, McKinley, Plate, Frosted, "Protection & Plenty, " 9 1/2 In.	32.50
Pressed Glass, McKinley, Plate, "Protection & Plenty, " Gold, 9 In.	22.50
Pressed Glass, McKinley, Tumbler, "Our Martyr President"	25.00
Pressed Glass, McKinley, Tumbler, Protection & Plenty	15.00
Pressed Glass, Meander, Bowl, Blue, Opalescent, 9 In.	32.00
Pressed Glass, Medallion, Butter	32.00
Pressed Glass, Medallion, Cake Stand, 9 1/2 In.	20.00
Pressed Glass, Medallion, Dish, Pickle, Blue	14.00
Pressed Glass, Medallion, Dish, Pickle, Green	15.00
Pressed Glass, Medallion, Goblet	14.00 To 15.00
Pressed Glass, Medallion, Goblet, Amber	23.00
Pressed Glass, Medallion, Goblet, Blue	35.00
Pressed Glass, Medallion, Pitcher, Water, Blue	40.00
Pressed Glass, Mellor, Goblet	6.50
Pressed Glass, Melrose, Compote, Flared Rim, 8 1/2 X 7 1/2 In.	22.00
Pressed Glass, Melrose, Goblet	14.50 To 15.00
Pressed Glass, Melrose, Pitcher, Water	24.00
Pressed Glass, Melrose, Plate, 6 In.	7.50
Pressed Glass, Melrose, Tray, Water	45.00
Pressed Glass, Melrose, Wine	12.50 To 18.75
Pressed Glass, Melton, Goblet	10.00
Pressed Glass, Memphis, Goblet	5.00
Pressed Glass, Menagerie, Sugar, Child's, Covered, Bear Shape	55.00
Pressed Glass, Michigan, Celery	15.50
Pressed Glass, Michigan, Creamer	14.00 To 17.50
Pressed Glass, Michigan, Creamer, Miniature	22.00
Pressed Glass, Michigan, Creamer, Yellow Eyes, Red Carnation	35.00
Pressed Glass, Michigan, Goblet	20.00
Pressed Glass, Michigan, Goblet, Cranberry & Gold Trim	39.50
Pressed Glass, Michigan, Goblet, Gold	22.50
Pressed Glass, Michigan, Pitcher, Water	27.50 To 30.00
Pressed Glass, Michigan, Pitcher, Water, Child's	22.00
Pressed Glass, Michigan, Relish, Gold	7.50
Pressed Glass, Michigan, Sauce, Ruby Flashed	10.00
Pressed Glass, Michigan, Spooner	14.00
Pressed Glass, Michigan, Spooner, Miniature	22.00
Pressed Glass, Michigan, Spooner, Pink Blush	28.50
Pressed Glass, Michigan, Toothpick	12.00 To 20.00
Pressed Glass, Michigan, Toothpick, Fiery Opalescent	20.00
Pressed Glass, Michigan, Toothpick, Robin's-Egg Blue	15.00
Pressed Glass, Michigan, Tumbler	9.50 To 23.75
Pressed Glass, Michigan, Vase, Flared, 8 1/4 In.	25.00
Pressed Glass, Michigan, Water Set, 10 Piece	190.00
Pressed Glass, Midget Loop, Goblet	5.00
Pressed Glass, Mikado Fan, Celery	8.50
Pressed Glass, Mikado Fan, Goblet	9.00 To 22.00
Pressed Glass, Mikado Fan, Nappy, Square	2.00
Pressed Glass, Millard, Pitcher, Water, Etched, Ruby Stained	95.00
Pressed Glass, Milton, Champagne	20.00
Pressed Glass, Milton, Goblet	13.50 To 20.00
Pressed Glass, Milton, Goblet, Findlay	13.00
Pressed Glass, Milton, Salt & Pepper, Amber	49.00
Pressed Glass, Milton, Wine	18.75
Pressed Glass, Minerva, Bowl, 6 In.	21.00
Pressed Glass, Minerva, Butter	50.00 To 60.00
Pressed Glass, Minerva, Butter, Covered	65.00
Pressed Glass, Minerva, Cake Stand, 10 1/2 In.	55.00
Pressed Glass, Minerva, Creamer	45.00 To 47.50
Pressed Glass, Minerva, Pitcher, Water	110.00
Pressed Glass, Minerva, Plate, Bread	40.00

Pressed Glass, Minerva, Plate, Bread, Straw Mark 42.00
Pressed Glass, Minerva, Sauce 16.00
Pressed Glass, Minerva, Sauce, Footed, 4 In. 8.00
Pressed Glass, Minerva, Spooner .... 30.00 To 35.00
Pressed Glass, Minerva, Sugar 20.00
Pressed Glass, Minnesota, Celery, 13 In. 25.00
Pressed Glass, Minnesota, Creamer, Gold Trim 16.00
Pressed Glass, Minnesota, Goblet 14.50
Pressed Glass, Minnesota, Goblet, Gold Trim .... |6.00
Pressed Glass, Minnesota, Jar, Cracker, 10 X 8 In. 65.00
Pressed Glass, Minnesota, Pitcher, Water, Tankard Type 37.50
Pressed Glass, Minnesota, Toothpick, Turning Purple 13.50
Pressed Glass, Mioton, Goblet, Pleat Band 8.00
Pressed Glass, Mioton, Goblet, Pleat Band, Flint .... 12.50 To 16.00
Pressed Glass, Mioton, Goblet, Ringed Stem 5.50
Pressed Glass, Mioton, Goblet, Ruby Stained 20.00
Pressed Glass, Mioton, Goblet, Scalloped Top 5.50
Pressed Glass, Mirror & Loop, Champagne 40.00
Pressed Glass, Mirror & Loop, Champagne, Flint 35.00
Pressed Glass, Mirror & Loop, Eggcup 30.00
Pressed Glass, Mirror & Loop, Eggcup, Flint .... 18.00 To 25.00
Pressed Glass, Mirror, Claret, Flint 50.00
Pressed Glass, Mirror, Compote, Flint, 10 In. 55.00
Pressed Glass, Mirror, Compote, 10 In. 55.00
Pressed Glass, Mirror, Creamer 90.00
Pressed Glass, Mirror, Creamer, Flint 85.00
Pressed Glass, Mirror, Goblet 24.00
Pressed Glass, Mirror, Goblet, Flint .... 23.00 To 26.00
Pressed Glass, Mirror, Spill, Flint 45.00
Pressed Glass, Mirror, Sugar, Covered 75.00
Pressed Glass, Mirror, Sugar, Covered, Flint .... 45.00 To 60.00
Pressed Glass, Mirror, Sugar, Flint .... 45.00 To 65.00
Pressed Glass, Mirror, Tumbler, Flint 50.00
Pressed Glass, Mirror, Wine 35.00
Pressed Glass, Mirror, Wine, Flint 30.00
Pressed Glass, Miss Columbia, Match Holder, Wall, Patent June 13, 1876 .... 48.00
Pressed Glass, Missouri, Cake Stand, Miniature 12.00
Pressed Glass, Missouri, Compote, Green, High Standard, 9 3/4 In. 35.00
Pressed Glass, Missouri, Pitcher, 7 In. 13.00
Pressed Glass, Missouri, Tumbler, Green 16.50
Pressed Glass, Mitered Bars, Celery .... 12.50 To 20.00
Pressed Glass, Mitered Bars, Goblet 10.50
Pressed Glass, Mitered Bars, Saltshaker 3.50
Pressed Glass, Mitered Bars, Sauce, Footed, 3 1/2 In. 5.50
Pressed Glass, Mitered Bars, Spooner 15.00
    Mitered Diamond Point, see Mitered Bars
Pressed Glass, Mitered Diamond, Saltshaker, Blue .... 18.00 To 25.00
Pressed Glass, Mitered Diamond, Tumbler, Amber 16.50
Pressed Glass, Mitered Diamond, Wine, Amber 27.50
Pressed Glass, Mitered Frieze, Goblet 14.50
Pressed Glass, Mitered Frieze, Sauce, Footed, 4 5/8 In. 5.50
Pressed Glass, Mitered Frieze, Sugar 12.00
Pressed Glass, Mitered Prisms, Goblet 5.00
Pressed Glass, Mitered Thumbprint Variant, Goblet 8.50
Pressed Glass, Mitered Thumbprint, Goblet 5.00
Pressed Glass, Model Peerless, Cordial 16.50
Pressed Glass, Model Peerless, Plate, 6 1/4 In. 7.50
Pressed Glass, Modiste, Goblet 8.50
Pressed Glass, Monkey Climber, Goblet 42.50
Pressed Glass, Monkey, Bowl, Waste 65.00
Pressed Glass, Monkey, Mug, Grabbing Tails, 4 In. 55.00
Pressed Glass, Monkey, Spooner 10.00
Pressed Glass, Monkey, Spooner, Scalloped Rim .... 55.00 To 75.00
Pressed Glass, Monkey, Sugar, Flint 45.00
Pressed Glass, Monkey, Tumbler .... 75.00 To 100.00
Pressed Glass, Monkey, Water Set, 5 Piece 525.00

Pressed Glass, Moon & Star Variant, Bottle, Water 20.00
Pressed Glass, Moon & Star, Bottle, Perfume, Flint 68.00
Pressed Glass, Moon & Star, Bowl, Berry, 7 1/4 In. 21.00
Pressed Glass, Moon & Star, Bowl, Berry, 9 In. .... 27.50 To 28.00
Pressed Glass, Moon & Star, Bowl, Footed, 6 In. 17.50
Pressed Glass, Moon & Star, Bowl, Oval, 8 X 6 In. 10.00
Pressed Glass, Moon & Star, Bowl, 6 In. 10.50
Pressed Glass, Moon & Star, Bowl, 9 X 4 In. 22.50
Pressed Glass, Moon & Star, Butter, Covered 45.00
Pressed Glass, Moon & Star, Cake Stand, 9 In. 30.00
Pressed Glass, Moon & Star, Celery .... 18.50 To 25.00
Pressed Glass, Moon & Star, Champagne 45.00
Pressed Glass, Moon & Star, Compote, Covered, 6 In. 38.00
Pressed Glass, Moon & Star, Compote, Scalloped Edge, High Standard, 10 In. 47.50
Pressed Glass, Moon & Star, Compote, 7 X 5 In. 25.00
Pressed Glass, Moon & Star, Creamer .... 35.00 To 45.00
Pressed Glass, Moon & Star, Creamer, Applied Handle 48.75
Pressed Glass, Moon & Star, Goblet .... 18.50 To 27.50

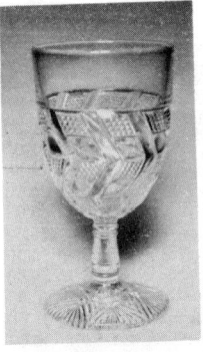

Pressed Glass, Mitered Diamond, Goblet

Pressed Glass, Oval,
Fine Ribbed, Cordial

Pressed Glass,
Moon & Star,
Whale Oil Lamp

Pressed Glass,
Star & Prunty,
Cylindrical Footed Vessel

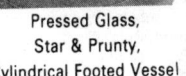

Pressed Glass,
Moon & Star, Tumbler

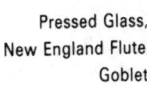

Pressed Glass,
New England Flute,
Goblet

Pressed Glass,
New England Pineapple,
Pitcher

Pressed Glass,
Moon & Star,
Covered Footed Bowl

Pressed Glass, Moon & Star, Goblet, Frosted	40.00
Pressed Glass, Moon & Star, Plate, Bread	32.50
Pressed Glass, Moon & Star, Relish	13.75
Pressed Glass, Moon & Star, Sauce, Footed, 4 In.	15.00
Pressed Glass, Moon & Star, Spill, Flint	39.50 To 40.00
Pressed Glass, Moon & Star, Spooner	32.50 To 45.00
Pressed Glass, Moon & Star, Spooner, Flint	40.00
Pressed Glass, Moon & Star, Sugar	25.00
Pressed Glass, Moon & Star, Sugar, Covered	185.00
Pressed Glass, Moon & Star, Syrup, Flint	110.00
Pressed Glass, Moon & Star, Tumbler	165.00
Pressed Glass, Moon & Star, Tumbler, Footed	65.00 To 165.00
Pressed Glass, Moon & Star, Tumbler, Footed, Flint	60.00 To 165.00
Pressed Glass, Moose Eye In Sand, Goblet	15.00
Pressed Glass, Morning Glory, Champagne	250.00
Pressed Glass, Morning Glory, Eggcup, Flint	135.00
Pressed Glass, Morning Glory, Sauce, Flint	28.00
Pressed Glass, Morning Glory, Tumbler, Footed	175.00
Pressed Glass, Morning Glory, Tumbler, Footed, Flint	160.00
Pressed Glass, Morning Glory, Wine	195.00
Pressed Glass, Morning Glory, Wine, Flint	145.00 To 180.00
Pressed Glass, Moses In Bulrushes, Plate, 7 In.	12.50
Pressed Glass, Mother Hubbard, Sugar, Blue, Covered	16.00
Pressed Glass, Mother Hubbard, Teapot, Blue	16.00
Pressed Glass, Mountain Laurel, Goblet	12.50
Pressed Glass, My Lady's Workbox, Goblet	14.50
Pressed Glass, Nail, Bowl, Berry, 3 1/2 In.	8.00
Pressed Glass, Nail, Celery	8.00
Pressed Glass, Nail, Pitcher, Milk, Etched	45.00
Pressed Glass, Nail, Pitcher, Water, Ruby Stained	65.00
Pressed Glass, Nail, Sauce, Footed	5.00
Pressed Glass, Nailhead, Butter, Covered	32.50
Pressed Glass, Nailhead, Cake Stand, 8 1/2 In.	15.00
Pressed Glass, Nailhead, Cake Stand, 10 1/2 In.	27.50
Pressed Glass, Nailhead, Plate, Handled, Square, 7 In.	10.00
Pressed Glass, Nailhead, Plate, Square, 7 In.	7.50
Pressed Glass, Nailhead, Plate, 9 In.	10.00
Pressed Glass, Nailhead, Plate, 9 1/4 In.	15.00
Pressed Glass, Nailhead, Sauce	4.50
Pressed Glass, Nailhead, Sugar & Creamer	48.00
Pressed Glass, Nailhead, Sugar, Covered	20.00
Pressed Glass, Narcissus Spray, Water Set, 5 Piece	35.00 To 40.00
Pressed Glass, Narcissus, Creamer	14.00
Pressed Glass, Nemesis, Goblet	12.00
Pressed Glass, Nestor, Sugar, Covered, Apple Green	40.00 To 45.00
Pressed Glass, Nestor, Toothpick, Light Green	32.50
Pressed Glass, New England Centennial, Goblet	75.00
Pressed Glass, New England Flute, Goblet, Flared Top, Knob Stem, Flint	15.00
Pressed Glass, New England Flute, Goblet, Flint, 5 1/2 In.	12.00
Pressed Glass, New England Flute, Wine	10.50
Pressed Glass, New England Pineapple, Compote, Footed, Flint, 5 X 8 In.	65.00
Pressed Glass, New England Pineapple, Creamer	150.00
Pressed Glass, New England Pineapple, Creamer, Flint	125.00
Pressed Glass, New England Pineapple, Dish, Honey	14.50
Pressed Glass, New England Pineapple, Dish, Honey, Flint	14.50
Pressed Glass, New England Pineapple, Dish, Sweetmeat, Covered, Flint	150.00
Pressed Glass, New England Pineapple, Eggcup	32.00 To 33.00
Pressed Glass, New England Pineapple, Eggcup, Flint	30.00 To 38.00
Pressed Glass, New England Pineapple, Goblet	32.00 To 40.00
Pressed Glass, New England Pineapple, Goblet, Flint	20.00 To 45.00
Pressed Glass, New England Pineapple, Goblet, Lady's, Flint	55.00
Pressed Glass, New England Pineapple, Pitcher, Water, Flint	250.00
Pressed Glass, New England Pineapple, Plate, Flint, 6 In.	65.00
Pressed Glass, New England Pineapple, Sauce	12.50
Pressed Glass, New England Pineapple, Spill	22.00
Pressed Glass, New England Pineapple, Spill, Flint	30.00

Pressed Glass, New England Pineapple, Spooner	22.00 To 32.00
Pressed Glass, New England Pineapple, Spooner, Flint	26.50 To 32.50
Pressed Glass, New England Pineapple, Sugar, Covered	78.00
Pressed Glass, New England Pineapple, Sugar, Covered, Flint	65.00 To 70.00
Pressed Glass, New England Pineapple, Sugar, Flint, C.1850	56.50
Pressed Glass, New England Pineapple, Tumbler	95.00
Pressed Glass, New England Pineapple, Tumbler, Flint	95.00
Pressed Glass, New England Pineapple, Tumbler, Whiskey, Handle, Flint, 3 In.	135.00
Pressed Glass, New England, Goblet	25.00
Pressed Glass, New Hampshire, Bowl, Berry, Pink Flashed	15.00
Pressed Glass, New Hampshire, Creamer	13.00 To 14.00
Pressed Glass, New Hampshire, Creamer, Cranberry Stained	14.00
Pressed Glass, New Hampshire, Cup, Punch	9.00
Pressed Glass, New Hampshire, Goblet	14.00
Pressed Glass, New Hampshire, Goblet, Cranberry Flashed Top	20.00
Pressed Glass, New Hampshire, Pitcher, Water	32.50
Pressed Glass, New Hampshire, Sauce, Flared	3.00
Pressed Glass, New Hampshire, Sauce, Pink Flashed	4.50
Pressed Glass, New Hampshire, Spooner	12.50 To 13.00
Pressed Glass, New Hampshire, Sugar & Creamer	14.00 To 15.50
Pressed Glass, New Hampshire, Sugar, Covered	17.50
Pressed Glass, New Hampshire, Syrup	32.50
Pressed Glass, New Hampshire, Toothpick	12.00
Pressed Glass, New Hampshire, Tumbler	9.50 To 10.00
Pressed Glass, New Jersey, Bowl, 8 In.	12.00
Pressed Glass, New Jersey, Dish, Mint, Footed	17.00
Pressed Glass, New Jersey, Dish, Pickle, Gold Trim, 4 X 8 In.	6.50
Pressed Glass, New Jersey, Goblet	14.00
Pressed Glass, New Jersey, Plate, 11 In.	16.50
Pressed Glass, New Jersey, Plate, 11 1/2 In.	10.00
Pressed Glass, New Jersey, Saltshaker	22.50
Pressed Glass, New Jersey, Saltshaker, Gold	22.00
Pressed Glass, New Jersey, Toothpick, Gold	18.50
Pressed Glass, New Jersey, Tumbler	9.50
Pressed Glass, New Jersey, Tumbler, Gold Trim	9.50 To 15.00
Pressed Glass, New York Honeycomb, Champagne	10.00 To 20.00
Pressed Glass, New York Honeycomb, Creamer, Applied Crimped Handle, Flint	45.00
Pressed Glass, New York Honeycomb, Goblet, Amber	23.00
Pressed Glass, New York Honeycomb, Goblet, Flint	10.00
Pressed Glass, New York Honeycomb, Sugar, Flint	18.00
Pressed Glass, Niagara Falls, Tray, Water	95.00
Pressed Glass, Niagara Falls, Tray, Water, Frosted	110.00
Pressed Glass, Nicotiana, Goblet	13.00
Pressed Glass, Nicotiana, Goblet, Etched	10.00
Pressed Glass, No.15, Tumbler, Pioneer	6.00
Pressed Glass, Nova Scotia Raspberry, Plate, 10 In.	20.00 To 25.00
Pressed Glass, Nova Scotia Tandem, Plate, 9 In.	13.75
Pressed Glass, Nova Scotia, Sauce, Footed, Scalloped Rim, 3 1/2 In.	3.00
Pressed Glass, Nursery Tales, Berry Set, Miniature, 7 Piece	140.00
Pressed Glass, Nursery Tales, Butter, Covered, Miniature	118.00
Pressed Glass, Nursery Tales, Butter, Covered, Swirled	28.50
Pressed Glass, Nursery Tales, Creamer, Miniature	35.00 To 42.00
Pressed Glass, Nursery Tales, Cup, Punch, Miniature	10.00 To 25.00
Pressed Glass, Nursery Tales, Pitcher, Water, Miniature	45.00
Pressed Glass, Nursery Tales, Plate, Child's, 6 In.	28.00
Pressed Glass, Nursery Tales, Sauce, Miniature	23.00
Pressed Glass, Nursery Tales, Spooner, Miniature	44.00
Pressed Glass, Nursery Tales, Sugar & Creamer, Child's	95.00
Pressed Glass, Nursery Tales, Sugar, Covered, Miniature	54.00
Pressed Glass, Nursery Tales, Sugar, Miniature	42.50
Pressed Glass, Nursery Tales, Table Set, 4 Piece	225.00
Pressed Glass, Nursery Tales, Water Set, Child's, 7 Piece	215.00
Pressed Glass, Oak Leaf Band With Loops, Goblet	10.00
Pressed Glass, Oak Leaf, Bowl, Shallow, Flint, 6 1/2 In.	35.00
Pressed Glass, Oak Leaf, Bowl, 6 1/2 X 1 1/4 In.	65.00
Pressed Glass, Oak Leaf, Dish, Pickle, Cathedral Border, Open Handles	15.00

Pressed Glass, Open Rose, Goblet

Pressed Glass,
Orange Peel, Goblet

Pressed Glass,
Moon & Stork, Goblet

Pressed Glass,
Oval Miter, Footed Salt

Pressed Glass, Oak Leaf, Salt, Master	25.00
Pressed Glass, Oak Wreath, Salt	20.00
Pressed Glass, Oak Wreath, Sauce	5.00
Pressed Glass, Oak Wreath, Spooner	8.50
Pressed Glass, Oaken Bucket, Pitcher, Water, Blue	37.50
Pressed Glass, Oaken Bucket, Spooner	12.50 To 17.50
Pressed Glass, Oaken Bucket, Toothpick	10.00
Pressed Glass, Ohio Inverted Thumbprint, Goblet	6.00
Pressed Glass, Ohio, Goblet	15.00
Pressed Glass, Ohio, Goblet, Etched Ivy & Leaf	18.50
Pressed Glass, Ohio, Goblet, Etched Lines	17.00
Pressed Glass, Old Abe, Sugar, Covered	69.00 To 135.00
One Hundred One, see 101	
Pressed Glass, Open Cryptic, Banana Stand, Child's	32.50
Pressed Glass, Open Plaid, Pitcher, Water	16.00
Pressed Glass, Open Plaid, Salt, Individual, 2 3/4 X 1 1/2 In.	3.00
Pressed Glass, Open Rose, Bowl, Green, Pedestal, Marked N, 6 1/2 In.	16.00
Pressed Glass, Open Rose, Eggcup	10.00 To 23.00
Pressed Glass, Open Rose, Goblet	13.50 To 21.50
Pressed Glass, Open Rose, Goblet, Buttermilk	22.00
Pressed Glass, Open Rose, Relish	11.00
Pressed Glass, Open Rose, Sauce	5.00
Pressed Glass, Open Rose, Spill	15.00
Pressed Glass, Open Rose, Spooner	15.00 To 18.50
Pressed Glass, Open Rose, Spooner, Footed	20.00
Pressed Glass, Open Rose, Sugar	10.00
Pressed Glass, Opposing Pyramids, Goblet	10.00
Pressed Glass, Opposing Pyramids, Tumbler	4.50
Pressed Glass, Opposing Pyramids, Wine, Ruby Stained	25.00
Pressed Glass, Optic Flute, Wine	5.00
Pressed Glass, Orange Peel Band, Goblet	7.50
Pressed Glass, Orange Peel, Sauce	3.75
Pressed Glass, Orange Peel, Sherbet	7.50
Oregon, see Beaded Loop, Skilton	
Pressed Glass, Oriental Fan, Goblet	11.00
Pressed Glass, Oriental, Creamer	20.00
Pressed Glass, Orion Inverted Thumbprint, Goblet	10.00
Pressed Glass, Ostrich Looking At The Moon, Goblet	50.00 To 90.00
Pressed Glass, Oswego Waffle, Goblet	7.50 To 8.00

Pressed Glass, Oval Miter, Goblet .... 8.00 To 25.00
Pressed Glass, Oval Miter, Goblet, Flint .... 18.00 To 33.00
Pressed Glass, Oval Miter, Sauce 6.00
Pressed Glass, Oval Miter, Spill 10.00
Pressed Glass, Oval Miter, Spooner .... 10.00 To 24.00
Pressed Glass, Oval Miter, Spooner, Flint 20.00
Oval Loop, see Question Mark
Pressed Glass, Oval Panels, Goblet 10.00
Pressed Glass, Oval Panels, Goblet, Flint .... 13.50 To 35.00
Pressed Glass, Oval Star, Butter, Child's .... 22.50 To 25.00
Pressed Glass, Oval Star, Butter, Covered .... 15.00 To 25.00
Pressed Glass, Oval Star, Creamer 18.50
Pressed Glass, Oval Star, Creamer, Child's .... 9.00 To 20.00
Pressed Glass, Oval Star, Pitcher, Water, Gold Trim, 4 1/4 In. 25.00
Pressed Glass, Oval Star, Spooner 14.50
Pressed Glass, Oval Star, Spooner, Miniature .... 9.00 To 16.00
Pressed Glass, Oval Star, Spooner, Miniature, Gold At Top 18.00
Pressed Glass, Oval Star, Sugar, Covered .... 20.00 To 21.50
Pressed Glass, Oval Star, Sugar, Child's 10.00
Pressed Glass, Oval Star, Sugar, Covered, Child's .... 15.00 To 16.50
Pressed Glass, Oval Star, Table Set, Child's, 3 Piece 57.00
Pressed Glass, Oval Star, Water Set, Child's, 7 Piece 125.00
Pressed Glass, Oval Star, Water Set, Child's, 8 Piece 90.00
Pressed Glass, Oval Thumbprint, Goblet, Gentleman's 10.00
Pressed Glass, Oval Thumbprint, Goblet, Lady's 10.00
Pressed Glass, Ovals & Circles, Mug, Flint 23.00
Pressed Glass, Ovals & Honeycombs, Goblet, Flint 7.50
Pressed Glass, Ovals With Long Bars, Tumbler, Footed, Flint 10.00
Pressed Glass, Owl & Possum, Goblet 45.00
Pressed Glass, Owl & Pussycat, Dome, Cheese 95.00
Pressed Glass, Owl In Fan, Goblet 18.00
Pressed Glass, Owl In Horseshoe, Mug, White 28.50
Pressed Glass, Owl, Relish, Frosted, Clear Eyes & Nose 18.50
Pressed Glass, Paisley With Purple Dots, Goblet 10.00
Pressed Glass, Paisley, Bowl, Gold Trim, 8 1/4 In. 22.50
Pressed Glass, Paling, Banded, Goblet 8.00
Pressed Glass, Paling, Goblet 6.00
Pressed Glass, Palm & Scroll, Bowl, Blue Opalescent, Fluted, Footed, 8 In. 26.00
Pressed Glass, Palm & Scroll, Sauce 4.00
Pressed Glass, Palm Beach, Sugar, Blue Opalescent, Covered 55.00
Pressed Glass, Palm Beach, Tumbler, Colored Grapes & Vines 23.50
Pressed Glass, Palm Leaf Fan, Cake Stand 16.00
Pressed Glass, Palm Stub, Goblet .... 11.00 To 13.00
Pressed Glass, Palmette, Celery .... 19.50 To 27.00
Pressed Glass, Palmette, Compote, Covered, 8 1/2 X 8 1/2 In. 55.00
Pressed Glass, Palmette, Compote, Low Footed, 8 1/2 In. 30.00
Pressed Glass, Palmette, Creamer 39.00
Pressed Glass, Palmette, Creamer, Applied Handle 25.00
Pressed Glass, Palmette, Eggcup .... 18.00 To 18.50
Pressed Glass, Palmette, Goblet .... 15.00 To 22.00
Pressed Glass, Palmette, Goblet, Buttermilk 9.00
Pressed Glass, Palmette, Plate, Bread, Blue, Round, Handled 20.00
Pressed Glass, Palmette, Spooner .... 14.50 To 22.50
Pressed Glass, Palmette, Sugar 9.00
Pressed Glass, Palmette, Tumbler 38.00
Pressed Glass, Pampas Flower, Creamer 10.00
Pressed Glass, Panel & Star, Celery 13.75
Pressed Glass, Paneled Acorn Band, Creamer, Applied Handle 30.00
Pressed Glass, Paneled Acorn Band, Eggcup 38.00
Pressed Glass, Paneled Acorn Band, Eggcup, Flint 38.00
Pressed Glass, Paneled Acorn Band, Goblet, Flint 32.00
Pressed Glass, Paneled Acorn Band, Wine 40.00
Pressed Glass, Paneled Acorn Band, Wine, Flint 35.00
Pressed Glass, Paneled Cane, Butter, Covered 26.00
Pressed Glass, Paneled Cane, Goblet .... 8.00 To 16.00
Pressed Glass, Paneled Cane, Jar, Cracker 24.00

Pressed Glass, Paneled Cane, Vase, Trumpet, 7 1/2 In.High 8.00
Pressed Glass, Paneled Cane, Wine, Amber 30.00
Pressed Glass, Paneled Cherry, Goblet .... 12.00 To 22.00
Pressed Glass, Paneled Cherry, Pitcher, Water 30.00
Pressed Glass, Paneled Cherry, Sauce .... 3.75 To 4.50
Pressed Glass, Paneled Cherry, Tumbler, Northwood 16.00
Pressed Glass, Paneled Daisies & Finecut, Goblet 8.50
Pressed Glass, Paneled Daisy & Button, Bowl, Berry, Emerald Green, Long 45.00
Pressed Glass, Paneled Daisy & Button, Bowl, Deep Green, 5 X 11 1/2 In. 27.50
Pressed Glass, Paneled Daisy & Button, Compote, Canary, 11 X 7 In. 57.50
Pressed Glass, Paneled Daisy & Button, Creamer 15.50
Pressed Glass, Paneled Daisy & Button, Goblet 12.00
Pressed Glass, Paneled Daisy & Button, Goblet, Blue 20.50
Pressed Glass, Paneled Daisy & Button, Sauce, Amber 8.00
Pressed Glass, Paneled Daisy & Button, Spooner 24.00
Pressed Glass, Paneled Daisy & Button, Sugar 35.00
   Paneled Daisy & Button, see also Daisy & Button with Amber Panels
Pressed Glass, Paneled Daisy, Bowl, Berry, 8 In. 18.00
Pressed Glass, Paneled Daisy, Bowl, 6 In. 12.50
Pressed Glass, Paneled Daisy, Bowl, 8 In. 18.00
Pressed Glass, Paneled Daisy, Cake Stand, 9 1/4 X 6 In. 21.50
Pressed Glass, Paneled Daisy, Cake Stand, 10 X 6 1/4 In. 26.00
Pressed Glass, Paneled Daisy, Celery .... 24.00 To 35.00
Pressed Glass, Paneled Daisy, Compote, Covered, 6 In. 35.00
Pressed Glass, Paneled Daisy, Compote, Covered, 9 X 5 1/2 In. 35.00
Pressed Glass, Paneled Daisy, Pitcher, Water 38.00
Pressed Glass, Paneled Daisy, Plate, Square, 9 In. 15.00
Pressed Glass, Paneled Daisy, Plate, Square, 9 1/4 In. 12.00
Pressed Glass, Paneled Daisy, Sauce 4.50
Pressed Glass, Paneled Daisy, Tray, Water, Scalloped Edge, 11 In. 20.00
Pressed Glass, Paneled Dewdrop, Celery 19.50
Pressed Glass, Paneled Dewdrop, Cordial, 3 1/4 In. 19.50
Pressed Glass, Paneled Dewdrop, Creamer 15.00
Pressed Glass, Paneled Dewdrop, Creamer, Child's, 3 1/2 In. 11.00
Pressed Glass, Paneled Dewdrop, Dish, Pickle, Handled 6.50
Pressed Glass, Paneled Dewdrop, Goblet .... 14.00 To 16.00
Pressed Glass, Paneled Dewdrop, Goblet, Pattern On Base 12.50
Pressed Glass, Paneled Dewdrop, Jar, Jam, Glass Lid 37.50
Pressed Glass, Paneled Dewdrop, Jar, Marmalade, Covered 24.50
Pressed Glass, Paneled Dewdrop, Mug, Applied Handle 30.00
Pressed Glass, Paneled Dewdrop, Pitcher, Milk 35.00
Pressed Glass, Paneled Dewdrop, Pitcher, Water 27.50
Pressed Glass, Paneled Dewdrop, Plate, Bread, 2 Handles, Oval, 9 X 12 1/2 In. .. 24.00
Pressed Glass, Paneled Dewdrop, Plate, 7 In. 13.50
Pressed Glass, Paneled Dewdrop, Plate, 10 In. 19.50
Pressed Glass, Paneled Dewdrop, Relish 12.50
Pressed Glass, Paneled Dewdrop, Sauce, Footed, 4 In. 6.00
Pressed Glass, Paneled Dewdrop, Sauce, Footed, 4 1/2 In. 7.50
Pressed Glass, Paneled Dewdrop, Spooner 11.00
Pressed Glass, Paneled Dewdrop, Sugar & Creamer 49.00
Pressed Glass, Paneled Dewdrop, Sugar, Covered 24.50
Pressed Glass, Paneled Dewdrop, Wine .... 14.00 To 25.00
Pressed Glass, Paneled Diamond Band, Goblet 10.00
Pressed Glass, Paneled Diamond Cross, Bowl, Deep Amber, 5 X 10 In. 20.00
Pressed Glass, Paneled Diamond Cross, Goblet 10.00
Pressed Glass, Paneled Diamond Cross, Pitcher, Water 12.50
Pressed Glass, Paneled Diamond Cross, Tumbler 12.50
Pressed Glass, Paneled Diamond Point, Dish, Honey 12.00
Pressed Glass, Paneled Diamond Point, Goblet .... 7.00 To 10.00
Pressed Glass, Paneled Diamond Point, Goblet, Blue 24.00
Pressed Glass, Paneled Diamonds & Finecut, Celery, Oblong, 9 X 6 In. 8.00
Pressed Glass, Paneled Diamonds & Finecut, Compote, 8 X 5 1/2 In. 14.00
Pressed Glass, Paneled Diamonds & Finecut, Creamer 15.00
Pressed Glass, Paneled Diamonds & Finecut, Spooner 15.00
Pressed Glass, Paneled Diamonds & Flowers, Goblet .... 14.00 To 14.50
Pressed Glass, Paneled Diamonds, Goblet .... 8.00 To 15.00

Pressed Glass,
Paneled Diamond &
Flowers, Goblet

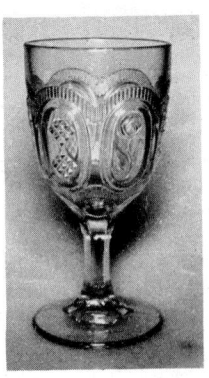

Pressed Glass,
Paneled Forget-Me-Not,
Marmalade Jar

Pressed Glass, Heavy Paneled, Finecut, Goblet

Pressed Glass, Paneled Diamonds, Goblet, Ruby & Clear	20.00
Paneled Dogwood, see Dogwood	
Pressed Glass, Paneled English Hobnail, Goblet	12.50
Pressed Glass, Paneled English Hobnail, Table Set, Child's, Blue, 3 Piece	75.00
Paneled Fan Top, see Shepherd's Plaid	
Pressed Glass, Paneled Fern, Goblet	18.00
Pressed Glass, Paneled Fine Tooth, Champagne	45.00
Pressed Glass, Paneled Fishscale, Bowl, 8 1/4 In.	12.50
Pressed Glass, Paneled Fishscale, Compote, Jelly	12.50
Pressed Glass, Paneled Fishscale, Pitcher, Water	20.00
Pressed Glass, Paneled Fishscale, Sauce, 4 In.	4.50
Paneled Flower, see Maine	
Pressed Glass, Paneled Flute, Wine, Long Stem	16.00
Pressed Glass, Paneled Forget-Me-Not, Butter, Covered	35.00
Pressed Glass, Paneled Forget-Me-Not, Butter, Green, Covered, Gold Trim, N	75.00
Pressed Glass, Paneled Forget-Me-Not, Cake Stand, 9 1/2 In.	18.50
Pressed Glass, Paneled Forget-Me-Not, Celery	15.00 To 24.00
Pressed Glass, Paneled Forget-Me-Not, Creamer	16.50 To 18.50
Pressed Glass, Paneled Forget-Me-Not, Goblet	15.00 To 22.00
Pressed Glass, Paneled Forget-Me-Not, Plate, Bread	28.50
Pressed Glass, Paneled Forget-Me-Not, Relish, 8 In.	14.50
Pressed Glass, Paneled Forget-Me-Not, Relish, 9 In.	15.50
Pressed Glass, Paneled Forget-Me-Not, Sauce, Light Blue	15.00
Pressed Glass, Paneled Forget-Me-Not, Sugar, Covered	28.00
Pressed Glass, Paneled Fruit, Sauce	4.50
Pressed Glass, Paneled Grape Band, Creamer, Pedestal Base	25.00
Pressed Glass, Paneled Grape Band, Eggcup	32.00
Pressed Glass, Paneled Grape Band, Eggcup, Flint	32.00
Pressed Glass, Paneled Grape Band, Goblet	11.00
Pressed Glass, Paneled Grape Band, Goblet, Buttermilk	20.00
Pressed Glass, Paneled Grape Band, Goblet, Flint	35.00
Pressed Glass, Paneled Grape Band, Sugar, Covered	65.00
Pressed Glass, Paneled Grape, Butter, Grape Finial	32.00
Pressed Glass, Paneled Grape, Goblet	7.50 To 20.00
Pressed Glass, Paneled Grape, Sauce	7.50
Pressed Glass, Paneled Grape, Sugar, Covered, Flint	50.00
Pressed Glass, Paneled Grape, Tumbler	10.00
Pressed Glass, Paneled Grape, Tumbler, Lemonade	8.00
Pressed Glass, Paneled Grape, Water Set, 5 Piece	65.00
Pressed Glass, Paneled Grape, Wine, Stemmed	8.50
Pressed Glass, Paneled Heather, Goblet	10.00
Pressed Glass, Paneled Heather, Sugar, Covered	15.00
Pressed Glass, Paneled Heather, Wine	9.00 To 13.00
Pressed Glass, Paneled Hobnail, Goblet	5.00
Pressed Glass, Paneled Iris, Wine	7.00 To 8.50
Pressed Glass, Paneled Ivy, Goblet	18.50
Pressed Glass, Paneled Jewels, Champagne	20.00
Pressed Glass, Paneled Jewels, Goblet	12.50 To 15.00

Pressed Glass, Paneled Jewels, Goblet, Findlay	13.00 To 15.00
Pressed Glass, Paneled Jewels, Wine	12.50 To 15.00
Pressed Glass, Paneled Julep, Goblet	12.50
Pressed Glass, Paneled Lattice, Wine	10.00
Pressed Glass, Paneled Long Jewels, Goblet	10.00 To 13.50
Pressed Glass, Paneled Medallion, Goblet	7.00
Pressed Glass, Paneled Nightshade, Celery	25.00 To 28.75
Pressed Glass, Paneled Nightshade, Goblet	15.00
Pressed Glass, Paneled Nightshade, Wine	20.00
Pressed Glass, Paneled Oval Finecut, Goblet	15.00
Pressed Glass, Paneled Ovals, Eggcup	22.00 To 35.00
Pressed Glass, Paneled Ovals, Eggcup, Flint	35.00
Pressed Glass, Paneled Ovals, Goblet	15.00
Pressed Glass, Paneled Ovals, Goblet, Flint	24.00 To 44.00
Pressed Glass, Paneled Ovals, Spooner	38.00
Pressed Glass, Paneled Palm, Bowl, 8 In.	10.00
Pressed Glass, Paneled Palm, Butter	22.00
Pressed Glass, Paneled Palm, Celery	22.00
Pressed Glass, Paneled Palm, Mug	8.00
Pressed Glass, Paneled Palm, Pitcher, Water, Pink On Clear, Gold Flash	75.00
Pressed Glass, Paneled Palm, Spooner	18.00
Pressed Glass, Paneled Palm, Sugar, Covered	20.00
Pressed Glass, Paneled Palm, Toothpick, Frog	20.00
Pressed Glass, Paneled Pleat, Goblet	12.00
Pressed Glass, Paneled Potted Flower, Goblet	15.00
Pressed Glass, Paneled Prism & Inverted Diamonds, Spill	20.00
Pressed Glass, Paneled Prism & Inverted Diamonds, Spooner	20.00
Pressed Glass, Paneled Rosette, Goblet	15.00
Pressed Glass, Paneled S, Goblet	10.00
Pressed Glass, Paneled Sawtooth, Goblet	14.00 To 16.00
Paneled Star & Button, see Sedan	
Pressed Glass, Paneled Star & Square, Goblet	9.50
Pressed Glass, Paneled Star, Celery	10.00
Pressed Glass, Paneled Stippled Bowl, Goblet	9.50
Pressed Glass, Paneled Stippled Bowl, Spooner	18.50
Pressed Glass, Paneled Strawberry, Compote, Sweetmeat, Covered	30.00
Pressed Glass, Paneled Sunflower, Goblet	11.00 To 15.00
Pressed Glass, Paneled Thistle, Banana Stand	45.00
Pressed Glass, Paneled Thistle, Basket, 7 In.	30.00
Pressed Glass, Paneled Thistle, Bowl, Footed, 6 1/4 X 2 1/4 In.	10.00
Pressed Glass, Paneled Thistle, Bowl, Footed, 7 X 2 In.	20.00
Pressed Glass, Paneled Thistle, Bowl, Footed, 8 3/4 X 3 In.	20.00
Pressed Glass, Paneled Thistle, Bowl, Footed, 9 X 3 1/4 In.	30.00
Pressed Glass, Paneled Thistle, Bowl, Oval, 1 3/4 X 7 1/2 X 5 1/4 In.	15.00
Pressed Glass, Paneled Thistle, Bowl, Ruffled Top, 11 In.Diameter	18.00
Pressed Glass, Paneled Thistle, Bowl, 7 X 5 In.	8.00
Pressed Glass, Paneled Thistle, Butter, Covered	35.00
Pressed Glass, Paneled Thistle, Cake Stand, 6 3/4 X 3 1/2 In.	32.00
Pressed Glass, Paneled Thistle, Cake Stand, 9 In.	22.50
Pressed Glass, Paneled Thistle, Cake Stand, 10 In.	15.00
Pressed Glass, Paneled Thistle, Celery, 10 X 5 In.	17.50
Pressed Glass, Paneled Thistle, Celery, 2 Handles, 4 1/2 X 5 1/2 In.	24.00
Pressed Glass, Paneled Thistle, Compote, Indented Stem, 7 X 8 In.	13.50
Pressed Glass, Paneled Thistle, Compote, Jelly, Stemmed, 5 1/2 X 8 In.	30.00
Pressed Glass, Paneled Thistle, Compote, 8 In.	24.00
Pressed Glass, Paneled Thistle, Cruet, Vinegar	19.50
Pressed Glass, Paneled Thistle, Cup, Punch, Footed, 2 3/4 In.	22.50
Pressed Glass, Paneled Thistle, Dish, Honey, Covered	35.00
Pressed Glass, Paneled Thistle, Dish, Honey, Covered, Footed, 2 Handled	30.00
Pressed Glass, Paneled Thistle, Dish, Pickle, 8 X 4 In.	13.50
Pressed Glass, Paneled Thistle, Doughnut Stand, 6 In.	24.50
Pressed Glass, Paneled Thistle, Goblet	10.00 To 30.00
Pressed Glass, Paneled Thistle, Goblet, Flared Top	25.00
Pressed Glass, Paneled Thistle, Mug, 3 In.High	20.00
Pressed Glass, Paneled Thistle, Pitcher, Milk, Footed, 7 X 4 In.	25.00
Pressed Glass, Paneled Thistle, Plate, Cake, Stemmed, 10 In.	20.00

Pressed Glass, Paneled Thistle, Plate, Square, 7 In. .... 11.00 To 18.50
Pressed Glass, Paneled Thistle, Plate, 7 1/2 In. 15.00
Pressed Glass, Paneled Thistle, Plate, 8 In. 15.00
Pressed Glass, Paneled Thistle, Plate, 10 In. 20.00
Pressed Glass, Paneled Thistle, Relish 18.00
Pressed Glass, Paneled Thistle, Relish, Ring Handle, 5 1/2 In. 15.00
Pressed Glass, Paneled Thistle, Rose Bowl, 5 In. 20.00
Pressed Glass, Paneled Thistle, Salt, Master, Footed 12.50
Pressed Glass, Paneled Thistle, Saltshaker .... 20.00 To 35.00
Pressed Glass, Paneled Thistle, Sauce, 3 In. 4.50
Pressed Glass, Paneled Thistle, Sauce, 4 In. 6.00
Pressed Glass, Paneled Thistle, Sherbet .... 6.00 To 20.00
Pressed Glass, Paneled Thistle, Spooner .... 18.50 To 20.00
Pressed Glass, Paneled Thistle, Sugar, Covered 27.50
Pressed Glass, Paneled Thistle, Sugar, 2 Handles 35.00
Pressed Glass, Paneled Thistle, Toothpick 32.50
Pressed Glass, Paneled Thistle, Toothpick, Signed 6.00
Pressed Glass, Paneled Thistle, Tumbler, 4 In. 30.00
Pressed Glass, Paneled Thistle, Tumbler, 4 3/4 In. 32.50
Pressed Glass, Paneled Thistle, Vase, Oval Flared Top, 5 1/2 In. 25.00
Pressed Glass, Paneled Thistle, Vase, 6 1/2 X 6 1/4 In. 30.00
Pressed Glass, Paneled Thistle, Wine .... 15.00 To 22.50
Pressed Glass, Paneled Thistle, Wine, Bee 13.00
Pressed Glass, Paneled Thumbprint, Compote, 5 X 6 In. 17.00
Pressed Glass, Paneled Thumbprint, Goblet 7.50
Pressed Glass, Paneled Thumbprint, Salt & Pepper 12.00
Pressed Glass, Paneled Wild Daisy, Goblet 10.00
Pressed Glass, Paneled Zipper, Pitcher, Water, Amber 26.00
Pressed Glass, Paneled Zipper, Sugar, Open, Scalloped, Gold Trim 7.00
Pressed Glass, Paneled 44, Goblet 9.00
Pressed Glass, Paneled 44, Salt & Pepper, Silver Trim 22.00
Pressed Glass, Paneled 44, Sugar & Creamer, Pink With Gold 35.00
Pressed Glass, Paneled, Cup & Saucer, Handleless, Flint 45.00
Pressed Glass, Paneled, Salt Dip, 3 Footed 6.50
Pressed Glass, Paneled, Tumbler, Flint 15.00
Pressed Glass, Paneled, Tumbler, Footed, Flint 25.00
Pressed Glass, Paris, Bowl, Shallow, 9 In. 8.00
Pressed Glass, Parrot & Fan, Plus, Goblet .... 25.00 To 35.00
Pressed Glass, Parrot, Bowl, Blue, Gold Trim, 8 1/2 In. 38.00
Pressed Glass, Parrot, Bowl, Blue, 8 1/2 In. 35.00
Pressed Glass, Parrot, Goblet .... 19.50 To 36.00
Pressed Glass, Parrot, Jug, Whiskey, Lock Top, Key 200.00
Pressed Glass, Parrot, Sauce 4.50
Pressed Glass, Parrot, Sauce, Footed 12.00
Pressed Glass, Parrot, Wine .... 33.00 To 37.00
    Pattee Cross, see Broughton
Pressed Glass, Pathfinder, Goblet 10.00
Pressed Glass, Patrician, Pitcher, Water, Amber 20.00
Pressed Glass, Patriotic, Bowl, Punch, Miniature 20.00
Pressed Glass, Pavonia, Butter, Covered 37.50
Pressed Glass, Pavonia, Butter, Covered, Etched 45.00
Pressed Glass, Pavonia, Butter, Covered, Pedestal 36.00
Pressed Glass, Pavonia, Butter, Covered, Ruby Stained .... 40.00 To 60.00
Pressed Glass, Pavonia, Cake Stand, Etched Oak Leaves & Acorn, 7 In. 27.50
Pressed Glass, Pavonia, Cake Stand, 9 1/4 In. 27.50
Pressed Glass, Pavonia, Celery, Etched 25.00
Pressed Glass, Pavonia, Celery, Etched, Low Type 22.50
Pressed Glass, Pavonia, Creamer, Ruby Stained .... 30.00 To 48.75
Pressed Glass, Pavonia, Goblet 20.00
Pressed Glass, Pavonia, Goblet, Etched 18.00
Pressed Glass, Pavonia, Goblet, Etched Leaf & Acorn 20.00
Pressed Glass, Pavonia, Pitcher, Milk, Etched 57.50
Pressed Glass, Pavonia, Pitcher, Water, Etched 45.00
Pressed Glass, Pavonia, Plate, Etched, Piecrust Edge, 6 1/2 In. 42.50
Pressed Glass, Pavonia, Plate, 4 In. 15.00
Pressed Glass, Pavonia, Salt Dip 4.00

Pressed Glass, Pavonia, Sauce	4.50
Pressed Glass, Pavonia, Sauce, Footed, 3 1/2 In.	6.00
Pressed Glass, Pavonia, Sugar, Ruby Stained	15.00
Pressed Glass, Pavonia, Tankard, Water	35.00
Pressed Glass, Pavonia, Tankard, Water, Etched	45.00
Pressed Glass, Pavonia, Tumbler, Etched	16.50
Pressed Glass, Pavonia, Tumbler, Ruby Stained, 4 In.	26.50
Pressed Glass, Pavonia, Wine, Etched	20.00
Pressed Glass, Pea Pods, Pitcher	18.50
Pressed Glass, Peacock Feather, Bowl, 5 1/4 In.	32.00
Pressed Glass, Peacock Feather, Bowl, 8 1/4 In.	21.50
Pressed Glass, Peacock Feather, Butter, Covered	28.00
Pressed Glass, Peacock Feather, Compote, Bonbon, Scalloped Rim, Low	22.00
Pressed Glass, Peacock Feather, Compote, Jelly, 2 In. High	10.00
Pressed Glass, Peacock Feather, Compote, 7 X 2 3/4 In.	28.00
Pressed Glass, Peacock Feather, Creamer	18.50
Pressed Glass, Peacock Feather, Cruet, 8 In. High	16.00
Pressed Glass, Peacock Feather, Mug	14.00
Pressed Glass, Peacock Feather, Pitcher, Water	26.00
Pressed Glass, Peacock Feather, Relish, Oval	23.00
Pressed Glass, Peacock Feather, Sauce, 4 1/4 In.	20.00
Pressed Glass, Peacock Feather, Sugar, Covered	20.00 To 30.00
Pressed Glass, Peacock Feather, Syrup, Applied Handle, Tin Top	14.00
Pressed Glass, Peacock Feather, Table Set, Sapphire Blue, Gold Trim, 4 Piece	185.00
Peacock's Eye, see Peacock Feather	
Pressed Glass, Peaflower, Mug, Amber	16.00
Pressed Glass, Pear, Butter, Acorn Finial	27.50
Pressed Glass, Pear, Goblet	15.00
Pressed Glass, Pebbled Loop & Dart, Sugar	12.00
Pressed Glass, Pebbled Swirl, Sauce	5.00
Pressed Glass, Pecorah, Goblet	10.00
Pressed Glass, Pecorah, Wine	12.00
Pressed Glass, Peerless, Champagne	25.00
Pressed Glass, Peerless, Eggcup, Saucer Base	16.00 To 25.00
Pressed Glass, Peerless, Goblet	12.50 To 18.00
Pressed Glass, Peerless, Spooner	12.00 To 25.00
Pressed Glass, Peerless, Sugar, Covered, Albany	18.50
Pressed Glass, Peerless, Tumbler, Amber	15.00
Pressed Glass, Peerless, Wine	14.00
Peerless, see also Model Peerless	
Pressed Glass, Pendleton, Goblet, Flint	48.00 To 55.00
Pressed Glass, Pennsylvania, Butter, Covered, Scalloped	35.00
Pressed Glass, Pennsylvania, Celery	24.00 To 38.00
Pressed Glass, Pennsylvania, Compote, Scalloped Rim, 9 X 6 1/2 In.	25.00
Pressed Glass, Pennsylvania, Creamer	10.00 To 38.00
Pressed Glass, Pennsylvania, Creamer, Child's	22.00
Pressed Glass, Pennsylvania, Creamer, Child's, Gold Trim	18.00
Pressed Glass, Pennsylvania, Creamer, Gold Trim	12.50
Pressed Glass, Pennsylvania, Goblet	7.50 To 15.00
Pressed Glass, Pennsylvania, Jar, Jam, Covered	40.00
Pressed Glass, Pennsylvania, Plate, Bread	18.50
Pressed Glass, Pennsylvania, Creamer, Small, Gold Trim	12.50
Pressed Glass, Pennsylvania, Creamer, Small, No Gold	10.00
Pressed Glass, Pennsylvania, Goblet	7.50 To 15.00
Pressed Glass, Pennsylvania, Sauce, Flat, 4 1/2 In., Gold	6.50
Pressed Glass, Pennsylvania, Spooner, Child's	16.00 To 23.50
Pressed Glass, Pennsylvania, Sugar, Child's	24.00
Pressed Glass, Pennsylvania, Sugar, Child's, Covered	28.00
Pressed Glass, Pennsylvania, Tumbler	7.00
Pressed Glass, Pennsylvania, Vase, Frosted, Centennial, 1876, 6 In.	45.00
Pressed Glass, Pennsylvania, Wine	15.00 To 32.50
Pressed Glass, Pentagon, Creamer, 4 In.	12.00
Pressed Glass, Pentagon, Creamer, 6 In.	14.00
Pressed Glass, Periwinkle, Saltshaker, Deep Red	29.00
Pressed Glass, Perkins, Cake Stand	9.00
Pressed Glass, Perkins, Cake Stand, Martinsville	8.00

Pressed Glass, Perkins, Sauce, Footed, 3 3/8 In.	4.00
Pressed Glass, Perkins, Spooner	19.00
Pressed Glass, Perkins, Sugar, Covered	19.00
Pressed Glass, Pert, Butter, Child's	40.00
Pressed Glass, Petalled Medallion, Butter, Ruby Stained	81.00
Pressed Glass, Petalled Medallion, Toothpick, Ruby Stained	22.00
Pressed Glass, Pheasant Cover, Dish	68.50
Pressed Glass, Pheasant Cover, Dish, Frosted Pheasant Finial	68.75
Pressed Glass, Pheasant Cover, Dish, Oval	68.50
Pressed Glass, Philadelphia Centennial, Goblet	25.00 To 40.00
Pressed Glass, Philadelphia, Goblet	15.00
Pressed Glass, Philadelphia, Goblet, Flint	30.00
Pressed Glass, Picket, Butter, Covered	29.50
Pressed Glass, Picket, Celery	19.75
Pressed Glass, Picket, Compote, 7 In.	27.50 To 35.00
Pressed Glass, Picket, Creamer	19.75
Pressed Glass, Picket, Goblet	5.50 To 15.00
Pressed Glass, Picket, Pitcher, Water	45.00
Pressed Glass, Picket, Salt	7.50
Pressed Glass, Picket, Salt, Individual	12.00
Pressed Glass, Picket, Spooner	11.50
Pressed Glass, Picket, Toothpick, Frosted	22.50
Pillar & Bull's-eye, see Thistle	
Pressed Glass, Pillar, Claret, Flint	29.50 To 40.00
Pressed Glass, Pillar, Goblet, Flint	40.00
Pressed Glass, Pillar, Tumbler, Flint	25.00
Pressed Glass, Pillar, Wine	45.00
Pressed Glass, Pillow & Sunburst, Plate, Scalloped Edge, 10 In.	10.00
Pressed Glass, Pillow & Sunburst, Water Set, Gold Trim, 6 Piece	75.00
Pillow Encircled, see Ruby Rosette	
Pinafore, see Actress	
Pressed Glass, Pineapple & Fan, Bowl, Waste	7.50
Pressed Glass, Pineapple & Fan, Bucket, Ice, Notched Top	39.50
Pressed Glass, Pineapple & Fan, Celery, Jar	22.00
Pressed Glass, Pineapple & Fan, Creamer	15.00
Pressed Glass, Pineapple & Fan, Creamer, Ruby Stained	30.00
Pressed Glass, Pineapple & Fan, Cup, Punch	4.00 To 5.00
Pressed Glass, Pineapple & Fan, Pitcher, Water, Tankard Type, Ruby Stained	55.00
Pressed Glass, Pineapple & Fan, Rose Bowl, 4 3/4 In.	9.50
Pressed Glass, Pineapple & Fan, Saltshaker	4.00
Pressed Glass, Pineapple & Fan, Saltshaker, Pewter Top	3.50
Pressed Glass, Pineapple & Fan, Spooner	9.00
Pressed Glass, Pineapple & Fan, Sugar	15.00
Pressed Glass, Pineapple & Fan, Sugar, Covered, Albany	21.00
Pressed Glass, Pineapple & Fan, Syrup	15.00
Pressed Glass, Pineapple & Fan, Whiskey Set, 7 Piece	65.00
Pressed Glass, Pineapple, Pitcher, Water	15.00
Pressed Glass, Pinecone, Muffineer, Pink	75.00
Pressed Glass, Pinwheel, Creamer, Ruby & Clear	20.00
Pressed Glass, Pinwheel, Goblet	10.00
Pressed Glass, Pinwheel, Plate, Flint, 4 3/4 In.	32.00
Pressed Glass, Pinwheel, Spooner, Ruby & Clear	20.00
Pressed Glass, Pinwheel, Tray, Ruby Stained, 10 In.	25.00
Pressed Glass, Pinwheel, Wine	8.00
Pressed Glass, Pioneer's Victoria, Berry Set, Ruby Stained, Set Of 7	135.00
Pressed Glass, Pioneer's Victoria, Bowl, Ruby Stained, 7 In.	35.00
Pressed Glass, Pioneer's Victoria, Goblet	10.00
Pressed Glass, Pioneer's Victoria, Goblet, Ruby Stained	30.00
Pressed Glass, Pioneer's Victoria, Pitcher, Water, Ruby Stained	45.00
Pressed Glass, Pioneer's Victoria, Tumbler, Ruby Stained	16.00 To 20.00
Pressed Glass, Pioneer's Victoria, Wine	13.00
Pressed Glass, Pitcairn, Goblet	8.00
Pressed Glass, Pitcairn, Sauce, Footed, 4 In.	4.50
Pressed Glass, Pittman, Goblet	9.00
Pressed Glass, Pittsburgh Honeycomb, Tumbler, Flint	20.00
Pressed Glass, Pittsburgh, Whiskey Taster, Flint	15.00

Pressed Glass, Pleated Bands, Covered Compote

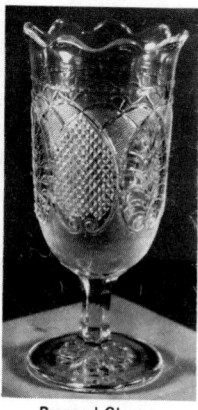

Pressed Glass, Princess Feather, Spooner

Pressed Glass, Primrose, Pitcher, 7 In.

Pressed Glass, **Plain Sunburst,** Goblet	12.50
Plain Smocking, see Smocking	
Pressed Glass, **Plain Tulip,** Goblet, Flint	25.00 To 40.00
Pressed Glass, **Pleat & Panel,** Cake Stand, 9 1/2 In.	22.50
Pressed Glass, **Pleat & Panel,** Cake Stand, 10 In.	27.50
Pressed Glass, **Pleat & Panel,** Celery	22.50 To 25.00
Pressed Glass, **Pleat & Panel,** Celery, Etched, Pedestal, Handled	18.50
Pressed Glass, **Pleat & Panel,** Creamer	22.50 To 35.00
Pressed Glass, **Pleat & Panel,** Plate, Bread	20.00 To 45.00
Pressed Glass, **Pleat & Panel,** Plate, Octagonal, 6 In.	9.00
Pressed Glass, **Pleat & Panel,** Plate, Square, 7 In.	10.00 To 12.50
Pressed Glass, **Pleat & Panel,** Plate, 7 In.	15.00
Pressed Glass, **Pleat & Panel,** Relish, Oblong	18.00
Pressed Glass, **Pleat & Panel,** Sauce, Footed	7.00
Pressed Glass, **Pleat & Panel,** Spooner	13.50 To 20.00
Pressed Glass, **Pleat & Panel,** Tray, Water	45.00
Pressed Glass, **Pleat & Panel,** Wine	37.50
Pressed Glass, **Pleat Band,** Compote, Greentown, 8 In.High	35.00
Pressed Glass, **Pleat Band,** Goblet	5.00 To 18.00
Pressed Glass, **Pleat Band,** Spooner, Child's, Gold Trim	14.00
Pressed Glass, **Pleat Band,** Tumbler, Greentown	6.50
Pressed Glass, **Plume & Block,** Nappy, Ruby Stained	15.00
Pressed Glass, **Plume & Block,** Pitcher, Milk	12.50
Pressed Glass, **Plume,** Bowl, Crimped, 8 In.	26.00
Pressed Glass, **Plume,** Bowl, Square, 8 In.	10.00
Pressed Glass, **Plume,** Bowl, Square, 8 1/4 In.	14.00
Pressed Glass, **Plume,** Bowl, Waste	35.00
Pressed Glass, **Plume,** Butter, Covered	30.00
Pressed Glass, **Plume,** Cake Stand, 8 1/2 In.	27.50
Pressed Glass, **Plume,** Celery	18.00 To 35.00
Pressed Glass, **Plume,** Compote, Low Foot, Crimped, 7 In.	30.00
Pressed Glass, **Plume,** Compote, 7 In.	32.00
Pressed Glass, **Plume,** Compote, 9 In.	28.00
Pressed Glass, **Plume,** Goblet, Flared & Etched	34.00
Pressed Glass, **Plume,** Sauce	5.00
Pressed Glass, **Plume,** Sauce, Flint	9.00
Pressed Glass, **Plume,** Sugar, Covered	23.00
Pressed Glass, **Plume,** Tumbler	28.00
Pressed Glass, **Plutec,** Wine	14.00
Pressed Glass, **Pogo Stick,** Sauce, Footed, 3 1/2 In.	5.00
Pressed Glass, **Pointed Hobnail,** Bowl, Berry, 9 In.	15.00
Pressed Glass, **Pointed Hobnail,** Jar, Mustard, Covered	9.50
Pressed Glass, **Pointed Hobnail,** Wine, Amber	17.50
Pressed Glass, **Pointed Jewel,** Compote, 4 1/2 In.	15.00

Pressed Glass, Pointed Jewel, Goblet .... 18.00 To 18.50
Pressed Glass, Pointed Jewel, Sauce 3.75
Pressed Glass, Pointed Jewel, Sugar, Covered, Findlay 35.00
    Pointed Paneled Daisy & Button, see Queen
    Pointed Thumbprint, see Almond Thumbprint
Pressed Glass, Polar Bear, Bowl, Waste, Frosted 55.00
Pressed Glass, Polar Bear, Goblet .... 55.00 To 85.00
Pressed Glass, Polar Bear, Goblet, Frosted .... 65.00 To 110.00
Pressed Glass, Polar Bear, Tray, Frosted, CGCO., 15 1/2 X 11 In. 110.00
Pressed Glass, Polar Bear, Tray, Water 150.00
Pressed Glass, Popcorn, Creamer 45.00
Pressed Glass, Popcorn, Pitcher, Water 39.50
Pressed Glass, Popcorn, Sugar, Ears 35.00
    Portland with Diamond Point Band, see Galloway
Pressed Glass, Portland, Compote, Covered, 9 1/2 X 6 1/2 In. 37.50
Pressed Glass, Portland, Creamer, Individual 7.00
Pressed Glass, Portland, Dish, Pickle, 9 In. 7.00
Pressed Glass, Portland, Goblet 22.50
Pressed Glass, Portland, Pitcher, Water, Overshot, Applied Handle 55.00
Pressed Glass, Portland, Saltshaker 7.50
Pressed Glass, Portland, Sauce, Canary, Birch Leaf 13.50
Pressed Glass, Portland, Sauce, Oval 7.00
Pressed Glass, Portland, Sugar & Creamer 37.50
Pressed Glass, Portland, Sugar & Creamer, Individual 12.00
Pressed Glass, Portland, Sugar, Purple 20.00
Pressed Glass, Portland, Toothpick 10.00
Pressed Glass, Portland, Toothpick, Gold Flashed 18.00
Pressed Glass, Portland, Tumbler, Gold Trim .... 12.00 To 12.50
Pressed Glass, Portland, Wine 18.50
Pressed Glass, Portland, Wine, Gold Trim 24.00
Pressed Glass, Post, Goblet, Etched .... 20.00 To 25.00
Pressed Glass, Postscript, Goblet .... 9.00 To 12.00
Pressed Glass, Powder & Shot, Creamer, Flint 125.00
Pressed Glass, Powder & Shot, Eggcup 65.00
Pressed Glass, Powder & Shot, Eggcup, Flint 52.00
Pressed Glass, Powder & Shot, Goblet .... 45.00 To 48.50
Pressed Glass, Powder & Shot, Goblet, Buttermilk 32.50
Pressed Glass, Powder & Shot, Goblet, Flint .... 35.00 To 48.50
Pressed Glass, Powder & Shot, Spill, Flint 28.00
Pressed Glass, Powder & Shot, Spooner .... 24.00 To 35.00
Pressed Glass, Powder & Shot, Spooner, Flint .... 28.00 To 36.00
Pressed Glass, Powder & Shot, Sugar, Covered 90.00
Pressed Glass, Powder & Shot, Sugar, Covered, Flint .... 70.00 To 85.00
    Prayer Rug, see Horseshoe
Pressed Glass, Pressed Block, Bowl, Flint, 8 1/2 In. 30.00
Pressed Glass, Pressed Block, Compote, Flint, 6 1/2 In. 38.00
Pressed Glass, Pressed Diamond Sauce, Amber, Square 7.50
Pressed Glass, Pressed Diamond, Bowl, Waste 15.00
Pressed Glass, Pressed Diamond, Celery 25.00
Pressed Glass, Pressed Diamond, Compote, Blue, Scalloped Edge, 8 3/4 In. 35.00
Pressed Glass, Pressed Diamond, Creamer, Amber 20.00
Pressed Glass, Pressed Diamond, Cup, Punch, Blue 12.50
Pressed Glass, Pressed Diamond, Insert, Pickle Castor, Silver Lid 15.00
Pressed Glass, Pressed Diamond, Pitcher, Water, Amber 45.00
Pressed Glass, Pressed Diamond, Salt, Amber, Boat Shape, Footed 7.50
Pressed Glass, Pressed Diamond, Spooner, Yellow 28.00
Pressed Glass, Pressed Leaf, Creamer 65.00
Pressed Glass, Pressed Leaf, Creamer, Flint 55.00
Pressed Glass, Pressed Leaf, Eggcup .... 21.00 To 25.00
Pressed Glass, Pressed Leaf, Eggcup, Flint .... 18.00 To 32.00
Pressed Glass, Pressed Leaf, Goblet .... 12.00 To 12.50
Pressed Glass, Pressed Leaf, Goblet, Buttermilk 9.00
Pressed Glass, Pressed Leaf, Goblet, Flint .... 12.50 To 30.00
Pressed Glass, Pressed Leaf, Pitcher, Water 47.50
Pressed Glass, Pressed Leaf, Pitcher, Water, Applied Handle, Flint 85.00
Pressed Glass, Pressed Leaf, Pitcher, Water, Flint 90.00

Pressed Glass, Pleat & Panel, Footed Bowl

Pressed Glass, Punty, Syrup, Opalescent

Pressed Glass, Pressed Leaf, Cordial

Pressed Glass, Princess Feather, Tazza

Pressed Glass, Prism With Diamond Point, Master Salt

Pressed Glass, Cupid & Psyche, Creamer

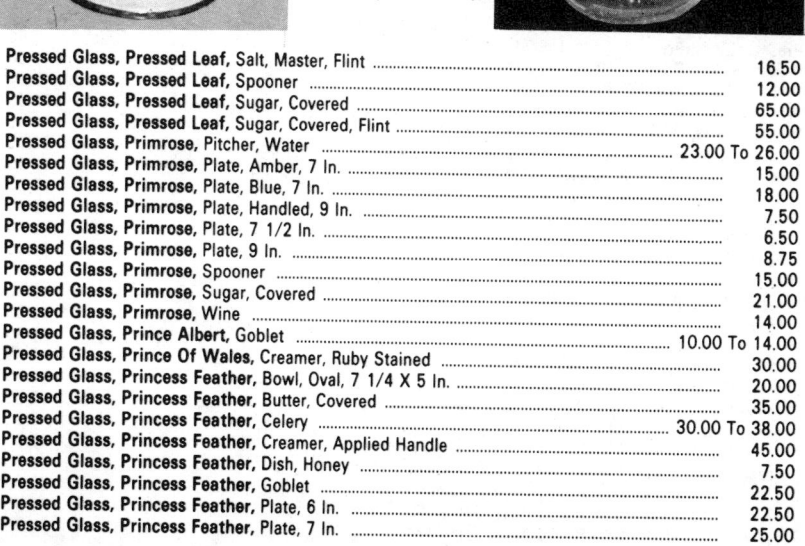

Pressed Glass, Pressed Leaf, Salt, Master, Flint	16.50
Pressed Glass, Pressed Leaf, Spooner	12.00
Pressed Glass, Pressed Leaf, Sugar, Covered	65.00
Pressed Glass, Pressed Leaf, Sugar, Covered, Flint	55.00
Pressed Glass, Primrose, Pitcher, Water	23.00 To 26.00
Pressed Glass, Primrose, Plate, Amber, 7 In.	15.00
Pressed Glass, Primrose, Plate, Blue, 7 In.	18.00
Pressed Glass, Primrose, Plate, Handled, 9 In.	7.50
Pressed Glass, Primrose, Plate, 7 1/2 In.	6.50
Pressed Glass, Primrose, Plate, 9 In.	8.75
Pressed Glass, Primrose, Spooner	15.00
Pressed Glass, Primrose, Sugar, Covered	21.00
Pressed Glass, Primrose, Wine	14.00
Pressed Glass, Prince Albert, Goblet	10.00 To 14.00
Pressed Glass, Prince Of Wales, Creamer, Ruby Stained	30.00
Pressed Glass, Princess Feather, Bowl, Oval, 7 1/4 X 5 In.	20.00
Pressed Glass, Princess Feather, Butter, Covered	35.00
Pressed Glass, Princess Feather, Celery	30.00 To 38.00
Pressed Glass, Princess Feather, Creamer, Applied Handle	45.00
Pressed Glass, Princess Feather, Dish, Honey	7.50
Pressed Glass, Princess Feather, Goblet	22.50
Pressed Glass, Princess Feather, Plate, 6 In.	22.50
Pressed Glass, Princess Feather, Plate, 7 In.	25.00

Pressed Glass, Princess Feather, Plate, 9 In.	35.00
Pressed Glass, Princess Feather, Spill	14.00
Pressed Glass, Princess Feather, Spooner	14.00 To 35.00
Pressed Glass, Princess Feather, Sugar	17.50 To 25.00
Pressed Glass, Princess Feather, Sugar, Covered	35.00
Princess Feather, see also Lacy Medallion	
Pressed Glass, Printed Hobnail, Bowl, Finger, Honey Amber	18.50
Pressed Glass, Printed Hobnail, Goblet	8.50 To 10.50
Pressed Glass, Printed Hobnail, Goblet, Knob Stem	6.00
Pressed Glass, Printed Hobnail, Toothpick, Emerald Green	20.00
Pressed Glass, Priscilla, Basket, Fruit	70.00
Pressed Glass, Priscilla, Bowl, Shallow, 8 1/2 In.	9.50
Pressed Glass, Priscilla, Butter	27.50
Pressed Glass, Priscilla, Butter, Covered	35.00
Pressed Glass, Priscilla, Compote, Tall Standard, 6 1/2 In.	47.50
Pressed Glass, Priscilla, Cup & Saucer, Findlay	25.00
Pressed Glass, Priscilla, Fruit Stand, Findlay	70.00
Pressed Glass, Priscilla, Pitcher, Lemonade	65.00
Pressed Glass, Priscilla, Pitcher, Water	65.00
Pressed Glass, Priscilla, Relish	22.50
Pressed Glass, Priscilla, Relish, Clover Shape, Findlay	21.00
Pressed Glass, Priscilla, Rose Bowl, Findlay, 3 In.	35.00
Pressed Glass, Priscilla, Sauce, Round	6.50
Pressed Glass, Priscilla, Sryup	45.00
Pressed Glass, Priscilla, Syrup, Pewter Lid	44.00
Pressed Glass, Priscilla, Syrup, Pewter Lid, Findlay	48.00
Pressed Glass, Priscilla, Toothpick	7.50 To 20.00
Pressed Glass, Priscilla, Tumbler	15.00
Pressed Glass, Priscilla, Wine	25.00 To 29.00
Pressed Glass, Prism & Broken Column, Goblet	10.00
Pressed Glass, Prism & Broken Column, Wine	6.00
Pressed Glass, Prism & Bull's-Eye Column, Wine	65.00
Pressed Glass, Prism & Bull's-Eye, Goblet	8.00 To 14.50
Pressed Glass, Prism & Clear Panels, Goblet	7.00
Pressed Glass, Prism & Crescent, Champagne	45.00
Pressed Glass, Prism & Crescent, Goblet, Flint	60.00
Pressed Glass, Prism & Daisy Bar, Goblet, Amber	15.00
Pressed Glass, Prism & Flattened Sawtooth, Goblet, Flint	35.00 To 42.00
Pressed Glass, Prism & Flattened Sawtooth, Spill	20.00
Pressed Glass, Prism & Flattened Sawtooth, Spill, Flint	25.00
Pressed Glass, Prism & Flattened Sawtooth, Spooner	20.00
Pressed Glass, Prism & Flattened Sawtooth, Spooner, Flint	25.00
Pressed Glass, Prism & Flute, Goblet	7.50
Pressed Glass, Prism & Hexagon, Saltshaker, Pair	16.50
Pressed Glass, Prism & Paneled Rosettes, Goblet	7.50
Pressed Glass, Prism & Sawtooth, Celery	55.00
Pressed Glass, Prism & Sawtooth, Celery, Flint	38.00
Pressed Glass, Prism & Sawtooth, Compote, Flint, 8 In.	30.00
Pressed Glass, Prism & Sawtooth, Goblet, Flint	17.50
Pressed Glass, Prism Arc, Plate, 6 3/4 In.	5.00
Pressed Glass, Prism Arc, Relish	8.50
Pressed Glass, Prism Arc, Sauce	5.00
Pressed Glass, Prism Bar, Goblet, Flint	10.00
Pressed Glass, Prism Bar, Table Set, 4 Piece	45.00
Pressed Glass, Prism Buttress, Goblet	10.00
Pressed Glass, Prism With Arches, Spill	30.00
Pressed Glass, Prism With Arches, Spooner	30.00
Pressed Glass, Prism With Bull's-Eye, Spooner	16.00
Pressed Glass, Prism With Diamond Point, Sugar, Flint	30.00
Pressed Glass, Prism With Double Block, Wine, Green	12.00
Pressed Glass, Prism With Loops, Goblet	6.00 To 7.00
Pressed Glass, Prism With Rayed Base, Champagne	45.00
Pressed Glass, Prism With Rayed Base, Champagne, Flint	40.00
Pressed Glass, Prism With Rayed Base, Creamer, Flint	70.00
Pressed Glass, Prism With Rayed Base, Goblet, Flint	26.00
Pressed Glass, Prism With Rayed Base, Spill, Flint	25.00

Pressed Glass, Prism With Rayed Base, Spooner 28.00
Pressed Glass, Prism With Rayed Base, Spooner, Flint .... 16.00 To 25.00
Pressed Glass, Prism With Rayed Base, Sugar, Covered, Flint 55.00
Pressed Glass, Prism With Rayed Base, Sugar, Flint 30.00
Pressed Glass, Prism, Compote, Low Standard, Flint, 7 1/2 In. 28.00
Pressed Glass, Prism, Compote, Serrated Edge, Low Standard, Flint, 8 In. 35.00
Pressed Glass, Prism, Goblet, Banded Top 6.00
Pressed Glass, Prism, Goblet, Flint .... 16.00 To 26.00
Pressed Glass, Prism, Pitcher, Water, Flint 110.00
Pressed Glass, Prism, Salt, Covered 35.00
Pressed Glass, Prism, Sauce, Flint, 4 In. 6.25
Pressed Glass, Prism, Spooner 25.00
Pressed Glass, Prism, Sugar 18.50
Pressed Glass, Prism, Sugar, Flint 18.50
Pressed Glass, Prize, Toothpick, Ruby Stained 18.00
Pressed Glass, Psyche & Cupid, Pitcher, Water 50.00
Pressed Glass, Psyche & Cupid, Sauce, Footed .... 5.50 To 8.00
Pressed Glass, Psyche & Cupid, Sugar, Covered 45.00
Pressed Glass, Psyche & Venus, Sauce, Footed 5.50
 Puffed Bands, see Snow Band
Pressed Glass, Pulaski Cube, Goblet 6.50
Pressed Glass, Punty & Scroll, Spill 35.00
Pressed Glass, Punty & Scroll, Spooner 35.00
Pressed Glass, Puritan, Butter 30.00
Pressed Glass, Puritan, Butter, Child's .... 18.00 To 25.00
Pressed Glass, Puritan, Cake Stand, Child's 25.00
Pressed Glass, Puritan, Creamer 25.00
Pressed Glass, Puritan, Creamer, Child's 15.00
Pressed Glass, Puritan, Goblet 10.00
Pressed Glass, Puritan, Goblet, Ruby & Clear 32.50
Pressed Glass, Puritan, Pitcher, Water, Ruby Stained 65.00
Pressed Glass, Puritan, Spooner 12.50
Pressed Glass, Puritan, Sugar 28.00
Pressed Glass, Puritan, Syrup, Ruby Stained 75.00
Pressed Glass, Puritan, Table Set, Miniature, 3 Piece 55.00
Pressed Glass, Puritan, Toothpick, Ruby Stained 34.00
Pressed Glass, Puritan, Tumbler, Ruby Stained 17.50
Pressed Glass, Quaker Lady, Bowl, Scalloped Edge, 6 1/2 In. 24.00
Pressed Glass, Quantico, Goblet 32.50
Pressed Glass, Quarter Block No.2, Cake Stand, 9 1/2 In. 15.00
Pressed Glass, Quarter Block, Tumbler 7.00
Pressed Glass, Quatrefoil, Butter, Covered 15.00
Pressed Glass, Quatrefoil, Creamer 18.00
Pressed Glass, Quebec Diamond Point Band, Wine 5.00
 Queen Anne, see Viking
Pressed Glass, Queen Victoria, Compote, 1837-1887, 5 In. 60.00
Pressed Glass, Queen, Creamer, Amber 23.50
Pressed Glass, Queen, Goblet 15.00
Pressed Glass, Queen, Goblet, Amber .... 24.00 To 26.00
Pressed Glass, Queen, Pitcher, Water 20.00
Pressed Glass, Queen, Pitcher, Water, Amber 37.50
Pressed Glass, Queen, Sauce, Blue 7.50
Pressed Glass, Queen, Sugar, Amber, Covered 27.50
Pressed Glass, Queen, Wine 14.00
 Queen's Necklace, see Jewel & Festoon
Pressed Glass, Question Mark, Sugar & Creamer 47.50
Pressed Glass, Quilted Phlox, Muffineer, Emerald Green 78.00
Pressed Glass, Quilted Phlox, Muffineer, Sapphire Blue, Gold Trim 88.00
Pressed Glass, Quixote, Salt 10.00
Pressed Glass, Rabbit Tracks, Goblet 13.50
Pressed Glass, Racing Deer, Pitcher, Water 95.00
Pressed Glass, Radiant, Compote, Findlay, 7 In. 21.00
Pressed Glass, Radiant, Tumbler 15.00
Pressed Glass, Rail Fence Band, Goblet .... 7.50 To 12.00
Pressed Glass, Raindrop, Berry Set, Blue, Footed, 7 Piece 125.00
Pressed Glass, Raindrop, Creamer, Blue 28.50

Pressed Glass, Raindrop, Pitcher, Water, Amber	45.00
Pressed Glass, Raindrop, Plate, Amber, Handled, 10 In.	7.50
Pressed Glass, Raindrop, Plate, Amber, 10 In.	8.75
Pressed Glass, Raindrop, Sauce, Amber, Footed, 4 1/8 In.	6.50
Pressed Glass, Raspberry & Grape, Creamer	42.00
Pressed Glass, Ray, Celery, Flint	85.00
Pressed Glass, Ray, Creamer	14.00
Pressed Glass, Ray, Pitcher, 10 1/2 In.	22.00
Pressed Glass, Ray, Sugar, Flint	30.00
Pressed Glass, Rayed Flower, Cake Stand	20.00
Pressed Glass, Rayed Flower, Tumbler, 4 1/4 In.	6.00
Pressed Glass, Rayed Flower, Wine	12.00
Pressed Glass, Rayed Heart, Compote, Jelly, Pale Green To Opalescent, 5 In.	45.00
Pressed Glass, Reardon, Goblet	7.50
Recessed Ovals with Block Band, see Recessed Ovals	
Pressed Glass, Recessed Ovals, Goblet	9.50 To 18.00
Pressed Glass, Red Block & Swirl, Berry Set, 7 Piece	85.00
Pressed Glass, Red Block, Bowl, 8 In.	80.00
Pressed Glass, Red Block, Butter, Covered	45.00
Pressed Glass, Red Block, Creamer	45.00
Pressed Glass, Red Block, Cup	22.00
Pressed Glass, Red Block, Goblet	30.00 To 35.00
Pressed Glass, Red Block, Mug	30.00
Pressed Glass, Red Block, Pitcher, Water	85.00 To 100.00
Pressed Glass, Red Block, Spill	20.00
Pressed Glass, Red Block, Spooner	20.00 To 32.00
Pressed Glass, Red Block, Sugar	20.00
Pressed Glass, Red Block, Sugar, Covered	35.00 To 55.00
Pressed Glass, Red Block, Table Set, 4 Piece	275.00
Pressed Glass, Red Block, Tumbler	18.50 To 35.00
Pressed Glass, Red Block, Water Set, Ruby Stained, 7 Piece	225.00
Pressed Glass, Red Block, Wine	32.00 To 32.50
Pressed Glass, Red Draped Block, Goblet	42.00
Pressed Glass, Red Draped Block, Pitcher, Water	150.00
Pressed Glass, Red Draped Block, Table Set, 3 Piece	285.00
Pressed Glass, Red Draped Block, Tumbler	35.00
Pressed Glass, Red Riding Hood & Wolf, Cup, Punch, Miniature	15.00
Regal, see Paneled Forget-me-not	
Pressed Glass, Regent, Berry Set, Amethyst, Gold, 7 Piece	285.00
Pressed Glass, Reticulated Cord, Sauce, Footed, 3 1/2 In.	6.50
Pressed Glass, Retort, Bowl, Findlay, 9 In.	20.00
Pressed Glass, Reverse S, Cup, Punch, Green, Gold Trim	7.00
Pressed Glass, Reverse S, Punch Set, Amethyst, 15 Piece	300.00
Pressed Glass, Reverse Torpedo, Butter, Covered	65.00
Pressed Glass, Reverse Torpedo, Compote, Jelly	38.00
Pressed Glass, Reverse Torpedo, Compote, Ruffled, 9 1/2 In.	45.00
Pressed Glass, Reverse Torpedo, Plate, 8 1/2 In.	42.50
Pressed Glass, Reverse Torpedo, Sauce, Sawtooth Rim	12.00
Pressed Glass, Reverse Torpedo, Toothpick, Ruby Stained	14.00 To 15.00
Pressed Glass, Reverse Torpedo, Tumbler	26.00
Pressed Glass, Reverse Torpedo, Wine, Ruby Stained	25.00
Pressed Glass, Reverse 44, Butter, Silver Decoration	45.00
Pressed Glass, Reverse 44, Goblet, Pink, Gold Trim	15.00
Pressed Glass, Reverse 44, Mug, Lemonade, Silver Trim, Handle, U.S.Glass Co.	16.00
Pressed Glass, Reverse 44, Pitcher, Water, Green Around Top	27.00
Pressed Glass, Reverse 44, Sugar, Covered	30.00
Pressed Glass, Reverse 44, Sugar, Silver Trim	20.00
Pressed Glass, Reverse 44, Toothpick	12.00 To 23.00
Pressed Glass, Rexford, Bowl, 8 In.	7.00
Pressed Glass, Rexford, Goblet	12.50
Pressed Glass, Rexford, Sugar, Covered	17.50
Pressed Glass, Ribbed Acorn, Compote, Covered, 5 In.Diameter	75.00
Pressed Glass, Ribbed Acorn, Compote, Sweetmeat, Covered, High Standard	58.00
Pressed Glass, Ribbed Acorn, Dish, Honey, Flint	35.00
Pressed Glass, Ribbed Acorn, Dish, Sweetmeat, Covered, Flint, 6 1/2 X 6 In.	67.50
Pressed Glass, Ribbed Acorn, Sweetmeat, Covered, 6 X 6 1/2 In.	37.50

Pressed Glass, Ribbed Forget-Me-Not, Butter, Covered 20.00
Pressed Glass, Ribbed Forget-Me-Not, Creamer, Amber 37.50
Pressed Glass, Ribbed Forget-Me-Not, Creamer, Child's, Blue 45.00
Pressed Glass, Ribbed Forget-Me-Not, Creamer, Miniature 17.50
Pressed Glass, Ribbed Forget-Me-Not, Creamer, 3 3/4 In.High 18.50
Pressed Glass, Ribbed Grape, Compote, Flint, 7 3/4 In. 28.00
Pressed Glass, Ribbed Grape, Creamer 45.00
Pressed Glass, Ribbed Grape, Goblet .... 24.50 To 35.00
Pressed Glass, Ribbed Grape, Goblet, Flint .... 23.00 To 35.00
Pressed Glass, Ribbed Grape, Plate, Flint, 6 In. 45.00
Pressed Glass, Ribbed Grape, Plate, 6 In. 45.00
Pressed Glass, Ribbed Grape, Sauce 12.50
Pressed Glass, Ribbed Grape, Spooner .... 21.00 To 35.00
Pressed Glass, Ribbed Grape, Spooner, Flint 29.00
Pressed Glass, Ribbed Grape, Spooner, Flint, Footed 30.00
Pressed Glass, Ribbed Grape, Sugar, Covered 75.00
Pressed Glass, Ribbed Ivy, Butter, Covered, Flint 78.00
Pressed Glass, Ribbed Ivy, Compote, Covered, 5 In.Diameter 85.00
Pressed Glass, Ribbed Ivy, Compote, High Standard, Flint, 9 In. 100.00
Pressed Glass, Ribbed Ivy, Compote, Inverted Bell Shape Bowl, Flint, 9 In. 195.00
Pressed Glass, Ribbed Ivy, Compote, Inverted Bowl Base, Flint, 8 In. 55.00
Pressed Glass, Ribbed Ivy, Compote, Low Standard, 7 3/4 In. 55.00
Pressed Glass, Ribbed Ivy, Dish, Sweetmeat, Covered, Flint 75.00
Pressed Glass, Ribbed Ivy, Eggcup .... 24.00 To 25.00
Pressed Glass, Ribbed Ivy, Eggcup, Flint .... 16.00 To 32.00
Pressed Glass, Ribbed Ivy, Goblet .... 35.00 To 40.00
Pressed Glass, Ribbed Ivy, Goblet, Flint .... 27.50 To 40.00
Pressed Glass, Ribbed Ivy, Salt, Beaded Rim, Footed, 2 3/4 In. 25.00
Pressed Glass, Ribbed Ivy, Sauce .... 7.00 To 10.00
Pressed Glass, Ribbed Ivy, Sauce, Flint 10.00
Pressed Glass, Ribbed Ivy, Spill, Flint .... 25.00 To 28.00
Pressed Glass, Ribbed Ivy, Spooner 28.00
Pressed Glass, Ribbed Ivy, Spooner, Flint .... 25.00 To 28.00
Pressed Glass, Ribbed Ivy, Spooner, Pedestal, Flint 30.00
Pressed Glass, Ribbed Ivy, Sugar, Covered, Flint 80.00
Pressed Glass, Ribbed Ivy, Sugar, Scalloped Top, Flint 30.00
Pressed Glass, Ribbed Ivy, Tumbler 75.00
Pressed Glass, Ribbed Ivy, Tumbler, Whiskey 75.00
Pressed Glass, Ribbed Ivy, Tumbler, Whiskey, Flint 55.00
Ribbed Leaf, see Bellflower
Ribbed Opal, see Beatty Rib
Pressed Glass, Ribbed Palm, Celery 75.00
Pressed Glass, Ribbed Palm, Celery, Flint 68.00
Pressed Glass, Ribbed Palm, Champagne 70.00
Pressed Glass, Ribbed Palm, Champagne, Flint 60.00
Pressed Glass, Ribbed Palm, Creamer 125.00
Pressed Glass, Ribbed Palm, Creamer, Flint 85.00
Pressed Glass, Ribbed Palm, Eggcup .... 22.50 To 40.00
Pressed Glass, Ribbed Palm, Eggcup, Flint .... 20.00 To 30.00
Pressed Glass, Ribbed Palm, Goblet .... 18.00 To 32.00
Pressed Glass, Ribbed Palm, Goblet, Flint .... 22.50 To 40.00
Pressed Glass, Ribbed Palm, Pitcher, Water, Flint 135.00
Pressed Glass, Ribbed Palm, Salt, Footed, Flint 20.00
Pressed Glass, Ribbed Palm, Sauce 16.00
Pressed Glass, Ribbed Palm, Spill, Flint .... 21.00 To 32.00
Pressed Glass, Ribbed Palm, Spooner 32.00
Pressed Glass, Ribbed Palm, Spooner, Flint .... 21.00 To 32.00
Pressed Glass, Ribbed Palm, Spooner, Footed, Flint 30.00
Pressed Glass, Ribbed Palm, Sugar .... 18.00 To 35.00
Pressed Glass, Ribbed Palm, Sugar, Flint .... 19.00 To 37.00
Pressed Glass, Ribbed Palm, Tumbler .... 27.00 To 75.00
Pressed Glass, Ribbed Palm, Tumbler, Flint 70.00
Pressed Glass, Ribbed Palm, Wine 45.00
Pressed Glass, Ribbed Palm, Wine, Flint 38.00
Ribbed Pineapple, see Prism & Flattened Sawtooth
Pressed Glass, Ribbed Sawtooth, Butter, Covered 30.00

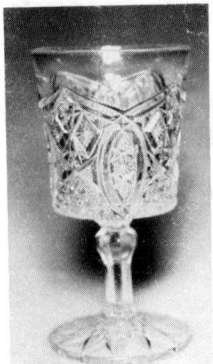

Pressed Glass, Rexford, Goblet

Pressed Glass, Ribbon With Double Bands, Goblet, Frosted

Pressed Glass, Roman Cross, Goblet

Pressed Glass, Oval & Cross Bar, Whiskey

Pressed Glass, Ribbed Spiral, Bowl, Blue Opalescent, Albany, 7 1/2 In.	23.00
Pressed Glass, Ribbed Spiral, Toothpick, Canary Opalescent, Albany	42.50
Pressed Glass, Ribbed Swirl, Muffineer, Amber	48.00
Pressed Glass, Ribbed Swirl, Saltshaker, Emerald Green, Gold Trim	20.00
Pressed Glass, Ribbon & Double Bars, Sauce, Frosted	4.50
Pressed Glass, Ribbon Band & Pendants, Goblet	30.00
Pressed Glass, Ribbon Candy, Cake Stand, 8 1/2 In.	15.00
Pressed Glass, Ribbon Candy, Cake Stand, 9 In.	17.50
Pressed Glass, Ribbon Candy, Cake Stand, 9 1/2 In.	23.50
Pressed Glass, Ribbon Candy, Creamer	15.00
Pressed Glass, Ribbon Candy, Plate, 10 3/8 In.	15.00
Pressed Glass, Ribbon Candy, Relish	10.00
Pressed Glass, Ribbon Candy, Spooner	11.25 To 25.00
Pressed Glass, Ribbon Candy, Spooner, Footed, 5 In.	12.00
Pressed Glass, Ribbon, Bowl, Admiral Dewey, 5 1/4 In.	10.00
Pressed Glass, Ribbon, Bowl, Waste, Frosted Bars	32.50
Pressed Glass, Ribbon, Butter, Covered	44.00
Pressed Glass, Ribbon, Butter, Covered, Flint	30.00
Pressed Glass, Ribbon, Butter, Covered, Frosted	45.00
Pressed Glass, Ribbon, Celery	20.00
Pressed Glass, Ribbon, Celery, Frosted	28.00
Pressed Glass, Ribbon, Compote, Covered, High Standard, 8 In.	55.00
Pressed Glass, Ribbon, Compote, Dolphin Base, Flint, 7 1/2 X 8 1/2 In.	150.00
Pressed Glass, Ribbon, Compote, Low Standard, Flint, 8 1/4 In.	28.00
Pressed Glass, Ribbon, Creamer	20.00
Pressed Glass, Ribbon, Goblet	13.50 To 23.00
Pressed Glass, Ribbon, Goblet, Bakewell Pears	13.50
Pressed Glass, Ribbon, Goblet, Straight Sides	10.00
Pressed Glass, Ribbon, Pitcher, Water, Flint	48.00
Pressed Glass, Ribbon, Sauce, Footed, 4 In.	9.50 To 10.00
Pressed Glass, Ribbon, Spooner, Clear	15.00
Pressed Glass, Ribbon, Table Set, Flint, 6 Piece	68.00
Pressed Glass, Richmond, Pitcher, Water, Etched	20.00
Ripple Band, see Ripple	
Pressed Glass, Ripple Sandwich, Wine	20.00
Pressed Glass, Ripple, Eggcup	12.50
Pressed Glass, Ripple, Goblet	7.50
Pressed Glass, Ripple, Spooner	25.00
Pressed Glass, Rising Sun, Cup & Saucer, Pink Suns	14.00

Pressed Glass, Rising Sun, Goblet	6.50
Pressed Glass, Rising Sun, Goblet, Gold Trim	15.00
Pressed Glass, Rising Sun, Toothpick, Gold Trim	18.00
Pressed Glass, Rising Sun, Tumbler	7.50
Pressed Glass, Roanoke, Berry Set, Ruby Stained, 5 Piece	60.00
Pressed Glass, Roanoke, Bowl, Ruby Stained, 10 In.	20.00
Pressed Glass, Robin Hood, Saltshaker	9.00
Rochelle, see Princess Feather	
Pressed Glass, Rock Crystal, Goblet	4.00
Pressed Glass, Rock Crystal, Sugar & Creamer, Amber	40.00
Pressed Glass, Roman Cross, Goblet	7.50 To 11.00
Pressed Glass, Roman Cross, Relish	3.75
Pressed Glass, Roman Key, Celery, Frosted, Flint	38.00
Pressed Glass, Roman Key, Eggcup	22.50
Pressed Glass, Roman Key, Goblet	14.00 To 37.50
Pressed Glass, Roman Key, Goblet, Flint	29.00
Pressed Glass, Roman Key, Goblet, Frosted	24.50
Pressed Glass, Roman Key, Goblet, Frosted, Flint	37.00
Pressed Glass, Roman Key, Sugar, Flint	30.00
Pressed Glass, Roman Rosette, Bowl, Berry	6.00
Pressed Glass, Roman Rosette, Butter, Covered	28.75
Pressed Glass, Roman Rosette, Cake Stand, 9 In.	32.00
Pressed Glass, Roman Rosette, Compote, Jelly, 4 1/2 In.	25.00
Pressed Glass, Roman Rosette, Creamer	12.00 To 30.00
Pressed Glass, Roman Rosette, Goblet	18.50
Pressed Glass, Roman Rosette, Mug	14.00
Pressed Glass, Roman Rosette, Plate, Bread	20.00
Pressed Glass, Roman Rosette, Plate, 5 1/4 In.	31.00
Pressed Glass, Roman Rosette, Relish, Oval	8.00
Pressed Glass, Roman Rosette, Sauce, 4 In.	22.00
Pressed Glass, Roman Rosette, Spooner	12.00
Pressed Glass, Roman Rosette, Wine	32.00 To 32.50
Romeo, see Block & Fan	
Rope Bands, see Clear Panels with Cord Band	
Pressed Glass, Rose Band, Creamer	9.50
Pressed Glass, Rose Band, Wine	12.50 To 20.00
Pressed Glass, Rose In Snow, Bowl, Straight Sided, 4 1/2 X 2 1/2 In.	15.00
Pressed Glass, Rose In Snow, Butter, Flat	25.00
Pressed Glass, Rose In Snow, Cake Stand	38.00 To 42.00
Pressed Glass, Rose In Snow, Compote, 6 X 4 1/2 In.	20.00
Pressed Glass, Rose In Snow, Creamer	22.50 To 30.00
Pressed Glass, Rose In Snow, Goblet	25.00 To 35.00
Pressed Glass, Rose In Snow, Goblet, Amber	15.00
Pressed Glass, Rose In Snow, Mug	16.50
Pressed Glass, Rose In Snow, Plate, 5 1/4 In.	19.50
Pressed Glass, Rose In Snow, Plate, 7 1/4 In.	19.00 To 22.50
Pressed Glass, Rose In Snow, Relish	14.75
Pressed Glass, Rose In Snow, Relish, 8 X 5 In.	12.50
Pressed Glass, Rose In Snow, Sugar & Creamer, Round	42.50
Pressed Glass, Rose In Snow, Sugar, Covered, Round	25.00
Pressed Glass, Rose In Snow, Sugar, Square	20.00
Pressed Glass, Rose In Snow, Table Set, Square, 4 Piece	120.00
Pressed Glass, Rose In Snow, Tumbler, Bar, Handled	35.00
Pressed Glass, Rose Of Sharon, Goblet	15.00
Pressed Glass, Rose Point Band, Butter, Covered	18.50
Pressed Glass, Rose Point Band, Cake Stand, 8 3/4 In.	16.50
Pressed Glass, Rose Point Band, Creamer	7.00
Pressed Glass, Rose Point Band, Sauce, 3 Footed	12.00
Pressed Glass, Rose Point Band, Sugar, Covered	13.00
Pressed Glass, Rose Sprig, Cake Stand, Octagon Shaped	18.00
Pressed Glass, Rose Sprig, Cake Stand, 9 In.	20.00
Pressed Glass, Rose Sprig, Celery, Sapphire Blue	50.00
Pressed Glass, Rose Sprig, Compote, Low Standard, 9 In.	10.00
Pressed Glass, Rose Sprig, Dish, Pickle	8.00
Pressed Glass, Rose Sprig, Goblet	13.00 To 15.00
Pressed Glass, Rose Sprig, Pitcher, Water	25.00 To 26.00

Pressed Glass,
Roman Rosette,
Creamer

Pressed Glass, Royal,
Butter, Covered

Pressed Glass,
Sandwich Star, Spill

Pressed Glass, Rose In Snow,
Creamer

Pressed Glass, Rose Sprig, Goblet

Pressed Glass, Rose Sprig, Pitcher, Water, Amber, 9 In.	50.00
Pressed Glass, Rose Sprig, Relish, Amber, Boat Shape, 8 In.	35.00
Pressed Glass, Rose Sprig, Sauce, Footed	10.00
Pressed Glass, Rose Sprig, Wine	22.00 To 28.00
Pressed Glass, Rosette & Palm, Cake Stand, 9 1/2 In.	10.50
Pressed Glass, Rosette & Palm, Celery	22.50
Pressed Glass, Rosette & Palm, Goblet	9.00 To 12.50
Pressed Glass, Rosette & Palm, Jar, Cracker	45.00
Pressed Glass, Rosette & Palm, Pitcher, Water	32.00
Pressed Glass, Rosette & Palm, Plate, Handled, 9 In.	10.00
Pressed Glass, Rosette & Palm, Wine	15.00 To 18.00
Pressed Glass, Rosette Band, Celery, Faceted, Ruffled Rim	22.00
Pressed Glass, Rosette Band, Compote, Covered, 12 X 8 In.	59.00
Pressed Glass, Rosette Band, Pitcher, Water, Etched	45.00
Pressed Glass, Rosette Band, Wine, Red Faceted	28.00
Rosette Medallion, see Feather Duster	
Pressed Glass, Rosette, Bowl, Covered, 7 1/4 In.	29.50
Pressed Glass, Rosette, Bowl, Covered, 7 1/2 In.	22.00
Pressed Glass, Rosette, Cake Stand, 8 1/2 X 4 1/4 In.	16.50
Pressed Glass, Rosette, Celery	18.00
Pressed Glass, Rosette, Compote, Jelly	9.50 To 12.50
Pressed Glass, Rosette, Creamer	15.00
Pressed Glass, Rosette, Dish, Pickle	9.00
Pressed Glass, Rosette, Goblet	12.50 To 15.50
Pressed Glass, Rosette, Pitcher, Milk	38.00
Pressed Glass, Rosette, Pitcher, Water	47.50
Pressed Glass, Rosette, Plate, Bread, Closed Handles	18.00
Pressed Glass, Rosette, Plate, Cake	20.00

Pressed Glass, Rosette, Relish	9.00
Pressed Glass, Rosette, Relish, Fish Shape	10.50
Pressed Glass, Rosette, Spooner	18.00
Pressed Glass, Rosette, Sugar, Covered	28.00
Pressed Glass, Royal Crystal, Butter, Covered, Ruby Stained	45.00
Pressed Glass, Royal Crystal, Butter, Ruby Stained	70.00 To 79.00
Pressed Glass, Royal Crystal, Cake Stand	22.50
Pressed Glass, Royal Crystal, Compote, 7 1/2 In.	16.00
Pressed Glass, Royal Crystal, Creamer, Ruby Stained	40.00
Pressed Glass, Royal Crystal, Goblet, Ruby Flashed	35.00
Pressed Glass, Royal Crystal, Pitcher, Water, Bulbous, Ruby Stained	80.00
Pressed Glass, Royal Crystal, Pitcher, Water, Tankard Type, Ruby Stained	70.00
Pressed Glass, Royal Crystal, Plate, 5 1/4 In.	7.50
Pressed Glass, Royal Crystal, Plate, 10 1/4 In.	18.00 To 19.50
Pressed Glass, Royal Crystal, Plate, 10 1/2 In.	12.50
Pressed Glass, Royal Crystal, Spooner, Ruby Stained	29.50 To 40.00
Pressed Glass, Royal Crystal, Sugar, Covered, Ruby Stained	45.00
Pressed Glass, Royal Crystal, Syrup	29.00
Pressed Glass, Royal Lady, Plate, Bread	55.00
Pressed Glass, Royal Lady, Sugar, Covered	25.00 To 45.00
Pressed Glass, Royal Oak, Butter, Covered, Miniature, Frosted To Clear	80.00
Pressed Glass, Royal Oak, Salt & Pepper, Frosted To Clear	50.00
Pressed Glass, Royal Oak, Spooner, Frosted & Clear	32.50
Royal, see Sprig	
Pressed Glass, Ruby Dot, Compote, Scalloped Rim, 7 X 5 1/2 In.	95.00
Pressed Glass, Ruby Dot, Plate, 6 3/8 In.	58.75
Pressed Glass, Ruby Dot, Plate, 8 3/8 In.	58.75
Pressed Glass, Ruby Dot, Relish	25.00
Pressed Glass, Ruby Dot, Salt & Pepper	75.00
Pressed Glass, Ruby Rosette, Bowl, Berry, 8 In.	20.00
Pressed Glass, Ruby Rosette, Saltshaker	15.00 To 22.50
Pressed Glass, Ruby Rosette, Sauce	15.00
Pressed Glass, Ruby Rosette, Spooner	15.50 To 20.00
Pressed Glass, Ruby Rosette, Tankard, Water	75.00
Pressed Glass, Ruby Rosette, Tumbler	25.00
Ruby Thumbprint, see King's Crown	
Pressed Glass, S Repeat, Pitcher, Water, Blue	125.00
Pressed Glass, S Repeat, Pitcher, Water, Gold Trim	85.00
Pressed Glass, S Repeat, Pitcher, Water, Purple, Gold Trim	85.00
Pressed Glass, S Repeat, Saltshaker	8.00
Pressed Glass, S Repeat, Tumbler, Amethyst	18.50 To 32.50
Pressed Glass, S Repeat, Tumbler, Blue	14.00 To 30.00
Pressed Glass, S Repeat, Wine, Sapphire Blue, Gold	30.00
Pressed Glass, Sage, Goblet	35.00
Pressed Glass, Sailboat Cover, Dish, Crossed Oars Over Lifesaver Finial	87.50
Sandwich Loop, see Hairpin	
Pressed Glass, Sandwich Star, Champagne, Flint	150.00
Pressed Glass, Sandwich Star, Compote, Flint, 8 1/2 In.	70.00
Pressed Glass, Sandwich Star, Creamer, Applied Handle	35.00
Pressed Glass, Sandwich Star, Spill	28.00
Pressed Glass, Sandwich Star, Spill, Flint	25.00 To 30.00
Pressed Glass, Sandwich Star, Spooner	28.00
Pressed Glass, Sandwich Star, Spooner, Flint	25.00 To 28.00
Pressed Glass, Sandwich Star, Wine, Flint	225.00
Pressed Glass, Santa Cover, Dish, Sleigh Base	60.00
Pressed Glass, Sawtooth & Star, Bowl, Ruby Stained, 8 In.	35.00
Pressed Glass, Sawtooth & Star, Bowl, Waste	6.50
Pressed Glass, Sawtooth & Star, Cup & Saucer, Ruby Stained	35.00
Pressed Glass, Sawtooth & Star, Goblet	9.00
Pressed Glass, Sawtooth & Star, Pitcher, Water	27.50
Pressed Glass, Sawtooth & Star, Plate, 10 1/4 In.	5.00
Pressed Glass, Sawtooth & Star, Tray, Water	25.00
Pressed Glass, Sawtooth Circle, Salt	26.00
Pressed Glass, Sawtooth Circle, Salt, Master, Flint, Pair	30.00
Pressed Glass, Sawtooth, Butter, Covered, Flint	65.00 To 110.00
Pressed Glass, Sawtooth, Butter, Flint	110.00

Pressed Glass, Sawtooth, Cake Stand	30.00 To 32.00
Pressed Glass, Sawtooth, Cake Stand, Wafer Connection Pedestal, Flint, 9 In.	25.00
Pressed Glass, Sawtooth, Celery	20.00 To 25.00
Pressed Glass, Sawtooth, Celery, Flint	26.00
Pressed Glass, Sawtooth, Celery, Knob Stem, Flint	55.00
Pressed Glass, Sawtooth, Celery, Scalloped Rim	27.50
Pressed Glass, Sawtooth, Celery, Stemmed	12.50
Pressed Glass, Sawtooth, Champagne	45.00
Pressed Glass, Sawtooth, Champagne, Knob Stem	40.00
Pressed Glass, Sawtooth, Champagne, Knob Stem, Flint	60.00
Pressed Glass, Sawtooth, Compote, Covered, Flint, 8 In.	110.00 To 125.00
Pressed Glass, Sawtooth, Compote, Covered, Flint, 8 1/4 X 7 1/2 In.	65.00
Pressed Glass, Sawtooth, Compote, Covered, Flint, 12 In.	80.00 To 95.00
Pressed Glass, Sawtooth, Compote, Flint, 7 1/2 In.	38.00
Pressed Glass, Sawtooth, Compote, Flint, 8 X 9 In.	25.00
Pressed Glass, Sawtooth, Compote, Low Standard, Flint, 8 In.	35.00
Pressed Glass, Sawtooth, Compote, 7 1/2 In.	38.00
Pressed Glass, Sawtooth, Creamer	14.00 To 35.00
Pressed Glass, Sawtooth, Creamer, Applied Crimped Handle, Footed, Flint	65.00
Pressed Glass, Sawtooth, Creamer, Applied Handle	30.00
Pressed Glass, Sawtooth, Creamer, Applied Handle, Flint	47.50 To 70.00
Pressed Glass, Sawtooth, Creamer, Flint	30.00 To 40.00
Pressed Glass, Sawtooth, Creamer, Footed	25.00
Pressed Glass, Sawtooth, Eggcup	25.00
Pressed Glass, Sawtooth, Eggcup, Flint	32.50 To 38.00
Pressed Glass, Sawtooth, Goblet	6.00 To 12.00
Pressed Glass, Sawtooth, Goblet, Banded	5.50
Pressed Glass, Sawtooth, Goblet, Etched	7.00
Pressed Glass, Sawtooth, Goblet, Flint	10.00 To 40.00
Pressed Glass, Sawtooth, Goblet, Knob Stem, Flint	18.00 To 41.00
Pressed Glass, Sawtooth, Goblet, Ruby Stained	20.00
Pressed Glass, Sawtooth, Goblet, 6 Sided Stem	15.00
Pressed Glass, Sawtooth, Pitcher, Milk, Applied Handle, Flint	65.00
Pressed Glass, Sawtooth, Relish, 3 Compartments, 4 X 10 In.	10.50
Pressed Glass, Sawtooth, Salt & Underplate	7.50
Pressed Glass, Sawtooth, Salt, Acorn Finial, Flint	85.00
Pressed Glass, Sawtooth, Salt, Covered	50.00
Pressed Glass, Sawtooth, Salt, Covered, Flint	35.00 To 62.50
Pressed Glass, Sawtooth, Salt, Covered, Footed	45.00
Pressed Glass, Sawtooth, Salt, Footed, Flint	20.00 To 24.50
Pressed Glass, Sawtooth, Salt, Master	22.00 To 35.00
Pressed Glass, Sawtooth, Salt, Master, Covered, Footed, Flint	60.00
Pressed Glass, Sawtooth, Salt, Master, Flint	14.00 To 22.50
Pressed Glass, Sawtooth, Salt, Master, Footed, Flint	20.00
Pressed Glass, Sawtooth, Spill	16.50
Pressed Glass, Sawtooth, Spill, Flint	22.50
Pressed Glass, Sawtooth, Spill, Gold Flashed, Flint	38.50
Pressed Glass, Sawtooth, Spooner	14.00 To 45.00
Pressed Glass, Sawtooth, Spooner, Child's	10.00 To 25.00
Pressed Glass, Sawtooth, Spooner, Flint	17.00 To 22.50
Pressed Glass, Sawtooth, Spooner, Gold Trim	38.50
Pressed Glass, Sawtooth, Sugar, Child's, Covered	35.00
Pressed Glass, Sawtooth, Sugar, Covered, Flint	35.00 To 65.00
Pressed Glass, Sawtooth, Table Set, Miniature, 4 Piece	97.50
Pressed Glass, Sawtooth, Tray, Water, 10 In.	8.00
Pressed Glass, Sawtooth, Tumbler	12.50 To 55.00
Pressed Glass, Sawtooth, Tumbler, Flint	30.00
Pressed Glass, Sawtooth, Tumbler, Footed	50.00
Pressed Glass, Sawtooth, Tumbler, Footed, Flint	35.00 To 45.00
Pressed Glass, Sawtooth, Tumbler, Ruby Stained	20.00
Pressed Glass, Sawtooth, Wine	10.00 To 75.00
Pressed Glass, Sawtooth, Wine, Flint	20.00 To 43.00
Pressed Glass, Sawtooth, Wine, Knob Stem	20.00 To 30.00
Pressed Glass, Sawtooth, Wine, Knob Stem, Flint	24.00 To 52.50
Pressed Glass, Sawtooth, Wine, New England Glass Co.	12.00

Pressed Glass, **Sawtoothed Honeycomb**, Toothpick, Gold Trim 14.00
Pressed Glass, **Saxon**, Butter 35.00
Pressed Glass, **Saxon**, Goblet 6.00
Pressed Glass, **Saxon**, Plate, Bread 12.00
Pressed Glass, **Scalloped Daisy**, Goblet, Green 15.00
Pressed Glass, **Scalloped Daisy**, Goblet, Gold Top 9.00
Pressed Glass, **Scalloped Daisy**, Mug, Etched Vintage, Ruby Stained 14.00
Pressed Glass, **Scalloped Daisy**, Mug, Ruby Stained 12.00
Pressed Glass, **Scalloped Daisy**, Sugar, Covered, Ruby Stained, Floral Design 30.00
Pressed Glass, **Scalloped Diamond Point**, Spooner .... 13.00 To 35.00
Pressed Glass, **Scalloped Diamonds**, Goblet, Clambroth 32.50
Pressed Glass, **Scalloped Lines**, Compote, Covered, 7 1/4 In.Diameter 25.00
Pressed Glass, **Scalloped Prism**, Goblet 8.50
Pressed Glass, **Scalloped Tape**, Celery .... 18.75 To 20.00
Pressed Glass, **Scalloped Tape**, Creamer .... 14.00 To 17.50
Pressed Glass, **Scalloped Tape**, Goblet .... 14.00 To 18.50
Pressed Glass, **Scalloped Tape**, Sugar, Covered .... 17.00 To 17.50
Pressed Glass, **Scalloped Tape**, Wine 14.50
Pressed Glass, **Scarab**, Goblet, Flint .... 80.00 To 90.00
Pressed Glass, **Scotch Plaid**, Plate, 6 In. 30.00
Pressed Glass, **Scroll & Daisy**, Creamer, Measuring Cup Type 10.50
Pressed Glass, **Scroll With Acanthus**, Bowl, Opalescent, 9 In. 18.50
Pressed Glass, **Scroll With Acanthus**, Compote, Jelly, Blue, Scalloped Edge 38.00
Pressed Glass, **Scroll With Acanthus**, Compote, Jelly, Green, Opalescent 25.00
Pressed Glass, **Scroll With Acanthus**, Pitcher, Water, Blue, Opalescent 85.00
Pressed Glass, **Scroll With Acanthus**, Sauce, Opalescent, 5 In. 7.50
Pressed Glass, **Scroll With Acanthus**, Sugar, Blue, Gold, Enamel 25.00
Pressed Glass, **Scroll With Acanthus**, Toothpick, Apple Green 48.00
Pressed Glass, **Scroll With Cane Band**, Butter, Amber Flashed, Covered 70.00
Pressed Glass, **Scroll With Cane Band**, Sugar, Covered, Ruby Stained 45.00
Pressed Glass, **Scroll With Cane Band**, Toothpick, Ruby Stained .... 12.00 To 22.50
Pressed Glass, **Scroll With Cane Band**, Tumbler, Yellow Flashing 22.50
Pressed Glass, **Scroll With Flowers**, Butter, Covered 23.00
Pressed Glass, **Scroll With Flowers**, Creamer 18.00
Pressed Glass, **Scroll With Flowers**, Eggcup .... 12.00 To 18.50
Pressed Glass, **Scroll With Flowers**, Eggcup, Handled .... 14.50 To 25.00
Pressed Glass, **Scroll With Flowers**, Goblet .... 8.00 To 14.00
Pressed Glass, **Scroll With Flowers**, Plate, Bread 11.00
Pressed Glass, **Scroll With Flowers**, Plate, Cake, Handles 22.50
Pressed Glass, **Scroll With Flowers**, Plate, Handled, 10 In. 25.00
Pressed Glass, **Scroll With Flowers**, Relish .... 7.50 To 9.00
Pressed Glass, **Scroll With Flowers**, Relish, Oblong, Handled 15.00
Pressed Glass, **Scroll With Flowers**, Spooner 16.00
Pressed Glass, **Scroll With Flowers**, Wine 14.50
Pressed Glass, **Scroll With Star**, Goblet 7.00
Pressed Glass, **Scroll With Star**, Plate, 8 1/4 In. 5.00
Pressed Glass, **Scroll**, Bowl, Flint, 8 In. 28.00
Pressed Glass, **Scroll**, Butter, Covered 25.00
Pressed Glass, **Scroll**, Creamer, Stippled Panels 9.50
Pressed Glass, **Scroll**, Goblet .... 9.00 To 13.50
Pressed Glass, **Scroll**, Goblet, Stippled 8.50
Pressed Glass, **Scroll**, Goblet, Buttermilk 14.00
Pressed Glass, **Scroll**, Spooner 12.00
Pressed Glass, **Scroll**, Spooner, Stippled 12.00
Pressed Glass, **Scroll**, Tumbler, Footed 15.00
Pressed Glass, **Scrolled Spray**, Sugar & Creamer, Sapphire, Covered 65.00
Pressed Glass, **Scrolled Sunflower**, Creamer 9.00
Pressed Glass, **Seashell**, Wine 17.50
Pressed Glass, **Sedan**, Creamer 15.00
Pressed Glass, **Sedan**, Goblet 12.50
Pressed Glass, **Sedan**, Salt, Master 12.50
Pressed Glass, **Sedan**, Sauce .... 4.00 To 4.75
Pressed Glass, **Sedan**, Wine 10.00
Pressed Glass, **Selby**, Goblet .... 9.00 To 11.00
Pressed Glass, **Seneca Loop**, Celery .... 37.00 To 60.00

Pressed Glass,
Scroll With Flowers, Goblet

Pressed Glass,
Sawtooth, Pomade

Pressed Glass, Shell & Tassel,
Compote, Covered

Pressed Glass, Seneca Loop, Compote, Flint, 7 1/2 X 5 In.	40.00
Pressed Glass, Seneca Loop, Compote, Flint, 8 1/2 X 7 3/4 In.	45.00
Pressed Glass, Seneca Loop, Compote, Fruit, Opaque Blue, Flint, 9 In.	145.00
Pressed Glass, Seneca Loop, Compote, Scalloped Edge, Flint, 8 1/4 X 8 In.	40.00
Pressed Glass, Seneca Loop, Compote, Scalloped, Flint, 10 In.	45.00
Pressed Glass, Seneca Loop, Compote, Scalloped, 1869, 10 In.	45.00
Pressed Glass, Seneca Loop, Cordial, Flint	35.00
Pressed Glass, Seneca Loop, Creamer, Flint	70.00
Pressed Glass, Seneca Loop, Eggcup	35.00
Pressed Glass, Seneca Loop, Eggcup, Flint	32.00 To 32.50
Pressed Glass, Seneca Loop, Goblet	9.00 To 35.00
Pressed Glass, Seneca Loop, Goblet, Flint	16.00 To 32.00
Pressed Glass, Seneca Loop, Mug, Applied Handle, Flint, 3 In.	18.00
Pressed Glass, Seneca Loop, Pitcher, Water, Applied Handle, Flint	82.00
Pressed Glass, Seneca Loop, Pitcher, Water, Flint	125.00
Pressed Glass, Seneca Loop, Salt, Footed, Flint	17.00
Pressed Glass, Seneca Loop, Spooner	7.50
Pressed Glass, Seneca Loop, Spooner, Flint	20.00
Pressed Glass, Seneca Loop, Sugar	20.00 To 24.00
Pressed Glass, Seneca Loop, Sugar, Covered, Flint	65.00
Pressed Glass, Seneca Loop, Tumbler, Footed	40.00
Pressed Glass, Seneca Loop, Tumbler, Footed, Flint	30.00 To 35.00
Pressed Glass, Seneca Loop, Wine	40.00
Pressed Glass, Seneca Loop, Wine, Flint	28.00
Pressed Glass, Sequoia & Crossbar, Plate, Bread, 8 X 12 In.	11.00
Pressed Glass, Sequoia, Goblet	12.00
Pressed Glass, Sequoia, Saltshaker	2.50 To 3.50
Pressed Glass, Sequoia, Spooner	25.00
Pressed Glass, Serrated Prism, Goblet, Banded, Gold Rim	5.00 To 12.00
Pressed Glass, Serrated Prism, Sugar, Green, Covered, Gold Trim	30.00
Pressed Glass, Sexton Flute, Goblet, Flint	15.00
Pressed Glass, Sheaf Of Wheat, Plate, Oval, 22 In.	24.00
Pressed Glass, Sheaf Of Wheat, Plate, 11 In.	24.00
Pressed Glass, Shell & Jewel, Bowl, Berry, Amber	10.50
Pressed Glass, Shell & Jewel, Cake Stand, 10 In.	47.50
Pressed Glass, Shell & Jewel, Compote, 7 1/2 X 7 In.	37.50
Pressed Glass, Shell & Jewel, Pitcher, Water	16.00 To 35.00
Pressed Glass, Shell & Jewel, Pitcher, Water, Blue, 7 1/4 In.	55.00
Pressed Glass, Shell & Jewel, Pitcher, 8 1/2 In.High	18.50
Pressed Glass, Shell & Jewel, Sauce	9.00
Pressed Glass, Shell & Jewel, Tumbler	12.00 To 16.00
Pressed Glass, Shell & Jewel, Tumbler, Blue	18.50 To 30.00
Pressed Glass, Shell & Jewel, Tumbler, Green	18.50
Pressed Glass, Shell & Jewel, Water Set, Blue, 7 Piece	225.00
Pressed Glass, Shell & Jewel, Water Set, 6 Piece	55.00

Pressed Glass, Shell & Tassel, Bowl, Gondola, 10 In.Long	30.00
Pressed Glass, Shell & Tassel, Bowl, Oval, Silver Plate Holder, 12 In.	48.00
Pressed Glass, Shell & Tassel, Bowl, Oval, 11 1/2 X 7 In.	23.00
Pressed Glass, Shell & Tassel, Butter, Covered	40.00
Pressed Glass, Shell & Tassel, Cake Stand, High Standard, 10 In.	25.00
Pressed Glass, Shell & Tassel, Cake Stand, Square, 10 In.	35.00
Pressed Glass, Shell & Tassel, Celery	22.50
Pressed Glass, Shell & Tassel, Compote, Jelly, Square	18.50
Pressed Glass, Shell & Tassel, Compote, 4 1/4 In.	33.00
Pressed Glass, Shell & Tassel, Compote, 7 In.High, 8 In.Square	32.00
Pressed Glass, Shell & Tassel, Compote, 7 3/4 In.	22.00
Pressed Glass, Shell & Tassel, Compote, 8 1/2 In.	35.00
Pressed Glass, Shell & Tassel, Creamer, Round	32.00
Pressed Glass, Shell & Tassel, Creamer, Square	28.50
Pressed Glass, Shell & Tassel, Goblet	23.00 To 35.00
Pressed Glass, Shell & Tassel, Plate, Bread, Square, 9 X 13 1/2 In.	28.00
Pressed Glass, Shell & Tassel, Platter, Oblong, 11 3/4 X 8 1/4 In.	33.00
Pressed Glass, Shell & Tassel, Relish, 9 X 6 In.	14.00
Pressed Glass, Shell & Tassel, Saltshaker, Sun Tint, Tin Top	20.00
Pressed Glass, Shell & Tassel, Sauce	7.50 To 9.50
Pressed Glass, Shell & Tassel, Sauce, Footed	14.50
Pressed Glass, Shell & Tassel, Sauce, Handled	6.00
Pressed Glass, Shell & Tassel, Sauce, Square, 4 In.	10.00
Pressed Glass, Shell & Tassel, Spooner	22.00
Pressed Glass, Shell & Tassel, Sugar	23.00
Pressed Glass, Shell & Tassel, Sugar & Creamer, Square	50.00 To 65.00
Pressed Glass, Shell & Tassel, Sugar, Covered, Dog's Head Finial	45.00
Pressed Glass, Shell & Tassel, Tray, Hollowed Shell Corners, 8 X 12 In.	27.50
Pressed Glass, Shepherd's Plaid, Butter, Covered	16.00 To 16.50
Pressed Glass, Shepherd's Plaid, Celery, 6 In.	20.00
Pressed Glass, Shepherd's Plaid, Creamer	12.00 To 15.00
Pressed Glass, Shepherd's Plaid, Spooner	7.00 To 10.00
Pressed Glass, Shepherd's Plaid, Sugar, Covered	15.00 To 18.00
Pressed Glass, Sheraton, Butter, Blue	50.00
Pressed Glass, Sheraton, Dish, Pickle, Amber	9.00
Pressed Glass, Sheraton, Goblet	15.50
Pressed Glass, Sheraton, Goblet, Blue	27.00
Pressed Glass, Sheraton, Pitcher, Milk	15.00 To 35.00
Pressed Glass, Sheraton, Pitcher, Water	45.00
Pressed Glass, Sheraton, Plate, 6 In.	12.50
Pressed Glass, Sheraton, Relish, Amber	16.00
Pressed Glass, Sheraton, Sauce, Footed, 3 1/2 In.	4.00
Pressed Glass, Sheraton, Spooner, Amber	17.50
Pressed Glass, Sheraton, Wine	16.00 To 16.50
Pressed Glass, Sherwood, Goblet	4.50
Pressed Glass, Sherwood, Goblet, Knob At Base	5.00
Pressed Glass, Shield Band, Goblet, Etched	8.50
Pressed Glass, Shields, Goblet	15.00
Pressed Glass, Shimmering Star, Butter, Covered	55.00
Pressed Glass, Shimmering Star, Sugar, Covered	45.00
Pressed Glass, Shimmering Star, Tumbler	12.00
Pressed Glass, Shimmering Star, Water Set, 7 Piece	110.00
Pressed Glass, Short Flute, Tumbler, Bar, Flint	15.00
Pressed Glass, Short Loops, Goblet	7.00
Pressed Glass, Short Loops, Goblet, Etched	25.00
Pressed Glass, Short Ribs, Goblet	5.00
Pressed Glass, Short Swirl, Goblet	6.00
Short Teasel, see Teasel	
Pressed Glass, Shoshone, Bowl, Ruby & Clear, 7 In.	23.00
Pressed Glass, Shoshone, Bowl, 2 Handles, 5 1/2 In.	8.00
Pressed Glass, Shoshone, Butter, Ruby Stained	65.00
Pressed Glass, Shoshone, Cake Stand, 9 In.	12.00
Pressed Glass, Shoshone, Compote, 5 1/2 X 4 1/2 In.	9.50
Pressed Glass, Shoshone, Creamer, Ruby Stained, 5 In.	30.00
Pressed Glass, Shoshone, Relish, Gold Trim, Oval	8.50
Pressed Glass, Shoshone, Spooner, Ruby Stained	30.00

Pressed Glass, Shoshone, Toothpick 16.50
Pressed Glass, Shovel, Goblet .... 6.50 To 12.00
Pressed Glass, Shovel, Tumbler 9.00
Pressed Glass, Shrine, Compote, Jelly 12.00
Pressed Glass, Shrine, Goblet 18.00
Pressed Glass, Shrine, Mug 18.50
Pressed Glass, Shrine, Pitcher, Water .... 32.00 To 45.00
Pressed Glass, Shrine, Relish 13.75
Pressed Glass, Shrine, Sauce 8.00
Pressed Glass, Shrine, Spooner .... 22.00 To 35.00
Pressed Glass, Shrine, Sugar, Covered 32.50
Pressed Glass, Shrine, Toothpick 25.00
Pressed Glass, Shrine, Tumbler 20.00
Pressed Glass, Shuttle, Celery .... 25.00 To 28.75
Pressed Glass, Shuttle, Celery, Footed 30.00
Pressed Glass, Shuttle, Cordial, Greentown, 3 1/8 In. 21.50
Pressed Glass, Shuttle, Cup, Punch .... 5.00 To 10.00
Pressed Glass, Shuttle, Wine 9.00
Pressed Glass, Shuttle, Wine, Greentown 15.00
Pressed Glass, Side Wheeler, Spooner 12.00
Pressed Glass, Silver Anniversary, Goblet .... 5.00 To 11.50
Pressed Glass, Singing Birds, Goblet 65.00
Pressed Glass, Sir Moses Montefiori, Plate, 10 In. 45.00
Pressed Glass, Siskyou, Goblet 8.50
Pressed Glass, Six Panel Finecut, Bowl, Berry, Amber Stain, 8 In., Findlay 35.00
Pressed Glass, Six Panel Finecut, Mug 18.00
Pressed Glass, Six Panel Finecut, Tumbler 13.00
Pressed Glass, Six Panel Finecut, Tumbler, Etched, Findlay 19.50
Pressed Glass, Skilton, Bowl, Ruby & Clear, 8 In. 32.50
Pressed Glass, Skilton, Butter, Covered, Ruby Stained 65.00
Pressed Glass, Slashed Swirl Band, Creamer, Tankard Type, 7 In. .... 14.00 To 19.00
Pressed Glass, Smocking, Butter, Covered 55.00
Pressed Glass, Smocking, Butter, Covered, Flint 50.00
Pressed Glass, Smocking, Butter, Flint 57.50
Pressed Glass, Smocking, Compote, Flint, 7 X 3 In. 37.00
Pressed Glass, Smocking, Compote, Low Standard, Flint, 7 In. 48.00
Pressed Glass, Smocking, Compote, Low Standard, Flint, 7 3/4 In. 58.00
Pressed Glass, Smocking, Compote, Low Standard, 7 3/4 In. 65.00
Pressed Glass, Smocking, Compote, Pointed Scalloped Rim, Flint, 7 3/4 In. 58.00
Pressed Glass, Smocking, Creamer 110.00
Pressed Glass, Smocking, Creamer, Flint .... 75.00 To 125.00
Pressed Glass, Smocking, Eggcup 45.00
Pressed Glass, Smocking, Eggcup, Flint 45.00
Pressed Glass, Smocking, Goblet, Flint .... 45.00 To 65.00
Pressed Glass, Smocking, Spill, Flint 30.00
Pressed Glass, Smocking, Spooner, Flint .... 30.00 To 32.50
Pressed Glass, Smocking, Sugar & Creamer, Cover, Applied Handle, Flint 160.00
Pressed Glass, Smocking, Sugar & Creamer, Cover, Flint 160.00 T3 180.00
Pressed Glass, Smocking, Sugar & Creamer, Vaulted 100.00
Pressed Glass, Smocking, Sugar, Covered, Flint .... 60.00 To 80.00
Pressed Glass, Smocking, Tumbler, Whiskey, Flint 80.00
Pressed Glass, Smocking, Wine, Flint 68.00
Pressed Glass, Snail, Banana Boat 110.00
Pressed Glass, Snail, Butter, Covered 45.00
Pressed Glass, Snail, Celery .... 27.50 To 30.00
Pressed Glass, Snail, Goblet 36.00
Pressed Glass, Snail, Pitcher, Water, Ruby Stained, Etched 85.00
Pressed Glass, Snail, Sauce, 4 In. 14.50
Pressed Glass, Snail, Spooner .... 15.50 To 24.50
Pressed Glass, Snail, Tumbler 35.00
Pressed Glass, Snail, Tumbler, Etched 23.75
Pressed Glass, Snake Drape, Goblet .... 12.50 To 19.00
Pressed Glass, Snakeskin & Dot Band, Goblet 12.00
Pressed Glass, Snakeskin & Dot, Cup Plate 8.00
Pressed Glass, Snakeskin & Dot, Cup Plate, Blue 40.00
Pressed Glass, Snakeskin & Dot, Plate, 8 In. 12.50

Pressed Glass, Star & Dewdrop,
Covered Butter Dish
(See Page 478)

Pressed Glass, Squirrel, Creamer
(See Page 478)

Pressed Glass, Shrine, Bowl
(See Page 476)

Pressed Glass,
Starflower, Sugar,
Nova Scotia, C.1800
(See Page 478)

Pressed Glass, Snow Band, Goblet	13.00 To 18.50
Pressed Glass, Snowdrop, Berry Set, Portland, 7 Piece	45.00
Pressed Glass, Snowdrop, Sauce Set, Portland, 5 Piece	20.00
Pressed Glass, Snowflake, Goblet	18.00 To 35.00
Pressed Glass, Spalding, Goblet	7.50
Spanish American, see Admiral Dewey	
Spanish Coin, see Columbian Coin	
Spartan, see Barred Star	
Pressed Glass, Spear Point & Daisy Band, Goblet	10.00
Pressed Glass, Spear Point & Daisy Band, Sauce, Ruby Stained	12.50
Pressed Glass, Spear Point & Daisy Band, Toothpick, Ruby Stained, 2 1/4 In.	10.00
Pressed Glass, Spear Point & Daisy Band, Wine	7.00
Pressed Glass, Spear Point & Frosted Band, Spooner, Ruby Stained, 4 1/8 In.	22.00
Pressed Glass, Spear Point & Frosted Band, Tumbler, Ruby Stained	18.00
Pressed Glass, Spear Point, Bowl, Ruby Stained, Oval, 10 X 7 In.	25.00
Pressed Glass, Spear Point, Goblet, Ruby Stained	20.00
Pressed Glass, Spear Point, Sugar, Covered	25.00
Pressed Glass, Spearhead, Celery	18.50
Pressed Glass, Spearhead, Goblet	9.00
Pressed Glass, Spiked Argus, Claret, Flint	55.00
Pressed Glass, Spiked Argus, Tumbler	45.00
Pressed Glass, Spiral & Maltese Cross, Creamer, Amber	16.50
Pressed Glass, Spirea Band, Butter, Blue, Covered	35.00
Pressed Glass, Spirea Band, Cake Stand, Honey Amber	45.00
Pressed Glass, Spirea Band, Celery	13.50
Pressed Glass, Spirea Band, Creamer, Amber	23.00
Pressed Glass, Spirea Band, Goblet	12.50
Pressed Glass, Spirea Band, Goblet, Amber	17.00 To 22.00
Pressed Glass, Spirea Band, Jar, Pickle, Covered	15.00
Pressed Glass, Spirea Band, Platter, Oval, Blue, 8 1/2 X 11 In.	24.00
Pressed Glass, Spirea Band, Relish, Amber	18.50
Pressed Glass, Spirea Band, Wine	14.00 To 16.00
Pressed Glass, Spirea, Plate, Bread	11.00
Pressed Glass, Spirea, Plate, Bread, Amber	18.00
Pressed Glass, Spirea, Salt & Pepper, Blue	15.00
Pressed Glass, Sprig, Bowl, Footed, 8 In.	17.50
Pressed Glass, Sprig, Bowl, Oval, 4 3/8 X 6 1/4 In.	12.50
Pressed Glass, Sprig, Cake Stand, High Standard, 10 In.	35.00
Pressed Glass, Sprig, Cake Stand, 10 In.	20.00
Pressed Glass, Sprig, Celery	24.50

Pressed Glass, Sprig, Compote, Covered, High Standard, 8 In. 42.50
Pressed Glass, Sprig, Compote, Covered, 7 In. 60.00
Pressed Glass, Sprig, Creamer 20.00
Pressed Glass, Sprig, Goblet .... 22.50 To 27.50
Pressed Glass, Sprig, Plate, Bread 19.50
Pressed Glass, Sprig, Relish 8.75
Pressed Glass, Sprig, Sauce 3.00
Pressed Glass, Sprig, Sauce, Footed .... 7.50 To 8.75
Pressed Glass, Sprig, Spooner 15.00
Pressed Glass, Sprig, Sugar .... 11.50 To 15.00
Pressed Glass, Sprig, Sugar & Creamer, Decorated Sugar 35.00
Pressed Glass, Square Waffle, Goblet 8.50
Pressed Glass, Squared Ashburton, Goblet, Flint 23.50
Pressed Glass, Squirrel Beside Tree Trunk, Salt Dip, Master, Portland 28.00
Pressed Glass, Squirrel, Pitcher, Water, 2 Acorns Under Rim .... 85.00 To 125.00
Pressed Glass, Squirrel, Sauce 12.50
Pressed Glass, Stag, Goblet 48.00
Pressed Glass, Stag, Mug, Amber 20.00
Pressed Glass, Star & Arches, Cup, Punch 6.00
Pressed Glass, Star & Arches, Punch Set, Miniature, 6 Piece 67.00
Pressed Glass, Star & Arches, Punch Set, Miniature, 7 Piece 75.00
Pressed Glass, Star & Buckle, Spill 35.00
Pressed Glass, Star & Buckle, Sugar 35.00
Pressed Glass, Star & Dart, Butter, Covered 70.00
Pressed Glass, Star & Dart, Butter, Covered, Flint 55.00
Pressed Glass, Star & Dart, Compote, Footed, Flint, 1950s, 6 In. 35.00
Pressed Glass, Star & Dart, Dish, Sweetmeat, Covered, Flint 48.00
Pressed Glass, Star & Dewdrop, Salt 4.00
Pressed Glass, Star & Feather, Plate, Amber, 7 In. 15.00
Pressed Glass, Star & File, Relish, Two Handles 8.75
Pressed Glass, Star & File, Wine 8.00
Pressed Glass, Star & Loop, Sugar, Covered 35.00
Pressed Glass, Star & Oval With Frosted Band, Celery 16.00
Pressed Glass, Star & Oval With Frosted Band, Tumbler .... 8.00 To 15.00
Pressed Glass, Star & Oval, Dish, Olive, Boat Shape 8.00
Pressed Glass, Star & Palm, Goblet .... 8.00 To 14.00
    Star & Punty, see Moon & Star
    Star Band, see Bosworth
Pressed Glass, Star In Bull's-Eye, Creamer, Gold Trim 12.00
Pressed Glass, Star In Bull's-Eye, Cruet, 6 In. 29.50
Pressed Glass, Star In Bull's-Eye, Cup, Punch 4.50
Pressed Glass, Star In Bull's-Eye, Mug 9.50
Pressed Glass, Star In Bull's-Eye, Relish 8.00
Pressed Glass, Star In Bull's-Eye, Saltshaker 8.00
Pressed Glass, Star In Bull's-Eye, Sauce, Gold Trim 6.50
Pressed Glass, Star In Bull's-Eye, Toothpick 10.00
Pressed Glass, Star In Honeycomb, Goblet .... 11.00 To 18.00
Pressed Glass, Star In Honeycomb, Wine 15.00
Pressed Glass, Star Medallion, Bowl, Hexagonal, Flint, 6 In. 80.00
Pressed Glass, Star Medallion, Bowl, 7 In. 10.00
Pressed Glass, Star Medallion, Relish, Oblong, 2 Handled 13.00
    Star of Bethlehem, see Bethlehem Star
Pressed Glass, Star Of David, Cup Plate, Stippled Hearts, Sunbursts, Flint 12.00
Pressed Glass, Star Rosetted, Bowl, Footed, 7 In. 7.50
Pressed Glass, Star Rosetted, Dish, Pickle 4.00
Pressed Glass, Star Rosetted, Goblet .... 15.00 To 18.00
Pressed Glass, Star Rosetted, Plate, "Good Mother, " 11 In. 25.00
Pressed Glass, Star Rosetted, Plate, Apple Green, 7 In. 12.50
Pressed Glass, Star Rosetted, Plate, 7 In. 6.00
Pressed Glass, Star Rosetted, Relish 4.50
Pressed Glass, Star Rosetted, Relish, Handled 4.50
Pressed Glass, Star Rosetted, Sauce, Footed, 4 In. 3.75
Pressed Glass, Star Rosetted, Sauce, Footed, 5 In. 6.00
Pressed Glass, Star Rosetted, Sauce, 4 In. 3.00
Pressed Glass, Star Rosetted, Spill, Flint 48.00
Pressed Glass, Star Rosetted, Sugar, Covered 25.00

Item	Price
Pressed Glass, Star Whorl, Goblet	10.00
Pressed Glass, Star Whorl, Goblet, Gold, Crooked	7.50
Pressed Glass, Stars & Bars, Creamer, Etched Leaves, Miniature	12.50
Pressed Glass, Stars & Bars, Cruet Set, Blue, Findlay, 4 Piece	175.00
Pressed Glass, Stars & Bars, Goblet	25.00
Pressed Glass, Stars & Bars, Salt & Pepper	14.00
Pressed Glass, Stars & Bars, Sauce, Footed, 3 1/2 In.	3.50
Pressed Glass, Stars & Bars, Spooner, Amber Panels	40.00
Pressed Glass, Stars & Bars, Spooner, Etched	20.00
Pressed Glass, Stars & Bars, Wine	8.00
Pressed Glass, Stars & Fan, Cake Stand, 9 1/2 In.	12.00
Pressed Glass, Stars & Stripes, Creamer	8.00 To 12.50
Pressed Glass, Stars & Stripes, Wine	6.00 To 8.00
Pressed Glass, States, Bowl, 8 X 4 In.	9.00
Pressed Glass, States, Compote, Tall Stem, 9 In.	27.50
Pressed Glass, States, Creamer	10.00
Pressed Glass, States, Creamer, Deep Green	30.00
Pressed Glass, States, Cup, Punch	6.50
Pressed Glass, States, Goblet	20.00 To 25.00
Pressed Glass, States, Nappy, 3 Handled	19.00
Pressed Glass, States, Plate, Gold Trimmed Scalloped Rim, 5 1/2 In.	20.00
Pressed Glass, States, Saltshaker, Glass Top	10.00
Pressed Glass, States, Spooner	20.00
Pressed Glass, States, Toothpick, Sanitary	20.00
Pressed Glass, States, Tumbler	15.00
Pressed Glass, States, Wine	12.00 To 22.50
Pressed Glass, States, Wine, Gold Flashed	20.00
Stayman, see Tidy	
Pressed Glass, Stedman, Champagne	38.00
Pressed Glass, Stedman, Champagne, Flint	30.00
Pressed Glass, Stedman, Creamer	30.00
Pressed Glass, Stedman, Creamer, Flint	70.00
Pressed Glass, Stedman, Eggcup, Flint	28.00
Pressed Glass, Stedman, Goblet	16.00 To 22.00
Pressed Glass, Stedman, Goblet, Barrel Shape, Rayed Base	25.00
Pressed Glass, Stedman, Goblet, Flint	23.00
Pressed Glass, Stedman, Sugar	15.00
Pressed Glass, Stedman, Sugar, Flint	30.00
Pressed Glass, Stedman, Wine, Flint	30.00
Pressed Glass, Stepped Hexagons, Sugar, Covered	80.00
Pressed Glass, Stepped Hexagons, Sugar, Covered, Flint	75.00
Stippled Band, see Stippled Bowl	
Pressed Glass, Stippled Bowl, Goblet	9.50
Pressed Glass, Stippled Bowl, Goblet, Flint	15.00 To 18.00
Pressed Glass, Stippled Bowl, Spooner, Scalloped Top, Flint	15.00
Pressed Glass, Stippled Butterfly, Cup Plate, Forget-Me-Not Edge, 3 In.	15.00
Pressed Glass, Stippled Cabbage Leaf, Celery	38.00
Pressed Glass, Stippled Chain, Goblet	10.00
Pressed Glass, Stippled Chain, Spooner	15.00
Pressed Glass, Stippled Cherry, Plate, 9 1/4 In.	22.00
Pressed Glass, Stippled Cherry, Sauce	3.50 To 3.75
Pressed Glass, Stippled Daisy, Bowl, Berry	9.75
Pressed Glass, Stippled Daisy, Tumbler	12.50
Pressed Glass, Stippled Double Loop, Creamer, 5 In.	17.50
Pressed Glass, Stippled Double Loop, Sugar, Covered	18.50
Pressed Glass, Stippled Festoon & Grape, Goblet, Clear Leaf	14.50
Pressed Glass, Stippled Forget-Me-Not, Cake Stand	20.00
Pressed Glass, Stippled Forget-Me-Not, Cake Stand, Findlay	32.50
Pressed Glass, Stippled Forget-Me-Not, Compote, 8 In.	35.00
Pressed Glass, Stippled Forget-Me-Not, Creamer	20.00
Pressed Glass, Stippled Forget-Me-Not, Goblet	25.00 To 32.50
Pressed Glass, Stippled Forget-Me-Not, Pitcher, Milk	45.00
Pressed Glass, Stippled Forget-Me-Not, Wine	42.00
Pressed Glass, Stippled Fuchsia, Goblet	16.50 To 18.50
Pressed Glass, Stippled Grape & Festoon, Goblet, Buttermilk	30.00
Pressed Glass, Stippled Grape & Festoon, Celery	28.00

Pressed Glass, Stippled Grape & Festoon, Goblet, Stippled Leaf	14.50
Pressed Glass, Stippled Grape & Festoon, Spooner, 5 In.	14.00
Pressed Glass, Stippled Grape & Festoon, Sugar, Open	28.00
Pressed Glass, Stippled Ivy, Compote, Covered, 6 In.	38.00
Pressed Glass, Stippled Ivy, Creamer, Applied Handle	45.00
Pressed Glass, Stippled Ivy, Eggcup	15.00
Pressed Glass, Stippled Ivy, Goblet	15.00
Pressed Glass, Stippled Ivy, Sauce	6.00 To 6.35
Pressed Glass, Stippled Leaf, Goblet	21.50
Pressed Glass, Stippled Magnet & Grape, Salt	16.00
Pressed Glass, Stippled Maidenhair Fern, Goblet	12.00 To 20.00
Pressed Glass, Stippled Maple Leaf, Plate, Cake, Footed, 9 1/2 In.	10.00
Pressed Glass, Stippled Maple Leaf, Sauce, Bark Handles & Feet	6.00
Pressed Glass, Stippled Medallion, Butter, Covered	50.00
Pressed Glass, Stippled Medallion, Butter, Covered, Flint	45.00
Pressed Glass, Stippled Medallion, Eggcup	30.00
Pressed Glass, Stippled Medallion, Eggcup, Flint	28.00
Pressed Glass, Stippled Medallion, Goblet	30.00
Pressed Glass, Stippled Medallion, Goblet, Flint	24.00 To 30.00
Pressed Glass, Stippled Medallion, Sauce	4.00 To 12.50
Stippled Paneled Flower, see Maine	
Stippled Peppers, Goblet	20.00
Pressed Glass, Stippled Peppers, Sauce	3.75
Pressed Glass, Stippled Roman Key, Goblet	18.00 To 25.00
Pressed Glass, Stippled Sandburr, Compote, Covered, High Standard, 7 1/4 In.	37.50
Pressed Glass, Stippled Sandburr, Sugar	15.00
Pressed Glass, Stippled Sandburr, Sugar, Covered	22.50
Pressed Glass, Stippled Sandburr, Tumbler, Lemonade	7.50
Stippled Scroll, see Scroll	
Stippled Star Variant, see Stippled Sandburr	
Pressed Glass, Stippled Star, Celery, Tall Pedestal	30.00
Pressed Glass, Stippled Star, Eggcup	35.00
Pressed Glass, Stippled Star, Spooner	16.00 To 20.00
Pressed Glass, Stippled Star, Spooner, Sandwich	45.00
Pressed Glass, Stippled Star, Sugar & Creamer, Applied Handle	55.00
Pressed Glass, Stippled Star, Tumbler	12.00
Pressed Glass, Stippled Starflower, Goblet	15.00
Stork Looking at the Moon, see Ostrich Looking at the Moon	
Pressed Glass, Stork, Creamer, Iowa City	45.00
Pressed Glass, Stork, Dish, Pickle, Frosted	20.00
Pressed Glass, Stork, Goblet, Frosted	16.50
Pressed Glass, Stork, Jar, Pickle, Frosted	40.00
Pressed Glass, Stork, Pitcher, Water	125.00
Pressed Glass, Stork, Plate, Bread, Frosted	23.00
Pressed Glass, Stork, Relish, Frosted	20.00
Pressed Glass, Stork, Spooner, 101 Border	15.00 To 20.00
Pressed Glass, Stork, Sugar	25.00
Pressed Glass, Stork, Table Set, Iowa City Glass Co., 4 Piece	285.00
Pressed Glass, Stork, Tray, Water, Frosted	75.00
Pressed Glass, Stove, Butter, Blue, Flatiron Finial	85.00
Pressed Glass, Stove, Butter, Flatiron Finial	65.00
Pressed Glass, Strawberry & Currant, Creamer	45.00
Pressed Glass, Strawberry & Currant, Goblet	13.00 To 25.00
Pressed Glass, Strawberry, Butter, Miniature	6.00
Pressed Glass, Strawberry, Compote, C.1870, 8 X 4 1/2 In.	22.50
Pressed Glass, Strawberry, Creamer	18.00
Pressed Glass, Strawberry, Pitcher, Water, Applied Handle, Bulbous	85.00
Pressed Glass, Strawberry, Relish	18.00
Pressed Glass, Strawberry, Sauce, Red Stained, Gold Trim	10.50
Pressed Glass, Strawberry, Spooner	25.00
Pressed Glass, Strawberry, Sugar, Covered, Sandwich	65.00
Pressed Glass, Strigil, Pitcher, Water, 6 1/2 In.	25.00
Pressed Glass, Strigil, Plate, Cake, 11 In.	12.00
Pressed Glass, Strigil, Vase, 6 In.	6.00
Pressed Glass, Strigil, Wine	15.00 To 15.50
Pressed Glass, Sugar Pear, Goblet	19.50

Pressed Glass, Sunbeam, Sugar, Blue, Gold Trim 15.00
Pressed Glass, Sunbeam, Toothpick .... 15.00 To 20.00
Pressed Glass, Sunbeam, Tumbler .... 2.00 To 2.50
Pressed Glass, Sunburst Medallion, Goblet 16.00
Pressed Glass, Sunburst Medallion, Pitcher, Water 16.00
Pressed Glass, Sunburst, Bowl, Banana 22.50
Pressed Glass, Sunburst, Butter, Covered 20.00
Pressed Glass, Sunburst, Celery .... 10.00 To 13.75
Pressed Glass, Sunburst, Creamer, Individual 7.50
Pressed Glass, Sunburst, Cup, Punch, Miniature 2.00
Pressed Glass, Sunburst, Plate, 7 In. 5.00
Pressed Glass, Sunburst, Sugar, Covered, Miniature 18.00
Pressed Glass, Sunburst, Table Set, Miniature, 4 Piece 42.00
Pressed Glass, Sunflower, Creamer 12.00
Pressed Glass, Sunflower, Goblet 16.50
Pressed Glass, Sunflower, Sugar 12.00
Pressed Glass, Sunflower, Water Set, Ruby Stained, Footed, 5 Piece 150.00
Pressed Glass, Sunk Daisy, Celery 12.50
Pressed Glass, Sunk Daisy, Creamer 12.00
Pressed Glass, Sunk Daisy, Goblet 12.00
Pressed Glass, Sunk Daisy, Jar, Cracker, Covered 45.00
Pressed Glass, Sunk Daisy, Tray, Condiment, 7 1/2 In. 7.50
Pressed Glass, Sunk Daisy, Tumbler 15.00
Pressed Glass, Sunk Honeycomb, Bottle, Wine, Ruby Stained 49.00
Pressed Glass, Sunk Honeycomb, Compote, High Standard, Ruby Stained, 8 In. 45.00
Pressed Glass, Sunk Honeycomb, Creamer, Ruby 27.50
Pressed Glass, Sunk Honeycomb, Cup, Punch, Ruby Stained 10.00
Pressed Glass, Sunk Honeycomb, Mug, Ruby Stained 15.00
Pressed Glass, Sunk Honeycomb, Pitcher, Water, Ruby Stained 60.00
Pressed Glass, Sunk Honeycomb, Syrup, Ruby Stained .... 55.00 To 75.00
Sunken Buttons, see Mitered Diamond
Pressed Glass, Sunken Teardrop, Creamer 15.00
Pressed Glass, Sunken Teardrop, Spooner, Footed 5.00
Sunrise, see Rising Sun
Pressed Glass, Swag & Bracket, Compote, Jelly 42.00
Pressed Glass, Swag & Bracket, Compote, Jelly, Green .... 25.00 To 30.00
Pressed Glass, Swag & Bracket, Creamer, Green, Opalescent 45.00
Pressed Glass, Swag & Bracket, Dish, Jelly, Green Opalescent 28.00
Pressed Glass, Swag & Bracket, Sauce, Amethyst 12.00
Pressed Glass, Swag & Bracket, Toothpick, Amethyst, Gold Trim 30.00
Pressed Glass, Swan Cover, Dish, Frosted & Clear Hobnail Base, 7 1/2 In. 59.00
Pressed Glass, Swan, Compote, Scalloped Top, 9 X 6 1/4 In. 25.00
Pressed Glass, Swan, Creamer 32.50
Pressed Glass, Swan, Dish, Pickle 15.00
Pressed Glass, Swan, Sauce, Footed 15.00
Pressed Glass, Swan, Sauce, Footed, 4 1/4 In. 9.50

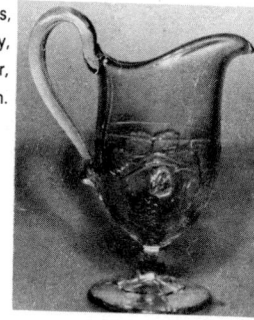

Pressed Glass,
Strawberry,
Creamer,
5 1/2 In.

Pressed Glass,
Stork,
Goblet, Frosted

Pressed Glass, Tandem Diamonds
With Thumbprint, Goblet

Pressed Glass, Swan .... 15.00 To 37.50
Pressed Glass, Swan, Spooner 15.00
Pressed Glass, Swan, Sugar 27.50
Pressed Glass, Sweetheart, Creamer .... 15.00 To 25.00
Pressed Glass, Sweetheart, Creamer, Miniature 9.50
Pressed Glass, Sweetheart, Dish, Arrowhead Shape, Marked Near Cut, 6 In. 14.00
Pressed Glass, Sweetheart, Mug .... 20.00 To 25.00
Pressed Glass, Sweetheart, Spooner, Miniature 32.00
Pressed Glass, Sweetheart, Sugar, Covered 28.00
Pressed Glass, Sweetheart, Sugar, Covered, Miniature 24.00
Pressed Glass, Sweetheart, Sugar, Miniature 95.00
Pressed Glass, Swimming Swan, Pitcher, Water 26.00
Pressed Glass, Swirl With Beaded Band, Goblet 27.50
Pressed Glass, Swirl, Butter 37.00
Pressed Glass, Swirl, Butter, Child's, Covered 22.00
Pressed Glass, Swirl, Candlestick, Miniature, Pair 22.00
Pressed Glass, Swirl, Cruet, Miniature 14.00
Pressed Glass, Swirl, Mug 40.00
Pressed Glass, Swirl, Spooner, Child's, Opalescent 30.00
Pressed Glass, Swirl, Sugar, Child's, Covered 85.00
Pressed Glass, Swirl, Table Set, Miniature, 4 Piece 32.50
Pressed Glass, Swirled Opal, Spooner 8.00
Pressed Glass, Sydney, Saltshaker .... 24.00 To 25.00
Pressed Glass, Tackle Block, Barrel, Goblet, Flint .... 25.00 To 58.00
Pressed Glass, Tackle Block, Goblet, Flint 45.00
Pressed Glass, Tacoma, Butter, Covered, Ruby Stained 45.00
Pressed Glass, Tacoma, Celery, Ruby Stained 35.00
Pressed Glass, Tacoma, Creamer, Ruby Stained 65.00
Pressed Glass, Tacoma, Pitcher, Water, Ruby Stained 7.50
Pressed Glass, Tacoma, Saltshaker 15.00
Pressed Glass, Tacoma, Sauce, Ruby Stained 30.00
Pressed Glass, Tacoma, Spooner, Ruby Stained 40.00
Pressed Glass, Tacoma, Sugar, Covered, Ruby Stained 27.50
Pressed Glass, Tacoma, Tumbler, Ruby Stained 35.00
Pressed Glass, Talisman Ashburton, Goblet, Flint 24.00
Pressed Glass, Tandem Bicycle, Goblet 12.50
Pressed Glass, Tandem Bicycle, Plate, 9 In. 9.50
Pressed Glass, Tandem Diamond & Thumbprint, Goblet ....
  Tape Measure, see Shields
Pressed Glass, Tappan, Butter, Child's, Teal Blue 45.00
Pressed Glass, Tappan, Butter, Covered, Miniature 20.00
Pressed Glass, Tappan, Creamer .... 14.00 To 15.00
Pressed Glass, Tappan, Creamer, Miniature 13.00
Pressed Glass, Tappan, Spooner, Miniature 30.00
Pressed Glass, Tappan, Sugar & Creamer, Blue, Cover, Miniature 75.00
Pressed Glass, Tappan, Table Set, Miniature, 4 Piece 27.50
Pressed Glass, Teardrop & Tassel, Pitcher 75.00
Pressed Glass, Teardrop & Tassel, Pitcher, Water 28.50
Pressed Glass, Teardrop & Tassel, Pitcher, 8 In. .... 6.50 To 8.75
Pressed Glass, Teardrop & Tassel, Sauce 11.00
Pressed Glass, Teardrop & Tassel, Sauce, Blue 42.50
Pressed Glass, Teardrop & Tassel, Spooner, Blue 50.00
Pressed Glass, Teardrop & Tassel, Sugar, Covered 20.00
Pressed Glass, Teardrop & Tassel, Tumbler .... 32.50 To 35.00
Pressed Glass, Teardrop & Tassel, Tumbler, Blue ....
  Teardrop & Thumbprint, see Teardrop
Pressed Glass, Teardrop Flower, Sugar, Light Blue, Covered .... 45.00 To 55.00
Pressed Glass, Teardrop, Compote, Jelly 15.00
Pressed Glass, Teardrop, Goblet 14.00
Pressed Glass, Teardrop, Wine .... 9.50 To 15.00
Pressed Glass, Teardrop, Wine, Etched 6.00
Pressed Glass, Teasel, Goblet .... 12.50 To 15.00
Pressed Glass, Teasel, Goblet, Gold Rim 12.50
Pressed Glass, Teasel, Relish 3.75
Pressed Glass, Teepee, Celery 13.00
Pressed Glass, Teepee, Goblet, Gold 15.00
Pressed Glass, Teepee, Spooner 11.50

Pressed Glass, Teepee, Spooner, Miniature	16.00
Pressed Glass, Tennessee Statehood, Mug, Frosted	40.00
Pressed Glass, Tennessee, Cake Stand, 8 1/2 In.	22.00
Pressed Glass, Tennessee, Mug	29.00
Pressed Glass, Tennessee, Toothpick	6.50 To 18.50
Pressed Glass, Texas Bluebell, Celery, Footed, 8 In.	22.00
Pressed Glass, Texas Bull's-Eye, Goblet	13.00 To 14.00
Pressed Glass, Texas Bull's-Eye, Sugar, Flint	15.00
Pressed Glass, Texas Bull's-Eye, Tumbler	15.00
Pressed Glass, Texas Bull's-Eye, Wine	10.00
Pressed Glass, Texas Campaign, Plate, 7 1/2 In.	40.00
Pressed Glass, Texas Centennial, Plate, With Flags, 8 In.	25.00
Pressed Glass, Texas Centennial, Sherbet, Stemmed	15.00
Pressed Glass, Texas Centennial, Tumbler, Cobalt	6.00
Pressed Glass, Texas Centennial, Tumbler, Iced Tea, Cobalt	7.00
Pressed Glass, Texas, Celery, Oval, 8 1/4 X 6 In.	28.50
Pressed Glass, Texas, Cordial	14.00
Pressed Glass, Texas, Creamer, Individual	12.00 To 15.00
Pressed Glass, Texas, Creamer, Small	10.00
Pressed Glass, Texas, Dish, Olive, Oval	22.00
Pressed Glass, Texas, Eggcup	20.00
Pressed Glass, Texas, Sauce	6.00
Pressed Glass, Texas, Sugar & Creamer	50.00
Pressed Glass, Texas, Sugar & Creamer, Individual, Gold Trim	15.00
Pressed Glass, Texas, Toothpick	10.00
Pressed Glass, Texas, Wine	28.50
Pressed Glass, Texas, Wine, Red & Clear	28.00
Pressed Glass, Thistle Shield, Goblet	18.50
Pressed Glass, Thistle, Cordial, Flint	55.00
Pressed Glass, Thistle, Goblet	16.50 To 18.00
Pressed Glass, Thistle, Goblet, Flint	48.00 To 55.00
Pressed Glass, Thistle, Sauce, Flat	6.50
Pressed Glass, Thistle, Tumbler	25.00
Pressed Glass, Thousand Faces, Cup & Saucer, C.1850	45.00
Pressed Glass, Thousand Faces, Cup & Saucer, Gold Trim	28.00
Pressed Glass, Threaded, Spooner, Miniature	14.00
Pressed Glass, Threaded, Table Set, 3 Piece	55.00
Pressed Glass, Three Bar Waffle, Goblet	7.50
Pressed Glass, Three Dolphins, Toothpick, Blue	45.00
Pressed Glass, Three Elk Medallions, Goblet	50.00
Pressed Glass, Three Face, Butter, Covered	72.50
Pressed Glass, Three Face, Cake Stand, 8 In.	65.00 To 87.50
Pressed Glass, Three Face, Cake Stand, 9 1/4 In.	65.00
Pressed Glass, Three Face, Cake Stand, 10 1/2 In.	110.00
Pressed Glass, Three Face, Celery	85.00
Pressed Glass, Three Face, Celery, Scalloped Rim	60.00
Pressed Glass, Three Face, Champagne	125.00
Pressed Glass, Three Face, Champagne, Etched	135.00
Pressed Glass, Three Face, Champagne, Saucer Type	125.00
Pressed Glass, Three Face, Compote, Covered, 6 X 4 3/4 In.	75.00
Pressed Glass, Three Face, Compote, Covered, 8 1/2 In.	110.00
Pressed Glass, Three Face, Compote, High Standard, 10 In.	62.50
Pressed Glass, Three Face, Compote, 6 In.	35.00
Pressed Glass, Three Face, Compote, 8 1/2 X 8 1/2 In.	67.00
Pressed Glass, Three Face, Creamer	65.00
Pressed Glass, Three Face, Creamer, Etched	35.00
Pressed Glass, Three Face, Creamer, Medallion Spout	72.50
Pressed Glass, Three Face, Creamer, Pedestal	90.00
Pressed Glass, Three Face, Goblet	45.00 To 75.00
Pressed Glass, Three Face, Jar, Cracker	300.00
Pressed Glass, Three Face, Pitcher, Water	200.00
Pressed Glass, Three Face, Salt & Pepper	67.00
Pressed Glass, Three Face, Salt Dip	15.00
Pressed Glass, Three Face, Salt Dip, Frosted	17.50
Pressed Glass, Three Face, Sauce, Footed, 4 In.	17.50
Pressed Glass, Three Face, Sherbet	45.00

Pressed Glass, Three Face, Spooner	65.00
Pressed Glass, Three Face, Sugar, Covered	75.00
Pressed Glass, Three Face, Sugar, Etched	100.00
Pressed Glass, Three Face, Wine	85.00
Pressed Glass, Three In One, Creamer, Individual	7.50
Pressed Glass, Three Panel, Berry Set, 8 Piece	48.50
Pressed Glass, Three Panel, Bowl, Amber, Flint, 8 1/2 In.	25.00
Pressed Glass, Three Panel, Bowl, Cracker, Blue	45.50
Pressed Glass, Three Panel, Bowl, Yellow, Footed, 7 In.	30.00
Pressed Glass, Three Panel, Compote, Amber, Low Standard, 7 1/2 In.	20.00
Pressed Glass, Three Panel, Compote, Amber, 9 In.	22.00
Pressed Glass, Three Panel, Creamer, Amber	27.50 To 43.00
Pressed Glass, Three Panel, Creamer, Blue	45.00
Pressed Glass, Three Panel, Goblet, Amber	26.50
Pressed Glass, Three Panel, Goblet, Blue	40.00
Pressed Glass, Three Panel, Sauce, Amber, Footed	12.00
Pressed Glass, Three Panel, Sauce, Blue, Footed	12.50
Pressed Glass, Three Panel, Sauce, Canary	14.00
Pressed Glass, Three Panel, Sauce, Footed	4.50
Pressed Glass, Three Panel, Spooner	11.00
Pressed Glass, Three Panel, Spooner, Blue	29.50
Pressed Glass, Three Shields, Butter	125.00
Pressed Glass, Three Shields, Butter, Blue	72.00
Pressed Glass, Three Stories, Goblet	14.50 To 20.00
Pressed Glass, Thumbprint Block, Goblet, Gold Rim	8.35
Pressed Glass, Thumbprint Block, Wine	10.00
Pressed Glass, Thumbprint, Banded, Goblet, Flint	16.00
Pressed Glass, Thumbprint, Barrel, Goblet	9.00
Pressed Glass, Thumbprint, Bowl, Etched, Ruby Stained, 6 1/2 In.	50.00
Pressed Glass, Thumbprint, Bowl, Finger, Amber, 4 1/2 X 2 3/4 In.	26.00
Pressed Glass, Thumbprint, Bowl, Footed, 5 In.	40.00
Pressed Glass, Thumbprint, Bowl, Ruby Stained, 7 1/2 In.	50.00
Pressed Glass, Thumbprint, Butter, Covered, Ruby Stained	65.00
Pressed Glass, Thumbprint, Cake Stand, Flint	60.00 To 68.00
Pressed Glass, Thumbprint, Cake Stand, Ruby Stained	250.00
Pressed Glass, Thumbprint, Celery, Flint	100.00
Pressed Glass, Thumbprint, Celery, Ruby Stained	45.00 To 55.00
Pressed Glass, Thumbprint, Celery, 12 In.	45.00
Pressed Glass, Thumbprint, Champagne	70.00
Pressed Glass, Thumbprint, Champagne, Flint	70.00
Pressed Glass, Thumbprint, Compote, Covered, Flint, 6 In.	45.00 To 69.50
Pressed Glass, Thumbprint, Compote, Covered, Flint, 8 1/2 In.	70.00
Pressed Glass, Thumbprint, Compote, Covered, High Standard, Flint, 7 1/4 In.	70.00
Pressed Glass, Thumbprint, Compote, Covered, Low Standard, Flint, 7 1/4 In.	60.00
Pressed Glass, Thumbprint, Compote, Covered, 6 In.	70.00
	69.50

Pressed Glass, Three Faces,
Covered Footed Bowl

Pressed Glass,
Three Faces, Goblet

Pressed Glass, Thumbprint, Pitcher

Pressed Glass, Thumbprint, Compote, High Standard, 5 In., Ruby Stained	50.00
Pressed Glass, Thumbprint, Compote, Jelly, Flint	16.50
Pressed Glass, Thumbprint, Compote, Jelly, Ruby Stained	65.00
Pressed Glass, Thumbprint, Compote, Low Standard, Flint, 8 3/4 In.	72.00
Pressed Glass, Thumbprint, Creamer	90.00
Pressed Glass, Thumbprint, Creamer, Flint	70.00
Pressed Glass, Thumbprint, Creamer, Ruby Stained, Etched	45.00
Pressed Glass, Thumbprint, Creamer, Ruby Stained, 3 In.	25.00
Pressed Glass, Thumbprint, Creamer, 2 Rows, Miniature	9.50
Pressed Glass, Thumbprint, Cup & Saucer, Ruby Stained	55.00
Pressed Glass, Thumbprint, Decanter, Wine	40.00
Pressed Glass, Thumbprint, Dish, Honey, Flint	10.00 To 12.50
Pressed Glass, Thumbprint, Doughnut Stand, 8 In.	13.00
Pressed Glass, Thumbprint, Goblet	12.00
Pressed Glass, Thumbprint, Goblet, Amethestine, 3 Rows	18.00
Pressed Glass, Thumbprint, Goblet, Flint	17.50 To 20.00
Pressed Glass, Thumbprint, Goblet, Knob Stem, Flint	35.00 To 60.00
Pressed Glass, Thumbprint, Goblet, Lady's, Knob Stem, Flint	50.00
Pressed Glass, Thumbprint, Goblet, Ruby Stained	30.00
Pressed Glass, Thumbprint, Goblet, 3 Row	16.00
Pressed Glass, Thumbprint, Nappy, Handled, Ruby Stained, 5 In.	65.00
Pressed Glass, Thumbprint, Pitcher, Milk, Ruby Stained	47.50
Pressed Glass, Thumbprint, Pitcher, Miniature	10.00
Pressed Glass, Thumbprint, Pitcher, Water	85.00
Pressed Glass, Thumbprint, Pitcher, Water, Bakewell Pears, Flint, 8 1/2 In.	175.00
Pressed Glass, Thumbprint, Pitcher, Water, Flint	250.00
Pressed Glass, Thumbprint, Pitcher, Water, Ruby Stained, Bulbous	75.00
Pressed Glass, Thumbprint, Salt & Pepper, Ruby Stained	33.00
Pressed Glass, Thumbprint, Salt, Master	6.50
Pressed Glass, Thumbprint, Salt, Master, Beaded Edge	25.00
Pressed Glass, Thumbprint, Saltshaker, Amber, Sterling Cap, Enamel Floral	25.00
Pressed Glass, Thumbprint, Sauce, Flint, 4 1/4 In.	9.00
Pressed Glass, Thumbprint, Spooner, Flint	35.00 To 45.00
Pressed Glass, Thumbprint, Spooner, Ruby Stained	25.00
Pressed Glass, Thumbprint, Spooner, Ruby Stained, Etched	30.00
Pressed Glass, Thumbprint, Spooner, Ruby Stained, Etched, Sawtooth Rim	35.00
Pressed Glass, Thumbprint, Sugar & Creamer, Ruby Stained	50.00
Pressed Glass, Thumbprint, Sugar, Covered	95.00
Pressed Glass, Thumbprint, Sugar, Covered, Ruby Stained	50.00
Pressed Glass, Thumbprint, Sugar, Flint	30.00
Pressed Glass, Thumbprint, Syrup, Amber	48.00
Pressed Glass, Thumbprint, Syrup, Amber, On Standard	70.00
Pressed Glass, Thumbprint, Tankard, Ruby Stained, 8 3/8 In.	68.00
Pressed Glass, Thumbprint, Tankard, Water, Ruby Stained	65.00
Pressed Glass, Thumbprint, Toothpick, Ruby Stained	21.50 To 25.00
Pressed Glass, Thumbprint, Toothpick, Ruby Stained, Etched	18.00
Pressed Glass, Thumbprint, Tumbler, Footed	38.50 To 45.00
Pressed Glass, Thumbprint, Tumbler, Footed, Flint, 3 1/2 In.	26.00
Pressed Glass, Thumbprint, Tumbler, Ruby Stained	27.50 To 30.00
Pressed Glass, Thumbprint, Tumbler, Ruby Stained, Etched	30.00
Pressed Glass, Thumbprint, Water Set, Blue, Reeded Amber Handle, Enameled	165.00
Pressed Glass, Thumbprint, Wine, Flint	25.00 To 55.00
Pressed Glass, Thumbprint, Wine, Ruby Stained	25.00
Pressed Glass, Tic-Tac-Toe, Goblet	10.00
Pressed Glass, Tidy, Eggcup	9.00 To 12.50
Pressed Glass, Tidy, Goblet	8.50 To 20.00
Pressed Glass, Tidy, Pitcher, Water, Applied Handle	24.00
Pressed Glass, Tile Band, Goblet	10.00
Pressed Glass, Tiny Finecut, Wine	10.00
Pressed Glass, Tiny Finecut, Wine, Green, 4 In.	15.00
Pressed Glass, Tiny Lion, Pitcher, Water	24.00 To 45.00
Pressed Glass, Tivoli, Goblet	7.00
Pressed Glass, Tobin, Goblet	12.00
Pressed Glass, Tobin, Sauce	4.00
Pressed Glass, Tokyo, Bowl, Berry, Opalescent, Scalloped, 8 In.	15.00
Pressed Glass, Tokyo, Butter, Green Opalescent	175.00

Pressed Glass, Tokyo, Dish, Pickle, Blue Opalescent, Oval, Turned-Up Sides 20.00
Pressed Glass, Tokyo, Dish, Pickle, Green Opalescent, Sides Turned Up 25.00
Pressed Glass, Tokyo, Pitcher, Water, Green Opalescent .... 95.00 To 150.00
Pressed Glass, Tokyo, Sugar, Green, Covered, Gold 38.00
Pressed Glass, Tokyo, Tumbler, Green Opalescent 30.00
Pressed Glass, Tokyo, Water Set, Gold Trim, 7 Piece 115.00
Tom Thumb, see Humpty-Dumpty
Pressed Glass, Tong, Celery, Flint 48.00
Pressed Glass, Tong, Sugar, Covered, Flint 80.00
Pressed Glass, Torpedo, Bowl, Etched, 8 1/4 In. 18.00
Pressed Glass, Torpedo, Bowl, 3 3/8 In. 22.00
Pressed Glass, Torpedo, Bowl, 7 1/4 In. 15.00
Pressed Glass, Torpedo, Bowl, 9 1/2 In. 22.00
Pressed Glass, Torpedo, Celery 25.00
Pressed Glass, Torpedo, Celery, Footed 17.50
Pressed Glass, Torpedo, Compote, High Standard, 6 In. 27.00
Pressed Glass, Torpedo, Creamer .... 20.00 To 35.00
Pressed Glass, Torpedo, Goblet .... 28.00 To 29.50
Pressed Glass, Torpedo, Pitcher, Milk .... 47.50 To 50.00
Pressed Glass, Torpedo, Pitcher, Water 56.00
Pressed Glass, Torpedo, Salt & Pepper 25.00
Pressed Glass, Torpedo, Sauce 7.50
Pressed Glass, Torpedo, Sauce, Footed, 3 1/2 In. 7.50
Pressed Glass, Torpedo, Sugar, Covered 32.50
Pressed Glass, Torpedo, Syrup .... 37.50 To 55.00
Pressed Glass, Torpedo, Tray, Water, 9 3/4 In. 42.50
Pressed Glass, Torpedo, Tumbler, Etched 22.50
Pressed Glass, Tree Bark, Tumbler, Amber 15.00
Pressed Glass, Tree Of Life With Hand, Compote, Jelly 45.00
Pressed Glass, Tree Of Life With Hand, Creamer .... 45.00 To 65.00
Pressed Glass, Tree Of Life With Hand, Creamer, Pittsburgh 55.00
Pressed Glass, Tree Of Life, Bowl, Birch Leaf Stem Handles, Portland, 10 In. 11.50
Pressed Glass, Tree Of Life, Bowl, Finger, Amber 20.00
Pressed Glass, Tree Of Life, Bowl, Finger, Blue, Portland 22.50
Pressed Glass, Tree Of Life, Bowl, Finger, Fluted 12.50
Pressed Glass, Tree Of Life, Bowl, Waste, Blue 27.50
Pressed Glass, Tree Of Life, Butter Pat, Amber 12.00
Pressed Glass, Gree Of Life, Cake Stand, Davis, Portland, 10 In. 89.50
Pressed Glass, Tree Of Life, Cake Stand, Samuel Stem, Davis, Portland, 12 In. 150.00
Pressed Glass, Tree Of Life, Cake Stand, Samuel Stem, Davis, 11 1/2 In. 150.00
Pressed Glass, Tree Of Life, Cake Stand, Samuel Stem, Portland, 9 In. 100.00
Pressed Glass, Tree Of Life, Cake Stand, 9 In. 65.00
Pressed Glass, Tree Of Life, Cake Stand, 9 In., Portland 100.00
Pressed Glass, Tree Of Life, Cake Stand, 10 In. 90.00
Pressed Glass, Tree Of Life, Celery .... 25.00 To 45.00
Pressed Glass, Tree Of Life, Celery, Flint 45.00
Pressed Glass, Tree Of Life, Compote, Davis, Portland, 8 1/2 In. .... 57.50 To 65.00
Pressed Glass, Tree Of Life, Compote, Hand Standard, 9 In. 45.00
Pressed Glass, Tree Of Life, Compote, PGCo., Portland, 7 3/4 In. 49.50
Pressed Glass, Tree Of Life, Eggcup, Amber, Portland 25.00
Pressed Glass, Tree Of Life, Epergne, Samuel Stem, Davis, 11 In. 175.00
Pressed Glass, Tree Of Life, Goblet 24.00
Pressed Glass, Tree Of Life, Goblet, Portland .... 22.00 To 32.50
Pressed Glass, Tree Of Life, Pitcher, Water 45.00
Pressed Glass, Tree Of Life, Plate, Boat Center, 8 In. 10.00
Pressed Glass, Tree Of Life, Plate, Bread, Portland 34.50
Pressed Glass, Tree Of Life, Sauce, Amber, 5 In. 11.50
Pressed Glass, Tree Of Life, Sauce, Blue, Leaf Shape, 4 In. 20.00
Pressed Glass, Tree Of Life, Sauce, Leaf Shape 12.50
Pressed Glass, Tree Of Life, Sauce, Portland 12.00
Pressed Glass, Tree Of Life, Sauce, Shell Shape 5.00
Pressed Glass, Tree Of Life, Sugar, Covered, PG&Co. 55.00
Pressed Glass, Tree Of Life, Sugar, Portland 18.50
Pressed Glass, Tree Of Life, Sugar, Silver Plate Holder 40.00
Pressed Glass, Tree Of Life, Tray, Ice Cream, PG&Co. 18.00
Pressed Glass, Tree Of Life, Tumbler, Lemonade 15.00

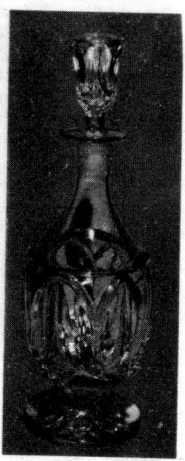

Pressed Glass, Tree Of Life,
Compote, 9 In.

Pressed Glass, Tree Of Life,
Open Compote

Pressed Glass, Tulip & Sawtooth, Decanter

Pressed Glass, Tree Of Life, Wine, Applied Handle	30.00
Pressed Glass, Trellis, Goblet	12.50
Pressed Glass, Trellis, Plate, 9 1/2 In.	5.00
Pressed Glass, Trellis, Plate, 10-Pointed Star Base, 9 1/2 In.	3.75
Pressed Glass, Tremont, Goblet	5.00
Pressed Glass, Triangles & Fans, Goblet	13.50
Pressed Glass, Triangular Prism, Butter, Covered, Flint	35.00
Pressed Glass, Triangular Prism, Celery	30.00
Pressed Glass, Triangular Prism, Celery, Flint	28.00 To 30.00
Pressed Glass, Triangular Prism, Goblet	7.50
Pressed Glass, Triangular Prism, Goblet, Flint	20.00 To 38.00
Trilby, see Valentine	
Pressed Glass, Triple Band & Fan, Goblet	12.00
Pressed Glass, Triple Beaded Band, Sauce, Footed, 3 1/2 In.	4.50
Pressed Glass, Triple Triangle, Creamer, Ruby Flashed	35.00
Pressed Glass, Triple Triangle, Goblet, Ruby Stained	24.50 To 32.50
Pressed Glass, Triple Triangle, Mug, Ruby Stained	12.00
Pressed Glass, Triple Triangle, Pitcher, Water, Ruby Stained	69.50
Pressed Glass, Triple Triangle, Plate, Cake, 11 In.	21.50
Pressed Glass, Triple Triangle, Spooner, Ruby	27.50
Pressed Glass, Triple Triangle, Sugar, Red Stained	30.00
Pressed Glass, Triple Triangle, Tumbler, Ruby Stained	24.00 To 55.00
Pressed Glass, Triple Triangle, Wine, Ruby Stained	25.00
Pressed Glass, Triple Triangle, Wine, Yellow & Clear	35.00
Pressed Glass, Tropical Villa, Celery	22.00
Pressed Glass, Tropical Villa, Celery, Etched	20.00
Pressed Glass, Tropical Villa, Sauce, Etched	6.50
Pressed Glass, Truncated Cube, Wine	5.00
Pressed Glass, Truncated Cube, Wine, Red Flashed	20.00
Pressed Glass, Tub On Sled, Salt, Master, Blue	32.50
Pressed Glass, Tulip & Acanthus, Bowl, Flint, 7 1/2 In.	65.00
Pressed Glass, Tulip & Honeycomb, Bowl, Punch, Miniature	17.00 To 22.00
Pressed Glass, Tulip & Honeycomb, Butter, Child's, Covered	22.50 To 35.00
Pressed Glass, Tulip & Honeycomb, Butter, 4 1/2 In.	30.00
Pressed Glass, Tulip & Honeycomb, Compote, Footed, Miniature, Scalloped Edge	18.00
Pressed Glass, Tulip & Honeycomb, Creamer, Miniature	12.50 To 25.00
Pressed Glass, Tulip & Honeycomb, Dish, Cheese, Domed Cover	35.00
Pressed Glass, Tulip & Honeycomb, Punch Set, Miniature, 7 Piece	75.00 To 95.00
Pressed Glass, Tulip & Honeycomb, Spooner	18.50
Pressed Glass, Tulip & Honeycomb, Spooner, Handled	24.00
Pressed Glass, Tulip & Honeycomb, Spooner, Miniature	10.00 To 25.00
Pressed Glass, Tulip & Honeycomb, Sugar & Creamer	27.50
Pressed Glass, Tulip & Honeycomb, Sugar, Covered, Miniature	20.00 To 25.00
Pressed Glass, Tulip & Honeycomb, Sugar, Miniature	7.00 To 27.00

Pressed Glass, Tulip & Honeycomb, Sugar, Miniature, 2 Handles 10.00
Pressed Glass, Tulip & Honeycomb, Table Set, Miniature, 4 Piece .... 65.00 To 100.00
Pressed Glass, Tulip & Honeycomb, Tureen, Covered, Miniature 18.00
Pressed Glass, Tulip & Sawtooth, Celery 32.00
Pressed Glass, Tulip & Sawtooth, Celery, Footed, Pair 87.00
Pressed Glass, Tulip & Sawtooth, Compote, 8 In. 70.00
Pressed Glass, Tulip & Sawtooth, Decanter, Applied Handle, Flint, Pint 64.00
Pressed Glass, Tulip & Sawtooth, Eggcup .... 22.00 To 45.00
Pressed Glass, Tulip & Sawtooth, Goblet, Flint 42.00
Pressed Glass, Tulip & Sawtooth, Salt, Footed, Pointed Edge 17.00
Pressed Glass, Tulip & Sawtooth, Spooner .... 18.00 To 30.00
Pressed Glass, Tulip & Sawtooth, Sugar, Flint 31.50
Pressed Glass, Tulip & Sawtooth, Tumbler .... 27.00 To 60.00
Pressed Glass, Tulip & Sawtooth, Tumbler, Flint .... 50.00 To 55.00
Pressed Glass, Tulip & Sawtooth, Wine 24.00
Pressed Glass, Tulip Petals, Wine 10.00
Pressed Glass, Tulip With Ovals, Celery 65.00
Pressed Glass, Tulip With Ovals, Celery, Flint 50.00
Pressed Glass, Tulip With Ovals, Pitcher, Water 175.00
Pressed Glass, Tulip With Ovals, Tumbler, Ale, Flint 38.00
Pressed Glass, Tulip With Ribs, Creamer 75.00
Pressed Glass, Tulip With Ribs, Creamer, Flint 70.00
Pressed Glass, Tulip With Ribs, Eggcup, Flint 38.00
Pressed Glass, Tulip With Ribs, Goblet, Flint .... 43.00 To 45.00
Pressed Glass, Tulip With Ribs, Sugar, Rope At Top & Base, Flint 30.00
Pressed Glass, Tulip, Celery .... 12.50 To 23.00
Pressed Glass, Tulip, Compote, Flint, 10 In. 80.00
Pressed Glass, Tulip, Goblet 20.00
Pressed Glass, Tulip, Goblet, Flint 30.00
Pressed Glass, Tulip, Salt Dip 6.00
Pressed Glass, Tulip, Salt Dip, Green 8.50
Pressed Glass, Tulip, Salt Dip, Pink 8.50
Pressed Glass, Tulip, Salt, Master 35.00
Pressed Glass, Turkey Gobbler, Sugar, Covered, Full Figure 50.00
Pressed Glass, Twin Showshoes, Creamer, Child's 15.00
Pressed Glass, Twin Snowshoes, Creamer 25.00
Pressed Glass, Twin Snowshoes, Spooner, Miniature 10.00
Pressed Glass, Two Band, Compote, Footed, Handles, 8 In. 12.50
Pressed Glass, Two Band, Plate, Open Handles, 10 3/4 In. 18.00
Pressed Glass, Two Band, Spooner 18.00
Pressed Glass, Two Panel, Butter, Apple Green 25.00
Pressed Glass, Two Panel, Celery, Blue 20.00
Pressed Glass, Two Panel, Goblet, Amber .... 25.00 To 32.00
Pressed Glass, Two Panel, Pitcher, Water 40.00
Pressed Glass, Two Panel, Pitcher, Water, Amber 47.50
Pressed Glass, Two Panel, Pitcher, Water, Green 47.00
Pressed Glass, Two Panel, Relish, Blue 18.00
Pressed Glass, Two Panel, Salt, Green 13.00
Pressed Glass, Two Panel, Sauce, Green .... 8.00 To 15.00
Pressed Glass, Two Panel, Tray, Water, Handled, Oval 37.50
Pressed Glass, Two Panel, Tumbler, Blue 29.50
Pressed Glass, Two Panel, Wine 14.00
Pressed Glass, U.S.Coin, Bowl, 8 In. 275.00
Pressed Glass, U.S.Coin, Cake Stand, Clear Coins 275.00
Pressed Glass, U.S.Coin, Cake Stand, 10 X 6 1/2 In. 375.00
Pressed Glass, U.S.Coin, Celery 225.00
Pressed Glass, U.S.Coin, Compote, Covered, 1892 Coins, Silver Dollars, 9 In. 400.00
Pressed Glass, U.S.Coin, Compote, Quarters, 7 In. 225.00
Pressed Glass, U.S.Coin, Goblet, Dimes 275.00
Pressed Glass, U.S.Coin, Pitcher, Water, Frosted Dollars, 1892, 9 1/2 In. 400.00
Pressed Glass, U.S.Coin, Plate, Bread, 1892 Dollars, 10 In. 350.00
Pressed Glass, U.S.Coin, Sauce .... 75.00 To 95.00
Pressed Glass, U.S.Coin, Sauce, Footed 165.00
Pressed Glass, U.S.Coin, Spooner 165.00
Pressed Glass, U.S.Coin, Sugar 35.00
Pressed Glass, U.S.Coin, Tumbler 150.00

Pressed Glass, Umbilicated Hobnail, Bowl, Etched, 7 In. 22.00
Pressed Glass, Umbilicated Sawtooth, Eggcup, Flint 35.00
Pressed Glass, Umbilicated Sawtooth, Tumbler, Whiskey, Flint 45.00
Pressed Glass, Umbilicated Sawtooth, Wine, Flint .... 22.00 To 33.00
Pressed Glass, Umbilicated Sawtooth, Wine, 4 1/2 In. 18.50
Pressed Glass, Umbilicated Sawtooth, Eggcup 22.00
Pressed Glass, Utah, Cake Stand, 8 1/2 In. 27.50
Pressed Glass, Utah, Creamer, Rose, Gold Trim 26.00
Pressed Glass, Utah, Pitcher, Water 30.00
Pressed Glass, Valencia Waffle, Celery 25.00
Pressed Glass, Valencia Waffle, Goblet .... 15.00 To 17.50
Pressed Glass, Valencia Waffle, Goblet, Ruby Stained 20.00
Pressed Glass, Valencia Waffle, Plate, Bread 18.50
Pressed Glass, Valencia Waffle, Relish 7.50
Pressed Glass, Valencia Waffle, Sauce 3.00
Pressed Glass, Valencia Waffle, Sauce, Amber, Footed, 4 In. 12.00
Pressed Glass, Valencia Waffle, Sauce, Apple Green, Footed 12.50
Pressed Glass, Valencia Waffle, Sauce, Blue, Footed, 4 In. 15.00
Pressed Glass, Valencia Waffle, Sauce, Ruby Stained 12.00
Pressed Glass, Valencia Waffle, Syrup, Amber 59.00
Pressed Glass, Valencia Waffle, Syrup, Flip-Off Top 29.50
Pressed Glass, Valencia Waffle, Tankard, Water 52.00
Pressed Glass, Valencia Waffle, Tray, Ice Cream, 10 3/4 X 7 3/4 In. 10.00
Pressed Glass, Valentine, Pitcher, Water .... 75.00 To 125.00
Pressed Glass, Variance Panels, Goblet 9.50
Pressed Glass, Vera, Compote, Frosted, 8 In. 42.50
Pressed Glass, Vera, Creamer 20.00
Pressed Glass, Vera, Sugar 25.00
Pressed Glass, Vera, Tumbler, Ruby Stained 25.00
Pressed Glass, Vermont, Butter, Green, Covered 58.00
Pressed Glass, Vernon Honeycomb, Celery, 10 In. 35.00
Pressed Glass, Vernon Honeycomb, Celery, Flint 52.50
Pressed Glass, Vernon, Celery 95.00
Pressed Glass, Vernon, Sugar 24.00
Pressed Glass, Vernon, Sugar, Flint 35.00
Pressed Glass, Versailles, Plate, Blue, 8 3/4 In. 3.75
Pressed Glass, Victoria, Dish, Sweetmeat, Covered, Flint 65.00
Pressed Glass, Vigilant, Tumbler 3.75
Pressed Glass, Viking, Butter .... 33.50 To 65.00
Pressed Glass, Viking, Butter, Covered 65.00
Pressed Glass, Viking, Compote, 8 In. 27.50
Pressed Glass, Viking, Creamer .... 24.00 To 30.00
Pressed Glass, Viking, Pitcher, Water .... 48.00 To 58.00
Pressed Glass, Viking, Salt & Pepper, Blue & Rose 29.00
Pressed Glass, Viking, Sauce, Footed, 4 1/2 In. .... 10.00 To 18.50
Pressed Glass, Viking, Sauce, 4 1/2 In. 5.75
Pressed Glass, Viking, Spooner .... 18.50 To 22.00
Pressed Glass, Viking, Sugar 25.00
Pressed Glass, Viking, Sugar & Creamer 60.00
Pressed Glass, Viking, Sugar, Covered .... 28.00 To 45.00
Pressed Glass, Viking, Swan, Green, 6 In. 15.00
Pressed Glass, Viking, Table Set, 4 Piece 112.00
Pressed Glass, Viking, Tumbler, Juice, Handled 45.00
Pressed Glass, Viking, Vase, Flared Top, 8 In. 28.50
Pressed Glass, Vine & Beads, Spooner 35.00
Pressed Glass, Vine & Beads, Spooner, Child's 21.00
Pressed Glass, Vine & Beads, Table Set, Child's, 4 Piece 100.00
Pressed Glass, Vine & Flower, Creamer, Amber 45.00
Pressed Glass, Vine & Flower, Spooner, Amber 40.00
Pressed Glass, Vine & Flower, Sugar, Amber, Covered 48.00
Pressed Glass, Vintage, Wine, Ruby Stained 25.00
    Virginia, see Galloway
Pressed Glass, Waffle & Thumbprint, Celery .... 65.00 To 95.00
Pressed Glass, Waffle & Thumbprint, Celery, Flint .... 65.00 To 90.00
Pressed Glass, Waffle & Thumbprint, Champagne, Flint .... 40.00 To 68.00
Pressed Glass, Waffle & Thumbprint, Claret, Flint 60.00

Pressed Glass,
Queen Anne,
Covered Compote

Pressed Glass,
Waffle & Thumbprint,
Flip Glass

Pressed Glass, Waffle & Thumbprint, Compote, Pointed Edge, 9 In.	65.00
Pressed Glass, Waffle & Thumbprint, Decanter, Bar Lip, Flint, 1/2 Pint	45.00
Pressed Glass, Waffle & Thumbprint, Decanter, 11 In.High	48.00
Pressed Glass, Waffle & Thumbprint, Dish, Sweetmeat, Covered, Flint	140.00
Pressed Glass, Waffle & Thumbprint, Eggcup	35.00 To 45.00
Pressed Glass, Waffle & Thumbprint, Eggcup, Flint	22.50 To 40.00
Pressed Glass, Waffle & Thumbprint, Flip, Flint	90.00
Pressed Glass, Waffle & Thumbprint, Goblet, Flint	45.00
Pressed Glass, Waffle & Thumbprint, Pitcher, Water, Flint	200.00
Pressed Glass, Waffle & Thumbprint, Spill	45.00
Pressed Glass, Waffle & Thumbprint, Spill, Flint	38.50
Pressed Glass, Waffle & Thumbprint, Spooner	15.00
Pressed Glass, Waffle & Thumbprint, Sugar, Covered, Flint	100.00
Pressed Glass, Waffle & Thumbprint, Tumbler, Footed	60.00
Pressed Glass, Waffle & Thumbprint, Tumbler, Footed, Flint	35.00
Pressed Glass, Waffle & Thumbprint, Wine, Flint, 4 1/2 In.	35.00
Pressed Glass, Waffle With Fan Top, Goblet	15.00
Pressed Glass, Waffle With Spearpoint, Celery	13.00
Pressed Glass, Waffle With Spearpoint, Goblet	10.00 To 12.00
Pressed Glass, Waffle, Butter, Covered	75.00
Pressed Glass, Waffle, Butter, Covered, Flint	60.00
Pressed Glass, Waffle, Butter, Flint	42.50 To 55.00
Pressed Glass, Waffle, Celery	60.00
Pressed Glass, Waffle, Celery, Flint	45.00 To 60.00
Pressed Glass, Waffle, Compote, Covered, 5 In.Diameter	70.00
Pressed Glass, Waffle, Creamer	140.00
Pressed Glass, Waffle, Creamer, Flint	125.00
Pressed Glass, Waffle, Creamer, Flint, 6 3/4 In.	85.00
Pressed Glass, Waffle, Eggcup	26.50
Pressed Glass, Waffle, Eggcup, Flint	33.00
Pressed Glass, Waffle, Goblet, Oswego	15.00
Pressed Glass, Waffle, Mug	7.50
Pressed Glass, Waffle, Plate, Flint, 6 In.	35.00
Pressed Glass, Waffle, Salt, Master	16.00
Pressed Glass, Waffle, Salt, Master, Amethyst, Rectangular, Serrated Rim	90.00
Pressed Glass, Waffle, Salt, Master, Amethyst, Rectangular, Serrated, Flint	80.00
Pressed Glass, Waffle, Salt, Master, Rectangular, Serrated Rim, Flint	16.00
Pressed Glass, Waffle, Saltshaker, Amber	10.00
Pressed Glass, Waffle, Sugar, Covered, Flint	100.00 To 125.00
Pressed Glass, Waffle, Sugar, Flint	125.00
Pressed Glass, Wagonette, Salt, Blue, 3 In.Long	29.50
Pressed Glass, Wahoo, Goblet	14.00
Washboard, see Adonis	
Pressed Glass, Washington & Lafayette, Mug	25.00
Pressed Glass, Washington Centennial, Butter, Covered	75.00
Pressed Glass, Washington Centennial, Cake Stand, 8 3/4 In.	28.00
Pressed Glass, Washington Centennial, Celery	45.00 To 62.50
Pressed Glass, Washington Centennial, Champagne	45.00 To 65.00

Pressed Glass, Washington Centennial, Compote, High Standard, 7 In.	35.00
Pressed Glass, Washington Centennial, Compote, High Standard, 8 In.	35.00
Pressed Glass, Washington Centennial, Compote, Scalloped Rim, 7 7/8 X 6 In.	65.00
Pressed Glass, Washington Centennial, Compote, Scalloped, High Stand, 8 In.	50.00
Pressed Glass, Washington Centennial, Creamer	60.00
Pressed Glass, Washington Centennial, Cup Plate, Star Rim	12.50
Pressed Glass, Washington Centennial, Dish, Pickle	30.00 To 35.00
Pressed Glass, Washington Centennial, Eggcup	36.00 To 48.50
Pressed Glass, Washington Centennial, Goblet	37.50 To 48.50
Pressed Glass, Washington Centennial, Pitcher, Milk	125.00
Pressed Glass, Washington Centennial, Pitcher, Water	62.00
Pressed Glass, Washington Centennial, Plate, Bread, Independence Hall	95.00
Pressed Glass, Washington Centennial, Plate, Bread, Washington Center	95.00
Pressed Glass, Washington Centennial, Plate, Cake	75.00
Pressed Glass, Washington Centennial, Relish, Bears' Claws Handles	65.00
Pressed Glass, Washington Centennial, Relish, Dated	65.00
Pressed Glass, Washington Centennial, Relish, Oval, 7 X 2 In.	16.50
Pressed Glass, Washington Centennial, Salt, Master, Oval	37.50
Pressed Glass, Washington Centennial, Sauce	10.00
Pressed Glass, Washington Centennial, Spooner	40.00 To 45.00
Pressed Glass, Washington Centennial, Sugar	22.50
Pressed Glass, Washington Centennial, Wine	48.00 To 57.50
Pressed Glass, Washington, Celery	65.00 To 75.00
Pressed Glass, Washington, Compote, 8 1/4 In.	39.50
Pressed Glass, Washington, Eggcup	30.00 To 65.00
Pressed Glass, Washington, Eggcup, Flint	58.00
Pressed Glass, Washington, Goblet	70.00
Pressed Glass, Washington, Goblet, Lady's, Flint	82.00
Pressed Glass, Washington, Salt, Master	45.00
Pressed Glass, Water Lily & Cattails, Bonbon, Green Opalescent, 2 Handled	16.00

Pressed Glass,
Wedding Ring, Goblet

Pressed Glass,
Wedding Ring, Syrup, Flint

Pressed Glass, Water Lily & Cattails, Bowl, Clear & Opalescent, 9 1/4 In.	35.00
Pressed Glass, Water Lily & Cattails, Tumbler, Lavender	45.00
Water Lily, see Rose Point Band	
Pressed Glass, Waterfall, Butter, Covered	19.00
Pressed Glass, Way Colonial, Tumbler, Whiskey	45.00
Pressed Glass, Wedding Bells, Butter, Cranberry Flashed	35.00
Pressed Glass, Wedding Bells, Tumbler	16.50
Pressed Glass, Wedding Ring, Goblet	12.50
Pressed Glass, Wedding Ring, Goblet, Flint	48.00 To 54.00
Pressed Glass, Wedding Ring, Syrup, Applied Handle, Tin & Pewter Top, Flint	60.00
Pressed Glass, Wedding Ring, Wine, Flint	22.00
Pressed Glass, Wee Branches, Creamer, Child's	55.00
Pressed Glass, Westmoreland, Celery	13.50
Pressed Glass, Westmoreland, Celery, Scalloped Top, 5 3/4 In.	10.00
Pressed Glass, Westmoreland, Dish, Candy, Covered, Footed	14.70
Pressed Glass, Westmoreland, Eggcup	13.00
Pressed Glass, Westmoreland, Pitcher, Water	25.00

Pressed Glass,
Westward Ho, Covered Dish

Pressed Glass,
Robin, Mug, Blue

Pressed Glass, Westward Ho, Butter, Covered	25.00 To 160.00
Pressed Glass, Westward Ho, Celery	95.00
Pressed Glass, Westward Ho, Celery, Frosted	75.00
Pressed Glass, Westward Ho, Compote, Covered, High Standard, 5 In.	175.00 To 225.00
Pressed Glass, Westward Ho, Compote, Covered, High Standard, 6 In.	135.00
Pressed Glass, Westward Ho, Compote, Covered, High Standard, 8 1/4 In.	175.00
Pressed Glass, Westward Ho, Compote, Covered, High Standard, 9 1/4 In.	350.00
Pressed Glass, Westward Ho, Compote, Covered, Low Standard, Oval, 8 X 5 In.	150.00
Pressed Glass, Westward Ho, Compote, Covered, Low Standard, 5 In.	275.00
Pressed Glass, Westward Ho, Compote, Covered, Low Standard, 7 In.	175.00
Pressed Glass, Westward Ho, Compote, Covered, Oval, 6 3/4 In.	145.00
Pressed Glass, Westward Ho, Compote, Indian Finial, 11 In.	90.00 To 135.00
Pressed Glass, Westward Ho, Compote, Low Standard, 8 3/4 In.	75.00
Pressed Glass, Westward Ho, Compote, Oval, 7 In.	125.00
Pressed Glass, Westward Ho, Compote, 8 In.	48.00
Pressed Glass, Westward Ho, Compote, 11 1/4 X 6 In.	145.00
Pressed Glass, Westward Ho, Cordial, 4 1/2 In.	125.00
Pressed Glass, Westward Ho, Creamer, 7 In.	72.50
Pressed Glass, Westward Ho, Goblet	50.00 To 65.00
Pressed Glass, Westward Ho, Goblet, Frosted	35.00
Pressed Glass, Westward Ho, Pitcher, Water	125.00 To 185.00
Pressed Glass, Westward Ho, Plate, Bread, Frosted Deer Handles	85.00
Pressed Glass, Westward Ho, Sauce, Footed	22.50
Pressed Glass, Westward Ho, Sauce, Frosted, Footed, 4 In.	12.00
Pressed Glass, Westward Ho, Sauce, 3 1/2 In.	17.50
Pressed Glass, Westward Ho, Sauce, 4 In.	20.00
Pressed Glass, Westward Ho, Spooner	65.00
Pressed Glass, Westward Ho, Spooner, Frosted	45.00
Pressed Glass, Westward Ho, Sugar	55.00
Pressed Glass, Westward Ho, Sugar & Creamer	65.00
Pressed Glass, Westward Ho, Wine, 5 In.	125.00
Pressed Glass, Wheat & Barley, Butter, Blue	55.00
Pressed Glass, Wheat & Barley, Cake Stand, 11 1/2 In.	35.00
Pressed Glass, Wheat & Barley, Compote, Jelly	14.50 To 15.00
Pressed Glass, Wheat & Barley, Compote, Jelly, Amber	25.00
Pressed Glass, Wheat & Barley, Creamer	18.50 To 24.00
Pressed Glass, Wheat & Barley, Goblet, Amber	20.00
Pressed Glass, Wheat & Barley, Plate, 7 In.	15.00
Pressed Glass, Wheat & Barley, Sauce, Footed	5.00
Pressed Glass, Wheat & Barley, Spooner	12.50
Pressed Glass, Wheat & Barley, Sugar & Creamer, Covered	38.00
Pressed Glass, Wheat & Barley, Sugar, Covered	18.00 To 38.00
Pressed Glass, Wheat & Barley, Tumbler	14.00
Pressed Glass, Wheat & Barley, Tumbler, Amber	24.00 To 25.00
Pressed Glass, Wheat Sheaf, Goblet	18.00 To 20.00
Pressed Glass, Wheat, Compote, Etched, Covered, 11 1/4 In.	45.00
Pressed Glass, Wheat, Pitcher, Water, Etched, 3 Footed	45.00
Pressed Glass, Wheat, Sauce, Porringer Handle	4.50

Pressed Glass, Whirligig, Bowl, Punch	9.00
Pressed Glass, Whirligig, Bowl, Punch, Miniature	17.50
Pressed Glass, Whirligig, Butter, Miniature	22.00
Pressed Glass, Whirligig, Creamer, Miniature	12.00 To 20.00
Pressed Glass, Whirligig, Cup, Punch	7.00
Pressed Glass, Whirligig, Spooner, Miniature	9.75 To 20.00
Pressed Glass, Whirligig, Sugar, Covered, Miniature	15.00
Pressed Glass, Whirligig, Sugar, Miniature	21.00
Pressed Glass, Whirligig, Table Set, Miniature, 4 Piece	60.00 To 90.00
Pressed Glass, Whirling Star, Bowl, Punch, Millersburg, Miniature	23.50
Pressed Glass, Whirling Star, Butter, Covered, Miniature	20.00 To 35.00
Pressed Glass, Whirling Star, Butter, Miniature	25.00
Pressed Glass, Whirling Star, Creamer, Child's	18.00
Pressed Glass, Whirling Star, Spooner, Child's	16.00
Pressed Glass, Whirling Star, Spooner, Millersburg, Miniature	10.00
Pressed Glass, Whirling Star, Table Set, Miniature, 3 Piece	65.00
Pressed Glass, Whitton, Goblet	12.50 To 22.00
Pressed Glass, Whitton, Spooner	12.00
Pressed Glass, Whitton, Tumbler	15.00
Pressed Glass, Wild Bouquet, Bowl, Berry, Opalescent Blue, 9 1/4 In.	78.00
Pressed Glass, Wild Fern, Goblet	7.50 To 12.00
Pressed Glass, Wild Rose With Bowknot, Tumbler, Frosted	18.50
Pressed Glass, Wild Turkey, Salt	12.50
Pressed Glass, Wildflower, Bowl, Amber, Footed, 8 In.	22.50
Pressed Glass, Wildflower, Bowl, Apple Green, Footed, 6 In.	15.00
Pressed Glass, Wildflower, Bowl, Apple Green, Footed, 7 In.	20.00
Pressed Glass, Wildflower, Bowl, Apple Green, Square, 6 In.	10.00
Pressed Glass, Wildflower, Bowl, Apple Green, Square, 8 In.	15.00
Pressed Glass, Wildflower, Bowl, Square, 7 In.	10.00
Pressed Glass, Wildflower, Bowl, Waste	20.00
Pressed Glass, Wildflower, Bowl, Waste, Amber	27.50
Pressed Glass, Wildflower, Bowl, Waste, Apple Green	27.50
Pressed Glass, Wildflower, Butter	23.00
Pressed Glass, Wildflower, Butter, Apple Green, Covered	35.00
Pressed Glass, Wildflower, Butter, Collared Base	27.00
Pressed Glass, Wildflower, Butter, Covered	18.50 To 35.00
Pressed Glass, Wildflower, Cake Stand, Amber, 9 In.	34.50
Pressed Glass, Wildflower, Cake Stand, Apple Green	52.00
Pressed Glass, Wildflower, Compote, Apple Green, Covered, Low Standard, 8 In.	37.50
Pressed Glass, Wildflower, Compote, Blue, Covered, 9 X 6 In.	50.00
Pressed Glass, Wildflower, Compote, Blue, 7 X 4 1/4 In.	43.50
Pressed Glass, Wildflower, Compote, 7 1/2 X 7 1/2 In.	18.50
Pressed Glass, Wildflower, Creamer	12.00 To 20.00
Pressed Glass, Wildflower, Creamer, Yellow	35.00
Pressed Glass, Wildflower, Goblet	17.50
Pressed Glass, Wildflower, Goblet, Amber	25.00
Pressed Glass, Wildflower, Goblet, Blue	25.00
Pressed Glass, Wildflower, Nappy, 5 3/4 In.	8.00
Pressed Glass, Wildflower, Pitcher, Water	12.50
Pressed Glass, Wildflower, Pitcher, Water, Amber	34.50
Pressed Glass, Wildflower, Pitcher, Water, Apple Green	38.00
Pressed Glass, Wildflower, Plate, Amber, Square, 10 In.	20.00
Pressed Glass, Wildflower, Plate, Cake, 10 In.	12.00
Pressed Glass, Wildflower, Plate, Square, 10 In.	12.50
Pressed Glass, Wildflower, Plate, 10 In.	12.50
Pressed Glass, Wildflower, Sauce, Amber, Footed, 4 In.	8.50
Pressed Glass, Wildflower, Sauce, Amber, Square, 4 In.	6.00
Pressed Glass, Wildflower, Sauce, Apple Green, Footed, 4 In.	10.00
Pressed Glass, Wildflower, Sauce, Apple Green, 4 In.	7.50
Pressed Glass, Wildflower, Sauce, Footed	5.00
Pressed Glass, Wildflower, Sauce, 4 In.	7.50
Pressed Glass, Wildflower, Spooner	7.50 To 12.00
Pressed Glass, Wildflower, Spooner, Green	22.00
Pressed Glass, Wildflower, Sugar	15.00 To 25.00
Pressed Glass, Wildflower, Sugar, Blue	28.00

Pressed Glass, Wildflower, Syrup, Apple Green .... 55.00 To 72.50
Pressed Glass, Wildflower, Table Set, 3 Piece 48.00
Pressed Glass, Wildflower, Tray, Apple Green, 8 X 11 In. 25.00
Pressed Glass, Wildflower, Tray, Blue, 9 1/4 X 4 In. 27.50
Pressed Glass, Wildflower, Tray, Cake, Metal Handle, Oblong 48.50
Pressed Glass, Wildflower, Tray, Water, Amber .... 35.00 To 37.50
Pressed Glass, Wildflower, Tray, Water, Apple Green, Oval 42.50
Pressed Glass, Wildflower, Tray, Water, Blue, Oval 35.00
Pressed Glass, Wildflower, Tumbler 15.00
Pressed Glass, Wildflower, Tumbler, Amber 24.00
Pressed Glass, Wildflower, Tumbler, Apple Green 24.00
Pressed Glass, Willow Oak, Bowl, Amber, 7 In. 20.00
Pressed Glass, Willow Oak, Bowl, Blue, 7 In. 25.00
Pressed Glass, Willow Oak, Bowl, Covered, 7 In. 12.50
Pressed Glass, Willow Oak, Bowl, Ice 38.00
Pressed Glass, Willow Oak, Bowl, Waste, Amber 30.00
Pressed Glass, Willow Oak, Bowl, Waste, Blue 35.00
Pressed Glass, Willow Oak, Butter .... 25.00 To 35.00
Pressed Glass, Willow Oak, Butter, Covered .... 23.50 To 34.50
Pressed Glass, Willow Oak, Cake Stand, 9 In. 15.00
Pressed Glass, Willow Oak, Cake Stand, 9 1/4 In.Diameter 16.00
Pressed Glass, Willow Oak, Compote, Amber, High Standard, 7 In. 30.00
Pressed Glass, Willow Oak, Compote, Covered, High Standard, 6 1/4 In. 37.50
Pressed Glass, Willow Oak, Creamer .... 17.50 To 25.00
Pressed Glass, Willow Oak, Creamer, Amber .... 28.00 To 43.00
Pressed Glass, Willow Oak, Creamer, Footed 22.00
Pressed Glass, Willow Oak, Goblet 20.00
Pressed Glass, Willow Oak, Goblet, Amber 30.00
Pressed Glass, Willow Oak, Goblet, Blue 35.00
Pressed Glass, Willow Oak, Mug 20.00
Pressed Glass, Willow Oak, Mug, Amber 25.00
Pressed Glass, Willow Oak, Pitcher, Milk .... 20.00 To 30.00
Pressed Glass, Willow Oak, Pitcher, Milk, Amber 37.50
Pressed Glass, Willow Oak, Pitcher, Water .... 37.50 To 38.75
Pressed Glass, Willow Oak, Pitcher, Water, Amber 55.00
Pressed Glass, Willow Oak, Pitcher, Water, Blue 50.00
Pressed Glass, Willow Oak, Plate, Amber, 7 In. 35.00
Pressed Glass, Willow Oak, Plate, Blue, 7 In. 18.00
Pressed Glass, Willow Oak, Plate, Bread 32.00
Pressed Glass, Willow Oak, Plate, Bread, Blue 20.00
Pressed Glass, Willow Oak, Plate, 7 In. 20.00
Pressed Glass, Willow Oak, Saltshaker 16.00
Pressed Glass, Willow Oak, Sauce, Blue 14.00
Pressed Glass, Willow Oak, Sauce, Light Blue, Side Handled .... 15.00 To 16.50
Pressed Glass, Willow Oak, Spooner .... 14.50 To 35.00
Pressed Glass, Willow Oak, Sugar .... 14.50 To 25.00
Pressed Glass, Willow Oak, Sugar & Creamer, Cover 55.00
Pressed Glass, Willow Oak, Sugar, Covered 35.00
Pressed Glass, Willow Oak, Tray, Oval, 10 1/2 In. 29.50
Pressed Glass, Willow Oak, Tray, Water .... 12.50 To 23.00
Pressed Glass, Willow Oak, Tumbler .... 15.00 To 23.75
Pressed Glass, Willow Oak, Tumbler, Amber 25.00
Pressed Glass, Willow Oak, Tumbler, Blue 30.00
Pressed Glass, Willow Oak, Water Set, 5 Piece 105.00
Pressed Glass, Windflower, Bowl, Cobalt, 8 In. 37.50
Pressed Glass, Windflower, Butter 55.00
Pressed Glass, Windflower, Butter, Covered 48.00
Pressed Glass, Windflower, Compote, Covered, Low Standard, 8 1/2 In. 60.00
Pressed Glass, Windflower, Creamer .... 20.00 To 35.00
Pressed Glass, Windflower, Eggcup .... 22.00 To 25.00
Pressed Glass, Windflower, Goblet, Amber 35.00
Pressed Glass, Windflower, Goblet, 5 3/4 In. 16.50
Pressed Glass, Windflower, Plate, Apple Green, Square, 9 3/4 In. 27.00
Pressed Glass, Windflower, Plate, Apple Green, Square, 10 In. 24.00
Pressed Glass, Windflower, Relish, Oblong 18.00
Pressed Glass, Windflower, Salt, Master 24.00

Pressed Glass, Windflower, Spooner	17.00
Pressed Glass, Windflower, Sugar	26.50
Pressed Glass, Windflower, Sugar, Covered	45.00 To 50.00
Pressed Glass, Windflower, Tray, Water, Apple Green	35.00
Pressed Glass, Windflower, Tumbler	45.00
Pressed Glass, Windflower, Wine	38.00

Winona, see Barred Hobnail
Wisconsin, see Beaded Dewdrop

Pressed Glass, Worcester, Banded, Goblet, Flint	24.00
Pressed Glass, Worcester, Belted, Champagne, Flint	20.00
Pressed Glass, Worcester, Belted, Eggcup, Flint	25.00
Pressed Glass, Worcester, Belted, Goblet, Flint	22.00 To 24.00
Pressed Glass, Worcester, Belted, Tumbler, Footed	45.00
Pressed Glass, Worcester, Belted, Tumbler, Footed, Flint	30.00 To 35.00
Pressed Glass, Worcester, Belted, Tumbler, Whiskey, Flint	25.00
Pressed Glass, Wreath & Shell, Spooner, Blue Opalescent	40.00

Wycliff, see Scroll with Star

Pressed Glass, Wyoming, Cake Stand, 8 3/4 In.	16.50
Pressed Glass, X-Ray, Compote, Jelly, Green	28.00
Pressed Glass, X-Ray, Sauce, Gold Trim	5.00 To 6.00
Pressed Glass, X-Ray, Spooner	16.00
Pressed Glass, X-Ray, Sugar, Covered, Pink Floral Enamel	22.50
Pressed Glass, X-Ray, Sugar, Green, Covered, Gold Trim	42.00
Pressed Glass, X-Ray, Toothpick, Green	30.00
Pressed Glass, X-Ray, Toothpick, Green, Gold Trim	35.00

Yale, see Crow's-Foot

Pressed Glass, Yankee Doodle, Tumbler, Etched	18.50
Pressed Glass, Yoked Loop, Compote, Low, Scalloped Rim, 8 1/2 In., Flint	30.00
Pressed Glass, Yoked Loop, Compote, Scalloped Top, Flint, 8 X 3 1/2 In.	25.00
Pressed Glass, Yoked Loop, Creamer	75.00
Pressed Glass, Yoked Loop, Creamer, Flint	75.00
Pressed Glass, Yoked Loop, Goblet, Flint	16.50 To 22.00
Pressed Glass, Yoked Loop, Sugar, Covered, Flint	90.00
Pressed Glass, Yoked Loop, Sugar, Flint	30.00
Pressed Glass, Yoked Loop, Tumbler, Whiskey, Flint	25.00
Pressed Glass, Yoked Loop, Tumbler, Whiskey, Handled, Flint	30.00
Pressed Glass, York Herringbone, Pitcher, Water	20.00
Pressed Glass, York Herringbone, Spooner, Ruby Stain	24.00
Pressed Glass, Yuma Loop, Goblet	18.00
Pressed Glass, Yuma Loop, Spooner	9.50 To 12.50
Pressed Glass, Yuma Loop, Spooner, Flint	12.50
Pressed Glass, Zipper Slash, Celery, Tall	14.00
Pressed Glass, Zipper Slash, Celery, Etched, 6 1/2 In.	14.00
Pressed Glass, Zipper Slash, Creamer, Applied Handle	22.50
Pressed Glass, Zipper Slash, Goblet	8.50
Pressed Glass, Zipper Slash, Goblet, Ruby & Clear	32.50
Pressed Glass, Zipper Slash, Spooner, Etched	20.00
Pressed Glass, Zipper, Box, Tin Lid, 2 In.	2.00
Pressed Glass, Zipper, Creamer	11.00 To 15.00
Pressed Glass, Zipper, Cruet, Vinegar	15.00
Pressed Glass, Zipper, Cup, Punch, Pedestal	12.00
Pressed Glass, Zipper, Dish, Cheese	35.00
Pressed Glass, Zipper, Goblet	14.00
Pressed Glass, Zipper, Jar, Dresser, Art Nouveau Lady On Sterling Lid	20.00
Pressed Glass, Zipper, Pitcher, Applied Handle, 9 In.	18.50
Pressed Glass, Zipper, Pitcher, Milk, Blue	55.00
Pressed Glass, Zipper, Pitcher, Water	15.00
Pressed Glass, Zipper, Pitcher, Water, Amber	45.00
Pressed Glass, Zipper, Spooner, Footed	12.00
Pressed Glass, Zipper, Sugar	15.00
Pressed Glass, Zipper, Sugar & Creamer, 4 1/2 In.	17.50

Zippered Block, see Cryptic

Pressed Glass, 77, Pitcher, Ruby Stained, Thompson, Miniature	22.00
Pressed Glass, 100-Eye, Goblet	7.00
Pressed Glass, 100-Eye, Sauce, Amber, Footed	10.00
Pressed Glass, 100-Eye, Wine, Amber	19.00

Pressed Glass, 100-Leaved Ivy, Compote, Jelly	10.00 To 13.50
Pressed Glass, 100-Leaved Rose, Butter, Covered	18.00
Pressed Glass, 100-Leaved Rose, Creamer	15.00
Pressed Glass, 100-Leaved Rose, Spooner	12.00
Pressed Glass, 101, Butter, Covered	20.00 To 37.50
Pressed Glass, 101, Creamer	17.00 To 37.50
Pressed Glass, 101, Creamer, Footed	15.00
Pressed Glass, 101, Goblet	12.00 To 15.00
Pressed Glass, 101, Plate, Bread, 8 In.	18.00
Pressed Glass, 101, Plate, 7 In.	12.00
Pressed Glass, 101, Plate, 8 1/2 In.	42.50
Pressed Glass, 101, Spooner	15.00
Pressed Glass, 101, Sugar, Covered	21.50
Pressed Glass, 251, Spooner, Blue Opalescent, Jefferson	48.00
Pressed Glass, 500, Berry Set, Blue, Gold Trim, King, 5 Piece	95.00
Pressed Glass, 808, Bowl, 8 In.	9.00
Pressed Glass, 808, Celery	18.50
Pressed Glass, 808, Plate, Bread, 9 In.	24.00
Pressed Glass, 808, Plate, 5 1/2 In.	5.00
Pressed Glass, 808, Plate, 8 In.	7.50
Pressed Glass, 808, Plate, 9 In.	16.50
Pressed Glass, 808, Wine	12.50 To 13.50
Pressed Glass, 808, Wine, Albany	19.50
Pressed Glass, 1,000-Eye Band, Goblet	12.00 To 24.00
Pressed Glass, 1,000-Eye, Box, Cigarette, Covered, Turtle Shape	18.50
Pressed Glass, 1,000-Eye, Celery, Amber, Knob Stem	35.00
Pressed Glass, 1,000-Eye, Compote, Amber, Scalloped, 3 Knob Stem, 7 1/4 In.	27.50
Pressed Glass, 1,000-Eye, Compote, High Standard, Square, 8 In.	45.00
Pressed Glass, 1,000-Eye, Compote, Low Standard, 7 1/2 In.	35.00
Pressed Glass, 1,000-Eye, Compote, Low Standard, 8 1/4 In.	44.00
Pressed Glass, 1,000-Eye, Compote, Three Knob, Amber, 7 1/4 In.	27.50
Pressed Glass, 1,000-Eye, Compote, 10 In.	29.50
Pressed Glass, 1,000-Eye, Creamer	40.00
Pressed Glass, 1,000-Eye, Eggcup, Blue	45.00
Pressed Glass, 1,000-Eye, Goblet, Amber	18.00
Pressed Glass, 1,000-Eye, Goblet, Blue	35.00
Pressed Glass, 1,000-Eye, Goblet, Canary	18.00
Pressed Glass, 1,000-Eye, Goblet, Knob Stem	25.00
Pressed Glass, 1,000-Eye, Lamp Base, Electric, 8 In.	20.00
Pressed Glass, 1,000-Eye, Mug, Amber	20.00
Pressed Glass, 1,000-Eye, Mug, Apple Green, 3 1/2 In.	20.00
Pressed Glass, 1,000-Eye, Mug, Blue	12.50
Pressed Glass, 1,000-Eye, Pitcher, Amber, Applied Handle, Bulbous, 7 In.	24.00
Pressed Glass, 1,000-Eye, Plate, Bread	16.00
Pressed Glass, 1,000-Eye, Plate, Cake, Amber	48.00
Pressed Glass, 1,000-Eye, Plate, Cake, Green	48.00
Pressed Glass, 1,000-Eye, Plate, Folded Corners, 8 In.	8.50
Pressed Glass, 1,000-Eye, Plate, Folded Corners, 10 In.	12.50
Pressed Glass, 1,000-Eye, Plate, Handled, Square, 8 In.	10.00
Pressed Glass, 1,000-Eye, Plate, Handled, Square, 10 In.	15.00
Pressed Glass, 1,000-Eye, Plate, Square, 8 In.	12.50
Pressed Glass, 1,000-Eye, Plate, 10 In.	18.50
Pressed Glass, 1,000-Eye, Platter, Amber, Square, 10 In.	25.00
Pressed Glass, 1,000-Eye, Salt & Pepper	20.00
Pressed Glass, 1,000-Eye, Sauce, Amber	9.00
Pressed Glass, 1,000-Eye, Sauce, 3 5/8 In.	12.00
Pressed Glass, 1,000-Eye, Sherbet, Opalescent, Footed	12.50
Pressed Glass, 1,000-Eye, Spooner, Apple Green	28.00
Pressed Glass, 1,000-Eye, Spooner, Knob Stem	35.00
Pressed Glass, 1,000-Eye, Spooner, Green, 3 Knob Stem	32.50
Pressed Glass, 1,000-Eye, Sugar, Apple Green, Knob Base	30.00
Pressed Glass, 1,000-Eye, Sugar, Covered	45.00
Pressed Glass, 1,000-Eye, Sugar, Green, Covered, Knob Stem	57.50
Pressed Glass, 1,000-Eye, Tray, Apple Green, Oval, 14 In.	47.00
Pressed Glass, 1,000-Eye, Twine Holder, Amber, 4 X 4 In.	45.00
Pressed Glass, 1,000-Eye, Vase, Fan, 8 X 9 In.	25.00

Print, see also Store, Poster, Print

Print, Ackermann, Promenade Dresses, London, 1809, Engraving, Color, 9 X 6 In. 10.00
Print, Alken, Breaking Cover, Framed, 9 1/2 X 12 In. 75.00
Print, Alken, Full Cry, Framed, 9 1/2 X 12 In. 75.00
Print, Alken, Ipswich, Preparing To Start, Framed, 18 X 22 In. 150.00
Print, Alken, The Death, Framed, 9 1/2 X 12 In. 75.00
Print, Alken, The Meeting, Framed, 9 1/2 X 12 In. 75.00
Print, Andersonville Stockade, Jerklapp, 1903, Color, 24 X 17 In. 35.00
Print, Baker, Abraham Lincoln, Lithograph, Oval Walnut Frame, 36 X 32 In. 350.00
Print, Bartlett, Cape Split, Black & White, 7 X 5 In. 9.50
Print, Bartlett, Centre Harbour, Lake Winnipisseogee, 1838, 7 X 4 3/4 In. 12.50
Print, Bartlett, Marketplace, Quebec, Black & White, 7 X 5 In. 9.50
Print, Bartlett, Mill On Rideau River Near Bytown, Black & White, 7 X 5 In. 9.50
Print, Bartlett, View Near Anthonys Nose, 1839, 7 X 4 3/4 In. 12.50
Print, Battle Of Manila, 1898, Smith, 1898, Lithograph, Color, 20 X 28 In. 65.00
Print, Charlotte Becker, When The Sandman Comes, 1929, 14 X 18 In. 4.00
Print, Christy, Awful Predicament, 1900, Black & White, 15 X 12 In. 10.00
Print, Christy, Cotillion, The, 1909 .... 16.00
Print, Condie, John Adams, 7 1/2 X 9 In. 100.00
  Print, Currier & Ives, see Currier & Ives
  Print, Currier, see Currier
Print, Custer's Last Fight, Budweiser, 1952, Framed, 30 1/2 X 20 1/2 In. 16.00
Print, Fangel, Sleeping Baby, In Chair, Bottle, 15 X 19 In. 5.00
Print, Fraser, Appeal To The Great Spirits, C.1930, Lithograph, Color, 16 In. 2.25
Print, Fraser, End Of The Trail, C.1930, Lithograph, Color, 12 X 16 In. 2.25
Print, Fry, Count Von Bismark, Engraving, Framed, 12 X 7 In. .... 100.00 To 125.00
Print, George Washington, Maurin, Paris, Lithograph, Color, 16 1/2 X 12 In. 100.00
Print, Girl With Doll, Fr.Brundage, 1899, Calendar, Color, Framed, 12 X 18 In. 20.00
Print, Godey, Fashion For May 1839, 9 1/2 X 7 1/2 In. 15.00
Print, Godey, Group Of Croquet Players, 11 1/2 X 15 In.Framed 14.00
Print, Grant, Swordfisherman, C.1875, Lithograph, 11 X 10 In. 125.00
Print, Gutman, Little Bit Of Heaven, Gold Frame, 15 X 15 In. 7.50
Print, Hacker, Enchantment, C.1900, Lithograph, Color, 14 X 22 In. 4.50
Print, Harnett, The Old Violin, 1887, Lithograph, Color, 35 X 24 In. 300.00
Print, Honore Daumier, La Charivari, 1844, Lithograph, 9 X 12 In. 50.00
Print, Icart, Girl & Greyhounds, Etching, 26 X 16 In. 225.00
Print, In Time For The Coach, Harris, 1848, Engraving, Color, 30 X 22 In. 50.00
Print, Japanese Woodblock, Samurai Warriors, C.1900, 14 X 9 1/4 In. 35.00
Print, Japanese, Hokusai-Oban Yoko-E, Great Wave 1800.00
Print, Johnson, Great Locofoco Juggernaut, 1838, 4 X 9 1/2 In. 200.00
Print, Lewis, Lady Marie, Hand Colored, Oval Mahogany Frame, 9 X 7 In. 12.00
Print, Lincoln Family, Copy Lincoln Museum, Steel Engraving, 31 X 24 In. 975.00
Print, Lodge, Attack On Bunker's Hill, 1782, Engraving, Color, 12 X 8 3/8 In. 110.00
Print, Map, British North America, Arrowsmith, 1846, 25 X 21 In. 50.00
Print, Map, French Florida, N.Bellin, C.1744, 7 1/2 X 10 In. 50.00

Print, Japanese,
Hokusai-Oban Yoko-E,
Great Wave

Print, Map, Georgia & Alabama, Johnson, 1863, Color, 22 X 16 In.	20.00
Print, Map, Indian Agencies In Nebraska, Colton, C.1870, 8 X 7 1/2 In.	50.00
Print, Map, Lake George, N.Y., Stoddard, 1906, Hydrographic, 8 Ft.X 16 In.	150.00
Print, Map, North America, S.A.Mitchell, Phila., 1860, Color, 14 X 11 In.	20.00
Print, Map, Northern Virginia, Corbett, 1861, Lithograph, Hoen, 22 X 26 In.	25.00
Print, Map, Panorama Of The Mississippi Valley, Magnus & Co., 1862, 26 In.	22.50
Print, Map, Philadelphia, 1876, Gray, Centennial Grounds, 25 X 17 In.	25.00
Print, Map, Plan Of Philadelphia, S.A.Mitchell, 1860, Color, 11 X 13 In.	17.50
Print, Map, Territory Of Utah, Froiseth, 1870, Hand Colored, 17 X 14 In.	74.50
Print, Map, U.S.& Territories, 1867, Land Office, Canvas Back, 56 X 29 In.	50.00
Print, Map, U.S.Military, Johnson, 1861, Color, 25 X 18 In.	35.00
Print, Map, United States, John Rapkin, 1864, Engraved, Color, 10 X 6 In.	22.50
Print, Map, Washington & North Carolina, Allis Co., 1863, 12 X 10 1/2 In.	350.00
Print, Map, 150 Miles Around Richmond, Magnus & Co., N.Y., 1864, 34 X 28 In.	22.50
Print, McLean, Jeff's Last Skedaddle, 1865, Lithograph, 20 X 14 In.	54.50
Print, Mucha, Monaco-Monte Carlo, 1879, 27 X 41 In.	2000.00
Print, Norman Rockwell, Barbershop Quartet, Lithograph, 28 1/2 X 22 In.	550.00
Print, Nutting, A Birch Approach, Framed, 16 X 13 In.	18.00 To 21.50
Print, Nutting, A Pink Bower, Framed, 15 In.	15.00
Print, Nutting, A Third Person Arriving, 1909, 9 1/2 X 12 1/2 In.	20.00
Print, Nutting, Bag & Baggage, Color, 16 X 13 1/2 In.	30.00
Print, Nutting, Birches, Framed, 7 X 5 In.	7.50
Print, Nutting, Bridesmaid Procession, Outdoor, Framed, 18 X 10 1/2 In.	20.00
Print, Nutting, Coming Out Of Rosa, Framed, Matted, 11 X 13 In.	22.50
Print, Nutting, Five O'Clock, Cottage Scene, Framed, 21 In.	21.00
Print, Nutting, Goose Chase Quilt, Interior, Framed, 4 3/4 X 2 1/2 In.	30.00
Print, Nutting, Honeymoon Drive, Framed, 7 1/2 X 9 1/2 In.	20.00
Print, Nutting, Honeymoon Drive, Framed, 18 1/2 X 15 1/2 In.	15.00
Print, Nutting, Jane, Framed, 9 1/2 X 4 1/2 In.	35.00
Print, Nutting, Larkspur Lady In Garden, Color, Framed, 20 1/2 X 17 1/2 In.	22.00
Print, Nutting, Larkspur, Framed, 16 X 14 In.	15.00
Print, Nutting, Life Of The Golden Age, The, Color, Framed	25.00
Print, Nutting, Pink Flowering Trees Reflected In Water, Framed, 5 X 7 In.	14.00
Print, Nutting, River Scene, 10 X 7 1/2 In.	8.00
Print, Nutting, Shore Acres, Framed, 19 X 10 In.	15.00
Print, Nutting, The Going Forth Of Betty, 9 1/2 X 7 1/2 In.	50.00
Print, Nutting, The Maple Sugar Cupboard, Interior, 10 X 7 In.	60.00
Print, Nutting, The Silent Shore, Framed, 18 X 15 In.	19.00
Print, Nutting, The Swimming Pool, Framed, 15 1/2 X 12 In.	17.00
Print, Nutting, The Way Through The Orchard, 17 X 14 In.	15.00
Print, Nutting, Two Ladies At Tea, Interior, Framed, 12 3/4 X 8 1/2 In.	30.00
Print, Nutting, Two Ladies In Bedroom, 1907, Framed, 11 X 8 1/2 In.	28.00
Print, Nutting, Very Satisfactory, Framed, 14 X 17 In.	24.00
Print, Parrish, Aladdin, 16 X 12 In.	15.00
Print, Parrish, Atlas, 16 X 12 In.	15.00
Print, Parrish, Bellerophon, 16 X 12 In.	15.00
Print, Parrish, Cassim, 16 X 12 In.	15.00
Print, Parrish, Community Plate, 2 Squires, 1918, 8 X 11 In.	10.00
Print, Parrish, Djer-Kiss Toilet Water, Girl In Swing, 11 X 14 In.	15.00
Print, Parrish, Djer-Kiss Toilet Water, Girl In Swing, 1922, 8 X 11 In.	10.00
Print, Parrish, Dreaming, 15 X 9 In.	10.00
Print, Parrish, Edison Mazda, Girl In Mountains, 1918, 8 X 11 In.	10.00
Print, Parrish, Garden Of Allah, Framed, 10 X 19 In.	35.00
Print, Parrish, Jell-O, King & Queen May Eat Thereof, 1922, 12 X 16 In.	15.00
Print, Parrish, King Albert's Book, Dies Irae On Horse, 1919, 9 X 11 In.	12.00
Print, Parrish, Old King Cole, Art Nouveau Oak Frame, 25 1/2 X 7 In.	22.50
Print, Parrish, Pandora's Box, 16 X 12 In.	15.00
Print, Parrish, Polly Put The Kettle On For Jell-O, 1924, 12 X 16 In.	15.00
Print, Parrish, Queen Gulnare, 16 X 12 In.	15.00
Print, Parrish, Sea Nymphs, 16 X 12 In.	15.00
Print, Parrish, The Canyon, Framed, 16 X 13 In.	30.00
Print, Peltro, Naval Engagement, John Paul Jones Squadron, 1781, 18 In.	375.00
Print, Prang, Basket Of Cherries, 1893, Adelaide Palmer, Lithograph, 21 In.	20.00
Print, Prang, Battle Of Antietam, 1887, Lithograph, Color, 21 1/4 X 15 In.	35.00
Print, Prang, Battle Of Antietam, 1887, Lithograph, Color, 23 X 17 In.	35.00
Print, Prang, Battle Of Kenesaw Mountain, 1887, Lithograph, Color, 21 In.	35.00

Print, Prang, Birch Tree & Water Scene, 1906, Gold Frame, 12 1/2 X 7 1/2 In.	10.00
Print, Prang, Bull Frog, 1883, Chromolithograph, 5 X 7 3/4 In.	7.00
Print, Prang, Butterflies, 1883, Chromolithograph, 5 X 7 3/4 In.	7.00
Print, Prang, Chillingham Cattle, 1883, Chromolithograph, 5 X 7 3/4 In.	7.00
Print, Prang, Finches, 1883, Chromolithograph, 5 X 7 3/4 In.	7.00
Print, Prang, Gorilla, 1883, Chromolithograph, 5 X 7 3/4 In.	9.00
Print, Prang, Harvest Mouse, 1883, Chromolithograph, 5 X 7 3/4 In.	7.00
Print, Prang, Landscape, 1888, Louis K.Harlow, Lithograph, 19 X 13 In.	30.00
Print, Prang, Leopard, 1883, Chromolithograph, 7 3/4 X 5 In.	9.00
Print, Prang, Lincoln, 1861, Lithograph, 8 1/2 X 6 1/2 In.	50.00
Print, Prang, Lion, 1883, Chromolithograph, 5 X 7 3/4 In.	9.00
Print, Prang, Paradise Fly Catchers, 1883, Chromolithograph, 5 X 7 3/4 In.	7.00
Print, Prang, Peaches, 1894, Adelaide Palmer, Lithograph, 15 X 21 In.	40.00
Print, Prang, Puma, 1883, Chromolithograph, 5 X 7 3/4 In.	7.00
Print, Prang, Resplendent Trogon, 1883, Chromolithograph, 7 3/4 X 5 In.	7.00
Print, Prang, Sea Lion, 1883, Chromolithograph, 5 X 7 3/4 In.	7.00
Print, Prang, Sloth Bear, 1883, Chromolithograph, 5 X 7 3/4 In.	7.00
Print, Prang, Stag, 1883, Chromolithograph, 5 X 7 3/4 In.	7.00
Print, Prang, Tiger, 1883, Chromolithograph, 5 X 7 3/4 In.	9.00
Print, Prang, Titmice, 1883, Chromolithograph, 5 X 7 3/4 In.	7.00
Print, Prang, Woodcock, 1883, Chromolithograph, 5 X 7 3/4 In.	7.00
Print, Preliminary Trial Of A Horse Thief, Carr & Green, 1877, Color, 30 In.	325.00
Print, Rackham, English Children At The Seashore, 1910, Color, 12 X 9 In.	12.50
Print, Rackham, Little Girl In Drifting Rowboat, 1909, Color, 10 X 7 In.	12.50
Print, Remington, The Moose, Framed, 1908, 16 X 20 In.	65.00
Print, Remington, The Smoke Signal, Framed, 24 X 14 In.	45.00
Print, Rosenthal, Camp Chase, Rhode Island, 1862, Color, 15 X 11 In.	22.50
Print, Seat Of War In America, Stanford, London, 1861, Color, 22 X 26 In.	50.00
Print, Seymour, Capture Of Frigate Macedonian, Etching & Aquatint, 17 In.	350.00
Print, Schell, Battle At Dam No.4, Potomac River, 1881, Wood Etching, 16 In.	25.00
Print, Shakers Dancing, A.Boyd Houghton, 1870, 13 1/2 X 10 1/2 In.	85.00
Print, Smith, John Hancock, Governor Of Boston, 1775, Mezzotint, 13 X 10 In.	325.00
Print, Werner, Infantry Attached By Indians, 1876, Color, 9 X 13 In.	45.00
Print, Wilson, Thomas Jefferson, Engraving, Walnut Frame, 12 X 7 In.	275.00
Print, Wolf Overlooking Snow-Covered Village, Drescher Co., 13 X 10 In.	6.00
Print, Wood, Jr., Lake Champlain, 1870, Chromolithograph, 14 X 8 In.	28.00
Purple Slag, see Slag, Purple	
Purse, Art Deco Frame, Hand-Embroidered Homestead & Floral	37.50
Purse, Change, Leather, German Silver	5.00
Purse, Lady's, German Silver, Oval	8.50
Purse, Silver With Ivory, "Polly Fairchild, Born 1789, Died 1873, " 2 In.	30.00
Purse, Vicuna, Golden Frame, Jewels	120.00

Quezal

Quezal glass was made from 1901 to 1920 by Martin Bach, Sr. He made iridescent glass of the same type as Tiffany.

Quezal, Bowl & Stand, Dessert, Amber Iridescent, Collared, C.1905, Set Of 12	650.00
Quezal, Bowl, Gold Iridescent, Pulled Design, 6 In.Diameter	150.00
Quezal, Bowl, Gold Iridescent, Ribbed, Flaring Lip, 6 In.	235.00
Quezal, Compote, White & Green Feathers Over Zipper Base, Gold Top, 6 In.	900.00
Quezal, Lamp, Lily, 7 Arm, Green Feathers On White, Gold Lining, 16 1/2 In.	2150.00
Quezal, Night-Light, Green, Gold, & White Feathered, 12 In.	1450.00
Quezal, Plate, Stretch, Gold & Blue Undertones, 6 1/2 In.	85.00
Quezal, Salt, Open, Gold Iridescent	125.00
Quezal, Salt, Ribbed, Stand-Up Collar, Iridescent, Signed	95.00
Quezal, Shade, Calcite & Gold, 5 In.High	65.00
Quezal, Shade, Calcite & Green Feather, Gold Aurene, 6 1/4 In.High	75.00
Quezal, Shade, Calcite, Gold Inside, Gold Line Decoration, 5 1/2 In.High	47.00
Quezal, Shade, Gold, Feathers, Gold Threading, 5 1/4 In.	100.00
Quezal, Shade, Gold, Hooked Feather On Opalescent, Signed, 6 In.	110.00
Quezal, Shade, Gold, Orange Drag Loop, 6 3/4 X 6 In.	125.00
Quezal, Shade, Gold, Red & Blue Highlights, 5 In., Set Of 5	300.00
Quezal, Shade, Green Gold Leaves, Random Threading, 6 In.	85.00
Quezal, Shade, King Tut & Zipper Pattern, Gold On White, 3 In.High	80.00
Quezal, Shade, Snakeskin, 5 In.	95.00
Quezal, Shade, White, Gold King Tut, Zipper Base, White Lined, 3 In., Set Of 3	240.00
Quezal, Vase, Amber Iridescent, Silver Repousse Overlay, C.1910, 11 1/2 In.	575.00

Quezal, Vase, Amber Oil Spots, Green Sworls, Applied Teardrops, C.1901, 6 In.	1150.00
Quezal, Vase, Dimpled Sides, Gold, Pink, & Blue Iridescent, 3 In.	175.00
Quezal, Vase, Gold Feathers On Green Opalescent, 9 X 5 In.Wide	1050.00
Quezal, Vase, Gold Iridescent, Dimpled Sides, Signed, 3 In.	162.50
Quezal, Vase, Gold Luster, Yellow & White Leaf Decoration, 9 1/2 In.	280.00
Quezal, Vase, Gold, Sterling Overlay, 5 In.	625.00
Quezal, Vase, Gold, 7 In.High	260.00
Quezal, Vase, Green & Gold Hearts, Applied Gold Webbing, Signed, 7 In.	525.00
Quezal, Vase, Opal & Yellow Luster Leaf Design On Gold, Ruffled, 9 1/4 In.	250.00
Quezal, Vase, Stick, Paperweight, Iridescent Gold, Blue & Pink Lights, 7 In.	265.00
Quezal, Vase, Sweetpea, Opal Glass, Green Luster Threads, Conical, 6 In.High	650.00
Quezal, Vase, Tumbler Shape, Flared Top & Base, Threading, Gold, 3 7/8 In.	139.00

Quilt, see Textile, Quilt

*Quimper pottery was made in Finistere, France, after 1900. Most of the
pieces found today were made during the twentieth century.A Quimper factory
has worked in France since the eighteenth century.*

Quimper, Bottle, Oil & Vinegar, Crossed	28.00
Quimper, Bowl, Signed, 6 1/4 In.	15.00
Quimper, Bowl, Woman With Flowers, 2 Handles, 5 1/4 In.	20.00
Quimper, Box, Sardine, Signed	45.00
Quimper, Chocolate Pot, Peasant Design	40.00
Quimper, Cruet Set, Yellow Ground, Floral Design, Holder & 2 Bottles	40.00
Quimper, Cup & Saucer, Peasant	15.00
Quimper, Cup & Saucer, Round, Marked France	15.00
Quimper, Cup & Saucer, Square	15.00
Quimper, Cup & Saucer, Yellow, Decorated	15.00
Quimper, Cup Plate, Peasant Woman	8.00
Quimper, Dish, Fish Shape, 4 In.	7.00
Quimper, Dish, Salt, Double, Figural Woman Peasant Handle	25.00
Quimper, Figurine, Dancing Children, Blue, Black, & Yellow, 10 In.High	42.00
Quimper, Figurine, Pair Of Shoes With Woman, 3 1/4 In., Pair	24.50
Quimper, Inkwell, Covered, Rose Floral Decoration, 3 Piece	49.00
Quimper, Inkwell, Double, Peasant Lady On White	38.50
Quimper, Inkwell, Shaped Like Peasant's Hat	50.00
Quimper, Knife Rest, Dutch Lady, Florals, Signed	24.00
Quimper, Knife Rest, Open Ends, 3 Sided	22.00
Quimper, Pitcher, 6 In.	24.00
Quimper, Plate, Breton Man, Yellow Border, Henriot, 9 1/2 In.	13.00
Quimper, Plate, Breton Woman, Yellow Border, Henriot, 9 1/2 In.	13.00
Quimper, Plate, Man Center, 8 In.	10.00
Quimper, Plate, Signed, 9 1/2 In.	18.00
Quimper, Plate, Soup, Portrait Center, Marked France, 8 In.	15.00
Quimper, Platter, Peasant Man On Buff, Floral Border, 11 X 17 In.	50.00
Quimper, Porringer, 3 7/8 In.	8.00
Quimper, Shoe, Pink, Blue Trim, 3 In., Pair	15.00
Quimper, Vase, Peasant Lady, Sectioned, 3 Footed, 5 In.	35.00

*Radford pottery was made by Alfred Radford in Broadway, Virginia,
Tiffin and Zanesville, Ohio, and Clarksburg, West Virginia, from 1891
until 1912. Jasperware, Ruko, Thera, Radera, and Velvety Art Ware
were made.*

Radford, Jardiniere, Ruko, Floral, Marked, 7 1/2 X 9 In.	200.00
Radford, Vase, Jasper, Green, White Cherubs On Gray Inset, Marked 14, 6 In.	155.00
Radford, Vase, Jasper, Light & Dark Green, Marked 18 On Bottom, 7 In.	180.00
Radford, Vase, Jasper, Twisted, Blue, 2 Cherubs On Each Side, Marked 57, 5 In.	150.00
Radford, Vase, Jasper, White Cherubs On Green, Marked 57, 5 3/4 In.	125.00
Radford, Vase, Thera, Matt, Floral On Blue, Similar To Owens Matt, 10 In.	225.00
Radio, Airline Detector, Mahogany, 1 Tube, Headphones, Battery, C.1919	55.00
Radio, Amplifier, Crystal, Radio Wonder, Amethyst Glass	42.00
Radio, Atwater Kent, Model 387, Beehive, Battery	45.00
Radio, Atwater Kent, Power Pack, Speaker, Wooden, 6 Tube	110.00
Radio, Emerson, Low-Boy, C.1931	95.00
Radio, Headphones, Western Electric, Patent 1918	15.00
Radio, Lafayette, Battery	15.00
Radio, Magazine, Radio Mirror, 1936	2.50

Radio, Magazine, What's On The Air, 1930	4.00
Radio, Montgomery Ward, 1923, Separate Morning Glory Speaker	40.00
Radio, Scott, Floor Model	300.00
Radio, Silvertone, Radionet, Wire Recorder, 15 X 25 1/2 X 32 1/4 In.	100.00
Radio, Zenith, Stratosphere, Floor Model, Inlaid Cabinet, Dual Speaker	700.00
Railroad, Ashtray, Chessie, Porcelain	10.00
Railroad, Bell, Brass, In Frame	500.00
Railroad, Booklet, Canadian Pacific Tours, 1915, Map	4.50
Railroad, Bowl, B.& O., Oval, Lamberton China, 5 1/2 In.	15.00
Railroad, Bowl, Finger, B.& O., Silver	10.00
Railroad, Bowl, Finger, N.Y.C., Silver	4.50
Railroad, Bowl, Soup, B.& O., Rimmed, Lamberton China, 9 In.	17.00
Railroad, Bowl, Vegetable, B&O, Light Blue, Oval, 5 3/4 In.	25.00
Railroad, Butter Pat, Baltimore & Ohio, Shenango, 1927	5.00 To 12.00
Railroad, Button, N.P.	.75
Railroad, Caboose Lamp & Bracket, Dressel, 19 In.	45.00
Railroad, Cards, Playing, Chessie, Deck	10.00
Railroad, Cards, Playing, Chessie, The Cat, Boxed Set	7.00
Railroad, Cards, Playing, Missouri Pacific, Boxed Set	7.50
Railroad, Cards, Playing, Mobile & Ohio, Deck	5.00
Railroad, Cards, Playing, Nickel Plate Road, Deck	5.00
Railroad, Cards, Playing, Northern Pacific, 1920s, Case & Score Pad, 2 Decks	60.00
Railroad, Cards, Playing, P.R.R., Pack	15.00
Railroad, Cards, Playing, Rio Grande	2.50
Railroad, Cards, Playing, Southern & Gulf, Deck	5.00
Railroad, Coffeepot, Pennsylvania R.R., Silver, 14 Ozs.	37.50
Railroad, Creamer, B.& O., Sterlings China	20.00
Railroad, Cup & Saucer, B & O, Blue & White, Shenango	18.00
Railroad, Cup & Saucer, B & O, Light Blue	30.00
Railroad, Cup, Soup, B & O, Light Blue	20.00
Railroad, Date Nail, Baltimore & Ohio, Round, Indent, No.11	.90
Railroad, Date Nail, Baltimore & Ohio, Round, Indent, No.12	.90
Railroad, Date Nail, Baltimore & Ohio, Round, Indent, No.13	.90
Railroad, Date Nail, Baltimore & Ohio, Round, Indent, No.14	.90
Railroad, Date Nail, Baltimore & Ohio, Round, Indent, No.15	.90
Railroad, Date Nail, Baltimore & Ohio, Round, Indent, No.16	.75
Railroad, Date Nail, Baltimore & Ohio, Round, Indent, No.17	.75
Railroad, Date Nail, Baltimore & Ohio, Round, Indent, No.18	.75
Railroad, Date Nail, Baltimore & Ohio, Round, Indent, No.19	.75
Railroad, Date Nail, Baltimore & Ohio, Round, Indent, No.20	.75
Railroad, Date Nail, Baltimore & Ohio, Round, Indent, No.21	.75
Railroad, Date Nail, Baltimore & Ohio, Round, Indent, No.22	.50
Railroad, Date Nail, Baltimore & Ohio, Round, Indent, No.23	.50
Railroad, Date Nail, Baltimore & Ohio, Round, Indent, No.24	.50
Railroad, Date Nail, Baltimore & Ohio, Round, Indent, No.25	.50
Railroad, Date Nail, Baltimore & Ohio, Round, Indent, No.26	.50
Railroad, Date Nail, Baltimore & Ohio, Round, Indent, No.27	.50
Railroad, Date Nail, Baltimore & Ohio, Round, Indent, No.28	.50
Railroad, Date Nail, Baltimore & Ohio, Round, Indent, No.29	.50
Railroad, Date Nail, Baltimore & Ohio, Round, Indent, No.30	.50
Railroad, Date Nail, Baltimore & Ohio, Round, Indent, No.31	.50
Railroad, Date Nail, Baltimore & Ohio, Round, Indent, No.32	.30
Railroad, Date Nail, Baltimore & Ohio, Round, Indent, No.33	.30
Railroad, Date Nail, Baltimore & Ohio, Round, Indent, No.34	.30
Railroad, Dish, Vegetable, B & O, Light Blue, 5 3/4 In.Long	25.00
Railroad, First Aid Box, Tin, New York Central, 18 X 5 X 2 In.	25.00
Railroad, Fork, A.T.& S.F.Ry., Silver	6.50
Railroad, Fork, Oyster, A.T.& S.F.Ry., Silver	6.50
Railroad, Fork, Salad, A.T.& S.F.Ry., Silver	6.50
Railroad, Fork, Union Pacific, Silver	4.00
Railroad, Globe, Lantern, Etched A.T. & S.F. On Clear	7.00
Railroad, Globe, Lantern, Etched P.R.R. On Clear, 4 1/2 In.	7.00
Railroad, Hammer, Sledge, L.& N.R.R.	18.00
Railroad, Hand Lantern, Brass, Top Inscribed Steamer No. 1	75.00
Railroad, Headrest Cover, P.R.R.	5.00
Railroad, Key, G.M.O., Brass	3.00

Railroad, Key, Switch, Brass, Marked West Md.	8.00
Railroad, Key, Switch, PRR, Brass	10.00
Railroad, Key, Switch, PRR, Nickel	15.00
Railroad, Kit, First Aid, P.C.	4.00
Railroad, Kit, Flare, Flagman's, Pacific Railroad	4.00
Railroad, Knife, A.T.& S.F.Ry., Silver	6.50
Railroad, Knife, Butter, A.T.& S.F.Ry., Silver	6.50
Railroad, Knife, Fruit, A.T.& S.F.Ry., Silver	6.50
Railroad, Knife, Union Pacific, Silver	4.00
Railroad, Ladder, Pullman Berth, Wooden, Covered Carpeting	.
Railroad, Lamp, Caboose, Kerosene, Brass	25.00
Railroad, Lamp, Wall, N.Y.Cent. System, Candle	50.00
Railroad, Lantern, Adlake B&M On Frame, Etched Globe, 5 3/8 In.	40.00
Railroad, Lantern, Adlake, Amber Globe	20.00
Railroad, Lantern, Adlake, Dressel, Clear Globe	20.00
Railroad, Lantern, Adlake, Squat, Blue Globe	20.00
Railroad, Lantern, Adlake, Squat, Clear Globe	20.00
Railroad, Lantern, Adlake, Squat, Red Globe	20.00
Railroad, Lantern, Adlake, Squat, Ribbed Red Globe	20.00
Railroad, Lantern, Armspear, P.R.R., Bell, Clear Globe, 5 1/2 In.	60.00
Railroad, Lantern, B & M Rel., Clear Globe	50.00
Railroad, Lantern, B & M, Clear Globe	12.75
Railroad, Lantern, B & O Rel., Clear Globe	40.00
Railroad, Lantern, B & O, Adlake, Etched Clear Globe, 5 3/8 In.	40.00
Railroad, Lantern, B & O, Squat Base, Ribbed Red Globe	20.00
Railroad, Lantern, B.R.& P.Ry., Dietz, Vesta, Etched Clear Globe	26.00
Railroad, Lantern, Baltimore & Ohio, Kerosene, Hand	19.00
Railroad, Lantern, Boston & Albany, Dietz, Vesta, 1923, Red Globe	35.00
Railroad, Lantern, Boston & Maine, Dietz, Vesta, Clear Globe	35.00
Railroad, Lantern, CRRofNJ Armspear, Clear Globe	50.00
Railroad, Lantern, CRRofNJ, Dressel, Clear Globe	50.00
Railroad, Lantern, Cheseapeake & Ohio, Kerosene, Hand	19.00
Railroad, Lantern, D & H, Squat, Etched Clear Globe	20.00
Railroad, Lantern, D.L.& W., Dietz 39, Bell, Clear Globe, 5 3/8 In.	40.00
Railroad, Lantern, D.L.& W., Vesta, Etched Clear Globe	20.00
Railroad, Lantern, D.L.& W., Vesta, Etched Red Globe	20.00
Railroad, Lantern, Dietz D-Lite, N.Y., U.S.A., 13 In.	35.00
Railroad, Lantern, Dietz, Bell Bottom, Round Handle, Tin, Clear Globe, 13 In.	50.00
Railroad, Lantern, Erie & Westlake R.R., 1895, Marked Globe, 5 3/8 In.	50.00
Railroad, Lantern, Erie On Frame & Clear Globe, Armspear, 5 3/8 In.	50.00
Railroad, Lantern, Erie R.R., Marked Clear Globe, 5 3/8 In.	40.00
Railroad, Lantern, Erie 39, Ham Marked Frame, Patent 1893, 5 3/8 In.	50.00
Railroad, Lantern, Erie, Brass Top, Clear Globe Marked 1883	60.00
Railroad, Lantern, Erie, Dressel, Squat, Clear Globe	20.00
Railroad, Lantern, French, 19th Century, Pair	390.00
Railroad, Lantern, G.N.Ry., Dressel, Blue Globe	26.00
Railroad, Lantern, German, Emblem, Carbide, Cast Brass Burner, 11 In.	15.00
Railroad, Lantern, German, Swastika, Carbide, Cast Brass Burner, 11 In.	20.00
Railroad, Lantern, Globe, Lantern, Red, 4 1/2 In.	6.00
Railroad, Lantern, Grand Trunk, Wright, Red Globe, Patent 1908, 5 3/8 In.	40.00
Railroad, Lantern, H.& H.R.R., Dressel, Clear Globe, 5 3/8 In.	40.00
Railroad, Lantern, Handlan, St.Louis, Kerosene, Ruby Glass	35.00
Railroad, Lantern, I.C.R.R., Red Globe	25.00
Railroad, Lantern, Illinois Central, Red Globe, 3 1/4 In.	17.50
Railroad, Lantern, Inspection Torch, Wabash R.R.	40.00
Railroad, Lantern, Inspector's, D.L.& W., Dietz, Ideal, Clear Etched Globe	25.00
Railroad, Lantern, L.G.& E.Co., Red Globe	25.00
Railroad, Lantern, L.V., Armspear, Raised Letters On Clear Globe, 5 3/8 In.	55.00
Railroad, Lantern, L.V., Dressel, Red Ribbed Globe, 9 In.	20.00
Railroad, Lantern, LSMS Rel, Marked Frame, Red Globe, 5 3/8 In.	40.00
Railroad, Lantern, LV, Caboose, Wall, Kerosene	50.00
Railroad, Lantern, LV, Vesta, Etched Clear Globe	20.00
Railroad, Lantern, Mo Pac, Handlan Marked Frame, 5 3/8 In.	20.00
Railroad, Lantern, N.Y. Central, Vesta, Red Globe	180.00
Railroad, Lantern, N.Y.C.S., Clear Marked Globe	14.75
Railroad, Lantern, N.Y.Cent, Red Globe, Dietz, Bell Bottom	65.00

Railroad, Lantern, N.Y.Central, Dietz, Bell Bottom, Blue Globe	37.50
Railroad, Lantern, N.Y.Central, Dietz, Bell Bottom, Clear Globe	50.00
Railroad, Lantern, N.Y.Central, Dietz, Bell Bottom, Red Globe	65.00
Railroad, Lantern, N.Y.N.H. & H.R.R., Clear Globe	14.75
Railroad, Lantern, NSRR, Dietz, Ideal, Clear Globe	25.00
Railroad, Lantern, NYNH&H Rel., Clear Globe	45.00
Railroad, Lantern, NYNH&H, Vesta, Clear Etched Globe	20.00
Railroad, Lantern, NYNH&H, Vesta, Clear Globe	20.00
Railroad, Lantern, P.& R., Armspear, Dietz, Clear Globe	50.00
Railroad, Lantern, P.& R., Armspear, Raised Letters On Globe, 6 In.	65.00
Railroad, Lantern, P.& R., The Adams, Marked Globe, 5 3/8 In.	50.00
Railroad, Lantern, P.R.R., Etched Amber Globe, 5 3/8 In.	55.00
Railroad, Lantern, P.R.R., Inspector's, Acme, Dietz, Reflector, 9 In.	50.00
Railroad, Lantern, P.R.R., Keystone, No.39, Etched Amber Globe, 5 3/8 In.	55.00
Railroad, Lantern, PRR Key 39, Clear Globe	50.00
Railroad, Lantern, PRR Key-Casey, Clear Globe	50.00
Railroad, Lantern, PRR Key-Casey, Red Globe	50.00
Railroad, Lantern, PRR On Frame, Dietz, Steel Clad, Marked Globe, 5 3/8 In.	40.00
Railroad, Lantern, PRRkey, Red Globe	50.00
Railroad, Lantern, Passenger Train Marker, Red Lens	50.00
Railroad, Lantern, Pennsylvania R.R., Key-Casey Frame, Red Globe	50.00
Railroad, Lantern, Rock Island Line, Patent 1909, Clear Globe	30.00
Railroad, Lantern, Sou, Red Globe, 5 3/8 In.	40.00
Railroad, Lantern, Supreme Embury Warsaw & N.Y.C., Electric, 5 3/8 In.	10.00
Railroad, Lantern, Westlake, P.R.R., Bell, Clear Globe, 1895, 5 1/2 In.	70.00
Railroad, Light, Wall, Adlake, Caboose	10.00
Railroad, Lock & Chain, Nor.& West., Script, Brass	15.00
Railroad, Lock & Chain, Switch, Sou R.R., Iron, Figure 8, Miller	10.00
Railroad, Lock & Key, B.& O., Brass	35.00
Railroad, Lock & Key, B.R.& P., Engineering Dept., Yale, Brass	20.00
Railroad, Lock & Key, D.L.& W., Climax, Newark, N.J., Iron Lock, Brass Key	25.00
Railroad, Lock & Key, L.& Nash., Brass	35.00
Railroad, Lock & Key, N&West In Script, Brass	25.00
Railroad, Lock, Chain, & Key, Sou Ry., Yale, Brass, Heavy Hasp	10.00
Railroad, Lock, Chain, & 2 Keys, R.& R.R.R., Howard 3 Co., Wooten's, 1866	32.50
Railroad, Lock, N&W, Bronze	12.00
Railroad, Lock, Norf Charlotte & St.Louis, Iron, Key	30.00
Railroad, Lock, Signal, NYNH & H, Brass	10.00
Railroad, Lock, Switch, Louisville & Nashville, Key, Brass	35.00
Railroad, Martini Set, Union Pacific Railroad, 4 Piece	22.50
Railroad, Mirror, Frisco Line, Pocket	30.00
Railroad, Oilcan, Brass, Long Spout, C.1890, 14 In.	17.50
Railroad, Oilcan, N.P.	12.50
Railroad, Oiler, L.V.R.R., Long Spout	20.00
Railroad, Padlock, B.R.	9.50
Railroad, Paperweight, Quanah, Acme, & Pacific, Glass, 4 In.	20.00
Railroad, Pass, Pennsylvania, 1876, Husband & Wife	8.00
Railroad, Pitcher & Underplate, Gravy, C.N., Porcelain	15.00
Railroad, Plate, Baltimore & Ohio, Blue & White, Lamberton China, 9 In.	30.00
Railroad, Plate, Dinner, B & O, Blue & White Train Scene, Shenango	20.00
Railroad, Plate, New York, New Haven, & Hartford, Indian Tree, 8 In.	18.00
Railroad, Plate, Salad, B.& O., Lamberton China, 8 1/4 In.	15.00
Railroad, Platter, Boston & Albany, 10 1/2 In.	10.00
Railroad, Platter, Denver & Rio Grande, 11 1/2 In.	10.00
Railroad, Platter, N.Y.Central, Buffalo China, 11 1/4 In.	10.00
Railroad, Platter, Steak, Santa Fe, Silver, Oval, 12 In.	15.00
Railroad, Poster, Pennsylvania Railroad, C.1930, 28 X 40 In.	30.00
Railroad, Poster, Pennsylvania Railroad, C.1935, 30 X 40 In.	30.00
Railroad, Sauce, Union Pacific, Blue Trim, 6 In.	5.00
Railroad, Sign, Quiet, Pullman Co., Cardboard, 6 X 9 In.	6.00
Railroad, Spoon, Cream Soup, A.T.& S.F.Ry., Silver	6.50
Railroad, Spoon, Grapefruit, A.T.& S F.Ry., Silver	6.50
Railroad, Spoon, Iced Tea, A.T.& S.F.Ry., Silver	6.50
Railroad, Spoon, Soup, A.T.& S.F.Ry., Silver	6.50
Railroad, Stove, Caboose, N.Y.O.& W., Cast Iron	100.00
Railroad, Sugar, Covered, C.B.& Q.R.R., Burlington Route, Silver	40.00

Railroad, Tablespoon, Union Pacific, Silver	4.00
Railroad, Tag, D.L.& W., Brass, Leather Strap	15.00
Railroad, Teakettle, Erie, Aluminum-Plated Cast Iron	45.00
Railroad, Tray, Crumb, G.T., Silver	18.00
Railroad, Tumbler, Pennsylvania R.R., N.Y. & Washington, D.C. Buildings	15.00
Railroad, Whistle, Backup, Sherburne Co., Boston, Compressed Air, Brass	25.00
Railroad, Whistle, Rear End Train, Sherburne, Compressed Air, 7 In.	25.00

Rainbow, see Mother-of-Pearl, Satin Glass

The Red Wing Pottery of Red Wing, Minnesota, was a firm started in 1878. It was not until the 1920s that art pottery was made. It closed in 1967. Rumrill pottery was made for George Rumrill by the Red Wing Pottery Company and other firms. It was sold in the 1930s.

Red Wing, Bowl & Frog, Green & Tan, Green Glazed Interior, 9 In.	18.00
Red Wing, Cornucopia, Dark Green, 7 1/2 In.	6.00
Red Wing, Cornucopia, White, Brown Trim, 8 1/2 In.	10.00
Red Wing, Jar, Cookie, Blue, Baker Boy	12.50
Red Wing, Jar, Cookie, Blue, Chef, Stamped Hand-Painted	20.00
Red Wing, Jar, Cookie, Blue, Dutch Girl, Stamped Hand-Painted, 10 In.	20.00
Red Wing, Jar, Cookie, Apple	10.00
Red Wing, Jar, Cookie, Chef	12.00
Red Wing, Pitcher, Leaf & Lines On Yellow, White Interior, 4 1/2 In.	1.50
Red Wing, Planter, Cream, Leaf Decoration, Impressed 866, 7 In.	8.00
Red Wing, Planter, Deep Red, Raised Decoration, Marked, 8 X 4 X 4 In.	6.00
Red Wing, Planter, Green, Reclining Lady & Deer, Impressed B2507, 14 X 5 In.	10.00
Red Wing, Pot, Marmalade, Figural, Apple, Liner	8.50
Red Wing, Vase, Bark Finish, Flowers, Mountain, Double Handles, 6 In.	35.00
Red Wing, Vase, Brown Outlined Roses On Ivory, Matt, Pedestal, 8 In.	7.50
Red Wing, Vase, Bud, Matte Pink, Handle, 7 In.	7.00
Red Wing, Vase, Cattails, Green Interior, Union Stoneware, 7 In.	8.00
Red Wing, Vase, Green, 7 1/2 In.	3.00
Red Wing, Vase, Red, Scalloped Edge, 7 1/2 In.	10.00
Red Wing, Vase, Roman Gods At Top, 2 Handled, Marked, 15 In.	65.00
Red Wing, Vase, Star Shape, Blue Gray, Mottled Glaze, 9 1/2 In.	8.00

Redware is a hard red stoneware that originated in the late 1600s and continues to be made. The term is also used to describe any common clay pottery that is reddish in color.

Redware, Bowl, For Settling Cream, Glazed Interior, 17 X 3 In.	100.00
Redware, Bowl, Light Brown Glaze In & Out, 6 X 4 1/4 In.	25.00
Redware, Box, Money, White Slip, Honey Glaze, 1880, 9 1/3 In.	60.00
Redware, Bust, Grant, Dated 1885, New England, 7 1/2 In.	175.00
Redware, Crock, Unglazed Outside, Lewis K.Tomlinson, Berks County, 7 In.	80.00
Redware, Figurine, Seated Monkey Holding Bucket, Pennsylvania, C.1850, 6 In.	650.00
Redware, Flowerpot, Square Top, Yellow Glazed Design, 5 In.High	30.00
Redware, Jar, Biscuit, Chinese, Raised Dragons	10.00
Redware, Jar, Snuff, Black Glazed, Wide Mouth, 6 1/4 X 5 In.	18.00
Redware, Jar, Wide Mouth, 5 In. Diameter Top, 5 3/4 In.	30.00
Redware, Jug, Handled, C.1850, 7 1/2 In.	30.00
Redware, Jug, Handled, 4 In.	40.00
Redware, Jug, Ovoid, 8 In.	20.00
Redware, Jug, Wine, High Glazed Outside, Green, 8 1/2 In.	100.00
Redware, Pitcher, Brown Mottled Glaze, C.1820, 6 1/2 In.High, Quart	75.00
Redware, Pitcher, New England, Glazed Inside, 10 In.	37.00
Redware, Pot, Bean, Covered	40.00
Redware, Strainer, Holes, Glazed Inside & Out, 5 In. Diameter	50.00
Redware, Teapot, Chinese, Applied Colored Figures On Sides & Lid, C.1850	85.00
Redware, Whistle, Bird Perched On Stand, White Slip, C.1850, 9 1/2 In.	55.00
Redwood, Vase, Floral On Floretta Weller Type Ground, 2 Handled, 5 In.	75.00
Redwood, Vase, Ovoid, Portrait Of Cavalier, 5 1/4 In.	45.00
Richard, Bottle, Perfume, Blue Cut To Bright Orange, Signed, Cameo, 5 In.	225.00
Richard, Vase, Cameo, Rust Raspberry Plants On Orange, 6 In.	215.00
Richard, Vase, Cut Cameo, Narrow Neck, Bulbous Base, 8 In.	275.00
Richard, Vase, Scenic, Tawny & Deep Purple Shades, 8 In.	350.00

 Ridgway pottery has been made in the Staffordshire District in England

since 1808 by a series of companies with the name Ridgway. The transfer-design dinner sets are the most widely known product. They are still being made.

Ridgway, Ashtray, Three Characters' Faces	5.00
Ridgway, Bowl, Cereal, Oriental, Light Blue, 6 1/4 In.	5.50
Ridgway, Bowl, Two Wellers, The, Pickwick Series, Black On Brown, 9 1/2 In.	39.00
Ridgway, Bowl, Vegetable, Covered, Oriental, Blue & White	22.50
Ridgway, Bowl, Vegetable, Covered, Palestine, Blue With White, 10 1/2 In.	48.00
Ridgway, Bowl, Vegetable, Oriental, Blue & White	16.00
Ridgway, Chocolate Pot, Portrait Of Maiden On Yellow, 9 In.	40.00
Ridgway, Cup & Saucer, Coaching Days, Caramel, Silver Rim	40.00
Ridgway, Cup & Saucer, Demitasse, Oriental, Blue & White	7.50
Ridgway, Cup & Saucer, Forget-Me-Not, Girl, English Village, Purple	38.00
Ridgway, Gravy Boat, Boston State House	125.00
Ridgway, Mug & Saucer, Coaching Days, Winter's Day, Fresh Teams, 2 Handled	40.00
Ridgway, Mug, Windmills & Sailships, Gold Tones, 5 In., Artist Signed	45.00
Ridgway, Pitcher, Classical Figures In Cameos, Grape & Leaf Border, 6 In.	65.00
Ridgway, Pitcher, Coaching Days, Pewter Lid, Luster Trim, 8 In.	45.00
Ridgway, Pitcher, Molded Cattails & Grass, Gray Parian, C.1835, 8 1/2 In.	85.00
Ridgway, Pitcher, Parian, Tavern Scene, Foliage, Footed, 1835, 8 1/4 In.	95.00
Ridgway, Pitcher, Salt Glaze, Brown Tavern Scene, 1835, 6 In.	62.00
Ridgway, Plate, Auld Brig A'Doon, 9 In.	25.00
Ridgway, Plate, Baronial Castles, Sundorn, Lavender, 8 1/2 In.	12.50
Ridgway, Plate, Blue Transfer Aladdin, C.1846, 7 1/2 In., Pair	12.00
Ridgway, Plate, City Hall, New York, Medium Blue, C.1820, 9 7/8 In., Pair	175.00
Ridgway, Plate, Coaching Days, Barry Lyndon Cracks A Bottle, Caramel, 9 In.	25.00
Ridgway, Plate, Coaching Days, In A Snowdrift, Silver Trim, 11 In.	40.00
Ridgway, Plate, Delaware, 1847, 10 1/2 In.	18.00
Ridgway, Plate, It's A Long Way To Tipperary, 1914, 9 In.	25.00
Ridgway, Plate, Marmora, Sepia, 9 In.	12.00
Ridgway, Plate, Oriental, Blue & White, 7 In.	4.00
Ridgway, Plate, Oriental, Blue & White, 8 3/4 In.	5.50
Ridgway, Plate, Oriental, Blue & White, 9 3/4 In.	6.50
Ridgway, Plate, Oriental, Light Blue, Gold Rim, Signed, 9 1/2 In.	12.50
Ridgway, Plate, Oriental, Light Blue, 6 3/4 In.	5.50
Ridgway, Plate, Oriental, Light Blue, 8 3/4 In.	7.50
Ridgway, Plate, Oriental, Pink, 10 In.	15.00
Ridgway, Plate, Soup, Oriental, Light Blue, 7 1/4 In.	5.50
Ridgway, Plate, Tam-O'-Shanter & Souter Johnny, 9 In.	20.00
Ridgway, Plate, University, Blue, C.1841, 10 1/2 In.	28.00
Ridgway, Plate, View From Ruggles House, Hudson River, Newburgh, 10 1/4 In.	40.00
Ridgway, Platter, Genevese, Blue, 16 In.	58.00
Ridgway, Platter, Oriental, Blue & White, 13 X 10 1/2 In.	16.50
Ridgway, Platter, Oriental, Blue & White, 15 X 12 1/2 In.	22.50
Ridgway, Saucer, Blue Transfer Oriental, 6 In., Pair	10.00
Ridgway, Tankard, Coaching Days, Brown, Silver Luster Trim, 12 In., Pair	270.00
Ridgway, Tankard, Coaching Days, Walking Up Hill, Winter's Day, 5 In.	38.00
Ridgway, Tea Set, Child's, Maidenhair Fern, Blue & White, 1883, 15 Piece	100.00
Ridgway, Tray, Coaching Days, In A Snowdrift, 12 1/2 In. Diameter	50.00
Ridgway, Tray, Coaching Days, Taking Up The Mails, Open Handles, 12 3/4 In.	52.00
Ridgway, Tureen, Oriental, Green On White, Square, 8 In.	45.00
Ridgway, Tureen, Soup, Lichfield, Blue & White, 3 Quart	38.00
Riviera Ware, Bowl, Serving, Red, Deep, Round, 8 1/2 In.	4.00
Riviera Ware, Butter, Light Green, Covered, 1 Lb.	17.50
Riviera Ware, Creamer, Yellow, 3 In.	2.50
Riviera Ware, Cup & Saucer, Yellow	3.00
Riviera Ware, Cup, Medium Blue	2.50
Riviera Ware, Gravy Boat, Yellow	4.00
Riviera Ware, Nappy, Ivory, 5 In.	2.50
Riviera Ware, Nappy, Light Green, 5 In.	2.50
Riviera Ware, Platter, Light Green, 11 1/2 In.	3.00
Riviera Ware, Saucer, Light Green	1.25
Riviera Ware, Sugar, Light Green	2.50
Roblin, Vase, Art Nouveau Design, 8 1/2 In.	85.00
Roblin, Vase, Art Nouveau Oriental Poppies, 8 In.	90.00

Rockingham in the United States is a brown glazed pottery with a tortoiseshell-like glaze. It was made from 1840 to 1900 by many American potteries. The mottled brown Rockingham wares were first made in England at the Rockingham factory. Other wares were also made by the English firm.

Rockingham, Bowl, Footed, Flaring, 10 1/4 X 4 1/2 In.	55.00
Rockingham, Creamer, Footed, June 14, 1843, 5 1/2 In.	48.00
Rockingham, Cup & Saucer, Large, June 14, 1843	48.00
Rockingham, Dish, Soap *Illus*	12.00
Rockingham, Dish, Soap, Raised Panels, 4 1/2 X 3 1/4 In.	38.00
Rockingham, Inkwell, Shell Shape, Cream Decorated With Gold, C.1820	68.00
Rockingham, Jar, Standing Pig, Brameld Type Glaze, C.1850, 8 3/4 In.	80.00
Rockingham, Mug, 3 In. *Illus*	15.00
Rockingham, Pan, Milk, 8 X 2 1/2 In.	38.00
Rockingham, Pitcher, Bennington Type, Leaf Decoration, Gallon	55.00
Rockingham, Pitcher, 5 In.	28.00
Rockingham, Quill Holder, English, 4 In. *Illus*	40.00
Rockingham, Sugar, Covered, Gold	8.00
Rockingham, Teapot, Portly Man, Hat Cover, Brameld Glaze, C.1850, 10 In.	40.00
Rockingham, Toby Mug, Portly Man, Hat Cover, Brameld Glaze, C.1850, 9 3/4 In.	80.00
Rockingham, Toby Mug, Tricorner Hat, Cable Neck, Flat Base, 6 In.	150.00

Rookwood pottery was made in Cincinnati, Ohio, from 1880 to 1960. All of this art pottery is marked, most with the famous flame mark. The R is reversed and placed back to back with the letter P. Flames surround the letters.

Rookwood, Ashtray, Beige Matte, 1937	9.00
Rookwood, Ashtray, Human Head Shape, Prognathic Lower Jaw, Olive Green, 1935	75.00
Rookwood, Basket, Brown & Green Glaze, Cream Floral, 2 Handles, Sohok, 11 In.	450.00
Rookwood, Bookend, Blue Rooks, Matte Finish, No.2274 1918 P, 6 In., Pair	125.00
Rookwood, Bookend, St.Francis & Animals, 1945, No.6883, 7 1/2 X 5 In., Pair	65.00
Rookwood, Bowl Vase, Matte Blue, 4 Pillars Form Legs, 1917, 7 1/2 In.	34.00
Rookwood, Bowl, Flower, Fishes On Side, Green, Pink Lining, 1929, 5 1/2 In.	38.50
Rookwood, Bowl, Greenish Tones, Low, 1915, 5 In.	18.50
Rookwood, Bowl, Light Blue Matte, Rook & Animals, 1927, 8 In.	35.00
Rookwood, Box, Covered, Cream & Blue, Floral, I.S., 1926, Round, 7 1/2 In.	250.00
Rookwood, Box, Pin, Floral On Brown, Mattie Foglesong, 1897, 3 X 1 7/8 In.	245.00
Rookwood, Box, Powder, Little Jack Horner Writing Name, Harriet Wilcox	425.00
Rookwood, Candleholder, Turquoise, Four Petals, 1921, 4 In., Pair	8.00
Rookwood, Candleholder, Yellow, 1 3/4 In., Pair	20.00
Rookwood, Candlestick, Brown Glaze, 2 Handled, 1885, 8 In., Pair	175.00
Rookwood, Candlestick, Light Green Glaze, Art Nouveau Design, 1900, 4 In.	15.00
Rookwood, Candlestick, Salmon Ground, Painted Daffodils, Abel, 1891, 6 In.	60.00
Rookwood, Candlestick, Shaded Blue, Art Nouveau, 1921, 3 1/4 In., Pair	18.00
Rookwood, Console Set, Floriform Candleholders, Blue, 1927, 3 Piece	65.00
Rookwood, Creamer, Cherries On Brown Glaze, C.A.B., 1894, 3 3/4 In.High	150.00
Rookwood, Creamer, Dragonflies On Gold & Cameo, H.H., 1883, 2 1/2 In.High	350.00

Rockingham, Quill Holder, English, 4 In.

Rockingham, Mug, 3 In.   Rockingham, Dish, Soap

Rookwood, Creamer, Standard Glaze, Yellow Mums, Caroline Steinle, 1894 .... 135.00
Rookwood, Ewer, Brown & Green, Marsh Scene, Gilt, McDonald, 1882, 12 In. 275.00
Rookwood, Ewer, Iris, Brown To Moss Green, Phlox, LEL, 1900, 4 1/3 In. 110.00
Rookwood, Ewer, Leaf & Berry On Brown, Leona Van Briggle, 1900, 5 3/4 In. 185.00
Rookwood, Ewer, Leaves & Acorns On Brown, Sadie Markland, 1895, 8 1/2 In. 225.00
Rookwood, Ewer, Standard Glaze, Laurel Blossoms, C Scroll Handle, 1890, 8 In. 300.00
Rookwood, Ewer, Tiger Lilies On Green & Orange, M.Norse, 1895, 6 X 6 In. 250.00
Rookwood, Figurine, Cat, Brown, 1911, 5 1/2 In. 250.00
Rookwood, Figurine, Seminude, White, Drapery Forms Bud Vase, 1922, 11 1/2 In. 85.00
Rookwood, Flower Frog, Matte Light Mustard, 1915, 4 1/4 X 1 3/4 In. 5.00
Rookwood, Flower Frog, Nude Negro Boy & 2 Monkeys, Blue Glaze, 1921, 5 In. 60.00
Rookwood, Fountain, Garden, Nude Child & Swan, C.J.Barnhorn, 1914, 35 In. 300.00
Rookwood, Humidor, Cigar, Glossy Yellow, Crest On Lid, 1940, 6 In. 80.00
Rookwood, Inkwell, Green With Incised Geometric Design, 3 1/2 In.High, 1903 .... 63.00
Rookwood, Inkwell, Lotus Form, Leaf Tray, Stem Handle, Green, 1906, 6 X 3 In. 39.00
Rookwood, Jar, Tobacco, Brown Matte, 3 Green Tulips, CAD, 1907, 5 1/4 In. 75.00
Rookwood, Jug, Brown Glaze, Ears Of Corn, Husks, Lenore Asbury, 1898, 7 1/2 In 265.00
Rookwood, Jug, Chocolate, Incised Stems & Leaves, Matte, 1882, 5 In. 275.00
Rookwood, Jug, Gray & Rust, Swallows, Foliage, Gold Flecks, ARV, 1884, 5 In. 225.00
Rookwood, Mantel Set, Blue, Pair Of 7 In. Handled Vases, 8 In. Bowl, 1925 .... 75.00
Rookwood, Mug, Beer, Barrel Shape, Cherubs, Green Glaze, 1886, 6 1/8 In. 300.00
Rookwood, Mug, Chestnut Leaves, H.E.W., 1890 .... 165.00
Rookwood, Mug, Green Matte, Decorated In Panels, 1903 .... 75.00
Rookwood, Mug, High Glaze, St.Bernard Dog, E.T.Hurly, 1900 .... 495.00
Rookwood, Mug, Matte Green, 5 In. 45.00
Rookwood, Mug, Standard Glaze, Puzzle, Yellow Floral, Lenore Asbury, 1898 .... 235.00
Rookwood, Paperweight, Fruit & Flower Basket, Yellow, Purple, Ivory, 1929, S.T 85.00
Rookwood, Paperweight, Monkey, Marked & Numbered, 4 In. 125.00
Rookwood, Paperweight, Rook, Blue, 1921 .... 40.00
Rookwood, Pitcher, Iris Glaze, Clover On Pink, C.S., 1901, 3 In. 150.00
Rookwood, Pitcher, Milk, Standard Glaze, Cherry Branches, LY, 1897, 4 In. 130.00
Rookwood, Pitcher, Rose Matte, Green Decoration, 1908, 5 In. 55.00
Rookwood, Pitcher, Standard Glaze, Yellow Green Floral On Brown, 1898, 3 In. 185.00
Rookwood, Pitcher, Triangular, 3 Spouts, Brown, Brown Floral, IB, 4 3/4 In. 170.00
Rookwood, Pitcher, Water, Redware, Unglazed, Floral Design, H.W., 1884, 5 In. 350.00
Rookwood, Plate, Autumn Leaves On Green & Beige, A.R.Valentien, 1882, 10 In. 60.00
Rookwood, Plate, Dogwood Branch On Peach Color, C.S., 1889, 9 In. 225.00
Rookwood, Plate, Green Matte, Flower & Leaf, AMV, 1901, 9 1/4 In. 95.00
Rookwood, Plate, Light Blue Ships On White, Marked M-6, 8 In. 15.00
Rookwood, Pocket, Wall, Wedgwood Blue, Petal Panels, Conical, 1925, 8 In. 32.00
Rookwood, Relish, Matte Wine Glaze, Leaf Shape, Green Shadings, 1914 .... 43.00
Rookwood, Rose Bowl, Iris Glaze, Mistletoe, White To Gray, L.L., 1904, 4 In. 140.00
Rookwood, Rose Bowl, Iris Glaze, Purple Violets, H.F., 1945, 4 In. 145.00
Rookwood, Tea Set, Light Blue Sailing Vessels On White, 1924, 3 Piece 150.00
Rookwood, Teapot, Pale Green, Mottled Pink, & Yellow, Incised, A.M.V. 175.00
Rookwood, Tile, Sea Horses On Gray Matte, 8 In. 20.00
Rookwood, Tray, Standard Glaze, 3 Angels & Clouds, H.E.W., 1891, 11 3/4 In. 1450.00
Rookwood, Trivet, Vellum, Raised Floral, 1925 Mark, Round, 6 In. 19.00
Rookwood, Vase, Aqua, Classic Band, 1921, 7 In. 18.00
Rookwood, Vase, Art Deco, Apple Green Glaze, 1930, 5 1/2 X 6 3/8 In. 25.00
Rookwood, Vase, Beige, 6 In. .... Illus 30.00
Rookwood, Vase, Blue Butterfly & Bird Decoration, XLV, 4 1/2 In. 11.00
Rookwood, Vase, Blue Flower Decoration, Elizabeth Lincoln, 11 In. 145.00
Rookwood, Vase, Blue Green Matte, Petallike Design, Dated 1906, 7 In. 24.50
Rookwood, Vase, Blue, Bell Like Floral At Top, 1928, 6 1/4 In. 22.50
Rookwood, Vase, Blue, Donkey Design, 4 1/2 X 4 1/2 In. 9.00
Rookwood, Vase, Blue, 1921, 5 1/2 In. 20.00
Rookwood, Vase, Bowl Type, Vellum, Water Lilies, Sara Sax, 1909, 4 X 8 In. 125.00
Rookwood, Vase, Brown, Leaf Molded, 5 Sided, No.6107, 1930, 4 In. 25.00
Rookwood, Vase, Brown, 1912, 7 X 8 In. 45.00
Rookwood, Vase, Bud, Cream & White Matte, Dated 1937, 6 In. 13.00
Rookwood, Vase, Bud, White, Art Deco Nude Behind Draped Pillar, 12 In. 85.00
Rookwood, Vase, Buttermilk, Roses & Lines, LNL Over CST, 1922, 6 In. 125.00
Rookwood, Vase, Cinnamon Color, 1935, 5 3/4 X 2 3/4 In. 39.00
Rookwood, Vase, Dark Purple To Brown, Red Floral, Green, 1923, 9 5/8 In. 32.00
Rookwood, Vase, Dark Yellow Matte Glaze, 3 Handles, RP, 1922, 3 1/2 In. 18.00

Rookwood, Vase, Beige, 6 In.
(See Page 507)

Rookwood, Vase, Dogwood, Blue Green, Wide Mouth, Wilhelmine Rehm, 7 X 4 In.	88.00
Rookwood, Vase, Eared, Green To Blue, Molded Figures, C.S.Todd, 6 In.	105.00
Rookwood, Vase, Floral Vellum, White Blossoms On Blue, L.A., 1919, 14 In.	245.00
Rookwood, Vase, Gray & Green, No.2739, 1926, 11 In.	60.00
Rookwood, Vase, Gray Brown, FR, 1916, 6 1/2 X 4 1/2 In.	60.00
Rookwood, Vase, Green Maroon Matte, Geometrics, WEH, 1911, 12 In.	125.00
Rookwood, Vase, Green Matte, Design Near Top, CAD, 1908, 4 1/2 X 5 In.	60.00
Rookwood, Vase, Green Thistles On White Gloss Glaze, M.A.D., 1900, 8 1/2 In.	125.00
Rookwood, Vase, Green To Burnt Orange, Sunflowers, LNL, 8 1/2 In.	85.00
Rookwood, Vase, Green To Mustard Yellow, Leaf Design, Sprague, 1890, 6 In.	188.00
Rookwood, Vase, Green To Rose To Pink Matte Glaze, 1928, Butterflies, 6 In.	22.50
Rookwood, Vase, Green, Oval, Ruffled, No.1167, 1930, 6 1/4 X 10 1/2 X 6 In.	50.00
Rookwood, Vase, High Glaze, Light To Brown, Water Lily, Lindeman, 1907, 8 In.	100.00
Rookwood, Vase, High Gloss Gray & Black Glaze, Dated 1954, 3 1/2 X 8 In.	10.00
Rookwood, Vase, Inverted Thumbprints, Beige & Tan, 1934, 4 X 5 In.	22.00
Rookwood, Vase, Iris Finish, Floral, Katherine Van Horne, 1908, 6 3/4 In.	225.00
Rookwood, Vase, Iris Glaze, Floral & Fruit, Artist Signed, 1911, 8 1/2 In.	175.00
Rookwood, Vase, Iris Glaze, Floral, Artist Signed, 1904, 4 1/4 In.	85.00
Rookwood, Vase, Iris Glaze, Flowers, Stalks, & Fronds, 1904, 4 1/2 In.	85.00
Rookwood, Vase, Iris Glaze, Nasturtiums, Black Bottom, I.B., 1907, 5 1/2 In.	175.00
Rookwood, Vase, Iris Glaze, Pink Flowers, O.G.Reed, 1903, 8 In.	175.00
Rookwood, Vase, Iris Glaze, Pink Roses, Fred Rothenbusch, 1902, 7 7/8 In.	265.00
Rookwood, Vase, Iris, Blue & White Bleeding Hearts, Irene Bishop, 1904, 7 In.	220.00
Rookwood, Vase, Iris, Cream To Gray, Berries & Leaves, I.B., 1907, 7 In.High	220.00
Rookwood, Vase, Iris, Edith Noonan, 1906, 7 In.	160.00
Rookwood, Vase, Jonquils Under Tan & Gold Glaze, Steinle, 1894, 5 In.	140.00
Rookwood, Vase, Lavender Drippings On Magenta, Gold Dust, 1932, 7 In., Pair	200.00
Rookwood, Vase, Leaves On Brown Glaze, LVB, 1900, 5 1/2 In.High	175.00
Rookwood, Vase, Light Blue, Darker Blue Specks, No.356F, 1922, 5 1/2 In.	30.00
Rookwood, Vase, Light Brown To Dark Green, Poppy Decoration, 1909, 7 In.	150.00
Rookwood, Vase, Matte Green & Rust, Octagonal, M Rauchfuss, C.1915, 8 In.	45.00
Rookwood, Vase, Matte Patterned, Shaded Rose, Gray, 1928, 6 1/4 In.	18.00
Rookwood, Vase, Matte Pink, 3 Handles, 1929, 4 1/2 X 3 7/8 In.Wide	22.50
Rookwood, Vase, Mottled Green, Greek Key, Matte Finish, Signed, 1900, 5 In.	72.00
Rookwood, Vase, Off-White, Flowers In Relief, 4 X 4 In.	9.00
Rookwood, Vase, Off-White, Gazelle Design, 1945, 4 1/4 In.	10.00
Rookwood, Vase, Off-White, 1945, 5 1/2 In.	9.00
Rookwood, Vase, Pillow, Brown Glaze, Daffodils, Laura Lindeman, 1900, 6 1/2 In	180.00
Rookwood, Vase, Pink Intaglio Glaze, 5 Pink Rabbits In Band, 1924, 6 1/2 In.	18.00
Rookwood, Vase, Pink To Gray Green Matte, Incised Roman Key, 1915, 11 In.	30.00
Rookwood, Vase, Pink To Gray Top, Embossed Vertical Petals, 1928, 6 In.	18.00
Rookwood, Vase, Plum Color, Rooks Around Base, 1916, 6 In.High	37.00
Rookwood, Vase, Plum, Molded Rooks, 1916, 6 In.	35.00
Rookwood, Vase, Pocket, Blue Flowers, Leaves, 1882, 4 1/2 In.	275.00
Rookwood, Vase, Poppies, Green Yellow Glazed, Dated, 9 Flames, 7 In.	145.00
Rookwood, Vase, Porcelain, Pastel Pink, Blue, Yellow, F.R., 1924, 6 1/2 In.	260.00

Rookwood, Vase, Portrait Of Elk, Standard Glaze, Hurley, 8 In., 1898 .... 575.00
Rookwood, Vase, Powder Blue, Slip Morning Glory, Handled, A.M.V., 1887, 8 In. 385.00
Rookwood, Vase, Raised Deer & Bushes On Light Blue, 1930, 7 1/2 In. 55.00
Rookwood, Vase, Reddish Brown, Batlike Figures, Mattie Foglesong, 7 In. 108.00
Rookwood, Vase, Reddish Brown, Blue Lining, Pussy Willows, 14 Flames, 5 In. 55.00
Rookwood, Vase, Rose Color, Band Of Vertical Rectangles, 1931, 6 1/2 In. 12.00
Rookwood, Vase, Scenic Vellum, Blue To Gray, F.Rothenbusch, 1919, 10 In. 195.00
Rookwood, Vase, Scenic Vellum, S.E.C., 9 In. 195.00
Rookwood, Vase, Soft Pink, Dated 1927, 7 In. 47.50
Rookwood, Vase, Standard Glaze, Autumn Leaves, Paneled, 1898, K.H., 8 In. 245.00
Rookwood, Vase, Standard Glaze, Berries & Leaves, SM, 1893, 3 1/4 In. 135.00
Rookwood, Vase, Standard Glaze, Clover, MM, 1901, 6 3/4 In. 123.00
Rookwood, Vase, Standard Glaze, Ducks At Play, 2 Handles, 1894, 6 In. 750.00
Rookwood, Vase, Standard Glaze, Flowers & Berries, CAB, 1898, 4 3/4 In. 105.00
Rookwood, Vase, Standard Glaze, Fruit & Foliage, Shirayamadani, 1891, 12 In. 450.00
Rookwood, Vase, Standard Glaze, Poppies, C.Steinle, 1893, 6 1/4 In. 227.50
Rookwood, Vase, Standard Glaze, Trumpet Flowers, CFB, 1902, 6 1/2 In. 175.00
Rookwood, Vase, Standard Glaze, Wild Roses, SC, 1899, 9 1/4 In. 175.00
Rookwood, Vase, Standard Glaze, Yellow Clover Slip, Steinle, 1898, 6 1/2 In. 140.00
Rookwood, Vase, Standard, Gold Roses & Leaves, William Klemm, 1901, 5 1/4 In. 100.00
Rookwood, Vase, Tan & Gold Glaze, Jonquils, Clara Lindeman, 1907, 6 3/4 In. 155.00
Rookwood, Vase, Tassel Design, Green With Rose Matte, 1917, 5 1/2 In. 17.50
Rookwood, Vase, Turquoise Semimatte, Floral & Leaf, 1926, 5 3/4 In. 26.00
Rookwood, Vase, Urn Shape, Earred, Green To Blue, Molded Leaf, Todd, 6 In. 115.00
Rookwood, Vase, Urn Shape, Robin's-Egg Blue, No.915D, 1926, 7 1/4 In. 45.00
Rookwood, Vase, Vellum Blue Glaze, Lavender Asters, C.Steinle, 1919 .... 155.00
Rookwood, Vase, Vellum, Art Nouveau Daisies, Blues, Louise Abel, 1920, 9 In. 150.00
Rookwood, Vase, Vellum, Black Rook Against Moon & Sky, 1907, 9 In. 250.00
Rookwood, Vase, Vellum, Blue Berry Vine On Pink To Yellow, P.C., 1917, 8 In. 115.00
Rookwood, Vase, Vellum, Daisies, Pastel Blue Shades, E.F.M., 1915, 8 In. 225.00
Rookwood, Vase, Vellum, Dogwood, Gray Green, E.Noonan, 1907, 7 In. 137.50
Rookwood, Vase, Vellum, Jug Shape, Brown, Art Design, Handled, 1906, 9 1/2 In. 75.00
Rookwood, Vase, Vellum, Robin's-Egg Blue, No Decoration, 1917, 9 In. 97.50
Rookwood, Vase, Vellum, Roses On Light To Dark Green, 1911, 8 In.High 165.00
Rookwood, Vase, Vellum, Water Lilies Around Top, Sara Sax, 1909, 4 X 8 1/2 In 125.00
Rookwood, Vase, Vellum, Winter Scene, Sallie Coyne, 1919, 11 In.High 245.00
Rookwood, Vase, Vellum, Woods & Creek, Cylindrical, F.R., 1913, 11 1/2 In. 280.00
Rookwood, Vase, Vines & Blueberries In Fuchsia & Blue, 11 X 20 In.Wide 125.00
Rookwood, Vase, Violet Color, Rooks At Bottom, Marked 1922, 7 In. 17.50
Rookwood, Vase, Wax Matte, Pink To Blue, Crocus, Shirayamadani, 1932, 7 In. 150.00
Rookwood, Vase, Wax Matte, Pink, Floral, Coyne, 1931, 5 In. 65.00
Rookwood, Vase, White Cameo Flowers On Blue Matte, A.V.B., 1887, 12 In.High 575.00
Rookwood, Vase, Yellow Gladiolas, Browns, Signed LNL, 1902, 9 In. 150.00
Rookwood, Vase, Yellow Matte Glaze, Flowers Between 5 Panels, 1926, 4 1/2 In 18.00
Rookwood, Vase, Yellow, Stylized Tulips, Molded, Shape 1907, Dated 1917, 5 In. 32.00
Rookwood, Vase, Yellow, White Gardenia, L.E.Lindeman, 6 1/2 In. 115.00
Rookwood, Vase, Yellow, 6 1/4 In. 20.00

Rose bowls were popular during the 1880s. Rose petals were kept in the open bowl to add fragrance to a room. The glass bowls were made with crimped tops, which kept the petals inside. Many types of Victorian art glass were made into rose bowls.

Rose Bowl, see also Porcelain, Rose Bowl, Pressed Glass, Rose Bowl, special art glass categories

Rose Bowl, Acid Etched Blossoms, Frosted Leaves, 5 1/2 In. 15.00
Rose Bowl, Blue Satin Glass, Crimped Rim, 4 1/2 In. 50.00
Rose Bowl, Blue Satin Glass, Footed, Enameled Flowers, 5 In.High 125.00
Rose Bowl, Cranberry Opalescent Bubbles, Ground Pontil, 4 1/2 In. 110.00
Rose Bowl, Satin Glass, Shell & Seaweed, White To Yellow, Crimped, 5 X 5 In. 145.00
Rose Bowl, Yellow To Cream, Enameled, Shell Pattern, 3 1/2 In.High 85.00
Rose Canton, Cup & Saucer, Demitasse 25.00
Rose Canton, Cup & Saucer, Famille Rose, Wishbone Handle, C.1825 .... 75.00
Rose Canton, Plate, Marked Made In China, 10 In. 18.00
Rose Canton, Tureen, Covered, Floral & Vegetables Inside, 11 X 8 1/2 In. 245.00
Rose Canton, Vase, Ewer Shape, Twig Handles, Floral & Bird Panels, 6 In. 80.00
Rose Canton, Vase, Exotic Birds & Flowering Trees, 10 1/2 In. 85.00

Rose Canton, Vase, 3 1/2 In. 30.00

Rose Medallion china was made in China during the nineteenth and twentieth centuries. It is a distinctive design picturing people, flowers, birds, and butterflies. They are colored in greens, pinks, and other colors.

Rose Medallion, Bowl & Underplate, Openwork, 8 1/2 & 9 1/8 In.	175.00
Rose Medallion, Bowl, Covered, Cabbage Rose Inside, 9 1/2 In.	325.00
Rose Medallion, Bowl, Dessert, Exposed Bisque Foot Rim, People, 6 In.	20.00
Rose Medallion, Bowl, Panels Of People & Roses, 4 Legs, 10 In.	55.00
Rose Medallion, Bowl, Panels Of Roses & People, Gold Trim, 10 X 4 In.	195.00
Rose Medallion, Bowl, Punch, 15 In.	495.00 To 575.00
Rose Medallion, Bowl, Rice, People In Windows, Raised Foot Rim, 5 1/2 In.	28.00
Rose Medallion, Bowl, 5 1/2 In.	50.00
Rose Medallion, Bowl, 11 1/2 In.	185.00
Rose Medallion, Box, Covered, Oriental Figures, Floral, 3 In.	29.50
Rose Medallion, Box, Covered, Round, 3 In.	50.00
Rose Medallion, Candlestick, C.1870, 10 In., Pair	575.00
Rose Medallion, Charger, 6 Panels, C.1840, 16 In.	300.00
Rose Medallion, Coffee Set, Roses, Birds, & Chinese Medallions, 6 Piece	225.00
Rose Medallion, Cup & Saucer	25.00 To 48.00
Rose Medallion, Cup & Saucer, Demitasse	25.00 To 35.00
Rose Medallion, Cup & Saucer, Demitasse, People, Butterflies, & Floral	16.65
Rose Medallion, Cup & Saucer, Made In China, Thin	25.00
Rose Medallion, Cup & Saucer, Octagonal, Decorated	22.50
Rose Medallion, Cup & Saucer, Orange Peel Ground, 6 Panels	65.00
Rose Medallion, Cup & Saucer, Wishbone Handle, Birds, Butterflies, C.1825	75.00
Rose Medallion, Cup, Wine, Pair	40.00
Rose Medallion, Dish, Casserole, Covered, 9 1/2 X 8 1/4 In.	350.00
Rose Medallion, Dish, Soap, Gold Finial, Liner, Pink & Gold Roses, 5 1/2 In.	145.00
Rose Medallion, Gravy Boat, Medallion Inside, Marked China, 3 1/2 X 8 In.	75.00
Rose Medallion, Ladle, Jelly, Canton	10.00
Rose Medallion, Pitcher, 10 In.	225.00
Rose Medallion, Plate, Cake, People, Butterflies & Floral, Bird Center, 8 In.	16.65
Rose Medallion, Plate, Marked China, 7 In.	24.00
Rose Medallion, Plate, Marked China, 8 1/2 In.	33.00
Rose Medallion, Plate, Orange Peel Ground, 6 Panels, 10 In.	65.00
Rose Medallion, Plate, People & Birds Cartouches, Toa Kuang, 9 1/2 In.	60.00
Rose Medallion, Plate, People In Window, 7 1/2 In., Pair	35.00
Rose Medallion, Plate, Scalloped Edge, 8 1/4 In.	35.00
Rose Medallion, Plate, 7 3/8 In.	20.00
Rose Medallion, Plate, 8 In.	30.00
Rose Medallion, Plate, 9 1/2 In.	25.00 To 50.00
Rose Medallion, Platter, Orange Peel Bottom, Oval, 16 1/2 X 14 1/4 In.	188.00
Rose Medallion, Platter, Orange Peel Ground, 6 Panels, 12 In.	167.50
Rose Medallion, Platter, Six Panels, C.1800, 11 1/2 X 14 In.	175.00
Rose Medallion, Pot, Hot Water, People In Windows, Handle, Pint	65.00
Rose Medallion, Sauce, On Dish Ring Base, 3 1/8 In.	15.00
Rose Medallion, Sugar & Creamer, People, Butterflies, & Floral, Bird Center	38.00
Rose Medallion, Teapot, Baroque Handle, High Dome Lid, 8 1/4 X 11 In.	585.00
Rose Medallion, Teapot, Double Wire Handle, Cylindrical Sides, 5 3/4 In.	50.00
Rose Medallion, Teapot, In Basket, Brass Clasp, 6 In.	72.50
Rose Medallion, Teapot, Straight Sided, 7 1/2 X 6 1/2 In.	250.00
Rose Medallion, Tray, 7 X 9 X 2 In.	75.00
Rose Medallion, Vase, Dragons At Neck, 10 In.	95.00
Rose Medallion, Vase, 8 In.	148.00

Rose O'Neill, see Kewpie

Rose Tapestry porcelain was made by the Royal Bayreuth Factory of Germany during the late nineteenth century. The surface of the ware feels like cloth.

Rose Tapestry, Basket, Apricot Roses, Royal Bayreuth, 5 1/4 X 4 3/4 In.	195.00
Rose Tapestry, Box, Covered, Dome Lid, Pink & Yellow Roses, 5 3/4 In. High	310.00
Rose Tapestry, Box, Powder, Covered, Gold, Footed, Green Mark	150.00
Rose Tapestry, Creamer, Lady & Horse Portrait, Royal Bayreuth, Blue Mark	135.00
Rose Tapestry, Creamer, Mountain Goats, Pinched Spout, Royal Bayreuth, 4 In.	125.00
Rose Tapestry, Creamer, Pinched Spout, Royal Bayreuth, Blue Mark	145.00

Rose Tapestry, Creamer, Royal Bayreuth, Blue Mark	195.00
Rose Tapestry, Creamer, 3 Color Roses, Pinched Spout, Royal Bayreuth	100.00
Rose Tapestry, Ewer, Relief Decoration, Royal Doulton, 8 In.	45.00
Rose Tapestry, Hair Receiver, Floral Decoration	150.00
Rose Tapestry, Hair Receiver, Pink & Yellow Roses, Gold Feet, Blue Mark	100.00
Rose Tapestry, Hair Receiver, Royal Bayreuth	125.00 To 150.00
Rose Tapestry, Hair Receiver, Yellow Roses, Royal Bayreuth	145.00
Rose Tapestry, Hair Receiver, 3 Color Roses, Footed, Blue Mark	150.00
Rose Tapestry, Hair Receiver, 3 Footed, Royal Bayreuth, Blue Mark	175.00
Rose Tapestry, Pitcher, Corset Shape, Pinched Spout, Royal Bayreuth, 4 In.	135.00
Rose Tapestry, Pitcher, Pinched Spout, Blue Mark, 4 1/4 In.	135.00
Rose Tapestry, Pitcher, Sheep With Ram, Royal Bayreuth, 3 In.	115.00
Rose Tapestry, Plate, Cake, Royal Bayreuth, Green Mark, 6 In.	75.00
Rose Tapestry, Plate, 3 Color Roses, Royal Bayreuth, Blue Mark, 7 1/2 In.	250.00
Rose Tapestry, Sauce, Royal Bayreuth, Blue Mark, 4 3/4 In.	40.00
Rose Tapestry, Shoe, Lace, Royal Bayreuth, Blue Mark, 5 X 2 1/2 In.	225.00
Rose Tapestry, Tray, Dresser, Colonial Lovers Scene, Blue Mark, 11 1/2 In.	195.00
Rose Tapestry, Tray, Dresser, Royal Bayreuth, Blue Mark, 10 X 7 1/2 In.	175.00
Rose Tapestry, Tray, Dresser, 3 Color Roses, Blue Mark, 11 X 8 In.	380.00
Rose Tapestry, Tray, 3 Color Roses On Floral Ground, Blue Mark, 11 X 8 In.	295.00
Rose Tapestry, Vase, Floral In Front Of Garden Gate, Rust Neck, 7 In.	110.00
Rose Tapestry, Vase, Goats In Mountains, Ear Handles, Footed, R.B., 2 1/4 In.	145.00
Rose Tapestry, Vase, Panels Of Blue & Green, E.B., Doulton, 11 In., Pair	95.00

MARKE

Rosenthal porcelain was established in Sels, Bavaria, in 1880. The German factory still continues to make fine-quality tableware and figurines.

Rosenthal, see also Mustache Cup

Rosenthal, Cup & Saucer, Demitasse, Art Nouveau Silver Overlay	20.00
Rosenthal, Cup & Saucer, Demitasse, Ivory, Gold Handle & Band Inside	20.00
Rosenthal, Cup & Saucer, Demitasse, Maroon Floral & Green, Gold, 1918	16.50
Rosenthal, Cup & Saucer, Demitasse, Rose Garlands, Gold	15.00
Rosenthal, Cup & Underplate, Bouillon, Floral Garland, Gold Handle	30.00
Rosenthal, Cup, Cream Soup, Gold Handles & Band Inside	12.50
Rosenthal, Figurine, Allegro, 1931, Artist Signed, 7 In.	95.00
Rosenthal, Figurine, Baby Eating Porridge, Bird On Bowl, 4 1/2 In.	65.00
Rosenthal, Figurine, Baby Kingfisher, Blue, On Stump, Green Mark, 4 1/2 In.	35.00
Rosenthal, Figurine, Bird, Perched On Branch, 5 3/4 In.	55.00
Rosenthal, Figurine, Brown Bear, Standing, White Base, 8 In.High	68.00
Rosenthal, Figurine, Dog, 5 In.	30.00
Rosenthal, Figurine, Green Frog On Gray Rock, 2 1/2 In.	18.50
Rosenthal, Figurine, Kingfisher On Branch, 6 In.High	65.00
Rosenthal, Figurine, Rooster, White, Red Comb, Heidenreich, Green Mark, 5 In.	50.00
Rosenthal, Goblet, Copper Wheel Cut Roses & Leaves, Paneled Stem, Pair	35.00
Rosenthal, Gravy Boat & Underplate, Sans Souci	30.00
Rosenthal, Group, Fox Cubs At Play, Freidenreich, 5 1/2 X 4 In.	115.00
Rosenthal, Plate, Fruit, Apple & Berries, Scalloped, Gold Border, 8 1/2 In.	40.00
Rosenthal, Plate, Fruit, C.1850, 8 1/2 In.	15.00
Rosenthal, Plate, Girl Sitting On Rock Center, Green & Gold Rim, 8 3/4 In.	30.00
Rosenthal, Plate, Gooseberries & Green On Pink, Yellow, & Blue, 8 1/2 In.	15.00
Rosenthal, Plate, Ivory Bavaria, Wild Rose, Gold Bands, 11 In., Set Of 12	240.00
Rosenthal, Plate, Octagonal, Floral, 8 7/8 In.	10.00
Rosenthal, Plate, Service, Coin Gold, Floral, Ivory, 11 In.	20.00
Rosenthal, Plate, Two Seminole Ladies In Center, Gold Band, 7 3/4 In.	10.50
Rosenthal, Vase, Flowering Morning Glory On White, C.1900, 5 3/4 In.High	40.00
Rosenthal, Vase, Portrait On Each Side, Covered, Handled, Deep Rose, 11 In.	265.00
Rosenthal, Vase, Roses, Gold Trim, 5 1/2 In.	20.00
Rosenthal, Vase, Trumpet, Sterling Overlay On Black Matte, 12 In.	100.00

Roseville Pottery Company was established in 1891 in Zanesville, Ohio. Many types of pottery were made, including flower vases.

Roseville, Ashtray, Bushberry, Brown, 3 1/2 X 6 1/2 In.	15.00
Roseville, Basket, Apple Blossom, Pink & Green, 9 In.High	25.00
Roseville, Basket, Freesia, White & Lavender Floral On Green, 7 In.	32.50
Roseville, Basket, Gold Peonies On Green, Irregular Shape Handle, 8 In.	29.50
Roseville, Basket, Magnolia, Brown, Tall Handle, 10 In.	40.00
Roseville, Basket, Magnolia, Burnt Orange, Brown, 8 In.High, 10 In.Across	18.00

Roseville, Basket, Ming Tree On White, Twig Handle, 14 In.	59.50
Roseville, Basket, Pinecone, Green, Attached Frog, Twig Handle, 8 In.	35.00
Roseville, Basket, Round Handles, Round Shape, No.389, 10 X 10 In.	30.00
Roseville, Basket, Rozane I, Oval Shape, 7 In.	15.00
Roseville, Basket, Snowberry On Green & Brown, 7 In.	32.50
Roseville, Basket, Wall, Magnolias On Blue Gray, 8 X 4 In.	25.00
Roseville, Basket, Wincraft, Glossy Variegated Blue, 9 3/4 X 8 In.	22.00
Roseville, Bookend, Pinecones On Green & Tan, Planters, 5 In., Pair	36.00
Roseville, Bowl & Flower Holder, Magnolia, Blue, 3 X 10 In.	35.00
Roseville, Bowl & Frog, Carnelian, Blue, 3 X 7 In.	23.00
Roseville, Bowl & Frog, Donatello, Low, 10 X 3 In.	21.00
Roseville, Bowl Vase, Mostique, Enameled Floral On Matte Pebbly, 3 In.	15.00
Roseville, Bowl, Apple Blossom, Rose Color, Handled, Marked 329-10, 4 1/2 In.	18.00
Roseville, Bowl, Apple Blossom, Twig Handles, 11 In.	12.00
Roseville, Bowl, Baneda, 6 Sided, Fruit On Blue, Open Handles, 11 In.	35.00
Roseville, Bowl, Blackberry, Low, 8 In.	25.00
Roseville, Bowl, Carnelian, Tan To Light Green, Marked RV, 5 X 5 3/4 In.	17.50
Roseville, Bowl, Centerpiece, Snowberry, Brown, 12 X 3 In.	25.00
Roseville, Bowl, Centerpiece, Zephyr Lily, Green, 14 X 3 1/2 In.	25.00
Roseville, Bowl, Clematis, Blue, 4 X 6 In.	17.00
Roseville, Bowl, Columbine, Pink, Double Handled, 8 In.	15.00
Roseville, Bowl, Columbine, Round, Blue, 9 In.	17.00
Roseville, Bowl, Console, Apple Blossom, Handled, Peach Color Inside, 6 In.	20.00
Roseville, Bowl, Console, Apple Blossoms On Green, Twig Handled, 8 1/2 In.	22.50
Roseville, Bowl, Console, Freesia, Green, 15 1/2 In.Long	16.00
Roseville, Bowl, Console, White Rose, Blue, 11 1/2 In.Diameter	15.00
Roseville, Bowl, Console, Zephyr Lily On Green & Brown, Handled, 14 In.	17.50
Roseville, Bowl, Covered, Handled, White, Blue Windmills & Sailboats, 7 In.	70.00
Roseville, Bowl, Dahlrose, Brown, 6 X 8 In.	45.00
Roseville, Bowl, Darsie, Turquoise, 7 In.	16.00
Roseville, Bowl, Dogwood, Green, Marked RV, 2 1/2 X 6 1/2 In.	22.50
Roseville, Bowl, Donatello, Footed, 6 1/2 In.High	35.00
Roseville, Bowl, Ferrella, Brown, Black Sticker, 8 X 5 1/4 In.	38.50
Roseville, Bowl, Florentine, Brown & Green, 7 1/2 In.	14.50
Roseville, Bowl, Florentine, Dark Color, Marked RV, 8 1/2 X 3 In.	17.50
Roseville, Bowl, Florentine, Light & Dark Browns, 7 In.	25.00
Roseville, Bowl, Florentine, Marked RV, 2 X 7 1/4 In.	17.50
Roseville, Bowl, Florentine, 6 X 2 1/2 In.	14.00
Roseville, Bowl, Freesia Line, Brown, Low, 6 X 2 In.	7.50
Roseville, Bowl, Fuchsia, Blue, Open Handled, 8 X 2 1/2 In.	40.00
Roseville, Bowl, Fuchsia, Pink Flowers On Blue Ground, 8 In.	40.00
Roseville, Bowl, Futura, Brown, Turquoise, & Terra-Cotta, 6 Sided, 8 In.	20.00
Roseville, Bowl, Gardenia Line, Green, Marked, 3 1/2 X 3 1/2 In.	7.50
Roseville, Bowl, Gardenia Line, Tan, 8 1/2 X 4 In.	12.50
Roseville, Bowl, Gardenia Line, White, Gray, 4 In.	10.00
Roseville, Bowl, Holly, Handled, 5 X 4 In.	45.00
Roseville, Bowl, Imperial I, 2 Handles, 8 In.Diameter	12.00
Roseville, Bowl, Jonquil, Brown, Sticker, 4 X 5 In.	20.00
Roseville, Bowl, Jonquil, 2 Handled, Gold Sticker, 4 1/2 X 6 In.	20.00
Roseville, Bowl, Laurel, Low, 6 1/2 In.	15.00
Roseville, Bowl, Magnolia, Dark Ground, Marked, 3 In.	7.00
Roseville, Bowl, Magnolia, Green Ground, Marked, 2 1/2 X 7 In.	12.00
Roseville, Bowl, Mostique, Marked RV, 3 X 7 In.	22.50
Roseville, Bowl, Mostique, 4 Color Geometrics On Gray, 3 X 5 1/2 In.	15.00
Roseville, Bowl, Pinecone, Green, Impressed Roseville USA, 6 1/2 X 4 In.	24.00
Roseville, Bowl, Silhouette, Turquoise, Green Panels, Oval, 8 In.	20.00
Roseville, Bowl, Snowberry, Blue, 5 1/2 In.	5.00
Roseville, Bowl, Snowberry, Green, 6 X 9 In.	20.00
Roseville, Bowl, Snowberry, Shaded Green, Rectangular, 11 In.	9.00
Roseville, Bowl, Sunflowers On Green Mottled & Tan, Handled, 7 1/2 In.	30.00
Roseville, Cachepot, Gardenia, 4 In.	10.00
Roseville, Candleholder, Donatello, 6 In.	23.00
Roseville, Candleholder, Ferrella, 4 In., Pair	25.00
Roseville, Candleholder, Green, Pink & Yellow Flowers, 2 In., Pair	8.50
Roseville, Candleholder, Ixia, Pink & Yellow Floral On Aqua, 2 In., Pair	11.50
Roseville, Candleholder, Oxblood, Leaf Spray, Heart Shape, 3 In.	5.00

Roseville, **Candleholder,** Snowberry, 2 1/2 In., Pair	12.00
Roseville, **Candlestick,** Clematis, Blue, 5 1/2 In.High, Pair	12.50
Roseville, **Candlestick,** Columbine Line, Rose & Green, 1145, 2 1/2 In., Pair	12.50
Roseville, **Candlestick,** Donatello, Band Of Cherubs, 8 1/2 In.High	26.00
Roseville, **Candlestick,** Freesia, Rust Color, 4 1/2 In., Pair	18.00
Roseville, **Candlestick,** Imperial Green, Sticker, 2 1/2 In., Pair	30.00
Roseville, **Candlestick,** Water Lily, Double, Green Ground, 4 X 7 1/2 In.	8.00
Roseville, **Centerpiece For Bowl,** Zephyr Lily, Turquoise, Marked, 5 In. High	155.00
Roseville, **Centerpiece,** Clematis, Handled, Blue, Rough Texture, 4 In.	8.00
Roseville, **Compote,** Donatello, 3 1/2 X 4 1/2 In.	15.00
Roseville, **Console Set,** Clematis, Red Flowers On Green, 3 Piece	32.00
Roseville, **Console Set,** Cremona, Blue, 4 1/4 In. Candles, 3 Piece	32.50
Roseville, **Console Set,** Futura, Mottled Brown & Green, 4 Piece	22.00
Roseville, **Console Set,** White Gardenias Green On Green, 3 Piece	19.50
Roseville, **Console Set,** Zephyr Lily, Blue, 3 Piece	25.00
Roseville, **Console Set,** Zephyr Lily, Brown, 3 Piece	25.00
Roseville, **Cornucopia,** Freesia, Brown With Yellow Flowers, 6 In.	7.50
Roseville, **Cornucopia,** Pinecone, Green, 6 In.	7.00
Roseville, **Creamer,** Child's, Dog, Signed	17.00
Roseville, **Ewer,** Columbine, Brown, 8 X 7 In.	35.00
Roseville, **Ewer,** Freesia, Lavender & White Floral On Green, 6 In.	38.00
Roseville, **Ewer,** Magnolia, Green, 6 In.High	22.00
Roseville, **Ewer,** Rozane, Royal, Holly, Marked Rozane RPCO, 6 1/2 In.	125.00
Roseville, **Ewer,** Zephyr Lily, Large Handle, Brown, 10 1/2 In.	30.00
Roseville, **Flower Frog,** Tuscany, Paper Sticker, 5 1/2 In.	13.50
Roseville, **Inkwell,** Rozane, Egypto, In Hoc Signo On Scroll, 3 3/4 In.	165.00
Roseville, **Jar,** Cookie, Columbine, Covered, 10 1/2 X 9 In.	40.00
Roseville, **Jardiniere,** Dahlrose, Green & Blue, 7 In.High	22.00
Roseville, **Jardiniere,** Dahlrose, Round, Open Handles At Top, 4 X 3 In.	22.50
Roseville, **Jardiniere,** Dahlrose, Round, Open Handles At Top, 6 X 6 In.	37.50
Roseville, **Jardiniere,** Dogwood II, 6 1/2 In.High	28.00
Roseville, **Jardiniere,** Donatello, 12 1/2 In.Diameter	45.00
Roseville, **Jardiniere,** Donatello, 6 X 7 In.	32.00
Roseville, **Jardiniere,** Donatello, 8 1/2 X 11 In.	65.00
Roseville, **Jardiniere,** Florentine, Green Band Of Grapes On Cream, 9 In.	32.00
Roseville, **Jardiniere,** Mostique, Gray, 8 In.	20.00
Roseville, **Jardiniere,** Mostique, Rough Gray Ground, Stylized Design, 13 In.	38.00
Roseville, **Jardiniere,** Pinecone I, Blue, Small	12.00
Roseville, **Jardiniere,** Pinecone, Blue, 4 1/2 X 7 In.	25.00
Roseville, **Jardiniere,** Pinecone, Green Matte, 8 1/2 X 11 In.	50.00
Roseville, **Jardiniere,** Rozane, Handled, 6 X 6 In.	20.00
Roseville, **Jardiniere,** White Lilies On Blue, 2 Handled, 2 Piece, 25 In.	125.00
Roseville, **Jug,** Rozane, Handled, Red, Yellow, & Blue Flowers, 7 1/2 In., B.M.	75.00
Roseville, **Lamp Base,** Freesia, Brown, 11 1/2 In.High	50.00
Roseville, **Mug,** Blue Bushberry, Marked U.S.A. 1, 3 1/2 In.	20.00
Roseville, **Mug,** Children & Cat	18.00
Roseville, **Mug,** Holly, 3 1/2 In.	7.50
Roseville, **Pitcher,** Lemonade, Magnolia, Dark Green Ground, Marked, 9 1/2 In.	30.00
Roseville, **Pitcher,** Marvo, Green, 7 1/2 In.High	68.00
Roseville, **Pitcher,** Pale Yellow, Kitchen Utensils, Medallions, 6 1/2 In.	11.00
Roseville, **Pitcher,** Rozane Egypto, Green Matte, Tricorner, Molded, 3 In.High	95.00
Roseville, **Pitcher,** Water, Ivory Pattern, 9 3/4 In.	28.00
Roseville, **Pitcher,** Water, Landscape, 1915	45.00
Roseville, **Pitcher,** Water, Magnolia, Green	45.00
Roseville, **Planter & 2 Candlesticks,** Burgundy Color, 12 1/2 X 3 In.	23.00
Roseville, **Planter,** Boat Shape, Mottled Blues On Blue, Grapes, 15 1/2 In.	38.00
Roseville, **Planter,** Brown To Rust, Yellow Flowers, 2 Handles, 10 In.	9.95
Roseville, **Planter,** Bushberry, Rectangular, Green, Brown Berries, 8 In.	13.00
Roseville, **Planter,** Dahlrose, Round, Brown Ground, Cream Flowers, 10 In.	16.00
Roseville, **Planter,** Donatello, 9 In.	27.50
Roseville, **Planter,** Hanging, Dogwood I, Rounded Bow Shape, 3 1/2 X 7 1/4 In.	25.00
Roseville, **Planter,** Magnolia, Brown, 5 X 7 In.	17.00
Roseville, **Planter,** Mostique, Gray Ground, Stylized Design, 9 In.	24.00
Roseville, **Plate,** Child's, Bunny	20.00
Roseville, **Pocket,** Foxglove Pink To Wine, Marked U.S.A. 1292, 8 In.	11.00
Roseville, **Pocket,** Wall, Blue, Moss, 8 1/2 In.	12.50

Roseville, Pocket, Wall, Dahlrose, Open Handled, 8 X 6 1/2 In.	25.00
Roseville, Pocket, Wall, Rosecraft, Vintage Line, Black, 9 In.	25.00
Roseville, Pocket, Wall, Zephyr Lily, Open Handled, Brown & Green, 8 In.	20.00
Roseville, Rose Bowl, Iris, No.357, 4 In.	12.00
Roseville, Rose Bowl, Pine Cone, Green, 7 In.Diameter	10.00
Roseville, Sugar & Creamer, White Berries On Green & Brown, Marked	20.00
Roseville, Sugar & Creamer, Wild Berry Decoration On Blue	17.50
Roseville, Sugar, Snowberry, Deep Red & Pink, 2 Handled	10.00
Roseville, Tea Set, Freesia Line, Brown, 3 Piece	65.00
Roseville, Tea Set, Peony, Pink, 3 Piece	65.00
Roseville, Tea Set, White Rose Line, Blue, 3 Piece	70.00
Roseville, Tumbler, Sunflower, 2 Handles, 5 1/2 In.High	16.50
Roseville, Urn, Florentine, 2 Handles, Cream & Green Swags, 8 1/2 In.	25.00
Roseville, Urn, Green & Rust, White Berries & Leaves, 2 Handles, 8 1/2 In.	14.75
Roseville, Urn, Water Lily, 6 In.High	19.50
Roseville, Vase, Acorn, Branch Handles, Blue Body, 14 1/2 In.High	35.00
Roseville, Vase, Acorns On Orange To Brown, Handled, 9 In.	40.00
Roseville, Vase, Apple Blossom, Green, 10 1/2 X 7 In.	35.00
Roseville, Vase, Apple Blossoms On Blue, Twig Handles, 10 1/4 In.	35.00
Roseville, Vase, Baneda, Squatty, Cherries, Leaves On Blue, 5 1/4 In.High	32.00
Roseville, Vase, Baneda, 2 Handled, 1 In. Diameter Top, 4 In.	15.00
Roseville, Vase, Berries, Branches, & Leaves On Green, Handles, 12 In.	50.00
Roseville, Vase, Blue & Green, Water Lilies, Double Handles, 7 In.	8.00
Roseville, Vase, Blue Drapery, 11 In.High	38.00
Roseville, Vase, Bowl Type, Morning Glory, 4 X 6 3/4 In.Wide	25.00
Roseville, Vase, Bud, Jonquils On Brown & Yellow, Open Handled, 7 In.	19.50
Roseville, Vase, Bud, Wincraft, Mottled Blues, Flower, Leaf Each Side, 6 In.	9.00
Roseville, Vase, Bud, Zephyr Lilies On Blue, Open Handled, 7 In.	15.00
Roseville, Vase, Bushberry, Blue, 9 In.High	18.00
Roseville, Vase, Bushberry, Brown, 6 In.	17.00
Roseville, Vase, Bushberry, Green, 6 In.	17.00
Roseville, Vase, Carnelian I, Medium Blue Over Light Blue, 8 In.High	28.00
Roseville, Vase, Cherry Blossom, 8 In.	20.00
Roseville, Vase, Cherry Blossoms, 2 Handles, 7 1/2 In.High	22.00
Roseville, Vase, Clematis, Dark Green, 15 1/2 In.	52.00
Roseville, Vase, Clematis, Green, Pink Flowers, 7 In.	17.00
Roseville, Vase, Clematis, Green, 2 Handles, 7 1/2 In.	18.00
Roseville, Vase, Clematis, Marked 192, 5 In.	15.00
Roseville, Vase, Clematis, White Flowers On Light Blue Ground, 7 1/2 In.	16.00
Roseville, Vase, Columbine On Pink To Green, 3 In.	15.00
Roseville, Vase, Columbine On Tan To Green, Squatty, 3 In.	15.00
Roseville, Vase, Columbine, Blue Flowers On Tan, 3 X 5 In.	15.00
Roseville, Vase, Corinthian, Double, 6 1/2 X 8 In.	22.50
Roseville, Vase, Corinthian, 8 1/2 In.	32.00
Roseville, Vase, Cornucopia, Tan & Brown, White Flowers, 6 In.High	8.50
Roseville, Vase, Cremona, Handled, 13 In.	27.50
Roseville, Vase, Cremona, White Floral On Beige, Leaves Form Handle, 11 In.	30.00
Roseville, Vase, Dawn, Handled, Green Floral On Cream, Square Base, 6 1/2 In.	30.00
Roseville, Vase, Dickensware, Dombey & Son, 2nd Line, 9 In.	325.00
Roseville, Vase, Donatello, Corset Shape, Bowed Handles, 6 1/4 In.	26.00
Roseville, Vase, Donatello, Cylindrical, Band Of Cherubs, 6 In., Unmarked	22.00
Roseville, Vase, Donatello, 10 In., Pair	70.00
Roseville, Vase, Double Bud, Donatello, 7 1/2 In.High	25.00
Roseville, Vase, Ferrella, Mottled Glaze, Reticulated, 9 1/4 In.	65.00
Roseville, Vase, Florentine, Double, 4 1/2 X 9 In.	15.00
Roseville, Vase, Florentine, Marked RV, 6 1/4 X 2 1/2 In.	14.00
Roseville, Vase, Florentine, Marked RV, 7 1/4 X 3 1/2 In.	14.00
Roseville, Vase, Florentine, Marked RV, 8 1/4 In.	20.00
Roseville, Vase, Florentine, Matte Brown, Leaves & Grapes, RV, 10 1/4 In.	30.00
Roseville, Vase, Flowers On Both Sides, Handled, No.822, 8 In.	25.00
Roseville, Vase, Foxglove, Blue, 8 In.	16.00
Roseville, Vase, Foxglove, Green, No.46, 7 1/4 In.	20.00
Roseville, Vase, Foxglove, Pink, 15 In.High	22.00
Roseville, Vase, Freesia, Blue, Handled, 10 1/2 In.High	20.00
Roseville, Vase, Freesia, Green, No.123, 9 1/2 In., Pair	50.00
Roseville, Vase, Freesia, Rust Color, Signed, 8 In.	20.00

Roseville, Vase, Fuchsia, Squatty, Blue, 2 Handles, 7 In.	30.00
Roseville, Vase, Fuchsias On Shaded Blue, Open Handled, 6 In.	25.00
Roseville, Vase, Futura, Blue To Cream To Blue, 4 In.	20.00
Roseville, Vase, Futura, Flower Design, 5 1/4 In.	20.00
Roseville, Vase, Futura, 6 X 5 X 4 3/4 In.	18.50
Roseville, Vase, Gardenia, Gray, 2 Handled, 6 X 2 1/4 In.	14.00
Roseville, Vase, Gardenia, Marked 57, 4 In.	9.00
Roseville, Vase, Green With Rust, Sprigs Of White Berries, 2 Handles, 8 In.	14.75
Roseville, Vase, Green, Pink Flowers, 7 1/2 In.	12.00
Roseville, Vase, Imperial, 7 In.	45.00
Roseville, Vase, Iris, Tan, 3 X 5 In.	20.00
Roseville, Vase, Ixia, Orange & Yellow, 8 In.High	26.00
Roseville, Vase, Ixia, Urn Shape, Pink & Yellow Floral On Aqua, 7 In.	18.00
Roseville, Vase, Jonquil, Gourd Shape, 2 Handles, 8 1/2 In.High	25.00
Roseville, Vase, Laurel On Yellow, Closed Handles, 8 In.	36.00
Roseville, Vase, Laurel, High Neck, 9 X 6 In.	38.50
Roseville, Vase, Laurel, Light Brown, Silver Sticker, 6 In.	20.00
Roseville, Vase, Lily On Green, 2 Handled, 18 In.	65.00
Roseville, Vase, Lily, Blue, 7 1/2 In.	20.00
Roseville, Vase, Lily, Marked 201, 7 In.	10.00
Roseville, Vase, Lily, Yellow & Pink, Green, Ground, 2 Handles, 7 In.	10.50
Roseville, Vase, Luffa, Open Handled, Green To Cream, White Floral, 8 In.	45.00
Roseville, Vase, Magnolia, Blue, 2 Handled, 9 X 9 In.	22.50
Roseville, Vase, Magnolia, Blue, 5 1/2 In.High, 7 1/2 In.Wide	16.00
Roseville, Vase, Magnolia, Brown, 2 Handled, 4 In.	9.00
Roseville, Vase, Magnolia, Burnt Orange, No.87, 6 1/4 In.	20.00
Roseville, Vase, Magnolia, White & Brown On Blue, Handles, 14 3/4 In.High	44.00
Roseville, Vase, Mara, 8 In.	350.00
Roseville, Vase, Moderine, Rose To White, 7 1/2 X 1 3/4 In.	14.00
Roseville, Vase, Molded Yellow Top, Brown Base, Yellow Flower, 10 In.	29.00
Roseville, Vase, Monticello, Open Handled, Black & White On Tan, 5 1/4 In.	40.00
Roseville, Vase, Monticello, Round, Black & White Design On Greenish, 5 In.	40.00
Roseville, Vase, Moss, Inverted Cone On Base, Green To Tan, Handled, 6 In.	27.50
Roseville, Vase, Moss, 9 In.High	22.00
Roseville, Vase, Mostique, Flared, Gray, Stylized Flowers, 10 X 5 1/4 In.	33.00
Roseville, Vase, Mostique, Flared, Matte Pebbly, Floral, 8 X 4 In.	25.00
Roseville, Vase, Mostique, Marked R, 10 In.	35.00
Roseville, Vase, Mostique, 11 In., Pair	52.00
Roseville, Vase, Mostique, 11 1/2 In.	20.00
Roseville, Vase, Panel, Brown With Orange Flowers, RV Mark, 6 1/2 In.	20.00
Roseville, Vase, Peonies On Gold To Green, Open Handles, 7 In.	25.00
Roseville, Vase, Peony, Green To Rose Shading, Double Handled, 7 In.	9.00
Roseville, Vase, Pinecone, Handled, Marked RV, 8 In.	28.00
Roseville, Vase, Pinecone, Blue, Leaves Form Handle, Irregular Top, 8 In.	35.00
Roseville, Vase, Pinecone, Blue, Signed, 8 In.	28.00
Roseville, Vase, Pinecone, Blue, 10 1/2 X 6 In.	25.00
Roseville, Vase, Pinecone, Brown, Handled, Marked 700-10, 10 In.	30.00
Roseville, Vase, Pinecone, Green, Impressed Roseville 846-9, 9 In.	27.00
Roseville, Vase, Pinecone, Trumpet Shape, Green To White, Twig Handle, 6 In.	18.50
Roseville, Vase, Pinecone, 6 1/2 In.	14.00
Roseville, Vase, Pink Tuscany, Conical, 5 In.	18.00
Roseville, Vase, Poppy, Green, No.872, 9 1/4 In.	30.00
Roseville, Vase, Primrose, Tan, 6 X 5 In.	20.00
Roseville, Vase, Rose Dahlias & Leaves, 2 Handled, No.1036, 6 1/2 In., Pair	15.00
Roseville, Vase, Rosecraft, Double, Hexagonal, Marked RV, 5 1/4 X 7 1/2 In.	25.00
Roseville, Vase, Royal Rozane, Purple Clover, Footed, J.Imlay, 6 1/2 In.	48.00
Roseville, Vase, Rozane, Berry & Leaf On Brown Glaze, Handled, 4 1/2 In.High	45.00
Roseville, Vase, Rozane, Cherries & Leaves, Lily Mitchell, 13 In.High	150.00
Roseville, Vase, Rozane, Clovers, High Glaze, Slender Neck, Handled, 8 1/4 In.	70.00
Roseville, Vase, Rozane, Compote Shape, Floral On White Stippled, 5 In.	45.00
Roseville, Vase, Rozane, Daffodils On Shaded Brown, 8 In.	75.00
Roseville, Vase, Rozane, Dark Brown High Glaze, Yellow & Red Floral, 9 In.	85.00
Roseville, Vase, Rozane, Nasturtiums, Flared Out Center, 7 In.	95.00
Roseville, Vase, Rozane, Orange & Green Foliage On Brown, 8 1/2 In.	125.00
Roseville, Vase, Rozane, Royal, Floral, Marked Rozane RPCO, 6 In.	75.00
Roseville, Vase, Rozane, Royal, Twisted, Holly, Artist W.M., 5 1/4 In.	210.00

Roseville, Vase, Silhouette, Green Leaf, 12 1/2 In. 25.00
Roseville, Vase, Silhouette, Nudes, Green, Marked, 8 X 7 In. 37.50
Roseville, Vase, Snowberry, Blue, Quarter Moon Shape, 7 In., Pair 25.00
Roseville, Vase, Snowberry, Green & Brown Ground, White Berries, 5 1/4 In. 16.00
Roseville, Vase, Snowberry, Green, 7 X 5 In. 18.00
Roseville, Vase, Sunflower, 10 1/2 X 6 In. 38.50
Roseville, Vase, Teasel, Lavender To Pink, 8 X 6 In. 20.00
Roseville, Vase, Thornapple On Brown To Tan, Cornucopia Shape, 6 In. 20.00
Roseville, Vase, Thornapple, White Blossoms On Blue, Open Handles, 6 In. 19.50
Roseville, Vase, Topeo, Mongol Red Glaze, 9 1/4 In. 100.00
Roseville, Vase, Tulip, Glossy, 8 In. 15.00
Roseville, Vase, Tuscany, Ivory Color, 2 Handles, 5 X 5 In.High 24.00
Roseville, Vase, Vintage, Brown, Grapes & Vines, 5 X 3 1/2 In.High 22.00
Roseville, Vase, Water Lily, Blue & White, 2 Handled, Marked, 15 X 11 In. 45.00
Roseville, Vase, Water Lily, Blue, Marked 174, 6 In. 12.50
Roseville, Vase, Water Lily, Green, 4 In. 15.00
Roseville, Vase, Water Lily, 8 1/2 In. 18.00
Roseville, Vase, White & Green Floral On Blue Green, 2 Handles, 8 1/2 In. 14.00
Roseville, Vase, White Floral On Blue, 4 1/2 In. 12.50
Roseville, Vase, White Rose On Brown, Triangle Handles, Marked H, 6 In. 15.00
Roseville, Vase, Wincraft, Brown To Chartreuse, Flower, Closed Handles, 8 In. 15.00
Roseville, Vase, Wincraft, Glossy Green, 9 In. 20.00
Roseville, Vase, Wincraft, Glossy Light Brown, 8 X 6 In. 17.00
Roseville, Vase, Wincraft, Mottled Wine & Gray, Thornapple, 10 3/8 In. 20.00
Roseville, Vase, Wincraft, Yellow & Brown Mottled, Brown Tree Trunks, 8 In. 16.00
Roseville, Vase, Wisteria, Open Handles, 6 1/2 In. 16.00
Roseville, Vase, Wisteria, 2 Handles, 7 1/2 In.High 28.00
Roseville, Vase, Zephyr Lily, Blue, Cream Lilies, Green Leaves, 12 1/2 In. 34.00
Roseville, Vase, Zephyr Lily, Brown, 6 X 4 In. 17.00
Roseville, Washstand Set, Juvenile Line, Rabbit, Green Band, 2 Piece 25.00

Roy Rogers, see also Clock
Roy Rogers, Button, Picture, Pinback 2.00
Roy Rogers, Dinner Set, 21 Piece 11.00
Roy Rogers, Flashlight, Signal Siren 12.00
Roy Rogers, Gun, Cap, Six Shooter, Metal 6.50
Roy Rogers, Hat, Quick Shooter, Gun In Felt Cowboy Hat .... 7.50 To 8.00
Roy Rogers, Holster Set, Leather, Illustrated Box With Metal Gun 10.50
Roy Rogers, Lunch Box & Thermos, C.1950 .... 12.00
Roy Rogers, Lunch Box & Thermos, Chuckwagon Shape, Lithographed, Tin 10.75
Roy Rogers, Spurs, Metal, Pair In Illustrated Box .... 7.00 To 7.50
Roy Rogers, Watch, Wrist, Dale Evans, Official, Leather Band 35.50
Royal Austria, Platter, Fish, Scalloped Edge, Wreath Of Roses, 21 In.Long 75.00
Royal Austria, Salt Dip, Hand-Painted 5.00

Royal Bayreuth porcelain was made in Germany during the late nineteenth and twentieth centuries. Many types of wares were made.

Royal Bayreuth, see also Old Ivory, Rose Tapestry, Sand Babies, Snow Baby, Sunbonnet Babies
Royal Bayreuth, Ashtray, Arab, Blue Mark 32.00
Royal Bayreuth, Ashtray, Bulldog, Caption Come On, Square, Green Mark 35.00
Royal Bayreuth, Ashtray, Corinthian, Cue Ball Shape, Blue Mark 110.00
Royal Bayreuth, Ashtray, Deer Hunting Scene 30.00
Royal Bayreuth, Ashtray, Elk, Blue Mark .... 39.50 To 67.00
Royal Bayreuth, Ashtray, Figural, Devil's Face, Green Mark 85.00
Royal Bayreuth, Ashtray, Fox Hunting Scene 30.00
Royal Bayreuth, Ashtray, Musical Cavaliers, Brown, Dixon, Blue Mark 27.00
Royal Bayreuth, Ashtray, Sheep In Mountain Pasture, Blue Mark 35.00
Royal Bayreuth, Berry Set, Cherries & Blossoms On Green, Blue Mark, 7 Piece 190.00
Royal Bayreuth, Bowl, Blown-Out, Gold Scalloped Rim, Blue Mark, 10 1/2 In. 85.00
Royal Bayreuth, Bowl, Pansy, Pearlized, Blue Mark, 10 In. 125.00
Royal Bayreuth, Bowl, Red Devil & Cards, C.1890 .... *Illus* 50.00
Royal Bayreuth, Bowl, Roses, Satin Finish, Blue Mark, 10 1/2 In. 70.00
Royal Bayreuth, Bowl, White To Green, Red Orchids, Gold, Blue Mark, 10 1/2 In 95.00
Royal Bayreuth, Box, Covered, Yellow Roses, Blue Mark, 3 1/2 In. 35.00
Royal Bayreuth, Box, Covered, 3 Cows In Meadow, Blue Mark, 4 1/4 X 5 In. 55.00
Royal Bayreuth, Box, Peacock On Cover, Browns, Blue Mark, 4 3/4 X 2 1/2 In. 37.00

Royal Bayreuth, Bowl,
Red Devil & Cards, C.1890
(See Page 516)

Royal Bayreuth, Cachepot, Man In Fishing Boat, 2 Handled, Blue Mark, 3 In.	39.00
Royal Bayreuth, Candleholder, Girl & Geese, Mountains, Blue Mark, 4 In.	42.50
Royal Bayreuth, Celery, Lobster, Blue Mark	55.00
Royal Bayreuth, Celery, Yellow Roses & Green Leaves On Pastel, Blue Mark	50.00
Royal Bayreuth, Chocolate Pot, Cobalt, White, & Gold, Blue Mark, 11 In.	35.00
Royal Bayreuth, Compote, Pastoral Farm Scene, Blue Mark, 10 In.	175.00
Royal Bayreuth, Condiment Set, Strawberry Figural, 3 Piece On Green Leaf	37.00
Royal Bayreuth, Creamer, Alligator	110.00 To 125.00
Royal Bayreuth, Creamer, Apple, Blue Mark	45.00 To 55.00
Royal Bayreuth, Creamer, Autumn Leaf, Blue Mark	85.00
Royal Bayreuth, Creamer, Black Bull, Red Horns & Ears, Green Mark	72.00
Royal Bayreuth, Creamer, Black Cat, Tettau Mark, 5 In.	85.00
Royal Bayreuth, Creamer, Black Crow, Blue Mark	75.00 To 85.00
Royal Bayreuth, Creamer, Butterfly	92.00
Royal Bayreuth, Creamer, Coachman, Signed	135.00
Royal Bayreuth, Creamer, Conch Shell, Mother-Of-Pearl, Blue Mark, 6 In.	54.00
Royal Bayreuth, Creamer, Conch Shell, Pearl Luster, 3 In.	48.00
Royal Bayreuth, Creamer, Conch Shell, White, Blues, Orange Highlights	35.00
Royal Bayreuth, Creamer, Corinthian, Black, Scenes, Blue Mark, 4 X 3 In.	55.00
Royal Bayreuth, Creamer, Corinthian, Black, 5 1/4 In.	47.50
Royal Bayreuth, Creamer, Cows & Trees, Yellow Bottom, Blue Mark, 3 1/2 In.	40.00
Royal Bayreuth, Creamer, Crab	45.00
Royal Bayreuth, Creamer, Crow, Black & White	65.00
Royal Bayreuth, Creamer, Devil & Cards, Blue Mark, 3 7/8 In.High	64.00
Royal Bayreuth, Creamer, Devil & Cards, Blue Mark, 4 In.	65.00
Royal Bayreuth, Creamer, Devil & Cards, Red Devil Handle, Green Mark, 4 In.	70.00
Royal Bayreuth, Creamer, Eagle, Tettau Mark	100.00
Royal Bayreuth, Creamer, Elk, Blue Mark	38.00 To 48.00
Royal Bayreuth, Creamer, Elk, Etched Coney Island 1908, Blue Mark	68.00
Royal Bayreuth, Creamer, Frog, Signed	90.00 To 105.00
Royal Bayreuth, Creamer, Fish's Head, Blue Mark	35.00
Royal Bayreuth, Creamer, Geranium	30.00
Royal Bayreuth, Creamer, Hand-Painted Ship On Stormy Sea, Blue Mark, 4 In.	42.00
Royal Bayreuth, Creamer, Hunter With Dog, 4 In.	46.00
Royal Bayreuth, Creamer, Lemon, Signed	70.00
Royal Bayreuth, Creamer, Lobster Handle, Cabbage Body, 3 3/4 In.	35.00
Royal Bayreuth, Creamer, Lobster On Lettuce Leaf, Blue Mark	45.00
Royal Bayreuth, Creamer, Lobster, Blue Mark, 3 1/2 In.	55.00
Royal Bayreuth, Creamer, Lobster, Green Mark, 5 1/4 In.	32.00
Royal Bayreuth, Creamer, Man In Mountain, Tettau Mark	90.00
Royal Bayreuth, Creamer, Man Leading Horses, Blue Mark	37.00
Royal Bayreuth, Creamer, Moose's Head, Blue Mark, 4 1/4 In.	39.00
Royal Bayreuth, Creamer, Mountain Goat, Blue Mark, 4 1/2 In.	42.00 To 110.00
Royal Bayreuth, Creamer, Musicians, Painted	70.00
Royal Bayreuth, Creamer, Orange, Blue Mark	65.00 To 90.00
Royal Bayreuth, Creamer, Poodle	45.00
Royal Bayreuth, Creamer, Poppy, Blue Mark	45.00 To 85.00

Royal Bayreuth, Creamer, Rose, Blue Mark 145.00
Royal Bayreuth, Creamer, Snail, Lobster Handle, Blue Mark 20.00
Royal Bayreuth, Creamer, Snow Baby, Miniature 35.00
Royal Bayreuth, Creamer, Spiky Shell, Pearl 65.00
Royal Bayreuth, Creamer, Tankard Shape, Arab On Horse, Blue Mark, 4 1/2 In. ... 55.00
Royal Bayreuth, Creamer, Tomato, Blue Mark, 3 In. 30.00
Royal Bayreuth, Creamer, Tomato, Blue Mark, 3 3/4 In. 35.00
Royal Bayreuth, Creamer, Town Crier, 4 1/4 In. 100.00
Royal Bayreuth, Creamer, Woodpecker Handle, Tree Trunk Body, 3 3/4 In. 35.00
Royal Bayreuth, Creamer, Yawning Mouth Fish, Blue Mark 72.00
Royal Bayreuth, Cup & Saucer, Demitasse, Pansy Figural 30.00
Royal Bayreuth, Cup & Saucer, Demitasse, Red, Sheep Border, Blue Mark 45.00
Royal Bayreuth, Cup & Saucer, Demitasse, Yellow Roses, Tettau Blue Mark 15.00
Royal Bayreuth, Cup & Saucer, Goats In Mountain Scenery, Blue Mark 39.50
Royal Bayreuth, Cup & Saucer, Jack & Jill, Blue Mark 40.00
Royal Bayreuth, Cup & Saucer, Pastoral Sheep Scene, Gold, Blue Mark 56.00
Royal Bayreuth, Cup & Saucer, Rose & Leaf, Blue Mark 18.50
Royal Bayreuth, Cup & Saucer, Young Girl & Geese, Village Scene, Blue Mark 38.00
Royal Bayreuth, Cup, Loving, 3 Handled, Cattle Scene, Blue Mark 50.00
Royal Bayreuth, Dish, Heart Shape, Little Boy Blue, Blue Mark, 4 1/2 X 4 In. 45.00
Royal Bayreuth, Dish, Jack & The Beanstalk, Blue Mark, 5 3/4 In. 40.00
Royal Bayreuth, Dish, Nut, Old Venice, Pierced Handled, Blue Mark, 8 In. 45.00
Royal Bayreuth, Hair Receiver, Lady On Horse On Lid, Gold Footed, Blue Mark ... 35.00
Royal Bayreuth, Hair Receiver, Ring-Around-The-Rosy, Blue Mark 95.00
Royal Bayreuth, Hatpin Holder, Entire Hunting Scene, Green Dish Base 85.00
Royal Bayreuth, Hatpin Holder, Fox Hunt, On Pedestaled Plate, Blue Mark 85.00
Royal Bayreuth, Hatpin Holder, Lavender Poppy, Blue Mark 175.00
Royal Bayreuth, Hatpin Holder, White Poppy, Blue Mark 125.00
Royal Bayreuth, Humidor, Chimpanzee 265.00
Royal Bayreuth, Jar, Cigarette, Cylindrical, Sheik In White Robe, Horse 50.00
Royal Bayreuth, Jar, Cookie, Poppy, Blue Mark 115.00
Royal Bayreuth, Jar, Cracker, Tomato, Covered 75.00
Royal Bayreuth, Jar, Mustard, Pansy, Stem Spoon, Blue Mark 60.00
Royal Bayreuth, Jar, Tobacco, Horse, Rider & Dogs, Pipes Hand On Each Side ... 150.00
Royal Bayreuth, Jar, Tomato, Covered, 3 1/2 X 3 In. 35.00
Royal Bayreuth, Jug, Hand-Painted Ship At Sea, Blue Mark, 4 In.High 42.00
Royal Bayreuth, Match Holder, Clown, Tub Shape Striker, Blue Mark 95.00
Royal Bayreuth, Match Holder, Hanging, Devil & Cards 125.00
Royal Bayreuth, Match Holder, Hanging, Fishermen Scene 85.00
Royal Bayreuth, Match Holder, Moose, Blue Mark 75.00
Royal Bayreuth, Mayonnaise Set, Lobster, 2 Piece 28.00
Royal Bayreuth, Mug, Beer, Devil & Cards, 5 In. 95.00
Royal Bayreuth, Mug, Coffee, 2 Dutch Children On Pier, Ships, 3 1/2 In. 49.00
Royal Bayreuth, Mug, Dutch Children By Gate, Sailing Ships, 3 1/2 In. 53.00
Royal Bayreuth, Mug, Little Boy Blue, Blue Mark 40.00
Royal Bayreuth, Mug, Penguin Trim, 3 Handles, Large Size 95.00
Royal Bayreuth, Nappy, Cabbage Leaf, Handled 12.00
Royal Bayreuth, Nappy, Leaf, Multicolored, 6 In. 28.00
Royal Bayreuth, Picher, Milk, Brown Roses, Pastoral Scene, 4 3/4 In.High 85.00
Royal Bayreuth, Picher, Water, Devil & Cards, 8 In.High 150.00
Royal Bayreuth, Pitcher, Arab With 2 Horses, 8 1/2 In. 75.00
Royal Bayreuth, Pitcher, Brittany Maids, Blue Mark, 5 In. 65.00
Royal Bayreuth, Pitcher, Brittany Scene, Scalloped Edging, 3 1/2 In. 58.00
Royal Bayreuth, Pitcher, Cavaliers On Green, A.Dixon, 5 1/2 In. 105.00
Royal Bayreuth, Pitcher, Children Playing In Winter, Green Mark, 3 In. 35.00
Royal Bayreuth, Pitcher, Cider, Figural, Gray Eagle, Blue Mark 175.00
Royal Bayreuth, Pitcher, Devil & Cards, 46 Ozs. 75.00
Royal Bayreuth, Pitcher, Figural, Flounder, Blue Mark, Quart 110.00
Royal Bayreuth, Pitcher, Frog, Green With Pink, 3 In. 40.00
Royal Bayreuth, Pitcher, Hunting Scene, Green, 5 7/8 In. 39.00
Royal Bayreuth, Pitcher, Lobster, 5 In. 30.00
Royal Bayreuth, Pitcher, Milk, Devil & Cards, Signed 225.00
Royal Bayreuth, Pitcher, Milk, Lamplighter, Blue Mark 165.00
Royal Bayreuth, Pitcher, Milk, Red Tomato 57.00
Royal Bayreuth, Pitcher, Milk, Ye Olde Crown & Scepter, Barrel, Blue Mark 145.00
Royal Bayreuth, Pitcher, Moose & Dogs, Blue Mark, 3 3/4 In. 65.00

Royal Bayreuth, Pitcher, Snow Baby, Blue Mark, 4 1/2 In. 155.50
Royal Bayreuth, Pitcher, Tomato, Hound & Elk At Top, Black Mark, 7 In. 85.00
Royal Bayreuth, Pitcher, Water, Apple, Blue Mark 145.00
Royal Bayreuth, Pitcher, Water, Devil & Cards, 8 In. 150.00
Royal Bayreuth, Pitcher, Water, Little Miss Muffet, 10 In. 175.00
Royal Bayreuth, Pitcher, Water, Lobster, 7 X 8 In. 125.00
Royal Bayreuth, Plate, Arab On Horseback, Blue Mark, 7 1/2 In. 35.00
Royal Bayreuth, Plate, Bopeep Pastoral Scene, Pink, Blue Mark, 7 1/2 In. 64.00
Royal Bayreuth, Plate, Cake, Handled, Sheik With 2 Horses, 10 5/8 In. 40.00
Royal Bayreuth, Plate, Clockface With Red Devil, 4 1/2 In. 95.00
Royal Bayreuth, Plate, Covered, Tomato On Lettuce Leaf, Ring Handle, 3 In. 35.00
Royal Bayreuth, Plate, Devil & Cards, Signed, 7 In. 85.00
Royal Bayreuth, Plate, Fishermen On Lake, Pine Trees, Birds, Blue Mark, 9 In. 110.00
Royal Bayreuth, Plate, Leaf, Stem Curls To Form Handle, Blue Mark, 4 In. 12.00
Royal Bayreuth, Plate, Little Boy Blue, Green To Pink, Blue Mark, 6 In. 85.00
Royal Bayreuth, Plate, Little Jack Horner, Blue Mark, 7 5/8 In. 45.00
Royal Bayreuth, Plate, Poppy, Open Handled, 10 1/2 In. 65.00
Royal Bayreuth, Plate, Ship In Storm Scene, Signed, 7 In. 25.00
Royal Bayreuth, Plate, 2 Maidens Filling Fishing Baskets, Blue Mark, 8 In. 39.50
Royal Bayreuth, Pot & Spoon, Mustard, Lobster 29.50
Royal Bayreuth, Pot, Mustard, Covered, Lobster 42.50
Royal Bayreuth, Pot, Mustard, Covered, Tomato, Blue Mark 37.00
Royal Bayreuth, Pot, Mustard, Red Poppy, Blue Mark 52.50
Royal Bayreuth, Pot, Mustard, Shell, Mother-Of-Pearl Murex 30.00
Royal Bayreuth, Relish, Cutout Handles, Dutch Boy & Girl Scene, Blue Mark 79.00
Royal Bayreuth, Relish, Lobster, Green Mark 35.00
Royal Bayreuth, Relish, Shell, Mother-Of-Pearl Murex, 8 In. 48.00
Royal Bayreuth, Rose Bowl, Little Boy Blue & Haystack, Blue Mark, 4 X 3 In. 50.00
Royal Bayreuth, Salt & Pepper, Devil & Cards .... 75.00 To 125.00
Royal Bayreuth, Salt & Pepper, Elk, Signed 55.00
Royal Bayreuth, Salt & Pepper, Murex, Blue Mark 45.00
Royal Bayreuth, Salt & Pepper, Purple Grape, Green Leaf Base, Blue Mark 53.00
Royal Bayreuth, Salt & Pepper, Red Pepper 35.00
Royal Bayreuth, Salt & Pepper, Toadstool 45.00
Royal Bayreuth, Saltshaker, Conch Shell, Blue & Orange On Pearlized 19.00
Royal Bayreuth, Saltshaker, Plum, Unmarked 15.00
Royal Bayreuth, Saltshaker, Woman Feeding Chickens 8.00
Royal Bayreuth, Saucer, Ring-Around-The-Rosy, Blue Mark 26.00
Royal Bayreuth, Stein, Blonde Girl Holding Candle, Blue Mark, Liter 120.00
Royal Bayreuth, Stein, Devil & Cards, 18 Ozs. 75.00
Royal Bayreuth, Stickpin Holder, Green Frog On Maroon, Blue Mark 127.50
Royal Bayreuth, String Holder, Figural, Rooster, Blue Mark 85.00
Royal Bayreuth, Sugar & Creamer, Dutch Girl & Boy Scene 60.00
Royal Bayreuth, Sugar & Creamer, Lobster, Blue Mark 95.00
Royal Bayreuth, Sugar & Creamer, Man Leading Horses, Blue Mark 20.00
Royal Bayreuth, Sugar & Creamer, Pastoral Scene 75.00
Royal Bayreuth, Sugar & Creamer, Purple Grape 125.00
Royal Bayreuth, Sugar & Creamer, Tomato, Cover, Blue Mark .... 58.00 To 65.00
Royal Bayreuth, Sugar, Little Bopeep 58.00
Royal Bayreuth, Sugar, Lobster, Covered, 3 3/4 In. 35.00
Royal Bayreuth, Sugar, Man Leading Horses, Blue Mark 23.00
Royal Bayreuth, Sugar, Tomato, Covered, 3 3/4 In., Blue Mark 35.00
Royal Bayreuth, Tankard, Pheasant, Blue Mark, 7 1/2 In. 85.00
Royal Bayreuth, Tea Set, Shell, Mother-Of-Pearl Murex, 3 Piece 175.00
Royal Bayreuth, Tea Set, Tomato, 3 Piece 95.00
Royal Bayreuth, Teapot, Murex Shell, Blue Mark 110.00
Royal Bayreuth, Teapot, Orange Figural, Covered 95.00
Royal Bayreuth, Teapot, Shell, Mother-Of-Pearl, Signed .... 85.00 To 110.00
Royal Bayreuth, Teapot, Tomato, Covered, 3 3/4 X 5 In., Blue Mark 65.00
Royal Bayreuth, Toby Mug, Coachman, Blue Mark, 4 1/2 In. 85.00
Royal Bayreuth, Toby Mug, Old Man Of The Mountain, 4 In. 40.00
Royal Bayreuth, Toothpick, Clown 85.00
Royal Bayreuth, Toothpick, Elk's Head .... 42.00 To 60.00
Royal Bayreuth, Toothpick, Moose, Footed, 3 Handles At Top, Blue Mark 42.50
Royal Bayreuth, Tray, Dresser, Misty Roses, 10 X 7 In. 60.00
Royal Bayreuth, Tray, Dresser, Open Handles, Floral, Blue Mark, 10 X 7 In. 60.00

Royal Bayreuth, Tray, Hunt Scene, 9 3/4 X 7 1/4 In.	95.00
Royal Bayreuth, Tray, Pin, Floral On Green & White, 4 X 4 1/2 In.	14.00
Royal Bayreuth, Tray, Pin, Hunt Scene, Blue Mark	35.00
Royal Bayreuth, Tray, Pin, Rose Garlands, Gold Leaf Border, 3 X 5 In.	35.00
Royal Bayreuth, Tray, Pin, Roses, Gold Decoration, 3 1/2 X 5 In.	15.00
Royal Bayreuth, Vase, Art Nouveau, Swans On Lake, Blue Mark, 6 In.	75.00
Royal Bayreuth, Vase, Cavalier, Signed Dixon, Blue Mark, 3 1/4 In.High	39.50
Royal Bayreuth, Vase, Coach Scene, 9 1/2 In.	65.00
Royal Bayreuth, Vase, Farmer & Scythe, Blue Mark, 4 1/2 In.	50.00
Royal Bayreuth, Vase, Musicians, Sterling Rim, Blue Mark, 3 1/2 In.	30.00
Royal Bayreuth, Vase, Musicians, Sterling Rim, 5 1/2 In.	30.00
Royal Bayreuth, Vase, Pastoral Scene, Green, Footed, Blue Mark, 5 1/4 In.	49.95
Royal Bayreuth, Vase, Pastoral Scene, 6 In.	42.00
Royal Bayreuth, Vase, Portrait, Girl, High Glaze, Dark Blue Ground, 6 In.High	120.00
Royal Bayreuth, Vase, Roses On Cream Ground, Gold Trim, Blue Mark, 3 1/2 In.	45.00
Royal Bayreuth, Vase, Roses, Lions' Heads Handles, Blue Mark, 7 In.	85.00
Royal Bayreuth, Vase, Scenic, Cachet, Fisherman In Boat, Handles, 2 3/4 In.	65.00
Royal Bayreuth, Vase, Scenic, Swans On Lake, Blue Mark, 3 3/4 In.	35.00
Royal Bayreuth, Vase, Sheik On Horse, Blue Mark, 4 In.	40.00
Royal Berlin, see also KPM	
Royal Berlin, Bowl, Covered, Russian Eagle & German Crest, C.1810, 6 1/4 In.	800.00
Royal Berlin, Cup & Saucer, Cup On 3 Claw Feet, Floral Medallions	50.00
Royal Berlin, Cup, Sweetmeat, 2 On Baroque Base, Male Cherub Standing, 1870	135.00
Royal Berlin, Figurine, St.Bernard Dog, Reclining, White, 9 1/2 In.	44.00
Royal Berlin, Plate, Floral Center, Magenta, Rococo Gold Border, 10 In., 8	200.00
Royal Berlin, Tea Set, Various Flowers & Insects, Embossed Border, 27 Piece	650.00
Royal Berlin, Teapot, Floral, Gold Gilding, 6 1/2 In.	90.00

Royal Bonn is the nineteenth century trade name for the Bonn China Manufactory established in 1755 at Bonn, Germany. A general line of porcelain dishes was made.

Royal Bonn, Bowl, Brown To Beige, Magenta & Cream Floral, Mehlem, 9 1/2 In.	16.00
Royal Bonn, Bowl, Delft, Windmills & Floral, 8 3/4 X 4 3/4 In.	47.50
Royal Bonn, Dish, Cheese, Aster Decoration	28.00
Royal Bonn, Dish, Cheese, Slant Top, Mums	30.00
Royal Bonn, Jardiniere, Persian Cashmere, Blues & Gold, 6 1/2 X 7 1/2 In.	85.00
Royal Bonn, Plate, Floral Sprays, Gold Edges, 8 1/4 In., Pair	12.00
Royal Bonn, Plate, Impressed Franz Art Mehlem, 9 In.	95.00 To 150.00
Royal Bonn, Vase, Beige, Colored Floral, Raised Gold, Lion Head Handle, 9 In.	65.00
Royal Bonn, Vase, Candlestick Type Top, Geometrics, Floral, 10 1/4 In.	145.00
Royal Bonn, Vase, Covered, Pink & Gold On Pale Green, 16 1/4 In.	225.00
Royal Bonn, Vase, Floral On Rust, Gold Trim, 8 1/2 In.	24.00
Royal Bonn, Vase, Gold Portrait Lady, 2 Handled, Mottled ....Color	25.00
Royal Bonn, Vase, Hand-Painted, Blue, Green, Orchid, & Rose Floral, 12 1/4 In.	87.50
Royal Bonn, Vase, Paintings Of Ladies, Signed, 17 In., Pair	260.00
Royal Bonn, Vase, Pastel Floral, 26 X 6 In.	150.00

DENMARK

Royal Copenhagen porcelain and pottery has been made in Denmark since 1772. It is still being made. One of their most famous wares is the Christmas Plate Series.

Royal Copenhagen, see also Collector, Plate, Royal Copenhagen	
Royal Copenhagen, Compote, White, Blue Flowers, 8 1/2 X 6 In.	55.00
Royal Copenhagen, Cup & Saucer, Blue On White	29.50
Royal Copenhagen, Cup & Tray, Cigarette, Cranuelle	15.00
Royal Copenhagen, Dish, Seashell Shape, Crab Sitting On Side, 9 1/2 In.	105.00
Royal Copenhagen, Figurine, Barefooted Boy Sitting On Rock, 12 1/2 In.	395.00
Royal Copenhagen, Figurine, Blue Point Siamese Cat, Signed R R, 7 3/4 In.	165.00
Royal Copenhagen, Figurine, Boxer Puppy Sitting Askew, 3 1/2 In.	48.00
Royal Copenhagen, Figurine, Boy, No.1659, 12 X 10 In.	250.00
Royal Copenhagen, Figurine, Dachshund, Sitting, 3 In.	62.00
Royal Copenhagen, Figurine, Deer Lying Down, 6 X 5 In.	75.00
Royal Copenhagen, Figurine, Kitten, Sitting, Green Eyes, 6 In.	64.00
Royal Copenhagen, Figurine, Mother Robin & 2 Babies, 3 1/4 In., Set Of 3	90.00
Royal Copenhagen, Figurine, Mouse On Ear Of Corn	45.00
Royal Copenhagen, Figurine, Pug, Sitting, Beige, 3 1/2 In.	42.00 To 47.00
Royal Copenhagen, Figurine, Reclining Cat, White & Gray, 5 1/2 In.	35.00

Royal **Copenhagen, Figurine,** Robin, Pastel Coloring, 2 1/4 In.	26.00
Royal **Copenhagen, Figurine,** Sitting Kitten, Gray & White, 6 In.	63.00
Royal **Copenhagen, Frog,** Sitting On Gray Rock, 2 1/2 In.	20.00
Royal **Copenhagen, Group,** Peasant Couple, 17 1/2 X 11 In.	550.00
Royal **Copenhagen, Group,** Sultan Kissing Nude Lady, C.1930, 9 1/2 In.	375.00
Royal **Copenhagen, Group,** Two Puppies At Play, 4 X 2 1/2 In.	65.00
Royal **Copenhagen, Group,** 2 Peasants, No.1352, 11 X 17 In.	450.00
Royal **Copenhagen, Inkstand,** Covered Well On 10 3/4 In. Tray, White, C.1900	100.00
Royal **Copenhagen, Plaque,** Parian, Night & Day, 15 In.Diameter, Framed	500.00
Royal **Copenhagen, Vase,** Shaded Blue, Art Nouveau Poppy, C.1900, 10 1/4 In.	130.00
Royal **Copenhagen, Vase,** White Art Nouveau Poppies On Blue, C.1900, 11 In.	130.00

Royal Crown Derby Company, Ltd., was established in England in 1876.
Royal Crown Derby, see also Crown Derby, Derby

Royal **Crown Derby, Bowl,** Daffodils, Shallow, 6 In.	32.50
Royal **Crown Derby, Cup & Saucer,** Demitasse, Blues, Pink, & White	35.00
Royal **Crown Derby, Vase,** Gold, Red, & Green Enamel On Pink, 2 Handles, 12 In.	225.00

Royal Doulton was the name used on pottery made after 1902. The Doulton Factory was founded in 1815. Their wares are still being made.
Royal Doulton, see also Doulton

Royal **Doulton, Ashtray,** Sairey Gamp, 3 In.	39.00
Royal **Doulton, Berry Set,** Sir Roger De Coverley, Horse Grooming, 7 Piece	150.00
Royal **Doulton, Bottle,** Perfume, Oriental Lady, Grossmith's, Thibet, 12 In.	110.00
Royal **Doulton, Bottle,** Sandeman, Original Label, 10 In.	45.00
Royal **Doulton, Bowl,** Berry, Coaching Day, 5 In.Diameter	13.50
Royal **Doulton, Bowl,** Bunnykins, Straight Sided, 6 In.	22.00
Royal **Doulton, Bowl,** Coaching Days, 8 In.	45.00
Royal **Doulton, Bowl,** Coaching Scene, Scalloped Edge, 1895 Mark, 5 1/4 In.	21.50
Royal **Doulton, Bowl,** Dickensware, Fagin, Signed Noke, 9 1/4 X 6 X 1 3/4 In.	55.00
Royal **Doulton, Bowl,** Dickensware, Micawber, Weller, & Pickwick, Noke, 8 In.	75.00
Royal **Doulton, Bowl,** Dickensware, Old Peggotty, 9 In.	45.00
Royal **Doulton, Bowl,** Dickensware, Poor Jo, Pierced Handles, 5 X 6 1/2 In.	36.00
Royal **Doulton, Bowl,** Dickensware, Tony Weller, 7 3/4 In.	50.00
Royal **Doulton, Bowl,** Izaac Walton Ware, Quotes Inside Rim, 8 In.	50.00
Royal **Doulton, Bowl,** Junket, Bunnykins, 7 1/2 In.	22.00
Royal **Doulton, Bowl,** Nursery Rhyme, Ride A Cock-Horse, 5 In.	36.00
Royal **Doulton, Bowl,** Oatmeal, Bunnykins, 6 In.	18.00
Royal **Doulton, Bowl,** Old Gaffers, 4 X 8 X 8 In.	90.00
Royal **Doulton, Bowl,** Punch, Coaching Scene, Royal Mail, Cream, 1920s, Gallon	125.00
Royal **Doulton, Bowl,** Punch, The Gleaners, 8 1/2 X 4 1/4 In.	65.00
Royal **Doulton, Bowl,** Rex Begonia Leaves In Blue, Green, Yellow, 8 3/4 In.	55.00
Royal **Doulton, Bowl,** Robert Burns Inside, 8 In.	65.00
Royal **Doulton, Bowl,** Titanian, Oval, 8 X 11 In.	65.00
Royal **Doulton, Bowl,** Vegetable, Coaching Days, Oval, 9 1/2 In.	35.00
Royal **Doulton, Bust,** Tony Weller, Marked A, Miniature	34.00
Royal **Doulton, Butter Pat,** Dickensware, Fagin, Signed Noke, 3 3/4 In.	18.50
Royal **Doulton, Butter Pat,** Dickensware, Tony Weller, Signed Noke, 3 3/4 In.	19.00
Royal **Doulton, Cachebox,** Green Tassels On Corners, Square, 3 In.	17.50
Royal **Doulton, Condiment Set,** Tans & Browns, 3 Piece, 2 1/2 In., Lambeth	80.00
Royal **Doulton, Creamer,** Bunnykins, Barbara Vernon, Marked A, 4 In.	15.00
Royal **Doulton, Creamer,** Dickensware, Bill Sykes	35.00
Royal **Doulton, Creamer,** Pied Piper, Toby Type, 1953	27.00
Royal **Doulton, Creamer,** Pink, Blue Mottled Decoration, 7 In.	27.50
Royal **Doulton, Creamer,** The Jackdaw Of Rheims, 4 In.	45.00
Royal **Doulton, Cup & Saucer,** Bunnykins	7.50 To 22.50
Royal **Doulton, Cup & Saucer,** Coaching Days	30.00 To 32.00
Royal **Doulton, Cup & Saucer,** Demitasse, Fox In Relief, Riding Crop Handle	20.00
Royal **Doulton, Cup & Saucer,** Demitasse, Madras, Artist Signed	20.00
Royal **Doulton, Cup & Saucer,** Demitasse, Relief Fox, Riding Crop Handle	20.00
Royal **Doulton, Cup & Saucer,** Dickensware, Bill Sykes	35.00
Royal **Doulton, Cup & Saucer,** Pomeroy	10.00
Royal **Doulton, Cup & Saucer,** Shakespeare Series	25.00
Royal **Doulton, Cup & Saucer,** Under The Green Tree	22.00
Royal **Doulton, Cup,** Fox Hunting, Yellow, Green Border, No.D-5104	28.00
Royal **Doulton, Cup,** Loving, George VI & Elizabeth Coronation, 1937, Noke	165.00

Royal Doulton, Dinner Set, Hunt Scenes, Charles Simpson, 31 Piece	250.00
Royal Doulton, Dish, Child's Feeding, Nursery Rhyme, 7 1/2 In.	35.00
Royal Doulton, Dish, Pin, Dickensware, Artful Dodger, Signed Noke, 4 1/4 In.	25.00
Royal Doulton, Dish, Serving, The Leather Boffal Inn, Oak Leaves, 11 1/2 In.	28.00
Royal Doulton, Eggcup, Bunnykins	3.00
Royal Doulton, Eggcup, Double, Grantham, Pair	18.50
Royal Doulton, Ewer, Blue, Swirled Gold Circles Band, BN, 9 1/2 In., Pair	95.00
Royal Doulton, Ewer, Dickensware, Little Nell, 8 1/2 In.	45.00
Royal Doulton, Figurine, Ardienne, Purple, HN2152, 1963	60.00
Royal Doulton, Figurine, Autumn Breezes, Green, Dated 1913, 8 In.	75.00
Royal Doulton, Figurine, Autumn Breezes, HN 1934, Red Dress, 8 In.	65.00
Royal Doulton, Figurine, Autumn Breezes, Young Lady In Red Dress, 7 1/2 In.	65.00
Royal Doulton, Figurine, Bather, HN 687, 7 1/2 In.	165.00
Royal Doulton, Figurine, Beez Fuz, 4 1/4 In.High	75.00
Royal Doulton, Figurine, Bonnie Lassie, 5 1/4 In.High	85.00
Royal Doulton, Figurine, Bull Terrier, Miniature	17.50
Royal Doulton, Figurine, Bulldog, Miniature	8.00
Royal Doulton, Figurine, Bumble, 4 In.	11.00
Royal Doulton, Figurine, Bunny, Sitting, 1 Ear Up, Flambe, 3 In.	19.50
Royal Doulton, Figurine, Carmen, HN1267, 7 In.	95.00
Royal Doulton, Figurine, Chloe, 2 3/4 In.High	75.00
Royal Doulton, Figurine, Churchill Bulldog With Flag On Back, 6 In.	60.00
Royal Doulton, Figurine, Curly Knob, HN 1627, 6 In.	175.00
Royal Doulton, Figurine, Dalmatian, 8 X 6 In.	32.00 To 45.00
Royal Doulton, Figurine, Darling, HN 1319, 7 1/2 In.	85.00
Royal Doulton, Figurine, Darling, 5 1/4 In.High	45.00
Royal Doulton, Figurine, Drake, Flambe, Standing, 6 1/2 In.	60.00
Royal Doulton, Figurine, Duck, Flambe, Swimming, 2 X 3 In.	20.00
Royal Doulton, Figurine, Duck, Flambe, 6 1/2 In.	45.00
Royal Doulton, Figurine, Elegance, Beige & Green, 7 3/4 In.	45.00
Royal Doulton, Figurine, Fat Boy, 4 In.High	20.00
Royal Doulton, Figurine, Fox Lying Down, Flambe, 5 In.	22.00
Royal Doulton, Figurine, Fox, Flambe, 9 In.	185.00
Royal Doulton, Figurine, Fox, Running, Flambe, 5 1/2 In.	19.50
Royal Doulton, Figurine, Foxhound, Miniature	8.00
Royal Doulton, Figurine, Genevieve, HN 1962, 8 In.	60.00
Royal Doulton, Figurine, Hare, Flambe, 1 3/4 In.Long	18.00
Royal Doulton, Figurine, Horse & Colt, Platform Base, 15 X 8 1/2 In.	160.00
Royal Doulton, Figurine, Horse & Colt, 16 & 8 In., Pair	175.00
Royal Doulton, Figurine, Janet, 4 In.High	75.00
Royal Doulton, Figurine, Jersey Milkmaid, HN 2057, Copyright 1949, 7 In.	65.00
Royal Doulton, Figurine, Lido Lady, HN1220, 7 In.	95.00
Royal Doulton, Figurine, Little Bopeep, 5 1/2 In.	55.00
Royal Doulton, Figurine, Little Bridesmaid, HN 1633, 5 1/4 In.	100.00
Royal Doulton, Figurine, Little Nell, 4 In.	11.00
Royal Doulton, Figurine, Lizana, 8 1/2 In.High	125.00
Royal Doulton, Figurine, Margery, HN 1413, 10 3/4 In.	225.00
Royal Doulton, Figurine, Mary Had A Little Lamb, HN 2048, 3 1/2 In.	45.00
Royal Doulton, Figurine, Mary, Mary, 1948, 5 In.	35.00
Royal Doulton, Figurine, Mask, HN733, 6 3/4 In.	95.00
Royal Doulton, Figurine, Mendicant, HN 1365, 5 1/4 X 3 1/2 In.	95.00
Royal Doulton, Figurine, Michele, Green Dress, 7 In.High	50.00
Royal Doulton, Figurine, Miss Demure, Pinks, 8 In.	45.00
Royal Doulton, Figurine, Miss Demure, 8 1/2 In.	70.00
Royal Doulton, Figurine, Monica, HN 1467, 4 1/2 In.	38.00
Royal Doulton, Figurine, Mr.Micawber, 4 In.	11.00
Royal Doulton, Figurine, Mr.Pickwick, 4 In.	11.00
Royal Doulton, Figurine, Owl, Flambe, 12 X 6 In.	225.00
Royal Doulton, Figurine, Paisley Shawl, 8 In.	55.00
Royal Doulton, Figurine, Paisley Shawl, 8 1/4 In.	95.00
Royal Doulton, Figurine, Pecksniff, 4 In.	11.00
Royal Doulton, Figurine, Persian Cat, 5 In.	18.00
Royal Doulton, Figurine, Pickwick, HN 556, 7 In.	135.00
Royal Doulton, Figurine, Polar Bear Sitting On Cake Of Ice, 2 X 2 X 4 In.	95.00
Royal Doulton, Figurine, Rabbit, Crouching, Flambe, 2 3/4 In.	28.00
Royal Doulton, Figurine, Rabbit, Flambe, 1 Ear Raised, 3 In.	20.00

Royal Doulton, Figurine, Rabbit, Flop Eared, Flambe, 2 1/2 In. 22.00
Royal Doulton, Figurine, Rag Doll, 5 In. 50.00
Royal Doulton, Figurine, Reclining Hare, Flambe, 4 In.Long 65.00
Royal Doulton, Figurine, Rose, 4 3/4 In.High 55.00
Royal Doulton, Figurine, Sairey Gamp, HN 558, 7 1/4 In. 160.00
Royal Doulton, Figurine, Sairey Gamp, 4 In. 11.00
Royal Doulton, Figurine, Sairey Gamp, 4 1/2 In.High 75.00
Royal Doulton, Figurine, Seated Bulldog With British Flag, C.1941, 4 In. 38.00
Royal Doulton, Figurine, Setter Dog With Large Bird, 5 1/2 In. 55.00
Royal Doulton, Figurine, Shire Horse, 7 1/4 In., Pair 175.00
Royal Doulton, Figurine, Snarling Tiger, Crouched Ready To Spring, 9 In. 70.00
Royal Doulton, Figurine, Standing Duck, Flambe, 3 In. 18.00
Royal Doulton, Figurine, Sweet & Twenty, HN 1298, 5 3/4 X 7 In. 135.00
Royal Doulton, Figurine, Sweet Anne, HN 1496, 7 In. 160.00
Royal Doulton, Figurine, Sweet Anne, 4 1/2 In. 75.00
Royal Doulton, Figurine, Sweeting, Young Lady In Full Pink Dress, 6 1/4 In. 30.00
Royal Doulton, Figurine, Sweeting, 1935, 6 1/2 In. 39.50
Royal Doulton, Figurine, The Moor, 18 In.High 230.00
Royal Doulton, Figurine, The Old King, 11 In. 145.00
Royal Doulton, Figurine, Tiger, Flambe, Signed Noke, 14 In. .... 158.00 To 250.00
Royal Doulton, Figurine, Uriah Heep, 7 1/4 In.High 95.00
Royal Doulton, Figurine, Victorian Lady, HN 1452, 7 1/2 In. 165.00
Royal Doulton, Gravy Boat, Coaching Days 45.00
Royal Doulton, Group, Horse & Colt, 16 X 8 In. 168.00
Royal Doulton, Hair Receiver, Coaching Ways 32.00
Royal Doulton, Humidor, Dickensware, Mr.Pickwick, Street Scene, Noke, 10 In. 50.00
Royal Doulton, Humidor, Sailing Ships On Blue Ground, Blue & Brown Border 50.00
Royal Doulton, Humidor, Tobacco, Arab Scene, Beige Trim, 6 1/2 In. 75.00
Royal Doulton, Humidor, Tobacco, Viking Ship, Dark Green Trim, 6 1/2 In. 75.00
Royal Doulton, Jar, Covered, Kyle Pattern, Shamrock Decoration, 3 1/4 In. 15.00
Royal Doulton, Jar, Dickensware, Tony Weller Waiting For Coach, Noke, 5 In. 39.00
Royal Doulton, Jar, Tobacco, Eliza Simmance, Gray, 6 1/2 In. 150.00
Royal Doulton, Jar, Tobacco, Glazed Tan With Blue, Embossed, Metal Bar 55.00
Royal Doulton, Jar, Tobacco, Steel Lid, Green Glaze, Brown Tree Bark, 6 In. 45.00
Royal Doulton, Jar, Tobacco, White Figures On Tan & Brown, Presser 45.00
Royal Doulton, Jardiniere, Green & Blue, Floral, F.J., 8 X 6 3/4 In. 73.00
Royal Doulton, Jardiniere, Leaf Pattern In Beige & Gray, Elm Leaf, 6 1/2 In 75.00
Royal Doulton, Jug, Harvest, 7 In. 54.00
Royal Doulton, Jug, Viking Ship, Brown To Beige, 9 In.High 110.00
Royal Doulton, Jug, Welsh Ladies Scenic, 2 In. 50.00
Royal Doulton, Lighter, Cigarette, The Beefeater 28.50
Royal Doulton, Match Holder, Art Deco Geometrics, Cobalt & Brown, C.1925 .... 60.00
Royal Doulton, Mug, Monk Decoration, Signed Noke 60.00
Royal Doulton, Mug, Shakespeare, Tan & Brown, House, 3 Handles, C.1910 .... 95.00
Royal Doulton, Mug, 3 Hound Handles & Toby Scenes, Hunting, 1902-37 .... 85.00
Royal Doulton, Pitcher, "Deaf, " Men & Car, Signed H.J.M., 6 In. 65.00
Royal Doulton, Pitcher, Aubrey Pattern, Blue & White, 10 1/3 In. 80.00
Royal Doulton, Pitcher, Bunnykins, Barbara Vernon, 6 1/4 In. 30.00
Royal Doulton, Pitcher, Falconry, Woman, Man, Castle, & Falcon, 4 1/2 In. 32.00
Royal Doulton, Pitcher, Five Men Playing Golf, C.1910, 8 1/2 In.High 60.00
Royal Doulton, Pitcher, Gleaner's, 6 In. 75.00
Royal Doulton, Pitcher, Gleaners, 9 In. 85.00
Royal Doulton, Pitcher, Gray Floral Band On Mottled Blue, 8 In. 48.50
Royal Doulton, Pitcher, Houses & Lake Scene, C.1935, 4 X 5 In. .... 48.00 To 52.00
Royal Doulton, Pitcher, Light To Dark Brown, Applied Handle, 3 1/4 In. 15.00
Royal Doulton, Pitcher, Milk, Canterbury Pilgrims 75.00
Royal Doulton, Pitcher, Milk, Dickensware, Bill Sykes, 5 In. 45.00
Royal Doulton, Pitcher, Monk, 6 Panels, 5 1/2 In.High 35.00
Royal Doulton, Pitcher, Owl Bordered, Cream, Leaves On Handle, 1902, 7 In. 50.00
Royal Doulton, Pitcher, Queen Elizabeth I, Signed Noke 58.00
Royal Doulton, Pitcher, Scenic With Young Woman, 4 1/4 In. 35.00
Royal Doulton, Pitcher, Three Musketeers, Made In England, 8 1/2 In. 37.50
Royal Doulton, Pitcher, Treasure Island, 1934, Noke & Fenton, 7 3/4 In. 195.00
Royal Doulton, Pitcher, Vase Type, Gray Band & Raised Floral On Blue, 8 In. 49.50
Royal Doulton, Pitcher, Watchman What Of The Night, 6 3/4 In. 37.50
Royal Doulton, Pitcher, Yellow Crackled, Greek Key, Brown Handle, 8 In. 85.00

Royal Doulton, Plaque, Flagship Of Lord Nelson, Raised, Dated 1939, 10 In. 37.50
 Royal Doulton, Plate, see also Gibson Girl, Plate
Royal Doulton, Plate & Mug, Child's, Bunnykins, Artist Signed, Set 25.00
Royal Doulton, Plate, Admiral, 10 1/2 In. .... 18.00 To 22.00
Royal Doulton, Plate, African Series, Elephant, 10 1/2 In. 20.00
Royal Doulton, Plate, Anne Hathaway's Cottage, 10 1/2 In. .... 22.00 To 35.00
Royal Doulton, Plate, Art Nouveau, 10 In. 30.00
Royal Doulton, Plate, Arundel Castle, Brown & Yellow, 10 1/2 In. 30.00
Royal Doulton, Plate, Baby's, Hush A Bye Baby, Baby In Basket 35.00
Royal Doulton, Plate, Becket's Martyrdom, 10 1/2 In. 40.00
Royal Doulton, Plate, Bow Valley, 10 1/2 In. 22.00
Royal Doulton, Plate, Bread & Butter, Coaching Days, 7 In. 20.00
Royal Doulton, Plate, Bunnykins, 7 In. 18.00
Royal Doulton, Plate, Cake, Floral, Octagonal 5.50
Royal Doulton, Plate, Changing Team, Coaching Scene, 10 1/2 In. 24.00
Royal Doulton, Plate, Coaching Days, White Ground, 5 1/2 In. Square 18.00
Royal Doulton, Plate, Coaching Days, 5 In. 15.00
Royal Doulton, Plate, Dickensware, Artful Dodger, 7 1/2 In. 28.00
Royal Doulton, Plate, Dickensware, Artful Dodger, 9 1/2 In. 35.00
Royal Doulton, Plate, Dickensware, Barkis, 10 1/2 In. .... 38.00 To 46.00
Royal Doulton, Plate, Dickensware, Bill Sykes, Noke, 10 1/2 In. 45.00
Royal Doulton, Plate, Dickensware, Captain Cuttle, 10 1/2 In. 45.00
Royal Doulton, Plate, Dickensware, Dick Swiveller, 10 1/2 In. 38.00
Royal Doulton, Plate, Dickensware, Fat Boy, 10 1/2 In. 45.00
Royal Doulton, Plate, Dickensware, Mr. Micawber, Noke, 10 1/2 In. 45.00
Royal Doulton, Plate, Dickensware, Sairey Gamp, 10 1/2 In. 45.00
Royal Doulton, Plate, Dickensware, Sydney Carton, Angry Mob, Yellow, 7 In. 20.00
Royal Doulton, Plate, Dickensware, The Admiral, 10 In. 35.00
Royal Doulton, Plate, Dickensware, Tony Weller, Noke, 10 1/2 In. 45.00
Royal Doulton, Plate, Dickensware, Trolly Veck, 10 1/2 In. 38.00
Royal Doulton, Plate, Dinner, Coaching Days 30.00
Royal Doulton, Plate, Doctor, 10 1/2 In. 18.00
Royal Doulton, Plate, Dutch Scene, Signed Noke, 10 1/2 In. 35.00
Royal Doulton, Plate, Elizabeth I At Moreton Hall, 10 In. 25.00
Royal Doulton, Plate, Elizabeth I At Moreton Hall, 10 1/4 In. 35.00
Royal Doulton, Plate, Embossed, Ivory, Scalloped Rim, 9 In. 8.00
Royal Doulton, Plate, English Milkmaid On Cobblestone Path, 10 1/2 In. 37.00
Royal Doulton, Plate, English Sampler, Cottage & Cows, 10 1/2 In. 45.00
Royal Doulton, Plate, Falconer, 10 1/4 In. .... 18.00 To 31.00
Royal Doulton, Plate, Fish, Gold Borders, Signed C. Hart, 9 In. 75.00
Royal Doulton, Plate, Flambe, Peasant With Bundle Of Straw On Back, 9 In. 75.00
Royal Doulton, Plate, Flambe, Veined Sung, 6 In. 25.00
Royal Doulton, Plate, Home Waters, W. E. Grace, 10 1/2 In. 45.00
Royal Doulton, Plate, Hunting Dog, 10 1/2 In. 15.00
Royal Doulton, Plate, Hunting Man, 10 1/2 In. 25.00
Royal Doulton, Plate, Jackdaw Of Rheims, 9 3/4 In. 35.00
Royal Doulton, Plate, Jackdaw Of Rheims, 10 1/2 In. 45.00
Royal Doulton, Plate, Jester, 10 In. 22.00
Royal Doulton, Plate, Jester, 10 1/2 In. 28.00
Royal Doulton, Plate, Katherine, 9 In. 32.00
Royal Doulton, Plate, Knights In Armor On Horseback, Old Mark, 10 1/2 In. 35.00
Royal Doulton, Plate, Long John Silver, 13 1/2 In. 55.00
Royal Doulton, Plate, Maritime Scenic, J. H. Plant, 10 5/8 In., Pair 195.00
Royal Doulton, Plate, Mayor, 10 1/2 In. .... 18.00 To 28.00
Royal Doulton, Plate, Men In Red Jackets Smoking Pipes, 10 1/2 In. 22.00
Royal Doulton, Plate, Merry Wives Of Windsor Scene, Black Rim, 13 In. 65.00
Royal Doulton, Plate, Midsummer Night's Dream, Octagonal, 9 1/2 In. 25.00
Royal Doulton, Plate, Niagara Falls, 10 1/2 In. 22.00
Royal Doulton, Plate, Nursery Rhymes, Old Mother Hubbard, 7 In. 12.50
Royal Doulton, Plate, Old Auto Series, 10 1/2 In. 65.00
Royal Doulton, Plate, Old English, Gypsies Around Campfire, 10 1/2 In. 45.00
Royal Doulton, Plate, Old Woman Flower Seller, 10 1/2 In. 27.50
Royal Doulton, Plate, Parson, 10 1/2 In. .... 18.00 To 22.00
Royal Doulton, Plate, Robert Burns, 10 1/2 In. 45.00
Royal Doulton, Plate, Robin Hood, Under The Greenwood Tree, 10 1/2 In. 45.00
Royal Doulton, Plate, Sailboats, Dark Green Border, 8 1/2 In. 12.00

Royal Doulton, Plate, Scotsman With Hunting Dogs, Artist Signed, 10 1/2 In.	30.00
Royal Doulton, Plate, Scottie Dog Against Scottish Highlands, 10 1/2 In.	37.00
Royal Doulton, Plate, Shakespeare, Orlando, Dated 1924, 8 1/2 In.	27.00
Royal Doulton, Plate, Should Auld Acquaintance, Brown, 10 In.	65.00
Royal Doulton, Plate, Sir Izaac Walton, I Care Not-, 10 1/2 In.	45.00
Royal Doulton, Plate, Solem, The Cobbler, 10 1/2 In.	35.00
Royal Doulton, Plate, Spaniel, 10 1/2 In.	25.00
Royal Doulton, Plate, Squire, 10 1/2 In.	18.00
Royal Doulton, Plate, Thatched Cottage & Man Caning Chair, 10 In.	25.00
Royal Doulton, Plate, To Market To Buy A Pig, 7 In.	45.00
Royal Doulton, Plate, Tower Of London, 10 1/2 In.	22.00
Royal Doulton, Plate, Tunis, Arabs Eating Under Tree, 10 1/2 In.	38.00
Royal Doulton, Plate, Two Musketeers, 10 1/2 In.	40.00
Royal Doulton, Plate, Under The Greenwood Tree, 9 1/2 In.	27.00
Royal Doulton, Plate, Under The Greenwood Tree, 10 1/2 In.	40.00
Royal Doulton, Plate, Vernon, 7 1/2 In.	8.00
Royal Doulton, Plate, White Horse & Coach, People, Black Edge, 10 In.	25.00
Royal Doulton, Plate, Woman With Tea Cup, Tea Cup Border, 10 1/4 In.	36.00
Royal Doulton, Plate, Woodley Dale, Marked Made In England, 10 In.	25.00
Royal Doulton, Pot, Salt, Tulips Inside, Deep Blue Outside, 2 1/2 In.	8.50
Royal Doulton, Sauce, Four Gaffers, 5 In.	45.00
Royal Doulton, Sugar & Creamer, Coaching Days	50.00
Royal Doulton, Syrup, Cobalt, Pewter Top, Gold Tapestry, Aqua Vines, Slater	75.00
Royal Doulton, Tazza, Blue, Pink Mottled Base, 4 1/2 In.	80.00
Royal Doulton, Tea Set, Royal Mailcoach, 21 Piece	275.00
Royal Doulton, Teacup & Saucer, The Cardinal, Lord Archbishop Of Rheims	10.00
Royal Doulton, Teapot, Santa In Toy Laden Reindeer Drawn Sleigh	90.00
Royal Doulton, Toby Mug, 'Arry, 1 1/4 In.	68.00
Royal Doulton, Toby Mug, 'Arry, 2 1/2 In.	38.00
Royal Doulton, Toby Mug, 'Arry, 6 In.	85.00
Royal Doulton, Toby Mug, Apothecary, 2 1/2 In.	7.50
Royal Doulton, Toby Mug, Apothecary, 4 1/2 In.	9.50
Royal Doulton, Toby Mug, Aramis, 4 1/2 In.	9.50
Royal Doulton, Toby Mug, 'Arriet, 7 In.	50.00
Royal Doulton, Toby Mug, Athos, 2 1/2 In.	6.00 To 25.00
Royal Doulton, Toby Mug, Auld Mac, Australia, 3 1/2 In.	50.00
Royal Doulton, Toby Mug, Auld Mac, C.1939, 6 1/2 In.	55.00
Royal Doulton, Toby Mug, Auld Mac, Marked A, 2 1/4 In.	27.00
Royal Doulton, Toby Mug, Auld Mac, Marked A, 2 1/2 In.	30.00 To 38.00
Royal Doulton, Toby Mug, Auld Mac, Marked A, 3 1/2 In.	28.00
Royal Doulton, Toby Mug, Auld Mac, Marked A, 6 In.	65.00
Royal Doulton, Toby Mug, Bacchus, 2 1/2 In.	22.00
Royal Doulton, Toby Mug, Bacchus, 7 In.	14.00
Royal Doulton, Toby Mug, Beefeater, Marked A, 2 1/2 In.	32.00
Royal Doulton, Toby Mug, Bootmaker, 6 In.	40.00
Royal Doulton, Toby Mug, Buz Fuz, Marked A, 3 1/2 In.	55.00 To 65.00
Royal Doulton, Toby Mug, Buz Fuz, 4 1/2 In.	9.50
Royal Doulton, Toby Mug, Captain Hook, 6 In.	60.00
Royal Doulton, Toby Mug, Cardinal, Marked A, 2 1/2 In.	38.00
Royal Doulton, Toby Mug, Cardinal, Marked A, 3 1/2 In.	25.00 To 50.00
Royal Doulton, Toby Mug, Cardinal, Marked A, 6 1/2 In.	55.00 To 80.00
Royal Doulton, Toby Mug, Cardinal, 2 1/2 In.	40.00
Royal Doulton, Toby Mug, Cardinal, 3 1/4 In.	35.00
Royal Doulton, Toby Mug, Cardinal, 3 1/2 In.	50.00
Royal Doulton, Toby Mug, Cavalier, Marked A, 3 1/2 In.	55.00
Royal Doulton, Toby Mug, Coachman, Coaches Around Top, 5 3/4 In.	28.50
Royal Doulton, Toby Mug, David Copperfield, 4 1/2 In.	9.50
Royal Doulton, Toby Mug, Dick Turpin, Gun Handle, 6 In.	125.00
Royal Doulton, Toby Mug, Dick Turpin, Marked A, 3 1/4 In.	40.00
Royal Doulton, Toby Mug, Dick Turpin, Marked A, 7 In.	60.00
Royal Doulton, Toby Mug, Dick Turpin, Mask Up, 2 1/2 In.	40.00
Royal Doulton, Toby Mug, Dick Whittington, 6 In.	195.00
Royal Doulton, Toby Mug, Drake, Marked A, 3 1/2 In.	55.00
Royal Doulton, Toby Mug, Drake, 3 In.	45.00
Royal Doulton, Toby Mug, Drake, 6 In.	85.00
Royal Doulton, Toby Mug, Falconer, 6 In.	40.00

Royal Doulton, Toby Mug, Farmer John, Marked A, 3 1/2 In. 37.50
Royal Doulton, Toby Mug, Fat Boy, Marked A, 2 1/2 In. .... 38.00 To 45.00
Royal Doulton, Toby Mug, Fat Boy, 1 In. 60.00
Royal Doulton, Toby Mug, Friar Tuck, 6 In. 125.00
Royal Doulton, Toby Mug, Gardener, 2 1/2 In. .... 8.50 To 18.00
Royal Doulton, Toby Mug, Gardener, 4 1/2 In. 9.50
Royal Doulton, Toby Mug, Gladiator, 6 In. 190.00
Royal Doulton, Toby Mug, Goaler, 2 1/2 In. 7.50
Royal Doulton, Toby Mug, Grammy, Marked A, 7 In. 55.00
Royal Doulton, Toby Mug, Granny, 4 1/2 In. 9.50
Royal Doulton, Toby Mug, Granny, 6 In. 50.00
Royal Doulton, Toby Mug, Guardsman, 2 1/2 In. 7.50
Royal Doulton, Toby Mug, Guardsman, 3 1/2 In. 25.00
Royal Doulton, Toby Mug, Gulliver, 6 In. 175.00
Royal Doulton, Toby Mug, Jockey, 6 In. 45.00
Royal Doulton, Toby Mug, John Barleycorn, Marked A, 3 1/2 In. 37.50
Royal Doulton, Toby Mug, John Barleycorn, Marked A, 6 In. 110.00
Royal Doulton, Toby Mug, John Barleycorn, Marked A, 6 1/2 In. 120.00
Royal Doulton, Toby Mug, John Barleycorn, 2 1/2 In. .... 38.00 To 45.00
Royal Doulton, Toby Mug, John Barleycorn, 3 1/2 In. .... 45.00 To 50.00
Royal Doulton, Toby Mug, John Barleycorn, 6 In. 125.00
Royal Doulton, Toby Mug, John Peel, Marked A, 2 1/4 In. 35.00
Royal Doulton, Toby Mug, John Peel, Marked A, 2 1/2 In. .... 38.00 To 45.00
Royal Doulton, Toby Mug, John Peel, Marked A, 3 1/4 In. 40.00
Royal Doulton, Toby Mug, John Peel, Marked A, 3 1/2 In. .... 40.00 To 55.00
Royal Doulton, Toby Mug, John Peel, 6 In. 110.00
Royal Doulton, Toby Mug, Johnny Appleseed, 6 In. .... 125.00 To 150.00
Royal Doulton, Toby Mug, Lawyer, 2 1/2 In. 8.50
Royal Doulton, Toby Mug, Lawyer, 3 1/2 In. 25.00
Royal Doulton, Toby Mug, Little Nell, 4 1/2 In. 9.50
Royal Doulton, Toby Mug, Lobsterman, 3 1/2 In. 25.00
Royal Doulton, Toby Mug, Lobsterman, 6 In. 40.00
Royal Doulton, Toby Mug, Long John Silver, 4 1/2 In. 9.50
Royal Doulton, Toby Mug, Long John Silver, 7 In. 45.00
Royal Doulton, Toby Mug, Lord Nelson, 6 In. 195.00
Royal Doulton, Toby Mug, Mikado, 3 1/2 In. 45.00
Royal Doulton, Toby Mug, Mikado, 6 In. 95.00
Royal Doulton, Toby Mug, Motorist, 4 1/2 In. 9.50
Royal Doulton, Toby Mug, Mr.Micawber, Marked A, 4 1/2 In. 60.00
Royal Doulton, Toby Mug, Mr.Micawber, 2 1/2 In. 38.00
Royal Doulton, Toby Mug, Mr.Micawber, 4 1/2 In. 9.50
Royal Doulton, Toby Mug, Mr.Pickwick, Marked A, 2 1/2 In. 38.00
Royal Doulton, Toby Mug, Mr.Pickwick, Marked A, 4 1/2 In. 60.00
Royal Doulton, Toby Mug, Mr.Pickwick, Marked A, 6 In. .... 95.00 To 110.00
Royal Doulton, Toby Mug, Musical, 6 1/2 In. 95.00
Royal Doulton, Toby Mug, Night Watchman, 2 1/2 In. 22.00
Royal Doulton, Toby Mug, Old Charley, Marked A, 2 In. 28.00
Royal Doulton, Toby Mug, Old Charley, Marked A, 2 1/2 In. .... 28.00 To 35.00
Royal Doulton, Toby Mug, Old Charley, Marked A, 3 1/2 In. .... 28.00 To 45.00
Royal Doulton, Toby Mug, Old Charley, Marked A, 6 In. 50.00
Royal Doulton, Toby Mug, Old Charley, 1 In. 60.00
Royal Doulton, Toby Mug, Old Charley, 3 1/2 In. 45.00
Royal Doulton, Toby Mug, Old Charley, 5 3/4 In. 38.00
Royal Doulton, Toby Mug, Old Charley, 6 In. 30.00
Royal Doulton, Toby Mug, Old King Cole, Marked A, 3 In. 35.00
Royal Doulton, Toby Mug, Old Salt, 6 In. 40.00
Royal Doulton, Toby Mug, Paddy, Marked A, 2 1/2 In. .... 38:00 To 40.00
Royal Doulton, Toby Mug, Paddy, Marked A, 3 1/2 In. .... 37.50 To 55.00
Royal Doulton, Toby Mug, Paddy, Marked A, 6 In. 58.00
Royal Doulton, Toby Mug, Paddy, 1 In. 60.00
Royal Doulton, Toby Mug, Paddy, 6 In. 90.00
Royal Doulton, Toby Mug, Parson Brown, Marked A, 3 1/4 In. 55.00
Royal Doulton, Toby Mug, Parson Brown, Marked A, 3 1/2 In. .... 37.50 To 50.00
Royal Doulton, Toby Mug, Parson Brown, 6 1/2 In. 65.00
Royal Doulton, Toby Mug, Pied Piper, 2 1/2 In. 8.50
Royal Doulton, Toby Mug, Pied Piper, 6 In. 45.00

Royal Doulton, Toby Mug, Punch & Judy Man, 6 In.	185.00
Royal Doulton, Toby Mug, Regency Beau, 6 In.	185.00
Royal Doulton, Toby Mug, Rip Van Winkle, 2 1/2 In.	8.50
Royal Doulton, Toby Mug, Robin Hood, 2 1/2 In.	8.50
Royal Doulton, Toby Mug, Robinson Crusoe, 2 1/2 In.	8.50
Royal Doulton, Toby Mug, Sairey Gamp, Marked A, 2 1/4 In.	17.00
Royal Doulton, Toby Mug, Sairey Gamp, Marked A, 2 1/2 In.	28.00
Royal Doulton, Toby Mug, Sairey Gamp, Marked A, 3 In.	35.00
Royal Doulton, Toby Mug, Sairey Gamp, Marked A, 3 1/4 In.	39.00
Royal Doulton, Toby Mug, Sairey Gamp, Marked A, 3 1/2 In.	37.50 To 45.00
Royal Doulton, Toby Mug, Sairey Gamp, Marked A, 6 In.	50.00 To 65.00
Royal Doulton, Toby Mug, Sairey Gamp, 2 1/2 In.	8.50 To 27.50
Royal Doulton, Toby Mug, Sairey Gamp, 3 In.	35.00
Royal Doulton, Toby Mug, Sairey Gamp, 4 1/2 In.	9.50
Royal Doulton, Toby Mug, Sairey Gamp, 5 3/4 In.	38.00
Royal Doulton, Toby Mug, Sairey Gamp, 6 In.	40.00
Royal Doulton, Toby Mug, Sairey Gamp, 6 1/2 In.	55.00
Royal Doulton, Toby Mug, Sam Weller, Marked A, 2 1/2 In.	38.00
Royal Doulton, Toby Mug, Sam Weller, Marked A, 3 1/2 In.	50.00
Royal Doulton, Toby Mug, Sam Weller, Marked A, 4 1/2 In.	60.00
Royal Doulton, Toby Mug, Sam Weller, Marked A, 6 In.	95.00
Royal Doulton, Toby Mug, Sam Weller, 1 In.	60.00
Royal Doulton, Toby Mug, Sam Weller, 1 1/4 In.	57.50 To 68.00
Royal Doulton, Toby Mug, Scaramouche, 6 In.	185.00
Royal Doulton, Toby Mug, Simon The Cellarer, Marked A, 3 In.	35.00
Royal Doulton, Toby Mug, Simon The Cellarer, Marked A, 3 1/2 In	45.00 To 65.00
Royal Doulton, Toby Mug, Simon The Cellarer, Marked A, 6 In.	85.00
Royal Doulton, Toby Mug, Simon The Cellarer, Marked A, 7 1/2 In.	50.00
Royal Doulton, Toby Mug, Simple Simon, 6 In.	175.00
Royal Doulton, Toby Mug, Sleuth, 4 1/2 In.	9.50
Royal Doulton, Toby Mug, Sleuth, 6 In.	40.00
Royal Doulton, Toby Mug, Smuggler, 4 1/2 In.	9.50
Royal Doulton, Toby Mug, St.George, 4 1/2 In.	9.50
Royal Doulton, Toby Mug, Tam-O'-Shanter, 4 1/2 In.	9.50
Royal Doulton, Toby Mug, Tiny Tim, 4 1/2 In.	9.50
Royal Doulton, Toby Mug, Toby Philpot, Marked A, 2 In.	30.00
Royal Doulton, Toby Mug, Toby Philpot, Marked A, 2 1/2 In.	38.00 To 40.00
Royal Doulton, Toby Mug, Toby Philpot, Marked A, 3 In.	35.00
Royal Doulton, Toby Mug, Toby Philpot, 3 1/2 In.	45.00
Royal Doulton, Toby Mug, Toby Philpot, 6 In.	80.00
Royal Doulton, Toby Mug, Tony Weller, Marked A, 2 1/2 In.	30.00 To 40.00
Royal Doulton, Toby Mug, Tony Weller, Marked A, 6 In.	110.00
Royal Doulton, Toby Mug, Tony Weller, 2 1/4 In.	38.00
Royal Doulton, Toby Mug, Tony Weller, 3 1/2 In.	45.00
Royal Doulton, Toby Mug, Tony Weller, 6 1/2 In.	75.00
Royal Doulton, Toby Mug, Touchstone, Marked A, 6 In.	150.00
Royal Doulton, Toby Mug, Touchstone, 6 In.	150.00 To 175.00
Royal Doulton, Toby Mug, Town Crier, 2 1/2 In.	35.00
Royal Doulton, Toby Mug, Town Crier, 3 1/2 In.	30.00
Royal Doulton, Toby Mug, Town Crier, 4 In.	20.00
Royal Doulton, Toby Mug, Vicar Of Bray, Marked A, 6 In.	195.00
Royal Doulton, Toby Mug, Vicar Of Bray, 6 In.	125.00
Royal Doulton, Toothpick, Dickensware, Artful Dodger, Noke	35.00
Royal Doulton, Toothpick, Dickensware, Mr.Pickwick In London, Noke, 2 1/4 In	33.00
Royal Doulton, Tray, Coaching Ways, 10 X 5 In.	32.00
Royal Doulton, Tray, Dickensware, Bill Sykes, 2 Handled, Noke, 11 X 5 In.	55.00
Royal Doulton, Tray, Dickensware, Fat Boy, 9 1/4 X 4 1/4 In.	55.00
Royal Doulton, Tray, Pin, Country Scene, Marked England	10.00
Royal Doulton, Tray, Stags & Trees, Hand-Tinted, 8 X 6 In.	20.00
Royal Doulton, Tray, Titanian, 8 X 6 1/4 In.	45.00
Royal Doulton, Tumbler, Hunt Scene, 6 1/2 In.High	15.00
Royal Doulton, Vase, Baluster Shape, Bacchus & Apollo With Lyre, Gold, 15 In	145.00
Royal Doulton, Vase, Brown & Blue Flowers, Stoneware, 8 1/2 In.High	30.00
Royal Doulton, Vase, Cardinal Wolsey, 8 In.	45.00
Royal Doulton, Vase, Deep Blue, Turquoise & White Tapestry, 12 In., Pair	140.00
Royal Doulton, Vase, Dickensware, Fagin, Signed Noke, 4 In.	34.00

Royal Doulton, Vase, Dickensware, Fagin, Signed Noke, 7 1/4 In.	90.00
Royal Doulton, Vase, Dickensware, Fat Boy, 2 Handled, 5 1/2 In.	50.00
Royal Doulton, Vase, Dickensware, Mr.Micawber, Signed Noke, 2 7/8 In.	35.00
Royal Doulton, Vase, Dickensware, Sam Weller & Mr.Pickwick, Square, 6 In.	115.00
Royal Doulton, Vase, Dickensware, The Artful Dodger, Signed Noke, 3 1/2 In.	35.00
Royal Doulton, Vase, Farmhouse, Wood Scene, Flambe, 7 1/2 In.	95.00
Royal Doulton, Vase, Flambe, Sung Pattern, Free Form, 5 In.	28.00
Royal Doulton, Vase, Flambe, Veined Sung, No.1614, 5 3/4 In.	24.00
Royal Doulton, Vase, Flambe, Veined Sung, No.1618, 9 1/2 In.	80.00
Royal Doulton, Vase, Flambe, Woodcut, 6 In.	40.00
Royal Doulton, Vase, Frank Pope, 7 In.	65.00
Royal Doulton, Vase, Impressed Leaf Pattern On Dark Green, 7 1/2 In., Pair	120.00
Royal Doulton, Vase, Maid Marian, 8 1/2 In.High	38.50
Royal Doulton, Vase, Pumpkin Luster, Geometrics, 6 Sided, Art Deco, 6 1/2 In.	20.00
Royal Doulton, Vase, Seaside Scene With People, Signed Noke, 5 1/2 In.	39.00
Royal Doulton, Vase, Sunflowers & Dots On Green & Blue, C.1920, 4 3/4 In.	52.50
Royal Doulton, Vase, Woodcut, Flambe, Farm Scene, 6 1/2 In.	30.00

Royal Dux is a Czechoslovakian pottery made at the turn of the twentieth century. Unfortunately, reproductions are now appearing on the market.

Royal Dux, Compote, Art Nouveau Lady Holding Shell, Green, Gold, 14 In.	195.00
Royal Dux, Figurine, Borzoi, 14 X 6 1/2 In.High	68.50
Royal Dux, Figurine, Cupid On Seashell, Frogs On Side, 12 In.High	255.00
Royal Dux, Figurine, Girl & Man Fisherpeople, 12 1/8 In., Pair	365.00
Royal Dux, Figurine, Milkmaid With Cow, 7 1/2 In.	195.00
Royal Dux, Figurine, Nude Scene, 14 In.High	225.00
Royal Dux, Figurine, Peasant Man & Woman With Basket, 17 In., Pair	300.00
Royal Dux, Figurine, Young Lady, Short Skirt, Holding Dove, Pink Mark, 11 In.	55.00
Royal Dux, Figurine, Young Woman, Barefooted, Holding Urn, 7 In.	40.00
Royal Dux, Group, Sheik With Dancing Girl, 3 In.	190.00
Royal Dux, Jar, Tobacco, Man's Head Smoking Pipe, Sleeping Cap Lid, 8 In.	50.00
Royal Dux, Planter, Seated Woman With 2 Sheep, 10 X 3 3/4 In.	195.00
Royal Dux, Plate, Brown, Pink, & Green Leaves On Yellow, 28 1/2 In.	22.00
Royal Dux, Shell, 2 Art Nouveau Women, Pink Triangle Mark, 18 In. High	490.00
Royal Dux, Vase, Boy On Conch Shell, 3 X 5 In.	225.00
Royal Dux, Vase, Boy Playing Flute, Girl & Lamb, Foliage, Flared, 12 In., Pair	295.00
Royal Dux, Vase, Bud, Pink Flowers On Ivory, 6 In.	18.00
Royal Dux, Vase, Figurine, Shepherd Girl & Boy, Beige, Gold, 16 1/2 In., Pair	425.00

Royal Flemish glass was made during the late 1880s in New Bedford, Massachusetts, by the Mt.Washington Glass Works. It is a colored satin glass decorated in dark colors with gold designs.

Royal Flemish, Box, Decorated	1000.00
Royal Flemish, Vase, Gold Winged Lizard, Stained Glass Windows, 6 1/4 In.	110.00
Royal Haeger, Pocket, Wall, Brown Glaze, Form Of 2 Leaves, 11 X 5 In.	8.00
Royal Haeger, Vase, Peacock, 12 In.	3.50
Royal Lancastrian, Vase, Cobalt Blue Matte, Bulbous, E.T.R., 7 1/2 In.	65.00
Royal Munich, Plate, Pink & White Roses, Gold Rim, 9 1/2 In.	18.50

Royal Rudolstadt, a German faience factory, was established in Thuringia, Germany, in 1721. Hard paste porcelain was made by E.Bohne after 1854. Late nineteenth and early twentieth-century pieces are most commonly found today. The later mark is a shield with the letters RW inside superseded by a crown and the words Royal Rudolstadt.

Royal Rudolstadt, see also Kewpie

Royal Rudolstadt, Basket, Floral On Cream, Gold Handle, 6 3/4 X 4 1/2 In.	45.00
Royal Rudolstadt, Berry Set, Painted Fruits, Gold Beaded Rim, 7 Piece	65.00
Royal Rudolstadt, Bowl, Salad, Roses, F.Kahn, 10 In.	22.50
Royal Rudolstadt, Celery, White, Blue Geometric Border, 12 1/2 X 5 1/2 In.	14.00
Royal Rudolstadt, Chocolate Set, Roses On Cream Ground, Gold Trim, 9 Piece	200.00
Royal Rudolstadt, Creamer, Floral On Biscuit, Molded Leaf Handle	16.50
Royal Rudolstadt, Creamer, Violets & Gold On Cream, Blue Mark	30.00
Royal Rudolstadt, Dish, Cheese & Cracker, White To Green, White Roses	19.00
Royal Rudolstadt, Dish, Veined Leaf, Flowers & Leaves, 7 1/2 In.	14.00
Royal Rudolstadt, Ewer, Green Bamboo Handle, Floral On Beige, 8 1/4 In.	35.00
Royal Rudolstadt, Hair Receiver, Hand-Painted Floral	22.00

Royal Rudolstadt, Hatpin Holder, Bluebird	45.00
Royal Rudolstadt, Jar, Cracker, Quilted, Floral On White, Gold, 7 1/2 In.	45.00
Royal Rudolstadt, Mayonnaise Set, Hand-Painted Violets, Gold, 3 Piece	32.50
Royal Rudolstadt, Pitcher, Cylindrical, Floral Design, 11 In.High	65.00
Royal Rudolstadt, Pitcher, Jug Shape, Monk On Browns, 7 1/2 In.	38.00
Royal Rudolstadt, Plaque, Violets & Lily Of The Valley, Gold Rim, 13 In.	40.00
Royal Rudolstadt, Plate, Cake, Pink Roses, Gold Trim, F.Kahn, Handled, 10 In.	25.00
Royal Rudolstadt, Plate, Fernlike Fronds In Autumn Colors, 9 1/2 In.	35.00
Royal Rudolstadt, Plate, Multicolored Roses, Blue & Gold Trim, 6 In.	25.00
Royal Rudolstadt, Plate, Pink Roses, Gold Rim, Artist Signed, 6 In., Pair	15.00
Royal Rudolstadt, Plate, Red Poinsettias, 8 1/2 In.	22.00
Royal Rudolstadt, Plate, Violets, Signed, 8 1/2 In.	22.50
Royal Rudolstadt, Sugar, Covered	16.50
Royal Rudolstadt, Toothpick, Baby Chick Out Of Egg, Gold Specks	27.50
Royal Rudolstadt, Tray, Violets & Sweet Peas, 12 1/2 In.	40.00
Royal Rudolstadt, Vase, Chinese Design On Ivory, C.1850, 6 1/2 In.	135.00
Royal Rudolstadt, Vase, Cream, Floral Decoration, Gold Handle, 9 In.	75.00
Royal Rudolstadt, Vase, Cupid On Front, Handled, Fluted Top, 8 In.	85.00
Royal Rudolstadt, Vase, Multicolor Floral, Gold, 11 1/2 In.	52.00
Royal Saxe, Bowl, Fruit, Blues, Gold, 3 Handled, 3 Sections, 7 In.	23.00
Royal Saxe, Plate, Cake, Open Handled, Fruit, Blues, Gold, 9 1/2 In.	29.00
Royal Saxe, Tray, Portrait, Sitting Bull, Rust, Gold, 10 X 6 1/2 In.	38.00
Royal Saxe, Vase, Portrait Medallion, Lady, Gold, Pedestal, 2 Handled, 10 In.	85.00

Royal Vienna was established in Vienna by Claude Innocentius du Paquier in 1719. The factory closed in 1865. Since then, various German and Austrian factories have reproduced Royal Vienna wares, complete with the original beehive mark.

Royal Vienna, see also Beehive

Royal Vienna, Bust, Art Nouveau Flower Pattern Nova, Bisque, 5 3/4 In.	90.00
Royal Vienna, Bust, General Jelacic, Bisque, 1849, 5 In.	38.00
Royal Vienna, Charger, Nude Lady & 3 Cupids, Frichling, 14 In.	325.00
Royal Vienna, Compote, Blue & Gold Decoration, 8 In.Diameter, 5 In.High	50.00
Royal Vienna, Cup & Saucer, Demitasse, Creselda, Signed A.Heer, Beehive	35.00
Royal Vienna, Cup, Demitasse, Blue & Gold Bands, Woman In Courtyard	85.00
Royal Vienna, Dish, Bone, Cobalt & Gold On White, Beehive Mark, Pair	35.00
Royal Vienna, Hair Receiver, Gold Banding, Mums, Footed	22.50
Royal Vienna, Plate, Angel, Signed C.Heer, 6 In.	58.50
Royal Vienna, Plate, Angel, Signed C.Heer, 7 In.	95.00
Royal Vienna, Plate, Brunette Gypsy Girl, Gold Border, Dark Green, 9 In.	75.00
Royal Vienna, Plate, Classical Seminude Figures, Green Border, 9 1/2 In.	27.50
Royal Vienna, Plate, Cloisonne Look, 9 1/2 In.	24.50
Royal Vienna, Plate, Full-Length Woman & Cherubs, Blue & Gold Border, 8 In.	195.00
Royal Vienna, Plate, Helen Of Paris, Dark Blue, Burgundy, & Gold Border, 9 In	385.00
Royal Vienna, Plate, Ladies Standing In Middle, Cobalt & Gold Border, 9 In.	295.00
Royal Vienna, Plate, Lovers & Cupids Scene, Allegorical, Yager, 8 In., Pair	295.00
Royal Vienna, Plate, Maroon, Blue, 9 In. *Illus*	365.00
Royal Vienna, Plate, Mythological Figures & Cupid, Gold, Beehive, 9 1/2 In.	75.00
Royal Vienna, Plate, Pink & Yellow Roses, Gold Edge, 9 1/2 In.	45.00
Royal Vienna, Plate, Portrait, Chief Little Wound, Beehive, 9 1/2 In.	90.00
Royal Vienna, Plate, Portrait, Cupid, Maroon & Gold Border, 9 1/4 In.	55.00
Royal Vienna, Plate, Portrait, White Rock Lady, Cobalt, Wagner, C.1840, 10 In.	250.00
Royal Vienna, Plate, Scenic Of 3 Grecians, Cobalt & Gold Border, 9 In.	95.00
Royal Vienna, Salt, Master, Empire, Tripod Support, Gold, 1818, 3 1/2 In.	145.00
Royal Vienna, Tea Caddy, Cobalt & Gold, 2 Figures, Huttman, 7 In.High	250.00
Royal Vienna, Urn, Covered, Angel, Square Base, 18 In.	350.00
Royal Vienna, Urn, Kauffmann, Square Base, 18 In.	350.00
Royal Vienna, Urn, Lady's Portrait, Gold Scrolls, 2 Handled, Beehive, 7 In.	65.00
Royal Vienna, Urn, 3 Hand-Painted Ladies On Front, Green, Handled, 18 In.	375.00
Royal Vienna, Vase, Panels Of Lovers In Garden, Purple, Blue, Gold, 4 1/2 In.	65.00
Royal Vienna, Vase, Portrait Of Odysseus & Kalypso, Preller, 11 1/2 In.	225.00
Royal Vienna, Vase, Portrait, Madame LeBrun, 10 1/2 In.	55.00

Royal Worcester porcelain was made in the later period of Worcester pottery, which was originally established in 1751. The Royal Worcester trade name has been used by Worcester Royal Porcelain Company, Ltd., since 1862.

Royal Vienna, Plate,
Maroon, Blue, 9 In.
(See Page 529)

Royal Worcester, Ewer,
1889, 11 3/4 In.

Royal Worcester, see also Sewing Tool, Thimble, Worcester

Royal Worcester, Basket, Beige, Gold Trim, 1892, 7 In.	125.00
Royal Worcester, Bottle, Perfume, Flat, Bird & Flowers, C.1862	48.00
Royal Worcester, Bowl, Beige, Gold Outlined Edge, Florals, 1900, 9 1/2 In.	99.00
Royal Worcester, Bowl, Bird Form On Pedestal Base, Floral, Gold, 1906, 9 In.	85.00
Royal Worcester, Bowl, Cream Ground, Lavender, Rose, Blue, Flowers, 9 X 8 In.	125.00
Royal Worcester, Bowl, White, Pierced Top, Roses, Violets, Cole, 1909, 6 In.	195.00
Royal Worcester, Bowl, Wild Roses & Violets On White, Footed, 1909, 6 In.	190.00
Royal Worcester, Box, Patch, Cream Ground, C.1910, 2 X 4 In.	55.00
Royal Worcester, Cake Stand, Lilac, Gold Bands, Purple Mark, 10 3/4 In.	95.00
Royal Worcester, Candlesnuffer, Figural, Nun In Habit, 1920, 3 1/2 In.	50.00
Royal Worcester, Candlesnuffer, Monk In Brown Robe	40.00
Royal Worcester, Candlesnuffer, Monk With Book	45.00
Royal Worcester, Candlesnuffer, Monk, Signed, 5 In.	29.50
Royal Worcester, Candlesnuffer, Toby & Punch, C.1880, Pair	225.00
Royal Worcester, Candlesnuffer, Woman's Head, Bonnet, Blonde Hair	100.00
Royal Worcester, Candlestick, Gold & White Beading, Snake-Like, 9 In., Pair	200.00
Royal Worcester, Chocolate Pot, Green Swirls On Ivorine, Purple Mark, 9 In.	170.00
Royal Worcester, Chocolate Pot, Melon Ribbed Spout, 18K Gold Trim	32.00
Royal Worcester, Creamer, Applied Gold Lily Pads On Cream, 1888	50.00
Royal Worcester, Creamer, Flowers On Beige Ground, Matte Finish, 5 In.	38.00
Royal Worcester, Cup & Saucer, Bouillon, Platinum Bands, Z-1319	22.00
Royal Worcester, Cup & Saucer, Demitasse, Bamboo Handle, C.1865	38.00
Royal Worcester, Cup & Saucer, Demitasse, Floral Sprigs, C.1940, 2 In.	12.00
Royal Worcester, Cup & Saucer, Demitasse, Lavender Floral, Gold, 1886	10.00
Royal Worcester, Cup & Saucer, Demitasse, Pheasants, F.Higgins, No.1587	35.00
Royal Worcester, Cup & Saucer, Demitasse, Rosemary	9.00
Royal Worcester, Cup & Saucer, Florals On Cream	25.00
Royal Worcester, Cup & Saucer, Pink, White, & Yellow Roses, Shiny Glaze, 1913	39.00
Royal Worcester, Cup & Saucer, Tea, Pink Floral Decoration	15.00
Royal Worcester, Demitasse Set, Yellow, Black & White Geometrics, 7 Piece	145.00
Royal Worcester, Ewer, Gold Snake Handle, Floral & Leaf, Purple Mark, 12 In.	375.00
Royal Worcester, Ewer, Ivorine, Butterflies & Floral, Dragon Handle, 12 In.	380.00
Royal Worcester, Ewer, Multicolored Floral, Gold, Serpent Handle, 11 1/2 In.	395.00
Royal Worcester, Ewer, Pink & Red Roses, Gold, Green, Hadley, 3 1/2 In.	98.00
Royal Worcester, Ewer, Rose Pink, Gold Lizard Handle, C.1883, 11 1/4 In.	150.00
Royal Worcester, Ewer, Tan, Enamel Floral, High Narrow Neck, 7 In.	165.00
Royal Worcester, Ewer, White, Relief Designs, Footed, Thin Neck, 13 1/2 In.	115.00
Royal Worcester, Ewer, 1889, 11 3/4 In. .... *Illus*	275.00
Royal Worcester, Figurine, August, Nude Girl By Sea, Doughty, 4 3/4 In.	78.00
Royal Worcester, Figurine, Dancing Lady, Gold Gown, Purple Mark, 13 In.	395.00
Royal Worcester, Figurine, Dutch Boy, F.Gertner, 5 1/2 In.	65.00
Royal Worcester, Figurine, Eastern Water Carrier, Male, C.1886, 9 In.	275.00
Royal Worcester, Figurine, Grandmother's Dress, F.G.Doughty, 6 In.High	70.00
Royal Worcester, Figurine, Michael, Artist F.G.Doughty, 3 1/4 In.Long	65.00
Royal Worcester, Figurine, Peter Pan, Gertner, C.1936, Purple Mark, 8 In.	95.00
Royal Worcester, Figurine, Saturday's Child, Girl, Black Mark, 5 1/2 In.	65.00
Royal Worcester, Figurine, Sorrow, Woman & Dove, Hand Over Eyes, 12 In.	450.00
Royal Worcester, Figurine, Wednesday's Child, Girl, Blue Mark, 6 3/4 In.	75.00

Royal Worcester, Figurine, White Rabbit, F.G.Doughty, 4 In.	40.00
Royal Worcester, Figurine, Woman, Jug On Head, Urn In Hand, 15 1/2 In.	295.00
Royal Worcester, Figurine, Woodland Dance, Girl With Animals, 5 1/2 In.	76.00
Royal Worcester, Figurine, Young Lad, Impressed 1876, 6 In.	86.00
Royal Worcester, Holder, Menu, Tree Trunk, Frog On Base, 7 1/2 In.High	115.00
Royal Worcester, Jar, Biscuit, Melon Style, Bulbous, 7 In.	95.00
Royal Worcester, Jar, Cracker, Ribbed, Hand-Painted, Purple Mark	180.00
Royal Worcester, Jar, Sweetmeat, Goose In Pastoral Scene, Locke	65.00
Royal Worcester, Jug, Matte Finish, Floral, 1896, 4 3/4 In.	55.00
Royal Worcester, Mug, White, Bird On Flowering Branch, Gold, 1897, 1 1/2 In.	55.00
Royal Worcester, Pitcher, Birds, Floral, & Cattails On Lemon, 1878, 9 In.	95.00
Royal Worcester, Pitcher, Cabbage Leaf, 4 In.	55.00
Royal Worcester, Pitcher, Daisies On Ivorine, Purple Mark, 6 In.	90.00
Royal Worcester, Pitcher, Flat Back, Flowers On Matte Beige, 5 In., Pair	150.00
Royal Worcester, Pitcher, Flat Back, Pastel Flowers, Purple Mark, 6 In.	65.00
Royal Worcester, Pitcher, Floral, Gold Trim, 1891, 5 In.High	75.00
Royal Worcester, Pitcher, Ivorine & Beige Swirls, Gold, Green Handle, 5 In.	85.00
Royal Worcester, Pitcher, Left Handed, Floral, Gold, Crimped Edge, 9 In.	105.00
Royal Worcester, Pitcher, Lion Head Spout, Paw & Leg Handle, Mums, 5 1/2 In.	125.00
Royal Worcester, Pitcher, Roses, Butterfly, Dragonfly, Gold Handle, 7 In.	85.00
Royal Worcester, Pitcher, Swirl, Beige & Ivorine, Rococo Handle, 5 1/2 In.	62.00
Royal Worcester, Pitcher, Yellow, Metallic Gold Leaves, 8 In.	65.00
Royal Worcester, Plate, Center Floral Sprays, Gold Border, 7 In.	15.00
Royal Worcester, Plate, Dessert, Blossom Time	3.75
Royal Worcester, Plate, Earl Of Manvers, Scalloped, Blue Mark, 8 3/4 In.	25.00
Royal Worcester, Plate, Flamingos In Scene, W.Powell, 1912, 9 1/4 In.	200.00
Royal Worcester, Plate, Flowers, Birds, & Eggs, Gold Border, 9 1/4 In.	39.50
Royal Worcester, Plate, Hand-Painted Flowers On Cream, 9 In.	45.00
Royal Worcester, Plate, Kenilworth Castle, Gold Trim, Pierced Rim, 1889, 9 In	58.00
Royal Worcester, Plate, Kidney Shape, Orange & Blue Oriental Design, 9 In.	35.00
Royal Worcester, Plate, Pink Flowers In Baskets, Green Band, 6 In.	9.00
Royal Worcester, Plate, Portraits Of Mayoress & Mayor, Lavender, 10 3/8 In.	20.00
Royal Worcester, Plate, Red & Blue Garlands, Green Border, 8 In., Pair	30.00
Royal Worcester, Plate, Service, Gold Medallion, Maroon Border, 10 1/2 In.	10.00
Royal Worcester, Plate, Shakespeare's Burial Place, Jeweled, 9 In.	98.00
Royal Worcester, Platter, Blue On White, 20 1/2 X 17 In.	125.00
Royal Worcester, Ring Tree, Floral On Cream, C.1904	55.00
Royal Worcester, Rose Bowl, Floral Design On Cream, 3 X 2 In.	35.00
Royal Worcester, Rose Bowl, Pale Yellow To White, Swirled, 1905, 2 3/4 In.	24.50
Royal Worcester, Rose Bowl, Yellow To Pink, 3 Shell Feet, 1900, 2 1/2 In.	48.00
Royal Worcester, Sauce, Astral	4.00
Royal Worcester, Sugar & Creamer, Floral, Gold, Pink, & Purple	39.50
Royal Worcester, Sugar & Creamer, Fluted, Gold Beading	75.00
Royal Worcester, Sugar & Creamer, Hand-Painted Floral On Cream	75.00
Royal Worcester, Sugar & Creamer, Leaf, Shaker Sugar, Sheffield Holder	185.00
Royal Worcester, Sugar & Creamer, Silver Luster	17.00
Royal Worcester, Tea Set, White, Floral & Ribbon Garland, 8 Piece	75.00
Royal Worcester, Teapot, Color Shakespeare House Scene, Bamboo Gold	115.00
Royal Worcester, Toothpick, Pinwheel, Red, Green, & Black, Oval, 2 1/2 In.	10.00
Royal Worcester, Tray, Heart Shape, Ivory, Irregular Gold Edge, 4 1/2 In.	22.50
Royal Worcester, Tray, Pin, Nude Child Holding Dish, Green Mark	40.00
Royal Worcester, Tureen, Soup, Blue & White Oriental Design, 9 1/2 In.	125.00
Royal Worcester, Tureen, Soup, Light Blue, Brown Trim, C.1878	45.00
Royal Worcester, Urn, Covered, Beige, Floral, Handled, Gold, 1900, 9 1/2 In.	265.00
Royal Worcester, Vase, Autumn Colorings, Spider Spinning Web, 13 In.High	150.00
Royal Worcester, Vase, Beige Floral, 2 Leaf Handles, 11 In.	150.00
Royal Worcester, Vase, Beige With Red & Pink Blossoms, Purple Mark, 13 In.	120.00
Royal Worcester, Vase, Beige, Floral, Gold Handles, 1888, 10 1/4 In.	140.00
Royal Worcester, Vase, Beige, Pink & Gold Floral, Gold Handles, 1895, 13 In.	165.00
Royal Worcester, Vase, Birds & Flowers, Gold Trim, Purple Mark, 5 1/4 In.	35.00
Royal Worcester, Vase, Covered, Loop Handles, Floral & Scrolls, 1895, 20 In.	300.00
Royal Worcester, Vase, Cream, Orange Poppies, Gold Trim, C.1852, 12 In.	175.00
Royal Worcester, Vase, Ewer Type, Colorful Flowers In Panels, 15 In.High	245.00
Royal Worcester, Vase, Gourd, Oriental Type, Cobalt & Gold, Flat, 1876	1000.00
Royal Worcester, Vase, Ivorine, Floral & Fern, 13 1/2 In., Pair	395.00
Royal Worcester, Vase, Light Blue, Jeweled Peacocks, 1895, 13 In., Pair	1800.00

Royal Worcester, Vase, Peacock, Landscape, 4 Panels, Green, Gold, 1909, 4 In.	130.00
Royal Worcester, Vase, Reticulated, Locke, 6 1/4 In.	150.00
Royal Worcester, Vase, White, Cube Shape, Lizard On Side, C.1872, 2 1/2 In.	68.00
Royal Worcester, Vase, 2 Maidens In Field, Deep Blue, Gold, 8 In.	45.00
Royal Worcester, Vase, 4 In. .... *Illus*	185.00
Royal Worcester, Wall Pocket, Floral & Gilt, Biscuit Ground, 8 In.	90.00

Roycroft products were made by the Roycrofter community of East Aurora, New York, in the late nineteenth and early twentieth centuries. The community was founded by Elbert Hubbard. The products included furniture, metalware, leatherwork, and jewelry.

Roycroft, Bookend, Hammered Metal, 5 1/2 X 2 3/4 In., Pair	12.00
Roycroft, Bookend, Open Center, Border Decoration, 8 1/2 In., Pair	25.00
Roycroft, Jug, Brown Glaze, 5 In.	10.00
Roycroft, Jug, Brown Glaze, 5 1/2 In.	10.00
Roycroft, Jug, Brown, Signed, 6 In.	20.00
Roycroft, Tray, Copper, Hammered, 8 In.	28.00
Roycroft, Vase, Hammered Metal, 4 3/4 In.	14.00
Rozenburg, Plate, Art Nouveau Floral, 6 In.	750.00
Rozenburg, Shoe, Art Nouveau Style, 4 1/2 In.	125.00
Rozenburg, Vase, Blue, Panels Of Yellow, Green, Purple, & Brown, 5 In.	210.00
Rozenburg, Vase, Dutch Boy, 4 Handles At Top, Blue, Yellow, Brown, 12 In.	225.00
Rozenburg, Vase, Egg Shell, Art Nouveau Design, 3 1/2 In.	650.00

RS Germany porcelain was made at the factory of Rheinhold Schlegelmilch after 1869 in Tillowitz, Germany. It was sold both decorated and undecorated.

RS Germany, see also RS Prussia

RS Germany, Basket, Candy, Marked	17.50
RS Germany, Basket, Gold Plated, 7 X 4 In.	45.00
RS Germany, Basket, Wide Gold Trim, Grapes, Leaves, & Scrolls, 6 3/4 In.	22.00
RS Germany, Bonbon, Scalloped, Blue & White Flowers On Pearly Ground, 4 In.	22.00
RS Germany, Bottle, Perfume, Bulbous, Sunflowers, 5 In.	23.00
RS Germany, Bowl, Black Outlined Embossed Gold Border, Roses, 10 1/4 In.	39.00
RS Germany, Bowl, Footed, Blue Mark, 6 In.	25.00
RS Germany, Bowl, Pink Orchid, Water Lilies, Gold, 4 Open Handles, 9 1/4 In.	75.00
RS Germany, Bowl, Roses, Open Handled, Square, 9 In.	22.00
RS Germany, Bowl, Three Poinsettias, Green Leaves, Artist Champin, 9 In.	25.00
RS Germany, Box, Puff, Art Deco, Blue, Gold	22.00
RS Germany, Box, Trinket, Ball Shape, Orange Poppies, Green Mark	18.00
RS Germany, Cake Set, Pink & White Roses, 5 Piece	25.00
RS Germany, Chamberstick, Ring Handle, Pearlized, 2 In.High	18.50
RS Germany, Creamer, Orange Poppies & Buds	7.50
RS Germany, Cruet, Red Rose On Yellow & White, Blue Mark, 4 In.	28.00
RS Germany, Cup & Saucer, Demitasse, Green Roses On Browns	15.00
RS Germany, Cup & Saucer, Demitasse, Pink Roses, Green Mark	18.00
RS Germany, Dish, Cheese & Cracker, Lilies On Green, Gold Trim	27.50
RS Germany, Dish, Pickle, Indian Chief's Head At Each End, White, Blue Mark	25.00
RS Germany, Dish, Pickle, Lady & 2 Children On Bench, Open Handled, Gold	38.00
RS Germany, Dresser Set, Pink Roses, Small Size, Blue Mark, 6 Piece	90.00
RS Germany, Fernery, White & Red Roses On Green, 8 X 4 In.	75.00
RS Germany, Hair Receiver & Powder Jar, Orange Pink Roses	35.00
RS Germany, Hair Receiver, Lilies Of The Valley On Green, Marked	15.00
RS Germany, Hatpin Holder, Green Floral	26.00
RS Germany, Hatpin Holder, Lilies Of The Valley On Greens	28.00
RS Germany, Hatpin Holder, One Rose	25.00
RS Germany, Hatpin Holder, Orange Poppies On Brown & Yellow, Green Mark	28.00
RS Germany, Hatpin Holder, Pink & White Roses On Green Ground, 4 1/2 In.	25.00
RS Germany, Hatpin Holder, Poppies On Green, Closed Bottom, Green Mark	24.00
RS Germany, Hatpin Holder, Roses, Green Mark	30.00
RS Germany, Hatpin Holder, White & Yellow Roses, Coin Gold, Etching	55.00
RS Germany, Hatpin Holder, White Roses On Green, 4 1/2 In.	27.00
RS Germany, Jar & Underplate, Jam, Lilies	25.00
RS Germany, Jar, Cookie, Handled, Floral, Heavy Gold, 6 X 5 In.	24.00
RS Germany, Jar, Cracker, 15K Gold Lacy Trim, Orchids & Tulips	68.00
RS Germany, Letter Holder, Farm Scene On Beige To White, Green Mark, 4 In.	45.00

RS Germany, **Nappy**, Pale To Deep Green, Poppy, Gold, Green Mark	5.50
RS Germany, **Pitcher**, Cider, Roses, Satin Finish, 7 X 6 In.	65.00
RS Germany, **Plate**, Cake, Gardenias & Daisies, Open Handles, 11 1/2 In.	27.00
RS Germany, **Plate**, Cake, Open Handled, White Lilies, 9 1/2 In.	24.00
RS Germany, **Plate**, Gold Beaded Rim, Greenish Floral, 6 In.	9.25
RS Germany, **Plate**, Grapes & Floral, Pierced Handles, 10 1/2 In.	16.50
RS Germany, **Plate**, Open Handled, Floral, Raised Leaves & Buds, Gold, 10 In.	40.00
RS Germany, **Plate**, Pansy, 8 1/2 In.	15.00
RS Germany, **Plate**, Pink & White Apple Blossoms, 11 In.	25.00
RS Germany, **Plate**, Pink Orchids On Green & Cream, Blue Mark, 6 1/4 In.	10.00
RS Germany, **Plate**, Poppies On White & Brown, Pierced Handles, 10 In.	24.00
RS Germany, **Plate**, Rust & White Tulips, Signed Schlegelmilch, 11 In.	25.00
RS Germany, **Plate**, Shepherd & Sheep On Path To House, 11 In.	65.00
RS Germany, **Plate**, White Floral On Cream To Brown, Signed, 6 1/2 In.	5.00
RS Germany, **Plate**, White Flowers On Green, Green Mark, 6 In.	4.50
RS Germany, **Plate**, White Roses On Pink, 6 1/2 In.	7.50
RS Germany, **Plate**, White To Olive Green, Pink Roses, 6 1/2 In.	15.00
RS Germany, **Plate**, 3 Calla Lilies, Gold Rim, 7 In.	14.50
RS Germany, **Plate**, 3 Ivory Roses, Gold Design & Border, 8 1/4 In.	22.00
RS Germany, **Pot**, Mustard, Roses	11.00
RS Germany, **Relish**, Cutout Ends, Gray Blue Border, Symbol Designs, Blue Mark	20.00
RS Germany, **Relish**, Floral, Open Handles, Green Mark, 9 In.	15.00
RS Germany, **Relish**, Hand-Painted	22.50
RS Germany, **Relish**, Pink Pansies	14.00
RS Germany, **Ring Tree**, 5 Branch, Gold Trim, Green Mark	18.50
RS Germany, **Salt Dip**, Rabbit's Ear Handles, Roses	15.00
RS Germany, **Sauce**, Lily	6.00
RS Germany, **Shaving Mug, see Shaving Mug**	
RS Germany, **Stein**, No.1191, 19 X 9 In.	225.00
RS Germany, **Sugar & Creamer**, Cover, Lilies On Beige	28.00
RS Germany, **Sugar & Creamer**, Easter Lilies On Cream, 6 Sided	30.00
RS Germany, **Sugar & Creamer**, Embossed Gold Decoration, Green Mark	28.00
RS Germany, **Sugar & Creamer**, Oblong, Yellow To Blue, Gold Trim	52.50
RS Germany, **Sugar**, Covered, Roses	10.00
RS Germany, **Sugar**, Pink Poppies, Brown & Green Foliage	18.00
RS Germany, **Syrup & Underplate**, Pink Poppies On White With Green	29.50
RS Germany, **Syrup Set**, Roses On Green, Gold Trim, 3 Piece	28.50
RS Germany, **Syrup**, Painted Bees On Flowers, Matte Finish, 5 1/2 In.	28.00
RS Germany, **Syrup**, Roses	15.00
RS Germany, **Tea Set**, Tan & Brown Luster, Pink Roses, 15 Piece	95.00
RS Germany, **Teacup & Saucer**, Pedestal Cup, Pink Flower, Saxe	12.50
RS Germany, **Teacup & Saucer**, Pink Roses On Tan Luster	10.00
RS Germany, **Teapot & Underplate**, Roses, 1 Cup Size	35.00
RS Germany, **Teapot & Underplate**, Roses, 2 Cup Size	35.00
RS Germany, **Teapot**, Woodland Colors With Dogwoods, Blue Mark	30.00
RS Germany, **Toothbrush Holder**, Pink Roses On Green To White, Scalloped	45.00
RS Germany, **Toothbrush Holder**, Wall, Gilt Floral, 3 X 4 In.	15.00
RS Germany, **Toothbrush Holder**, Wall, White & Gold	18.50
RS Germany, **Toothpick & Attached Underplate**, Pink Flowers, Green Mark	32.50
RS Germany, **Toothpick**, Pale Green, Roses, Gold, 3 Handled	45.00
RS Germany, **Toothpick**, Roses, Gold Decoration, Two Handles, Green Mark	25.00
RS Germany, **Toothpick**, Roses, Gold Trim	35.00
RS Germany, **Toothpick**, White Dogwood On Brown, 2 Handled	30.00
RS Germany, **Tray**, Dresser, Floral, Gold Trim	18.00
RS Germany, **Tray**, Dresser, Pierced Handles, Morning Glories, Gold, 11 1/2 In.	24.00
RS Germany, **Tray**, Pin, Handled, Roses	22.50
RS Germany, **Tray**, Pin, Pierced Handles, Morning Glories, Gold, Green Mark	14.00
RS Germany, **Tray**, Pin, White & Yellow Roses, Scalloped, 5 1/2 X 3 1/4 In.	25.00
RS Germany, **Vase**, Yellow & Pink Roses On Cream To Caramel, 6 In., Pair	17.00
RS Poland, **Vase**, Poppies, Bulbous, 12 1/2 X 4 1/2 In.	100.00

 RS Prussia porcelain was made at the factory of Rheinhold Schlegelmilch after 1869 in Tillowitz, Germany. The porcelain was sold decorated or undecorated.

RS Prussia, see also RS Germany

RS Prussia, **Berry Set**, Green & White, Red Mark, 7 Piece	275.00

RS Prussia, Plate, Snow Bird,
Black Trim, 7 3/4 In.
(See Page 535)

Royal Worcester, Vase, 4 In.
(See Page 532)

RS Prussia, Tankard, 15 In.
(See Page 536)

RS Prussia, Berry Set, Magnolias, 4 Green Scalloped Panels, 7 Piece	250.00
RS Prussia, Berry Set, Pink Roses On Green Shading, Red Mark, 5 Piece	175.00
RS Prussia, Bowl, Apple Blossoms On Green, Red Mark, 10 In.	60.00
RS Prussia, Bowl, Bas-Relief Floral & Feather, Scalloped, 9 In.	20.00
RS Prussia, Bowl, Bluebirds & Cottage, Red Mark, 14 X 9 In.	600.00
RS Prussia, Bowl, Fall Season, Red Mark, 11 In.	525.00
RS Prussia, Bowl, Fruit, Blownout Flowers, Gold, Forest, 10 In.	85.00
RS Prussia, Bowl, Fruit, Giant Roses, Footed, Handles, 7 1/2 X 3 1/4 In.	95.00
RS Prussia, Bowl, Fruits On Blue, Red Mark, 10 1/2 In.	75.00
RS Prussia, Bowl, Gold Scallops, Roses, Green Lattices, Red Mark, 10 1/4 In.	71.00
RS Prussia, Bowl, Light Blue Panels & Gold Scrolls, Red Mark, 10 1/2 In.	140.00
RS Prussia, Bowl, Light Green Ground, Pink Roses, Gold Trim, Red Mark, 10 In.	85.00
RS Prussia, Bowl, Lilac & Turquoise, Raised Gold, Red Mark, 10 1/4 In.	110.00
RS Prussia, Bowl, Melon Boys, Dog, Playing Dice, Red Mark, 11 In.	395.00
RS Prussia, Bowl, Pale Green, Lilac Decoration, Red Mark, 10 In.	65.00
RS Prussia, Bowl, Pastel Orchid & Beige Leaves Edged In Gold, 10 1/2 In.	40.00
RS Prussia, Bowl, Pink Roses In Wreaths, Red Mark, 10 In.	72.50
RS Prussia, Bowl, Pink Roses On White, Gold Scalloped Edge, Red Mark, 10 In.	85.00
RS Prussia, Bowl, Roses & Leaves, Pale Blue Border, Gold At Top, 10 1/2 In.	65.00
RS Prussia, Bowl, Salad, Scalloped, Floral, Lavender & Yellow, 10 In.	55.00
RS Prussia, Bowl, Satin Finish, Footed, 7 In.	65.00
RS Prussia, Bowl, Snowbirds, Red Mark, 15 In.	2550.00
RS Prussia, Bowl, Starfish Pattern, Roses, 10 1/2 In., Unsigned	58.00
RS Prussia, Bowl, Swans, Water, Bluebirds, 3 Legs, 9 1/2 In.	235.00
RS Prussia, Bowl, Tan Ground, Dark Red Roses, Gold Trim, 10 In.	85.00
RS Prussia, Bowl, Vegetable, Gold Tracery & Chains, Roses, 8 1/4 In.	65.00
RS Prussia, Bowl, Wild Rose Decoration, Handled, Scalloped, Red Mark, 11 In.	55.00
RS Prussia, Bowl, 2 Color Roses, Satin Finish, Red Mark, 10 In.	120.00
RS Prussia, Bowl, 5 White Roses On Olive, Scalloped, Gold, Red Mark, 11 In.	70.00
RS Prussia, Cake Set, Pink Roses, Gold, Red Mark, 7 Piece	225.00
RS Prussia, Celery, Blue, White Flowers, Gold Dots & Trim, Poppies, Red Mark	175.00
RS Prussia, Celery, Open Handled, White Magnolias, Raised Gold, 12 In.	60.00
RS Prussia, Celery, Rabbits In Thicket, Berry Blossom Vines, Red Mark	150.00
RS Prussia, Celery, Water Lilies & Swallows On White, Red Mark, 12 In.	125.00
RS Prussia, Chocolate Pot, Gray Green Satin Ground, Yellow Floral, Red Mark	115.00
RS Prussia, Chocolate Pot, Pink & Green Floral	35.00
RS Prussia, Chocolate Pot, Pink & White Carnations On Green, Red Mark	115.00
RS Prussia, Chocolate Pot, Pink Roses, Green Leaves, Red Mark	95.00
RS Prussia, Chocolate Pot, Roses, Tan & Pink Shading, Scalloped Foot	100.00
RS Prussia, Chocolate Pot, Swans, Water Lilies, Mauve To Beige, Red Mark	245.00
RS Prussia, Chocolate Pot, White Daisy, Green Leaves, Red Mark	95.00
RS Prussia, Chocolate Pot, White Violets On White, Floral Shape Top	160.00
RS Prussia, Chocolate Pot, Yellow Floral, Pearlized, Red Mark	95.00
RS Prussia, Chocolate Set, Art Nouveau Shape, Blownout Florals, 9 Piece	135.00
RS Prussia, Chocolate Set, Floral, Red Mark, 9 Piece	185.00
RS Prussia, Chocolate Set, Green & Rose, Red Mark, 9 Piece	325.00
RS Prussia, Chocolate Set, Light Green, Roses, Gold Trim, 6 Piece	400.00

RS Prussia, Chocolate Set, 3 Color Roses On Green, Red Mark, 12 Piece 450.00
RS Prussia, Coffeepot, Roses, Art Nouveau Style, Red Mark, 9 1/2 In. 225.00
RS Prussia, Creamer, Pink Flowers, Green Vines, Gold Outline, Red Mark 23.50
RS Prussia, Creamer, Swan 49.00
RS Prussia, Creamer, Turquoise On White, Pink Roses, Footed 22.00
RS Prussia, Cup & Saucer, Bouillon, Pearlized, Red Mark 46.00
RS Prussia, Cup & Saucer, Chocolate, Eggshell Finish, Swans On Water 75.00
RS Prussia, Cup & Saucer, Demitasse, Floral, Gold Trim, 8 Gold Feet, Red Mark 48.00
RS Prussia, Cup & Saucer, Demitasse, Pink Roses, Green Trim, Red Mark 35.00
RS Prussia, Cup & Saucer, Green & Gray Ferns, White, Scalloped, Red Mark 28.50
RS Prussia, Cup, Chocolate, Dogwood, Red Mark 20.00
RS Prussia, Dessert Set, Aqua, Pink Floral, Red Mark, 6 Piece 135.00
RS Prussia, Dish, Pickle, Dogwood Blossoms, Gold Trim, Red Mark 40.00
RS Prussia, Dish, Pickle, Open Handled, Pink Roses, Beaded, Scalloped Edge 48.00
RS Prussia, Dish, Relish, Pink & Yellow Roses On Green, Scalloped Edge 38.00
RS Prussia, Dish, Shell & Leaf Figural, Double Scroll Handle, 8 1/4 In. 47.00
RS Prussia, Dresser Set, Pink Blossoms, Gold Trim, Satin Finish, 3 Piece 150.00
RS Prussia, Hair Receiver, Basket Of Flowers 85.00
RS Prussia, Hair Receiver, Pink Roses, Gold Points, 8 Pointed Star Shape 30.00
RS Prussia, Hatpin Holder & Attached Covered Box, White, Pink Roses, Footed 125.00
RS Prussia, Hatpin Holder & Pin Tray, 1 Piece, Roses, Tan & White, Red Mark 265.00
RS Prussia, Hatpin Holder, Floral On Purple Pink, 3 Tall Legs, Red Mark 110.00
RS Prussia, Hatpin Holder, Pink Flowers, White With Blue Trim, Red Mark 135.00
RS Prussia, Hatpin Holder, Roses On Pastel, Scalloped Bottom, Red Mark 75.00
RS Prussia, Jar, Cookie, Roses, Bouquets, Gold Tracery, 2 Handles, Red Mark 140.00
RS Prussia, Jar, Cookie, White, Floral & Green Leaves, Red Mark 110.00
RS Prussia, Jar, Cracker, Pink Flowers, Red Mark 175.00
RS Prussia, Jar, Cracker, Satin Finish, Pink Roses 67.50
RS Prussia, Jar, Cracker, Water Lilies On Lake, Blue & White, Red Mark 295.00
RS Prussia, Match Holder, Wall, Swan Pattern, Striker 30.00
RS Prussia, Muffineer, Footed, White, Roses, Gold Edges, Red Mark 65.00
RS Prussia, Muffineer, Swans, Red Mark 75.00
RS Prussia, Pitcher, Left Handed, Pink Roses & Green On White, 5 1/4 In. 75.00
RS Prussia, Pitcher, Lemonade, Lilies, Green 185.00
RS Prussia, Pitcher, Milk, Floral On Cream, Gold Trim, Red Mark, 8 Cup Size 65.00
RS Prussia, Pitcher, Milk, Pink Roses, White Carnations On Blue, Red Mark 165.00
RS Prussia, Plate, Blue & Gold, 8 In. 60.00
RS Prussia, Plate, Cake, Pierced Handles, Roses, Red Mark, 10 1/2 In. 65.00
RS Prussia, Plate, Cake, Pink Roses 22.00
RS Prussia, Plate, Cake, Roses, Salmon To White, 2 Handled, Red Mark, 10 In. 45.00
RS Prussia, Plate, Cookie, Pink Roses, Gold Enamels, Garland, 9 1/2 In. 65.00
RS Prussia, Plate, Floral, Red Mark, 8 1/2 In. 85.00
RS Prussia, Plate, Gold Edge, Beading, & Fleur-De-Lis, Roses, 8 7/8 In. 49.00
RS Prussia, Plate, Green, Pink & Lavender Roses, Red Mark, 10 1/2 In. 85.00
RS Prussia, Plate, Handled, Ruffled Rim, Cream & Green, Bouquet, 9 3/4 In. 120.00
RS Prussia, Plate, Lily-Of-The-Valley, Scalloped, Pastel, 9 In., Set Of 6 .... 350.00
RS Prussia, Plate, Mauve Roses On Yellow, Gold, Red Mark, 7 1/2 In. 35.00
RS Prussia, Plate, Open Handled, Floral & White Buds On Green, 10 1/4 In. 59.00
RS Prussia, Plate, Open Handles, Cream, Pink, Lavender, Green, & White, 9 In. 110.00
RS Prussia, Plate, Pearlized, Carnations Center, Gold, Red Mark, 8 1/2 In. 85.00
RS Prussia, Plate, Pink & Yellow Roses Shading To Blue, Red Mark, 6 In. 25.00
RS Prussia, Plate, Pink Carnations On Brown & White, Red Mark, 8 In. 32.50
RS Prussia, Plate, Pink Floral, Gold Piecrust Edge, Red Mark, 8 1/2 In. 70.00
RS Prussia, Plate, Pink Poppies, Irregular Edge, 8 1/2 In. 60.00
RS Prussia, Plate, Puffed Floral Edge, Pastel Shades, Red Mark, 8 In. 65.00
RS Prussia, Plate, Roses On Yellow & Green, Gold Rim, Red Mark, 8 1/2 In. 75.00
RS Prussia, Plate, Ruffled Upward, Floral, Gold Tracery & Stars, 7 3/4 In. 43.00
RS Prussia, Plate, Snowbird, Black Trim, 7 3/4 In. .... *Illus* 600.00
RS Prussia, Plate, Spring Season, Gold Decoration, Red Mark, 8 In. 700.00
RS Prussia, Plate, Star Shape, Roses, Gold, Red Mark, 6 In. 28.00
RS Prussia, Plate, Swans, Red Mark, 7 1/2 In. 65.00
RS Prussia, Plate, Turkey In Forest, Lake, Bluebirds, Red Mark, 10 In. 225.00
RS Prussia, Plate, White Apple Blossoms, Gold Edge, Red Mark, 8 1/2 In. 55.00
RS Prussia, Plate, Wild Roses, Scalloped Sections, Red Mark, 10 In. 65.00
RS Prussia, Plate, Winter Season's Portrait, Red Mark, 9 In. 595.00
RS Prussia, Relish, Jeweled, Gold Drape, Rose Garlands, Green & Tan, Red Mark ... 150.00

RS Prussia, Sauce, Pink Rose Center, Green & Orchid, Gold, Red Mark	15.00
RS Prussia, Sauce, Raised Deep Scallops, Pink Roses, Red Mark, 3 X 5 In.	95.00
RS Prussia, Sauce, Roses, Red Star Mark	15.00
RS Prussia, Shaving Mug, see Shaving Mug	
RS Prussia, Sugar & Creamer, Bluebirds, Pedestal, Jeweled, Red Mark	440.00
RS Prussia, Sugar & Creamer, Cover, Hanging Baskets Of Roses On Green	75.00
RS Prussia, Sugar & Creamer, Cover, Melon Ribbed, Gold, Floral, Red Mark	120.00
RS Prussia, Sugar & Creamer, Ferns, Roses, & Lilies On Green, Red Mark	125.00
RS Prussia, Sugar & Creamer, Iridescent Mauve, Floral, Red Mark	75.00
RS Prussia, Sugar & Creamer, Melon Boys, Green, Jeweled, Red Mark	1250.00
RS Prussia, Sugar & Creamer, Pearlized, Floral, Gold Scrollwork	160.00
RS Prussia, Sugar & Creamer, Roses, Green & Gold, 8 Footed, Red Mark	87.50
RS Prussia, Sugar & Creamer, Roses, Red Mark	55.00
RS Prussia, Sugar, Covered, White, Yellow Flowers	65.00
RS Prussia, Sugar, Green Garlands, Lilac Trim	37.50
RS Prussia, Sugar, Pink Roses On Pale Blue	37.50
RS Prussia, Syrup, Green & Yellow Ground, Pink Roses, Red Mark	85.00
RS Prussia, Table Set, Pink Roses & Blown-Out Floral On Blue, 4 Piece	300.00
RS Prussia, Tankard, 15 In. ....*Illus*	2300.00
RS Prussia, Tankard, Blown-Out Flowers, White Roses, Red Mark, 12 In.	250.00
RS Prussia, Tankard, Gold Fleur-De-Lis, Roses, Blue Chains, Red Mark, 7 In.	65.00
RS Prussia, Tea Set, Pink Roses & Hydrangeas, Gold Tracery, 3 Piece	250.00
RS Prussia, Teapot, Dogwood Blossoms On Gray Luster, Red Mark	75.00
RS Prussia, Teapot, Pearlized, Red Mark	70.00
RS Prussia, Toothpick, White, Gold, Red Roses, Footed, 2 Handled, Red Mark	70.00
RS Prussia, Tray, Celery, Open Handles, Pastel Colors, Roses, 12 X 6 In.	65.00
RS Prussia, Tray, Dresser, Floral, Turned-Up Rim, Red Mark, 11 In.	85.00
RS Prussia, Tray, Dresser, Orchids	65.00
RS Prussia, Tray, Dresser, Pink & Red Roses, 7 X 11 In.	50.00
RS Prussia, Tray, Dresser, Satin, Flowers, Gold Trim, Red Mark, 12 1/2 X 9 In.	77.00
RS Prussia, Tray, Dresser, Yellow Roses, Cutout Handles, 6 X 3 1/2 In.	42.00
RS Prussia, Tray, Pink Roses & White Lilacs, Pearlized Border, 7 X 14 In.	80.00
RS Prussia, Tray, Rose Center, Jeweled Luster Border, Red Mark, 12 X 8 In.	110.00
RS Prussia, Vase, Melon Boy, Pearlized Jewels, 10 In.	110.00
RS Prussia, Vase, Melon Boy, Red Mark, 4 In.High	310.00
RS Prussia, Vase, Melon Boy, Red Mark, 6 1/2 In.	300.00
RS Prussia, Vase, Pheasant In Garden Scene, 2 Handles, 7 1/4 In.	95.00
RS Prussia, Vase, Spring Season, Handled, Red Mark, 10 1/2 In.	550.00
RS Prussia, Vase, Springtime, Gold Handles, 9 In.High, Pair	950.00
RS Prussia, Vase, Tiger & Tigress In Browns & Yellows, Round, 5 1/2 In.	300.00

Rubena Verde is a Victorian glassware that was shaded from red to green. It was first made by Hobbs, Brockunier and Company of Wheeling, West Virginia, about 1890.

Rubena Verde, Bowl, Finger, Fluted Rim, Thumbprint	69.00
Rubena Verde, Epergne, Center Ruffled Trumpet Vase, Green, Petals, 11 In.	115.00
Rubena Verde, Epergne, Single Trumpet Vase, Base Bowl, 11 In.High	125.00
Rubena Verde, Pitcher, Blown, Polished Pontil, Quart Size	115.00
Rubena Verde, Pitcher, Water, Square Mouth	300.00
Rubena Verde, Vase, Cranberry To Green, Applied Rigaree & Floral, 10 In.	125.00
Rubena Verde, Vase, Cranberry To Green, Daisies, Bird, & Bug, 8 1/4 In.	145.00

Rubena is a glassware that shades from red to clear. It was first made by George Duncan and Sons of Pittsburgh, Pennsylvania, about 1885.

Rubena, Bottle, Dresser, Mouth Lotion & Listerine, Clear Stopper, 5 In., Pair	48.00
Rubena, Bowl, Waste, Pointed Hobnail	60.00
Rubena, Butter, Covered, Thumbprint	98.00
Rubena, Butter, Pointed Hobnail	145.00
Rubena, Castor Set, 4 Bottle	195.00
Rubena, Celery, Inverted Thumbprint	35.00
Rubena, Charger, Diamond-Quilted, Ground Pontil, 11 1/2 In.High	50.00
Rubena, Compote, Fluted, 3 In.	30.00
Rubena, Creamer, Pointed Hobnail	85.00
Rubena, Muffineer, Cranberry To Clear Threaded Pattern	76.00 To 85.00
Rubena, Muffineer, Inverted Blocks, Silver Plate Domed Lid, 6 1/2 In.	69.50
Rubena, Muffineer, Royal Oak, Deep Cranberry, Northwood	110.00

Rubena, Pitcher, Crackle, Clear Reeded Handle, Square Mouth, 5 1/2 In.	75.00
Rubena, Pitcher, Inverted Thumbprint, Applied Reeded Handle, 5 In.	55.00
Rubena, Pitcher, Water, Frosted, Royal Ivy	145.00
Rubena, Pitcher, Water, Opal	95.00
Rubena, Rose Bowl, Ribbed, Crimped Top, 3 1/4 X 4 In.	50.00
Rubena, Rose Bowl, Ribbed, Gold Decoration, 6 X 7 In.	65.00
Rubena, Saltshaker, Inverted Thumbprint, Tall Type	35.00
Rubena, Saltshaker, Royal Oak	35.00
Rubena, Sauce, Royal Ivy	29.00
Rubena, Sugar, Covered, Pointed Hobnail	110.00
Rubena, Syrup, Cranberry To Clear, Opalescent Coin Spot	95.00
Rubena, Tankard, Etched Peace & Happiness, Flowers, & Scrolls, 9 1/4 In.	125.00
Rubena, Tumbler, Etched Heron	24.50
Rubena, Tumbler, Inverted Thumbprint	34.00
Rubena, Vase, Bud, Gold & White Enamel Decoration, 7 In.	47.50 To 62.50
Rubena, Vase, Cranberry, Gold & Enamel Floral, 10 1/2 In.	60.00
Rubena, Vase, Pink Enamel Roses, Gold, 8 1/4 In.	28.50

*Ruby glass is a dark red color. It was a Victorian and twentieth-century
ware. The name means many different types of red glass.*

Ruby Glass, see also Cranberry Glass, Pressed Glass, Souvenir

Ruby Glass, Bell, 12 In.High	88.00
Ruby Glass, Boot, Stained, Dated 1905, 3 In.	17.00
Ruby Glass, Bottle, Perfume & Snuff, Mordan, Sterling Caps, 4 3/4 In.	92.00
Ruby Glass, Bottle, Perfume, French, White Cased, Gold, C.1840, 6 3/4 In.	75.00
Ruby Glass, Bottle, Perfume, Gold Enamel Floral, Leaf, & Beading, 3 In.	65.00
Ruby Glass, Bottle, Perfume, Sterling Overlay, 3 1/4 In.High	65.00
Ruby Glass, Bowl, Engraved 1/2 In. Pewter Rim, Ribbed, Low, 4 X 12 In.	40.00
Ruby Glass, Bowl, Silver Plate Holder, Bird Handles, Ball & Claw Feet, 3 In.	30.00
Ruby Glass, Bowl, Spear Point & Daisy Band, Souvenir, N.T., 1910, 8 1/4 In.	6.00
Ruby Glass, Bowl, Thumbprint, Etched Leaves, 7 1/2 X 3 In.	42.50
Ruby Glass, Bowl, Thumbprint, 7 1/4 X 2 1/2 In.	32.50
Ruby Glass, Box, Jewelry, Enameled Flowers, Gold Trim, Brass Fittings, Round	140.00
Ruby Glass, Butter, Covered, Thumbprint, Etched Leaves	57.50
Ruby Glass, Champagne, Knob Stem	28.35
Ruby Glass, Compote, Thumbprint, 8 1/4 X 7 1/2 In.	49.50
Ruby Glass, Creamer, Button Arches, Souvenir, Mother, 1911	18.00
Ruby Glass, Creamer, Button Arches, Souvenir, Portal, N.D., 4 1/4 In.	24.00
Ruby Glass, Creamer, Heart Band, Souvenir, Annandale, Minn.	16.00
Ruby Glass, Creamer, Heart Band, Souvenir, Dubuque, Iowa	15.00
Ruby Glass, Creamer, Heart Band, Souvenir, Victoria, Minn.	14.00
Ruby Glass, Creamer, Thumbprint, "Minnie 1905"	47.50
Ruby Glass, Cup & Saucer, Dianna	5.00
Ruby Glass, Cup, Lacy Medallion, Souvenir, Canaan, Maine, Gold Trim	20.00
Ruby Glass, Cup, Punch, Button Arches, Souvenir, Montevideo	20.00
Ruby Glass, Cup, Punch, Button Arches, Souvenir, Stule, N.D.	14.00
Ruby Glass, Dish, Candy, Center Handle, 22 X 3 In.	25.00
Ruby Glass, Goblet, Thumbprint, Souvenir, Cedar Rapids, Iowa	22.50 To 25.00
Ruby Glass, Jar, Jam, Squatty, Hollow Knob	20.00
Ruby Glass, Mug, Button Arches, Souvenir, Albie, S.D.	16.50
Ruby Glass, Mug, Button Arches, Souvenir, Mattie, Hot Springs, Ark.	16.50
Ruby Glass, Mug, Button Arches, Souvenir, 1903	12.50
Ruby Glass, Mug, Button Arches, Souvenir, 1908	8.00
Ruby Glass, Mug, Child's, Button Arches, Souvenir, 1905	8.00
Ruby Glass, Mug, Engraved Midwinter Fair, San Francisco, 1894	20.00
Ruby Glass, Mug, For A Good Boy In Gold, 3 In.	65.00
Ruby Glass, Mug, Lacy Medallion, Souvenir, H.M.Sherman, 1906	29.00
Ruby Glass, Mug, Red Block, Souvenir, World's Fair, 1893	18.00
Ruby Glass, Mug, Souvenir, Atlantic City, 1897, Stained	15.00
Ruby Glass, Mug, Souvenir, Atlantic City, 1904, Stained	15.00
Ruby Glass, Mug, Sunk Honeycomb, Souvenir, N.D.	17.00
Ruby Glass, Mug, Sunk Honeycomb, Souvenir, Tena Olsen, 1906	18.00
Ruby Glass, Pitcher, Button Arches, Souvenir, Portland, 1905, 10 In.	22.00
Ruby Glass, Pitcher, Button Arches, Souvenir, 1930, 4 In.	18.50
Ruby Glass, Pitcher, Milk, Button Arches, Etched Merry Xmas, 1904	35.00
Ruby Glass, Salt, Square	8.00

Ruby Glass, Saltshaker, Punty Band, Souvenir, Papa, 1908, Pewter Top	10.00
Ruby Glass, Sauce, Button Arches, Souvenir, Tyler, Minn.	12.50
Ruby Glass, Shot Glass, "Momence, Ill."	9.50
Ruby Glass, Table Set, Dogwood, Stained, Gold Floral & Leaf, 1908, 4 Piece	175.00
Ruby Glass, Toothpick, Colorado, Souvenir, Indiana, Pa.	12.00
Ruby Glass, Toothpick, Stained, Souvenir, Brocton Fair, 1902	25.00
Ruby Glass, Tumbler, Button Arches, Souvenir, 1906	21.50
Ruby Glass, Tumbler, Little Berries At Base	8.50
Ruby Glass, Tumbler, Pavonia, Souvenir, Hannah Fair	17.00
Ruby Glass, Tumbler, Red Block, Souvenir, Flora Lang, 1890	25.00
Ruby Glass, Tumbler, Wedding, Stained	45.00
Ruby Glass, Vase, Floriform, Lily, Art Nouveau, C.1900, 7 In.	22.50
Ruby Glass, Vase, Stained, Open Crocus Bloom Form, Gold, 10 1/2 In., Pair	48.00
Ruby Glass, Vase, Tulip Shape, Enameled Grapes, Leaves, Gold Vines, 7 In.	42.00
Ruby Glass, Wine, Button Arches, Souvenir, Balfour, N.D., Stained	25.00
Ruby Glass, Wine, King's Crown, Souvenir, Chicago	15.00
Ruby Glass, Wine, Teardrop, Souvenir, Dodgeville, 1904	16.00
Ruby Glass, Wine, Thumbprint, Gold Edged, Buffalo In White	12.00
Ruby Glass, Wine, Zipper Slash, Souvenir, Gettysburg, 1863	25.00
Rug, see Textile, Rug	
Rumrill, Planter, Swan, Pink, 5 X 5 1/2 In.	5.00
Rumrill, Vase, Cream Color, 2 Swan Neck Handles, Semimatte, 4 1/2 In.	4.50
Rumrill, Vase, Floral On Cream, 8 In.	12.50
Rumrill, Vase, Green To Cream, Ruffled Lip, 2 Handles, 8 1/2 In.	15.00
Sabino, Bottle, Perfume, Opalescent, Five Dancing Nudes, Pineapple Stopper	55.00
Sabino, Dish, Shell Shape, Iridescent, 7 X 4 In.	35.00
Sabino, Figurine, Art Deco Nude, Hair Cascading To Base, C.1925, 7 In.	90.00
Sabino, Figurine, Bird, Opalescent, Signed, 4 In.	20.00
Sabino, Figurine, Fish, Opalescent, Signed, 6 In.	20.00
Sabino, Figurine, Squirrel, Opalescent Glass, 3 In.	30.00
Sabino, Figurine, Stork, Gold Iridescent, Signed Paris, 7 1/4 In.	85.00
Sabino, Knife Rest, Bird, Signed	20.00
Sabino, Knife Rest, Butterfly, Signed	20.00
Sabino, Knife Rest, Fish, Signed	20.00
Sabino, Knife Rest, Snail, Signed	20.00
Sabino, Knife Rest, Squirrel, Signed	20.00
Sabino, Owl, Opalescent, 4 1/4 In.	55.00
Sabino, Vase, Frosted, Frieze Of Flying Geese, C.1935, 15 3/4 In.	60.00
Sabino, Vase, Opalescent, Smocked, 1/2 In. Opening At Top, Signed, 5 In.	47.50
Saddle, Cavalry, U.S., Girth, Stirrups	110.00
Saddle, Western, Tooled Leather, Brown	39.00

Salopian ware was made by the Caughley Factory of England during the eighteenth century. The early pieces were in blue and white with some colored decorations. Many of the pieces called Salopian are elaborate color-transfer decorated tablewares made during the late nineteenth century.

Salopian, Cup & Saucer	175.00
Salopian, Mug, Turquoise	100.00
Salt & Pepper, see Pressed Glass, Porcelain, etc.	

Salt glaze is a hard, shiny glaze that was developed for pottery during the eighteenth century. It is still being made.

Salt Glaze, Bowl, Pierced Rim, Molded Medallion Center, C.1750, 8 7/8 In.	100.00
Salt Glaze, Dish, Sweetmeat, 6 Heart Shape Compartments, C.1745, 8 1/4 In.	600.00
Salt Glaze, Figurine, King & Queen, French, White, 7 1/2 In., Pair	25.00
Salt Glaze, Figurine, Shepherdess, White, Similar To Bennington, 10 In.	47.50
Salt Glaze, Flagon, Enamel Bouquets, Round, 1769, 6 1/2 In.	1400.00
Salt Glaze, Group, Three Pot Dogs & Keg, Brown Paint, 6 1/2 X 5 In.	30.00
Salt Glaze, Inkwell, Stoneware, Drum Shape, Relief Floral Band, C.1800, 3 In.	48.00
Salt Glaze, Jug, Bacchanalian, White, T.Meigh, 1844, 11 1/4 In.	150.00
Salt Glaze, Jug, Milk, Pectin Shell, Pyriform, 3 Footed, C.1740, 4 1/8 In.	225.00
Salt Glaze, Jug, Stoneware, 1858, 6 3/4 In.High	58.00
Salt Glaze, Jug, White, Pewter Hinged Lid, 2 Women & Spinning Wheel, 9 In.	75.00
Salt Glaze, Mold, 6 Pointed Star, Separated By Smaller Points, C.1745, 4 In.	250.00
Salt Glaze, Pitcher, Buff, Masks, Grapes, Leaves, & Scrolls, 8 1/2 In.	65.00
Salt Glaze, Pitcher, Embossed Cattails, 7 In.	42.00

Salt Glaze, Pitcher, England, Embossed Lilies & Leaves, 7 1/4 In.	40.00
Salt Glaze, Pitcher, Gray, Blue Decoration, 7 1/2 In.	25.00
Salt Glaze, Pitcher, Greenish Blue, Bird In Bulrushes, Palm Trees, 8 3/4 In.	35.00
Salt Glaze, Pitcher, Raised Fern, Flowers, Thorn Handle, 1835, 8 In.High	125.00
Salt Glaze, Pot & Underplate, Meat, Pierced Lid, Rice Pattern, C.1745	800.00
Salt Glaze, Pot, Mustard, Acorn Knip On Lid, Strap Handle, C.1750, 3 In.	80.00
Salt Glaze, Syrup, Impressed Mosaic Stourbridge, Gray, Pewter Top, C.1850	36.00
Salt Glaze, Teabowl & Saucer, Enamel Bouquets, C.1765	250.00
Salt Glaze, Teapot & Trivet, Stoneware, Oriental Motif, 6 3/4 & 6 1/2 In.	52.50
Salt Glaze, Teapot, Diamond Shape, Serpent Spout, Greek Key, C.1745	900.00
Salt Glaze, Teapot, Recumbent Camel, Howdah Neck, Fish Handle, C.1745	1000.00
Salt Glaze, Teapot, White, Neptune's Face, Cranes, Shell Finial, C.1835, 8 In.	145.00
Sampler, see Textile, Sampler	

Samson and Company, a French firm specializing in the reproduction of collectible wares of many countries and periods, was founded in Paris in the early nineteenth century. Chelsea, Meissen, Famille Verte, and Oriental Lowestoft are some of the wares that have been reproduced by the company. The company uses a variety of marks to distinguish its reproductions. It is still in operation.

Samson, Figurine, Duck Standing In Rushes, C.1850, 11 1/4 In., Pair	400.00
Samson, Figurine, Hound, Arita, Seated, Gilt Bell, 15 3/8 In., Pair	500.00
Samson, Group, Palmist & Lass, C.1890, 8 3/4 In.	150.00
Samson, Urn, American Eagle & Shield, Upright Handles, C.1850, 13 In., Pair	375.00
Samson, Vase, Oriental, Cylinder, 11 In.High	105.00
Sand Babies, Plate, Royal Bayreuth, Blue Mark, 9 In.	110.00
Sand Babies, Plate, Royal Bayreuth, 6 1/4 In.	65.00
Sand Babies, Tray, Dresser, Blue Mark, Oblong, 9 X 3 In.	110.00

Sandwich glass is any one of the myriad types of glass made by the Boston and Sandwich Glass Works in Sandwich, Massachusetts, between 1825 and 1888. It is often very difficult to be sure whether a piece was really made at the Sandwich factory because so many types were made there and similar pieces were made at other glass factories. The McK numbers refer to the book American Glass by George P. and Helen McKearin.

Sandwich Glass, see also Pressed Glass, etc.

Sandwich Glass, Basket, Calling Card, Blue, Hobnail, Wire Rim, 4 1/2 In.	22.50
Sandwich Glass, Basket, Yellow With Pink Overshot, Clear Base, 10 In.	140.00
Sandwich Glass, Berry Set, Chrysanthemum Leaf, Gold Trim, 6 Piece	100.00
Sandwich Glass, Bottle, Cobalt Blue, 12 In.	75.00
Sandwich Glass, Bottle, Cologne, Amethyst, 12 Panels, 4 1/2 In.	55.00
Sandwich Glass, Bottle, Cologne, Cobalt, 11 Panels, 4 1/2 In.	55.00
Sandwich Glass, Bottle, Cologne, Green, 12 Panels, 4 1/2 In.	55.00
Sandwich Glass, Bottle, Cologne, Flint, Open Pontil, C.1800, McK G I-9	50.00
Sandwich Glass, Bottle, Cologne, Peacock Blue Green, 12 Sided, 5 In.	70.00
Sandwich Glass, Bottle, Scent, Amethyst, McK 241	45.00
Sandwich Glass, Bottle, Scent, Cobalt, McK 241	40.00
Sandwich Glass, Bottle, Scent, Fiery Opalescent, McK 241	32.00
Sandwich Glass, Bottle, Scent, Flint, Pewter Cap, McK 241-28, Blue	40.00
Sandwich Glass, Bottle, Scent, Flint, Pewter Cap, McK 241-28, Opalescent	32.00
Sandwich Glass, Bottle, Scent, Flint, Pewter Cap, McK 241, Amethyst	45.00
Sandwich Glass, Bottle, Scent, Flint, Pewter Cap, McK 241, Blue	40.00
Sandwich Glass, Bottle, Scent, Flint, Pewter Cap, McK 241, Fiery Opalescent	32.00
Sandwich Glass, Bottle, Scent, Flint, Pewter Cap, McK 241, Opalescent	26.00
Sandwich Glass, Bottle, Scent, Sapphire, McK 241	40.00
Sandwich Glass, Bowl & Underplate, Finger, Sapphire Blue, Threaded, Ruffled	45.00
Sandwich Glass, Bowl, Covered, White, Clear Cased, Portrait On Front, 6 In.	125.00
Sandwich Glass, Bowl, Flint, Princess Feather Medallion With Star, 7 In.	58.00
Sandwich Glass, Bowl, Flint, Rayed Peacock's-Eye, Lacy, 7 1/2 In.	65.00
Sandwich Glass, Bowl, Intermediate Period, McK 149-1, 6 In.	48.00
Sandwich Glass, Bowl, Oak Leaf, Shallow, 6 1/2 X 1 1/4 In.	70.00
Sandwich Glass, Bowl, Peacock's-Eye, Lacy, Flint, 6 1/4 In.	55.50
Sandwich Glass, Bowl, Peacock's-Eye, Lacy, Rayed, Flint, 7 1/2 In.	65.00
Sandwich Glass, Bowl, Robin's-Egg Blue, Threaded, Curlicue Feet, 4 1/2 In.	75.00
Sandwich Glass, Butter, Silver Plate Lid & Stand, Bull Finial	45.00
Sandwich Glass, Candlestick, Dolphin, C.1840, 8 In.High, Pair	135.00
Sandwich Glass, Candlestick, Flower Cup Nozzle, C.1850, 7 In., Pair	40.00

Sandwich Glass, Candlestick, Petal & Loop, Clambroth, C.1835, 6 3/4 In.Pair	275.00
Sandwich Glass, Candlestick, Petal & Loop, 7 In.High	75.00
Sandwich Glass, Celery, Flint, Gothic Arch, Lacy	90.00 To 110.00
Sandwich Glass, Compote, Lacy, 10 1/2 X 6 In.	750.00
Sandwich Glass, Compote, Mirror, 7 1/2 In.	95.00
Sandwich Glass, Creamer, Baroque, Frosted, Lacy	150.00
Sandwich Glass, Creamer, Lacy, Miniature	60.00
Sandwich Glass, Cup Plate, Bunker Hill Monument, Flint	18.00 To 25.00
Sandwich Glass, Cup Plate, Concentric Ring Heart, Flint	25.00
Sandwich Glass, Cup Plate, Eagle With Olive Branch, Flint	25.00
Sandiwch Glass, Cup Plate, Flint, Fiery Opalescent	32.00 To 50.00
Sandwich Glass, Cup Plate, Fort Meigs Cabin, Flint	25.00
Sandwich Glass, Cup Plate, Hairpin, Lacy, Flint	19.00
Sandwich Glass, Cup Plate, Heart Pattern	17.50
Sandwich Glass, Cup Plate, Heart Variant	10.00
Sandwich Glass, Cup Plate, Heart, Opalescent	115.00
Sandwich Glass, Cup Plate, Henry Clay, McK-181-28	35.00
Sandwich Glass, Cup Plate, Log Cabin & Cider Barrel, Flint	25.00
Sandwich Glass, Cup Plate, Major General W.H.Harrison, Flint	25.00
Sandwich Glass, Cup Plate, Shell, Lacy	22.00
Sandwich Glass, Cup Plate, Stippled Diamond Border, Star & Hobnails, Lacy	10.00
Sandwich Glass, Cup Plate, Stippled Heart, Lacy	18.00
Sandwich Glass, Cup Plate, 12 Heart, Lacy	25.00
Sandwich Glass, Decanter, Flat Diamond & Panel, Quart, Pair	125.00
Sandwich Glass, Dish, Octagonal Beehive, Lacy, 9 1/4 In.	95.00
Sandwich Glass, Dish, Rectangular, Lacy, Gothic Arch & Leaf, 5 X 7 1/2 In.	60.00
Sandwich Glass, Dish, Scalloped Shell, Cranberry Overshot, 28 Ribs, 9 In.	165.00
Sandwich Glass, Dispenser, String, Etched Floral Dome, Wooden Base, 6 In.	175.00
Sandwich Glass, Goblet, Clambroth, Satin Finish, Inscribed Base, Dated 1856	85.00
Sandwich Glass, Inkwell, Hollow Crystal Ball, Hinged Lid, 3 Ball Feet, 5 In.	75.00
Sandwich Glass, Inkwell, Star, Molded Base, Blown, Cut Hinged Lid, 3 3/4 In.	75.00
Sandwich Glass, Jar, Pomade, Muzzled Black Bear, Black Amethyst, 3 1/2 In.	150.00
Sandwich Glass, Lamp Base, Fleur-De-Lis Stem, Swirled Rib Font, 8 In.	75.00
Sandwich Glass, Lamp, see Lamp	
Sandwich Glass, Lampshade, Fairy, Applied Cranberry Leaves, 6 In., Pair	65.00
Sandwich Glass, Match Holder, Cobalt Blue, Monkey On Side	85.00
Sandwich Glass, Pitcher, Amber, Overshot, Clover Leaf Top, Ribbed, 8 1/2 In.	115.00
Sandwich Glass, Pitcher, Overshot, Blue, Amber Ribbed Handle, 7 In.	95.00
Sandwich Glass, Pitcher, Overshot, Cranberry, Tankard Type, 11 In.High	125.00
Sandwich Glass, Pitcher, Overshot, Ice Bladder Hand, Applied Handle, C.1865	85.00
Sandwich Glass, Pitcher, Overshot, Twisted Rope Handle, 9 1/2 In.High	110.00
Sandwich Glass, Pitcher, Water, Cranberry Thumbprint, Square Top	200.00
Sandwich Glass, Pitcher, Water, Ewer Shape, Overshot, Pink, Applied Handle	275.00
Sandwich Glass, Plate, Beehive, Lacy, Flint, Mold Defect, 9 1/2 In.	65.00
Sandwich Glass, Plate, Dessert, Crackle, Champagne, Gold Edge, 6 1/4 In.	8.25
Sandwich Glass, Plate, Grill Center, Serpentine Border, Lacy, Flint, 6 In.	50.00
Sandwich Glass, Plate, Heart Variant, Flint, 5 In.	50.00
Sandwich Glass, Plate, Lacy, Flint, 6 In.	24.00
Sandwich Glass, Plate, Lacy, Washington Variant, Acorn, 6 In.	32.50
Sandwich Glass, Plate, Peacock's-Eye & Thistle, Lacy, 8 In.	87.50
Sandwich Glass, Plate, Shell Pattern, Lacy, 6 In.	35.00 To 45.00
Sandwich Glass, Plate, Toddy, Roman Rosette, Lacy, Flint, 5 In.	24.00
Sandwich Glass, Salt, Aqua, Lacy, Flint	140.00
Sandwich Glass, Salt, Baroque, Lacy, Frosted, Pedestal	150.00
Sandwich Glass, Salt, Boat Shape, Flint	80.00
Sandwich Glass, Salt, Christmas, Amber	30.00
Sandwich Glass, Salt, Lacy, Strawberry Diamond, Footed	45.00
Sandwich Glass, Salt, Oval, Lacy, Flint	125.00
Sandwich Glass, Salt, Strawberry Diamond, Lacy, Flint	80.00
Sandwich Glass, Sauce, Crossed Swords, Lacy, Flint, 4 1/2 In.	18.00
Sandwich Glass, Sauce, Flint, Peacock's-Eye, Lacy, 4 1/2 In.	20.00
Sandwich Glass, Sauce, Princess Feather, Lacy, Flint, 4 1/2 In.	15.00
Sandwich Glass, Shade, Etched Daisy & Fern, 8 X 5 1/2 In.	60.00
Sandwich Glass, Sugar, Acanthus, Lacy	75.00
Sandwich Glass, Syrup, Amber & Clear, Etched, Pewter Lid	75.00
Sandwich Glass, Syrup, Blown, Star & Buckle, Applied Hollow Handle, Tin Lid	95.00

Sandwich Glass, Tieback, Curtain, Opalescent, Pewter Stems, 3 In., Pair	100.00
Sandwich Glass, Tieback, Flint, Fiery Opalescent, Pewter Stem, 2 1/2 In.	15.00
Sandwich Glass, Tieback, Flint, Opalescent, Brass Stem, 2 1/2 In.	28.00
Sandwich Glass, Tieback, Flint, Opalescent, Brass Stem, 3 In.	28.00
Sandwich Glass, Tieback, Flint, Opalescent, Brass Stem, 4 1/2 In.	28.00
Sandwich Glass, Tieback, Flint, Opalescent, Pewter Stem, 2 1/2 In.	28.00
Sandwich Glass, Tieback, Flint, Opalescent, Pewter Stem, 3 In.	28.00
Sandwich Glass, Tieback, Flint, Opalescent, Pewter Stem, 4 1/2 In.	28.00
Sandwich Glass, Tieback, Sunburst, Opalescent, Pewter Stem, 4 1/4 In., Pair	27.50
Sandwich Glass, Tieback, 6 Petal Flower, Pewter Shank, 2 1/4 In., Pair	25.00
Sandwich Glass, Tray, Ice Cream, Overshot, 7 X 13 X 2 In.	48.00
Sandwich Glass, Tray, Lacy, Flint, 6 1/2 In.	40.00
Sandwich Glass, Tray, Lacy, Scrolled Leaf & Fleur De Lis, 5 X 6 1/2 In.	65.00
Sandwich Glass, Tray, Scrolled Leaf & Fleur-De-Lis, Lacy, Flint, 6 1/2 In.	40.00
Sandwich Glass, Tumbler, Amethyst, Blown, Fish	110.00
Sandwich Glass, Tumbler, Clambroth, Blown, Fish	80.00
Sandwich Glass, Vase, Fireglow, Flared, Taffy Color, Daisies, 12 In.	95.00
Sandwich Glass, Vase, Milk Glass, Swamp Bird, Waffle Base, 6 In., Pair	45.00
Sandwich Glass, Vase, Tulip Shape, Applied Rigaree, Ruffled Top, 8 In.	30.00
Sandwich Glass, Whiskey Taster, 9 Panel, Flint	15.00

Sarreguemines pottery was first made in Lorraine, France, about 1770. Most of the pieces found today date from the late nineteenth century.

Sarrgeuemines, see also Kate Greenaway

Sarreguemines, Basket, Faience, Pheasant Top, 2 Handles, 11 X 7 1/4 In.	62.50
Sarreguemines, Pitcher, Double Face, 8 3/4 In.	68.00
Sarreguemines, Pitcher, Man's Head Shape, Smiling, Roman Striped Hat, 7 In.	45.00
Sarreguemines, Pitcher, Turquoise Inside, C.1770, 7 In.	75.00
Sarreguemines, Plate, Asparagus, Majolica Type, Round	25.00
Sarreguemines, Plate, Cake, Fables De La Fontaine, 7 1/8 In., Set Of 6	30.00
Sarreguemines, Plate, French Nursery Rhymes, Pink Border, 15 In.	135.00
Sarreguemines, Plate, Spain, Bullfighting Scenes, 8 In., Set Of 12	100.00
Sarreguemines, Stein, Pink, Black Hunting Scene, Pewter Lid, 1/2 Liter	95.00
Sarreguemines, Tray, Couples Dancing & House, Handled, 8 1/4 X 4 7/8 In.	20.00
Sarreguemines, Vase, Floral & Geometric Design On Blue, 13 1/2 In.	58.00

Satin glass is a late nineteenth-century art glass. It has a dull finish that is caused by a hydrofluoric acid vapor treatment. Satin glass was made in many colors and sometimes had applied decorations.

Satin Glass, Basket, Herringbone Mother-Of-Pearl, Frosted Handle, 10 In.	225.00
Satin Glass, Bowl, Apricot To White, Ruffled, Clear Border, 8 1/2 In.	80.00
Satin Glass, Bowl, Finger, White To Yellow, Diamond-Quilted, White Lining	85.00
Satin Glass, Bowl, Flower, Pearl, Blown-Out Pattern, Brass Top, 22 In.	85.00
Satin Glass, Bowl, Pink & White, Mother-Of-Pearl, Fluted, 4 1/2 X 3 In.	100.00
Satin Glass, Box, Jewel, Brass Trim, Red, 4 1/2 X 3 In.	85.00
Satin Glass, Box, Jewel, Egg Shape, Bronze Frame, Flowers, Leaves, Twigs, 4 In.	165.00
Satin Glass, Candlestick, Black, Cable & Band Stem, 8 1/2 In.	14.00
Satin Glass, Candlestick, Black, Gilt Borders, Footed, 6 In.High, Pair	40.00
Satin Glass, Compote, Pale Pink To Deep Rose, Ruffled, Cased, 12 X 5 In.	175.00
Satin Glass, Console Set, Black, Twisted Candlesticks, Flat Bowl, 3 Piece	55.00
Satin Glass, Creamer, Enamel Scroll, Silver Handle, Rim, & Lip	85.00
Satin Glass, Epergne, Blue, Fluted, Enamel Lily Top, Stag Base, 24 1/2 In.	275.00
Satin Glass, Epergne, Blue, Ruffled Compote, 11 In.	65.00
Satin Glass, Ewer Vase, Deep To Light Pink, Frosted Twisted Handle, 13 In.	140.00
Satin Glass, Ewer, Blue, Overlay, Frosted Handles, Bluebirds, Floral, 10 In.	87.50
Satin Glass, Ewer, Green, Diamond-Quilted, Applied Camphor Handle, 6 1/2 In.	110.00
Satin Glass, Ewer, Pink To Rose, Applied Frosted Handles, Ribbed, 9 1/2 In.	150.00
Satin Glass, Ewer, Pink, Melon Ribbed, Camphor Cases & Handle, 9 In.	175.00
Satin Glass, Ewer, Raspberry To White, Jeweled Butterfly Center, 8 In.	120.00
Satin Glass, Ewer, Yellow To White, Applied Camphor Handle, 6 1/2 In.	60.00
Satin Glass, Jar, Biscuit, Pink, Quilted, Blown-Out, Sterling Lid, 7 In.	200.00
Satin Glass, Jar, Biscuit, Red, Quilted, Puffed, Silver Fittings	135.00
Satin Glass, Jar, Biscuit, White Ground, Yellow Daisies, Pink Band	150.00
Satin Glass, Jar, Cookie, Pink, Diamond Puff, Silver Plate Top	90.00
Satin Glass, Jar, Cracker, Blue, Enamel Floral, Bar Finial, 7 In.	145.00
Satin Glass, Jar, Cracker, Pink & White, Lilac Decorated, 8 1/2 In.	145.00

Satin Glass, Jar, Cracker, Pink, Quilted	165.00
Satin Glass, Lamp Base, Red, Artichoke, Chimney, Miniature	75.00
Satin Glass, Lamp, Hanging, Red, Iris, 12 In.	450.00
Satin Glass, Lamp, Red, Cherubs On Open Lattice Pewter Base, 1895, 21 In.	400.00
Satin Glass, Lamp, Red, Lion's Face, Brass Band, Pewter Base, 4-30-95, 23 In.	400.00
Satin Glass, Lamp, White, Ribbed Base, Green Painted Leaf, 1867, Miniature	40.00
Satin Glass, Lamp, Yellow, Mother-Of-Pearl, Caroline Decoration, Miniature	300.00
Satin Glass, Pepper Shaker, Opaque, Letter P	18.00
Satin Glass, Perfumer, Pink, Enameled, Flared Stopper, 5 In.	85.00
Satin Glass, Pitcher, Rainbow, Pink & Blue Stripes, Coinspot, 9 1/2 In.	795.00
Satin Glass, Pitcher, Water, Frosted & Pink, Candy Stripes, Applied Handle	125.00
Satin Glass, Pitcher, Water, Green, Umbrella Leaf, 8 1/2 In.	168.00
Satin Glass, Pitcher, Water, Orange To Clear, Mother-Of-Pearl Herringbone	850.00
Satin Glass, Pitcher, Water, Pink, Florette, Frosted Handle	225.00
Satin Glass, Plaque, Pansy, White, 11 1/2 In.	18.00
Satin Glass, Ring Tree, Pink	10.00
Satin Glass, Rose Bowl, Blue, Crimped Rim, 4 1/2 In.	56.00
Satin Glass, Rose Bowl, Blue, Herringbone, Seaweed Designs, 3 3/4 X 3 1/2 In	245.00
Satin Glass, Rose Bowl, Blue, Overlay, Enameled Fruit, Crimped, 4 5/8 In.	195.00
Satin Glass, Rose Bowl, Blue, Overlay, Jeweled, Enamel Floral, 4 1/2 In.	95.00
Satin Glass, Rose Bowl, Blue, Ruffled Top, White Lining, Blown, 4 In.	65.00
Satin Glass, Rose Bowl, Deep Blue, Diamond-Quilted, Scalloped, 3 1/2 X 4 In.	160.00
Satin Glass, Rose Bowl, Deep Pink, Enamel Floral, Crimped Top, 3 In.	85.00
Satin Glass, Rose Bowl, Gray, Mauve Enamel Floral, Butterfly, 5 1/4 In.	65.00
Satin Glass, Rose Bowl, Green Shaded, 5 In.	65.00
Satin Glass, Rose Bowl, Lemon To White, 8 In. Crimped Top, 3 1/2 In.	47.50
Satin Glass, Rose Bowl, Pink To Lavender, Rough Pontil, 4 In.	65.00
Satin Glass, Rose Bowl, Pink To White, Blue Dotted Flowers, Handles, 4 X 8	125.00
Satin Glass, Rose Bowl, Pink, Cased White, 4 X 4 1/2 In.	75.00
Satin Glass, Rose Bowl, Pink, Light To Dark, Ruffled Top, 5 In.	125.00
Satin Glass, Rose Bowl, Robin's-Egg Blue, Ruffled Edge, Cased, 4 In.	68.00
Satin Glass, Rose Bowl, Rose, Ruffled, White Lining, Blown, 5 In.	85.00
Satin Glass, Rose Bowl, White, Jack-In-The-Pulpit, 5 3/4 In. At Back	100.00
Satin Glass, Rose Bowl, White, Yellow Roses, Pinched Top, 5 1/4 In.	60.00
Satin Glass, Rose Bowl, Wild Rose Color, 5 X 5 1/2 In.	85.00
Satin Glass, Rose Bowl, Yellow Shaded, 5 1/2 In.	70.00
Satin Glass, Rose Bowl, Yellow To White Base, 4 1/2 In.	55.00
Satin Glass, Rose Bowl, Yellow To White, Pansies, Coralene Outlines, 5 In.	75.00
Satin Glass, Rose Bowl, Yellow To White, Pansies, Pinched Top, 5 In.	65.00
Satin Glass, Rose Bowl, Yellow To White, Shell & Seaweed, 5 X 5 1/2 In.	180.00
Satin Glass, Rose Bowl, Yellow, Crimped Top, 3 1/2 In.	55.00
Satin Glass, Salt & Pepper, White, Sunset	28.00
Satin Glass, Saltshaker, Figural Hand, Camphor, Petal Detail, 3 1/8 In.	19.00
Satin Glass, Saltshaker, Opaque, Letter S	18.00
Satin Glass, Saltshaker, Pink, Cord & Tassel	30.00
Satin Glass, Saltshaker, Pink, Periwinkle	30.00
Satin Glass, Saltshaker, Yellow, Egg Shape, Blue & White Flowers	42.00
Satin Glass, Sugar & Creamer, Red, Silver Rims & Handles	125.00
Satin Glass, Syrup, Cream Ground, Pink Roses	85.00
Satin Glass, Syrup, Red, Applied Handle, Hinged Metal Top, 1887, 6 In.	125.00
Satin Glass, Toothpick, Green, Shell & Seaweed, Challinor	35.00
Satin Glass, Toothpick, Pink, Florette	30.00 To 50.00
Satin Glass, Tumbler, Blue To White	40.00
Satin Glass, Tumbler, Mother-Of-Pearl, White Raindrops	95.00
Satin Glass, Tumbler, Pink, Diamond-Quilted Mother-Of-Pearl	85.00
Satin Glass, Tumbler, Pink, Florette	68.00
Satin Glass, Tumbler, Yellow To White, Diamond-Quilted Mother Of Pearl	43.50
Satin Glass, Urn, Chartreuse & Red, Bead & Drape, Bronze Trim, 19 In., Pair	275.00
Satin Glass, Vase, Apricot To Pale Pink, Ruffled, Frosted Feet, 9 In.High	75.00
Satin Glass, Vase, Apricot To Salmon, Ruffled, Jeweled, Handled, 10 In., Pair	400.00
Satin Glass, Vase, Apricot To White, Bulbous, Ruffled Top, 5 In.High, Pair	240.00
Satin Glass, Vase, Black, Flowers, 4 3/4 In.	55.00
Satin Glass, Vase, Blown, Pink & White Opaque Stripes, Ruffled, 8 1/4 In.	98.00
Satin Glass, Vase, Blue, Diamond-Quilted Mother-Of-Pearl, Ruffled, 8 1/4 In.	225.00
Satin Glass, Vase, Blue, Floral, Gold, Ruffled, 4 Applied Camphor Feet, 10 In.	70.00
Satin Glass, Vase, Blue, Overlay, Frosted Feet, Floral, White Lining, 9 In.	75.00

Satin Glass, Vase, Bud, White To Rose, Gold Grasses, 9 1/2 In.	30.00
Satin Glass, Vase, Butterscotch To Yellow To White, Cased, Seaweed, 7 In.	130.00
Satin Glass, Vase, Butterscotch, Cased, Raindrop, Crimped, Ruffled, 6 1/2 In.	95.00
Satin Glass, Vase, Butterscotch, Diamond-Quilted, Ruffled, White Lined, 7 In.	75.00
Satin Glass, Vase, Butterscotch, 6 In.	135.00
Satin Glass, Vase, Cased, Blackbirds Perched On Branches, Florals, 8 1/2 In.	65.00
Satin Glass, Vase, Cased, Deep To Light Butterscotch, 6 3/4 In.	160.00
Satin Glass, Vase, Chartreuse, Ribbon Mother-Of-Pearl, Scalloped, 4 1/8 In.	195.00
Satin Glass, Vase, Citron, Rose Threading, Pink Lined, 10 In.	750.00
Satin Glass, Vase, Citron, Rose Threading, Pink Lined, 10 1/2 In.	850.00
Satin Glass, Vase, Clear Cased, Pink & Maroon Pulled Feathers, 3 3/4 In.	85.00
Satin Glass, Vase, Cylindrical, Rose To Pink, Gold Enameled Flowers, 7 In.	300.00
Satin Glass, Vase, Dark To Light Pink, Bulbous, 8 In., Pair	87.50
Satin Glass, Vase, Deep To Light Salmon, Diamond-Quilted, Cased, 12 1/2 In.	175.00
Satin Glass, Vase, Lily, Pink, Diamond-Quilted, 6 In.High	145.00
Satin Glass, Vase, Multicolor, 8 In.	600.00
Satin Glass, Vase, Pink, Overlay, Frosted Feet, Enameled, 9 5/8 In., Pair	175.00
Satin Glass, Vase, Rose, Pansies, Coralene Stems, Camphor Feet, 10 In.	85.00
Satin Glass, Vase, Salmon To Pink, Enameled Floral & Red Bird, 7 In.	115.00
Satin Glass, Vase, Trumpet Shape, Blue Ribbon, Crimped Top, 8 1/2 In.High	105.00
Satin Glass, Vase, White To Pink, Crimped Top, Applied Handles, 8 In.	145.00

Satin Glass, Webb, see Webb

Satsuma is a Japanese pottery with a distinctive creamy beige crackled
glaze. Most of the pieces were decorated with blue, red, green, orange, or gold.
Almost all the Satsuma found today was made after 1860. Japanese faces
are often a part of the decorative scheme.

Satsuma, see also Button, Satsuma

Satsuma, Bottle, C.1850, 11 3/4 In.	*Illus*	400.00
Satsuma, Bowl, Decorated, 11 1/2 X 7 1/2 In.		65.00
Satsuma, Bowl, Floral, 7 In.		100.00
Satsuma, Box, Fan Shaped, Figural & Floral Design, Gold Beading, 2 X 5 In.		38.00
Satsuma, Box, Ivory, Bird On Lid, Footed, Floral, Round, 3 In.		85.00
Satsuma, Box, Lift-Off Lantern Top, Gold, Red, Dark Blue, C.1840, 6 In., Pair		185.00
Satsuma, Burner, Incense, Domed Lid, 3 Monster Mask Feet, C.1850, 11 3/4 In.		600.00
Satsuma, Button, Florals, 1 1/2 In.		45.00
Satsuma, Button, Peacock Design, 3/4 In.		25.00
Satsuma, Button, Robe, Geisha Girl On Cream, 1 1/8 In.		35.00
Satsuma, Cup & Saucer, Demitasse, Wisteria, Black Decoration		55.00
Satsuma, Cup & Saucer, Intricate Floral Decoration		11.00
Satsuma, Cup & Saucer, Japanese Family		50.00
Satsuma, Figurine, Geisha Girl, Enameling & Gold, 12 In.High		250.00
Satsuma, Humidor, Octagon, War Lords, Orange, Brown, & Green, 7 1/2 In.High		65.00
Satsuma, Inkwell, Japanese Children Medallions, Gold Beading, 15 In.		35.00
Satsuma, Jar, Covered, Tall Box On 3 Legs, Various Butterflies, 4 In.		180.00
Satsuma, Jar, Ginger, Panels Of People & Flowers, Orange, Blue, 6 In.High		65.00
Satsuma, Jar, Rose, Figures, Heavy Gold, 8 In.		195.00
Satsuma, Jar, Rose, Potpourri, Figures, Heavy Gold, 3 In.		50.00
Satsuma, Jar, Tear Finial, Chinese Military Figures On Cream, 32 In., Pair		2600.00
Satsuma, Jar, Temple, 14 Samurai Warriors, 3 On Horseback, 10 1/2 In.		250.00
Satsuma, Jug, Water Scene, 4 1/4 In.		13.50
Satsuma, Napkin Ring, Tricornered		7.50
Satsuma, Pitcher, Purple Wisteria, 3 In.		14.75
Satsuma, Pitcher, White Ground, Beaded Children, Orange & Blue, 7 In.High		49.50
Satsuma, Plate, Hawk Frightening Flight Of Small Birds, C.1870, 7 1/4 In.		34.00
Satsuma, Plate, 1, 000 Flower, 8 1/2 In.		35.00
Satsuma, Sugar & Creamer, Covered, Millefiori Pattern, C.1750		175.00
Satsuma, Tea Set, Brown Jewels On Orange, Green, & Red, Faces, 11 Piece		85.00
Satsuma, Tea Set, Dragon & Figures, Gold Encrusted, Seal Mark, 11 Piece		375.00
Satsuma, Tea Set, Dragons, Gold, C.1850, 7 Piece		700.00
Satsuma, Tea Set, Floral & Bird Design, Raised, 3 Piece		135.00
Satsuma, Tea Set, Japanese Woman & 4 Men Scene, Gold, 15 Piece		295.00
Satsuma, Tea Set, Wisteria On Beige, Gold Dragon Finials, 3 Piece		125.00
Satsuma, Urn, 4 1/4 In., Pair		235.00
Satsuma, Vase, Arhat & Kwannon In Garden Of Western Paradise, 1850, 3 Ft.		1200.00
Satsuma, Vase, Arhat & Sages, Floral, Shishi Mask Handles, C.1850, 35 3/4 In.		1250.00

Satsuma, Vase, Banjo Shape, 2 Handled, 3 In.	115.00
Satsuma, Vase, Birds, Floral, & Landscape On Buff, C.1850, 3 Ft.	800.00
Satsuma, Vase, Blue & Gold Decoration, Figures, 10 In.High, Pair	100.00
Satsuma, Vase, C.1850, 15 In. *Illus*	225.00
Satsuma, Vase, Cobalt Ground, Enameled Oriental Figures, 10 X 13 In.	75.00
Satsuma, Vase, Detailed Figures, Gold Trim, 4 In.	35.00
Satsuma, Vase, Dragon & Coin Medallions, Pate-Sur-Pate Pebbled, 1840, 8 In.	150.00
Satsuma, Vase, Gold Foil Fans, Birds, & Floral, Tear Shape, C.1850, 25 In.	275.00
Satsuma, Vase, Group Of Figures, Gold Fan Handles, Orange & Cream, 11 In.	65.00
Satsuma, Vase, Group Of Figures, White Ring Handles, Orange & Cream, 11 In.	65.00
Satsuma, Vase, Oriental Figures On Deep Blue, 12 In.	100.00
Satsuma, Vase, Rust Ground, Raised Enamel Decoration, 15 1/2 In.High	85.00
Satsuma, Vase, Scenic, Bamboo Shoots, Gilding, C.1850, 7 1/2 In.	160.00
Satsuma, Vase, Thousand Face Panels, Cobalt Ground, 6 In.	110.00
Satsuma, Vase, Warrior, Gold & Enamel, 3 1/2 In.	65.00
Satsuma, Vase, Woman On Front, 2 Handled, C.1850, 9 3/4 In.	65.00
Satsuma, Vase, 2 Warrior Scenes, 2 Handles, Fluted Top, 12 1/4 In.	75.00
Satsuma, Vase, 7 In. *Illus*	165.00
Scale, American Weight & Fortune, 1 Cent	75.00
Scale, Balance, Brass & Steel, Tole Case, 5 X 3 In.	32.00
Scale, Balance, Brass, Weights, Case	12.00
Scale, Baume's, Hydrometers, Wood Tube, Mercury, Dated 5/12/12	50.00
Scale, Candy Store, Standard, Oval Brass Scoop Type, Cast Iron Base, Green	30.00
Scale, Candy, Patent 1927, Brass Scoop Pan	45.00
Scale, Century Weighing Machine, Drugstore, Penny, C.1920	85.00
Scale, Chatillon, No.3, Patent 1891, Brass, Spring Balance, To 24 Lbs.	5.00
Scale, Daniel Alonso, Valladolid, Brass, Double S Scroll Bar, 36 3/4 In.	350.00
Scale, Detecto, Brass Band, 100 Pound	14.00
Scale, Egg, Klein	3.50
Scale, Egg, Oakes, Weight, 6 1/2 In.	12.00
Scale, Egg, Tin	6.00
Scale, Gold Miner's, Hand Type, Brass Pans & Weights	15.00
Scale, Gold Miner's, Portable, Brass Center Balance, Brays, & 5 Weights	39.50
Scale, Gold Miner's, Portable, C.1849, Brass, Embossed American Eagle	64.50
Scale, Gold, Jeweler's, Glass, Mahogany Drawer, Brass Balance, 19 1/2 In.	135.00
Scale, Handy, The, 25 Pound Capacity, 6 In. Hooks On Each End	5.00
Scale, Hanson, Model 8910, Spring, To 100 Pounds	12.50
Scale, Jockey's, Mahogany, C.1850, 28 In. *Illus*	500.00
Scale, John Chatillon & Sons, New York, Iron, Brass Measure, 4 Weights	85.00
Scale, Patent 1840, Plunger Type, Brass, 8 Ozs.	38.00
Scale, Platform, Country Store	50.00
Scale, R.D.Simpson, Edinburgh, Brass, 34 In. High	300.00
Scale, Relouze, Spring	5.00
Scale, Standard, Counter, Metal, Glass Platform, Dated 1911, 34 1/2 In.	75.00
Scale, Tea, Williams, London, C.1850, Hand Held, Brass, Copper Pans	60.00
Scale, Toledo, 1909, Milk Glass, Brass Pan	55.00

Schneider   Schneider Glassworks was founded in 1903 at Epinay-sur-Seine, France, by Charles and Ernest Schneider. Art glass was made between 1903 and 1930. The company still produces clear crystal glass.

Schneider, Candlestick, Brown & Orange, Purple Stem, C.1930, 11 In., Pair	350.00
Schneider, Compote, Orange & Brown, Dark Rim, Signed, 8 In.	138.00
Schneider, Compote, Ribbed, Orange Base, Red Top, Wrought Iron Stand, 8 In.	225.00
Schneider, Vase, Cuspidor Shape, Mottled, Taffy, Reddish & White, 5 In.High	95.00
Schneider, Vase, Ewer, Royal Blue Top, Rust Red Handle, 6 1/2 In.	185.00
Schneider, Vase, Footed, Yellow, Orange, & White Mottled, 5 In.	90.00
Schneider, Vase, Frosted, Fiddlebacks, Round Foot, C.1925, 5 In.	90.00
Schneider, Vase, Green To Frosted, Black Base, Impressed Deco Design, 8 In.	145.00
Schneider, Vase, Mauve & White, Signed, 23 1/2 In.	250.00
Schneider, Vase, Mottled Blue & Orange, Cased, Shield Shape, C.1930, 19 In.	150.00
Schneider, Vase, Mottled Lilac & Purple, Clear Casing, C.1930, 15 3/4 In.	80.00
Schneider, Vase, Urn Shape, Mottled Red, White, & Taffy, 5 X 4 1/2 In.	95.00
Schneider, Vase, Wheel Carved, 1920, 18 1/4 In. *Illus*	375.00
Schneider, Vase, Yellow & Green, Cameo, Red Poppies, C.1920, 12 1/2 In.	425.00

Scrimshaw is bone or ivory or whale's teeth carved by sailors and others for

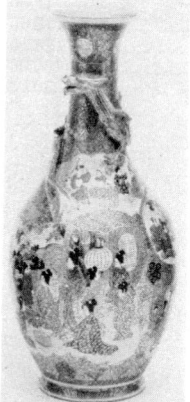

Satsuma, Bottle, C.1850, 11 3/4 In.
(See Page 543)

Satsuma, Vase, C.1850, 15 In.
(See Page 544)

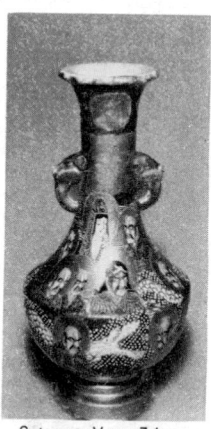

Satsuma, Vase, 7 In.
(See Page 544)

entertainment during the sailing ship days. Some scrimshaw was carved as
early as 1800.

Scrimshaw, Antler, Holder, Knife .... Illus	175.00
Scrimshaw, Busk, Elongated Heart, Sailing Vessels, 15 1/2 In.	200.00
Scrimshaw, Case, Vesta, Sailing Vessel, Sterling, Hallmarked, London, 1880	400.00
Scrimshaw, Ditty Box, Shipping Scenes, Wooden, Hubbard, 1830, 4 1/2 In.	400.00
Scrimshaw, Gavel, Ring Turnings, 8 1/2 In.	200.00
Scrimshaw, Walrus Tusk, Cribbage Board, Dated 1907, 12 In.	150.00
Scrimshaw, Jagging Wheel, Form Of Stylized Antelope, 7 In.	425.00
Scrimshaw, Walrus Tusk, American Indian, Illinois, Nelsons, 17 3/4 In.	175.00
Scrimshaw, Walrus Tusk, Bars Triton, American Eagle, J.Crispin, 1850, 20 In.	1300.00
Scrimshaw, Walrus Tusk, Eskimo, Cribbage Board, Alaska Shoreline, 25 In.	250.00
Scrimshaw, Walrus Tusk, Nelson, Nile, & Trafalgar, Silver Mounted, 8 In.	175.00
Scrimshaw, Walrus Tusk, Reserve Portraits, 25 In.	225.00
Scrimshaw, Walrus Tusk, Whaling Scene, Bars Emerald, Burns, 1852, 15 1/4 In.	650.00
Scrimshaw, Whale's Tooth, Abraham Lincoln Splitting Rails, 7 1/2 In.	400.00
Scrimshaw, Whale's Tooth, American Whaler, Maiden & Sailor, 6 In.	250.00
Scrimshaw, Whale's Tooth, Corkscrew, Black, Starr & Frost Silver End, 6 In.	95.00
Scrimshaw, Whale's Tooth, Crossed Harpoons, American, C.1850, 6 In.	100.00
Scrimshaw, Whale's Tooth, Harpooner In Bow of Longboat, 5 1/4 In.	275.00
Scrimshaw, Whale's Tooth, Hinged Bradd Lid, Charles W.Morgan, 1841, 4 In.	450.00
Scrimshaw, Whale's Tooth, Lincoln & Hamlin, 7 In. .... Illus	350.00
Scrimshaw, Whale's Tooth, Maiden, American Sailing Vessel, 5 1/2 In.	250.00
Scrimshaw, Whale's Tooth, Man On Shore & Sea Monsters, 7 In.	750.00
Scrimshaw, Whale's Tooth, Phoenix & Francis, New Bedford, 1825, 5 In.	475.00
Scrimshaw, Whale's Tooth, Phoenix & 2 Other Whalers, 1844, 4 1/2 In.	300.00
Scrimshaw, Whale's Tooth, Sailing Vessel & Union Jack, 1838, 8 1/2 In.	600.00
Scrimshaw, Whale's Tooth, Sailing Vessel, Ann Alexander, 1851, 6 3/4 In.	150.00
Scrimshaw, Whale's Tooth, Sailing Vessel, Mars, American Flag, 6 1/2 In.	700.00
Scrimshaw, Whale's Tooth, Ships United States & Macedonia, 5 1/2 In.	250.00
Scrimshaw, Whale's Tooth, Slave Kissing Lincoln's Hand, 6 1/4 In.	350.00
Scrimshaw, Whale's Tooth, Whaler, Dead Whale & Longboats, 7 In.	650.00
Scrimshaw, Whale's Tooth, Whaler, Inscribed Phoenix, New Bedford, 5 In.	200.00
Scrimshaw, Whale's Tooth, Whaler, James Whitby, New Bedford, 5 1/4 In.	500.00
Scrimshaw, Whale's Tooth, Whaler, Longboats & Harpooners, 6 In.	600.00
Scrimshaw, Whale's Tooth, Whaler, Morning Star, Floral, & Scroll, 3 1/2 In.	200.00
Scrimshaw, Whale's Tooth, Whaler, Morning Star, New Bedford, 5 1/2 In.	175.00
Scrimshaw, Whale's Tooth, Whaler, Phoenix, N.B., 5 In.	350.00
Scrimshaw, Whale's Tooth, Whaler, The Cape Of Good Hope, 1890, 7 1/2 In.	200.00
Scrimshaw, Whale's Tooth, Whaling Scene On Both Sides, 6 In.	250.00

Scrimshaw, Whale's Tooth, World Globe, American, & British Flag, 6 In. 225.00
Scrimshaw, Whale's Tooth, 3 Whalers & American Flag, 5 In. 275.00
Scrimshaw, Whalebone, "Lizzy, " Stamp Seal, 2 1/2 In. 24.75
Scrimshaw, Whalebone, Sperm Whale, Bone Pivot, 13 In. 1300.00
Scrimshaw, Whalebone, Spoon, Geometric Designs, 6 In. 20.00
Scuttle Mug, see Shaving Mug, Scuttle
SEG, see Paul Revere Pottery

Sevres porcelain has been made in Sevres, France, since 1769. Many copies of the famous ware have been made. The name originally referred to the works of the Royal Factory. The name now includes any of the wares made in the town of Sevres, France.

Sevres, Bowl, Royal Blue, Gold Floral, White Interior, Ormolu Frame, 5 In. 35.00
Sevres, Box, Jewel, Courting Scenes On Red, 4 X 8 In. 90.00
Sevres, Box, Louis Philippe On Hinged Lid, S.Maurice, 9 1/2 X 4 1/2 In. 325.00
Sevres, Box, Ormolu Lid & Mounts, Bleu Celeste & Yellow, C.1890, 10 In. 300.00
Sevres, Burner, Pastille, Autumn Leaves On Powder Blue, Art Nouveau Style 140.00
Sevres, Cachepot, C.1850, 6 In., Pair .... Illus 900.00
Sevres, Candelabra, Dore Bronze, 5 Arm, 21 In., Pair 1250.00
Sevres, Candelabra, 3 S Scroll Ormolu Arms, Tripod Base, C.1850, 17 In., Pair 175.00
Sevres, Creamer, Cobalt & Gold, Panels Of Cherub, Noel, 1761 .... 425.00
Sevres, Cup & Saucer, Coffee, Gros Bleu, 3 Duchess Portraits, C.1850 .... 800.00
Sevres, Figurine, Rabbit, Bisque, M.Marx, C.1895, 7 1/4 In. 350.00
Sevres, Group, Courtesan & Lover, C.1741, 13 X 12 In. 1250.00
Sevres, Group, Le Larcin De La Rose, Terra-Cotta, Wood Socle, C.1850, 20 In. 125.00
Sevres, Inkstand, Champleve Enamels, Insert Of Angels 395.00
Sevres, Plate, Chop, Red Poinsettias, Gold Rim, 10 1/2 In. 25.00

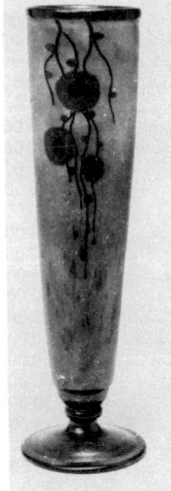

Schneider, Vase,
Wheel Carved, 1920, 18 1/4 In.
(See Page 544)

Scale, Jockey's, Mahogany, C.1850, 28 In.
(See Page 544)

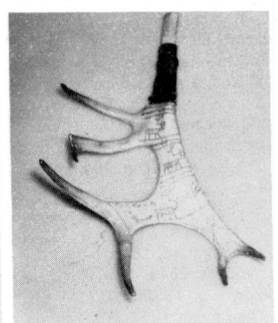

Scrimshaw, Antler, Holder, Knife
(See Page 545)

Scrimshaw, Whale's Tooth,
Lincoln & Hamlin, 7 In.
(See Page 545)

Sevres, Cachepot, C.1850, 6 In., Pair
(See Page 546)

Sewing Tool, Darner, Silver Handle, Wooden Egg
(See Page 548)

Sevres, Plate, Cupids Holding Roses, Gold Trim, C.1848, 9 1/2 In.	95.00
Sevres, Plate, Full Figures Of Woman & Man, Floral Border, 9 In.	68.50
Sevres, Plate, Pink Roses On Pastel Green, 10 1/2 In.	12.50
Sevres, Plate, Portrait, Lady, Pink Border, Gold, Jeweled, 9 1/2 In., Pair	125.00
Sevres, Plate, Portrait, Louis Philippe, D.Montebello, Morin, C.1845, 10 In.	95.00
Sevres, Plate, Woman's Portrait, Dark Blue Border, 9 In.	75.00
Sevres, Tea Set, Hunting Scene, Signed Depres, 3 Piece	225.00
Sevres, Tray, Cherubs In Medallion, Blue & Gold Band, 1846, 8 X 11 1/2 In.	150.00
Sevres, Tray, Receiving, White, Oyster Shell Shape	29.50
Sevres, Urn, Covered, Ormolu Mounted, Gros Bleu, Gilt, C.1850, 37 In., Pair	1300.00
Sevres, Urn, Hand-Painted Scenics, Pivot, 1771, 38 1/2 In.High	6500.00
Sevres, Vase, Covered, Pedestal, Portrait Scenes, Cobalt, Gold, 16 In.	350.00
Sevres, Vase, Dome Cover, Bleu De Roi, Enamel, Ormolu Trim, C.1850, 13 In.	475.00
Sevres, Vase, Glass, Signed, 5 1/4 In.	350.00
Sevres, Vase, Gold Tracery, Blue, Openwork Handles, Artist Signed, 20 In.	350.00
Sevres, Vase, Pottery, Mottled Red & Yellow, 5 In.	45.00

Sewer tile figures were made by workers in the sewer tile factories in the Ohio area during the late nineteenth and early twentieth centuries.

Sewer Tile, Man's Head, 5 In.	45.00
Sewer Tile, Owl, Sitting, 14 1/4 In.	195.00
Sewer Tile, Tree Stump, 14 In.	55.00
Sewing Tool, Basket, Peking Glass Beads, Oriental Coins, 7 1/2 In.	15.50
Sewing Tool, Basket, Reed, Beading, 12 X 6 In.	12.00
Sewing Tool, Bird, Brass, Double Cushion	45.00
Sewing Tool, Bird, Brass, Embossed Feathers 3 Concentrics, 1853	39.00
Sewing Tool, Bird, Brass, One Cushion, Dated 1853	37.50
Sewing Tool, Bird, Brass, Red Velvet Pincushion	45.00
Sewing Tool, Bird, Brass, Revolving Cushion, Norton, 1853	55.00
Sewing Tool, Bird, Dated 1853	37.00
Sewing Tool, Bird, Marked Germany, Pincushion	27.00
Sewing Tool, Bobbin, Wooden, Light Tone, Patina, 9 1/4 In.	8.00
Sewing Tool, Box, Needle, Staffordshire, 2 3/4 X 1 1/2 In.	45.00
Sewing Tool, Box, Pincushion Top, Silver Plate, Victorian	30.00
Sewing Tool, Box, Victorian, Inlaid Wood, Tray, Quilted Lid Pocket, 11 In.	150.00
Sewing Tool, Cabinet, Wooden, Drawer, Spool Holder Pulls Out, 11 X 8 1/2 In.	24.00
Sewing Tool, Case, Needle & Thread, Crocheted Hat	8.00
Sewing Tool, Case, Needle, Carved Ivory, 3 1/2 In.	8.00
Sewing Tool, Case, Needle, Mechanical Barrel	18.00
Sewing Tool, Case, Needle, Mechanical Urn	28.00
Sewing Tool, Case, Needle, Ornate, Hallmarked	25.00
Sewing Tool, Case, Needle, Sterling Silver, Design	12.50
Sewing Tool, Case, Scissors, Sweet Grass	8.00

Sewing Tool, Casket, Lacquer, Chinese, Wood, Brass Handles & Paw Feet, 14 In. 135.00
Sewing Tool, Darner, End-Of-Day, Bulbous 35.00
Sewing Tool, Darner, Globe, Black, Sterling Medallion 20.00
Sewing Tool, Darner, Silver Handle, Wooden Egg .... *Illus* 15.00
Sewing Tool, Darner, Spatter Glass, Pink, Ruby, White, & Clear, 10 In. 62.00
Sewing Tool, Darner, White Nailsea Loopings In Cobalt, Handles 45.00
Sewing Tool, Egg, Darning, Milk Glass, Blown, 6 In. 12.00
Sewing Tool, Egg, Darning, Sterling Silver Handle, Black Egg, 3 3/4 In. 15.00
Sewing Tool, Holder, Needle, Carved Ivory 30.00
Sewing Tool, Holder, Thimble, Sterling, Nutmeg Shape 19.00
Sewing Tool, Holder, Thread, Sterling Silver, 4 Cherubs' Heads .... 55.00 To 75.00
Sewing Tool, Holder, Thread, Sterling Silver, Raised Design .... 25.00 To 35.00
Sewing Tool, Hoops, Embroidery, see Shaker, Hoops, Embroidery
Sewing Tool, Machine, Embroidery, Perfection, Instructions 5.00
Sewing Tool, Measurer, Sterling Silver, Clamp 18.50
Sewing Tool, Mender, Glove, Sterling, Egg Shape Ends, Twisted Bar 30.00
Sewing Tool, Pincushion, see also Shaker, Pincushion, Souvenir,
Pincushion
Sewing Tool, Pincushion & Tape Measure, Doll, Felt, Japan 5.00
Sewing Tool, Pincushion & Thimble In Hand-Carved Dutch Shoes, 3 In. 10.00
Sewing Tool, Pincushion, Bronze Slipper 4.50
Sewing Tool, Pincushion, Cavorting Cherubs Encircle Holder, Gorham, 4 In. 75.00
Sewing Tool, Pincushion, Chair, Carved Whalebone & Ivory 25.00
Sewing Tool, Pincushion, China Kitten, String Attached To Ball 18.00
Sewing Tool, Pincushion, Doll, Flowing Dress 5.00
Sewing Tool, Pincushion, Doll, Germany, Blonde Curls, Fan, 3 1/2 In. 4.50
Sewing Tool, Pincushion, Doll, Young Girl, Bonnet, Flowers In Arm 8.50
Sewing Tool, Pincushion, Hitler, 1941, Plaster 20.00
Sewing Tool, Pincushion, Iron Kitten 6.50
Sewing Tool, Pincushion, Lady's Shoe Shape, Gold Finish 3.95
Sewing Tool, Pincushion, On Back Of Bisque Elephant, 3 3/4 In. 15.00
Sewing Tool, Pincushion, Oriental Doll's Head, In Handled Basket 14.00
Sewing Tool, Pincushion, Velvet, Sterling Silver Openwork Holder, 2 In. 14.00
Sewing Tool, Pincushion, Wooden, Bunker Hill 13.00
Sewing Tool, Scissors, Embroidery, Sterling Handles 16.00
Sewing Tool, Scissors, Stork Shape, Germany 8.50
Sewing Tool, Shuttle, Tatting, Sterling Silver 10.00
Sewing Tool, Shuttle, Wooden, Williams, Millbury, Mass., Metal Tips, 17 In. 18.00
Sewing Tool, Spoon Holder & Pincushion, Brass & Iron, 2 Tiers, 9 In. 15.75
Sewing Tool, Tape Measure, see also Store, Tape Measure
Sewing Tool, Tape Measure, Alarm Clock, Hands Turn When Tape Is Pulled 68.00
Sewing Tool, Tape Measure, Celluloid, Bird 28.00
Sewing Tool, Tape Measure, Celluloid, House 28.00
Sewing Tool, Tape Measure, Celluloid, Pig 20.00
Sewing Tool, Tape Measure, Celluloid, Plum, Leaves, Owl, & Floral Basket 30.00
Sewing Tool, Tape Measure, Hard Plastic, Dressmaker's Dummy 8.00
Sewing Tool, Tape Measure, Metal Cat On Top 28.00
Sewing Tool, Tape Measure, Silver Plate, Ornate 19.00
Sewing Tool, Tape Measure, Unger Bros. Sterling Case 30.00
Sewing Tool, Thimble & Etui, Staffordshire, Gilt Metal Mounts, C.1770, 5 In. 230.00
Sewing Tool, Thimble & Needle Case, Horn & Wood, C.1820 .... 19.00
Sewing Tool, Thimble, Brass 1.50
Sewing Tool, Thimble, Caverswall, England, Hand-Painted Flowers 12.50
Sewing Tool, Thimble, Child's, Brass 8.00
Sewing Tool, Thimble, Cloisonne, On Brass, Mother's Day 7.50
Sewing Tool, Thimble, Copper Clad Stove Advertising 2.50
Sewing Tool, Thimble, English Silver, Enameled Band, Bird On Sides 28.50
Sewing Tool, Thimble, Florals, Ribbed Pattern, Sterling, Pat.May 28, 89 .... 12.00
Sewing Tool, Thimble, Gold, Allover Floral 75.00
Sewing Tool, Thimble, Gold, Bright Cut Leaves & Scrolls, Beaded Base 48.00
Sewing Tool, Thimble, Gold, Chased Rim, Engraved Lulu 24.00
Sewing Tool, Thimble, Gold, Engraved H N H From L N, Size 8 .... 38.00
Sewing Tool, Thimble, Gold, Garland Of Flowers, 14K 35.00
Sewing Tool, Thimble, Gold, Ornate Scroll Band, Size 8 .... 45.00
Sewing Tool, Thimble, Gold, Raised Ornate Flowers 75.00
Sewing Tool, Thimble, Gold, Raised Scroll Base, Scenic Band 65.00

Sewing Tool, Thimble, Gold, Repousse Band 45.00
Sewing Tool, Thimble, Gold, 10K, Carved Rim, Engraved, Size 7 .... 45.00
Sewing Tool, Thimble, Gold, 10K, Scalloped, Raised Scroll Rim, Size 7 .... 45.00
Sewing Tool, Thimble, Greek Silver, Enamel Floral & Decoration 31.00
Sewing Tool, Thimble, Hammersley, Hand-Painted Violets 10.00
Sewing Tool, Thimble, Kirby Shoe Repair, Metal .... .25
Sewing Tool, Thimble, Liberty National Life Insurance, Plastic 1.25
Sewing Tool, Thimble, Limoges Porcelain 8.50
Sewing Tool, Thimble, Marked Germany, Band Of 3 Stars 3.50
Sewing Tool, Thimble, Panama, Metal Case, Thread & Needle Carrier 25.00
Sewing Tool, Thimble, Peters Shoes 4.50
Sewing Tool, Thimble, Petit Point On Metal, Garden 8.50
Sewing Tool, Thimble, Porcelain, Royal Worcester, Birds, Artist Signed 15.00
Sewing Tool, Thimble, Quilting 3.00
Sewing Tool, Thimble, Royal Worcester, Bridal, Bluebirds & Apple Blossoms 10.00
Sewing Tool, Thimble, Royal Worcester, Hand-Painted Birds 12.50
Sewing Tool, Thimble, Royal Worcester, Hand-Painted Flowers 12.50
Sewing Tool, Thimble, Royal Worcester, Hand-Painted Fruit 12.50
Sewing Tool, Thimble, Ships & Lighthouse Engraved, 1882 .... 85.00
Sewing Tool, Thimble, Silver Gilt, Plain & Ornate Panels, Ruby In Each 65.00
Sewing Tool, Thimble, Silver Plate On Brass, Valentine Hearts 8.50
Sewing Tool, Thimble, Silver Plate, Our Lady Of Fatima 8.50
Sewing Tool, Thimble, Silver, Marked England 3.00
Sewing Tool, Thimble, Silver, Mexico 2.00
Sewing Tool, Thimble, Sterling Silver, Birds 12.00
Sewing Tool, Thimble, Sterling Silver, Birmingham, England, Enameled 22.50
Sewing Tool, Thimble, Sterling Silver, European, Diamond-Cut Edge 9.50
Sewing Tool, Thimble, Sterling Silver, Flowered Base 11.00
Sewing Tool, Thimble, Sterling Silver, German, Enameled Roses On Ribbon 50.00
Sewing Tool, Thimble, Sterling Silver, German, Raised Shield 32.50
Sewing Tool, Thimble, Sterling Silver, Handmade 3.00
Sewing Tool, Thimble, Sterling Silver, Marie In Band, Blossoms, McClinton 12.00
Sewing Tool, Thimble, Sterling Silver, Narrow Border 6.00
Sewing Tool, Thimble, Sterling Silver, Persian, Cutwork 15.00
Sewing Tool, Thimble, Sterling Silver, Wide Border 8.00
Sewing Tool, Thimble, Sterling Silver, 10 Sided, Decorated 11.00
Sewing Tool, Thimble, Sterling, Gold Band, Initial, Size 11 .... 18.00
Sewing Tool, Thimble, Sterling, Wide Band Of English Roses 20.00
Sewing Tool, Thimble, Sterling, Wide Band With English Rose 20.00
Sewing Tool, Thimble, Tailor's, Lady's 1.50
Sewing Tool, Thimble, Westminster Abbey & Abbey Crest, Silver 23.00
Shaker, Advertisement, Shaker Cough Syrup, Black & White, 13 X 7 In. ... 20.00
Shaker, Advertisement, Shaker Sarsaparilla, Union Village, 10 X 9 In. 22.50
Shaker, Almanac, 1885, 7 1/2 X 6 In. 25.00
Shaker, Almanac, 1886, 9 X 5 3/4 In. 22.50
Shaker, Bag, Seed, Turnip, Enfield, Planting Directions 12.00
Shaker, Basket, Cheese, 23 1/2 In. Diameter 90.00
Shaker, Basket, Covered, Signed Denison, 23 X 12 1/4 X 8 1/2 In. 85.00
Shaker, Basket, Handle, Cone Shape Bottom, Round, Deep 70.00
Shaker, Basket, Laundry, 27 X 9 1/2 In. 55.00
Shaker, Basket, Sewing, Oval Bentwood Handle, 10 X 11 In. 95.00
Shaker, Basket, Sewing, Pincushion & Pouches, Labeled Oak 1903, 8 1/2 In. 115.00
Shaker, Basket, Sewing, Sabbathday Lake, Silk Lining, 2 1/2 X 6 1/2 In. ... 42.50
Shaker, Basket, 2 Handled, 8 X 16 In. 65.00
Shaker, Basket, 2 1/2 X 8 In. 55.00
Shaker, Beater, Carpet, 24 In. Long 30.00
Shaker, Board, Pressing, Mount Lebanon, 7 1/2 X 22 3/4 In. 90.00
Shaker, Bonnet, Gray Color, 13 In. Long 17.50
Shaker, Bonnet, Straw, 9 In. Long 45.00
Shaker, Book, A Summary View Of The Millennial Church, Wells, 1823 ..... 50.00
Shaker, Book, Christ's First & Second Appearing, 1856, 2nd Edition 50.00
Shaker, Book, Mount Lebanon Cedar Boughs, 1895 .... 22.50
Shaker, Book, Therapeutical Powers & Properties Of Veratrum Viride, 1858 ... 12.50
Shaker, Booklet, Correspondence, Mary F.C. & Sarah L., 1868 .... 22.50
Shaker, Booklet, The Donkey Puzzle, Shaker Drug Remedies, 5 1/2 X 4 1/2 In. ... 17.50
Shaker, Bookmark, Woven Silk, Mount Lebanon, C.1900 .... 60.00

Shaker, Bootjack, 23 In. High	55.00
Shaker, Bottle, Apothecary, Fluid Ext. Tongua Dipterix, Blown, Aqua, 2 Quart	60.00
Shaker, Bottle, Pickle, Shaker Pickles, E.D.Pettengil Co., Me., 1872, 8 In.	95.00
Shaker, Bottle, Pickles, E.D.Pettengil Co., Me., 1871, Cathedral, 7 3/4 In.	95.00
Shaker, Bowl, Maple, Handled, Signed EB, 14 1/2 In. Diameter	230.00
Shaker, Box, Bentwood, Copper Nails, Oval, 1 1/4 X 3 1/2 In.	65.00
Shaker, Box, Bentwood, Copper Nails, Oval, 5 1/2 X 2 1/4 In.	50.00
Shaker, Box, Candle, Sliding Top, 6 1/2 X 17 1/2 In.	160.00
Shaker, Box, Document, Trunk, Red Paint, 8 X 17 1/2 In.	160.00
Shaker, Box, Garden Seeds, Mount Lebanon, Red, 23 1/4 X 3 1/2 In.	115.00
Shaker, Box, Knife, Handle, Blue Color, 13 X 8 1/2 In.	60.00
Shaker, Box, Oval, 10 X 4 1/4 In.	60.00
Shaker, Box, Sewing, Labeled Sabbathday Lake, Square, 3 1/2 In.	40.00
Shaker, Box, Sewing, Oval, Canterbury, Pink Silk Lining, 6 X 7 1/4 In.	90.00
Shaker, Box, Sewing, Pincushion, Spool Cabinet, 2 Drawers, Lydia Crosby, 1847	110.00
Shaker, Box, Sewing, Wooden, Sabbathday Lake, Oval, Pink Lining	135.00
Shaker, Box, Sewing, 9 1/2 X 7 1/2 In.	150.00
Shaker, Box, Spice, Slide Top, 4 X 8 In.	85.00
Shaker, Box, Sugared Nuts, Mount Lebanon, C.1900, Paper, Fabric Handle	10.00
Shaker, Box, Vegetable Seed, Yellow Paint, 5 Partitions Inside, 21 3/4 In.	125.00
Shaker, Bucket, Gray Paint, 12 In. High	50.00
Shaker, Bucket, Oval, Mustard Paint, 9 1/4 X 10 In.	95.00
Shaker, Bucket, Sugar, Wooden, Covered, Wire & Wood Handle, 6 1/2 X 6 In.	35.00
Shaker, Calendar, 1882, Mount Lebanon, Cooking Recipies, 35 Pages	20.00
Shaker, Can, Milk, Tin, 2 Gallon	*Illus* 55.00
Shaker, Candle Dryer, Alfred, 34 In. High	*Illus* 400.00
Shaker, Churn, Butter	*Illus* 205.00
Shaker, Churn, Tin	*Illus* 175.00
Shaker, Churn, Wooden, Red Paint, 27 X 18 1/2 X 11 In.	250.00
Shaker, Comb, Shampoo, Wooden	30.00
Shaker, Cover, Seat, Wool Fleece, Purple, 25 X 15 In.	*Illus* 40.00
Shaker, Creamer, Mount Lebanon, N.Y., Porcelain	190.00
Shaker, Dipper, Wooden, New Lebanon, C.1800, Natural Finish, 4 In.	95.00
Shaker, Dryer, Candle, Alfred Community, Turntable Top, 30 Candles, 34 In.	400.00
Shaker, Duster, Wool, Fabric Hanger, 14 1/2 In. Long	40.00
Shaker, Easel, For Cleaning & Painting Storm Windows, 6 Ft.2 In.	90.00
Shaker, Firkin, Apple Sauce, J.S.Kaime, N.H., Wooden, Wire Handle, 7 In.	120.00
Shaker, Furniture, see Furniture	
Shaker, Handle, Mop, Labeled 25 EP	10.00
Shaker, Hanger, Clothes, Wooden, Flat, 17 In. Long	7.50
Shaker, Hanger, Clothes, Wooden, Initial B, 14 In. Long	13.00
Shaker, Hanger, Initials MB, Wooden, Round, 16 1/2 In. Long	20.00
Shaker, Hanger, Wooden, Initials MJ, 18 3/4 In. Long	22.50
Shaker, Hat, Lady's, Quilted, 16 In. Long	25.00
Shaker, Hat, Lady's, Winter Fur Trim	15.00
Shaker, Holder, Funnel, Wooden, Enfield Dispensary, 13 X 12 In.	105.00
Shaker, Holder, Funnel, Wooden, Medicine House, Mount Lebanon, 18 1/2 In.	100.00
Shaker, Hoops, Embroidery, 8 In.	15.00
Shaker, Kerchief, Initials JB, Harvard, 41 X 40 In.	65.00
Shaker, Label, Extract Of Butternut, Juglans Cineria, D.M., New Lebanon, N.Y.	8.00
Shaker, Label, Extract Of Deadly Nightshade, Atropa Belladonna, N.Y.	16.00
Shaker, Label, Extract Of Sarsaparilla, Aralia Nudicaulis, New Lebanon	13.00
Shaker, Lapboard, Pine, Folding, Hinge Tapes, 37 In. Long	105.00
Shaker, Lifter, Pie, 16 1/2 In. Long	22.50
Shaker, Lifter, Stove Lid, 15 In. Long	20.00
Shaker, Measure, Bentwood, From 4 1/2 To 11 In., Nest Of 5	155.00
Shaker, Measure, United Society Shakers, Gloucester, Me., Green Paint, 8 In.	70.00
Shaker, Measure, 8 X 14 1/4 In. Diameter	60.00
Shaker, Measurer, Tin, Quart	*Illus* 45.00
Shaker, Paddle, Apple Butter, Mount Lebanon, 1830-40, 42 X 14 1/2 In.	30.00
Shaker, Pail, Seed, Covered, 9 1/2 X 12 In.	40.00
Shaker, Pail, Seed, Painted Yellow Grain, 9 X 12 In.	55.00
Shaker, Peg Board, 6 Pegs, 33 X 2 1/4 In.	85.00
Shaker, Pick, Mount Lebanon, 1830-40, 35 1/2 In. High	45.00
Shaker, Pincushion With Spool Holder, Cloth Covering, 5 1/2 In. High	60.00
Shaker, Pincushion, East Canterbury, Blue, White Leather Trim, 2 In.	25.00

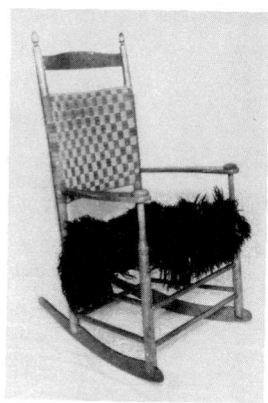

Shaker, Cover,
Seat, Wool Fleece,
Purple, 25 X 15 In.
(See Page 550)

Shaker, Rocker
(See Page 552)

Shaker, Can, Milk,
Tin, 2 Gallon
(See Page 550)

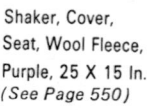

Shaker, Candle Dryer, Alfred, 34 In. High
(See Page 550)

Shaker, Churn, Tin
(See Page 550)

Shaker, Measurer, Tin, Quart
(See Page 550)

Shaker, Stove, Box
(See Page 552)

Shaker, Washbasin, Wire Handle, 10 1/2 In.
(See Page 552)

Shaker, Churn, Butter
(See Page 550)

Shaker, Postcard, Shaker Bridge, Enfield, N.H., 1910	8.00
Shaker, Postcard, Shaker Village, Ayer, Mass., 1908	6.00
Shaker, Price List, Medicinal Herbs, Mount Lebanon, 1872, 13 X 8 1/4 In.	12.50
Shaker, Rack, Drying, Wooden, Leather Hinges, 3 Fold, 3 Footed, 68 In.	140.00
Shaker, Rack, Drying, 41 1/2 X 33 1/2 In.	85.00
Shaker, Rack, Pill Drying, Sabbathday Lake, 1880, Sister R.Mildred Barker	55.00
Shaker, Rack, Towel, Black Finish, 28 X 23 1/4 In.	105.00
Shaker, Reward Notice, Stolen Property, Seed Store, Hancock Village, 1839	40.00
Shaker, Rocker .... Illus	350.00
Shaker, Rug, Woven, Sabbathday Lake, Abigail C.Blazo, 1810, 12 X 15 Ft.	750.00
Shaker, Rug, 39 X 96 In.	150.00
Shaker, Seat Cover, Chair, Purple Wool Fleece, On Woven Mat, 25 X 15 In.	40.00
Shaker, Shirt, Man's, Homespun Linen, Initials EB, 36 In. Long	130.00
Shaker, Shovel, Enfield, N.H., 55 In. High	52.50
Shaker, Sieve, Bentwood, Woven Horsehair Mesh, 12 1/4 X 5 In.	32.50
Shaker, Sieve, Horsehair, 12 In. Diameter	40.00
Shaker, Sieve, Silk & Bentwood, 2 1/4 X 7 In.	30.00
Shaker, Sifter, Bentwood, Wire Mesh, Labeled Seeds, 17 In. Diameter	67.50
Shaker, Sleeve, Ironing, Wooden, 31 X 9 In.	125.00
Shaker, Stool, Wagon, 7 1/2 X 7 X 13 In.	45.00
Shaker, Stove, Box .... Illus	450.00
Shaker, Swift, Maple, Table Clamp, Hancock, 23 In. High	170.00
Shaker, Tongs, Harvard, 14 1/2 In. Long	35.00
Shaker, Tub, Oval, Handled, 14 X 10 In.	200.00
Shaker, Washbasin, Tin, Canterbury, Wire Hanger, 28 1/2 X 26 1/2 In.	25.00
Shaker, Washbasin, Wire Handle, 10 1/2 In. .... Illus	25.00

Shaving mugs were popular from 1860 to 1900. Many types were made, including occupational mugs featuring pictures of the man's job. There were scuttle mugs, silver-plated mugs, glass-lined mugs, and others.

Shaving Mug, A Present In Gold, Purple Flowers, Brown Leaves, Soap Saver	22.50
Shaving Mug, Archie J.Stoddard In Gold, White & Black Child, Limoges	27.00
Shaving Mug, Azaleas, Signed Germany	8.50
Shaving Mug, Blue Panels With Pink Roses, Gold, Ornate Handle, Brandenburg	35.00
Shaving Mug, Brown Shading, Elks, Germany	12.50
Shaving Mug, Carnival Glass, Orange Tree, Blue	31.00
Shaving Mug, Crockery Type, Roses	9.50
Shaving Mug, Derby Silver Plate, Chased, Milk Glass Insert	27.00
Shaving Mug, Eagle, Flag, & Shield, Gold Name & Rim, Red, White, & Blue	85.00
Shaving Mug, Excelsior, Patent Sept.20, 1870, Left Handed, Floral, 3 1/2 In.	16.00
Shaving Mug, "F.L.T. Walter H. Haynes, " White, Gold Trim	25.00
Shaving Mug, Foresters Of America, T & V Limoges	22.00
Shaving Mug, Hand-Painted, Divider	20.00
Shaving Mug, Ironstone, Medium Blue & Gold Bands	18.00
Shaving Mug, Ironstone, Tea Leaf, Gridley	55.00
Shaving Mug, Ironstone, White, Roses	10.00
Shaving Mug, McKinnis & Flowers, Porcelain, 3 1/2 In.	38.00
Shaving Mug, Milk Glass, Patent Shaving Mug, July 16, 1867	23.00
Shaving Mug, Nippon, Floral, Gold Trim, Marked	45.00
Shaving Mug, Nippon, Owl, Brown Eyes, Beaded Handle & Top, Green M Mark	68.00
Shaving Mug, Occupational, Arm & Hammer, Gold Trim	45.00
Shaving Mug, Occupational, Banker, M.S.Bowen, T & V Limoges Lange & Co.	165.00
Shaving Mug, Occupational, Carpenter, John Burger	65.00
Shaving Mug, Occupational, Engine With Wood Carrier, D & C	95.00
Shaving Mug, Occupational, Farmer Taking Grain To Market	95.00
Shaving Mug, Occupational, Farmer, Wagon & 2 Horses, KPM, Germany	95.00
Shaving Mug, Occupational, Gold Name, Blue Drapery, Limoges	50.00
Shaving Mug, Occupational, Gold Ribbon & Name, Royal Austria, Green Wreath	50.00
Shaving Mug, Occupational, Horizontal Steam Engine, Gold Band	75.00
Shaving Mug, Occupational, Jeweler's, Personalized	95.00
Shaving Mug, Occupational, Man Sitting At Desk, AK France	75.00
Shaving Mug, Occupational, Musician, Tuba	115.00
Shaving Mug, Occupational, Pool Table, T & V Limoges	60.00
Shaving Mug, Occupational, Telegrapher	100.00
Shaving Mug, Pink Luster, Embossed Flowers & Leaves	17.50
Shaving Mug, Pink Roses On White, Double Looped Handle, Gold, Soap Deck	23.50

Shaving Mug, Porcelain, Violets & Green Foliage	18.50
Shaving Mug, Portrait, Brunette, Gold Trim, Browns, R.C.Bavaria	40.00
Shaving Mug, Pottery Type, G.Y.Kridler In Gold Scroll, Fuchsia & White	23.50
Shaving Mug, "Raymond Sulliven, Corpus Christi, Texas, Xmas 1912, " Violets	35.00
Shaving Mug, R.S.Germany, Roses	62.50
Shaving Mug, R.S. Prussia, Floral, Footed, Red Mark	85.00
Shaving Mug, R.S.Prussia, Pearlized, Red Mark	78.00
Shaving Mug, R.S. Prussia, Yellow Roses On Cream & Beige	65.00
Shaving Mug, Scuttle, Blue, English, Signed James Kent, 4 X 6 In.	35.00
Shaving Mug, Scuttle, Decorated	8.00
Shaving Mug, Scuttle, George VI & Elizabeth Coronation, Porcelain	38.50
Shaving Mug, Scuttle, Green & Gold Trim	20.00
Shaving Mug, Scuttle, Orange To Yellow, 4 X 6 In.	20.00
Shaving Mug, Scuttle, Shell Body, Floral	25.00
Shaving Mug, Scuttle, Shell, White	18.50
Shaving Mug, Scuttle, Union, 1870, Florals	20.00
Shaving Mug, Scuttle, White Shell	18.50
Shaving Mug, Silver Plate, Flowered Body, Brush	18.00
Shaving Mug, Silver Plate, Monogram, Porcelain Liner	12.50
Shaving Mug, Silver, Brush & Brush Rest, Milk Glass Insert, C.1890	35.00
Shaving Mug, Soap Divider, Porcelain, 3 3/4 In.	22.50
Shaving Mug, Tin, Brush Holder On Side, Soap Tray In Top, 4 In.	35.00
Shaving Mug, Triple Plate Silver, Royal Mfg.Co., Brush Rest, Floral	25.00
Shaving Mug, U.S.Flags, Eagle, & Deer, Liberty, Unity, Benevolence, & Concord	27.50
Shaving Mug, White, Floral	8.50
Shaving Mug, White, Gold Flowers, Green & Blue Leaves	18.00

Shawnee pottery was made in Zanesville, Ohio, from 1935 until 1961.
Shawnee also produced pottery for George Rumrill during the late 1930s.

Shawnee, Creamer, Cat	7.50
Shawnee, Creamer, Corn	8.50
Shawnee, Jar, Cookie, Clown	15.00
Shawnee, Jar, Cookie, Puss In Boots	5.00
Shawnee, Planter, Black Threads On Orange, Wash Boiler Shape, 6 7/8 In.	3.50
Shawnee, Planter, Chihuahua Dog With Doghouse, 7 In.	4.00
Shawnee, Planter, Orange & Gold Basket Weave, Square, 4 Feet, 3 1/2 In.	2.00
Shawnee, Planter, Yellow Doe & Fawn On Green, 5 1/2 X 6 3/4 In.	3.50
Shawnee, Salt & Pepper, Corn King Pattern	12.00
Shawnee, Salt & Pepper, Girl & Boy	6.00
Shawnee, Salt & Pepper, Puss 'n Boots	8.50
Shawnee, Salt & Pepper, Tom, Tom, The Piper's Son	8.50
Shawnee, Vase, Applied Deer, 9 In.	3.00
Shawnee, Vase, Planter Type, 2 Deer, 6 1/2 In.	3.00
Sheffield, see Silver, Sheffield	
Shellwork, Bureau, 9 In. .... *Illus*	32.50

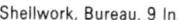

Shellwork, Bureau, 9 In.

Shellwork, Valentine, Sailor's, Heart, Framed 225.00
Shellwork, Valentine, Sailor's, Home Again & Heart, Hinged, Pair 450.00
Shenango, Jar, Mustard, Hotel, Maroon On White, C.1910 .... 4.25
Shenango, Pot, Cream, Hotel, Green On White, C.1910 .... 3.25
Shenango, Sugar, Hotel, Green On White, C.1910 .... 4.25
Ship, American Eagle, Pilot House, Carved & Gilt Wood, C.1850, 47 In. 700.00
Ship, Bag, Ditty, Sailmaker's, Canvas, Implements Inside, C.1850, 16 In. 64.50
Ship, Binoculars, U.S.Navy Night Glass, Brass, Leather Grips 25.00
Ship, Box, Ditty, Ivory Whale On Bentwood Lid, Oval, 5 In. 100.00
Ship, Card, Clipper Peruvian, Coleman's California Line, C.1850, 6 1/2 In. 250.00
Ship, Card, Clipper William Tell, Coleman's California Line, C.1850 .... 225.00
Ship, Chart, Northern Part Of Indian Ocean, Sayer, 1787, 24 X 36 In. 70.00
Ship, Chart, Reduit De L'Ocean Occidental, Dheulland, 1742, 25 X 37 In. 165.00
Ship, Chest, Medicine, Mahogany, Hinged Top, Brass Handle, 14 Bottles, C.1840 ...... 195.00
Ship, Chest, Sea, Wood & Iron, Painting In Lid, American, C.1850, 22 X 8 In. 425.00
    Ship, Clock, see Clock, Ship's
Ship, Compass, E.Vion, Paris, C.1900, Black Enamel Body, 9 In. 55.00
Ship, Compass, Maine Fishing Boat, Wet 35.00
Ship, Compass, New England, Oak Box 45.00
Ship, Creamer, White Star Steamship, Cunard, Clews, 3 X 2 X 2 In. 20.00
Ship, Dividers, English, C.1850, Proportional, German Silver, Steel Tips 30.00
Ship, Dividers, Navigation, English, C.1850, Brass, Steel Points, 8 In. 28.00
Ship, Eagle, Pilothouse, Carved Wood, C.1850, 36 X 25 In. 800.00
Ship, Figurehead, Gentleman, Carved & Painted Wood, C.1850, 37 In. 1600.00
Ship, Hook, Grappling, American, Iron, Hand-Forged, C.1750, Braided Rope 125.00
Ship, Instruments, Drawing, Brass, Steel, & Ivory, English, 1800, Fishskin Case 145.00
Ship, Lantern, Anchor, Brass & Copper 265.00
Ship, Lantern, Blue Glass, 10 In. 60.00
Ship, Lantern, Govt.Contract Key.Ware 50.00
Ship, Lantern, Masthead 265.00
Ship, Log, Bark Mary & Louisa Of New York, 1861-1862 .... 185.00
Ship, Log, Clipper John Quincy Adams, 1848-1849 .... 475.00
Ship, Log, Merchantman Gloucester, 1838-1839, Leatherbound 250.00
Ship, Log, Taffrail, Negus Patent, Brass 2 In. Dial, Rotator 115.00
Ship, Masthead, Eagle, Carved Wood & Gilt Wood, Maine, C.1850, 48 In. 1100.00
Ship, Menu, Caronia, Ship Pictured 2.50
Ship, Model, Anchor, Brass, Marble Base, 4 1/2 In. 57.50
Ship, Model, Ferry Boat, Carved Wood, Painted, C.1890, 23 In. 200.00
Ship, Model, Viking, Gokstad, Oak Hull, Oars, Shields, 40 In. 175.00
Ship, Model, Whaler, Honqua, Whalebone, C.1850, Case, 26 1/2 X 19 In. 2300.00
Ship, Model, Whaler, 3 Masted, Wooden Base, C.1850, 34 In. 525.00
Ship, Model, 3 Masted Sailing Ship, C.1840, 28 In. 150.00
Ship, Model, 3 Masted Sailing Vessel, Wood & Ivory, Glass Case, 20 1/2 In. 650.00
Ship, Nameplate, U.S.Brinckerhoff Paddlewheeler, 5 X 1 1/2 In. 200.00
Ship, Orrery, French, C.1850, Brass Center Post, Gold Leaf Wood Sphere 850.00
Ship, Pantograph, English, C.1850, Brass, Cloth Covered Lead Pivot Weight 195.00
Ship, Papers, Schooner Armada, 1860, Boston To New Orleans 60.00
Ship, Papers, Schooner Helios, 1858, New Orleans To Liverpool 60.00
Ship, Plate, Mess, British Man-O'-War, Staffordshire, C.1900, 9 1/2 In. 64.50
Ship, Plate, Officers' Mess, British Man-O'-War, Staffordshire, 10 In. 97.50
Ship, Poster, Sold By Auction, The American Ship Clinton, 1849, 17 X 11 In. 84.50
Ship, Quadrant, Spencer, Barret & Co., London, Black Ebony, Brass, Ivory, 1810 ...... 325.00
Ship, Quadrant, T.D.Lillie & Co., New Orleans, Brass, C.1820, 10 In. 550.00
Ship, Rule, Captain Field's Improved Parallel, Boxwood, English, C.1900 .... 50.00
Ship, Rule, Gunter, John Rabone & Son, Warranted, Boxwood, C.1860, 24 In. 225.00
Ship, Rule, Gunter, Navigator's, Initials J.S.M., Boxwood, C.1800, 24 In. 175.00
Ship, Rule, Parallel, Rolling, U.W.W., Birmingham, Brass, C.1900, Pine Case 70.00
Ship, Sector, English, C.1810, Boxwood, Brass Hinge, 6 1/4 In. 55.00
Ship, Sextant, Paget Angel, Boxed, 4 1/2 In. 125.00
Ship, Sextant, Sounding, Hughes & Son, London, Paget, Angle, C.1895 .... 170.00
Ship, Sextant, Spencer Barrett & Co., London, Brass & Wood, C.1850, 14 In. 250.00
Ship, Sign, S.S.Imperator Steamship, Tin On Brass Plate, 1911, 46 X 36 In. 150.00
Ship, Sounder, Wigzell's Patent, England, C.1910, Brass, Pressure Type 130.00
Ship, Spyglass, Berge, London, C.1810, Longitude By Moons Of Jupiter 375.00
Ship, Spyglass, Gilbert & Wright, London, C.1789, Mahogany Barrel, Brass Trim 295.00
Ship, Steam Engine Indicator, Richard's, Elliot Bros., London, C.1890, Brass 75.00

Ship, Tea Set, White Star Steamship, Cunard, Clews, Art Deco, 4 Piece	110.00
Ship, Telescope, Mahogany, Brass Tubes, Ferrules & Cap, Opens To 24 In.	22.00
Ship, Timing Glass, Second Log, English, C.1890, Brass Case	65.00
Ship, Trumpet, Captain's Speaking, Copper, C.1820, 19 1/2 In.	195.00
Ship, Watch, Hamilton, Lancaster, Pa., Gimbaled, Brass, Mahogany Box	295.00
Ship, Wheel, Anderson Mfg.Co., Iron, Wood Handles, Brass Tips, 44 In.	185.00
Ship, Wheel, Brass Hub, Inlaid Wood, 42 In.	290.00
Ship, Wheel, Brass Inlay & Hub, 36 In.	255.00
Ship, Wheel, Brass, Oak Grips, 24 In.	165.00
Ship, Wheel, Handmade, Wood, Brass Center Hub, 6 Spokes, Inlays, 25 In.	145.00

Shirley Temple dishes, blue glassware, and any other souvenir-type objects with her name and picture are now collected.

Shirley Temple, Book, How I Raised Shirley Temple, Her Mother, 1935	25.00
Shirley Temple, Book, Just A Little Girl	8.50
Shirley Temple, Book, Little Colonel	7.00 To 10.00
Shirley Temple, Book, Little Playmate	8.50
Shirley Temple, Book, Littlest Rebel, Peple, 1939	7.00
Shirley Temple, Book, Now I Am Eight	12.00
Shirley Temple, Book, On The Movie Lot	8.50
Shirley Temple, Book, Shirley Temple's Story Book	6.00
Shirley Temple, Book, Shirley Temple's Treasury Book	6.00
Shirley Temple, Book, Susannah Of The Mounties, Muriel Denison, 1936	15.00
Shirley Temple, Book, Twinkle Toes	8.50
Shirley Temple, Creamer, Picture	8.50 To 15.00
Shirley Temple, Doll, Composition, Long Dress & Pantaloons, 24 In.	155.00
Shirley Temple, Doll, Composition, Wig, Dressed, 13 In.	75.00
Shirley Temple, Doll, Composition, Wig, Dressed, 22 In.	135.00
Shirley Temple, Doll, Composition, 16 In.	60.00
Shirley Temple, Doll, Composition, 25 In.	120.00
Shirley Temple, Doll, Dressed As Texas Ranger, 23 In.	65.00
Shirley Temple, Doll, Horseman, Composition, Little Colonel, 1930s, 18 In.	95.00
Shirley Temple, Doll, Ideal, Composition, Dressed, 18 In.	85.00
Shirley Temple, Doll, Ideal, Dressed, 14 In.	29.50
Shirley Temple, Doll, Ideal, 12 In.	5.00 To 22.50
Shirley Temple, Doll, Long Dress, 24 In.	150.00
Shirley Temple, Doll, Vinyl, Flirty Eyes, 18 In.	35.00
Shirley Temple, Doll, Vinyl, 15 In.	10.00
Shirley Temple, Doll, Vinyl, 1957, 12 In.	35.00
Shirley Temple, Figurine, Salt Glaze, 6 1/2 In.	37.50
Shirley Temple, Mirror, America's Sweetheart, Heidi, 1937, 2 1/4 In.	4.50
Shirley Temple, Mirror, Pocket, America's Sweetheart, Heidi, 1937, 2 1/4 In.	4.00
Shirley Temple, Mirror, Pocket, Heidi Movie, Fox Film Corp., 1937, 2 In.	15.00
Shirley Temple, Mug	12.00
Shirley Temple, Music Sheet, Animal Crackers In My Soup, 1935	10.00
Shirley Temple, Music Sheet, Stowaway, Illustrated	8.50
Shirley Temple, Nightgown & Cap, For 12 In. Doll, Red Flannel	10.50
Shirley Temple, Photograph, Black & White, 10 X 7 In.	4.00
Shirley Temple, Photograph, Framed, Signed, 8 X 5 3/4 In.	8.50
Shirley Temple, Photograph, 1936, Framed	10.00
Shirley Temple, Raincoat & Hat, Red Polka Dot, Size 12	5.00
Shirley Temple, Ring, Celluloid	5.00
Shirley Temple, Scrapbook, C.1930	22.50
Shirley Temple, Trunk, Doll's, 14 X 7 X 8 In.	25.00
Silesia, Bowl, Nut, White Flowers, Gold, 4 1/2 In.	18.00
Silesia, Bowl, Underplate, & Ladle, Mayonnaise, Hand-Painted, Marked	35.00
Silesia, Celery, Art Nouveau Band With Ladies' Heads, 11 1/2 In.	30.00
Silesia, Celery, Swans, Water Lilies, Gold Beading, Pierced Ends, 12 1/2 In.	19.00
Silesia, Jar, Biscuit, Blue Jewel Sets, Floral, Bronze Handle, 12 In.	145.00
Silesia, Plate, Gooseberries, 8 1/2 In.	27.50
Silesia, Plate, Hand-Painted Poppies & Leaves, 7 In.	12.50
Silesia, Plate, Purple Floral On White, Ruffled Edge, 8 In.	10.00
Silesia, Punch Set, Grapes Outside & Inside, 13 Piece	550.00
Silesia, Relish, Handled, Yellow & White Daisies, Tan, R.S.Tillowitz, 11 In.	16.00
Silesia, Sugar & Creamer, White Roses On Green	20.00
Silesia, Syrup & Underplate, Roses On Ecru To White, Gold, R.S.Tillowitz	28.00

Silesia, Vase, White & Pink Roses On Cream, Gold, 2 Handled, 10 1/2 In. 62.50
Silhouette, see Picture, Silhouette
  Silver deposit glass was made during the late nineteenth and early twentieth
  centuries. Solid sterling silver was applied to the glass by a chemical
  method so that a cutout design of silver metal appeared against a clear or
  colored glass. It is sometimes called silver overlay.
Silver Deposit, Bottle, Cologne, Emerald Green, Floral, 5 In. 110.00
Silver Deposit, Bottle, Cordial, Green, Gondolier & Scrolls, 10 1/2 In. 19.00
Silver Deposit, Bottle, Perfume, 3 1/2 In. 15.00
Silver Deposit, Bottle, Sterling Floral & Vines, 3 1/2 In. Wide At Bottom 60.00
Silver Deposit, Bowl, Dolphin, 4 Footed, 10 1/2 X 4 In. 18.00
Silver Deposit, Bowl, Floral & Concentrics, Pedestal, 9 1/4 X 5 1/2 In. 12.50
Silver Deposit, Cordial Set, Emerald Green, 7 Piece 35.00
Silver Deposit, Creamer, Latticework & Four-Leaf Clover 3.95
Silver Deposit, Decanter, Blown, Ornate Overlay, 8 1/2 In. 85.00
Silver Deposit, Decanter, 12 In. 65.00
Silver Deposit, Goblet, Cocktail, Silver Rim, 3 3/4 In. 3.50
Silver Deposit, Jug, Claret, Lime Green Glass, Reeded Handle, Gorham, 8 In. 250.00
Silver Deposit, Jug, Claret, Lime Green, Reeded Handle, Gorham, 8 1/4 In. 195.00
Silver Deposit, Pitcher, Sauce, Signed Rockwell, 6 X 3 In. 25.00
Silver Deposit, Plate, Crystal, 5 1/2 In. 6.50
Silver Deposit, Bowl, Fluted, 5 1/4 In. 12.00
Silver Deposit, Plate, Green, 6 Sided, 7 In. 15.00
Silver Deposit, Salt & Pepper 7.50
Silver Deposit, Salt, Sherbet Shape, Footed 8.50
Silver Deposit, Sugar & Creamer, Floral Design, Open 40.00
Silver Deposit, Tray, Sandwich, Wild Roses, Silver Rim, 11 1/2 In. 22.50
Silver Deposit, Tumbler, Lemonade, Bands & Bars, Monogram Blank 7.95
Silver Deposit, Tumbler, Monogram DD, 4 In. 15.00
Silver Deposit, Vase, Blue Iridescent, Loetz Style, Floral, C.1900, 5 1/2 In. 225.00
Silver Deposit, Vase, Emerald Green, 7 1/2 In. 53.50
Silver Deposit, Vase, Three Wild Ducks, Silver Rims, 8 1/2 In. 27.00
Silver Deposit, Washstand Set, Sterling, Engraved Floral, 2 Piece 85.00
Silver Deposit, Water Set, Amethyst, Floral Design, 4 Piece 97.50
Silver Plate, see also Silver, Sheffield
Silver Plate, Ashtray, Golfer On Corner, Derby, Patent 11/2/26 .... 40.00
Silver Plate, Basket, Bread, Pierced, Meriden, C.1905, 12 In. 18.00
Silver Plate, Basket, Cake, Birds, Fruit, Floral, & Landscape, Meriden, 10 In. 39.00
Silver Plate, Basket, Cake, Footed, James W.Tufts Co. 35.00
Silver Plate, Basket, Cake, Middletown 10.50
Silver Plate, Basket, Embossed Swan, Pairpoint, Round, 5 1/2 In. 26.00
Silver Plate, Basket, Floral, Vines, Birds, & Insects, Footed, Tufts, 10 In. 38.00
Silver Plate, Basket, Victorian, Allover Cupids & Figures, 16 In.High 85.00
Silver Plate, Bowl, Serving, Scalloped Edge, English, EPC, 10 In. 7.50
Silver Plate, Bowl, Vegetable, Covered, Repousse, 2 Handled, Wilcox, 9 1/2 In. 65.00
Silver Plate, Box, Collar Button, "A Friend In Need, " Rutland, Vt. 11.50
Silver Plate, Box, Hairpin, Pairpoint 15.00
Silver Plate, Brush, Hair, Art Nouveau Lady, Ribbons, & Floral, Hope Co., Pair 10.00
Silver Plate, Butter, Cow Finial, 4 Legs, Chased, Simpson, Hall Miller Co. 75.00
Silver Plate, Butter, Dome Cover, Insert 13.50
Silver Plate, Butter, Dome Top, Knife Rest, Chased, Simpson, Hall Miller Co. 45.00
Silver Plate, Butter, Domed Cover, Handled, Footed, Peacocks, Webster Mfg. 35.00
Silver Plate, Butter, Liner, Footed, Meriden 14.00
Silver Plate, Cake Stand, Embossed Patterning On Bowl & Rim, Double Handle 38.00
Silver Plate, Candlesnuffer & Tray, 10 In. ....*Illus* 65.00
Silver Plate, Case, Stamp, Embossed Cupids & Florals, 1 1/2 X 2 1/4 In. 15.00
Silver Plate, Castor, see Castor
Silver Plate, Celery, Full-Length Woman On Each Side, Etched Liner 75.00
Silver Plate, Chest, Jewel, Roll Top, Bird & Floral, Meriden, 1878, 6 In. 68.00
Silver Plate, Cigar Piercer, Dog, Carved Leaf Handle, Sheffield, 5 1/2 In. 74.00
Silver Plate, Coffeepot, Crest, Domed Lid, Scroll Handle, Elkington, C.1880 .... 110.00
Silver Plate, Coffeepot, Floral On Lid, Handle, Spout, & Feet, Meriden, 8 In. 85.00
Silver Plate, Coffeepot, Rochester Stamping Works 35.00
Silver Plate, Coffeepot, Stand & Cup, Quadruple, Middletown Silver Co. 165.00
Silver Plate, Coffeepot, Wooden Handle, J.L.Hudson Co., 1928, Pint 17.50

Silver Plate, Candlesnuffer & Tray, 10 In.
(See Page 556)

Silver Plate, **Compote**, Dolphin Stem, Handled, Meriden, 6 X 4 In.	26.00
Silver Plate, **Cooler**, Water, Ornate, Victorian, E.G.Webster & Bros., N.Y.	135.00
Silver Plate, **Cup & Saucer**, Coffee, Floral Spray, Barbour Bros., 1880s	23.50
Silver Plate, **Cup**, Demitasse, Walter Baker Chocolate, Dutch Girl In Relief	6.50
Silver Plate, **Cup**, Folding, Art Nouveau Embossed Lid, Dated 1897	15.00
Silver Plate, **Cup**, Gold Washed Inside, Tufts, 3 1/2 In.	18.00
Silver Plate, **Dish**, Candy, Boat Shape, Pierced, Pairpoint, 1885	20.00
Silver Plate, **Dish**, Candy, Oval, Repousse Rim, Raised Base, Gorham, 5 X 8 In.	8.00
Silver Plate, **Fork & Spoon**, Serving, Horn Handles, M B & Co., 12 In.	24.50
Silver Plate, **Fork**, Ice Cream, Fancy Tines, Wm.Rogers, Set Of 6	20.00
Silver Plate, **Fork**, Meat, Rogers & Bro., C.1910, 6 3/4 In.	7.00
Silver Plate, **Fork**, Oyster, Engraved Floral, Rogers Bros., 1847, Set Of 12	35.00
Silver Plate, **Fork**, Salad, Elton, Rogers & Bro., C.1910	1.25
Silver Plate, **Frame**, Pickle Castor, Footed, Tongs Hanger For Cover, Tufts	65.00
Silver Plate, **Hair Receiver**, Nude Girls Picking Flowers, Covered, 4 In.High	15.00
Silver Plate, **Hair Receiver**, Ornate, Quadruple, Wilcox, Meriden, Conn.	35.00
Silver Plate, **Humidor**, Cigar, Raised Cigars & Man's Head, Tufts	65.00
Silver Plate, **Humidor**, Figural, Dog Sitting On Top, Derby Silver Co., 6 In.	135.00
Silver Plate, **Inkwell**, Repousse Decoration, Signed Wilcox	32.00
Silver Plate, **Jar**, Sweetmeat, Cranberry Insert, Simpson, Hall, Miller & Co.	75.00
Silver Plate, **Jar**, Sweetmeat, 6 Panels With Men's Heads, Cranberry Liner	85.00
Silver Plate, **Juicer**, Lemon, Meriden	50.00
Silver Plate, **Knife Bread**, Art Nouveau, Engraved Blade, Sheffield	22.50
Silver Plate, **Knife Rest**, Apostles On Each End	22.00
Silver Plate, **Knife Rest**, Cupid On Each End	10.00
Silver Plate, **Knife Rest**, Peacock, 4 In.Long	19.00
Silver Plate, **Knife Rest**, Prehistoric Beasts Form Ends	30.00
Silver Plate, **Knife**, Dinner, Sterling Ferrules, J.E.Caldwell, 10	100.00
Silver Plate, **Knife**, Luncheon, Pearl Handle, Ornate Bands, Meriden, 6	39.00
Silver Plate, **Knife**, Table, Tiger Lily Pattern, Reed & Barton	3.00
Silver Plate, **Ladle**, Punch, W.F.Rogers, C.1910, 11 In.	15.00
Silver Plate, **Muffineer**, Band Of Raised Fruits, Hearts Border, Tufts	35.00
Silver Plate, **Muffineer**, Victorian	20.00
Silver Plate, **Mug**, Child's, Garlands & Daisies, Meriden	8.00
Silver Plate, **Mug**, Initials, Henry Turner Of Pattington, C.1750, 1/2 Pint	15.00
Silver Plate, **Mug**, see Mustache Cup	
Silver Plate, **Napkin Ring**, see Napkin Ring	
Silver Plate, **Pitcher**, Ice Water, Swivel Stand, Porcelain Lined, Wilcox, 1878	200.00
Silver Plate, **Pitcher**, Water, Hand Hammered, Derby Co., 2 Quart	17.50
Silver Plate, **Plate**, Bread, Lilies & Lily Pads, Quadruple, St.Louis, 13 In.	25.00
Silver Plate, **Plate**, Cake, Scalloped Pedestal, Ornate Allover Design, 12 In.	30.00
Silver Plate, **Rack**, Toast, 7 Racks, Oval, Openwork Base, Bun Feet, 7 In.	35.00
Silver Plate, **Salt & Pepper**, Occupied Japan	2.85
Silver Plate, **Salt Dip**, Shell Shape, Canterbury, Pair	15.00
Silver Plate, **Salt**, Bowl Supported By Shovel, Inscribed, 1795-1895, 3 In.	25.00
Silver Plate, **Salt**, Feather Embossing, W.B.Mfg.Co., 2 In.	23.00
Silver Plate, **Salt**, Master, Meriden, Footed, Blue Glass Liner, 3 X 5 In.	38.00
Silver Plate, **Salt**, Master, Pedestal, Feathers, Blue Crystal Liner, W.B.Co.	20.00
Silver Plate, **Saltshaker**, Figural Chicken	11.00
Silver Plate, **Saltshaker**, Figural Owl, Glass Eyes	20.00

Silver Plate, **Scissors,** On Brass, Stoeker, Germany, SMF Sclinge	18.50
Silver Plate, **Scoop,** Crumb, Art Nouveau Design, Bone Handle, 1887	10.50
Silver Plate, **Server,** Berry, Etched Flowers, Towle & Son, 8 1/2 In.	8.00
Silver Plate, **Server,** Cake, Ornate, Rogers & Brother, Conn., C.1910, 10 In.	7.50
Silver Plate, **Server,** Coffee, The Palace Hotel, Reed & Barton, Hinged Lid	50.00
Silver Plate, **Spoon & Fork,** Child's, 1847 Rogers Brothers	6.50
Silver Plate, **Spoon,** Berry, Ornate, Pierced, Wm. Rogers, 1904	6.00
Silver Plate, **Spoon,** Demitasse, Grape, Rogers, 1881	3.00
Silver Plate, **Spoon,** Demitasse, Heritage, Roger Bros., Set Of 12	18.00
Silver Plate, **Spoon,** Dessert, Fiddleback, S.Baker & Son	12.50
Silver Plate, **Spoon,** Ice Cream Soda, Twisted Handle	5.00
Silver Plate, **Spoon,** Master Salt, Gorham, Patent 1896	2.75
Silver Plate, **Spoon,** Master Salt, Olive, Rogers, Smith & Co., C.1856	3.95
Silver Plate, **Spoon, Souvenir, see Souvenir, Spoon, Silver Plate**	
Silver Plate, **Spoon,** Tomato Serving, Orchid, Pierced, Rogers & Hamilton, 1900	10.00
Silver Plate, **Spooner & Butter,** Meriden ....*Illus*	65.00
Silver Plate, **Spooner,** Handled, Blue Thumbprint Insert, J.Rogers Co.	65.00
Silver Plate, **Spooner,** Incised, Footed, Handled, Victorian, Rogers	11.00
Silver Plate, **Spreader,** Butter, Elton, Rogers & Bro., C.1910, 5 1/2 In.	1.10
Silver Plate, **Strainer,** Tea, Cobalt Blue Liner, Floral Embossed	10.00
Silver Plate, **Strainer,** Tea, English, Pierced, Handled	8.50
Silver Plate, **Sugar & Creamer,** Beading At Top, Poole Silver Co., Mass.	18.00
Silver Plate, **Sugar & Creamer,** English, Hallmarked, 1/2 Pint Size	20.00
Silver Plate, **Sugar & Creamer,** Footed, Fleur-De-Lis, MMS&EPNS	35.00
Silver Plate, **Sugar & Creamer,** Raised Leaves & Grapes, Reed & Barton	55.00
Silver Plate, **Sugar & Creamer,** Rococo Rims, Legs, & Handles, Swirled Ribbed	55.00
Silver Plate, **Sugar & Creamer,** Signed Derby	20.00
Silver Plate, **Sugar & Spooner,** Bird Finial, Rogers Bros., 9 In.	75.00
Silver Plate, **Syrup,** Hinged Lid, Swirl Flutings, Quadruple, Meriden	23.00
Silver Plate, **Syrup,** Quadruple, Pairpoint	100.00
Silver Plate, **Tablespoon,** Elton, Rogers & Bro., C.1910	2.25
Silver Plate, **Tea & Coffee Set,** Engraved Pheasants, Gorham, 1874, 7 Piece	940.00
Silver Plate, **Tea Set,** Ornate Scroll Band, Forbes, 5 Piece	65.00
Silver Plate, **Tea Set,** Paneled, Queen City Silver Co., 3 Piece	65.00
Silver Plate, **Tea Set,** Pedestal, Reeded Borders, Forbes, 3 Piece	65.00
Silver Plate, **Tea Set,** Quadruple, Pairpoint, 5 Piece	125.00
Silver Plate, **Tea Set,** Reeded Borders, Pedestal Base, Forbes, 3 Piece	65.00
Silver Plate, **Teakettle On Stand,** Queen Anne, Wooden Handle, 17 In.	125.00
Silver Plate, **Teapot,** Pairpoint	50.00
Silver Plate, **Toothpick,** Bird On Rim, "Looking For A Pick," 3 1/4 In.High	37.50
Silver Plate, **Toothpick,** Chick, Egg, & Wishbone	20.00
Silver Plate, **Toothpick,** Chicken On Wishbone, Embossed S/P Co.	24.00
Silver Plate, **Toothpick,** Cupid With Wings	30.00
Silver Plate, **Toothpick,** Dog, Glass Eyes, Derby, No.2204	65.00
Silver Plate, **Toothpick,** Figural, Chick On Wishbone, Warren Silver Co.	17.00
Silver Plate, **Toothpick,** Figural, Owl On Branch, Middletown, C.1864	24.75

Silver Plate, Spooner & Butter, Meriden

Silver Plate, Toothpick, Man's Opera Hat, 2 In.High	38.00
Silver Plate, Toothpick, Pair Of High Boots With Spurs, Fox, Reed & Barton	35.00
Silver Plate, Toothpick, Standing Bear & Holder On Round Base, Pairpoint	58.50
Silver Plate, Toothpick, Woman Alongside Holder, Derby, 3 1/2 In.	30.00
Silver Plate, Tray, Oblong, Nickel Silver, Wallace, 8 1/2 X 12 In.	9.00
Silver Plate, Tray, Victorian, 10 Sided, Reed & Barton, 11 In.	25.00
Silver Plate, Urn, Tea, Burner, Engraved, Webster Co., C.1870, 1/2 Gallon	95.00
Silver Plate, Vase, Bud, Reed & Barton, 5/8 In.Square	8.00
Silver Resist, Candlestick, Grape Pattern, 6 In., Pair	75.00
Silver Resist, Jug, Bands & Sprigs, Iron Red Blossoms, C.1825, 4 1/2 In.	40.00
Silver Resist, Jug, Blue Floral & Vines Panels, C.1815, 4 3/4 In.	240.00
Silver Resist, Jug, Creamware, Flowering Vine, Ocher Fret Rim, C.1815, 6 In.	90.00
Silver Resist, Pitcher, Creamware, Bulbous, Flowers & Leaves, 4 1/2 In.	125.00
Silver Resist, Plate, Silver & Iron Red Border, 7 In.	50.00
Silver Resist, Sugar, Flower Design	75.00
Silver Resist, Tea Set, Amber Glass, Scenic, 14 Piece	75.00
Silver Springs, Pitcher, Pink, White, Black, & Green Swirl, Signed, 3 1/2 In.	6.00
Silver, American, see also Tiffany, Silver, Silver, Sterling	
Silver, American, Basket, Cake, Engraved Foliage, Gale & Son, 1852, 14 1/4 In.	375.00
Silver, American, Basket, Cake, Medallion Heads, Beading, Krider, Coin, 9 In.	725.00
Silver, American, Basket, Cake, Pierced Handle, Bailey & Co., Coin, 12 In.	1100.00
Silver, American, Basket, Cake, Twig Handles, Lincoln & Foss, Coin, 13 In.	575.00
Silver, American, Basket, Sugar, Grapes & Vines, Stebbins & Co., C.1850	175.00
Silver, American, Beaker, Festoon Collar, Hutton, C.1795, 3 1/2 In., Pair	1100.00
Silver, American, Beaker, Flared Top, Lows, Ball & Co., Coin, 3 1/2 In.	285.00
Silver, American, Beaker, Molded Border, Hazen, C.1830, 3 5/8 In., Pair	700.00
Silver, American, Beaker, Molded Border, Shepard, Ky., C.1830, 3 3/8 In., Pair	750.00
Silver, American, Beaker, Molded Lip & Foot, Kendrick, C.1840, 2 3/4 In.	200.00
Silver, American, Beaker, Swelling Body, Shepherd & Boyd, C.1810, 3 In., Pair	750.00
Silver, American, Beaker, Tapered, Molded Borders, Sharrard, C.1850, 3 1/4 In.	375.00
Silver, American, Bookmark & Paper Knife, Engraved Floral, Wells, N.Y., 1791	35.00
Silver, American, Bowl, Dessert, Dome Lid, Footed, Krider, C.1860, 11 1/2 In.	900.00
Silver, American, Bowl, Female Mask Handles, Wood & Hughes, C.1850, 12 In.	150.00
Silver, American, Bowl, Fruit, Repousse, Footed, Dominick & Haff, C.1800, 9 In.	375.00
Silver, American, Bowl, Pedestal Foot, Chased, Ewan, C.1830, 7 In.	550.00
Silver, American, Bowl, Repousse Floral, S.Kirk & Son, 5 In.	50.00
Silver, American, Bowl, Vegetable, Lion Finial, Gorham, C.1865, 15 In.	700.00
Silver, American, Bowl, Waste, Reeded Edge, Armstrong, Phila., 1806, 5 1/8 In.	550.00
Silver, American, Buckle, Reeded Shape, Pons, Boston, C.1800, 3 3/4 In., Pair	250.00
Silver, American, Butter, Dome Lid, Footed, Jones, Ball & Poor, C.1850	400.00
Silver, American, Butter, Dome Lid, Repousse, Liner, Kirk, C.1885, 7 1/8 In.	525.00
Silver, American, Butter, Pierced Gilt Insert, Dome Lid, Wood & Hughes, 1865	350.00
Silver, American, Can, Daniel Rogers, R.I., 1770 .... *Illus*	2200.00
Silver, American, Can, Footed, Double Scroll Handle, Parker, C.1750, 5 1/8 In.	1000.00
Silver, American, Can, Pear Shape, Molded Lip & Foot, Handle, Burt, C.1790	1800.00

Silver, American, Can, Daniel Rogers, R.I., 1770

Silver, American, Can, Reeded Strap Handle, Footed, Churchill, Boston, C.1815	160.00
Silver, American, Candelabra, 5 Arm, Pierced Base, Starr, C.1900, 14 In., Pair	1350.00
Silver, American, Candlesticks, Pierced Dome Base, C.1900, 11 1/4 In., Pair	500.00
Silver, American, Case, Card, Chain, Engraved Design, Albert Coles, C.1850	75.00
Silver, American, Castor, Lighthouse, Domed, Pierced, Nys, C.1710, 6 3/8 In.	7500.00
Silver, American, Centerpiece, Chased, Grapevine, Starr, C.1860, 11 1/2 In.	750.00
Silver, American, Centerpiece, Pierced Rim, Vase Shape, Footed, C.1900, 9 In.	450.00
Silver, American, Coffee Set, Flowering Foliage, Gorham, C.1900, 3 Piece	300.00
Silver, American, Coffeepot, Applied Leaf, Arden & Bro., Coin, 13 In.	650.00
Silver, American, Coffeepot, Helmet Shape, Key Pattern, Robert Rait, C.1860	475.00
Silver, American, Coffeepot, Pedestal, Acorn Finial, Lownes, C.1820, 11 In.	950.00
Silver, American, Compote, Applied Copper Leaved, Gorham, 1881, 14 In.	500.00
Silver, American, Compote, Geometrics, Handled, Kidney & Johnson, Coin, 12 In.	325.00
Silver, American, Compote, Loose Ring Handles, Greek Key Banding, Coin, 7 In.	250.00
Silver, American, Compote, Pierced Rim, Trumpet Feet, C.1900, 7 1/2 In.	225.00
Silver, American, Compote, Pierced, Black, Starr & Frost, C.1900, 16 1/2 In.	750.00
Silver, American, Creamer, Berries & Foliage, Helmet Shape, Eoff, C.1830	250.00
Silver, American, Creamer, Boat Shape, Gadroon Lip, Gale & Son, C.1855	150.00
Silver, American, Creamer, Boat Shape, Pedestal Foot, Boehme, C.1800, 7 In.	350.00
Silver, American, Creamer, Fluted Helmet Shape, Revere, Jr., C.1798, 7 In.	4500.00
Silver, American, Creamer, Hinged, Lipped Spout, Jones, Boston, 1810, 6 In.	500.00
Silver, American, Creamer, Pear Shape, 3 Hoof Feet, Roosevelt, C.1760, 4 In.	1100.00
Silver, American, Creamer, Pear Shape, 3 Hoof Feet, S.J., C.1770, 4 1/4 In.	900.00
Silver, American, Creamer, Scroll Handle, Hoof Feet, Hammersley, C.1770	2000.00
Silver, American, Cruet, 4 Cut Glass Bottles, Domed Base, Harding, C.1850	200.00
Silver, American, Crumber, Bright Cut Thistles, Gale & Son, C.1823, Coin	39.95
Silver, American, Cup, Applied Floral Band Base, Harding Co., Coin, 4 1/2 In.	125.00
Silver, American, Cup, Applied Hearts, Tifft & Whiting, Coin, 2 1/4 In.	285.00
Silver, American, Cup, Barrel Shape, Repousse Roses, Foster, Coin, 4 1/2 In.	145.00
Silver, American, Cup, Beaded Band Top & Bottom, Gorham, 2 7/8 In.	65.00
Silver, American, Cup, Bulbous, Repousse, Footed, Evans & Co., Coin, 3 In.	110.00
Silver, American, Cup, Cylindrical, Beaded, Tifft & Whiting, Coin, 4 In.	110.00
Silver, American, Cup, Cylindrical, Beaded, Tifft & Whiting, Coin, 4 1/2 In.	130.00
Silver, American, Cup, Cylindrical, Medallions, Names & Dates, Coin, 4 In.	150.00
Silver, American, Cup, Engine Turned, Footed, Sharp, Bailey & Co., Coin, 5 In.	125.00
Silver, American, Cup, Engraved Helen, Wood & Hughes, C.1845, 2 1/2 In.	32.50
Silver, American, Cup, Engraved Palm Fronds, Trumpet Foot, Gorham, 1865	200.00
Silver, American, Cup, Reeded Foot, Bulbous, Crosby & Foss, Boston, Coin, 4 In.	135.00
Silver, American, Cup, 2 Loop Handles, Whiting Mfg.Co., C.1890, 7 7/8 In.	175.00
Silver, American, Cup, 3 Reeded Loop Handles, Starr, C.1906, 8 1/2 In.	350.00
Silver, American, Dish, Meat, Pierced Foot, C.1900, 18 In.	450.00
Silver, American, Etui, Fox Hunt, Cottager, Barber & Whitwell, 1882, 5 In.	450.00
Silver, American, Fish Slice, Engraved Fish On Blade, A.E.Armiger, 11 In.	95.00
Silver, American, Fish Slice, Gadroon, Pierced Blade, Engraved, W.& H., Coin	60.00
Silver, American, Fork, A.C.Benedict, N.Y.C., Coin, 8 In.	16.50
Silver, American, Fork, Akerly & Briggs, Coin	17.00
Silver, American, Fork, Beaded Edge, Vanderslice, Calif., Coin	18.00
Silver, American, Fork, Butler & McCarty, Coin, 8 In.	15.50
Silver, American, Fork, Cold Meat, Olive, Ball, Black & Co., Coin	20.00
Silver, American, Fork, Cold Meat, Oval With Dart, Coin	16.00
Silver, American, Fork, Dessert, Fiddle & Thread, Low, Ball, & Co., 1845, Coin	14.50
Silver, American, Fork, Dessert, Initial W, Palmer & Batchelder, Coin	29.75
Silver, American, Fork, Dinner, Beaded Handle, Initial H, 1861, Coin	11.69
Silver, American, Fork, Dinner, Fiddle & Thread, Engraved, Coin	25.00
Silver, American, Fork, Dinner, Fiddle Tip, Raised Design, Cole, C.1840, Coin	25.00
Silver, American, Fork, Dinner, Olive, Harding, Boston, C.1830, Coin	21.40
Silver, American, Fork, Dinner, Round End, Harding, Boston, C.1840, Coin	15.00
Silver, American, Fork, Fiddle & Thread, Lows, Ball & Co., Coin	14.25
Silver, American, Fork, Fiddle Thread, Ball, Black & Co., N.Y.C., Coin, Pair	35.00
Silver, American, Fork, Fiddle, Savage, C.1820, Set Of 12	400.00
Silver, American, Fork, King's Pattern, Sharp, Bailey & Co., Phila., Coin	20.00
Silver, American, Fork, Luncheon, Fiddle & Thread, R.T.& Co., Coin	25.50
Silver, American, Fork, Luncheon, Fiddle Top, Raised Design, Cole, C.1840, Coin	24.15
Silver, American, Fork, Luncheon, Olive, Steele, Conn., C.1840, Coin	20.50
Silver, American, Fork, Olive, C.A.Mudge & Co., Coin, 5 1/2 In., Pair	35.00
Silver, American, Fork, Olive, N.Harding & Co., Boston, Coin, 6 3/4 In.	15.00

Silver, American, Goblet, Repousse Floral Design, 6 In. 150.00
Silver, American, Goblet, Stepped Pedestal, Flared, Lincoln & Reed, Coin 225.00
Silver, American, Jug, Milk, Flower Finial, Chased, Eoff & Phyfe, C.1845, 7 In. 150.00
Silver, American, Kettle On Lampstand, Hot Water, Foliate, Kirk, C.1885 .... 400.00
Silver, American, Kettle On Lampstand, Hot Water, Whiting Co., C.1900, 12 In. 325.00
Silver, American, Knife & Fork, Fish, Virginian, Gorham, Floral, 1904 .... 125.00
Silver, American, Knife, Butter Serving, Farrington & Hunnewell, C.1835, Coin 12.75
Silver, American, Knife, Butter Serving, French Thread, Harding, C.1845, Coin 12.00
Silver, American, Knife, Butter Serving, Initial P, Harding, C.1850, Coin 12.75
Silver, American, Knife, Butter Serving, Olive, Engraved, Clark, C.1850, Coin 13.75
Silver, American, Knife, Butter Serving, Thread, Bailey & Co., C.1848, Coin 12.75
Silver, American, Knife, Butter Serving, Twombly & Smith, C.1850, Coin 13.75
Silver, American, Knife, Butter, Hall & Hewson, Albany, N.Y., Coin 29.00
Silver, American, Knife, Butter, Newell Harding, Boston, C.1850 .... 12.75
Silver, American, Knife, Butter, Twisted Handle, Duhme & Co., C.1839, Coin 28.00
Silver, American, Knife, Crumb, Olive Leaf, Jones, Ball & Poor, 1845, Coin 68.00
Silver, American, Knife, Fruit, Pocket, Engraved, Coin 9.95
Silver, American, Ladle, Cream, Fiddle Handle, Smith & Chamberlain, C.1835 .... 28.00
Silver, American, Ladle, Gravy, Bigelow Bros. & Kennard, Boston, C.1845, Coin 35.00
Silver, American, Ladle, Gravy, Cottage Type Pattern, H.Harding & Co., Coin 35.00
Silver, American, Ladle, Gravy, Fiddle Handle, Currier & Trott, C.1836, Coin 32.00
Silver, American, Ladle, Gravy, Fiddle Thread, Shell Bowl, J.S.& Co., Coin 45.00
Silver, American, Ladle, Gravy, Fiddle Tip Handle, Harding, C.1835, Coin 35.00
Silver, American, Ladle, Gravy, Fiddle, Farnam & Ward, Conn., Coin 65.00
Silver, American, Ladle, Gravy, Initial S, F.Curtis & Co., C.1840, Coin 24.75
Silver, American, Ladle, Gravy, Mayflower, K.Kirk & Son, C.1846, Coin 50.00
Silver, American, Ladle, Gravy, Modified Fiddle, H.Sargeant & Co., Coin 30.00
Silver, American, Ladle, Gravy, Palmer & Batchelder, Boston, C.1850, Coin 26.75
Silver, American, Ladle, J.Holister, Oswego, 1850, Coin, 6 In. 17.00
Silver, American, Ladle, Mustard, Bigelow Bros. & Kennard, C.1845, Coin 9.95
Silver, American, Ladle, Mustard, Bright Cut, Wakefield, C.1830, Coin 9.95
Silver, American, Ladle, Mustard, Fiddle Tip, Skinner, N.Y., C.1820, Coin 18.00
Silver, American, Ladle, Mustard, Marked Coin 8.75
Silver, American, Ladle, Mustard, Ribbed Shell Bowl, J.B.Hill, N.H., Coin 18.00
Silver, American, Ladle, Olive, H.Harding & Co., Boston, C.1850, Coin 29.75
Silver, American, Ladle, Pierced, Shell Bowl, Gorham, R.I., C.1840 .... 35.00
Silver, American, Ladle, S.D.Choates, Louisville, Coin, 7 In. 55.00
Silver, American, Ladle, Sauce, Fiddle Tip, H.Rosenberg, Coin 35.00
Silver, American, Ladle, Sauce, Fiddle Tip, Hourglass, Dennison, Adams, Coin 35.00
Silver, American, Ladle, Sauce, Fiddle Tip, Jennings Brothers, Coin 35.00
Silver, American, Ladle, Sauce, J.W.Root, C.1830, Coin 24.75
Silver, American, Ladle, Sauce, Steward, Stevens & Dewey, Coin 22.75
Silver, American, Ladle, Soup, Elongated Fiddle, Bradbury, C.1815 .... 175.00
Silver, American, Ladle, Soup, Fiddle Handle, Oval Bowl, Hewson & Brower, 1845 .... 110.00
Silver, American, Ladle, Soup, Fiddle Tip, Hyde & Goodrich, C.1830, Coin 350.00
Silver, American, Ladle, Soup, Fiddle Tip, Whiting, Coin, 12 1/2 In. 125.00
Silver, American, Ladle, Soup, Fiddle, Isaac Hutton, N.Y., C.1810, 13 5/8 In. 285.00
Silver, American, Ladle, Soup, Jenny Lind, McMullen & Hamilton, Coin 100.00
Silver, American, Ladle, Soup, Olive, Bailey & Co., Coin, 11 1/2 In. 95.00
Silver, American, Ladle, Soup, Oval Bead, Wood & Hughes, N.Y.C., Coin, 13 In. 115.00
Silver, American, Ladle, Soup, Pan's Pipes & Thyrsus, Gorham, C.1870, 13 In. 100.00
Silver, American, Ladle, Soup, Ram's & Devil's Heads, H.H., 1862, Coin 125.00
Silver, American, Ladle, Strawberry & Leaf, Gold Washed Bowl, 7 1/2 In.Long 55.00
Silver, American, Ladle, Twisted Horn Handle, Ward, Sr., Conn., C.1706, Coin 225.00
Silver, American, Mug, S Scroll Handle, Footed, Edwards, C.1740, 4 1/2 In. 300.00
Silver, American, Pastry Server, Bright Cut Engraving, Fenno & Hale, C.1840 .... 34.75
Silver, American, Pencil, Automatic, Red Jewel End, Engraved, Coin 12.50
Silver, American, Pick, Nut, Squirrel End, Peter Krider, Phila., C.1860, Coin 30.00
Silver, American, Pitcher, Milk, Grape Finial, Hinged, Gale & Son, Coin, 9 In. 425.00
Silver, American, Pitcher, Milk, Repousse, Sharp, Bailey & Co., Coin, 9 In. 325.00
Silver, American, Pitcher, Repousse, Chased, Forbes, C.1838, 16 1/4 In. 1600.00
Silver, American, Pitcher, Water, C Scroll Handle, Spreading Foot, C.1900 .... 525.00
Silver, American, Pitcher, Water, Guilloche Borders, Kinsey, Ohio, C.1845 .... 450.00
Silver, American, Pitcher, Water, Helmet Shape, Foliage, Reed & Barton, C.1900 .... 200.00
Silver, American, Pitcher, Water, Martele Style, Repousse, Gorham, C.1899 .... 675.00
Silver, American, Pitcher, Water, Masonic Emblems, Wood & Hughes, Coin, 12 In. 500.00

Silver, American, Porringer, Saunders Pitman, R.I., 1800

Silver, **American,** Pitcher, Water, Repousse, Bigelow & Kennard, C.1848	550.00
Silver, **American,** Pitcher, Water, Repousse, Chased, Domed Foot, Hayden, C.1850	550.00
Silver, **American,** Pitcher, Water, Repousse, Kirk & Son, C.1900, 12 In.	500.00
Silver, **American,** Pitcher, Water, Repousse, Starr, 1888, 7 1/2 In.	300.00
Silver, **American,** Plate, Bread & Butter, Pierced Border, C.1900	35.00
Silver, **American,** Plate, Service, Pierced Border, C.1900, 11 3/8 In.	165.00
Silver, **American,** Porringer, Saunders Pitman, R.I., 1800 ....*Illus*	700.00
Silver, **American,** Pot, Mustard, Wm.Eley, 1805, 4 Troy Ozs.	428.00
Silver, **American,** Salt Cellar, Bombe, Shell & Scroll Feet, Syng, C.1760, Pair	1900.00
Silver, **American,** Salt Cellar, Reeded Rim, 3 Hoof Feet, Gorham, C.1860, Pair	110.00
Silver, **American,** Salver, Ball & Claw Feet, Bailey & Co., Coin, 6 1/4 In.	195.00
Silver, **American,** Salver, Dolphins & Floral, Lincoln & Reed, Coin, 7 In.	275.00
Silver, **American,** Scoop, Marrow, Edward Watson, Boston, C.1810, Coin	24.75
Silver, **American,** Server, Dessert, Engraved Scene In Oval, Hart & Co., Coin	55.00
Silver, **American,** Server, Olive, Bright Cut, Fenno & Hale, Me., C.1840, Coin	39.75
Silver, **American,** Server, Pastry, Bright Cut, Fenno & Hale, C.1840, Coin	34.75
Silver, **American,** Server, Pie, Flat Button Top, Gothic Engraving, W.& H., Coin	65.00
Silver, **American,** Server, Tomato, Flat, Olive, Wood & Hughes, C.1845, Coin	39.75
Silver, **American,** Shell, Sugar, Bowknot, Engraved Grapes In Bowl, Coin	18.00
Silver, **American,** Shell, Sugar, C.W.Wilcox, Berlin, Conn., C.1850, Coin	13.75
Silver, **American,** Shell, Sugar, Cottage, Jaccard & Co., St.Louis, 1861, Coin	16.00
Silver, **American,** Shell, Sugar, E.Reuse, Coin	16.00
Silver, **American,** Shell, Sugar, Engraved, Farrington & Hunnewell, C.1835, Coin	13.75
Silver, **American,** Shell, Sugar, Fiddle Tip, Lakeman, Mass., Coin	18.00
Silver, **American,** Shell, Sugar, Fiddle Tip, Wood & Hughes, Coin	22.50
Silver, **American,** Shell, Sugar, Flared Handle, Wakefield, N.H., Coin	17.50
Silver, **American,** Shell, Sugar, Initials J.W.C., Wood & Hughes, C.1845, Coin	13.75
Silver, **American,** Shell, Sugar, Initials, Squire & Lander, N.Y., C.1846, Coin	13.75
Silver, **American,** Shell, Sugar, Initials, Twombly & Smith, C.1850, Coin	13.75
Silver, **American,** Shell, Sugar, Joseph Raynes, Coin	15.00
Silver, **American,** Shell, Sugar, M.F.& C.H.Stillwell, N.Y., C.1845, Coin	13.75
Silver, **American,** Shell, Sugar, McKay, Spear & Br., C.1835, Coin	13.75
Silver, **American,** Shell, Sugar, Modified Fiddle, Hewett, Coin	12.00
Silver, **American,** Shell, Sugar, Olive Pattern, Dexter & Haskins, C.1850	13.75
Silver, **American,** Shell, Sugar, Palmer & Batchelder, Coin	15.00
Silver, **American,** Shell, Sugar, Round End, Palmer & Batchelder, C.1840, Coin	15.00
Silver, **American,** Shovel, Salt, Coin	15.00
Silver, **American,** Shovel, Salt, Wm.Root, Mass., Coin	18.00
Silver, **American,** Shovel, Sugar, Adams & Farnsworth, Boston, Coin	29.00
Silver, **American,** Shovel, Sugar, Fiddleback, J.Gorham & Son, R.I., Coin	30.00
Silver, **American,** Shovel, Sugar, R.H.Bailey, Woodstock, Vt.	90.00
Silver, **American,** Siphon, C.1850, Coin, 15 1/2 In.	300.00
Silver, **American,** Snuffbox, Hinged, John Noyes, 1749, Engraved, Coin, 2 3/4 In.	275.00
Silver, **American,** Spoon, Berry, Pierced Gold Washed Bowl, N.Harding, Coin	42.00
Silver, **American,** Spoon, Child's, Turned-Down Handle, Currier, C.1830, Coin	15.00
Silver, **American,** Spoon, Child's, 2 Part Construction, Wilson, C.1805, Coin	16.00
Silver, **American,** Spoon, Coffee, Coffin End, C.Babbit, Coin	20.00

Silver, American, Spoon, Demitasse, John Goodhue, Mass., C.1822, Coin	12.75
Silver, American, Spoon, Demitasse, Medallion, Stevenson, Coin	15.00
Silver, American, Spoon, Dessert, Coffin End, 2 Parts, R.Wilson, Coin	35.00
Silver, American, Spoon, Dessert, Fiddle Tip, Forbes, N.Y., C.1837, Coin	10.00
Silver, American, Spoon, Dessert, Fiddle Tip, Hourglass Form, Bailey, Coin	15.00
Silver, American, Spoon, Dessert, Fiddle Tip, Hourglass Form, Ferren, Coin	17.50
Silver, American, Spoon, Dessert, Fiddle Tip, Hourglass Form, Hale, Coin, Pair	30.00
Silver, American, Spoon, Dessert, Fiddle Tip, Hourglass Form, L.Simons, Coin	13.50
Silver, American, Spoon, Dessert, Fiddle Tip, Hourglass Form, Myers, Coin, Pair	30.00
Silver, American, Spoon, Dessert, Fiddle Tip, Hourglass Form, Sanborn, Coin	15.00
Silver, American, Spoon, Dessert, Fiddle Tip, Squire & Lander, N.Y.C., Coin	17.50
Silver, American, Spoon, Dessert, Fiddle Tip, W.Boning, Phila., Coin	16.00
Silver, American, Spoon, Dessert, Fiddle Tip, 2 Part, J.G.Thompson, Coin	13.60
Silver, American, Spoon, Dessert, Fiddle Top, Mills & Forristall, C.1835, Coin	10.00
Silver, American, Spoon, Dessert, Fiddle, Gorham & Webster, R.I., Coin, Pair	30.00
Silver, American, Spoon, Dessert, Fiddle, Hourglass Form, Perkins, Coin	12.50
Silver, American, Spoon, Dessert, Modified Fiddle, B.Dexter, N.B., Coin	15.00
Silver, American, Spoon, Dessert, Pointed Handle, Moulton, C.1810, Coin	20.00
Silver, American, Spoon, Dessert, Rounded, Farrington & Hunnewell, Coin, Pair	25.00
Silver, American, Spoon, Dessert, Shell Top, Flowers & Leaves, C.1815, Pair	40.00
Silver, American, Spoon, Dessert, Shellback, J.P.Bull	18.00
Silver, American, Spoon, Dessert, Washington Medallion, Harding & Co., Coin	15.00
Silver, American, Spoon, Fiddleback, Cary, C.1850, Coin, 5 3/8 In.	15.00
Silver, American, Spoon, Fiddleback, Chaffee, Coin, 6 In.	15.00
Silver, American, Spoon, G.Baker, R.I., Coin	10.00
Silver, American, Spoon, Initials, Palmer & Batchelder, 1815, Coin, 5 3/4 In.	15.00
Silver, American, Spoon, Master Salt, E.Lownes, Phila., C.1820, Coin	9.75
Silver, American, Spoon, Master Salt, Gorham, R.I., C.1835, Coin	8.95
Silver, American, Spoon, Master Salt, Initials, Gooding, C.1820, Coin	8.95
Silver, American, Spoon, Master Salt, Initials, Lows, Ball & Co., C.1840, Coin	8.95
Silver, American, Spoon, Master Salt, S.V.& Co., Coin, Pair	12.50
Silver, American, Spoon, Master Salt, Shell Handle, N.Harding & Co., Coin	11.65
Silver, American, Spoon, Mustard, Fiddle, Hourglass Form, E.Mead, Mo., Coin	25.00
Silver, American, Spoon, Mustard, Fiddle, T.Ireland, Coin	20.00
Silver, American, Spoon, Mustard, Godley, N.Y., C.1843, Coin	25.00
Silver, American, Spoon, Mustard, Initials, Bacon & Smith, C.1830, Coin	9.95
Silver, American, Spoon, Mustard, Medallion, Hotchkiss & Schreuder, N.Y., Coin	30.00
Silver, American, Spoon, Mustard, Oval Thread, Jones, Ball & Co., Coin	18.00
Silver, American, Spoon, Salt, Engraved Emily, Bigelow & Bros., C.1840, Coin	12.00
Silver, American, Spoon, Salt, Fiddle Tip, Bigelow & Kennard, C.1845, Coin	12.00
Silver, American, Spoon, Salt, Fiddle, Baldwin & Jones, Boston, Coin, Pair	25.00
Silver, American, Spoon, Salt, Fine, Lows, Ball & Company, Boston, 1840	12.00
Silver, American, Spoon, Salt, Master, Farrington & Hunnewell, Boston, C.1835	9.00
Silver, American, Spoon, Salt, Medallion, Wood & Hughes, Coin	25.00
Silver, American, Spoon, Salt, Oval Thread, Jones, Ball & Co., Boston, Coin	9.00
Silver, American, Spoon, Salt, Oval Thread, Shreve & Stanwood, Boston, Coin	9.00
Silver, American, Spoon, Salt, Thread, Bailey & Co., Phila., C.1848, Coin	8.95
Silver, American, Spoon, Serving, Coffin Handle, I.W.Forbes, N.Y., C.1810	15.00
Silver, American, Spoon, Serving, Gold Washed Bowl, Bailey & Co., C.1850, Coin	55.00
Silver, American, Spoon, Serving, Oval Thread, Shovel Bowl, B.K.& C., Coin	45.00
Silver, American, Spoon, Serving, Pierced Bowl, Garrett, Phila., C.1850, Coin	50.00
Silver, American, Spoon, Serving, Raised Tip, Castle, N.Y., C.1837, Coin	25.00
Silver, American, Spoon, Serving, Ram & Devil, Clark & Biddle, 1852, Coin	38.00
Silver, American, Spoon, Serving, Sheaf Of Wheat, Floral, Crosby & Loss, Coin	32.50
Silver, American, Spoon, Serving, Turned-Down Handle, Lakeman, C.1819, Coin	20.00
Silver, American, Spoon, Serving, Twisted Handle, Shell Bowl, F.& H., Coin	45.00
Silver, American, Spoon, Serving, Twisted Handle, Shell Bowl, Smith, Coin	45.00
Silver, American, Spoon, Serving, Twisted Stem, Medallion, Cole, Coin	55.00
Silver, American, Spoon, Serving, Washington Medallion, Harding & Co., Coin	55.00
Silver, American, Spoon, Stuffing, Bright Cut, Harding, C.1835, Coin, 12 In.	95.00
Silver, American, Spoon, Stuffing, Ram's & Devil's Heads, H.H., 1862, Coin	125.00
Silver, American, Spoon, W.Barker On Handle, Matson, Coin	7.50
Silver, American, Spreader, Cheese, Initials E.S.L., Cole, N.Y., C.1844, Coin	11.75
Silver, American, Spreader, Engraved, Farrington & Hunnewell, Boston, Coin	18.00
Silver, American, Spreader, Fiddle Thread, Hollow Handle, Cole, Coin, Pair	25.00
Silver, American, Spreader, Medallion, Turned Handle, H.& S., N.Y., Coin	25.00

Silver, American, Spreader, Olive, Farrington & Hunnewell, Boston, Coin	15.00
Silver, American, Spreader, Ordway, Coin, 6 3/4 In.	10.00
Silver, American, Spreader, Strawberry, Engraved Blade, Harmon, Coin	18.00
Silver, American, Sugar & Creamer, Acanthus Leaves, Ball, Black & Co., C.1860	375.00
Silver, American, Sugar & Creamer, Butterfly Finial, Harding, C.1830, Coin	750.00
Silver, American, Sugar & Creamer, Helmet Sugar, Wishart, N.Y., C.1784, Coin	1500.00
Silver, American, Sugar, Beading & Medallions, Albert Cole	245.00
Silver, American, Sugar, Dome Lid, Boat Shape, Richardson, Jr., C.1800	900.00
Silver, American, Sugar, Pear Shape, Repousse Grapes, Wood & Hughes, Coin	385.00
Silver, American, Tablespoon, A.C.Benedict, N.Y.C., Coin	15.00
Silver, American, Tablespoon, A.O.Fairchild, Coin	10.00
Silver, American, Tablespoon, B.E.Cook, Coin	14.00
Silver, American, Tablespoon, B.Pitman, R.I., C.1850, Coin	9.75
Silver, American, Tablespoon, Basket Of Flowers, Head, G, Lion, & D Marks, Coin	45.50
Silver, American, Tablespoon, Basket Of Flowers, Leopard, E, Star, Bird, Coin	50.00
Silver, American, Tablespoon, Basket Of Flowers, William Smith, N.Y.C., Coin	54.50
Silver, American, Tablespoon, Beaded Edge, Vanderslice, Calif., Coin	18.00
Silver, American, Tablespoon, Bird With Sprig In Beak, Byrnes, C.1795	62.50
Silver, American, Tablespoon, Bright Cut Floral, Lane, C.1850, Coin	12.75
Silver, American, Tablespoon, Bright Cut, DT In Cartouche, Shell Back, Coin	50.00
Silver, American, Tablespoon, Bright Cut, J.R.Reed & Co., C.1846, Coin	12.75
Silver, American, Tablespoon, Bright Cut, Thomas Eayres, Coin	150.00
Silver, American, Tablespoon, C.T.Emery, Coin	15.00
Silver, American, Tablespoon, Coffin End, Bright Cut, Keeler, N.Y.C., Coin	45.00
Silver, American, Tablespoon, Coffin End, Bright Cut, Milne, N.Y.C., Coin	45.00
Silver, American, Tablespoon, Coffin End, J * E In Cartouche, Coin	45.00
Silver, American, Tablespoon, Coffin End, M & W In Rectangle, Coin	45.00
Silver, American, Tablespoon, Coffin End, Pointed Drop, Haverstock, Jr., Coin	45.00
Silver, American, Tablespoon, Coffin End, Pointed Drop, WL, Coin	45.00
Silver, American, Tablespoon, Coffin End, Ridgway, Boston, C.1800, Coin	75.00
Silver, American, Tablespoon, Coffin End, Thomas Emery, Boston, Coin	45.00
Silver, American, Tablespoon, Drop On Bowl Back, J.& P. Targee, C.1800, Coin	60.00
Silver, American, Tablespoon, Engraved Adams, Franklin, R.I., C.1815, Coin	14.75
Silver, American, Tablespoon, Engraved, B.S.F.& Co., C.1820, Coin	12.75
Silver, American, Tablespoon, Engraved, Farrington & Hunnewell, C.1845, Coin	13.75
Silver, American, Tablespoon, Engraved, Harding & Co., C.1830, Coin	30.00
Silver, American, Tablespoon, Engraved, Paul Revere, Jr., C.1790	1100.00
Silver, American, Tablespoon, Farrington & Hunnewell, Boston, Engraved, Coin	64.50
Silver, American, Tablespoon, Fiddle & Shell, Shepherd & Boyd, C.1820	20.50
Silver, American, Tablespoon, Fiddle Handle, Lincoln & Reed, C.1830, Coin	14.00
Silver, American, Tablespoon, Fiddle Handle, Tanner & Cooley, Utica, N.Y., 4	68.00
Silver, American, Tablespoon, Fiddle Thread, Sharp, Bailey & Co., Coin	12.75
Silver, American, Tablespoon, Fiddle Tip, Clark, Coit & Cargill, Coin, Pair	50.00
Silver, American, Tablespoon, Fiddle Tip, D.B.Miller, Coin	15.00
Silver, American, Tablespoon, Fiddle Tip, Inscribed Bristol, J.& G., Coin	14.00
Silver, American, Tablespoon, Fiddle Tip, Lascelle, Coin	18.00
Silver, American, Tablespoon, Fiddle Tip, Lewis Kimball, N.Y., Coin	19.00
Silver, American, Tablespoon, Fiddle Tip, P.Crasnon, Coin	15.00
Silver, American, Tablespoon, Fiddle Tip, Tanner & Cooley, N.Y., C.1840, Coin	16.50
Silver, American, Tablespoon, Fiddle Tip, W.M.Root, Mass., 1860, Coin, Pair	35.00
Silver, American, Tablespoon, Fiddle, Alfred Lockwood, N.Y.C., Coin	17.50
Silver, American, Tablespoon, Fiddle, Erastus Cook, Rochester, N.Y., Coin, Pair	35.00
Silver, American, Tablespoon, Fiddle, Hourglass Form, E.E.Bailey, N.H., Coin	35.00
Silver, American, Tablespoon, Fiddle, Hourglass Form, J.M.Ford, Coin, Pair	30.00
Silver, American, Tablespoon, Fiddle, Hourglass, Beasom & Reed, N.H., Coin	15.00
Silver, American, Tablespoon, Fiddle, Isaiah Lukens, Phila., Coin, Pair	55.00
Silver, American, Tablespoon, Fiddle, Joseph Ketcham, N.Y.C., Coin	18.50
Silver, American, Tablespoon, Fiddle, Joseph Shoemaker, Phila., Coin, Pair	75.00
Silver, American, Tablespoon, Fiddle, R & W Wilson, Phila., Coin	15.00
Silver, American, Tablespoon, Fiddle, William Moulton IV, Mass., Coin	25.00
Silver, American, Tablespoon, Flared Handle, Harding & Co., Boston, C.1835	30.00
Silver, American, Tablespoon, Flared Handle, Lakeman, Mass., C.1819, Coin	22.00
Silver, American, Tablespoon, Initials J.M.W., M & A, Utica, N.Y., C.1840, Coin	12.75
Silver, American, Tablespoon, Initials M.A.R., Parker, C.1840, Coin	8.95
Silver, American, Tablespoon, Initials, Ambrose Martin, Phila., C.1840, Coin	13.75
Silver, American, Tablespoon, Initials, H.Sargeant, Mass., C.1825, Coin	13.75

Silver, American, Tablespoon, Initials, Wolcott & Gelston, C.1824, Coin	13.75
Silver, American, Tablespoon, King's Pattern, Jones, Ball & Poor, Coin, Pair	45.00
Silver, American, Tablespoon, Mary On Handle, Daniel White, Coin	12.00
Silver, American, Tablespoon, N & F T, Coin	12.50
Silver, American, Tablespoon, N.Harding, Coin	13.50
Silver, American, Tablespoon, Old English, Bright Cut, Sayre, N.Y., C.1800	22.50
Silver, American, Tablespoon, Old English, Paul Revere, C.1775	650.00
Silver, American, Tablespoon, Old English, Van Voorhis, C.1785, Pair	200.00
Silver, American, Tablespoon, Palmer & Batchelder, C.1850, Coin	8.95
Silver, American, Tablespoon, Palmer & Batchelder, C.1850, Coin, Pair	24.75
Silver, American, Tablespoon, Pointed End, Unmarked, Coin	15.00
Silver, American, Tablespoon, Pointed Handle, Moulton, Mass., C.1830, Coin	25.00
Silver, American, Tablespoon, Raised Thread, Harris & Stanwood, C.1835, Coin	18.00
Silver, American, Tablespoon, Round End, Harding, Boston, C.1840, Coin	18.00
Silver, American, Tablespoon, Round End, John Vernon, N.Y.C., Coin	55.00
Silver, American, Tablespoon, Script Initials, Anchor & Star, Coin	14.00
Silver, American, Tablespoon, Tipped Forward, J.Rogers, R.I., Coin	100.00
Silver, American, Tablespoon, Tipped Forward, Underhill & Vernon, Coin	95.00
Silver, American, Tablespoon, Vent, N.H.	40.00
Silver, American, Tablespoon, W.L.Kox, C.1850, Marked Coin	9.75
Silver, American, Tablespoon, W.Mitchell, Jr., Richmond, Va., C.1795	40.00
Silver, American, Tea & Coffee Set, Art Nouveau, Mauser Co., C.1900, 6 Piece	1600.00
Silver, American, Tea & Coffee Set, Floral Swags, C.1900, 6 Piece	2300.00
Silver, American, Tea & Coffee Set, J.E.Caldwell, Phila., Miniature, 5 Piece	175.00
Silver, American, Tea & Coffee Set, Leaf Band, Gale & Wood, C.1860, 5 Piece	1300.00
Silver, American, Tea & Coffee Set, Pedestal, Kirk & Son, C.1880, 5 Piece	1600.00
Silver, American, Tea & Coffee Set, Pierced Bases, C.1900, 5 Piece	2000.00
Silver, American, Tea & Coffee Set, Repousse, Schultz & Co., C.1900, 5 Piece	2000.00
Silver, American, Tea Caddy, Applied Copper Design, Howard & Co., 1879	110.00
Silver, American, Tea Caddy, Hinged Dome Lid, Bright Cut, Sayre, C.1800, 8 In.	1700.00
Silver, American, Tea Caddy, Repousse, R.Kirk & Son, Coin, 5 1/2 In.	325.00
Silver, American, Tea Set, Acorns & Oak Leaves, Thomson, C.1820, 3 Piece	1300.00
Silver, American, Tea Set, Applied Banding, Bard & Lamont, Coin, 6 Piece	4400.00
Silver, American, Tea Set, Applied Floral & Leaf, Lewis, Phila., Coin, 6 Piece	5000.00
Silver, American, Tea Set, Bright Cut, Urn Finials, Forbes, C.1805, 3 Piece	700.00
Silver, American, Tea Set, Engraved, Bud Finials, Fletcher, C.1830, 3 Piece	1500.00
Silver, American, Tea Set, Inverted Pear Shape, Thomson, C.1820, 3 Piece	1100.00
Silver, American, Tea Set, Pedestal, Ball, Tompkins & Black, C.1840, 3 Piece	750.00
Silver, American, Tea Set, Repousse Grapevines, Boyce, N.Y., Coin, 4 Piece	2800.00
Silver, American, Tea Set, Repousse, Chased, Howard & Co., C.1880, 3 Piece	175.00
Silver, American, Tea Set, Repousse, Chased, Kirk & Son, C.1880, 6 Piece	2700.00
Silver, American, Tea Set, Repousse, Footed, Kirk & Son, C.1880, 5 Piece	1750.00
Silver, American, Tea Set, Repousse, Pedestal, Gale & Son, 1852, 4 Piece	850.00
Silver, American, Tea Set, Repousse, Pineapple Finials, C.1860, 3 Piece	700.00
Silver, American, Tea Set, Vase Shape, Lownes, C.1790, 6 Piece	7500.00
Silver, American, Teapot, Bright Cut, Wood Handle, Hutton, N.Y., C.1795	650.00
Silver, American, Teapot, Domed Lid, Bud Finial, Haddock, Lincoln & Foss, 1860	170.00
Silver, American, Teapot, Vase Shape, Bright Cut, Urn Finial, Md., C.1810	600.00
Silver, American, Teapot, Weaver, Phila., 1825 *Illus*	950.00
Silver, American, Teaspoon, A.Sanborn, Lowell, Mass., C.1850, Coin	6.50
Silver, American, Teaspoon, B.Pitman, R.I., C.1850, Coin	34.75
Silver, American, Teaspoon, Baker, Providence, R.I., C.1820, Coin, 6	42.00
Silver, American, Teaspoon, Basket Of Flowers, Moore, N.Y., Coin	23.50
Silver, American, Teaspoon, Basket Of Flowers, New York, Coin	25.00
Silver, American, Teaspoon, Basket Of Flowers, Stebbins & Howe, N.Y.C., Coin	25.00
Silver, American, Teaspoon, Bigelow & Brothers, Boston, C.1840	6.00
Silver, American, Teaspoon, Bright Cut, C.W.Wilcox, Berlin, Conn., Coin	6.95
Silver, American, Teaspoon, Bright Cut, CD In Cartouche, Coin	25.00
Silver, American, Teaspoon, Bright Cut, JM In Rectangle, Coin	25.00
Silver, American, Teaspoon, Bright Cut, N.G.Wood & Son, Boston, Coin	5.95
Silver, American, Teaspoon, Bright Cut, William Grigg, N.Y. & N.S., Coin	27.50
Silver, American, Teaspoon, C.T.Emery, Coin	8.00
Silver, American, Teaspoon, C.1820, Coin	5.95
Silver, American, Teaspoon, Churchill, Boston, C.1800, Coin, 4	40.00
Silver, American, Teaspoon, Coffin End, Barton, Mass. & N.Y., Coin	25.00
Silver, American, Teaspoon, Coffin End, Dodge, Providence, Coin, Pair	65.00

Silver, American, Teapot,
Weaver, Phila., 1825
(See Page 565)

Silver, American, Teaspoon, Coffin End, Forbes, N.Y.C., Coin	21.25
Silver, American, Teaspoon, Coffin End, Hallmarks Eagle, B, & Indian, Coin	15.00
Silver, American, Teaspoon, Coffin End, Hart, Conn., Coin	30.00
Silver, American, Teaspoon, Coffin End, Initial L, C.1790, Coin	9.95
Silver, American, Teaspoon, Coffin End, Loring, Boston, Coin	25.00
Silver, American, Teaspoon, Coffin Top, Stanton, Coin	10.00
Silver, American, Teaspoon, Corbett, Keene, N.H., Coin	25.00
Silver, American, Teaspoon, E.J.Austin, Coin	8.00
Silver, American, Teaspoon, Engraved M.J.Cheswill, B.S.F.& Co., C.1820, Coin	6.75
Silver, American, Teaspoon, Engraved OAW, Fenno & Hale, Me., C.1840, Coin	12.00
Silver, American, Teaspoon, Engraved S.A.Fowler, Moulton, C.1820, Coin, 5	33.50
Silver, American, Teaspoon, Engraved, C.Lord, C.1810, Coin	7.25
Silver, American, Teaspoon, Engraved, Gennet, N.Y., Coin	10.00
Silver, American, Teaspoon, Engraved, Pear & Bacall, Boston, C.1850, Coin	6.95
Silver, American, Teaspoon, F.A.Makepeace, C.1850, Coin	5.75
Silver, American, Teaspoon, Fiddle & Shell, Star, C Star Hallmarks, Coin	18.00
Silver, American, Teaspoon, Fiddle Tip, Farrington & Hunnewell, C.1835, Coin	7.00
Silver, American, Teaspoon, Fiddle Tip, Harding & Co., C.1830, Coin	10.00
Silver, American, Teaspoon, Fiddle Tip, Hourglass Form, Adell & Co., Coin	9.00
Silver, American, Teaspoon, Fiddle Tip, Hourglass Form, F.& H., Boston, Coin	10.00
Silver, American, Teaspoon, Fiddle Tip, Hourglass Form, Skerry, Boston, Coin	10.00
Silver, American, Teaspoon, Fiddle Tip, Hourglass Form, W.& O., Lewiston, Coin	8.50
Silver, American, Teaspoon, Fiddle Tip, John Gray, Phila., C.1811, Coin	15.00
Silver, American, Teaspoon, Fiddle Tip, Tanguy, Phila., C.1801, Coin	16.00
Silver, American, Teaspoon, Fiddle Tip, 2 Part, J.G.Thompson, Coin	7.75
Silver, American, Teaspoon, Fiddle, Adrian Holmes, N.Y.C., Coin, Pair	18.00
Silver, American, Teaspoon, Fiddle, Beecher, Conn., Coin	16.00
Silver, American, Teaspoon, Fiddle, Bessac, N.Y., Coin	10.00
Silver, American, Teaspoon, Fiddle, Colin V.G.Forbes, N.Y.C., Coin	8.25
Silver, American, Teaspoon, Fiddle, D.Goldsmith, Troy, N.Y., Coin	6.50
Silver, American, Teaspoon, Fiddle, E.Mead, St.Louis, Mo., Coin	19.00
Silver, American, Teaspoon, Fiddle, Fletcher & Gardiner, Boston, Coin	18.00
Silver, American, Teaspoon, Fiddle, Forman, N.Y., Coin, Pair	18.00
Silver, American, Teaspoon, Fiddle, H.B.Myer, Newburgh, N.Y., Coin	10.00
Silver, American, Teaspoon, Fiddle, Hewell Harding, Boston, Coin	5.00
Silver, American, Teaspoon, Fiddle, Hobart, Conn., Coin	16.00
Silver, American, Teaspoon, Fiddle, Hutton, N.Y., Coin	21.25
Silver, American, Teaspoon, Fiddle, J.Abbot, Coin, Pair	10.00
Silver, American, Teaspoon, Fiddle, Moulton IV, Mass., Coin	15.00
Silver, American, Teaspoon, Fiddle, Nathaniel & Thomas Foster, Mass., Coin	12.50
Silver, American, Teaspoon, Fiddle, Osborn, Utica, N.Y., Coin	20.00
Silver, American, Teaspoon, Fiddle, W.Pitkin, Coin	8.00
Silver, American, Teaspoon, Fiddle, 2 Parts, McCully, C.1825, Coin, Pair	14.00
Silver, American, Teaspoon, Flared Handle, Appleton, Mass., C.1850, Coin	9.00
Silver, American, Teaspoon, Flared Handle, Bailey & Co., Me., C.1825, Coin	9.00

Silver, American, Teaspoon, Flared Handle, Beasom & Reed, N.H., Coin	7.00
Silver, American, Teaspoon, Flared Handle, Beasom & Reed, N.H., C.1830, Coin	10.00
Silver, American, Teaspoon, Gorham & Thurber, R.I., C.1850, Coin	7.00
Silver, American, Teaspoon, Hallett & Buckland, Coin	7.00
Silver, American, Teaspoon, Hammered, C.A.W.Crosby, Coin	15.00
Silver, American, Teaspoon, J.H.Clark, Coin	7.50
Silver, American, Teaspoon, J.Lowe, N.Y., C.1828, Coin	5.95
Silver, American, Teaspoon, Joseph Raynes, Lowell, Mass., 1835, Coin	10.00
Silver, American, Teaspoon, Knowles & Ladd, R.I., C.1850, Coin	6.65
Silver, American, Teaspoon, Mayflower, S.Kirk & Son, Baltimore, C.1846, Coin	16.00
Silver, American, Teaspoon, Medallion, Brower & Son, Albany, N.Y., Coin	19.25
Silver, American, Teaspoon, Monroe & De Friez, St.Louis, 1848, Coin, Pair	22.00
Silver, American, Teaspoon, N.Harding, Boston, Coin	8.50
Silver, American, Teaspoon, Olive, Jones, Ball & Co., Boston, Coin	7.50
Silver, American, Teaspoon, Olive, N.Harding & Co., Boston, Coin	7.50
Silver, American, Teaspoon, Oval Thread With Leaf, A.Cole, N.Y.C., Coin	6.75
Silver, American, Teaspoon, Oval Thread, C.Hulse, Coin	5.75
Silver, American, Teaspoon, Oval Thread, P.L.Taylor, Brooklyn, N.Y., Coin	8.00
Silver, American, Teaspoon, Page Bros., C.1850, Coin	7.45
Silver, American, Teaspoon, Plain Tip, F.Richmond, Providence, C.1815, Coin	15.00
Silver, American, Teaspoon, Plain Tip, Lowell & Senter, Me., Coin, Pair	25.00
Silver, American, Teaspoon, Plain Tip, O.D.Seymour, Hartford, C.1843, Coin	15.00
Silver, American, Teaspoon, Pointed End, Burr, Providence, Coin	18.35
Silver, American, Teaspoon, Pointed End, Myers, Phila., Coin, Pair	75.00
Silver, American, Teaspoon, Pointed End, W.Terry, Enfield, Conn., Coin	35.00
Silver, American, Teaspoon, Pointed End, Warner, C.1800, Coin, Pair	25.00
Silver, American, Teaspoon, Pointed Handle, Crittenden, Ohio, C.1840, Coin	10.50
Silver, American, Teaspoon, Rounded End, HW In Cartouche, Coin	18.00
Silver, American, Teaspoon, Rounded End, Martin, Phila., Coin	21.50
Silver, American, Teaspoon, Rounded End, Wiltberger, Phila., Coin	20.00
Silver, American, Teaspoon, S.A.Brown, N.Y., Coin	8.50
Silver, American, Teaspoon, Samuel Sargent, Middlebury, Vt., Coin	90.00
Silver, American, Teaspoon, Sheaf Of Wheat, E.Putnam, Boston, 1825, Coin	33.00
Silver, American, Teaspoon, Turned-Down Handle, Clark, N.Y., C.1836, Coin	9.00
Silver, American, Teaspoon, Turned Down Handle, Cook, N.Y., C.1836, Coin	8.50
Silver, American, Teaspoon, Turned Down Handle, Gill, Mass., C.1810, Coin	12.00
Silver, American, Teaspoon, 2 Part, Logan, N.Y., C.1805, Coin	12.00
Silver, American, Tongs, Basket Of Flowers, E.Benjamin, Conn., Coin	75.00
Silver, American, Tongs, Claw Ends, Initial F, Jones, Lows, & Ball, C.1839, Coin	39.75
Silver, American, Tongs, Fiddle, Oval Bowl, Chased Leaf, McKeen, Coin, 6 In.	65.00
Silver, American, Tongs, Fiddle, Oval Bowl, J.B.Jones, Boston, Coin, 6 In.	50.00
Silver, American, Tongs, Fiddle, Shell Bowl, R.& W.Wilson, Phila., Coin, 6 In.	55.00
Silver, American, Tongs, Oval Thread, Claw Ends, Harding & Co., Coin, 6 In.	25.00
Silver, American, Tongs, Sugar, Bright Cut, Lamson, Boston, C.1790, Coin	60.00
Silver, American, Tongs, Sugar, Shell Ends, Huntington, C.1850, Coin, 6 1/2 In.	39.75
Silver, American, Tongs, Sugar, Shell Nippers, Scalloped Arms, F.Rath, N.Y.	42.00
Silver, American, Tongs, Tea, Birds' Claws Ends, C.Bond, C.1835, Coin	35.00
Silver, American, Tongs, Tea, Oval Spoon Ends, R.& W.Wilson, Coin, 6 In.	45.00
Silver, American, Tongs, Tea, Spoon Ends, A.G.Peck, Ohio, C.1823, Coin	48.00
Silver, American, Tray, Birds & Floral, Jones, Ball & Poor, C.1846, 25 In.	1000.00
Silver, American, Tray, Cutout Handles, Caldwell & Co., C.1900, 26 In.	1000.00
Silver, American, Tray, Pierced Rim, Loop Handles, C.1900, 33 1/2 In.	1300.00
Silver, American, Tray, Presentation, Polish, Gorham, C.1910, 21 In.	450.00
Silver, American, Tray, Serving, Pierced Rim, C.1900, 13 1/2 In.	300.00
Silver, American, Tray, Serving, Pierced Rim, C.1900, 14 1/2 In.	350.00
Silver, American, Tureen, Sauce, Dome Lid, Ball, Tompkins & Black, C.1850	350.00
Silver, American, Urn, Sugar, Covered, Williamson, Phila., 1794, 11 1/2 In.	1500.00
Silver, American, Vase, Lions' Heads Handles, Lincoln & Foss, Coin, 9 1/4 In.	425.00
Silver, American, Waiter, Applied Leaves Rim, Footed, Ewan, C.1830, 8 In.	700.00
Silver, Austrian, Box, Seal, Gilt, Drum Shape, Armorial, Francis I, C.1810	250.00
Silver, Austrian, Fork, C.1872	3.50
Silver, Austrian, Knife, C.1872	3.50
Silver, Austrian, Scoop, Sugar, C.1872	3.50
Silver, Austrian, Snuffbox, Book Form, Engraved, C.1850, 3 1/2 X 2 In.	65.00
Silver, Austrian, Tea Caddy, Infuser, & Spoon, Traveling, Klinkosch, C.1890	150.00
Silver, Austrian, Teakettle On Lampstand, Dome Lid, Scroll Feet, 1840	425.00

Silver, Austrian, Tongs, Sugar, Openwork Filigree, Schott, C.1850, 6 In. 18.00
Silver, Belgian, Candlestick, Domed Circular Base, Chased, 1784, 12 In., Pair 2900.00
Silver, Chinese, Bottle, Snuff, Carved, 2 1/2 In. 325.00
Silver, Chinese, Case, Card, Filigree, Top 1/3 Lifts Off, 3 3/4 X 2 1/2 In. 38.00
Silver, Danish, Box, Spice, Hinged Lid & Base, Chased, Hansen, C.1790, 3 In. 170.00
Silver, Danish, Snuffbox, Bombe, Chased, Hunting Scene, Wissing, C.1750 .... 350.00
Silver, Danish, Spoon, Serving, Thread Edge, C.1820, 14 In. 125.00
Silver, Dutch, Basket, Sweetmeat, Embossed, Openwork, C.1854, 6 In. 140.00
Silver, Dutch, Box, Tobacco, Bombe, Chased, Putto Finial, I.R., 1765, 7 In. 1200.00
Silver, Dutch, Chair, Sedan, 6 1/2 In. 400.00
Silver, Dutch, Creamer, Cow, Tail Looped To Form Handle, 5 1/2 In. 200.00
Silver, Dutch, Cup, Wedding, Repousse Floral, Sterling, .925, 5 1/2 In. 72.00
Silver, Dutch, Cup, Wedding, Repousse, 925 Sterling, 5 1/2 In. 78.00
Silver, Dutch, Ladle, Soup, Fiddle Thread, Armorials, C.1750, 14 3/4 In. 85.00
Silver, Dutch, Snuffbox, Flat Lid, Bright Cut, C.1785, 1 3/8 X 1 X 1 1/2 In. 125.00
Silver, Dutch, Snuffbox, Flat Lid, Bright Cut, C.1800, 1 3/8 X 1 X 1 1/2 In. 135.00
Silver, Dutch, Spoon, Demitasse, Amsterdam, Set Of 6 .... 35.00
Silver, Dutch, Spoon, Orange, Bright Cut, Gondola Shape Bowl, C.1850 .... 7.50
Silver, Dutch, Tea Caddy, Cone Finial, Chased, Shells & Ovals, 1744, 5 1/8 In. 225.00
Silver, Dutch, Tea Caddy, Domed Lid, Pinecone Finial, I.T., 1804, 5 3/4 In. 375.00
Silver, English, Basket, Cake, Boat Shape, Grapevine, Hennell, 1809, 11 In. 425.00
Silver, English, Basket, Cake, Engraved, Barnard, 1829, 12 1/4 In. 550.00
Silver, English, Basket, Cake, Pierced, Peter & Ann Bateman, 1793, 15 In. 850.00
Silver, English, Basket, Dessert, Pierced, Pedestal, Frisbee, 1795, 12 In. 1050.00
Silver, English, Basket, Sugar, Hinged Handle, Filigree, Cranberry Insert 57.50
Silver, English, Basket, Sweetmeat, Pierced, Hester Bateman, 1787, 6 3/4 In. 525.00
Silver, English, Basket, Sweetmeat, Pierced, Oval, T.F., 1767, 6 In. 200.00
Silver, English, Basket, Sweetmeat, Pierced, Scroll Feet, E.A., 1769, 6 In. 250.00
Silver, English, Bookmark, Pierced Trowel, Birmingham, 1897, 3 1/4 In. 35.00
Silver, English, Bowl, Dessert, Boat Shape, Chased, Martin & Hall, 1885, 8 In. 225.00
Silver, English, Bowl, Dessert, Shell Handled, London, 1812, 10 3/8 In. 475.00
Silver, English, Bowl, Everted Rim, Georgian, 8 5/8 In. 100.00
Silver, English, Bowl, Georgian, Fluted Swirl, Domed Foot, 10 1/2 In. 425.00
Silver, English, Bowl, Gilt, Chased, Dome Foot, Hilland, C.1738, 4 In. 1500.00
Silver, English, Bowl, Monteith, Repousse, J.A.J.S., 1882, 12 1/4 In. 1350.00
Silver, English, Bowl, Spiral Fluted, Applied Shells, Archambo, 1742, 7 In. 2000.00
Silver, English, Bowl, Spiral Fluted, Engraved, Grundy, 1757, 7 In. 2300.00
Silver, English, Box, Clock Form, Slip On Lid, Taylor, 1798, 1 1/4 In. 180.00
Silver, English, Box, Counter, Profile Of Queen Anne, T.K., C.1705, 1 In. 90.00
Silver, English, Box, Gilt, State Of The Nation, George III, 2 In. 275.00
Silver, English, Box, Heart Shape, Floral On Lid, Gold Wash Interior, 3 In. 40.00
Silver, English, Box, Patch, 2 Figures & Building, R.B., C.1690, 1 1/2 In. 200.00
Silver, English, Box, Taper, Folding Handle, Engraved, C.1800, 2 In. 100.00
Silver, English, Box, Taper, Ring Handle, Chased, Phipps & Robinson, 1806 .... 200.00
Silver, English, Candelabra, Female Busts, 4 Arm, Crichton, 1910, 18 In., Pair 3900.00
Silver, English, Candlestick, Square Dished Base, Cafe, 1762, 10 1/4 In., Pair 2000.00
Silver, English, Case, Vesta, Inverted Mushroom Shape, 1888, 2 1/4 In. 225.00
Silver, English, Casket, Gilt, Sarcophagus Shape, Barnard, 1884, 9 In. 2000.00
Silver, English, Centerpiece, Goldsmiths & Silversmiths, 1927, 16 3/4 In. 500.00
Silver, English, Centerpiece, Twisted Vine Column, Smith, 1836, 29 1/2 In. 7000.00
Silver, English, Chocolate Pot, Domed Lid, Leaves, Footed, Bailey, 1750 .... 1200.00
Silver, English, Coffee Set, Octagonal Baluster Shape, I.W., 1842, 3 Piece 950.00
Silver, English, Coffeepot, Acorn Finial, Wood Handle, Berthelot, 1752 .... 700.00
Silver, English, Coffeepot, Engraved Oak & Acorns, Hennell, 1797 .... 950.00
Silver, English, Coffeepot, Pear Shape, Chased, More, 1761, 10 In. 1150.00
Silver, English, Coffeepot, Urn Finial, Dome Lid, Farren, 1733, 8 3/4 In. 2300.00
Silver, English, Condiment Set, Banded, Birmingham, 3 Piece 20.00
Silver, English, Creamer, Boat Shape, Scroll Handle & Feet, 1756 .... 175.00
Silver, English, Creamer, Cow, Applied Fly & Floral, Schuppe, 1762, 6 In. 2200.00
Silver, English, Creamer, Embossed Cows, Scroll Handle, Mills, 1751 .... 100.00
Silver, English, Creamer, Ovoid Shape, Medallion, Newcastle, 1794 .... 95.00
Silver, English, Cruet Stand, 4 Bottles, Ball Feet, Square, AB, C.1812 .... 150.00
Silver, English, Cruet, John Delmester, 1763, 11 1/4 In. .... Illus 1100.00
Silver, English, Cruet, 5 Bottles, Shell & Scroll Feet, Wood, 1753, 11 In. 1600.00
Silver, English, Cup, Caudle, Chased, S Scroll Handles, Parr, 1704 .... 1000.00
Silver, English, Cup, Caudle, Double Scroll Handles, 1690, 3 3/8 In. 900.00

Burmese vase, Mt. Washington Glass Works, c. 1880–90.

Enameled milk glass mug, c. 1793.

Free-blown glass celery, American(?), c. 1840.

Bristol glass mug, early 18th century.

Whale oil lamp with pressed glass base, New England, c. 1830.

Tiffany glass flower bowl, c. 1900.

Glass vases by Louis Tiffany, c. 1900.

Austrian overlay glass vase, c. 1845.

Ruby glass vase, mid-19th century.

Mary Gregory glass vase, c. 1885.

American mahogany game table, c. 1825–30. Famille rose garniture set, Chinese export porcelain, c. 1740.

Mahogany blanket chest, Pennsylvania, 1786.

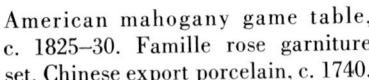

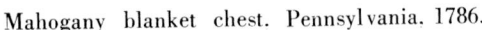

Pine cabinet, carved, painted black and gilded, c. 1860. Laminated rosewood armchair, Charles A. Baudouine, New York, c. 1855.

Cast-iron stove, c. 1835. Stencil decorated Windsor side chair, New England, c. 1825.

Empire parlor, 1815–45.

Maple chest of drawers, Samuel Dunlap II, New Hampshire, 1775–90.

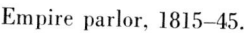

Curly maple child's bed, New England, c. 1825.

Simon Willard tall clock, mahogany and birch, Roxbury, Massachusetts, 1790–1810.

Willard's patented 8-day banjo clock, c. 1820.

Banjo clock with reverse painting on glass, Aaron Willard, c. 1820.

Lyre-shaped wall clock, Abiel Chandler, Concord, New Hampshire, 1829–44.

Secretary bookcase, mahogany on tulipwood and pine, S. J. John, Cincinnati, 1848.

Massachusetts Queen Anne table; English Chippendale hanging shelf. Eighteenth-century dresses.

Crotch mahogany organ, George Jardine, New York, c. 1880.

Corner cupboard of tulipwood decorated in imitation of crotch mahogany, Pennsylvania, 1815–25.

Mahogany desk and chair, The Standard Furniture Co., Cincinnati, c. 1900–10.

Country Hepplewhite secretary bookcase, c. 1800–1815.

Desk and chair of maple in imitation of bamboo, New York, c. 1875–85.

Pewter coffeepot by Sellew & Co., Cincinnati, c. 1840. Ohio iron.

Silver tea set, Robert and William Wilson, Philadelphia, c. 1825–46.

Brass camphene lamp, Cornelius & Son, Philadelphia, 1843.

Glass and metal astral lamp, American, c. 1835–40.

Table lamp with leaded glass Tiffany shade. c. 1900.

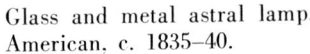

Federal-style mirror, gilt pine, reverse glass painting of Landing of Columbus, c. 1810. Table, mahogany with curly maple veneer, American, c. 1810.

Tiger maple and tulipwood worktable by William Tygart, North Bloomfield, Ohio, c. 1830. Pair of painted-wood side chairs, Baltimore, c. 1830. Pennsylvania painted-wood wedding box, 18th century.

Early 19th-century land office.

Table, mahogany with curly maple veneer, American, c. 1810.

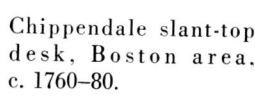

Chippendale slant-top desk, Boston area, c. 1760–80.

Mahogany and white pine chest of drawers. New England. c. 1820.

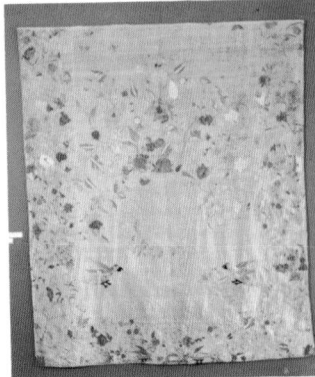

Late Empire card table and chair of mahogany and white pine. American. Mahogany side chair. c. 1840.

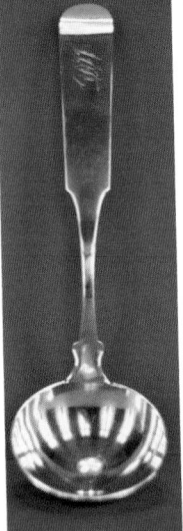

Coin silver soup ladle. Wilson McGrew. Cincinnati. c. 1824.

Pennsylvania Chippendale chest of drawers of walnut and tulipwood. c. 1780.

Appliqued linen bed cover of homespun linen, American. c. 1840.

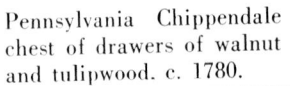

Silver, English, Cup, Covered, 2 Handled, Armorial, Spilsbury, 1739, 12 In. 1700.00
Silver, English, Cup, Vase Shape, Grotesque Masks, 2 Handled, 1772, 21 In. 1000.00
Silver, English, Dish, Chafing, Pierced Hearts, Footed, Ward, 1712, 6 In. 1000.00
Silver, English, Dish, Entree, Greyhound Finial, Sheffield Liner, Storr, 1820 .... 2300.00
Silver, English, Dish, Meat, Gadroon Border, Wakelin & Garrard, 1799, 17 In. 725.00
Silver, English, Dish, Venison, Well & Tree, Garrard, 1837, 24 1/2 In. 1200.00
Silver, English, Epergne, Pierced Boat Baskets, R.G., 1770, 15 1/4 In. 3600.00
Silver, English, Fork, Fiddle Thread Shell, Mary Chawner, 1839 .... 26.50
Silver, English, Fork, Old English Thread, Smith & Fearn, 1788 .... 25.00
Silver, English, Fork, Sucket, 2 Prong At End, Bowl At Other, Matthew, 1712 .... 400.00
Silver, English, Fork, Traveling, Mother-Of-Pearl Handle, C.1790 .... 55.00
Silver, English, Grater, Nutmeg, Repousse, Acorn Shape, Massey, C.1755 .... 140.00
Silver, English, Jug On Lampstand, Coffee, Repousse, W.C., 1757, 11 1/2 In. 450.00
Silver, English, Jug, Beer, Engraved Crests, Repousse, Garden, 1752, 8 3/4 In. 1900.00
Silver, English, Jug, Beer, Molded Foot, Scroll Handle, Johnston, 1764, 11 In. 1450.00
Silver, English, Jug, Coffee, George & Charles Fox, 1853 .... *Illus* 1150.00
Silver, English, Jug, Hot Water, Pear Shape, Domed Lid, Heming, 1759, 9 In. 375.00
Silver, English, Kettle On Lampstand, Hot Water, Melon Shape, Storr, 1835 .... 2300.00
Silver, English, Kettle On Lampstand, Hot Water, Reeded, Fountain, 1799 .... 1300.00
Silver, English, Kettle On Lampstand, Hot Water, Repousse, Storr, 1828 .... 2600.00
Silver, English, Kettle On Lampstand, Hot Water, Shell Feet, 1897, 13 In. 425.00
Silver, English, Knife, Cheese, Carved Ivory Handle, Birmingham, C.1825 .... 20.00
Silver, English, Knife, Pistol Handle, Chased, Steel Blade, Brent, 1814 .... 33.50
Silver, English, Ladle, GL, London, C.1837, 7 In. 42.00
Silver, English, Ladle, King's Pattern, C.L., London, C.1837, 7 In. 48.00
Silver, English, Ladle, Peter & Anne Bateman, C.1797, 5 In. 45.00
Silver, English, Ladle, Soup, Old English, Smith & Fearn, London, C.1792 .... 150.00
Silver, English, Ladle, Soup, Old English, Wrigglework, T.T., 1778 .... 100.00
Silver, English, Ladle, Soup, Onslow, Shell Bowl, G.B., 1762 .... 200.00
Silver, English, Ladle, Tubular Handle, Rattail Terminal, B.B., 1690, 17 In. 650.00
Silver, English, Match Safe, Honeycomb Design, Birmingham, 1918 .... 28.00
Silver, English, Matchbox, Bright Cut, Striker, Carrying Ring, C.1857 .... 25.00
Silver, English, Muffineer, Octagonal, 8 1/2 In. 85.00
Silver, English, Nip, Stork Shape, Eley, Fearn & Chawner, 1807, 5 In., Pair 225.00
Silver, English, Pepper Shaker, Mary Johnson, 1729 .... *Illus* 600.00
Silver, English, Pillbox, Birmingham, C.1900, Round, 1 In. 20.00
Silver, English, Pot, Mustard, Gilt, Embossed, Armorial, I.W., 1819, 3 3/4 In. 350.00
Silver, English, Salt Cellar, Bombe, Hoof Feet, A.M., 1865 .... 50.00
Silver, English, Salt Cellar, Bombe, Scroll Feet, Eaton, 1819 .... 100.00
Silver, English, Salt Cellar, Bombe, Shell & Hoof Feet, H.C., 1761, Pair 150.00
Silver, English, Salt Cellar, Bombe, 3 Hoof Feet, Hennell, 1752, Pair 225.00
Silver, English, Salt Cellar, Pierced, Blue Glass Liner, W.C., 1794 .... 75.00
Silver, English, Salt Cellar, Pierced, Footed, Blue Glass, H.Bateman, 1776 .... 125.00
Silver, English, Salt Cellar, Winged Paw Feet, Smith, 1819, 4 In. 120.00
Silver, English, Salt Celler, Boat Shape, Scroll Handle, A.T., 1797 .... 112.50

Silver, English, Cruet,
John Delmester, 1763,
11 1/4 In.
(See Page 568)

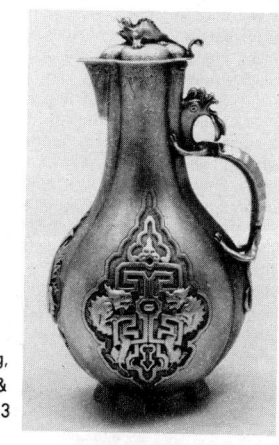

Silver, English, Jug,
Coffee, George &
Charles Fox, 1853

Silver, English, Salt, Master, Raised Shell, Mary Chawner, London, C.1839, Pair	32.00
Silver, English, Salver, Armorial, Gadrooned, Carter, 1771, 13 3/4 In.	1100.00
Silver, English, Salver, Ball & Claw Feet, Embossed, Carter, 1774, 13 1/2 In.	800.00
Silver, English, Salver, Footed, Courtauld, 1714, 13 In.	950.00
Silver, English, Salver, Gadroon Edge, Ball & Claw Feet, Capper, 1768, 12 In.	525.00
Silver, English, Salver, Gadroon Rim, Engraved, S.H., 1817, 18 1/2 In.	1100.00
Silver, English, Salver, Pierced Border, Footed, Robinson, 1753, 12 1/2 In.	500.00
Silver, English, Salver, Scroll Rim, Floral, C.C.Pilling, 1902, 10 In.	150.00
Silver, English, Salver, Shell & Scroll Rim, Footed, Caper, 1762, 10 In.	500.00
Silver, English, Sauceboat, Boat Shape, Scroll Feet, White, C.1750, Pair	475.00
Silver, English, Sauceboat, Engraved, Footed, Fray & Fuller, 1744, Pair	3000.00
Silver, English, Sauceboat, Leaf Capped Scroll Handle, Videau, 1758	650.00
Silver, English, Scoop, Marrow, Crown Engraved On Back, Fennell, 1791	125.00
Silver, English, Seal, Fob, Vinaigrette, Gilt, Pierced, 1871, 1 1/2 In.	250.00
Silver, English, Server, Sandwich, Fiddle, Peter & Wm.Bateman, 1809, 12 In.	150.00
Silver, English, Shoehorn, Engraved Edity, Birmingham, 1900-01	13.00
Silver, English, Skewer, Crested, Shell Grip, T.& W. Chawner, C.1759	125.00
Silver, English, Snuffbox, Applied Profile Of Duke Of Wellington, Shaw, 1827	375.00
Silver, English, Snuffbox, Boat Shape, 2 Compartment, W.P., B.S., C.1790	425.00
Silver, English, Snuffbox, Engine Turned, W.E., 1811, 3 In.	100.00
Silver, English, Snuffbox, Exeter Cathedral, Mills, 1846, 2 5/8 In.	350.00
Silver, English, Snuffbox, George III, Hinged, Agate Dome, 1798, 2 1/2 In.	200.00
Silver, English, Snuffbox, Gilt, Abbotsford House, Taylor & Perry, 1836, 3 In.	600.00
Silver, English, Snuffbox, Gilt, Chased, Engine Turned, Bettridge, 1825, 3 In.	250.00
Silver, English, Snuffbox, Oval, Engraved, Peter & Ann Bateman, 1792	1600.00
Silver, English, Snuffbox, Victorian Mansion, Mills, 1844, 3 In.	250.00
Silver, English, Snuffbox, Warwick Castle, Chased, Yapp & Woodward, 1847	750.00
Silver, English, Snuffbox, Warwick Castle, Repousse, Mills, 1838, 3 1/2 In.	650.00
Silver, English, Snuffbox, Windsor Castle, Engine Turned, Mills, 1838, 3 In.	350.00
Silver, English, Spoon, Demitasse, Bearded Man Holding Book, Cherub's Head	10.00
Silver, English, Spoon, Demitasse, Feather Edge, Chester, 1781	18.50
Silver, English, Spoon, Demitasse, Rounded Ends, 1893, Set Of 12	60.00
Silver, English, Spoon, Dessert, Old English, Langlands, Fr., Newcastle, 1801	25.00
Silver, English, Spoon, Dessert, Reverse Fiddleback, Exeter, 1866	35.00
Silver, English, Spoon, Dessert, Reverse Fiddleback, London, 1831	35.00
Silver, English, Spoon, Dessert, Reverse Fiddleback, London, 1835	35.00
Silver, English, Spoon, Dessert, Reverse Fiddleback, London, 1842	35.00
Silver, English, Spoon, Dessert, Reverse Fiddleback, Newcastle, 1849	35.00
Silver, English, Spoon, Dressing, Fiddle & Shell, Eley, Fearn, & Chawner, 1812	95.00
Silver, English, Spoon, Dressing, Fiddle Pattern, T B, London, 1809, 12 In.	85.00
Silver, English, Spoon, Dressing, Fiddle, TB, London, 1808, 12 In.	85.00
Silver, English, Spoon, Elongated Ridge, Short Handle, Swanson, 1761	65.00
Silver, English, Spoon, Elongated Ridge, Short Handle, W.L., C.1761	65.00
Silver, English, Spoon, Gravy, Raised Panel On Handle, 1753, 10 3/4 In.	125.00
Silver, English, Spoon, Picture Back, Scroll, John Spackman, London, C.1741	100.00
Silver, English, Spoon, Serving, Bright Cut, Engraved, Peter & Ann Bateman	50.00
Silver, English, Spoon, Serving, Hester Bateman	150.00
Silver, English, Spoon, Serving, Peter & William Bateman, Pair	80.00 To 125.00
Silver, English, Spoon, Straining, Old English, Pierced, Hester Bateman, 1780	250.00
Silver, English, Spoon, Stuffing, Crested, Sutton, London, C.1793	120.00
Silver, English, Spoon, Stuffing, Henry Sardet, London, 1799, 12 In.Long	95.00
Silver, English, Spoon, Stuffing, 1884, 12 In.Long	65.00
Silver, English, Spoon, Tea Caddy, Fiddle Handle, Shell Bowl, GR, 1820	85.00
Silver, English, Spoon, Turkey, Ornament On Handle, London, 1829	80.00
Silver, English, Strainer, Pierced Concentric Quatrefoils, London, 1782	125.00
Silver, English, Strainer, Tea, Openwork Handles, E.P.N.S.	8.50
Silver, English, Sugar, Spreading Foot, Eliza Godfrey, 1729	375.00
Silver, English, Tablespoon, Bright Cut, Extended Drop, Sutton, 1793	95.00
Silver, English, Tablespoon, Drop On Back Of Bowl, JG & FP, 1810	50.00
Silver, English, Tablespoon, Fiddle, Eley & Fearn, London, 1815, 8 3/4 In.	50.00
Silver, English, Tablespoon, King's Pattern, I.B., 1828	29.50
Silver, English, Tablespoon, Repousse, Scalloped, Gilt, Smith & Fearn, 1786	75.00
Silver, English, Tankard, Molded Foot, Scroll Handle, London, C.1680, 8 In.	9250.00
Silver, English, Tankard, Reeded Bands, P.& A.Bateman, 1798, 7 3/8 In.	1300.00
Silver, English, Taperstick, Caryatid, Schuppe, 1767, 5 5/8 In., Pair	1800.00
Silver, English, Tea & Coffee Set, Fluted, Double Lip Creamer, 1830, 4 Piece	2300.00

Silver, English, Tea Caddy,
Joseph Fainell, 1718

Silver, English, Pepper Shaker,
Mary Johnson, 1729
(See Page 569)

Silver, English, Tea Caddy,
Joseph Fainell, 1718, 5 In.

Silver, English, Tea & Coffee Set, Repousse, Craddock & Reid, C.1818, 4 Piece	1900.00
Silver, English, Tea Caddy, Joseph Fainell, 1718 .... *Illus*	650.00
Silver, English, Tea Caddy, Joseph Fainell, 1718, 5 In. .... *Illus*	750.00
Silver, English, Tea Caddy, Slide In Base, Dome Lid, Newton, C.1725, 5 In.	275.00
Silver, English, Tea Set, Fluted, Ivory Finial, I.P., 1814, 3 Piece	375.00
Silver, English, Tea Set, Leaf Capped Handles, Angell, 1814, 4 Piece	1400.00
Silver, English, Teapot, Engraved, Scroll Feet, Scroll Handle, Storr, 1830	900.00
Silver, English, Teapot, Ovoid, Engraved Medallion, Wood Handle, London, 1799	350.00
Silver, English, Teaspoon, King's Pattern, Wm.Bell, London, C.1823, Pair	22.00
Silver, English, Tongs, Sugar, Acorn Grips, Hester Bateman, C.1788	100.00
Silver, English, Tongs, Sugar, Apostle Handle, Birmingham, 1897, 4 In.	32.00
Silver, English, Tongs, Sugar, Line Design, Peter & Wm. Bateman, 1813	75.00
Silver, English, Tray, Bracket Handles, Engraved, Barnard, 1894, 29 3/4 In.	1200.00
Silver, English, Tray, Loop Handled, Hutton & Sons, London, 1900, 25 3/4 In.	950.00
Silver, English, Tray, Piecrust Edge, Footed, Bateman, C.1801, 6 3/4 In.	50.00
Silver, English, Tureen, Sauce, Domed Lid, Boat Shape, Storr, 1800, Pair	450.00
Silver, English, Urn, Tea, Embossed, Engraved, Smith & Sharp, 1765, 20 In.	1900.00
Silver, English, Urn, Tea, George III, Vase Shape, Fennell, 1784, 21 In.	2800.00
Silver, English, Vinaigrette & Scent Bottle, Cannon Form, 1873, 2 7/8 In.	450.00
Silver, English, Vinaigrette & Scent Flask, Parcel Gilt, J.B., 1871	275.00
Silver, English, Vinaigrette, Balmoral Castle, Repousse, Taylor & Perry, 1835	525.00
Silver, English, Vinaigrette, Book Form, Ledsam, Vale & Wheller, 1829	250.00
Silver, English, Vinaigrette, Crystal Palace, W.D., 1850, 1 1/4 In.	150.00
Silver, English, Vinaigrette, Floral, Cathedral, J.T., 1842, 1 5/8 In.	300.00
Silver, English, Vinaigrette, Gilt, Abbotsford House, Mills, 1837, 1 3/4 In.	425.00
Silver, English, Vinaigrette, Gilt, Brighton Pavilion, J.L., 1829, 1 3/8 In.	350.00
Silver, English, Vinaigrette, Gilt, Chinese Fretwork, Pemberton, 1805	200.00
Silver, English, Vinaigrette, Gilt, Chrysanthemum Form, Willmore, C.1825	475.00
Silver, English, Vinaigrette, Gilt, Engraved, Pierced, Shaw, 1816, 1 1/2 In.	200.00
Silver, English, Vinaigrette, Gilt, Grapes & Leaves, Pierced, W.P., 1814	170.00
Silver, English, Vinaigrette, Gilt, Mosaic Capitol Of Rome, Mills, 1835	650.00
Silver, English, Vinaigrette, Gilt, Newstead Abbey, Mills, 1837, 1 1/2 In.	475.00
Silver, English, Vinaigrette, Gilt, Snail Form, Linwood, 1804, 1 1/4 In.	350.00
Silver, English, Vinaigrette, Gilt, St.George's Chapel, Taylor & Perry, 1839	500.00
Silver, English, Vinaigrette, Gilt, Traveler & Dog, Linwood, 1811, 1 1/4 In.	400.00
Silver, English, Vinaigrette, Gilt, Warwick Castle, Taylor & Perry, 1839	500.00
Silver, English, Vinaigrette, Kenilworth Castle, Clark, 1839, 1 3/4 In.	300.00
Silver, English, Vinaigrette, Lantern Form, Hinged, Red & Green Glass, 1873	275.00
Silver, English, Vinaigrette, London Stock Exchange, Mills, 1844, 1 5/8 In.	500.00
Silver, English, Vinaigrette, Martyr's Cross, Oxford, A.T., 1853, 1 5/8 In.	375.00
Silver, English, Vinaigrette, Newcastle Town Hall, C.W., S.D., C.1850	300.00
Silver, English, Vinaigrette, Pierced, Foliage, R.B., 1802, 1 1/8 In.	100.00

Silver, English, Vinaigrette, Strawberry Shape, Pierced, H.& T., 1863 .... 400.00
Silver, English, Vinaigrette, Warwick Castle, Mills, 1841, 1 1/2 In. 350.00
Silver, English, Vinaigrette, Westminster Abbey, Pierced, Willmore, 1842 .... 400.00
Silver, English, Vinaigrette, Windsor Castle, J.T., 1844, 1 5/8 In. 350.00
Silver, English, Vinaigrette, Windsor Castle, Pierced, Mills, 1827, 1 1/2 In. 450.00
Silver, English, Waiter, Armorial, Fluted Feet, T.B., J.H., 1884, 9 1/4 In. 275.00
Silver, English, Waxjack, Domed Base, Scroll Handle, Chawner, 1790, 7 In. 300.00
Silver, English, Waxjack, Round Base, Spring Operated, Smith & Sharp, 1763 .... 675.00
Silver, French, Beaker, Flared Lip, Gadrooned Border, Jouette, C.1775, 4 In. 300.00
Silver, French, Beaker, Tulip Shape, Chased Foot, Gilt Interior, C.1809 .... 150.00
Silver, French, Box, Applied 3 Color Gold Floral, Michelin, 1763, 3 1/2 In. 750.00
Silver, French, Box, Rectangular, Birds, Rabbit, & Plants In Niello, 3 In. 110.00
Silver, French, Chalice & Paten, Gilt, Hexafoil Base, Engraved, C.1890 .... 175.00
Silver, French, Chocolate Pot, Dome Lid, Swivel Finial, Vancoubert, 1783 .... 475.00
Silver, French, Dish, Dessert, Pierced Bellflowers, Footed, C.1890, 9 In., Pair 325.00
Silver, French, Pepper Mill, Hallmarked Sterling, 3 3/4 In. 20.00
Silver, French, Plate, Service, Gilt, Armorial, Reeded Edge, Biennais, 1809 .... 1165.00
Silver, French, Pot, Mustard, Ivory Lid & Spoon, Puiforcat, C.1900, 3 In. 140.00
Silver, French, Salt Cellar, Openwork, Cut Glass Liner, Courtois, C.1835 .... 27.50
Silver, French, Salt Cellar, Openwork, Paw Supports, Prion, 1782, Pair 150.00
Silver, French, Snuffbox, Cherub On Goat On Lid, C.1850, 2 1/4 X 1 1/2 In. 65.00
Silver, French, Spoon, Crowned Crest On Back, Rennes, C.1744 .... 95.00
Silver, French, Spoon, Sugar Sifter, Threaded Shell, Hallmarked, 6 In. 20.00
Silver, French, Taster, Wine, Beaded Band, Reeded Scrolled Handle, C.1809 .... 100.00
Silver, French, Taster, Wine, Repousse, Gadrooned, C.1819, 3 In. 95.00
Silver, German, Bag, Mesh, Chain, 2 1/2 X 2 In. 8.00
Silver, German, Beaker, Double, Gilt, Chased, S H, C.1650, 5 3/8 In. 2100.00
Silver, German, Beaker, Hebrew Inscription, I.I.B., C.1770, 3 1/4 In. 700.00
Silver, German, Bowl, Chased, Fruit, Scroll Feet, Oval, C.1900, 8 In. 110.00
Silver, German, Box, Jewel, Table Form, Wings Fold, C.1890, 2 X 2 1/2 In. 450.00
Silver, German, Box, Sugar, Bombe, Oval, Domed Cover, I.B., C.1777, 3 3/4 In. 800.00
Silver, German, Candlestick, Square Base, Laurel Border, C.1781, 9 In., Pair 600.00
Silver, German, Case, Jewel, Bombe, Pierced, Drawer, C.1790, 4 In. 450.00
Silver, German, Cup, Covered, Parcel Gilt, Man & Tree Trunk Stem, C.1620 .... 350.00
Silver, German, Cup, Whiskey, Gold Washed Inside, 2 In Leather Case 100.00
Silver, German, Dish, Sweetmeat, Chased, Floral, Footed, C.1770, 6 3/4 In. 70.00
Silver, German, Inkwell, Hinged, Saucer Base, Courting & Tavern Scene 25.00
Silver, German, Snuffbox, Coins In Lid, Octagonal, B.D., C.1790, 4 In. 275.00
Silver, German, Snuffbox, Gilt, Boar Shape, C.B., C.1720, 4 1/4 In. 1600.00
Silver, German, Spoon, Basting, Hanoverian, C.G.F., C.1750, 14 1/4 In. 250.00
Silver, German, Spoon, Woman Figural Handle, Hallmarked, 2 1/2 In. 45.00
Silver, Irish, Bowl, Fluted, Engraved, Mask & Paw Feet, C.1750, 6 5/8 In. 700.00
Silver, Irish, Candlestick, Square Base, Engraved, Dublin, C.1740, 8 In., Pair 1450.00
Silver, Irish, Cup, Leaf Capped Double Scroll Handles, Walker, C.1755 .... 400.00
Silver, Irish, Ladle, Tubular Handle, Rattail Terminal, T.M., C.1710 .... 1300.00
Silver, Irish, Plate, Dinner, Armorial, Gadrooned Rim, Nowlan, 1821, 10 In. 275.00
Silver, Irish, Salver, Adam Style, Jackson, C.1780, 9 1/4 In. 400.00
Silver, Irish, Snuffbox, Oval, Engraved, Keating, 1798, 3 In. 110.00
Silver, Irish, Spoon, Serving, Fiddleback, Samuel Neville, Dublin, C.1819 .... 30.00
Silver, Irish, Tongs, Sugar, Bright Cut, Oval Grips, John Stoyte, C.1790 .... 60.00
Silver, Italian, Candlestick, Chased, Round Base, C.1800, 10 1/8 In., Pair 450.00
Silver, Italian, Case, Sealing Wax, Cupids, Accarise, C.1900, 6 1/8 In. 130.00
Silver, Japanese, Figurine, Cicada, Hinged Wings & Legs, Muneyoshi, 3 In. 650.00
Silver, Japanese, Group, Monkey & 2 Young, Sadakatsu, C.1850, 5 1/8 In. 1500.00
Silver, Portuguese, Candlestick, Openwork Stem, A.P.C., C.1850, 10 In., Pair 450.00
Silver, Russian, see also Faberge
Silver, Russian, Basket, Basket Weave, Ovchinnikov, C.1890, 5 In. 350.00
Silver, Russian, Basket, Kremlin Center, Pierced Handles, 1880, 16 In. 1500.00
Silver, Russian, Basket, Pierced Floral & Fruit Border, Footed, 1835, 13 In. 1000.00
Silver, Russian, Beaker, Repousse Birds & Flames, Petrov, 1790, 3 1/2 In. 525.00
Silver, Russian, Beaker, Repousse Birds, Flames, & C Scrolls, 1760, 3 1/2 In. 550.00
Silver, Russian, Beaker, Repousse Birds, Flames, & C Scrolls, 1775, 3 1/8 In. 425.00
Silver, Russian, Beaker, Repousse, Chased, Eagles, C.1850, 3 1/4 In. 350.00
Silver, Russian, Bowl, Covered, Lobes, Gadroon Rim, 1832, 2 3/8 In. 90.00
Silver, Russian, Box, Parcel Gilt & Niello, Man & Child On Lid, C.1820, 3 In. 200.00
Silver, Russian, Butter Pat, Plain Buttons, 2 5/8 In.Square 11.00

Silver, Russian, Case, Cigar, Niello, Basket Weave, I.F., Moscow, 1875 .... 450.00
Silver, Russian, Case, Cigarette, Carved War Scene, Hallmarked 84 .... 225.00
Silver, Russian, Case, Cigarette, Double, Woman On Trapeze, C.1900, 6 3/4 In. 325.00
Silver, Russian, Case, Cigarette, Engraved Strapwork, C.1880, 4 1/4 In. 30.00
Silver, Russian, Case, Cigarette, Niello, Cigarettes In Cyrillic, 1891 .... 325.00
Silver, Russian, Case, Cigarette, Niello, Imperial Eagle, Moscow, 1880 .... 250.00
Silver, Russian, Case, Cigarette, Parcel Gilt & Niello, Peter The Great, 1820 .... 275.00
Silver, Russian, Case, Cigarette, Peasants, Cabochon Purple Stone, C.1900 .... 175.00
Silver, Russian, Case, Cigarette, Time Changes All, Samorokok, C.1900 .... 250.00
Silver, Russian, Casket, Curved Lid, Filigree, Pierced, Footed, 1857, 2 3/8 In. 100.00
Silver, Russian, Casket, Filigree, Domed Lid, Foliate Scrolls, C.1850, 2 In. 100.00
Silver, Russian, Casket, Hinged, Filigree, Foliate Scrolls, Footed, 1847, 4 In. 150.00
Silver, Russian, Casket, Hinged, Filigree, Foliate Scrolls, Footed, 1860, 3 In. 150.00
Silver, Russian, Cover, For Book Of Gospels, Repousse, Gilt, Kostroma, 1866 .... 450.00
Silver, Russian, Cup, Vodka, Geometrics, 1 5/8 In. 20.00
Silver, Russian, Cup, Vodka, Geometrics, 2 In. 25.00
Silver, Russian, Cup, Vodka, Geometrics, 2 1/4 In. 30.00
Silver, Russian, Cup, Vodka, Geometrics, 2 3/8 In. 45.00
Silver, Russian, Cup, Vodka, House Motif, 2 In. 25.00
Silver, Russian, Cup, Vodka, House Motif, 2 1/4 In. 30.00
Silver, Russian, Cup, Vodka, House Motif, 2 3/8 In. 45.00
Silver, Russian, Egg, Easter, Chased, Christ Is Risen, Moscow, C.1900, 3 In. 400.00
Silver, Russian, Egg, Easter, Gilt, Lacquer Stand, Ovchinnikov, C.1900, 4 In. 425.00
Silver, Russian, Figurine, Pushka Under Cannon, Gilt, Sazikov, 1851, 7 1/4 In. 4500.00
Silver, Russian, Fork, Marked 84 .... 25.00
Silver, Russian, Goblet, Chased Floral Panels, Wiberg, 1846, 8 3/8 In. 400.00
Silver, Russian, Goblet, Gilt & Niello, Buildings Medallions, C.1840, 5 In. 450.00
Silver, Russian, Goblet, Lobed Lid & Base, Man & Cane Stem, C.1750, 17 In. 900.00
Silver, Russian, Holder Tea Glass, Gilt & Niello, St.Basil's, Semenov, 1863 .... 500.00
Silver, Russian, Kovsh, Chased Dragons' Heads & Floral, Ovchinnikov, C.1850 ...... 675.00
Silver, Russian, Ladle, Fiddleback, Pierced Bowl, 1856, 7 1/2 In. 85.00
Silver, Russian, Ladle, Soup, 1815, 14 1/2 In. 300.00
Silver, Russian, Plaque, Catherine The Great, Gilt, Niello, C.1770, 4 3/4 In. 275.00
Silver, Russian, Salt Dip, Etched Floral, 3 Ball Feet, Marked 84 .... 45.00
Silver, Russian, Salt, Master, 3 Feet, Moscow 1781, 2 1/2 In.Diameter 65.00
Silver, Russian, Seal, Bogatyr On Horse, Cyrillic SV, Arnd, C.1850, 4 In. 3100.00
Silver, Russian, Server, Cake, Hallmarked 84 .... 55.00
Silver, Russian, Snuffbox, Gilt & Niello, Hunt Scene, Kaltikov, 1836, 3 In. 225.00
Silver, Russian, Spoon, Twisted Handle, Gold Washed, 1886, 4 1/4 In. 21.65
Silver, Russian, Sugar, Dome Lid & Base, Foliage, Uvarov, C.1820 .... 500.00
Silver, Russian, Tablespoon, Hallmarked, Pair 35.00
Silver, Russian, Tablespoon, Initials F.F., Dated 1859, Marked 84 .... 38.00
Silver, Russian, Tankard, Domed Lid, Ball Feet, Chased, Ovchinnikov, 1870, 8 In. ... 1000.00
Silver, Russian, Tankard, Domed Lid, Geometrics, C Scroll Handle, 1859, 8 In. 925.00
Silver, Russian, Tankard, Parcel Gilt, Hinged, Empress Anna, C.1730, 6 1/2 In. 2600.00
Silver, Russian, Tankard, Parcel Gilt, Hinged, Medallion Scenes, C.1720, 8 In. 3300.00
Silver, Russian, Tankard, Parcel Gilt, Hinged, Swedish Style, C.1720, 8 In. 4100.00
Silver, Russian, Tankard, Simulated Barrel, Siever, 1856, 5 1/4 In. 600.00
Silver, Russian, Tea Caddy, Niello, Floral In Meander Borders, C.1886, 6 In. 375.00
Silver, Russian, Teaspoon, Marked 84 .... 20.00
Silver, Russian, Teaspoon, Twisted Handle, Pair 35.00
Silver, Russian, Tongs, Engraved, Hallmarked, 5 1/2 In. 35.00
Silver, Russian, Tongs, Sugar, Pineapple Motif, Bright Cut, 1842 .... 75.00
Silver, Russian, Tray, Beaded Edge, Chlebnikov, C.1900, Oval, 12 3/8 In. 300.00
Silver, Scottish, Chamberstick, Reeded Border, Robertson, 1793, 5 1/2 In. 250.00
Silver, Scottish, Creamer, S Scroll Handle, Aytoun, 1725 .... 200.00
Silver, Scottish, Ladle, Punch, WM, Edinburgh, 1804, 14 1/2 In. 175.00
Silver, Scottish, Salver, Foliate Rim, Arthur, 1835, 12 1/2 In. 375.00
Silver, Scottish, Teapot, Inverted Pear Shape, Kerr & Dempster, 1752 .... 900.00
Silver, Scottish, Waxjack, Wood Base, Spring Operated, Gairdner, C.1790, 6 In. 300.00
    Silver, Sheffield, see also Silver Plate
Silver, Sheffield, Basket, Bread, 13 X 2 1/4 In. 65.00
Silver, Sheffield, Basket, Engraved Fox, Pierced, 14 In. 175.00
Silver, Sheffield, Caddy, Tea, Allover Embossed Grapes, Vines, Leaves, 5 In. 32.00
Silver, Sheffield, Candelabra, Palm Leaves, 3 Arm, C.1805, 16 In., Pair 200.00
Silver, Sheffield, Candelabra, 3 Arm, G & S Co., 1929, 20 1/2 In., Pair 900.00

	140.00
Silver, Sheffield, Candlestick, C.1800, 14 In., Pair	1600.00
Silver, Sheffield, Candlestick, Square Base, Floral, Winter, 1776, 11 In., Pair	75.00
Silver, Sheffield, Cigar Piercer, Figural, Irish Setter, 5 1/2 In.	650.00
Silver, Sheffield, Cooler, Wine, Armorials, Pedestal Base, C.1820, Pair	130.00
Silver, Sheffield, Cooler, Wine, Grapevine Rim, Foliate Handles, C.1820	750.00
Silver, Sheffield, Cooler, Wine, Reeded Flying Scroll Handles, C.1815, Pair	1600.00
Silver, Sheffield, Cooler, Wine, Warwick Vase Copy, 1907, 13 1/2 In.	84.00
Silver, Sheffield, Cutter, Cigar, Figural, Irish Setter	225.00
Silver, Sheffield, Dish, Cheese, Hinged Lid, Hot Water Base, C.1800, 8 1/2 In.	800.00
Silver, Sheffield, Dish, Entree, Covered, Warmer, George III, C.1810, Pair	350.00
Silver, Sheffield, Dish, Souffle, Footed, Robert Cadman, C.1790, 7 1/2 In.	185.00
Silver, Sheffield, Fish Set, Ivory Handles, Engraved, 14 Piece	32.00
Silver, Sheffield, Knife, Pearl Handled, 8	120.00
Silver, Sheffield, Salt Cellar & Stand, Gilt Interior, C.1810, Set Of 4	87.50
Silver, Sheffield, Salt Cellar, Pierced, Blue Glass, Morton, 1779	33.00
Silver, Sheffield, Salt, Master, Dixon & Son, C.1835	400.00
Silver, Sheffield, Salver, Armorial, Floral, Scrolls, Gainsford, 1826, 11 In.	78.00
Silver, Sheffield, Sander, Marked H.J., 2 In.	25.00
Silver, Sheffield, Server, Cheese, Pearl Handle, 1867	68.00
Silver, Sheffield, Tea Set, C.1840, 3 Piece	55.00
Silver, Sheffield, Teapot, Squatty Boat Shape, Bright Cut, C.1810	95.00
Silver, Sheffield, Teapot, 1810 Style	500.00
Silver, Sheffield, Tray, Foliate & Gadroon Handles, Amorial, C.1800, 19 In.	11.50
Silver, Sheffield, Tray, Pierced, N.S. & P.S. Co., 10 1/4 In.	625.00
Silver, Sheffield, Tray, Tea, Shell & Foliate Handles, Footed, Boulton, C.1810	700.00
Silver, Sheffield, Tureen, Soup, Foliate Ring Finial, Handled, C.1820, 16 In.	200.00
Silver, Sheffield, Urn, Hot Water, Ivory Finial On Spigot, C.1785, 21 In.	120.00
Silver, Sheffield, Waxjack, Oval Base, 4 Panel Supports, C.1800, 7 In.	25.00
Silver, Siamese, Creamer, Symbolic Dancers In Repousse, 3 Paw Feet, Squirrel	325.00
Silver, South American, Candlestick, Knopped Stem, C.1820, 10 1/2 In., Pair	225.00
Silver, Spanish, Chalice, Gilt Interior, Pear Knop, Domed Base, S A, C.1700	100.00
Silver, Spanish, Snuffbox, Engraved Basket Of Flowers & Strapwork, C.1725	

*Sterling silver is made with 925 parts of silver out of 1, 000 parts of metal.
The word sterling is a quality guarantee used in the United States after
about 1860.*

Silver, Sterling, see also Silver, American

Silver, Sterling, Basket, Cupids, Gold Washed, Ball, Black & Co., 11 In.	325.00
Silver, Sterling, Basket, Rose, Hand-Chased Handle, Stieff, 11 In.	390.00
Silver, Sterling, Bookmark, Princess Ingrid, Frank M.Whiting	25.00
Silver, Sterling, Bottle, Perfume, Repousse, Dominick & Haff, 5 1/2 In., Pair	375.00
Silver, Sterling, Bowl, Angel, Gold Wash Interior, Gorham, C.1870, 4 In.	275.00
Silver, Sterling, Bowl, Centerpiece, Cutout Sides, Gold Wash, Gorham, 12 In.	175.00
Silver, Sterling, Bowl, Lotus Blossom Shape, Engraved, Chinese, C.1885, 7 In.	325.00
Silver, Sterling, Box, Flowers & Scrolls In Relief, Footed, 1 1/2 X 2 1/2 In	15.00
Silver, Sterling, Box, Heart Shape, Stein On Lid, Embossed, English, 2 1/4 In.	55.00
Silver, Sterling, Box, Repousse Cover, Gorham, 1 1/8 In.Diameter	16.00
Silver, Sterling, Buckle, Pansies, 2 Sections, Unger Bros. 3 7/8 In.	60.00
Silver, Sterling, Butter, Covered, Dragonfly, Bigelow & Kinnard, Liner	145.00
Silver, Sterling, Buttonhook, Art Nouveau, Gorham, 6 1/2 In.	20.00
Silver, Sterling, Buttonhook, Art Nouveau, Repousse Handle Of Dolphins	15.00
Silver, Sterling, Buttonhook, Initial, Gorham, 8 In.	5.95
Silver, Sterling, Candelabra, 3 Arm, Gadrooned, Hamilton, 12 In., Pair	98.00
Silver, Sterling, Candlestick, Corinthian Column, Beaded, Gorham, 10 In.	90.00
Silver, Sterling, Carving Set, Ornate, Monogram M, Lion, Anchor, & G, 3 Piece	60.00
Silver, Sterling, Case, Card, Art Nouveau Full Body Woman In Relief, Kerr	95.00
Silver, Sterling, Case, Cigarette, Russian, Engraved Wheat, Poppies, & Bird	125.00
Silver, Sterling, Centerpiece, Allover Chasing, Gorham, C.1896, 20 X 15 In.	1250.00
Silver, Sterling, Cigarette Case, Reclining Elephant, 4 1/4 X 3 In.	175.00
Silver, Sterling, Clip, Desk, Female Figure Reading Book, Unger Bros., C.1900	90.00
Silver, Sterling, Coffee Set, After Dinner, Art Nouveau, Gorham, 3 Piece	300.00
Silver, Sterling, Coffeepot, Chased Floral, Reed & Barton, Quart, 10 In.	195.00
Silver, Sterling, Coffeepot, Demitasse, Repousse, Bone Handle, Gorham, 1901	90.00
Silver, Sterling, Compote, Footed, Openwork Sides, Floral, 3 X 7 1/2 In.	40.00
Silver, Sterling, Compote, Open Handles, Engraved, 6 3/4 X 6 In.	40.00
Silver, Sterling, Compote, Raised Roses, Buds, & Foliage, Low, 4 X 4 3/4 In.	25.00

Silver, Sterling, Compote, Repousse, Stieff, 8 1/2 X 4 In.	195.00
Silver, Sterling, Container, Toothbrush, Repousse, Gorham, 1887	115.00
Silver, Sterling, Creamer, Figural Cow, Embossed Floral Decoration, 4 In.	150.00
Silver, Sterling, Creamer, Helmet, Cut & Pricked Design, London, 1803	185.00
Silver, Sterling, Creamer, Helmet, Reeded Handle, London, 1817, 3 3/4 In.	185.00
Silver, Sterling, Cup & Saucer, Demitasse, Willet Belleek Liner	20.00
Silver, Sterling, Dish, Candy, Poppies, Repousse, Dec.20, 1901, 7 X 5 1/2 In.	38.00
Silver, Sterling, Dish, Candy, Repousse Decoration, Wavy Edge, 5 In.Diameter	35.00
Silver, Sterling, Dish, Candy, Rolled Edge, Repousse Floral, S.Kirk & Son	75.00
Silver, Sterling, Dish, Nut, Oval, International, C.1900	8.00
Silver, Sterling, Dish, Salt, Square, Gorham, 3 In.	10.00
Silver, Sterling, Dresser Set, Delft Inserts, 4 Piece	260.00
Silver, Sterling, Dresser Set, 6 Piece	70.00
Silver, Sterling, Figurine, English Bulldog, Standing, 3 X 4 1/2 In.	155.00
Silver, Sterling, Figurine, Irish Setter, Lying, 2 1/2 X 4 1/2 In.	150.00
Silver, Sterling, Figurine, Knight, Embossed, Ivory Face, Stones, 5 1/2 In.	140.00
Silver, Sterling, Figurine, Poodle, Sitting Up, 3 1/2 In.High	126.00
Silver, Sterling, Figurine, Sandpiper, 3 1/2 In.High	177.00
Silver, Sterling, Fish Slice, Cutout Fish & Stars Blade, Gale & Hayden	95.00
Silver, Sterling, Fish Slice, Openwork Blade, Wood & Hughes, 1863	75.00
Silver, Sterling, Flask, Art Nouveau, Woman & Cigarette, Unger Bros., 6 In.	250.00
Silver, Sterling, Flask, Gorham, Fish, Dragonfly, & Flora, C.1883, 4 1/2 In.	75.00
Silver, Sterling, Fork & Spoon, Salad Serving, Rustic, Towle, C.1895	60.00
Silver, Sterling, Fork, Meat Serving, Art Nouveau Floral, Wallace	30.00
Silver, Sterling, Fork, Serving, Engraved, Gold Washed, Gorham, 9 1/4 In.	30.00
Silver, Sterling, Fork, Serving, Flowers & Leaves, Gorham, 1896	9.95
Silver, Sterling, Fork, Similar To King's Pattern, John Walton, C.1846	10.00
Silver, Sterling, Hat, Mexican, "Pepsi Cola Convention, Mexico, 1967, " 11 In.	60.00
Silver, Sterling, Holder, Paper, Lion Holding Shield, Spring Type, Wing Mark	55.00
Silver, Sterling, Knife & Fork, Fruit, Female Mask Handles, Gorham, C.1870	60.00
Silver, Sterling, Knife, Butter Serving, Grape Design, Gordon & Co., C.1850	12.75
Silver, Sterling, Knife, Carving, Art Deco Design, George Jensen, C.1920	45.00
Silver, Sterling, Knife, Paper, Ivory Blade, Dominick & Haff, C.1900, 12 In.	90.00
Silver, Sterling, Knife, Paring, Violet, Hollow Handle, Wallace	18.00
Silver, Sterling, Label, Liquor, Brandy	27.50
Silver, Sterling, Label, Scotch, Stieff, With Chain, 1 X 2 In.	18.00
Silver, Sterling, Ladle, Antique Lily, Whiting, 1882, Betty On Back	50.00
Silver, Sterling, Ladle, Applied Gold & Copper Cherries, Gorham, C.1880	65.00
Silver, Sterling, Ladle, Gravy, Imperial Queen, Whiting, 1893	45.00
Silver, Sterling, Ladle, Sauce, Scrolled Handle, Gold Washed, Taylor, 1890	25.00
Silver, Sterling, Ladle, Soup, Feather Edging, Bruff, Maryland, C.1760	350.00
Silver, Sterling, Ladle, Spiral Leaf With Shell, Birmingham, 1885, 7 In.	65.00
Silver, Sterling, Match Safe, Bulldog, "Your Match"	68.00
Silver, Sterling, Match Safe, Fisherman	46.00
Silver, Sterling, Match Safe, Ornate Borders, Gorham	30.00
Silver, Sterling, Matchbox, Fish Scale, Hinged Top, Cartouche, Holland	35.00
Silver, Sterling, Mirror, Hand, Art Nouveau Woman's Head, Unger Bros.	85.00
Silver, Sterling, Mirror, Hand, Art Nouveau, Bride Of The Wave, Unger Bros.	95.00
Silver, Sterling, Muffineer, Urn Shape On Round Base, S.Kirk & Son, C.1910	58.00
Silver, Sterling, Mug, Child's, Chased & Embossed, Floral & Bird, Gorham	85.00
Silver, Sterling, Napkin Ring, see Napkin Ring	
Silver, Sterling, Paper Clip, 3 Scalloped Triangle, 1911, Howard, N.Y., 3 In.	45.00
Silver, Sterling, Pick, Nut, Ornate, Victorian	16.00
Silver, Sterling, Pitcher, Initials S.A., Gorham, Pint, 4 1/2 In.	150.00
Silver, Sterling, Pitcher, Water, Repousse, Whiting, 7 1/4 In.	550.00
Silver, Sterling, Porringer, Child's, Handleless, Nursery Scenes, 4 X 2 In.	55.00
Silver, Sterling, Purse, Evening, Mesh, Gilt, Unger Bros., C.1900	250.00
Silver, Sterling, Purse, Mesh, 5 Flowing Haired Women's Heads, Chain	135.00
Silver, Sterling, Rattle, Baby Head With Bonnet, Mother-Of-Pearl Handle	85.00
Silver, Sterling, Ring Tree, English, Hallmarked, Embossed Floral Designs	50.00
Silver, Sterling, Salt & Spoon, Cobalt Enamel, Danish	10.00
Silver, Sterling, Salt, Beaded Edge, 3 Shell Feet, Gold Wash, Harris, 1877	22.50
Silver, Sterling, Server, Cake, Engraved, Gold Washed, Gorham, 12 In.	30.00
Silver, Sterling, Server, Fish, Twisted Handle Center, Shaw, Texas	65.00
Silver, Sterling, Server, Pie, Gladstone, Amston, C.1890	50.00
Silver, Sterling, Shears, Grape, Repousse Figural Of Boy & Girl	38.00

Silver, Sterling, Shell, Sugar, Bright Cut, Oval Bowl, Albert Cole	20.00
Silver, Sterling, Spoon, Berry, Rope Twist Handle, Floral, Gold Washed, Gorham	60.00
Silver, Sterling, Spoon, Bonbon, Heart Shape, Baltimore, Schofield, 4 In.	25.00
Silver, Sterling, Spoon, Bonbon, Marked R.W.& S., 1910	13.00
Silver, Sterling, Spoon, Caddy, Leaf Shape, Trefoil Handle, Germany, C.1820	10.00
Silver, Sterling, Spoon, Demitasse, Gorham, Dated June 3, 1902	8.00
Silver, Sterling, Spoon, Dessert, Strasbourg, Gorham	14.00
Silver, Sterling, Spoon, Mote, Twisted Handle, Sharp, Phila., Bailey & Co.	25.00
Silver, Sterling, Spoon, Platter, Medallion, Wood & Hughes, 8 1/2 In.	45.00
Silver, Sterling, Spoon, Serving, Holding Tureen Handle, Gorham	38.00
Silver, Sterling, Spoon, Serving, Crescent, Knowles, Victorian	17.00
Silver, Sterling, Spoon, Serving, Engraved Pineapple, Gold Wash, Kennard	35.00
Silver, Sterling, Spoon, Serving, Gold & Copper Cherries, Gorham, C.1880	65.00
Silver, Sterling, Spoon, Serving, Henry VIII Figural Handle, Starr, 1875	85.00
Silver, Sterling, Spoon, Serving, Luxembourg, Gorham, C.1890	28.50
Silver, Sterling, Spoon, Serving, Marlborough, Heart Shape, R.& B., C.1906	23.00
Silver, Sterling, Spoon, Serving, Pineapple Engraving, Bigelow Kennard, 9 In.	35.00
Silver, Sterling, Spoon, Serving, Roses & Leaves Handle, A.Stowell & Co.	16.00
Silver, Sterling, Spoon, Souvenir, see Souvenir, Spoon, Sterling	
Silver, Sterling, Spreader, Butter, Coventry, I.S.& Co., 1916	2.75
Silver, Sterling, Stand, Floral, Footed, Cole, N.Y.C., C.1863, Oval, 10 1/2 In.	95.00
Silver, Sterling, Stick File, Lady's Desk, Initials, Black, Starr & Frost	9.50
Silver, Sterling, Sugar & Creamer, Demitasse, Bailey, Banks & Biddle, 1909	38.00
Silver, Sterling, Sugar & Creamer, Shreve, Crump & Low	45.00
Silver, Sterling, Tablespoon Hinged To Teaspoon, Metcalf Co., N.Y.	25.00
Silver, Sterling, Tablespoon, Armor, Whiting, 1871, Pair	30.00
Silver, Sterling, Tablespoon, Bead Pattern, Whiting, Pair	28.00
Silver, Sterling, Tablespoon, Florentine, Alvin	17.50
Silver, Sterling, Tablespoon, King's Pattern, Dom & Haff, 1905	16.00
Silver, Sterling, Tazza, Pierced, Berry & Whitmore, 5 In.	40.00
Silver, Sterling, Tea Ball, Acorn Shape, Black, Starr & Frost	40.00
Silver, Sterling, Tea Ball, Plump Strawberry Shape, Raised Leaf, Paye-Baker	75.00
Silver, Sterling, Tea Ball, Shape Of Witch's Kettle, Raised Design	35.00
Silver, Sterling, Tea Ball, Shaped Like Covered Teapot	35.00
Silver, Sterling, Tea Caddy, Repousse, Howard & Co., Patent 1895, 4 1/2 In.	80.00
Silver, Sterling, Tea Egg, English, Locks Closed With Pin On Chain, 1889	19.00
Silver, Sterling, Tea Set, Art Nouveau Design, Wallace, 1864, 3 Piece	210.00
Silver, Sterling, Teaspoon, Birth Record, Figural Stork	22.00
Silver, Sterling, Teaspoon, Gorham, R.I., Patent 1861	8.25
Silver, Sterling, Teaspoon, U.S.A. For Belgium World War I Relief	8.50
Silver, Sterling, Teaspoon, 5 O'Clock, Victorian, Scrollwork, 1870, 12	68.00
Silver, Sterling, Thimble, see Sewing Tool, Thimble, Sterling	
Silver, Sterling, Tongs, Roses, Gorham, 4 1/8 In.	9.95
Silver, Sterling, Tongs, Sugar, Claw Handles, Bancroft Bros.	9.00
Silver, Sterling, Tongs, Sugar, Openwork Arms, S.Kirk & Son	48.00
Silver, Sterling, Tongs, Tea, Ivy, Gorham, 1868, Initials E.F., 6 1/2 In.	22.50
Silver, Sterling, Toothpick & Connecting Salt & Pepper, Marked GHF	22.50
Silver, Sterling, Traveling Set, Man's, Leather Case, International, 3 Piece	35.00
Silver, Sterling, Tray, Footed, Engraved BBS, Gorham, 1893, 7 In.	85.00
Silver, Sterling, Tray, Raised Figures Scene, London, 1925, 5 In.	29.00
Silver, Sterling, Vase, Art Nouveau, Narcissus, Handles, C.1900, Towle, 7 In.	245.00
Silver, Sterling, Vase, Repousse, Florals, Black, Starr & Frost, C.1880, 8 In.	210.00
Silver, Swedish, Tablespoon, Oval, C.1858	35.00
Silver, Venetian, Tablespoon, Pointed Handle, C.1837, Pair	38.00
Silver, Viennese, Cutter, Cigar, Horn, Elk's Head, Red Eyes, C.1890	135.00
Silver, West Indian, Ladle, Soup, Old English, I.Burke, St.Kitts, C.1880	300.00

Sinclaire cut glass was made by H.P.Sinclaire and Company of Corning, New York, between 1905 and 1929. Pieces were made of crystal as well as amber, blue, green, or ruby. Only a small percentage of Sinclaire glass is marked.

Sinclaire, Bowl, Engraved Fern & Floral, 9 X 4 In.	135.00
Sinclaire, Bowl, Salad, Amethyst, Marked With S In Wreath, 8 In.	75.00
Sinclaire, Plate, Amethyst, Marked With S In Wreath, 8 In.	75.00

Slag glass is streaked with several colors. There were many types made from about 1880. Pink slag was an American Victorian product of unknown origin. Purple and blue slag were made in American and English factories. Red slag is a very late Victorian product. Other colors are known, but are of less importance to the collector. The letters B-xx refer to the book "Milk Glass" by E.Belknap.

Slag, Blue, Compote, Jelly, Fern & Coral Bowl, Stippled Base, 4 1/2 In.High	35.00
Slag, Blue, Plate, Basket Weave, English, Sowerby Mark, 8 7/8 In.	20.00
Slag, Blue, Salt, Kettle Shape, Sowerby Marked, Dated Sept.18, 1877	50.00
Slag, Butterscotch, Spooner, Swan Handles	95.00
Slag, Caramel, see Chocolate Glass	
Slag, Green, Cachepot, Relief Plants On Sides, 6 1/2 In.	70.00
Slag, Green, Cake Stand, Waffle, High Standard, Atterbury, 10 In.	135.00
Slag, Green, Jardiniere, Straight Sides, Relief Flowers, 6 1/4 X 6 1/2 In.	85.00
Slag, Lavender, Saltshaker, Oval & Fan	32.00
Slag, Pink, Jar, Jam, Inverted Fan & Feather	1000.00
Slag, Pink, Toothpick, 4 White Ball Feet, Scalloped Top, 2 In.	350.00
Slag, Pink, Tumbler .... *Illus*	250.00
Slag, Purple, Bowl, Dart & Bar, Diamond Frieze, C.1850, 5 3/4 In., Set Of 4	90.00
Slag, Purple, Bowl, Fruit, Acanthus, Atterbury, 9 1/2 In.	82.50
Slag, Purple, Bowl, Fruit, Melon, Atterbury, 9 1/2 In.	82.50
Slag, Purple, Bowl, Raindrop, Flint	90.00
Slag, Purple, Bowl, Ruffled, Footed, B-297a	40.00
Slag, Purple, Butter, Covered	38.50 To 145.00
Slag, Purple, Cake Stand, Dart & Bar	90.00
Slag, Purple, Cake Stand, Ringed Foot, 9 In.	100.00
Slag, Purple, Candlestick, Reeded Columnar Standard, C.1850, 8 1/2 In., Pair	175.00
Slag, Purple, Candlestick, Three Dolphins On Base, English, Pair	135.00
Slag, Purple, Celery, American, C.1850 .... *Illus*	100.00
Slag, Purple, Celery, Fluted	85.00
Slag, Purple, Celery, Jeweled, B-295b	55.00
Slag, Purple, Celery, 8 1/4 In.High	95.00
Slag, Purple, Compote, Covered, 8 1/2 X 8 In.	100.00
Slag, Purple, Compote, Jelly, Davidson Marked, Flint	55.00
Slag, Purple, Compote, Open, Dart Bar, High Standard, 8 1/4 X 8 1/2 In.	60.00
Slag, Purple, Creamer, Fish Shape, Dated Nov.24, 1882	135.00
Slag, Purple, Creamer, Mosaic, 4 In., B-296c	20.00
Slag, Purple, Creamer, Sunflower, B-31	38.50
Slag, Purple, Cup & Saucer, Demitasse, Signed	45.00
Slag, Purple, Dish, Candy, Crimped Edge, Flint	23.00
Slag, Purple, Dish, Candy, Low, Ruffled Edge	55.00
Slag, Purple, Dish, Hen Cover, Basket Weave Base, 4 In.	225.00
Slag, Purple, Dish, Hen Cover, White Head	275.00
Slag, Purple, Dish, Salt, Fish Shape, Cockleshell, C.1850, Pair	80.00
Slag, Purple, Goblet, Twig Foot	75.00

Slag, Pink, Tumbler

Slag, Purple, Celery,
American, C.1850

Slag, Purple, Inkwell	25.00
Slag, Purple, Match Holder, Footed, Straight Sided, 3 3/4 In.	26.65
Slag, Purple, Match Holder, Square, 4 In.	30.00
Slag, Purple, Mug, Embossed Nesting Birds, Cat On Bottom	45.00
Slag, Purple, Mug, Handled, Grapes	25.00
Slag, Purple, Pitcher, Water, Flower & Panel	170.00
Slag, Purple, Pitcher, Water, Raindrop	225.00
Slag, Purple, Plate, Closed Lattice Edge, 10 1/2 In.	80.00
Slag, Purple, Plate, English, Open Edge, Sowerby Mark, 8 In.	65.00
Slag, Purple, Plate, Open Edge, Basket Weave Design, 8 In.	45.00
Slag, Purple, Plate, Open Edge, 10 In.	65.00 To 86.00
Slag, Purple, Platter, Notched Border, Pebble Cavetto, C.1850, 13 In., Pair	80.00
Slag, Purple, Platter, Open Edge, B-291b	85.00
Slag, Purple, Relish, English, Double, Open Handles	55.00
Slag, Purple, Salt & Pepper, Beaded Oval Motif On Four Sides	75.00
Slag, Purple, Salt, Scalloped Edge, Floral Design	32.00
Slag, Purple, Saltshaker, Seashell	30.00 To 40.00
Slag, Purple, Sauce, 3 Swans Around Sides, 5 In.	35.00
Slag, Purple, Shot Glass, "Just A Thimble Full"	35.00
Slag, Purple, Shot Glass, "Just A Thimble Full, " Beaded, 2 1/2 In.	75.00
Slag, Purple, Shot Glass, "Just A Thimble Full, " Embossed, Raindrop	45.00
Slag, Purple, Spooner, Oval Medallion	80.00
Slag, Purple, Spooner, Scroll With Acanthus	38.00
Slag, Purple, Sugar & Creamer, English, Sowerby Mark	95.00
Slag, Purple, Sugar & Creamer, Holly Design, B-288b-C	95.00
Slag, Purple, Sugar, Flower Bands, Footed, 4 In. Diameter At Top	22.00
Slag, Purple, Toothpick, Bushel Basket Shape, 2 Handles, 2 X 2 1/2 In.	37.50
Slag, Purple, Toothpick, Scroll With Acanthus, Northwood, C.1885	55.00
Slag, Purple, Toothpick, Scrolled Rim, 3 Handles, 1877 Registry Mark, 3 In.	34.00
Slag, Purple, Tumbler, Davidson Marked, Says Half Pint On Base, B-319-290	43.00
Slag, Purple, Tumbler, Sowerby Mark, 3 1/2 In., B-319-290F	48.00
Slag, Purple, Tumbler, Whiskey, Ten Panel, Sowerby, 3 In.	40.00
Slag, Purple, Vase, English, Ring & Flower, Cylindrical, 6 In., Pair	130.00
Slag, Purple, Vase, Grapes, Leaves & Vines Intertwined, Leaf Base, 5 3/4 In.	95.00
Slag, Purple, Vase, Oriental Figures, Square, Sowerby, 5 In.	68.00
Slag, Purple, Vase, Paneled Flower, 4 X 4 1/4 In.	30.00
Slag, Purple, Vase, Tulip Shape, Leaf Pedestal, 6 1/4 In.	42.00
Slag, Red & Turquoise, Butter, Flying Swan	150.00
Slag, Red, Bowl, 2 X 8 1/2 In.	35.00
Slag, Red, Compote, Fenton, 8 1/2 In.	50.00

Sleepy Eye pottery was made to be given away with the flour products of the
Sleepy Eye Milling Co., Sleepy Eye, Minnesota, from about 1893 to
1952. It is a heavy stoneware with blue decorations, usually the famous
profile of an Indian.

Sleepy Eye, Pitcher, Cobalt & White, Blue Rim, 5 1/2 In.	60.00
Sleepy Eye, Pitcher, Cobalt & White, Diamond Mark, 8 In.	85.00
Sleepy Eye, Pitcher, Cobalt & White, 4 1/2 In.	59.50
Sleepy Eye, Pitcher, 5 1/2 In.	40.00
Sleepy Eye, Pitcher, 6 1/2 In.	60.00
Sleepy Eye, Vase, 8 In.	85.00
Sleepy Eye, Vase, 9 In.	95.00

Slip is a thin mixture of clay and water, about the consistency of sour cream,
that is applied to the pottery for decoration. If the pottery is made with
red clay, the slip is mixed with yellow clay.

Slipware, Barrel, Spirit, Redware, Cream Slip, Chailey, Sussex, 1791, 4 In.	85.00
Slipware, Bowl, Pennsylvania, C.1750, Yellow On Brick Red, 13 1/4 In.	200.00
Slipware, Bowl, Red, Black Splotched, 7 1/4 In.	150.00
Slipware, Box, Money, Dovecote, Brown Spots On Buff, C.1850, 6 1/2 In.	200.00
Slipware, Charger, Tulips, Brown Glaze, Octagonal, C.1790, 14 1/4 In.	375.00
Slipware, Cradle, Redware, Birds, Brown & Ocher, C.1850, 10 3/4 In.	400.00
Slipware, Dish, Baking, Pennsylvania, C.1790, Yellow On Brown, 13 1/2 In.	825.00
Slipware, Dish, Baking, Redware, Cream Slip, Honey Glaze, C.1750, 13 1/2 In.	200.00
Slipware, Dish, Baking, White Bird & Zigzags, Piecrust Rim, 1794, 15 1/4 In.	250.00
Slipware, Jug, Redware, Sgraffito, Clear Peacocks, Ilminster, 1809, 10 In.	275.00

Slipware, Jug, Redware, White Bird In Flight, C.1770, 5 3/4 In.	
Slipware, Mug, Owl, Cover Forms Cup, Brown Slip, Scroll Handle, 7 3/4 In.	130.00
Slipware, Plate, Angleworms, Red, 7 In.Diameter	250.00
Slipware, Plate, Pie, New England, C.1820, Yellow On Brick Red, 11 7/8 In.	100.00
Slipware, Whistle, Redware, White Slip, Manganese Glaze, C.1850, 9 3/4 In.	600.00
	60.00

Smith Brothers glass was made after 1878. The owners had worked for the Mt.Washington Glass Company in New Bedford, Massachusetts, for seven years before going into their own shop. Some of the designs were similar.

Smith Brothers, Bowl, Cream Satin, Easter Greetings In Gold, 4 In.	90.00
Smith Brothers, Bowl, Finger, Floral, 2 Handled Silver Plate Holder	125.00
Smith Brothers, Creamer, Contrasting Colors In Pansies, Rampant Lion Mark	225.00
Smith Brothers, Dish, Sweetmeat, Raised Gold & Enamel On Pansies, Signed	275.00
Smith Brothers, Jar, Biscuit, Satin Finish, Shasta Daisies, Silver Lid, 7 In.	225.00
Smith Brothers, Jar, Blue To White, Melon Ribbed, Floral, Covered, 5 1/4 In.	195.00
Smith Brothers, Jar, Cookie, Biscuit, Melon Ribbed, Water Lilies & Leaves	375.00
Smith Brothers, Jar, Cookie, Melon Ribbed, Gold Outlined Acorns & Leaves	395.00
Smith Brothers, Jar, Cookie, Rampant Lion, Pansy Decoration, Silver Lid	195.00
Smith Brothers, Jar, Covered, Biscuit Color, Melon Ribbed, Floral, 3 3/4 In.	285.00
Smith Brothers, Jar, Covered, Melon Ribbed, Floral Decoration, 4 In.	150.00
Smith Brothers, Jar, Covered, Melon Shaped, Floral Design, 3 1/2 X 5 1/2 In.	295.00
Smith Brothers, Jar, Cracker, Blue Wisteria On Cream, Rampant Lion Signed	375.00
Smith Brothers, Jar, Cracker, White, Floral, Silver Bail & Lid, 7 1/2 In.	125.00
Smith Brothers, Jar, Cracker, Wisteria Decoration	400.00
Smith Brothers, Jar, Melon Ribbed, Biscuit Body, Pansies & Leaves, 3 3/4 In.	285.00
Smith Brothers, Jar, Ribbed, Daisies, Rampant Lion Signature, 4 In.	155.00
Smith Brothers, Muffineer, Green To White, Wine Colored Lilies, Glossy	125.00
Smith Brothers, Muffineer, Urn Shape, Blue Acid, Pink & White Daisies	165.00
Smith Brothers, Salt, Egg Shape, Lay Down	35.00
Smith Brothers, Toothpick, Vertical Ribs, Enamel Dots At Top, Floral	90.00
Smith Brothers, Vase, Cylindrical, Enameled Stork, Pink, 4 1/2 In.High	75.00
Smith Brothers, Vase, Gold, Mottled, Red & Yellow Roses, 8 1/2 In.	265.00
Smith Brothers, Vase, Milk Glass, Green, Bird On Branch, 8 1/4 In.High	50.00
Snow Baby, German Porcelain, Arms Outstretched, 2 1/4 In.	22.50
Snow Baby, Sitting, Legs Bent, 2 1/2 In.	65.00
Snow Baby, Standing, 2 1/4 In.	35.00
Snuff Bottle, see Bottle, Snuff	
Snuffbox, Birch, Hinged, Oval Mother-Of-Pearl Inset, 4 1/4 X 1 X 2 1/2 In.	35.00
Snuffbox, Brass, Shaped Like Book, Tin Lined, C.1780, 4 X 2 3/4 In.	110.00
Snuffbox, Lacquer, Black, Tortoiseshell Lid, 3 1/2 X 1 3/4 X 1 In.	36.00
Snuffbox, Mother-Of-Pearl, Egg Shape, Chain Handle	18.00
Snuffbox, Stewart Plaid, White Figure, Round	18.00
Snuffbox, Tan & Gray Agate, Bronze Dore Sides, C.1840, 1 3/4 X 1 In.	95.00

Soapstone is a mineral that was used for foot warmers or griddles because of its heat-retaining properties. Chinese soapstone carvings of the nineteenth and twentieth centuries are found in many antique shops.

Soapstone, Bookend, Carved Urns & Flowers, 4 1/2 In., Pair	32.50
Soapstone, Bookend, Vase With Flowering Plant, 4 X 5 In., Pair	22.50
Soapstone, Carving, Grape Cluster, Rose Red & Rose Beige, 5 1/2 X 4 In.	45.00
Soapstone, Cup, Wine, Chinese, Recessed Foot Rim, Gray Green, 2 1/4 In.	10.00
Soapstone, Figurine, Elephant, Raised Trunk, Marked China, 2 3/4 In.	21.00
Soapstone, Figurine, Foo Dog, Red, 5 In.	80.00
Soapstone, Figurine, Jovial Buddha, White, Black & Gray Base, 3 1/4 In.	25.00
Soapstone, Figurine, Lion, 3 In.	6.50
Soapstone, Figurine, Man With Foot On Dog, Carved, 5 1/2 In.	75.00
Soapstone, Figurine, War Lord, Carved, Pedestal, 12 In.	35.00
Soapstone, Group, Woman & Man, Carved, Beige, 7 1/2 In.	75.00
Soapstone, Match Holder, Monkey Feeding Bird, Floral, 3 In.	30.00
Soapstone, Vase, Blacks, Browns, & Beige, Birds & Floral, 7 X 10 In.	40.00
Soapstone, Vase, Double, Floral & Leaves Between Vases & Base, 5 3/4 In.	25.00
Soapstone, Vase, Double, Flowers In Center, Caramel Color, 4 In.	17.50
Soapstone, Vase, Double, Green To Rust, 4 X 6 X 9 In.	48.00
Soapstone, Vase, Double, Light Gray, Carved Floral, 5 X 8 In.	30.00
Soapstone, Vase, Floral Carved Dark Brown To Tan At Top, 12 In.	75.00

Soft Paste, Bowl & Plate,
Single Rose, C.1820

Soft Paste, Teapot, Strawberry,
C.1820, 5 5/8 In.

Soapstone, Vase, Floral Carved Gray To Light Rust, 3 1/2 X 4 In.	10.00
Soapstone, Vase, Floral Carved Gray To Rust, 3 X 3 In.	7.50
Soapstone, Vase, Flowers On Side, 6 In.High	35.00
Soapstone, Vase, Light Rust Carved Floral, 4 1/2 X 4 1/2 In.	25.00
Soapstone, Whistle, Figural, Fish, Carved *Illus*	8.50
Soft Paste, Bowl & Plate, Single Rose, C.1820 *Illus*	325.00
Soft Paste, Dinner Set, Blue Butterflies, Miniature, 50 Piece	500.00
Soft Paste, Gravy Boat, Strawberry, Pink Luster	75.00
Soft Paste, Mug, Child's, Blue & White, "Blind Man's Buff, " 2 1/2 In.	38.00
Soft Paste, Plate, Blue, Milk Maid, 7 1/2 In.	18.00
Soft Paste, Plate, Country Scene Transfer, Polychrome Rim, 6 1/2 In.	98.00
Soft Paste, Plate, Strawberry, 6 1/4 In.	150.00
Soft Paste, Plate, Strawberry, 8 1/4 In.	195.00
Soft Paste, Teabowl & Drinking Saucer, Strawberry, Handleless *Illus*	130.00
Soft Paste, Teapot, Strawberry, C.1820, 5 5/8 In. *Illus*	400.00
Souvenir, Ashtray, Chicago World's Fair, Brass	5.00
Souvenir, Ashtray, New Orleans, Held By Scotties, Metal	6.00
Souvenir, Bathtub, Black Amethyst, Basin, Wyoming, Gold Edge	8.00
Souvenir, Binoculars, St.Louis Exposition, 1904, 2 Views	20.00
Souvenir, Bookmark, Sterling, Embossed Mountain Sheep, Rocky Mountain Park	5.00
Souvenir, Bowl, Des Moines, Ia., RCA Dog & Horn On Edge, Germany, 4 In.	6.50
Souvenir, Creamer, Grove City, Minn., Hand-Painted	3.75
Souvenir, Creamer, Mother, Pressed Glass, Colorado, Green, Gold Trim, 5 1/4 In	20.00
Souvenir, Creamer, Revere Beach, 1905, Pressed Glass, Colorado, Green, Gold	24.50
Souvenir, Creamer, Wildwood, 1904, Red & Clear	17.50
Souvenir, Dish, Bone, Chicago Exposition, 1893, Brown Border	7.00
Souvenir, Dish, Lookout Inn, Lookout Mountain, Tenn., Square, 5 In.	2.95
Souvenir, Dish, Nut, Old Memorial Hall & Library, Lancaster, Mass., England	7.00
Souvenir, Hand, Frosted, World's Columbian Exposition, 1893, Libbey	35.00
Souvenir, Knife, Sterling Silver, Home Insurance, N.Y.	18.00
Souvenir, Letter Opener, Wood, Indian Head, Santa Fe, New Mexico	9.00
Souvenir, Lighter, Cigarette, Camel, Dearborn Village, Chicago, 1893 Fair	17.50
Souvenir, Match Holder, Gadsden, Ala., Ruby & Clear, Heart Design	15.00
Souvenir, Mug, In Fond Remembrance, Pressed Glass, Rose In Snow	16.00
Souvenir, Mug, Lake Webb, Weld, Maine, Purple, 2 1/2 In.	12.00
Souvenir, Mug, Logan, O., Pressed Glass, Beaded Swirl, Blue, Gold Beading	15.00
Souvenir, Mug, Neenah, Wis., Electric Blue, 2 3/4 X 2 7/8 In.	16.50
Souvenir, Mug, New Orleans, La., Robert E.Lee Monument	7.95
Souvenir, Mug, Newark, N.J., Flashed Ruby, 2 1/2 In.	15.00
Souvenir, Mug, Princeton, Figural Football, 1905	75.00
Souvenir, Mug, San Antonio, Texas, Ruby Flashed	14.00
Souvenir, Mug, University Of Pennsylvania, Figural Football, 1905	75.00
Souvenir, Mug, Westfield, Wis., Pressed Glass, Colorado, Green, Miniature	14.00
Souvenir, Mug, World's Fair, 1904, Ruby Flashed	15.00
Souvenir, Mug, 1910, Ruby & Clear, Heart Design	15.00
Souvenir, Pincushion, New York, Shoe, Occupied Japan	12.00

Souvenir, Plate, Alaska-Yukon-Pacific Exposition, 1909, German, 10 In.	42.00
Souvenir, Plate, Avalon Bay, Catalina Island, Calif., Hand-Painted, 6 1/4 In.	4.75
Souvenir, Plate, Blackpool, Fruit, Gilt Openwork Border, 8 In.	7.00
Souvenir, Plate, Duquesne, Comandery No.72, Pittsburgh, Open Edge, 5 1/2 In.	8.00
Souvenir, Plate, Natural Bridge, Va., Hand-Painted, 7 In.	4.75
Souvenir, Plate, Porcelain, Providence, R.I., Union Depot, Blue & White, 8 In.	8.00
Souvenir, Plate, President McKinley, Porcelain, 8 In.	25.00
Souvenir, Plate, Prospect Point, Niagara Falls, Gold Trim, 9 3/4 In.	13.00
Souvenir, Relish, Lillie, Pressed Glass, Daisy & Button	12.50
Souvenir, Salt & Pepper, Gloucester, Mass., Negro	5.00
Souvenir, Saltshaker, Columbian Exposition, 1893, Egg On End, Gold	48.00
Souvenir, Sauce, North Dakota, Blue & Gold, China	2.00
Souvenir, Spoon, A Present From A Friend, Metal, Mother-Of-Pearl Bowl	7.50
Souvenir, Spoon, Amsterdam, Holland, Buildings, Silver Plate, Demitasse	4.00
Souvenir, Spoon, California, Silver Plate	4.00
Souvenir, Spoon, Coin Silver, Columbian Exposition, 1892, Demitasse	7.50
Souvenir, Spoon, Colorado Mountains & Mules	14.00
Souvenir, Spoon, Copper, Crafts Exposition, L.A., Indian Handle	12.50
Souvenir, Spoon, Copper, Michigan College Of Mines, Houghton	6.50
Souvenir, Spoon, English Silver, Glastonbury Abbey, Enamel, 1900	8.00
Souvenir, Spoon, Illinois, Silver Plate	4.00
Souvenir, Spoon, Indian Chief Calumet, Nickel Silver	8.00
Souvenir, Spoon, Iowa, Silver Plate	4.00
Souvenir, Spoon, Mexican Silver, Tijuana, Coin Finial, Demitasse	7.00
Souvenir, Spoon, Minnesota, Silver Plate	4.00
Souvenir, Spoon, Missouri, Silver Plate	7.00
Souvenir, Spoon, New Hampshire, Rogers, 1881	3.75
Souvenir, Spoon, New Mexico, Silver Plate	4.00
Souvenir, Spoon, New York, Silver Plate	4.00
Souvenir, Spoon, Pennsylvania, Silver Plate	4.00
Souvenir, Spoon, Silver Plate, Century Of Progress, 1933	6.00
Souvenir, Spoon, Silver Plate, Chicago World's Fair, 1933, Administration	6.00
Souvenir, Spoon, Silver Plate, Chicago World's Fair, 1933, Science Court	6.00
Souvenir, Spoon, Silver Plate, Columbian Exposition, 1892	4.50
Souvenir, Spoon, Silver Plate, New York World's Fair, 1939, Theme Building	7.50
Souvenir, Spoon, Sterling Silver, Alaska, State Seal, Scenes, Jos.Mayer	23.00
Souvenir, Spoon, Sterling Silver, Albert Lee, Minnesota In Bowl, Holly	12.75
Souvenir, Spoon, Sterling Silver, Albion College, Girl Graduate Handle	20.00
Souvenir, Spoon, Sterling Silver, Alma Mater	33.50
Souvenir, Spoon, Sterling Silver, American Indian, Bow & Tomahawk, Demitasse	12.00
Souvenir, Spoon, Sterling Silver, Atlantic City, Demitasse	10.00
Souvenir, Spoon, Sterling Silver, BPOE, Watertown, S.D., Cutout Elk	15.00
Souvenir, Spoon, Sterling Silver, Babylon, Demitasse	10.00
Souvenir, Spoon, Sterling Silver, Balance Rock	7.00
Souvenir, Spoon, Sterling Silver, Battleship Maine, Demitasse	10.00
Souvenir, Spoon, Sterling Silver, Bellows Falls, Vt., 1902	9.95
Souvenir, Spoon, Sterling Silver, Berlin, Demitasse	10.00
Souvenir, Spoon, Sterling Silver, Bessie	16.00
Souvenir, Spoon, Sterling Silver, Birmingham, Pictures	10.00
Souvenir, Spoon, Sterling Silver, Boerenherberg, Embossed Tavern, Nut	20.00
Souvenir, Spoon, Sterling Silver, Boston	12.00
Souvenir, Spoon, Sterling Silver, Boston, Demitasse	5.95 To 15.00
Souvenir, Spoon, Sterling Silver, Boston, The Hub On Handle, Pot Of Beans	17.00
Souvenir, Spoon, Sterling Silver, Brighton, British Royal Arms, Demitasse	4.95
Souvenir, Spoon, Sterling Silver, Brooklyn Bridge, N.Y.	7.00 To 16.00
Souvenir, Spoon, Sterling Silver, Buffalo, Figural Buffalo	14.00
Souvenir, Spoon, Sterling Silver, Buffalo, N.Y., Demitasse	8.00 To 10.50
Souvenir, Spoon, Sterling Silver, Burgett Park, Demitasse, Gold Bowl	8.00
Souvenir, Spoon, Sterling Silver, CB & Q RRY Shops, Havelock, Neb.	8.00
Souvenir, Spoon, Sterling Silver, California Miner, "Delta"	25.00
Souvenir, Spoon, Sterling Silver, Capital, Washington, D.C., Library	9.95
Souvenir, Spoon, Sterling Silver, Capital, Washington, D.C., Treasury	9.95
Souvenir, Spoon, Sterling Silver, Capitol, Richmond, Negro Head	14.00
Souvenir, Spoon, Sterling Silver, Capitol, Richmond, Va., Demitasse	7.95
Souvenir, Spoon, Sterling Silver, Capitol, Washington, D.C.	16.00
Souvenir, Spoon, Sterling Silver, Carthage, Mo. Courthouse, Missouri Seal	18.00

Souvenir, Spoon, Sterling Silver, Chicago	7.00 To 12.50
Souvenir, Spoon, Sterling Silver, Chicago, Bust Of Indian	10.00
Souvenir, Spoon, Sterling Silver, Chicago, Mar.4, 1837	15.00
Souvenir, Spoon, Sterling Silver, Chief Seattle, Totem Pole, Demitasse	15.00
Souvenir, Spoon, Sterling Silver, Cincinnati	16.00
Souvenir, Spoon, Sterling Silver, Cincinnati, Tyler A.Davidson Fountain	30.00
Souvenir, Spoon, Sterling Silver, City Of Baltimore, Monument	12.50
Souvenir, Spoon, Sterling Silver, College Boy, Figural	28.00
Souvenir, Spoon, Sterling Silver, College Girl, Figural	28.00
Souvenir, Spoon, Sterling Silver, Columbian Exposition	16.00
Souvenir, Spoon, Sterling Silver, Columbian Exposition, 1893, Demitasse	11.00
Souvenir, Spoon, Sterling Silver, Columbine, Demitasse	6.00
Souvenir, Spoon, Sterling Silver, County Court House, Danbury, Conn.	11.00
Souvenir, Spoon, Sterling Silver, Court House, Duluth	7.50
Souvenir, Spoon, Sterling Silver, Daisy, Demitasse	6.00
Souvenir, Spoon, Sterling Silver, Dallas, Texas, Enameled Bowl	45.00
Souvenir, Spoon, Sterling Silver, Daytona, Fla., Palm Tree On Handle	9.95
Souvenir, Spoon, Sterling Silver, December, Holly	20.00
Souvenir, Spoon, Sterling Silver, Delaware Water Gap, Pa., Indian Handle	22.00
Souvenir, Spoon, Sterling Silver, Delaware, 4 1/4 In.	10.00
Souvenir, Spoon, Sterling Silver, Denver, Colo., Burled Handle	12.00
Souvenir, Spoon, Sterling Silver, Detroit, Windsor, Indian Bust Handle, Small	7.95
Souvenir, Spoon, Sterling Silver, Dover, Twisted Handle, Demitasse	5.50
Souvenir, Spoon, Sterling Silver, Duluth	11.00
Souvenir, Spoon, Sterling Silver, Duray, Colorado, Demitasse	10.00
Souvenir, Spoon, Sterling Silver, Eads Jetty, New Orleans	24.00
Souvenir, Spoon, Sterling Silver, Easter, Chick End, Demitasse	30.00
Souvenir, Spoon, Sterling Silver, Elk	22.50
Souvenir, Spoon, Sterling Silver, Elka Park	16.00
Souvenir, Spoon, Sterling Silver, Elyria, Ohio, Lion, Anchor & G Marks	8.95
Souvenir, Spoon, Sterling Silver, Everett, Wash., Demitasse	8.00
Souvenir, Spoon, Sterling Silver, Excelsior Springs, Mo.	10.00
Souvenir, Spoon, Sterling Silver, Fernbank Lock & Dam, Cinn.	9.95
Souvenir, Spoon, Sterling Silver, Florida, Cutout Palm Tree Handle	9.95
Souvenir, Spoon, Sterling Silver, Flower Of The Month, August, Tea Size	15.00
Souvenir, Spoon, Sterling Silver, Fort Dearborn, Chicago, 1808-57, Demitasse	10.50
Souvenir, Spoon, Sterling Silver, Fort Dearborn, Douglas Monument	9.95
Souvenir, Spoon, Sterling Silver, Fort Dearborn, Masonic Building, Teepee	15.00
Souvenir, Spoon, Sterling Silver, Fort Pitt In Bowl, Twisted Handle	20.00
Souvenir, Spoon, Sterling Silver, Fort Pitt, Figural Fort, Demitasse	9.00
Souvenir, Spoon, Sterling Silver, Fort Ticonderoga, Ethan Allen	13.00
Souvenir, Spoon, Sterling Silver, Fort Ticonderoga, 1775	22.50
Souvenir, Spoon, Sterling Silver, Fredonia, N.Y., Demitasse	7.00
Souvenir, Spoon, Sterling Silver, G.A.R., 1894	27.50
Souvenir, Spoon, Sterling Silver, General Miles, Camp Cuba Libre	30.00
Souvenir, Spoon, Sterling Silver, Georgia State, Terminal Station Bowl	24.00
Souvenir, Spoon, Sterling Silver, Girl Graduate, Full Figure	40.00
Souvenir, Spoon, Sterling Silver, Grand Canyon, Demitasse	7.00
Souvenir, Spoon, Sterling Silver, Grand Rapids, Wis.	12.00
Souvenir, Spoon, Sterling Silver, Grangeville, Colo., Western Girl	35.00
Souvenir, Spoon, Sterling Silver, Greater New York, Gold Washed Bowl	12.00
Souvenir, Spoon, Sterling Silver, Haskell In't, Indian's Head	18.00
Souvenir, Spoon, Sterling Silver, Hoover Cottage, Wooster, Ohio	12.00
Souvenir, Spoon, Sterling Silver, Hoover, 3 1/2 In.	5.00
Souvenir, Spoon, Sterling Silver, Hoover, 4 1/2 In.	7.00
Souvenir, Spoon, Sterling Silver, Horticultural Hall, Chicago, 1898	16.00
Souvenir, Spoon, Sterling Silver, Hotel Eastman, Hot Springs, Ark.	12.00
Souvenir, Spoon, Sterling Silver, Idaho, State Seal Finial, Engraved Bowl	16.50
Souvenir, Spoon, Sterling Silver, Illinois City Hall, Belleville	16.00
Souvenir, Spoon, Sterling Silver, Illinois, Eagle Top	16.50
Souvenir, Spoon, Sterling Silver, Indiana	16.00
Souvenir, Spoon, Sterling Silver, Jacksonville, Fla., Palm Trees, Alligator	9.95
Souvenir, Spoon, Sterling Silver, Jamestown Exposition, Figural Pocahontas	19.50
Souvenir, Spoon, Sterling Silver, January, Aquarius, Demitasse	7.00
Souvenir, Spoon, Sterling Silver, Kaiser, Wm.Der Crosse	16.00
Souvenir, Spoon, Sterling Silver, Kingston, N.Y., Peter Stuyvesant Figure	25.00

Souvenir, Spoon, Sterling Silver, Knickerbocker	24.50
Souvenir, Spoon, Sterling Silver, Knights Templars, Demitasse	12.50
Souvenir, Spoon, Sterling Silver, Laconia, N.H. High School	9.95
Souvenir, Spoon, Sterling Silver, Lake Champlain, Demitasse	7.95
Souvenir, Spoon, Sterling Silver, Lake Champlain, Indian's Head Top	7.95
Souvenir, Spoon, Sterling Silver, Landing Of Pilgrims	12.00
Souvenir, Spoon, Sterling Silver, Lawrence, Kansas, State University	9.95
Souvenir, Spoon, Sterling Silver, Lawton In Bowl, Indian Handle, Demitasse	12.00
Souvenir, Spoon, Sterling Silver, Lillian, Twisted Handle, Demitasse	8.00
Souvenir, Spoon, Sterling Silver, Log Cabin Handle	20.00
Souvenir, Spoon, Sterling Silver, Los Angeles	12.00
Souvenir, Spoon, Sterling Silver, Los Angeles, Angel Finial	22.50
Souvenir, Spoon, Sterling Silver, Los Angeles, Mt.Lowe R.R., Mission	9.95
Souvenir, Spoon, Sterling Silver, Louisville, Ky., Engraved Bowl, Demitasse	6.50
Souvenir, Spoon, Sterling Silver, Machinery Hall, Demitasse	10.00
Souvenir, Spoon, Sterling Silver, Maine, 4 1/4 In.	10.00
Souvenir, Spoon, Sterling Silver, Maryland, State Seal Finial, Demitasse	8.50
Souvenir, Spoon, Sterling Silver, Meadsville, Pa., 1892	12.00
Souvenir, Spoon, Sterling Silver, Memphis Skyline	42.00
Souvenir, Spoon, Sterling Silver, Miami, Fla.	9.00
Souvenir, Spoon, Sterling Silver, Miles City, Demitasse	8.00
Souvenir, Spoon, Sterling Silver, Minnehaha Falls, Christmas, Demitasse	15.50
Souvenir, Spoon, Sterling Silver, Missouri Mule, "I'm From Missouri"	12.00
Souvenir, Spoon, Sterling Silver, Missouri State, World's Fair, 1904	24.00
Souvenir, Spoon, Sterling Silver, Missouri, St.Joseph In Bowl	30.00
Souvenir, Spoon, Sterling Silver, Moll Pitcher, Figural, Witch & Cat	28.50
Souvenir, Spoon, Sterling Silver, Montana	8.00
Souvenir, Spoon, Sterling Silver, Montreal, Crown Finial, Bowl Scene	16.50
Souvenir, Spoon, Sterling Silver, Mt.Holy Cross, Demitasse	7.00
Souvenir, Spoon, Sterling Silver, Mt.Ranier, Everett, Wash., 1905, Demitasse	7.50
Souvenir, Spoon, Sterling Silver, Mt.Ranier, Seattle, Wash., Mayer Bros.	12.00
Souvenir, Spoon, Sterling Silver, Mt.Vernon	13.00
Souvenir, Spoon, Sterling Silver, Nebraska	8.00
Souvenir, Spoon, Sterling Silver, Negro Island, Camden, Me.	12.00
Souvenir, Spoon, Sterling Silver, New Castle, Pa., Demitasse	10.00
Souvenir, Spoon, Sterling Silver, New Orleans	8.00
Souvenir, Spoon, Sterling Silver, New York City Skyline, 1911	28.50 To 42.00
Souvenir, Spoon, Sterling Silver, New York World's Fair, 1939	12.00
Souvenir, Spoon, Sterling Silver, New York, Flatiron Building	20.00
Souvenir, Spoon, Sterling Silver, New York, Flatiron Building, Demitasse	7.50
Souvenir, Spoon, Sterling Silver, New York, Pan American Exposition	32.00
Souvenir, Spoon, Sterling Silver, New York, Tiffany & Co.	12.00
Souvenir, Spoon, Sterling Silver, Newburgh, Cutout Washington's Quarters	12.00
Souvenir, Spoon, Sterling Silver, Niagara Falls In Bowl, Good Luck Handle	24.00
Souvenir, Spoon, Sterling Silver, Niagara Falls, Demitasse	7.00
Souvenir, Spoon, Sterling Silver, Niagara Falls, Enameled Top	9.95
Souvenir, Spoon, Sterling Silver, Niagara Falls, Indian Maid & Canoe	15.00
Souvenir, Spoon, Sterling Silver, Nome, Alaska, Miner's Tools, Demitasse	8.00
Souvenir, Spoon, Sterling Silver, North Carolina, Mustard	25.00
Souvenir, Spoon, Sterling Silver, Ocean City, N.J., Good Luck, Demitasse	7.00
Souvenir, Spoon, Sterling Silver, Ohio	12.50
Souvenir, Spoon, Sterling Silver, Oklahoma, Alva In Bowl	15.00
Souvenir, Spoon, Sterling Silver, Old Point Comfort, Fort Monroe	15.00
Souvenir, Spoon, Sterling Silver, Old South Church, Boston, Demitasse	15.00
Souvenir, Spoon, Sterling Silver, Omaha, Demitasse	8.00
Souvenir, Spoon, Sterling Silver, Order Of The Owls, 3 Owls At Top	3.95
Souvenir, Spoon, Sterling Silver, Oregon, Embossed Handle	14.50
Souvenir, Spoon, Sterling Silver, Pan American Exposition	22.50
Souvenir, Spoon, Sterling Silver, Pan American Exposition, Demitasse	12.50
Souvenir, Spoon, Sterling Silver, Panama California Exposition, 1915	9.95
Souvenir, Spoon, Sterling Silver, Panama Pacific Exposition, 1915	18.00
Souvenir, Spoon, Sterling Silver, Paris, Texas	8.00
Souvenir, Spoon, Sterling Silver, Paris, Texas, Star, Steer	14.00
Souvenir, Spoon, Sterling Silver, Pasadena, Standing Bear	9.00
Souvenir, Spoon, Sterling Silver, Pennsylvania, Soldiers' & Sailors'	16.00
Souvenir, Spoon, Sterling Silver, Philadelphia, Demitasse	10.00

Souvenir, Spoon, Sterling Silver, Pike's Peak, Signal Station, Demitasse	8.50
Souvenir, Spoon, Sterling Silver, Pine Bluff, Arkansas, Demitasse	9.00
Souvenir, Spoon, Sterling Silver, Plymouth Rock	9.95
Souvenir, Spoon, Sterling Silver, Plymouth, Mass., John Alden & Priscilla	11.00
Souvenir, Spoon, Sterling Silver, Poland Spring Water, Figural	35.00
Souvenir, Spoon, Sterling Silver, Portage, La Prairie, Snowshoe At Top	8.00
Souvenir, Spoon, Sterling Silver, Portland	16.00
Souvenir, Spoon, Sterling Silver, Post Office, Kansas City, Mo.	9.50
Souvenir, Spoon, Sterling Silver, Providence	12.00
Souvenir, Spoon, Sterling Silver, Quebec, Enamel, Gold Wash, Pierced, Nut	20.00
Souvenir, Spoon, Sterling Silver, Richfield Springs, N.Y., Bandstand	12.50
Souvenir, Spoon, Sterling Silver, Roberts County Court House, Sisseton, S.D.	9.95
Souvenir, Spoon, Sterling Silver, Rochester, Minn., 1910	5.50
Souvenir, Spoon, Sterling Silver, Sacramento, California	10.00
Souvenir, Spoon, Sterling Silver, San Diego, 2 Palm Trees	9.95
Souvenir, Spoon, Sterling Silver, San Diego, 6 Scenes In Bowl	12.00
Souvenir, Spoon, Sterling Silver, San Francisco	8.00
Souvenir, Spoon, Sterling Silver, San Gabriel Mission, California	15.00
Souvenir, Spoon, Sterling Silver, Santa Fe, Demitasse	10.00
Souvenir, Spoon, Sterling Silver, Santa, Baby's, Figural, Loop Handle	32.00
Souvenir, Spoon, Sterling Silver, Santa, Demitasse	9.50
Souvenir, Spoon, Sterling Silver, Sarnia, Canada, Demitasse	10.00
Souvenir, Spoon, Sterling Silver, Seattle, Demitasse	7.00
Souvenir, Spoon, Sterling Silver, Seven Falls, Colorado	9.95
Souvenir, Spoon, Sterling Silver, Shawnee Indian's Head, Covered Wagon	15.00
Souvenir, Spoon, Sterling Silver, Sparta, Wis., Lion, Anchor & G Marks	8.95
Souvenir, Spoon, Sterling Silver, Spokane, Demitasse	10.00
Souvenir, Spoon, Sterling Silver, Springfield, Illinois	8.00
Souvenir, Spoon, Sterling Silver, St.Anthony's Falls, Minneapolis, Minn.	25.00
Souvenir, Spoon, Sterling Silver, St.Augustine, Fla.	16.00
Souvenir, Spoon, Sterling Silver, St.Louis World's Fair, 1904	24.00
Souvenir, Spoon, Sterling Silver, St.Louis, Indian On Globe	18.00
Souvenir, Spoon, Sterling Silver, St.Louis, Wheat Stalk Handle	8.00
Souvenir, Spoon, Sterling Silver, St.Paul 93	16.00
Souvenir, Spoon, Sterling Silver, Stratford-On-Avon, Birmingham, 1894, Nut	20.00
Souvenir, Spoon, Sterling Silver, Sunny South, Negro Child	27.50
Souvenir, Spoon, Sterling Silver, Tacoma Harbor Scene, Indian Handle	18.00
Souvenir, Spoon, Sterling Silver, Texas, Demitasse	10.00
Souvenir, Spoon, Sterling Silver, The Antlers, Colorado Springs, Demitasse	7.50
Souvenir, Spoon, Sterling Silver, Totem Pole Handle	28.00
Souvenir, Spoon, Sterling Silver, Tottenham, Canada, Demitasse	7.50
Souvenir, Spoon, Sterling Silver, Trans-Missippi & International, 1898	9.95
Souvenir, Spoon, Sterling Silver, Trinity Church, Boston, Demitasse	7.95
Souvenir, Spoon, Sterling Silver, University Of Missouri	8.00
Souvenir, Spoon, Sterling Silver, Washington State	22.50
Souvenir, Spoon, Sterling Silver, Washington, Capitol Finial, Demitasse	6.50
Souvenir, Spoon, Sterling Silver, Washington, D.C., Bust Of Washington	8.00
Souvenir, Spoon, Sterling Silver, Washington, D.C., Demitasse	6.95
Souvenir, Spoon, Sterling Silver, Watch Hill, R.I., Lily, Whiting	15.00
Souvenir, Spoon, Sterling Silver, Watergap	7.00
Souvenir, Spoon, Sterling Silver, Wayside Inn	12.00
Souvenir, Spoon, Sterling Silver, Webster City, Iowa, Demitasse	9.50
Souvenir, Spoon, Sterling Silver, Westminster Abbey, London, Demitasse	10.00
Souvenir, Spoon, Sterling Silver, White House	16.00
Souvenir, Spoon, Sterling Silver, White House, D.C., Demitasse	10.00
Souvenir, Spoon, Sterling Silver, Winston Churchill	11.00
Souvenir, Spoon, Sterling Silver, Woman's Building	18.00
Souvenir, Spoon, Sterling Silver, Woman's Building, Demitasse	10.00
Souvenir, Spoon, Sterling Silver, Woman's Head On Handle, Demitasse	7.00
Souvenir, Spoon, Sterling Silver, World's Columbian Exposition	15.00
Souvenir, Spoon, Sterling Silver, World's Fair, Chicago, Demitasse	10.00
Souvenir, Spoon, Sterling Silver, World's Fair, 1893	24.00
Souvenir, Spoon, Sterling Silver, Yellowstone Park, Bear Handle, Demitasse	8.00
Souvenir, Spoon, Sterling Silver, Zodiac, June, Cancer	12.75
Souvenir, Spoon, Sterling Silver, Zodiac, November	18.00
Souvenir, Spoon, Sterling Silver, Zodiac, October, Patent 1894	15.00

Souvenir, Spoon, Sterling Silver, Zodiac, Pisces, Engraved Jean, 1895	7.95
Souvenir, Spoon, Sterling Silver, 12 O'clock, Demitasse	7.00
Souvenir, Teacup, Soldiers' Monument, Sheboygan, Wis.	5.50
Souvenir, Toothpick, Hilbert, Wis., Ruby Stained, Pedestal, 2 Handled	15.00
Souvenir, Toothpick, Hudson, Wis., Ruby Stained	12.00
Souvenir, Toothpick, Ithaca, Ruby Stained	12.00
Souvenir, Toothpick, Lena, 1909, Pressed Glass, Colorado, Green	18.00
Souvenir, Toothpick, Lewis & Clark Expedition, 1905, Ruby Stained	22.50
Souvenir, Toothpick, McReynolds, 1906, Ruby Stained	12.00
Souvenir, Toothpick, Niagara Falls, 1907, Flashed Red & Clear, Mug Shape	6.00
Souvenir, Toothpick, Rossland, B.C., Ruby Stained	18.50
Souvenir, Toothpick, Waukesha Beach, Ruby Stained	12.00
Souvenir, Tray, Pan American Exposition, 1901, Aluminum, 5 1/4 X 3 1/2 In.	8.50
Souvenir, Tray, Pin, New York Central Railroad, Johnsville Station, German	3.50
Souvenir, Tumbler, Boston, Austrian, 3 3/4 In.	15.00
Souvenir, Tumbler, Buffalo, 1903, Clear Glass, 3 1/2 In.	3.95
Souvenir, Tumbler, Columbian Exposition, 1893, Red Flashed	14.00
Souvenir, Tumbler, Engraved Christmas, 1893, Pressed Glass, Red & White	45.00
Souvenir, Tumbler, Etched Minnie 1894 & Fancywork, Clear Glass	7.00
Souvenir, Tumbler, Pan American Exposition, Buffalo, 1901	10.00
Souvenir, Tumbler, St.Augustine, Fla., Pot Metal	4.00
Souvenir, Wine, Compliments Of City Bakery, La Moure, N.D., Ruby Stained	15.00

Spangle glass is multicolored glass made from odds and ends of colored glass rods. It includes metallic flakes of mica covered with gold, silver, nickel, or copper. Spangle glass is usually cased with a thin layer of clear glass over the multicolored layer.

Spangle Glass, see also Vasa Murrhina

Spangle Glass, Basket, White, Gold Mica, Yellow Inside Crystal Handle, 10 In.	175.00
Spangle Glass, Creamer, Cobalt Overlaid With Clear, Mica Flecks, 6 1/2 In.	175.00
Spangle Glass, Rose Bowl, Light To Dark Blue, Crimped Top, 4 In.	58.00
Spangle Glass, Vase, Blue Cased With Amber, Green Gold Flakes, Floral, 8 In.	50.00
Spangle Glass, Vase, White & Gold Spatter, Ribbed, Bulbous, 5 In.	18.00

Spanish lace is a Victorian glass pattern that seems to have white lace on a colored background. Blue, yellow, cranberry, and clear glass was made with this distinctive white pattern.

Spanish Lace, Bowl, Cranberry To Clear, Ruffled, 10 7/8 X 4 1/2 In.	85.00
Spanish Lace, Bride's Basket, Fluted Cranberry Rim, Van Bergh Frame, 10 In.	125.00
Spanish Lace, Celery, Vaseline, Crimped Top, Ferns	40.00
Spanish Lace, Celery, Yellow, Ruffled Top, 6 X 4 1/2 In.	45.00
Spanish Lace, Cruet, 7 1/2 In. *Illus*	145.00
Spanish Lace, Lemonade Set, Opalescent, 5 Piece	195.00
Spanish Lace, Muffineer, Clear & Opalescent	27.50 To 32.00
Spanish Lace, Muffineer, Cranberry, Wide Ribbed Swirl	85.00
Spanish Lace, Pitcher, Water, Blue Opalescent, Bulbous	52.00
Spanish Lace, Pitcher, Water, Green	85.00
Spanish Lace, Rose Bowl, Blue, Daisy & Fern, 4 1/2 X 3 3/4 In.	35.00
Spanish Lace, Saltshaker, Blue	18.00
Spanish Lace, Saltshaker, White	16.00
Spanish Lace, Syrup, Blue, Opalescent, Wide Paneled, Squatty	90.00
Spanish Lace, Tumbler, Blue	25.00
Spanish Lace, Tumbler, Cranberry	95.00
Spanish Lace, Vase, Pale Vaseline, White Lace, Ruffled Rim, 4 In.	45.00
Spanish Lace, Vase, Pink Satin, 7 1/2 In.High	95.00
Spanish Lace, Vase, White, Ruffled Edge, 6 In.	60.00

Spatter glass is a multicolored glass made from many small pieces of different colored glass.

Spatter Glass, Basket, Opalescent Chartreuse, Ruffled, Leaf Feet, 8 1/4 In.	68.50
Spatter Glass, Basket, Smoky Aventurine Color, Thorn Handle, 6 In.	55.00
Spatter Glass, Basket, White Casing, Melon Ribbed, Clear Thorn Handle, 7 In.	110.00
Spatter Glass, Bowl, Midwestern, Cased, Blues & Yellows, 9 X 3 In.	50.00
Spatter Glass, Bowl, Pink & White, Ribbed, 7 In.	38.00
Spatter Glass, Eggcup, Blue With White, Clear Cased, Gold, Footed	23.00
Spatter Glass, Pitcher, Milk, Pink & White On Clear, Bulbous, 6 X 5 In.	65.00

Spanish Lace, Cruet, 7 1/2 In.
(See Page 585)

Spatterware, Pitcher, Blue & White, 3 1/2 In.

Spatter Glass, Pitcher, Water, Cranberry & White On Clear, Thumbprint	80.00
Spatter Glass, Saltshaker, Pink & White On Clear	20.00
Spatter Glass, Toothpick, Maroon & White, Clear Casing	65.00
Spatter Glass, Tumbler, Inverted Thumbprint, Red, White, Clear	30.00
Spatter Glass, Vase, Black Amethyst Top, Yellow Base, 8 In.	20.00
Spatter Glass, Vase, Cranberry, Butterscotch & Gold Swirls, 10 1/2 In., Pair	150.00
Spatter Glass, Vase, Czechoslovakia, Black, Multicolor, Red Lined, 9 1/2 In.	25.00
Spatter Glass, Vase, Czechoslovakia, Red Top, Green Spatter Base, 8 In.	18.00
Spatter Glass, Vase, Czechoslovakia, White Lining, 8 In.	30.00
Spatter Glass, Vase, Gourd, 3 Layers Of Cased Glass, Enameled, 5 In.	69.00
Spatter Glass, Vase, Greens & Blacks, Graduates From Bottom To Top, 7 In.	20.00
Spatter Glass, Vase, Oxblood Red & White, Cased, Lined In Yellow, 6 In.	40.00
Spatter Glass, Vase, Pinched Sides, English Silver Hallmarked Top, 7 In.	35.00
Spatter Glass, Vase, Pink, Green, & White Flecked, Ruffled Rim, 5 1/2 In.	35.00
Spatter Glass, Vase, Pinks & Reds On White, 10 1/2 In., Pair	90.00
Spatter Glass, Vase, Reddish Orange, Gilt & White Birds & Flowers, 9 In.	125.00

Spatterware is a creamware or soft-paste dinnerware decorated with spatter designs. The earliest pieces were made during the late eighteenth century, but most of the wares found today were made from 1800 to 1850. The spatterware dishes were made in the Staffordshire District of England for sale on the American market.

Spatterware, Bowl, Blue, Schoolhouse Design, 5 1/4 X 3 1/4 In.	195.00
Spatterware, Creamer, Brown, 2 1/2 In.	70.00
Spatterware, Cup & Saucer, Handleless, Green & Brown Flower On White	24.00
Spatterware, Cup & Saucer, Handleless, Green Fan On White, Stick	24.00
Spatterware, Cup & Saucer, Handleless, Red & Green On White, Stick	22.00
Spatterware, Cup & Saucer, Victorian Lady, Yellow Border	8.00
Spatterware, Cup, Fort, Handleless	48.00
Spatterware, Pitcher, Blue & White, 3 1/2 In. .... *Illus*	68.00
Spatterware, Pitcher, Blue, Rose Pattern, 6 Sided, Swelling Shape, 6 1/4 In.	275.00
Spatterware, Plate, Blue, Sunflower Center, 9 In.	100.00
Spatterware, Plate, Green Fan On White, Stick, 9 In.	22.00
Spatterware, Plate, Peafowl, Blue Border, Red, Green, & Blue, 7 1/2 In.	125.00
Spatterware, Platter, Red, Green Transfer American Eagle, C.1850, 17 3/4 In.	250.00
Spatterware, Tea Set, Child's, Allerton & Sons, C.1890, 3 Piece	45.00
Spatterware, Teabowl & Saucer, Blue, Rose Design	125.00
Spatterware, Teabowl & Saucer, Green, Peafowl Design	175.00
Spatterware, Teabowl & Saucer, Schoolhouse, C.1820	300.00
Spatterware, Vase, Blue & Green, 13 In.	27.50
Spelter, Figurine, Buffalo, 3 1/2 In.	10.00
Spelter, Figurine, Ceres, Sitting, White Lead, Bronze Finish, 9 X 9 In.	35.00
Spelter, Figurine, Elephant, Trunk Down, Germany, 3 In.	9.00

Spelter, Figurine, Roman Soldier & Lady, Bronze Finish, 11 1/2 In., Pair	50.00
Spelter, Figurine, Stag, Hand Colored, 5-Pointed Antlers, C.1910, 4 5/8 In.	17.50
Spelter, Figurine, World War I German Soldier, Bronze Finish, 6 In.	64.50
Spelter, Inkwell, Horse's Head Poking Out Of Stall, Gold Plated, 5 X 5 In.	48.00
Spelter, Striker, Table Match, Rats On Each Side Of Urn, 3 1/2 In.	60.00
Spinning Wheel, see Tool, Spinning Wheel	

Spode pottery, porcelain, and bone china were made by the Stoke-on-Trent Factory of England founded by Josiah Spode about 1770. The firm became Copeland and Garrett from 1833 to 1847, then W.T.Copeland or W.T.Copeland and Sons until the present time. The word Spode appears on many pieces made by the Copeland Factory. Most antique dealers include all the wares under the more familiar name of Spode.

Spode, see also Copeland

Spode, Basket, Potpourri, Pierced Lid, Green Glaze, C.1815, 4 3/4 In.	100.00
Spode, Bowl & Underplate, Ivory & White, Gold Edge, 2 Handled, 7 1/4 In.	35.00
Spode, Bowl, Chinoiserie, Light Blue, Openwork, Oblong, C.1800, 9 In.	75.00
Spode, Bowl, Transfer Printed Oriental Shrubbery, C.1815, 7 1/2 In., Pair	60.00
Spode, Cup & Saucer, Cabbage, Enamel & Gilt Overglaze, C.1820	65.00
Spode, Cup & Saucer, Doll's, Colored Leaf, Copeland, 2 1/2 In. Saucer	22.00
Spode, Invalid Feeder, Verona, Light Blue, C.1880, 5 In.	28.00
Spode, Jar, Tobacco, White Embossed Males On Gray, 4 In.	25.00
Spode, Jug, Floral On White, C.1830, 4 In.	40.00
Spode, Pitcher, Milk, Delft, Scenic, Florals	35.00
Spode, Plate, Cake, Lausanne, Medium Blue, Footed, C.1820	47.50
Spode, Plate, Constitution Hall, Phila., Light Blue, Copeland, 10 In.	9.00
Spode, Plate, Floral Center, Gold & Cobalt, Scalloped, 9 In.	39.50
Spode, Plate, Green Ground, Pink Flower, Grapes, & Birds, 8 1/4 In.	20.00
Spode, Plate, Memorial Hall, Phila., Light Blue, Copeland, 10 In.	9.00
Spode, Plate, Passionflowers, Roses, Blue & White, C.1830, 10 In.	35.00
Spode, Plate, Peacock & Hen With Peonies, Hand-Painted, C.1815, 8 In.	30.00
Spode, Spill, White Floral On Gray, 3 1/2 In.	5.00
Spode, Tureen & Stand, Sauce, Cone Knop, Dolphin Handles, C.1820, 8 In.	80.00
Spode, Tureen, Covered, Spode Tower, Deep Blue, Rectangular, 10 In.	40.00

Spongeware is very similar to spatterware in appearance. The designs were applied to the ware by daubing the color. Many dealers do not differentiate between the two wares and use the names interchangeably.

Spongeware, Bowl, Blue Sponge On Buff, 4 X 3 In.	12.00
Spongeware, Bowl, Blue, Wire Bail, Wooden Handle, 10 In.	60.00
Spongeware, Bowl, Blue, 4 1/2 X 5 In.	40.00
Spongeware, Bowl, Mottled Brown & Green On Cream, 11 Paneled Sides, 8 In.	18.00
Spongeware, Bowl, Red, Blue, & Brown, Tapered Bottom, 9 1/4 In.	50.00
Spongeware, Bowl, Red, Blue, & Brown, 9 In.	50.00
Spongeware, Crock, Salt, Blue	35.00
Spongeware, Cup & Saucer, Blue, Large, Handle, 3 In.High	60.00
Spongeware, Pitcher, Blue Sponge On Buff, 9 In.	68.00
Spongeware, Pitcher, Blue, Dutch Girl & Boy Kissing, Windmill, 7 In.	40.00
Spongeware, Pitcher, Blue, 8 X 5 In.	70.00
Spongeware, Pitcher, Blue, 9 In.	70.00
Spongeware, Plate, Apples & Leaves In Center, Leaves Around Rim, 9 In.	30.00
Spongeware, Plate, Pie, Blue, 10 1/2 In.	55.00
Spongeware, Platter, Blue, Oval, 12 In.	50.00
Spongeware, Platter, Dark Blue, Ironstone, 13 X 10 In.	22.50
Spongeware, Spittoon, Blue Banded, 8 In.	38.00
Spongeware, Spittoon, Blue, Kitchen	45.00
Spongeware, Spittoon, Blue, 2 Center Bands	55.00
Spongeware, Spittoon, Blue, 4 3/4 In.Diameter	45.00
St.Louis, Bowl, Dark Green Floral On Light Green, Cameo, Nancy, 2 1/4 In.	165.00
St.Louis, Box, Covered, Wine Color Floral Cameos On Gray, Gilt, 5 In.	275.00
St.Louis, Plate, Festival Hall, Openwork, 1904, 7 1/4 In.	15.00
St.Louis, Vase, Galle Type, Plum Color Berries & Leaves, Nancy, 5 In.	250.00
St.Louis, Vase, Teardrops, Amethyst Threading & Base, Art Verrier, 6 In.	65.00

Staffordshire is a district in England where pottery and porcelain have been made since the 1900s. Thousands of types of pottery and porcelain have been made in the hundreds of factories that operated in the area. Some of the most famous factories have been listed separately. See Royal Doulton, Royal Worcester, Spode, Wedgwood, and others.

Staffordshire, see also Flow Blue

Staffordshire, Bank, Cottage, 5 In.High	37.50
Staffordshire, Basket & Stand, Pearlware, Pierced, C.1790, 9 & 11 3/4 In.	70.00
Staffordshire, Basket, Fish, Fish On Bed Of Leaves, C.1845, 19 1/4 In.	90.00
Staffordshire, Bonbonniere, Finch Form, Metal Base, C.1790, 1 1/2 In.	140.00
Staffordshire, Bonbonniere, Finch Form, Purple, Yellow, Metal Mounts, C.1790	325.00
Staffordshire, Bonbonniere, Finch Form, Russet, Metal Mounts, C.1790	475.00
Staffordshire, Bonbonniere, Finch Form, Yellow, Metal Mounts, C.1790	325.00
Staffordshire, Bonbonniere, Pug's Head Form, Metal Mounts, C.1790, 1 1/4 In.	325.00
Staffordshire, Bonbonniere, Spaniel Form, Black, White, Metal Mounts, C.1790	550.00
Staffordshire, Bonbonniere, Watch Form, Gilt Metal Mounts, C.1760, 2 In.	275.00
Staffordshire, Bottle, Scent, Pear Shape, Gilt Metal Stopper, C.1770, 4 In.	250.00
Staffordshire, Bottle, Scent, Pear Shape, Silver Mounts, C.1765, 3 1/2 In.	325.00
Staffordshire, Bottle, Scent, Strawberries & Plums Form, Gilt Metal, C.1770	375.00
Staffordshire, Bowl, Flowers & Vase, Deep Blue, Stone China, 6 1/2 In.	18.00
Staffordshire, Bowl, Fruit & Flower, Light Blue, Handled, H.M.J., 9 1/2 In.	50.00
Staffordshire, Bowl, Mikado, Brown & Yellow, Furnival & Sons, 1881, 10 In.	17.50
Staffordshire, Bowl, Old Tower, Blue & White, 5 In.	8.00
Staffordshire, Bowl, Punch, Chrysanthemums On Green, T.& T., C.1875, 16 In.	125.00
Staffordshire, Bowl, Scenic, Brown & White, 5 1/2 X 3 In.	9.50
Staffordshire, Bowl, Temple, PWC3., 12 In.	28.50
Staffordshire, Bowl, Vegetable, American Marine, Brown, Ashworth, 8 3/4 In.	30.00
Staffordshire, Bowl, Vegetable, Chinese Tree, Booths	15.00
Staffordshire, Bowl, Vegetable, Covered, Iris, Light Blue, 10 1/2 In.	25.00
Staffordshire, Bowl, Vegetable, Kyber, Mulberry, J.Meir, 8 1/4 X 10 In.	55.00
Staffordshire, Bowl, Vegetable, Rose Finial, Ning Po, Mulberry	45.00
Staffordshire, Bowl, Waste, Rose, Mulberry, 3 3/4 X 5 1/2 In.	38.00
Staffordshire, Bowl, Waste, Temple, Purple, PWC3.	18.00
Staffordshire, Box, Covered, Little Girl Sitting In Chair, 8 In.High	175.00
Staffordshire, Box, Egg, Chicks & Shell Cover, Nest Base, C.1850, 8 1/2 In.	125.00
Staffordshire, Box, Egg, Duck Cover, Blue Water Base, C.1890, 11 1/4 In., Pair	175.00
Staffordshire, Box, Egg, Eggs Cover, Leafy Vines Base, C.1850, 7 1/8 In.	80.00
Staffordshire, Box, Egg, Guinea Hen Cover, Grass Base, C.1890, 8 3/8 In.	110.00
Staffordshire, Box, Egg, Hen Cover, Grass Base, C.1890, 7 1/2 In.	100.00
Staffordshire, Box, Egg, Hen Cover, Nest Base, Gilding, C.1890, 9 In., Pair	60.00
Staffordshire, Box, Patch, A Trifle From Bath, White, Metal Mounts, C.1790	180.00
Staffordshire, Box, Patch, A Trifle From Bridgwater, Metal Mounts, C.1790	160.00
Staffordshire, Box, Patch, A Trifle From Chatham, Gilt Metal Mounts, C.1790	180.00
Staffordshire, Box, Patch, A Trifle From Cheltenham, Metal Mounts, C.1790	130.00
Staffordshire, Box, Patch, A Trifle From Grantham, Pink, Metal Mounts, C.1790	120.00
Staffordshire, Box, Patch, A Trifle From Lincoln, Blue, Metal Mounts, C.1790	150.00
Staffordshire, Box, Patch, A Trifle From London, Blue, Metal Mounts, C.1790	200.00
Staffordshire, Box, Patch, A Trifle From Milford, Blue, Metal Mounts, C.1790	225.00
Staffordshire, Box, Patch, A Trifle From Ramsgate, Blue, Metal Mounts, C.1790	170.00
Staffordshire, Box, Patch, Balloon Ascent, Pink Ribbons, Metal Mounts, C.1790	160.00
Staffordshire, Box, Patch, Boy & Dog In Front Of Mirror Lid, Chest Base	50.00
Staffordshire, Box, Patch, Boy & Dog On Cover, Chest Of Drawers Base, Footed	50.00
Staffordshire, Box, Patch, Cheltenham Spa, White, Metal Mirror, C.1790	150.00
Staffordshire, Box, Patch, Dan De Lion, Pink, Metal Mounts, C.1790, 1 1/4 In.	100.00
Staffordshire, Box, Patch, Dishes On Cover, Table Base, Footed, Round	50.00
Staffordshire, Box, Patch, Egg Shape	18.00
Staffordshire, Box, Patch, Floral On White & Blue, Metal Mounts, C.1790	80.00
Staffordshire, Box, Patch, Floral On White, Gilt Metal Mounts, C.1760	100.00
Staffordshire, Box, Patch, Florettes	18.00
Staffordshire, Box, Patch, Gilt & Blue On White, C.1790, 2 In.	200.00
Staffordshire, Box, Patch, Girl & Boy At Kitchen Table, Metal Mounts, C.1790	250.00
Staffordshire, Box, Patch, Inscription On White, Metal Mounts, C.1790, 2 In.	225.00
Staffordshire, Box, Patch, King's Gate On Lavender, Metal Mounts, C.1790	130.00
Staffordshire, Box, Patch, Louis XVI Portrait, Blue, Metal Mounts, C.1790	190.00
Staffordshire, Box, Patch, Milsom Street On White, C.1790, 2 In.	150.00
Staffordshire, Box, Patch, Nelson & Victory, White, Metal Mounts, C.1790	160.00
Staffordshire, Box, Patch, Orange Slipper With Blue Bow On Cover, Footed	30.00
Staffordshire, Box, Patch, Oval Table With Tea Set	32.00

Staffordshire, **Box,** Patch, Oval, Orange Slipper With Large Blue Bow	35.00
Staffordshire, **Box,** Patch, Present From Ivanhoe Baths, Metal Mounts, C.1790	120.00
Staffordshire, **Box,** Patch, Ramsgate Pier, Blue, Metal Mounts, C.1790, 2 In.	190.00
Staffordshire, **Box,** Patch, Spaniel Form, Black, White, Metal Mounts, C.1790	350.00
Staffordshire, **Box,** Patch, Spaniel Form, Red, White, Metal Mounts, C.1790	475.00
Staffordshire, **Box,** Patch, St.Michael's Mount, Lavender, Metal Mounts, C.1790	200.00
Staffordshire, **Box,** Patch, Strawberry Hill, Purple, Metal Mounts, C.1775	310.00
Staffordshire, **Box,** Patch, Tea Set On Lid, Base Is Table, Gold, Green	50.00
Staffordshire, **Box,** Patch, The Absent Not Forgotten, Metal Mounts, C.1770	80.00
Staffordshire, **Box,** Patch, The Pump Room On White, Metal Mounts, C.1790	100.00
Staffordshire, **Box,** Patch, The Victory Of Earl Howe, 1794, Metal Mounts	170.00
Staffordshire, **Box,** Patch, Trifle From Sidmouth, White, Metal Mounts, C.1790	110.00
Staffordshire, **Box,** Patch, Virtue & Manners, Lavender, Metal Mounts, C.1770	175.00
Staffordshire, **Box,** Trinket, Altar, Gold	14.00
Staffordshire, **Box,** Trinket, Boy & Dog On Lid	25.00
Staffordshire, **Box,** Trinket, Boy In High Chair With Dog Begging, 3 1/2 In.	45.00
Staffordshire, **Box,** Trinket, Children Playing	55.00
Staffordshire, **Box,** Trinket, Crown, Scepter, Orb, & Sword	23.00
Staffordshire, **Box,** Trinket, Draped Table Shape, Gray, Dishes, 3 X 3 1/4 In.	48.00
Staffordshire, **Box,** Trinket, Fireplace Base, Open Hearth, Child On Lid	22.00
Staffordshire, **Box,** Trinket, Fireplace, Mirror Frame, Gold Trim, 4 X 3 In.	48.00
Staffordshire, **Box,** Trinket, Florets & Corsage On Lid, Rectangular	18.00
Staffordshire, **Box,** Trinket, Hen, Rooster, & 3 Chicks On Lid, Oval, 3 3/4 In.	35.00
Staffordshire, **Box,** Trinket, Little Red Riding Hood	22.00
Staffordshire, **Box,** Trinket, Polychrome, Winged Angel & Dove, Rectangular	45.00
Staffordshire, **Box,** Trinket, Washstand With Mirror, 5 X 3 In.	48.00
Staffordshire, **Box,** Trinket, Woman, Man, & Dove, Multicolored	22.00
Staffordshire, **Box,** Trinket, 2 Standing Children On Lid, St.Bernard Dog	22.00
Staffordshire, **Burner,** Pastille, Cottage, Gold Outlining, 4 1/2 X 3 3/4 In.	75.00
Staffordshire, **Burner,** Pastille, Cottage, Moss On Roof, Blue & White, 6 In.	75.00
Staffordshire, **Bust,** John Wesley, Wood, C.1820, 10 3/4 In.	225.00
Staffordshire, **Bust,** Shakespeare, Multicolored, 9 In.	35.00
Staffordshire, **Butter Pat,** Brown Transfer Daffodil, Square	4.00
Staffordshire, **Case,** Scent Bottle, Floral, Gilt, Pink, Metal Mounts, C.1790	80.00
Staffordshire, **Case,** Scent Bottle, Sepia & Gilt On Lavender, Metal, C.1750	170.00
Staffordshire, **Castle,** 2 Turretts, Lilac & Purple, Moss, C.1830, 4 3/4 In.	250.00
Staffordshire, **Cigar Holder,** Water Barrel, Basket For Matches	25.00
Staffordshire, **Coffeepot,** Oriental Deer Park, Deep Blue, C.1810, High Domed	225.00
Staffordshire, **Coffeepot,** Spotted Deer, Dark Blue, High Dome, C.1810	250.00
Staffordshire, **Compote,** Castle Scenes, Spode, C.1810, 12 1/4 X 4 1/2 In.	110.00
Staffordshire, **Cottage,** Garden Pavillion, 2 Story, C.1835, 6 3/4 In.	150.00
Staffordshire, **Cottage,** Marked .... *Illus*	85.00
Staffordshire, **Cottage,** Pavilion, 2 Story, Pierced Windows, C.1835, 8 In.	100.00

Staffordshire, Cup Plate,
Castle Garden, 3 3/4 In., Pair
(See Page 590)

Staffordshire, Cottage, Marked

Staffordshire, Cottage, Salmon Pink, 2 Stories, Gables, C.1850, 7 1/2 In. 150.00
Staffordshire, Cottage, Two Chimneys, Pink Roof, Green Trim 60.00
Staffordshire, Cottage, 3 Pointed Gables, Moss Encrusted, C.1830, 4 1/2 In. 100.00
Staffordshire, Creamer, Cow, White, Orange, Green Base, Covered, 5 In. 125.00
Staffordshire, Creamer, Lighthouse Shape, Light Blue Transfer Scene, 5 In. 28.00
Staffordshire, Creamer, Storks & Foliage 8.50
Staffordshire, Cup & Saucer, Arabian, Pink, Handleless, Dillon 22.00
Staffordshire, Cup & Saucer, Barlboro Hall, Derbyshire, Blue, Handleless 55.00
Staffordshire, Cup & Saucer, Basket & Flower, Deep Blue, Stubbs & Kent 53.00
Staffordshire, Cup & Saucer, Black Transfer New Orleans, Stevenson 85.00
Staffordshire, Cup & Saucer, Child's, Sylvan, Dark Blue, Cauldon, England 7.50
Staffordshire, Cup & Saucer, Cottage Girl, Purple 33.00
Staffordshire, Cup & Saucer, Demitasse, Pansies 24.00
Staffordshire, Cup & Saucer, Doll's, Flower Design 20.00
Staffordshire, Cup & Saucer, Doll's, Flower, Crown Staffordshire 20.00
Staffordshire, Cup & Saucer, English Lake Scene, Medium Blue, C.1820 .... 45.00
Staffordshire, Cup & Saucer, English Scene, The Cottage Girl, Purple 33.00
Staffordshire, Cup & Saucer, Garden, Light Blue, Handleless, Mayer, Longport 24.00
Staffordshire, Cup & Saucer, Handleless, Indian Shells, Green On White 25.00
Staffordshire, Cup & Saucer, Handleless, Light Blue 20.00
Staffordshire, Cup & Saucer, Handleless, Ning Po, Mulberry 25.00
Staffordshire, Cup & Saucer, Handleless, Rose, Mulberry 32.00
Staffordshire, Cup & Saucer, India Scene, Elephants With Howdahs, Purple 19.00
Staffordshire, Cup & Saucer, Jeddo, Mulberry, Handleless 37.50
Staffordshire, Cup & Saucer, Lafayette At Franklin's Tomb, Handleless, Blue 200.00
Staffordshire, Cup & Saucer, Mt.Vernon, Seat Of Washington, Transfer 110.00
Staffordshire, Cup & Saucer, Pink, Handleless, Wood 88.00
Staffordshire, Cup & Saucer, Rose, Mulberry, Handleless 58.00
Staffordshire, Cup & Saucer, Salt Lake City, Pink 17.00
Staffordshire, Cup & Saucer, Spanish Scene, Alhambra, Sepia, C.1840 .... 18.00
Staffordshire, Cup & Saucer, Swan, Dark Pink 88.00
Staffordshire, Cup & Saucer, Toddy, Alhambra, Sepia, C.1840 .... 18.00
Staffordshire, Cup & Saucer, Wadsworth Tower, Dark Blue, Enoch Wood 335.00
Staffordshire, Cup & Saucer, Women With Harp & Man, Pink & Green, C.1820 .... 16.00
Staffordshire, Cup Plate, American Marine, Sepia 35.00
Staffordshire, Cup Plate, Asiatic Palaces, Dark Blue 30.00
Staffordshire, Cup Plate, Battery New York, Dark Blue, Enoch Wood 125.00
Staffordshire, Cup Plate, Battery Park, Dark Blue, Enoch Wood 150.00
Staffordshire, Cup Plate, Black & White Oriental Scene, Adams, 4 In. 25.00
Staffordshire, Cup Plate, Blue & White, Flowers, Butterfly Center, 3 3/4 In. 18.00
Staffordshire, Cup Plate, Boston Mails, Gentlemen's Cabin, Black & White 50.00
Staffordshire, Cup Plate, Brown & White Chalet Scene, 4 In. 22.00
Staffordshire, Cup Plate, Brown Classical Buildings & Garden 26.00
Staffordshire, Cup Plate, Canova, Medium Blue 15.00
Staffordshire, Cup Plate, Canova, Pink, T.Mayer, 4 In. 12.00
Staffordshire, Cup Plate, Castle Garden, 3 3/4 In., Pair .... Illus 275.00
Staffordshire, Cup Plate, Dark Brown Quail Center, Birds In Medallion 28.00
Staffordshire, Cup Plate, Flower & Scroll, Mulberry Transfer, Elkin, C.1840 .... 12.00
Staffordshire, Cup Plate, Green Transfer, Children Fishing, 3 3/4 In. 15.00
Staffordshire, Cup Plate, Hop Pickers, Pink 24.00
Staffordshire, Cup Plate, Hyena, Quadrupeds, Blue & White, Woods, 4 1/4 In. 45.00
Staffordshire, Cup Plate, Italian Scene, Pink, Enoch Wood, 3 7/8 In. 25.00
Staffordshire, Cup Plate, Light Blue Castle Scene, Floral Border, Alcock 15.00
Staffordshire, Cup Plate, Pink Ship, Green Shells Border, 4 3/4 In. 30.00
Staffordshire, Cup Plate, Pompeii, Light Blue, Alcock, 4 1/8 In. 20.00
Staffordshire, Cup Plate, Stag Center, Pink Luster 24.00
Staffordshire, Cup Plate, Transfer Floral, Purple To Mulberry, Elkin & Co. 12.00
Staffordshire, Cup Plate, Village Scene With Church & Houses, Brown 24.00
Staffordshire, Cup Plate, Vincennes, Mulberry, J.Alcock, 4 1/8 In. 24.00
Staffordshire, Cup Plate, Virginia And Her Goats, Sepia 20.00
Staffordshire, Cup, Canova, Pink, T.Mayer 20.00
Staffordshire, Cup, Florilla 15.00
Staffordshire, Cup, Flower With Vase, Dark Blue, Handleless 18.00
Staffordshire, Cup, Loving, Bargeware, White Slip On Dark Brown, C.1850 .... 20.00
Staffordshire, Cup, Loving, Grange Symbols, 2 Ocher Frogs Inside, C.1825 .... 85.00
Staffordshire, Cup, Stirrup, Fox's Head, Mottled Red, Black, & White, 5 In. 125.00
.... 35.00

Staffordshire, Cup, Stirrup, Greyhound, Gray Sepia, C.1825, 6 3/4 In.	850.00
Staffordshire, Cup, Stirrup, Hound Mask, Black Spots, C.1820, 4 1/2 In.	60.00
Staffordshire, Cup, Stirrup, Hound Mask, Brown Markings, C.1820, 4 3/4 In.	150.00
Staffordshire, Dish, Cheese, Covered, Blue & White, Square	65.00
Staffordshire, Dish, Hen Cover, Caramel Basket Weave Base, Eggs, 9 In.	135.00
Staffordshire, Dish, Hen Cover, Nest Base, 3 1/2 In.	48.50
Staffordshire, Dish, Hen Cover, Tan Basket Weave Base, 8 In.	225.00
Staffordshire, Dish, Leaf Shape, Pearlware, Green Outlined, C.1780, 5 3/8 In.	40.00
Staffordshire, Doghouse, Brown Spotted Dog & Pup, C.1835, 4 In.	140.00
Staffordshire, Etui, Asparagus Form, Gilt Metal Mounts, C.1790, 5 1/4 In.	150.00
Staffordshire, Etui, Floral Bouquets On Dark Blue, Metal Mounts, C.1770	140.00
Staffordshire, Etui, Floral, Gilt Leaves, Dark Green, C.1790, 3 3/4 In.	60.00
Staffordshire, Etui, Turquoise, Sheep Scene, Gilt Metal Mounts, C.1770	190.00
Staffordshire, Figurine, A.M., Shoeshine Boy & P.M., Newsboy, 13 In., Pair	150.00
Staffordshire, Figurine, Actress, Victorian, Playing Mandolin, C.1850, 11 In.	30.00
Staffordshire, Figurine, Barefoot Girl In Smock, Water Ewer, 2 X 5 X 9 In.	50.00
Staffordshire, Figurine, Benjamin Franklin, Standing, C.1850, 15 1/2 In.	400.00
Staffordshire, Figurine, Bird On Log, Speckled, 1930, 3 1/2 In.	30.00
Staffordshire, Figurine, Boy, Seated, Brown Coat, Pratt Type, C.1790, 3 In.	30.00
Staffordshire, Figurine, Calico Cat On Blue Cushion, C.1850, 4 In., Pair	35.00
Staffordshire, Figurine, Cat And The Fiddle, 4 1/2 In.	35.00
Staffordshire, Figurine, Cat Sitting On A Pillow, 7 1/2 In.	45.00
Staffordshire, Figurine, Cat, Ocher & Blue Spots, C.1890, 3 In., Pair	475.00
Staffordshire, Figurine, Charlotte At Tomb Of Werther, C.1820, 9 In.	100.00
Staffordshire, Figurine, Clock, Scottish Piper & His Lass, 13 1/2 In.	65.00
Staffordshire, Figurine, Cockerel, Standing, Yellow, Gray, & Red, C.1800, 8 In.	325.00
Staffordshire, Figurine, Crier, Black Costume, C.1820, 7 1/4 In.	120.00
Staffordshire, Figurine, Dalmatian, Seated, Gilt Chain, C.1850, 7 In., Pair	150.00
Staffordshire, Figurine, Daniel Flanked By Lions, Oval Base, 9 1/2 In.High	75.00
Staffordshire, Figurine, Dog, Copper Luster Trim, Black Feet, 12 In, Pair	95.00
Staffordshire, Figurine, Dog, Decorated, 7 In.	30.00
Staffordshire, Figurine, Dog, Reclining, Spotted, C.1810, 6 In., Pair	150.00
Staffordshire, Figurine, Dog, White, Black & Pink Spots, 8 In.	35.00
Staffordshire, Figurine, Dog, 12 In.	65.00
Staffordshire, Figurine, Florence Nightingale, Standing, C.1850, 14 In.	160.00
Staffordshire, Figurine, Girl & Boy, Bocage, Walton, C.1825, 5 3/4 In., Pair	275.00
Staffordshire, Figurine, Hen On Yellow Base, 8 X 6 In.	120.00
Staffordshire, Figurine, Hen, Green Grass, White Eggs, Basket Weave, 4 In.	30.00
Staffordshire, Figurine, Hunter & His Dog, C.1850, 10 1/4 In.	80.00
Staffordshire, Figurine, John Milton, Standing, C.1850, 11 1/4 In.	30.00
Staffordshire, Figurine, King Charles Spaniel, Purple Spots, 8 1/2 In., Pair	85.00
Staffordshire, Figurine, Lady Holding Tray Of Pheasants, 15 In.	37.50
Staffordshire, Figurine, Lion Slayer, Hunter & Lion, 16 1/2 In.	60.00
Staffordshire, Figurine, Lion, Standing, Paw On World Globe, C.1825, 13 In.	250.00
Staffordshire, Figurine, Lost Piece, Maiden With Broom, C.1820, 9 1/8 In.	40.00
Staffordshire, Figurine, Man On Horse, Deer Over Saddle, Black, Gold, 14 In.	45.00
Staffordshire, Figurine, Milkmaid & Companion, With Cow, C.1850, 6 In., Pair	150.00
Staffordshire, Figurine, Milkmaid & Companion, With Cow, C.1850, 8 In., Pair	80.00
Staffordshire, Figurine, Poodle, Seated, Gilt Collar, C.1850, 8 1/8 In., Pair	80.00
Staffordshire, Figurine, Poodle, Seated, Pebble Coat, C.1850, 8 1/2 In., Pair	110.00
Staffordshire, Figurine, Poodle, Seated, Pebble Coat, C.1850, 9 1/2 In., Pair	130.00
Staffordshire, Figurine, Poodle, White, Red Flower Basket, 3 1/4 In.	38.00
Staffordshire, Figurine, Poodles, White, 8 1/2 In.High, Pair	60.00
Staffordshire, Figurine, Prince Of Wales, Standing, Chair, Book, 10 1/2 In.	75.00
Staffordshire, Figurine, Prodigal's Return, 3 X 7 X 13 In.	75.00
Staffordshire, Figurine, Rarey Standing Before A Horse, C.1850, 9 1/4 In.	150.00
Staffordshire, Figurine, Robert Burns & Highland Mary, 13 In., Pair	65.00
Staffordshire, Figurine, Robin Hood, Tree Trunk Vase, Flat Back, 14 1/2 In.	75.00
Staffordshire, Figurine, Samson & The Lion, C.1850, 11 In.	300.00
Staffordshire, Figurine, Spaniel, Gilt Collar, C.1850, 10 1/4 In., Pair	160.00
Staffordshire, Figurine, Spaniel, Seated, Gold Collar, C.1850, 7 3/4 In., Pair	85.00
Staffordshire, Figurine, Spaniel, Seated, Red Spotted, C.1860, 3 3/4 In.	40.00
Staffordshire, Figurine, Spaniel, 10 1/2 In., Pair	65.00
Staffordshire, Figurine, Squirrel, Eating, Brown Glaze, C.1850, 7 3/8 In.	950.00
Staffordshire, Figurine, Squirrel, Eating, White, Ralph Wood, C.1770, 8 In.	1400.00
Staffordshire, Figurine, The Lion Slayer, 16 1/2 In.	125.00

Staffordshire, Figurine, Tiger, Male & Female, Seated, 7 In., Pair	135.00
Staffordshire, Figurine, Tinker, Striding, Black Top Hat, C.1820, 6 3/8 In.	125.00
Staffordshire, Figurine, Wellington, Standing, C.1850, 13 3/8 In.	175.00
Staffordshire, Figurine, Whippet & Dead Hare, Recumbent, C.1840, 11 In., Pair	175.00
Staffordshire, Figurine, Whippet Dog, Cobalt Base, Quill Holder, 6 1/2 In.	45.00
Staffordshire, Figurine, Whippet Dog, Seated, Oval Base, Biscuit, 5 In.	28.00
Staffordshire, Figurine, Whippet With Hare In Mouth, 7 3/4 In.	65.00
Staffordshire, Figurine, Whippet, Red Coat, Black Collar, C.1860, 7 1/2 In.	30.00
Staffordshire, Figurine, Whippet, Scratching Its Ear With Foot, 5 In.	30.00
Staffordshire, Flask, Agateware, Ring, Bird Center, Tans, C.1850, 13 7/8 In.	300.00
Staffordshire, Flask, Double, Flattened, Man's Portraits, C.1825, 7 5/8 In.	60.00
Staffordshire, Font, Holy Water, Wall Type, Christ In Color, Raised Flowers	12.00
Staffordshire, Grater, Nutmeg, Egg Shape, Floral, Pink, Metal Mounts, C.1790	80.00
Staffordshire, Grater, Nutmeg, Lemon Form, A Margate Gift, C.1790	375.00
Staffordshire, Gravy Boat, Rochester Castle Bridge, 1792, Johnson Bros.	20.00
Staffordshire, Gravy Boat, Temple, Purple, PWCo.	22.00
Staffordshire, Group, Babes In Woods, Guardian Angel, 8 In.	30.00
Staffordshire, Group, C.1800, Pair .... *Illus*	500.00
Staffordshire, Group, Cobbler & His Wife, 7 In.	45.00
Staffordshire, Group, Cottage, Cupola On Roof, Dogs At Door, C.1820, 6 In.	70.00
Staffordshire, Group, Couple Embracing In Floral Arbor, 10 X 7 In.	47.50
Staffordshire, Group, Couple Sitting Above Clock, 14 In.	40.00
Staffordshire, Group, Couple Waltzing, Hard Paste, C.1850, 9 In.	150.00
Staffordshire, Group, Cows With Calves, Bocage, C.1825, 5 7/8 In.	170.00
Staffordshire, Group, Elijah & The Widow, C.1800, 9 3/4 In.	180.00
Staffordshire, Group, Lady & Kneeling Suitor, C.1850, 10 3/4 In., Pair	225.00
Staffordshire, Group, Lovers In Bower, Dog, White, Black Hair, Gold, 15 In.	33.50

Staffordshire, Group, C.1800, Pair

Staffordshire, Group,
Uncle Tom & Eva,
1852, 5 3/8 In.
(See Page 593)

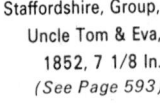

Staffordshire, Group,
Uncle Tom & Eva,
1852, 7 1/8 In.
(See Page 593)

Staffordshire, Group, Lovers, Flowering Bocage, C.1825, 7 In. 160.00
Staffordshire, Group, Robin Hood, 2 Men, Dog, 14 1/2 X 9 In. 97.50
Staffordshire, Group, Shepherd & Companion Musician, Bocage, C.1825, 7 In. 225.00
Staffordshire, Group, Two Guardsmen With Dog, 12 In. 32.50
Staffordshire, Group, Two Lovers, White & Gold Clothes, 4 1/2 In. 50.00
Staffordshire, Group, Uncle Tom & Eva, C.1850, 8 3/8 In. 175.00
Staffordshire, Group, Uncle Tom & Eva, 1852, 5 3/8 In. .... *Illus* 200.00
Staffordshire, Group, Uncle Tom & Eva, 1852, 7 1/8 In. .... *Illus* 250.00
Staffordshire, Group, 2 Girls With Clock, 6 1/4 In. 37.50
Staffordshire, Hatpin Holder, Scenic, Blue & White 45.00
Staffordshire, Inkwell, Napoleon 75.00
Staffordshire, Inkwell, Reclining Deer, Double Inserts, Quill Socket, 9 In. 175.00
Staffordshire, Inkwell, Triple Tulip Shape, Maroon Tulips, C.1850, 4 In. 200.00
Staffordshire, Inkwell, Whippet, Recumbent, Iron Red, C.1850, 4 3/4 In., Pair 100.00
Staffordshire, Jar, Ginger, Covered, Flowers, Crown Staffordshire, 1 1/2 In. 20.00
Staffordshire, Jar, Ginger, Doll's, Covered, Flower Design, 1 1/2 In. 20.00
Staffordshire, Jug, Bacchus Mask, Grotesque Brown Handle, C.1820, 7 5/8 In. 80.00
Staffordshire, Jug, Canary Yellow, Black Country Scene, C.1810, 5 3/4 In. 150.00
Staffordshire, Jug, Canary Yellow, Silver Luster Decoration, C.1815, 4 In. 300.00
Staffordshire, Jug, Club Day & Poem, Black Transfer, C.1815, 6 1/8 In. 125.00
Staffordshire, Jug, Dark Rose Camaieu Floral, Wood, C.1820, 7 3/8 In. 30.00
Staffordshire, Jug, Hunt, Raised Applied Scene, Hunters, Gray & Brown, 5 In. 50.00
Staffordshire, Jug, Josiah Wedgwood Bust, Enameled, Cooper & Co., 5 1/2 In. 125.00
Staffordshire, Jug, Mask, Black Beard, C.1815, 4 5/8 In. 175.00
Staffordshire, Jug, Mask, 3 Color Masks, Dark Brown Body, C.1815, 5 In. 150.00
Staffordshire, Match Holder, Boy & Animal Against Tree 35.00
Staffordshire, Match Holder, Double, Pink High Top Shoes 18.00
Staffordshire, Mug, Brown & White, Marked French-Wileman, Applied Handle 8.00
Staffordshire, Mug, Child's, Canary Yellow, "For Loving A Book," C.1825 .... 180.00
Staffordshire, Mug, Child's, Canary Yellow, Girl & Boy Transfer, C.1825 .... 125.00
Staffordshire, Mug, Child's, Canary Yellow, Lafayette & Washington, C.1820 .... 375.00
Staffordshire, Mug, Child's, Franklin's Maxims, Green Transfer, C.1850 .... 70.00
Staffordshire, Mug, Molded Carousers, Sepia Frog Inside, C.1890, 4 3/4 In. 60.00
Staffordshire, Mug, Scuttle, Flower Decorated, Foley 15.00
Staffordshire, Mug, 2 Men With Foundling Baby, Brown Transfer, 2 1/3 In. 22.00
Staffordshire, Nodder, Woman & Little Boy, 8 & 6 1/2 In., Pair 150.00
Staffordshire, Ornament, Chimney, Barefoot Girl & Ewer, C.1850, 9 In. 50.00
Staffordshire, Ornament, Chimney, Barefooted Girl In Blue Smock, 9 In. 50.00
Staffordshire, Ornament, Chimney, Blue Coated Girl On Bridge, Swan, 9 In. 55.00
Staffordshire, Ornament, Chimney, Prodigal's Return, Woman & Man, 13 1/2 In. 63.00
Staffordshire, Penholder, Dog On Blue Pillow, 4 In. Across Base 40.00
Staffordshire, Penholder, Parrot On White Tree Trunk, Lamb, 5 1/4 In. 70.00
Staffordshire, Penholder, White Dog With Black Spots, Blue Pheasant 40.00
Staffordshire, Penholder, White Dog With Black Spots, Yellow Pillow 40.00
Staffordshire, Pitcher, Bargeware, Brown Glaze, Applied Floral, C.1850, 6 In. 70.00
Staffordshire, Pitcher, Brown Spotted Hound Handle, C.1840, 6 3/4 In. 30.00
Staffordshire, Pitcher, Eagle & Niagara Falls, Blue, Mier & Son, 1837, 10 In. 100.00
Staffordshire, Pitcher, Figural, The Exchequer From Mikado, 9 1/2 In. 87.50
Staffordshire, Pitcher, Milk, Chasing The Ostrich, Sepia 38.00
Staffordshire, Pitcher, Ring Puzzle, Stoneware, Blue Glaze, C.1850, 11 In. 130.00
Staffordshire, Pitcher, Rose, Mulberry, 5 1/4 In. 28.00
Staffordshire, Pitcher, Sitting Spaniel, Copper Luster Spots, C.1850, 10 In. 75.00
Staffordshire, Pitcher, Spaniel, Copper Luster, White Ground, 10 In. High 68.00
    Staffordshire, Plate, see also Ship Plate
Staffordshire, Plate, Abbey Ruins, Pink, Scalloped, T.& J.Mayer, 10 In. 20.00
Staffordshire, Plate, Adelaide Bower, Green & White, 9 In. 9.00
Staffordshire, Plate, Ailanthus, Black Transfer, C & W, 9 1/4 In., Pair 15.00
Staffordshire, Plate, Aleppo, Black Transfer, C & Y, C.1844, 9 1/2 In., Pair 15.00
Staffordshire, Plate, Alhambra, Blue, Castle Scene, 10 In. 10.00
Staffordshire, Plate, Alhambra, Castle, Black & White, England, 10 In. 8.00
Staffordshire, Plate, American Marine, Blue, 10 1/4 In. 35.00
Staffordshire, Plate, American Villa, Dark Blue, 10 In. 100.00
Staffordshire, Plate, Annapolis Basin, N.S., Blue, R.& M., 10 In. 35.00
Staffordshire, Plate, Arms Of New York, Blue, Mayer, C.1829, 10 In. 375.00
Staffordshire, Plate, Arms Of New York, Dark Blue, Mayer, 10 In. 750.00
Staffordshire, Plate, Asia Displayed, Black, Hall, 10 1/2 In. 38.00

Staffordshire, Plate, Bakers Falls, Hudson River, Purple, 9 In.	45.00
Staffordshire, Plate, Baronial Castles, Sundorn, Lavender, Ridgway, 8 1/2 In.	12.50
Staffordshire, Plate, Battle Of Bunker Hill, Blue, R & M Co., 9 3/4 In.	22.00
Staffordshire, Plate, Blantyre, Purple, Alcock, 9 1/2 In.	28.00
Staffordshire, Plate, Blind Man's Bluff, Mulberry, Black Rim, 5 3/4 In.	50.00
Staffordshire, Plate, Blue Transfer Greenwich, 9 1/2 In.	25.00
Staffordshire, Plate, Boston Massacre, 1770, Pink, R.M., 10 In.	36.00
Staffordshire, Plate, Boston Statehouse, Blue, Enoch Wood, 9 3/4 In.	70.00
Staffordshire, Plate, Brooklyn, Blue & White, R & M, 6 In.	9.00
Staffordshire, Plate, Brown Transfer Daffodil, 7 1/2 In.	9.00
Staffordshire, Plate, Calcutta, Mulberry, 8 3/4 In.	20.00
Staffordshire, Plate, Canova, Blue, 8 In.	20.00
Staffordshire, Plate, Canova, Brown, 9 1/2 In.	10.50
Staffordshire, Plate, Canova, Green, 10 1/2 In.	20.00
Staffordshire, Plate, Canova, Light Blue Transfer, T & J Mayer, 9 1/2 In.	25.00
Staffordshire, Plate, Capitol, Washington, Dark Blue, Stevenson, 10 In.	225.00
Staffordshire, Plate, Carolina, Hall, Purple, 10 1/4 In.	35.00
Staffordshire, Plate, Catskill Mountain House, Rose, 10 1/2 In.	70.00
Staffordshire, Plate, Cattle Scene, L.& A., C.1840, 9 1/2 In.	25.00
Staffordshire, Plate, Chicago, Green, Rowland & Marcellus, 10 In.	15.00
Staffordshire, Plate, Chief Justice Marshall Troy, Dark Blue, Wood, 10 In.	195.00
Staffordshire, Plate, Circassia, Dark Blue, Alcock, 6 1/4 In.	24.00
Staffordshire, Plate, City Of Benares, Hall, Blue, 6 1/2 In.	58.00
Staffordshire, Plate, Classic Ruins, Polychrome, Raised Border, 6 In.	38.00
Staffordshire, Plate, Commodore Paul Jones, Blue, B & D, 9 3/4 In.	22.00
Staffordshire, Plate, Compton Verney, Dark Blue, Wood, C.1818, 8 1/2 In.	32.00
Staffordshire, Plate, Corean, Mulberry, Eagle Mark, 9 3/4 In.	28.00
Staffordshire, Plate, Corean, Mulberry, P.W.& Co., 10 In. 15.00 To	18.00
Staffordshire, Plate, Corean, Mulberry, 8 3/4 In.	17.00
Staffordshire, Plate, Dartmouth College, N.H., Blue & White, 7 In.	7.95
Staffordshire, Plate, Don Quixote Series, Dark Blue, 6 3/4 In.	150.00
Staffordshire, Plate, Dr.Syntax Taking Possession, 1890, 10 1/4 In.	95.00
Staffordshire, Plate, Duke Of York, Pearlware, C.1790, 8 3/4 In.	375.00
Staffordshire, Plate, Erford, Edwards, Dark Blue, 10 3/8 In.	18.00
Staffordshire, Plate, Esholt House, Yorkshire, Dark Blue, Wood, 10 1/4 In.	100.00
Staffordshire, Plate, European Scenery, Black & White, Wood, 7 In., Pair	15.00
Staffordshire, Plate, European Scenery, Pink, Wood, 10 1/2 In.	33.00
Staffordshire, Plate, Fairmount Near Philadelphia, Stubbs, 10 In.	150.00
Staffordshire, Plate, Faulkbourn Hall, Dark Blue, Stevenson, C.1820, 10 In.	45.00
Staffordshire, Plate, Florentine Fountain, Dark Pink, 10 1/2 In.	30.00
Staffordshire, Plate, Florentine, Dark Blue, Mayer, 9 3/4 In.	18.00
Staffordshire, Plate, Garden Scenery, Medium Blue, Mayer, 8 1/2 In.	28.00
Staffordshire, Plate, Garibaldi, Beside Horse, Floral & Leaf Border, 8 In.	38.00
Staffordshire, Plate, Guy's Cliff, Warwickshire, Blue & White, 10 1/8 In.	72.00
Staffordshire, Plate, Hartford, Conn., Pink, Jackson, 10 1/2 In.	78.00
Staffordshire, Plate, Henry & Virginia Assembly, Blue & White, 9 In.	35.00
Staffordshire, Plate, Independence Hall, Blue, 9 In.	25.00
Staffordshire, Plate, Iris, Light Blue, 7 In.	10.00
Staffordshire, Plate, Iris, Light Blue, 8 In.	12.00
Staffordshire, Plate, Iris, Light Blue, 9 In.	15.00
Staffordshire, Plate, Japan Flowers, Green Transfer, R.M.W.& Co., 8 In.	8.50
Staffordshire, Plate, Jenny Lind, Purple, 9 In.	25.00
Staffordshire, Plate, King's Western Gloucestershire, Blue, Riley, 8 3/4 In.	58.00
Staffordshire, Plate, Knight Templar, 1907, Saratoga, N.Y., Gold Rim, 8 In.	36.00
Staffordshire, Plate, Lafayette At Washington's Tomb ... Illus	275.00
Staffordshire, Plate, Lakewood, N.J., Dark Blue, 10 In.	22.00
Staffordshire, Plate, Landing Of Lafayette, Blue, 10 In.	165.00
Staffordshire, Plate, Landing Of Lafayette, Dark Blue, 9 3/4 In.	150.00
Staffordshire, Plate, Landing Of Pilgrims, Dark Blue, 9 In.	45.00
Staffordshire, Plate, Landing Of Pilgrims, Enoch Wood, 5 3/4 In.	85.00
Staffordshire, Plate, Lavender, Abbey 1790 England, 10 1/2 In.	12.00
Staffordshire, Plate, Leighton, 9 In.	20.00
Staffordshire, Plate, Madras, Deep Purple, 8 1/8 In., Pair	38.00
Staffordshire, Plate, Marine, Brown, 8 In.	20.00
Staffordshire, Plate, Milanese Pavilion, Purple, J.Hall, 9 1/8 In.	19.00
Staffordshire, Plate, Millennium, Isaiah II, Sepia, 10 1/2 In.	39.00

Staffordshire, Plate, Montevideo, Connecticut, Deep Pink, Adams, 7 In.	38.00
Staffordshire, Plate, Moral Maxims, Pink, Clews, 10 1/2 In.	55.00
Staffordshire, Plate, Ning Po, Mulberry, R.H.Co., 8 1/2 In.	22.00
Staffordshire, Plate, Obelisk At Catania, Blue, Don Pottery, C.1820, 10 In.	32.50
Staffordshire, Plate, Olympia, Medium Blue, P.W.& Co., 9 1/4 In.	28.00
Staffordshire, Plate, Oriental Palace, Light Blue, C.1800, 9 3/4 In.	35.00
Staffordshire, Plate, Oriental Scenery, Dark Blue, Hall, 1830, 9 3/4 In.	45.00
Staffordshire, Plate, Pain's Hill, Surrey, Dark Blue, 10 In.	55.00
Staffordshire, Plate, Parisian Chateau, Brown & White, 9 In.	9.00
Staffordshire, Plate, Park Theatre N.Y., 10 In., Stevenson	185.00
Staffordshire, Plate, Pearlware, Carnation, C.1820, 9 7/8 In.	350.00
Staffordshire, Plate, Pelew, Mulberry, Challinor, 9 1/2 In.	20.00
Staffordshire, Plate, Penn's Treaty, Light Blue, 7 1/2 n.	45.00
Staffordshire, Plate, Penn's Treaty, Sepia, T.G., 9 In.	38.50
Staffordshire, Plate, Peruvian, Mulberry, 7 In.	15.00
Staffordshire, Plate, Pilgrim Memorial Monument, Blue, 9 In.	18.50
Staffordshire, Plate, Pittsfield Elm, Dark Blue, 6 3/4 In.	140.00
Staffordshire, Plate, Plymouth, Blue & White, R.& M., 10 In.	17.00
Staffordshire, Plate, Plymouth, Mass., Blue, R & M, 9 3/4 In.	30.00
Staffordshire, Plate, Quadruped, Dark Blue, John Hall, C.1810, 10 In.	50.00
Staffordshire, Plate, Rose, Mulberry, Challinor, 9 7/8 In.	18.00
Staffordshire, Plate, Scott's Illustrations & Waverley, Blue & White, 8 In.	15.00
Staffordshire, Plate, Soup, Arms Of New York, Blue, Mayer, C.1829, 9 7/8 In.	350.00
Staffordshire, Plate, Soup, Boston State House, Blue, Marked Rogers	80.00
Staffordshire, Plate, Soup, Boston State House, Deep Blue, Rogers, 10 1/2 In.	95.00
Staffordshire, Plate, Soup, Fairmount, Stubbs, Eagle Border, Blue, 10 In.	145.00
Staffordshire, Plate, Soup, Fishkill, Hudson River, Brown, 11 In.	75.00
Staffordshire, Plate, Soup, Floral, Sepia, 10 In., Pair	58.00
Staffordshire, Plate, Soup, North Fishkill, Hudson River, Brown, 10 In.	75.00
Staffordshire, Plate, Soup, Tams, Eagle, Villa Park, London, Dark Blue, 10 In.	90.00
Staffordshire, Plate, Soup, The Bosporus, Pink, R.Hall & Co., 10 1/4 In.	12.00
Staffordshire, Plate, Souvenir Of Cleveland, Blue, 9 In.	20.00
Staffordshire, Plate, States, Dark Blue, 6 3/4 In.	155.00
Staffordshire, Plate, Texas Campaign, Lavender, JB, 10 1/2 In.	65.00
Staffordshire, Plate, Texas Campaign, Light Blue, J.B., 10 1/2 In.	45.00
Staffordshire, Plate, Toddy, Scenic Center, Mulberry, Floral Border, 5 1/8 In.	18.00
Staffordshire, Plate, Togo, Green Transfer, FW&Co., 8 In.	9.00
Staffordshire, Plate, Troy From Mt.Ida, Hudson River, Sepia, 10 1/2 In.	62.00
Staffordshire, Plate, Vandyke, Pink, S.Alcock, C.1840, 9 In.	30.00
Staffordshire, Plate, Venice, Blue & White, Woods & Sons, 10 In.	10.00
Staffordshire, Plate, Vincennes, Purple, Alcock, 7 1/4 In.	14.00
Staffordshire, Plate, Washington Crossing Delaware, Blue, B & D, 9 3/4 In.	22.00
Staffordshire, Plate, Waterworks, Philadelphia, Purple, Jackson, 9 In.	68.00

Staffordshire, Plate, Lafayette At Washington's Tomb
(See Page 594)

Staffordshire, Saltshaker, Man, 6 In.
(See Page 596)

Staffordshire, Plate, William Penn's Treaty, Brown, 8 1/2 In.	45.00
Staffordshire, Plate, William Penn's Treaty, Sepia, Godwin, 10 1/2 In.	58.00
Staffordshire, Plate, Woodlands Near Philadelphia, Blue, Stubbs, 6 In.	135.00
Staffordshire, Plate, 25 Year Reign Of Queen Wilhelmina, Blue, 9 In.	36.50
Staffordshire, Platter, Blue Transfer Lotus Blossoms, White, C.1830, 20 In.	50.00
Staffordshire, Platter, Boston And Bunker Hill, States Border, 13 X 7 In.	225.00
Staffordshire, Platter, Boston Mails, Black & White, 12 X 15 In.	85.00
Staffordshire, Platter, Brown Floral, Stoke, 8 X 11 In.	30.00
Staffordshire, Platter, Dr.Syntax, Noble Hunting Party, Dark Blue, 17 In.	375.00
Staffordshire, Platter, English River Scene, C.1825, 16 3/4 In.	78.00
Staffordshire, Platter, Indian Temple View, Blue, Herculaneum, C.1815, 19 In.	110.00
Staffordshire, Platter, Iris, Light Blue, 14 1/2 In.	25.00
Staffordshire, Platter, L'Abbaye De Bon Port Fondee, Blue, C.1830, 12 In.	125.00
Staffordshire, Platter, Lake George, Pink, Oval, 13 In.	150.00
Staffordshire, Platter, Meat, Black Transfer Roselle, Meir, C.1848, 16 In.	30.00
Staffordshire, Platter, Milanese Pavilion, Purple, J.Hall, 12 1/2 In.	45.00
Staffordshire, Platter, Mogul Scenery, Mayer, Purple, 12 In.	43.00
Staffordshire, Platter, Ontario Lake, Purple, J.Heath, 13 1/4 In.	45.00
Staffordshire, Platter, Oriental, Blue, Marked Wear, 17 X 21 In.	165.00
Staffordshire, Platter, Quadruped, Rhinoceros, Deep Blue, Hall, 17 In.	160.00
Staffordshire, Platter, Residence Of Lafayette, Blue, Wood, C.1819, 19 In.	325.00
Staffordshire, Platter, Rhone Scenery, Mulberry, 16 X 12 1/2 In.	55.00
Staffordshire, Platter, Richard Jordan, Purple, 13 1/2 In.	175.00
Staffordshire, Platter, River Scene, Blue & White, C.1820, 13 X 9 In.	80.00
Staffordshire, Platter, Rose, Mulberry, E.Challinor, 17 3/4 X 14 In.	48.00
Staffordshire, Platter, Strawberries, Mulberry, Octagonal, C.1840, 16 In.	75.00
Staffordshire, Platter, Tivoli, Light Blue, 8 Sided, Oblong, 15 In.	37.00
Staffordshire, Platter, Venetian, Blue & White, G.H., C.1880, 17 1/2 In.	85.00
Staffordshire, Platter, Vincennes, Mulberry, Alcock, 10 1/2 In.	35.00
Staffordshire, Platter, Vincennes, Mulberry, 13 In.	55.00
Staffordshire, Pot, Pepper, Man In Tricornered Hat Holds Mug, 6 In.	69.50
Staffordshire, Relish, Corean, Mulberry, Handled, 10 Sided, 9 X 5 1/2 In.	24.00
Staffordshire, Relish, Historical Scene, Shell Shape, Sepia	45.00
Staffordshire, Rocker, Agateware, Red & Cream, Honey Glaze, C.1850, 7 3/8 In. _Illus_	125.00
Staffordshire, Saltshaker, Man, 6 In.	32.00
Staffordshire, Saucer, Pearlware, King's Rose, C.1820	30.00
Staffordshire, Saucer, Pink & Gold Luster, Floral, 4 3/8 In.	6.00
Staffordshire, Snuffbox, Artist's Palette, White, Metal Mounts, C.1770	275.00
Staffordshire, Snuffbox, Couple In Landscape, White, Metal Mounts, C.1780	110.00
Staffordshire, Snuffbox, Figures Fishing On White, Metal Mounts, C.1760	325.00
Staffordshire, Snuffbox, Floral On Blue, Gilt Metal Mounts, C.1760, 3 In.	875.00
Staffordshire, Snuffbox, Floral On Pink, Metal Mounts, C.1770, 3 3/8 In.	150.00
Staffordshire, Snuffbox, Floral On Yellow, Gilt Metal Mounts, C.1760, 3 In.	500.00
Staffordshire, Snuffbox, Floral On Yellow, Metal Mounts, C.1780, 2 1/2 In.	325.00
Staffordshire, Snuffbox, Street Scene, Ruins, White, Metal Mounts, C.1760	325.00
Staffordshire, Spill, Figural, Cow & Calf, Black, C.1850, 10 3/4 In., Pair	100.00
Staffordshire, Spill, Figural, Cow & Calf, Stump Vase, C.1850, 11 In., Pair	130.00
Staffordshire, Stand, Teapot, Gold Band, Round, 6 1/2 In.	10.00
Staffordshire, Sugar & Creamer, Iris, Light Blue	40.00
Staffordshire, Sugar, Covered, Brown Transfer Daffodil	20.00
Staffordshire, Sugar, Covered, Siam, Clementson	32.00
Staffordshire, Sugar, Rose, Mulberry, Covered, Handled, 7 3/8 In. _Illus_	48.00
Staffordshire, Sugar, Washington Standing At Tomb	350.00
Staffordshire, Tea Set, Brown Transfer Child & Cats, 24 Piece	68.00
Staffordshire, Tea Set, Child's, Alaska, 13 Piece	60.00
Staffordshire, Tea Set, Child's, May, Allerton, 15 Piece	85.00
Staffordshire, Tea Set, Strawberry Luster, C.1820, 23 Piece	175.00
Staffordshire, Teakettle, Bargeware, Brown Glaze, Applied Trim, 1888, 8 In. _Illus_	90.00
Staffordshire, Teapot, Lafayette At Washington's Tomb _Illus_	450.00
Staffordshire, Teapot, Landing Of Lafayette	700.00
Staffordshire, Teapot, Scenic, Dark Blue & White, 10 In.	300.00
Staffordshire, Teapot, Walled Garden, Flowerpots, Medium Blue, 1825	110.00
Staffordshire, Tile, Bust Of Lincoln, Eastwood Tile Works, 6 X 9 In.	85.00
Staffordshire, Toby Mug, Flushed Face, Green Coat, Pink Pants, C.1830, 9 In.	100.00
Staffordshire, Toby Mug, Full Figure, Tree Branch Handle, 5 1/2 In.	55.00
Staffordshire, Toby Mug, Hearty Good Fellow, Yellow Breeches	50.00

Staffordshire, Teapot,
Lafayette At Washington's Tomb
(See Page 596)

Staffordshire, Sugar, Washington Standing At Tomb
(See Page 596)

Staffordshire, Teapot, Landing Of Lafayette
(See Page 596)

Staffordshire, Toby Mug, Woman & Man, Royal Purple Dress, 2 In., Pair	15.00
Staffordshire, Tower, Octagonal, Yellow, Pierced Windows, C.1835, 8 1/8 In.	150.00
Staffordshire, Tumbler, Views Of Plymouth, Blue, R.& M., 1906	22.50
Staffordshire, Tureen, Vegetable, Archery, Sepia, Leaf Finial	78.00
Staffordshire, Tureen, Vegetable, Cabbage Rose Finials, Dark Blue, Pair	375.00
Staffordshire, Tureen, Vegetable, Oriental Scene, Pavilion, Green & White	48.00
Staffordshire, Urn, Covered, Flow Blue, 22 In.High, 13 In.Diameter, Pair	195.00
Staffordshire, Vase, Blue Floral, C & H Mark, Tunstall, 6 In.	15.00
Staffordshire, Vase, Blue Onion Type Design, Gold Scrolled Handles, 5 In.	6.00
Staffordshire, Vase, Boy & Girl With Birds, Cobalt & Orange On White, 8 In.	40.00
Staffordshire, Vase, Hand-Painted, 4 3/4 In., Pair	18.00
Staffordshire, Vase, Robin Hood, 2 Men, Dog, & Tree Trunk, 14 1/2 In.	75.00
Staffordshire, Vase, Tulip Form, Maroon & Yellow Tulip, C.1820, 3 3/4 In.	275.00
Staffordshire, Vase, Tulip Form, Puce & Green, Gilt, C.1825, 6 1/4 In., Pair	250.00
Staffordshire, Vase, 2 Human Masks, Impressed C Wilson, C.1820, 6 1/8 In.	50.00
Staffordshire, Washstand Set, Doll's, Roses, 2 In. Basin, 2 Piece	18.00
Staffordshire, Whistle, Bird On Branch	30.00
Staffordshire, Whistle, Boy Holding Rabbit	30.00
Staffordshire, Whistle, Monkey On Branch	30.00
Staffordshire, Whistle, Owl	30.00

*Stangl pottery was organized in 1929, succeeding the
Fulper Pottery Company. Stangl porcelain birds are popular
collectibles.*

Stangl, Ashtray, Antique Gold, 9 X 9 In.	14.00
Stangl, Ashtray, Pink, Black, White Designs, Signed	8.50
Stangl, Bird, Black, Yellow, Rose, Blue Beak, 3 1/2 In.	18.00

Stangl, Bird, Bluebird, Double, 8 In.	45.00
Stangl, Bird, Bluebird, Yellow Belly, 4 1/4 In.	15.00
Stangl, Bird, Bluebird, 3 1/2 In.High	20.00
Stangl, Bird, Bluejay, MMF, 5 1/2 In.	20.00
Stangl, Bird, Cardinal On Stump, 6 1/2 In.High	18.00
Stangl, Bird, Cockatoo, Artist JVF, No.3580, 9 In.	60.00
Stangl, Bird, Cockatoo, Pink With Blue, 6 In.	20.00
Stangl, Bird, Cockatoo, Pink, Double, 9 1/2 In.	32.50
Stangl, Bird, Cockatoo, Rose Colored, Green Tropical Plant, 10 In.High, Pair	45.00
Stangl, Bird, Duck, Artist MLF, No.3443, 13 In.	135.00
Stangl, Bird, Hen & Rooster, 9 3/4 In., Pair	55.00
Stangl, Bird, Key West Quail Dove, No.3454, 9 In.	80.00
Stangl, Bird, Kingfisher, 3 1/2 In.	15.00 To 22.50
Stangl, Bird, Mother & 3 Young Goldfinches On Bough, E.M.F., 12 In.	49.00
Stangl, Bird, Owl, On Flowering Branch, Pink, M.L. No.34059, 6 1/2 In.	25.00
Stangl, Bird, Pair Of Bluebirds, Artist V, No.3176D, 8 In.	75.00
Stangl, Bird, Parakeet, Green, Double, 7 1/2 In.	45.00
Stangl, Bird, Parakeet, Yellow, Double, On Branch, Wide Base, 5 1/4 In.	45.00
Stangl, Bird, Parakeet, 4 1/4 In.High	17.50
Stangl, Bird, Parrot Eating Worm, No.3449, 6 1/2 In.	48.00
Stangl, Bird, Parrot, Green, Yellow, & Brown, 5 1/2 In.	27.50
Stangl, Bird, Parrot, Pink, 6 1/2 In., Pair	14.00
Stangl, Bird, Parrot, 9 In.	38.00
Stangl, Bird, Pheasant, Brown, Artist DM, No.3491, 12 In.	75.00
Stangl, Bird, Pheasants, Pair, 11 1/2 X 5 1/2 In.	60.00
Stangl, Bowl, Covered, Divided, 7 1/2 X 3 1/4 In.	10.50
Stangl, Bowl, Terra Rose, Covered, Made In Trenton USA, 5 3/4 In.	9.00
Stangl, Box, Cigarette, Terra Rose, Green, Ashtray Lid, No.11	6.00
Stangl, Pitcher, Bright Green, Pink Lined, Stamped Terrarose, 4 In.	4.50
Stangl, Plate, Starflower, Olive Green, White Floral, 10 In.	7.00
Stangl, Pocket, Wall, Nautilus, Yellow, Chambered, Impressed 3238, 8 In.	15.00
Stangl, Teapot, Flora, 2 Cup Size	5.95
Stangl, Vase, Antique Gold, Ruffled, 5 1/4 X 4 3/4 In.	9.50
Stangl, Vase, Blue, White Dancing Lady, 8 1/2 In.	8.50
Stangl, Vase, Chartreuse, Leaping Eland, 9 1/2 In.	8.50
Stangl, Vase, Corncuopia, Terra Rose, 7 In.	7.00
Stangl, Vase, Gold & Silver Finish, Ruffled Edge, 6 In.	10.00
Stangl, Vase, Light Blue, 2 Handled, Marked No.3110, 7 In.	6.50
Stangl, Vase, Silver & Gold Iridescent, 7 1/2 In.	22.00
Stangl, Vase, Terra Rose, 8 X 5 In.High	14.00

Star Holly is a milk glass type of glass made by the Imperial Glass Company of Bellaire, Ohio, in 1957. The pieces were made to look like Wedgwood jasperware. White holly leaves appear against colored borders of blue, green, or rust. It is marked on the bottom of every piece.

Star Holly, Plate, Blue Border, Imperial, 7 In.	35.00
Star Holly, Plate, Green Border, Imperial, 7 In.	35.00

Steins have been used for over 500 years. They have been made of ivory, porcelain, stoneware, faience, silver, pewter, wood, or glass in sizes up to nine gallons. Although some were made by Meissen, Capo-Di-Monte, and other famous factories, most were made in Germany. The words Geschutz or Musterschutz on a stein are the German for patented or registered mark, not company names.

Stein, Blown, 1/2 Liter, Thumbprint, Pewter Lid & Thumblift, Porcelain Inset	58.50
Stein, Cameo Court Scene, Pewter Lid, 2 Liter, Marked * & Red Mark	228.00
Stein, Character, Munich Maid, Porcelain, 1/2 Liter	225.00
Stein, Cut Glass, German Engraving, Guitar On Thumb Rest, 1/2 Liter	75.00
Stein, Dragoon Regimental, Kaiser Nicholas II, Lithophane, 6/10 Liter	350.00
Stein, Faience, Dated 1773, 10 1/2 In.	Illus 850.00
Stein, Flint Glass, Gothic Arches With Coats Of Arms & Crowns, 1871, 7 In.	45.00
Stein, Frankfort, Germany, Blue & Beige, 7 In.	85.00
Stein, German, Blue On Gray, German Verse, Portrait Thumbrest, 1 Liter	75.00
Stein, German, Faience, C.1750, 9 3/4 In.	Illus 800.00
Stein, German, Faience, Pewter Mounted, 8 1/2 In.	Illus 850.00
Stein, German, Man & Woman In Swiss Costumes, 3 Liter, 17 1/2 In.High	25.00

Stein, German, Faience,	Stein, German, Faience,	Stein, Faience,
C.1750, 9 3/4 In.	Pewter Mounted, 8 1/2 In.	Dated 1773, 10 1/2 In.
(See Page 598)	*(See Page 598)*	*(See Page 598)*

Stein, German, Marked 575 & 4, Blue, Beige Figures, Pewter Lid, 1/2 Liter	40.00
Stein, German, Music Box, 10 1/2 In.	85.00
Stein, German, No.6391, Figures & Legend, Pewter Lid, 9 3/4 In.	95.00
Stein, German, Thumbprints In Glass, Pewter Lid, 1/2 Liter	40.00
Stein, German, 2 Liter, Lovers & Angels, Pewter Top, 16 3/4 In.	115.00
Stein, German, 2 Liter, Men Serving Beer To Soldiers, Pewter Top, 16 In.	115.00
Stein, Germany, Commemorating Steuben Tavern, Times Square, 9 In., Pair	38.00
Stein, Germany, No.11071, 1/2 Liter, Ivory Figures On Dark Blue, Pewter Top	46.00
Stein, Geschutz Gerschlitz, No.1179, 1/2 Liter, Couple, Tree Bark Handle	75.00
Stein, Geschutz, Germany, Etched Garden Scene, Pewter Lid, Liter	125.00
Stein, HB, 1/2 Liter, Relief Of Card Players	65.00
Stein, Knight & Royal Lady, Silver Plate Lid & Thumbpiece, 15 1/2 In.	135.00
Stein, Lithophane, Windmill & Sailboats, Delft, Pewter Fittings, 1/2 Liter	125.00
Stein, M & W, 1/2 Liter, PUG Couple	65.00
Stein, M & W, 1/2 Liter, PUG Target & Rifles, 1893, Eagle Shield	85.00
Stein, Massachusetts Institute Of Technology, Cream, Pewter Top, 9 In.	90.00
Stein, Mettlach, see Mettlach, Stein	
Stein, Military, Porcelain, Soldier's Coat, Gun, & Hat, Lithophane, 1/2 Liter	125.00
Stein, Monk, Rust Robe, Lithophane, 1/2 Liter	225.00
Stein, Musical, Hand-Painted Scene Of Man & Woman, Pewter Lid, 1/2 Liter	135.00
Stein, Musical, 1/2 Liter, Embossed Scene In Lid, "Tells Capella"	85.00
Stein, Musterschutz, Figural, Benjamin Franklin Finial, 7 In.	150.00
Stein, Musterschutz, Singing Pig, 7 In.	450.00
Stein, Nun, Lithophane, 1/2 Liter	250.00
Stein, Pewter, Glass Bottom, Covered, Fraternity Emblem, 6 X 4 In.	49.50
Stein, Pewter, Silver Wedding Anniversary, 1/2 Liter	125.00
Stein, Pottery, German, Couple Drinking, 1/2 Liter	25.00
Stein, Pottery, Pewter Base & Rim, Dated 1696, 1 Liter	350.00
Stein, Regimental, Porcelain, Lithophane, 1/2 Liter	175.00
Stein, Skull Resting On Book, 1/2 Liter	295.00
Stein, 3 Monks Sitting At Table, Brown & Tans, Dolphin Handle, 5 1/2 In.	32.50

*Stereo cards that were made for stereopticon viewers became popular after
1840. Two almost identical pictures were mounted on a stiff cardboard backing
so that, when viewed through a stereoscope, a three-dimensional picture could be
seen.*

Stereo Card, Alaska, Dyea Trail	3.50
Stereo Card, Alaska, Eskimo	3.50
Stereo Card, Alaska, President Harding	3.50
Stereo Card, Alaska, Railroad	3.50

Stereo Card, Alaska, Steamer	3.50
Stereo Card, Alaska, Totem Poles	3.50
Stereo Card, Alhambra Court In Crystal Palace, London, Gray Square Mount	5.00
Stereo Card, Bashful Lover, Comedy, 23	10.00
Stereo Card, Battle Of Gettysburg, 4	5.00
Stereo Card, Carter's Photo Gallery, N.Y. City, Yellow Square Mount	5.00
Stereo Card, Columbian Exposition, 6	3.00
Stereo Card, Cotton Industry In Dallas, Texas, Keystone, 10 In.	5.00
Stereo Card, Crystal Palace, London, Interior, Yellow Square Mount	7.00
Stereo Card, Grand Canyon, Arizona, 18	9.00
Stereo Card, Falls On The Moriston, Frith, Gray Square Mount	3.00
Stereo Card, Heroes Of Santiago, 1898	5.00
Stereo Card, Japan, 10	12.00
Stereo Card, Japanese & Russian Battle At Port Arthur, 82	20.00
Stereo Card, Japanese Silk, Industry, 16	9.00
Stereo Card, McKinley & Wife, Burial, 7	6.00
Stereo Card, Mexico, Keystone, 11	5.50
Stereo Card, New French Cook, 12	6.00
Stereo Card, Niagara, 3	2.00
Stereo Card, President Grant & Party, Yellow Mount	7.00
Stereo Card, San Francisco Earthquake & Fire, 1906, Color, 55	25.00
Stereo Card, Santa	1.00
Stereo Card, Sears Roebuck Series, 50	15.00
Stereo Card, South America, Keystone, 20	10.00
Stereo Card, Spanish American War, Color, 22	25.00
Stereo Card, U.S.A., Keystone, 20	9.95
Stereo Card, Versailles Castle, France, Langenheim, Pa., 1854	25.00

Stereoscopes, or stereopticons, were used for viewing the stereo cards. The hand viewer was invented by Oliver Wendell Holmes, although more complicated table models were used before his was placed in production in 1859.

Stereoscope, E.C.White Co., Wooden, Sliding Attachment, 37 Views	38.00
Stereoscope, France, Mahogany & Maple, Double View Type, 46 Cards	95.00
Stereoscope, Hand Type Viewer, Sliding Adjustment	14.75
Stereoscope, Metal Hood, 30 Cards	35.00
Stereoscope, Patent 1901, Cards	21.50
Stereoscope, Wooden	12.00

Sterling Silver, see Silver, Sterling

Steuben glass was made at the Steuben Glass Works of Corning, New York. The factory, founded by Frederick Carder and T.C.Hawkes, Sr., was purchased by the Corning Glass Company. They continued to make glass called Steuben. Many types of art glass were made at Steuben. The firm is still producing glass of exceptional quality.

Steuben, see also Aurene

Steuben, Ashtray, Green, Quilted, Amethyst Leaf Decoration, 6 X 6 1/4 In.	80.00
Steuben, Atomizer, Perfume, Gold Iridescent	145.00
Steuben, Basket, Gold Aurene, 18 In.High	850.00
Steuben, Block, Flower, Matted Figure Of Kneeling Child, 7 1/2 In.High	175.00
Steuben, Bottle, Perfume, Celeste Blue, Signed, 10 In.	95.00
Steuben, Bottle, Perfume, Gold Aurene, Melon Shape, 5 1/2 In.High	395.00
Steuben, Bottle, Perfume, Pink Swirled, Silver Mica Flecks, Green Handles	425.00
Steuben, Bowl & Base, Calcite, Gold Aurene Interior, 11 3/4 & 4 3/4 In.	155.00
Steuben, Bowl & Underplate, Finger, Amethyst	35.00
Steuben, Bowl & Underplate, Finger, Black Reeding On Clear Glass	45.00
Steuben, Bowl & Underplate, Finger, Opalescent Pink, Oriental Poppy, Carder	445.00
Steuben, Bowl, Amber, Swirled, Mica Flecks, Applied Prunts, Blue Foot, 12 In.	125.00
Steuben, Bowl, Blue, 10 In.	425.00
Steuben, Bowl, Bubbly, Green Threading On Ruffled Edge, 12 In.	75.00
Steuben, Bowl, Calcite, Gold, Label In Pontil, 10 X 2 1/2 In.	225.00
Steuben, Bowl, Centerpiece, Calcite, Gold, 14 X 2 In.	175.00
Steuben, Bowl, Centerpiece, Cluthra, Blue, Domed Pedestal Base, 9 3/4 In.	225.00
Steuben, Bowl, Centerpiece, Ivory, Ruffled, Ring Wafer, Domed Base, 8 In.	155.00
Steuben, Bowl, Centerpiece, Verre De Soie, Rolled Inward, 8 1/2 In.	38.00
Steuben, Bowl, Cluthra, Mulberry, 9 1/4 X 2 3/4 In.	175.00
Steuben, Bowl, Finger, Amethyst, Signed	30.00

Steuben, Bowl, Finger, Green Jade 105.00
Steuben, Bowl, Gold Aurene & Calcite, Small Foot, Flaring, 8 In.Diameter 165.00
Steuben, Bowl, Gold Iridescent, Fleur-De-Lis Mark, 7 In. 75.00
Steuben, Bowl, Green, Fluted, Pedestal, Pontil Mark, 6 In. 35.00
Steuben, Bowl, Ivory, Grotesque, Transparent Ruffled Top, 12 X 7 In. 200.00
Steuben, Bowl, Oval, Bubble Base, Gold Threading, 14 In. 225.00
Steuben, Bowl, Oval, Signed, 10 In. 185.00
Steuben, Bowl, Plum Jade, 3 Layer Acid Cut Back, 4 X 6 In. 995.00
Steuben, Bowl, Verre De Soie, 12 In. 60.00
Steuben, Candlestick, Calcite, Blue Aurene, Flat Top, 5 1/2 In., Pair 750.00
Steuben, Candlestick, Cranberry Swirl, Clear Stem, 6 In., Pair 400.00
Steuben, Candlestick, Flemish Blue, Clear Wafer, Hollow Stem, 12 In., Pair 150.00
Steuben, Candlestick, Green, Bubbly, Threading, 14 In., Pair 125.00
Steuben, Candlestick, Ivorene, 3 1/2 In. 155.00
Steuben, Candlestick, Rosaline & Alabaster, Petticoat Base, 9 1/2 In., Pair 550.00
Steuben, Champagne, VanDyke, Clear Foot & Top, Rosa Stem, 5 1/2 In., 8 .... 525.00
Steuben, Compote, Amber, Ribbed, Green Stem, Scalloped Rim, 8 In. 65.00
Steuben, Compote, Amethyst, 12 Blown-Out Ribs, 2 1/2 In.High, 6 In.Diameter 50.00
Steuben, Compote, Calcite & Gold Aurene, Rolled Edge, 3 1/4 In.High 200.00
Steuben, Compote, Calcite & Gold Aurene, 6 X 6 In. 190.00
Steuben, Compote, Calcite, Blue, 5 X 6 In. 450.00
Steuben, Compote, Crystal, 4 Part Open Stem, Signed, 9 1/8 X 4 3/4 In. 110.00
Steuben, Compote, Gold Ruby Appearing Amber, 8 1/2 X 8 In. 105.00
Steuben, Compote, Green Bowl, Clear Stem, 7 In.Diameter, 3 In.High 165.00
Steuben, Compote, Green, Mica, Air Trap, Art Deco Style, 5 X 6 1/2 In. 225.00
Steuben, Compote, Ivorene, Curlicue Stem, 4 1/2 X 7 In. 275.00
Steuben, Compote, Rosaline, Alabaster Base, Boat Shape, 10 X 6 X 5 In. 250.00
Steuben, Compote, Silverina Air Trap, Pomona Green, 7 X 8 In., Pair 750.00
Steuben, Compote, Verre De Soie, Pedestal, 6 In.Diameter, 2 3/4 In.High 85.00
Steuben, Compote, 4 Column Base, Signed, 10 In. 120.00
Steuben, Console Set, Oriental Poppy, Green Stems On 6 In. Candles, 3 Piece 1450.00
Steuben, Console Set, Venetian, Ruby, Black Edges, Berry Prunts, 3 Piece 375.00
Steuben, Cup & Saucer, Rosaline, Jade Pink, Alabaster Handle, Demistasse 200.00
Steuben, Dipper, Rosaline, Alabaster Handle, Miniature 65.00
Steuben, Dipper, Salad, Rosaline, Alabaster Handle 75.00
Steuben, Dresser Set, Cut Glass, Engraved Floral, Enameled Sterling, 4 Piece 225.00
Steuben, Figurine, Pheasant, Cut Glass, Signed, 12 In. 475.00
Steuben, Figurine, Pheasant, Cut Glass, 12 3/4 In. 750.00
Steuben, Flower Block, Deep Amethyst, 2 Tier, 4 X 2 1/2 In. 25.00
Steuben, Flower Block, Matted Figure Of Kneeling Child, 2 Piece, 7 1/2 In. 175.00
Steuben, Goblet, Amethyst Bowl, Alabaster Foot & Stem, 6 In. 55.00
Steuben, Goblet, Green Jade, Alabaster Foot, Twisted Stem, 7 In.High 138.00
Steuben, Goblet, Lavender Bowl, Alabaster Stem & Foot, 6 In. 68.00
Steuben, Goblet, Oriental Poppy, Pink With Green Stems, Carder 225.00
Steuben, Goblet, Salmon Orange Bowl, Alabaster Stem & Foot, 6 1/2 In. 50.00
Steuben, Goblet, Selenium Red, Etched Vintage, Signed 155.00
Steuben, Goblet, Water, Ruby Cerise 20.00
Steuben, Lamp Base, Deep Blue Cut To Brown Jade, 12 1/2 In. 1275.00
Steuben, Lamp Base, Jade Over Alabaster, Bird & Urn, Brass Fittings, 11 In. 450.00
Steuben, Lampshade, Ivorene, Vine & Berry Edge, Acanthus Bottom, 16 In. 95.00
Steuben, Plate, Green Jade, Alabaster Acid Cut Back, 6 In. 35.00
Steuben, Plate, Green Jade, Cut To Alabaster Floral Garlands, 9 1/4 In. 100.00
Steuben, Plate, Jade, Blue, Unsigned, 8 1/2 In. 55.00
Steuben, Plate, Jade, Green, Unsigned, 8 1/2 In. 33.00
Steuben, Plate, Pink Threading, Clear Center, Signed, 8 1/4 In. 38.00
Steuben, Plate, Rosaline, Cut To Alabaster Florals All Around, 8 1/2 In. 55.00
Steuben, Plate, Rosaline, 8 1/2 In.Diameter, Pair 235.00
Steuben, Rose Bowl, Pedestal Base, Gold, Applied Prunts, 9 1/2 X 4 1/2 In. 360.00
Steuben, Salt Dip, Amber, Green Foot, Signed 47.50
Steuben, Salt, Pedestal, Signed, 2 In., Set Of 6 .... 110.00
Steuben, Salt, Verre De Soie, Pedestal 65.00
Steuben, Shade, Calcite, Gold Lining, Signed, 5 In. 50.00
Steuben, Shade, Gas, Gold Feathers On Ivory, Gold Aurene Inside, 4 In. 85.00
Steuben, Shade, Gold Iridescent, Ribbed, 5 In. 50.00
Steuben, Shade, Gold Iridescent, Ribbed, 7 In. 58.00
Steuben, Sherbet & Underplate, Aquamarine 125.00

Steuben, Sherbet & Underplate, Calcite, Aurene Interior	210.00
Steuben, Sherbet & Underplate, Celeste Blue, Signed	50.00
Steuben, Sherbet & Underplate, Crystal, Black Reeding, Signed	39.50
Steuben, Sherbet & Underplate, Gold Calcite	100.00
Steuben, Sherbet & Underplate, Green Jade, Alabaster Pedestal, 4 In. High	85.00
Steuben, Sherbet & Underplate, Green Jade, Alabaster Stem & Base	70.00
Steuben, Sherbet & Underplate, Rosaline, Alabaster Stem & Base	120.00
Steuben, Sherbet & Underplate, Verre De Soie	55.00
Steuben, Sherbet & Underplate, Verre De Soie, Pedestal Stem	40.00
Steuben, Sherbet & Underplate, Verre De Soie, 6 In. Plate	55.00
Steuben, Sherbet, Oriental Poppy, Pink & Green	250.00
Steuben, Sherbet, Rosaline & Alabaster	80.00
Steuben, Sherbet, Rosaline, Pink, Alabaster Twisted Stem	125.00
Steuben, Sugar & Creamer, Blue Bubbled Glass, Blue Threaded	51.00
Steuben, Tazza, Green Jade, Alabaster Pedestal Stem, 8 1/8 X 2 1/8 In.	59.00
Steuben, Toothpick, Rosaline	50.00
Steuben, Tumbler, Blue Crystal, Cone Dome Base & Top	11.00
Steuben, Tumbler, Bristol Yellow, Inverted Cone Base, Cone Top	25.00
Steuben, Tumbler, Crystal, Black Reeding, Handled, Signed	35.00
Steuben, Tumbler, Iced Tea, Matsu-No-Ke, Crystal, Amethyst Handle & Prunt	60.00
Steuben, Tumbler, Lemonade, Pale Yellow	9.00
Steuben, Tumbler, Purple Crystal, Long Cone Top	25.00
Steuben, Tumbler, Red Metallic Luster, White Cased Inside, 4 In.	100.00
Steuben, Tumbler, Selenium Red, Pedestal, Octagonal Top, Signed	45.00
Steuben, Tumbler, Verre De Soie, Cobalt Handle, 5 1/4 In.	39.00
Steuben, Urn, Covered, Moonlight, Topaz Wheel Stem, Applied Rim	105.00
Steuben, Urn, Ivorene, Signed Incised Script, 8 In.	190.00
Steuben, Vase, Acid Cut Iridescent Floral On Blue, 7 1/2 X 4 1/2 In.	325.00
Steuben, Vase, Alabaster With Green Leaves & Flowers, Acid Cutback, 4 In.	850.00
Steuben, Vase, Amethyst, Bubble, Signed, 7 In.	100.00
Steuben, Vase, Blue Crystal, Ribbed, Flaring, 14 1/2 In.	125.00
Steuben, Vase, Blue, Elongated Thumbprint, White Ribbing, Signed, 4 In.	175.00
Steuben, Vase, Bud, Green Jade, Stellate Support, C.1920, 8 3/8 In., Pair	200.00
Steuben, Vase, Calcite, Trumpet, Stretched Aurene Interior, 6 In.	145.00
Steuben, Vase, Classic, Blue Cluthra, Signed, 8 In.High	650.00
Steuben, Vase, Classic, Rose Cluthra, Signed, 6 1/2 In.	500.00
Steuben, Vase, Clear, Blue Threading, 6 In.High	80.00
Steuben, Vase, Cluthra, Black To White, 6 1/2 In., Unsigned	200.00
Steuben, Vase, Cornucopia, Ivorene, Ribbed Body, Ruffled Rim, 6 In.	275.00
Steuben, Vase, Covered, Venetian Style, Yellow Rigaree, Footed, 12 1/2 In.	135.00
Steuben, Vase, Diamond Quilted, Clear, Blue Threaded Neck & Flared Top, 8 In	80.00
Steuben, Vase, Fan, Bristol Yellow Crystal, Signed, 8 1/4 In.	90.00
Steuben, Vase, Fan, Emerald Green, Triple Wheel Wafer, Ball Stem, 8 3/4 In.	75.00
Steuben, Vase, Fan, Vaseline Green, Cobalt Threading, Marked, 8 In.	75.00
Steuben, Vase, Flared Top, Pink Threading, 3 In.High	48.00
Steuben, Vase, Flemish Blue, Rolled Rim, Signed, 10 In.	65.00
Steuben, Vase, Free-Blown, 3 Handles, Wafer Foot, C.1950, 6 In.	30.00
Steuben, Vase, Garnet, Signed, 8 In.	230.00
Steuben, Vase, Gold Iridescent, Signed, 10 In.	445.00
Steuben, Vase, Green Crystal, Ribbed, 5 1/2 In.High	78.00
Steuben, Vase, Green Jade, White, Tricornered, Signed, 8 In.	155.00
Steuben, Vase, Green To Clear, Grotesque, 9 In.	135.00
Steuben, Vase, Ivorine, Amethyst Base, 8 In.High	200.00
Steuben, Vase, Ivory, 10 1/2 In.High	495.00
Steuben, Vase, Jack-In-The-Pulpit, Amber Iridescent, C.1904, 6 In.	350.00
Steuben, Vase, Lily, Ivorene, Trumpet & 2 Jack-In-The-Pulpits, C.1920, 12 In.	275.00
Steuben, Vase, Overlay, Silver & Purple, Art Deco, Carder, 7 In., Pair	850.00
Steuben, Vase, Paperweight, Blue, 6 1/2 In.High, Signed	425.00
Steuben, Vase, Rosaline Cluthra, 11 1/2 X 27 In.	750.00
Steuben, Vase, Rosaline, Alabaster Base, Amphora Shape, Signed, 9 X 5 1/2 In.	350.00
Steuben, Vase, Selenium Red, Ruffled Top, Half Ball & Wafer Stem, 8 1/4 In.	117.00
Steuben, Vase, Shade Type, Peacock Blue, Ribbed, 5 1/2 In.High	295.00
Steuben, Vase, Stick, Turquoise Blue Jade, Alabaster Base, 8 In.	195.00
Steuben, Vase, Trumpet, Deep Blue Iridescent, Ribbed, C.1905, 5 1/2 In.	200.00
Steuben, Vase, Tyrian, Blue Gray Hooked On White & Blue, C.1916, 8 1/4 In.	2800.00
Steuben, Vase, Urn Shape, Green Jade, M Shape Alabaster Handles, 10 1/4 In.	450.00

Steuben, Vase, Verre De Soie, Quilted, Pink Threaded, 8 In. High 225.00
Steuben, Vase, Verre De Soie, 10 In. 95.00
Steuben, Vase, Wisteria, Orchid, Ribbed, Pedestal Foot, 6 1/4 X 8 1/2 In. 125.00
Steuben, Vase, 2 Applied Ovals Near 3 In. Base, 6 1/2 In. 65.00
Steuben, Wine, Amethyst 40.00
Steuben, Wine, Domed Topaz Base & Bowl, 5 3/4 In., Signed 26.00
Steuben, Wine, Rosaline, Alabaster Stem, Unsigned 45.00
Steuben, Wine, Ruby Red, Clear Spiral Stem, Carder 65.00
Steuben, Wine, Topaz & Green, Pedestal Stem, 5 3/4 In. 26.00

Stevengraphs are woven pictures made like ribbons. They were manufactured
by Thomas Stevens of Coventry, England, and became popular in 1862.
Stevengraph, A Birthday Wish, Red Rose, Tassel, Inscription, 7 1/2 In. 75.00
Stevengraph, A Merry Christmas, Eliza Cook, Bird & Holly, 9 In. 35.00
Stevengraph, Bookmark, "First In Peace, " Washington, Crossed Flags 49.75
Stevengraph, Bookmark, Centennial, 1776-1876, 6 1/2 In. 65.00
Stevengraph, Bookmark, Coach Scene, Christmas Verse, Signed, 1872 .... 75.00
Stevengraph, Bookmark, Compliments Of The Season, Brown, Gold, 5 In. 35.00
Stevengraph, Bookmark, George Washington Centennial 150.00
Stevengraph, Bookmark, Pharaoh's Daughter Finding Moses, T.Stevens 95.00
Stevengraph, Bookmark, Philadelphia Centennial, 1876 .... 85.00
Stevengraph, Called To The Rescue, Heroism At Sea, Cardboard Mount 125.00
Stevengraph, Clifton Suspension Bridge 375.00
Stevengraph, Compliments Of The Season, The, Scene, Tassel, 6 X 1/2 In. 55.00
Stevengraph, Death Of Nelson, The, Framed 225.00
Stevengraph, Faith, Hope, & Charity, Inscription, 9 1/4 X 2 In. 85.00
Stevengraph, For Auld Lang Syne, Iris On White, Tassel, 5 1/2 X 1 1/4 In. 42.00
Stevengraph, For Life Or Death, Framed 250.00
Stevengraph, Forth Bridge, The 350.00
Stevengraph, Good Old Days 85.00
Stevengraph, Home Sweet Home, Inscription, Tassel, 7 1/2 X 1 1/2 In. 75.00
Stevengraph, Horse Race, Columbian Exposition, Gold Frame 110.00
Stevengraph, Iroquois 500.00
Stevengraph, Lady Godiva 145.00
Stevengraph, Late Earl Of Beaconsfield 185.00
Stevengraph, Madonna & Child 1500.00
Stevengraph, Many Happy Returns Of The Day, Floral, Another Year 55.00
Stevengraph, Meet, The 175.00
Stevengraph, Mizpah, Fuchsia To Top, Tassel, Inscription, 6 X 1 1/2 In. 75.00
Stevengraph, New Year's Greeting, Inscription, Tassel, 9 1/4 X 2 In. 75.00
Stevengraph, Old Tyne Bridge, The 750.00
Stevengraph, Philadelphia Centennial, 1776-1876, 7 In. 42.50
Stevengraph, President & Mrs. Cleveland, Pair 225.00
Stevengraph, Remember Me, Roses, Inscription, Tassel, 6 X 1 1/2 In. 50.00
Stevengraph, Royal Jubilee Exhibition, Newcastle-On-Tyne 450.00
Stevengraph, Rt.Hon. W.E. Gladstone, M.P. 95.00
Stevengraph, Start, The, 1879, Color 125.00
Stevengraph, W.G.Grace 500.00
Stevengraph, Wesley, Bust, Bible, Inscription, Tassel, 7 3/4 X 1 1/2 In. 95.00
Stevengraph, Wishing You A Merry Christmas & A Happy New Year, 5 X 1 In. 37.00
Stevengraph, Ye Ladye Godiva 185.00
Stevengraph, Young Lady On Candlestick Phone, Flag, Rose Border, 17 X 22 In 40.00

Stevens & Williams of Stourbridge, England, made many types of art glass.
Stevens & Williams, Basket, Moire, Curled Pink Handle, 9 In. 225.00
Stevens & Williams, Blue, Applied Drape & Feet, 15 In., Pair 195.00
Stevens & Williams, Bowl, Ruffle, Rainbow, 4 Colors, 11 In.Diameter 450.00
Stevens & Williams, Bowl, Three Color Rainbow, Enameled Floral, 4 1/2 In. 360.00
Stevens & Williams, Bowl, Tortoiseshell Glass, Gold Birds, 7 In. 125.00
Stevens & Williams, Cruet, Arboresque, White Crackle, Amber Stopper, 8 In. 210.00
Stevens & Williams, Inkwell, Intaglio Blossoms, Silver Lid, 3 1/2 X 4 In. 195.00
Stevens & Williams, Parfait, Green Jade, Alabaster Wafer & Pedestal, 6 In. 50.00
Stevens & Williams, Pitcher, Cider, Candy Stripe, Frosted Handle, 6 In. 175.00
Stevens & Williams, Rose Bowl, Pear & Apple On Clear, Leaves & Stems, 10 In 245.00
Stevens & Williams, Vase, Blue & Brown Swirl Satin, Lemon Interior, 7 In. 850.00
Stevens & Williams, Vase, Blue Ribbon Mother-Of-Pearl, Pewter Holder, 8 In. 112.50

Stevens & Williams, Vase, Blue To White, Allover Flowers & Leaves, 8 In.	275.00
Stevens & Williams, Vase, Brown Tapestry Mother-Of-Pearl, 7 3/4 In.	750.00
Stevens & Williams, Vase, Cornucopia, Enameled, Applied Feet & Bottom, 9 In.	120.00
Stevens & Williams, Vase, Crackle, Dragonflies & Floral, 5 In., Pair	70.00
Stevens & Williams, Vase, Cranberry, Applied Clear Rigaree, 7 1/2 X 5 In.	49.00
Stevens & Williams, Vase, Jack-In-The-Pulpit, Striped, 13 5/8 In., Pair	395.00
Stevens & Williams, Vase, Lemon Crackle, Insects & Flowers, 5 In., Pair	73.00
Stevens & Williams, Vase, Lemon Opalescent, Ruffled Top, 16 In.	45.00
Stevens & Williams, Vase, Peachblow Color, Applied Flowers & Vines, 10 In.	350.00
Stevens & Williams, Vase, Peachblow Colors, Enameled Floral, 10 In.High	110.00
Stevens & Williams, Vase, Rose To Cream, Intaglio Dragonfly & Frog, 11 In.	1195.00
Stevens & Williams, Vase, Swirled Mother-Of-Pearl, American Beauty, 8 In.	450.00
Stevens & Williams, Vase, White, Applied Green & Amber Leaves, 4 In.	80.00
Stevens & Williams, Vase, Yellow Crackle, Floral & Dragonflies, 6 In., Pair	78.00
Stevens & Williams, Water Set, Pink & White Peppermint Swirl, 5 Piece	275.00
Stiegel Type, Bottle, Flint, Half Post Method, Enameled, C.1750, 7 In.	215.00
Stiegel Type, Flask, Ovoid, 19 Diamonds, 6 In.	125.00
Stiegel Type, Flip, Covered, Acorn Finial, Floral Devices, C.1790, 11 In.	275.00
Stiegel Type, Flip, Incised Floral, Swags, & Birds, C.1790, 8 1/2 In.	60.00
Stiegel Type, Pitcher, Flint, 16 Ribs, Applied Blue Rim, 5 1/2 In.	75.00
Stiegel Type, Pitcher, Milk, Amber, Threading At Top Rim	95.00
Stiegel Type, Salt, Master, Expanded Diamond, Sloping Foot, 2 3/8 In.	100.00
Stiegel Type, Tumbler, Copper Etched Sailing Designs	22.50
Stiegel, Tumbler, Blown, 16 Ribs, Etched Floral	200.00
Stiegel, Wine, Blown, Flint	200.00
Stockton, Vase, Flowers & Leaves On Brown Glaze, Marked Rekston, 10 In.High	140.00

Stoneware is a coarse glazed and fired potter's ware that is used to make crocks, jugs, etc.

Stoneware, Barrel, Water, Gray, Cobalt Flower, Spigot, 15 X 11 In.	175.00
Stoneware, Bottle, Ink, Dark Brown Splashes On Light Brown	35.00
Stoneware, Bowl, Cowden, Light Brown Glaze, 8 1/2 X 4 3/4 In.	25.00
Stoneware, Box, Money, Buff, Brown Salt Glaze, Conical Finial, C.1850, 5 In.	20.00
Stoneware, Box, Salt, Wall, Wooden Top, Blue Design, 6 1/4 X 4 In.	40.00
Stoneware, Churn, Crock, Western Stoneware In Leaf & No.3	12.00
Stoneware, Crock, Cobalt Backward Pheasant & Whites, Utica, 3 Gallon	175.00
Stoneware, Crock, Cobalt Bird & White, Utica, 3 Gallon	100.00
Stoneware, Crock, Cobalt Fuchsia & Leaf On Tan, Salt Glaze, Eared, 5 Gallon	68.50
Stoneware, Crock, Cobalt Grouse On Branch & Ottman Bros, N.Y., 4 Gallon	90.00
Stoneware, Crock, Cobalt Large Bird, 4 Gallon	100.00
Stoneware, Crock, Covered, Gray, Cobalt Design, "Ice Water," 11 X 15 In.	200.00
Stoneware, Crock, Eagle Decoration, 3 Gallon	250.00
Stoneware, Crock, Hamilton & Jones, Greensboro, Pa., 2 Gallon	65.00
Stoneware, Crock, J.H.Dipple, Pa. & Tulip On Gray, Salt Glaze, 4 Gallon	75.00
Stoneware, Crock, Roberts, Binghamton, N.Y., 13 1/2 In. .... *Illus*	225.00
Stoneware, Crock, Southbridge, Mass., C.1850, Cobalt Bird, Branch, 12 1/2 In.	250.00

Stoneware, Crock, Roberts, Binghamton, N.Y., 13 1/2 In.

Stoneware, Crock, Wide Mouth, Glazed Inside & Out, Front Design, 9 In.	40.00
Stoneware, Gallipot, Vinegar, Spout, Round, Brown, 5 1/2 In., Pair	25.00
Stoneware, Inkwell, Cone Shape, Tan, 2 3/4 In.	22.00
Stoneware, Jar, Covered, Gray, Blue Decoration, 5 In.	12.00
Stoneware, Jar, Cowden, Wide Mouth, Medium Brown Glaze In & Out, 6 1/2 In.	25.00
Stoneware, Jar, Storage, Ocher Leaves, No.1 In Circle, 10 1/2 In.	47.00
Stoneware, Jar, Wide Mouth, Brown Glaze Inside & Out, Cowden, 6 1/2 In.	25.00
Stoneware, Jug, Batter, Brown, Bulbous, Handle, Spout, 10 In.	25.00
Stoneware, Jug, Bear Holding Cub, Brown Glaze, Monkey Handle, C.1850, 11 In.	175.00
Stoneware, Jug, Blue Decoration, Norton Bennington, Vt., Gallon	63.00
Stoneware, Jug, Cobalt Bird On Branch & J.& E. Norton, Vt., 1 1/2 Gallon	150.00
Stoneware, Jug, Cobalt Bird On Branch & Whites, Utica, Gallon	95.00
Stoneware, Jug, Cobalt Bird On Stump & West Troy Pottery, 2 Gallon	125.00
Stoneware, Jug, Cobalt Running Bird & Whites, Utica, 2 Gallon	95.00
Stoneware, Jug, Cobalt Scrolls, Handled, Gallon	20.00
Stoneware, Jug, Cobalt Star & Leaf Spray, F.A.Plaisted, Gardiner, 13 In.	48.00
Stoneware, Jug, Cobalt 1863 & Whites, Utica, Gallon	150.00
Stoneware, Jug, Covered, Cobalt Brushwork, Loop Handles, C.1850, 14 In.	175.00
Stoneware, Jug, Cowden, Dark Brown Glaze, Handle, 8 In.	25.00
Stoneware, Jug, Dark Blue Floral Grouping, Tyler & Co., New York, Gallon	26.00
Stoneware, Jug, E & LP Norton, Bennington, Vt., Cobalt Flower, 2 Gallon	68.00
Stoneware, Jug, Green & Blue Bird On Flower, 2 Gallon	95.00
Stoneware, Jug, Hand-Painted 1880 3 Masted Schooner At Sea, Gallon	20.00
Stoneware, Jug, Honey, Cowden, Medium Brown Glaze In & Out, Handle, 7 In.	45.00
Stoneware, Jug, Hunt, Hound Handle, 4 1/4 In.High	75.00
Stoneware, Jug, Incised Flower On Dark, Gallon	425.00
Stoneware, Jug, W.H.Leheu And Co., Strasburg, Va., Tulip, 2 Gallon	75.00
Stoneware, Pitcher, Batter, Cobalt Tulip & Whites, Binghamton	195.00
Stoneware, Pitcher, Blue & White, Apricot, 5 In.	45.00
Stoneware, Pitcher, Blue Dutch Girl & Boy Kissing & Windmill, 6 3/4 In.	40.00
Stoneware, Pitcher, Blue Gray, Relief Tavern Scene, Leaf Borders, 9 1/2 In.	85.00
Stoneware, Pitcher, Blue Sponge Decoration, Handle, 9 In.High	70.00
Stoneware, Pitcher, Blue, Cows, 8 In.	45.00
Stoneware, Pitcher, Brown, Reeded Handle, 8 1/2 In.	25.00
Stoneware, Pitcher, Buff & Lavender Blue, Rose Trellis, 7 3/4 In.	37.50
Stoneware, Pitcher, Gray, Blue Spatter, 3 Quart, 8 3/4 In.	55.00
Stoneware, Pitcher, Milk, Embossed Paneled Scales, Flower Medallions, Blue	17.50
Stoneware, Pitcher, Salt Glaze Type, Blue Gray, Carnation & Buttercup, 9 In.	45.00
Stoneware, Pitcher, Swastika Design Center, Blue Bands, Large	30.00
Stoneware, Pitcher, Two Blue Bands Top & Bottom, 7 1/2 In.High	25.00
Stoneware, Plate, Brown Transfer Venus, Pearl, P.W.& Co., 9 3/4 In.	12.00
Stoneware, Spittoon, Tan	8.00
Stoneware, Syrup, Gray, Peacock Decoration, East Aurora, N.Y.	35.00
Stoneware, Vase, Two Tone Blues, 12 1/2 In.	35.00
Stonware, Jug, White's Utica, Cobalt, Running Bird, 2 Gallon	145.00
Store, see also Card, Advertising, Coffee Grinder, Tool, Scale	
Store, Animal Mill, For Butter Churn, C.1800, 5 X 4 X 2 In.	200.00
Store, Ashtray, Ball Fruit Jar, Square, 4 In.	2.00
Store, Ashtray, Charles Dunn Machinery, Kansas City, Mo., Glass	17.50
Store, Ashtray, Continental Tire	5.00
Store, Ashtray, Coor's Beer, Ceramic	2.00
Store, Ashtray, Dobbs' Hats, Brown Glass, Top Hat Shape	6.00
Store, Ashtray, Goodyear Tire	7.00
Store, Ashtray, Mr.Peanut, Figure Center, Gold Plated Metal	15.00
Store, Ashtray, Pete's Cafe, Boonville, Missouri, Drunk On Lamppost, Iron	8.50
Store, Ashtray, Tire, PA RUBBER CO., JEANNETTE, PA., 3 X 4 IN.	16.75
Store, Back Bar & Waiting Bench, Barbershop, Oak, Carved, 1909, Berninghaus	500.00
Store, Badge, Kellogg's Pep	3.00
Store, Bag, George Washington Cut Plug Tobacco, Quilted Top, 62 X 79 In.	35.00
Store, Bag, Oceanic Cut Plug Tobacco, C.1914, Cloth	.70
Store, Bank, Eight O'Clock Coffee, Tin	4.00
Store, Banner, Kansas Sun Choice Wheat Flour, Linen, Embroidered, 29 In.	95.00
Store, Banner, Smith Organ & Piano, 22 X 17 In.	16.00
Store, Bar, Back, Marble, Nickel Silver Base, Mirror, Hanging Lamps, 8 Ft.	900.00
Store, Barometer & Thermometer, Labeled Cottage, 3 X 9 In.	25.00
Store, Barrel, Briggs' Tobacco, Wooden, Quart	10.00

Store, Basket, Berry, Splint, Handled, 3 X 3 1/2 In.	12.00
Store, Basket, Egg, Wire, Folding, 8 1/2 X 11 In.	3.50
Store, Basket, Egg, Wire, 6 In.	9.00
Store, Basket, Jewel Tea, 6 1/2 In.	10.00
Store, Basket, Rye, 10 In.	18.00
Store, Basket, Splint & Raffia Weave, 11 1/2 X 17 In.	10.00
Store, Basket, Splint, Swing Handle, Handmade, C.1850, 10 In.	55.00
Store, Basket, Woven, Green, Round, 5 1/2 X 3 1/2 In.	1.50
Store, Basket, Woven, Oval, 6 1/2 X 7 1/4 In.	5.50
Store, Bin, Coffee, King Bee, Wood, Stenciling On Front	165.00
Store, Bin, Golden Rule Blend Coffee, Gold & Black Letters On Green, Ohio	40.00
Store, Bin, J.M.Bour's Co. Coffee, Gold Letters On Green	65.00
Store, Bin, Sweet Cuba Tobacco, Green	58.00
Store, Bit, Medicine, Horse, Dr.LeGear	45.00
Store, Blotter, Duffy's Malt Whiskey	3.00
Store, Blotter, Ink, Buster Brown Shoes, Tige	2.00
Store, Blotter, Shadow, Blue	8.00
Store, Blotter, Shoe Repair, Pictures Of Washington To Hoover, 1930	1.00
Store, Booklet, Palace Theatre Presents Madame Sarah Bernhardt, 1912	16.00
Store, Booklet, Premium Stamp, L.H.Parke Co., Coffee & Tea, 1912	4.50
Store, Booklet, Quo Vadis, 1913, Silent Version	8.00
Store, Bootjack, see also Iron, Bootjack	
Store, Bootjack, Beetle, Gilt	22.00
Store, Bootjack, Musselman's Plug Tobacco, Cast Iron, 10 In.	35.00
Store, Bootjack, Patent 1859, Step On Clamp	20.00
Store, Bootjack, Pittsburgh Novelty Works, Buggy Wrench End, Iron, 13 In.	50.00
Store, Bottle Capper, Iron	4.00
Store, Box, Bee, 3 Compartments, Wooden	22.00
Store, Box, Blasting Caps, Miner's, Sliding Lid, Dovetailed, 10 1/2 X 5 In.	25.75
Store, Box, Blueberry, Maine, Wooded Pegs, Copper Nails, Round, Quart	6.00
Store, Box, Carter's Ink, Wooden, Red & Black, Quart Size	20.00
Store, Box, Cheese, D.Beal On Bottom, Rosehead & Square Nails, Round, 7 In.	35.00
Store, Box, Coffee, Capital, Wooden, Floor Model, Slant Lift Lid, Stenciled	135.00
Store, Box, Coffee, Jersey, Floor Model, Slant Lift Lid, Stenciled	145.00
Store, Box, Daniel Boone Cigars, C.C.Bickel & Co., Wooden	4.50
Store, Box, Display, Esterbrook, Wooden, Drawer, Glass Top, Painted	25.00
Store, Box, Display, Unrivalled Crackers, James McClurg & Co., 12 In. ..... *Illus*	50.00
Store, Box, Dr.LeGear's Poultry Prescription, 6 1/2 In.	3.00
Store, Box, Dr.LeGear's Stock Powders, Trial Size	7.00
Store, Box, Fun To Wash Washing Powder, C.1890, Negro Mammy, 5 X 7 X 3 In.	5.00
Store, Box, Gold Dust Washing Powder, Orange, Black, & White, 5 Ozs.	4.00
Store, Box, Grape Nuts, Tin, Yellow & Black, 14 Ozs.	3.00
Store, Box, Ivin's Spiced Wafers, Wooden, 21 X 14 X 10 In.	39.00
Store, Box, Ke-No Cigars, Wooden	2.00

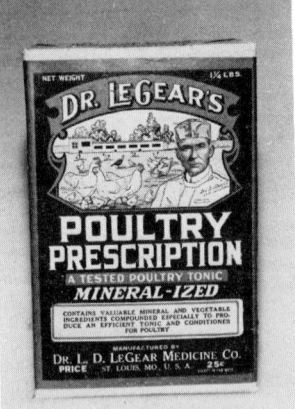

Store, Box, Dr.Le Gear's Poultry Prescription, 6 1/2 In.

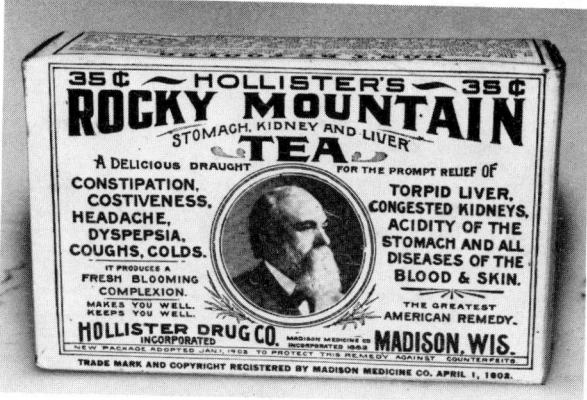

Store, Box, Rocky Mountain Tea, Paper, 5 X 3 In.

Store, Box, Kentucky Twist Tobacco, Pine, 20 X 10 X 8 In.	15.00
Store, Box, Mason's Shoe Blacking, Black Man's Picture, 7 X 11 X 5 In.	25.00
Store, Box, Page's Seed, Oak, Hinged Lid, 12 Compartments, 11 X 7 1/2 In.	15.00
Store, Box, Pencil, Boy Scouts In Camp On Cover, C.1918	3.95
Store, Box, Pencil, Oak, Sliding Cover, 10 X 1 In.	5.00
Store, Box, Pencil, Round, 2 Part, 9 In.	12.00
Store, Box, Quaker Puffed Rice	3.00
Store, Box, Quaker Puffed Wheat	3.00
Store, Box, Remington Express DuPont Shotgun Shells, Pine, 15 X 9 X 9 In.	10.00
Store, Box, Rocky Mountain Tea, Paper, 5 X 3 In.	*Illus* 3.00
Store, Box, S.S.Marvin Biscuits, Paper Label, 11 1/2 X 10 X 10 In.	28.00
Store, Box, Schrafft's Candy, Metal Hinged	3.00
Store, Box, The Saturday Evening Post Cigars	2.25
Store, Box, Tyrell's Hygienic Aid, Wooden, Dovetailed	5.00
Store, Box, Union Pacific Railroad Cigars	2.25
Store, Box, W.H.Bull's Herb & Iron Blood Purifier, Pine, 18 X 11 X 11 In.	15.00
Store, Box, Walker's Cracker Jack Headache Cure, Wooden, 9 X 7 X 3 In.	12.00
Store, Box, Winchester Shotgun Cartridges, Pine, Tongue & Groove, 15 X 9 In.	10.00
Store, Broadside, Auction, Daisy Cows, C.1910, 9 X 13 In.	7.50
Store, Broadside, John Wilkes Booth In Damon & Pythias, 1864, 14 1/2 In.	450.00
Store, Broadside, John Wilkes Booth In Pescara, 1863, 6 X 18 In.	450.00
Store, Broadside, Queen Of Baltimore 5 Cent Cigar, C.1850, 18 X 24 In.	20.00
Store, Broadside, Statue Of Liberty, 1887, 8 X 14 In.	20.00
Store, Bucket, Guaranteed Laundry Powder, Swift & Co., Wooden, 25 Lbs.	14.00
Store, Bucket, Hellick's Peanut Butter, Wire Handle, 2 Lbs.	7.50
Store, Bucket, Maple Sap, Wooden, 2 1/2 Gallon	4.50
Store, Button, Buster Brown Bread, Pinback	5.00
Store, Button, Colonel Roscoe Turner, H.J.Heinz, C.1930, Pinback	5.00
Store, Button, Dan Dunn, Evening Ledger Comics, Pinback	3.50
Store, Button, Felix The Cat, Evening Ledger Comics, Pinback	4.50
Store, Button, Joe DiMaggio, Pinback	3.00
Store, Button, Kellogg's Pep, Uncle Walt	2.50
Store, Button, Planter's Peanut, Mr.Peanut, Celluloid, Pinback, C.1930	2.25
Store, Buttonhook, see also Art Nouveau, Buttonhook, Brass, Buttonhook, Silver Plate, Buttonhook, Silver, Sterling, Buttonhook	
Store, Buttonhook & Shoehorn, Sterling Silver, Folding, Leather Case	25.00
Store, Buttonhook, Art Nouveau Woman's Profile, Sterling Silver	15.00
Store, Buttonhook, Celluloid	4.00
Store, Buttonhook, Connie & Mayer	1.50
Store, Buttonhook, Glove, Folding, Mother-Of-Pearl Handle, 1 5/8 In. Closed	5.95
Store, Buttonhook, Glove, Gold Plated, Ring	4.00
Store, Buttonhook, Glove, Ivory Handle	5.00
Store, Buttonhook, Glove, Sterling Silver	5.95
Store, Buttonhook, Glove, Sterling Silver, Folding	12.50

Store, Buttonhook, Ornate Handle, 6 1/2 In.	10.50
Store, Buttonhook, Ornate Sterling Silver Handle, 7 1/2 In.	4.95
Store, Buttonhook, Sir Raleigh Spats	1.50
Store, Buttonhook, Sterling Silver, Repousse	20.00
Store, Buttonhook, Wooden Handle	6.00
Store, Cabinet, Angel Dainty Dyes, Wooden, Stenciled Front	65.00
Store, Cabinet, Bread, Counter, Wooden, Glass On 3 Sides	50.00 To 150.00
Store, Cabinet, Buston Leathers, Wooden, Glass Front, 16 X 15 X 10 In.	45.00
Store, Cabinet, Clark's Mile End, Chestnut, 2 Drawer, Floral, 21 X 14 In.	95.00
Store, Cabinet, Clark's, Spool, Oak, 2 Drawer	75.00
Store, Cabinet, Diamond Dye, Tin Front, Maypole	490.00
Store, Cabinet, Diamond Dye, Tin, Children With Balloon	200.00
Store, Cabinet, Diamond Dye, 24 X 15 In.	175.00
Store, Cabinet, Dr.Moyer's Horse & Cattle Medicines, Wooden, 12 X 11 In.	225.00
Store, Cabinet, Dyola Dye, Wooden, Tin On Front Door	100.00
Store, Cabinet, Myers Co., Rochester, Display, Oak, Cubbyhole	45.00
Store, Cabinet, O.N.T. Spool, Walnut, 2 Drawer	69.00
Store, Cabinet, Putnam Dye, General Putnam On Horse, Tin	25.00
Store, Cabinet, Spice, Sauer's Flavoring Extracts, 3 Glass Sides, 20 In.	110.00
Store, Cabinet, Spool, Clark's, Oak, 2 Drawer	65.00
Store, Cabinet, Spool, Clark's, 2 Drawers, Ruby Glass Inserts, Brass Knobs	75.00
Store, Cabinet, Spool, Merrick's, Oak, Brass Ring Pulls, 5 Drawer, 30 In.	285.00
Store, Cabinet, Spool, Oak, Curved Glass Front, 1867, 50 In.	250.00
Store, Cabinet, Spool, Oak, 4 Drawer	150.00
Store, Cabinet, Thread, Star, Metal, 2 Drawer	25.00
Store, Cage, Dice, From Saloon In Colorado	65.00
Store, Calendar, see also Dionne Quintuplet, Calendar, Shaker, Calendar	
Store, Calendar, C.1920, Singer Sewing Machine, Perpetual, Tin	49.00
Store, Calendar, Fairy Soap, 1900	10.00
Store, Calendar, 1883, Dr.Morse's Indian Root Pills, Indian On Horseback	4.50
Store, Calendar, 1892, All The Year Through, Envelope	5.00
Store, Calendar, 1897, Hood's Sarsaparilla, Figural Victorian Child	6.50
Store, Calendar, 1898, Winchester, Hunting Scene, 15 X 8 In.	27.95
Store, Calendar, 1899, Colgate & Co., Patriot's	6.00
Store, Calendar, 1901, E.E.K. 10 Cent Cigars, Girl & Telephone	34.00
Store, Calendar, 1903, Pabst Malt Extract, Scroll, Geisha, 36 In.	45.00
Store, Calendar, 1906, Seattle, Washington, Dutch Girl & Boy, Hardboard	5.00
Store, Calendar, 1910, Prudential, Girl Blowing Bubbles	5.00
Store, Calendar, 1913, John P.Dant, Louisville, Ky., Grandpa & Grandma	25.00
Store, Calendar, 1916, J.J.Thompson, General Blacksmith	10.00
Store, Calendar, 1925, Holland Flower Girl, Signed Print	3.00
Store, Calendar, 1925, Sunshine Girl, Signed Print	3.00
Store, Can, Black Powder Blasting, Colorado, Funnel Nozzle, 13 In.	10.00
Store, Can, Brownie Salted Pecans, United Fig & Date Co., 1915, 5 Pound	25.00
Store, Can, Burgermeister Beer, 2 Pack In Cardboard Holder	4.00
Store, Can, Cream, 10 Quart	8.00
Store, Can, Ginna, Bret Harte Pictures, Heathen Chinee, Tin, 4 1/2 In.	12.00
Store, Can, Heinz Olives, Black, Circle Design, Gallon	35.00
Store, Can, Ice Cream, 5 Gallon	5.00
Store, Can, Imperial Coal Oil, 3 Ft.	25.00
Store, Can, Johnson's Milco Malt, 16 Ozs.	3.00
Store, Can, Milk, Schoolhouse, Wooden Stopper, Tin, Pint	7.75
Store, Can, Milk, Tin, 2 Gallon	7.00
Store, Can, Milk, Tin, 3 Gallon	7.00
Store, Can, Oil, Lithographed, 2 Gallon	1.40
Store, Cane, Boye Needle, Wood & Tin, Children & Lady, 19 In.	67.00
Store, Case, Cavalier Cigarettes, Plastic	1.00
Store, Case, Eveready Batteries, Battery Tester, Sheet Metal, 15 X 9 In.	42.50
Store, Case, J.P.Coats Co. Thread & Yarn, 4 Drawer, Table Model, 3 Ft.	150.00
Store, Case, Motorcycle Tool, Leather, Handle, 6 X 3 1/2 X 3 1/2 In.	10.00
Store, Case, Optician's, Walnut, Brass Trim, 49 Lenses	45.00
Store, Case, Scissors, Terry, Revolving Cylinder In Middle, 11 X 11 X 28 In.	85.00
Store, Case, Stamp, Hamilton Watch, Celluloid	12.00
Store, Case, Thurlow, Homeo Cures, Wooden, 1891, 15 X 10 X 5 1/2 In.	55.00
Store, Cash Drawer, Tucker Alarm Till, Country Store	30.00

609

Store, Cash Register, Model 567, Brass Feet, Mahogany Case, 66 In.	575.00
Store, Cash Register, National, Copper, Dated 1908, Rings To 1 Dollar	300.00
Store, Cash Register, National, Hand Crank, Brown	35.00
Store, Cash Register, National, Patent Date 1905, Brass	325.00
Store, Cash Register, National, Series 336, Brass	225.00
Store, Cash Register, National, Size 356-G, Brass, Ornate	250.00
Store, Cash Register, National, Wood Grain, Marble Shelf, Up To 1 Dollar	75.00
Store, Cash Register, National, 1903, Chest Type, 5 Drawer	125.00
Store, Chair, Barber, Child's, Horse's Head On Front Of Seat, Adjustable	275.00
Store, Chair, Dentist's, Victorian, Walnut, Leather, & Iron	79.00
Store, Charm, Cracker Jacks, Tin Clock	10.00
Store, Charm, Swift's Premium Ham	2.50
Store, Check Protector, Royal, Rouse Maf.Co., Patent May 3, 1898, 5 1/4 In.	17.50
Store, Cigar Store Indian, Counter Top, Plaster, Painted, C.1880, 32 1/2 In.	225.00
Store, Cigar, Exploding, Makes Fan, C.1880	15.00
Store, Claw, Police Restraint Device, Patent May 18, 1884, Nickel Plated	54.50
Store, Cleaner, Bean, Treadle, Clipper Patent 1902	85.00
Store, Clip, Bill, L.F.Grammes & Sons, Allentown, Pa., Brass, Girl's Head	4.95
Store, Clip, Paper, Los Angeles Rubber Stamp Co., Metal	3.00
Store, Clipboard, Van Leer, Phila., Universal, Calendar, Brass, 8 X 5 In.	17.00
Store, Clock, Dr.Pepper, Electric, C.1940	40.00
Store, Clock, Dr.Pepper, Red Brick Background	50.00
Store, Clock, Utica Club Beer, Steins & Glass Of Beer, Electric, 15 In.	35.00
Store, Coaster, A-1 Beer, Metal	5.00
Store, Coaster, Canadian Ace Beer, Metal	5.00
Store, Coaster, Simon Pure Beer, Metal	5.00
Store, Coffee Grinder, see Coffee Grinder	
Store, Coil, Tesla, A.Gaiffe, Paris, C.1900, Mahogany Base, 16 In.	450.00
Store, Collar, Sled Dog Harness	17.50
Store, Comb, Clothier, Lebanon, Pa., Aluminum, Handsaw Shape	7.50
Store, Comb, Good Housekeeping, Aluminum	2.00
Store, Container, Barrabee Cookies, Tin, Glass Front, 10 X 10 X 11 In.	20.00
Store, Container, Gum, Adams Pure Chewing Gum, Glass, 12 In.High	38.50
Store, Container, Porter Candy, Cardboard, C.1930, 13 X 8 X 3 In.	6.00
Store, Cork Sizer, 4 Slots, Cast Iron, 10 In.	35.00
Store, Corkscrew & Bottle Cap Opener, Sterling Container, Ashlee	22.50
Store, Corkscrew & Bottle Opener, Green River Whiskey, Metal	9.00
Store, Corkscrew & Bottle Opener, Lemp Brewing Co., Wooden Handle, 1893	15.00
Store, Corkscrew Inside 8 Mm. German Bullet	3.00
Store, Corkscrew, Anheuser Busch, Bottle Shape, Metal, Brass Label	6.00
Store, Corkscrew, Old Forester Whiskey, Louisville, Bullet Shape	12.00
Store, Corn Husker, Black Hawk, Dated 1903	12.50
Store, Corn Husker, Hand Crank, Cast Iron	6.50
Store, Corn Husker, Universal, Brass, 1882	20.00
Store, Counter, Grain Bin Merchandiser, 30 Glass Fronted Bins, 12 Ft.	845.00
Store, Coupon, Gas Ration, 1943	3.50
Store, Cradle, Kleinert's Waterproof Baby Pants, Tin, 12 1/2 X 7 1/2 In.	75.00
Store, Creamer, Kellog's, Glass, 3 In.	3.50 To 9.50
Store, Cribbage Board, Lash's Kidney & Liver Bitters	45.00
Store, Crock, A.P.Donagho, Parkersburg, W.Va., Blue Stenciled, 11 In.	14.00
Store, Crystal Ball, Sepharial, 1920, Black Box, Instructions	50.00
Store, Cup & Saucer, Baker's Chocolate, Shelley, La Belle Chocolate On Cup	23.00
Store, Cup, Cyclist's, Telescopic, 1900, Cyclists On Cover	16.00
Store, Cup, Measuring, Health Club Baking Powder	4.25
Store, Cup, Measuring, Planter's Peanuts, Tin	25.00
Store, Cutter, Cigar, Brumoff Mfg.Co., 1902, Double Matchbox	65.00
Store, Cutter, Cigar, Mala Fond & Co., Detriot, Mich., Finger	4.50
Store, Cutter, Cigar, May & Schubert Manufacturers, Cast Iron Pig	65.00
Store, Cutter, Cigar, Miller Bros., Knife, Copper Handle, Single Blade	20.00
Store, Cutter, Cigar, Nude Woman Sitting On Potty, Brass, 1 1/2 In.	100.00
Store, Cutter, Cigar, Stratton & Storm Segars, Figural Indian, Owl, 1 1/2 Ft.	800.00
Store, Cutter, Tobacco, Brown's Mule Store	35.00
Store, Cutter, Tobacco, Cast Iron, Enterprise Mfg.Co., Philadelphia	25.00
Store, Cutter, Tobacco, Counter Type, Iron	20.00
Store, Cutter, Tobacco, Five Brothers	35.00
Store, Cutter, Tobacco, Star Store	30.00

Store, Cylinder, Wallpaper Printing, Aluminum, Brass Designs, C.1830 .... 15.00
Store, Cylinder, Wallpaper, Printing, Maple, Brass Designs, C.1830 .... 25.00
Store, Cylinger, Wallpaper, Printing, Maple, Brass Designs, 24 X 6 In. 35.00
Store, Decoder, ROA, 1935, Secret Society Code Book, Premium 30.00
Store, Dipper, Ice Cream, Cone Shape, Tin 10.00
Store, Dish, Schrafft's Chocolates, Imitation Cut Glass 8.00
Store, Dispenser, Candy, Metal Spring Door, 18 X 6 X 6 In. 45.00
Store, Dispenser, Iced Tea, N.E.Tea Co., Black Amethyst Base, Barrel Shape 25.00
Store, Dispenser, Matches, Kool Cigarettes, Tin, Penguin 6.00
Store, Dispenser, Mission Orange Syrup 90.00
Store, Dispenser, Syrup, Emerald Isle, Shamrock Shape, Vaseline & Milk Glass 165.00
Store, Display, Emilla Garcia Cigars, Stand-Up, C.1920, 26 X 40 In. 26.00
Store, Display, Garcia Grande Cigars, Tin, Electric Lighter 35.00
Store, Display, Moth-Ene Moth Proofer, C.1915, Stand-Up, 26 X 40 In. 20.00
Store, Display, Old Grand Dad, Hourglass, Pedestal, Metal, Swivel Shape 19.50
Store, Display, Red Comet Fire Control, Gray Wood Stand, 2 Bonds, 16 In. 35.00
Store, Display, Winchester Super X Model Autoloading Shotgun, 18 In. 20.00
Store, Dryer, Corn, Cast Iron, 19 In. 15.00
Store, Duster, Turkey Feather, Hoag's Columbus Janitor 15.00
Store, Engine, Gasoline, 3 Horsepower, Stationary, 2 Fly Wheels 300.00
Store, Engine, Hot Air Pump, Erickson, 1890 .... 900.00
Store, Engine, Steam, Bronze & Copper, Vertical, 9 1/2 X 6 1/2 In. 90.00
Store, Eyecup, Italian, Crystal, Pedestal, 2 3/4 In. 12.00
Store, Eyecup, John Bull Patent 1917, Clear Glass 3.75
Store, Eyecup, Wilson, Wine Color, Double, Hard Plastic, Nosepiece 8.50
Store, Fan Hanger, Hambone Cigars 6.00
Store, Fan Hanger, James Bryce Cigars, C.1910 .... 2.00
Store, Fan Hanger, Red Dot Cigars, 2 Sided 4.50
Store, Fan Hanger, Toiletine, 1913, 2 Sided 6.00
Store, Fan, Ceiling, Ice Cream Parlor, Wooden Blades 95.00
Store, Fan, Dr.Pepper, C.1930, Hand 5.00
Store, Fan, Moxie, Pretty Girl 15.00
Store, Fan, Sloan Ice Cream, C.1900, 9 In. 7.00
Store, Fan, Toiletine For Bruises, Double Face, Hanging, 1913, 10 In. 9.50
Store, Figurine, Campbell's Kid, Bisque, 9 In. 12.50
Store, Figurine, Mellin's Food-Our Baby, Bisque Tot In High Chair, 5 In. 26.00
Store, Filler, Alcohol Lamp, Patent 1908, Metal, Screw Top, 3 In. 5.00
Store, Flashlight, Everready, Patent 1899 .... 9.00
Store, Flashlight, Winchester, Chrome, 15 In. 17.50
Store, Fly Trap, Applied Neck Ring, C.1780, 6 3/4 In. .... *Illus* 45.00

Store, Fly Trap, Applied Neck Ring, C.1780, 6 3/4 In.

Store, Fork, Butcher, Wrought Iron, 13 In. 15.00
Store, Fork, Planter's Peanuts, Mr.Peanut, Silver Plate 5.00
Store, Funnel & Measure, Apothecary, Clear Glass, 5 & 5 1/2 In. 25.00
Store, Goblet, Jelly, Marked Ball, Tin Cover 3.00
Store, Graduate, Pharmacist's, 8 Ozs. 2.00
Store, Grater, Fels Naphtha Soap 5.00
Store, Grinder, Corn, Clamp Down, Cast Iron 12.50
Store, Grinder, Meat, Butcher's, Hobart, Electric, 2 Horse Power 150.00
Store, Grinder, Peanut, Planter's 15.00
    Store, Gum Machine, see Store, Machine, Gum ball
Store, Gum Stand, Teaberry, Crystal 9.00
Store, Hammer, See's Candy, Metal 5.00
Store, Hanger, Coat, Collapsible, Nickel Plated, Patent 1913, Leather Case 2.95
Store, Harness Brass, Openwork Star In Crescent, 3 In. Diameter 14.00
Store, Hat Block, Wooden, Paco, Adjustable 8.00
Store, Hatpin, Malleable Steel Range Mfg.Co., Ind., Stove On Pin, 8 In. 6.50
Store, Holder, Broom, Hanging, Umbrella Shape, Wire 75.00
Store, Holder, Catalogue, Sears 15.00
Store, Holder, Cigar, Counter, Lankering Cigar Company, Brass 15.00
Store, Holder, Hose, Negro, Sprinklin' Sambo, Tin, 30 In. 45.00
Store, Holder, String & Bag, Wire, Round, 14 X 14 In. 25.00
Store, Holder, String, Ball, Cast Iron, Lacy, 4 In. 25.00
Store, Holder, String, Beehive .... 16.00 To 20.00
Store, Holder, String, Beehive, Iron 25.00
Store, Holder, String, Beehive, Ribbed Glass, 5 3/4 X 5 In. 20.00
Store, Holder, String, Bullman, Iron, Screws To Counter 15.00
Store, Holder, String, Clown's Head, 7 1/2 In. 7.50
Store, Holder, String, Figural, Apple 8.00
Store, Holder, String, Humpty-Dumpty, Glazed 5.00
Store, Holder, String, Iron, Ball Of Twine Shape 35.00
Store, Holder, String, Man In Top Hat Smoking Pipe, Wall Type 12.00
Store, Holder, String, Wall Type, Dutch Boy Smoking Pipe 10.00
Store, Hook, Corn Husking 1.25
Store, Hook, Harness, Made From Tree Branch, Carved, 15 In. & 10 In., Pair 20.00
Store, Humidor, Bulldog Tobacco 35.00
Store, Humidor, La Palina Cigars, Glass, Congress Cigar Co., 7 X 6 In. 27.50
Store, Hydrometer, Taylor, Pair 6.00
Store, Hydrometer, W.T.& T.V.Gendar, N.Y., Silver, Copper Handle, Ivory Dials 195.00
Store, Hygrometer, Friez Instruments Co., Chelsea Movement, Steel Case 55.00
Store, Jar, Buffalo Cold Cream, Larkin Co., Prunus Blossoms, 2 Ozs. 17.50
Store, Jar, Jumbo Brand Peanut Butter, Frank Tea & Spice Co., O., Pint 2.00
Store, Jar, Planter's Peanuts, 5 Pound 24.00
Store, Jar, Red Balt Tobacco, Counter Piece 15.00
Store, Jar, Sunshine Coffee, Embossed, Lb. 2.50
Store, Jug, A.P.Donagho, Parkersburg, W.Va., Blue Stenciled, 1/2 Gallon 17.00
Store, Jug, A.P.Donagho, Parkersburg, W.Va., Blue Stenciled, Gallon 17.00
Store, Jug, E.Swasey & Co., Portland, Maine, Brown & White, Gallon 8.50
Store, Jug, Handles, Pouring Spout, 2 Gallon 5.00
Store, Jug, S.S.Pierce Co., Boston, Gray, Gallon 8.50
Store, Keg, Powder, F.Jepson, Wooden, Wood Hoops & Plug, 6 X 4 1/2 In. 17.00
Store, Key, Jail, 5 In. 1.75
Store, Key, Jail, 7 In. 1.75
Store, Key, Ranch, 5 In. 1.75
Store, Key, Ranch, 7 In. 1.75
Store, Knife, Alexander Drug Co., Miller Bros., Ivory Handle, Single Blade 15.00
Store, Knife, Babe Ruth Bat 40.00
Store, Knife, Banana, Russell, Green River Works 10.00
Store, Knife, Boning, Green River On Blade, Russel, Thumb Guard 14.00
Store, Knife, Butcher, Russell, Green River Works, No.2333-9, 14 1/2 In. 10.00
Store, Knife, Meat Chopping, Metal, Single Curved Blade 10.00
Store, Knife, Nehi Soda, Shape Of Leg 30.00
Store, Knife, Nu-Grape, Metal 20.00
Store, Knife, Pocket, Coles Tobacco 8.00
Store, Knife, Pocket, Planter's Peanut, White Handle, Mr.Peanut, C.1960 .... 3.00
Store, Knife, Pocket, Wolf's Whiskey, Cigar Cutter & Corkscrew 12.00
Store, Knife, Purina, Red & White Checked Handle, 3 Blades 10.00

Store, Knife, Ralston, Tom Mix 25.00
Store, Label, Cigar, Paid In Full, Gold Embossed, 6 X 10 In. 2.00
Store, Label, Morning Sip Roast Coffee, C.1910, 9 X 22 In. 4.50
Store, Label, Rudolph Valentino Cigar, C.1925, 6 X 9 In. 3.50
Store, Last, Shoe, Child's, Wooden, Size 7 To 14, Per Pair 1.00
Store, Lifter, Hatbox, Falcon, Wooden, Kohn, Co., New Orleans, 36 In. 22.00
Store, Light, Wall, Carling's Black Label Beer 17.00
Store, Lighter, Cigar, Counter, Electric 40.00
Store, Lighter, Cigar, Figural, Scottish Hunter, Gas, 18 In. 100.00
Store, Lighter, Cigarette, Bowers Manufacture, World War II, Windproof ... 12.00
Store, Lighter, Cigarette, Camel Cigarettes, Lithographed, Metal 2.75
Store, Lighter, Cigarette, Chesterfield Cigarettes, Lithographed, Metal 2.75
Store, Lighter, Cigarette, Diamond Salt, Lighthouse Shape, Metal, 6 In. ... 8.00
Store, Lighter, Cigarette, Lucky Strike Cigarettes, Lithographed, Metal 2.75
Store, Lighter, Cigarette, Playboy Club 3.00
Store, Lighter, Cigarette, Salem 5.00
Store, Lighter, Miller Beer, Boxed 2.50
Store, Lock & Key, Sargent Builders' Upright Rim Store Door Deak Lock ... 10.00
Store, Lock, F.S.Hardware Co., Nokey, Brass, 2 1/4 X 2 In. 5.00
Store, Loom, Weaving, Pine, Table Top 65.00
    Store, Lunch Box, see also Disneyana, Lunch Box, Hopalong
    Cassidy, Lunch Box, Roy Rogers, Lunch Box
Store, Lunch Box, Airplane, Train, Motor Boats, & Skaters, C.1930 .... 4.00
Store, Lunch Box, Central Union Tobacco .... 14.00 To 35.00
Store, Lunch Box, Country Club Tobacco .... 120.00 To 225.00
Store, Lunch Box, Crow-Mo-Smokers' Tobacco 75.00
Store, Lunch Box, Dan Patch Tobacco 38.00
Store, Lunch Box, Dixie Kid, Black 135.00
Store, Lunch Box, Dixie Queen Tobacco .... 30.00 To 35.00
Store, Lunch Box, Dixie Queen Tobacco, Basket Weave 7.00
Store, Lunch Box, Fashion 70.00
Store, Lunch Box, Genuine Sweet Cuba Tobacco 18.00
Store, Lunch Box, Green Turtle Cigars 65.00
Store, Lunch Box, H & O 35.00
Store, Lunch Box, Handbag Tobacco 25.00
Store, Lunch Box, Just Suits 16.00
Store, Lunch Box, King Koal Stripped Tobacco 45.00
Store, Lunch Box, Laredo Tobacco 25.00
Store, Lunch Box, Leader Cut Plug 22.50
Store, Lunch Box, Lorillard Stripped Smoking Tobacco, Brown Check, 9 In. 24.00
Store, Lunch Box, Mayo's Cut Plug Tobacco 85.00
Store, Lunch Box, Mayo's Cut Plug, Dark Blue & Silver 12.00
Store, Lunch Box, Mayo's Tobacco 30.00
Store, Lunch Box, Patterson's Seal Cut Plug Tobacco .... 12.50 To 15.00
Store, Lunch Box, Pedro Tobacco .... 12.00 To 30.00
Store, Lunch Box, Plowboy Tobacco 55.00
Store, Lunch Box, Red Tiger Tobacco 32.00
Store, Lunch Box, Redicut Tobacco 50.00
Store, Lunch Box, Schaffer & Co., Shoe Sellers, Canton, O., Metal 10.00
Store, Lunch Box, Sensation Cut Plug Smoking Tobacco 175.00
Store, Lunch Box, Sensible Tobacco 16.00
Store, Lunch Box, Sweet Cuba Tobacco 20.00
Store, Lunch Box, Tiger Tobacco, Blue 20.00
Store, Lunch Box, Tiger Tobacco, Red 32.00
Store, Lunch Box, U.S.Marine Cut Plug Tobacco 10.00
Store, Lunch Box, U.S.Marine Tobacco, Basket Weave 16.00
Store, Lunch Box, Union Leader Cut Plug Tobacco, Slot In Top .... 8.00 To 15.00
Store, Lunch Box, Union Leader Tonacco 35.00
Store, Lunch Box, Warnick & Brown Tobacco .... 20.00 To 50.00
Store, Lunch Box, Winner Cut Plug Tobacco .... 30.00 To 40.00
Store, Lunch Box, Winner Tobacco 70.00
Store, Lunch Box, Worker Cut Plug Tobacco, Green 15.00
Store, Lunch Box, Worker Tobacco 65.00
Store, Machine, Arcade Gum Ball Shooting Gallery, 1 Cent, 18 X 10 X 24 In. 75.00
Store, Machine, Arcade Roll-A-Dice, 1 Cent 22.00
Store, Machine, Aspirin, 10 Cents ....

Store, Machine, Astroscope, 5 Cents 150.00
Store, Machine, Athletic Scale, Test Your Grip, 1 Cent 80.00
Store, Machine, Baseball, Pop Up, Wood, 5 Cents 125.00
Store, Machine, Basketball, Long Shot, 1 Cent 80.00
Store, Machine, Blasting, DuPont, Wood 65.00
Store, Machine, Bubble, Cast Iron, Motorized 69.50
Store, Machine, Buckley, Iron Claw, Arcade 650.00
Store, Machine, Card Vendor, Dispenses Movie Stars Photos 48.00
Store, Machine, Challanger Guns, Coin-Operated, 5 Cents .... 150.00 To 175.00
Store, Machine, Chicago Pro Basketball, Arcade, Coin 250.00
Store, Machine, Chicago Pro-Hockey, Arcade, Coin 250.00
Store, Machine, Cigarette, Wall, Metal, World War II, 3 Ft.X 10 In. 15.00
Store, Machine, Cub Gum Ball, 1 Cent, Vest Pocket Size 75.00
Store, Machine, Daval 5 Cent Gum, Slot, Free Games 150.00
Store, Machine, Gum Ball, Bones, Penny Slot 160.00
Store, Machine, Gum Ball, Buffalo 169.00
Store, Machine, Gum Ball, Pace Co., Chicago, 1933, Metal, Black, 11 X 9 In. .. 165.00
Store, Machine, Gum Ball, Races, Penny Slot 195.00
Store, Machine, Gum Ball, Wooden, Pistol Shoots Penny At Bell 150.00
Store, Machine, Gum Ball, 1 Armed Bandit, Bear Tavern 200.00
Store, Machine, Gum Vendor, Key, 1 Cent 29.00
Store, Machine, Hot Nut, 5 Cent, World War I Period, 14 X 7 In. 35.00
Store, Machine, Jaw Teaser, 1 Cent 14.50
Store, Machine, Jeweler's Engraving, Nickel Plate, Oak Bench, 23 X 19 In. .. 165.00
Store, Machine, Jigsaw Pinball, Coin-Operated, 5 Cents 395.00
Store, Machine, Kicker Catcher, Arcade 85.00
Store, Machine, Knitting, Family, Gearhart's, 1914, Ribbon Attachment .. 32.00
Store, Machine, Knitting, Sock & Mitten, Gearhart's, 1906, Cast Iron ... 60.00
Store, Machine, Leather Cutting, To 12 In. Wide 85.00
Store, Machine, Marvel, Penny Slot 125.00
Store, Machine, Match Dispenser, Oak & Iron, Patent 1910, Penny 85.00
Store, Machine, Medical, Violet Ray, Case 26.00
Store, Machine, Metal Medal Stamper 400.00
Store, Machine, Metal Typer, Supply Of Medals 495.00
Store, Machine, Mill's, Gum, 1 Cent 15.00
Store, Machine, Mutoscope, Caught Between The Acts, Electric, 5 Cents ... 450.00
Store, Machine, Mutoscope, Diggers, Penny Arcade, Iron Claw Retrieves .. 375.00
Store, Machine, Mutoscope, Seeing Is Believing, Electric, 5 Cents 450.00
Store, Machine, Optical, Self Test, Wooden, Patent 1928 .... 13.00
Store, Machine, Pace Comet, 1937, Pays In Gold Balls, 10 Cents 300.00
Store, Machine, Paper Match Book, Dispenser, Hawkeye Novelty Co., C.1920 .. 25.00
Store, Machine, Peanut, Aluminum & Glass, 13 In.High 40.00
Store, Machine, Pencil Dispenser, 5 Cents 25.00
Store, Machine, Personality Indicator, Electric, Stand, 5 Cents 150.00
Store, Machine, Poker, J.P.Mills, Jockey, 7-18-02, 5 Reel 750.00
Store, Machine, Pulver Chewing Gum, Policeman Hits Man On Head, Penny .. 200.00
Store, Machine, Pulver Gum, Mechanical Clown, 1 Cent 125.00
Store, Machine, Pulver Chewing Gum, Yellow Kid On Blue 75.00
Store, Machine, Question Answerer, Electric 395.00
Store, Machine, Red Pin Bowler, Chicago, Coin Operated, 7 Ft.10 In.X 6 Ft. .. 250.00
Store, Machine, Renu-Life Electric-Violet Ray Generator, 4 Electrodes .. 30.00
Store, Machine, Romance Register, Electric, Stand, 5 Cents 150.00
Store, Machine, Rug, Wilson Easy Way, Wood, 6 1/2 In. 14.00
Store, Machine, Saw Filing 85.00
Store, Machine, Select-O-Veno Tab Gum, 1 Cent 15.00
Store, Machine, Shooting Gallery, English, Reward Of Gift 400.00
Store, Machine, Silent Mystery, Mill's, 5 Cent Slot 750.00
Store, Machine, Slot, German, Wall, Half Dollars 175.00
Store, Machine, Slot, Rotomint, German, Electric, 5 Cent Coin 295.00
Store, Machine, Slot, Silver King, 1922, 5 Cent Slot, 24 1/2 X 14 In. ... 850.00
Store, Machine, Slot, Watling, Roll-A-Top, 5 & 10 Cents .... 400.00 To 850.00
Store, Machine, Sultan's Harem, Peep, Penny Slot 250.00
Store, Machine, U.S.Marshal, Coin-Operated, 10 Shots For 5 Cents 75.00
Store, Machine, U.S.Postage Stamp Dispenser, Porcelain, 19 1/2 X 8 In. .. 35.00
Store, Machine, Winshurst, L.Bonetti, Paris, C.1900, Black Wooden Base .. 295.00
Store, Machine, X-Ray & Electro-Vibration, F.Gottschalk, Md. 22.50

Store, Machine, 4 Cent Stamp 24.00
Store, Mailbox, George Collins Co., Glass, Embossed 17.50
Store, Mannequin, Lady, Corset Model, Camp Anatomical Supports, 25 In. 110.00
Store, Map, see also Print, Map
Store, Map Holder, Schoolhouse, Oak Case, Maps, Copyright 1914, 48 X 40 In. 115.00
Store, Map, Schoolhouse, Denoyer Gepper & Co., 1934, 7 Maps, 45 X 54 In. 100.00
Store, Match Holder, Dockash Stove Factory, Scranton, Pa., Tin, Hanging 23.00
Store, Match Holder, Dr.Pepper, C.1930, Tin 5.00
Store, Match Holder, Dr.Shoop's Health Coffee Imitation, Wall, Tin 8.00
Store, Match Holder, Humpty-Dumpty, Marked Patent Pending 6.50
Store, Match Holder, Old Judson Whiskey, Tin, Lithographed Scene 12.00
Store, Match Holder, Pabst Brewing Co., Pocket 17.50
Store, Match Holder, Safe Home, Tin, 5 In. 12.00
Store, Match Holder, San Felice Cigars, Pocket, Folding, Celluloid Center 19.00
Store, Match Holder, Table, New Haven, Patent 1864, Self Closing 18.00
Store, Match Safe, Anheuser Busch, Brass 16.00
Store, Match Safe, Anheuser Busch, Nickel Plated Brass 18.00
Store, Match Safe, Crystal Palace, Silver 18.00
Store, Match Safe, Murphy Varnish, Pocket, Brass 9.50
Store, Match Safe, Standard Oil Co., Barrel 18.50
Store, Match Safe, Wall, D.A.Baker, Warrenville, Ct., Wooden, Barrel Shape 7.75
Store, Matchbox Holder, Dr.Pepper, Green With Black, Patent Novelty, Fulton 4.95
Store, Matchbox Holder, Smokit Berkshire 5 Cent Cigar, Pocket 8.50
Store, Matchbox, Blazer's, Man Riding Bicycle 2.00
Store, Measure, Cloth, Putnam's Improved Cloth Chart, Chrome Plated Brass 15.00
Store, Measuring Glass, Dr.Burkhardt's Vegetable Compound, 2 Tablespoons 3.50
Store, Measuring Glass, Wetherall's For The Blood, Sarsaparilla 8.00
Store, Megaphone, St.Louis Cardinals, Baseball, Cardboard 3.00
Store, Menu, Willard's Hotel, Washington, D.C., 1862, 16 X 7 In. 20.00
Store, Meter, Gas, Coin, 1890 .... 30.00
Store, Microscope Set, Gilbert, Dated 1938, Original Wooden Box 16.00
Store, Microscope, Bausch & Lomb Optical Co. 19.50
Store, Mill, Sausage, Keen Kutter 4.00
Store, Mirror, Aetna, 3 1/2 In. 10.00
Store, Mirror, Angelus Marshmallows, 2 Angels On Box, Pocket 20.00
Store, Mirror, Bell's Coffee, Pocket 20.00
Store, Mirror, Campbell's Soups, Pocket 10.00
Store, Mirror, Cavitt's System Regulator, 2 In. 4.00
Store, Mirror, Copperclad Ranger, Oval, Pocket 5.00
Store, Mirror, Duffy's Pure Malt Whiskey, Pocket .... 10.00 To 24.00
Store, Mirror, Electric Burglar Alarms, 3 1/2 In. 12.00
Store, Mirror, Game, Putting Mice In Traps On Back, Pocket 7.00
Store, Mirror, Gamewell, Shape Of Fire Alarm Box, 17 X 10 In. 45.00
Store, Mirror, Grinnel Bros. Music House, Factory, Pocket 16.00
Store, Mirror, H.W.Gossard Co., Chicago, Lady Trying On Corset, Pocket 22.00
Store, Mirror, Hand, Jewish Daily Forward Newspaper, 1916, Calendar On Back 12.00
Store, Mirror, Hand, Plastic, Marked Florence, 1866, Embossed, 5 In. 45.00
Store, Mirror, Hires, Pocket 15.00
Store, Mirror, Hotel Pontchartrain, Brass, Pocket, Hand Mirror Shape 12.00
Store, Mirror, Klienert's Dress Shields, Pocket 15.00
Store, Mirror, Kregel Casket Co., St.Louis, Mo., 4 In. 12.50
Store, Mirror, Massachusetts Mutual Life Insurance, Pocket 17.50
Store, Mirror, Odd Fellows, Pocket .... .75
Store, Mirror, Pepsi Cola, Girl Holding Bottle, 15 1/2 X 13 1/2 In. 20.00
Store, Mirror, Van Camps Pork & Beans, Dutch Girl & Boy, Pocket 20.00
Store, Mirror, Vance's Shoes, Lady, Pocket 16.00
Store, Mirror, Vincent Pianos, Lady, Pocket 16.00
Store, Mirror, Zunder's Ginger Cordial, 4 In. 35.00
Store, Mold, see also Pewter, Mold, Tin, Mold
Store, Mold, Candy, Maple Leaf, Tin, 6 X 11 In., 6 Molds 22.00
Store, Mold, Cap, Wooden, Dated 1854 .... 13.50
Store, Mold, Chocolate, Begging Dog, 4 X 11 In. 37.50
Store, Mold, Chocolate, Boy In Knickers, 4 X 11 In. 37.50
Store, Mold, Chocolate, Grandfather Clocks, Helm, Randle & Smith, Birmingham 15.00
Store, Mold, Chocolate, Lamb 20.00
Store, Mold, Chocolate, Little Girl With Large Hair Ribbon, 4 X 11 In. 37.50

Store, Mold, Cigar, 10 Tube, Wooden, 2 Piece	20.00
Store, Mold, Jello Imprinted On Bottom, Aluminum	2.00
Store, Mold, Maple Sugar, Boy & Girl, Pair	40.00
Store, Mortar & Pestle, Wood, Maple	20.00
Store, Mug, Blatz Beer, Pottery, Barrel Shape, 4 1/2 In.	8.00
Store, Mug, Drink Hires Root Beer, Little Boy Smiling, Villeroy & Boch	75.00
Store, Mug, Drink Modox, Embossed, Indian, Glass	7.00 To 19.00
Store, Mug, Hires Root Beer, Crockery	12.00
Store, Mug, Lowenbrau Beer, Stoneware	4.50
Store, Mug, Michelob Beer	6.00
Store, Mug, Moxie	15.00
Store, Mug, Nesbitt's Hot Chocolate, Pottery	6.00
Store, Mug, Ranier Brewing Co., Judge & Sunflowers, Germany	35.00
Store, Mug, Red Wing Hamm's Krug Klub	25.00
Store, Mug, Schlitz Beer	5.00
Store, Mug, Smith's Musty Ale, Phila., Pottery	14.00
Store, Mug, Tuborg Beer, Horn	4.50
Store, Mug, Utica Club Beer, 6 In.	3.00
Store, Net, Horsefly, Leather, Pair	28.50
Store, Nut Set, Mr.Peanut, Tin, 7 Piece	22.00
Store, Nut Set, Planters Peanuts, 5 Piece	10.00
Store, Nutcracker, Metal, Woldert Grocery Company, Clamp Style	12.50
Store, Nutcracker, Perfection Co., Patent 1914, Metal, Clamps To Counter	12.50
Store, Oilcan, DeLaval, 1/2 Gallon	6.50
Store, Opener, Bottle, Dewar's, Bottle Shape, Metal	8.00
Store, Opener, Bottle, Esslinger's Premium Beer, Bottle Shape	2.50
Store, Opener, Bottle, Fox River Valley Dairy, Patent 1912, 5 1/2 In.	5.00
Store, Opener, Bottle, Iroquois Indian Beer, Figural	12.00
Store, Opener, Bottle, Nu-Grape, Flat	5.00
Store, Opener, Bottle, Pepsi Cola, Bottle Shape, Metal, 4 In.	6.00
Store, Opener, Bottle, Pepsi Cola, 1940, Metal, 4 1/2 In.	4.50
Store, Opener, Bottle, Pickwick Ale, Green Wooden Handle, 1903, 4 1/2 In.	10.00
Store, Opener, Bottle, Sterling Silver Handle, Flower Design, 5 3/4 In.	6.95
Store, Opener, Can, Keen Kutter, Cast Iron	3.50
Store, Opener, Letter, Army Rifle, Vulcan On Red Mountain, Birmingham, Ala.	9.00
Store, Opener, Letter, Borden's, Elsie The Cow, Brass	5.00
Store, Opener, Letter, Day Wood Heel Co., O., Indian Warrior, Brass, 9 In.	15.00
Store, Opener, Letter, Goat's Hoof Handle, Celluloid Blade	7.00
Store, Opener, Letter, Metropolitan Life Insurance Co., Bronze, 8 3/4 In.	2.95
Store, Opener, Letter, Mother-Of-Pearl & Sterling Silver, 5 3/8 In.	5.95
Store, Opener, Letter, Mother-Of-Pearl Handle, Sword Shape, 6 5/8 In.	3.95
Store, Opener, Letter, Nabisco, Boy	10.00
Store, Opener, Letter, Pittsburgh Steel	4.00
Store, Opener, Letter, Silver Plate, Dagger, Fleur-De-Lis, Cross Of Lorraine	8.00
Store, Opener, Letter, Sterling Silver Handle, Flower On Handle	6.95
Store, Opener, Letter, Victor Evans, Patent Attorneys, Brass	6.00
Store, Opener, Letter, White Warner Co., Household Ranges, Nickel Plated	2.95
Store, Package, Beechnut Tobacco, 1926 Stamp, Contents	2.00
Store, Package, Fragrant Tobacco, Contents	7.00
Store, Package, Good Cheer Tobacco, Contents	7.00
Store, Package, Landmark Tobacco, Contents	7.00
Store, Package, Little Bopeep Tobacco, 1874, 5 X 6 In.	4.50
Store, Package, Long Distance Smoking Tobacco, C.1890, 4 X 12 In.	4.00
Store, Package, Lucky Strike Cigarettes	3.50
Store, Package, Marconi Brand Tobacco, Contents	7.00
Store, Package, Ojibwa Fine Cut Tobacco, C.1890, 4 X 12 In.	4.00
Store, Package, Red Man Tobacco, 1926 Stamp, Contents	2.00
Store, Package, Rum & Honey Tobacco, 1926 Stamp, Contents	2.00
Store, Package, Seven Seas Tobacco, 1926 Stamp, Contents	2.00
Store, Package, Snow Apple Tobacco, 1926 Stamp, Contents	2.00
Store, Package, Snow Shoe Tobacco, 4 X 12 In.	4.00
Store, Package, Spear Head Tobacco, Free Sample, Contents	7.00
Store, Package, Strawberry Cut Tobacco, 1874, 5 X 6 In.	4.50
Store, Package, Strawberry Cut Tobacco, 1874, 6 X 4 In.	4.50
Store, Package, Sure Go Tobacco, Contents	7.00
Store, Package, Wine Shag Tobacco, 1926 Stamp, Contents	2.00

Store, Padlock & Key, Wilson-Bohannon, Brass, Sliding Escutcheon	12.50
Store, Pail, Bail, 1 Piece Fiber Board, Lockport, N.Y., 1882, 9 X 11 1/2 In.	24.00
Store, Pail, Cuban Star Tobacco	38.00
Store, Pail, Duco Tobacco, Eagle	35.00
Store, Pail, Eight Brothers Tobacco	22.00
Store, Pail, George Washington Tobacco, 6 X 3 3/4 In.	16.00
Store, Pail, Gold Belt Tobacco	30.00
Store, Pail, Home Comfort Tobacco	25.00
Store, Pail, Miners & Puddlers Tobacco	20.00 To 30.00
Store, Pail, Nigger Hair Tobacco, Brown	50.00 To 60.00
Store, Pail, Nigger Hair Tobacco, Yellow	90.00
Store, Pail, Ox Heart Peanut, Yellow Picture Of Apple, 10 In.	21.00
Store, Pail, Patterson's Seal Cut Plug Tobacco	17.00
Store, Pail, Plowboy Tobacco	16.00
Store, Pail, Pure Kettle Rendered Lard, Sander Brothers, 4 1/2 Lbs.	11.00
Store, Pail, Sensible Tobacco	22.00
Store, Pail, Sultana Peanut Butter, 2 Children, Lb.	12.00
Store, Pail, Summertime Tobacco	15.00 To 19.00
Store, Pail, Sweet Lotus Tobacco	40.00
Store, Pail, Tiger Tobacco	16.00
Store, Pail, Union Leader Cut Plug Tobacco	85.00
Store, Pail, Warnick & Brown Tobacco, Tan, 7 1/2 X 5 In.	12.00
Store, Painting, Margarita Tobacco, Can & 2 Pipes, Wooden Frame, 12 X 9 In.	50.00
Store, Pedometer, Jack Armstrong, Red, Black, & White, 2 3/4 In.	10.00
Store, Pen & Pencil Combination, Gold Filled, Retractable, Red Stone Tip	4.75
Store, Pen, Black & Gold, Case	4.95
Store, Pen, Desk, Mother-Of-Pearl	5.00
Store, Pen, Fountain, Diplomat, 1920s, Mother-Of-Pearl, 14K Gold Fittings	8.00
Store, Pen, Fountain, Lady's, Art Nouveau Style, Sterling Silver	10.00
Store, Pen, Fountain, Miracle, Green Marbelized	2.00
Store, Pen, Fountain, Sheaffer, Gold Point	3.00
Store, Pen, Moore's Improved Non-Leakable Fountain, Patent 1893-96-1903	4.95
Store, Pen, Mother-Of-Pearl Handle, Case	7.00
Store, Pen, Mother-Of-Pearl, Gold Point, Embossed Shaft, 5 1/2 In.	10.00
Store, Pen, Sterling Silver, Ornate Etched, 6 3/4 In.	30.00
Store, Pencil, Mechanical, Blue & Orange Marbelized	2.00
Store, Pencil, Mechanical, Eversharp, Gold Filled	2.00
Store, Pencil, Mechanical, German, Embossed, Black & White, Marbelized	2.00
Store, Pencil, Mechanical, Railroad, Soo Line	5.00
Store, Pencil, Retractable, Gold Finish, Loop For Chain	2.95
Store, Pencil, Retractable, Sterling Silver, Loop For Hanging	4.95
Store, Penknife, Bollard's Own Old Bourbon Engraved In Metal, 3 1/4 In.	7.00
Store, Penknife, Life & Casualty Insurance, Brass, 2 Blades	7.00
Store, Penlight, Winchester	5.00
Store, Photoscope, Penny Arcade, Coin-Operated, Stereo Strip Tease Cards	150.00
Store, Pillbox, Cascarets Pills, Brass, Enameled Letters & Decoration	25.00
Store, Pin, Heinz Pickle	1.50 To 3.00
Store, Pitcher, Hirsh Bros. & Co., Pottery, White Glaze, 5 In.	18.00
Store, Pitcher, Indiana Cider & Vinegar Co., Indianapolis, Pottery, 7 In.	16.00
Store, Pitcher, Orange Crush, 10 In.	15.00
Store, Pitcher, R.M.Hughes & Co., Fruit Vinegar, Louisville, Pottery, 8 In.	17.00
Store, Pitcher, Water, Bells Scotch Whiskey	10.00
Store, Pitcher, Water, Black Velvet Whiskey	7.00
Store, Pitcher, Water, Jewel Tea	12.00
Store, Pitcher, Water, Passport Scotch Whiskey	10.00
Store, Pitcher, Water, Smirnoff	7.00
Store, Pitcher, Water, Teacher's Scotch Whiskey	7.00 To 10.00
Store, Pitcher, Water, V.O.Whiskey	10.00
Store, Pitcher, Water, 100 Pipers Scotch Whiskey	10.00
Store, Plaque, Falstaff Beer, Fishing, Lithograph On Wood, C.1960, 15 In.	13.50
Store, Plaque, Farmer's Supply, Washington, Stag, Christmas, Tin, 10 In.	20.00
Store, Plate, Borden Co., Elsie The Cow, 7 In.	12.00
Store, Plate, Calvert's Whiskey, C.1915, Owl Drinking, Porcelain, 10 In.	8.00
Store, Plate, Hot, Jewel Tea, Footed, 9 In.	8.50
Store, Plate, Philip Boileau Stoves, 1907, Lady In Blue Hat, 8 1/4 In.	11.25
Store, Plate, Ruffner's Cafe, Phila., Portrait, Tin, 10 In.	23.00

Store, Plate, Smith & Powell, Newport News, Va., 8 In.	12.00
Store, Plate, The Bungalow Lunch System, Inc., McNicol China, 7 In.	15.00
Store, Post Office Cage, Clerk Window, Oak, 42 X 50 In.	400.00
Store, Post Office, Wooden, 4 Glass Sections, Cage, Letter Drop, 68 In. Long	295.00
Store, Poster, see also Disneyana, Poster	
Store, Poster, Alexander, The Man Who Knows, Magic, C.1908, 40 X 80 In.	95.00
Store, Poster, Arm & Hammer, Paper, 11 1/2 X 14 1/2 In.	4.00
Store, Poster, Auction, Shoat, Woodcut Of Pig, C.1910, 20 X 13 In.	7.00
Store, Poster, Baltimore Fashion Show & Pageant, Lithograph, C.1930, 26 In.	60.00
Store, Poster, Barnum & Bailey Circus, Olga Bondi, C.1910, 14 X 18 In.	50.00
Store, Poster, Billy The Kid, Black & White, 14 X 22 In.	18.00
Store, Poster, Chesterfield Cigarettes, Streetcar, C.1930, 10 X 17 In.	6.00
Store, Poster, Climax, The Grand Old Chew, C.1900, 10 In.	10.00
Store, Poster, Clyde Beatty Circus, Lions & Tigers, C.1935, 20 X 30 In.	30.00
Store, Poster, Cole & Walter's 4 Ring Wild Animal Circus, 28 X 21 In.	9.50
Store, Poster, Cole Bros. Circus, Jumbo, The 2nd, C.1935, 20 X 30 In.	20.00
Store, Poster, Cooper Bros. Circus & Wild West, C.1910, 30 X 40 In.	50.00
Store, Poster, Cooper Bros. Circus, Different Acts, C.1920, 10 X 27 In.	8.00
Store, Poster, Deliverance, Movie, 1972, 28 X 40 In.	5.00
Store, Poster, Edwin Booth In Hamlet, Boston, 1867, 6 X 12 In.	32.00
Store, Poster, Garneau Crackers, 1885, Victorian Lady, Paper, 22 In.	110.00
Store, Poster, Henderson Motorcycles, C.1910, 11 X 14 In.	12.00
Store, Poster, J.P.Alley's Hambone Cigars, 5 Cents, 7 In. Diameter	15.00
Store, Poster, Jack Frost Fontaine, C.1900, 11 X 15 In.	10.00
Store, Poster, Keller, The Magician, Strobridge, 1894, 30 X 40 In.	110.00
Store, Poster, Marvel Cigarettes, C.1930s, Die Cut, 9 In.	9.00
Store, Poster, Pears Soap, 1892, 2 Peasant Girls, Chromolithograph, 33 In.	75.00
Store, Poster, Prang's Easter Cards, D.Fausel, C.1890, 18 X 24 In.	35.00
Store, Poster, Ringling Bro., Barnum & Bailey, Lions, Strobridge, 14 X 22 In.	45.00
Store, Poster, Ringling Bros.Barnum & Bailey, Lion, Strobridge, 20 X 30 In.	25.00
Store, Poster, Ringling Bros.Barnum & Bailey, Orland Mara, 1933, 20 X 30 In.	35.00
Store, Poster, Royal Gloss Corn Starch, C.1890, 14 X 25 In.	39.00
Store, Poster, Smith & Wesson Pistols, 1854, Copyright 1944, 37 X 23 In.	70.00
Store, Poster, Stuebner's Sons Shaving Mugs, N.Y., C.1890, 14 X 18 In.	15.00
Store, Poster, Telegraphers Of The World, 1871, 14 X 17 In.	50.00
Store, Poster, Uncle John's Syrup, N.E.Maple Syrup Co., Boston, C.1910	15.00
Store, Poster, Union Leader Tobacco, Uncle Sam & Tin, C.1910, 24 In.	25.00
Store, Poster, Union Leader Tobacco, Uncle Sam Smoking Pipe, C.1910, 22 In.	20.00
Store, Poster, Winchester, Toonerville Trolley, Fontaine Fox, 1915, 50 In.	120.00
Store, Poster, World's Greatest Flyer 5 Cent Cigar, Streetcar, 8 X 20 In.	8.50
Store, Potlid, Cherry Toothpaste	8.50
Store, Press, Printing, Monarch Junior	8.50
Store, Print, Falstaff Beer, Famous Fishing Place, C.1960, 13 1/4 X 15 In.	17.50
Store, Program, Theatre, White Knight Cigar, 10 X 13 In.	10.00
Store, Pump, Gasoline, Skelly, Motor Power Diesel Fuel On Inserts	24.00
Store, Purse, Green River Whiskey, Leather, Gold Lettering, 2 1/2 X 3 In.	17.00
Store, Puzzle, Jigsaw, Lipton's Tea, 125 Pieces, Dated 1933	9.00
Store, Puzzle, Jigsaw, New & True Coffee	2.50
Store, Pyrographic Box, Dated 1910, Floral Decorated	25.00
Store, Rack, Hat, American Wringer Co.'s Horseshoe Brand, Wooden, 65 In.	68.00
Store, Radio, Pepsi Cola, Transistor, General Electric	17.50
Store, Razor, Anticor Safety Corn Shaves, Nickel Plated Brass, 1911	5.95
Store, Razor, Electric, Tark, C.1930	20.00
Store, Razor, German Steel, Bone Handled, World's Fair, 1904 On Blade	20.00
Store, Razor, Gillette, Brass Greek Key Case, 3 In.	25.00
Store, Razor, Rolls, English, Folding, Metal Case	10.00
Store, Razor, Safety, Autostop, Valet, Brass	3.00
Store, Razor, Straight, "The Razor That Fits Your Face," Nickel Plate Trim	3.75
Store, Razor, Straight, Bengal Razors, Cadman & Sons, Sheffield, Set Of 7	64.50
Store, Razor, Straight, Bindley Hardware, German	4.00
Store, Razor, Straight, Charles Buck, Millbury, Mass., Yellow Plastic Handle	10.00
Store, Razor, Straight, D.H.Lory, N.Y.	20.00
Store, Razor, Straight, F.Reynolds, Sheffield, C.1860, Green Horn Handle	49.50
Store, Razor, Straight, Imperial	4.00
Store, Razor, Straight, Marked Germany On Blade	12.00
Store, Razor, Straight, Ornate Sterling Frame	60.00

Store, Razor, Straight, Peerless, Ivory Handle, Marked In Gold On Blade 3.95
Store, Razor, Straight, Sheffield, Engraved Columbian Exposition, 1893 .... 15.00
Store, Razor, Straight, Thomas Turner 4.00
Store, Razor, Straight, Turham 4.00
Store, Razor, Straight, Wostenholm, Engraved Blade 5.00
Store, Razor, Wade & Tucke, Sheffield, Diamond Edge, Tortoiseshell Handle 5.00
Store, Razor, Weck, Leather Case 3.50
Store, Reel, Clothesline, Wooden, Handled, Rectangular, Dated 1866 .... 13.00
Store, Robe, Buffalo Hide, 58 X 68 In. 47.50
Store, Robe, Buggy, Dog's Head Design, Ornate 12.50
Store, Rope, Woven Horsehair, 20 Ft. 10.00
Store, Safe, Black, Gold & Red Trim, Rose On Inside Door, 2 Ft. High 450.00
Store, Salt & Pepper, Budweiser Beer, 4 In. 2.00
Store, Salt & Pepper, R.C.A., Victrola With Horn & Dog, Gold Finish 15.00
Store, Saltshaker, Blatz Beer, Amber, Pair 9.00
Store, Sander, Pounce, Tin, Red, Cylindrical, Flared Top, 3 In. 32.00
Store, Sander, Pounce, Tin, 8 Sided, Painted, 2 3/4 In. 25.00
Store, Schooner, Morlein's National Lager Beer, Glass, 6 1/2 In., Pair 24.00
Store, Scoop, Mr.Peanut, Full Figure 5.95
Store, Scooter, Lang's Hardware Store, Wooden 20.00
Store, Scraper, Pot, Henkel's Flour 4.00
Store, Separator, Cream, Anchorholth, 1916, Nickel Plated 75.00
Store, Separator, Cream, Superior, Sets On Legs, 10 Gallon 15.00
Store, Shaker, Ovaltine, Tin 7.50
Store, Sharpener, Razor, Wood & Metal, 14 X 13 X 6 In. 18.00
Store, Sharpener, Scissors, Diamond, Dated 1896 .... 3.00
Store, Sharpening Stone, Knife, Winchester, 1930s 11.75
Store, Shoe, Button, Iron, For Mannequin, 6 1/2 In. 20.00
Store, Shoe, Heineken's Beer, Wooden, Picture Of Dutch Boy 10.50
Store, Shoe, Hood's Rubbers, Metal 6.50
Store, Shoe, Lady's, High Button, Spain, For Wilbar's, C.1920, Pair 12.50
Store, Shoe, Lady's, High Top, Laced, Black, Pair 15.00
Store, Shoe, Marked Shenanigans, Salesman's Sample, 5 1/2 In., Pair 10.00
Store, Shot Glass, Chapin & Gore, Embossed 15.00
Store, Shot Glass, Dallomand Cream Rye, Enamel Lettering 7.00
Store, Shot Glass, Dr.Harter's, Embossed, Stemmed 12.00
Store, Shot Glass, E.Bros.Star Whiskey, Paneled, Enamel Lettering 7.00
Store, Shot Glass, Erie Club Whiskey, 1890 .... 4.00
Store, Shot Glass, Frosted Lettering Advertising Whiskey 9.00
Store, Shot Glass, Hayner's Whiskey, Barrel & Horseshoe, Etched 7.00
Store, Shot Glass, J.H.Carson Rye 4.00
Store, Shot Glass, Martha Hill Rye 4.00
Store, Shot Glass, Rothschild Bros., Buffalo, N.Y., Etched 4.00
Store, Shot Glass, Trost Bros. Whiskey, Louisville 3.00
Store, Shot Glass, Woodland, Crigler & Crigler, Ky., Red Letters 6.00
Store, Showcase, Remington Pocket Clasp Knives, Wooden, Hinged Door, 15 In. 250.00
Store, Showcase, Walnut, Turned Legs, 11 Ft. Long 90.00
Store, Sign, A.C.Oil Filter, Tin, 10 X 29 In. 17.50
Store, Sign, Ajax Beer, Tin & Cardboard, 11 X 29 In. 12.00
Store, Sign, Andy Gump Cigars, Embossed Paper, C.1930, 4 X 4 In. 3.00
Store, Sign, Arm & Hammer Baking Soda, Porcelain, White On Red, 9 X 12 In. 25.00
Store, Sign, Ballantine Beer, 1954 Yankee Team Pictures, 15 X 16 In. 16.50
Store, Sign, Belmont Whiskey, Max Selliger & Co., Reverse On Glass, 9 In. 16.00
Store, Sign, Bixby Shoe Polish, Paper Lithograph On Wood, 7 X 10 In. 10.00
Store, Sign, Blueck's Beer, Tin, Color, 17 3/4 X 21 In. 40.00
Store, Sign, Braehm's Bitters, C.1915, Aluminum, 12 X 6 In. 16.00
Store, Sign, Buck Cigars, Cutout Deer's Head, Tin, 12 In. 36.00
Store, Sign, Budweiser Beer, Bar, Electric, 27 1/2 X 15 In. 82.95
Store, Sign, Bulldog Segars, Red Bulldogs On Green, 1907, Cardboard, 19 In. 45.00
Store, Sign, Burma Shave, C.1930, Comic Breakfast Scene, Cardboard, 20 In. 25.00
Store, Sign, Busch Bavarian Beer, Electric, 45 1/4 X 9 1/2 In. 65.00
Store, Sign, Busch Beer, A & Eagle, Plastic, 10 1/2 X 10 3/4 In. 18.95
Store, Sign, Carling's Black Label Beer, Electric, Fiber Optics, 14 In. 72.50
Store, Sign, Carling's Nine Pints Of The Law, C.1930, 21 X 12 In. 45.00
Store, Sign, Carling's Red Cap Ale, Tin, 18 X 13 In. 6.50
Store, Sign, Centlivre Tonic, 1905, Nurse, Color, 22 X 12 In. .... 25.00 To 35.00

Store, Sign, Cetacolor, C.1910, Cloth, 36 X 24 In. 35.00
Store, Sign, Champagne Velvet Beer, Man Fishing, Tin, 20 1/2 X 15 1/4 In. 32.00
Store, Sign, Cheer-Up Drink, C.1930, Embossed, Tin, 17 X 7 In. 7.00
Store, Sign, City Club Beer, St.Paul, Minn., Embossed Tin, 28 X 11 In. 30.00
Store, Sign, Colonial Club Cigars, C.1910, 2 Sided, 18 X 9 In. 9.00
Store, Sign, Cook's Beer, Southern River Scene, Tin, 28 1/4 X 22 In. 100.00
Store, Sign, Cook's Goldblume Beer & Ale, Evansville, Ind., 19 X 8 1/4 In. 3.00
Store, Sign, Daisy Tonic, C.1905, Tin, 6 X 9 In. 9.00
Store, Sign, Dandro Solvent, C.1930, Tin, 13 X 10 In. 9.00
Store, Sign, Devilish Good Cigars, Chain For Hanging, Tin, 13 3/4 X 9 3/4 In 75.00
Store, Sign, Diamond Dyes, Children With Balloons, Tin, 20 X 11 1/2 In. 125.00
Store, Sign, Dolly Madison Cigars, C.1910, Embossed, Tin, 21 X 5 In. 12.00
Store, Sign, Dr.Cox's Barbed Wire Liniment, Cardboard, Framed, 14 X 20 In. 17.00
Store, Sign, Dr.Jayne's Tonic Vermifuge, C.1910, Tin, 10 X 7 In. 25.00
Store, Sign, Dr.Lynas' Hair Grower, C.1920, Cardboard, 13 X 10 In. 4.50
Store, Sign, Dr.Lynas' Hair Grower, Cardboard, Framed, 10 X 14 In. 12.00
Store, Sign, Dr.Pepper, White Letters On Red, Tin, 30 X 12 In. 8.00
Store, Sign, Drink Utica Club Ginger Ale, Tin, 23 X 11 In. 30.00
Store, Sign, Drink Utica Club Pilsner Brew, Tin, 23 X 11 In. 30.00
Store, Sign, Duquesne Pilsner Beer, Electric, 1910, Reverse Painting, 25 In. 79.95
Store, Sign, Dutchess Trousers, 10 Cents A Button, 1 Dollar A Rip, Tin, 26 In 25.00
Store, Sign, Eagle Vignette, U.S.Revenue License To Operate, C.1864, 11 In. 15.00
Store, Sign, Early Times Whiskey, Log Cabin Distillery, Plaster, 29 In. 125.00
Store, Sign, Fairies Starch, C.1920, Cardboard, 15 X 10 In. 2.50
Store, Sign, Fatima Cigarettes, 1909, Paper, 36 X 26 In. 175.00
Store, Sign, Fisk, Time To Retire, Metal, 24 X 70 In. 18.00
Store, Sign, Fix, C.1930, Cardboard & Metal, 21 X 3 In. 3.50
Store, Sign, Four Roses Whiskey, Game Animals In Cabin, Tin, 4 X 3 Ft. 450.00
Store, Sign, French Meat Market, Cow's Head, Cast Iron, 19 X 17 In. 325.00
Store, Sign, GA Stores, Reverse Painting On Glass, 10 In. Diameter 20.00
Store, Sign, Gem City Ice Cream, C.1930, Embossed, Tin, 20 X 12 In. 7.00
Store, Sign, Ginita Cigars, C.1910, Lithograph, Cardboard, 21 X 11 In. 7.00
Store, Sign, Globe Brewing Co., Utica, N.Y., 1935, Indian Maiden, 28 In. 85.00
Store, Sign, Golden Wedding Whiskey, 3 Gents Imbibing, Tin, 20 X 13 In. 40.00
Store, Sign, Goldyrock Birch Beer, C.1930, Embossed, Tin, 16 X 10 In. 8.00
Store, Sign, Goodwill Soap, 32 X 19 In. 85.00
Store, Sign, Gra-Rock Ginger Ale, Tin, 11 X 28 In. 7.50
Store, Sign, Grape Nuts Girl With Dog, Tin, 30 X 20 In. 250.00
Store, Sign, Green River Whiskey, Paper Under Glass, 24 X 16 In. 65.00
Store, Sign, Green River Whiskey, 1919, Negro & Horse, Cardboard, 30 X 22 In. 25.00
Store, Sign, Hambone Sweets Cigar, C.1927, Negro Aviator, Round, 7 In. 7.50
Store, Sign, Helmar Cigarettes, 1909, Paper, 36 X 26 In. 145.00
Store, Sign, Hires, C.1930, Embossed Tin, 27 X 10 In. 32.00
Store, Sign, Hoffman Brewing Co., C.1910, Lithograph, Paper, 31 X 21 In. 20.00
Store, Sign, Hommel Wine, C.1897, Lithograph, Paper, 26 X 20 In. 70.00
Store, Sign, Honest Scrap Tobacco, Dog & Cat, Paper, 30 X 22 In. 235.00
Store, Sign, Humphries' Specifics, Girl & Lion, Blue, Tin, 22 X 17 In. 75.00
Store, Sign, Independent Brewing Co., 1910, 20 X 15 In. 150.00
Store, Sign, James Lewis Cigars, C.1910, Aluminum, 9 X 6 In. 6.00
Store, Sign, Korbel Champagne, C.1915, Tin, 19 X 12 In. 50.00
Store, Sign, La Flor De Carvallio Cigars, C.1900, Tin, Wood Frame, 21 In. 75.00
Store, Sign, Lion Coffee, C.1920, Embossed, Tin, 28 X 5 In. 14.00
Store, Sign, Little General Bread, Yellow, Canvas, 27 X 45 In. 12.00
Store, Sign, Mail Pouch Tobacco, C.1930, Porcelain, 12 X 3 In. 17.00
Store, Sign, Majestic Beer, Phila., 1912, Old Timers Drinking, 20 X 14 In. 85.00
Store, Sign, Marquette National Fire Insurance, Tin, Wood, 19 In. 45.00
Store, Sign, Marvel Cigarettes, C.1935, Cardboard, Standup, 24 X 17 In. 8.00
Store, Sign, Mason's Old Fashioned Root Beer, Tin, Thermometer, 26 In. 35.00
Store, Sign, Mayo's Cut Plug Tobacco, Rooster, Porcelain, 13 X 6 1/2 In. 100.00
Store, Sign, McCoy's Real Wild West Circus, 1938, Tin, 20 X 30 In. 50.00
Store, Sign, Medical Officer, The Border Regt., Wooden, 11 X 6 1/2 In. 37.50
Store, Sign, Miller High Life, Self Framed, Tin, 26 1/2 X 18 1/2 In. 95.00
Store, Sign, Mission Orange, Bottle Picture, Tin, 45 X 12 In. 18.50
Store, Sign, Morning Sip Coffee, 1923, Lithograph, Paper, 21 X 11 In. 6.00
Store, Sign, Moxie, Girl, C.1920, Reverse On Glass, 10 X 8 In. 37.50
Store, Sign, Murad Cigarettes, Lithograph, 25 1/2 X 17 In. 125.00

Store, Sign, Murad Turkish Cigarettes, Soldier On Horse, 43 X 29 In.	300.00
Store, Sign, Napoleon Cigars, C.1915, Lithograph, Paper, 20 X 10 In.	25.00
Store, Sign, New England Pale Ale, C.1900, Embossed Tin, 14 X 7 In.	20.00
Store, Sign, Norka Orange Drink, C.1940, Tin, 24 X 24 In.	6.00
Store, Sign, Norka Orange, C.1950, Tin, 24 X 12 In.	3.00
Store, Sign, Old Dutch Cleanser, Porcelain, Lady, 10 Cents, 32 X 19 In.	200.00
Store, Sign, Old Gold Cigarettes, Cloth, C.1935, 48 X 20 In.	21.00
Store, Sign, Old North Cigarettes, C.1920, Cardboard, Stand Up, 11 X 8 In.	9.00
Store, Sign, Omar Cigarettes, Tin, 14 X 8 In.	35.00
Store, Sign, Orange Flower 5 Cent Cigar, Cardboard, C.1900, 6 X 10 In.	9.00
Store, Sign, Ox Head Ale, 16 X 12 1/2 In.	45.00
Store, Sign, Pabst Blue Ribbon Beer, Blackboard, 26 X 14 In.	15.00
Store, Sign, Pabst Blue Ribbon Beer, Electric, Plastic, 29 1/4 X 9 3/4 In.	31.50
Store, Sign, Pabst Blue Ribbon Beer, Reverse Under Glass, 14 X 11 In.	25.00
Store, Sign, Pabst Blue Ribbon Beer, Wooden, Weight Lifter Of 1950s, 23 In.	21.95
Store, Sign, Pay Car Tobacco, Tin, 17 X 14 In.	35.00
Store, Sign, Pepsi-Cola, Blackboard, Tin, 19 1/2 X 30 In.	16.95
Store, Sign, Pepsi-Cola, Restaurant, C.1940, Wooden, 12 X 22 In.	25.00
Store, Sign, Pepsi-Cola, Tin, Embossed Enamel, 31 X 12 In.	6.00
Store, Sign, Pepsi-Cola, Tin, 30 X 10 In.	12.75
Store, Sign, Piccaninny Freese, 1922, Cardboard, 12 X 9 In.	22.00
Store, Sign, Pioneer Basket, C.1920, Cardboard, 16 X 13 In.	9.00
Store, Sign, Piunas California Wines, C.1930, Light-Up, 13 X 11 In.	45.00
Store, Sign, Pompeian Beauty Cream, 1926, Masquerade Ball, 25 1/2 X 7 In.	16.00
Store, Sign, Postal Telegraph, International System, Porcelain, 16 X 31 In.	30.00
Store, Sign, Potosi Beer, Blue, Silver, & Red, Metal, C.1936, 10 X 7 In.	3.00
Store, Sign, Poulterer's, W.Kinstler, Pa., C.1850, Wooden Rooster, 24 In.	450.00
Store, Sign, Railway Express Agency, Porcelain, Red & White, 7 X 7 In.	14.00
Store, Sign, Ramon's Nerve & Bone Oil, Cardboard, Color, 5 1/2 X 6 In.	7.00
Store, Sign, Rasola Cigars, 1907, Lady, Low Cut Dress, Tin, 14 In.	100.00
Store, Sign, Red Dot Cigars, C.1900, Round, 8 In.	10.00
Store, Sign, Red Dot Cigars, C.1938, Stand-Up, Cardboard, 18 X 13 In.	4.50
Store, Sign, Red Man Chewing Tobacco, C.1940, Tin, 14 X 5 In.	4.50
Store, Sign, Red Man, America's Best Chew, Tin, 5 X 15 In.	12.50
Store, Sign, Red Rock Cola, 1939, Embossed, Tin, 32 X 8 In.	14.00
Store, Sign, Rheingold Cold Beer, Electric, 36 X 13 In.	17.50
Store, Sign, Rockford Watches, Woman & Man Boarding Train, C.1900, 24 In.	150.00
Store, Sign, Rooster Snuff, C.1930, Tin, 20 X 4 In.	7.00
Store, Sign, Round Oak Stoves, Stand-Up, Cardboard, Round, 14 In.	15.00
Store, Sign, Royal Crown, Tin.1936, 12 X 30 In.	15.00
Store, Sign, S.S.S. For Rich Red Blood, White On Red, Metal, 9 X 19 1/2 In.	13.50
Store, Sign, Satin Skin Powder, 1903, Lithograph, Paper, 42 X 26 In.	23.00
Store, Sign, Schaefer Beer, Beer & Food, Electric, 35 X 14 In.	15.00
Store, Sign, Seminola Cigars, C.1910, Velvet Cloth, 13 X 9 In.	45.00
Store, Sign, Shell Kerosene, C.1930, 2 Sided, Steel, 21 X 17 In.	12.00
Store, Sign, Smith Bros. Cough Drops, Embossed Tin, 28 X 11 In.	45.00
Store, Sign, Smoke Caton Quality Cigars, Tin, 3 X 12 In.	3.00
Store, Sign, Spiffy Cola, C.1935, Embossed, Tin, 34 X 12 In.	22.00
Store, Sign, Spud Cigarettes, Girl & Dog, Cardboard, 31 X 24 In.	75.00
Store, Sign, Standing Horse, Iron, C.1850, 17 1/2 In.	200.00
Store, Sign, Star Brand Shoes Are Better, Tin, 14 X 20 In.	22.00
Store, Sign, Stoodite For Plowshares, Porcelain, 7 X 19 1/2 In.	20.00
Store, Sign, Stroh's Beer, Plastic, Bar With Customers, 17 1/2 X 14 1/2 In.	5.00
Store, Sign, Studebaker, 1939, Framed, 26 X 21 In.	30.00
Store, Sign, Tanner's, Horse's Head, Red Paint, Iron, C.1850, 35 In.	800.00
Store, Sign, Tobacconist, Man, Smoking Pipe, Metal, Painted, C.1850, 24 In.	900.00
Store, Sign, Tokio Cigarettes, Slave Child, Cardboard, 31 X 22 In.	125.00
Store, Sign, Trolley Car Conductor's License, Boston, 1898, 10 X 8 In.	15.00
Store, Sign, Uncle John Syrup, C.1920, Lithograph, Cardboard, 18 X 12 In.	4.50
Store, Sign, Velvet Tobacco, C.1935, Cloth, 60 X 30 In.	11.00
Store, Sign, Viceroy Cigarettes, C.1954, Girl, Tin, 28 X 17 In.	5.00
Store, Sign, Vicks Vaporub & Drops, Porcelain, Door Push Plate, "Come In"	22.50
Store, Sign, Virginia Cigarettes, Blonde Bathing Beauty, Tin, 21 X 13 In.	15.00
Store, Sign, Walter Beer, Eau Claire, Wis., Milk Glass, Copper Frame, 33 In.	200.00
Store, Sign, Wildroot, Dick Tracy, Fearless Fosdick, Cardboard, 25 X 31 In.	21.50
Store, Sign, Winchester Repeating Arms, C.1890, Counter, 14 X 10 In.	60.00

Store, Skates, Ice, Winchester, Pair	9.00
Store, Skates, Roller, Best-Ever-Built, 3 Wheels In A Row, Pair	22.50
Store, Slate, Schoolhouse, Mortised Frame	14.00
Store, Sleigh, Bob, Studebaker, 1890	350.00
Store, Sleigh, Pony, Red Velvet Upholstery	450.00
Store, Slicer, Meat, Electric	75.00
Store, Snowshoe, Made By C.A.Lund, Hastings, 1943, 10 X 58 In., Pair	125.00
Store, Spigot, Bung, Pine, Hand-Hewn, Tubular, 20 In.	10.00
Store, Spigot, For Barrel, Wooden, 8 1/4 In.	7.50
Store, Spittoon, Porcelain Covered Iron, C.1920	12.00
Store, Spoon, Allentown Crockery Co., Allentown, Pa.	3.95
Store, Spoon, Campbell's Soup, Little Girl	5.00
Store, Spoon, Duffy's Pure Malt Whiskey-A Medicine, Glass, Loop Handle	7.50
Store, Spoon, Gerber's, Baby	5.00
Store, Spoon, Larkin	15.00
Store, Spoon, Log Cabin Syrup	5.00
Store, Spoon, Mixing, Kellogg's, Wooden	3.00
Store, Spoon, Planter's Peanut, Perforations In Round Bowl	5.00
Store, Spoon, Planter's Peanuts, Plastic	1.50
Store, Stamp, Harrisville, R.I. Post Office, Hand, C.1900	32.00
Store, Stamp, Sheep, Rectangular Block, Leather Raised Letters, 4 1/2 In.	32.00
Store, Stand, Clark's Teaberry Gum, Vaseline Glass, 4 1/2 X 7 In.	24.50
Store, Stand, Display, Wrigley, Tin	20.00
Store, Stand, Shoe Repair, 2 Iron Shoes, 3 Pieces	5.25
Store, Stand, Wig, Walnut, Mushroom Top, Turned Pedestal, 16 In.	9.00
Store, Statue, Winchester Pony Express Rider, Cast Metal, 7 1/2 In.	42.00
Store, Stein, Falstaff Beer, Boot, Presentation, 30 Ozs.	18.50
Store, Stein, Pabst, Flip Top, Paper Label, Miniature	10.00
Store, Stereoscope, see Stereoscope	
Store, Stickpin, Brown & Sharpe Hair Clippers, Clippers Shape	4.95
Store, Stickpin, Cash Register Co.	5.50
Store, Stickpin, Gorton's Fish Foods, Gold Finish, Shape Of Fish	3.95
Store, Stickpin, International Harvester Co.	5.50
Store, Stickpin, John Deere	12.00
Store, Stickpin, Libby Food Products	3.95
Store, Stickpin, Mascot Tobacco, Brass Bulldog	10.00
Store, Stillyard, Wrought Iron, Red Spade End, Hooks & Weights, 19 In.	15.00
Store, Stopper, Lash's Bitters, Metal, Patent 1910	5.00
Store, Stretcher, Glove, Sterling Handle	18.50
Store, Strop, Razor, Kriss Kross, Original Box	4.00
Store, Tablet, School, Picture Of Deanna Durbin On Cover	4.00
Store, Tally Board, Apple Bag, Pine, Peg Holes For Counting, 16 In.	20.00
Store, Tap, Maple Syrup, For Trees, Patent 1877	2.50
Store, Tape Measure, see also Sewing Tool, Tape Measure	
Store, Tape Measure, Calvert's Whiskey, Bottle Figural	5.00
Store, Tape Measure, Fab	8.50
Store, Tape Measure, Shape Of Ship, Celluloid, Germany, C.1900	22.50
Store, Target, Shooting Gallery, Card Suits On Steel Plate, 25 In.	135.00
Store, Target, Shooting Gallery, Moving, 2 Roosters, Arcade, Iron, 10 X 4 In.	18.50
Store, Target, Shooting Gallery, Scowling Human Face, Steel Plate, 24 In.	225.00
Store, Target, Shooting Gallery, Steel, Clown's Face, 27 In.	250.00
Store, Taster, Cheese, Ring Handle, Steel Channel, 1915, 26 In.	17.00
Store, Teapot, Jewel Tea, Figural Aladdin	15.00
Store, Teapot, Lipton Tea, Dark Green	6.50
Store, Teapot, Salada Tea, Blue Pottery, 1 Cup Size	7.50
Store, Teapot, Salada Tea, Light Green, Embossed	8.00
Store, Telegraph Key, Wooden Base, 7 X 4 3/4 In.	20.00
Store, Telescope, Tully-Islington, C.1850, Brass, Tripod, 5 Ft.7 In.	475.00
Store, Thermometer, Arbuckles' Coffee, C.1920, Tin, 19 X 4 In.	25.00
Store, Thermometer, Brew Kettle, Copper, Moeller, N.Y., Brass Chain	25.00
Store, Thermometer, John Deere Tractor & Plow, Mirror, 12 In.	9.50
Store, Thermometer, Orange Crush, Brown Ribbed Bottle	15.00
Store, Thermometer, Pepsi-Cola, 1957, 27 X 7 In.	23.95
Store, Thermometer, Pepsi-Cola, 1963	8.00
Store, Thermometer, Ramons-Brownie Pills, Little Boy Doctor, 21 In.	20.00
Store, Thermometer, Stegmaier Beer, 1953, 9 1/4 In. Diameter	16.95

Store, Tie Presser, Jim Dandy, Eiman Sales, Kansas City, Mo. 7.00
Store, Tie Tac, Winchester Gun 3.00
Store, Tie Tac, Winchester Shotgun Shell, Brass 3.00
Store, Tin, Acme Coffee, Lb. 11.00
Store, Tin, After Dinner Salted Peanuts, 10 Pound 25.00
Store, Tin, Amorita Tobacco, Pocket 35.00
Store, Tin, Bagdad Tobacco, Pocket 30.00
Store, Tin, Bagley's Old Colony Tobacco, Pocket 20.00
Store, Tin, Bagley's Sweet Tips Tobacco, Pocket 6.00
Store, Tin, Banquet Orange Pekoe Tea, McCormick, Orange, Green, 10 In. 10.00
Store, Tin, Battle Royal Cut Plug Tobacco, Sailboat & Anchors, 4 1/2 In. 8.00
Store, Tin, Battleship Coffee, 3 Lbs. 22.00
Store, Tin, Belfast Cut Plug Tobacco, Pocket 18.00
Store, Tin, Belfast Cut Plug Tobacco, 5 X 3 In. 10.00
Store, Tin, Belfast Tobacco, 6 X 4 In. 5.00
Store, Tin, Ben Franklin Coffee, Red & Gold, 3 Lbs. 75.00
Store, Tin, Benton Mixture Tobacco, 4 1/2 X 3 1/4 X 2 1/4 In. 35.00
Store, Tin, Betsy Ross Shoe Polish, Picture Of Betsy, 1910 .... 6.00 To 7.00
Store, Tin, Between The Acts Cigars, 3 X 6 In. 9.00
Store, Tin, Big Ben Tobacco, Pocket 6.50
Store, Tin, Big Ben Tobacco, Store Canister 15.00
Store, Tin, Blanke's Coffee, Trunk Design, 9 X 5 X 4 1/2 In. 22.00
Store, Tin, Blue Boar Tobacco, Store Canister 25.00
Store, Tin, Borden's Malted Milk, 8 In. 13.00
Store, Tin, Boscul Coffee, Pound 6.40
Store, Tin, Briggs Pipe Mixture Tobacco, Round 10.00
Store, Tin, Brotherhood Tobacco, 6 X 4 X 3 In. 24.00
Store, Tin, Browne's Peanuts, 10 Lb., Orange & Black 30.00
Store, Tin, Brownie Salted Pecans, United Fig & Date Co., 1915, 5 Pound 25.00
Store, Tin, Buchannan & Lyall's Blue Label Cut Plug Tobacco, Pocket 35.00
Store, Tin, Buchannan & Lyall's Red Label Cut Plug Tobacco, Pocket 15.00
Store, Tin, Buckingham Tobacco, Pocket 9.00
Store, Tin, Campbell's Coffee, 4 Pounds 25.00
Store, Tin, Campfire Marshmallow, Boy Scouts Around Campfire, Pound 12.50
Store, Tin, Carmen Brand Prophylactics, 1 Dozen Rubbers On Reverse 4.50
Store, Tin, Central Union Cut Plug Tobacco, 6 X 4 X 3 In. .... 8.50 To 18.00
Store, Tin, Cheloong's Canton Ginger, Flat, 8 Ozs. 8.00
Store, Tin, Chesterfield Cigarettes, Flat 50 .... 4.00
Store, Tin, Chocolate Laxative, Little Girl, "Tak-A-Lax, " 3 3/4 In. 4.00
Store, Tin, Chocolates, Netherlands, Merchants On Barge Scene, 6 X 4 In. 7.00
Store, Tin, Christy's Coffee, 2 Lbs. 35.00
Store, Tin, Cleo Brand Prophylactics, 1 Dozen Rubbers On Reverse 4.50
Store, Tin, Coffee-After Glow, Bail Handle, 4 Pound 22.00
Store, Tin, Columbia Needles 3.00
Store, Tin, Craven A Cigarettes, 100s Size 7.00
Store, Tin, Crescent Club Mixture Tobacco, 4 1/2 X 3 1/4 X 2 3/4 In. 25.00
Store, Tin, Crescent Crackers, Red, Square, 9 In. 15.00
Store, Tin, Culture Tobacco, Pocket 22.00
Store, Tin, Dan Patch Tobacco, 6 X 4 X 3 In. .... 8.50 To 16.00
Store, Tin, Dial Tobacco, C.1900, Pocket 1.50
Store, Tin, Dial Tobacco, Pocket .... 1.75 To 12.00
Store, Tin, Dixie Queen Tobacco, 4 X 6 In. 25.00
Store, Tin, Dr.R.S.Parker's Sure Kidney Pills, 3 1/2 In. .... Illus
Store, Tin, Dr.Simmon's Laxative Medicine, 1929 .... 1.00
Store, Tin, Dr.Simmon's Liver Medicine 4.00
Store, Tin, Edgemont Crackers, White & Green, 8 In. 3.00
Store, Tin, Edgeworth Sliced Plug Pipe Tobacco, 4 1/2 X 3 1/4 In. 8.00
Store, Tin, Edgeworth Tobacco, Pocket .... 2.20 To 4.50
Store, Tin, Edgeworth Tobacco, Punched In Sides, 6 1/2 In. 10.00
Store, Tin, Edgeworth Tobacco, Store Canister 12.00
Store, Tin, Edgeworth Tobacco, 4 1/2 X 3 1/2 In. .... 20.00 To 30.00
Store, Tin, Epicure Tobacco, Pocket 4.00
Store, Tin, Eve Tobacco, Pocket 45.00
Store, Tin, Eve, Cube Cut Tobacco, Pocket 55.00
Store, Tin, Gallaher's Snuff, Round 7.00
Store, Tin, Glendora Coffee, C.1930, Wire Bail, 5 Pound 20.00

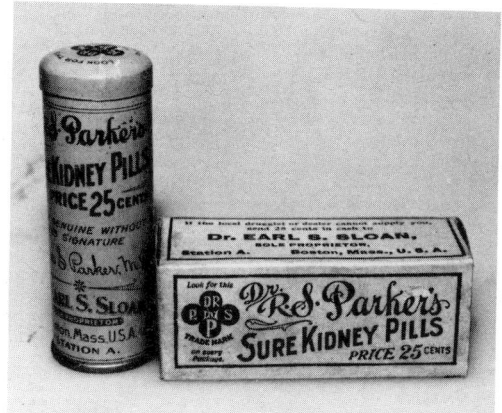

Store, Tin, Dr.R.S.Parker's Sure Kidney Pills, 3 1/2 In.
(See Page 622)

Store, Tin, Huntley & Palmer, 8 In.

Store, Tin, Glove Kid Peanut Butter, 10 Lb.	25.00
Store, Tin, Gold Dust Scouring Cleanser, 1930s	6.00
Store, Tin, Gold Medal Coffee, Lb.	12.00
Store, Tin, Gold Shore Tobacco, 7 X 5 X 4 In.	25.00
Store, Tin, Golden Brown Peanuts, 10 Pound	20.00
Store, Tin, Grain Tobacco, Pocket	20.00
Store, Tin, Granulated 54 Tobacco, Pocket	11.00
Store, Tin, Green Mountain Asthma Cure, Rupert, Vt., 4 1/2 In.	28.00
Store, Tin, Handsome Dan Mixture Tobacco	19.00
Store, Tin, Heckerman Peanut Products, 10 Pound	25.00
Store, Tin, Heinze Peanut Butter, 10 Lbs.	12.00
Store, Tin, Herman Sonntag's Violin Strings	7.00 To 10.00
Store, Tin, Hi-Plane Tobacco, Pocket	10.00 To 12.00
Store, Tin, Honest Labor Tobacco, 4 1/2 X 2 1/2 X 1 In.	13.00
Store, Tin, Humo Cigars, 2 1/2 X 5 1/2 X 9 In.	6.50
Store, Tin, Huntley & Palmer Biscuits, Bell, When Ye Doe Ring, Etc., 6 In.	33.00
Store, Tin, Huntley & Palmer Biscuits, Embossed Dragon, Flower Border, 6 In.	36.00
Store, Tin, Huntley & Palmer Biscuits, Syrian Table, Hexagonal, 6 1/2 In.	50.00
Store, Tin, Huntley & Palmer, 8 In.	*Illus* 50.00
Store, Tin, Hus Chocolates, Netherlands, Dutch Family At Dinner, 6 X 4 In.	8.00
Store, Tin, J.B.Pace Roll Cut Tobacco, 6 X 4 In.	17.00
Store, Tin, J.Goldmark's Percussion Caps, Patent 1867, 2 1/2 In.	4.95
Store, Tin, Jack & Jill Coffee, Bucket Shape, 4 Lbs.	10.00
Store, Tin, Jewel Tea, 8 In.	4.00
Store, Tin, Just Suits Cut Plug Tobacco, Pocket	25.00
Store, Tin, Just Suits Tobacco, Store Canister	45.00
Store, Tin, Juyler's Crystallized Ginger	6.00
Store, Tin, Keen's Mustard, Hunter's Return On Lid, Square, 7 X 5 1/2 In.	38.50
Store, Tin, Kentucky Club Tobacco, C.1940, Pocket	1.50
Store, Tin, Kentucky Club Tobacco, C.1945, Pocket	1.50
Store, Tin, Kentucky Club Tobacco, Pocket	1.50 To 1.75
Store, Tin, Kentucky Club Tobacco, 1949, Pocket	1.25
Store, Tin, Kis-Me If You Wish Gum, Brass, Square, 1 1/2 In.	22.00
Store, Tin, Krisp Krunch Peanut, 1 Pound	5.00
Store, Tin, Laredo Tobacco, Red, 6 X 4 In.	12.00
Store, Tin, Laredo Tobacco, 6 X 4 In.	9.00
Store, Tin, Layton's Baking Powder, C.1910, Paper Label, Cats, 8 Ozs.	3.00
Store, Tin, Lipton Ceylon Tea, 5 Pound	35.00
Store, Tin, Lipton Tea, 4 X 6 In.	15.00
Store, Tin, Long's Oxheart Peanut Butter, Lb.	7.00
Store, Tin, Lucky Strike Cigarettes, Christmas, Flat 50	5.00

Store, Tin

2.50 To 15.00

Store, Tin, Lucky Strike Cigarettes, Flat 50 .... 4.50
Store, Tin, Lucky Strike Cigarettes, Green, Pocket 12.00
Store, Tin, Lucky Strike Cigarettes, Holds 100, Promotion Sticker 17.00
Store, Tin, Lucky Strike Tobacco, Hasker & Marcuse, 4 1/2 X 2 3/4 X 1 In. 50.00
Store, Tin, Luzainne Coffee & Chicory, 3 Pound 4.50
Store, Tin, Marlboro Cigarettes, Flat 50 .... 6.00
Store, Tin, Maxwell House Coffee, C.1910, 6 In. Diameter 22.00
Store, Tin, Mayo's Cut Plug Tobacco, Round, 6 In. 5.00
Store, Tin, Merry Widow's, Embossed, 1 1/2 In. 22.00
Store, Tin, Montclair Brand Breakfast Cocoa, Sears Roebuck, 5 Pound ... 8.00 To 10.00
Store, Tin, Morning Sip Dry Roast Coffee, Paper Label, Lb. 30.00
Store, Tin, Mosemann's Peanut Butter, 25 Pound 57.00
Store, Tin, National Pretzel, Scranton, Eagle Design, Glass Lid, 15 In. 12.50
Store, Tin, Nut House Of Lynn, Mass., Home Of Good Nuts, 2 1/2 In. 25.00
Store, Tin, Old Master Coffee, 2 Lbs. 25.00
Store, Tin, Old Virginia Cut Plug Tobacco, Pocket 16.50
Store, Tin, Our Triumph Brands Tea, Boston Tea Party, Yellow, 6 X 4 In. 8.50
Store, Tin, Parke Davis, Materia Medica Specimen, Glass In Lid, 2 1/2 In. 23.00
Store, Tin, Parke's Coffee, Pull Ring On Lid, Orange & Ivory, 5 Pound .... 22.00 To 65.00
Store, Tin, Pastime Tobacco 30.00
Store, Tin, Pat Hand Tobacco, Pocket 17.00
Store, Tin, Peachey Tobacco, Pocket 20.00
Store, Tin, Penn's Tobacco, Rectangular, 6 1/2 X 6 1/2 X 2 3/4 In. 7.00
Store, Tin, Penn's 30 Cent Plug Tobacco, Dozen 2.50
Store, Tin, Pile Cure, Miniature 12.00
Store, Tin, Planter's House Coffee, Lb. 15.00
Store, Tin, Planter's Peanut, 10 Lbs. 25.00
Store, Tin, Planter's, Brown & Gold, 5 Lb. 50.00
Store, Tin, Planter's, Salt-In-Shell, White, 10 Lb. 40.00
Store, Tin, Planters Pennant Brand Salted Peanuts, Lithographed, 10 Lbs. 30.00
Store, Tin, Polar Bear Brand Coffee, Pound 85.00
Store, Tin, Popper's Ace, Plane On 3 Sides, Glass Lid, 6 X 7 X 8 1/2 In. 10.00
Store, Tin, Postum Cereal, Beverage, 4 Ozs. 8.50
Store, Tin, Pride Of Virginia Tobacco, 4 1/2 X 2 1/2 X 1/2 In. 8.50
Store, Tin, Pride Of Virginia Tobacco, 5 1/2 X 3 X 1 1/2 In. .... .73
Store, Tin, Prince Albert Tobacco, C.1920, Pocket .... .45 To 1.00
Store, Tin, Prince Albert Tobacco, Pocket .... 13.00 To 30.00
Store, Tin, Q Boid Tobacco, Pocket 10.00
Store, Tin, Rawleigh's Antiseptic Salve 3.75
Store, Tin, Rawleigh's Pure Ground Cinnamon, Red, White & Gold, 5 X 3 In. 11.00
Store, Tin, Red Bird Coffee, Lb. .... 3.00 To 8.00
Store, Tin, Red Jacket Tobacco, Pocket 2.50
Store, Tin, Red Top Snuff 30.00
Store, Tin, Regal Cube Cut Tobacco, Pocket 8.00
Store, Tin, Rette Chocolates, Netherlands, Scenic, 8 1/2 X 5 1/4 X 3 1/4 In. 3.50
Store, Tin, Rich's Canton Ginger 4.00
Store, Tin, Rich's Canton Ginger, Flat 10.00
Store, Tin, Richmond Club Mixture Tobacco, Red & Gold, 4 1/2 X 3 1/2 In. 17.00
Store, Tin, Richmond Mixture Tobacco, Ginna, 4 1/2 X 3 1/2 In. 15.00
Store, Tin, Richmond Mixture Tobacco, Hasker & Marcuse, 4 1/2 X 3 1/2 In. 145.00
Store, Tin, Roly Poly, Mammy, Mayo Tobacco 125.00
Store, Tin, Roly Poly, Mammy, U.S.Marine Tobacco .... *Illus* 190.00
Store, Tin, Roly Poly, Storekeeper 32.00
Store, Tin, Seminole Coffee, Picture Of Indian, Label, 4 1/4 X 5 1/2 In. 35.00
Store, Tin, Shakespeare Tobacco, 4 1/2 X 3 1/2 X 2 1/4 In. 6.50
Store, Tin, Sheik Prophylactics, Sheik On Camel On Lid, Square, 1920s 15.00
Store, Tin, Silver Sea Coffee, Lb. 1.50
Store, Tin, Sir Walter Raleigh Tobacco, Pocket 4.00
Store, Tin, Sozodont Powder, Man Brushing Teeth 15.00
Store, Tin, Sphinx Mixture Tobacco, Pocket .... 10.00 To 22.00
Store, Tin, Stag Tobacco, Pocket 47.00
Store, Tin, Sterling Tobacco, Green, Store Tin 32.00
Store, Tin, Sterling Tobacco, Store Can 25.00
Store, Tin, Summer Time Tobacco, Store Canister 10.00
Store, Tin, Sunshine Biscuits, Washington View, Hinged, 12 X 11 X 3 In. 130.00
Store, Tin, Sure Shot Tobacco, Store Canister ....

Store, Tin, Roly Poly, Storekeeper
(See Page 624)

Store, Tin, Sweet Burley Tobacco, Store Canister	60.00
Store, Tin, Sweet Burley Tobacco, 6 X 4 In.	15.00
Store, Tin, Sweet Burley Tobacco, 11 In.	35.00
Store, Tin, Sweet Clover Tobacco, Pocket	45.00
Store, Tin, Sweet Cuba Tobacco, Green & Red, Round, Pound	15.00
Store, Tin, Sweet Cuba Tobacco, Store Canister	30.00 To 40.00
Store, Tin, Swift's Peanut Butter, 25 Pounds, White & Black	25.00
Store, Tin, Target Tobacco, Pocket	12.00
Store, Tin, Taroid Pile Cure	2.50
Store, Tin, Three Feathers Tobacco, Pocket	35.00
Store, Tin, Three States Mixture Tobacco, 4 1/2 X 3 1/4 X 1 In.	6.00
Store, Tin, Tiger Tobacco, Store Canister	55.00 To 60.00
Store, Tin, Turkey Coffee, 3 Pound	50.00
Store, Tin, Tuxedo Kentucky Club Tobacco, Pocket	2.50
Store, Tin, Tuxedo Tobacco, 1902 Stamp, Pocket	7.00
Store, Tin, Twin Oaks Tobacco, Pocket	5.00 To 16.00
Store, Tin, Union Leader Tobacco, C.1900, Pocket	1.50
Store, Tin, Union Leader Tobacco, Eagle, Trial Sample	12.00
Store, Tin, Union Leader Tobacco, Picture Of Uncle Sam, Pocket	13.00 To 32.00
Store, Tin, Union Leader Tobacco, Pocket	1.75 To 2.00
Store, Tin, Union Leader Tobacco, 1917 Stamp, Pocket	17.00
Store, Tin, Union Leader Tobacco, Trial Sample, Eagle	12.00
Store, Tin, Velvet Tobacco, C.1900, Pocket	1.25
Store, Tin, Velvet Tobacco, Pipe On Front, Pocket	15.00
Store, Tin, Velvet Tobacco, Pocket	.40 To 6.00
Store, Tin, Victrola Stylus	3.50
Store, Tin, Vienna Coffee, Lb.	12.00
Store, Tin, Watkin's Talcum Powder, Lady's Purse Size, Spring Loaded End	6.50
Store, Tin, Watson's Cough Drop, 7 X 5 1/2 In.	22.00
Store, Tin, White Bear Brand Coffee, Durand & Kasper, Pound	21.00
Store, Tin, Wiley's D.R. Scalp Treatment, C.1910, 10 X 5 X 4 In.	7.00
Store, Tin, Wiley's Scalp Treatment, 1920s, Gallon	8.00
Store, Tin, Woolson's Vienna Coffee, 3 Lbs.	20.00
Store, Tin, World's Navy Plug Tobacco, 3 Lbs.	38.00
Store, Tin, Yale Tobacco, Green & Black, 4 1/2 X 3 1/2 X 2 1/4 In.	8.00
Store, Tin, Yankee Boy, Pocket Type	120.00
Store, Tin, Young & Smylie Licorice, Brooklyn, N.Y., Glass Front, 7 1/2 In.	20.00
Store, Token, Bulldog Ale, Copper	11.00
Store, Token, Worcester Salt, Brass	2.00
Store, Tongs, For Lifting Chocolates From Box, Marquise Chocolates, 4 In.	3.75
Store, Toothpick & Master Salt, Fort Wayne Outfitters	18.00
Store, Trap & Cage, Rat, Wire, Oblong Oval Shape, 8 1/2 X 15 In.	13.00
Store, Trap, Rat, Wire, 18 X 7 In.	23.00
Store, Tray, Ballantine's Ale, Glass Of Beer, 13 1/4 In.	9.95
Store, Tray, Brass, Compliments Of Empire Cream Separator Co., 4 3/4 In.	12.00
Store, Tray, Budweiser Beer, Lithographed, Metal, Red, 10 In.	8.00
Store, Tray, Counter, U-Tah-Na Chocolates, Tin, 5 1/2 X 7 1/2 In.	8.00

	125.00
Store, Tray, Cyslimic Water, Topless Lady, 13 X 10 In.	2.50
Store, Tray, Dental, Milk Glass	27.50
Store, Tray, Indianapolis Beer, Tavern Fireplace Scene, 13 X 10 In.	12.00
Store, Tray, Iroquois Beer, Buffalo, N.Y., Round, 13 In.	9.95
Store, Tray, Kaier's, American & Canadian Competition, Brussels, 1950, 12 In.	35.00
Store, Tray, Lawrence Welk & Alice Dancing, Metal, 9 X 14 In.	11.50
Store, Tray, Michelob Beer, 13 In.	14.50
Store, Tray, Muehlebach Beer, Round, 12 In.	10.00
Store, Tray, Pepsi-Cola, 7 X 5 In.	4.50
Store, Tray, Pin, Clover Brand Shoes Are Always Just Correct, Kittens	35.00
Store, Tray, Tip, Black & White Scotch, Dogs, 4 X 6 In.	9.00
Store, Tray, Tip, Brown Forman Whiskey, Rectangular	10.00 To 22.00
Store, Tray, Tip, Carnation Milk, Cows In Meadow, Oval	15.00
Store, Tray, Tip, Century Beer, Round	12.00
Store, Tray, Tip, Cherry Blossoms	35.00
Store, Tray, Tip, Cottoline, Negroes In Cottonfield	16.00
Store, Tray, Tip, Cunard Line, R.M.S. Aquitania, Picture Of Ship	10.00 To 30.00
Store, Tray, Tip, DeLaval Cream Separators	10.00
Store, Tray, Tip, Dey's Dry Goods, Syracuse, N.Y.	16.00 To 22.00
Store, Tray, Tip, Fairy Soap	12.00 To 28.00
Store, Tray, Tip, Globe Wernicke Sectional Bookcases, N.M.	28.00
Store, Tray, Tip, Hyroler Whiskey, C.1910	12.50
Store, Tray, Tip, Indianapolis Brewing Co., Lieber's Gold Medal Beer	10.00
Store, Tray, Tip, Fairy Soap, 4 1/4 In.	40.00
Store, Tray, Tip, Iroquois Brewing, Buffalo, Picture Of Indian	15.00
Store, Tray, Tip, King's Pure Malt, Oval	15.00
Store, Tray, Tip, Krueger Beer, Round	12.00 To 12.50
Store, Tray, Tip, Marilyn Monroe, Nude, Round	35.00
Store, Tray, Tip, Merit Separator Co., Omaha, Nebr.	7.00
Store, Tray, Tip, Miller's High Life Beer, 1952	16.00
Store, Tray, Tip, Old Scotch Whiskey, Antiquary, The, Tan, Red, & Black, 4 In.	18.50
Store, Tray, Tip, Phil.Schneider Brewing Co., Century Bottled Beer	35.00
Store, Tray, Tip, President Suspenders, Lady, Under Glass	9.00
Store, Tray, Tip, Prudential, Oval	26.00
Store, Tray, Tip, R.M.S.Aquitania, 1913, Cunard Line, 4 X 6 In.	22.00
Store, Tray, Tip, Ranges, Baby Chicks	30.00
Store, Tray, Tip, Red Raven Splits, Man & Raven	17.00
Store, Tray, Tip, Red Raven, Ask The Man, Pittsburgh Exposition, 1905	22.00 To 23.50
Store, Tray, Tip, Resinol Soap & Ointment, Ample Boosomed Lady	8.00
Store, Tray, Tip, Rock Of Gibralter	17.50
Store, Tray, Tip, Rockford Watches, Gross, Canton, Mo.	24.00
Store, Tray, Tip, Rockford Watches, Lancaster, Pa.	15.00
Store, Tray, Tip, Saratoga Star Spring Water, 4 1/2 In.	3.00
Store, Tray, Tip, Schenley's Reserve Whiskey, Aluminum	17.00
Store, Tray, Tip, Schweppes Ginger Ale, Blue Willow, China, 4 3/4 In.	25.00 To 35.00
Store, Tray, Tip, Sears Roebuck, Factory	3.50
Store, Tray, Tip, Simon Pure Beer	.50
Store, Tray, Tip, Sprite, Painted, Tin, 7 X 6 In.	15.00
Store, Tray, Tip, Stollwerck Cocoa	25.00
Store, Tray, Tip, Welsbach Lightning, Mother & Child, Round	12.50
Store, Tray, Tip, White Top Champagne, Picture Of Bottle	27.00
Store, Tray, Valley Forge Beer, Washington & Flag, 12 In.	4.95
Store, Trowel, Dean St.Builders Supply Co., Taunton, Ma., Brass, 6 In.	1.00
Store, Tube, Larkin, Buffalo, Stick Shaving Cream, Screw Cap, Metal	12.00
Store, Tumbler, Coors' Beer, Etched	3.00
Store, Tumbler, Fountain, Pepsi-Cola, C.1940	3.75
Store, Tumbler, Gillette Award, Golden Horseshoe, 1956	6.50
Store, Tumbler, Jewel Tea, Frosted	12.00
Store, Tumbler, Los Angeles Brewery, Carmel Mission Picture, 1771, 3 In.	10.00
Store, Tumbler, Margo Root Beer, Etched	10.00
Store, Tumbler, Moxie, Orange Band	12.00
Store, Tumbler, Old German Lager Beer, Etched	1.00
Store, Tumbler, Pepsi-Cola, 75th Anniversary	12.00
Store, Tumbler, Schlitz Beer, Etched	12.00
Store, Tumbler, Seattle Beer, Etched	15.00
Store, Tumbler, Soda, Green River, Syrup Line	

Store, Valve, Pump, Wooden, Leather Bushing, 3 1/4 X 10 In.	9.00
Store, Vaporizer, Cresolene, Pat. Off. Reg. England 1901, Original Box	30.00
Store, Vibrator, Eureka Co., C.1905, Attachments, Instructions, & Box	16.00
Store, Wagon, Child's, Berry Bros. Varnish	37.50
Store, Wagon, Concession, On 1911 International Truck Frame, 6 Ft.	3500.00
Store, Warmer, Boot, Stove Top, Oval, Tin, Dated 1872, 11 X 21 In.	65.00
Store, Warmer, Foot, Buggy, Stone	6.00
Store, Warmer, Foot, Iron	48.00
Store, Warmer, Foot, Pierced Tin, Turned Posts, Square, 10 In.	65.00
Store, Warmer, Foot, Walnut Frame, Pierced Diamonds In Tin, Wire Bail, 9 In.	75.00
Store, Weaner, Calf, So-Boss, Simonsen, Chain Halter	12.50
Store, Weather House, Lovejoy's Improved, Metallic, Man & Woman, 7 1/2 In.	58.00
Store, Wheelbarrow, Wooden, S.A.Smith Mfg., Brattleboro, Vt., Iron Tire	40.00
Store, Whip Holder, Buggy	5.00
Store, Whiskey Set, Royal Velvet, White Lettering, 7 Piece	55.00
Store, Whistle, Delco Light, Wooden	7.50
Store, Yoke, Goat, Neck, Brasses & Brass Bell	22.00
Stove, see Fire, Stove	
Strawberry, see Soft Paste	
Stretch Glass, Bowl & Flower Frog, Blue, Footed, Shallow, 7 In.	20.00
Stretch Glass, Bowl, Blue Opaque, 8 In.	30.00
Stretch Glass, Bowl, Blue Panels, Deep, 9 1/4 In.	18.00
Stretch Glass, Bowl, Blue, 9 In.	22.00
Stretch Glass, Bowl, Blue, 10 In.	24.00
Stretch Glass, Bowl, Champagne Color, Imperial, 12 X 3 1/2 In.	38.00
Stretch Glass, Bowl, Frosty White, 7 3/4 X 3 5/8 In.	27.00
Stretch Glass, Bowl, Green, Shallow, 6 In.	9.50
Stretch Glass, Bowl, Green, 7 1/2 In.Diameter	18.00
Stretch Glass, Bowl, Iridescent Yellow, Imperial, 10 In.	48.00
Stretch Glass, Bowl, Iridescent, Curved-In Edge, 6 1/2 X 3 1/4 In.	14.00
Stretch Glass, Bowl, Light Amber, 10 X 3 5/8 In.	30.00
Stretch Glass, Bowl, Light Green, 7 3/4 X 2 In.	18.00
Stretch Glass, Bowl, Peacock Blue, Iridescent, 10 In.	45.00
Stretch Glass, Bowl, Pink, Low Pedestal, Ribbed Melon Sections, 11 In.	26.00
Stretch Glass, Bowl, Pink, Melon Shape, Rolled Edge, Fenton, 6 1/2 X 11 In.	35.00
Stretch Glass, Bowl, Sapphire Blue, Footed, 10 1/2 In.	25.00
Stretch Glass, Bowl, Sapphire Blue, Shallow, 10 In.	17.50
Stretch Glass, Bowl, Sapphire Blue, 5 3/4 X 2 1/4 In.	17.00
Stretch Glass, Bowl, Yellow, Shallow, 8 5/8 In.	11.00
Stretch Glass, Bowl, Yellow, 10 1/2 In.	18.00
Stretch Glass, Candlestick, Blue, 8 1/2 In.High, Pair	35.00
Stretch Glass, Candlestick, Green, Clear Stem, 4 In., Pair	16.00
Stretch Glass, Candlestick, Green, Scalloped, Round Base, 9 1/2 In., Pair	95.00
Stretch Glass, Candlestick, Lime Green, 8 1/4 In., Pair	25.00
Stretch Glass, Candlestick, Mint Green, 7 In.	8.00
Stretch Glass, Candlestick, Pastel Green, 8 1/2 In., Pair	21.00
Stretch Glass, Candlestick, Pink, 3 3/4 In., Pair	15.00
Stretch Glass, Candlestick, Sapphire Blue, 3 1/2 In.High, Pair	20.00
Stretch Glass, Candlestick, Sapphire Blue, 7 In., Pair	25.00
Stretch Glass, Candlestick, Sapphire Blue, 8 1/2 In., Pair	25.00
Stretch Glass, Compote, Blue, Ruffled Edge, 5 In.	15.00
Stretch Glass, Compote, Candy, Lime, 5 3/4 In.	15.00
Stretch Glass, Compote, Yellow, Footed, Shallow, 8 1/2 In.	10.00
Stretch Glass, Compote, Yellow, Low Standard, 8 In.	6.00
Stretch Glass, Compote, Yellow, 8 1/8 In.	16.00
Stretch Glass, Dish, Candy, Blue, Covered, 15 Panels, 6 1/2 In.	24.00
Stretch Glass, Dish, Candy, Blue, Covered, 9 In.	25.00
Stretch Glass, Dish, Candy, Blue, Footed, Covered, 6 1/2 In.	10.00
Stretch Glass, Dish, Candy, Lime Green, Covered, 6 Ribs	25.00
Stretch Glass, Dish, Candy, Marigold, Covered, 6 Panels, 9 1/2 In.	25.00
Stretch Glass, Dish, Candy, Mint Green, Covered, 16 Panels, 6 In.	17.00
Stretch Glass, Dish, Candy, Mint Green, Covered, 16 Panels, 9 In.	25.00
Stretch Glass, Dish, Candy, Mint Green, Covered, 8 In.	24.00
Stretch Glass, Dish, Sundae, Pink	16.00
Stretch Glass, Goblet, Blue, Footed	13.00
Stretch Glass, Plate, Blue, 8 In.	12.00

Stretch Glass, Plate, Chop, White, Black Border, 12 In. 25.00
Stretch Glass, Plate, Green, 8 In. 6.00
Stretch Glass, Plate, Iridescent Green, 7 1/2 In. 6.00
Stretch Glass, Plate, Pink, 8 In. 12.00
Stretch Glass, Plate, Sapphire Blue, 10 In. 1.00
Stretch Glass, Plate, Yellow, 7 1/2 In. 6.00
Stretch Glass, Salt, Pedestal, Apple Green, 1 3/4 In. X 3 In. Diameter 17.50
Stretch Glass, Server, Green, Handled, 11 In. 20.00
Stretch Glass, Sherbet & Underplate, Sapphire Blue 22.00
Stretch Glass, Toothpick, Ice Blue, 3 In. High 70.00
Stretch Glass, Tray, Sandwich, Marigold, Clear Center Handle 12.00
Stretch Glass, Tray, Sandwich, Mint Green, 10 1/2 In. 17.00
Stretch Glass, Tray, Sandwich, Sapphire Blue, Center Handle 18.50
Stretch Glass, Tumbler, Red Metallic Luster, White Interior, 3 1/2 In. 35.00
Stretch Glass, Vase, Apple Green, Cylindrical, 9 1/2 In. 27.00
Stretch Glass, Vase, Fan, Green, Melon Ribbed, 9 1/2 In. High 18.50
Stretch Glass, Vase, Fan, Ice Green, 7 3/4 X 10 In. 35.00
Stretch Glass, Vase, Fan, Iridescent, Dolphin, Handled, 5 1/4 In. 32.00

Sunbonnet Babies were first introduced in 1902 in the Sunbonnet Babies Primer. The stories were by Eulalie Osgood Grover, illustrated by Bertha Corbett. The children's faces were completely hidden by the sunbonnets, and had been pictured in black and white before this time. The color pictures in the book were immediately successful. The Royal Bayreuth China Company made a full line of children's dishes decorated with the Sunbonnet Babies.

Sunbonnet Babies, Ashtray, Cleaning, Royal Bayreuth, Blue Mark, Square, 4 In. 95.00
Sunbonnet Babies, Book, In Mother Goose Land, Copyright 1907 .... 25.00
Sunbonnet Babies, Book, Overall Boys, Grover .... 22.50 To 35.00
Sunbonnet Babies, Book, Primer, 1902, Color Illustrations 22.00
Sunbonnet Babies, Book, Primer, 1902, 1st Edition 65.00
Sunbonnet Babies, Book, Sunbonnet A.B.C. Hornbook 35.00
Sunbonnet Babies, Book, The Sunbonnet Twins 85.00
Sunbonnet Babies, Chocolate Pot, Child's 225.00
Sunbonnet Babies, Creamer, Sweeping, Royal Bayreuth .... *Illus* 100.00

Sunbonnet Babies, Creamer,
Sweeping, Royal Bayreuth

Sunbonnet Babies, Cup & Saucer, Coffee, Fishing, Gold Handle, Blue Mark 185.00
Sunbonnet Babies, Cup & Saucer, Demitasse, Washing & Scrubbing, Blue Mark 165.00
Sunbonnet Babies, Cup, Hanging Clothes 40.00
Sunbonnet Babies, Dish, Candy, 3 Beach Babies, 8 Sided, Royal Bayreuth 57.00
Sunbonnet Babies, Dish, Feeding, Cleaning, Royal Bayreuth, Blue Mark, 7 In. 120.00
Sunbonnet Babies, Doorstop, Iron 15.00
Sunbonnet Babies, Feeding Set, Snow Babies, Royal Bayreuth, 2 Piece 150.00
Sunbonnet Babies, Hatpin Holder & Trinket Tray, Combination, 1 Piece 145.00
Sunbonnet Babies, Jar, Powder, Covered, Ironing, Blue Mark, 3 1/4 In. 185.00
Sunbonnet Babies, Jar, Powder, Covered, Washing & Scrubbing, Blue Mark 195.00

Sunbonnet Babies, Mug, Sweeping, Royal Bayreuth, Blue Mark .... 95.00 To 130.00
Sunbonnet Babies, Opener, Letter, Figural Handle, Cast Iron 16.00
Sunbonnet Babies, Paperweight, Baby Kissing Overall Boy, 3 1/4 In. 75.00
Sunbonnet Babies, Paperweight, Oblong 5.00
Sunbonnet Babies, Picture, Cleaning Day, B.L.Corbett, 1904, Frame, 6 X 8 In. 35.00
Sunbonnet Babies, Picture, Mending Day, B.L.Corbett, 1904, Frame, 6 X 8 In. 35.00
Sunbonnet Babies, Pitcher, Mending, Royal Bayreuth, Blue Mark, 4 In. 120.00
Sunbonnet Babies, Plate, Cake, Washing & Hanging, Handled, Blue Mark, 11 In. 300.00
Sunbonnet Babies, Plate, Cleaning, 6 In. 35.00
Sunbonnet Babies, Plate, Fishing, Royal Bayreuth, Blue Mark, 8 1/2 In. 120.00
Sunbonnet Babies, Plate, Fishing, 6 In. 35.00
Sunbonnet Babies, Plate, Ironing, Royal Bayreuth, Blue Mark, 7 1/4 In. 97.50
Sunbonnet Babies, Plate, Mending, Carnation-McNicol, 7 1/4 In. 62.50
Sunbonnet Babies, Plate, Sweeping, Royal Bayreuth, Blue Mark, 6 In. 100.00
Sunbonnet Babies, Plate, Tuesday's Scene, 7 5/8 In. 89.50
Sunbonnet Babies, Postcard, Baby Fishing, 1907, Printed On Silk 10.00
Sunbonnet Babies, Postcard, Cleaning Day, J.J.Austen 10.00
Sunbonnet Babies, Postcard, Easter, Sunbonnet Sue, Set Of 7 .... 64.00
Sunbonnet Babies, Postcard, Fishing, Leather 4.50
Sunbonnet Babies, Postcard, In The Good Old Summer Time, 1906, Nude Babies 10.00
Sunbonnet Babies, Postcard, Mary's Little Lamb, Ullman 10.00
Sunbonnet Babies, Postcard, Monday, Ullman 10.00
Sunbonnet Babies, Postcard, Paying Toll, Signed D.Dixon, 1905 .... 6.00
Sunbonnet Babies, Postcard, Saying Grace, 1905 .... 8.00
Sunbonnet Babies, Postcard, Seven Days Of The Week, Ullman, 7 .... 35.00 To 49.00
Sunbonnet Babies, Postcard, Sunday, Ullman 10.00
Sunbonnet Babies, Postcard, The Lovers, J.J.Austen 10.00
Sunbonnet Babies, Postcard, Thursday, Ullman 10.00
Sunbonnet Babies, Postcard, Wash Day, J.J.Austen, 1908 .... 10.00
Sunbonnet Babies, Postcard, 6 A.M. To 6 P.M., Ullman Mfg.Co., 1906, 6 .... 50.00
Sunbonnet Babies, Saltshaker, Cleaning, Royal Bayreuth, Blue Mark 125.00
Sunbonnet Babies, Saucer, Scrubbing, Royal Bayreuth, 5 In. 38.00
Sunbonnet Babies, Shoe, Fishing Scene 225.00
Sunbonnet Babies, Sugar & Creamer, Cover, Washing & Scrubbing, Blue Mark 350.00
Sunbonnet Babies, Sugar, Open 85.00
Sunbonnet Babies, Tea Set, Limoges China, Dated 1915, 16 Piece 195.00
Sunbonnet Babies, Tray, Mending, Diamond Shape, Blue Mark, 5 3/4 In. 165.00
Sunbonnet Babies, Vase, Wall, Cleaning, Cup For Flowers, Blue Mark, 4 In. 225.00

> Sunderland luster is a name given to a characteristic pink luster made by
> Leeds, Newcastle, and other English firms during the nineteenth century.
> The luster glaze is metallic and glossy and sometimes appears to have bubbles
> as a decoration.

Sunderland, Bowl, Transfer River Wear & Mariner's Compass, C.1850, 10 In. 225.00
Sunderland, Chalice, Silver, Copper Interior, Bulbous, C.1820, 4 In. 60.00
Sunderland, Garniture Set, Pink Splash, Double Ring Handles, C.1925, 3 Piece 200.00
Sunderland, Jug, Ancient Order Of Foresters & River Wear, C.1825, 5 5/8 In. 150.00
Sunderland, Jug, British Sailing Ship & Cast-Iron Bridge, C.1925, 4 7/8 In. 80.00
Sunderland, Jar, Mariner's Arms, Domed Lid, Strap Handles, C.1850, 4 1/2 In. 75.00
Sunderland, Jug, Northumberland, C.1815 .... Illus 450.00
Sunderland, Jug, Pink Ruins & Farm Buildings, C.1925, 6 1/4 In. 125.00
Sunderland, Jug, Pink, 7 3/4 In., Pair .... Illus 400.00
Sunderland, Jug, The Sailor's Tear, 6 1/2 In.High 248.00
Sunderland, Jug, The Shipwright's Arms, Abbey, C.1790, Black Transfer, 8 In. 275.00
Sunderland, Pitcher, A West View Of Iron Bridge, Masonic Poem, C.1825, 7 In. 150.00
Sunderland, Pitcher, A West View Of Iron Bridge, Masonic Poem, C.1825, 9 In. 225.00
Sunderland, Pitcher, Argonaut Shell, Black Snipe Shooting Transfer, 6 In. 110.00
Sunderland, Pitcher, Crimea & Masonic Emblems, C.1855, 6 In. 150.00
Sunderland, Pitcher, Frigate In Full Sail, C.1850, 9 In. 250.00
Sunderland, Pitcher, Snipe Shooting & Coursing, Black Transfer, Pink, 9 In. 110.00
Sunderland, Plaque, British & French Sailor, 8 1/2 In. 30.00
Sunderland, Plaque, Man-O'-War Northumberland, C.1850, 8 1/2 In., Pair 150.00
Sunderland, Plaque, Travelers, Indian Landscape, C.1850, 8 3/4 In., Pair 100.00
Sunderland, Plaque, Verse, Prepare To Meet Thy God.Brown Border, 8 X 9 In. 80.00
Sunderland, Plate, Sailing Ship, Gray's Pottery, 10 1/2 In. 24.00
Sunderland, Toby Mug, Shakespeare 20.00

Sunderland, Jug, Northumberland, C.1815
(See Page 629)

Sunderland, Jug, Pink, 7 3/4 In., Pair
(See Page 629)

Sunderland, Vase, Tulip, Pink Splash, 6 Spouts, C.1825, 7 1/2 In., Pair	275.00
Superman, Badge, 1945	3.00
Superman, Doll, Clark Kent, Rubber, 4 In.	4.50

Sundial, see Clock, Sundial
Sword, see Weapon, Sword
Taffeta Glass, see Carnival Glass
Tapestry, Porcelain, see Rose Tapestry
Tea Caddy, see Furniture, Tea Caddy
Tea Leaf, see Ironstone, Tea Leaf

Teco

Teco pottery is the art pottery line made by the Terra-Cotta Tile Works of Terra-Cotta, Illinois. The company was founded by William D.Gates in 1881. The Teco line was first made in 1902 and continued into the 1920s. It included over 500 designs, made in a variety of colors and glazes.

Teco, Pitcher, Brown & Black, Gold Flecks, 4 In.High	60.00
Teco, Vase, Matte Green, Marked Teco, 9 In.	57.00
Telephone, Candlestick, Bell Box	55.00
Telephone, Danish, Dial	19.00
Telephone, Desk, American Automatic Electric Sales Co., Tin, 1920s	22.50
Telephone, Desk, Crank	8.50
Telephone, Kellogg, 1928, Cradle, Cloth Cord, Felt Base	7.00 To 9.00
Telephone, Pay Phone Box, Iron, 1911	25.00
Telephone, Pay, Iron, Gray, 1912, Nickel	25.00
Telephone, Wall, Kellogg, 1901, Oak	100.00

Teplitz refers to art pottery manufactured by a number of companies in the Teplitz-Turn area of Bohemia during the late nineteenth and early twentieth centuries. The Amphora Porcelain Works and the Alexandra Works were two of these companies.

Teplitz, Basket, Art Deco Flowers, Blue, 6 X 7 In.	25.00
Teplitz, Figurine, Camel & Rider, Amphora, Pastel Colors, 13 1/2 In., Pair	475.00
Teplitz, Plate, Incised & Raised Christmas Scene, Amphora, 10 In.	45.00
Teplitz, Urn, Art Deco, Scenic Forest, Raised Mushrooms, 6 1/2 In.High	145.00
Teplitz, Urn, Greenish Glaze, Purple Highlights, Gold Flowers, Amphora, 14 In	200.00
Teplitz, Vase, Amphora, Art Nouveau, Green & Red Flowers On Brown, 19 In.	295.00
Teplitz, Vase, Amphora, Blue, Gourd Shape, Gold Outlined Butterflies, 7 In.	100.00
Teplitz, Vase, Amphora, Blues, Mulberry, Beige, & Browns, 4 Handles, 9 In.	75.00
Teplitz, Vase, Amphora, Dragon Handled, Gold On Green, Berries, 10 In.	129.00
Teplitz, Vase, Amphora, Gold Matte, Poppies & Pods, 9 In.	60.00
Teplitz, Vase, Amphora, Gourd Shape, Butterflies & Bees, Spider Webs, 6 In.	110.00

Teplitz, Vase, Amphora, Half Dressed Man Kneeling On Blue, 7 1/2 In.	75.00
Teplitz, Vase, Amphora, Inlaid Jewels, 7 1/2 In.	110.00
Teplitz, Vase, Amphora, Iridescent Blue & Purple, Jeweled, Bulldog, 13 In.	275.00
Teplitz, Vase, Amphora, Lady On Side, Applied Floral, Lavender Pink, 21 In.	300.00
Teplitz, Vase, Amphora, Man, Incised, Enameled, 5 1/2 In.	25.00
Teplitz, Vase, Amphora, Pebbled, Raised Glossy Floral, 7 1/2 In.	18.00
Teplitz, Vase, Amphora, Raised Bird & Art Deco Designs On Beige, 6 1/2 In.	18.00
Teplitz, Vase, Amphora, Raised Bluebird, Glossy Art Deco Design, 6 1/2 In.	25.00
Teplitz, Vase, Amphora, Rooster, Incised, Enameled, 5 1/2 In.	25.00
Teplitz, Vase, Blue Gray, Inlaid Boy With Bowl Looking At Moon, 6 In.	54.00
Teplitz, Vase, Enameled Sinbad, Costumed, 5 In.	34.00
Teplitz, Vase, Pedestal, Cream, Gold Greek Key & Scrolls, Insects, 13 1/2 In.	125.00
Teplitz, Vase, Pitcher Type, Blue Daisies & Leaves, White, 10 In.High	82.50
Teplitz, Vase, Portrait, Enamel Jewels, Floral & Leaves, Green, 5 1/2 In.	45.00
Teplitz, Vase, Royal Blue Glossy Ground, Gold Enameled Birds & Leaves, 9 In	50.00
Terra-Cotta, Medallion, Benjamin Franklin Portrait, Baptiste, C.1780, 4 In.	300.00
Terra-Cotta, Mug, Raised Dragon & Symbols, Dragontail Handle, 6 1/2 In.	65.00
Terra-Cotta, Teapot, Chinese, Turquoise, Crabstock Spout & Handle	20.00
Terra-Cotta, Vase, Chocolate Brown, Relief Cameo Heads, English, 10 In., Pair	58.00

Textile includes all types of table linens and household linens such as coverlets, quilts, fabrics, etc.

Textile, see also World's Fair items

Textile, Apron, Lawn, Silk Ribbon, Crochet Top	5.00
Textile, Bag, Lady's, Silver Mesh	18.50
Textile, Banner, Russian School, Embroidered, C.1890, 27 1/4 X 26 In.	60.00
Textile, Bedspread, Crocheted, Pinwheel Pattern, 101 X 75 In.	52.50
Textile, Bedspread, Hand-Crocheted, Fringed, 80 X 72 In.	42.50
Textile, Bedspread, Hand-Crocheted, Popcorn Stitch, Ecru, Double Bed Size	72.50
Textile, Bedspread, Hand-Crocheted, 101 X 94 In.	52.50
Textile, Bedspread, Marseilles, Woven, Cut Corners, Fringe, 84 X 88 In.	20.00
Textile, Blanket, Homespun, Center Seam, Natural, Black Bands, 64 X 76 In.	10.00
Textile, Blouse, British Officer's, C.1840, Red Wool, 65 Brass Buttons	84.50
Textile, Blouse, U.S.Army, Summer Campaign, Spanish American War, Cotton, Tan	94.50
Textile, Bonnet, Pumpkin, Silk, Quilted, Padded, C.1750	15.00
Textile, Bookmark, Silk, Poem, God's Best, Holly, 1904	12.00
Textile, Carpet, Art Deco, Geometric Center, C.1930, 10 Ft.X 10 Ft.3 In.	850.00
Textile, Coat, Child's, Victorian, Peach Velvet, Grand Maison De Blanc, N.Y.	30.00
Textile, Coat, Man's, Cutaway, 3 Button, C.1890	25.00
Textile, Coat, Man's, Prince Albert, C.1860	25.00
Textile, Coat, U.S.Officer's, Frock, C.1870, Navy Blue Wool, 9 Brass Buttons	84.50
Textile, Corset, Handmade, Bone Eyelets, C.1850	12.50
Textile, Corset, Handmade, Buckskin Reinforced, C.1850	12.00
Textile, Corset, Lady's, Lacing, White, C.1900	5.00

Linen or wool coverlets were made during the nineteenth century. Most of the coverlets date from 1800 to 1850. Four types were made, the double woven, jacquard, summer and winter, and overshot.

Textile, Coverlet, Chintz, Quilted, Pineapple Sprigs On Brown, C.1790, 92 In.	175.00
Textile, Coverlet, Geometric Design, Two Shades Gold & White, 89 X 72 In.	70.00
Textile, Coverlet, Homespun, Red & White, Fringed, Geometrics, Double Size	175.00
Textile, Coverlet, Jacquard, Mary Tuthill, 1822 .... *Illus*	650.00
Textile, Coverlet, Jacquard, Tan, Blue & Red Geometrics, U.S.Capitol	85.00
Textile, Coverlet, Pennsylvania Dutch, Red, White, Blue, Green, Dated 1851	375.00
Textile, Coverlet, Red & White, Reversible Floral, 1854, 78 X 90 In.	275.00
Textile, Coverlet, Woven, Blue & White, 90 X 66 In.	85.00
Textile, Coverlet, Woven, Ira Hadsell, N.Y., 1854, Red & White, 78 X 90 In.	275.00
Textile, Dress & Petticoat, Infant's, White Calico, Embroidered	6.00
Textile, Dress, Child's, Red, White Lace, C.1840	30.00
Textile, Dress, Flapper, 1925, Satin, Velvet Fringe, Boa, Size 8	50.00
Textile, Dress, Wedding, C.1880, 2 Piece	25.00
Textile, Dress, 1920s, Silk, Crochet, Gray & Yellow Stripes	22.50
Textile, Duster, Auto, Man's, Silk	8.00
Textile, Flag, U.S.A., 13 Stars, C.1865, 4 Ft.4 In. X 5 Ft.1 In.	100.00
Textile, Handkerchief, Child's, Queen Of Hearts, Poem, Square, 10 1/2 In.	8.50

Textile, Hat, see also Shaker, Hat

Textile, Hat, Buster Brown Type, Fuzzy, Ear Lugs	6.00
Textile, High Hat, Silk, Black, Corded	20.00
Textile, Jacket, Mandarin, Silk, Yellow, Embroidered, Size 12	28.00
Textile, Kerchief, see also Shaker, Kerchief	
Textile, Kerchief, Spanish American War, Silk, Square, 20 In.	50.00
Textile, Knickers, Golf, Man's, Linen	7.00
Textile, Lap Robe, Horse With Glass Eye, Brown, 4 1/2 X 3 1/2 Ft.	18.00
Textile, Petticoat, Embroidered Nainsook	7.00
Textile, Petticoat, Lady's, Muslin, Full Length, Tucks, Embroidery	4.00
Textile, Photograph, On Silk, Negro Child, Seated In Chair, 16 X 12 In.	150.00
Textile, Pillow Cover, Lawn, Cutwork, Crocheting, Square, 18 In.	5.00
Textile, Pillow, From Summer Winter Coverlet, C.1840, Red, White, & Blue	8.00
Textile, Purse, Cocktail Size, Minipoint Floral	23.00
Textile, Purse, Victorian, Petit Point, Gilt Handle & Rim	15.00
Textile, Quilt, Basket Design, Handmade, 84 X 82 In.	75.00
Textile, Quilt, Black Calico, Roses, Handmade, 70 X 74 In.	50.00
Textile, Quilt, Broken Pieced Star, Pink & White, Quaker Path, 88 X 96 In.	100.00
Textile, Quilt, Calico, 1876 Centennial Banner In Center, 72 X 72 In.	225.00
Textile, Quilt, Centennial 1776 Banner, Reds, Handmade, 84 X 84 In.	175.00
Textile, Quilt, Child's, Star Pattern, Blue On White, 62 X 62 In.	35.00
Textile, Quilt, Child's, Star Pattern, Pale Blue On White, 32 X 32 In.	35.00
Textile, Quilt, Crazy, Cradle, 32 In.Square	52.00
Textile, Quilt, Crazy, Embroidered Floral, Tatted Edge, C.1900, 38 X 48 In.	40.00
Textile, Quilt, Crazy, Velvet, Silk & Satin, 1886, Grandma, 84 X 52 In.	95.00
Textile, Quilt, Crib, Rose Of Sharon, Pennsylvania, C.1850	165.00
Textile, Quilt, Doll Carriage, Rabbit, Organ Grinder, Handmade, 15 X 20 In.	22.50
Textile, Quilt, Double Wedding Ring, Yellow, 78 X 83 In.	90.00
Textile, Quilt, Friendship, 1902, 74 X 74 In.	60.00
Textile, Quilt, Improved 9 Patch, Purple & White, Quaker Path, 78 X 86 In.	100.00
Textile, Quilt, Irish Chain, Pink & Green On Muslin, 82 X 86 In.	45.00
Textile, Quilt, Irish, Chain, Stairsteps Quilting, White On Green, 86 In.	45.00
Textile, Quilt, Lincoln Log, Silk & Velvet, 40 X 58 In.	128.00
Textile, Quilt, Patchwork, Basket, Red, Yellow, & White, 68 X 76 In.	55.00
Textile, Quilt, Patchwork, Cross Trail, Red, White, & Blue, 74 X 82 In.	60.00
Textile, Quilt, Patchwork, Handmade, Star Center, Blues, 70 X 80 In.	55.00
Textile, Quilt, Patchwork, Ribbon, Prints, 70 X 75 In.	60.00
Textile, Quilt, Patchwork, Victorian, Silk & Velvet, 60 X 60 In.	85.00
Textile, Quilt, Patchwork, Yo-Yo, Pastels, Green Lined, Twin Bed Size	45.00
Textile, Quilt, Star In A Star, Dark & Light Blue, 82 X 91 In.	95.00
Textile, Quilt, Tulip Pattern, Handmade, 66 X 84 In.	50.00
Textile, Quilt, Washing Pavement, Silk & Velvet, 58 In.Square	135.00
Textile, Robe, Carriage, Hunter Green & Rust, Leaves On Cream, 5 X 4 Ft.	32.50
Textile, Robe, Lap, Wool, Plaid, Fringe, 52 X 72 In.	42.50

Textile, Coverlet, Jacquard, Mary Tuthill, 1822
(See Page 631)

Textile, Rug, C.1850, 38 1/2 In.
(See Page 633)

Textile, Robe, Lap, Woolen, Horse's Head Center, Chase Label, 46 X 56 In. 32.50
    Textile, Rug, see also Shaker, Rug
Textile, Rug, Bokhara, 4 X 9 Ft. 3 In. 125.00
Textile, Rug, C.1850, 38 1/2 In. .... 800.00 *Illus*
Textile, Rug, Caucasian, Geometrics, White, 28 X 48 In. 42.50
Textile, Rug, Hooked, American Clipper Ship, C.1850, 4 1/2 Ft. X 30 In. 525.00
Textile, Rug, Hooked, Candy Stripe, 3 1/2 X 5 Ft. 9.50
Textile, Rug, Hooked, Centennial, 1776-1876, American, C.1850, 35 X 23 In. 325.00
Textile, Rug, Hooked, Chevrons Bands, Greek Key, 6 Ft.2 In. X 4 1/2 Ft. 200.00
Textile, Rug, Hooked, Floral, American, C.1850, 5 Ft. X 6 Ft.2 In. 200.00
Textile, Rug, Hooked, Floral, American, C.1850, 5 Ft.1 In. X 30 In. 75.00
Textile, Rug, Hooked, G.A.R., Dated 1861-1866, 30 X 60 In. 75.00
Textile, Rug, Hooked, New England, C.1850, Floral Reserve, 6 Ft.3 1/2 In. 1400.00
Textile, Rug, Hooked, New England, C.1850, Girl & Sailor, 47 X 37 In. 500.00
Textile, Rug, India, Princess, Wool, Vegetable Dyed, 12 X 28 Ft. 4500.00
Textile, Rug, Iran, 13 Ft.5 In. X 29 In. 400.00
Textile, Rug, Lilihan, 4 X 7 In. 115.00
Textile, Rug, Persian, Silk, 25 1/2 X 45 1/2 In. 37.50
Textile, Rug, Wall, Eagle Clutching American Flag, Blue Ground, 19 X 20 In. 150.00
Textile, Sailor Bloomer Outfit, Lady's, Navy Blue, 2 Piece 8.50

*Samplers were made in the United States during the early 1700s. The
best examples were made from 1790 to 1840. Long narrow samplers are usually
older than the square ones. Early samplers just had stitching or alphabets.
The later examples had numerals, borders, and pictorial decorations. Those
with mottoes are mid-Victorian.*

Textile, Sampler, Agnes Rattrey, 1786, Alphabet, Floral, 16 1/2 X 15 In. 275.00
Textile, Sampler, Alphabet, Dated 1819, 14 X 20 In. 100.00
Textile, Sampler, Barbara Hendarson, 1787, Linen, Needlework, 13 1/2 In. 425.00
Textile, Sampler, Basket Of Flowers, Trees, Bird, Eliza Jane, 21 X 16 1/2 In. 145.00
Textile, Sampler, Christina & F.Summers, 21 1/2 X 20 1/4 In. 100.00
Textile, Sampler, Elizabeth Abraham, 1811, Alphabet, Adam & Eve, 16 1/2 In. 275.00
Textile, Sampler, Genealogical, Husband Born 1776, 10 1/2 X 8 1/2 In. 175.00
Textile, Sampler, Genealogical, May 17, 1776, 8 1/2 X 10 1/2 In. 125.00
Textile, Sampler, Girl In Fancy Dress, House, Cow, 1837, Framed 275.00
Textile, Sampler, Handloomed Linen, Framed, 17 X 10 In. 87.00
Textile, Sampler, Margaret Hopkins, 1808, Adam & Eve, Birds, 16 X 12 In. 275.00
Textile, Sampler, Mary Ann Ten Eyck, C.1790, Alphabet, 17 X 7 1/2 In. 60.00
Textile, Sampler, Needlepoint, Floral & Verse, 1842, 22 X 26 In.Framed 250.00
Textile, Sampler, Ruth Huntington, 1787, 10 X 16 In. .... *Illus* 650.00
Textile, Sampler, Sarah Clark, 1803, 12 X 11 In. 275.00
Textile, Shawl, Embroidered Allover Flowers, Fringe, 51 X 56 In. 65.00
Textile, Shawl, Paisley, Scotland, Wool, Square, C.1860, 5 Ft.5 In. 80.00
Textile, Shawl, Silk, Black, White Silk Embroidered Floral, C.1920, 48 In. 75.00
Textile, Shirt, Man's, Dress, White, Collar Band, Stiff Front .... 3.00 To 7.00
    Textile, Shirt, see also Shaker, Shirt

Textile, Sampler, Ruth Huntington,
1787, 10 X 16 In.

Textile, Shoe, Baby's, Crocheted, Leather Sole, Eclipse, 1907, Size 3, Pair	15.00
Textile, Skirt, Lady's, 1 Piece Bustle & Hoop, C.1880	15.00
Textile, Slipper, Child's, Japanese, Embroidered, Handwoven Sole, Pair	15.00
Textile, Tablecloth & 9 Napkins, Linen Damask, Greek Key Borders, 82 In.	25.00
Textile, Tablecloth & 12 Napkins, Banquet, Madeira, Cutwork, 86 X 70 In.	125.00
Textile, Tablecloth, Banquet, Rose Pattern On White, 72 X 106	13.00
Textile, Tablecloth, Battenberg, Handmade, Round, 33 In.	12.50
Textile, Tablecloth, Cutwork, Scallops, Handmade, Cotton, Round, 65 In.	20.00
Textile, Tablecloth, Hand-Crocheted, Off-White, Flowers & Leaf, 66 X 76 In.	32.00
Textile, Tablecloth, Hand-Crocheted, Round, Fringe, 48 In.	12.00
Textile, Tablecloth, Linen, Battenberg & Irish Lace, Round, 72 In.	35.00
Textile, Tablecloth, Linen, Ecru, Cutwork, Embroidered, 52 X 66 In.	25.00
Textile, Tablecloth, Linen, Hemstitched, 72 X 60 In.	9.50
Textile, Tablecloth, Lunch, Irish Linen, Medallion, Cutwork, 38 In.	7.00
Textile, Tablecloth, Russian, Mauve Velvet, Embroidered, C.1850, 34 X 33 In.	120.00
Textile, Tapestry, Anecdotic, Skating Scene, C.1890, 10 Ft.9 In. X 6 Ft.	3500.00
Textile, Tapestry, Aubusson, Court Scene, Castles, C.1850, 7 Ft.11 In.	1500.00
Textile, Tapestry, Aubusson, Hanging Hunting Trophies, C.1850, 8 Ft.	1000.00
Textile, Tapestry, Aubusson, Millefleurs, Court Lady & Man, C.1850, 6 Ft.	1300.00
Textile, Tapestry, Aubusson, Shepherdess On Swing, Suitor, C.1890, 9 Ft.	2500.00
Textile, Tapestry, Aubusson, Verdure, Damsel In Swing, 2 Youths, C.1850, 9 Ft.	1200.00
Textile, Tapestry, Belgium, Arabian Dancing Girls, 13 X 18 In.	27.50
Textile, Tapestry, Courtyard Scene, French, Machine, C.1900, 3 X 2 In.	135.00
Textile, Tapestry, Diana & Apollo, Dogs, C.1890, 6 Ft.5 In. X 5 Ft.10 In.	1200.00
Textile, Tapestry, French, Mother & 2 Children, Chicken, C.1850, 6 Ft.9 In.	1500.00
Textile, Tapestry, French, People Scene, 5 X 6 Ft.	18.00
Textile, Tapestry, French, Shepherdess & Suitor, Ruins, C.1850, 6 Ft.9 In.	450.00
Textile, Tapestry, French, Verdure, Horsemen & Hounds, C.1850, 5 Ft.6 In.	1400.00
Textile, Tapestry, Hunting, Hunter & Lady, C.1890, 6 Ft.3 In. X 4 Ft.8 In.	1600.00
Textile, Tapestry, Mars & Venus, C.1890, 6 Ft.2 In. X 7 Ft.4 In.	5100.00
Textile, Tapestry, Millefleurs, Feudal Life, C.1890, 6 Ft.7 In. X 7 Ft.	3500.00
Textile, Tapestry, Pastoral, December, The Months Of Lucas, C.1890, 7 Ft.	1600.00
Textile, Tapestry, Pastoral, Girl & Boy, C.1890, 6 Ft.2 In. X 7 Ft.	3000.00
Textile, Tapestry, Pastoral, Shepherdess & Shepherd, C.1890, 5 X 6 Ft.	750.00
Textile, Tapestry, Romulus & Remus, Wolf, Alexander, C.1890, 7 X 6 Ft.	2800.00
Textile, Tapestry, Spirit Of St.Louis, Portraits Of Aviators, 52 X 16 In.	75.00
Textile, Tapestry, Verdure, Crane Center, C.1890, 4 Ft.3 In. X 5 Ft.5 In.	300.00
Textile, Tapestry, Verdure, Large Bird, C.1890, 5 Ft.1 In. X 6 Ft.3 In.	400.00
Textile, Throw, Piano, Damasque, Rose, Aqua, & Tan, Fringed, 71 X 47 In.	10.00
Textile, Top Hat, Beaver, Leather Case	45.00
Textile, Top Hat, Silk, Folding, Pirs, New York	25.00
Textile, Topcoat, Cownie Tanning Company, Black Hair On Leather	135.00
Textile, Towel, Demask, Floral, Hemstitched, Drawnwork, 21 X 40 In.	3.50
Textile, Towel, Damask, Greek Key Borders, Crochet Inserts, 18 X 35 In.	3.50
Textile, Towel, Linen, Huck, Embroidered Scalloped Ends, 23 X 33 In.	2.50
Textile, Towel, Linen, Monogrammed, Hem Stitched, 20 X 40 In.	2.00
Textile, Undergarment, Combination, Lady's, Nainsook, Lace	5.00
Textile, Waistcoat, Gentleman's, Blue Wool, Embroidered, C.1780	225.00

Tiffany glass was made by louis Comfort Tiffany, the American glass designer who worked from about 1879 to 1933. His work included iridescent glass, art nouveau styles of design, and original contemporary styles. He was also noted for his stained glass windows, his unusual lamps, bronze work, pottery, and silver.

Tiffany Bronze, Blotter End, Chinese Pattern, 19 X 2 1/2 In., Pair	90.00
Tiffany Bronze, Blotter End, Grape Pattern, Dore, 19 In., Pair	75.00
Tiffany Bronze, Blotter End, Modeled Design, Greek Key, 19 X 2 1/4 In., Pair	75.00
Tiffany Bronze, Blotter End, Zodiac, 12 In., Pair	80.00
Tiffany Bronze, Blotter End, Zodiac, 19 1/2 In., Pair	135.00
Tiffany Bronze, Blotter, Hand, Adam Pattern, Gold Dore, 5 1/2 In.	45.00
Tiffany Bronze, Blotter, Hand, Red & Pink Enamel, 6 In.	150.00
Tiffany Bronze, Blotter, Pine Needle, Rolling	65.00
Tiffany Bronze, Bookend, Gold Dore, Woman Buddha Figure, 6 In., Pair	190.00
Tiffany Bronze, Bookend, Zodiac & Circle & Line, Dark Patina, 6 In., Pair	150.00
Tiffany Bronze, Bookend, Zodiac & Circle & Line, Gold Dore, 6 In., Pair	150.00
Tiffany Bronze, Bowl, Molded Flowers & Abalone Border, Gold, 9 In.	125.00

Tiffany Bronze, Box, American Indian, Gold Dore, Hinged, 4 3/4 X 3 In.	125.00
Tiffany Bronze, Box, Byzantine, Gold Dore, Hinged, Cedar Lined, 5 X 4 In.	250.00
Tiffany Bronze, Box, Cigar, Zodiac, Wood Line, 6 X 6 1/2 In.	245.00
Tiffany Bronze, Box, Jewelry, Abalone, Gold Dore Finish, Leaf Design	400.00
Tiffany Bronze, Box, Stamp, Grape, Green Glass	125.00
Tiffany Bronze, Box, Zodiac, Hinged, Dark Patina, 5 1/4 X 3 1/2 X 1 In.	150.00
Tiffany Bronze, Box, Zodiac, Hinged, 7 X 3 X 1 1/2 In.	195.00
Tiffany Bronze, Candlestick, Enamel, Fabrique Shade, Gold Dore, 10 1/2 In.	650.00
Tiffany Bronze, Candlestick, Gilt, Pierced Standard, C.1892, 11 1/4 In., Pair	350.00
Tiffany Bronze, Candlestick, Gold Dore Finish, 3 Ball Feet, 8 1/2 In.High	350.00
Tiffany Bronze, Candlestick, Jeweled, Gold Tulip Shade, 13 In.High	1200.00
Tiffany Bronze, Candlestick, Zodiac, 6 In.High, Pair	450.00
Tiffany Bronze, Candlestick, 19 In., Pair	400.00
Tiffany Bronze, Compote, Gold Dore, Etched Border, 3 3/4 X 3 In.	75.00
Tiffany Bronze, Compote, Gold Dore, Intaglio Leaves & Vines, 10 In.	650.00
Tiffany Bronze, Corner, Blotter, Pine Needle, Set Of 4	95.00
Tiffany Bronze, Creamer, Gold Color, Signed, 2 3/4 In.	350.00
Tiffany Bronze, Desk Set, Abalone, C.1900, 7 Piece	475.00
Tiffany Bronze, Desk Set, Grapevine, 6 Piece	285.00
Tiffany Bronze, Desk Set, Indian Pattern, Owls Heads, 3 Piece	300.00
Tiffany Bronze, Desk Set, Zodiac, 4 Piece	150.00
Tiffany Bronze, Desk Set, Zodiac, 7 Piece	440.00 To 625.00
Tiffany Bronze, Figurine, Bulldog, Gold Dore	275.00
Tiffany Bronze, Frame, Chinese Pattern, Easel Type, 7 1/4 X 6 In.	90.00
Tiffany Bronze, Frame, Easel Type, Chinese Pattern, 7 1/4 X 6 In.	95.00
Tiffany Bronze, Frame, Easel Type, Pink & Red Enamel, 6 X 5 1/4 In.	225.00
Tiffany Bronze, Frame, Easel, Zodiac & Lines, Beveled Glass, 12 X 15 In.	275.00
Tiffany Bronze, Holder, Pen, Pine Needle, Easel	40.00
Tiffany Bronze, Inkwell, Chinese Pattern, Octagon Shape, 4 1/2 In.High	225.00
Tiffany Bronze, Inkwell, Double, 14K Gold Venetian Design, 5 In.	225.00
Tiffany Bronze, Inkwell, Grapevine, Dore	165.00 To 185.00
Tiffany Bronze, Inkwell, Pine Needle, Small, Caramel Glass	155.00
Tiffany Bronze, Inkwell, Zodiac, Glass Liner, No.1072	195.00
Tiffany Bronze, Inkwell, Zodiac, Large	225.00
Tiffany Bronze, Jar, Grapevine, Urn Shape, Dark Patina, 2 In.	55.00
Tiffany Bronze, Jar, Scent, Turquoise Stones, Gold Dore, Repousse, 3 In.	750.00
Tiffany Bronze, Lamp Base, Counter Balance, Scrolled Arm, C.1899, 14 In.	1000.00
Tiffany Bronze, Lamp Base, No.320, 4 Stems, Round Base, Floral Sockets, 8 In.	275.00
Tiffany Bronze, Lamp Base, Oil, Gadrooned, 3 Legs, C.1899, 18 1/2 In.	550.00
Tiffany Bronze, Letter Holder, Zodiac, Gold Dore, Center Divider, 6 In.	110.00
Tiffany Bronze, Letter Opener, Adam Pattern, Gold Dore, 9 1/2 In.	75.00
Tiffany Bronze, Letter Opener, Amber Slag Glass Insert, 9 In.Long	75.00
Tiffany Bronze, Letter Opener, Chinese Pattern, 10 In.	50.00
Tiffany Bronze, Letter Rack, Adam Pattern, Gold Dore, 2 Parts, 10 In.	175.00
Tiffany Bronze, Letter Rack, Bronze Grapevine Over Green Glass, 6 In.	150.00
Tiffany Bronze, Letter Rack, Chinese Pattern, 3 Compartments, 12 X 8 In.	225.00
Tiffany Bronze, Letter Rack, Modeled Design, Greek Key, 3 Part, 12 In.	200.00
Tiffany Bronze, Letter Rack, Zodiac, 3 Compartments, 12 In.	225.00
Tiffany Bronze, Letter Seal, Scarab	135.00
Tiffany Bronze, Magnifying Glass, Grapevine	175.00
Tiffany Bronze, Match Holder, No.1104	65.00
Tiffany Bronze, Match Stand, Zodiac	130.00
Tiffany Bronze, Pad, Calendar, Zodiac	100.00
Tiffany Bronze, Pad, Memo, American Indian, No.1188, 4 1/2 X 7 1/2 In.	72.00
Tiffany Bronze, Pad, Memo, Pine Needle, Dark Patina	89.00
Tiffany Bronze, Pad, Memo, Zodiac, Dark Patina	125.00
Tiffany Bronze, Paper Clip, Zodiac, Dore	85.00
Tiffany Bronze, Paperclip, Abalone	100.00
Tiffany Bronze, Paperclip, Bronze & Glass, Spider Web Pattern	60.00
Tiffany Bronze, Paperweight, Bulldog, Gold Dore, 2 In.	110.00
Tiffany Bronze, Paperweight, Pine Needle	95.00
Tiffany Bronze, Planter, Marsh Marigold Fern, Dark, 10 3/4 X 3 1/2 In.	1100.00
Tiffany Bronze, Plate, Deep, Overall Snakeskin Finish, 9 In.	25.00
Tiffany Bronze, Plate, Peacock, Gold Dore, 8 In.	195.00
Tiffany Bronze, Platter, Gold Dore, Abalone Discs, 9 In.	125.00
Tiffany Bronze, Scale, Letter, Zodiac, Dark Patina, 3 1/4 X 3 X 1 1/2 In.	225.00

Tiffany Bronze, Scale, Postal, Grapevine	165.00
Tiffany Bronze, Scissors, Gold Dore, Steel Blades, 9 In.	150.00
Tiffany Bronze, Tray, Adam Pattern, Gold Dore, Handled, 9 1/2 In.	65.00
Tiffany Bronze, Tray, Dore, Egyptian Design, 9 In.	100.00 To 115.00
Tiffany Bronze, Tray, Dore, Oriental Symbols On Brick Red Enamel, 10 In.	120.00
Tiffany Bronze, Tray, Egyptian Motifs Around Border, 9 In.	95.00
Tiffany Bronze, Tray, Pen, American Indian	70.00
Tiffany Bronze, Tray, Pen, Grapevine	75.00
Tiffany Bronze, Tray, Pen, Modeled Design, Greek Key, 9 1/2 X 3 In.	60.00
Tiffany Bronze, Tray, Pen, Zodiac	70.00
Tiffany Bronze, Vase, Line Patterns, Flared Top, Dark Patina, 6 1/2 In.	250.00
Tiffany Glass, Base, Lamp, Blue Candle	450.00
Tiffany Glass, Bonbon, Gold Iridescent, Applied Punts, Ribbed, 4 1/4 In.	175.00
Tiffany Glass, Bottle, Pale Gold, Free-Form, Signed, L.C.T. D2609, 3 1/2 In.	135.00
Tiffany Glass, Bottle, Perfume, Amber & Blue, Silver Mounts, C.1892, 7 In.	1100.00
Tiffany Glass, Bowl & Underplate, Finger, Amber Iridescent, Prince, C.1892	110.00
Tiffany Glass, Bowl & Underplate, Finger, Amber Iridescent, Queen, C.1902	175.00
Tiffany Glass, Bowl & Underplate, Finger, Gold Favrile	200.00
Tiffany Glass, Bowl & Underplate, Finger, Gold Iridescent, Applied Prunts	300.00
Tiffany Glass, Bowl & Underplate, Finger, Gold Iridescent, Signed L.C.T.	325.00
Tiffany Glass, Bowl & Underplate, Finger, Gold, Pinch Twist Design	395.00
Tiffany Glass, Bowl, Amber Iridescent, Intaglio Vines, C.1892, 6 3/4 In.	400.00
Tiffany Glass, Bowl, Amber Iridescent, Ribbed, Crenated Rim, C.1892, 7 In.	200.00
Tiffany Glass, Bowl, Amber Iridescent, Ribbed, Scalloped, C.1892, 8 1/2 In.	175.00
Tiffany Glass, Bowl, Amber Iridescent, Round Foot, Ruffled, C.1907, 5 In.	150.00
Tiffany Glass, Bowl, Amber Iridescent, 4 Splayed Feet, C.1908, 4 In.	400.00
Tiffany Glass, Bowl, Amber, Spiraling Ribs, C.1892, 6 3/4 In.	300.00
Tiffany Glass, Bowl, Aquamarine, Crackle, Optic Ribbed, 1898, 10 1/4 In.	300.00
Tiffany Glass, Bowl, Aquamarine, Pale Green, Orange Blossoms, C.1904, 5 In.	1900.00
Tiffany Glass, Bowl, Aurene, Blue, 12 In.	1000.00
Tiffany Glass, Bowl, Blue Iridescent, Ribbed, Serpentine Lip, C.1892, 7 In.	375.00
Tiffany Glass, Bowl, Centerpiece, Dusty Rose, Optic Devices, C.1920, 11 In.	475.00
Tiffany Glass, Bowl, Cut Grape Leaves, L.C.Tiffany Favrile, 9 3/4 In.	795.00
Tiffany Glass, Bowl, Diatreta, Peacock Blue, 4 1/4 In.Diameter	500.00
Tiffany Glass, Bowl, Gold Iridescent, Footed, Low, 4 X 1 In.	165.00
Tiffany Glass, Bowl, Gold Iridescent, Signed L.C.T., 4 1/2 X 1 7/8 In.	135.00
Tiffany Glass, Bowl, Gold Iridescent, Signed LCT No.8918, 4 1/2 In.	225.00
Tiffany Glass, Bowl, Gold Iridescent, Signed, No.5-1403, 7 X 2 1/2 In.	295.00
Tiffany Glass, Bowl, Green Iridescent Rim To Clear, Leaves, C.1920, 8 In.	350.00
Tiffany Glass, Bowl, Iridescent Gold, Low Footed, L.C.T. Favrile, 4 X 1 In.	150.00
Tiffany Glass, Bowl, Pastel White With Yellow Trim, 10 1/2 In.	550.00
Tiffany Glass, Box, Cigarette, Gold Iridescent, Hinged, Bronze Feet, 6 In.	250.00
Tiffany Glass, Box, Cigarette, Hinged Lid, Gold Iridescent, 4 Bronze Feet	250.00
Tiffany Glass, Candelabrum, 2 Arm, Amber & Green Sworls, C.1902, 9 In.	750.00
Tiffany Glass, Candlestick, Blue, Twisted, 8 In.	275.00
Tiffany Glass, Candlestick, Gold Iridescent, Ribbed, Scalloped Base, 12 In.	300.00
Tiffany Glass, Candlestick, Gold Iridescent, Vertical Ribs, 12 In.	300.00
Tiffany Glass, Candlestick, Ribbed White Opalescent, Pink Top, 11 1/2 In.	450.00
Tiffany Glass, Candlestick, Rock Crystal, Art Nouveau Flowers, 4 1/2 X 3 In	600.00
Tiffany Glass, Centerpiece, Pastel Green, Free-Form Leaf Pattern, 6 In.	350.00
Tiffany Glass, Chalice, Gold With Blue Highlights	170.00
Tiffany Glass, Chalice, Tulip Design Cup, 6 In. Stem, 12 In.	295.00
Tiffany Glass, Champagne, Intaglio Cut, No.1197, 5 1/2 In.	285.00
Tiffany Glass, Champagne, Opalescent, Turquoise & White Stripes On Clear	250.00
Tiffany Glass, Champagne, Turquoise, White Loopings, Opalescent Edge	250.00
Tiffany Glass, Compote, Amber, Ribbed, Scalloped Lip, C.1907, 3 5/8 In.	275.00
Tiffany Glass, Compote, Calcite, Green, 5 Green Leaves, Scalloped, 4 1/4 In.	450.00
Tiffany Glass, Compote, Gold Iridescent, Intaglio Leaf & Vine, 6 In.	425.00
Tiffany Glass, Compote, Green Iridescent, White With Gold Pedestal, 7 In.	425.00
Tiffany Glass, Compote, Yellow Crackle Lip, Iridescent Foot, C.1919, 5 In.	300.00
Tiffany Glass, Cordial, Gold	135.00
Tiffany Glass, Cordial, Green & Blue On Bowl, Amber Cut Stem	155.00
Tiffany Glass, Cup, Green Decoration, Signed & Numbered, 2 3/4 In.	325.00
Tiffany Glass, Cup, Nut, Gold, Crimped Edge, Favrile, Signed	118.00
Tiffany Glass, Cup, Punch, Favrile, Gold Wtih Red & Blue, 3 1/2 In.High	175.00
Tiffany Glass, Decanter, Gold, Applied Prunts, 10 1/2 In.	525.00

Tiffany Glass, Dish, Mint, Gold Iridescent, Leaf & Vine Pattern, 5 3/4 In. 150.00
Tiffany Glass, Dish, Mint, Gold Iridescent, Raised Edge, 3 3/4 In. 110.00
Tiffany Glass, Dish, Mint, Millefiori, Gold Iridescent, Leaf & Vine, 6 In. 350.00
Tiffany Glass, Dish, Nut, Gold Iridescent, L.C.T., No.Q6606, 6 In. 295.00
Tiffany Glass, Dish, Nut, Gold Iridescent, L.C.Tiffany Inc., 3 In. 150.00
Tiffany Glass, Dish, Tortoiseshell, Green, Free Form, Red Interior, 2 1/2 In. 250.00
Tiffany Glass, Epergne, Floriform, Single, 18 In.High 795.00
Tiffany Glass, Epergne, Gold, Floriform, 16 In. 675.00
Tiffany Glass, Goblet, Amber Iridescent, Pink & Blue Highlights 165.00
Tiffany Glass, Goblet, Deep Blue, Bell Shape Bowl, C.1917 .... 200.00
Tiffany Glass, Goblet, Gold, Blue Highlights, Favrile, Signed & Numbered 175.00
Tiffany Glass, Goblet, Pale Yellow, Optic Ribbed, Twisted Stem, 8 1/2 In. 300.00
Tiffany Glass, Jar, Blue Stopper, Blue To Green, C.1910, 4 In. 500.00
Tiffany Glass, Lamp Base, Amber, Intaglio Vines & Leaves, C.1892, 10 In. 275.00
Tiffany Glass, Liqueur Set, Amber Iridescent, C.1892, 5 Piece 525.00
Tiffany Glass, Liqueur Set, Gold & Blue Iridescent, Threaded, 9 Piece 2500.00
Tiffany Glass, Liqueur Set, Pale Green Iridescent, Sworled, C.1902, 12 Piece 1300.00
Tiffany Glass, Liqueur, Gold, Signed L.C.T., 4 3/4 In. 107.00
Tiffany Glass, Liqueur, Green Pastel 225.00
Tiffany Glass, Medal, Victory, May 24, 1926, Gold Iridescent, L.C.T. 500.00
Tiffany Glass, Panel, Tiffany Studios, Blue Purple, Leaded, C.1900, 5 Ft. 2600.00
Tiffany Glass, Parfait, Pastel Aqua, 6 1/2 In.High 225.00
Tiffany Glass, Pitcher, Cameo & Intaglio Cut, Sterling Top & Handle, 13 In. 2500.00
Tiffany Glass, Pitcher, Cameo Opal Glass, Green Luster Top, 6 1/4 In.High 3500.00
Tiffany Glass, Pitcher, Miniature, Gold Favrile, 2 3/4 In.High 335.00
Tiffany Glass, Plate, Blown, Gold, Stretched Edge, 7 3/4 In. 300.00
Tiffany Glass, Plate, Green To White, Bronze Holder, Enamel, C.1900, 10 In. 450.00
Tiffany Glass, Plate, Miniature, Gold Iridescent, Scalloped Border, 7 3/8 In 135.00
Tiffany Glass, Plate, Opalescent, Green To Clear, Panels, 8 1/4 In. 225.00
Tiffany Glass, Salt, Favrile, Gold, Raised Prunts, 2 1/4 X 1 1/4 In. 135.00
Tiffany Glass, Salt, Gold Iridescent, Raised Prunts, 2 1/4 In. 135.00
Tiffany Glass, Salt, Gold, Blue Highlights, Scalloped, 2 1/2 X 1 In. 125.00
Tiffany Glass, Salt, Kettle, 2 X 1 1/2 In. 145.00
Tiffany Glass, Salt, Master, Crimped Top, Signed LCT 6304, 3 In. 135.00
Tiffany Glass, Salt, Master, Gold, Threading, Blue Highlights 145.00
Tiffany Glass, Salt, Pastel Green, Signed 275.00
Tiffany Glass, Salt, Ruffled, Signed L.C.T. 85.00
Tiffany Glass, Salt, Silver Blue Highlights, Crimped Top, Signed L.C.T. 98.00
Tiffany Glass, Salt, Silver Blue, Footed, Applied Prunts 145.00
Tiffany Glass, Salt, Witch's Pot 120.00
Tiffany Glass, Saucer, Pastel Green, L.C.T. Favrile, 5 3/4 In. 175.00
Tiffany Glass, Scarab, Blue Iridescent, 3/4 In. 35.00
Tiffany Glass, Seal, Three Scarab Beetles Shape, White Tones, 1 3/4 In. 150.00
Tiffany Glass, Shade, Bright Green, Geometrics & Floral, Scallops, 5 1/2 In. 250.00
Tiffany Glass, Shade, Hanging, Amber Iridescent, Feathered, C.1892, 15 In. 325.00
Tiffany Glass, Shade, Hanging, Dome, Deep Emerald, Ivy Leaves, Leaded, 24 In. 4000.00
Tiffany Glass, Shade, Linenfold, Aqua & Green, 5 X 5 1/2 In. 250.00
Tiffany Glass, Sherbet, Turquoise, White Loopings, Opalescent Edge 240.00
Tiffany Glass, Shot Glass, Dimpled, Signed & Numbered 175.00
Tiffany Glass, Shot Glass, Gold Iridescent, Pinched-In Sides, 2 In. 110.00
Tiffany Glass, Shot Glass, Rainbow Hues, Dimpled, Signed L.C.Tiffany 120.00
Tiffany Glass, Tazza, Amber Iridescent, Rod Standard, C.1892, 6 1/8 In. 175.00
Tiffany Glass, Tile, Red & Orange Decorated, Square, 4 In. 40.00
Tiffany Glass, Tile, Red & Orange, 4 In. 40.00
Tiffany Glass, Toothpick, Pinch Sided, Gold Favrile 395.00
Tiffany Glass, Trivet, Cypriote, Blue, Gold Iridescent, Bronze Feet, 4 In. 225.00
Tiffany Glass, Tumbler, Gold, Applied Prunts 275.00
Tiffany Glass, Tumbler, Gold, Favrile, Footed, 4 1/2 In. 110.00
Tiffany Glass, Vase, Agate, Blue To Ocher Green Base, C.1904, 6 In. 350.00
Tiffany Glass, Vase, Agate, Gold, Yellow Zipper, Stand-Up Collar, 3 1/2 In. 900.00
Tiffany Glass, Vase, Amber & Pink, Floriform Opening, Brass Base, 18 In. 1500.00
Tiffany Glass, Vase, Amber Iridescent, Green Vines & Leaves, C.1916, 12 In. 900.00
Tiffany Glass, Vase, Amber Iridescent, Intaglio Maple Leaves, C.1915, 7 In. 675.00
Tiffany Glass, Vase, Amber Iridescent, Purple & Amber Banding, C.1892, 1 In. 250.00
Tiffany Glass, Vase, Amber Iridescent, 4 Green Leaves At Base, 1915, 10 In. 325.00
Tiffany Glass, Vase, Amber, Gold, Green, & White Feathers, C.1905, 2 1/4 In. 375.00

Tiffany Glass, Vase, Amber, Intaglio Green Vines & Leaves, C.1917, 12 In. 1000.00
Tiffany Glass, Vase, Amber, Millefiori Blossoms, C.1907, 6 3/4 In. 850.00
Tiffany Glass, Vase, Amber, Millefiori, Inverted Pyriform, C.1920, 2 3/4 In. 675.00
Tiffany Glass, Vase, Amber, Optic Rib, Magenta & Fuchsia Tones, 6 1/4 In. 590.00
Tiffany Glass, Vase, Aquamarine & White, Footed, Flared Top, 6 1/2 In. 225.00
Tiffany Glass, Vase, Aquamarine & White, Footed, Optic Stripes, 6 1/2 In. 225.00
Tiffany Glass, Vase, Aquamarine, Blue Neck, Amber Band, C.1910, 12 1/2 In. 1200.00
Tiffany Glass, Vase, Aurene, Gold, 3 Dimples, 5 In. 269.00
Tiffany Glass, Vase, Black Amethyst, Blue & Amber Ferns, C.1892, 13 In. 900.00
Tiffany Glass, Vase, Black Decorated, Yellow Line Decoration, 3 1/2 In. 800.00
Tiffany Glass, Vase, Blue Iridescent, Covered, Dimpled, Pedestal, 4 In. 675.00
Tiffany Glass, Vase, Blue Iridescent, Floral & Tendrils, C.1892, 17 1/2 In. 1300.00
Tiffany Glass, Vase, Blue To Purple Base, Signed, 4 1/4 In. 450.00
Tiffany Glass, Vase, Blue To Silver Blue, Footed, C.1919, 10 In. 850.00
Tiffany Glass, Vase, Blue, Zipper Type Pattern, Tapers To Top, 12 In. 575.00
Tiffany Glass, Vase, Brown, Favrile, Leaf Decoration, 7 1/2 In.High 900.00
Tiffany Glass, Vase, Bud, Amber Iridescent, Green Vines & Leaves, 1915, 6 In. 425.00
Tiffany Glass, Vase, Bud, Amber, Green Leafage, Triangular Base, 1915, 14 In. 300.00
Tiffany Glass, Vase, Bud, Bronze Holder, Tapered, 13 In. 500.00
Tiffany Glass, Vase, Bud, Gold Iridescent, Bronze Holder, 13 1/4 In. 275.00
Tiffany Glass, Vase, Bud, Gold, Green Leaves From Base, L.C.T., Favrile, 8 In. 385.00
Tiffany Glass, Vase, Bud, Gold, Green Leaves, Bronze Holder, 13 1/2 In. 420.00
Tiffany Glass, Vase, Bud, Gold, Swirled, Favrile, 3 1/2 In. 185.00
Tiffany Glass, Vase, Bud, Opalescent Cream Iridescent, Green Leaves, 8 In. 395.00
Tiffany Glass, Vase, Bud, Pastel White, Gold Flame Decoration, 8 1/4 In. 425.00
Tiffany Glass, Vase, Bud, Two Piece, Hexagon Shape, Emerald Green, 13 In. 275.00
Tiffany Glass, Vase, Bud, 2 Piece, Bronze Holder, Gold Iridescent, 13 1/4 In. 275.00
Tiffany Glass, Vase, Cabinet, Favrile, White Opaque, Two Ears, 3 In.High 225.00
Tiffany Glass, Vase, Calcite, Footed, Flaring Rim, 4 1/2 In. 435.00
Tiffany Glass, Vase, Canary Opalescent, Webb & Swag Design, 5 In. 895.00
Tiffany Glass, Vase, Cypriote, Iridescent Gold With Brown, 7 1/2 In. 1800.00
Tiffany Glass, Vase, Deep Blue Iridescent, Amber Zigzags, C.1904, 3 1/4 In. 700.00
Tiffany Glass, Vase, Deep Blue Iridescent, Ribbed Foot, C.1919, 18 7/8 In. 400.00
Tiffany Glass, Vase, Deep Blue, Yellow Loops & Scrolls, C.1892, 9 In. 2800.00
Tiffany Glass, Vase, Elephant's Foot, Copper Blue Iridescent, 3 1/4 In. 675.00
Tiffany Glass, Vase, Floriform, Amber, Ribbed, Domed Base, C.1900, 15 In. 425.00
Tiffany Glass, Vase, Floriform, Bronze & Glass, Blue, Gold, & Green, 14 In. 4500.00
Tiffany Glass, Vase, Floriform, C.1902, 12 In. ....*Illus* 1500.00
Tiffany Glass, Vase, Floriform, Green Pulled Leaf On Amber, 13 In. 950.00
Tiffany Glass, Vase, Floriform, Green, Spiral Ribs, C.1921, 15 1/4 In. 450.00
Tiffany Glass, Vase, Floriform, Iridescent, Pink Highlights, 7 1/4 In. 490.00
Tiffany Glass, Vase, Floriform, Pink Amber Crackle, Green, C.1905, 11 In. 1200.00
Tiffany Glass, Vase, Floriform, Red Amber, Green Feathers, C.1902, 11 3/4 In. 1200.00
Tiffany Glass, Vase, Floriform, Red Amber, Green Leaf, White Rim, 1873, 20 In. 1800.00
Tiffany Glass, Vase, Floriform, Red Decoration, Yellow Pulled Leaf, 9 In. 3500.00

Tiffany Glass, Vase, Floriform, C.1902, 12 In.

Tiffany Glass, Vase, Free Form, Peacock Blue, Silver & Gold, 5 In. 950.00
Tiffany Glass, Vase, Gold Iridescent, Applied Ears, Stand-Up Collar, 4 In. 300.00
Tiffany Glass, Vase, Gold Iridescent, Green Leaf & Vine, 3 1/2 In. 450.00
Tiffany Glass, Vase, Gold Iridescent, Green Leaf, Bronze Holder, 26 In. 750.00
Tiffany Glass, Vase, Gold Iridescent, Pulled Handles, 5 In. 165.00
Tiffany Glass, Vase, Gold Iridescent, Red Design, Blue Feather, 3 In. 900.00
Tiffany Glass, Vase, Gold Iridescent, 8 Section Pattern, 3 1/2 In. 325.00
Tiffany Glass, Vase, Gold Luster With Millefiori Decoration, 4 1/2 In. 2000.00
Tiffany Glass, Vase, Gold, Handled, L.C.Tiffany 1018-149K, 3 In. 265.00
Tiffany Glass, Vase, Gold, Red Design, Blue Peacock's Feather, 3 X 3 In. 900.00
Tiffany Glass, Vase, Gooseneck, Green, Amber Feathers, C.1910, 12 In. 4000.00
Tiffany Glass, Vase, Gourd, Red Pulled Feathers On Green, Signed, 10 In. 600.00
Tiffany Glass, Vase, Green Iridescent, Amber Interior, C.1910, 6 3/4 In. 200.00
Tiffany Glass, Vase, Green, Free-Form, Molded Applied Handles, 6 1/2 In. 535.00
Tiffany Glass, Vase, Melon Shape, Gold Iridescent, 1 1/2 X 1 3/4 In. 325.00
Tiffany Glass, Vase, Miniature, Red Cameo On Canary Yellow, 3 In. 2500.00
Tiffany Glass, Vase, Mirrored Amber, Looping, C.1896, 7 1/2 In. 650.00
Tiffany Glass, Vase, Paperweight, Amber, Green & Yellow Leaves, C.1900, 12 In 2500.00
Tiffany Glass, Vase, Paperweight, Gold, White & Green Leaves, 6 In. 3500.00
Tiffany Glass, Vase, Paperweight, Intaglio Leafage, C.1892, 9 In. 3600.00
Tiffany Glass, Vase, Paperweight, Salmon Convolvuli, C.1907, 6 In. 2800.00
Tiffany Glass, Vase, Peacock Blue Iridescent, Dimpled, Ribbed, 4 1/2 In. 475.00
Tiffany Glass, Vase, Red Blue, Orange Crackle On White Lining, 7 3/4 In. 85.00
Tiffany Glass, Vase, Red Gold, Egyptian Decorated, Stand-Up Collar, 10 In. 1500.00
Tiffany Glass, Vase, Trumpet, Alabaster, Feathers, Bronze Base, C.1892, 12 In. 300.00
Tiffany Glass, Vase, Trumpet, Amber, Bronze Base, C.1892, 17 5/8 In. 300.00
Tiffany Glass, Vase, Trumpet, Amber, Green Leaves & Vines, C.1917, 12 In. 475.00
Tiffany Glass, Vase, Trumpet, Amber, Green Leaves, C.1916, 10 In. 550.00
Tiffany Glass, Vase, Trumpet, Amber, Green, Bronze Holder, C.1892, 14 1/2 In. 300.00
Tiffany Glass, Vase, Trumpet, Blue, Bronze Floriform Support, C.1899, 18 In. 350.00
Tiffany Glass, Vase, Trumpet, Deep Blue, Ribbed, C.1919, 16 In. 650.00
Tiffany Glass, Vase, Trumpet, Gold Iridescent, Cut, Signed, 6 1/2 In. 195.00
Tiffany Glass, Vase, Trumpet, Opalescent, Ribbed, Green Interior, 1900, 15 In. 575.00
Tiffany Glass, Vase, Trumpet, Pastel Yellow To Clear, 12 In.High 575.00
Tiffany Glass, Vase, Urn Form, Amber, Ribbed, Hobnails, C.1896, 3 1/2 In. 250.00
Tiffany Glass, Vase, Verre De Soie, Gold Free-Form Vines & Leaves, 8 In. 875.00
Tiffany Glass, Vase, Waisted Shape, Gold, Pink Highlights, Signed, 8 In. 365.00
Tiffany Glass, Vase, White, Gold Damascene Hook & Feather, 7 1/4 In. 950.00
Tiffany Glass, Vase, Yellow Green, Amber & Green Feathers, C.1913, 20 In. 900.00
Tiffany Glass, Vase, Yellow With Red & Black Leaves & Vines, 10 In.High 2500.00
Tiffany Glass, Vase, Zipper Decorated, Red & Green With Yellow, 8 1/2 In. 1200.00
Tiffany Glass, Window, Leaded, Blossoms, Green Leaves, C.1900, 30 X 23 In. 2500.00
Tiffany Glass, Wine Set, Gold Iridescent, Dimpled Glasses, 7 Piece 1250.00
Tiffany Glass, Wine, Cone Top, Twisted Stem, Signed 120.00
Tiffany Glass, Wine, Hock, Gold, Double Twist Stem 165.00
Tiffany Glass, Wine, Opalescent, Reactive, Green To Clear, Panels, 7 In. 235.00
Tiffany Glass, Wine, Pastel Blue & White Stem, 8 In.High 250.00
Tiffany Glass, Wine, Pastel Green, 4 1/2 In. 166.65
Tiffany Glass, Wine, Pastel, Opalescent To Bright Green, Signed, 6 In. 195.00
Tiffany Pottery, Bowl, Avocado & Black, Mother Bird & 2 Young, C.1904, 5 In. 550.00
Tiffany Pottery, Bowl, Blue, Green, Pink, & White, Fishes, Waves, C.1904, 5 In. 900.00
Tiffany Pottery, Bowl, Bronze, Gilt, Honesty Blossoms, C.1910, 2 1/4 In. 100.00
Tiffany Pottery, Bowl, Bronze, Silver, Floral, Green Interior, C.1910, 3 In. 200.00
Tiffany Pottery, Bowl, Buff & Avocado Glaze, Birds In Nest, 1904, 5 1/2 In. 300.00
Tiffany Pottery, Bowl, Celadon Glaze, Depressed Rim, C.1904, 5 In. 100.00
Tiffany Pottery, Bowl, Covered, Bronze, Fruiting Branches, C.1910, 4 In. 500.00
Tiffany Pottery, Bowl, Flower, Animals On Blue To Green To White, 8 In. 950.00
Tiffany Pottery, Ewer, Blue Green, Cattails, Integral Handle, C.1904, 12 In. 125.00
Tiffany Pottery, Ewer, Cattails, Green & White Interior, C.1904, 12 1/2 In. 100.00
Tiffany Pottery, Flower Holder, Blossoms On Vines, Pierced, C.1904, 9 In. 175.00
Tiffany Pottery, Flower Holder, 5 Petaled Blossoms On Vines, C.1904, 8 In. 300.00
Tiffany Pottery, Jar, Covered, Avocado, Pendant Vines & Fruit, C.1904, 9 In. 425.00
Tiffany Pottery, Jar, Dome Cover, Bronze, Green Glaze, C.1910, 8 3/4 In. 700.00
Tiffany Pottery, Vase, Avocado Glaze, Sea Blue Splashes, C.1901, 16 In. 200.00
Tiffany Pottery, Vase, Avocado To Mint Green, Blossoms, C.1904, 12 In. 350.00
Tiffany Pottery, Vase, Blue Green Matte, Ring Turned Foot, C.1904, 15 In. 140.00

Tiffany Pottery, Vase, Blue, Black, Green, & White, 3 Handles, 9 In.	750.00
Tiffany Pottery, Vase, Brown To Rust To Mustard, Beaded, 6 1/2 In.	650.00
Tiffany Pottery, Vase, Brown, Black & Deep Salmon, Waisted, C.1904, 4 1/2 In.	120.00
Tiffany Pottery, Vase, Buff Color, Unglazed, Relief Leaves & Vines, 10 In.	400.00
Tiffany Pottery, Vase, Buff, Maple Leaves On Crosshatching, C.1901, 14 In.	90.00
Tiffany Pottery, Vase, Buff, Pendant Berries & Leaves, C.1904, 10 In.	175.00
Tiffany Pottery, Vase, Buff, Pendant Berries & Leaves, C.1904, 8 In.	100.00
Tiffany Pottery, Vase, Buff, Wild Orchids & Grasses, C.1904, 12 3/4 In.	100.00
Tiffany Pottery, Vase, Chocolate Glaze, Ocher Patches, C.1904, 7 In.	175.00
Tiffany Pottery, Vase, Cream, Wildflowers, Baluster, C.1904, 9 1/2 In.	325.00
Tiffany Pottery, Vase, Dark Brown Drippings Over Light Brown, 9 1/2 In.	325.00
Tiffany Pottery, Vase, Emerald To Deep Green, Gourd Shape, C.1904, 10 In.	175.00
Tiffany Pottery, Vase, Fern Fronds, Blue Green Interior, C.1904, 10 In.	125.00
Tiffany Pottery, Vase, Green, Buff, & Ocher, Ear Of Corn, C.1904, 12 1/2 In.	550.00
Tiffany Pottery, Vase, Green, Calla Lilies, Pierced Upper, C.1904, 11 1/4 In.	500.00
Tiffany Pottery, Vase, Lime To Avocado Crackle, Collared Rim, C.1904, 9 In.	90.00
Tiffany Pottery, Vase, Matte Pastel Yellow, Flaring Shoulder, C.1904, 9 In.	90.00
Tiffany Pottery, Vase, Mint Green, Berry Laden Branches, C.1904, 10 1/4 In.	300.00
Tiffany Pottery, Vase, Ocher & Avocado, Fruiting Branches, 1904, 10 1/4 In.	325.00
Tiffany Pottery, Vase, Pods & Leaves On Streaked Mustard, C.1904, 6 1/4 In.	200.00
Tiffany Pottery, Vase, Sea Green Matte, Flaring Base, C.1904, 16 In.	140.00
Tiffany Pottery, Vase, Speckled Blue, Branches & Pods, C.1910, 6 3/4 In.	325.00
Tiffany Pottery, Vase, Sworled Ocher, Mustard, Green, & Blue, C.1904, 6 In.	150.00
Tiffany Silver, Basket, Octagonal, Floral Garlands, Gadrooned, 7 In.	200.00
Tiffany Silver, Bowl, Chrysanthemum, Perforated, 9 X 4 X 4 1/2 In.	65.00
Tiffany Silver, Bowl, Foliate Rim, Embossed Foliage, C.1900, 9 1/2 In.	225.00
Tiffany Silver, Bowl, Punch, Plique A Jour & Champleve Enamel, 1920, 14 In.	2600.00
Tiffany Silver, Bowl, 9 1/4 X 2 1/2 In.	165.00
Tiffany Silver, Box, Stamp, Paperweight, Acorn Lid, Repousse, Floral	35.00
Tiffany Silver, Chamberstick, Repousse, Square Tray, 5 1/4 In.	300.00
Tiffany Silver, Child's Set, Nursery Rhyme, Fork, Spoon, Knife	235.00
Tiffany Silver, Cocktail Sword, Set Of 6 In Box	55.00
Tiffany Silver, Compote, Repousse, Cutout Base & Top, 8 X 4 In.	185.00
Tiffany Silver, Creamer, Floral Band Around Top, Monogrammed	35.00
Tiffany Silver, Dish, Chafing, Ivory Handled, 3 Piece, 1930s	55.00
Tiffany Silver, Dish, Entree, Reversible Cover, Repousse, C.1890, Pair	850.00
Tiffany Silver, Dresser Set, Dated 6/29/1875, 14 Piece	1450.00
Tiffany Silver, Fork & Helper, Sardine, Ornate	50.00
Tiffany Silver, Fork, Cold Meat, Pat.1885	52.50
Tiffany Silver, Fork, Dinner, Beekman, 8 In.	18.50
Tiffany Silver, Fork, Luncheon, Leaf & Line	8.50
Tiffany Silver, Fork, Salad, C.1875	24.75
Tiffany Silver, Fork, 3 Tined, Cherries & Leaves On Handle, Set Of 8	140.00
Tiffany Silver, Knife, Butter Serving, King James	18.00
Tiffany Silver, Knife, Cheese, Saratoga	30.00
Tiffany Silver, Knife, Tea, Wave Edge, Initialed, 7 1/2 In.	13.00
Tiffany Silver, Ladle, Mayonnaise, Olive Pattern	27.00
Tiffany Silver, Ladle, Mustard, Long Handled, 5 1/2 In.	9.95
Tiffany Silver, Loving Cup, Plain, 15 In.High	850.00
Tiffany Silver, Napkin Ring, Engraved Circular Bands & Bob	25.00
Tiffany Silver, Nutcracker	45.00
Tiffany Silver, Paper Clip, Fleur-De-Lis, Shield Shape Back, 2 1/4 X 2 In.	45.00
Tiffany Silver, Perfume, Plain, Engraved Front, 3 1/2 In.High	45.00
Tiffany Silver, Pitcher, Water, Repousse, Chased Floral, C.1855, 11 1/2 In.	700.00
Tiffany Silver, Plate, Bread, Boat Shape, Cutout Ends, 10 1/2 In.	48.00
Tiffany Silver, Sachet, Footed, Perforated Top, Gold Washed, 2 In.High	50.00
Tiffany Silver, Salt Dip, Gold Washed Interior, Rosebud Finial On Lid	22.00
Tiffany Silver, Salt Dip, Shell Shape, Monogram HCK	15.50
Tiffany Silver, Salt, Footed, 1 1/8 In., Pair	35.00
Tiffany Silver, Salver, Engraved Palm Fronts, Footed, C.1870, 15 In.	500.00
Tiffany Silver, Sauceboat, Loop Handle, Beaded Border, C.1854, 7 In.	150.00
Tiffany Silver, Sauceboat, Repousse, Reeded Loop Handle & Rim, C.1890, Pair	375.00
Tiffany Silver, Server, Berry, Persian Pattern, Scoop Form, C.1872	95.00
Tiffany Silver, Snuffbox, Hinged, Engraved, 2 Compartments, 5 1/2 In.	55.00
Tiffany Silver, Spoon, Berry, Strawberries & Leaves, Gold Washed	85.00
Tiffany Silver, Spoon, Demitasse, Twisted Handle, Leaf Bowl	14.00

Tiffany Silver, Spoon, Dessert, Beekman, 1869 .... 15.50
Tiffany Silver, Spoon, Dessert, Monogram, Set Of 6 .... 75.00
Tiffany Silver, Spoon, Dessert, Raised Pears, Leaves, Vines On Stippled 16.50
Tiffany Silver, Spoon, Iced Tea, Leaf Shaped Bowl 19.00
Tiffany Silver, Spoon, Master Salt, Initial M, Patent 1869 .... 7.95
Tiffany Silver, Spoon, Salt, Double Beaded Borders, Pair 18.00
Tiffany Silver, Spoon, Serving, Gold Washed 40.00
Tiffany Silver, Spoon, Serving, Pierced, Greek Mythology Handle, C.1878 ...... 145.00
Tiffany Silver, Spoon, Serving, Richelieu, Gold Washed Bowl, 9 In. 75.00
Tiffany Silver, Spoon, Vegetable, Hamilton, Slotted 25.00
Tiffany Silver, Tablespoon, Medallion, Set Of 6 .... 250.00
Tiffany Silver, Tazza, Champleve Enamel, Molded Foot, C.1920, 8 7/8 In. 225.00
Tiffany Silver, Tea & Coffee Set, Repousse, Engraved, C.1890, 6 Piece 3600.00
Tiffany Silver, Tea & Coffee Set, Strapwork, C.1880, 7 Piece 1800.00
Tiffany Silver, Teaspoon, Graduated Leaves On Handle, 1899, Set Of 6 .... 105.00
Tiffany Silver, Teaspoon, Jack & Jill Figural Handle, Inscribed Robert 32.00
Tiffany Silver, Teaspoon, Raised Gourds & Vine 12.50
Tiffany Silver, Tongs, Sugar, Art Nouveau 40.00
Tiffany Silver, Tongs, Sugar, Audubon, Gold Washed, 1891 .... 35.00
Tiffany Silver, Tongs, Sugar, Winthrop 18.00
Tiffany Silver, Toothpick, Footed 55.00
Tiffany Silver, Tray, Repousse Swirl Border, 10 In. Diameter 200.00
Tiffany Silver, Vase, Paneled, Flared, Footed, 7 In. 75.00
Tiffany Silver, Wine, 4 In. 39.50
Tiffany pieces made of all combinations of materials
Tiffany, Ashtray, Bronze & Green Glass, Cutout Grapes, Matchbox Holder 155.00
Tiffany, Ashtray, Bronze Hinged Mount, Amber Blue, C.1900, 5 In. 275.00
Tiffany, Ashtray, Pierced Bronze, Amber Iridescent Bowl, C.1900, 12 In. 500.00
Tiffany, Box, Gold Dore Bronze, Abalone Leaves, Hinged, 4 X 2 1/4 In. 125.00
Tiffany, Box, Gold Dore Bronze, Amber Slag Glass, Pine Needle, Lid, 4 X 2 In. ... 125.00
Tiffany, Box, Gold Dore Bronze, Enameled Design, Covered, Round, 4 1/4 In. ... 200.00
Tiffany, Box, Stamp, Bronze, Spider Web, Green Glass, 4 Bun Feet, 4 X 2 In. ... 85.00
Tiffany, Candelabrum, Bronze & Glass, 5 Ft.1 3/4 In. .... *Illus* 5100.00

Tiffany, Bronze & Glass Candelabrum, 5 Ft. 1 3/4 In.

Tiffany, Candelabrum, Bronze & Green Glass, 2 C Scroll Arms, C.1902, 15 In. 625.00
Tiffany, Candleholder, Bronze & Green Blown Glass, 17 In. 265.00
Tiffany, Candlestick & Snuffer, Bronze & Glass, Triangular Bottom, 11 In. 1100.00
Tiffany, Candlestick, Bronze & Glass, Cutout, Tripod 4 Footed Base, 13 In. 550.00
Tiffany, Candlestick, Bronze & Green Glass, C.1900, 17 5/8 In. 800.00
Tiffany, Candlestick, Bronze, Magnolia, Jade Green Glass Top, 15 In. 750.00
Tiffany, Candlestick, Dore Bronze, Gold Favrile Shade, 15 In. 325.00
Tiffany, Candlestick, Gilt Bronze, Amber Floriform Shade, C.1899, 21 1/2 In. 425.00
Tiffany, Candlestick, Gold Dore Bronze, Green Glass At Top, 15 In., Pair 750.00
Tiffany, Candlestick, Gold Iridescent Tulip On Bronze Holder, 17 1/2 In. 550.00

Tiffany, Clock, Alarm, 8 Day	75.00
Tiffany, Clock, American Indian, Gold Dore Bronze, Key Wind, 5 1/2 In.	675.00
Tiffany, Clock, Bronze & Enamel, Ball Feet, Square, 5 1/2 In.	1125.00
Tiffany, Clock, Bronze & Enamel, Line & Scroll Pattern, 6 X 4 1/2 In.	975.00
Tiffany, Clock, Crystal Regulator, Bronze Case, Mercury Pendulum	700.00
Tiffany, Clock, Desk, Zodiac, Round Face, 8 Sided, 4 1/4 In.	350.00
Tiffany, Clock, Grandfather, Westminster & Whittington Chimes, Gilt Case	1650.00
Tiffany, Clock, Herschede Works, Cincinnati, Westminster Chimes, Wooden	295.00
Tiffany, Clock, Herschede Works, Westminster Chime, Wooden Case	375.00
Tiffany, Clock, Mantel, Black & Silver Inlay	450.00
Tiffany, Clock, Mantel, Brass, Raised White Porcelain Numbers, 3 Weeks	400.00
Tiffany, Clock, Mantel, Marble & Ormolu, C.1860	500.00
Tiffany, Clock, Regulator, Crystal & Bronze Case	550.00
Tiffany, Cross, 14K Gold, 1 1/4 In.	35.00
Tiffany, Desk Set, Bookmark, Bronze & Glass, Signed, 10 Piece	2000.00
Tiffany, Desk Set, Bronze & Abalone, 9 Piece	1850.00
Tiffany, Desk Set, Bronze, Favrile Glass, Blue Waves, C.1909, 10 Piece	900.00
Tiffany, Figurine, Lady Holding Tambourine, Silver Plated Bronze, 16 In.	850.00
Tiffany, Frame, Bronze, Abalone Floral & Leaf, Easel Type, 6 X 6 1/2 In.	125.00
Tiffany, Frame, Picture, Pine Needle, Bronze, Amber Glass, Easel, 6 X 8 In.	160.00
Tiffany, Inkwell, Bronze & Blown Glass, Pyramid Shape, Hinged, 3 1/2 In.	1000.00
Tiffany, Inkwell, Bronze & Enamel, Ball Feet, Favrile Insert, 2 1/2 In.	450.00
Tiffany, Inkwell, Bronze & Glass, Adam Pattern, Hinged, Gold Dore, 4 In.	175.00
Tiffany, Inkwell, Bronze & Glass, Spanish, Raised Dragons, Hinged, 6 In.	450.00
Tiffany, Inkwell, Bronze & Red Enamel, Hinged, Ball Feet, 3 3/4 In.	350.00
Tiffany, Inkwell, Bronze Crab, Oyster Shell Cover, Hinged, C.1906	1800.00
Tiffany, Inkwell, Bronze, Hinged Lid, Grapevine, Mottled Amber Insert, C.1902	200.00
Tiffany, Inkwell, Bronze, Raised Enamel Geometrics, Glass Insert, Square	450.00
Tiffany, Inkwell, Crystal, Hinged Sterling Cover, Signed, 3 In.	65.00
Tiffany, Inkwell, Pine Needle, Bronze, Amber Glass Insert	150.00
Tiffany, Lamp, Acorn, Bronze Base, Glass Tiles Domical Shade, C.1899, 21 In.	1100.00
Tiffany, Lamp, Adjustable Double Arm, Bronze, Gold Shades, 20 In.	1100.00
Tiffany, Lamp, Autumn Leaf, Orange & Gold, Green Leaf, Bronze Base, 18 In.	4500.00
Tiffany, Lamp, Bridge, Bronze, Green Domical Shade, C.1899, 4 Ft.8 1/2 In.	1600.00
Tiffany, Lamp, Bridge, Counterbalance, Bronze, Green Shade, C.1900, 5 Ft.	1200.00
Tiffany, Lamp, Bronze Art Nouveau Base, Amber & Red Shade, C.1900, 12 In.	450.00
Tiffany, Lamp, Bronze Base, Green Glass Tiles Parasol Shade, C.1910, 26 In.	1400.00
Tiffany, Lamp, Bronze Base, Intaglio Leaf On Amber Helmet Shade, 20 In.	1800.00
Tiffany, Lamp, Bronze Base, Ocher Paneled Domical Shade, Acorns, 22 1/2 In.	2200.00
Tiffany, Lamp, Bronze Domical Shade, Bookmark Pattern, C.1899, 14 1/2 In.	225.00
Tiffany, Lamp, Desk, Bell Shape, Gold Favrile Shade, 12 In.High	750.00
Tiffany, Lamp, Desk, Blue & Green Swirl Shade	850.00
Tiffany, Lamp, Desk, Brass, Curved Arm Holding Shade, 9 In.	375.00
Tiffany, Lamp, Desk, Bronze & Glass, Curved Arm, 7 In.Diameter Shade	1500.00
Tiffany, Lamp, Desk, Bronze Base & Shade, Curved Arm, 5 In. Diameter Base	750.00
Tiffany, Lamp, Desk, Bronze Base, Chinese Pattern On Shade, 17 In.	1500.00
Tiffany, Lamp, Desk, Bronze Base, 2 Arms, Bell Shape, Gold Shades, 13 In.	750.00
Tiffany, Lamp, Desk, Bronze, Chinese Pattern, 10 X 9 In.	300.00
Tiffany, Lamp, Desk, Gold Feathering On Butterscotch Shade, 13 In.	650.00
Tiffany, Lamp, Desk, Ivy Leaf, Green, Yellow & White, Bronze Base, 14 In.Diam.	2000.00
Tiffany, Lamp, Desk, Metal, Bookmark Domical Shade, C.1899, 15 1/2 In.	350.00
Tiffany, Lamp, Desk, Turtleback, Amber, White, & Gold, Bronze Base, 15 1/8 In.	2500.00
Tiffany, Lamp, Desk, Turtleback, Golden, Rounded Bronze Base, 14 In.Diameter	3600.00
Tiffany, Lamp, Desk, Zodiac, Dore Bronze, 13 In.	600.00
Tiffany, Lamp, Dogwood, Pattern On Base, Red, Green, White, & Amber, 28 In.	2500.00
Tiffany, Lamp, Dogwood, White & Pink Flowers, Bronze Base, 16 In.Diameter	6500.00
Tiffany, Lamp, Dragonfly, Bronze Tree Trunk Base, Favrile Shade, 1899, 18 In.	9000.00
Tiffany, Lamp, Floor, Aladdin, Bronze, Blue & Gold Swirled Shade, 53 In.	1700.00
Tiffany, Lamp, Floor, Bronze Base, Gold Damascene On Blue Shade, 55 In.	1800.00
Tiffany, Lamp, Gilt Bronze Base, Amber Linenfold Shade, C.1899, 24 In.	3300.00
Tiffany, Lamp, Gone With The Wind, Gold & Green Favrile, Enameled, 17 In.	1500.00
Tiffany, Lamp, Green Favrile Glass, 20 In.	2500.00
Tiffany, Lamp, Lily, 3-Light, Amber Shades, C.1899, 14 In.	1200.00
Tiffany, Lamp, Lily, 3-Light, Gold Iridescent Shades, Signed, 9 In.	1165.00
Tiffany, Lamp, Lily, 5 Branch, Gold & Optic Rib Lilies, Bronze, 23 In.	2200.00
Tiffany, Lamp, Linenfold, Bronze Base, 12 Panels, 1937, 17 In.	1400.00

Tiffany, Lamp, Miniature, Gone With The Wind, Favrile Shade, 14 In.High	950.00
Tiffany, Lamp, Mosque, White, Blue Feathers, Gold Trim, 8 1/2 In.	1200.00
Tiffany, Lamp, Nautilus, Bronze Mermaid Base, Deep Green, Gudebrod, 8 In.	7500.00
Tiffany, Lamp, Nautilus, Bronze Mermaid Base, Deep Green, 16 In.	7500.00
Tiffany, Lamp, Night-Light, Gold Bronze On Base, Gold Torch Shade, 7 3/4 In.	350.00
Tiffany, Lamp, Student, Bronze, Domical Milk Glass Shades, C.1899, 30 In.	3000.00
Tiffany, Lamp, Table, Apple Blossom, Raised Root, Bronze Footed Base, 22 In.	5200.00
Tiffany, Lamp, Table, Arabian, Brown & Gold On Brown Base & Shade, 19 In.	2500.00
Tiffany, Lamp, Table, Byzantine, Bronze Base, Favrile Glass, 21 In.	9500.00
Tiffany, Lamp, Table, Dogwood, Bronze Base, Leaded Shade, 19 In.	6000.00
Tiffany, Lamp, Table, Dogwood, Bronze Footed Base, White & Pink, 21 In.	6500.00
Tiffany, Lamp, Table, Fabrique, Bronze Footed Base, Linen Fold, Gold, 23 In.	3000.00
Tiffany, Lamp, Table, Herringbone, Bronze Base & Cap, Leaded Shade, 22 In.	3100.00
Tiffany, Lamp, Table, Ivy Leaf, Bronze Base, Leaded Shade, 19 In.	2500.00
Tiffany, Lamp, Table, Leaf, Bronze Footed Base, Blue Green Mottled, 22 In.	3500.00
Tiffany, Lamp, Table, Sunset, Bronze Base, Leaded Shade, 24 In.	3100.00
Tiffany, Lamp, Table, Sunset, Bronze Twisted Base, Orange Gold, 27 In.	3000.00
Tiffany, Lamp, Table, Woodbine, Bronze Base, Leaded Shade, 16 In.	6800.00
Tiffany, Lantern, Turtleback, Blue Green & Red, Bronze, 6 X 9 In.	1500.00
Tiffany, Lantern, Turtleback, 4 Turtlebacks, Blue Green, Bronze, 12 In.	1800.00
Tiffany, Letter Holder, Bronze & Abalone, Line & Swirl, Enamel, 6 1/2 In.	175.00
Tiffany, Letter Opener, Venetian, Bronze	95.00
Tiffany, Letter Rack, Bronze, Green Slag Glass, Pine Needle, 2 Sections	175.00
Tiffany, Magnifying Glass, Bronze, Zodiac, 9 In.	145.00
Tiffany, Ornament, Butterfly, Bronze & Glass, C.1899, 7 1/2 In.	1500.00
Tiffany, Paperweight, Gold Dore Bronze, Abalone Disks, Octagonal, 4 In.	95.00
Tiffany, Pedestal, Walnut Base, Mosaic Tiles, C.1890, 33 In.	2500.00
Tiffany, Rack, Letter, Brass, Jeweled, Arabesque Carved	250.00
Tiffany, Rack, Pen, Cutout Grapes, Caramel Striated Glass, Upright, 5 In.	135.00
Tiffany, Ring, Scarab, Red Iridescent, 14K Gold Mounting	95.00
Tiffany, Scissors, Gold Dore Bronze & Steel, Line Design, 9 In.	150.00
Tiffany, Tray, Pen, Abalone, Bronze, Signed	100.00
Tiffany, Tray, Pen, Zodiac, Dore Bronze	65.00
Tiffany, Wiper, Quill, Grape & Vine, Dore Bronze & Amber Glass, Insert	95.00

Tiffin Glass Company of Tiffin, Ohio, was a subsidiary of the United States Glass Co.of Pittsburgh, Pa. Black satin glass, made by the company between 1923 and 1926, is very popular among collectors. Other types were also made.

Tiffin, Bowl Vase, Black Satin, Red Coralene Poppies, Label, 7 In.	30.00
Tiffin, Compote, Crystal, Paper Label, 5 X 7 In.	8.00
Tiffin, Console Set, Black Satin, Lace Edge 8 1/2 In. Compote, 3 Piece	60.00
Tiffin, Dish, Cake, Black Satin, Center Handle, 9 3/4 In.	12.50
Tiffin, Figurine, Dog, Amber, Jeweled Eyes, 7 In.High, Seated	125.00
Tiffin, Figurine, Dog, Amber, 7 X 7 In.	125.00
Tiffin, Vase, Black Satin, Paper Label, 9 In.	13.50
Tile, see also Nippon, Tile, and various ceramic categories	
Tile, French Porcelain, Hand-Painted Scene, Frame, Square, 7 1/2 In., Pair	185.00
Tile, French, Floral, Artist Signed, 9 1/2 X 10 1/2 In.	10.00
Tile, Shakespearean Scene, Blue & Tan, Square, 6 In.	9.50
Tile, Tea, Pink Flowers Center, Gold Trim, Round, 6 In.	6.00
Tin, see also Store	
Tin, Ashtray Cigarette Dispenser, Mechanical Donkey, Canyon City, 10 In.	20.00
Tin, Bathtub, Child's	28.50 To 55.00
Tin, Bottle, Hot Water, Curved For Stomach Or Back	18.00
Tin, Box, Candle, Oval, Wall Type, Wood Handle, 20 In.	110.00
Tin, Box, Candle, Oval, Wall, Green, Shepherd Scene, 14 1/4 In.	110.00
Tin, Box, Document, Dome Cover, Green Paint, Hand-Painted Flowers	35.00
Tin, Box, Pencil, Jackie Coogan Picture, Yellow Paint	7.00
Tin, Box, Punched Spread Eagle Design, Handle, 7 1/2 X 5 X 2 In.	30.00
Tin, Box, Salt, Green, Wooden Lid	15.00
Tin, Box, Spice, Gilt Crystallized Finish, 4 Containers, 4 3/8 X 3 In.	34.50
Tin, Box, Tobacco, Painted, 18th Century Figures, Hinged, C.1790, 7 In.	275.00
Tin, Can, Sprinkling, Flower, Soldered Strap Handle, Quart	6.00
Tin, Candleholder, Marked BB On Base, Push-Up, 6 7/8 In.	15.00
Tin, Candleholder, 4 Glass Sides, 11 In.	37.50

Tin, Candlesnuffer, Cone Shape, Long Handled, 9 In.	25.00
Tin, Candlesnuffer, Japanese, Cone Shape	18.00
Tin, Case, Comb, Victorian	3.50
Tin, Case, Comb, Wall, Eagle & Sheild On Back, Green, 6 1/4 X 7 In.	20.00
Tin, Case, Pipe, Shape Of Pipe, For Clay Pipe, Hunleys Peerless Ale	8.95
Tin, Coffeepot, Pressed-In Design, 1865, 9 In.	35.00
Tin, Cup, Child's, Old Mother Hubbard & Cow Jumped Over The Moon	6.00
Tin, Dipper, 7 X 5 In.	10.00
Tin, Downspout, Star & Moon Ornaments, Painted, C.1850, 15 In., Pair	60.00
Tin, Funnel, Gallon	5.00
Tin, Holder, Match, Slipper Shape, Pierced Oriental Figures	9.00
Tin, Horn, Dinner, 17 In.	10.00
Tin, Lamp Filling Can, Whale Oil, One Quart Capacity	4.00
Tin, Lunch Box, Tin, Lithographed	3.50
Tin, Match Holder, Oak Leaf, Acorn For Matches, Pierced, Niagara Falls	8.00
Tin, Match Holder, Petticoat, Blue Japanned Base, 4 In.	35.00
Tin, Match Safe, Double, Red Paint, 5 X 4 1/4 In.	10.00
Tin, Match Safe, Hanging, Flat, Hinged Lid, 1 1/2 X 3 1/2 In.	10.00
Tin, Match Safe, Pocket, Diamond Match Co., Wax Matched, Hinged, Striker	4.50
Tin, Measure, Pint, Side Handle	4.95
Tin, Measure, Pint, Side Handle, Long Pouring Spout	3.95
Tin, Mold, Candle, 2 Tube	54.00
Tin, Mold, Candle, 6 Tube	30.00
Tin, Mold, Candle, 6 Tube, Attached Top & Bottom	74.00
Tin, Mold, Candle, 8 Tube	16.00
Tin, Mold, Candle, 8 Tube, Pennsylvania Dutch, 10 In.	50.00
Tin, Mold, Candle, 9 Tube, Side Handle	50.00
Tin, Mold, Candle, 12 Tube	12.00 To 84.00
Tin, Mold, Candle, 12 Tube, Pennsylvania Dutch, 3 Rows Of 4	50.00
Tin, Mold, Candle, 12 Tube, 10 1/2 In. High	55.00
Tin, Mold, Chocolate, Rooster, 2 Piece	15.00
Tin, Mold, Chocolate, Santa, Peaked Hat, E., N.A.Y.	15.00
Tin, Mold, Ice Cream, Cone Shape, Scoop, Brass Pins, 3 1/4 In.	18.00
Tin, Mold, Jello, Child's, Embossed Rabbit On Bottom	4.00
Tin, Pitcher, Kerosene, To Refill Lamps, Handled, 6 In.	6.50
Tin, Pitcher, Measuring, 4 Quart	18.00
Tin, Plate, AYP Exposition, 1909, 3 Ladies, 9 1/2 In.	35.00
Tin, Plate, Child's, Enamel Kate Greenaway Girl & Boy, "Hickory Dickory"	12.00
Tin, Plate, Lady's Portrait, 10 In.	28.00
Tin, Plate, Polo Game, C.1910, 10 In.	27.50
Tin, Sander, Ink, Cylindrical, Dish Top & Base, C.1750, 3 1/2 X 3 In.	30.00
Tin, Scoop, Circular Back, Strap Handle, 4 In.	4.50
Tin, Scoop, Closed Back & Top, Tubular Handle, 9 In.	4.50
Tin, Scoop, Oval, Thumb Rest Handle, 9 In.	4.50
Tin, Skimmer, Perforated, Hole For Hanging, 6 X 6 In.	3.50
Tin, Snuffbox, Hinged, Oval, Dated 1860, 2 1/4 X 3 1/4 In.	12.00
Tin, Spittoon, Blue, Gilt Bordering	15.00
Tin, Strainer, Milk House, Perforated Bottom, Tapered Sides, Handle, 10 In.	12.00
Tin, Strainer, Tea, Lithographed Bowl, Wooden Handle	2.75
Tin, Tea & Coffee Caddy, Cone Shape, Japanning, Gold Letters, 6 In., Pair	30.00
Tin, Toothpick, Hat, Turned-Down Brim, C.1850, 1 3/4 In.	18.00
Tin, Tray, Admiral Dewey, Chas.Schonk Lithograph, Chicago, 12 In.	28.00
Tin, Tray, Battleship, Maine, Chas.Schonk Lithograph, Chicago, 12 In.	28.00
Tin, Tumbler, Bar, 2 1/4 In., Set Of 5	45.00
Tin, Urn, Painted, 12 In., Pair	Illus 325.00

Toby mugs have been made since the seventeenth century.

Toby Mug, see also Royal Doulton, Toby Mug, Staffordshire, Toby Mug

Toby Mug, Black Faced Man With Curly Hair, Stoneware Type, 4 3/4 In.	37.00
Toby Mug, Captain Cuttle, Beswick, England, 5 In.	18.50
Toby Mug, Colonial Man With Pipe & Glass, Blue, Copper Luster Trim, 5 In.	100.00
Toby Mug, Colonial Man, Deep Blue Coat, Copper Luster Trim, 5 In.	75.00
Toby Mug, Davy Jones, Clayton-Sterling, England, 9 1/2 In.	75.00
Toby Mug, Dickens, English, 3 1/4 In.	7.00
Toby Mug, Friar, Ruby Flashed, Clear Handle	75.00

Tin, Urn, Painted, 12 In., Pair
(See Page 644)

Tole, Canister, 7 In.

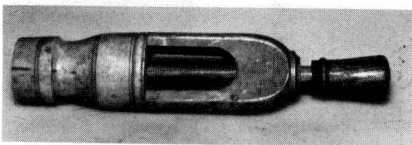

Tool, Corker, Wooden, 12 In.
(See Page 646)

Toby Mug, German Soldier, Bennington Type Pottery, English, 4 1/2 In.	22.50
Toby Mug, Happy Face, Snuffbox In Hand, Yellow Vest, 8 1/2 In.High	95.00
Toby Mug, King Neptune, Seahorse Handle, Shorter & Sons, 7 In.	19.00
Toby Mug, Lady In Tricornered Hat & Apron, 3 In.	7.50
Toby Mug, Laughing Face, Removable Tricorne Hat, Brown, 9 1/2 In.	175.00
Toby Mug, Old Lady, 3 In.	10.00
Toby Mug, Pluto, Lancaster Sandland, 4 In.	42.00
Toby Mug, Punch, Wain & Sons, England, 6 3/4 In.	22.00
Toby Mug, Scrooge, Beswickware, Made In England, 7 1/2 In.	25.00
Toby Mug, Seated Man, Green Coat, Brown Hat, English, 4 In.	11.00
Toby Mug, The Squeaker, Burlington, England	18.00
Toby Mug, Town Crier, Clayton-Sterling, England, 9 3/4 In.	75.00
Toby Mug, Town Crier, Green, Shorter & Sons, 3 1/2 In.	14.00
Toby Mug, William Penn, American, Indian's Head Handle, 6 1/2 I	90.00 To 225.00
Toilet Bowl, Salesman's Sample, Flowers Strewn, C.1870, 5 1/4 In.High	125.00
Tole, Box, Candle, Oval, Black, 8 1/2 In.Diameter	30.00
Tole, Box, Document, Black, Gold Stencil, "Sec'y Treas., " 13 X 6 X 9 1/2 In.	65.00
Tole, Box, Document, Gold & Red Stenciled, Sec'y Treas.St.J.W.W.Co., 13 In.	85.00
Tole, Box, Document, The St.J.W.W.Co., Gold & Red Stenciled, 13 X 6 X 9 In.	85.00
Tole, Box, Floral On Green, 10 X 3 In.	20.00
Tole, Box, Japanned On Cover, Pull Top, 5 X 4 X 3 In.	40.00
Tole, Box, Spice, Rectangular, Handle, 6 Containers Inside, 9 X 6 1/2 In.	30.00
Tole, Box, Spoon & Fork Spelled Out, Gold Stencil, 10 X 8 In.	32.00
Tole, Candlestick, Push-Up, Loop Handled Base, C.1850, 14 1/2 In.	225.00
Tole, Canister, 7 In.	*Illus* 160.00
Tole, Foot Warmer, Pennsylvania Dutch Decoration, Inset	62.00
Tole, Plate, Bread, Oval, 14 In.	29.50
Tole, Scoop, Ice Cream, Cone Shape	10.00
Tole, Spill, Conical, Silver, Hand-Painted Gold Trim, C.1650, 11 1/2 In.	90.00
Tole, Sugar, Covered, Pennsylvania Dutch, Dutch Design	35.00
Tole, Tray, English, Gold Chinoiserie On Green, C.1830, Round, 7 1/2 In.	65.00
Tole, Tray, Flowers In Urn, Stencil & Free Hand, Floral Border, 24 1/2 In.	65.00
Tole, Tray, Pierced Handles, Ribbon Tied Summer Flowers, C.1850, 19 In.	125.00
Tole, Tray, Pierced Handles, Young Man & Hunting Dog, C.1820, 30 1/2 In.	175.00
Tole, Tray, Urn Of Fruit, 8 Sided, 22 X 16 In.	35.00
Tom Mix, Movie, The Escape, 16 Mm.	8.00
Tom Mix, Photograph, 10 X 8 In.	7.00

Tool, see also Iron, Kitchen, Store, Tin, Wooden

Tool, Adze, Cooper's	17.50
Tool, Adze, Gutter, Wrought Iron	45.00
Tool, Altimeter, Barometric, Pocket, T.W.S.I., Ltd., London, Brass, C.1900	60.00
Tool, Angle Of Refraction Apparatus, Lerebours Et Secretan A Paris, 1845	315.00
Tool, Anvil Vise, C Type Jaws, 21 X 5 In.	25.00
Tool, Anvil, Blacksmith's, 135 Pounds	125.00
Tool, Astrologer's Quibla Dial, Persian, C.1890, Engraved Brass Plates	275.00
Tool, Auger, Hub, Wheelwright's, Hand-Forged, Tapered, Wood T Handle, 13 In.	15.00
Tool, Ax, Nickel Plated, Raised Work Aikens, 4 1/2 In.	4.95
Tool, Bag Spreader, Wooden, Bow Shape, 9 X 14 In.	30.00
Tool, Bevel, Nautical, Swing Blade, Wood, Copper Mounts, Ivory, C.1890, 19 In.	28.00
Tool, Bit Brace & Wagon Wrench Combination, Iron, Wooden, 10 X 6 In.	55.00
Tool, Bit Brace, Walnut, Slip-On Chuck, C.1750, 4 1/2 X 14 In.	195.00
Tool, Bit, Auger, Winchester, 3/8 In.	12.50
Tool, Broadax, Steel Inset, Short Offset Handle, 8 1/2 In.	22.00
Tool, Calipers, Hand-Forged Iron, Heart Shape Thumbscrew, 11 In.	45.00
Tool, Candle Dryer, Wooden, 4 Pronged	45.00
Tool, Chisel, Corner	8.50
Tool, Compass, Geomancer's, Chinese, C.1850, Boxwood, Center Compass	160.00
Tool, Compass, Miner's, Shuttleworth, London, Mahogany, Hinged Cover, 7 In.	195.00
Tool, Compass, Surveyor's, Mining, Troughton & Simms, London, C.1830, Brass	275.00
Tool, Compass, Surveyor's, Pocket, France, C.1900, Brass, 4 In.	90.00
Tool, Compass, Surveyor's, Thaxter & Son, Boston, C.1830, Mahogany, 7 In. .... Illus	450.00
Tool, Corker, Wooden, 12 In.	27.00
Tool, Corn Flail, Hand-Hewn	35.00
Tool, Cow Horn, For Whetstone, Belt Connection, 8 In.	10.00
Tool, Croze, Cooper's, Sawtooth, Red Paint	45.00
Tool, Croze, Cooper's, V Blade	45.00
Tool, Crucible, Mining, 9 1/2 X 7 1/2 In.	20.00
Tool, Divider, Carpenter's, Handwrought Iron, Wing Nut, 16 In.	25.00
Tool, Doctor, see Doctor	
Tool, Drawing Instruments, Davis & Son, London & Derby, C.1875, Oak Case	95.00
Tool, Fleam, Iron, Spring Type	50.00
Tool, Flytrap, Wire Screen, Funnel & Cylinder Shape, 9 In.	25.00
Tool, Froe, Cooper's, Hand-Forged, 10 1/2 In. Handle, 9 In.	25.00
Tool, Froe, Splitting	19.00
Tool, Gauge, Draw, Harness Maker's, Rosewood Handle	12.50
Tool, Hammer & Pick, Horse Hoof Cleaning	7.00
Tool, Hammer, Claw, Hand-Forged Iron, Wooden Handle, 4 In. Head	15.00
Tool, Hammer, Tack, Hand-Forged Iron, Wooden Handle, 3 3/4 In. Head	12.00
Tool, Hatchel, Flax, Iron Teeth, On Cherry Board, 15 X 3 1/2 In.	7.00
Tool, Hatchel, Flax, Nails Held To Pine By Punched Tin, J.M. 1812, 13 In.	35.00
Tool, Hatchel, Flax, Rectangular, Spike Tooth, Cherry Board, 22 X 4 In.	10.00
Tool, Hatchel, Flax, Weathered Pine Board, Nails, 29 X 10 In.	25.00
Tool, Hatchel, Hand Pierced Around Tin Spike Holder, Carving	20.00
Tool, Hatchel, 3 In. Spikes On Walnut Board, Dated 1801, 11 In.	35.00
Tool, Hatchet, Carpenter's, Hewing, Handle	5.00
Tool, Hog Scraper, Wooden Handle	3.75
Tool, Hone, Ax, Keen Kutter	3.50
Tool, Hone, Pocket, Winchester, Round	8.00
Tool, Hook, Lobster Bait, Hand Wrought Iron, 14 In.Long	18.00
Tool, Horn Tip, For Wet Stone For Farmer's Scythe, Hook For Belt, 6 1/2 In.	15.00
Tool, Husker, Corn, Leather, Hand	4.00
Tool, Hydrometer, Sikes, Joseph Long, London, Brass, Ivory, 8 In.	60.00
Tool, Iron, Curling, Folding, Wooden Handles	4.50
Tool, Knife, Chamfer, Hand-Forged Iron, Wood Handles, Cooper's, Curved, 15 In.	20.00
Tool, Level, Brassbound	2.75
Tool, Level, Builder's, Bubble, English, C.1890, Brass, Mahogany Case	40.00
Tool, Level, Engineer's, English, C.1820, Brass, Inverted Image, 11 5/8 In.	95.00
Tool, Level, Surveyor's, American, C.1890, Brass, 15 3/4 In.	225.00
Tool, Level, Wye, Megarey, New York, C.1830, Brass, 20 In.	515.00
Tool, Loom, Tape, Norway, Hand-Carved, Blue Paint, Dated 1819	40.00
Tool, Microscope, C.Reichert, Vienna, C.1885, Brass	145.00
Tool, Microscope, Carl Zeiss, Germany, C.1875, Brass	325.00
Tool, Microscope, Casella, London, C.U850, Brass, Mahogany Case	170.00
Tool, Microscope, J.Swift & Son, London, C.1900, Brass, Student's	175.00

Tool, **Microscope**, James W.Queen & Co., Phila., C.1870, Bronzed Iron Base 55.00
Tool, **Microscope**, Nairne, London, C.1774, Brass, Mahogany Chest 1695.00
Tool, **Microscope**, Pillischer, London, C.1890, Brass, Claw Foot Base 125.00
Tool, **Microscope**, R & J Beck, London, C.1872, Wenham, Brass 375.00
Tool, **Microscope**, Swift & Son, London, C.1890, Oil Immersion Objective 55.00
Tool, **Microscope**, W.Gregory & Co., London, C.1870, Brass, Student's 135.00
Tool, **Microscope**, Willett & Jewel, England, C.1825, Brass, Tripod Base 340.00
Tool, **Microscope**, Zentmayer, Phila., C.1850, Dissecting, Brass 130.00
Tool, **Nail Header**, Square Hole 14.00
Tool, **Nail Puller**, Hand-Forged Iron, 13 In. 7.00
Tool, **Net**, Horsefly, Orange, Black & White Bands, C.1920 ...... 10.00
Tool, **Niddy Noddy**, Bird's-Eye Maple 25.00
Tool, **Noon Indicator**, F.Dent's Patent, Meridian, London, C.1890, Brass 275.00
Tool, **Oil Stone**, Pine Frame, Handled, 6 3/4 In. 18.00
Tool, **Picker**, Cranberry, Wood, 6 Tines 65.00
Tool, **Plane**, Block, Wooden, 7 In. 8.00
Tool, **Plane**, Cabinetmaker's, Table, Brass Legs, 10 X 7 In. 29.75
Tool, **Plane**, Cooper's Header, Walnut, 6 1/4 X 2 1/2 In. 50.00
Tool, **Plane**, Empire Tool Co., Jack, Wooden, 16 In. 9.00
Tool, **Plane**, Jointer, Wooden, 22 In. 12.00
Tool, **Plant**, Winchester, Wooden, 10 In. 30.00
Tool, **Plucker**, Cooper's, McKenzie, Shaped Wedge, Earlike Handles 85.00
Tool, **Plumb Board**, Red Pine, Brass Plumb On Line, 30 In. 35.00
Tool, **Pointer**, Spoke 6.00
Tool, **Protractor**, Elliott Bros., London, C.1890, Brass, Pine Case 60.00
Tool, **Pulley**, Hay, Wooden 4.00
Tool, **Punch**, Leather, Finger, 1/16 In. 8.00
Tool, **Race Wheel**, Hand-Forged Iron, 8 1/2 X 15 In. 30.00
Tool, **Race Wheel**, Traveler, Handwrought Iron, Wooden Handle 15.00
Tool, **Reamer**, Bung 8.50
Tool, **Reel**, Yarn, Maple & Ash, Pegged, 23 X 30 In. 150.00
Tool, **Refraction Demonstrator**, Soleil Fils, Opticien, Paris, C.1890 ...... 75.00
Tool, **Riveting**, Horse Harness, Cast Iron 2.50
Tool, **Router**, Coachmaker's, Maple, Cast Steel Blade, 7 1/2 In. 30.00
Tool, **Router**, Coachmaker's, Cast Steel Blade, Walnut, Patent 1880, 4 X 2 In. 28.00
Tool, **Rug Beater**, Windsor, N.Y., Bentwood, 41 1/4 In. 12.00
Tool, **Rug Beater**, Wire 3.50
Tool, **Rule & Level**, Map Maker's, Casella, London, C.1850, Alidade, Brass 130.00
Tool, **Rule**, Folding, Brassbound 4.00
Tool, **Rule**, Slide, Bate, London, C.1825, Excise Officer's, Boxwood, Brass 195.00
Tool, **Rule**, Slide, Fowler's, England, C.1900, Pocket Watch Type, Aluminum 58.00
Tool, **Rule**, Slide, Stanley Trade Mark, Sines & Logs, C.1910, Bracket Mount 150.00
Tool, **Rule**, Stanley, Folding, Wood & Brass, 6 In. 5.00
Tool, **Saw**, Keyhole, Maple Handle, 12 1/2 In. 12.00
Tool, **Scorper**, Bowlmaker's, Closed, 2 In. Blade, 15 In. 35.00
Tool, **Scorper**, Cast Steel, Double Handle, Square, 4 1/2 X 5 In. 25.00
Tool, **Screwdriver**, Carstairs, 3 In. 4.00
Tool, **Screwdriver**, Gun, Winchester, 4 Blades 5.00
Tool, **Screwdriver**, Wooden Handle, 7 In. 5.00
Tool, **Scribe**, Carpenter's, Wooden 2.50
Tool, **Scythe**, Barley, Handwrought, Signed B.Y. 25.00
Tool, **Shave**, Spoke, Wooden 10.00
Tool, **Shaver**, Ice, Gem, North Brothers 9.50
     Tool, **Shovel**, see Shaker, Shovel
Tool, **Spectroscope**, John Browning, London, C.1875, Hand, Brass 135.00
Tool, **Speculum**, Veterinarian's, Rectactor, Handwrought, 14 In. 14.00
Tool, **Spyglass**, B.Martin, London, C.1780, Brass Barrel, Telescopic 265.00
Tool, **Spyglass**, Dollond, London, C.1780, Wooden Barrel, 3 Draw, Brass Fittings 165.00
Tool, **Stamp**, J.Falkner, Hand-Forged, Ring Handle, 1 Piece, 14 3/4 In. 25.00
Tool, **Stick**, Wash, 2 Tine, Hand-Hewn Wood, 1 Piece, 31 In. 7.00
Tool, **Telescope**, Gilbert & Co., London, C.1820, Portable, Mahogany Barrel 390.00
Tool, **Telescope**, J.R.Champlin, N.H., C.1880, Wooden Barrel, Brass Mounts 950.00
Tool, **Telescope**, J.Watson, London, C.1820, Brass, Tripod, Case 1095.00
Tool, **Telescope**, Lefevre, Paris, C.1890, Brass Barrel, Tripod Base 575.00
Tool, **Telescope**, Ross Ltd., London, C.1890, Brass Barrel, Table Stand 495.00
Tool, **Telescope**, W.& S.Jones, London, C.1800, Brass Barrel, Tripod Stand 1350.00

Tool, Tinder Pouch, Leather, Silver & Brass Trim, 4 1/4 In.	140.00
Tool, Tongs, Blacksmith's, Cast Iron, 23 In.	10.00
Tool, Tongs, Blacksmith's, Wrought Iron, 19 In.	6.00
Tool, Tongs, Blacksmith's, Wrought Iron, 22 In.	6.00
Tool, Tongs, Ice, Cast Iron	6.50
Tool, Tongs, Ice, W.T.Wood Co.	7.00
Tool, Tooth Puller, Dental, Iron, 7 In.	30.00
Tool, Torch, Blow, Brass	6.00
Tool, Torch, Gasoline, Brass, 6 X 3 In.	9.50
Tool, Trammel, Betty Ratchet, 12 In.	150.00
Tool, Trammel, Cast Iron	20.00
Tool, Trammel, Chain With Twisted Links, Cast Iron	45.00
Tool, Trammel, Chain, Cast Iron	20.00
Tool, Trammel, Sawtooth, Wrought Iron, C.1750, 38 In.	55.00
Tool, Transit Instrument, Heller & Brightly, Phila., C.1875, Brass, Case	360.00
Tool, Transit Instrument, John Browning, London, C.1870, Brass, 14 In.	625.00
Tool, Transit Instrument, Surveyor's, John Bliss & Co., N.Y., 1870, Brass	450.00
Tool, Trap, Bear, Custom Made, 35 X 14 In.	150.00
Tool, Trap, Bear, Grizzly, Custom Made, 51 X 13 In.	250.00
Tool, Trap, Bear, Newhouse, No.2	11.00
Tool, Trap, Bear, Newhouse, No.3	13.00
Tool, Trap, Bear, Newhouse, No.4	14.00
Tool, Trap, Bear, Newhouse, No.5	130.00 To 160.00
Tool, Trap, Bear, No 6 Model, 42 In.	225.00
Tool, Trap, Chicken Mite, Wooden	2.50 To 3.50
Tool, Trap, Mole	2.50
Tool, Trap, Mouse, Glass, Stand, Patent 1918	7.00
Tool, Trap, Mouse, Self Resetting, Wood, Wire, & Tin, Patent	52.00
Tool, Trap, Mouse, The Delusion, Patent 1876 & 1877, Blue Painted Tin, 5 In.	50.00
Tool, Trap, Patent, Self Resetting, Wood, Wire, & Tin	52.00
Tool, Trap, Rat, Wire Basket, Barrel Shape, Spring Door, 15 In. Long	13.00
Tool, Traveler, Wheelright's	20.00
Tool, Veterinary's, For Putting Rings In Hog's Nose, Iron, 1872	10.00
Tool, Wagon Jack, Wooden, 34 In.	35.00
Tool, Wagon Wheel Making, Iron & Wood, A.A.Wood & Sons Co.	30.00
Tool, Wheel Traveler, Wrought Iron	22.00
Tool, Wheelbarrow, Wooden, Wooden Spokes & Hub	14.00
Tool, Wheelwright Traveler, Wrought Iron, Loop Handle	35.00
Tool, Whetstone, Advertising On Back, Round, 2 1/4 In.	4.00
Tool, Whetstone, Oil, Inset In Covered Pine Box, Rectangular, 7 1/2 X 3 In.	20.00
Tool, Whetstone, Sears & Roebuck Co., Chicago, Lady & Scale Of Justice	12.50
Tool, Winder, Watchmaker's, Main Spring, English, C.1750, Brass & Steel	55.00
Tool, Winder, Yarn, New England, C.1750, Maple, Stick Legs, 35 In.	60.00
Tool, Wool Carder, Wooden, Pair	12.00
Tool, Wrench & Bit Stock Combination, P.Lownetraut, N.J., Patent 1894	30.00
Tool, Wrench, Buggy, Cast Iron	1.50 To 2.00
Tool, Wrench, Monkey, Dated 1882	2.50
Tool, Wrench, Pipe, Winchester, 14 In.	20.00
Tool, Wrench, Rope Bed	13.00
Tool, Wrench, S End, Winchester, 7/16 & 1/2 In.	15.00
Tool, Wrench, USS End, Winchester, 5/16 & 3/8 In.	12.50
Tool, Wrench, Wagon Wheel, Hand-Forged	6.50
Tool, Yoke, Ox, Oak, Hand-Hewn, Iron Bows	75.00
Tool, Yoke, Sap, Blue Paint, 40 In.	39.00
Tool, Yoke, Sap, Wooden Bucket Hooks, Dated 1868	32.00

Toothpick holders are sometimes called toothpicks by collectors. The
variously shaped containers made to hold the small wooden toothpicks are of
glass, china, or metal. Most of the toothpicks are Victorian.

Toothpick, see also other categories such as Bisque, Slag, etc.

Toothpick, Art Glass, Pink, White Overlay, Pontiled	30.00
Toothpick, Bisque, Boy Taking Off Shirt	35.00
Toothpick, Chick With Wishbone, New Amsterdam Silver Co.	25.00 To 32.50
Toothpick, Clear Glass Basket, Side Handles	6.00
Toothpick, Coal Bucket Shape, Blue Glass	22.00
Toothpick, Green Glass, Paneled Sides, Bronze Lid, 3 1/2 In.	5.00

Toothpick, **Green Metal**, Tan Pig At Side, Insert	12.00
Toothpick, **Green**, Gold, Beaded Top, Etched A.L.S.	16.00
Toothpick, **Monkey On Tree Stump**, Blue	35.00
Toothpick, **Owl**, Metal	27.50
Toothpick, **Potbellied & Hunchbacked Punch**, Crocked Hat, Porcelain, 6 In.	65.00
Toothpick, **Rabbit**, Silver Plate	38.00
Toothpick, **Ribbed Swirl**, Amber Top, Frosted Base	58.00
Toothpick, **Two Cherubs Holding Barrel**	17.50

*Tortoiseshell glass was made during the 1800s and after by the Sandwich
Glass Works of Massachusetts and some firms in Germany. Tortoiseshell
glass has been reproduced.*

Tortoiseshell **Glass, Basket**, Raspberry Cased, Amber Thorn Handle, 8 In.	145.00
Tortoiseshell **Glass, Vase**, Fluted Panels, Pedestal Base, 8 3/4 In.	35.00
Tortoiseshell **Glass, Vase**, Ribbed, Beaded, 6 In.	75.00
Tortoiseshell **Glass, Vase**, V Shape, Amber, Ribbed, 14 In.High	75.00
Tortoiseshell, **Bottle**, Snuff, Chinese, 2 1/2 In.	200.00
Tortoiseshell, **Box**, Gold Mounted, Champleve Miniatures, C.1830, 3 1/4 In.	725.00
Tortoiseshell, **Box**, Patch, Oblong, 4 Ivory Feet, 2 1/4 X 1 1/4 In.	45.00
Tortoiseshell, **Comb**, Hair, 9 Amber Stones	35.00
Tortoiseshell, **Comb**, Mustache, Sterling Silver Holder	24.00
Tortoiseshell, **Comb**, Silver Back, Chased Floral & Scroll, 4 1/2 In.	16.00
Tortoiseshell, **Comb**, 9 Large Amber Stones	35.00
Tortoiseshell, **Holder**, Cigarette, Gold Tip, Leather Case	15.00
Tortoiseshell, **Lorgnette**, Openwork, 11 In. Handle	35.00
Tortoiseshell, **Pocketbook**, Double Strap, 8 X 4 1/2 In.	125.00
Tortoiseshell, **Snuffbox**, Delaye, Gold Mounted, En Grisaille On Lid, 1820	725.00
Tortoiseshell, **Snuffbox**, French, Gilt Silver Hinge, Gouache On Lid, C.1820	60.00
Tortoiseshell, **Snuffbox**, French, Silver Mounted, En Grisaille Inset, C.1820	125.00
Tortoiseshell, **Snuffbox**, Gold Mounted, Red & White Agate On Lid, C.1820	350.00
Tortoiseshell, **Snuffbox**, Jouer Aux Cartes, Card Playing Scene	200.00
Tortoiseshell, **Snuffbox**, Paris, Gold Mounted, Miniature On Lid, C.1798, 3 In. ...	325.00
Tortoiseshell, **Toothpick**, Jackknife Form, Brass Picks, 2 In. Closed	8.50
Toy, see also Card, Disneyana, Doll, Game, Marble, Orphan Annie	
Toy, **Airplane**, Bomber, Wyandotte, 13 In. Wingspan	5.00
Toy, **Airport**, Lithograph, Tin, Superior, 19 X 24 X 11 In.	25.00
Toy, **Alligator With Native On Back**, Windup, Tin, Chein	20.00
Toy, **Ambulance**, White Rubber Tires, 2 Piece Body, Tootsie Toy	30.00
Toy, **Aquaplane**, Windup, Lithographed, Tin, J.Chein, 9 In.	12.75
Toy, **Areo Circus**, Newton, 1931	65.00
Toy, **Arkitoy Wood Construction Set**, No.3, Carrom Industries, C.1940	7.50
Toy, **Auto Mac**, Windup, Plastic, Marx, 13 In.	12.00
Toy, **Auto Speedway**, Jr., Lithographed, Tin, Automatic Toy Co.	8.75
Toy, **Auto Uncle**, Windup, Tin, Lehmann	280.00
Toy, **Avengers**, Metal, British, C.1966, Boxed	15.00
Toy, **B.O. Plenty**, Windup, Lithographed, Tin, Marx .... 42.50 To 55.00	
Toy, **B.O.Plenty**, Tin, Mechanical, Marx	55.00
Toy, **Baby Chick**, Windup, Tin, Chein	8.00
Toy, **Baby Grand Piano**, Petite Princess Fantasy Furniture	7.50
Toy, **Babyland Nursery**, Lithographed, Tin, Marx	8.50
Toy, **Balking Mule**, Windup, Tin, Lehmann	135.00
Toy, **Banjo Player**, Clockwork, Secor, C.1880	2700.00
Toy, **Barn**, Cow & Horse, 9 1/2 X 7 In. .... *Illus*	195.00
Toy, **Barn**, Red Robin, Wooden, 3 Stalls, Marked Converse, 12 X 12 X 8 In.	65.00
Toy, **Baseball Glove**, Child's, Spalding Bros., 1876	28.00
Toy, **Baseball**, New York Giants, 1954 World Series, Autographed	50.00
Toy, **Bat**, Baseball, Jackie Robinson, Standard Size	8.50
Toy, **Bathinette**, Doll's, Wooden, Strombecker, For 8 In. Doll	5.00
Toy, **Bed**, Baby Doll's, Shaker, Harvard, 32 X 16 In.	200.00
Toy, **Bed**, Doll's, American, C.1890, Mahogany .... *Illus*	80.00
Toy, **Bed**, Doll's, Brass, Castors, Feather Mattress & Pillow, 22 X 13 1/2 In. ...	75.00
Toy, **Bed**, Doll's, Brass, Chintz Coverlet, 22 X 16 In.	135.00
Toy, **Bed**, Doll's, Brass, Mattress & Springs, 19 1/2 X 19 In.	125.00
Toy, **Bed**, Doll's, Brass, 29 X 18 In.	250.00
Toy, **Bed**, Doll's, Canopied, Lace Spread & Canopy, 33 X 33 X 20 In.	90.00

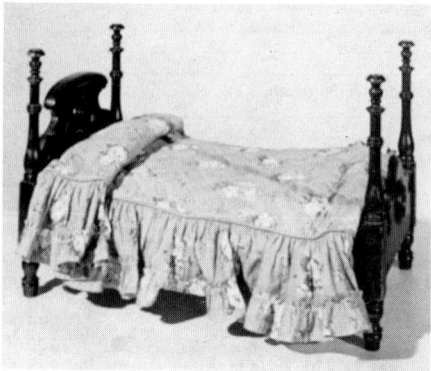

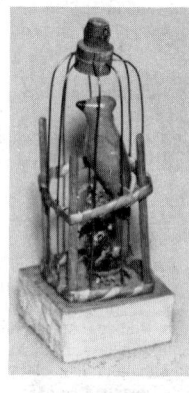

Toy, Bird,
Squeaker, 5 In.

Toy, Bed, Doll's, American, C.1890, Mahogany
(See Page 649)

Toy, Barn, Cow & Horse, 9 1/2 X 7 In.
(See Page 649)

Toy, Bed, Doll's, Canopy, Folding, Canopy & Spread, 13 In.	27.50
Toy, Bed, Doll's, Double Decker, Wooden, Strombecker, For 8 In. Doll	8.00
Toy, Bed, Doll's, Hardwood, Canopy, Salesman's Sample, 33 X 30 X 20 In.	90.00
Toy, Bed, Doll's, Maple, Hickory Rails, Turned Posts, C.1840, 26 In.	4.00
Toy, Bed, Doll's, Victorian, Brass, Bedding, 22 In.	45.00
Toy, Bed, Doll's, Victorian, Walnut, Bedding, 22 In.	38.00
Toy, Bed, Doll's, Wooden, Canopy, Spread, Sham, & Canopy, C.1950, 15 X 12 In.	25.00
Toy, Bed, Doll's, 4 Poster, Wooden, Strombecker, For 8 In. Doll	8.50
Toy, Bed, Dollhouse, Brass	9.50
Toy, Bedroom Set, Tootsie Toy, 3 Piece	12.50
Toy, Beetle, Windup, Tin, Lehmann	50.00
Toy, Beetle, Wings Flap Up & Down, Friction, Lithographed, Tin, Japan, Pre-War	2.00
Toy, Bellringer, Dancing Girl & Boy, Watrous Mfg.Co., Conn., Iron	325.00
Toy, Bicycle, see Bicycle	
Toy, Bird, Squeaker, 5 In. *Illus*	135.00
Toy, Block Set, Building, Schoenhut, Dated 1927, Original Box	35.00
Toy, Boat, Fishing, Pole & 5 Fish, Wooden, Keystone, 12 In.	7.00
Toy, Boat, Spring Wind Motor, Bavaria, 8 In.	45.00
Toy, Bomb, Dog's Head, Long Nose, Spring, Nickeled, Iron, 2 In.	75.00
Toy, Bomb, Powder Keg, Nickeled, Iron, 1 1/2 In.	100.00
Toy, Bombo The Monk, Windup, Lithographed, Tin, Unique Art, 10 In.	36.50
Toy, Bombo, The Monk, Windup, Lithographed, Tin, Unique Art, 6 In.	36.50
Toy, Bomb, Chinaman, Single Face, Iron, 1876, 1 1/2 In.	75.00
Toy, Book, Coloring, Presidents Of The U.S., Planters Peanut, 1950s	5.00
Toy, Bow & Arrow Set, Little Beaver, From Red Ryder, Wooden	9.00
Toy, Boy Skier, Windup, Tin, Chein	22.00
Toy, Bubbling Boy, Windup, Lithographed, Tin, Japan, 7 1/2 In.	7.50
Toy, Buggy, Doll's, Wicker, Marked Germany	8.00
Toy, Bunny Pushing Wagon, Wooden Wheels, Lithographed, Tin, Chein	7.00
Toy, Bus Terminal, Lithographed, Hardboard & Celluloid, Keystone	13.50
Toy, Bus, Cast Iron, Hubley, 8 In.	20.00
Toy, Bus, Coast To Coast, Cast Iron, Arcade, 10 In.	70.00

Toy, Bus, Double Deck, Cast Iron, Rubber Wheels, Painted, 9 In.Long	100.00
Toy, Bus, Fageol, Duel Wheels, Arcade, 12 1/2 In.	145.00
Toy, Bus, Greyhound, A Century Of Progress, Arcade, 10 In.	40.00
Toy, Bus, Greyhound, A Century Of Progress, Arcade, 12 In.	45.00
Toy, Bus, Greyhound, Arcade, 9 In.	55.00
Toy, Bus, Liberty, Driver, Friction, Red, Black Trim, Green Wheels, Marx, 5 In.	30.00
Toy, Bus, Solid Nickeled Wheels, Red, Gilt Trim, Cast Iron, Arcade, 8 In.	85.00
Toy, Bus, Sun Rubber, 1939	5.00
Toy, Busy Mike, Sand, Lithographed, Tin, Chein, 7 In.	9.00
Toy, Cabin Cruiser Boat, Windup, Lithographed, Tin, Lindstrom, 15 In.	8.00
Toy, Canary Warbler, Holds Water, Slush, C.1904	2.00
Toy, Cannon, Iron, Patented 1895, 5 1/4 In.	25.00
Toy, Cap Pistol, Animated Lightning Express, Cast Iron, 5 In.	300.00
Toy, Captain Video & His Video Rangers, Space Ships, Dumont Television	11.00
Toy, Car & House Trailer, Hubley Nos.2278 & 2279	140.00
Toy, Car & Ramp, Clockwork, Technofix, Lithographed, Tin, Germany, 1948	23.00
Toy, Car, Chrysler Airflow, Tin, Cast Iron, Hubley, 4 1/2 In.	35.00
Toy, Car, Coupe, Green, Cast Iron, C.1920, 5 In.	35.00
Toy, Car, FEX1111, Windup, Metal, Schuco, U.S.Zone Germany, 6 In.	7.50
Toy, Car, Fire Chief, Hoge, 15 In.	60.00
Toy, Car, Ford Coupe, Rumble Seat, Arcade No.116	80.00
Toy, Car, Ford Sedan, Nickel Spoke Wheels, Green, Cast Iron, Arcade, 5 In.	120.00
Toy, Car, G-Man Pursuit, Cast Iron, Marx, 15 In.	65.00
Toy, Car, Jaguar, XK140, Metal, Tootsie Toy, 5 In.	4.75
Toy, Car, Leaping Lena, Clockwork, Ferdinand Strauss, C.1922	95.00
Toy, Car, Mercedes 190 SL, Metal, Tootsie Toy, 5 In.	4.75
Toy, Car, Model T Ford, Painted, Cast Iron, Arcade	34.00
Toy, Car, Model T Ford, 4 Door, Cast Iron, Arcade, 6 In.	45.00
Toy, Car, Monorail, Windup, Circular Track, Lithographed, Tin, Germany, 5 In.	23.50
Toy, Car, Nash, Red & Yellow, 4 Door, Tin	6.00
Toy, Car, Porsche, Red, Metal, Tootsie Toy, 5 In.	4.75
Toy, Car, Race, Hubley No.2241, 7 1/2 In.	45.00
Toy, Car, Racer, Cast Iron, Hubley, 6 3/4 In.	30.00
Toy, Car, Racer, Silver Bullet, Patent 1/26/25, 25 1/2 In.	65.00
Toy, Car, Railway, N.Y.C., Black, Barclay, 1 1/2 In.	2.00
Toy, Car, Roadster, Friction, Rubber Wheels, Lithographed, Tin, Marx, 11 In.	8.00
Toy, Car, Roadster, Windup, Lithographed, Tin, Marx, 6 In.	7.25
Toy, Car, Sedan, Red, Cast Iron, C.1929, 4 1/4 In.	35.00
Toy, Car, Studebaker Electric, 1910, Plastic, Revell, C.1950	4.50
Toy, Car, Taxi, Yellow, Arcade No.3	45.00
Toy, Car, Touring, Cast Iron, A.C.Williams, 9 1/2 In.	385.00
Toy, Car, Uncle Wiggily, Painted, Windup, Tin, Howard Garis, 1935	28.00
Toy, Car, Whoopee, Clockwork, Tin, Marx	35.00
Toy, Car, Yellow, Black Running Board, Cast Iron, Wyandotte, 5 In.	30.00
Toy, Cart, Munitions, 2 Mule, Negro Driver, Iron, Hubley	750.00
Toy, Cash Register, Benjamin Franklin, Tin, South Bend Mfg.Co., 7 1/2 In.	75.00
Toy, Cash Register, Cooper, 8 Button, Embossed, U.S. Shield, Kamkap	39.00
Toy, Cash Register, Tom Thumb	10.00
Toy, Cement Mixer, Painted, Jaeger	75.00
Toy, Chair, Doll, Pine, 6 1/2 In.High, Pair	10.00
Toy, Chandelier, Dollhouse, Milk Glass Globes	12.00
Toy, Charleston Trio, Windup, Tin, Marx, C.1920	175.00
Toy, Charlie McCarthy, Benzine Buggy, Mechanical, Tin, Marx, 7 In., 1938	100.00
Toy, Charlie McCarthy, Tin, Windup, Marx, C.1930	40.00
Toy, Chest, Cedar, Doll's, Metal Lock & Key, 4 Feet, 6 1/2 X 3 1/2 In.	6.50
Toy, Chicken, Lays Eggs When Handle Is Turned, Metal, Baldwin Mfg.Co.	13.00
Toy, Chicken, Windup, Lithographed, Tin, Chein, 4 In.	8.75
Toy, Church, Musical, Chein	20.00
Toy, Church, Wooden, Lithographed, Keystone, To Assemble, 11 X 8 In.	8.75
Toy, Circus Set, Bisque, Occupied Japan, 10 Piece	10.00
Toy, Circus, Hardboard & Wood, Painted, National Playthings, 1946	6.75
Toy, Circus, Humpty-Dumpty, Animals & Tent, Schoenhut, 13 Pieces	7.00
Toy, Climbing Monkey, Lehmann, 1903, Original Box	12.00 To 95.00
Toy, Clown The Magician, Battery Operated, Cragstan	26.50
Toy, Clown Walks On Hands, Windup, Lithographed, Tin, Chein, 5 In.	15.00
Toy, Coffee Grinder, see Coffee Grinder	

Toy, Construction Camp Set, Lithographed, Tin, Marx, Original Box	17.00
Toy, Contractor's Wagon, Cast Iron	120.00
Toy, Couch, Doll's, Gold Upholstering, Wooden Frame, 14 In.	45.00
Toy, Cow, Calfskin, Moos When Head Is Moved, Wooden Platform	75.00 To 190.00
Toy, Cowboy, Lead, Lincoln Log Co., 2 1/2 In., 7 In Tepee Shape Box	6.00
Toy, Cradle, Doll's, Hooded, Pine, C.1860, 15 In.	20.00
Toy, Cradle, Doll's, Hooded, 20 X 10 X 7 In.	36.00
Toy, Cradle, Doll's, Swinging, Wooden, Handmade, Patchwork Quilt, 22 In.	35.00
Toy, Cradle, Doll's, Wicker, C.1850, 24 In.	40.00
Toy, Crane, Rubber Wheels, Lithographed, Metal, Wyandotte, 20 In.	9.00
Toy, Crap Shooting Gambling Man, Battery-Operated, Cragstan	21.00 To 32.50
Toy, Crap Shooting Monkey, Battery Operated, Cragstan	18.00
Toy, Crawling Beetle, Mechanical, Lehmann, 1895, 4 In.	65.00 To 100.00
Toy, Crocodile, Windup, Lithographed, Tin, Gama, U.S.Zone, Germany, 7 In.	8.50
Toy, Crone Wtih Basket, Walks, Tin, Mechanical, C.1910	200.00
Toy, Cruiser, Cabin, Clockwork, Lithographed, Tin, Lindstrom, 14 1/2 In.	15.00
Toy, Cupboard, Doll's, Oak, Hutch, Glass Door, Drawer, 18 In.	25.00
Toy, Dancing Indian, Windup, Lithographed, Tin, Lindstrom, C.1930	15.00
Toy, Dancing Man At Hollywood & Vine, Key Wind, Tin, Occupied Japan, 9 In.	12.00
Toy, Davy Crockett Indian Target Set, Lithographed, Hardboard, Keystone	11.00
Toy, Deering Thresher, Arcade, 12 In.Long, Decal	75.00
Toy, Delivery Wagon, Cast Iron, Kenton	200.00
Toy, Dining Room Furniture, Wooden, Nancy Forbes, 7 Piece	5.00
Toy, Dining Room Set, Dollhouse, Walnut, C.1930, 8 Pieces With Dishes	28.00
Toy, Dirigible Carousel, Tin, Mechanical, C.1910	300.00
Toy, Dishes, Doll's, Enameled Tin, 23 Pieces	15.00
Toy, Doll Carriage, Lithographed Scenes Of Girls With Dolls, 8 1/2 In.	35.00
Toy, Doll, see Doll	
Toy, Dollhouse, Colonial, 1930s Style, Lithographed, Cardboard, 19 In.	8.50
Toy, Dollhouse, Jefferson Manor, Lithographed, Masonite, Borgfeldt, C.1940	23.50
Toy, Dollhouse, Lithographed Cardboard, 1914, Collapsible, 20 X 14 In.	18.00
Toy, Donald Duck, Windup, Plastic, Mavco Products	15.00
Toy, Donkey Cart, Cast Iron, Hubley	220.00
Toy, Donkey, Stuffed, Cast Iron Wheels, Glass Eyes, 12 In.Long	35.00
Toy, Dopey, Eyes Move, Tin, Marx, 8 In.High	100.00
Toy, Dresser, Doll's, Hankies, 8 In.	25.00
Toy, Dresser, Doll's, Oak, 3 Drawer, Mirror, 10 In.	25.00
Toy, Dresser, Doll's, 3 Drawer, Hanging Side, Mirror, 15 X 6 In.	50.00
Toy, Dump Truck, Windup, Metal, Marx, 9 In.	9.00
Toy, Easter Band Parade, 6 Bisque Chicks With Instruments, Japan	12.00
Toy, Easter Egg, Musical, Mattel	3.00
Toy, Egg Laying Goose, Windup, Lithographed, Tin, Linemar, 9 In.	12.50
Toy, El Toro And The Bull, Battery Operated, Lithographed, Tin, Cragstan	22.50
Toy, Elephant, Nodding, Celluloid, Gray, Blanket On Back, 6 1/2 In.Long	12.00
Toy, Elmer, The Elephant, Rubber, W.D.E. Seberling	25.00
Toy, Elsie, The Borden Cow, Wooden, Jointed, Barn Shaped Box, 6 In.	10.00
Toy, Engine, Airplane, Stunt Model, Fox 35	25.00
Toy, Engine, Marx, No.1998, Union Pacific	20.00
Toy, Engine, Steam, Weeden, Wick In Tin Container, Wheel, C.1930, 7 In.	25.00
Toy, Engine, Train, Lionel, No.225, Diesel, Blue	5.00
Toy, Engine, Train, Lionel, No.1055, Diesel, The Texas Special, Red	5.00
Toy, Engine, Train, Lionel, No.1095, Diesel, Twin, 2 In Box	12.00
Toy, Engine, Train, Marx, No.666	8.00
Toy, Engine, Train, Marx, No.1829	20.00
Toy, Express Wagon Drawn By Goat, Iron, Driver	45.00
Toy, Farm Set, Hard Rubber, Arcor, 17 Piece	12.50
Toy, Farm Set, Metal, Tootsie Toy, 7 Piece	26.50
Toy, Farm Set, Rubber Animals, Lithographed, Tin, Marx	11.00
Toy, Finnegan, Windup, Lithographed, Tin, Unique Art	38.50
Toy, Fire Engine Pumper, Cast Iron, Turner Toys, 15 In.	50.00
Toy, Fire Engine, Hubley No.504	45.00
Toy, Fire Engine, Hubley No.526, 10 1/2 In.	50.00
Toy, Fire Engine, Pumper, 2 Horse, Red, Wilkins, 19 In.	90.00
Toy, Fire Engine, Pumper, 2 White Horses, Silver, Dent, 21 In.	155.00
Toy, Fire Engine, Steam Pumper, 3 Horse, Cast Iron, Dent, 21 In.	105.00
Toy, Fire Pumper, Steam, 3 Horse, Iron, Carpenter, 1880	450.00

Toy, Fort Superior, Rifle By Daisy, Lithographed, Tin, 23 X 17 In.	12.50
Toy, Fox & Duck, Tin, Mechanical, C.1910	260.00
Toy, Fred Flintstone, Riding Dino, Windup, Lithographed, Tin, Marx, 9 In.	12.00
Toy, G.I.Joe & His K-9 Pups, Windup, Lithographed, Tin, Unique Art	35.00
Toy, G.I.Joe In His Jouncing Jeep, Windup, Lithographed, Tin, Unique Art	40.00
Toy, Game, see Game	
Toy, Garage, Lithographed, Tin, Marx, 9 X 6 In.	6.75
Toy, Gas Pump, Tin, Old Style, 7 1/2 In.High	15.00
Toy, Gertie The Galloping Goose, Tin, Windup, 1930s	35.00
Toy, Good Time Charlie, Tin, Lithographed, Battery Operated	23.50
Toy, Goose, Windup, Tin, Unique Art Co., 10 In.	42.00
Toy, Guitar, Mickey Mouse, Plastic, Marx, 19 In.	7.00
Toy, Gun, see also Buck Rogers, Gun, Roy Rogers, Gun, Gene	
Autry, Gun	
Toy, Gun, Aeromatic Glider, Shoots Wood Planes, Metal, 9 In.	6.00
Toy, Gun, Aeromatic Glider, Steel	7.00
Toy, Gun, American Boy, Metal, Dated Nov.1919, 5 1/2 In.	6.50
Toy, Gun, Beckwith-Chandler Co., High Grade Varnishes, Nickel Plate	125.00
Toy, Gun, Blank Shooter, Cast Iron, Kenton	15.00
Toy, Gun, Cap, Big Bill, Cast Iron, Kenton, 6 In.	7.00
Toy, Gun, Cap, Big Bill, Embossed, Cast Iron	7.50
Toy, Gun, Cap, Big Chief, Spur Trigger, 6 Sided Barrel, Iron, 3 1/2 In.	20.00
Toy, Gun, Cap, Border Patrol, Marked K, Roll Type	6.50
Toy, Gun, Cap, Bronco	5.00
Toy, Gun, Cap, Colt, 1880, 5 1/2 In.	20.00
Toy, Gun, Cap, Cowboy, Spur Trigger, Iron, 3 3/4 In.	20.00
Toy, Gun, Cap, Dandy Police, 38, Revolving Cylinder, Iron, Hubley, 6 In.	11.75
Toy, Gun, Cap, Echo, Made In U.S.A., Single Shot, Iron, 4 1/2 In.	8.90
Toy, Gun, Cap, Flintlock Jr., Hubley	12.00
Toy, Gun, Cap, Fox, Trigger Guard Sawed Off, Iron, 5 1/2 In.	5.00
Toy, Gun, Cap, Gem, Trigger Guard, Iron, 5 1/2 In.	10.00
Toy, Gun, Cap, GIP, Trigger Guard, Iron, 5 1/2 In.	25.00
Toy, Gun, Cap, Kilgore Invisible	10.00
Toy, Gun, Cap, King, Cast Iron, 4 1/2 In.	9.00
Toy, Gun & Cap, King, Spur Trigger, Iron, 5 In.	30.00
Toy, Gun, Cap, Lasso'em Bill, Red Rubies In Handle, Cast Iron, 9 In.	20.00
Toy, Gun, Cap, Model, Trigger Guard, Iron, 1890, 5 1/2 In.	10.00
Toy, Gun, Cap, NAP, Spur Trigger, Iron, 4 1/4 In.	25.00
Toy, Gun, Cap, Pal, Hubley	7.50
Toy, Gun, Cap, Pet, Trigger Guard, Iron, 4 1/2 In.	20.00
Toy, Gun, Cap, Pluch, Spur Trigger, Iron, 4 In.	20.00
Toy, Gun, Cap, Ranger, Repeater, Metal, 8 In.	4.50
Toy, Gun, Cap, Ranger, Takes Roll Of Caps, Iron, 5 1/2 In.	11.75
Toy, Gun, Cap.Scout, Trigger Guard, Iron, 1900, 7 In.	20.00
Toy, Gun, Cap, Smith & Wesson, Cast Iron, 6 In.	15.00
Toy, Gun, Cap, Smith & Wesson, 3 1/2 In.	7.00
Toy, Gun, Cap, Stallion 38, Repeater, Metal, Nichols, 10 In.	4.50
Toy, Gun, Cap, Texan, Jr., Repeater, Gold Plated, Hubley, 1957, Pair	8.75
Toy, Gun, Cap, Texan, Jr., Repeater, Metal, Hubley, 10 In.	6.00
Toy, Gun, Cap, Texan, 38, Hubley	5.00
Toy, Gun, Cap, Texas Ranger, Repeater, Die Cast Metal, Fancy Grips, 9 In.	7.00
Toy, Gun, Cap, The Lone Rider, Buzz Henry, Metal, 8 In.	6.50
Toy, Gun, Cap, Wild Bill Hickok, Repeater, Bronzed Handle, Die Cast, 10 In.	7.50
Toy, Gun, Clicker, American Boy, 1919	10.00
Toy, Gun, Cody Colt, Automatic, Paper Buster, Plastic Steer's Head, 1940s	17.00
Toy, Gun, Combat, Windup, Lithographed, Tin, Marx, 7 In.	7.25
Toy, Gun, Fiber Dummy, Army 45, Holster	4.00
Toy, Gun, Fiber Dummy, Far West Ranger, Holster	4.00
Toy, Gun, G-Man Automatic, Clockwork, C.1935, Marx	12.00 To 20.00
Toy, Gun, Hubley, Flintlock, 5 1/2 In.	3.75
Toy, Gun, Machine, Hand Crank, Lithographed, Tin, 21 In.	5.50
Toy, Gun, Paper Shooter, Super Nu-Matic, Steel	7.00
Toy, Gun, Pet, White Metal	3.00
Toy, Gun, Spitfire, Cast Iron, Stevens	12.00
Toy, Gun, Spitfire, Hip, Nichols, 8 1/2 In.	4.50
Toy, Gun, Spud, Cossman, Metal, 6 In.	3.75

Toy, Gun, Stallion 32, Repeater, 6 Shooter, Metal, Nichols	5.75
Toy, Gun, Water, Tin, Occupied Japan	2.00
Toy, Ham & Sam Piano, Keywind, Strauss, 1921	25.00
Toy, Hansom Cab, Cast Iron, Dent No.57	95.00
Toy, Happy Hooligan, Windup, Tin, Chein, King Features, 1932	150.00
Toy, Happy Hooligan Nodder, Kenton, Cast Iron, 1911	1100.00
Toy, Happy Hooligan Police Patrol, Cast Iron, Kenton, C.1910	4100.00
Toy, Happy, The Dancer, Tin Puppet, C.1910, 10 In.	15.00
Toy, Harold Lloyd Figure, Mechanical, Tin, Marx	200.00 To 255.00
Toy, Hay Loader, Wooden, Rubber Wheels, 23 In.Long	14.00
Toy, Hen, Mechanical, Lays Eggs, Baldwin	12.00
Toy, Hercules Ferris Wheel, Disney Characters, Tin, Windup, 17 In., Chein	47.50
Toy, High Chair, Doll's, Pine, Lifting Tray, C.1880, 15 In.	20.00
Toy, Hobbyhorse, Carved & Painted Wood, Leather Saddle, C.1850, 43 In.	225.00
Toy, Hobbyhorse, Painted Wood, Leather Saddle, Rockers, 41 1/2 In.	150.00
Toy, Hobbyhorse, Wooden, Painted White, Leather Fittings, 38 In.	90.00
Toy, Hometown Movie Theatre, Lithographed, Tin, C.1920	13.75
Toy, Hook & Ladder Outfit, Lithographed Paper On Wood, C.1890	1500.00
Toy, Hopping Frog, Japan, 1930	20.00
Toy, Horse & Buggy, Clockwork, American Toy Co., C.1875	1500.00
Toy, Horse-Drawn Street Cleaner, Cast Iron, Wilkens	1050.00
Toy, Horseless Carriage, Key Wind, Tin, DRGM Germany	85.00
Toy, Huckleberry Hound, Knickerbocker, 1958, 18 In.	9.50
Toy, Ice Wagon, 2 Horses, Driver, Hubley, Cast Iron	135.00
Toy, Indian Doing War Dance, Windup, Lithographed, Tin, Lindstrom, 1930s	15.00
Toy, Indian, Lead, Made In Japan, C.1936, 2 1/2 In., Set Of 5	6.50
Toy, Jack-In-The-Box, Popeye, Matell, 1951	8.00
Toy, Jazzbo Jim Dancer, Mechanical, Tin, Strauss, 1921, 10 In.	100.00 To 150.00
Toy, Jeep, Metal, Tootsie Toy	1.75
Toy, Jeep, Willys, 4 Characters, Plastic, Walt Disney, 1940s	20.00
Toy, Jeep, 3 Soldiers, Lithographed, Tin, Arnold, Germany, 7 In.	13.50
Toy, Jenny The Baling Mule, Tin, Mechanical, C.1920	75.00
Toy, Jocko, The Climbing Monkey, Lithographed, Tin, Linemar, 7 In.	7.00
Toy, Jolly Joe, GI In Jeep, Windup, Tin, Marx	30.00
Toy, Jumbo The Elephant, 4 Rubber Wheels, Composition, Hubley, 6 In.	9.50
Toy, Jumbo, The Circus Elephant, Rubber Wheels, Composition, Hubley, 5 In.	9.00
Toy, Jumping Jeep, Windup, Lithographed, Tin, Marx	20.00 To 26.50
Toy, Keno, Goose	*Illus* 450.00
Toy, Kiddie Kar, Red, Wooden, Tin Wheels, Rubber Tires, 17 In.	20.00
Toy, Kiddie Kart, Wooden, For 2 Year Old, C.1900	9.50
Toy, Kitchen Appliances Set, Little Miss, Linemar, 4 Piece	7.50
Toy, Lansing Road Grader, Metal, Slick Toy, 16 In.	12.50
Toy, Lantern, Roy Rogers, Ranch, Battery-Operated, Lithographed, Tin, 8 In.	12.00
Toy, Li'l Abner Band, Windup, Tin, Lehmann	75.00
Toy, LoLo, Windup, Tin, Lehmann	95.00
Toy, Locomotive, Pioneer Express, Tin, 24 In.	22.00

Toy, Keno, Goose

Toy, Lone Ranger Ranch, Lithographed, Rubber, Vinyl, & Tin, Marx	15.00
Toy, MacGregor, Scotchman, Batter	
Toy, Mail Plane, Windup, Tin, Strauss	36.00
Toy, Mallard Duck, Windup, Tin, U.S.Zone, Germany, 5 In.	15.00
Toy, Man At Grindstone, Tin, Mechanical	15.00
Toy, Man On Motorcycle, Tin, Mechanical, 1914	150.00
Toy, Man On Trapeze, Windup, Lithographed, Tin, Wyandotte, 9 In.	19.00
Toy, Masuyama, Rickshaw, Windup, Lehmann	400.00
Toy, Mickey Mouse, see Mickey Mouse	
Toy, Miss Friday, The Typist, Battery-Operated, Lithographed, Tin	16.00
Toy, Model Kit, Oil Tanker, Wooden, Ideal Airplane Co., 14 In.	5.75
Toy, Model Kit, Submarine Chaser, Wooden, Ideal Airplane Co., 14 In.	5.75
Toy, Modern Farm Set, Rubber Accessories, Lithographed, Tin, Marx, C.1950	11.50
Toy, Monkey In Cowboy Outfit & Machine Gun, Windup, Lithographed, Tin, Japan	6.00
Toy, Monkey With Cymbals & Drum, Mechanical, Tin, 8 In.High, C.1900	37.50
Toy, Monkey, Zippo, Mechanical, Climbs String, Marx	55.00
Toy, Monkeys Swinging, Pull, Cast Iron	500.00
Toy, Monorail Car & Track, Windup, Lithographed, Tin, Germany, 1945	20.00
Toy, Moth On Wheels, Windup, Tin, Plastic Wings, Occupied Japan	10.00
Toy, Mother's Little Helper Kitchen Tools, 5 Piece, 1930s	25.00
Toy, Moto Run, Lithographed, Tin, Marx, 1949, 5 Vehicles, Tunnel, Toll House	35.00
Toy, Motor Ship, "United States, " Friction, Lithographed, Tin, Japan, 6 In.	3.00
Toy, Motorcycle Cop, Blue, Cast Iron, Champion, 7 In.	48.00
Toy, Motorcycle Cop, Red, Black Rubber Tires, Cast Iron, Made In U.S.A.	25.00
Toy, Motorcycle Cop, Sidecar, Blue, Red Sidecar, Cast Iron, Champion, 6 In.	45.00
Toy, Motorcycle, Cast Iron, Champion, 5 In.	20.00
Toy, Mouse, Windup, Schuco, U.S.Zone, Germany	6.00
Toy, Mule, Wood, Schoenhut, 8 In.Long	25.00
Toy, Musician & Dancer, Clockwork, Italian, C.1900	375.00
Toy, Naughty Boy, Windup, Lehmann, 1910	375.00
Toy, Naughty Duck, Chases A Bee, Windup, Cragstan	3.75
Toy, Naughty Duck, Chases Butterfly, Windup, Cragstan	4.00
Toy, Negro Dancer, Windup, Occupied Japan	32.50
Toy, Old Witch, Pull, Animated	35.00
Toy, Overland Circus Wagon, Cast Iron, Kenton	160.00
Toy, Oxcart, Driver, Hubley, 1920	115.00
Toy, Packard Patrician Auto, Tootsie Toy, Original Box	7.25
Toy, Paddy's Pride, Tin, Mechanical, Walter Stock, German, C.1900	185.00
Toy, Peacock, Walking With Squeak, German, 1907	75.00
Toy, Peacock, Tin, Mechanical	75.00
Toy, Pecking Parrot, Windup, Lithographed, Tin, Lindstrom, 5 1/2 In.	6.50
Toy, Penguin, Fur On Tin, Mechanical, Japan, 1930	35.00
Toy, Piano, Bliss, Scenes Of Cherubs	50.00
Toy, Piano, Mary Lu, Walnut, J.C.Penney Co.	30.00
Toy, Piano, Player, Electric, 1 Roll	10.00
Toy, Piano, Schoenhut, Baby Grand	25.00
Toy, Piano, Schoenhut, Baby Grand, Wooden, Red Paint, 8 X 10 X 5 1/2 In.	7.50
Toy, Piano, Schoenhut, Baby Grand, Wooden, 11 1/4 X 12 1/2 X 5 1/4 In.	11.00
Toy, Piano, Schoenhut, Ivory, Schoenhut In Gold, 20 X 16 1/2 In.	50.00
Toy, Piano, Schoenhut, 8 Keys	9.50
Toy, Piano, Schoenhut, 15 Keys, 15 1/2 X 9 1/2 X 7 1/2 In.	40.00
Toy, Pig, Windup, Tin, West Germany, 5 In.	15.00
Toy, Pinocchio, Mechanical, Walt Disney, 1939	32.00
Toy, Playpen, Lithographed, Tin, Chein, 7 X 7 X 4 In.	6.75
Toy, Pluto Pop-Up Kritter, Windup, Fisher Price	12.00
Toy, Polar Bear, Clockwork, Plush, Glass Eyes	50.00
Toy, Polar Bear, Windup, Plush Covering, Glass Eyes, Lehman	25.00
Toy, Pony, Mechanical, Fur Covered, C.1920	50.00
Toy, Poodle, Gray, Jointed, Glass Eyes, Leather Nose, Steiff, 18 X 15 In.	15.00
Toy, Porter Pushing Baggage Cart, German, 1910	125.00
Toy, Printing Set, Favorite Funnies, Stamperkraft, 1935, 14 Stamps	50.00
Toy, Projector, Western Movie, Spring Loaded, Mattel, C.1947, 8mm. Film	10.00
Toy, Puzzle Blocks, McLauglin, C.1890	130.00
Toy, Rabbit & Cart, Kenton, 5 In.	60.00
Toy, Racer, Cast Iron, Hubley, No.179, 5 1/4 In.	25.00
Toy, Railroad Set, Windup, Lithographed, Tin, Ranger, 3 Cars & Track, Etc.	15.00

Toy, Railroad Transfer, Clockwork, George Brown, C.1870	5500.00
Toy, Rake Hay, Dump, Cast Iron, Arcade, 5 In.	35.00
Toy, Rake, Hay, Dump, Arcade, 7 In.	65.00
Toy, Rattle, Baby's, Sterling Silver, Pearl Ring, Little Boy Blue	45.00
Toy, Rifle, Air, Daisy, Cast Iron & Brass, 31 In.	65.00
Toy, Rifle, Gene Autry, Cork Popping, Wooden Handle, 1946	6.50
Toy, Road Construction Set, No.6000, Metal, Tootsie Toy, 11 Piece	30.00
Toy, Road Construction Set, Tootsie Toy, 1950s, Boxed Set	19.00
Toy, Roadster, Windup, Lithographed, Tin, Marx	9.75
Toy, Roller Coaster With Car, Tin, Windup, Chein, 19 X 19 In.	35.00
Toy, Roller Coaster, Jet, Clockwork, Wolverine	20.00
Toy, Roller Skates, Patent, Richard Lahey, April 30, 1895	35.00
Toy, Rooster Pulling A Cart, Lithographed, Metal, Wyandotte, 8 In.	4.75
Toy, Rooster, Tin, Mechanical	20.00
Toy, Roy Rogers Rodeo Ranch, Lithographed, Tin, Marx	10.50
Toy, Royal Dressing Table, Doll's, Petite Princess Fantasy	6.50
Toy, Running Duck, Tin, Mechanical, C.1910	55.00
Toy, Sadiron, Child's, 4 1/4 In.	4.95
Toy, Sand, Oriental, Boy Pops In And Out	300.00
Toy, Scale, Confectioner's, Penny Toy, Tin, Germany, 3 In.	3.75
Toy, Scales, Toledo, Cast Iron, 4 X 4 In.	22.00
Toy, Sedan, Black Paint, Cast Iron, Arcade, 5 In.	40.00
Toy, Sedan, Green, Gold Trim, Tin, German, 3 1/2 In.	25.00
Toy, See-Saw, Clockwork, Ives, C.1875	4000.00
Toy, See-Saw, Woman Pops Out Of Chimney, Clockwork	2100.00
Toy, Sewing Machine, Betsy Ross	15.00
Toy, Sewing Machine, Child's, Singer	12.00 To 20.00
Toy, Sewing Machine, Child's, Stichwell, Floor Model	65.00
Toy, Sewing Machine, Little Miss, Lindstrom	10.00
Toy, Ship, Tootsie Toy, 4 1/2 In.	6.00
Toy, Shoe, Doll's, White Leather, Buckle On Pointed Toe, Heel, Pair	22.00
Toy, Shuttling Switcher Freight Train, Battery Operated, Tin, Cragstan	20.00
Toy, Singing Canary, Celluloid & Tin, Occupied Japan, 5 In.	6.25
Toy, Skater Bunny, Windup, Cragstan, 9 In.	4.50
Toy, Skeeter Duck, Windup, Lithographed, Tin, Lindstrom	23.50
Toy, Ski Boy, Windup, Lithographed, Tin, Chein, C.1940	21.50
Toy, Ski Boy, Windup, Lithographed, Tin, Chein, 8 In.	21.00 To 26.00
Toy, Ski Jumper, Lithographed, Wood & Tin, Wolverine, 26 In.	22.00
Toy, Sled, Child's, Handmade, Hex Signs	48.00
Toy, Sleigh, Child's, Oak Rocker, Beads Across	20.00
Toy, Sleigh, Child's, White, Stenciled, Brass Bells	150.00
Toy, Slingshot, Zip-Zip, Patent 1918	2.50
Toy, Sofa, Chair, & Footstool, Tootsie Toy, C.1930	9.00
Toy, Soldier Set, The Foreign Legion, Lead, Hand-Painted, 7 Piece	69.00
Toy, Soldier, Composition, Leyla, Germany, 3 In., Set Of 8	16.50
Toy, Soldiers On Parade, Milton Bradley, C.1910	15.00
Toy, Space Set, Rex Mars, Lithographed, Tin, Marx, 1950s	11.50
Toy, Speed Racer, Windup, Lithographed, Tin, Marx	22.50
Toy, Speedboat, Clockwork, Lithographed, Tin, Chein, 7 In.	10.00
Toy, Speedboat, Clockwork, World War II, Wood Body, Keystone, 10 In.	15.00
Toy, Speedboy Delivery, Tin, Windup, Marx	35.00
Toy, Spinet Piano & Stool, Wood, Schoenhut	85.00
Toy, Station House, Lionel, Tin	20.00
Toy, Steam Boiler, Electric, Weeden, 9 In.	40.00
Toy, Steam Engine, Live, Cast Iron	725.00
Toy, Steam Engine, Weeden, No.648, Iron & Brass	35.00
Toy, Steam Shovel, Iron, Swivels, 14 In.High, 20 In.Long	55.00
Toy, Stove, Acme, Iron, 6 Burners, Pots & Pans	84.00
Toy, Stove, Dollhouse, Baby, Iron, 2 3/4 X 2 1/4 In.	45.00
Toy, Stove, Eagle, Iron, 4 1/4 X 10 In.	75.00
Toy, Stove, Gas Range, Royal, High Back, Cast Iron, 5 X 3 In.	15.00
Toy, Stove, Gas Range, 2 Burner, Iron, Royal, 4 1/2 X 3 1/4 In.	9.95
Toy, Stove, Little Orphan Annie, Large Size	22.00
Toy, Stove, Nuremberg, 2 Ovens, 5 Burners, Utensils, Tin, 9 1/2 X 9 In.	45.00
Toy, Stove, Royal, Iron, 4 X 8 In.	75.00
Toy, Suitcase, Doll's, Drawer, Hardboard, 16 X 9 1/4 X 9 In.	20.00

Toy, Surrey, Lancaster, Hubley No.58	45.00
Toy, Surrey, 1 Seat, Lancaster, Hubley No.174	90.00
Toy, Sweeping Mammy, Windup, Lithographed, Tin, Lindstrom, C.1930	52.00
Toy, Swinging Girl, Animated, Pull, Bisque Head Doll	600.00
Toy, Swinging Girl, Clockwork, Ives, C.1880	850.00
Toy, Table & 4 Chairs, Dollhouse, Wooden	3.00
Toy, Table, Dressing, Royal, Petite Princess Fantasy Furniture	6.50
Toy, Tailspin Pug, Terrier Dog, Windup, Lithographed, Tin, U.S., 4 1/2 In.	5.00
Toy, Talking Railroad Station, Lithographed, Hardboard, Keystone	10.50
Toy, Tank, Army, Friction, Occupied Japan, 2 In.	1.75
Toy, Tank, U.S., Hard Rubber, White Rubber Wheels, Sun Rubber, 6 X 5 In.	7.25
Toy, Tank, World War I, Clockwork, Popup Soldier, Tin, Marx	25.00
Toy, Taxi, Tricky, Marx	10.00
Toy, Taxi, Windup, Rubber Wheels, Lithographed, Tin, Lupor, 7 In.	6.00
Toy, Tea Set, Child's, Children Design, Tin, Ohio Art Co., 13 Piece	20.00
Toy, Teapot, Child's, Tin, 3 1/2 In.	27.00
Toy, Teddy Bear, German, Buff Color, Stuffed With Excelsior, 23 In.	25.00
Toy, Teddy Bear, Steiff, C.1930, 4 In.	10.00
Toy, Telephone Boss, Bear At Desk, Battery-Operated, Linemar	23.50
Toy, Telephone, see Disneyana, Telephone	
Toy, The Blacksmith Bear, Battery-Operated	16.50
Toy, Thomas Concert, Clockwork, Animated, C.1890	300.00
Toy, Tin Lizzie, Windup	60.00
Toy, Tin Trolley Car, C.1880	500.00
Toy, Tip Top Porter, Tin, Mechanical, C.1920	80.00
Toy, Tortoise Carrying Baby Turtle, Windup, Lithographed, Tin, Japan	5.75
Toy, Tractor, Avery, Hubley, 4 3/4 In.	45.00
Toy, Tractor, Blue, White Tires, Cast Iron, Arcade, 5 1/4 In.	30.00
Toy, Tractor, Caterpillar, Arcade No.269	315.00
Toy, Tractor, Clockwork, Rubber Treads, Gray & Red, Patent 1916, Woodhaven	22.00
Toy, Tractor, Driver, Balloon Tires, Green, Cast Iron, Allis-Chalmers, 13 In	100.00
Toy, Tractor, Driver, Gray, Red Wheels, Cast Iron, Fordson, 5 3/4 In.	50.00
Toy, Tractor, Driver, Red, Tires, Cast Iron, Marked HR, 5 1/2 In.	30.00
Toy, Tractor, Driver, Rubber Tires, Red, Cast Iron, Arcade, 4 1/2 In.	30.00
Toy, Tractor, Farm, McCormick-Deering, Arcade, No.10-20	50.00
Toy, Tractor, Red, White Tires, Cast Iron, Arcade, 5 3/4 In.	30.00
Toy, Tractor, Rubber Wheels, Diecast Metal, Hubley, 12 In.	15.00
Toy, Tractor, Rubber Wheels, Metal, Hubley, 6 In.	6.50
Toy, Tractor, Spreader, Balloon Tires, Arcade	5.00
Toy, Trailer, Lonesome Pine, Oval, Marx	8.00
Toy, Train Engine & Tender, Lionel No.390, Standard Gauge	150.00
Toy, Train Set, American Flyer No.4000, Standard Gauge, 3 Piece	190.00
Toy, Train Set, American Flyer, No.307, 2 Piece	10.00
Toy, Train Set, American Flyer, O Gauge, 4 Piece	75.00
Toy, Train Set, American Flyer, Passenger, Clockwork, 4 Piece	95.00
Toy, Train Set, American Flyer, S Gauge, Red, 3 Piece	80.00
Toy, Train Set, Cor Cor, Caboose, Tank Cars, Hopper, & Tender	75.00
Toy, Train Set, Gilbert, American Flyer, 1938, 9 Piece	125.00
Toy, Train Set, Ives, Passenger, Clockwork, 5 Piece	175.00
Toy, Train Set, Ives, Passenger, O Gauge, No.3253, 4 Piece	220.00
Toy, Train Set, Lionel, Freight, Standard Gauge, No.385E, 6 Piece	495.00
Toy, Train Set, Lionel, No.212, U.S.Marine Corps, 2 Piece	10.00
Toy, Train Set, Lionel, No.249e, Gray, 2 Piece	65.00
Toy, Train Set, Lionel, No.1654, 2 Piece	15.00
Toy, Train Set, Lionel, Nos.8, 337, & 338, 3 Piece	135.00
Toy, Train Set, Marx, Key Wind, Steel, New York Central On Engine, 6 Piece	65.00
Toy, Train Set, Marx, No.666, 2 Piece	10.00
Toy, Train Set, Marx, 1927, 30 Piece	25.00
Toy, Train Set, Mary, Key Wind, C.1930, Tracks, 4 Piece	33.00
Toy, Train Set, Moto Run, Lithographed, Tin, Marx, 1949, 10 Piece	35.00
Toy, Train Set, Passenger, Diesel Engine, German, 5 Piece	79.95
Toy, Train Set, Shuttling Switcher Freight, Cragstan, 8 Piece	20.00
Toy, Train Set, The Tiny Town Train, 1880, Cardboard, Lithographed, 7 Piece	20.00
Toy, Train Set, Z Gauge, Freight, Metal Engine, 4 Cars, Track, 7 Piece	59.95
Toy, Train, Alpine Express, Windup, Lithographed, Tin, Tunnels	18.50
Toy, Train, Box Car, American Flyer No.4018, Standard Gauge	27.50

Toy, Train, Caboose, American Flyer No.4011, Standard Gauge	26.00
Toy, Train, Caboose, Lionel No.517	25.00
Toy, Train, Cattle Car, Lionel No.513, Green, Yellow Roof, Standard Gauge	20.00
Toy, Train, Dining Car, Lionel No.431, Standard Gauge	210.00
Toy, Train, Engine & Tender, American Flyer No.4671, Cast Iron	240.00
Toy, Train, Engine & Tender, Lionel No.6, N.Y.C. & H.R.R.R.	440.00
Toy, Train, Engine & Tender, Lionel No.384, Standard Gauge	135.00
Toy, Train, Engine & Tender, Lionel No.1835	250.00
Toy, Train, Engine & 2 Cars, Dent, Cast Iron, 38 In.	110.00
Toy, Train, Engine, American Flyer No.10, Windup, Cast Iron	30.00
Toy, Train, Engine, American Flyer No.3105, Blue	16.00
Toy, Train, Engine, American Flyer No.3195, Cast Iron	30.00
Toy, Train, Engine, Lionel No.2339, Wabash	45.00
Toy, Train, Engine, Lionel No.400E	525.00
Toy, Train, Engine, Lionel No.746	130.00
Toy, Train, Engine, Lionel 408E	360.00
Toy, Train, Engine, Lionel No.1120, .027 Gauge	24.50
Toy, Train, Engine, Pass Car, & Caboose, American Flyer Nos.1097 & 1120	45.00
Toy, Train, Gondola Coal Car, Lionel No.512	17.50
Toy, Train, Lightning Express Railroad Engine, Tin, Rider	27.50
Toy, Train, Lionel No.419, Baggage & Parlor Car	200.00
Toy, Train, Mail Car, Lionel No.332, Standard Gauge	20.00
Toy, Train, Observation Car, Lionel No.190	70.00
Toy, Train, Observation Car, Lionel No.490, Standard Gauge	200.00
Toy, Train, Parlor Car, Lionel No.18	60.00 To 65.00
Toy, Train, Parlor Car, Lionel No.418	170.00
Toy, Train, Pennsylvania R.R., Clockwork	120.00
Toy, Train, Pull, Wooden Wheels, Lithographed, Tin, Wolverine, 17 In.	8.00
Toy, Train, Windup, Marx, 1942, Tracks, 4 Pieces	32.50
Toy, Trolley Car, Tin, Lithographed, Chein, 8 In.	12.00
Toy, Trolley, Electric Railway, No.2 Gauge, Carlisle & Finch, C.1900	595.00
Toy, Trolley, Orange, Mechanical, Tin, Kingsbury Keene, N.H., No.784, 14 In.	110.00
Toy, Truck, see also Coca-Cola, Truck	
Toy, Truck & Trailer, Motor Express, Hubley No.2287, 8 In.	65.00
Toy, Truck, Auto Haulaway, Rubber Wheels, 1950 Cars, Metal, Structo, 21 In.	13.75
Toy, Truck, Baby, Red, Arcade, 11 In.	160.00
Toy, Truck, Cement, Die Cast, Rubber Wheels, Hubley, 10 In.	10.50
Toy, Truck, Coal, Marx, 13 In.	25.00
Toy, Truck, Dodd's Alderney Dairy, Sheet Metal, Rubber Tires, 1930s, 18 In.	45.00
Toy, Truck, Dodge, Stake-Bed, Slush, 1940s, 5 1/2 In.	7.00
Toy, Truck, Dump, Baby, Red, Arcade, 11 In.	125.00
Toy, Truck, Dump, Buddy L, Deluxe Rider, Rubber Wheels, 24 In.	20.00
Toy, Truck, Dump, Green, Rubber Tires, Cast Iron, Arcade, 13 In.	100.00
Toy, Truck, Fire Ladder, Dent, 8 1/2 In.	50.00
Toy, Truck, Fire, Battery Operated, Lithographed, Tin, Marx, 13 In.	9.00
Toy, Truck, Fire, Kenton, 15 In.	140.00
Toy, Truck, Fire, Rubber Wheels, Die Cast, Metal Masters, 10 In.	9.50
Toy, Truck, Gas & Motor Oil, Cast Iron, Champion, 8 In.	45.00
Toy, Truck, Gasoline, Iron, "Mack," 1930, 13 In.	30.00
Toy, Truck, Gasoline, Yellow, Steel Wheels, Cast Iron, C.1930, Mack, 5 In.	45.00
Toy, Truck, Hook & Ladder, Cast Iron, Turner, 15 In.	50.00
Toy, Truck, Hook & Ladder, Driver, 3 Horses, Kenton	250.00
Toy, Truck, Hook & Ladder, 2 Horse, Cast Iron, Lancaster, 28 In.	80.00
Toy, Truck, Ladder, Dent, 10 In.	35.00
Toy, Truck, Pickup, Metal, Tootsie Toy	1.75
Toy, Truck, Red & Yellow, Structo, 1911	35.00
Toy, Truck, Sand & Gravel, Lithographed, Metal, Marx, 12 In.	6.50
Toy, Truck, Shovel, Cast Iron, Hubley No.726	65.00
Toy, Truck, Stake, Barclay, 4 1/2 In.	18.00
Toy, Truck, Stake, Cast Iron Wheels, Mack, 5 In.	30.00
Toy, Truck, Stake, Ford, Cast Iron, Arcade, 7 In.	50.00 To 55.00
Toy, Truck, Stake, No.614, Cast Iron, Hubley	35.00
Toy, Truck, Stake, White Rubber Wheels, Cast Iron, Mack, 5 In.	40.00
Toy, Truck, Towing, White & Green, Buddy L, 22 In.	15.00
Toy, Truck, Water Tower, Boston, Mass., Metal, Keystone, 24 In.	37.00
Toy, Truck, Windup, Rubber Wheels, Metal, Structo, 12 In.	12.50

Toy, Truck, Wrecker, Arcade, 6 In.	60.00
Toy, Trunk, see also Trunk	
Toy, Trunk, Doll's, Camelback, Wooden, 12 X 8 X 8 In.	55.00
Toy, Trunk, see also Trunk	
Toy, Tut-Tut, Man In Car Blowing Horn, Lehmann	175.00
Toy, TV Set, see Disneyana, TV Set	
Toy, Typewriter, Dial, Marx, Original Box	14.00
Toy, Typewriter, Dial, Tin, Marx, 1930, 10 X 6 In.	22.50
Toy, Typewriter, Tom Thumb	10.00
Toy, U.S.A., Rocket Space Ship, Rubber Wheels, Friction, Lithographed, Tin	7.00
Toy, U.S.Tank, White Rubber Wheels, Hard Rubber, Sun Rubber, 6 X 5 In.	7.25
Toy, Vacation Land Airplane Ride, Windup, Lithographed, Tin, Japanese	4.75
Toy, Velocipede, Clockwork, Stevens & Brown, C.1870	400.00
Toy, Waddling Duck With Cane, Windup, Lithographed, Tin, Chein	9.75
Toy, Wagon, Contractor's Dump, 2 Horse, Dent, 15 In.	45.00
Toy, Wagon, Covered, 2 Horses, Cast Iron, Kenton	110.00
Toy, Wagon, Delivery, Horse, Kenton	125.00
Toy, Wagon, Fire Hose, 1 Horse, Iron, Carpenter, 1884	450.00
Toy, Wagon, Fire Patrol, Wikens, 12 In.	45.00
Toy, Wagon, Fire, Ladder, Cast Iron, Kenton, 12 In.	50.00
Toy, Wagon, Hook & Ladder, 2 Horse, Cast Iron, Lancaster, 25 In.	40.00
Toy, Wagon, Hook & Ladder, 3 Horse, Cast Iron, Lancaster, 28 In.	85.00
Toy, Wagon, Ice, 1 Horse, Dent, 14 In.	160.00
Toy, Wagon, Ice, 2 Horse, Dent, 12 In.	45.00
Toy, Wagon, Iron Wheels, Tin, Brown & Co., Conn., C.1870 .... Illus	5500.00
Toy, Wagon, Stake, 2 Horse, Cast Iron, Kenton, 15 In.	200.00
Toy, Wagon, Truck, 1 Horse, Dent, 16 In.	90.00
Toy, Wagon, 1 Horse, Cast Iron, Kenton No.5, 15 In.	40.00
Toy, Wagon, 1 Horse, Kenton No.3, 15 In.	85.00
Toy, Walking Peacock, Japan, 1930s	40.00
Toy, Walking Turtle, German, 1905	85.00
Toy, Walt Disney Cartoon Theatre, View Master, Metal & Plastic, Boxed	15.50
Toy, Washing Machine, Lithographed Children, Tin, Chein	15.00
Toy, Washing Machine, Wooden	24.00
Toy, Water Pump, Tin, C.1890	120.00
Toy, Whee-Wiz Auto Racer, Windup, Lithographed, Tin, Marx, C.1930, 13 In.	85.00
Toy, Whirligig, Confederate Soldier, Wooden, Carved, Painted, C.1850, 18 In.	2000.00
Toy, Whirligig, 2 Male Figures, Tin & Wood, Painted, C.1850, 12 In.	150.00
Toy, Whistle, Sergeant Preston, Steel, Brass Plated	10.00
Toy, Whistling Bird, Tin, Mechanical	45.00
Toy, Woman & Churn, Clockwork, Ives, C.1880	450.00
Toy, Woman's Rights, Clockwork, Ives, C.1880 .... Illus	1200.00
Toy, Xylophone, Pinky Lee, Boxed	7.00
Toy, Zilotone, Mechanical, Tin, Wolverine, 1930	135.00
Toy, Zulu, Windup, Tin, Lehmann	175.00
Trap, see Tool, Trap	

Treen are small wooden objects such as mugs, spoons, and bowls. The term is early English but is used in the United States in many areas.

Treen, Bowl, Carved Handles, American, C.1790, 15 1/2 In.	300.00
Treen, Bowl, Domed Base, Molded Edge & Side, C.1850, 26 In.	450.00
Treen, Bowl, Footed, 5 In. .... Illus	45.00
Treen, Bowl, Molded Edge, C.1850, 20 1/4 In.	350.00
Treen, Bowl, Molded Edge, C.1850, 22 1/2 In.	500.00
Treen, Bowl, Molded Rim, Sloping Sides, American, C.1790, 16 In.	225.00
Treen, Bowl, Pierced Handles, Oval, American, C.1790, 24 In.	750.00
Treen, Bowl, Porridge	95.00
Treen, Chalice, Maple, 7 In. .... Illus	128.00
Treen, Eggcup, Turned Maple, 2 3/4 In.	28.00
Treen, Eggcup, Turned, Pedestal	23.00
Treen, Glove Powderer, Turned	15.00
Trent Art, Tile, Olive Green Medallion, Impressed Mark, Square, 4 In.	8.00
Trenton, Tile, Bas Reliefs, Framed Medallion, Round, 4 In.	24.00

Trivets are now used to hold hot dishes. Most of the late nineteenth and early twentieth century trivets were made to hold hot irons. Iron or brass

Toy, Wagon, Iron Wheels, Tin, Brown & Co., Conn., C.1870
(See Page 659)

Toy, Woman's Rights, Clockwork,
Ives, C.1880
(See Page 659)

Treen, Bowl, Footed, 5 In.
(See Page 659)

Treen, Chalice, Maple, 7 In.
(See Page 659)

reproductions are being made of many of the old styles. The H-xx numbers
refer to the book "Trivets" by Dick Hankerson.

Trivet, Brass & Iron, M.A.C.Isaacs, Professor Of Hebrew, 12 1/4 In.	175.00
Trivet, Brass, Cast, Heart Top, Sunburst Center, 3 Peg Feet, 9 1/4 In.Long	20.00
Trivet, Brass, China, Openwork Center, Floral, 4 Footed, Square, 5 In.	4.95
Trivet, Brass, Design, Handled, 8 1/2 In.	15.00
Trivet, Brass, Flatiron, Lacy Heart, Handled, Footed, 7 1/2 X 3 1/2 In.	36.00
Trivet, Brass, Horseshoe, Eagle At Top, Clasped Hands In Center	12.75
Trivet, Brass, Marked China, Openwork Center, Flower Border, Footed, 5 In.	4.95
Trivet, Brass, 2 Inverted Hearts, Handled, 7 In.	15.00
Trivet, Brass, 4 Feet, 6 Sides, Flower Border, Openwork Center, 5 1/2 In.	7.95
Trivet, Buffalo Pottery, Blue Willow, 1918, Round, 6 In.	15.00
Trivet, Cast Iron, Colt, Rectangular, Handle, 6 1/2 In.	35.00
Trivet, Cast Iron, Vine, Rectangular, Handle, 8 In.	20.00
Trivet, Child's, Cutwork	4.50
Trivet, Hex Sign, Dutch Lacy, Cast Iron	8.50
Trivet, Iron, Bar & Holes Variant, H-75	5.95
Trivet, Iron, Bar & Holes, H-75	5.95
Trivet, Iron, Bar & Holes, H-93	5.95
Trivet, Iron, Buster Brown's Dog Tige, 3 Footed, 5 1/2 X 2 In.	22.00
Trivet, Iron, Cathedral No.6, Handled, H-37	6.95
Trivet, Iron, Chevrons, H-69	6.95
Trivet, Iron, Child's, Lacy Double Point, H-154	5.95

Trunk, English, 1672, Leather, Brass, On Stand, 45 In.

Union Porcelain Works, Vase,
Century, Firing Flaw
(See Page 662)

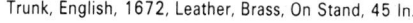

Trivet, Iron, Enterprise Mfg.Co., Phila., U.S.A.	8.00
Trivet, Iron, Ferrosteel Urn, H-121	6.95
Trivet, Iron, Geometric No.3, H-86	6.95
Trivet, Iron, Heart, Footed, Handled	14.00
Trivet, Iron, Heart, Handle, H-50	6.95
Trivet, Iron, Horseshoe & Bird, Hand Holding Heart & Quiver Of Arrows	11.75
Trivet, Iron, Horseshoe & Eagle, Good Luck, Similar To H-9	11.75
Trivet, Iron, Horseshoe With Eagle, H-9	11.75
Trivet, Iron, I Want U, Strauss Gas Iron Co., Phila., H-148	6.95
Trivet, Iron, Letter B, H-113	7.95
Trivet, Iron, Letter C, H-138	6.95
Trivet, Iron, Mule Shoe, H-89	6.95
Trivet, Iron, Octagon Waffle, H-76	6.95
Trivet, Iron, Royal, Crown & Maltese Cross, H-85	6.95
Trivet, Iron, Spider Web, H-90	4.95
Trivet, Iron, Star & Sunburst, Cleveland Foundry Co., H-122	6.95
Trivet, Iron, Target, Handled, H-55	6.95
Trivet, Iron, Triangular, 3 Curled Feet, Handle, C.1890, 9 1/4 X 3 3/4 In.	38.00
Trivet, Iron, 2 Hearts & W, Handled, 8 1/2 In.	17.00
Trivet, Iron, 4 Footed, Round, 5 In., H-70	7.95
Trivet, Masonic, Brass, 3 Feet, 9 1/2 In.Long, 1 3/8 In.High	27.50
Trivet, Silver Plate, Pairpoint, Pierced Flower & Scroll, Footed, 8 1/4 In.	25.00
Trivet, Sterling Silver Overlay On Glass, Flowers & Vines, 5 In.	28.00
Trivet, Wire, To Hold Iron, Handled, Footed, 10 X 5 In.	8.00
Trunk, Cunard Stickers On Top, C.1904, 40 X 21 1/2 X 13 In.	400.00
Trunk, Doll's, Northern Pacific Railroad Sticker, Tin, Handle, 10 In.	7.00
Trunk, English, 1672, Leather, Brass, On Stand, 45 In. *Illus*	1150.00
Trunk, Rawhide, Domed Lid, Nail Design, Dated 1784, 5 X 10 In.	40.00
Trunk, Stagecoach, American, C.1750, Wooden, Arched Lid, Black Leather, Brass	185.00
Tucker, Pitcher, Philadelphia, C.1825, Floral Bouquet, Gilding, 9 1/4 In.	425.00
Typewriter, Berwin Superior	15.00
Typewriter, Blickensderfer No.7, Wooden Carrying Case	75.00
Typewriter, Oliver, No.5	20.00
Umbrella, Black Silk, Sun, Fish Handle	18.00
Umbrella, Black Taffeta, Ruffled, Collapsible, 29 1/2 In. Opened	15.00
Umbrella, Handle, Child's, Porcelain, Portrait, Blonde Boy, Gold, Blue	23.00
Umbrella, Handle, Porcelain, Gold On Purple, Nymph & Lady, 2 1/2 In.	55.00
Umbrella, Handle, Porcelain, Young Couple On Mauve, Gilt Silver Ends, 4 In.	55.00
Umbrella, Parasol, Child's, Japanese Bamboo, Cloth	8.50
Umbrella, Parasol, Godey, Navy Silk, Collapsible Handle	40.00
Umbrella, Parasol, Patriotic, Bamboo Sticks, Paper, C.1905, 22 In. Opened	9.00
Union Porcelain Works, Plate, Oyster, Clamshell Shape, Patent 1881, 9 In.	60.00
Union Porcelain Works, Plate, Oyster, Greenpoint, Asymmetrical, 8 1/4 In.	50.00

Union Porcelain Works, Vase, Century, American History, C.1876, 22 1/4 In. 1400.00
Union Porcelain Works, Vase, Century, Firing Flaw .... *Illus* 850.00

Val St.Lambert   *Val St.Lambert Cristalleries of Belgium was founded by Messieurs*
               Kemlin and Lelievre in 1825. The company is still in operation.
Val St.Lambert, Bottle, Perfume, Cranberry, Frosted, Jewels, Cameo, 6 In. 95.00
Val St.Lambert, Bottle, Perfume, Frosted, Cranberry Floral, Silver Cap, 6 In. 95.00
Val St.Lambert, Box, Bust Of Mother & Baby On Lid, Round, 4 In. 65.00
Val St.Lambert, Box, Olive Green, Woman & Baby Etched Bust, Round, 5 1/2 In. 55.00
Val St.Lambert, Tumbler, Frosted & Cranberry, Cameo, Signed 150.00
Val St.Lambert, Vase, Cameo, Orange Overlay, Wooded Scene, 14 In.High 750.00
Val St.Lambert, Vase, Fruit & Floral Branches On Clear, C.1900, 17 1/2 In. 1700.00
Val St.Lambert, Vase, Fruit Laden Branches On Frosted Gray, C.1900, 6 In. 350.00
Val St.Lambert, Vase, Purple Poppies & Leaves On Frosted, Cameo, 8 1/2 In. 295.00
Val St.Lambert, Vase, Red Iris Cut To Frosted Green, Square, 10 In. 175.00
Val St.Lambert, Vase, Reds & Pinks, Cameo, Signed, 6 1/2 In. 195.00
Val St.Lambert, Vase, Trumpet, Green Cut Overlay, 5 Panels, Footed, 12 In. 165.00
Vallerystahl, Compote, Blue Milk Glass, Ornate Molded Designs, Square, 6 In. 70.00
Vallerystahl, Dish, Dog Cover, Embossed Floral Base, Signed 115.00
Vallerystahl, Eggcup Set, Hen Sitting On Eggs, 9 Piece 175.00
Vallerystahl, Flowerpot, Green Glass, Embossed Grapes, 3 1/4 In. 7.50
Vallerystahl, Plate, Clear Golden, 8 1/2 In. 30.00
Vallerystahl, Pot, Honey, Figural Beehive, Milk Glass 24.00

         Van Briggle Pottery was made by Artus Van Briggle in Colorado
         Springs, Colorado, after 1901. Mr.Van Briggle had been a decorator at
         the Rookwood Pottery of Cincinnati, Ohio, and he died in 1904. His
         wares were original and had modeled relief decorations with a soft dull glaze.
Van Briggle, Ashtray, Matte Persian Rose, Diamond Shape, 6 X 3 1/2 In. 10.00
Van Briggle, Bookend, Owl, Turquoise Ming, Marked, 5 In., Pair 50.00
Van Briggle, Bookend, Squirrels, Turquoise Ming, 7 1/2 In., Pair 50.00
Van Briggle, Bowl & Frog, Persian Rose, Flowers & Leaves, 7 1/2 In. 24.00
Van Briggle, Bowl & Frog, Stylized Dragonflies, 3 Frogs On Rock, 8 1/2 In. 75.00
Van Briggle, Bowl, Green Matte, Artist Marked, 5 1/4 X 7 In. 52.50
Van Briggle, Bowl, Molded Acorns & Oak Leaves On Blues, 1910, 5 1/2 In. 90.00
Van Briggle, Bowl, Mountain Craig Blue, Stylized Dragonflies, 8 1/2 In. 35.00
Van Briggle, Bowl, Mountain Craig Brown, Stylized Dragonflies, 8 1/2 In. 40.00
Van Briggle, Bowl, Mulberry, Stylized Floral, Dated 1917, 3 X 6 1/2 In. 50.00
Van Briggle, Bowl, Turquoise Ming, Butterflies At Rolled-In Top, 6 3/4 In. 10.00
Van Briggle, Candleholder, Persian Rose, Blue, Leaf & Floral, 3 3/4 In., Pair 8.50
Van Briggle, Candleholder, Turquoise Ming, 2 Arm, Floriform, 7 In. 18.00
Van Briggle, Candlestick, Deep Red Blue, 9 In., Pair 22.50
Van Briggle, Candlestick, Double, Matte Turquoise Ming, 4 1/2 In., Pair 22.00
Van Briggle, Candlestick, Matte Persian Rose, Tulips, 3 5/8 In., Pair 20.00
Van Briggle, Console Set, Matte Burgundy, 4 Piece 32.00
Van Briggle, Console Set, Shaded Maroon, Petal Shape, 5 Piece 36.00
Van Briggle, Ewer, Honey Glaze, Anna Van Briggle, 12 In. 26.00
Van Briggle, Figurine, Dog, Persian Rose Color, 2 In. 18.00
Van Briggle, Figurine, Donkey, Dated '47, 3 1/2 In. 30.00
Van Briggle, Flower Frog, Shell, Turquoise Ming Blue, 6 3/4 X 5 X 3 In. 10.00
Van Briggle, Jar, Covered, Closed Handles, Rose To Blue, 4 In. 15.00
Van Briggle, Lamp, Figural, Lady With Urn On Shoulder, Maroon, 10 In. 55.00
Van Briggle, Pitcher, Green, 7 In. 12.00
Van Briggle, Plate, Pale Blue To Dark Green Center, Decorated, 6 In. 30.00
Van Briggle, Salt & Pepper, Turquoise Ming, Penguins, Marked, 4 1/4 In. 20.00
Van Briggle, Sugar & Creamer, Hexagonal Shape, Persian Rose, 2 1/8 In. 18.50
Van Briggle, Vase, Brown & Green, Small Neck, Iris, 5 1/2 In. 15.00
Van Briggle, Vase, Brown, Green Raised Pattern, 5 In. 15.50
Van Briggle, Vase, Bud, Maroon, 9 In. 15.00
Van Briggle, Vase, Bud, Mulberry Color, Dated 1917, 7 1/2 In. 45.00
Van Briggle, Vase, Bud, Persian Rose, Marked, 8 In. 18.00
Van Briggle, Vase, Bud, Triple, Blue Black, Marked Anna Van Briggle, 7 In. 25.00
Van Briggle, Vase, Bulbous, Raised Leaf Design, Turquoise Ming, 4 1/2 In. 18.50
Van Briggle, Vase, Butterfly Design, Turquoise Ming, 5 3/4 In.High 18.50
Van Briggle, Vase, Green Floral On Persian Red, 5 In. 30.00
Van Briggle, Vase, Magenta, Blue, & Brown, Leaves Decoration, 4 1/2 In. 15.00

Van Briggle, Vase, Maroon & Blue, 13 In.	85.00
Van Briggle, Vase, Maroon Glaze, White Accents, Blossoms, 1920, 5 In.	48.00
Van Briggle, Vase, Maroon, Molded Indians' Heads, 11 In.	100.00
Van Briggle, Vase, Matte Turquoise Ming, Crescent Moon, Pedestal, 7 1/2 In.	25.00
Van Briggle, Vase, Molded Arches, Dark Blue, 7 In.High	28.00
Van Briggle, Vase, Mountain Craig Brown, Stylized Tulips, Signed, 4 1/4 In.	40.00
Van Briggle, Vase, Persian Rose & Purple, Bulbous, Straight Top, 4 In.	18.00
Van Briggle, Vase, Persian Rose, Marked Van Briggle, Colorado Springs, 4 In.	10.00
Van Briggle, Vase, Persian Rose, Stylized Butterflies, Marked, 3 3/4 In.	20.00
Van Briggle, Vase, Persian Rose, Stylized Leaves, Marked, 8 3/4 In.	10.00
Van Briggle, Vase, Pillow, Turquoise Ming, Marked, 3 1/2 X 4 In.	7.50
Van Briggle, Vase, Rose Bowl Type, Blue To Green, Leaves, 4 1/2 In.	14.00
Van Briggle, Vase, Tulip Shape, Blue Green Vellum Glaze, 1948, 3 1/2 In.	12.50
Van Briggle, Vase, Tulip Shape, Off-White Matte Glaze, 3 1/2 In.	35.00
Van Briggle, Vase, Tulip, Blue To Wine Red, 4 1/2 In.	16.00
Van Briggle, Vase, Turquoise Blue, Marked Van Briggle USA, 5 1/2 In.	10.00
Van Briggle, Vase, Turquoise Ming, Art Nouveau Design, 1918, 7 In.High	23.50
Van Briggle, Vase, Turquoise Ming, Stylized Acorns, Marked, 3 X 6 In.	10.00
Van Briggle, Vase, Turquoise Ming, Twisted Shape, 7 1/2 In.	22.00

*Vasa Murrhina is the name of a glassware made by the Vasa Murrhina
Art Glass Company of Sandwich, Massachusetts, about 1884. The
glassware was transparent and was embedded with small pieces of colored glass
and metallic flakes. Some of the pieces were cased. The same type of glass
was made in England. Collectors often confuse Vasa Murrhina glass with
aventurine, spatter, or spangle glass. There is much confusion about what
actually was made by the Vasa Murrhina Factory.*

Vasa Murrhina, see also Spangle Glass

Vasa Murrhina, Artichoke, Pink Spatter Highlights	60.00
Vasa Murrhina, Basket, Bride's, Light Blue To White, Thorn Handle, 10 In.	95.00
Vasa Murrhina, Basket, Butterscotch, Gold Flecks, Clear Handle, 6 In.	85.00
Vasa Murrhina, Basket, Melon Ribbed, Silver Flakes, Amber Handle, 6 1/4 In.	85.00
Vasa Murrhina, Pitcher, Green, Silver Speckles, Ruffled, 9 1/2 In.High	60.00
Vasa Murrhina, Tumbler, Cream, Blue & Pink Spatter, Amber Cased	75.00
Vasa Murrhina, Tumbler, Green	25.00
Vasa Murrhina, Tumbler, Pink, Silver Mica Flakes	50.00
Vasa Murrhina, Vase, Blue, Clear Thorn Handles, Ruffled Top, 7 1/2 In.	65.00
Vasa Murrhina, Vase, C.1850, 10 1/2 In.	60.00
Vasa Murrhina, Vase, Cobalt, Silver Spots, 8 1/2 In.	75.00
Vasa Murrhina, Vase, Custard & Cranberry, Gold Aventurine Flecks, 10 In.	115.00
Vasa Murrhina, Vase, Jack-In-The-Pulpit, 4 Color Spatter, 7 In.	55.00
Vasa Murrhina, Vase, Pink Cased, Mica Flakes, Melon Ribbed, Ruffled, 7 In.	42.00

Vasa Murrhina, see also Spangle Glass

*Vasart is the signature used on a late type of art glass made by the
Streathearn Glass Company of Scotland.*

Vasart, Bowl, Mottled Yellow Base, Blue Top, Semifooted, 5 In.	35.00
Vasart, Bowl, Mottled Yellow Base, Mottled Blue Top, Footed, 4 3/4 In.	35.00
Vasart, Bowl, Mottled Yellow To Blue Top, Semifooted, Signed, 5 X 2 1/2 In.	35.00
Vasart, Bowl, Shallow, Clambroth, Pink & Blue Decoration, 8 1/2 In.	75.00

*Vaseline glass is a greenish yellow glassware resembling petroleum jelly.
Some vaseline glass is still being made in old and new styles. Pressed
glass of the 1870s was often made of vaseline-colored glass. The old glass
was made with uranium, but the reproductions are being colored in a different
way. See Pressed Glass for more information about patterns that were also
made of vaseline-colored glass.*

Vaseline Glass, Basket, 9 In.High To Top Of Handle	26.50
Vaseline Glass, Berry Set, Alaska, Opalescent, 7 Piece	375.00
Vaseline Glass, Berry Set, Daisy & Button, Triangular, 9 Piece	90.00
Vaseline Glass, Berry Set, Maple Leaf, Open Log Feet, 5 Piece	85.00
Vaseline Glass, Bowl, Adonis, 9 In.	18.00
Vaseline Glass, Bowl, Beaded Drape, Fluted Edge, 4 Footed, 7 1/2 In.	25.00
Vaseline Glass, Bowl, Berry, Diamond-Quilted, 8 In.	25.00
Vaseline Glass, Bowl, Berry, Fluted Scrolls, Opalescent	36.00
Vaseline Glass, Bowl, Finger, Diamond-Quilted	10.00

Vaseline Glass, Bowl, Finger, Opalescent Coin Spot	19.00
Vaseline Glass, Bowl, Fruit, Footed, Greentown, 8 1/4 X 3 1/2 In.	58.50
Vaseline Glass, Bowl, Maple Leaf, 10 X 6 1/4 X 3 1/2 In.	35.00
Vaseline Glass, Bowl, Rose Sprig, Footed, 10 In.	32.00
Vaseline Glass, Bowl, Tree Of Life, Shallow, PG&Co., 5 3/8 X 1 3/8 In.	22.00
Vaseline Glass, Bowl, Tricornered, Threading, Scalloped, 3 Footed, 7 1/2 In.	23.00
Vaseline Glass, Bowl, Waste, Maple Leaf	45.00
Vaseline Glass, Bowl, Wildflower, Square, 7 1/2 In.	12.50
Vaseline Glass, Bucket, Marked Patent, 2 X 2 In.	20.00
Vaseline Glass, Butter Pat, Daisy & Button, Maltese Cross Shape	6.50
Vaseline Glass, Butter, Covered, Wildflower, On Stand	55.00
Vaseline Glass, Butter, Rose In Snow, Round	35.00
Vaseline Glass, Butter, Wreath & Shell, Covered	95.00
Vaseline Glass, Cake Stand, Finecut, 9 In.	38.50
Vaseline Glass, Cake Stand, Leaf & Panel, 8 1/2 In.	28.00
Vaseline Glass, Cake Stand, Turned-Up Edge, C.1940	15.00
Vaseline Glass, Candleholder, Lime Green, 7 In., Pair	42.00
Vaseline Glass, Candlestick, Dolphin, Stepped Base, C.1835, 10 1/2 In., Pair	450.00
Vaseline Glass, Case, Comb, Daisy & Button, Bowfront, Pierced For Hanging	32.50
Vaseline Glass, Celery, Daisy & Button With V Ornament	45.00
Vaseline Glass, Celery, Pressed Diamond	30.00
Vaseline Glass, Champagne, Daisy & Button With Thumbprint Stripe	35.00
Vaseline Glass, Compote, Jelly, Wheat & Barley	20.00
Vaseline Glass, Compote, Rose In Snow, 7 X 8 In.	55.00
Vaseline Glass, Compote, Three Panel, 7 X 4 In.	38.50
Vaseline Glass, Compote, Willow Oak, High Standard, 7 In.	55.00
Vaseline Glass, Console Set, Cut To Clear, Flowers, 3 Piece	85.00
Vaseline Glass, Creamer, Alaska, Opalescent	55.00
Vaseline Glass, Creamer, Argonaut Shell, Opalescent	52.50
Vaseline Glass, Creamer, Cathedral	35.00
Vaseline Glass, Creamer, Fluted Scroll, Opalescent	35.00 To 60.00
Vaseline Glass, Creamer, Maple Leaf	35.00 To 55.00
Vaseline Glass, Creamer, Oaken Bucket	29.50
Vaseline Glass, Creamer, Opalescent, Embossed Cherry & Wreath	30.00
Vaseline Glass, Creamer, Rose Sprig	49.50
Vaseline Glass, Creamer, Three Panel	30.00
Vaseline Glass, Creamer, Wildflower	25.00
Vaseline Glass, Creamer, 1, 000-Eye, Three Knob	65.00
Vaseline Glass, Cruet, Gold Band	65.00
Vaseline Glass, Cruet, Inverted Thumbprint, Clear Handle, 6 1/2 In.	65.00
Vaseline Glass, Decanter, Crystal Handle & Steeple Stopper, 10 In.	75.00
Vaseline Glass, Decanter, Diamond, 11 In.	24.00
Vaseline Glass, Dish, Candy, Footed, Triangular	12.00
Vaseline Glass, Dish, Divided, Holder	15.00
Vaseline Glass, Dish, Pickle, Cane, Boat Shape, 7 1/2 In.	14.00
Vaseline Glass, Dish, Pickle, Finecut & Panel, 8 In.	14.50
Vaseline Glass, Goblet, Basket Weave	12.50 To 20.00
Vaseline Glass, Goblet, Cane	26.00
Vaseline Glass, Goblet, Horizontal Oval Frames, Flint	45.00
Vaseline Glass, Goblet, Inverted Thumbprint	12.50 To 15.00
Vaseline Glass, Goblet, Inverted Thumbprint With Star	30.00
Vaseline Glass, Goblet, Inverted Prism	12.50
Vaseline Glass, Goblet, Maple Leaf	125.00
Vaseline Glass, Goblet, Three Panel	35.00
Vaseline Glass, Goblet, Two Panel	17.50
Vaseline Glass, Goblet, Wildflower	25.00 To 30.00
Vaseline Glass, Goblet, Windflower	26.50
Vaseline Glass, Gum Stand, Teaberry	15.00
Vaseline Glass, Hat, Daisy & Button, 3 3/4 In.	40.00
Vaseline Glass, Match Holder, Monkey	43.00
Vaseline Glass, Match Holder, Threaded, 2 1/2 X 3 1/2 In.	15.00
Vaseline Glass, Muffineer, Diamond, Ribbed Panels, Skirt, Tin Top, 5 1/4 In.	45.00
Vaseline Glass, Muffineer, Opalescent Flowers & Fernery, Bulbous	50.00
Vaseline Glass, Muffineer, Swirl, Opalescent	65.00
Vaseline Glass, Mug, Daisy & Button With V Ornament	20.00
Vaseline Glass, Mug, 1, 000-Eye	21.50

Vaseline Glass, Perfume, 6 Sided, Bulbous Base, Steeple Stopper, 7 1/2 In.	22.50
Vaseline Glass, Pitcher, Austrian, Miniature	30.00
Vaseline Glass, Pitcher, Milk, Zipper	55.00
Vaseline Glass, Pitcher, Water, Basket Weave	27.50
Vaseline Glass, Pitcher, Water, Cane	48.00
Vaseline Glass, Pitcher, Water, Finecut	46.00
Vaseline Glass, Pitcher, Water, Leaf	44.00
Vaseline Glass, Pitcher, Water, Two Panel, 9 1/2 In.	68.50
Vaseline Glass, Plate, Bread, Maple Leaf	35.00
Vaseline Glass, Plate, Bread, 1, 000-Eye	18.00
Vaseline Glass, Plate, Maple Leaf, 11 In.	30.00
Vaseline Glass, Plate, Ribbed Top & Underneath, Irregular Rim, 9 1/4 In.	24.00
Vaseline Glass, Plate, Wildflower, Square, 10 In.	18.00
Vaseline Glass, Relish, Wildflower, Rectangular	17.50
Vaseline Glass, Rose Bowl, Sapphire At Top, White Enameled Flowers	85.00
Vaseline Glass, Salt & Pepper, Swirled, Speckled	89.00
Vaseline Glass, Salt, Diamond-Quilted, Rectangular	12.50
Vaseline Glass, Salt, Diamond With Button	4.50
Vaseline Glass, Salt, Footed	6.00
Vaseline Glass, Salt, Hexagonal	16.00
Vaseline Glass, Saltshaker, Mitered Diamond	15.00
Vaseline Glass, Saltshaker, Pressed Diamond	10.00
Vaseline Glass, Saltshaker, Wildflower	24.00
Vaseline Glass, Sauce Set, Lion's Leg, Paw Feet, Square, 5 Piece	165.00
Vaseline Glass, Sauce, Alaska, Opalescent	35.00 To 38.00
Vaseline Glass, Sauce, Cathedral, Footed	21.00
Vaseline Glass, Sauce, Dewey	18.50
Vaseline Glass, Sauce, Everglades, Footed, Oval, 5 1/4 X 4 1/4 In.	28.00
Vaseline Glass, Sauce, Iris & Meander, 4 1/4 In.	21.50
Vaseline Glass, Sauce, Maple Leaf, Leaf Shape, 5 3/8 In.	6.00
Vaseline Glass, Sauce, Maple Leaf, Leaf Shape, 6 In.	7.50
Vaseline Glass, Sauce, Pressed Diamond	4.00
Vaseline Glass, Sauce, Three Panel	12.50
Vaseline Glass, Sauce, Two Panel	12.00
Vaseline Glass, Sauce, Valencia Waffle, Footed	12.50
Vaseline Glass, Sauce, Wheat & Barley, Footed	13.50
Vaseline Glass, Sauce, Wildflower	8.50
Vaseline Glass, Shade, Gas, Hobnail, Ruffled, 5 In.	48.00
Vaseline Glass, Spooner, Alaska, Opalescent	47.50
Vaseline Glass, Spooner, Cathedral	25.00
Vaseline Glass, Spooner, Fluted Scroll, Northwood	26.00
Vaseline Glass, Spooner, Fluted Scroll, Opalescent	35.00
Vaseline Glass, Spooner, Fluted Scrolls, Opalescent, Northwood	42.00
Vaseline Glass, Spooner, Ribbed Spiral, Opalescent	48.00
Vaseline Glass, Spooner, Three Panel, 5 In.	40.00
Vaseline Glass, Sugar, Covered, Maple Leaf	50.00
Vaseline Glass, Sugar, Dewey	35.00
Vaseline Glass, Sugar, Honeycomb, Covered	30.00
Vaseline Glass, Sugar, 3 Panel	32.50
Vaseline Glass, Syrup, Columbia, Gold	95.00
Vaseline Glass, Syrup, Diamond Spearhead	88.00
Vaseline Glass, Syrup, Reverse Rib	85.00
Vaseline Glass, Table Set, Fluted Scroll, Opalescent, 4 Piece	285.00
Vaseline Glass, Toothpick, Columbia, Gold	40.00
Vaseline Glass, Toothpick, Daisy & Button, Hat Shape, 2 5/8 In.	22.75
Vaseline Glass, Toothpick, Diamond Point Heart	5.00
Vaseline Glass, Toothpick, Diamond Point, Hat Shape	16.00
Vaseline Glass, Toothpick, Hobnail, Opalescent	20.00
Vaseline Glass, Toothpick, Petticoat	30.00
Vaseline Glass, Tray, Currier & Ives, Dog & Rabbit Series, 12 In.	52.00
Vaseline Glass, Tray, Jewel, Alaska, 4 X 2 In.	25.00
Vaseline Glass, Tray, Maple Leaf, 13 X 10 In.	65.00
Vaseline Glass, Tray, Water, Daisy & Button, Triangular, Handled, 12 1/2 In.	95.00
Vaseline Glass, Tray, Water, Scenic, Basket Weave Border, 12 In.	26.00
Vaseline Glass, Tray, Water, Wildflower	32.50
Vaseline Glass, Tray, Wildflower, Oval, 13 In.	27.50

Vaseline Glass, Tumbler, Cane	25.00
Vaseline Glass, Tumbler, Daisy & Button, Wide Band	21.50
Vaseline Glass, Tumbler, Daisy & Button, 3 3/4 In.	15.00
Vaseline Glass, Tumbler, Dewey	37.50
Vaseline Glass, Tumbler, Maple Leaf	50.00
Vaseline Glass, Tumbler, Whiskey, Diamond-Quilted, Blue Reeded Handle	20.00
Vaseline Glass, Tumbler, Wreathed Shell, Opalescent	36.00
Vaseline Glass, Vase, Green, Flared At Top To 4 1/2 In., 9 In.	35.00
Vaseline Glass, Vase, Inverted Thumbprint, 5 In.	15.00
Vaseline Glass, Vase, Ribbed Spiral, Albany, 9 3/4 In.	32.50
Vaseline Glass, Vase, Trumpet, 9 In.High	35.00
Vaseline Glass, Wine, Cathedral	32.00 To 38.00
Vaseline Glass, Wine, Daisy & Button With V Band	29.00
Vaseline Glass, Wine, Diamond-Quilted	15.00
Vaseline Glass, Wine, Inverted Thumbprint	15.00
Vaseline Glass, Wine, Mitered Diamond	21.50

Venetian glass has been made near Venice, Italy, from the thirteenth to the twentieth century. Thin colored glass with applied decorations is favored although many other types have been made.

Venetian Glass, Basket, Crackle, Green, Pink Flowers, Applied Handle, 7 In.	50.00
Venetian Glass, Candlestick, Dolphin, 14 In.High	85.00
Venetian Glass, Champagne, Cranberry, Cherubs & Grapevines At Top	59.50
Venetian Glass, Champagne, Green, Gold Flecks, Dolphin Stem, Onyx Eyes, 1869	60.00
Venetian Glass, Chandelier, 5 Arms, Pink & Blue Decoration, 30 In.	1100.00
Venetian Glass, Goblet, Blown Dolphin Stem, Gold Speckled	28.50
Venetian Glass, Sherbet & Underplate, Clear With Gold, Swirl Stem, 8	110.00
Venetian Glass, Tumbler, Opaque Net, Gold Rim	7.50
Venetian Glass, Urn, Pedestal Base, Applied Handle, Pale Pink, 8 1/2 In.	45.00
Venetian Glass, Vase, Deep Red, Rough Pontil, 10 In.	45.00
Venetian Glass, Vase, Green Blue, Blown, Painted Figures, C.1850, 7 In.	125.00
Venetian Glass, Vase, Purple, Enameled Floral, Ruffled Crimped Top, 10 In.	45.00
Venetian Glass, Wine, Cranberry, Cherubs & Grapevines At Top	49.50

Verlys

Verlys glass was made in France after 1931. Verlys was also made in the United States. The glass is either blown or molded. The American glass is signed with a diamond-point-scratched name, but the French pieces are marked with a molded signature.

Verlys, Bowl, Centerpiece, Frosted & Clear, Pierced Work, 17 X 15 X 3 In.	115.00
Verlys, Bowl, Directoire Blue, Raised Roses, 5 1/4 In.	60.00
Verlys, Bowl, Frosted Roses, Signed, 5 1/2 In.	20.00
Verlys, Bowl, Pinecones, Signed, 6 In.	45.00
Verlys, Bowl, Water Lily, Pattern No.1259, Signed, 13 3/4 In.	85.00
Verlys, Coupe, Raised Pigeons In Brown Wash, Pedestal, 4 1/2 X 6 1/2 In.	115.00
Verlys, Dish, Pinecone, Frosted, 6 In.	12.00
Verlys, Plaque, 3 Swirling Fish, 9 In.	85.00
Verlys, Vase, Fan, Two Lovebirds, Branch & Berry On Pedestal, 4 1/2 In.	50.00
Verlys, Vase, Frosted Butterflies In Relief, Script Signed, 5 In.	40.00
Verlys, Vase, Opalescent, Wheat & Thistle, Rolled-Out Rim, 9 In.	160.00
Verlys, Vase, Seasons, Crystal, Etched, 8 1/4 In.High, 5 In.Diameter, Pair	425.00

Verre de soie glass was first made by Frederick Carder at the Steuben Glass Works from about 1905 to 1930. It is an iridescent glass of soft white or very, very pale green. The name means glass of silk, and it does resemble silk. Other factories have made verre de soie, and some of the English examples were made of different colors. Verre de soie is an art glass and is not related to the iridescent pressed white carnival glass mistakenly called by its name.

Verre De Soie, see also Steuben	
Verre De Soie, Bottle, Perfume, Melon Ribbed, 3 In.	38.00
Verre De Soie, Salt, Etched, Sterling Base Marked 2467D, 1 3/4 In.	55.00
Verre De Soie, Vase, Floriform, Ruffled Crackle Rim, C.1915, 10 1/8 In.	150.00
Verre De Soie, Vase, Jack-In-The-Pulpit Top, Twisted Stem, 8 In., Pair	125.00
Verre De Soie, Water Set, Blown, Free-Form, Applied Handle, 5 Piece	85.00
Vienna Art, Plate, Candle Girl ....*Illus*	30.00
Vienna Art, Plate, Front Signed A.Beck ....*Illus*	20.00

Vienna Art, Plate, Candle Girl
(See Page 666)

Vienna Art, Plate, Front Signed A.Beck
(See Page 666)

Vienna Art, Plate, Portrait, Brunette, Coca-Cola, 10 In.	15.00
Vienna, Vase, Ormolu Mounts, Allegorical Figure, Landscape, C.1890, 25 In.	700.00

Vieux Paris, or Old Paris, is porcelain ware that is known to have been made in Paris in the eighteenth or early nineteenth century but has no identifying manufacturer's mark.

Vieux Paris, Cup & Saucer	28.00
Vieux Paris, Plate, White, 3 Pink Roses, Green & Brown Leaves, C.1800, 9 In.	20.00
Vieux Paris, Tea Set, White, Gold Trim, Rosebud Finial, C.1840, 15 Piece	275.00

Villeroy & Boch Pottery of Mettlach, Germany, was founded in 1841. The firm made many types of pottery, including the famous Mettlach steins.

Villeroy & Boch, Cruet, Oil, Onion Variant, Flow Blue, 8 1/2 In.	35.00
Villeroy & Boch, Cup, Handleless	12.50
Villeroy & Boch, Match Holder, Frog, White Crackle Glaze	40.00
Villeroy & Boch, Pitcher, Pink & White Raised Decoration, 9 In.	75.00
Villeroy & Boch, Pitcher, Red Flowers & Green Leaves On White, 7 1/2 In.	45.00
Villeroy & Boch, Plate, Hanging, Green Pond Lilies On Cream, 11 1/2 In.	45.00
Villeroy & Boch, Plate, Red & Green, 10 In.	18.00
Villeroy & Boch, Tile, Windmill & Boat Scene, Blue, Square, 6 In.	12.00
Villeroy & Boch, Vase, Gray, Beige Couples & Scrolls, Silver Trim, 6 1/2 In.	55.00
Villeroy & Boch, Vase, Silver Luster Trim, Beige Figure On Gray, 7 1/2 In.	155.00
Villeroy & Boch, see also Mettlach	
Volkstadt, Figurine, Comic In Underwear Battling 2 Insects, K.Ens, 9 In.	85.00
Volkstadt, Figurine, Frog, Singing, Decorated, 4 1/2 In.	95.00
Volkstadt, Figurine, Frog, Singing, Green, 5 In.	85.00
Volkstadt, Figurine, Thrushlike Bird On Branch, Candleholder Top, 5 In.	35.00
Wallendorf, Compote, Chinoiserie, Woman & Child, 15 X 11 In.	450.00
Walrath, Vase, Matte, Fruit & Leaves, Tan, Green, & Burnt Orange, C.1910, 4 In.	75.00
Walt Disney, see Disneyana	

Warwick china was made in Wheeling, West Virginia, in a pottery factory founded in 1887.

Warwick, Mug, Indian On Front, Ioga, 4 1/4 In.High	35.00
Warwick, Mug, Minstrel Playing Banjo, Brown Tones	29.00
Warwick, Syrup, Pewter Top	35.00
Warwick, Vase, Handled, Grecian Type Girl, Brown To Beige, Loga Mark, 12 In.	60.00
Warwick, Vase, Loga, Brown Glaze, 2 Running Hounds, R.K.Beck, 12 In.	85.00
Warwick, Vase, Pillow Shape, 3 Snow Geese, Gold Rim, Helmet Mark, 7 In.	48.00
Warwick, Vase, Portrait, Roberta, Basket Handle, 10 In.	50.00
Watch Chain, Gentleman's, Sterling Silver, Albert	4.00
Watch Chain, Man's, English Sterling Hallmarks, 1848-49	26.00
Watch Chain, 14K Gold, Foxtail, Art Nouveau Opal Slide, 60 In.	290.00

Watch fobs were worn on watch chains. They were popular during Victorian times and after.

Watch Fob, American Veterinary Medical Association, Kansas City, 1917	12.75
Watch Fob, B.& T.R.R., Leather, Crossed Flags	15.00
Watch Fob, B.F.O.E., Elk's Head, Metal	3.50
Watch Fob, Brass Jail Key, Leather Strap	19.00
Watch Fob, Brass, Lady's Head	4.00
Watch Fob, Bronze, State Of Massachusetts, State Seal, Strap Type	5.00
Watch Fob, Buff Survey	8.00
Watch Fob, Caterpillar Advertising	2.50
Watch Fob, Columbian Exposition, 1893, Watch Shape	8.00
Watch Fob, Diesel Caterpillar Tractor Co., Peoria, Ill., Tractor Shape	18.00
Watch Fob, Earl Ridge, Kansas City, U.S.Emblem	19.00
Watch Fob, Elks, Double Gold Chain, Jeweled Eyes & Seal	30.00
Watch Fob, Elks, Mounted On Leather Ribbons, Chain & Clasp	17.50
Watch Fob, F.O.E., Eagle Emblem	12.50
Watch Fob, Gold Floral Center, Blue Stone, Pearl Charm, Short Chain	18.00
Watch Fob, Green River Whiskey, Horseshoe Shape	7.00
Watch Fob, Independence Hall, Phila., P.E.Sharpless Co., Acorn Milk	7.95
Watch Fob, Indian On Brass Owl Body	15.00
Watch Fob, International Harvester Co., 1831-1931, Strap Type	4.95
Watch Fob, Iowa State Seal	15.00
Watch Fob, Jamestown Exposition, 1907, Nickel	10.00 To 25.00
Watch Fob, KOTM, Oriental Tent & Globe, Strap Type	4.95
Watch Fob, Keystone Watch Co., Columbian Exposition	6.50
Watch Fob, Lincoln's Profile, Illinois Watch Co., 1865, Bronze	22.00
Watch Fob, Marmarth, North Dakota	6.00
Watch Fob, McCormick-Deering Farm Machines, Strap Type	25.00
Watch Fob, Mesh Type, Gold Filled	13.50
Watch Fob, Michigan Power Equipment, Double Sided	12.00
Watch Fob, Modern Woodmen Of America, Rock Island, Ill.	12.50
Watch Fob, New Departure Brake, Brass	15.00
Watch Fob, New York State Fair, Syracuse, 1918	6.00
Watch Fob, Old Dutch Cleanser, Brass, Enamel	10.00
Watch Fob, Old Home Week, Orleans, Mass., 1921, Strap Type	3.95
Watch Fob, Paul Revere Life Insurance Co., Man Riding Horse	10.00
Watch Fob, Pewter, Sitting Owl Shape, Ring At Top, 7/8 In.	12.00
Watch Fob, Republique Francaise Exposition, 1889	7.00
Watch Fob, Russel Company, Silver	9.50
Watch Fob, St.Louis Exposition, 1904, Sterling Silver, 2 Tokens & Chain	25.00
Watch Fob, Statue Of Liberty, Strap Type	4.95
Watch Fob, Steamship	6.50
Watch Fob, Sterling Silver, Initials M S C N	15.00
Watch Fob, Sterling Silver, Strap Type, Flower Border	9.95
Watch Fob, Sterling, Embossed Flowing Haired Woman On 3 Linked Medallions	65.00
Watch Fob, The Girl Of The Pingree Shoe	20.00
Watch Fob, Wheeling Sheet Metal	6.00
Watch Fob, Woven Wire, Engraved Center, Gold Filled, Signet Slide & Charm	18.00
Watch Fob, Yankee Division Reunion, July 24, 1921	8.00
Watch Fob, 22nd Firemen's Convention, 1915, Indian Chief Guyasuta	19.95
Watch, see also Gene Autry, Watch, Disneyana, Watch, Hopalong Cassidy, Watch, Roy Rogers, Watch	
Watch, A.W.Co., Coin Silver Hunting Case To Open Face Convertible	100.00
Watch, Ball & Co., Cleveland, .925 Silver Open Face Case, 1883	80.00
Watch, Ball Commercial, Railroad, Gold Case, 17 Jewel	45.00
Watch, Ball, Official Railroad Standard, Engraved Case, 21 Jewel	120.00
Watch, Bartlett, C.1860, Silver Open Face Case, Key Wind, 17 Jewel	115.00
Watch, Bentley & Beck, England, C.1820, Open Face Silver Case, Duplex	265.00
Watch, Berwyn, Sterling Open Face Case, Dust Cover, 7 Jewel	25.00
Watch, Bun, 14K Gold Filled Case, 60 Hour	120.00
Watch, Buster Brown Shoes, 1913	140.00
Watch, C.& B. Company, Nickel Case, Marked Centennial 1776-1876	45.00
Watch, Calendar, Hebdomas Style, Silver Case, 8 Day, Stem Wind	245.00
Watch, Calendar, Silver Case, Jeweled, Stem Wind, Pin Set, 47 Mm.	195.00
Watch, Calendar, Silver Hunting Case, Pin Set, Stem Wind, Jeweled, 46 Mm.	255.00
Watch, Chain, Lady's, Gold, Green Opal Slide, 27 In.	30.00

Watch, Chain, Lady's, Pearl In Slide 42.00
Watch, Columbian, Lady's, Gold Filled Hunting Case, Engraved, 7 Jewel 65.00
Watch, Courvoisier Freres, Chaux-De-Fonds, 18K Gold Hunting Case 385.00
Watch, Crosswaithe, C.1765, Porcelain, Fusee, Chain 175.00
Watch, D.Edmonds, Liverpool, Silver Pair Case, Fusee, Key Wind 185.00
Watch, David Taylor, London, Open Face Silver Case, C.1850, 19 Jewel 120.00
Watch, Digital, Silver Case, Jeweled Lever Movement, 46 Mm. 270.00
Watch, E.Howard, Open Face, Keystone Howard White Case, 21 Jewel 95.00
Watch, Earle Of Philadelphia, Seth Thomas, Open Face Case, 15 Jewel 65.00
Watch, Elgin, Aluminum Silver Hunting Case, Lever Set, 13 Jewel 50.00
Watch, Elgin, Coin Silver Hunting Case, Engraved, Key Wind 75.00
Watch, Elgin, Crescent, Street Model, Gold Filled Open Face Case, 21 Jewel 100.00
Watch, Elgin, Engraved Gold Filled Hunting Case, 7 Jewel 85.00
Watch, Elgin, G.M.Wheeler, Gold Filled Case, 17 Jewel 60.00
Watch, Elgin, Gold Filled Hunting Case, Engraved, 15 Jewel, Size 18 .... 67.50
Watch, Elgin, Gold Filled Hunting Case, Nickel Movement, 17 Jewel 95.00
Watch, Elgin, Gold Filled Hunting Case, Winds At 3 Lever Set 85.00
Watch, Elgin, Lady's, Engraved Double Case, Dated 1908, Porcelain Face 150.00
Watch, Elgin, Lady's, Gold Filled Hunting Case, Lever Set 90.00
Watch, Elgin, Lady's, 14K Gold Filled Hunting Case, 1902 .... 75.00
Watch, Elgin, Lever Set, Size 18 .... 40.00
Watch, Elgin, Montgomery Dial, 20K Yellow Gold Filled Case, 19 Jewel 85.00
Watch, Elgin, National, Silverine Open Face Case, Key Wind, 7 Jewel 85.00
Watch, Elgin, Navigator's, Timer, Nickel Case, 1/5 Second 23.00
Watch, Elgin, Nickel Open Face Case, 15 Jewel 18.00
Watch, Elgin, Railroad, Open Face 25 Year Case, 1886 .... 70.00
Watch, Elgin, Railroad, Raymond Model, Gold Filled Open Face Case, 21 Jewel 110.00
Watch, Elgin, Raymond, Yellow Gold Filled Case, 21 Jewel 115.00
Watch, Elgin, Raymond, 10K Yellow Gold Filled Case, 23 Jewel 145.00
Watch, Elgin, Silver & Black Enamel Open Face Case 125.00
Watch, Elgin, Silver Hunting Case, Kennedy & Co. Movement, Key Wind 125.00
Watch, Elgin, Silveroid Open Face Engine Turned Case, 17 Jewel 22.00
Watch, Elgin, White Gold Filled Open Face Case, 15 Jewel 22.00
Watch, Elgin, White Gold Octagonal Open Face Case, 7 Jewel 30.00
Watch, Elgin, Yellow Gold Filled Case, 7 Jewel 50.00
Watch, Elgin, Yellow Gold Filled Hunting Case, 17 Jewel 58.00
Watch, Elgin, Yellow Gold Filled Open Face Case, Ruby, C.1910, 17 Jewel 68.00
Watch, Elgin, Yellow Gold Filled Open Face Case, 15 Jewel 15.00
Watch, Elgin, 14K Gold Open Face Center Hinged Case, 17 Jewel 55.00
Watch, Elgin, 20 Year Open Face Monogramed Case, 1908, 15 Jewel 65.00
Watch, Faveur, Silver Plate Case, Visible Balance Wheel, 47 Mm. 175.00
Watch, Ferdinand Engelscholk, C.1720, Silver Case, Verge .... Illus 900.00
Watch, French, Calendar, Gunmetal Case, 8 Day, Pin Set, Stem Wind 265.00
Watch, G.P.Bates Ludham 65353, Verge, Silver Pair Case, 1839, Key Wind 135.00
Watch, Geneva, J.M.Gondal, Sterling Hunting Case, C.1880, 13 Jewel 125.00
Watch, Geo.Pierce, Lowell, Mass., Open Face Silver Case, 1849, Fusee, Lever ... 95.00
Watch, Gold Base Metal Open Face Case, Quarter Hour Repeater, Pin Set 375.00
Watch, Gordino, Liverpool, Engraved 18K Gold Case, Key Wind, 45 Mm. 350.00
Watch, Graf Zeppelin 150.00
Watch, Gruen, Semithin, White Gold Filled Open Face Case, 21 Jewel 40.00
Watch, Gruen, 25K Yellow Gold Filled Case, 17 Jewel 60.00
Watch, Hamilton, Engraved Gold Case, Hand Set, 17 Jewel 55.00
Watch, Hamilton, Engraved Gold Filled Open Face Case, 17 Jewel 85.00
Watch, Hamilton, Engraved Gold Filled Open Face Case, 5 Positions, 19 Jewel .. 65.00
Watch, Hamilton, Gold Filled Open Face, Porcelain Face, 17 Jewel 65.00
Watch, Hamilton, Model 940, Railroad, Lever Set, Gold Filled Case, 21 Jewel 67.00
Watch, Hamilton, Model 992, Railroad, Yellow Gold Filled Case, 21 Jewel 77.00
Watch, Hamilton, Montgomery Dial, 10K Yellow Gold Filled Case, 19 Jewel 145.00
Watch, Hamilton, Montgomery Dial, 10K Yellow Gold Filled Case, 21 Jewel 125.00
Watch, Hamilton, Railroad, Model 992, 21 Jewels, C.1910 .... 70.00
Watch, Hamilton, Railway Special, Gold Filled Open Face Case, 21 Jewel 100.00
Watch, Hamilton, Stainless Steel Case, 24 Hour Dial, 21 Jewel 75.00
Watch, Hamilton, White Gold Filled Engraved Case, 21 Jewel 145.00
Watch, Hamilton, Yellow Gold Filled Case, 17 Jewel 65.00
Watch, Hamilton, 1898, Permanent Yellow Gold Case, 21 Jewel 135.00
Watch, Hampden, Gold Inlay Of Train In Silver Open Face Case, 17 Jewel 125.00

Watch, Hampden, Yellow Gold Filled Hunting Case, 7 Jewel 48.00
Watch, Hampden, Yellow Gold Filled Open Face Case, 17 Jewel 18.00
Watch, Hunting Case, Engraved Scenes, Silver, 21 Jewel 60.00
Watch, Illinois, Bunn Special, Stainless Steel Open Face Case, 21 Jewel 85.00
Watch, Illinois, Gold Filled Open Face Case, Lever Set, 17 Jewel 65.00
Watch, Illinois, Gold Filled Open Face Case, 24 Jewel, Size 18 .... 500.00
Watch, Illinois, Santa Fe Special, Hunting Case, 21 Jewel 110.00
Watch, Illinois, Silveroid Open Face Case, 17 Jewel 15.00
Watch, Illinois, Transparent Hunting Case, Lincoln Movement, Lever Set 58.00
Watch, Illinois, Yellow Gold Filled Open Face Case, Dust Cover, 17 Jewel 28.00
Watch, Imperial, Yellow Gold Case, Size 12 .... 40.00
Watch, Ingersoll, Big Bad Wolf 130.00
Watch, Ingraham Biltmore, Pocket 22.50
Watch, Ingraham, Viceroy, Silver 15.00
Watch, J.E.Caldwell Co., 18K Gold Open Face Case, 21 Jewel 250.00
Watch, John Ellicot, London, 1775, Gilt Silver Case .... *Illus* 800.00
Watch, Lady's, Swiss, 185 Gold Open Face Case, Key Wind, Inscribed 1870 .... 175.00
Watch, London, C.1730, Silver Case, Calendar .... *Illus* 600.00
Watch, Longines, Man's, Sterling Case, 15 Jewel 50.00
Watch, Longines, Tiffany & Co., Silver & Black Enamel Open Face 150.00
Watch, Lord Elgin, Gold Filled Open Face Case, 1935, 21 Jewel 70.00
Watch, Melchior Jewelers, Algoma, Wis., Silveroid Open Face Case, 15 Jewel 15.00
Watch, N.P.Knapp Special, Engraved Gold Open Face Case, 17 Jewel, Chain 45.00
Watch, N.Robert, Lady's, Gold Filled Hunting Case, 7 Jewel 55.00
Watch, Plojoux Geneve Demi Chronometre No.1302, 18K Gold Hunting Case 195.00
Watch, Pocket, Dice Numbers, Wind Up & Shoot Craps 29.00
Watch, Pocket, Sevens Seas Nautical, 1938, Clipper Ship Center 45.00
Watch, Pocket, Waltham, George Washington, Key Wind, Silveroid Case 55.00
Watch, R.Jean Gosselin, C.1710, Repeating .... *Illus* 300.00
Watch, Railway Special, Pocket, Gold Case, 23 Jewel 140.00
Watch, Reliance, Yellow Gold Filled Open Face Case, Lever Set, 7 Jewel 18.00
Watch, Robert Roscoe, Liverpool, 14K Gold Hunting Case, Key Wind 200.00
Watch, Rockford, Gold Filled Hunting Case, Visible Escapement, 17 Jewel 125.00
Watch, Rotating Risque Scenes, Silver Plate Case, Jeweled Lever, 47 Mm. 385.00
Watch, Saml.A.Eaton Boston, 3240, Verge, Silver Pair Case, 1804, Key Wind 175.00
Watch, Seth Thomas, Gold Filled Open Face Case, 17 Jewel 45.00
Watch, Skull, 18th Century Movement, Chain Of Skulls 800.00

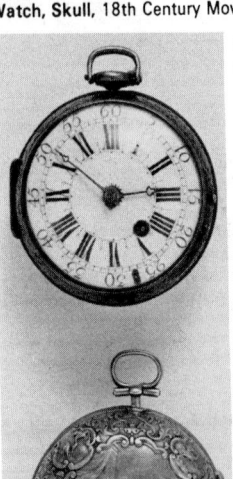

Watch, R.Jean Gosselin,
C.1710, Repeating

Watch, John Ellicot, London,
1775, Gilt Silver Case

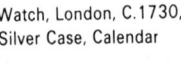

Watch, London, C.1730,
Silver Case, Calendar

Watch, Ferdinand Engelscholk,
C.1720, Silver Case, Verge
(See Page 669)

Watch, South Bend, Nickel Open Face Case, Style 211, 17 Jewel	60.00
Watch, Spirit Of St.Louis Commemorative	175.00
Watch, St.Imier, No.17649, 1874, Silver Case, Key Wind	50.00
Watch, St.Imier, Sterling Hunting Case, Lever Set, 15 Jewel	60.00
Watch, Standard, New Era, Silveroid Open Face Case, 7 Jewel	15.00
Watch, Stop, Medical Corps, Stop	40.00
Watch, Studebaker, Gold Filled Open Face Case, 8 Positions, 21 Jewel	95.00
Watch, Sun, Frank Buck Explorer's	12.50
Watch, Sundial Pocket Model, Ansonia, Brass Case, 2 X 3 In.	22.00
Watch, Swiss, Calendar, Gunmetal Case, Jeweled Lever Escapement, 59mm.	285.00
Watch, Swiss, Calendar, Silver Case, Stem Wind, Pin Set, 15 Jewel	145.00
Watch, Swiss, Chronograph, Silver Case, Pin Set, 47 Mm.	105.00
Watch, Swiss, Chronograph, 14K Gold Open Face Case, Second Hand	435.00
Watch, Swiss, Gunmetal Case, Visible Lever Escapement, 48 Mm.	220.00
Watch, Swiss, Repeater, Gunmetal Case, Stem Wind, Pin Set, 47 Mm.	375.00
Watch, Swiss, Silver Hunting Case, Repeater, Pin Set, Jeweled, 47 Mm.	595.00
Watch, Swiss, Yellow Gold Filled Octagonal Open Face Case, 15 Jewel	15.00
Watch, Turkish, Silver Hunting Case, Key Wind, Second Hand, 45 Mm.	105.00
Watch, U.S.Ordnance, Stainless Steel Case, Wrist, Waterproof	25.00
Watch, Waltham, Crescent, Railroad, 21 Jewels, Gold Filled Case	60.00
Watch, Waltham, Engraved Gold Filled Hunting Case, Riverside Movement	90.00
Watch, Waltham, Gold Filled Hunting Case, 21 Jewel	150.00
Watch, Waltham, Gold Filled Nickel Open Face Case, C.1889, Size 18	35.00
Watch, Waltham, Gold Filled Open Face Case, Eagle On Back	85.00
Watch, Waltham, Gold Filled 20 Year Hunting Case, Engine Turned	47.50
Watch, Waltham, Lady's, Gold Filled Hunting Case, Porcelain Dial	77.00
Watch, Waltham, Lady's, 14K Gold Hunting Case, Engraved, Slide Chain	265.00
Watch, Waltham, Model 645, Gold Filled Open Face Case, 21 Jewel	95.00
Watch, Waltham, Navigator's, Timer, Stainless Steel Case, 1/10 Second	18.00
Watch, Waltham, Railroad, Gold Case, 17 Jewel	45.00
Watch, Waltham, Riverside, 14K Gold Case, 15 Jewel	140.00
Watch, Waltham, Silver Hunting Case, Engraved, Porcelain Dial, 15 Jewel	65.00
Watch, Waltham, Sterling Silver Open Face Case, Swing-Out Works, 17 Jewel	80.00
Watch, Waltham, Vanguard, Gold Filled Open Face Case, 23 Jewel	125.00
Watch, Waltham, 14K Yellow Gold Filled Open Face Case, 7 Jewel	25.00
Watch, Waltham, 20 Year Open Face Case, 1919, 15 Jewel	70.00
Watch, Waltham, 20 Year Open Face Engraved Case, 1900, 17 Jewel	80.00
Watch, Willm.King 51485 London, Verge, Silver Pair Case, 1801, Key Wind	150.00
Watch, Wrist, Cinderella, Pink Face, Leather Strap	20.00
Watch, Wrist, Green Hornet, 2 Way Radio, Battery Operated	5.50
Watch, Wrist, Lady's, 2 Diamonds, 17 Jewel	22.00
Watch, Wrist, Planter's Peanuts	20.00
Watch, Zorro	15.00
Watch, 20 Dollar Gold Coin, Wrist	1200.00

Waterford type glass resembles the famous glass made in the Waterford Glass Works in Ireland. It is a clear glass that was often cut for decoration. Modern glass is still being made in Waterford, Ireland.

Waterford, Bonbonniere, 14 1/2 X 6 In., Pair	550.00
Waterford, Celery, Gold Bands, Pedestal, 8 X 5 1/2 In.	95.00
Waterford, Epergne, Bowl On Pedestal With Vase In Center, 18 1/2 In.High	250.00
Waterford, Salt, Footed, Oblong, Double Curved, Basket Shape, 3 1/2 X 2 In.	50.00

WAVE CREST WARE

Wave Crest glass is a white glassware manufactured by the Pairpoint Manufacturing Company of New Bedford, Massachusetts, and some French factories. It was then decorated by the C.F.Monroe Company of Meriden, Connecticut. The glass was painted pastel colors and decorated with flowers. The name Wave Crest was used after 1898.

Wave Crest, Barrel, Biscuit, Pink & Brown Daisies On Blue	175.00
Wave Crest, Bowl, Cream, Swirled, Pansies, Ormolu Handles, Gold Rim, 10 In.	195.00
Wave Crest, Bowl, Dresser, Lavender, Blue & Purple Flowers, 4 1/2 In.	85.00
Wave Crest, Bowl, Ormolu Handles, 7 X 2 1/2 In.	195.00
Wave Crest, Box, Biscuit, Green Satin, Enamel Chrysanthemums, Brass Fittings	325.00
Wave Crest, Box, Blue & White Floral, Round, 7 1/4 In.	350.00
Wave Crest, Box, Blue Floral, Brown Leaves, Ormolu Handles, Square, 3 In.	77.00

Wave Crest, Box, Blue Floral, Ormolu Handles, 4 1/4 In.	47.00
Wave Crest, Box, Blue, Yellow Flowers, 5 1/2 X 2 1/4 In.	72.00
Wave Crest, Box, Cigar, Shell Lid, Aqua, Pink Tea Roses, Red Banner Mark	325.00
Wave Crest, Box, Cigar, Shell Lid, Pale Yellow, Pink Floral, "Cigars"	290.00
Wave Crest, Box, Cigar, Shell Lid, Pale Yellow, Pink Flowers, Red Banner Mark	325.00
Wave Crest, Box, Collars & Cuffs In Gold Outlined Mauve, White To Blue	500.00
Wave Crest, Box, Collars & Cuffs, Hinged, Cream To Lemon, Round, 7 1/4 In.	400.00
Wave Crest, Box, Covered, Pink, Brook & Tree, 4 X 2 3/4 In.	200.00
Wave Crest, Box, Covered, Shell Shape, Enamel Floral, 4 1/4 In.	165.00
Wave Crest, Box, Flowers On Top, Blue, Pink Base, Brass Collar, 4 In.	155.00
Wave Crest, Box, Helmschmied Swirl, 4 X 4 X 4 In.	195.00
Wave Crest, Box, Hinged, Blue & White, Pink Floral, Scrolls, Square, 3 1/4 In.	135.00
Wave Crest, Box, Hinged, Blue To White, Enamel Floral & Scrolls, Round, 3 In.	145.00
Wave Crest, Box, Hinged, Cupid Decoration, 5 X 2 1/4 In.	375.00
Wave Crest, Box, Hinged, Hand-Painted Floral, Puffs, 7 In.	375.00
Wave Crest, Box, Hinged, Hand-Painted Floral, Signed, 7 In.	315.00
Wave Crest, Box, Hinged, Pale Green, Raised Pink & White Floral, Round, 4 In.	135.00
Wave Crest, Box, Hinged, Pink & White, Scrolls & Blue Bouquets, 3 1/2 In.	165.00
Wave Crest, Box, Hinged, Puffy, Floral Decoration, 6 In.	375.00
Wave Crest, Box, Hinged, Robin's-Egg Blue, Floral, Square, 7 In.	325.00
Wave Crest, Box, Hinged, Swirled, Blue Blossoms, Square, 3 In.	70.00
Wave Crest, Box, Hinged, White & Pink, Forget-Me-Nots, Ormolu Fittings, 3 In.	145.00
Wave Crest, Box, Hinged, White, Water Lily, Square, 4 1/2 In.	325.00
Wave Crest, Box, House Scene On Lid, Beige Satin, Round, 3 1/2 In.	275.00
Wave Crest, Box, Jewel, Hinged, Blue Cartouche, Floral, Square, 7 In.	375.00
Wave Crest, Box, Jewel, Hinged, Off-White, Swirl, Floral, Ormolu Feet, 8 In.	695.00
Wave Crest, Box, Jewel, Pink & White Enamel Flowers, Swirled, 7 In.	100.00
Wave Crest, Box, Jewel, Shell Scroll, Green Lining, 3 X 2 1/2 In.	135.00
Wave Crest, Box, Jewel, Hinged, Swirled, Helmschmied, 7 In.	210.00
Wave Crest, Box, Jewel, Tan & Pink, Blue & Yellow Birds, 7 In.	450.00
Wave Crest, Box, Jewel, Hinged, White, Swirl & Floral, Ormolu Feet, 8 In.	695.00
Wave Crest, Box, Marbelized Dark Blue, Pink Mum, Round, 4 5/8 In.	170.00
Wave Crest, Box, Pale Pink Raised Roses, 4 Footed, 6 X 3 In.	175.00
Wave Crest, Box, Pin, Enamel Floral, Ormolu Collar & Handles, Red Mark, 6 In.	75.00
Wave Crest, Box, Pink Floral, Liner, Red Banner Mark, Round, 4 1/2 In.	95.00
Wave Crest, Box, Pink To Yellow, Raised S Swirls, 5 In.	45.00
Wave Crest, Box, Pink, Blue Flowers, White Beading, Round, 4 In.	170.00
Wave Crest, Box, Powder, Hinged, Cream, Blue Florals, Round, 3 In.	95.00
Wave Crest, Box, Ring, Floral & Enamel Beading On Lid, Pale Pink, Signed	200.00
Wave Crest, Box, Scenic, Signed, Round, 3 1/2 In.	250.00
Wave Crest, Box, Shell On Lid, Beige, Enamel Floral, Round, 4 1/4 In.	165.00
Wave Crest, Box, Trinket, Blue & White, Applied Leaves, Ormolu Rim, R.B., 5 In	135.00
Wave Crest, Box, Trinket, Blue, Ormolu Collar & Handles, R.B., 3 1/2 In.	115.00
Wave Crest, Box, Trinket, Blue, Shell Design, Painted Floral, R.B., 4 1/4 In.	70.00
Wave Crest, Box, Trinket, Off-White, Shell & Scroll, Ormolu Collar, R.B., 4 In	85.00
Wave Crest, Box, White To Blue Swirl, Floral, Helmschmied, Square, 3 1/2 In.	200.00
Wave Crest, Box, Yellow & Orange On Lid, Blown-Out Pansy, Round, 3 1/2 In.	300.00
Wave Crest, Box, Yellow, Blue & Green Floral, Signed, 5 In.	68.00
Wave Crest, Casket, Jewel, Blue, Shells, Ormolu Legs, 4 X 3 1/2 In.	267.00
Wave Crest, Creamer, Satin, Swirl, Yellow & Brown Floral, 3 1/4 In.	80.00
Wave Crest, Hair Receiver, Blue, Red Banner Mark, 4 1/2 X 3 1/4 In.	215.00
Wave Crest, Holder, Letter, Decorated, 6 X 4 1/4 X 3 1/2 In.	145.00
Wave Crest, Holder, Letter, Egg Crate, Ormolu Rim, Signed	200.00
Wave Crest, Holder, Letter, Puffy Ground, Violets, 6 X 3 1/2 In.	145.00
Wave Crest, Humidor, Tobacco, Blue, Apricot Flowers, Wreath, 5 1/4 X 3 7/8 In	295.00
Wave Crest, Jar, Biscuit, Mums, Squatty	225.00
Wave Crest, Jar, Cookie, Cream, Daisies & Scrolls, Gold Washed Fittings	95.00
Wave Crest, Jar, Cracker, Blue & White Classical Figures, Bulbous	115.00
Wave Crest, Jar, Cracker, White & Tan, Swirled, 7 1/4 In.	165.00
Wave Crest, Jar, Cracker, White Satin, Mums, Puffed Blank	200.00
Wave Crest, Jar, Cracker, Yellow, Pink, Crescent Moon & Sea, White Beading	195.00
Wave Crest, Jar, Rose, Covered, Pink To White, Decorated, 6 1/4 In.	75.00
Wave Crest, Muffineer, Beige & White, Pink Roses, Swirl, Helmschmied	195.00
Wave Crest, Muffineer, Scroll Top, Panels Of Blue Scrolls & Floral	145.00
Wave Crest, Muffineer, White To Yellow Satin, Pastel Ferns	170.00
Wave Crest, Planter, Blue, Pink Blossoms, Brass Insert, Square, 5 1/4 In.	250.00

Wave Crest, Planter, Ivory, Ferns, Metal Loop Handles, Red Banner Mark, 7 In.	250.00
Wave Crest, Planter, Ivory, Pink Fern, Gray Leaves, Brass Insert, Square, 7 In	225.00
Wave Crest, Planter, Pink, Brown, & White, Floral, Metal Insert, 6 1/2 In.	125.00
Wave Crest, Salt & Pepper, Floral	50.00
Wave Crest, Salt & Pepper, Off-White, Puffy Florals, Pewter Tops, Square	135.00
Wave Crest, Salt & Pepper, Swirled, Enameled Daisies	90.00
Wave Crest, Saltshaker, Enameled Flowers & Birds, Tulip Shape	30.00
Wave Crest, Sugar & Creamer, Silver Plate Cover, Handles, & Rims, Pink	225.00
Wave Crest, Sugar, Silver Plate, Cover & Handles, Floral Transfer, 6 In.	57.00
Wave Crest, Syrup, Blue, Flowers, Brass Lid & Collar, Bulbous	85.00
Wave Crest, Toothpick, White, Yellow & Salmon Pansies, Ormolu Feet	165.00
Wave Crest, Tray, Pin, Green, Orange Kitten Decoration, 3 In.	95.00
Wave Crest, Tray, Pin, Pink & Blue Daisies, Ornate Ormolu Pedestal	95.00
Wave Crest, Tray, Ring, Blue Flowers, Ormolu Handles, 4 In.	55.00
Wave Crest, Vase, Blue, Classical Scene, 18 In.	950.00
Wave Crest, Vase, Blue, 2 Maidens In Garden, Floral, Bronze Handles, 18 In.	795.00
Wave Crest, Vase, Bud, Pink To Blue, Ewer Shape, Ormolu Fittings, T.M., 7 In.	285.00
Wave Crest, Vase, Green Leaf, Pink Floral, Fleur-De-Lis, 8 1/2 In.	125.00
Wave Crest, Vase, Molded Scrolls, Blue Astors, Ormolu Handles & Feet, 14 In.	350.00
Wave Crest, Vase, Pink & Blue Cosmos, Raised Shells, Ormolu Holder, 9 1/2 In	175.00
Wave Crest, Vase, Violets, White Dotted Top, Footed Ormolu Base, 6 1/4 In.	130.00
Wax, Medallion, Wall, Charles Dickens Seated In Chair, Oval, 4 3/4 X 3 In.	75.00
Weapon, Ax, Belt, Colonial American, C.1760, Wooden Handle	235.00
Weapon, Bayonet & Scabbard, U.S., 1917	9.50
Weapon, Bayonet, American Revolutionary, Triangular Forged Blade	59.50
Weapon, Bayonet, British Martini-Henry Rifle, C.1876, Leather Sheath	32.50
Weapon, Bayonet, British Martini-Henry Rifle, Socket, C.1876, 25 In.	14.50
Weapon, Bayonet, British Saber Type, Socket, C.1820	59.50
Weapon, Bayonet, Cadet Type, Civil War, Socket, Brass Tipped Sheath	49.50
Weapon, Bayonet, Cadet Type, Marked U.S., Socket, Small Bore Rifle	37.50
Weapon, Bayonet, Cadet Type, U.S., Socket, Triangular Blade	29.50
Weapon, Bayonet, Civil War, Socket, Brass Tipped Leather Sheath	54.50
Weapon, Bayonet, Enfield .577 Musket, Brass Mounted Leather Sheath	47.50
Weapon, Bayonet, Fencing, M1912, Leather Covered Steel Blade	34.50
Weapon, Bayonet, French Chassepot M1866 Rifle, Sheath, Brass Handle	22.50
Weapon, Bayonet, French Gras Bolt Action M1874 Rifle, Iron Sheath	14.50
Weapon, Bayonet, Infield .577 Percussion Musket, C.1853	19.50 To 29.50
Weapon, Bayonet, Lebel M1866 Rifle, Iron Sheath & Hilt, 4 Cornered Blade	22.50
Weapon, Bayonet, Nazi Dress, Iron Sheath, Engraved Blade, Black Grips	89.50
Weapon, Bayonet, Nazi Dress, Iron Sheath, Engraved Blade, Stag Grips	89.50
Weapon, Bayonet, Schmidt-Rubin M1911, Iron Sheath	19.50
Weapon, Bayonet, Springfield Rifle, M1873, U.S.Army, Socket, Sheath	22.50
Weapon, Bayonet, Springfield 1898 Krag Rifle, Iron Sheath	22.50
Weapon, Bayonet, Vetterli Bolt Action Rifle, 1882, Leather Sheath	22.50
Weapon, Bayonet, Winchester M1895 Military Musket, Cross Guard	34.50
Weapon, Bayonet, Winchester 1873 Musket, Socket, Triangular Blade	37.50
Weapon, Bayonet, World War II, Presentation, R.A.D.	110.00
Weapon, Belt, British Naval Captain's, Brass Buckle, C.1850	22.50
Weapon, Belt, British Naval Officer's Sword, Brass Buckle, C.1850	17.50
Weapon, Cutlass, British Navy, 1845, Wilkinson, London, Iron Hilt & Grips	195.00
Weapon, Cutlass, U.S.Naval, M1826, Iron Scabbard, Starr, Maple Grips	275.00
Weapon, Dagger, Japanese, Ivory Hilt, Steel Blade, Carved, Etched, 12 In.	50.00
Weapon, Dagger, Nazi Storm Trooper's, Sheath, Brown Wood Handle	97.50
Weapon, Dagger, Russian, Silver & Niello Mounts, Leather Sheath, C.1850	225.00
Weapon, Dagger, Scottish Highland, Skein Dhu, Stocking, C.1820, Enamel, Silver	325.00
Weapon, Derringer, A.Wurfflein, Phila., .38 Caliber, German Silver	650.00
Weapon, Derringer, American Arms Co., Wheeler Patent, .22 Caliber, Brass	250.00
Weapon, Derringer, Bitterlick, Nashville, German Silver, Gold Band Inlay	850.00
Weapon, Derringer, Deringer, Phila., Percussion, Iron, Gold Bands, .41 Caliber	850.00
Weapon, Derringer, Eclipse, .25 Caliber, Single Shot, Iron, Bird's Head Butt	54.50
Weapon, Derringer, F.Glassick & Co., Memphis, Tenn., .44 Caliber, Silver	650.00
Weapon, Derringer, Glassick, Memphis, Tenn., .46 Caliber, German Silver	650.00
Weapon, Derringer, Korean, C.1880, Percussion, Black Powder	40.00 To 45.00
Weapon, Derringer, Remington, Over & Under, Rubber Grips	235.00 To 350.00
Weapon, Derringer, Remington, Vest Pocket, Engraved, Ivory Grips	325.00
Weapon, Derringer, Stevens, Model 41, .22 Caliber, Walnut Grips	59.50

Weapon, Dirk, British Naval Officer's, C.1800, Lion's Head Pommel	175.00
Weapon, Dirk, British Naval Officer's, C.1810, Brass Sheath, Ivory Handle	145.00
Weapon, Dirk, British Naval, C.1810, Brass Sheath & Hilt, Gold Finish	225.00
Weapon, Dirk, Russian Naval, Cipher Of Nicholas II, Ivory Grips	195.00
Weapon, Flask, Powder, Brass, Deer & Pine Tree	30.00
Weapon, Flask, Powder, Leather, Brass Fittings, 9 In.	30.00
Weapon, Flask, Powder, Pewter With Brass Shell Decoration, 9 In.	50.00
Weapon, Gun, Colt .45, Brass, Handmade, Abalone Grips, Miniature, 2 1/4 In.	175.00
Weapon, Gun, Colt .45, Brass, Handmade, Pearl Grips, Miniature, 2 In.	175.00
Weapon, Gun, Lyle, Black Powder, 28 In. Barrel, Brass Trim	475.00
Weapon, Gun, Whaline, New Bedford, Brass, Breech Loading, 34 In.	650.00
Weapon, Harpoon, Whaling, Toggle Iron, Wood Shaft, C.1840, Macy, New Bedford	195.00
Weapon, Horn, Powder, Dr.T.S.Hitchick, Oswego, N.Y., Carved, C.1850, 15 In.	275.00
Weapon, Knife, see also Lone Ranger, Knife, Store, Knife	
Weapon, Knife & Scabbard, Bolo, U.S.Marine Corps	22.00
Weapon, Knife, Australian, World War II, Knuckle Duster, Ake Reg'd	135.00
Weapon, Knife, Austrian Trench Combat, World War I, Wooden Handle	54.50
Weapon, Knife, Bone Grips, 2 Blades, Folding, Cast Iron	5.00
Weapon, Knife, Bone Grips, 2 Blades, Folding, 3 In. Case, Cast Iron	5.00
Weapon, Knife, Bowie, Confederate, Engraved C.S.A. Clip Blade, 18 In.	142.00
Weapon, Knife, Bowie, Confederate, Starr Contract, 1818, D Shape Handle	425.00
Weapon, Knife, Bowie, J.Rodgers & Sons, Sheffield, Leather Sheath, Stag Grips	110.00
Weapon, Knife, Bowie, James Rodgers, Sheffield, C.1860, Ebony Grips	225.00
Weapon, Knife, Bowie, Joseph Rodgers & Sons, Leather Sheath, Stag Grips	97.50
Weapon, Knife, Bowie, Landers, Frary & Clark, Conn., Leather Sheath	97.50
Weapon, Knife, Bowie, Marked Miss.-1861, Leather Sheath	250.00
Weapon, Knife, Bowie, Rodgers & Co., Sheffield, Leather Sheath, Cast Steel	225.00
Weapon, Knife, Bowie, Stag Grip, Engraved N.Y. & Death To Traitors, 10 In.	75.00
Weapon, Knife, Boy Scout, Bone Grips, 4 Blades, Folding, Cast Iron	5.00
Weapon, Knife, Camillus, N.Y.C., Bone Grips, 3 Blades, Cast Iron, 3 In.	5.00
Weapon, Knife, Carved Ivory Handle & Case, Dragons, 8 1/2 In.	85.00
Weapon, Knife, Cattaraugus, Little Valley, N.Y., Pocket, Brass	35.00
Weapon, Knife, Eagle Co., Single Blade, Stainless Steel Handle, 3 1/4 In.	28.00
Weapon, Knife, Fighting, World War II, Cattaraugus, No.2250, Engraved 1943	78.00
Weapon, Knife, Hooked Blade, 3 Fold, Cast Iron	10.00
Weapon, Knife, Joseph Rodgers & Sons, Leather Sheath, German Silver Handle	295.00
Weapon, Knife, Navy, Russell, Wooden Handle, Brass	60.00
Weapon, Knife, New England Whaler, Ka-Bar	5.00
Weapon, Knife, Pen, Pocket, Sterling Silver, Loop For Chain	6.95
Weapon, Knife, Pocket, Civil War Centennial, 1961	3.50
Weapon, Knife, Pocket, George Unite, Birmingham, England, C.1910, Pearl, Silver	20.00
Weapon, Knife, Pocket, Hammered Sterling, 1 Blade, 1 Curved Pick	15.00
Weapon, Knife, Pocket, Indian Motorcycles, Key Chain On End, Brass Color	3.50
Weapon, Knife, Pocket, Nu Grape Soda, Pearl Handle	6.50
Weapon, Knife, Pocket, Presidents To Teddy Roosevelt, Metal Handle	39.75
Weapon, Knife, Pocket, Winchester, Centennial, 1866-1966, Pearlite Handle	4.50
Weapon, Knife, Pocket, Winchester, Pearllike Handle, 2 Blade, 1866-1966	5.00
Weapon, Knife, Remington, Bullet On Handle	450.00
Weapon, Knife, Remington, R-1806, Silver Bullet, Single Blade, Bone Handle	25.00
Weapon, Knife, Straight, 1 Blade, Cast Iron, 8 3/4 In.	5.00
Weapon, Knife, U.S.Trench, M1917, Leather Sheath, Iron Mounts	74.50
Weapon, Knife, U.S.Trench, M1917, Marked U.S.L.F.& C.-1917	54.50
Weapon, Knife, U.S.Trench, M1918, Wooden Grips	54.50
Weapon, Knife, Walden, N.Y., Press Button	20.00
Weapon, Knife, Winchester, 3 In.	90.00
Weapon, Knife, World War II Issue, Camillus, N.Y., Plastic Sheath	59.50
Weapon, Kris, Javanese, Brass Sheath & Hilt, Grotesque Javanese God	89.00
Weapon, Lance & Harpoon, Whale, Hand-Forged, C.1840, Wooden Shaft	295.00
Weapon, Lance, Bomb, Whaling, Cunningham & Cogen, New Bedford, Brass, C.1870	29.50
Weapon, Lance, Bomb, Whaling, Grudcho & Eggers Patent, 1857, 16 In.	94.50
Weapon, Lance, Bomb, Whaling, Pierce & Eggers, New Bedford, Brass, 18 In.	97.50
Weapon, Lance, Whale, Hand-Forged, Leaf Shape Blade, C.1840, 6 Ft.2 In.	195.00
Weapon, Luger, German M1914 Military, Semi Automatic, Walnut Grips	295.00
Weapon, Luger, Mauser, 1939, Nazi Markings, Walnut Grips	225.00
Weapon, Mold, Bullet, Kentucky Rifle, Iron	9.00
Weapon, Mold, Bullet, W.C., Patent 1844, .44 Caliber, Ladle, Loader	50.00

Weapon, Mold, Bullet, Winchester 15.00
Weapon, Musket, American, Revolutionary War, Maple Stock 2250.00
Weapon, Musket, Joslyn, Fire Breach, Conversion, 1864 .... 325.00 To 450.00
Weapon, Musket, Starr, U.S.Model 1816, Single Shot, Full Stock, .69 Caliber 145.00
Weapon, Pepperbox, Bacon, .22 Caliber, 6 Shot, Iron Frame, Rosewood Grips 100.00
Weapon, Pepperbox, Remington, Zig-Zag, .22 Caliber, Gutta-Percha Grips 650.00
Weapon, Pepperbox, Sharp & Hankins, .32 Caliber, Gutta-Percha Grips 350.00
Weapon, Pistol, Adkin, English, .60 Caliber, Double Barrel, Percussion 850.00
Weapon, Pistol, Allen & Thurber, Target, .34 Caliber, Boxlock, Walnut Grips 250.00
Weapon, Pistol, Dueling, English Flintlock, Sharpe & Keene, Pair 1795.00
Weapon, Pistol, Dueling, Robinson, Phila., C.1840, .44 Caliber, Pair 495.00
Weapon, Pistol, Dueling, Van Wart Son & Co., London, .52 Caliber, Silver 350.00
Weapon, Pistol, Freeman, Strand, London, British Officer's, C.1840, Brass, Iron 1500.00
Weapon, Pistol, Gould Model No.37, Stevens, Target, .22 Caliber 175.00
Weapon, Pistol, Indian, W.L.Grant, C.1870, Single Shot, .32 Caliber 85.00
Weapon, Pistol, Percussion, Single Shot, Stag Grips, 5 In. 45.00
Weapon, Pistol, Powder Tester, C.1750, Flintlock, Walnut Stock, 15 In. 350.00
Weapon, Pistol, Purdy, London, .36 Caliber, Boxlock, Percussion, German Silver 125.00
Weapon, Pistol, Remington Arms Co., Gambler's, .41 Caliber, Rubber Grips 175.00
Weapon, Pistol, Savage, Automatic, .380 Caliber, Rubber Grips 145.00
Weapon, Pistol, Smith & Wesson, 2nd Model, .22 Caliber, Single Shot 145.00
Weapon, Pistol, W.W.Marston, N.Y., Boxlock, Percussion, Pocket, Iron Frame 74.50
Weapon, Powder Flask, American Brass & Cap Company, Wreath & Shield 34.00
Weapon, Powder Flask, Brass, Cannons, Eagles, & Flags, C.1832 .... 150.00
Weapon, Powder Horn, Brass, Hunting Scene 52.00
Weapon, Powder Horn, Engraved, Churst, Arrows, & Trees, Wood Stopper, 9 In. 175.00
Weapon, Powder Horn, European, Relief Carved, Brass Spout, 14 In. 48.00
Weapon, Powder Horn, Indian Teepees, Tom Sands, 1862, 13 In. 300.00
Weapon, Powder Horn, Kentucky Rifle, 9 1/2 In. 25.00
Weapon, Powder Horn, Map Of Kentucky Territory, 1776, 8 In. 150.00
Weapon, Powder Horn, Mermaids, Floral Sprays, & Birds, C.1850, 7 In. 410.00
Weapon, Powder Horn, Steer's Horn, Carved Mouthpiece, 12 In. 15.00
Weapon, Revolver, .32 Caliber, 6 Shot, Brass Frame, Rosewood Grips 375.00
Weapon, Revolver, Adams' Patent, English, .44 Caliber, Copper Flask 750.00
Weapon, Revolver, Aetna No.2, Patent 1876, .32 Caliber, 5 Shot, Rubber Grips 34.50
Weapon, Revolver, Allen & Wheelock, .31 Caliber, 5 Shot, Walnut Grips 185.00
Weapon, Revolver, Bacon, Norwich, Conn., .31 Caliber, 5 Shot, Engraved Floral 225.00
Weapon, Revolver, Colt M1851, Navy, .36 Caliber, For Shoulder Stock 750.00
Weapon, Revolver, Colt, Officer's Model, Patent 1884, 1900, 1905, .38 Caliber 145.00
Weapon, Revolver, Colt, Official Police, .38 Caliber, Walnut Grips 135.00
Weapon, Revolver, Colt, Python, .357 Magnum, Walnut Grips 210.00
Weapon, Revolver, Colt, Trooper, .38 Caliber, Walnut Grips 125.00
Weapon, Revolver, Deane & Son, London, Tranter Patent, .30 Caliber, 5 Shot 275.00
Weapon, Revolver, Hi-Standard, Sentinel, .22 Caliber, 9 Shot 37.50
Weapon, Revolver, Iver Johnson, .32 Caliber, Owlhead Design Rubber Grips 34.50
Weapon, Revolver, Mass.Arms Co., Adam's Patent, Navy, Civil War, .36 Caliber 350.00
Weapon, Revolver, Merwin & Bray Firearms Co., N.Y., .28 Caliber, 5 Shot 225.00
Weapon, Revolver, Merwin Hulbert, .38 Caliber, 5 Shot, Burd's Head Butt 74.50
Weapon, Revolver, Percussion, Remington, Engraved, C.1860 .... 125.00
Weapon, Revolver, Pond, .32 Caliber, 6 Shot, Iron Frame, Rosewood Grips 175.00
Weapon, Revolver, Remington, New Model, Police, .38 Caliber, 5 Shot 250.00
Weapon, Revolver, Remington, Smoot, New Line, No.1, .30 Caliber, Rubber Grips 325.00
Weapon, Revolver, Remington, Smoot, New Line, No.2, .32 Caliber, Rubber Grips 150.00
Weapon, Revolver, Rogers & Spencer, Army, Civil War, .44 Caliber 495.00
Weapon, Revolver, Smith & Wesson, Hand Ejector, Model 1905, .38 Caliber 74.50
Weapon, Revolver, Smith & Wesson, Hand Ejector, M1903, .32 Caliber, 6 Shot 84.50
Weapon, Revolver, Smith & Wesson, Hand Ejector, U.S.Army Model 1899 .... 295.00
Weapon, Revolver, Smith & Wesson, Model 1 1/2, .32 Caliber, Engraved 325.00
Weapon, Revolver, Smith & Wesson, Model 2, Army, .32 Caliber, Rosewood Grips 375.00
Weapon, Revolver, Smith & Wesson, Model 3, .32/.44 Caliber, Rubber Grips 395.00
Weapon, Revolver, Smith & Wesson, Target, K-22, .22 Caliber, Walnut Grips 97.50
Weapon, Revolver, Tomes Son & Melvain, N.Y., .31 Caliber, 5 Shot, Engraved 295.00
Weapon, Revolver, U.S.Revolver Co., Hammerless, .38 Caliber, 5 Shot 34.50
Weapon, Revolver, Wesson & Seavitt, Civil War 690.00
Weapon, Rifle, Birmingham Small Arms Co., 1907, Military Training, .22 Cal. 84.50
Weapon, Rifle, Burnside Carbine, Civil War, Percussion, Breech Loading 395.00

Weapon, Rifle, Gross' Patent, 1st Model, Infantry, Carbine.52 Caliber	550.00
Weapon, Rifle, J.P.Sauer & Son, Prussia, Mauser Action, Sporting	550.00
Weapon, Rifle, J.Widmer, Newark, .40 Caliber, Target, Percussion	1250.00
Weapon, Rifle, Kentucky Fullstock, Octagonal Barrel, 36 Caliber, Golcher	425.00
Weapon, Rifle, Kentucky Halfstock Plains, Octagonal Barrel, Brass Fittings	395.00
Weapon, Rifle, Lindner, Lamson & Co., Vermont, 1865, Carbine, Cavalry	750.00
Weapon, Rifle, Marlin Ballard No.9, .38/.55 Caliber, Single Shot	950.00
Weapon, Rifle, Maynard, Sporting, .22 Caliber, 1873 Model	185.00
Weapon, Rifle, Quackenbush, Herkimer, N.Y., Haviland & Gunn Patent	39.50
Weapon, Rifle, Remington, Armory, 1917, Russian Bolt Action, Mosin M1891	59.50
Weapon, Rifle, Remington, Halfstock, Patch Box	385.00
Weapon, Rifle, Remington, No.7, Target, .22 Caliber, Single Shot	1850.00
Weapon, Rifle, Ross, M1910, Sporting, Bolt Action, .28 Caliber	195.00
Weapon, Rifle, Savage, Model 1899, .22 Caliber, Walnut Stock	135.00
Weapon, Rifle, Sharp & Hankins Carbine, U.S.Navy, Civil War, .52 Caliber	450.00
Weapon, Rifle, Sharp's New Model, 1863, Cavalry Carbine	750.00
Weapon, Rifle, Snider Patent, British, .577 Caliber, Breech Loading	375.00
Weapon, Rifle, Springfield 45/70, U.S.Army, M1884, Trap Door, Bayonet	195.00
Weapon, Rifle, Springfield, M1873, .45/.70 Caliber	250.00
Weapon, Rifle, Springfield, M1884, .45/.70 Caliber, Trap Door	295.00
Weapon, Rifle, Springfield, U.S.M1870, Trap Door, .50/.70 Caliber	195.00
Weapon, Rifle, Springfield, U.S.M1873, Trap Door, 45/70, Engraved	395.00
Weapon, Rifle, Vetterli Carbine, M1878, Swiss	97.50
Weapon, Rifle, Winchester '92 Carbine, Saddle Ring, .25/.20 Caliber	750.00
Weapon, Rifle, Winchester Carbine, Model '94, .30/.30 Caliber, Shotgun Butt	175.00
Weapon, Rifle, Winchester Carbine, M1872, Saddle Ring, .32/.20 Caliber	395.00
Weapon, Rifle, Winchester Carbine, 1873, .44 Caliber	250.00
Weapon, Rifle, Winchester, Model 53, Take Down, .25/.20 Caliber	275.00
Weapon, Rifle, Winchester, Model 73, 32-20 Caliber, 22 In. Barrel	80.00
Weapon, Rifle, Winchester, M1892, .38/.40 Caliber, Octagonal Barrel	395.00
Weapon, Rifle, Winchester, M1894, .30/.30 Caliber, Carbine Butt Plate	225.00
Weapon, Rifle, Winchester, M1894, Carbine, Saddle Ring, .32/.40 Caliber	595.00
Weapon, Rifle, Winchester, 1886, .40/.65 Caliber, Shotgun Butt	750.00
Weapon, Rifle, Winchester, 1886, Series 42, Flat Base, Tapered Front Point	37.50
Weapon, Saber & Scabbard, Ames, Civil War, Cavalry, 1864	125.00
Weapon, Saber & Scabbard, Union Light Cavalry, 1862, 35 In.	250.00
Weapon, Saber Bayonet, Colt Revolving Rifle, M1855, Iron Guard, 22 In.	34.50
Weapon, Saber Bayonet, U.S., Brass Scaled Grips, 20 In.	34.50
Weapon, Saber Bayonet, U.S., Leather Sheath, Brass Hilt	89.50
Weapon, Saber Bayonet, U.S.Navy M1861 Rifle, Collins & Co., Hartford	135.00
Weapon, Saber, Confederate Cavalry, Phrygian Helmet Type Pommel	275.00
Weapon, Saber, Tiffany & Co., N.Y., C.1840, Iron Guard, Dragoon Pattern	125.00
Weapon, Saber, U.S.Cavalry Officer's, M1872, Iron Scabbard, Brass Hilt	135.00
Weapon, Saber, U.S.Cavalry Officer's, 1812, Ivory Grips, Silver Mounts	1250.00
Weapon, Saber, U.S.Cavalry, 1905, Ames Co., Iron Hilt, Sharkskin Grips	325.00
Weapon, Saber, U.S.Cavalry, 1906, Ames Co., Iron Hilt, Sharkskin Grips	275.00
Weapon, Saber, U.S.Light Artillery, M1840, Scabbard, Ames, Leather Grips	195.00
Weapon, Saber, U.S.Officer's, 1902, Henderson-Ames Co., Presentation	550.00
Weapon, Shotgun, Colt, 10 Gauge, Double Barrel, Outside Hammers	275.00
Weapon, Shotgun, Heym, Suhl, Germany, 20 Gauge, Hammerless, Pistol Grip Stock	595.00
Weapon, Shotgun, Parker, 10 Gauge, Double Barrel, Outside Hammer, C.1878	425.00
Weapon, Shotgun, Remington, 10 Gauge, Double Barrel, Outside Hammers	325.00
Weapon, Shotgun, Remington, 12 Gauge, Double Barrel, Hammerless	350.00
Weapon, Shotgun, Winchester, M1887, 12 Gauge, Lever Action, Pistol Grip Stock	74.50
Weapon, Shotgun, Winchester, M1897, 12 Gauge, Pump, Take Down, Pistol Grip	175.00
Weapon, Sword & Scabbard, Caucasian, C.1890, Hebraic Inscriptions, 23 In.	325.00
Weapon, Sword & Scabbard, U.S.Militia Staff Officer's, C.1850, Ames Co.	225.00
Weapon, Sword & Scabbard, U.S.Navy Officer's, M1852, Brass Guard	84.50
Weapon, Sword & Scabbard, Union Officer's Dress, C.1870	50.00
Weapon, Sword, British Foot Officer's, 1795, Leather Scabbard, Brass Hilt	195.00
Weapon, Sword, British Hunting, Royal Cipher, C.1750, Brass Hilt, Stag Grips	325.00
Weapon, Sword, Civil War Officer's, 1850, Scabbard, Brass Grips & Mounts	650.00
Weapon, Sword, Civil War Staff Officer's, M1850, Iron Scabbard, Ames	325.00
Weapon, Sword, French Infantry, 1831, Leather Scabbard, Roman Pattern Type	59.50
Weapon, Sword, French Naval Officer's, C.1850, Leather Scabbard, Brass Hilt	250.00
Weapon, Sword, French Officer's Dress, C.1810, Brass Hilt, Animal Pommel	195.00

Weapon, Sword, Gentleman's Colichemarde, C.1770, English Silver Hilt	750.00
Weapon, Sword, German Cavalry Officer's, C.1850, Iron Hilt, D Shape Guard	135.00
Weapon, Sword, Hunting, Engraved Blade, Brass Hilt, Horn Grip, C.1760, 20 In.	125.00
Weapon, Sword, Imperial German Officer's, C.1870, Iron Scabbard, Brass Hilt	97.50
Weapon, Sword, Imperial German Officer's, C.1890, Leather Scabbard	125.00
Weapon, Sword, Japanese, Samurai, C.1900, Wooden Case	110.00
Weapon, Sword, Mounted German Officer's, C.1780, Brass Hilt, Sharkskin Grips	650.00
Weapon, Sword, Netherlands Army Officer's, Brass Hilt, Presentation	975.00
Weapon, Sword, Oriental, Snakeskin Case, Gold Leaves & Stems, 23 In.Long	150.00
Weapon, Sword, Sawfish Nose, 5 Pointed Star Inlayed In Wood Handle, 3 In.	330.00
Weapon, Sword, U.S.Artillery Officer's, C.1812, Leather Scabbard, Eaglehead	295.00
Weapon, Sword, U.S.Infantry Officer's, C.1850, Leather Scabbard, Brass Hilt	325.00
Weapon, Sword, U.S.Infantry Officer's, M1850, Iron Scabbard, Ames	325.00
Weapon, Sword, U.S.Infantry Officer's, 1850, Leather Scabbard, Brass Hilt	145.00
Weapon, Sword, U.S.Medical Staff's, M1840, Brass Hilt & Grips, Inscribed	650.00
Weapon, Sword, U.S.Militia Staff Officer's, 1850, Brass Hilt, Helmet Pommel	87.50
Weapon, Sword, U.S.Musician's, M1840, Ames, Brass Hilt & Grips	64.50
Weapon, Sword, U.S.Navy Ceremonial, Sheath, Belt, & Epaulets, C.1900	150.00
Weapon, Sword, U.S.Noncommissioned Officer's, C.1790, W.Rose, Phila.	595.00
Weapon, Sword, U.S.Revolutionary Foot Officer's, Scabbard, Brass Hilt	795.00
Weapon, Sword, U.S.Staff & Field Officer's, M1860, Iron Scabbard, Brass Hilt	150.00
Weapon, Sword, Union Officer's, Iron Scabbard, Phrygian Helmet Pommel	350.00
Weapon, Sword, Union Officer's, 1850, Brass Scabbard & Hilt, Presentation	595.00
Weapon, Telescope, For Stevens Rifle, No.438, 19 1/2 In.	59.50
Weapon, Telescope, For Winchester Rifle, Model A-5, 16 In.	74.50
Weather Vane, American Eagle On Orb, Spread Winged, Copper, C.1850, 14 In.	200.00
Weather Vane, American Eagle On Orb, Spread Winged, Copper, C.1850, 37 In.	550.00
Weather Vane, American Eagle, Spread Winged, Dome Base, Tin, C.1850, 6 Ft.	500.00
Weather Vane, Arrow, Marked Shinn, Ruby Glass Ball	26.50
Weather Vane, Birds, Copper, 4 Direction, 21 X 19 In.	37.50
Weather Vane, Cow, Copper, C.1850, 30 In.	525.00
Weather Vane, Dove On Orb, Gilt Copper, C.1850, 18 In.	1600.00
Weather Vane, Eagle On Banderole, Sheet Iron, 4 Ft.7 In.	190.00
Weather Vane, Eagle, Spread Wine, Repousse, Copper, C.1850, 30 X 26 In.	1400.00
Weather Vane, General Washington On Horseback, Cast Iron, C.1850, 15 In.	450.00
Weather Vane, Horse & Sulky, Copper, C.1850, 34 1/2 In.	900.00
Weather Vane, Horse, Copper, 24 In. *Illus*	425.00
Weather Vane, Horse, Trotting Horse, C.1850, 29 1/2 In.	170.00
Weather Vane, Hunting Dog In Grass, Sheet Iron, C.1850, 46 In.	425.00
Weather Vane, Indian Brave, Drawn Bow, Sheet Iron, C.1850, 24 1/2 In.	475.00
Weather Vane, Indian Drawing His Bow, Sheet Copper, C.1850, 4 1/2 Ft.	400.00
Weather Vane, Prancing Horse, Cast Iron, C.1850, 4 Ft.	150.00
Weather Vane, Reindeer, Sheet Iron, C.1850, 4 Ft.4 1/4 In.	130.00
Weather Vane, Running Horse, Copper, Gilt, Cast Head, C.1850, 20 In.	300.00
Weather Vane, Running Horse, Flowing Mane, Copper, C.1850, 47 1/2 In.	1200.00
Weather Vane, Running Horse, Sheet Iron, C.1850, 30 In.	450.00
Webb Burmese, Bowl, Enamel Decoration, 6 Sided, 2 3/4 In. High	400.00
Webb Burmese, Rose Bowl, Enamel Floral, Miniature	375.00

Weather Vane, Horse, Copper, 24 In.

Webb Burmese, Rose Bowl, Enameled Leaf & Vine Design, 3 1/2 X 2 1/4 In.	335.00
Webb Burmese, Rose Bowl, Peach To Yellow, Florals, Crimped Top, 2 1/2 In.	295.00
Webb Burmese, Rose Bowl, Pink To Yellow, Eight Crimped Top, 3 X 2 In.	225.00
Webb Burmese, Tumbler, Ivy Vine With Green Leaves, 2 1/4 In.	275.00
Webb Burmese, Tumbler, Juice	325.00
Webb Burmese, Vase, Peach To Yellow, Pedestal, Ruffled Top, Red Buds, 4 In.	365.00,
Webb Burmese, Vase, Ruffled Top & Pedestal Foot, Red Buds, 3 7/8 In.	345.00
Webb Burmese, Vase, Yellow To Pink, Five Petal Top, 4 In.	295.00

Webb glass was made by Thomas Webb & Sons of Stourbridge, England.
Many types of art and cameo glass were made by them during the Victorian era.

Webb, Basket, Tulip Shape, Pink To Green Rim, Applied Frosted Handle, 7 In.	240.00
Webb, Bottle, Cameo, Silver Top, Blue & White Winged Figure, Floral, Woodall	6500.00
Webb, Bottle, Perfume, Citron & White, Repousse Cap, Cameo, 7 In.	875.00
Webb, Bottle, Perfume, Hinged Sterling Lid, Blue & White Daisies, 3 In.	350.00
Webb, Bottle, Perfume, Laydown, Raisin Color, White Floral Carvings, 5 In.	450.00
Webb, Bottle, Perfume, Laydown, Cameo, Cranberry & White	450.00
Webb, Bottle, Scent, Blue, Butterfly, Gold Prunus, Sterling Top	395.00
Webb, Bowl & Stand, Bride's, Mother-Of-Pearl Satin, Enameled, 12 1/2 In.	425.00
Webb, Bowl, Bride's, Melon Ribbed, Enamel Floral, Cherry To Pink, 6 1/2 In.	65.00
Webb, Bowl, Cut Velvet, Basket Weave, Cloverleaf Top, Red To Pink, 6 1/2 In.	265.00
Webb, Cup, Punch, Blue Satin, Frosted Handle, Pink Floral, White Lining	85.00
Webb, Ewer, Mother-Of-Pearl, Pink, Applied Thorn Handle, 10 In.	195.00
Webb, Ewer, Mother-Of-Pearl, Rainbow, Applied Clear Handle, 10 In.	975.00
Webb, Ewer, Rainbow Mother-Of-Pearl, Herringbone, Clear Handle, 11 In.	985.00
Webb, Ewer, Satin, Apricot, Enamel Decoration, Thorn Handles, 12 1/2 In, Pair	295.00
Webb, Flask, Pocket, Ovoid, Hinged Lock Top, Citron, White Floral, 5 1/4 In.	725.00
Webb, Jar, Cookie, Cameo, Acid Cut Back, Pink Flowers	395.00
Webb, Lamp Base, Cameo, White Pansies & Butterfly On Citron, 3 Footed, 4 In.	550.00
Webb, Lamp, Kerosene, Quilted Pink Mother-Of-Pearl, Brass Feet, 14 In., Pair	500.00
Webb, Pitcher, Apricot, Enameled, Thorn Handle, Satin, 13 In.	195.00
Webb, Plaque, Simulated Ivory, Signed, 9 In.	950.00
Webb, Rose Bowl, Alexandrite, Blue To Fuchsia, Amber Honeycomb, 2 3/4 In.	725.00
Webb, Salt Dip, Blue With White, Cameo	275.00
Webb, Salt Dip, Citron With White, Cameo	275.00
Webb, Tumbler, Pink, Tufted, White Lining, Signed	115.00
Webb, Urn, Covered, Butterfly, Jeweled Wings, Blue Florals, 11 In.High	225.00
Webb, Vase, Amber, Acid Cut Leaves & Flowers, 6 1/4 In.	64.0-
Webb, Vase, Amber, Blue, & Clear, Intaglio Cut, 9 X 5 1/2 In.	175.00
Webb, Vase, Anemones On Yellow, White Hearts, Teardrop Shape, C.1890, 24 In.	5700.00
Webb, Vase, Citron, Embossed Butterfly & Flowers, 4 In.	135.00
Webb, Vase, Cut Glass, Flower-Filled Baskets, Geo Woodall, C.1890, 8 3/4 In.	400.00
Webb, Vase, Enameled Birds, Flowers, Leaves, & Vines, Blue Ground, 14 In.High	295.00
Webb, Vase, Intaglio Cut Blue & Amber On Clear, 9 X 5 1/2 In.	175.00
Webb, Vase, Ivory, Floral & Leaf, Pinched Scalloped Top, 4 In.	595.00
Webb, Vase, Mother-Of-Pearl, Frosted Base With Thorns, Blown, 12 In.	295.00
Webb, Vase, Mother-Of-Pearl, Salmon, 6 In.	195.00
Webb, Vase, Pastel Green Satin, Enameled, Jeweled, 9 In.	95.00
Webb, Vase, Pink, Enameled Butterflies & Flowers, Ruffled, 9 In., Pair	220.00
Webb, Vase, Quilted Peach Opalescent, Blue Enamel Flowers, 6 In.	95.00
Webb, Vase, Satin Glass, Green To Yellow, Gold Prunus Blossoms, 8 In.High	495.00
Webb, Vase, Satin Glass, Green, White, & Brown Prunus, 8 1/2 In.	125.00
Webb, Vase, Satin, Quilted, Pink, Applied Clear Handles, 9 1/2 In.High	330.00
Webb, Vase, Stick, Burgundy Ground, Gold & Silver Enameled Design, 9 1/2 In.	295.00
Webb, Vase, Tortoiseshell Glass, Bulbous, Enameled Flowers, 10 In.High	95.00
Webb, Vase, White Flowers & Butterflies On Rose, Cameo, 2 X 2 In.	450.00
Webb, Vase, White To Lemon, Intaglio Cut, Signed, 7 In.	795.00

WEDGWOOD

Wedgwood pottery has been made at the famous Wedgwood Factory in
England since 1759. A large variety of wares has been made, including the
well-known jasperware, basalt, creamware, and even a limited amount of porcelain.

Wedgwood, Ashtray, Green, Spade, 1955	10.00
Wedgwood, Ashtray, Lilac, Spade Shape	40.00
Wedgwood, Ashtray, Terra-Cotta, Heart Shape	40.00
Wedgwood, Barrel, Biscuit, Deep Blue	125.00
Wedgwood, Barrel, Cracker, Dark Blue & White, Silver Lid & Ball Feet	135.00

Wedgwood, **Basket**, Potpourri, Jasperware, White, Pierced Lid, C.1815, 5 1/2 In. 110.00
Wedgwood, **Beaker**, Basalt, Black, Basket Weave, 2 Rams' Masks, 7 1/2 In. 90.00
Wedgwood, **Bowl**, Basalt, Black, Classical Figures, C.1750, 8 In. 195.00
Wedgwood, **Bowl**, Basalt, Black, Drapery Festoons, Footed, 6 1/8 In. 70.00
Wedgwood, **Bowl**, Basalt, Black, Grapes, Leaves, & Twigs Border, 10 In. 75.00
Wedgwood, **Bowl**, Basalt, Classical Relief, 5 1/2 In. 75.00
Wedgwood, **Bowl**, Berry, Fairyland Luster, Turtle In Center, Blue, 3 3/4 In. 142.50
Wedgwood, **Bowl**, Butterfly Luster, 8 Sided Panel, Gold With Purple, 7 In. 445.00
Wedgwood, **Bowl**, Caneware, Leaf Shape, 8 X 8 In. 105.00
Wedgwood, **Bowl**, Creamware, Basket Weave Center, Green Strapwork, 11 X 9 In. 145.00
Wedgwood, **Bowl**, Creamware, Green Scenic Design, 1879, 15 1/4 X 4 1/2 In. 90.00
Wedgwood, **Bowl**, Faience, Oval, Oriental Design, C.1895, 8 1/2 X 7 1/2 In. 38.00
Wedgwood, **Bowl**, Fairyland Luster, Arabic Boy Center, Footed, 3 3/4 In. 275.00
Wedgwood, **Bowl**, Fairyland Luster, Birds, Blue, Orange Inside, 2 3/4 In. 95.00
Wedgwood, **Bowl**, Fairyland Luster, Birds, Blue, Orange Inside, 5 1/2 In. 225.00
Wedgwood, **Bowl**, Fairyland Luster, Blue, Dragons, 8 5/8 In.Diameter 195.00
Wedgwood, **Bowl**, Fairyland Luster, Butterflies, Orange Bronze, 3 3/4 In. 155.00
Wedgwood, **Bowl**, Fairyland Luster, Butterfly Center, Flared, 4 3/8 In. 235.00
Wedgwood, **Bowl**, Fairyland Luster, Dragons, Blue, Mother-Of-Pearl In, 4 In. 145.00
Wedgwood, **Bowl**, Fairyland Luster, Dragons, Blue, Mother-Of-Pearl In, 9 In. 375.00
Wedgwood, **Bowl**, Fairyland Luster, Dragons, Blue, Octagonal, 3 1/2 In. 90.00
Wedgwood, **Bowl**, Fairyland Luster, Dragons, Octagonal, 4 In. 275.00
Wedgwood, **Bowl**, Fairyland Luster, Foo Dogs, Green, Mother-Of-Pearl In, 3 In. 75.00
Wedgwood, **Bowl**, Fairyland Luster, Foo Dogs, Hummingbirds, Octagonal, 4 In. 265.00
Wedgwood, **Bowl**, Fairyland Luster, Hummingbirds, Blue, Orange In, 3 1/2 In. 165.00
Wedgwood, **Bowl**, Fairyland Luster, Hummingbirds, Blue, Orange Inside, 5 In. 195.00
Wedgwood, **Bowl**, Fairyland Luster, Hummingbirds, Geese, Orange Interior, 8 In. 385.00
Wedgwood, **Bowl**, Fairyland Luster, Hummingbirds, Mottled Orange, 3 1/4 In. 149.00
Wedgwood, **Bowl**, Fairyland Luster, Maroon, Blue Inside, Octagonal, 4 1/2 In. 650.00
Wedgwood, **Bowl**, Fairyland Luster, Maroon, Blue & Green Inside, 7 1/4 In. 295.00
Wedgwood, **Bowl**, Fairyland Luster, Persian Ornament, Blue Green, 2 3/8 In. 85.00
Wedgwood, **Bowl**, Fairyland Luster, Turtle In Center, Portland Mark, 3 3/4 In. 145.00
Wedgwood, **Bowl**, Fairyland Luster, 3 Gold Dragons On Green, 5 X 2 1/2 In. 325.00
Wedgwood, **Bowl**, Harbor View, Deep Blue, C.1850, 8 1/2 In. 30.00
Wedgwood, **Bowl**, Jasperware, Blue, White Child & Putti, C.1780, 8 1/4 In. 350.00
Wedgwood, **Bowl**, Jasperware, Blue, White Seated Lady & Child, C.1790, 8 In. 325.00
Wedgwood, **Bowl**, Luster, Blue Exterior With Hummingbirds, Orange Inside, 8 In 325.00
Wedgwood, **Bowl**, Majolica, Marked 1870, 14 X 9 1/4 In. 165.00
Wedgwood, **Bowl**, Potpourri, Drabware, Blue Floral Band, Handled, C.1810, 5 In. 150.00
Wedgwood, **Bowl**, Salad, Jasperware, Dark Blue, Silver Plate Rim, 8 In. 150.00
Wedgwood, **Box**, Bean, Jasperware, Terra-Cotta, White Decoration 125.00
Wedgwood, **Box**, Bean, Jasperware, White, Green Trim, England 250.00
Wedgwood, **Box**, Cigarette, Covered, Cobalt Blue, 5 In. 95.00
Wedgwood, **Box**, Covered, Lilac & White Jasperware, 1 3/4 X 1 1/8 In. 75.00
Wedgwood, **Box**, Dresser, Basalt, White Figures On Lid, Heart Shape, 5 X 4 In. 65.00
Wedgwood, **Box**, Patch, White Cameo Bust Of Washington, Blue Ground, 3 X 2 In. 95.00
Wedgwood, **Box**, Pentefoil, Lilac, 3 3/4 X 3 X 1 3/8 In. 95.00
Wedgwood, **Box**, Pentefoil, Terra-Cotta, 3 3/4 X 3 X 1 3/8 In. 95.00
Wedgwood, **Box**, Powder, Green Jasper, Laurel Wreath Design, Silver Rim, 4 In. 180.00
Wedgwood, **Box**, Terra-Cotta, Square, 4 X 4 X 1 3/4 In. 105.00
Wedgwood, **Bust**, Homer, Basalt, Black, Bentley, C.1774, 21 In. 4700.00
Wedgwood, **Bust**, Shakespeare, Black Basalt, 12 1/2 In. 525.00
Wedgwood, **Bust**, Sir Isaac Newton, Basalt, Black, Bentley, 18 In. 3500.00
Wedgwood, **Bust**, Socrates, Basalt, Black, Bentley, C.1775, 19 In. 3000.00
Wedgwood, **Button**, Jasperware, Blue, White Florette, 1/2 In., Set Of 12 .... 50.00
Wedgwood, **Button**, Jasperware, Pale Blue, Pierced, 1/2 In., Set Of 12 .... 50.00
Wedgwood, **Cachepot & Tray**, Blue Jasper, White Figures, 2 In.High 165.00
Wedgwood, **Cachepot**, Basalt, Black, Six Muses, Ring Handled, 7 1/8 In. 130.00
Wedgwood, **Cachepot**, Terra-Cotta, Marked Wedgwood, 4 1/4 X 4 3/4 In. 225.00
Wedgwood, **Can & Saucer**, Coffee, Jasperware, Black, White Relief 450.00
Wedgwood, **Candlestick**, Basalt, Black, Muses, Columnar Stem, 6 3/4 In., Pair 90.00
Wedgwood, **Candlestick**, Blue Fruiting Vines On White, 7 3/4 In., Pair 90.00
Wedgwood, **Candlestick**, Dark Blue Jasper, 5 In., Pair 150.00
Wedgwood, **Candlestick**, Jasperware, Black, White, 7 In., Pair 250.00
Wedgwood, **Candlestick**, Jasperware, Dark Blue, White Trim, 8 In. 135.00
Wedgwood, **Candlestick**, Jasperware, Deep Blue, White Classical Ladies, 5 In. 95.00

Wedgwood, Candlestick, Jasperware, Light Blue, 6 In., Pair	145.00
Wedgwood, Candlestick, Jasperware, Pale Blue, White 2 Muses, 6 1/8 In., Pair	90.00
Wedgwood, Candlestick, Terra-Cotta, 6 1/4 In., Marked Wedgwood, Pair	295.00
Wedgwood, Chess Set, Black Basalt & Blue Jasper, Arnold Machin	1150.00
Wedgwood, Cigar Rest, Black, White, Marked Wedgwood, 4 1/2 X 2 In.	85.00
Wedgwood, Coffee Set, Basalt, Widow Finials, 15 Piece	300.00
Wedgwood, Coffeepot, Rockingham Glaze, 8 In.	150.00
Wedgwood, Compote, Jasperware, Blue, White Trim, Seated Child Finial, 9 In.	400.00
Wedgwood, Compote, Lilac, Rams' Heads, 3 7/8 X 6 In.	195.00
Wedgwood, Compote, Queensware, Gray, White Trim, 6 1/4 In.	35.00
Wedgwood, Compotier, Lilac, Silver Tray, 5 X 3 1/2 X 7/8 In.	55.00
Wedgwood, Creamer, Basalt, Black, Classical Motifs, 3 1/2 X 3 1/4 In.	35.00
Wedgwood, Creamer, Basalt, Classical Relief, 4 X 2 In.	45.00
Wedgwood, Creamer, Chariot & Grecian Figures	42.00
Wedgwood, Creamer, Dark Blue Jasperware, Cameo Design, 5 1/4 In.High	95.00
Wedgwood, Creamer, Hunt Scene, Hound Handle, Gold, Relief	50.00
Wedgwood, Creamer, Individual, Terra-Cotta, 2 1/2 In.	105.00
Wedgwood, Creamer, Salt Glaze, Berries, Leaves, & Vines In Relief, 4 In.	95.00
Wedgwood, Cup & Saucer, Basalt, Black, Relief Decoration	125.00
Wedgwood, Cup & Saucer, Basalt, Floral Bas Relief	65.00
Wedgwood, Cup & Saucer, Coffee, Jasperware, Pale Blue, Cupid & Maiden, C.1780	200.00
Wedgwood, Cup & Saucer, Demitasse, Basalt, Black	35.00
Wedgwood, Cup & Saucer, Demitasse, Terra-Cotta, White Trim	95.00
Wedgwood, Cup & Saucer, Doulton Beaufort	10.00
Wedgwood, Cup & Saucer, Drabware	115.00
Wedgwood, Cup & Saucer, English Landscape, Turquoise	60.00
Wedgwood, Cup & Saucer, Gray Green Jasper, Twig Handle, Releif Figures	80.00
Wedgwood, Cup & Saucer, Jasperware, Lilac, White Trim	135.00
Wedgwood, Cup & Saucer, Jasperware, Pale Blue, Wishbone Handle	110.00
Wedgwood, Cup & Saucer, Jasperware, Terra-Cotta, White Trim	95.00
Wedgwood, Cup & Saucer, St.Austell	10.00
Wedgwood, Cup, Fairyland Luster, Dragons & Snakes, Blue, 3 Handled	80.00
Wedgwood, Cup, Jasperware, Double Scroll Handles, Footed, C.1810, Pair	210.00
Wedgwood, Cup, Loving, Fairyland Luster, Blue, Dragon, Pearl Inside, 2 In.	150.00
Wedgwood, Cup, Loving, Jasperware, 3 Handles, Dark Blue, White Trim, 2 1/2 In.	125.00
Wedgwood, Dish, Basket Shape, Creamware, Oval, England, 7 1/4 X 9 In.	30.00
Wedgwood, Dish, Candy, Jasperware, Black, White Portrait Of Churchill, 4 In.	7.50
Wedgwood, Dish, Caneware, Leaf Shape, Fern Frond Center, 10 3/4 In.	70.00
Wedgwood, Dish, Cheese, Domed Lid, Shocking Pink, Acorns & Oak Leaves	300.00
Wedgwood, Dish, Cheese, Domed, Cupid With Bow, Grape Bands, 9 1/4 In.	190.00
Wedgwood, Dish, Game Pie, Caneware, Rabbit Knop, Hanging Game, 1870, 8 3/4 In.	100.00
Wedgwood, Dish, Game, Caneware, Bunches Of Grapes, Cauliflower, 8 X 6 In.	195.00
Wedgwood, Dish, Game, Caneware, Cauliflower, C.1840	295.00
Wedgwood, Dish, Scallop Shell, Pink To Yellow At Handle, 8 3/8 In.	30.00
Wedgwood, Dish, Sweetmeat, Terra-Cotta & White, Diamond Shape	35.00
Wedgwood, Ewer, Majolica, C.1850, 8 5/8 In. ....*Illus*	300.00
Wedgwood, Figurine, Nymph At Well, Basalt, Black, 13 In.	1600.00
Wedgwood, Flowerpot, Basalt, Flare Shape, Fluted Rims, Embossed Floral, 3 In.	115.00
Wedgwood, Garniture Set, Queensware, Grapes, Leaves, & Twigs, 10 In., 3 Piece	145.00
Wedgwood, Gravy Boat & Attached Underplate, Queensware, Bullfinch, 8 In.	28.00
Wedgwood, Hair Receiver, Dark Blue Jasperware	95.00
Wedgwood, Heel, Shoe, Green Jasperware, Pair	55.00
Wedgwood, Humidor, Blue Jasper, Silver Rim, Tamper, 6 1/2 X 4 In.	215.00
Wedgwood, Ironstone, Tea Leaf, see Ironstone, Tea Leaf	
Wedgwood, Jar, Basalt, Black, Florette Knop, Sacrifice To Peace, C.1825, 5 In.	70.00
Wedgwood, Jar, Biscuit, Blue, White Design, C.1800	110.00
Wedgwood, Jar, Biscuit, Deep Blue, White Figures Scene, 10 In.	125.00
Wedgwood, Jar, Biscuit, Deep Blue, White Figures Scene, 8 X 6 In.	110.00
Wedgwood, Jar, Biscuit, Jasperware, Black, White Relief Figures	260.00
Wedgwood, Jar, Biscuit, Jasperware, Black, Yellow Lions' Heads & Floral	750.00
Wedgwood, Jar, Biscuit, Jasperware, Blue, Maidens, Acorn Knop, 8 1/2 In.	80.00
Wedgwood, Jar, Biscuit, Jasperware, Green, Lilac & White, Silver Fittings	250.00
Wedgwood, Jar, Biscuit, Jasperware, Green, Silver Plate Fittings	150.00
Wedgwood, Jar, Biscuit, Jasperware, Green, White Dancing Maidens, 8 In.	475.00
Wedgwood, Jar, Biscuit, Jasperware, Lilac & White, 5 1/2 In.	240.00

Wedgwood, Plate,
Majolica, 1871, 15 1/8 In.
(See Page 683)

Wedgwood, Ewer,
Majolica, C.1850, 8 5/8 In.
(See Page 680)

Wedgwood, Jug, Milk,
Cornflower, C.1765

Wedgwood, Jar, Biscuit, Jasperware, Lilac, Green, & White	750.00
Wedgwood, Jar, Biscuit, Jasperware, Lilac, Sacrifice To Peace, Silver Lid	250.00
Wedgwood, Jar, Biscuit, Jasperware, Yellow, Black Relief Figures	450.00
Wedgwood, Jar, Biscuit, Jasperware, 2 Tone Blue, White Relief	395.00
Wedgwood, Jar, Candy, Jasperware, Black, 8 Cathedral Cities, 4 1/2 In.	45.00
Wedgwood, Jar, Cracker, Jasperware, Blue, Silver Plated Handle & Rim	115.00
Wedgwood, Jar, Cookie, Jasperware, Blue, Silver Plated Lid & Bail	135.00
Wedgwood, Jar, Cracker, Blue, White Relief Figures, Silver Plate & Ivory	110.00
Wedgwood, Jar, Cracker, Green, Greek Design, Silver Plate Handles	145.00
Wedgwood, Jar, Mustard, Blue, Reticulated Silver Plate Hinged Lid, Insert	40.00
Wedgwood, Jar, Mustard, Jasperware, Dark Blue & White, 3 3/4 X 3 1/2 In.	55.00
Wedgwood, Jardiniere, Green, White Grecian Scenes, 4 1/2 X 5 In.	128.00
Wedgwood, Jardiniere, Jasperware, Blue, Muses & Flower Garlands, 9 X 8 In.	125.00
Wedgwood, Jardiniere, Jasperware, Dark Blue, White Lion's Heads, 7 In.	95.00
Wedgwood, Jardiniere, Jasperware, Dark Green, 5 X 4 1/2 In.	140.00
Wedgwood, Jardiniere, Jasperware, Emerald Green, Grecian Scenes, 5 In.	140.00
Wedgwood, Jardiniere, Jasperware, Green, Relief Classical Border, 8 3/4 In.	190.00
Wedgwood, Jug, Ale, Black, Coat Of Arms, St.Johns, 3 1/2 In.	50.00
Wedgwood, Jug, Ale, Cambridge, Redware, 7 In.	49.50
Wedgwood, Jug, Ale, Redware, Cambridge, Glazed Inside, Matte Out, 8 In.	75.00
Wedgwood, Jug, Ale, Rossico Antico, Cambridge, Pewter Lid & Rim, 6 1/2 In.	135.00
Wedgwood, Jug, Ale, Rossico Antico, Coat Of Arms, 4 1/4 In.	50.00
Wedgwood, Jug, Basalt, Black, Vertical Flutes, Strap Handle, C.1820, 4 1/2 In.	40.00
Wedgwood, Jug, Basalt, Rose, Thistle, Shamrock, & Harp, 4 In.	90.00
Wedgwood, Jug, Caneware, 2 Concentric Horizontal Bands, C.1790, 7 1/4 In.	60.00
Wedgwood, Jug, Copper Resist, Hunting Scene, C.1920, 7 In.	62.00
Wedgwood, Jug, Jasperware, Blue, White Sacrifice To Peace, 5 In.	25.00
Wedgwood, Jug, Jasperware, Dark Blue, White Trim, 3 X 2 3/4 In.	95.00
Wedgwood, Jug, Jasperware, Olive Green, England, 5 In.	135.00
Wedgwood, Jug, Jasperware, Olive Green, Rope Handle, 7 1/2 In.	250.00
Wedgwood, Jug, Jasperware, Pale Blue & White, 7 In.	145.00
Wedgwood, Jug, Jasperware, Terra-Cotta & White, 5 X 7 In.	135.00
Wedgwood, Jug, Jasperware, Terra-Cotta, White Trim, 5 X 6 In.	150.00
Wedgwood, Jug, Landing Of Roger Williams, Brown On Cream, 4 1/2 X 5 In.	60.00
Wedgwood, Jug, Milk, Blue, Doric, 6 In.	300.00
Wedgwood, Jug, Milk, Cornflower, C.1765 .... *Illus*	425.00
Wedgwood, Jug, Portrait Of Longfellow, 9 X 6 1/2 In.	165.00
Wedgwood, Jug, Silver Luster, Pink Ferrara Pattern, Etruria, 5 1/4 In.High	75.00
Wedgwood, Jug, Upright, Capri Enamel, Basalt, Gilt Decoration, 7 1/2 In.	345.00
Wedgwood, Jug, Upright, Olive Green Jasper, 7 1/2 X 6 In.	155.00
Wedgwood, Match Holder & Striker, Majolica, Green, Brown, Yellow, 4 In.	75.00
Wedgwood, Match Holder, Blue, White Cameos, Striker Inside, 3 3/4 X 2 In.	30.00
Wedgwood, Match Holder, Lilac, Peach Tint, Marked Wedgwood, 2 3/8 In.	105.00
Wedgwood, Matchbox, Jasperware, Black, White Trim, Miniature	150.00
Wedgwood, Matchbox, Jasperware, Blue, White Cameos, Striker, 1867, 3 3/4 In.	50.00
Wedgwood, Matchbox, Lilac, Oblong, 3 1/2 X 1 7/8 X 1 1/8 In.	50.00

Wedgwood, Medallion, Jasperware, Blue, Earl Cowper, C.1790, 3 7/8 In.	180.00
Wedgwood, Medallion, Jasperware, Green, Cupids, Floral Garlands, 7 In., Pair	325.00
Wedgwood, Medallion, Jasperware, Dark Blue, White Grecian Figure, 1 1/4 In.	27.00
Wedgwood, Medallion, Jasperware, Green, White Bearded Man's Head, 1 7/8 In.	110.00
Wedgwood, Medallion, Jasperware, Pale Blue, Euripides, C.1780, 1 3/4 In.	160.00
Wedgwood, Medallion, Jasperware, Pale Blue, Mr.Stuart, C.1790, 3 5/8 In.	190.00
Wedgwood, Mortar & Pestle, Best Composition, Wooden Handle, Size No.2	80.00
Wedgwood, Muffineer, Deep Blue, White Figures & Trees, 7 X 3 3/4 In.	195.00
Wedgwood, Mug, Dark Green, 5 1/2 In.	25.00
Wedgwood, Mug, Fairyland Luster, 3 Handles, Hummingbirds, Orange Interior	175.00
Wedgwood, Mug, Lavender Raised Figures On White	27.00
Wedgwood, Mug, Pearlware, Blue & Orange Flowers	23.00
Wedgwood, Mug, Queensware, Dickens, 4 3/4 In.	16.00
Wedgwood, Pitcher & Bowl, Historical Blue & Gray Scenes, 17 In.Diameter	125.00
Wedgwood, Pitcher, Basalt, Black, Flaxman Figures, Grapes, 6 1/2 In.	115.00
Wedgwood, Pitcher, Basalt, Dark Blue, White Figures, 6 In.	135.00
Wedgwood, Pitcher, Basalt, Foo Dog Enamel Trim, Kenlock Ware, 4 1/2 In.	145.00
Wedgwood, Pitcher, Blue Satin Ground, White Flaxman Figures, 4 1/2 In.	65.00
Wedgwood, Pitcher, Blue, White Classical Figures, 5 In.	65.00
Wedgwood, Pitcher, Copper Luster, Fallow Deer, 2 3/4 In.	40.00
Wedgwood, Pitcher, Covered, Deep Blue, White Figures & Grapevine, 7 1/4 In.	115.00
Wedgwood, Pitcher, Dark Blue, White Cameos, 1877, Pint	130.00
Wedgwood, Pitcher, Drabware, Cloverleaf Lid, Gold Band, C.1830, 5 1/2 In.	175.00
Wedgwood, Pitcher, Garfield, 1831-1881 & American Eagle, 7 1/2 In.	450.00
Wedgwood, Pitcher, Hound Handle, Polychrome Hunt Scenes, 5 In.High	90.00
Wedgwood, Pitcher, Jasperware, Deep Blue, Roman Figures & Key, 7 In.	150.00
Wedgwood, Pitcher, Jasperware, Olive Green, Etruscan, 3 1/2 X 3 1/4 In.	55.00
Wedgwood, Pitcher, Jasperware, Olive Green, White Classical Figures, 6 In.	72.50
Wedgwood, Pitcher, Jasperware, Pale Blue, White Trim, 6 In.	65.00
Wedgwood, Pitcher, Jasperware, Rope Handle, 4 In.	32.00
Wedgwood, Pitcher, Longfellow, Cream, Story Titles, 6 1/4 X 9 In.	95.00
Wedgwood, Pitcher, Olive Green, Rope Handle, 4 In.	145.00
Wedgwood, Pitcher, Queensware, Pink Women & Cupids On White, 4 3/4 In.	37.00
Wedgwood, Pitcher, Rossico Antico, Enameled Flowers, 5 In.	195.00
Wedgwood, Pitcher, Royal Blue, White Glasgow Angel & Greek Figures, 8 In.	75.00
Wedgwood, Planter, Wall, Majolica, Bird's Nest & Bird, C.1873, 9 X 7 In.	335.00
Wedgwood, Plaque, Basalt, Oval, Classical Relief, 9 1/2 X 7 In.	125.00
Wedgwood, Plaque, Black & White Jasper, Aristotle Looking At Skull, 4 In.	150.00
Wedgwood, Plaque, Jasperware, Lilac, White Classical Figure, Oval, 4 X 3 In.	275.00
Wedgwood, Plaque, Jasperware, Pale Blue, Classical Maiden & Frond, 4 3/8 In.	40.00
Wedgwood, Plaque, Jasperware, Pale Green, Maiden & Cornucopia, 6 In.	60.00
Wedgwood, Plaque, Jasperware, Pale Green, Maidens, Cupid, & Putto, 11 In.	275.00
Wedgwood, Plate, Academic Building, West Point, Pink, C.1930, 10 In.	25.00
Wedgwood, Plate, Basket Of Fruit Center, Yellow Border, 8 1/4 In.	8.00
Wedgwood, Plate, Birthplace Of Whittier, Blue, 1901, 9 1/4 In.	24.00
Wedgwood, Plate, Black, White Bust Of Josiah Wedgwood, 1930, 9 1/4 In.	28.50
Wedgwood, Plate, Boston Tea Party, Blue, 9 1/8 In.	20.00
Wedgwood, Plate, Bunker Hill Monument, Blue, 9 1/4 In.	21.00
Wedgwood, Plate, Butterfly Luster, Blue, Butterfly In Center, 9 In.	175.00
Wedgwood, Plate, Cake, Bramble, Flow Blue, Pedestal, C.1860, 9 1/2 In.	82.50
Wedgwood, Plate, Cake, Jasperware, Pale Green, Domed Lid, Sacrifice To Peace	160.00
Wedgwood, Plate, Cake, Royal Blue, White Greek Figures, Handled, 12 In.	75.00
Wedgwood, Plate, Caneware, Openwork Rim, 6 In.	25.00
Wedgwood, Plate, Caneware, 8 1/2 In.	85.00
Wedgwood, Plate, Chinese Motif, Blue & White, C.1879, HH, 9 1/2 In.	22.50
Wedgwood, Plate, Clipper Ship Anne McKin, Brown Transfer, 1938, 9 1/4 In.	12.50
Wedgwood, Plate, Clipper Ship N.B.Palmer, Brown Transfer, 1938, 9 1/4 In.	12.50
Wedgwood, Plate, Clipper Ship Young America, Brown Transfer, 1908, 9 1/4 In.	12.50
Wedgwood, Plate, Drabware, Grapevines On Basket Weave, C.1825, 8 1/4 In.	25.00
Wedgwood, Plate, Faneuil Hall, Blue, 9 1/8 In.	20.00
Wedgwood, Plate, February, Kate Greenaway Girl & Boy, Etruria, 10 In.	90.00
Wedgwood, Plate, Ferrara, Lavender Shades, 9 1/4 In., Set Of 12	125.00
Wedgwood, Plate, First Church, Hartford, Conn., Blue, 1900, 8 In.	15.00
Wedgwood, Plate, Grant Hall, West Point, Pink, C.1930, 10 In.	25.00
Wedgwood, Plate, Grant's Tomb, Blue, 9 1/8 In.	26.00
Wedgwood, Plate, Jones McDuffee & Stratton, 1810-1910, Blue, 10 In.	35.00

Wedgwood, Plate, Leaf, Dark Green, 8 1/2 In.	13.50
Wedgwood, Plate, Library, West Point, Pink, C.1930, 10 In.	25.00
Wedgwood, Plate, Louise, Dated 1881, 8 5/8 In.	11.00
Wedgwood, Plate, Majolica, Brown Daisy Center, C.1880, 7 In.	14.00
Wedgwood, Plate, Majolica, Green, Sunflower, Lattice Edge, C.1875, 8 1/2 In.	15.00
Wedgwood, Plate, Majolica, Raised Florals, Brown Daisy Center, C.1880, 7 In.	14.00
Wedgwood, Plate, Majolica, 1871, 15 1/8 In. *Illus*	375.00
Wedgwood, Plate, Mayflower Arriving, Blue & White, 9 In.	19.00
Wedgwood, Plate, Minute Man Parker, Blue & White Floral Edge, 10 1/2 In.	14.00
Wedgwood, Plate, Mt.Vernon Bicentennial, 10 In.	18.00
Wedgwood, Plate, Old Cadet Chapel, West Point, Pink, C.1930, 10 In.	25.00
Wedgwood, Plate, Pastime, Polychrome Scene Of Children, 8 In.	32.00
Wedgwood, Plate, Pearlware, Ranunculus, C.1870, 9 1/4 In.	38.00
Wedgwood, Plate, Pearlware, Shell Shape, Pink On Cream, 8 1/2 In.	45.00
Wedgwood, Plate, Portrait Of A Girl, Blue Floral, 9 1/2 In.	15.00
Wedgwood, Plate, Princeton University, 1930, 10 3/4 In.	15.00
Wedgwood, Plate, Queensware, Grapes, Leaves, & Twigs, 10 In.	30.00
Wedgwood, Plate, Rome Scenes, Archbishop Cushing, Boston, 10 1/2 In.	25.00
Wedgwood, Plate, Saratoga Springs, Blue, Hotel Medallion Border, 10 In.	25.00
Wedgwood, Plate, Signed Ada Brooke Drake 1910, 10 In.	28.00
Wedgwood, Plate, South Platform At Fort Ticonderoga, Blue, 9 1/4 In.	21.00
Wedgwood, Plate, The Capitol, Deep Blue, 1901, 9 In.	20.00
Wedgwood, Plate, The White House, Deep Blue, 1901, 9 In.	20.00
Wedgwood, Plate, Theodore Roosevelt, Floral Border, Blue & White, 9 In.	24.00
Wedgwood, Plate, Torbay, White, Green Scenic Center, 10 1/4 In., Set Of 6	55.00
Wedgwood, Plate, Trinity Church, Boston, 9 In.	14.50
Wedgwood, Plate, U.S.Military Academy, Blue & White, 10 In.	25.00
Wedgwood, Plate, University Of California, 1923, Blue, Hoover, 10 3/8 In.	30.00
Wedgwood, Plate, University Of Michigan, 1935, Blue, Hoover, 10 3/8 In.	30.00
Wedgwood, Plate, Ventnor, 10 3/4 In.	10.00
Wedgwood, Plate, Washington Hall, West Point, Pink, C.1930, 10 In.	25.00
Wedgwood, Plate, Wellesley College, Blue & White, 9 1/4 In.	25.00
Wedgwood, Plate, World's Columbian Exposition, Blue & White, 8 1/4 In.	9.50
Wedgwood, Plate, Yale University, Blue & White, Etruria, 10 In.	12.00
Wedgwood, Platter, Blue Willow, Doves, 9 X 11 In.	40.00
Wedgwood, Platter, Columbia, Sepia, Brown, & Green, Ironstone, 10 X 13 1/4 In.	37.50
Wedgwood, Platter, Ironstone, Red Roses, Scalloped & Embossed Edge, 17 In.	15.00
Wedgwood, Platter, Majolica, Basketweave, Butterflies, & Floral, 12 In.	53.00
Wedgwood, Platter, Mandarin, Bottle Pattern, Blue, C.1764, 14 X 10 1/2 In.	76.00
Wedgwood, Platter, Queen Charlotte, Blue & White, 16 1/2 X 12 1/2 In.	38.00
Wedgwood, Platter, Yale College & State House, 1832, Blue, C.1935, 20 In.	65.00
Wedgwood, Pot, Covered, Jasperware, Blue & White, 4 1/2 In.	90.00
Wedgwood, Pot, Jam, Dark Blue, Silver Plate Lid, 4 In.	35.00
Wedgwood, Pot, Jam, Jasperware, Black, Silver Plate Lid & Spoon	135.00
Wedgwood, Pot, Jam, Jasperware, Dark Blue, Silver Plate Lid & Spoon	65.00
Wedgwood, Pot, Jam, Jasperware, Lilac, Silver Plate Lid & Spoon	225.00
Wedgwood, Pot, Jam, Light Blue, Classical Figures, Dated 1955 & 1956, Pair	48.00
Wedgwood, Pot, Mustard, White Hunt Scene On Cobalt, Brass Lattice Top	150.00

Wedgwood, Teapot, Cornflower, C.1765   Wedgwood, Tea Caddy, Cornflower, C.1765

(See Page 684)   *(See Page 684)*

Wedgwood, Relish, Queensware, Light Green & Mulberry Design	35.00
Wedgwood, Salad Set, Ivory, Berries & Foliage, Silver Mounted, 3 Piece	150.00
Wedgwood, Salt & Pepper, Blue Jasperware, Steeple Form, Cupids, 4 In.	43.00
Wedgwood, Sauce, Ventnor, 4 3/4 In.	5.00
Wedgwood, Saucer, Jasperware, Olive, Medallions Of Children At Edge	4.00
Wedgwood, Saucer, Three Powder Blue Plaques With White Cherubs	27.50
Wedgwood, Sherbet, Fairyland Luster, Orange, Footed, 4 In.	185.00
Wedgwood, Sherbet, Fairyland Luster, Tiger, Orange, Mother-Of-Pearl Inside	185.00
Wedgwood, Spill, Basalt, Floral Bas Relief, 5 In., Pair	150.00
Wedgwood, Spill, Black, White Rams' Heads, Marked Wedgwood	155.00
Wedgwood, Spill, Jasperware, Dark Blue, Acanthus Leaves, 5 1/4 In.	95.00
Wedgwood, Sugar & Creamer, Light Blue, Classical Figures, Dated '55 & '58	48.00
Wedgwood, Sugar & Creamer, Ferrara, Etruria, England	50.00
Wedgwood, Sugar, Covered, Jasperware, Crimson	750.00
Wedgwood, Sugar, Jasperware, Olive Green, White Trim, 5 X 4 In.	65.00
Wedgwood, Sugar, Light Blue, Classical Figures, Dated '57	25.00
Wedgwood, Sugar, Stoneware, Custard Color, Apple Tree Branches, C.1820	175.00
Wedgwood, Syrup, Lion's Head On Lid, Classical Figures, 7 In.	125.00
Wedgwood, Tankard, Lilac, England, 7 1/2 In.	285.00
Wedgwood, Tea Caddy, Cornflower, C.1765 *Illus*	275.00
Wedgwood, Tea Set, Basalt, Black, Widow Knops, C.1820, 3 Piece	175.00
Wedgwood, Tea Set, Basalt, Widow Finials, 3 Piece	225.00
Wedgwood, Tea Set, Cobalt Blue, Teapot, Sugar, & Creamer	145.00
Wedgwood, Tea Set, Dark Blue Jasper, St.Louis Shape, 3 Piece	245.00
Wedgwood, Tea Set, Jasperware, Dark Blue, White Edward VIII, 1937, 3 Piece	650.00
Wedgwood, Teabowl & Saucer, Jasperware, Pale Blue, Cupid & Children, C.1780	175.00
Wedgwood, Teabowl & Saucer, Jasperware, Pale Blue, Putti & Bird, C.1780	350.00
Wedgwood, Teabowl, Jasperware, Blue, Domestic Employment, C.1790	190.00
Wedgwood, Teacup & Saucer, Basalt, Black, Classical Scenes, C.1820	50.00
Wedgwood, Teacup & Saucer, Jasperware, Pale Blue, Mythological Vignettes	100.00
Wedgwood, Teacup & Saucer, Lilac, Brewster	85.00
Wedgwood, Teapot & Trivet, Basalt, Widow Finial, 7 1/2 X 3 1/2 In.	135.00
Wedgwood, Teapot, Bennington Finish, Brown Glaze, C.1830, 3 In.	120.00
Wedgwood, Teapot, Black Basalt, Black Classical Figures, 5 In.High	95.00
Wedgwood, Teapot, Caneware, Sheaf Of Wheat Knop, Basketwork, C.1817	175.00
Wedgwood, Teapot, Caneware, Spaniel Knop, Arabesque Bands, C.1817	125.00
Wedgwood, Teapot, Caneware, Spaniel On Cushion Finial, 8 1/2 X 5 In.	195.00
Wedgwood, Teapot, Cornflower, C.1765 *Illus*	225.00
Wedgwood, Teapot, Dark Blue & White Jasperware, Ornate Silver Lid, 3 X 7 In	115.00
Wedgwood, Teapot, Dark Blue, White Classical Figures, 2 Cup Size	65.00
Wedgwood, Teapot, Green Jasper, White Figures, Cylindrical, C.1895, 3 1/2 In.	75.00
Wedgwood, Teapot, Jasperware, Blue, Domestic Employment, Templeton, C.1790	125.00
Wedgwood, Teapot, Jasperware, Green, White Figures & Leaves, 7 1/2 In.	65.00
Wedgwood, Teapot, Jasperware, Pale Blue, Classical Figures, 1869	50.00
Wedgwood, Teapot, Rosso Antico Capri Enamel, Impressed Etruria	450.00
Wedgwood, Teapot, Rosso Antico, Pierced Knop, Black Relief, C.1820	150.00
Wedgwood, Teapot, Smear Glaze, Flower Finial, 6 1/2 In.	150.00
Wedgwood, Teapot, State Visit To Canada, 1939, Cobalt	95.00
Wedgwood, Tile, April	40.00
Wedgwood, Tile, Calendar, 1891	45.00
Wedgwood, Tile, Calendar, 1906	34.50
Wedgwood, Tile, Calendar, 1909	34.50
Wedgwood, Tile, Calendar, 1911	34.50
Wedgwood, Tile, Calendar, 1911, Jones, McDuffee & Stratton, Framed	40.00
Wedgwood, Tile, Calendar, 1912	34.50
Wedgwood, Tile, Calendar, 1913	34.50
Wedgwood, Tile, Calendar, 1913, Jones, McDuffee & Stratton, Framed	40.00
Wedgwood, Tile, Calendar, 1914	34.50
Wedgwood, Tile, Calendar, 1915	34.50
Wedgwood, Tile, Calendar, 1917	34.50
Wedgwood, Tile, Calendar, 1917, Jones, McDuffee & Stratton, Framed	40.00
Wedgwood, Tile, Calendar, 1918	34.50
Wedgwood, Tile, July	40.00
Wedgwood, Tile, Midsummer Night's Dream, Puck, Blue & White, Square, 8 In.	40.00
Wedgwood, Tile, Old North Church, Salem Street	35.00
Wedgwood, Toothpick, Green, Seahorses & Heraldic Shield	45.00

Wedgwood, Vase,
Jasperware, Green,
White, C.1850, Pair

Wedgwood, Vase,
Covered,
C.1850, 11 7/8 In.

Wedgwood, Tray, Cake, Basalt, Classical Relief Border, 10 X 8 1/2 In.	125.00
Wedgwood, Tray, Heart Shape, Yellow Jasper, White Relief, 4 5/8 X 3 1/4 In.	300.00
Wedgwood, Tray, Pin, Green, Scalloped Rim, Round, C.1960, 4 1/4 In.	10.00
Wedgwood, Tray, Silver, Jasperware, Lilac, White Trim	55.00
Wedgwood, Tub, Butter, Basalt, Black, Silver Plate Lid & Stand, Husks, 5 In.	120.00
Wedgwood, Tureen & Stand, Pearlware, Pierced Lid, Blue Laurel, C.1790, 11 In.	300.00
Wedgwood, Tureen, Covered, Peony Shape, Green, Orange, & Gold, C.1910	115.00
Wedgwood, Urn, Jasperware, Blue, Covered, White Figures, Footed, Handled, 8 In.	375.00
Wedgwood, Urn, Jasperware, Pale Blue, White Four Muses, Handled, 9 1/4 In.	170.00
Wedgwood, Vase, Basalt, Black, Art Nouveau Persian Style Floral, 10 3/8 In.	50.00
Wedgwood, Vase, Basalt, Black, Covered, Classical Maidens, C.1820, 5 3/4 In.	125.00
Wedgwood, Vase, Basalt, Black, Wheel Turned Ribbing, Pedestal, 5 In.	85.00
Wedgwood, Vase, Basalt, Floral Bas Relief, Flared Top, 5 In.	75.00
Wedgwood, Vase, Bud, Fairyland Luster, Butterflies, Mother-Of-Pearl, 5 In.	195.00
Wedgwood, Vase, Bud, Jasperware, Dark Blue, Wedgwood Only, 5 In.	65.00
Wedgwood, Vase, Bulbous, Blue & White, Ladies Playing Instruments, 5 In.	55.00
Wedgwood, Vase, Covered, C.1850, 11 7/8 In. .... *Illus*	600.00
Wedgwood, Vase, Dark Blue, White Classical Figures, 2 Handled, 6 In.	125.00
Wedgwood, Vase, Dark Blue, White Figures, 4 1/4 In.	68.00
Wedgwood, Vase, Deep Blue, White Ladies & Musical Instruments, 5 In.	55.00
Wedgwood, Vase, Deep Blue, 2 White Classical Figures, Bulbous, 7 In.	125.00
Wedgwood, Vase, Deep Green, White Figures, 5 1/4 In.	50.00
Wedgwood, Vase, Fairyland Luster, Candlemas, Dark Blue, Portland, 7 1/2 In.	1100.00
Wedgwood, Vase, Fairyland Luster, Dragon, Blue, Aqua Interior, 11 In.	325.00
Wedgwood, Vase, Fairyland Luster, Dragon, Dark Blue, 8 In.	165.00
Wedgwood, Vase, Fairyland Luster, Flame, Pixies & Fairies, Green, 3 In.	850.00
Wedgwood, Vase, Fairyland Luster, Hummingbird, 8 3/4 In.	425.00
Wedgwood, Vase, Fairyland Luster, Mother-Of-Pearl Dragon, 4 1/2 In.	145.00
Wedgwood, Vase, Fairyland Luster, Phoenix Birds, Royal Blue, 7 In.	250.00
Wedgwood, Vase, Fairyland Luster, Ruby, Firbolgs, Mother-Of-Pearl In., 4 In.	495.00
Wedgwood, Vase, Fairyland Luster, Trumpet, Hawthorn Bush & Fairy, 6 In.	595.00
Wedgwood, Vase, Flame Butterfly Luster, Gold Flowers, Portland Mark, 5 In.	165.00
Wedgwood, Vase, Imari Pattern, 12 In.	120.00
Wedgwood, Vase, Jasperware, Blue, White Putti, Dog, & Boar's Head, 13 1/8 In.	275.00
Wedgwood, Vase, Jasperware, Dark Blue, Portland, White Relief, 8 1/8 In.	210.00
Wedgwood, Vase, Jasperware, Dark Blue, Portland, 6 In.	198.00
Wedgwood, Vase, Jasperware, Dark Blue, White Trim, Portland, 8 In.	450.00
Wedgwood, Vase, Jasperware, Green, White, C.1850, Pair .... *Illus*	900.00
Wedgwood, Vase, Jasperware, White, Green Leaves, Lilac Floral, 3 3/4 In.	750.00
Wedgwood, Vase, Portland, Florals & Figurines, White, Bail Handle, 6 In.High	165.00
Wedgwood, Vase, Potpourri, Acorn Knop, White & Lilac, C.1810, 9 In.	550.00
Wedgwood, Vase, Spill, Basalt, Floral Relief, 5 In.High, Pair	150.00
Wedgwood, Washstand Set, Corn Pattern, J.Wedgwood, 2 Piece	125.00
Wedgwood, Washstand Set, Pearlware, Flow Blue Pattern, 2 Piece	310.00
Wedgwood, Washstand Set, Red Berries, Green Vines, & Black On White, 2 Piece	95.00

Weller pottery was first made in 1873 in Fultonham, Ohio. The firm moved

WELLER to Zanesville, Ohio, in 1882. Art wares were first made in 1893. Hundreds of lines of pottery were made including Louwelsa, Eocean, Dickens, and Sicardo before the pottery closed in 1948.

Weller, Ashtray, Duck, White Glaze, Signed Weller Pottery, 4 1/2 In.	25.00
Weller, Ashtray, Woodcraft, Match Holder, Square, 6 In.	37.50
Weller, Basket, Cameo, Peach, 7 1/2 In.	14.00
Weller, Basket, Delsa, Yellow & Pink Pansy On White, 7 X 3 1/4 In.	18.50
Weller, Basket, Flemish, Brown, Red Flowers, Grapes, Handled, Footed, 6 In.	15.00
Weller, Basket, Green, Block Marked, 9 In.	32.50
Weller, Bottle, Ollas Water, 12 1/2 In.High	40.00
Weller, Bowl & Frog, Marvo, Ink Stamped Wellerware, 2 1/2 X 8 3/4 In.	20.00
Weller, Bowl & Frog, Woodrose, 4 1/2 In.	18.00
Weller, Bowl Vase, Dupont, Matte Ivory Crosshatched, Pink Roses, 6 1/4 In.	26.00
Weller, Bowl Vase, Marbelized, Ivory Shades On Dark Brown, 6 7/8 In.	37.50
Weller, Bowl Vase, Raised Rope & Bow On Blue, 7 1/2 In.	15.00
Weller, Bowl, Ansonia, Green, 4 1/2 In.	12.00
Weller, Bowl, Baldwin, Blue, 5 X 8 In.	45.00
Weller, Bowl, Burntwood, Mythological Animals, 6 In.	15.00
Weller, Bowl, Burntwood, 5 In.	10.00
Weller, Bowl, Classic Line, Cream Semigloss, Script Signed, 10 In.	17.50
Weller, Bowl, Console, Marvo, Tan & Green, Scalloped, 8 In., Unmarked	25.00
Weller, Bowl, Forest, 3 1/2 In. High	45.00
Weller, Bowl, Forest, 7 In.	35.00
Weller, Bowl, Lily, Blue Green Outside, Gold Inside, 7 1/2 In.Diameter	12.00
Weller, Bowl, Louwelsa, Grayish Lavender Ground, Yellow Flower, 4 In.	10.00
Weller, Bowl, Nut, Woodcraft, Squirrel Sitting On Side, Unmarked, 4 X 5 In.	65.00
Weller, Bowl, Roma Line, 3 X 5 3/4 In.	10.00
Weller, Bowl, Roma, 2 Handled, 4 Footed, Marked, 3 X 7 In.	25.00
Weller, Bowl, Sabrinian, Oval Shape, Lavender, Seahorses, 8 1/2 In.	48.50
Weller, Bowl, Sabrinian, 2 X 8 In.	17.50
Weller, Bowl, Silvertone, Floral On Blue Lavender, Flaring, 3 3/8 In.	47.50
Weller, Bowl, Woodcraft, 3 Foxes, Block Weller Mark, 4 1/2 X 7 1/2 In.	85.00
Weller, Bowl, Woodrose, Yellow Rose On Brown Ground, 6 In.Diameter	28.00
Weller, Candleholder, Ansonia, Green, 2 1/2 In.High, Pair	12.00
Weller, Candleholder, Glendale, Flying Bird In Tree With Eggs, 2 In., Pair	45.00
Weller, Candlestick, Blue Matte, Berries & Twigs, 10 In.	40.00
Weller, Candlestick, Cameo Line, Salmon Color, Paper Label, 1 1/2 In., Pair	12.50
Weller, Candlestick, Orange Iridescent Drape, 9 X 4 3/4 In.	55.00
Weller, Candlestick, White Roses On Green, Marked M & E, 2 1/2 In., Pair	9.50
Weller, Centerpiece & Flower Holder, Ivoris, White, 17 X 7 In.	47.25
Weller, Cornucopia, Wild Rose Design, Tan, Script Mark, 6 In.	10.00
Weller, Creamer, Hand-Painted Duck On 1 Side, Ink Stamp Mark, 3 3/4 In.	25.00
Weller, Creamer, Ivory, Bird, Ducks, Squirrel, & Rabbit, 2 3/4 In.	30.00
Weller, Creamer, Zona	6.00
Weller, Cup, Friendship, Louwelsa, Three Handles, Ear Of Corn, No Mark	65.00
Weller, Cup, Zona, Duck Decoration	12.00
Weller, Ewer, Louwelsa, Nasturtium On Brown, 4 In.High	80.00
Weller, Ewer, Louwelsa, Yellow & White Crocus On Tan To Brown, HW, 6 In.	95.00
Weller, Ewer, Oak Leaf, Brown, 9 In.High	23.00
Weller, Figurine, Dog, Woodcraft, Turquoise & Brown, 5 X 8 1/2 In.	50.00
Weller, Figurine, Log, Woodcraft, Handle, 9 1/2 In.	16.00
Weller, Flower Frog, Butterfly & Roses, Artist's Initials	22.00
Weller, Flower Frog, Coppertone, Signed	18.00
Weller, Flower Frog, Green Frog Sitting Under Open Lily	20.00
Weller, Flower Frog, Kingfisher, 9 In.	70.00 To 75.00
Weller, Flower Holder, Naked Child Holding Grapes, Turquoise, 7 1/2 In.High	17.00
Weller, Frog On Lily Pad, Copper Tone	34.00
Weller, Frog, Coppertone, Ink Stamped Weller Pottery, 2 1/4 In.	50.00
Weller, Frog, Flower, Muskota, Nude Woman With Swan, 7 X 8 In.	95.00
Weller, Frog, Muskota, Kingfisher	65.00
Weller, Humidor, Burntwood, Incised Florals, 5 1/2 In.	90.00
Weller, Jar, Tobacco, Roma, 9 Sided, Block Weller Mark, 7 In.	45.00
Weller, Jardiniere, Baldin, Apples & Leaves On Matte Beige, 5 1/2 In.	35.00
Weller, Jardiniere, Barrel Shape, Tulips On White, 12 In.	25.00
Weller, Jardiniere, Blue Ware, Classical, 3 Feet, 9 X 11 In.	140.00
Weller, Jardiniere, Claywood, Large Stylized Flowers, 8 X 8 In.	28.00

Weller, Jardiniere, Dickensware, Brown Glaze, Floral, 1st Line, 9 X 7 In.	110.00
Weller, Jardiniere, Etna, Gray High Gloss, Roses, 9 1/4 In.	86.00
Weller, Jardiniere, Etna, Maroon Pansies Around Top, 6 X 7 In.	30.00
Weller, Jardiniere, Etna, Wine Colored Irises, 8 In.	50.00
Weller, Jardiniere, Fairfield, Cream, Raised Cherubs, 6 1/2 X 8 In.	24.00
Weller, Jardiniere, Floral, Pedestal, 3 Footed, 8 X 6 In.	45.00
Weller, Jardiniere, Forest, Shaped Like Flower Pot, 4 1/2 X 5 In.	55.00
Weller, Jardiniere, Louwelsa, Red Poppy Decoration, 8 X 8 In.	120.00
Weller, Jardiniere, Patra, Signed, 9 X 8 1/2 In.	40.00
Weller, Jardiniere, Roma, Three Footed, Tan & Green, Roses, 5 X 6 In.	30.00
Weller, Jardiniere, Sicardo, Metallic Luster, Embossed Lotus Pods, 30 In.	850.00
Weller, Jug, Dickensware, 2nd Line, Pillow, Indian With Feathers, 5 In.	285.00
Weller, Jug, Russet Flowers On Brown, Artist Signed, 5 X 4 In.	55.00
Weller, Lamp Base, Dickensware, High Glaze, Nasturtium & Leaves, 9 In.	325.00
Weller, Lamp Base, Muskota, Fisherboy, 11 In.High	175.00
Weller, Lamp Base, Roma, 10 In.	50.00
Weller, Lamp, Aurelian, Pear Shape, Yellow Iris On Brown, Knaus, 16 In.	425.00
Weller, Letter Holder, Turado, Coral & Turquoise On Green, 6 X 3 1/4 In.	160.00
Weller, Mug, Burntwood, Incised Floral Decoration, Unsigned	38.00
Weller, Mug, Dickensware, Monk, Matte Green, Gold, & Blue, 2nd Line	125.00
Weller, Mug, Dickensware, Stag & Tree, 2nd Line, Artist G., 6 3/4 In.	175.00
Weller, Mug, Dickensware, 1st Line, High Glaze, Swallows Perched In Tree	395.00
Weller, Mug, Hudson, White Pansies On Blue Gray, Green Leaves, 5 1/2 In.	45.00
Weller, Mug, Ivory, Leaf In Low Relief Around Mug, 5 In.High, Unmarked	20.00
Weller, Mug, Louwelsa, Friendship, Flying Swallow Decoration, 3 Handles	395.00
Weller, Pedestal, Aurelian, 16 In.High	75.00
Weller, Pitcher, Art Nouveau, Woman Figure On Matte Glaze, 8 In.	70.00
Weller, Pitcher, Etna, Blue Flowers On Gray Shaded, 6 In.	48.00
Weller, Pitcher, Etna, Pink Cyclamen On Gray, Slender, 6 1/4 In.	55.00
Weller, Pitcher, Forest, High Glaze, 8 In.High	75.00
Weller, Pitcher, Glossy Salmon, Horizontal Ribbing, 5 X 6 In.	18.00
Weller, Pitcher, Louwelsa, Orange & Green Grapes On Brown, E.R., 12 1/2 In.	105.00
Weller, Pitcher, Louwelsa, Standard Brown Glaze, Grapes, ER, 12 1/2 In.	105.00
Weller, Pitcher, Louwelsa, Standard Glaze, Raspberry, 12 In.	135.00
Weller, Pitcher, Water, Cobalt, 5 1/4 In.	20.00
Weller, Pitcher, Zona, Cream Color, Rabbit & Bluebird, 4 In.High	20.00
Weller, Planter, Blue Drapery, Molded Sprigs Of Pink Roses, Dark Blue, 6 In.	20.00
Weller, Planter, DuPont, Cream, Red Roses & Vines On Basket Weave, 9 In.	22.00
Weller, Planter, Footed, Roba, Brown, White Bellflowers, Green Leaves, 6 In.	16.00
Weller, Planter, Forest, Round, Green Interior, 8 X 3 1/4 In.High	24.00
Weller, Planter, Knifewood, Floral Pattern, Cream, Tan, 2 X 6 In.	25.00
Weller, Planter, Roma, Square, Red Roses On White Ground, 3 1/2 In.	13.00
Weller, Planter, Roma, 6 In.Square, 3 1/2 In.High	20.00
Weller, Planter, Tutone, Triangle Form, 7 1/4 X 3 1/2 In.	175.00
Weller, Planter, Woodcraft, Three Foxes, Openwork Lattice, 5 X 6 1/2 In.	65.00
Weller, Plate, Louisiana Purchase Exposition, General Grant Figure, 5 In.	75.00
Weller, Ramekin & Underplate, Covered, Green Basket Weave	7.50
Weller, Rose Bowl, Turada, High Gloss Black, Creamy Inlaid Pattern, 5 In.	95.00
Weller, Tankard, Aqua Matte, White Dogwood, Cameo, Script Signature, 12 In.	28.00
Weller, Tankard, Art Nouveau, Green Matte, 23 In.	225.00
Weller, Tankard, Dickensware, Stag In Forest, 15 In.High	300.00
Weller, Tankard, Etna, 2 Red Carnations, 10 1/2 In.	74.00
Weller, Tankard, Green Bottom, White Top, Purple Grapes, 11 1/2 In.	50.00
Weller, Tankard, Louwelsa, Blackberry Design On Brown, 14 1/2 In.	245.00
Weller, Tankard, Louwelsa, Grape Decoration On Brown Glaze, 12 1/2 In.High	125.00
Weller, Tankard, Standard Glaze, Monk, Artist Signed, 14 In.	425.00
Weller, Teapot, Forest, Glossy Glaze, 6 In.High	150.00
Weller, Teapot, Glossy Rose, Gold Design, 8 X 5 In.	25.00
Weller, Teapot, Tea Rose, Pumpkin Shape, Green Stem Finial, DE, Quart	43.00
Weller, Teapot, Terra-Cotta, Green At Top, House In Landscape, DE, 3 In.	80.00
Weller, Tray, Marble, Block Signature, 14 X 2 In.	88.00
Weller, Turtle, Coppertone, Script Mark Weller Pottery, 4 In.	50.00
Weller, Turtle, Coppertone, Script Mark Weller Pottery, 6 In.	65.00
Weller, Umbrella Stand, Etna, Pink To Gray, Imitation Jewels, 20 In.	175.00
Weller, Umbrella Stand, Teakwood, 22 In.High	150.00

Weller, Vase, Alvin, Fan Shaped, Matte Green, Relief Vines, Fruit, 5 Holes	25.00
Weller, Vase, Andsley, Water Lilies & Cattails, 9 In.	25.00
Weller, Vase, Ansonia, Matte Green, Ruffled Top, 10 In.High	30.00
Weller, Vase, Ardsley, Green Ribbed Body, Cattails, Flowers, 7 1/2 In.	24.00
Weller, Vase, Art Nouveau, Matt Floral, Green, Pink, & Yellow, 12 1/2 In.	40.00
Weller, Vase, Art Nouveau, Raised Floral On Brown Glaze, 5 1/2 In.	70.00
Weller, Vase, Art Nouveau, Shell Type Pillow, Block Weller Mark, 7 In.	80.00
Weller, Vase, Aurelian, Pillow, Brown, Yellow, Orange, & Green, Terry, 5 1/2 n.	150.00
Weller, Vase, Baldin, Apple, Autumn Coloring, 5 1/2 In.	36.50
Weller, Vase, Blue & Decorated, Pink & Green Floral On Royal Blue, 9 In.	22.00
Weller, Vase, Blue & Decorated, Six Sided, Purple Band, 6 In.High	28.00
Weller, Vase, Blue Decorated, Blackberries, A.H., 10 1/2 In.	275.00
Weller, Vase, Blue Drapery, Pink Roses & Sprigs On Dark Blue Matte, 3 In.	20.00
Weller, Vase, Blue Drapery, Square, Blue Ground, Pink Roses, 7 In.High	22.50
Weller, Vase, Bodin, 1920, 7 In.	30.00
Weller, Vase, Bonita Line, Blue Daisy Type Floral, Artist Signed, 5 3/4 In.	32.50
Weller, Vase, Bonita Line, Bluebell Type Floral, Artist Signed, 4 1/4 In.	32.50
Weller, Vase, Bonita, Artist Signed Hester Pillsbury, 7 1/2 In.	45.00
Weller, Vase, Bonita, Matte Cream, 2 Handled, Floral, 5 1/4 In.	34.00
Weller, Vase, Bouquet, Dogwood Blossoms, 3 Twig Handles, Signed W, 6 In.	15.50
Weller, Vase, Bud, Alvin, Fan, Embossed & Painted Apple Trees, Signed B, 6 In.	10.00
Weller, Vase, Bud, Alvin, Triple, Vine & Flowers, 4 1/4 In.High	22.50
Weller, Vase, Bud, Alvin, 7 1/2 In.High	28.00
Weller, Vase, Bud, Baldin, 9 In.High	18.00
Weller, Vase, Bud, Cornish, Handled, Berries On Blue Matte, 8 1/2 In.	22.00
Weller, Vase, Bud, Hudson, Dark Blue, Small Pink & Rose Flowers, 12 In.	45.00
Weller, Vase, Bud, Lasa, Slender, Scenic, Signed, 7 In.	135.00
Weller, Vase, Bud, Standard Glaze, Pansies On Brown, Turned Top, 8 In.	60.00
Weller, Vase, Burntwood, Ducks, 3 In.	25.00
Weller, Vase, Burntwood, Fish, 2 1/4 In.	20.00
Weller, Vase, Burntwood, Spider Web Panels, 3 1/2 In.	14.00
Weller, Vase, Cameo, Urn Shape, Turquoise, White Roses & Leaves, 11 In.High	23.00
Weller, Vase, Cameo, White Rose & Foliage On Green Ground, Handles, 8 In.	22.00
Weller, Vase, Cameo, 2 Handled, Tan Background, 5 X 6 1/2 In.	10.00
Weller, Vase, Cameo, 2 Handled, Tan Background, 7 X 6 1/2 In.	11.00
Weller, Vase, Chase, White Cameo Hunter & Dogs On Tan, Script, 11 1/2 In.	175.00
Weller, Vase, Chengtu Red Bottom, Fulper Type Green Top, Dripping, 9 1/2 In.	22.50
Weller, Vase, Chengtu, Stamped Weller Pottery, 11 In.	55.00
Weller, Vase, Chengtu, 7 X 12 In.	55.00
Weller, Vase, Clewell, Incised Design, Block Weller Mark, 5 X 2 1/2 In.	110.00
Weller, Vase, Coppertone, Green, 2 Handled, 7 X 8 In.	38.50
Weller, Vase, Coppertone, Signed, 6 In.	25.00
Weller, Vase, Cornish Pattern, Tan, Script Mark, 9 In.	17.50
Weller, Vase, Dark Green Matte, Inpressed Signature, 5 1/2 X 2 1/2 In.	35.00
Weller, Vase, Dickensware, Orange Poppies On Sea Green, 6 In.	110.00
Weller, Vase, Dickensware, 1st Line, Classic Shape, Water Lilies, 10 In.	88.00
Weller, Vase, Dickensware, 1st Line, Monk With Mandolin, 15 In.	185.00
Weller, Vase, Dogwood Blossoms, Peach Color, Green Leaves, 11 In.High	14.00
Weller, Vase, Dogwood On Green, Script Signature, 5 1/2 In.	10.00
Weller, Vase, Dresden, Boats, Water, Land, & 5 Windmills, 16 In.	175.00
Weller, Vase, Dupont, Matte Gray & Cream Crosshatched, Roses, 9 In.	30.00
Weller, Vase, Eocean, Floral, Artist LJB, Block Weller Mark, 6 3/4 In.	75.00
Weller, Vase, Eocean, Red Rose On Dark To Light Gray, 6 1/2 In.	30.00
Weller, Vase, Etched Matte, Grapes On Gold, Block Weller, 10 1/2 In.	55.00
Weller, Vase, Ethel, Profile Smelling Rose, 9 In.High	80.00
Weller, Vase, Etna, Dark To Light Gray, Yellow Poppy, Double Handle, 4 In.	35.00
Weller, Vase, Etna, Gray Glaze, Floral, Corset Shape, 4 1/2 In.	55.00
Weller, Vase, Etna, Hydrangias, Cylindrical, 6 1/2 In.	33.00
Weller, Vase, Etna, Marked Weller On Side, 11 In.	58.00 To 80.00
Weller, Vase, Etna, Pale Gray To Dark Gray, Glossy, Pink Flower, 8 1/2 In.	52.50
Weller, Vase, Etna, Pink Mums On Dark To Light Gray, 15 In.High	125.00
Weller, Vase, Etna, Pink To Gray, Poppies, 10 In.High	45.00
Weller, Vase, Etna, Teardrop Shape, Pink Morning Glories, 7 In.	52.00
Weller, Vase, Etna, White To Gray, Floral Decoration, 14 In.High	80.00
Weller, Vase, Floretta, Brown Glaze, Grapes, 11 1/2 In.	60.00
Weller, Vase, Floretta, Brown, Green Grapes, 2 Handles, 7 1/2 In.	65.00

Weller, Vase, Floretta, Floral On Brown, Marked Floretta Weller, 7 In.	75.00
Weller, Vase, Floretta, Gold Grapes On Brown, Vine Handles, 8 1/4 In.	58.00
Weller, Vase, Floretta, Handles, Puffed Out Grapes & Scrolls, 7 1/2 In.	75.00
Weller, Vase, Floretta, Light To Dark Gray, Relief Rose, 5 In.High	50.00
Weller, Vase, Floretta, Ruffled Border, Brown Glazed, Raised Grapes, 7 1/2 In.	75.00
Weller, Vase, Forest, Block Signature, 8 1/2 In.	30.00
Weller, Vase, Forest, Flared Top, Unmarked, 5 X 10 In.High	36.00
Weller, Vase, Green, Double Handled, Bulbous, Signed, 17 X 6 In.	12.00
Weller, Vase, Hanging, Ivory Matte, Raised Floral, 6 1/2 In.	12.00
Weller, Vase, Hester Pillsbury, Dark Blue, White Shooting Stars, 6 In.	105.00
Weller, Vase, High Glaze, Gray, Pink, Turquoise, & Green, Floral, 3 5/8 In.	55.00
Weller, Vase, Hudson, Blue To Gray, Baluster Shape, Timberlake, 8 In.	95.00
Weller, Vase, Hudson, Dark Blue Floral, 7 In.	35.00
Weller, Vase, Hudson, Dark Royal Blue, Band Of Pink Flowers, 9 In.High	68.00
Weller, Vase, Hudson, Gray Green Top, Lavender Base, Blue Flowers, 10 In.High	35.00
Weller, Vase, Hudson, Pink To Gray, Lily Of The Valley, Artist, 8 In.	100.00
Weller, Vase, Ivory, Art Nouveau Mermaids & Embossing, 13 X 7 In.	85.00
Weller, Vase, Japbirdmal, Japanese Figure & Trees, Signed CMM, 7 In.	300.00
Weller, Vase, Jeweled, Blue Slip Flying Fish Sgraffito, 11 In.	165.00
Weller, Vase, Jug Type, Louwelsa, Yellow Orchids, H.Mitchell, 4 1/2 In.	75.00
Weller, Vase, Knifewood, Great Horned Owl, 9 In.	100.00
Weller, Vase, Lasa, Chalice Shape, Tree Design, 8 In.	125.00
Weller, Vase, Lasa, Gourd Shape, Palm Trees Scene On Gold, 6 In.	130.00
Weller, Vase, Lasa, Green, Magenta, Blues, 5 1/2 In.High X 3 1/2 In.Wide	135.00
Weller, Vase, Lasa, Landscape On Metallic, Signed, 6 In.	130.00
Weller, Vase, Lasa, Palm Trees, Mountains, Water, & Setting Sun, 10 In.	110.00
Weller, Vase, Lasa, Scenic, Iridescent Coloring, 8 1/2 In.	175.00
Weller, Vase, Lasa, Sea, Mountain, Land, Palm Trees, 6 In.High	145.00
Weller, Vase, Lasa, Signed Weller Lasa On Side, 3 1/2 X 3 1/2 In.	95.00
Weller, Vase, Lasa, Slender, 7 1/2 X 2 1/2 In.	95.00
Weller, Vase, Lasa, Tree & Mountain Scene, Gold, Magenta, Green, & Blue, 4 In.	134.00
Weller, Vase, Light Blue, Weller In Script, Initial A, 6 In.	9.50
Weller, Vase, Lilac, Art Deco, Pleated Sides, Panels, 8 3/4 In.	25.00
Weller, Vase, Louwelsa, Brown Glaze, Floral, 6 In.	60.00
Weller, Vase, Louwelsa, Brown To Green, Pansies, Bulbous At Shoulder, 9 In.	78.00
Weller, Vase, Louwelsa, Clover Decoration, 4 Sided, 4 In.	99.50
Weller, Vase, Louwelsa, Cylinder, Nasturtiums, H.P., 14 1/2 In.High, Pair	300.00
Weller, Vase, Louwelsa, Daffodil On Mahogany, Signed J.I., 8 In.	115.00
Weller, Vase, Louwelsa, Dark Brown, Yellow & Orange, Crocus, 7 1/2 In.	55.00
Weller, Vase, Louwelsa, Floral On Mahogany, Yellow, & Green, 4 1/2 In.	70.00
Weller, Vase, Louwelsa, Floral, Signed HM, 6 In.	62.50
Weller, Vase, Louwelsa, Floral, Signed Hester Pillsbury, 7 In.	75.00
Weller, Vase, Louwelsa, Iris On Dark Brown Glaze, 7 In.High	95.00
Weller, Vase, Louwelsa, Jonquils Under Standard Glaze, Hoskins, 11 In.	115.00
Weller, Vase, Louwelsa, Lavender Wisteria On Light To Dark Green, 13 In.	134.00
Weller, Vase, Louwelsa, Leaves & Berries, Signed LJB, 14 In.	88.00
Weller, Vase, Louwelsa, Long Neck, Rosebuds On Brown Glaze, 5 5/8 In.	65.00
Weller, Vase, Louwelsa, Pansies On Green To Brown, Bulbous, 2 Handles, 6 In.	58.00
Weller, Vase, Louwelsa, Pillow, Pansies, 4 1/2 In.	57.00
Weller, Vase, Louwelsa, Raised White Design On Matt Blue Gray, 7 In.	70.00
Weller, Vase, Louwelsa, Rose Decoration, Hester Pillsbury, 12 In., Pair	255.00
Weller, Vase, Marbelized, Gray Maroon, 9 X 4 1/2 In.	45.00
Weller, Vase, Marvo, Cylinder, Flared Top, Brown & Green, 8 1/2 In.High	15.00
Weller, Vase, Marvo, Gray, Incised, 7 In.	12.00
Weller, Vase, Marvo, Green With Rubbed On Brown, 6 1/2 In.High	28.00
Weller, Vase, Matte Finish, 5 1/2 In.	15.00
Weller, Vase, Matte Glaze, Bleeding Hearts, 2 Handles, M-F22, 6 In.	9.50
Weller, Vase, Matte Green, Molded Design At Bottom, Block Weller, 6 In.	12.50
Weller, Vase, Matte Green, Square, Marked, 6 X 2 In.	12.50
Weller, Vase, Matte, Morning Glories On Pink To Green, Pillsbury, 8 1/4 In.	95.00
Weller, Vase, Medium Green, Twisted Pillow Shape, Script Mark, 5 In.	12.50
Weller, Vase, Oak Leaf Pattern, Blue, Script Mark, 9 In.	12.50
Weller, Vase, Oak Leaf, 6 1/2 In.High	15.00
Weller, Vase, Pansies On Dark To Light Brown, Louwelsa Type, 6 1/2 In.	35.00
Weller, Vase, Pearl Gray, Mauve Apples & Greens, Signed, 8 1/4 In.	55.00
Weller, Vase, Pinecone, 10 X 5 1/2 In.	22.50

Weller, Vase, Roba, 6 In.High 17.50
Weller, Vase, Roma, Cylinder, Pink Rose On Brown Ground, Blue Bow, 8 In. 29.50
Weller, Vase, Roma, 4 Sided, Incised Branches, Leaves, 8 In.High 21.00
Weller, Vase, Roses, Buds, & Leaves Cn Blue, 11 In. 35.00
Weller, Vase, Rudlor, Apple Blossom, Green, Open Handled, 8 3/4 In. 20.00
Weller, Vase, Seascape At Sunset, Matte Finish, Signed, 8 1/2 In. 165.00
Weller, Vase, Seneca, Pastel Blue, Tree, Footed, Ruffled, 5 In. 10.00
Weller, Vase, Sgraffito Of Flying Fish, Pale Blue, Jeweled, Signed, 11 In. 195.00
Weller, Vase, Sicardo, Broad Base, Wide Neck, 5 1/2 X 3 In. 300.00
Weller, Vase, Sicardo, Classic Shape, Iridescent, 5 3/4 In.High 185.00
Weller, Vase, Sicardo, Floral & Vine, Pale Blue To Purple & Green, 4 1/2 In. 175.00
Weller, Vase, Sicardo, Flower & Leaf On Green, 6 In. 95.00
Weller, Vase, Sicardo, Gold, Red, Purple, Blue, & Green, Floral, 6 In. 195.00
Weller, Vase, Sicardo, Gourd Shape, Cherries, Green & Violet, 5 In. 128.50
Weller, Vase, Sicardo, Green Metallic Floral Design, 5 In.High 205.00
Weller, Vase, Sicardo, Green, Blue, & Purple Iridescence, Bulbous, 4 1/2 In. 145.00
Weller, Vase, Sicardo, Green, Blue, Purple, High Relief Floral, 17 1/2 In. 1000.00
Weller, Vase, Sicardo, Oak Leaves & Acorns, Classical Shape, Signed, 7 In. 215.00
Weller, Vase, Silvertone, Pink, Blue, Lavendar Ground, Raised Flowers, 8 In. 50.00
Weller, Vase, Sky Blue, White Stars, Pillsbury, 5 3/4 X 6 1/4 In. 105.00
Weller, Vase, Slip Painted Yellow Floral On Gray, 6 In. 26.00
Weller, Vase, Stellar, Black With White Comet Decoration, Signed T.M. 75.00
Weller, Vase, Sudonia, Blue Ground, Green Leaves, Square Base, 11 In.High 34.50
Weller, Vase, Teakwood, Tree Design, Rudolph Lorber, 13 In. 60.00
Weller, Vase, Triple Tree Trunk, Woodcraft Line, Daisies, 9 In., Pair 55.00
Weller, Vase, Tutone, Dark Rose Top, Light Green Bottom, Flower, 6 In.High 10.00
Weller, Vase, Tutone, White & Yellow Floral, 2 Handled, Marked Weller, 10 In. 8.00
Weller, Vase, Velva, Brown, Incised Script, 6 In. 20.00
Weller, Vase, Wall, Woodcraft, Tree Background, Squirrel & Acorn, 9 In. 57.50
Weller, Vase, Wall, Woodcraft, White Owl, 11 In. 52.00
Weller, Vase, Water Lilies On Pale To Royal Blue, Pillsbury, 10 In. 35.00
Weller, Vase, Wild Rose, Peach, Pink Flowers, Green Leaves, 8 In.High 13.00
Weller, Vase, Wild Rose, Sea Green, 2 Handled, Impressed Weller, 9 1/2 In. 15.00
Weller, Vase, Wild Rose, 6 1/2 In. 10.00
Weller, Vase, Wild Rose, 6 3/4 In. 15.00
Weller, Vase, Woodcraft, Pink Dogwood Blossoms, 9 1/4 In. 22.00
Weller, Vase, Woodcraft, Tree Stump, Green Leaves, 2 Handles, 8 1/4 In. 50.00
Weller, Vase, 2 Parakeets On Front, Plants, Trees, 9 In. 48.00
Weller, Wall Pocket, Marengo, Trees & Mountains, 8 1/2 In. 75.00
Weller, Wall Pocket, Rose & Ribbon, 7 1/2 In.High 12.00
Weller, Wall Pocket, Woodcraft, Squirrel Chewing Acorn 28.00
Weller, Wall Pocket, Woodcraft, Squirrel Sitting At Bottom, 9 In. 60.00
Wells Fargo, Certificate, Stock, Signed Henry Wells & Wm.S.Fargo, 1864 .... 35.00
Wells Fargo, Certificate, Stock, Wm.Fargo & John Butterfield, 1856 .... 75.00
Wells Fargo, Deed, Gold Mine, Combination Lode, 1863 .... 50.00
Whieldon Type, Figurine, Ram, Recumbent, Brown Coat, C.1860, 5 1/2 In. 500.00
Whieldon Type, Plate, Cartouches On Black, Octagonal, C.1765, 8 7/8 In., Pair 350.00
Whieldon, Tea Caddy, Pineapple, Yellow Ocher, Tin Cover, C.1765 .... 625.00
Whieldon, Teapot, Cauliflower, Scroll Handle, C.1765, 4 In. 70.00
Willow, see Blue Willow
Windowpane, Bull's-Eye, Hand-Pressed, C.1900, Light Opal, 1 1/2 In. 1.35
Windowpane, Bull's-Eye, Hand-Pressed, C.1900, Stained Amber, 2 In. 1.95
Windowpane, Bull's-Eye, Hand-Pressed, C.1900, Stained Dark Amber, 2 In. 1.95
Windowpane, Bull's-Eye, Hand-Pressed, C.1900, Stained Emerald, 1 1/2 In. 1.35
Windowpane, Bull's-Eye, Hand-Pressed, C.1900, Stained Green, 1 1/4 In. 1.25
Windowpane, Bull's-Eye, Hand-Pressed, C.1900, Stained Ruby, 1 1/2 In. 1.35

Wooden, Bowl, Burl, 20 1/2 In.

(See Page 691)

Windowpane, Bull's-Eye, Hand-Pressed, C.1900, Yellow Opal, 1 3/4 In.	1.45
Windowpane, Bull's-Eye, Hand-Pressed, C.1900, 2 In.	1.95
Windowpane, Bull's-Eye, Hand-Pressed, C.1900, 2 5/8 In.	2.35
Windowpane, Stained Glass, Leaded, Round, Graduated From 10 To 17 In., 3	150.00
Windowpane, Stained Glass, Leaded, 3 Ft.4 In.X 6 Ft.2 In.	250.00
Wood Carving, Bear, 3 X 4 1/2 In.	25.00
Wood Carving, Birds & Flowers, Gilt Wood, Framed, 8 X 6 In.	55.00
Wood Carving, Boy Scout Emblem, Eagle, Oval, "Be Prepared," 13 X 9 1/2 In.	45.00
Wood Carving, Confederate Infantryman, Tom Jones, 21 In.	450.00
Wood Carving, Dutch South African Seal, Black Ebony, Ceylon, 1901, 3 In.	64.50
Wood Carving, Eagle, Gilt, American School, C.1850, 34 X 26 In.	1100.00
Wood Carving, Eagle, Serpent In Talons, Train, N.Y., C.1800, Gilt, 13 In.	675.00
Wood Carving, Eagle, Wings Spread, On Rockwork Base, IO X 46 1/2 In.	325.00
Wood Carving, Lion, Spear Through Him, Swiss, Signed Viruti, 7 In.	22.00
Wood Carving, Noah's Ark & Animals, Painted, C.1850, 191 Pieces	1100.00
Wood Carving, Ono No Komachi, Seated On Tree, Inlaid Horn, C.1850, 6 In.	175.00
Wood Carving, Panel, Oak, Victories Of Nelson, Napoleonic Era, 50 X 10 In.	650.00
Wood Carving, Plaque, Anchor, Gilt Finish, Black Ground, C.1780, 7 In., Pair	195.00
Wood Carving, Plaque, Eagle, Wings Spread, Claws On Rod, C.1850, 27 In.	1000.00
Wood Carving, Seal Of The State Of Pennsylvania, C.1850, 26 In.	75.00
Wood Carving, Seal, London & Northwestern Railway, 1846, 12 In.	175.00
Wooden, Carousel Horse, see Carousel, Horse	
Wooden, Barrel, Biscuit, English, Porcelain Lined, Silver Plate Lid & Trim	10.00
Wooden, Barrel, Biscuit, Golden Oak, Silver Bands & Handle, China Liner	25.00
Wooden, Barrel, Carrying Bail, 11 In.	25.00
Wooden, Basket, Square, Folding Top Handle, 7 1/4 X 9 1/4 In.	15.00
Wooden, Basket, Square, Stationary Top Handle, 8 X 8 X 4 In.	15.00
Wooden, Bootjack, Walnut	10.00
Wooden, Bowl & Ladle, Russian, Black, Gold, & Bittersweet, 6 In.	22.00
Wooden, Bowl, Burl, 20 1/2 In. .... Illus	350.00
Wooden, Bowl, Hand-Carved Spread Winged Eagles, C.1790, 12 In.	95.00
Wooden, Bowl, Maple, Burl, 9 1/4 X 3 1/2 In.	160.00
Wooden, Bowl, Rectangular, Pine, 19 X 11 X 4 In.High	50.00
Wooden, Bowl, Salad, Maple, One Piece Of Wood, Square, 21 1/2 X 14 1/2 In.	45.00
Wooden, Bowl, Salad, Maple, 17 In.	75.00
Wooden, Bowl, Salad, Oblong, 17 1/2 X 9 1/2 In.	20.00
Wooden, Bowl, Tiger Maple, 10 1/2 X 11 In.	55.00
Wooden, Box, Bible, Carved Oak, Hinged Slant Lid, 12 1/2 X 26 1/2 In.	120.00
Wooden, Box, Bible, Oak, Carved Frieze, 12 1/2 X 26 1/2 In.	300.00
Wooden, Box, Burr Walnut, Hinged Mirror Plate, Brass Handles, C.1875, 13 In.	40.00
Wooden, Box, Camphor, Hand-Carved Boar's Head, Hinged, 4 X 2 1/2 In.	65.00
Wooden, Box, Candle, Pine, Hanging, Handmade, Square Nails, 9 X 9 In.	46.00
Wooden, Box, Candle, Pine, Sliding Lid, Dovetailed, 10 X 5 X 5 In.	38.00
Wooden, Box, Candle, Walnut, Sliding Top, Carved Thumb Hold & Crest, 7 In.	30.00
Wooden, Box, Cigarette, Inlaid Pearl, Copper, Ivory, & Brass, Pair	55.00
Wooden, Box, Collar, Gutta-Percha Of Farm Tools On Lid, Square, 4 3/4 In.	19.75
Wooden, Box, Document, American, C.1850, Painted & Grained, Hinged, 15 In.	30.00
Wooden, Box, Jewel, Natural Oak, Flower Carved Top, 11 1/2 X 7 1/2 In.	18.00
Wooden, Box, Jewelry, Gentleman's, Rosewood, Silver Trim, 6 X 3 1/2 X 2 In.	23.50
Wooden, Box, Pencil, Slide Drawer, Stenciled, 9 X 2 In.	6.50
Wooden, Box, Pipe, Rhode Island, C.1740, Pine, Pierced, 26 X 6 In.	600.00
Wooden, Box, Tunbridge Ware, Walnut, Inlaid Hinged Lid, 8 3/4 X 6 3/4 In.	49.95
Wooden, Box, Vanity, Black Walnut, Mirror Inside Lid, 11 X 8 X 3 1/2 In.	22.00
Wooden, Box, Wall, New England, C.1800, Pine, Pierced Crest, 13 In.	200.00
Wooden, Box, Wall, Pine, Painted Sailing Vessel, C.1800, 15 In.	150.00
Wooden, Box, 3 Hex Signs On Hinged Lid, Dovetailed, 19 X 49 X 18 In.	300.00
Wooden, Bucket, Covered, 2 Lapped Bands, Wood Pins, Bail, 10 In.	30.00
Wooden, Candleholder, Brass Insert, 6 In., Pair	8.00
Wooden, Candleholder, Turned, Fancy, 15 In.	25.00
Wooden, Canteen, C.1750, Barrel Type, Iron Bands & Handle, Green Paint, 7 In.	125.00
Wooden, see also Kitchen, Store, Tool	
Wooden, Chest, Jewel, Rosewood, Oriental, Jade Medallion On Lid, 8 1/2 In.	75.00
Wooden, Cigar Store Indian, Bust Of Maiden, C.1850, 18 In.	225.00
Wooden, Cigar Store Indian, Head, Headdress, C.1850, 19 1/2 X 15 In.	150.00
Wooden, Cigar Store Indian, Squaw, Holding Cigars, Papoose, 52 In.	150.00
Wooden, Comb, Hair, Carved, Diamond Shape Hole For Hanging, 12 In.	35.00

Wooden, Cup, Dicing, Maple, C.1750, Bone Dice, 2 1/4 In.	38.00
Wooden, Dipper, Hand-Carved Out Of 1 Piece Of Wood, Fancy Handle, 22 In.	70.00
Wooden, Egg, Easter, Lacquer, Christ Rising From Tomb, Lukutin, C.1850, 4 In.	300.00
Wooden, Egg, Easter, Lacquer, Savior's Gate Of Kremlin, Lukutin, C.1820, 3 In.	175.00
Wooden, Egg, Easter, Lacquer, St.Igor, Book Of Gospels, Lukutin, C.1850, 3 In.	225.00
Wooden, Egg, Easter, Pique, Silver Inlaid, Alexandra Feodorovna, C.1890, 4 In.	425.00
Wooden, Egg, Easter, Russian, Pique, Silver Inlaid, C.1850, 2 3/4 In.	300.00
Wooden, Figurine, Abraham Lincoln, Carved, Painted, C.1850, 33 1/4 In.	400.00
Wooden, Figurine, Angel, Indian, Polychrome, Gilt, C.1850, 27 1/2 In., Pair	375.00
Wooden, Figurine, Bear, Victorian, On Hind Legs, 6 1/2 In.	22.00
Wooden, Figurine, Buddha, Gilt, Seated, Burma, C.1850, 9 In.	40.00
Wooden, Figurine, Chinese Rat Catcher With Box & Club, 2 X 2 1/2 In.	125.00
Wooden, Figurine, Jovial Buddha Holding Ball & Sack, 6 1/2 X 3 1/2 In.	40.00
Wooden, Figurine, Mother & Child, Indian, Polychrome, 21 In.	50.00
Wooden, Figurine, Rooster, Carved, Painted, C.1850, 8 In.	175.00
Wooden, Figurine, Rooster, Carved, Painted, Pennsylvania, C.1850, 7 In.	600.00
Wooden, Figurine, Seated Monkey Scratching Buttocks, Male Organs, 1 3/4 In.	100.00
Wooden, Fork, 4 Tines, MB Young Burned In Top, 66 In.	75.00
Wooden, Group, 2 Adult Beasts, Gilt Eyes, 35 In.	140.00
Wooden, Hair Receiver, Walnut, 2 1/2 X 2 3/4 In.	9.50
Wooden, Hatpin Holder, Ebony, Victorian	14.00
Wooden, Humidor, Rosewood, Brass Clad, Hinged Lid	39.00
Wooden, Keg, Rum, American, C.1760, Iron Bands, Separate Staves, Oval, 9 In.	145.00
Wooden, Keg, Rum, Hollowed-Out Tree, Carved Hoops, 6 In.	84.50
Wooden, Keg, Rum, Hollowed-Out Tree, Ring Turnings, Red Paint, 8 1/2 In.	84.50
Wooden, Keg, Rum, Revolutionary Period, Hollowed-Out Tree, Pocket, 6 In.	79.50
Wooden, Keg, Rum, Revolutionary Period, Iron Hoops, Blue Paint, 5 X 3 In.	97.50
Wooden, Lighter, Candle, Handled, 28 1/2 In	30.00
Wooden, Mask, Dance, Balinese, Green, 12 In.	125.00
Wooden, Match Holder, Chip Carved, Captive Ring, 4 1/4 In.	18.00
Wooden, Matchbox, Piedra Dura Mosaic Panel, Black, Hinged, 3 In.	65.00
Wooden, Mold, Butter, Cow Pattern, 1 Lb.	25.00
Wooden, Mold, Butter, Geometric Flower Design, 1 Lb.	24.00
Wooden, Mold, Cigar, 10 Hole	10.50
Wooden, Nutcracker, Carved Bear's Head, Glass Eyes, C.1850	52.00
Wooden, Nutcracker, Face Of Dog, Glass Eyes	35.00
Wooden, Plate, Bread, Russian, Embossed Sheaf Of Wheat, Sickle, Plow, 11 In.	65.00
Wooden, Plate, Bread, 11 In.	22.00
Wooden, Plate, Polish Mountaineer's Profile, Hand-Carved, 11 In.	7.00
Wooden, Salt & Pepper, Wooden Screw-In Top, Painted Decoration	8.00
Wooden, Sander, Pounce, Desk, Turned Maple, 3 In.	24.00
Wooden, Shoe, Lady's, High Button Style, Ebony, Carved, 9 1/2 In.	86.00
Wooden, Snuffbox, Nickel Trim, 4 Leaf Clover On Lid, Oval, 2 3/4 In.	6.95
Wooden, Spooner, Pincushion On Top	6.50
Wooden, Stamp, Butter, Stylized Leaf Design, 3 1/2 In.	18.00
Wooden, Sugar, Covered, Dated 1858, 4 In.	50.00
Wooden, Sugar, Covered, Lignum Vitae, Turned Pedestal Base, 7 In.	150.00

Wooden, Telephone, see Telephone

Worcester, Cooler, Fruit, Barr, Flight & Barr, 1807, Pair
(See Page 693)

Worcester, Plate, Blue Scalework,
1st Period, 7 3/4 In.
(See Page 693)

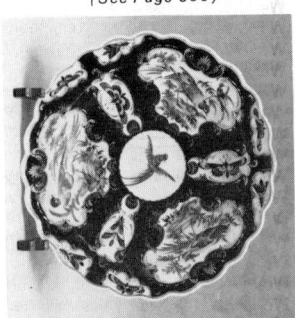

Wooden, Vase Holder, Myrtlewood, Glass Liner, 4 In.	5.00
Wooden, Watch Holder, Mahogany, Tall Case Clock, 13 1/4 In.	90.00
Wooden, Watch Holder, Sandalwood, Portal Shape, 36 Figures, 1860, 6 In.	50.00
Wooden, Wheel, From Hand Drawn Fire Apparatus, 5 Ft.	100.00
Wooden, Whirligig, Indian In Canoe, Carved, Painted, C.1850, 15 In.	800.00
Wooden, Whirligig, Sailor Boy, Carved, Painted, 15 In.	325.00
Wooden, Whirligig, Woodcutter, Carved, Painted, 14 In.	175.00
Worcester, see also Royal Worcester	
Worcester, Barrel, Biscuit, Hadley, Birds & Floral On Pink & Ivorine, 7 In.	225.00
Worcester, Bowl & Underplate, Covered, Handled, Oval, Chamberlain, 1800, 8 In.	285.00
Worcester, Bowl, Blossom Finial On Lid, Dr.Wall Period, 5 X 5 In.	195.00
Worcester, Candleholder, Rosy Beige, Etched With Gold, 4 1/2 In.	49.00
Worcester, Candlestick, Peach To Ecru To Biscuit, 9 In.	92.00
Worcester, Coaster, Wine, Peacock Decoration, J.Lewis, 4 1/2 In.	90.00
Worcester, Cooler, Fruit, Barr, Flight & Barr, 1807, Pair .... *Illus*	1300.00
Worcester, Creamer, Bands Of Gold Berries & Vines, Flight, Barr & Barr, 1820	135.00
Worcester, Creamer, Pear Shape, Green, Vertical Stripes, Gold, Kerr & Binns	115.00
Worcester, Cup & Saucer, Chocolate, Royal Lily, Crescent Mark, C.1790	110.00
Worcester, Cup & Saucer, Demitasse, Mediterranean Scenes	50.00
Worcester, Cup & Saucer, Flight, Barr & Barr	40.00
Worcester, Jar, Biscuit, Relief Leaves & Cascading Floral, Locke	75.00
Worcester, Jug, Masked Spout, Puce, Gold Decoration, C.1771, 12 In.High	600.00
Worcester, Muffineer, Pheasant In Grass, Beige Ground, Metal Top	45.00
Worcester, Planter, Nude Children Playing, 4 Footed, 4 Sided, C.1862, 8 In.	350.00
Worcester, Plate, Blue Scalework, 1st Period, 7 3/4 In. .... *Illus*	650.00
Worcester, Teapot, Armorial, Stag, Chamberlain, C.1797	450.00
Worcester, Teapot, Floral Finial, Dr.Wall Period, C.1770, 6 3/4 In.High	400.00
Worcester, Vase, English Sterling Collar, Leaf On Ivory, Locke, 6 In., Pair	85.00
Worcester, Vase, Gold & Silver Floral On Ivory, Purple Mark, 15 In.	350.00
Worcester, Vase, Hadley Ware, White, Navy & Gray Relief Designs, 6 In.High	165.00
Worcester, Wall Pocket, Acorns & Oak Leaves, Autumn Colors, Grainger, 4 In.	95.00
Worcester, Wall Pocket, Ivorine, Gold Gilded Leaves, C.1890, 8 In.	135.00
World War I, Box, Metal, Queen Mary's Gift To Troops, 1914, 3 X 5 In.	18.00
World War I, Buckle, Belt, German Infantryman's, Iron, "Gott Mit Uns"	9.50
World War I, Buckle, Belt, German Sergeant's, Brass, "Gott Mit Uns"	12.50
World War I, Buckle, German Dress Parade	20.00
World War I, Buckle, German, Iron, "Providentiae Memor"	24.50
World War I, Case, Cigarette, German, 1914, Iron Cross On Front	15.00
World War I, Club, Billy, U.S. Soldier's, Carved Wood, "France 1917-18"	84.50
World War I, Dogtag, A.E.F., Set Of 2	3.50
World War I, Front Plate, Eagle, German Spike Helmet	
World War I, Goggles, Aviator's, Green Tinted Isinglass Panels	17.50
World War I, Goggles, Splinter, Steel, Mask Shape, Leather Covering	175.00
World War I, Goggles, Splinter, Steel, Olive Finish	59.50
World War I, Hat, Brown Felt, Leather Band, 11th Inf., Mass. State Guard	10.00
World War I, Hat, German Army Field, Green Wool, Red Band, Dated 1915	59.00
World War I, Helmet, Bavarian Private's, Iron Fittings, Leather Lining	185.00
World War I, Helmet, German Infantryman's, Spike, Iron Fittings	145.00
World War I, Helmet, German, Jager, Rifleman's, Patent Leather, Iron Fittings	225.00
World War I, Helmet, German, Steel, Leather Lining	59.50
World War I, Helmet, U.S.A., Baden, E.M., Iron Fittings, Dated 1915	195.00
World War I, Helmet, U.S.Doughboy's, Trench, Steel, Olive Paint	7.50
World War I, Knife & Scabbard, Bolo	22.00
World War I, Map, Meuse-Argonne Offensive, Nov.20, 1918, 29 In.	20.00
World War I, Pillow, Crying, Forget Me Not, Lovers, Eagle, & Poem	20.00
World War I, Pilot Wings, Sterling Silver	45.00
World War I, Poster, America We Love You, 1917, Color, 16 X 20 In.	22.50
World War I, Poster, Americans All, H.C.Christy, 28 X 40 In.	59.00
World War I, Poster, Be Patriotic, Pledge To Save Food, 20 X 30 In.	28.00
World War I, Poster, Berlin Or Bust, Pershing, Framed, 22 X 18 In.	18.00
World War I, Poster, Biplanes, War Savings Stamps, C.L.Bull, 20 X 30 In.	40.00
World War I, Poster, Buy War Savings Stamps, C.L.Bull, Color, 20 X 30 In.	15.00
World War I, Poster, Clear The Way, H.Christy, 20 X 30 In.	50.00
World War I, Poster, Colored Man Is No Slacker, 1918, Lithograph	31.00
World War I, Poster, Come Over Boys, Irish To British Army, 38 X 58 In.	28.00
World War I, Poster, Duty Calls, 22 X 18 In.	15.00

World War I, Poster, Emprunt National, France, Marc, 36 X 43 In. 60.00
World War I, Poster, Feed A Fighter, W.Morgan, 20 X 30 In. 25.00
World War I, Poster, Food Is Ammunition, Don't Waste It, 20 X 30 In. 30.00
World War I, Poster, Food Will Win The War, 20 X 30 In. 28.00
World War I, Poster, France, War Loan, Lithograph, 36 X 44 In. 40.00
World War I, Poster, France, War Loan, 3 Men & Flag, Lithograph, 36 X 44 In. 75.00
World War I, Poster, Great Britain, Zeppelin Raids, F.Brangwyn, 30 X 20 In. 95.00
World War I, Poster, Help The Horse To Save The Soldier, 20 X 30 In. 125.00
World War I, Poster, Help Them With Your War Savings Stamps, 20 X 30 In. 10.00
World War I, Poster, Hunger Does Not Breed Reform, A.Triedler, 20 X 30 In. 20.00
World War I, Poster, I Want You For U.S.Army, J.M.Flagg, 30 X 40 In. 225.00
World War I, Poster, Irish Canadian Rangers, Linen, 28 X 40 In. 75.00
World War I, Poster, Join The Navy, Babcock, 30 X 40 In. 65.00
World War I, Poster, Keep Him First, Chas.Livingston Bull, 20 X 30 In. 20.00
World War I, Poster, Keep Him Free, C.L.Bull, Linen Mounted, 20 X 30 In. 50.00
World War I, Poster, Keep These Off The U.S.A., Norton, 30 X 40 In. 60.00
World War I, Poster, Kitchener's Overseas Battalion, Canada, 28 X 40 In. 75.00
World War I, Poster, Marines, Soldiers Of The Sea, Leyendecker, 30 S 40 In. 67.00
World War I, Poster, Motor Corps Of America, Christy, Linen, 32 X 44 In. 140.00
World War I, Poster, Order Coal Now, J.C.Leyendecker, 22 X 30 In. 55.00
World War I, Poster, Pour Forger Une France Puissante, 34 X 43 In. 40.00
World War I, Poster, Save Products Of Land, Eat Fish, C.L.Bull, 20 X 30 In. 25.00
World War I, Poster, Sottoscrivete Al Prestito, Italy, 40 X 58 In. 70.00
World War I, Poster, Tank Week, British, For War Loans, 20 X 30 In. 30.00
World War I, Poster, The Greatest Mother In The World, 20 X 30 In. 25.00
World War I, Poster, Treat 'em Rough, Join The Tanks, 26 X 40 In. 90.00
World War I, Poster, Women Of America, Save Your Country, 30 X 40 In. 37.00
World War I, Saddlebag, U.S.Cavalry, Leather, Brown, Brass Buckles 39.50
World War I, Sewing Kit, Soldier's Issue, In Canvas Bag 22.00
World War I, Shovel, Trench, German Infantryman's, Steel, Wooden Handle 24.50
World War I, Tunic, British General's Dress, Scarlet, Gold Bullion 195.00
World War II, Ax, Fireman's Dress, Nazi, Silver Blade, Pike End, Engraved 139.00
World War II, Bayonet & Scabbard, German 14.00
World War II, Bayonet & Scabbard, Nazi, Frog With Swastika 15.00
World War II, Belt, Signal Cartridge, Navy 6.00
World War II, Billfold, U.S.Army, Leather, Calendar 3.50
World War II, Book, Ration .... 1.00 To 5.00
World War II, Buckle, Belt, Luftwaffe 20.00
World War II, Button, Mechanical, Uncle Sam, Rope, Hitler's Neck, Pinback 30.00
World War II, Canteen, Nazi 22.50
World War II, Cap, Japanese Sailor's, Blue Wool, Pillbox Type 37.50
World War II, Case, Cartridge, German 3.00
World War II, Cutlass & Scabbard, Nazi, Forestry Scene On Blade 39.50
World War II, Cutlass, Forestry, Nazi, Presentation, Bronze Hilt, 9 1/2 In. 39.00
World War II, Dagger & Scabbard, Hitler Youth, Motto On Blade, 1937 .... 24.00
World War II, Dagger & Scabbard, Nazi, Air Force, Yellow Grip 158.00
World War II, Dagger & Scabbard, Nazi, S.S., Motto On Blade 140.00
World War II, Dagger, Nazi, Presentation, Forestry Scene On Blade 38.00
World War II, Flag, Afrika Korps 40.00
World War II, Flag, Japanese Battle, Square, 25 In. 15.00
World War II, Helmet, G.I. Issue, Infantry, Steel, Chin Strap 10.00
World War II, Helmet, Infantry Issue, Marked L.Kruger, Steel 10.00
World War II, Helmet, Japanese Army, Steel 60.00
World War II, Helmet, Nazi, Afrika Korps Officer's, Pith, Olive Felt 59.50
World War II, Helmet, Nazi, Afrika Korps, Pith, Tan, Red Linen Lining 59.50
World War II, Helmet, Nazi, Naval Officer's Parade, White, Summer, Pith 275.00
World War II, Helmet, Nazi, Naval, Pith, Tan, Brass Insignia 115.00
World War II, Helmet, Nazi, Paratrooper's, Steel, Leather Lining 250.00
World War II, Helmet, Luftwaffe Police, Steel, Decal, Eagle & Swastika 135.00
World War II, Phone, Army Field 29.50
World War II, Poster, Build The Mystery Ship, War Stamps, 30 X 20 In. 17.00
World War II, Poster, Buy Extra Bonds, Let 'em Have It, 30 X 20 In. 10.00
World War II, Poster, Enlist Now In The U.S.Army, 1940, 40 X 28 In. 30.00
World War II, Poster, Remember Me, I Was At Bataan, A.Brock, 30 X 20 In. 20.00
World War II, Poster, Russian Infantryman, Your Friend, 24 X 18 In. 20.00
World War II, Poster, U.S.Marines, Let's Go Geg 'em, 1942, 44 X 32 In. 25.00

World War II, Poster, Wanted, Adolf Hitler, C.1942, 12 X 9 In.	3.50
World War II, Poster, We've Made A Monkey Out Of You, Hitler, 24 X 18 In.	8.00
World War II, Writing Kit, Illustrations	2.25
World's Fair, see also Coca-Cola items, Copper, Ashtray, Milk Glass items, Souvenir, Spoon	
World's Fair, Ashtray, Chicago, 1933, Federal Building	7.00
World's Fair, Ashtray, Chicago, 1933, Science Hall	3.00
World's Fair, Bandana, Pan American Exposition, Silk, Square, 24 In.	65.00
World's Fair, Banner, New York, 1939, Cotton, Orange, Blue, & White	3.00
World's Fair, Book, Guide, New York, 1939	6.00
World's Fair, Book, Official View, Chicago, 1933	2.00
World's Fair, Bookmark, 1939, Metal	8.50
World's Fair, Card, Playing, Chicago, Sky Ride, Deck	3.50
World's Fair, Charm, Pan American Exposition, See Through, Bronze	25.00
World's Fair, Coaster, 1939, Composition	4.00
World's Fair, Cup & Saucer, Chicago, 1893, English China, Floral	250.00
World's Fair, Handkerchief, Jamestown Exposition, 1907, Silk	17.00
World's Fair, Hatchet, 1893, Washington, Libbey Glass Co., Toledo, O.	45.00
World's Fair, Kerchief, St.Louis, 1904, Temple Of Fraternity, 20 In.	22.00
World's Fair, Key, Master Company, 1933, Good Luck	3.50
World's Fair, Knife, Pocket, Chicago, 1933, 2 Blades, Plastic Handle	25.00
World's Fair, Knife, Pocket, 1939	6.00
World's Fair, Match Holder, St.Louis, 1904, Pocket, Machinery Buildings	18.00
World's Fair, Mirror, Pocket, Chicago, 1898, Gutta-Percha, 2 3/4 In.	65.00
World's Fair, Mug, Herbie, 1893, Ruby Flashed, 4 In.	25.00
World's Fair, Opener, Letter, Bookmark, Century Of Progress, 1933	3.00
World's Fair, Opener, Letter, Chicago, 1933, Chemical Elements	2.00
World's Fair, Opener, Letter, St.Louis, 1904, Cherub On Handle, White Metal	15.00
World's Fair, Opener, Letter, 1933, Key Shape	7.00
World's Fair, Pin, 1939, Light Blue & Green Enamel, Rhinestones	13.00
World's Fair, Plate, New York, 1940, Charles Murphy Artist, Laughlin, 10 In.	15.00
World's Fair, Plate, 1939, The American Potter, 7 1/4 In.	12.00
World's Fair, Purse, Change, Chicago, 1892, Leather, Brass Frame	30.00
World's Fair, Purse, Coin, St.Louis, 1904	10.00
World's Fair, Shaker, Cocktail, Century Of Progress, 1934, Aluminum	7.50
World's Fair, Spoon, Highball, 1939, Glass	1.00
World's Fair, Tape Measure, Philadelphia Sesquicentennial, 1926	20.00
World's Fair, Thermometer, St.Louis, 1904, Hatchet, Mother-Of-Pearl Inlay	17.00
World's Fair, Tray, Crumb, Chicago, 1933, Federal, Travel, & Science Buildings	5.00
World's Fair, Tumbler, Chicago, 1933	3.00
Yellowware, Mold, Ear Of Corn, 6 1/2 In.	20.00
Yellowware, Mold, Rabbit, 8 In.	35.00
Yellowware, Mold, Strawberry, 3 1/2 In.	15.00
Zane, see also Peters & Reed	
Zane, Bowl, Blue, Ink Stamped Zane Ware, 3 1/2 X 7 1/4 In.	4.00
Zane, Bowl, Enameled Pink Flowers On Gold Crackle, 10 In.	45.00
Zane, Bowl, Sheen Ware, Brown & Blue, Flower Frog, 8 X 2 1/2 In.	12.50
Zane, Vase, Blue, Black Specks, 2 Handles, P&R, 8 1/2 In.	45.00
Zane, Vase, Bud, Sheen Ware, Tan, Brown, Blue, & Gray, 8 1/2 In.	8.50
Zane, Vase, Cream, Marked Zane Ware, 8 X 5 In.	30.00

Zanesville Art Pottery was founded in 1900 by David Schmidt in Zanesville, Ohio. The firm made faience, umbrella stands, jardinieres, and pedestals. It worked until 1962.

Zanesville Pottery, Tankard, La Moro, Brown, Slip Berries, MCVR, 15 1/2 In.	195.00
Zanesville Pottery, Vase, La Moro, Blooming Clover, Artist Signed, 7 In.	150.00
Zanesville Pottery, Vase, La Moro, Pansies On Dark Brown, Footed, 9 1/2 In.	65.00
Zanesville Pottery, Vase, La Moro, Standard Glaze, Floral, Marked, 9 1/4 In.	90.00
Zanesville, Vase, Wild Rose On Brown Glaze, 14 In.High, Not Marked	65.00
Zanesville Pottery, Vase, Wild Rose On Brown Glaze, 14 In.	65.00

Zsolnay pottery was made in Hungary after 1855.

Zsolnay, Bowl, Enameled Pink Flowers On Gold Crackled Ground, 10 In.	45.00
Zsolnay, Cachepot, Enameled, Reticulated, Five Steeple Castle Mark, 5 In.	85.00
Zsolnay, Figurine, Deer, Lying, Metallic Blue Green, Artist Signed, 5 X 5 In.	130.00
Zsolnay, Figurine, Does Lying Together, Iridescent Blue Green, 3 X 6 In.	130.00

Zsolnay, Figurine, Hawk Sitting, Metallic Luster, 2 1/2 In. 80.00
Zsolnay, Figurine, Lying Deer, Iridescent Luster Blue Green, 5 X 5 In. 130.00
Zsolnay, Garniture Set, Caramel Color, Birds, Floral, Bronze Stands, 3 Piece 450.00
Zsolnay, Group, Pair Of Does Lying Together, Blue Green Metallic, 6 1/2 In. 135.00
Zsolnay, Inkwell, Nude Woman By Well, Sgraffito, Yellow, Purple, Green, 4 In. 150.00
Zsolnay, Jar, Cookie, 2 Eared Handles, 1 In. Tin Top With Turnable Insert 65.00
Zsolnay, Pitcher, Griffin Handle, Floral & Gold On Rose, 7 1/2 In. 195.00
Zsolnay, Pitcher, Pebble Green & White, Turret Top, 12 In. 50.00
Zsolnay, Pitcher, Pebbly Green, Turret Top, Bulbous, 12 In. 50.00
Zsolnay, Platter, Dark Blue, Red Yellow Gold Luster Design, 11 In. 325.00
Zsolnay, Vase, Conical, Gray Green, Horizontal Ribbing, Floral, 4 3/4 In. 150.00
Zsolnay, Vase, Conical, Red, Persian Designs Frieze, Millennium, 8 In. 275.00
Zsolnay, Vase, Crystalline, Blue Radiating Sunburst Effect, 3 X 6 In. 140.00
Zsolnay, Vase, Crystalline, Powder Blue, 3 X 6 In. 135.00
Zsolnay, Vase, Double Gourd Shape, Bluebells Against Coppery Ground, 19 In. 625.00
Zsolnay, Vase, Double Gourd Shape, Ivorine Ground, Enameled Floral, 11 In. 100.00
Zsolnay, Vase, Iridescent Dark Green, 12 3/4 In. 200.00
Zsolnay, Vase, Mottled Green & Yellow, Mermaid In Relief, 4 1/2 In. 130.00
Zsolnay, Vase, Sea Green Leaves & Stylized Flowers On Beige, Handles, 14 In 380.00